Safety Symbols

These safety symbols are used in laboratory and field investigations in this book to indicate possible hazards. Learn the meaning of each symbol and refer to this page often. *Remember to wash your hands thoroughly after completing lab procedures.*

SAFETY SYMBOLS	HAZARD	EXAMPLES	PRECAUTION	REMEDY
DISPOSAL	Special disposal procedures need to be followed.	certain chemicals, living organisms	Do not dispose of these materials in the sink or trash can.	Dispose of wastes as directed by your teacher.
BIOLOGICAL	Organisms or other biological materials that might be harmful to humans	bacteria, fungi, blood, unpreserved tissues, plant materials	Avoid skin contact with these materials. Wear mask or gloves.	Notify your teacher if you suspect contact with material. Wash hands thoroughly.
EXTREME TEMPERATURE	Objects that can burn skin by being too cold or too hot	boiling liquids, hot plates, dry ice, liquid nitrogen	Use proper protection when handling.	Go to your teacher for first aid.
SHARP OBJECT	Use of tools or glassware that can easily puncture or slice skin	razor blades, pins, scalpels, pointed tools, dissecting probes, broken glass	Practice common-sense behavior and follow guidelines for use of the tool.	Go to your teacher for first aid.
FUME	Possible danger to respiratory tract from fumes	ammonia, acetone, nail polish remover, heated sulfur, moth balls	Make sure there is good ventilation. Never smell fumes directly. Wear a mask.	Leave foul area and notify your teacher immediately.
ELECTRICAL	Possible danger from electrical shock or burn	improper grounding, liquid spills, short circuits, exposed wires	Double-check setup with teacher. Check condition of wires and apparatus. Use GFI-protected outlets.	Do not attempt to fix electrical problems. Notify your teacher immediately.
IRRITANT	Substances that can irritate the skin or mucous membranes of the respiratory tract	pollen, moth balls, steel wool, fiberglass, potassium permanganate	Wear dust mask and gloves. Practice extra care when handling these materials.	Go to your teacher for first aid.
CHEMICAL	Chemicals that can react with and destroy tissue and other materials	bleaches such as hydrogen peroxide; acids such as sulfuric acid, hydrochloric acid; bases such as ammonia, sodium hydroxide	Wear goggles, gloves, and an apron.	Immediately flush the affected area with water and notify your teacher.
TOXIC	Substance may be poisonous if touched, inhaled, or swallowed.	mercury, many metal compounds, iodine, poinsettia plant parts	Follow your teacher's instructions.	Always wash hands thoroughly after use. Go to your teacher for first aid.
FLAMMABLE	Open flame may ignite flammable chemicals, loose clothing, or hair.	alcohol, kerosene, potassium permanganate, hair, clothing	Avoid open flames and heat when using flammable chemicals.	Notify your teacher immediately. Use fire safety equipment if applicable.
OPEN FLAME	Open flame in use, may cause fire.	hair, clothing, paper, synthetic materials	Tie back hair and loose clothing. Follow teacher's instructions on lighting and extinguishing flames.	Always wash hands thoroughly after use. Go to your teacher for first aid.

Eye Safety
Proper eye protection must be worn at all times by anyone performing or observing science activities.

Clothing Protection
This symbol appears when substances could stain or burn clothing.

Animal Safety
This symbol appears when safety of animals and students must be ensured.

Radioactivity
This symbol appears when radioactive materials are used.

Handwashing
After the lab, wash hands with soap and water before removing goggles.

Teacher Edition

Biology

Glencoe Science

Authors

Alton Biggs, Whitney Crispen Hagins, William G. Holliday, Chris L. Kapicka, Linda Lundgren, Ann Haley MacKenzie, William D. Rogers, Marion B. Sewer, Dinah Zike

McGraw Hill Education

The McGraw·Hill Companies

Education

Send all inquiries to:
McGraw-Hill Education
8787 Orion Place
Columbus, OH 43240-4027

ISBN: 978-0-07-894585-4 (Teacher Edition)
MHID: 0-07-894585-2 (Teacher Edition)
ISBN: 978-0-07-894586-1 (Student Edition)
MHID: 0-07-894586-0 (Student Edition)

Printed in the United States of America.

6 7 8 9 10 11 12 DOW 20 19 18 17 16 15 14

Contents in Brief

Online Guide

connectED.mcgraw-hill.com

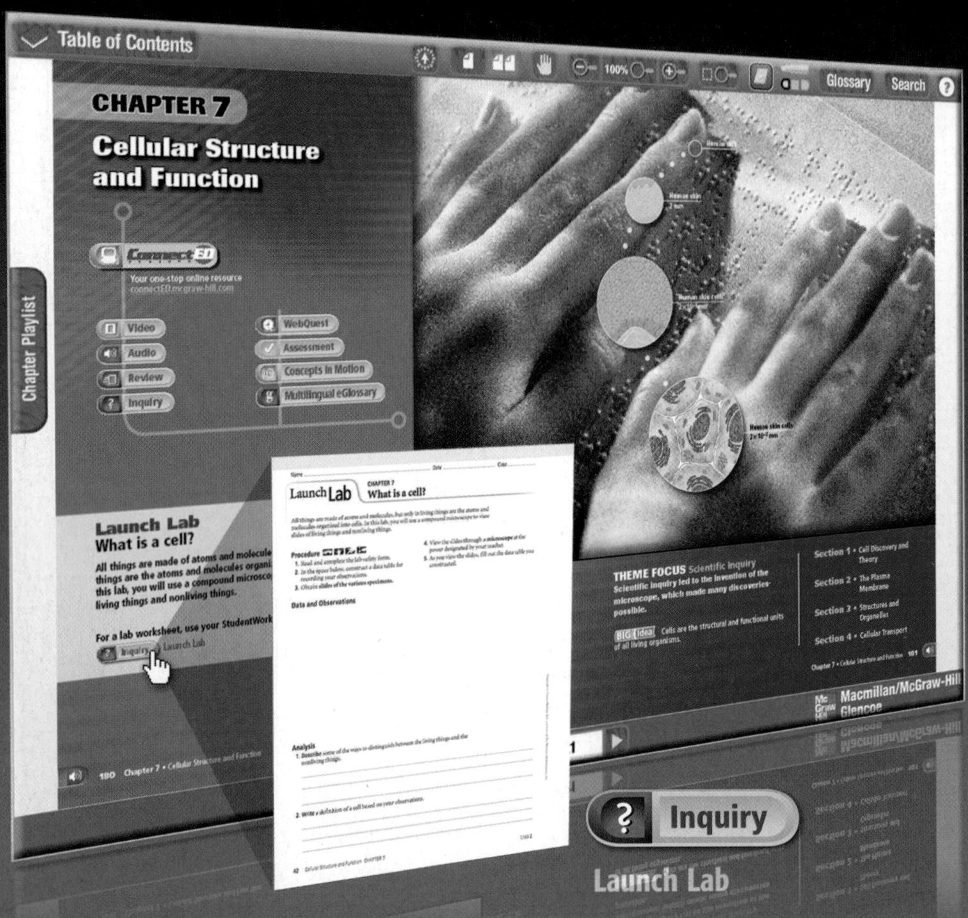

ConnectED

Your Digital Science Portal

Video

See the science in real life through these exciting videos.

Audio

Click the link and you can listen to the text while you follow along.

Review

Try these interactive tools to help you review the lesson concepts.

Inquiry

Explore concepts through hands–on and virtual labs.

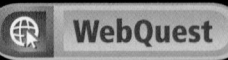

WebQuest

These web-based challenges relate the concepts you're learning about to the latest news and research.

The icons in your online student edition link you to interactive learning opportunities. Browse your online student book to find more.

Concepts in Motion Animation

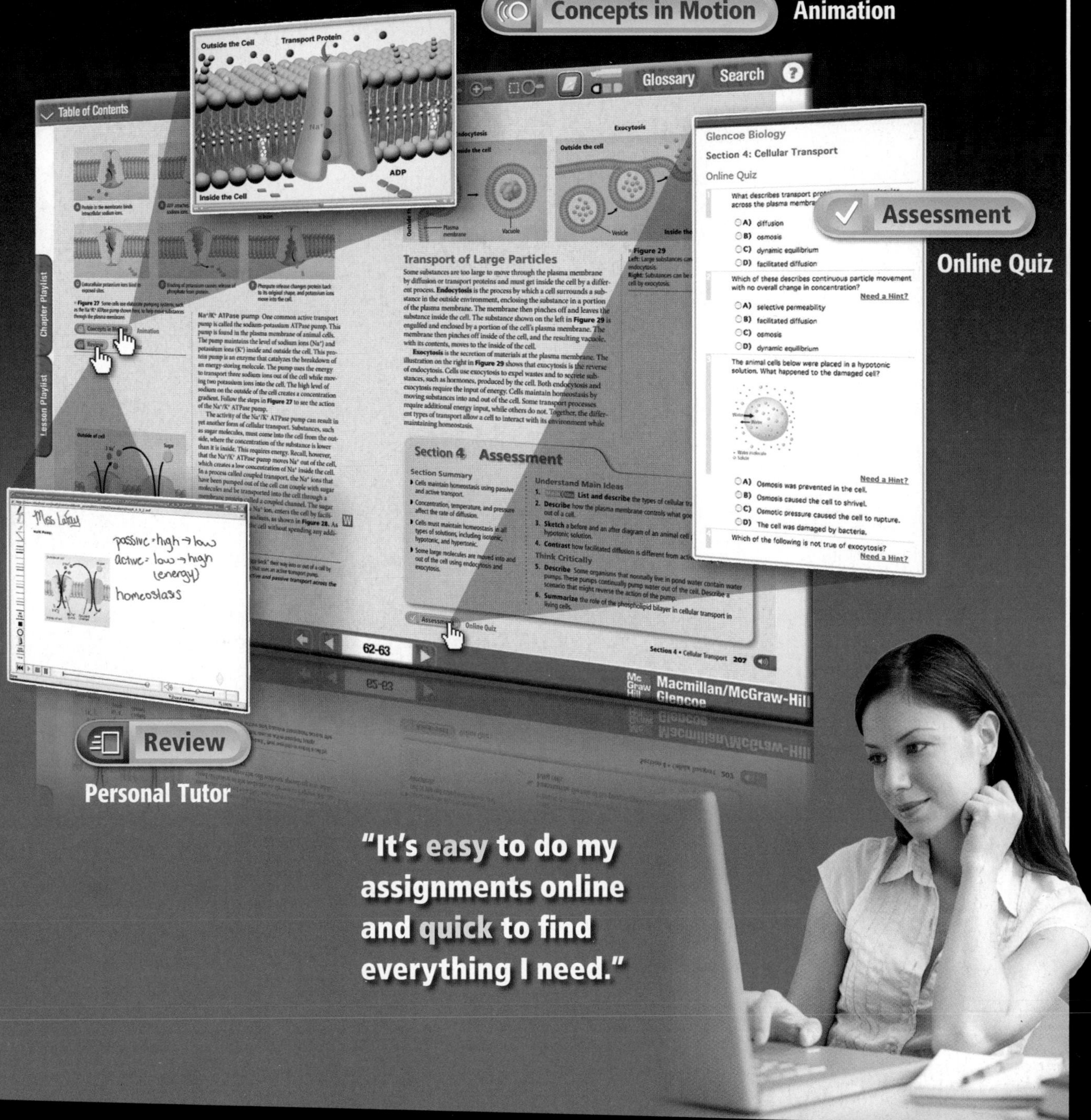

Assessment Online Quiz

Review Personal Tutor

"It's easy to do my assignments online and quick to find everything I need."

Assessment

Check how well you understand the concepts with online quizzes and practice questions.

Concepts in Motion

The textbook comes alive with animated explanations of important concepts.

Multilingual eGlossary

Read key vocabulary in 13 languages.

About the Authors

Alton Biggs has been a biology educator in Texas public schools for more than 30 years. He has a BS and an MS in biology from Texas A & M University—Commerce. Mr. Biggs was the founding president of the Texas Association of Biology Teachers in 1985, received the National Association of Biology Teachers' (NABT) Outstanding Biology Teacher Award for Texas in 1982 and 1995, and in 1992 was the president of the NABT.

Whitney Crispen Hagins teaches biology at Lexington High School in Lexington, Massachusetts. She has a BA and an MA in biological sciences from Mount Holyoke College and an MAT from Duke University. In 1998, she received NSF funding for the development of molecular biology activities. In 1999, she was a Massachusetts NABT Outstanding Biology Teacher Award recipient. In 2005, she was awarded the Siemens Foundation AP Award for Math and Science Teachers for Massachusetts. She works with the Wisconsin Fast Plant Program to develop curriculum, and she enjoys sharing ideas and activities at national meetings.

William G. Holliday is a science education professor at the University of Maryland (College Park), and before 1986, a professor at the University of Calgary (Alberta, Canada). He served as president of the National Association for Research in Science Teaching and later as an elected board member to the National Science Teachers Association. He has an MS in biological sciences and a PhD in science education. Dr. Holliday's multifaceted teaching experience totals more than 40 years.

Chris L. Kapicka is a retired faculty member from Northwest Nazarene University in Nampa, Idaho. She has a BS in biology from Boise State University, an MS in bacteriology and public health from Washington State University, and a PhD in cell and molecular physiology and pharmacology from the University of Nevada Medical School. In 1986, she received the Presidential Award for Science Teaching, and in 1988, she was awarded NABT's Outstanding Biology Teacher Award.

Linda Lundgren has more than 25 years of experience teaching science at the middle school, high school, and college levels, including ten years at Bear Creek High School in Lakewood, Colorado. For eight years, she was a research associate in the Department of Science and Technology at the University of Colorado at Denver. Ms. Lundgren has a BA in journalism and zoology from the University of Massachusetts and an MS in zoology from The Ohio State University. In 1991, she was named Colorado Science Teacher of the Year.

Ann Haley MacKenzie currently teaches at Miami University in Oxford, Ohio, where she works with future high school science teachers and teaches a life science inquiry course. She is the editor of *The American Biology Teacher* for the National Association of Biology Teachers. Dr. MacKenzie has a BS in biology from Purdue University, an MEd in secondary education from the University of Cincinnati, and an EdD in curriculum and instruction from the University of Cincinnati. She is a former Ohio Teacher of the Year and Presidential Award Winner for Secondary School Science.

William D. Rogers is a faculty member in the Department of Biology at Ball State University in Muncie, Indiana. He has a BA and an MA in biology from Drake University and a Doctor of Arts in biology from Idaho State University. He has received teaching awards for outstanding contributions to general education, and he has also received funding from the American Association of Colleges and Universities to study different approaches to science teaching.

Marion B. Sewer is an assistant professor at the Georgia Institute of Technology and a Georgia Cancer Coalition Distinguished Scholar. She received a BS in biochemistry from Spelman College in 1993 and a PhD in pharmacology from Emory University in 1998. Dr. Sewer studies how the integration of various signaling pathways controls steroid hormone biosynthesis.

Dinah Zike is an international curriculum consultant and inventor who has developed educational products and three-dimensional, interactive graphic organizers for more than 30 years. As president and founder of Dinah-Might Adventures, L.P., Ms. Zike is the author of more than 100 award-winning educational publications, including *The Big Book of Science.* She has a BS and an MS in educational curriculum and instruction from Texas A & M University. Dinah Zike's *Foldables* are an exclusive feature of McGraw-Hill textbooks.

Contributing Writer

Thomas Matthiesen
Tissue Engineer
Chicago, IL

Thomas Matthiesen wrote, consulted, and provided photographs for Chapter 34's Cutting Edge Biology feature.

Teacher Advisory Board and Reviewers

Teacher Advisory Board

The Teacher Advisory Board gave the authors, editorial staff, and design team feedback on the content and design of the Student Edition. We thank these teachers for their hard work and creative suggestions.

Chuck Cambria
Springfield North High School
Springfield, OH

Michelle M. Lewis
Lancaster High School
Lancaster, OH

Pamela J. Schumm
Wawasee High School
Syracuse, IN

Sharon Seckel
Canal Winchester High School
Canal Winchester, OH

Sara Haughn
Pickerington High School Central
Pickerington, OH

Daniel J. Regelski
New Albany High School
New Albany, OH

Danielle S. Scrase
Sycamore High School
Cincinnati, OH

Paula Weaver
Seymour High School
Seymour, IN

Reviewers

Each teacher reviewed selected chapters of *Glencoe Biology* and provided feedback and suggestions for improving the effectiveness of the instruction.

Beth Adams, EdS
Cartersville High School
Cartersville, GA

Michele Wonser Altavilla
Elk River High School
Elk River, MN

Elaine Asmus
Snake River High School
Blackfoot, ID

Shelley Barker
Danville High School
Danville, IL

Stephanie L. Baron
Patrick Henry High School
San Diego, CA

Rochelle Battersby
Sanford F. Calhoun High School
Merrick, NY

Ann Blackwell
Travelers Rest High School
Travelers Rest, SC

Fran S. Bouknight
Brookland-Cayce High School
Cayce, SC

Kimberly A. Brown
East Ridge High School
Chattanooga, TN

John H. C. Chipley
Palma High School
Salinas, CA

Melissa C. Donham
Little Rock Central High School
Little Rock, AR

William A. Donovan, Jr.
Amesbury High School
Amesbury, MA

Erica Dosch, BSN, MEd
Connetquot High School
Bohemia, NY

Julie Ertmann
University City High School
University City, MO

Mark Fife
Centerville High School
Centerville, OH

Sasha Hammond
Yakima School District
Yakima, WA

Kenneth L. Harms
Tigard High School
Tigard, OR

David Iott
Holden High School
Holden, MO

Rebecca Jackson
Summerville High School
Summerville, SC

Clinton A. Kennedy
Cascade JR/SR High School
Cascade, ID

Kristen Holly Kent
Pioneer Valley High School
Santa Maria, CA

Deborah L. Krause, EdD
West Orange Public Schools
West Orange, NJ

Kimberly Lane-Hinton
Whitney Young Magnet High School
Chicago, IL

Samantha A. Long
Carlisle High School
Carlisle, PA

Charlotte Parnell
Sullivan High School
Sullivan, MO

Cynthia A. Pousman
Davidson Fine Arts Magnet School
Augusta, GA

Rebekah R. Ravgiala, EdD
Merrimack High School
Merrimack, NH

Gail Raymond
Anchorage School District
Anchorage, AK

Kathryn A. Roberts
Lakeside Public High Schools
Hot Springs, AR

Tracy Rojo
Tucker High School
Tucker, GA

Pamela D. Sherley
Chicago Public Schools
Chicago, IL

Gary R. Smith
Pinelands Regional High School
Tuckerton, NJ

Sue Whitsett
Fond du Lac High School
Fond du Lac, WI

Karen Ann Wickersham
Troy High School
Troy, MI

Consultants

Content Consultants

Content consultants each reviewed selected chapters of *Glencoe Biology* for content accuracy and clarity.

Larry Baresi, PhD
Associate Professor of Biology
California State University, Northridge
Northridge, CA

Janice E. Bonner, PhD
Associate Professor of Biology
College of Notre Dame of Maryland
Baltimore, MD

Renea J. Brodie, PhD
Assistant Professor of Biological Sciences
University of South Carolina
Columbia, SC

Luis A Cañas, PhD
Assistant Professor
Department of Entomology/OARDC
The Ohio State University
Wooster, OH

John S. Choinski, Jr., PhD
Professor of Biology
Department of Biology
University of Central Arkansas
Conway, AR

Dr. Lewis B. Coons, PhD
Professor of Biology
The University of Memphis
Memphis, TN

Cara Lea Council-Garcia, MS
Biology Lab Coordinator
The University of New Mexico
Albuquerque, NM

Dr. Donald S. Emmeluth, PhD
Department of Biology
Armstrong Atlantic State University
Savannah, GA

Diana L. Engle, PhD
Ecology Consultant
University of California Santa Barbara
Santa Barbara, CA

John Gatz, PhD
Professor of Zoology
Ohio Wesleyan University
Delaware, OH

Alan D. Gishlick, PhD
National Center for Science Education
Oakland, CA

Yourha Kang, PhD
Assistant Professor of Biology
Iona College
New Rochelle, NY

Mark E. Lee, PhD
Assistant Professor of Biology
Spelman College
Atlanta, GA

Judy M. Nesmith, MS
Lecturer—Biology
University of Michigan—Dearborn
Dearborn, MI

Hay-Oak Park, PhD
Associate Professor
Department of Molecular Genetics
The Ohio State University
Columbus, OH

Carolyn F. Randolph, PhD
President NSTA 2001–2002
Assistant Executive Director
The SCEA
Columbia, SC

David A. Rubin, PhD
Assistant Professor of Physiology
Illinois State University
Normal, IL

Malathi Srivatsan, PhD
Assistant Professor of Biology
State University of Arkansas
Jonesboro, AR

Laura Vogel, PhD
Associate Professor of Biological Sciences
Illinois State University
Normal, IL

VivianLee Ward, MS
Director of CyberEducation; Codirector of Fellows Program; Project Director Access Excellence @ the National Health Museum
Washington, DC

Safety Consultants

Safety Consultants reviewed labs and lab materials for safety and implementation.

Jack Gerlovich
School of Education
Department of Teaching and Learning
Drake University
Des Moines, IA

Dennis McElroy
Director of Curriculum
Assistant Director for Technology
School of Education
Graceland University
Lamoni, IA

Reading Consultant

Dr. Douglas Fisher provided expert guidance on prototypes, Real-World Reading Links, and the reading strand.

Douglas Fisher, PhD
Professor of Language and Literacy Education
San Diego State University
San Diego, CA

Standardized Test Practice Consultant

Dr. Ralph Feather provided expert guidance on effective standardized test practice questions.

Ralph Feather, PhD
Assistant Professor of Education
Bloomsburg University of Pennsylvania
Bloomsburg, PA

Lab Tester

Science Kit performed and evaluated the Student Edition labs and additional Teacher Edition material, providing suggestions for improving the effectiveness of student instructions and teacher support.

Science Kit and Boreal Laboratories
Tonawanda, NY

Reviewers, Consultants, and Contributing Writers for the Teacher Edition

Contributing Writers

Each writer contributed professional development articles for the Classroom Solutions handbook on pages 10T–26T. Dr. Fisher also reviewed the instructional design of the Teacher Edition.

Douglas Fisher, PhD
Professor of Language and Literacy Education
San Diego State University
San Diego, CA

Emily M. Schell, EdD
Visiting Professor
San Diego State University
San Diego, CA

English Learner Consultants

The English learner consultants evaluated EL activities and provided additional support for English learners.

Laurie Weaver, MS EdD
Assoc. Prof. of Bilingual, ESL, and Multicultural Education
University of Houston-Clear Lake
Houston, TX

Patricia Juárez
Coordinator III
Sacramento City Unified School District
Sacramento, California

Reviewers

Each reviewer provided feedback and suggestions regarding the effectiveness of the science instruction.

Kelly R. Morrow, MS
Science Instructor
Flathead High School
Kalispell, MT

Rebecca K. Johns, MEd
Biology Teacher
Troy High School
Troy, MI

Kate DeSantis, MS, PhD abd
Biology Teacher
Lenape High School
Medford, NJ

Shannon Durkin
Research Specialist
University of Pittsburgh
Pittsburgh, PA

Shannon Reep, MEd
Intervention Specialist
Olentangy Local Schools
Powell, OH

Melissa L. Shirley
Science Dept. Chair
Olentangy Liberty High School
Powell, OH

Misconceptions Consultants

The misconceptions consultants reviewed *Clarify a Misconception* activities and the effectiveness of the science instruction.

Richard Storey, PhD
Chancellor and Professor of Biological Sciences
University of Montana-Western
Dillon, MT

Dr. John Trowbridge, PhD
Associate Professor
Southeastern Louisiana University
Hammond, LA

Teacher Handbook

Table of Contents

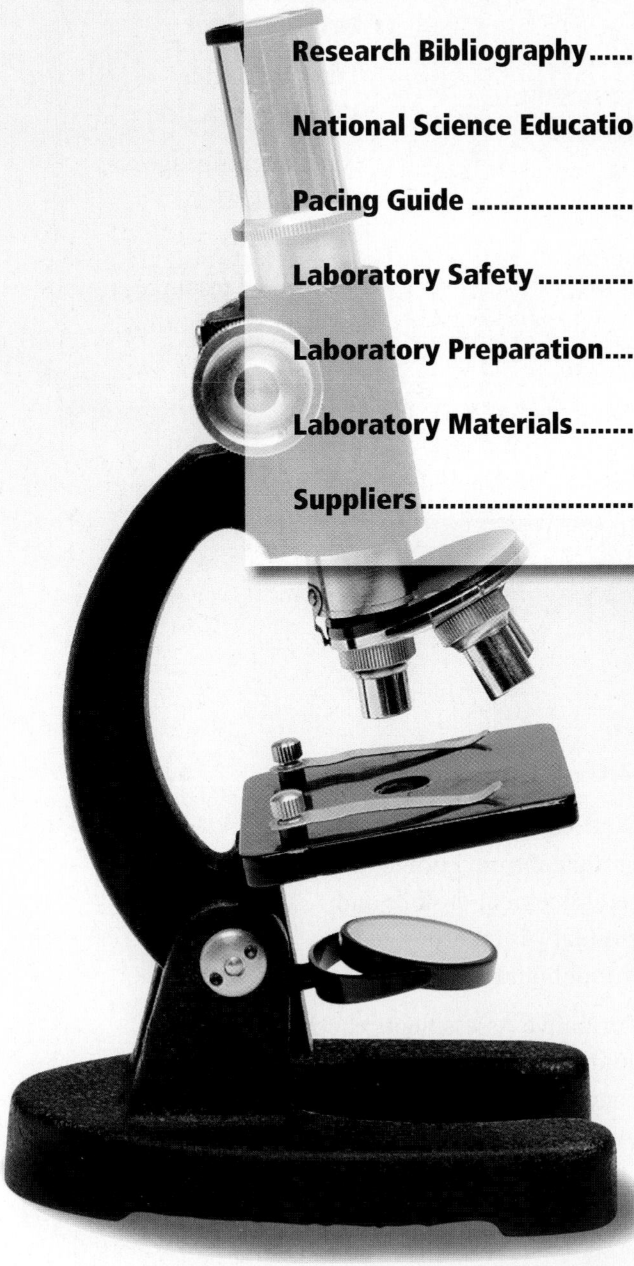

Program Design

Welcome to the Teacher Edition of *Glencoe Biology*. We have created this teacher edition based on input from experienced biology teachers and educational consultants. Our goal is provide you with research-based teaching strategies and activities, which are labeled for you at point-of-use.

Hierarchical Structure

- **Level 1: THEMES** *Glencoe Biology* is organized around five themes—scientific inquiry, diversity, energy, homeostasis, and change.
- **Level 2:** BIG Idea Each chapter has a Big Idea, which summarizes the chapter content in an overarching statement.
- **Level 3:** MAIN Idea Each section of the chapter has a Main Idea that describes the focus of the section. The Main Ideas within a chapter support the Big Idea of the chapter.

Differentiated Instruction

- Leveled activities and options for differentiated instruction help meet the needs of all students.

Assessment and Intervention

- Lessons provide standards practice.
- Assessments gauge student mastery of standards.
- Additional resources provide intervention options.

Standards-Based Instruction

Point-of-Use

- Strategies and activities apply directly to content.
- Letter icons on your reduced Student Edition pages show you where and when to teach each concept.

Review and Reinforcement

- Scaffolding—support for the gradual introduction and reinforcement of skills and content—is incorporated throughout the lessons.
- Formative Assessments check student understanding of key concepts and provide opportunities for reteaching at the end of each section.

Understanding the Letter Icons

The letter icons on the reduced Student Edition pages identify the type of strategy or activity. They are placed at point-of-use to show you where and when to teach each concept. See the key below to learn about the various types of strategies and activities.

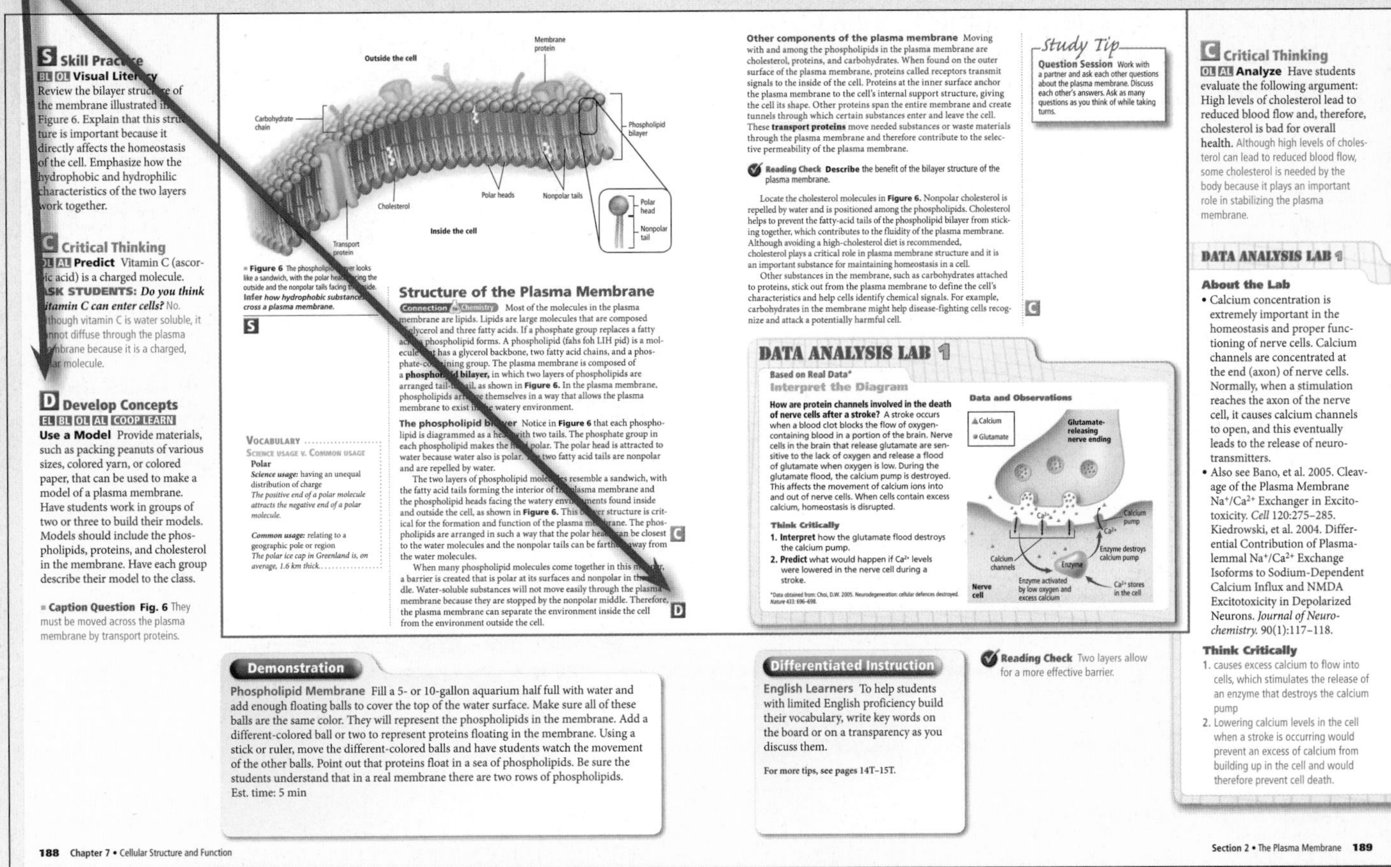

S Skill Practice
BL OL Visual Literacy Review the bilayer structure of the membrane illustrated in Figure 6. Explain that this structure is important because it directly affects the homeostasis of the cell. Emphasize how the hydrophobic and hydrophilic characteristics of the two layers work together.

C Critical Thinking
OL AL Predict Vitamin C (ascorbic acid) is a charged molecule. **ASK STUDENTS:** ***Do you think vitamin C can enter cells?*** No. Although vitamin C is water soluble, it cannot diffuse through the plasma membrane because it is a charged, polar molecule.

D Develop Concepts
EL BL OL AL COOP LEARN
Use a Model Provide materials, such as packing peanuts of various sizes, colored yarn, or colored paper, that can be used to make a model of a plasma membrane. Have students work in groups of two or three to build their models. Models should include the phospholipids, proteins, and cholesterol in the membrane. Have each group describe their model to the class.

Caption Question Fig. 6 They must be moved across the plasma membrane by transport proteins.

Figure 6 The phospholipid bilayer looks like a sandwich, with the polar heads facing the outside and the nonpolar tails facing the inside.
Infer how hydrophobic substances cross a plasma membrane.

S

VOCABULARY
SCIENCE USAGE V. COMMON USAGE
Polar
Science usage: having an unequal distribution of charge
The positive end of a polar molecule attracts the negative end of a polar molecule.
Common usage: relating to a geographic pole or region
The polar ice cap in Greenland is, on average, 1.6 km thick.

Structure of the Plasma Membrane

Connection to Chemistry Most of the molecules in the plasma membrane are lipids. Lipids are large molecules that are composed of glycerol and three fatty acids. If a phosphate group replaces a fatty acid, a phospholipid forms. A phospholipid (fahs foh LIH pid) is a molecule that has a glycerol backbone, two fatty acid chains, and a phosphate-containing group. The plasma membrane is composed of a **phospholipid bilayer,** in which two layers of phospholipids are arranged tail-to-tail, as shown in **Figure 6.** In the plasma membrane, phospholipids arrange themselves in a way that allows the plasma membrane to exist in the watery environment.

The phospholipid bilayer Notice in **Figure 6** that each phospholipid is diagrammed as a head with two tails. The phosphate group in each phospholipid makes the head polar. The polar head is attracted to water because water also is polar. The two fatty acid tails are nonpolar and are repelled by water.

The two layers of phospholipid molecules resemble a sandwich, with the fatty acid tails forming the interior of the plasma membrane and the phospholipid heads facing the watery environments found inside and outside the cell, as shown in **Figure 6.** This bilayer structure is critical for the formation and function of the plasma membrane. The phospholipids are arranged in such a way that the polar heads can be closest to the water molecules and the nonpolar tails can be farthest away from the water molecules. C

When many phospholipid molecules come together in this manner, a barrier is created that is polar at its surfaces and nonpolar in the middle. Water-soluble substances will not move easily through the plasma membrane because they are stopped by the nonpolar middle. Therefore, the plasma membrane can separate the environment inside the cell from the environment outside the cell. D

Other components of the plasma membrane Moving with and among the phospholipids in the plasma membrane are cholesterol, proteins, and carbohydrates. When found on the outer surface of the plasma membrane, proteins called receptors transmit signals to the inside of the cell. Proteins at the inner surface anchor the plasma membrane to the cell's internal support structure, giving the cell its shape. Other proteins span the entire membrane and create tunnels through which certain substances enter and leave the cell. These **transport proteins** move needed substances or waste materials through the plasma membrane and therefore contribute to the selective permeability of the plasma membrane.

Reading Check Describe the benefit of the bilayer structure of the plasma membrane.

Locate the cholesterol molecules in **Figure 6.** Nonpolar cholesterol is repelled by water and is positioned among the phospholipids. Cholesterol helps to prevent the fatty-acid tails of the phospholipid bilayer from sticking together, which contributes to the fluidity of the plasma membrane. Although avoiding a high-cholesterol diet is recommended, cholesterol plays a critical role in plasma membrane structure and it is an important substance for maintaining homeostasis in a cell.

Other substances in the membrane, such as carbohydrates attached to proteins, stick out from the plasma membrane to define the cell's characteristics and help cells identify chemical signals. For example, carbohydrates in the membrane might help disease-fighting cells recognize and attack a potentially harmful cell. C

Study Tip
Question Session Work with a partner and ask each other questions about the plasma membrane. Discuss each other's answers. Ask as many questions as you think of while taking turns.

DATA ANALYSIS LAB 1
Based on Real Data*
Interpret the Diagram

How are protein channels involved in the death of nerve cells after a stroke? A stroke occurs when a blood clot blocks the flow of oxygen-containing blood in a portion of the brain. Nerve cells in the brain that release glutamate are sensitive to the lack of oxygen and release a flood of glutamate when oxygen is low. During the glutamate flood, the calcium pump is destroyed. This affects the movement of calcium ions into and out of nerve cells. When cells contain excess calcium, homeostasis is disrupted.

Think Critically
1. **Interpret** how the glutamate flood destroys the calcium pump.
2. **Predict** what would happen if Ca^{2+} levels were lowered in the nerve cell during a stroke.

*Data obtained from: Choi, D.W. 2005. Neurodegeneration: cellular defences destroyed. *Nature* 433: 696–698.

Data and Observations

C Critical Thinking
OL AL Analyze Have students evaluate the following argument: High levels of cholesterol lead to reduced blood flow and, therefore, cholesterol is bad for overall health. Although high levels of cholesterol can lead to reduced blood flow, some cholesterol is needed by the body because it plays an important role in stabilizing the plasma membrane.

DATA ANALYSIS LAB 1

About the Lab
- Calcium concentration is extremely important in the homeostasis and proper functioning of nerve cells. Calcium channels are concentrated at the end (axon) of nerve cells. Normally, when a stimulation reaches the axon of the nerve cell, it causes calcium channels to open, and this eventually leads to the release of neurotransmitters.
- Also see Bano, et al. 2005. Cleavage of the Plasma Membrane Na^+/Ca^{2+} Exchanger in Excitotoxicity. *Cell* 120:275–285. Kiedrowski, et al. 2004. Differential Contribution of Plasmalemmal Na^+/Ca^{2+} Exchange Isoforms to Sodium-Dependent Calcium Influx and NMDA Excitotoxicity in Depolarized Neurons. *Journal of Neurochemistry.* 90(1):117–118.

Think Critically
1. causes excess calcium to flow into cells, which stimulates the release of an enzyme that destroys the calcium pump
2. Lowering calcium levels in the cell when a stroke is occurring would prevent an excess of calcium from building up in the cell and would therefore prevent cell death.

Demonstration
Phospholipid Membrane Fill a 5- or 10-gallon aquarium half full with water and add enough floating balls to cover the top of the water surface. Make sure all of these balls are the same color. They will represent the phospholipids in the membrane. Add a different-colored ball or two to represent proteins floating in the membrane. Using a stick or ruler, move the different-colored balls and have students watch the movement of the other balls. Point out that proteins float in a sea of phospholipids. Be sure the students understand that in a real membrane there are two rows of phospholipids.
Est. time: 5 min

Differentiated Instruction
English Learners To help students with limited English proficiency build their vocabulary, write key words on the board or on a transparency as you discuss them.
For more tips, see pages 14T–15T.

Reading Check Two layers allow for a more effective barrier.

188 Chapter 7 • Cellular Structure and Function

Section 2 • The Plasma Membrane 189

Key for Using the Teacher Edition

R **Reading Strategy** activities help you teach reading skills and vocabulary.

C **Critical Thinking** strategies require students to use higher-order thinking skills to apply and extend what they have learned.

S **Skill Practice** strategies help students organize information and use visuals for comprehension.

W **Writing Support** activities provide writing opportunities that help students comprehend the content.

D **Develop Concepts** activities use various strategies, such as scaffolding and clarifying misconceptions, to help teachers gauge and plan for students' concept development.

Differentiated Instruction

Activity Leveling

Teaching strategies and activities have been coded for ability level appropriateness. A competency level is given for each activity using the following code:

AL Activities for students working above grade level
OL Activities for students working on grade level
BL Activities for students working below grade level
EL Activities for English learners

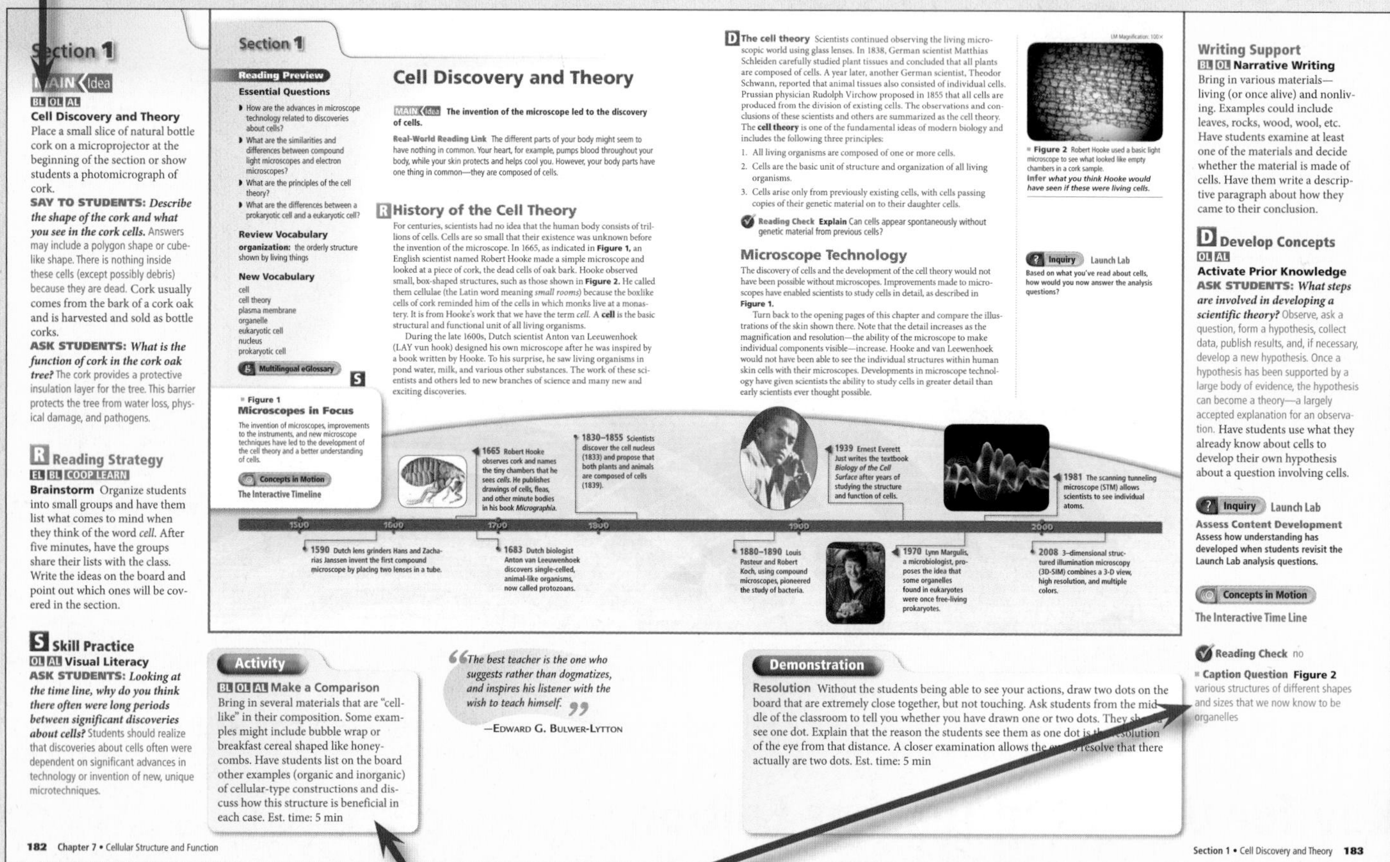

Section 1

MAIN Idea

BL OL AL

Cell Discovery and Theory Place a small slice of natural bottle cork on a microprojector at the beginning of the section or show students a photomicrograph of cork.

SAY TO STUDENTS: *Describe the shape of the cork and what you see in the cork cells.* Answers may include a polygon shape or cube-like shape. There is nothing inside these cells (except possibly debris) because they are dead. Cork usually comes from the bark of a cork oak and is harvested and sold as bottle corks.

ASK STUDENTS: *What is the function of cork in the cork oak tree?* The cork provides a protective insulation layer for the tree. This barrier protects the tree from water loss, physical damage, and pathogens.

R Reading Strategy

EL BL COOP LEARN

Brainstorm Organize students into small groups and have them list what comes to mind when they think of the word *cell*. After five minutes, have the groups share their lists with the class. Write the ideas on the board and point out which ones will be covered in the section.

S Skill Practice

OL AL **Visual Literacy**

ASK STUDENTS: *Looking at the time line, why do you think there often were long periods between significant discoveries about cells?* Students should realize that discoveries about cells often were dependent on significant advances in technology or invention of new, unique microtechniques.

Section 1

Reading Preview

Essential Questions

- How are the advances in microscope technology related to discoveries about cells?
- What are the similarities and differences between compound light microscopes and electron microscopes?
- What are the principles of the cell theory?
- What are the differences between a prokaryotic cell and a eukaryotic cell?

Review Vocabulary

organization: the orderly structure shown by living things

New Vocabulary

cell
cell theory
plasma membrane
organelle
eukaryotic cell
nucleus
prokaryotic cell

Multilingual eGlossary

Cell Discovery and Theory

MAIN Idea **The invention of the microscope led to the discovery of cells.**

Real-World Reading Link The different parts of your body might seem to have nothing in common. Your heart, for example, pumps blood throughout your body, while your skin protects and helps cool you. However, your body parts have one thing in common—they are composed of cells.

History of the Cell Theory

For centuries, scientists had no idea that the human body consists of trillions of cells. Cells are so small that their existence was unknown before the invention of the microscope. In 1665, as indicated in **Figure 1**, an English scientist named Robert Hooke made a simple microscope and looked at a piece of cork, the dead cells of oak bark. Hooke observed small, box-shaped structures, such as those shown in **Figure 2**. He called them cellulae (the Latin word meaning *small rooms*) because the boxlike cells of cork reminded him of the cells in which monks live at a monastery. It is from Hooke's work that we have the term *cell*. A **cell** is the basic structural and functional unit of all living organisms.

During the late 1600s, Dutch scientist Anton van Leeuwenhoek (LAY vun hook) designed his own microscope after he was inspired by a book written by Hooke. To his surprise, he saw living organisms in pond water, milk, and various other substances. The work of these scientists and others led to new branches of science and many new and exciting discoveries.

The cell theory Scientists continued observing the living microscopic world using glass lenses. In 1838, German scientist Matthias Schleiden carefully studied plant tissues and concluded that all plants are composed of cells. A year later, another German scientist, Theodor Schwann, reported that animal tissues also consisted of individual cells. Prussian physician Rudolph Virchow proposed in 1855 that all cells are produced from the division of existing cells. The observations and conclusions of these scientists and others are summarized as the cell theory. The **cell theory** is one of the fundamental ideas of modern biology and includes the following three principles:

1. All living organisms are composed of one or more cells.
2. Cells are the basic unit of structure and organization of all living organisms.
3. Cells arise only from previously existing cells, with cells passing copies of their genetic material on to their daughter cells.

Reading Check **Explain** Can cells appear spontaneously without genetic material from previous cells?

Microscope Technology

The discovery of cells and the development of the cell theory would not have been possible without microscopes. Improvements made to microscopes have enabled scientists to study cells in detail, as described in **Figure 1**.

Turn back to the opening pages of this chapter and compare the illustrations of the skin shown there. Note that the detail increases as the magnification and resolution—the ability of the microscope to make individual components visible—increase. Hooke and van Leewenhoek would not have been able to see the individual structures within human skin cells with their microscopes. Developments in microscope technology have given scientists the ability to study cells in greater detail than early scientists ever thought possible.

LM Magnification: 100×

Figure 2 Robert Hooke used a basic light microscope to see what looked like empty chambers in a cork sample.
Infer *what you think Hooke would have seen if these were living cells.*

Inquiry Launch Lab
Based on what you've read about cells, how would you now answer the analysis questions?

Figure 1
Microscopes in Focus
The invention of microscopes, improvements to the instruments, and new microscope techniques have led to the development of the cell theory and a better understanding of cells.

Concepts in Motion
The Interactive Timeline

1590 Dutch lens grinders Hans and Zacharias Janssen invent the first compound microscope by placing two lenses in a tube.

1665 Robert Hooke observes cork and names the tiny chambers that he sees cells. He publishes drawings of cells, fleas, and other minute bodies in his book *Micrographia*.

1683 Dutch biologist Anton van Leeuwenhoek discovers single-celled, animal-like organisms, now called protozoans.

1830–1855 Scientists discover the cell nucleus (1833) and propose that both plants and animals are composed of cells (1839).

1880–1890 Louis Pasteur and Robert Koch, using compound microscopes, pioneered the study of bacteria.

1939 Ernest Everett Just writes the textbook *Biology of the Cell Surface* after years of studying the structure and function of cells.

1970 Lynn Margulis, a microbiologist, proposes the idea that some organelles found in eukaryotes were once free-living prokaryotes.

1981 The scanning tunneling microscope (STM) allows scientists to see individual atoms.

2008 3-dimensional structured illumination microscopy (3D-SIM) combines a 3-D view, high resolution, and multiple colors.

1500 1600 1700 1800 1900 2000

Activity

BL OL AL **Make a Comparison** Bring in several materials that are "cell-like" in their composition. Some examples might include bubble wrap or breakfast cereal shaped like honeycombs. Have students list on the board other examples (organic and inorganic) of cellular-type constructions and discuss how this structure is beneficial in each case. Est. time: 5 min

"The best teacher is the one who suggests rather than dogmatizes, and inspires his listener with the wish to teach himself."
—Edward G. Bulwer-Lytton

Demonstration

Resolution Without the students being able to see your actions, draw two dots on the board that are extremely close together, but not touching. Ask students from the middle of the classroom to tell you whether you have drawn one or two dots. They should see one dot. Explain that the reason the students see them as one dot is the resolution of the eye from that distance. A closer examination allows the eye to resolve that there actually are two dots. Est. time: 5 min

Writing Support

BL OL **Narrative Writing**
Bring in various materials—living (or once alive) and nonliving. Examples could include leaves, rocks, wood, wool, etc. Have students examine at least one of the materials and decide whether the material is made of cells. Have them write a descriptive paragraph about how they came to their conclusion.

D Develop Concepts

OL AL

Activate Prior Knowledge
ASK STUDENTS: *What steps are involved in developing a scientific theory?* Observe, ask a question, form a hypothesis, collect data, publish results, and, if necessary, develop a new hypothesis. Once a hypothesis has been supported by a large body of evidence, the hypothesis can become a theory—a largely accepted explanation for an observation. Have students use what they already know about cells to develop their own hypothesis about a question involving cells.

Inquiry Launch Lab
Assess Content Development
Assess how understanding has developed when students revisit the Launch Lab analysis questions.

Concepts in Motion
The Interactive Time Line

Reading Check no

Caption Question **Figure 2**
various structures of different shapes and sizes that we now know to be organelles

182 Chapter 7 • Cellular Structure and Function

Section 1 • Cell Discovery and Theory 183

Answers and Additional Support

Along the bottom of the Teacher Edition, you will find

- answers to questions in the student edition;
- demonstrations and activities that help you quickly and easily address key concepts;
- *Content-Background* elements that provide you with additional content information;
- *Differentiated-Instruction* strategies that help you meet the needs of all students;
- *Research Citations* that highlight specific educational strategies and cite the research that supports them.

Planning and Teaching the Unit

Preview the Unit activity helps students make connections among the content areas covered in the unit.

Clarify a Misconception elements provide a question to elicit common student misconceptions and an explanation to help dispel that misconception.

Themes give an overview of how each of the five themes of *Glencoe Biology* is covered in the unit.

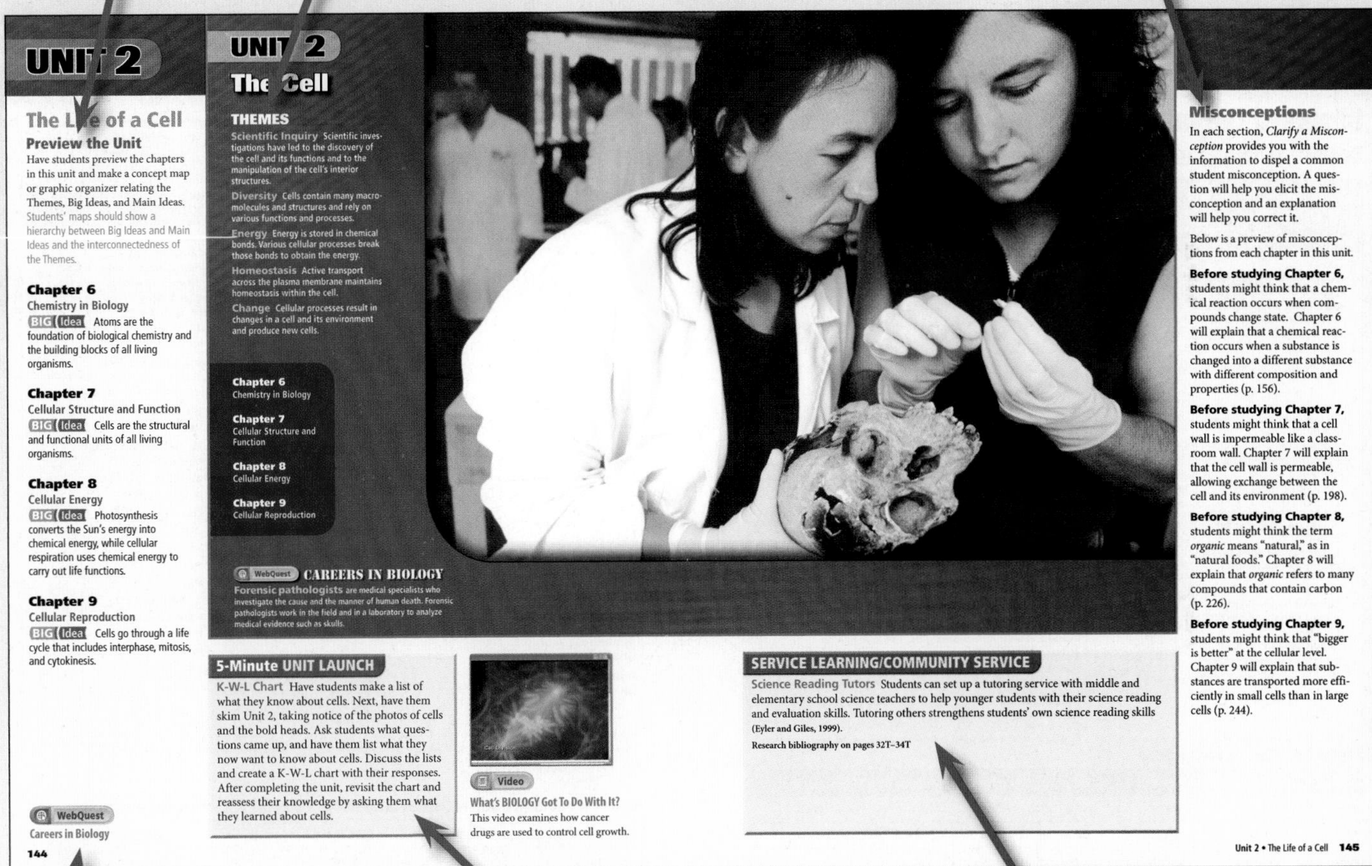

UNIT 2

The Life of a Cell

Preview the Unit

Have students preview the chapters in this unit and make a concept map or graphic organizer relating the Themes, Big Ideas, and Main Ideas. Students' maps should show a hierarchy between Big Ideas and Main Ideas and the interconnectedness of the Themes.

Chapter 6
Chemistry in Biology
BIG Idea Atoms are the foundation of biological chemistry and the building blocks of all living organisms.

Chapter 7
Cellular Structure and Function
BIG Idea Cells are the structural and functional units of all living organisms.

Chapter 8
Cellular Energy
BIG Idea Photosynthesis converts the Sun's energy into chemical energy, while cellular respiration uses chemical energy to carry out life functions.

Chapter 9
Cellular Reproduction
BIG Idea Cells go through a life cycle that includes interphase, mitosis, and cytokinesis.

WebQuest
Careers in Biology

144

UNIT 2

The Cell

THEMES

Scientific Inquiry Scientific investigations have led to the discovery of the cell and its functions and to the manipulation of the cell's interior structures.

Diversity Cells contain many macromolecules and structures and rely on various functions and processes.

Energy Energy is stored in chemical bonds. Various cellular processes break those bonds to obtain the energy.

Homeostasis Active transport across the plasma membrane maintains homeostasis within the cell.

Change Cellular processes result in changes in a cell and its environment and produce new cells.

Chapter 6 Chemistry in Biology
Chapter 7 Cellular Structure and Function
Chapter 8 Cellular Energy
Chapter 9 Cellular Reproduction

WebQuest **CAREERS IN BIOLOGY**

Forensic pathologists are medical specialists who investigate the cause and the manner of human death. Forensic pathologists work in the field and in a laboratory to analyze medical evidence such as skulls.

5-Minute UNIT LAUNCH

K-W-L Chart Have students make a list of what they know about cells. Next, have them skim Unit 2, taking notice of the photos of cells and the bold heads. Ask students what questions came up, and have them list what they now want to know about cells. Discuss the lists and create a K-W-L chart with their responses. After completing the unit, revisit the chart and reassess their knowledge by asking them what they learned about cells.

Video
What's BIOLOGY Got To Do With It?
This video examines how cancer drugs are used to control cell growth.

SERVICE LEARNING/COMMUNITY SERVICE

Science Reading Tutors Students can set up a tutoring service with middle and elementary school science teachers to help younger students with their science reading and evaluation skills. Tutoring others strengthens students' own science reading skills (Eyler and Giles, 1999).

Research bibliography on pages 32T–34T

Misconceptions

In each section, *Clarify a Misconception* provides you with the information to dispel a common student misconception. A question will help you elicit the misconception and an explanation will help you correct it.

Below is a preview of misconceptions from each chapter in this unit.

Before studying Chapter 6, students might think that a chemical reaction occurs when compounds change state. Chapter 6 will explain that a chemical reaction occurs when a substance is changed into a different substance with different composition and properties (p. 156).

Before studying Chapter 7, students might think that a cell wall is impermeable like a classroom wall. Chapter 7 will explain that the cell wall is permeable, allowing exchange between the cell and its environment (p. 198).

Before studying Chapter 8, students might think the term *organic* means "natural," as in "natural foods." Chapter 8 will explain that *organic* refers to many compounds that contain carbon (p. 226).

Before studying Chapter 9, students might think that "bigger is better" at the cellular level. Chapter 9 will explain that substances are transported more efficiently in small cells than in large cells (p. 244).

Unit 2 • The Life of a Cell 145

WebQuests give students an opportunity to further explore a topic or career while sharpening their research skills.

Service Learning/Community Service is an activity or project that engages students in meaningful community service that relates biology to the real world.

5-Minute Unit Launch is a short preteaching activity that will help you introduce students to the content covered in the unit.

Planning the Chapter

Planning pages appear at the beginning of each chapter.

Chapter Organizers detail all section objectives, standards covered, and materials needed to teach the chapter.

ConnectED is an online portal that holds and organizes all of your ancillary and technology resources for intervention, enrichment, reinforcement, and review.

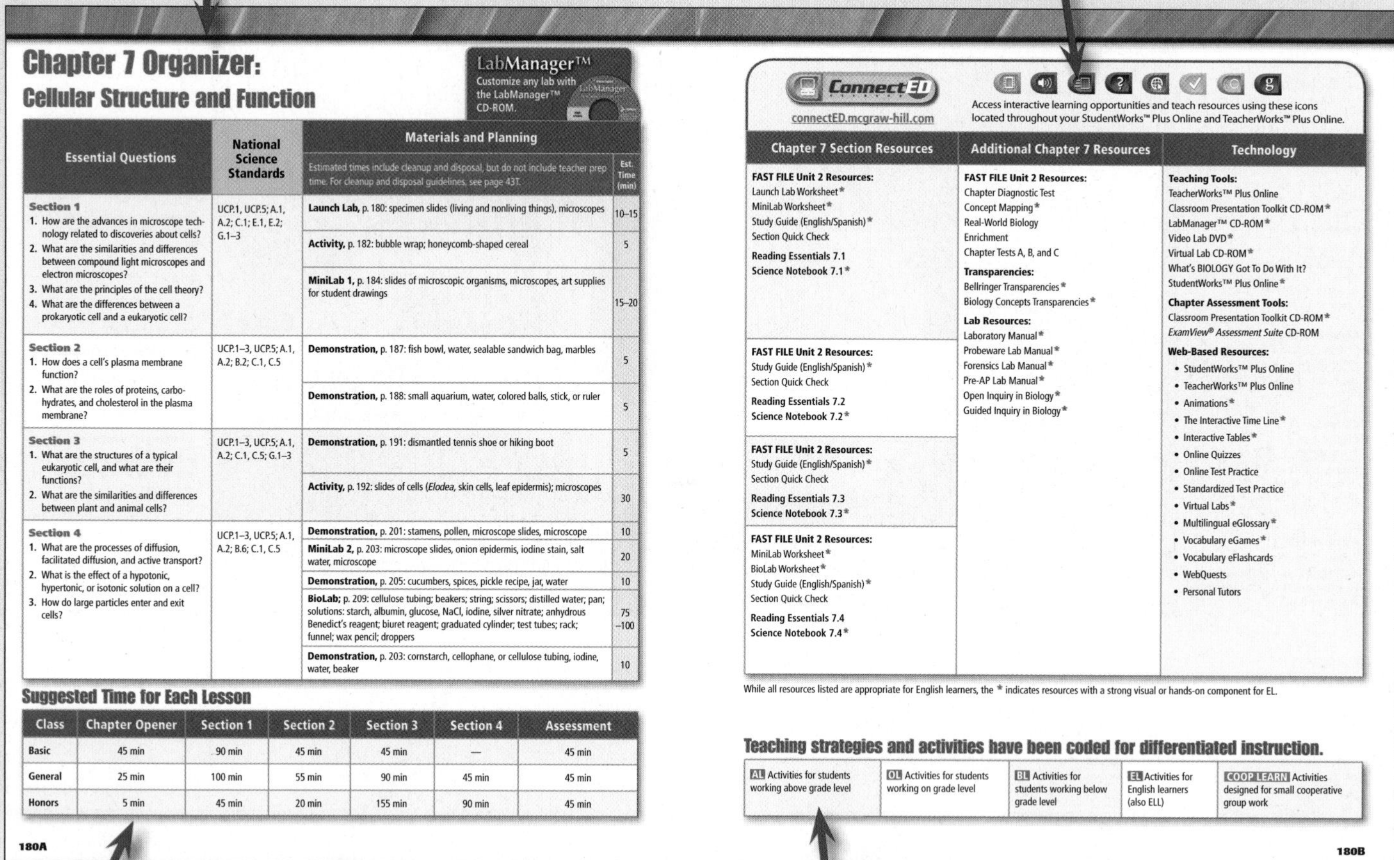

Chapter 7 Organizer:
Cellular Structure and Function

LabManager™
Customize any lab with the LabManager™ CD-ROM.

Essential Questions	National Science Standards	Materials and Planning: Estimated times include cleanup and disposal, but do not include teacher prep time. For cleanup and disposal guidelines, see page 43T.	Est. Time (min)
Section 1 1. How are the advances in microscope technology related to discoveries about cells? 2. What are the similarities and differences between compound light microscopes and electron microscopes? 3. What are the principles of the cell theory? 4. What are the differences between a prokaryotic cell and a eukaryotic cell?	UCP.1, UCP.5; A.1, A.2; C.1; E.1, E.2; G.1–3	**Launch Lab,** p. 180: specimen slides (living and nonliving things), microscopes	10–15
		Activity, p. 182: bubble wrap; honeycomb-shaped cereal	5
		MiniLab 1, p. 184: slides of microscopic organisms, microscopes, art supplies for student drawings	15–20
Section 2 1. How does a cell's plasma membrane function? 2. What are the roles of proteins, carbohydrates, and cholesterol in the plasma membrane?	UCP.1–3, UCP.5; A.1, A.2; B.2; C.1, C.5	**Demonstration,** p. 187: fish bowl, water, sealable sandwich bag, marbles	5
		Demonstration, p. 188: small aquarium, water, colored balls, stick, or ruler	5
Section 3 1. What are the structures of a typical eukaryotic cell, and what are their functions? 2. What are the similarities and differences between plant and animal cells?	UCP.1–3, UCP.5; A.1, A.2; C.1, C.5; G.1–3	**Demonstration,** p. 191: dismantled tennis shoe or hiking boot	5
		Activity, p. 192: slides of cells (*Elodea,* skin cells, leaf epidermis); microscopes	30
Section 4 1. What are the processes of diffusion, facilitated diffusion, and active transport? 2. What is the effect of a hypotonic, hypertonic, or isotonic solution on a cell? 3. How do large particles enter and exit cells?	UCP.1–3, UCP.5; A.1, A.2; B.6; C.1, C.5	**Demonstration,** p. 201: stamens, pollen, microscope slides, microscope	10
		MiniLab 2, p. 203: microscope slides, onion epidermis, iodine stain, salt water, microscope	20
		Demonstration, p. 205: cucumbers, spices, pickle recipe, jar, water	10
		BioLab; p. 209: cellulose tubing; beakers; string; scissors; distilled water; pan; solutions: starch, albumin, glucose, NaCl, iodine, silver nitrate; anhydrous Benedict's reagent; biuret reagent; graduated cylinder; test tubes; rack; funnel; wax pencil; droppers	75–100
		Demonstration, p. 203: cornstarch, cellophane, or cellulose tubing, iodine, water, beaker	10

Suggested Time for Each Lesson

Class	Chapter Opener	Section 1	Section 2	Section 3	Section 4	Assessment
Basic	45 min	90 min	45 min	45 min	—	45 min
General	25 min	100 min	55 min	90 min	45 min	45 min
Honors	5 min	45 min	20 min	155 min	90 min	45 min

180A

ConnectED
connectED.mcgraw-hill.com

Access interactive learning opportunities and teach resources using these icons located throughout your StudentWorks™ Plus Online and TeacherWorks™ Plus Online.

Chapter 7 Section Resources	Additional Chapter 7 Resources	Technology
FAST FILE Unit 2 Resources: Launch Lab Worksheet* MiniLab Worksheet* Study Guide (English/Spanish)* Section Quick Check **Reading Essentials 7.1** **Science Notebook 7.1***	**FAST FILE Unit 2 Resources:** Chapter Diagnostic Test Concept Mapping* Real-World Biology Enrichment Chapter Tests A, B, and C **Transparencies:** Bellringer Transparencies* Biology Concepts Transparencies* **Lab Resources:** Laboratory Manual* Probeware Lab Manual* Forensics Lab Manual* Pre-AP Lab Manual* Open Inquiry in Biology* Guided Inquiry in Biology*	**Teaching Tools:** TeacherWorks™ Plus Online Classroom Presentation Toolkit CD-ROM* LabManager™ CD-ROM* Video Lab DVD* Virtual Lab CD-ROM* What's BIOLOGY Got To Do With It? StudentWorks™ Plus Online* **Chapter Assessment Tools:** Classroom Presentation Toolkit CD-ROM* *ExamView® Assessment Suite* CD-ROM **Web-Based Resources:** • StudentWorks™ Plus Online • TeacherWorks™ Plus Online • Animations* • The Interactive Time Line* • Interactive Tables* • Online Quizzes • Online Test Practice • Standardized Test Practice • Virtual Labs* • Multilingual eGlossary* • Vocabulary eGames* • Vocabulary eFlashcards • WebQuests • Personal Tutors
FAST FILE Unit 2 Resources: Study Guide (English/Spanish)* Section Quick Check **Reading Essentials 7.2** **Science Notebook 7.2***		
FAST FILE Unit 2 Resources: Study Guide (English/Spanish)* Section Quick Check **Reading Essentials 7.3** **Science Notebook 7.3***		
FAST FILE Unit 2 Resources: MiniLab Worksheet* BioLab Worksheet* Study Guide (English/Spanish)* Section Quick Check **Reading Essentials 7.4** **Science Notebook 7.4***		

While all resources listed are appropriate for English learners, the * indicates resources with a strong visual or hands-on component for EL.

Teaching strategies and activities have been coded for differentiated instruction.

AL Activities for students working above grade level	OL Activities for students working on grade level	BL Activities for students working below grade level	EL Activities for English learners (also ELL)	COOP LEARN Activities designed for small cooperative group work

180B

Lesson Pacing provides three different pacing suggestions for the chapter. When used in conjunction with the Pacing Guide on page 36T, you can tailor the pace of your instruction to the individual needs of your classes.

Leveling Key describes the differentiated instruction labels used throughout the Teacher Edition.

Teaching the Chapter

Introduce the Chapter and *Big Idea* at the beginning of each chapter will help you to teach the standards.

ConnectED icons are placed at point of use in the student edition and teacher edition to point out where specific technology components can be used. In your StudentWorks™ Plus Online and eTeacherEdition Online, these are live links.

Introduce the Chapter is a question about the chapter opening photo. The image and question will engage students in the chapter content.

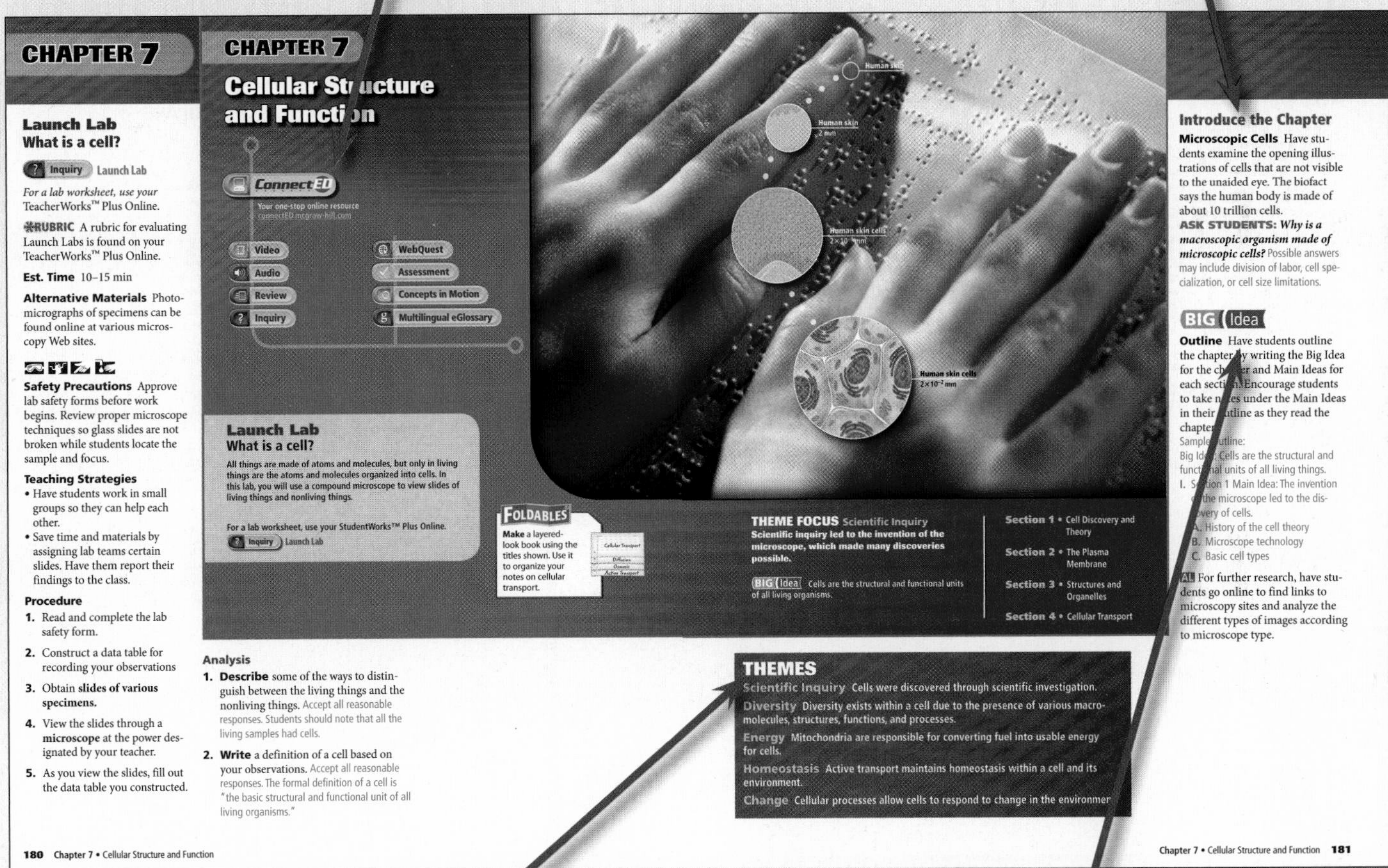

CHAPTER 7

Launch Lab
What is a cell?

Inquiry Launch Lab

For a lab worksheet, use your TeacherWorks™ Plus Online.

RUBRIC A rubric for evaluating Launch Labs is found on your TeacherWorks™ Plus Online.

Est. Time 10–15 min

Alternative Materials Photomicrographs of specimens can be found online at various microscopy Web sites.

Safety Precautions Approve lab safety forms before work begins. Review proper microscope techniques so glass slides are not broken while students locate the sample and focus.

Teaching Strategies
- Have students work in small groups so they can help each other.
- Save time and materials by assigning lab teams certain slides. Have them report their findings to the class.

Procedure
1. Read and complete the lab safety form.
2. Construct a data table for recording your observations
3. Obtain **slides of various specimens.**
4. View the slides through a **microscope** at the power designated by your teacher.
5. As you view the slides, fill out the data table you constructed.

CHAPTER 7

Cellular Structure and Function

ConnectED
Your one-stop online resource
connectED.mcgraw-hill.com

Video · Audio · Review · Inquiry · WebQuest · Assessment · Concepts in Motion · Multilingual eGlossary

Launch Lab
What is a cell?

All things are made of atoms and molecules, but only in living things are the atoms and molecules organized into cells. In this lab, you will use a compound microscope to view slides of living things and nonliving things.

For a lab worksheet, use your StudentWorks™ Plus Online.
Inquiry Launch Lab

Analysis
1. **Describe** some of the ways to distinguish between the living things and the nonliving things. Accept all reasonable responses. Students should note that all the living samples had cells.
2. **Write** a definition of a cell based on your observations. Accept all reasonable responses. The formal definition of a cell is "the basic structural and functional unit of all living organisms."

FOLDABLES
Make a layered-look book using the titles shown. Use it to organize your notes on cellular transport.

THEME FOCUS Scientific Inquiry
Scientific inquiry led to the invention of the microscope, which made many discoveries possible.

BIG Idea Cells are the structural and functional units of all living organisms.

Section 1 • Cell Discovery and Theory
Section 2 • The Plasma Membrane
Section 3 • Structures and Organelles
Section 4 • Cellular Transport

THEMES
Scientific Inquiry Cells were discovered through scientific investigation.
Diversity Diversity exists within a cell due to the presence of various macromolecules, structures, functions, and processes.
Energy Mitochondria are responsible for converting fuel into usable energy for cells.
Homeostasis Active transport maintains homeostasis within a cell and its environment.
Change Cellular processes allow cells to respond to change in the environmen

Introduce the Chapter

Microscopic Cells Have students examine the opening illustrations of cells that are not visible to the unaided eye. The biofact says the human body is made of about 10 trillion cells.
ASK STUDENTS: ***Why is a macroscopic organism made of microscopic cells?*** Possible answers may include division of labor, cell specialization, or cell size limitations.

BIG Idea

Outline Have students outline the chapter by writing the Big Idea for the chapter and Main Ideas for each section. Encourage students to take notes under the Main Ideas in their outline as they read the chapter.
Sample outline:
Big Idea: Cells are the structural and functional units of all living things.
I. Section 1 Main Idea: The invention of the microscope led to the discovery of cells.
A. History of the cell theory
B. Microscope technology
C. Basic cell types

AL For further research, have students go online to find links to microscopy sites and analyze the different types of images according to microscope type.

180 Chapter 7 • Cellular Structure and Function

Chapter 7 • Cellular Structure and Function 181

Themes are listed for each chapter in the teacher wrap. Use this information to help students make connections among the themes of biology and the content they are studying.

BIG Idea activities help students understand the conceptual structure of the chapter—starting with the Big Idea overarching the chapter to the Main Ideas that are the focus of each section.

Assessment: Sections

Student activities and questions throughout the book provide opportunities for ongoing assessment and remediation.

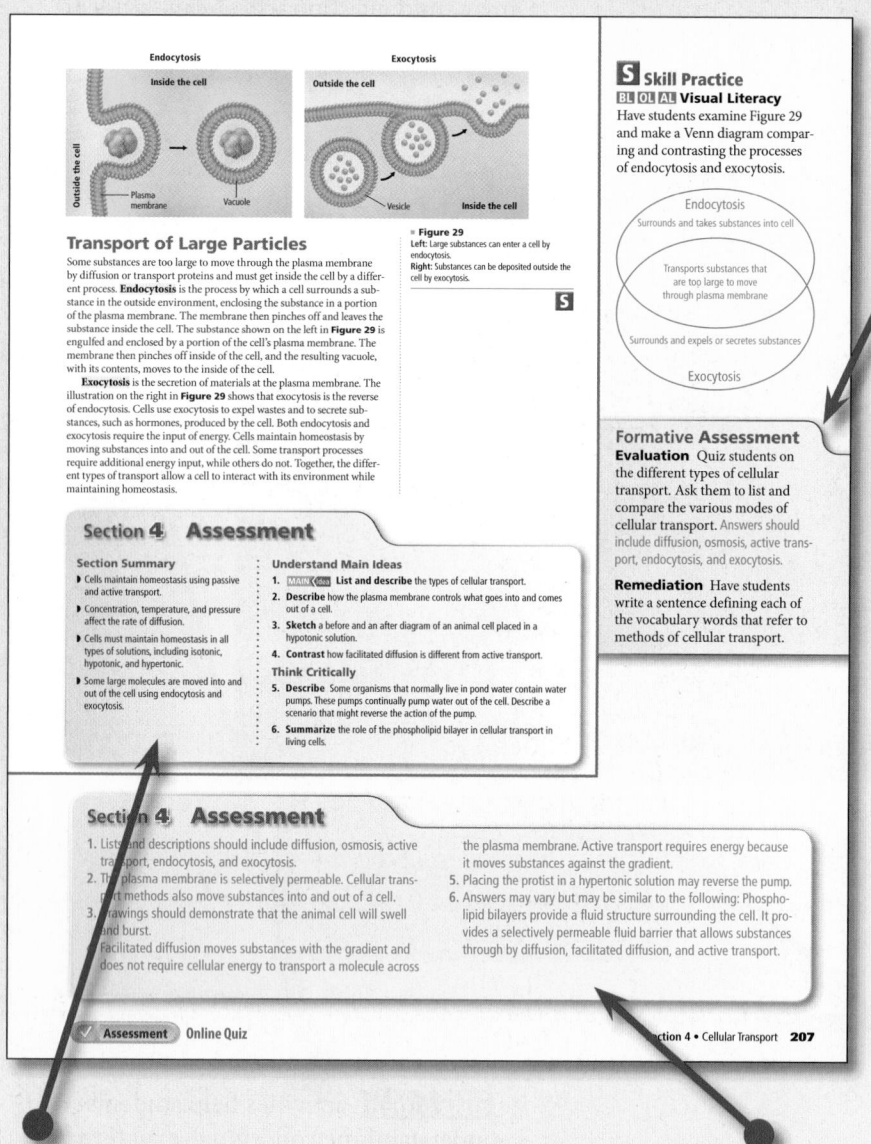

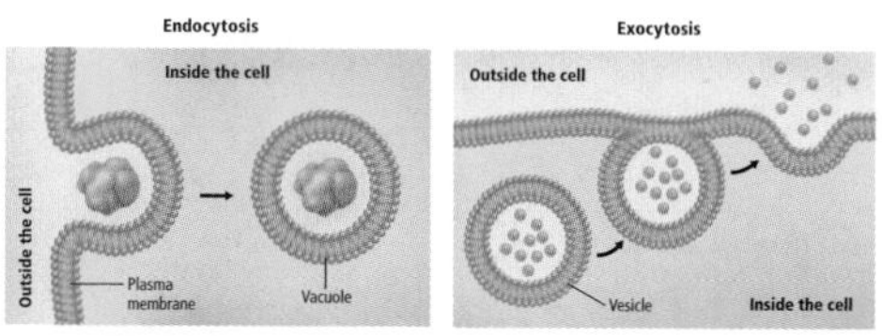

▪ **Figure 29**
Left: Large substances can enter a cell by endocytosis.
Right: Substances can be deposited outside the cell by exocytosis.

Transport of Large Particles

Some substances are too large to move through the plasma membrane by diffusion or transport proteins and must get inside the cell by a different process. **Endocytosis** is the process by which a cell surrounds a substance in the outside environment, enclosing the substance in a portion of the plasma membrane. The membrane then pinches off and leaves the substance inside the cell. The substance shown on the left in **Figure 29** is engulfed and enclosed by a portion of the cell's plasma membrane. The membrane then pinches off inside of the cell, and the resulting vacuole, with its contents, moves to the inside of the cell.

Exocytosis is the secretion of materials at the plasma membrane. The illustration on the right in **Figure 29** shows that exocytosis is the reverse of endocytosis. Cells use exocytosis to expel wastes and to secrete substances, such as hormones, produced by the cell. Both endocytosis and exocytosis require the input of energy. Cells maintain homeostasis by moving substances into and out of the cell. Some transport processes require additional energy input, while others do not. Together, the different types of transport allow a cell to interact with its environment while maintaining homeostasis.

S Skill Practice
BL OL AL Visual Literacy
Have students examine Figure 29 and make a Venn diagram comparing and contrasting the processes of endocytosis and exocytosis.

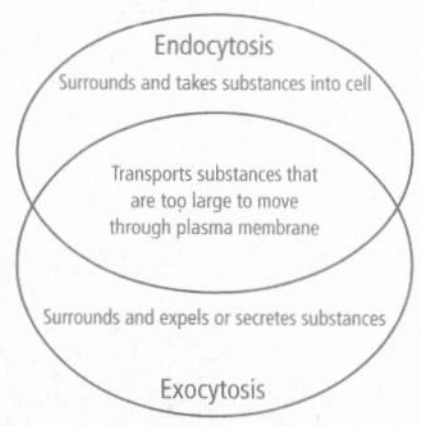

Formative Assessment
Evaluation Quiz students on the different types of cellular transport. Ask them to list and compare the various modes of cellular transport. Answers should include diffusion, osmosis, active transport, endocytosis, and exocytosis.

Remediation Have students write a sentence defining each of the vocabulary words that refer to methods of cellular transport.

Section 4 Assessment

Section Summary
- Cells maintain homeostasis using passive and active transport.
- Concentration, temperature, and pressure affect the rate of diffusion.
- Cells must maintain homeostasis in all types of solutions, including isotonic, hypotonic, and hypertonic.
- Some large molecules are moved into and out of the cell using endocytosis and exocytosis.

Understand Main Ideas
1. MAIN Idea **List and describe** the types of cellular transport.
2. **Describe** how the plasma membrane controls what goes into and comes out of a cell.
3. **Sketch** a before and an after diagram of an animal cell placed in a hypotonic solution.
4. **Contrast** how facilitated diffusion is different from active transport.

Think Critically
5. **Describe** Some organisms that normally live in pond water contain water pumps. These pumps continually pump water out of the cell. Describe a scenario that might reverse the action of the pump.
6. **Summarize** the role of the phospholipid bilayer in cellular transport in living cells.

Section 4 Assessment

1. Lists and descriptions should include diffusion, osmosis, active transport, endocytosis, and exocytosis.
2. The plasma membrane is selectively permeable. Cellular transport methods also move substances into and out of a cell.
3. Drawings should demonstrate that the animal cell will swell and burst.
4. Facilitated diffusion moves substances with the gradient and does not require cellular energy to transport a molecule across the plasma membrane. Active transport requires energy because it moves substances against the gradient.
5. Placing the protist in a hypertonic solution may reverse the pump.
6. Answers may vary but may be similar to the following: Phospholipid bilayers provide a fluid structure surrounding the cell. It provides a selectively permeable fluid barrier that allows substances through by diffusion, facilitated diffusion, and active transport.

Assessment Online Quiz

Section 4 • Cellular Transport 207

Formative Assessments provide a mid-chapter evaluation of a key concept and a reteaching activity for students struggling to meet that learning objective.

Section Assessments provide students with summary statements and questions that tie to the learning objectives for that section.

Answers to all assessment questions are found in the Teacher Edition.

Assessment: Chapters

Vocabulary Review and **Understand Main Ideas** assess comprehension of the vocabulary and concepts in each section.

Constructed Response and **Think Critically** require students to demonstrate higher-order thinking and use their writing skills.

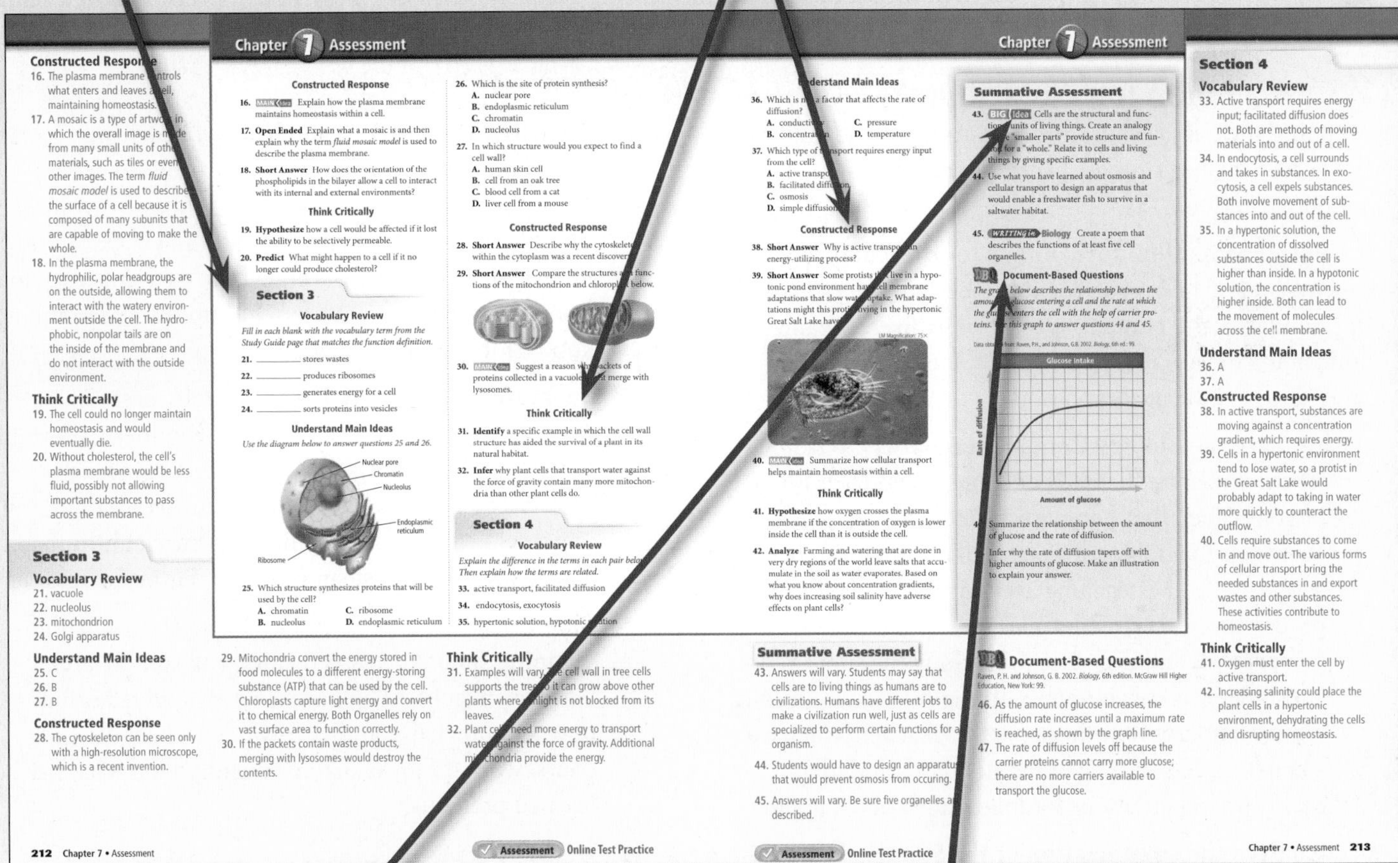

Big Idea Question asks students to apply everything that they have learned in the chapter.

Document-Based Questions connect students to real-world applications as they evaluate real data from current research. Students analyze graphs, charts, and other displays of data from recognized scientific journals and classic historic documents.

Backward Mapping

How can my instruction help students succeed in a standards-based system?

by Emily M. Schell, Ed.D.

Content standards articulate what students should know and be able to do in every biology classroom. Effective instructional planning based in the standards and maximizing available resources is essential for meaningful teaching and learning of biology. Planning instruction with educational goals in mind makes for the most effective teaching.

How do I map my curriculum?

Mapping the curriculum from beginning to end, and from the end to the beginning—backward mapping—makes for solid instruction.

Mapping out the curriculum allows teachers to achieve several goals. These goals include a better understanding of the standards and content-specific objectives, organization and pacing of the curriculum, and focused assessment related to specific goals and objectives.

✓ **Analyze the Biology Content Standards** To begin, teachers analyze the body of content standards for biology. Then they compare and contrast these standards to additional sources of information that support effective teaching and learning in biology. This process works best with colleagues who bring varying perspectives and expertise to teaching the subject. As a result of this collaboration, strengths and weaknesses of the standards become apparent. Teachers will have a better understanding of the standards and identify concerns and questions for follow-up while mapping.

✓ **Analyze the Organization of the Standards-Based Content** Most biology teachers agree with researchers that biology is best taught in order from simple to complex living organisms. However, some state standards either do not or cannot present the content in order from simple to complex living organisms. Rich discussions about themes and concepts tend to emerge, and teachers identify meaningful methods for presenting complicated and overlapping information. In this way, students will see the connections that transcend the "simple to complex" order.

✓ **Identify the Content and Order of Teaching** A plan is developed to present content in a certain order. Incorporating content that is either missing from the standards or is essential in building background knowledge with students enters the curriculum map as well. Outside resources brought into the classroom are good supplements.

✓ **Separate Overlapping Units** Identify areas of instruction related to the Themes, Big Ideas, or Main Ideas. It is at this stage that backward planning is introduced for the development of instructional units, which will support the grade-level curriculum map. The instruction must support the planned assessment.

✓ **Map Curriculum at Each Grade Level** Curriculum planning should be shared among all subject-area teachers. Teachers will have a better understanding of what knowledge and skills students bring to their coursework if they take into consideration what has been learned previously.

How do I use backward mapping?

After a year-long course of study is mapped out, further develop each unit through backward mapping. Start with the end in mind—know your curricular goals and objectives at the outset, which are often found in the content standards and articulated in the curriculum maps.

Once goals have been determined, teachers develop assessments that will show progress toward those goals and objectives. In the final step of this backward mapping process, teachers determine meaningful teaching and learning strategies and identify useful resources that support the assessment.

To use backward mapping in developing your units of instruction, consider the following steps:

Step One: Know Your Targets

First, identify exactly what students must know and do in this unit. Analyze content standards and any other resources that support curricular goals and objectives for this unit. As you plan, ask yourself:

- ✓ What do I want my students to know as a result of this unit?
- ✓ What skills will students develop during the course of this unit?
- ✓ How do I describe these goals clearly and concisely to my students so they understand where we should be at the end of this unit?
- ✓ What essential knowledge will students need to access to make sense of this information?
- ✓ Do my instructional goals align with strategies identified in the curriculum map?
- ✓ Have I introduced any Big Ideas that are pertinent to this content?

Step Two: Identify and Develop Assessments

Second, consider the multiple forms of formal and informal assessments that will help you determine to what degree each student has achieved the stated goals and objectives seen in Step One. Some assessments are embedded throughout the instructional unit, while others come at the end of the unit. Some assessments are performance-based, while others are not. Some are authentic applications of information and skills, while others require the formal recall of information. Ask yourself:

- ✓ What do I want to know and see from each student?
- ✓ What are the best methods for students to demonstrate what they know and can do based on the goals and objectives?
- ✓ How many assessments do I need to determine what students know and can do?
- ✓ How will I balance informal and formal assessments?
- ✓ How will I assess students with diverse learning styles, skills, and abilities?
- ✓ How can I prepare and support students?
- ✓ How will these assessments promote student progress in biology?
- ✓ At what time(s) during the unit will I administer these assessments?

Step Three: Develop Meaningful Instruction

After the assessments for the unit have been determined, consider the meaningful and effective teaching strategies that will support learning and student achievement on assessments. While developing lesson plans for instruction, ask yourself:

- ✓ How will students learn what they are expected to know?
- ✓ How will I engage students in the concepts of this unit?
- ✓ In what ways might students relate or connect to this information?
- ✓ What research-based strategies will be most effective with my students and in these studies?
- ✓ How will I differentiate my instruction to meet the diverse needs of my students?
- ✓ How will I scaffold or provide access to the curriculum for my English learners?
- ✓ What vocabulary requires attention in this unit?
- ✓ How much time will I have to effectively teach this unit?
- ✓ How will I use the textbook and other resources to support the goals and objectives for this unit?
- ✓ What lessons will I develop?
- ✓ In what sequence will I teach these lessons during this unit?
- ✓ How will these lessons support the assessments from Step Two?

Step Four: Locate and Manage Resources

Effective teaching and learning of biology requires the use of multiple forms of text and varied resources. Consider what you have available in your classroom, including your textbook, and identify resources you will add in order to teach this unit successfully. Ask yourself:

- ✓ What parts of the textbook are required for the lessons determined in Step Three?
- ✓ What ancillary materials are needed for the lessons in this unit?
- ✓ What Web sites will I recommend to students to support these lessons?
- ✓ Do I need to contact guest speakers or obtain outside resources?
- ✓ What literature resources are available to support this unit?

Emily Schell is a visiting professor at San Diego State University and social studies education director at SDSU City Heights Educational Collaborative, San Diego, CA.

Meeting the Diverse Needs of Students

by Douglas Fisher, Ph.D.

Today's classroom contains students from a variety of backgrounds with a variety of learning styles, strengths, and challenges. As teachers, we are facing the challenge of helping each student reach their educational potential. With careful planning, you can address the needs of all students in the biology classroom. The basis for this planning is universal access. When classrooms are planned with universal access in mind, fewer students require specific accommodations.

What is universal design?

Universal design was first conceived in architectural studies when businesspeople, engineers, and architects began making considerations for physical access to buildings. The idea was to plan the environment in advance to ensure that everyone had access. As a result, the environment would not have to be changed later for people with physical disabilities, people pushing strollers, workers who had injuries, or others for whom the environment would be difficult to negotiate. The Center for Universal Design, www.design.ncsu.edu/cud, defines universal design as: *The design of products and environments to be usable by all people, to the greatest extent possible, without the need for adaptation or specialized design.*

Universal Design and Access in Education

Researchers, teachers, and parents in education have expanded the development of built-in adaptations and inclusive accommodations from architectural space to the educational experience, especially in the area of curriculum.

In 1998, the National Center to Improve the Tools of Educators (NCITE), in partnership with the Center for Applied Special Technology (CAST), proposed an expanded definition of universal design focused on education: *In terms of learning, universal design means the design of instructional materials and activities that allow the learning goals to be achievable by individuals with wide differences in their abilities to see, hear, speak, move, read, write, understand English, attend, organize, engage, and remember.*

How does universal design work in education?

Universal design and access, as they apply to education and schooling, suggest the following:

✓ **Inclusive Classroom Participation** Curriculum should be designed with all students and their needs in mind. *Glencoe Biology* was designed for a wide range of students. For example, because English learners and students who struggle with reading will use this textbook, vocabulary is specifically taught and reinforced. Similarly, the teacher-support materials provide multiple instructional points to be used depending on the needs of the students in each class. Further, the main ideas are identified for all learners. Throughout the text, there are multiple opportunities to activate students' prior knowledge. Connections between what students know and think about are made throughout the text.

✓ **Maximum Text Readability** In universally designed classrooms that provide access for all students, texts use direct language, clear noun-verb agreements, and clear construct-based wording. In addition to these factors, the *Glencoe Biology* text uses embedded definitions for difficult terms, provides for specific instruction in reading skills, uses a number of visual representations, and includes note-taking strategies.

✓ **Adaptable and Accommodating** The content in this textbook can be easily translated, read aloud, or otherwise changed to meet the needs of students in the classroom. The section and end-of-chapter assessments provide students with multiple ways of demonstrating their content knowledge while also ensuring that they have practice with thinking in terms of multiple-choice questions. Critical thinking and analysis skills also are practiced.

How is differentiated instruction the key to universal access?

To differentiate instruction, teachers must acknowledge student differences in background knowledge and current reading, writing, and English language skills. They also must consider student learning styles and preferences, interests, and needs, and react accordingly. There are a number of general guidelines for differentiating instruction in the classroom to reach all students, including:

Link Assessment With Instruction Assessments should occur before, during, and after instruction to ensure that the curriculum is aligned with what students do and do not know. Using assessments in this way allows you to plan instruction for whole groups, small groups, and individual students. Backward mapping, in which you establish the assessment before you begin instruction, is also important.

Clarify Key Concepts and Generalizations Students need to know what is essential and how this information can be used in their future learning. In addition, students need to develop a sense of the Big Ideas—ideas that transcend time and place.

Emphasize Critical and Creative Thinking The content, process, and products used or assigned in the classroom should require that students think about what they are learning. While some students may require support, additional motivation, varied tasks, materials, or equipment, the overall focus on critical and creative thinking allows for all students to participate in the lesson.

Include Teacher- and Student-Selected Tasks A differentiated classroom includes both teacher- and student-selected activities and tasks. At some points in the lesson or day, the teacher must provide instruction and assign learning activities. In other parts of the lesson, students should be provided choices in how they engage with the content. This balance increases motivation, engagement, and learning.

Below is an example of a classroom activity for teaching Mendelian inheritance. It is followed by an example of the methods this text provides teachers for differentiating instruction to meet all students' needs.

Classroom Activity	Strategies for Differentiating this Activity:
Display an illustration that shows a simple monohybrid cross of the traits studied by Gregor Mendel. Next to the illustration, show a Punnett square that predicts the results of such a cross. Discuss with students general information regarding Mendel, his studies, and the particular monohybrid cross that is displayed.	• Ask students to imagine that they are reporters living in the time when Mendel performed his research. Have them write a newspaper article introducing the general public to Mendel's research. • Have students create a concept map tracing a monohybrid cross through the second generation. Be sure they indicate dominant and recessive alleles. • Obtain and display some of Mendel's actual data for monohybrid crosses. Ask students to compare the real data to the ratios predicted by Punnett squares. Ask them how they think scientists recognize patterns in data. • Have students research Mendel and the environment in which he worked. Ask them to write a two-page report on Mendel and his contributions. • Give students an assortment of large and small paper clips. Have them use two coin flips to choose two paper clips (heads = large; tails = small). Repeat 20 times. Tell them that large clips represent dominant traits, and small clips represent recessive ones. Ask them to compare their paper clip ratios to the predicted results of a monohybrid cross of heterozygous parents.

Classroom Solutions

How do I support individual students?

The majority of students will thrive in a classroom based on universal access and differentiated instruction. However, wise teachers recognize that no single option will work for all students and there might be students who require unique systems of support to be successful.

Tips for Instruction

The following tips for instruction can support your efforts to help all students reach their maximum potential.

- ✓ Survey students to discover their individual differences. Use interest inventories of their unique talents so you can encourage contributions in the classroom.
- ✓ Be a model for respecting others. Adolescents crave social acceptance. The student with learning differences is especially sensitive to correction and criticism, particularly when it comes from a teacher. Your behavior will set the tone for how students treat one another.
- ✓ Expand opportunities for success. Provide a variety of instructional activities that reinforce skills and concepts.
- ✓ Establish measurable objectives and decide how you can best help students meet them.
- ✓ Celebrate successes and make note of and praise "work in progress."
- ✓ Keep it simple. Point out problem areas if doing so can help a student affect change. Avoid overwhelming students with too many goals at one time.
- ✓ Assign cooperative group projects that challenge all students to contribute to solving a problem or creating a product.

How do I reach students who have learning disabilities?

- ✓ Provide support and structure. Clearly specify rules, assignments, and responsibilities.
- ✓ Practice skills frequently. Use games and drills to help maintain student interest.
- ✓ Incorporate many modalities into the learning process. Provide opportunities to say, hear, write, read, and act out important concepts and information.
- ✓ Link new skills and concepts to those already mastered.
- ✓ If possible, allow students to record answers on audiotape.
- ✓ Allow extra time to complete assessments and assignments.
- ✓ Let students demonstrate proficiency with alternative presentations, including oral reports, role plays, and art or musical projects.
- ✓ Provide outlines, notes, or tape recordings of lecture material.
- ✓ Pair students with peer helpers, and provide class time for pair interaction.

How do I reach students who have behavioral challenges?

- ✓ Provide a structured environment with simple and clearly defined schedules, rules, seat assignments, and safety procedures.
- ✓ Reinforce appropriate behavior and model it for students.
- ✓ Cue distracted students back to the task through verbal and nonverbal signals and teacher proximity.
- ✓ Set small goals that can be achieved in the short term. Work for long-term improvement in the big areas.

How do I reach students who have physical challenges?

- ✓ Openly discuss with the student any uncertainties you have about when to offer aid.
- ✓ Ask parents or therapists and students what special devices or procedures are needed and whether any special safety precautions need to be taken.
- ✓ Welcome students with physical challenges into all class activities, including field trips, special events, and classroom and community projects.
- ✓ Provide information to assist class members and parents in their understanding of support needed.

How do I reach students who have visual impairments?

- ✓ Facilitate independence. Modify assignments as needed.
- ✓ Teach classmates how and when to serve as visual guides.
- ✓ Limit unnecessary noise in the classroom if it distracts the student with visual impairments.
- ✓ Provide tactile models whenever possible.
- ✓ Foster a spirit of inclusion. Describe people and events as they occur in the classroom. Remind classmates that the student with visual impairments cannot interpret gestures and other forms of nonverbal communication.
- ✓ Provide taped lectures and reading assignments for use outside the classroom.
- ✓ Team the student with a sighted peer for written assignments.

How do I reach students who have hearing impairments?

- ✓ Seat students where they can see your lip movements easily and where they can avoid any visual distractions.
- ✓ Avoid standing with your back to the window or other light source.
- ✓ Use an overhead projector so you can maintain eye contact while writing information for students.
- ✓ Make sure students sit where they can see all speakers.
- ✓ Post all assignments on the board, or hand out written instructions.
- ✓ If the student has a manual interpreter, allow both student and interpreter to select the most favorable seating arrangements.
- ✓ Teach students to look directly at each other when they speak.

How do I reach English learners?

- ✓ Remember, students' abilities to speak English do not reflect their academic abilities.
- ✓ Try to incorporate students' cultural experience into your instruction. The help of a bilingual aide may be effective.
- ✓ Avoid any references in your instruction that could be construed as cultural stereotypes.
- ✓ Preteach important vocabulary and concepts.
- ✓ Encourage students to preview text before they begin reading, noting headings.
- ✓ Remind students not to ignore graphic organizers, photographs, and charts, graphs, and tables, since there is much information in these visuals.
- ✓ Use demonstrations and specimens whenever possible to build background knowledge and understanding. For example, you can display different types of leaves in order to facilitate an understanding of classification.

How do I reach students who are working above level?

- ✓ Make arrangements for students to take selected subjects early and to work on independent projects.
- ✓ Ask "what if" questions to develop high-level thinking skills. Establish an environment safe for risk taking in your classroom.
- ✓ Emphasize concepts, theories, ideas, relationships, and generalizations about the content.
- ✓ Promote interest in biology by inviting students to make connections to other disciplines that interest them.
- ✓ Let students express themselves in alternative ways, such as creative writing, acting, debates, simulations, drawing, or music.
- ✓ Provide students with a catalog of helpful resources, including agencies that provide free and inexpensive materials, appropriate community services and programs, and community experts who might be called upon to speak to your students.
- ✓ Assign extension projects that allow students to solve real-life problems related to their communities.

Douglas Fisher is a professor at San Diego State University, San Diego, CA.

Academic Vocabulary

How can I help my students learn academic vocabulary?

What is academic English?

Academic English is the language used by the educated and by leaders in business, academic, and other professional disciplines. It is the language used in courts of law and in professional books, including textbooks. This type of English contains specific linguistic features that are associated with academic disciplines like biology. Proficiency in reading and using academic English is especially related to long-term success in all parts of life.

Academic vocabulary is the basis for academic English. By reinforcing academic vocabulary and academic English, teachers can help learners to access authentic, academic texts—not simplified texts that "dummy down" the content. In this way, they can provide information that will help build their students' background knowledge rapidly.

What is academic vocabulary?

By the time children have completed elementary school, they must have acquired the knowledge needed to understand academic vocabulary. How many words should they acquire to be able to access their textbooks? A basic 2,000-word vocabulary of high-frequency words makes up 87 percent of the vocabulary of academic texts. Eight hundred other academic words comprise an additional 8 percent of the words. Three percent of the remaining words are technical words. The remaining 2 percent are low-frequency words. There might be as many as 123,000 low-frequency words in academic texts.

Why should students learn academic vocabulary?

English learners who have mastered a basic 2,000-word vocabulary are ready to acquire the majority of general words found in their academic texts.

Knowledge of academic words combined with continued acquisition of general words can significantly boost an English learner's comprehension level of academic texts. English learners who learn and practice these words before they graduate from high school are likely to be able to master academic material with more confidence and speed. They waste less time and effort in guessing words or consulting dictionaries than those who only know the basic 2,000 words that characterize general conversation.

Also, consider academic success in terms of measurement and assessment—state standards-based assessments, the SAT, and the ACT—with regard to word mastery. All demand an understanding of academic vocabulary.

How do I include academic vocabulary and academic English in my teaching?

- ✓ Teachers can provide their students with rich samples of academic vocabulary and help students understand and attend to the academic English in their text.
- ✓ To develop academic English, learners must have already acquired a basic proficiency in the grammar of everyday English.
- ✓ Academic English should be taught within contexts that make sense. In terms of instruction, teaching academic English includes providing students with access to core curriculum—in this case, biology.
- ✓ Academic English arises not only from knowledge of a linguistic code and cognition, but also from social practices in which academic English is used to accomplish communicative goals. The acquisition of academic vocabulary and grammar is necessary to advance the development of academic English.

Tips for Teaching Academic Vocabulary

Expose students to academic vocabulary. Provide students with sufficient exposure to academic words.

Do not ignore English learners in this process. They can learn academic vocabulary before they are completely fluent in everyday English.

Encourage broader learning by helping students build academic vocabulary. Students who have mastered the basic academic vocabulary are ready to continue acquiring words from the rest of the groups.

To help determine which words are in the 2,000-word basic group, refer to Coxhead's Academic Word List available through your eTeacherEdition Online.

Guidelines for Teaching Academic Vocabulary:

There are a number of guidelines that teachers can use when teaching academic English and vocabulary.

- ✓ direct and planned instruction
- ✓ models—that have increasingly difficult language
- ✓ attention to form—pointing out linguistic features of words
- ✓ practice
- ✓ motivation
- ✓ instructional feedback
- ✓ assessment—on a regular basis

Classroom Activity: Writing About Ecology

As an example of teaching academic vocabulary, when the class studies ecology, you could give students an impromptu writing assignment. Ask them to write a short essay about one of the topics listed below in the left column. Have students use as many of the academic vocabulary words in the right column as they can in their essays. Give students a time limit for their writing. When students have completed the assignment, ask student volunteers to share their writing. Help them use academic words correctly.

Topic	Academic Vocabulary
Cycles in nature (water, carbon, nitrogen, phosphorus)	chemical
	cycle
	energy
	environment
	interact
Conservation and change in wilderness areas	area
	benefit
	challenge
	community
	diverse
	implement
	regulate
	stress
	succession
	sustain

Test-Taking Strategies

How can I help my students succeed on tests?

It's not enough for students to learn biology facts and concepts—they must be able to show what they know in a variety of test-taking situations.

How can I help my students do well on objective tests?

Objective tests might include multiple choice, true/false, and matching questions. Applying the following strategies can help students do their best on objective tests.

Multiple-Choice Questions

✓ Students should read the directions carefully to learn what answer the test requires—the best answer or the right answer. This is especially important when answer choices include "all of the above" or "none of the above."

✓ Advise students to watch for negative words in the questions, such as *not, except, unless,* and *never*. If the question contains a negative, the correct answer choice is the one that does not fit.

✓ Students should try to mentally answer the questions before reading the answer choices.

✓ Students should read all the answer choices and cross out those that are obviously wrong. Then they should choose an answer from those that remain.

True/False Questions

✓ It is important that students read the entire question before answering. For an answer to be true, the entire statement must be true. If one part of a statement is false, the answer should be marked *False*.

✓ Remind students to watch for words like *all, never, every,* and *always*. Statements containing absolute words such as these are often false.

Matching Questions

✓ Students should read through both lists before they mark any answers.

✓ Unless an answer can be used more than once, students should cross out each choice as they use it.

✓ Using what they know about grammar can help students find the right answer. When matching a word with its definition, the definition is often the same part of speech (noun or verb, for example) as the word.

How can I help my students do well on essay tests?

Essay tests require students to write a thorough and well-organized answer to a question or questions. Help students use the following strategies on essay tests.

Read the Question

The key to writing successful essays lies in reading and interpreting questions correctly. Teach students to identify and underline key words in the questions, and to use these words to guide them in understanding what the question asks. Help students understand the meaning of some of the most common key words, listed in the chart below.

Analyze	To **analyze** means to systematically and critically examine all parts of an issue or event.
Classify or Categorize	To **classify** or **categorize** means to put people, things, or ideas into groups, based on a common set of characteristics.
Compare and Contrast	To **compare** is to show how things are similar, or alike. To **contrast** is to show how things are different.
Describe	To **describe** means to present a sketch or impression. Rich details help to flesh out a description.
Discuss	To **discuss** means to systematically write about all sides of an issue or event.
Evaluate	To **evaluate** means to make a judgment and support it with evidence.
Explain	To **explain** means to clarify or make plain.
Illustrate	To **illustrate** means to provide examples or to show with a picture or other graphic.
Infer	To **infer** means to read between the lines or to use knowledge and experience to draw conclusions, make a generalization, or form a prediction.
Justify	To **justify** means to prove or to support a position with specific facts and reasons.
Predict	To **predict** means to tell what will happen in the future, based on an understanding of prior events and behaviors.
State	To **state** means to briefly and concisely present information.
Summarize	To **summarize** means to give a brief overview of the main points of an issue or event.

Plan and Write the Essay

After students understand the question, they should follow the steps below to develop and write their essays.

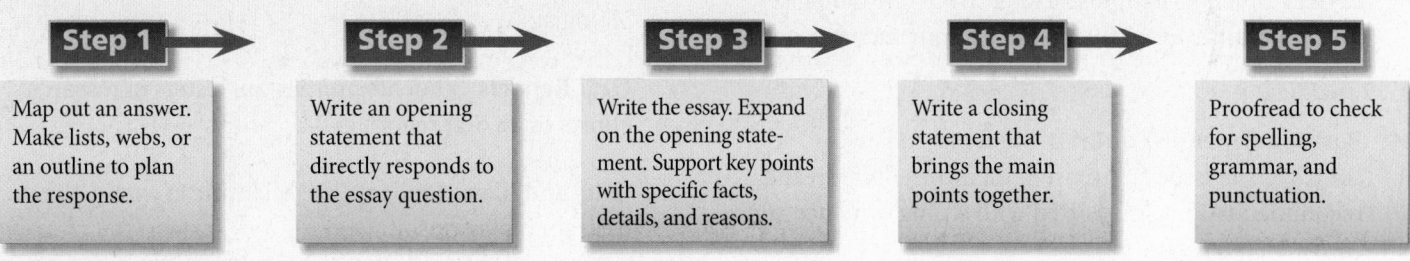

Step 1 → Map out an answer. Make lists, webs, or an outline to plan the response.

Step 2 → Write an opening statement that directly responds to the essay question.

Step 3 → Write the essay. Expand on the opening statement. Support key points with specific facts, details, and reasons.

Step 4 → Write a closing statement that brings the main points together.

Step 5 Proofread to check for spelling, grammar, and punctuation.

SAT/ACT Prep: How can I help my students prepare for the SAT, the ACT, and other standardized tests?

Students can follow the steps below to prepare for a standardized test.

- ✓ **Read About the Test** Students can familiarize themselves with the format of the test, the types of questions that will be asked, and the amount of time they will have to complete the test.
- ✓ **Review the Content** Consistent study throughout the school year will help students build biology knowledge and understanding. If there are specific objectives or standards that are tested on the exam, help students review these facts or skills to be sure they are proficient.
- ✓ **Practice** Provide practice, ideally with released tests, to build students' familiarity with the content, format, and timing of the actual exam. Students should practice all the types of questions they will encounter on the test—multiple choice, short answer, and extended response.
- ✓ **Analyze Practice Results** Help students improve test-taking performance by analyzing their test-taking strengths and weaknesses. Spend time discussing students' completed practice tests, explaining why particular answers are right or wrong. Look for patterns in errors and then tailor your instruction to the appropriate skills or biology content.

Alternative Assessment Strategies

How can I go beyond tests to assess students' understanding of biology facts and concepts?

In response to the growing demand for accountability in the classroom, educators must use multiple assessment measures to accurately gauge student performance. In addition to quizzes, tests, essay exams, and standardized tests, assessment today uses a variety of performance-based measures and portfolio opportunities.

What are some typical performance-based assessments?

There are many kinds of performance-based assessments. They all share one common characteristic: they challenge students to create written or oral reports that demonstrate what they know. One good way to present a performance assessment is in the form of an open-ended question.

Writing

Performance-based writing assessments challenge students to apply their knowledge of biology concepts and information in various ways. Writing activities are most often completed by one student, rather than by a group.

✓ **Journals** Students write from the perspective of a biologist, either current or historical.

✓ **Letters** Students compose a letter from one biologist to another or from a biologist to a family member or other audience.

✓ **Position Paper or Editorial** Students explain a controversial issue and present their own opinion and recommendations, supported with strong evidence and convincing reasons.

✓ **Newspaper** Students write a variety of stories from the perspective of a reporter.

✓ **Biographies and Autobiographies** Students write about biologists either from the third-person point of view (biography) or from the first person (autobiography).

✓ **Creative Stories** Students integrate scientific events into a piece of fiction.

✓ **Poems and Songs** Students follow the conventions of a particular type of song or poem as they tell about a biologist or scientific event.

✓ **Research Reports** Students synthesize information from a variety of sources into a well-developed report.

Oral Presentations

Oral presentations allow students to demonstrate their biology literacy before an audience. Oral presentations are often group efforts, although this need not be the case.

✓ **Simulations** Students hold simulations, or reenactments, of actual events, such as famous experiments or discoveries.

✓ **Debates** Students debate two or more sides to a scientific policy or issue. Students can debate from a contemporary perspective or through role-playing, from the viewpoint of a historical character.

✓ **Interview** Students conduct a mock interview of a biologist.

✓ **Oral Reports** Students present the results of research efforts in an oral report.

✓ **Skits and Plays** Students use scientific events as the basis for a play or skit.

Visual Presentations

Visual presentations allow students to demonstrate their scientific understanding in a variety of visual formats. Visual presentations can be either group or individual projects.

✓ **Model** Students make a model to demonstrate or represent a process or structure.

✓ **Museum Exhibit** Students create a rich display of materials around a topic. Typical displays might include models, illustrations, photographs, videos, writings, and audiotaped presentations.

✓ **Graph or Chart** Students analyze and represent scientific data in a line graph, bar graph, table, or other chart format.

✓ **Drawing** Students represent or interpret a scientific event or period through illustration, including political cartoons.

✓ **Posters and Murals** Posters and murals might include graphs, charts, tables, maps, time lines, diagrams, illustrations, photographs, and text that reflect students' understanding of scientific information.

✓ **Quilt** Students sew or draw a design for a patchwork quilt that shows a variety of perspectives, events, or issues related to a key topic.

✓ **Videotapes or DVDs** Students film a video or DVD to preserve a simulation of a scientific event. Students can also film plays they have written that incorporate biology in some way.

✓ **Multimedia Presentation or Slideshow** Students create a computer-generated multimedia presentation containing scientific information and analysis.

How are performance assessments scored?

There are a variety of means available to evaluate performance tasks. Some or all of the following methods can be used.

✓ **Scoring Rubrics** A scoring rubric is a set of guidelines for assessing the quality of a process and/or product. It sets out criteria used to distinguish acceptable responses from unacceptable ones, generally along a scale from excellent to poor.

RUBRIC A variety of modifiable rubrics are available on your eTeacherEdition Online.

✓ **Models of Excellent Work** Teacher-selected models of excellent work give a concrete illustration of what is expected and help students set goals for their own projects.

✓ **Student Self-Assessment** Common methods of self-assessment include ranking work in relation to the model, using a scoring rubric, and writing their own goals and then evaluating how well they have met these goals. Regardless of the method or methods students use, they should be encouraged to evaluate their behaviors, processes, and the finished product.

✓ **Peer or Audience Assessment** Many of the performance tasks target an audience other than the classroom teacher. If possible, an audience of peers should give the students feedback. Have the class work together to create rubrics for specific projects.

✓ **Observation** As students carry out their performance tasks, you might want to formally observe students at work. Start by developing a checklist, identifying the specific behaviors and knowledge you expect students to demonstrate. Then observe students as they carry out performance tasks and check off these items on your checklist as you observe them.

✓ **Interviews** As a form of ongoing assessment, you might want to conduct interviews with students, asking them to analyze, explain, and assess their participation in performance tasks. When projects take place over an extended period of time, you can hold periodic interviews as well as exit interviews. In this way, you can gauge the status of the project and guide students' efforts along the way.

Web Strategies

How can I use the Internet to teach biology?

From the Internet to round-the-clock live newscasts, teachers and students have never before had so much information at their fingertips. With all the choices available, it is sometimes difficult to determine where to turn for reliable content and what to do with it once you have found it. In today's world, biology teachers use the Internet as a source of up-to-the-minute information for students and teach students how to find and evaluate sources on their own.

What's available on the Internet?

✓ **Teacher-Focused Web Sites** These Web sites provide teaching tips, detailed lesson plans, and links to other sites of interest to teachers and students.

✓ **Scientific Data** Research data has been catalogued and placed on the Web. These sites are rich depositories of statistics for all scientific endeavors.

✓ **Geographical Information** The Web holds a variety of geographical resources, from historical and physical maps; to interactive mapping programs; to information about plants, animals, people, and places in the United States and around the world.

✓ **Statistics** Government Web sites are rich depositories for statistics of all kinds, including information about populations, habitats, bioinformatics, diseases, and other topics relating to biology.

✓ **Reference Sources** Students can access full-text versions of encyclopedias, dictionaries, atlases, and other reference books, as well as databases containing millions of journal and newspaper articles.

✓ **News** Traditional media sources—including television, radio, newspapers, and newsmagazines—sponsor Internet sites that provide almost-instantaneous news updates, as well as in-depth news coverage and analysis. Extensive archives facilitate research on past news stories.

✓ **Topical Information** Among the most numerous Web sites are those organized around a particular topic or issue, such as biotechnology. These Internet pages may contain essays, analyses, and other commentaries, as well as primary source documents, maps, photographs, video and audio clips, bibliographies, and links to related online resources.

✓ **Organizations** Many organizations, such as research institutes, post Web pages that provide online exhibits, archives, and other information.

✓ **Social Media** Many people use resources on the Web to interact with people on an interpersonal level. These resources are known collectively as social media. Some teachers and schools have begun to use social media to foster learning experiences. Discuss using social media in your classroom with your school administrators.

Finding Things on the Internet

The greatest asset of the Internet—its vast array of materials —is also its greatest deterrent. Many excellent biology-specific sites provide links to relevant content. Using Internet search engines can also help you find what you need.

✓ A search engine is an Internet search tool. You type in a keyword, name, or phrase, and the search engine lists the URLs for Web sites that match your search. However, a search engine may find things that are not at all related or may miss sites that you would consider of interest. The key is to find ways to define your search.

✓ Not all search engines are the same. Each seeks out information a little bit differently. Different search engines use different criteria to determine what constitutes a "match" for your search topic. The Internet contains numerous articles that compare search engines and offer guidelines for choosing those that best meet your needs.

✓ An advanced search allows you to refine the search by using a phrase or a combination of words. The way to conduct an advanced search varies from one search engine to another; check the search engine's Help feature for information. Encourage students to review this information regularly for each of the search engines they use.

How do I teach students to evaluate Web sites?

Anyone can develop a Web site. Web content is easy to change, too, so webmasters constantly update their Web sites by adding, modifying, and removing content. These characteristics make evaluating Web sites more challenging than evaluating traditional print resources. Teach students to evaluate Web resources critically, using the questions and criteria below.

1 **Purpose:** What is the purpose of the Web site or Web page? Is it an informational Web page, a news site, a business site, an advocacy site, or a personal Web page? Many sites serve more than one purpose. For instance, a news site may provide current events accompanied by banner ads that market the products advertisers think readers might want.

2 **URL:** What is the URL or Web address? Where does the site originate? That can sometimes tell you about the group or business behind the Web page. For example, URLs whose domain names end in *.edu* and *.gov* indicate that the site is connected to an educational institution or a government agency, respectively.

A *.com* suffix usually means that a commercial or business interest hosts the Web site, but it might also indicate a personal Web page. A nonprofit organization's Web address might end with *.org*.

3 **Authority:** Who wrote the material or created the Web site? What qualifications does this person or group have? Who has ultimate responsibility for the site? If the site is sponsored by an organization, are the organization's goals clearly stated?

4 **Accuracy:** How reliable is the information? Are sources listed so that they can be verified? Is the Web page free from surface errors in spelling and grammar? How does it compare with other sources you've found on the Web and in print?

5 **Objectivity:** If the site presents itself as an informational site, is the material free from bias? If there is advertising, is it easy to tell the difference between the ads and other features? If the site mixes factual information with opinion, can you spot the difference between the two? If the site advocates an opinion or viewpoint, is the opinion clearly stated and logically defended?

6 **Currency:** When was the information first placed online? Is the site updated on a regular basis? When was the last revision? If the information is time-sensitive, are the updates frequent enough?

7 **Coverage:** What topics are covered on the Web site? What is the depth of coverage? Are all sides of an issue presented? How does the coverage compare with other online and print sources?

Using WebQuests with Glencoe Biology

A WebQuest is a web-based inquiry project requiring research, analysis, and synthesis of information. They can be as simple or complex as you would like them to be. The simplest WebQuest format is a word processing document with hyperlinks. A good WebQuest includes a doable task that requires the students to use higher-level thinking skills.

Glencoe Biology provides career-based WebQuests for each Unit, and WebQuest extensions for each end-of-chapter feature. These WebQuests encourage students to explore various careers and topics in Biology. Each *Glencoe Biology* WebQuest results in a synthesis project.

You can create your own WebQuest by following three simple steps.

1. Identify a topic that you want your students to explore.
2. Decide what task you want your students to accomplish by completing the WebQuest. This can be a paper, a project, a video, or debate… the sky's the limit!
3. Find Web sites that you want the students to use in their WebQuests and create a document with the hyperlinks to distribute to the students.

Additional resources for creating your own WebQuests are available online.

English Learners (EL)

How can I reach English learners in the biology classroom?

American classrooms reflect the rich and diverse cultural heritage of the American people. Students come from different ethnic backgrounds and different cultural experiences into a common classroom that must assist all of them in learning. Multicultural and/or bilingual students often speak English as a second language or not at all. In providing for EL students, the focus needs to be on overcoming the language barrier. It is important not to confuse ability in speaking and reading English with academic ability or intelligence. In general, the best method to assist EL students is to provide them with a variety of ways to learn, apply, and be assessed on the concepts. *Glencoe Biology* has risen to this challenge with a full complement of ancillaries and technology for English learners.

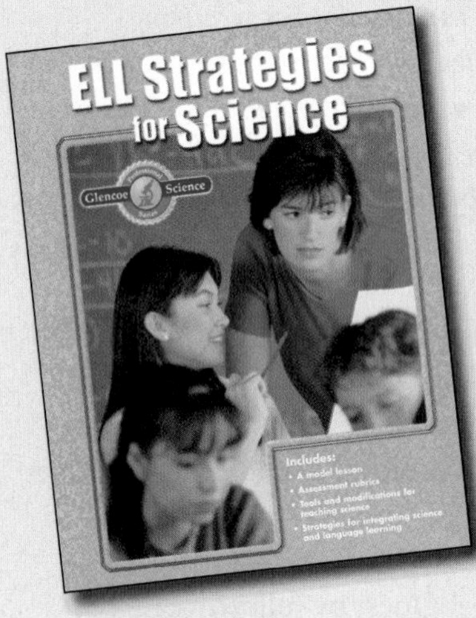

ELL Strategies for Science provides practical tools and suggests modifications that can help students master scientific concepts while developing their English language skills. The book focuses on methods for successful inclusion of EL students in the science classroom. These strategies rely not only on teacher intervention but also on student intervention to create ownership of the learning process.

The Spanish Student Edition of *Glencoe Biology* facilitates the learning of science concepts for students whose first language is Spanish.

The StudentWorks™ Plus Online and StudentWorks™ Plus DVD-ROM include Spanish audio summaries of each chapter to aid the reading comprehension of English learners in the science classroom.

The English/Spanish Glossary/Glosario in both the English and Spanish versions of *Glencoe Biology's* Student Edition helps native Spanish speakers learn science vocabulary.

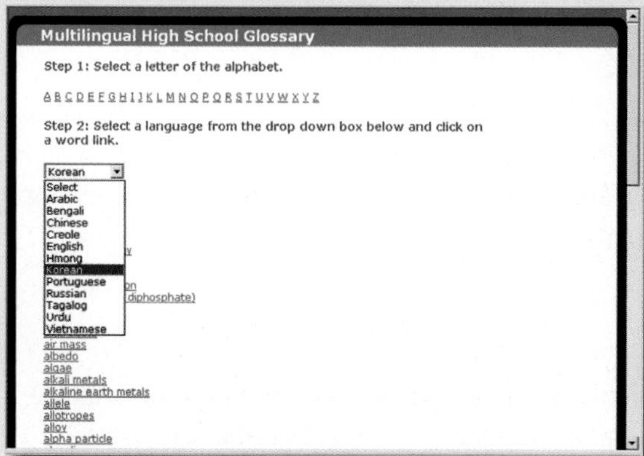

Multilingual eGlossary

The online Multilingual Science Glossary helps speakers of many languages learn science vocabulary. The glossary includes the following languages: Arabic, Bengali, Chinese, English, Haitian Creole, Hmong, Korean, Portuguese, Russian, Spanish, Tagalog, Urdu, and Vietnamese.

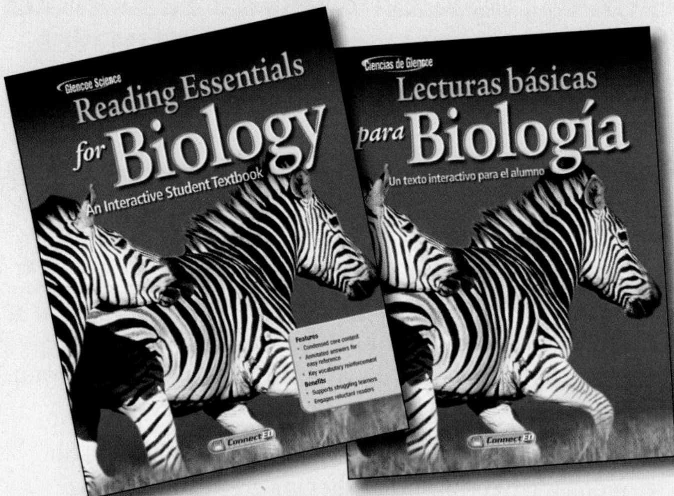

Reading Essentials for Biology (in English and Spanish) is designed to help students use recognized reading strategies to improve their reading-for-information skills. The supporting activities help students practice basic writing skills, find main ideas, review vocabulary terms, and more.

Science Notebook is a note-taking guide designed to help students succeed in learning science content. It contains note-taking tools based on the Cornell Note-Taking System.

EL strategies in the Teacher Wraparound Edition provide teachers with additional support for EL students in the science classroom. Blue asterisks on the A and B pages before each chapter indicate which ancillary and technology products would be useful to EL students.

Reading Strategy

EL BL Review and Preview Divide the class into dominant language groups. While English language students work independently, preview the main ideas and vocabulary with the other groups, allowing them to confer and collaborate with one another in their respective primary languages. Continue with the lesson in English, then regroup and review the key concepts and resolve any concepts that remain unclear.

Inquiry-Based Instruction

***How is inquiry used in* Glencoe Biology?**

In *Glencoe Biology,* the process of inquiry models scientific practice, encouraging problem-solving strategies and developing critical-thinking skills. Inquiry gets students actively involved in the learning process by allowing them to determine materials, procedures, or the topics and questions they want to investigate.

Inquiry Continuum

Inquiry-based instruction can be understood as a continuum. Levels range from a very structured activity in which students are guided through a scientific investigation to open inquiry in which students plan and conduct their own scientific study. It is important to gradually build students' inquiry skills so that they can learn to ask their own questions and apply critical thinking and problem-solving skills. The chart below illustrates the changing roles of the teacher and student as the level of inquiry increases.

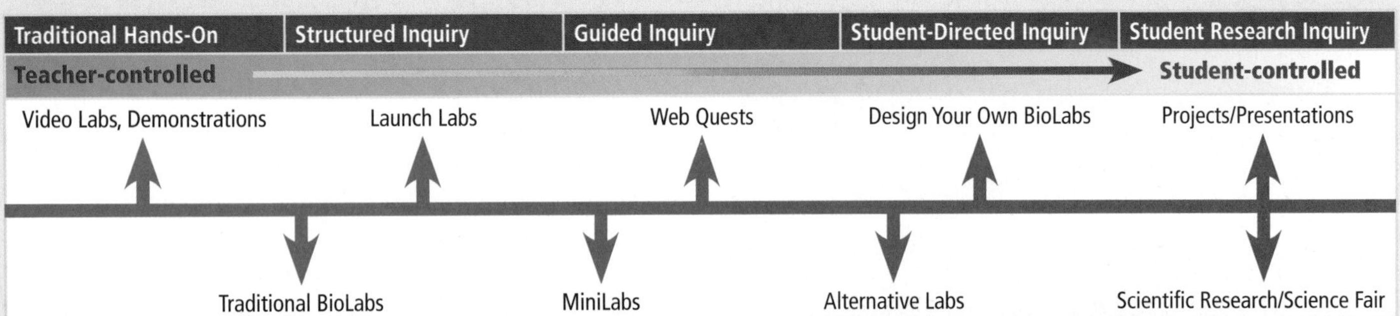

Teaching Tips for Incorporating Inquiry in the Biology Classroom

Inquiry in biology takes time, as students learn the content and build problem-solving skills. Use the following techniques to implement inquiry in the biology classroom.

- ✓ In the beginning of the school year, some students will need more guidance if they are unfamiliar with the practice of scientific inquiry. You might need to teach them how to ask testable questions, make observations, collect reliable data, and use evidence to support their conclusions, as you establish the safety guidelines and behavioral expectations for your lab. Students soon will learn that they can take chances in asking and answering questions and not be afraid of being wrong.
- ✓ Early on, plan and set up long-term experiments and projects with students that they can observe and potentially manipulate throughout the year.
- ✓ Give your students a more guided activity that relates hard-to-understand concepts and skills. Then allow them to explore on their own with a wider variety of materials.
- ✓ Have students brainstorm questions they would like to explore. As a class, choose 1 or 2 reasonable questions that each group will explore on its own. (This is very helpful if you are trying to cover a specific topic or standard.)
- ✓ Divide classes into groups. One group might require more supervision, or could work more closely with you, while other groups can work more independently.
- ✓ Use Problem-Based Learning (PBL) as a framework for inquiry. Exploring local issues is a great way to engage students. For example, if your community has noticed a decline in your native frog population, you and your students could conduct an investigation to determine the cause of the decline. By placing labs into a real-world context, students feel their participation is more relevant and important.
- ✓ Encourage students to rely on the data they collect. If their data or results are unexpected, help them to problem-solve to determine what might have happened.
- ✓ As an alternative assessment tool, have students teach their classmates about the concepts they explore. This is especially effective at the end of the year when students know the teacher's expectations.
- ✓ Build in time for debriefing/discussion so that you make sure that students do not leave the experience with misconceptions. Discussion and elaboration of their ideas will help you determine the depth of their understanding.

Glencoe Professional Development

Science, YES! (Your Education Solution)

Educational Strategies DVD and Workshop Facilitation Guide

This set of five videos emphasizes key issues in science education: Literacy Strategies, Differentiated Instruction, English Learners, Standards-Based Instruction, and Assessment Strategies.

Educational Strategies DVD

Each video begins with a discussion on the topic, providing a clear overview of the key issue and its importance in science education. Next, viewers see lesson excerpts from various science classrooms that demonstrate instructional strategies and techniques used to address the video topic. In place of the classroom demonstrations, the *Standards-Based Instruction and Assessment Strategies* videos present excerpts of science department meetings. In these segments, viewers watch department meeting collaboration to determine local curriculum and assessment.

Workshop Facilitation Guide

The Facilitation Guide contains workshop activities and information for conducting the workshops. Workshop activities foster participants' discussion and collaboration. Each workshop activity provides opportunities for science teachers to evaluate, discuss, and extend the strategies demonstrated in the video.

Educational Strategies Online Professional Development

Science, YES! Educational Strategies Online is comprised of five individual modules. These online modules, including Literacy Strategies, Differentiated Instruction, English Learners, Standards-Based Instruction, and Assessment Strategies, emphasize techniques used to teach science. Each online module contains video, interactive content, and a variety of online learning tools.

Online learners watch video clips of educational commentary and science classroom video delivered over the Web. Tools, such as a glossary, standards links, and lists of Web resources, are included throughout. Module content encourages online learners to discuss ideas with others in their online community through the discussion board.

The modules may be taken individually or they may be taken together as a university course. An electronic portfolio can be used to verify module completion for university credit. They can be combined with other modules to develop custom courses. A module takes 6-8 hours to complete and contains six content segments—Introduce, Model, Practice, Assess, Classroom Connection and Textbook Tie. Segments divide the content into shorter manageable chunks of learning, making it easy for a busy teacher to complete the module.

Unit Resources

These unit resource books contain effective content, lab, and assessment activity worksheets that will strengthen every student's understanding of *Glencoe Biology*.

Each *FAST FILE* includes:

1. Diagnostic Tests (All levels)
2. Launch Lab Worksheets
3. MiniLab Worksheets
4. BioLab Worksheets
5. Real-World Biology (On level)
6. Enrichment (Above level)
7. Concept Mapping (On level)
8. Study Guides (Below level)
9. Spanish Study Guides
10. Section Quick Checks (Scaffolded)
11. Chapter Tests
    Test A (Below level)
    Test B (On level)
    Test C (Above level)

Reading in Biology

Reading Essentials for Biology

- is written 2–3 grade levels below the student edition in English and Spanish;
- emphasizes only the most essential content to help struggling readers and learners;
- contains various reading strategies to help students improve their reading-for-information skills.

Science Notebook

- implements the Cornell Note-Taking System;
- helps students use their textbooks more effectively;
- can be used with the *Glencoe Biology Student Edition* and *Reading Essentials for Biology.*

Transparencies

Bellringers One hundred eleven full-color visuals and scaffolded questions accompany every *Glencoe Biology* section. These transparencies will capture students' attention by connecting biology and the real world.

Biology Concepts One hundred fifty full-color transparencies of essential Student Edition art help you teach basic biology concepts.

Transparencies are all available through your eTeacherEdition Online. Project them digitally or make your own transparencies to best meet your students' needs.

Lab Manuals

Biology Lab Manual A mix of classic and design-your-own labs provides students with varying skill levels.

Probeware for Biology Lab Manual Ten labs provide students with the opportunity to use a probeware data-collection system to integrate technology in the classroom.

Biology Pre-AP Lab Manual This manual contains 17 lab activities designed for a high school pre-AP biology curriculum. Each activity is based on the AP-recommended lab topics.

Forensics Lab Manual Ten hands-on labs emphasize scientific inquiry as a way of thinking and problem solving. The high-interest topics reinforce concepts and relate scientific processes to technological and societal issues.

Open Inquiry in Biology Ten interesting and in-depth projects challenge advanced students.

Guided Inquiry in Biology Ten inquiry-based labs increase students' independence in stating hypotheses, designing and performing investigations, and collecting and analyzing data.

Teacher Classroom Resources

ConnectED

connectED.mcgraw-hill.com

This is the complete solution for managing student and teacher resources.

Includes:

- eTeacherEdition Online
- StudentWorks™ Plus Online
- access to online quizzes, online test practice, and standardized test practice
- interactive activities to review chapter concepts, including Personal Tutors, Vocabulary eFlashcards, Vocabulary eGames, and videos
- Multilingual eGlossary
- Animations, Interactive Tables, and The Interactive Timeline
- WebQuests
- And much, much more!

eTeacherEdition Online

eTeacherEdition Online

Use your all-in-one teacher resource center to personalize lesson plans, access resources, or make a to-do list.

Includes:

- interactive Student Edition with integrated Teacher Support
- editable worksheets
- program blackline masters
- also available on DVD-ROM

StudentWorks Plus

StudentWorks™ Plus Online

This is the student's backpack solution.

Includes:

- complete Interactive Student Edition
- audio integrated throughout text (English and Spanish)
- activities and resources
- access to all student worksheets
- also available on DVD-ROM

Classroom Presentation Toolkit

Classroom Presentation Toolkit CD-ROM

Lesson planning is simple with editable Microsoft® PowerPoint® presentations. Use this tool to teach key concepts from each section or customize your own presentations.

Includes:

- video, audio, and animations
- interactive graphics
- image bank
- section presentations
- all transparencies

ExamView® Assessment Suite

ExamView® Assessment Suite

Create and customize tests easily and quickly with this convenient test platform.

Includes:

- QuickTest Wizard to create assessments
- standards-based questions that can easily be incorporated into your tests
- capability to modify tests for a desired difficulty level
- capability to track students' progress using the Teacher Management System

LabManager™

LabManager™ CD-ROM

LabManager makes individualizing labs easy. Search the database by topic, time required, materials, and key words. Choose from thousands of labs and edit them to suit your needs or use our template to create your own labs.

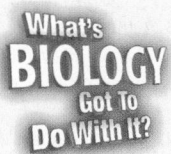

Video Labs DVD

Video Labs Include:

- step-by-step lab procedures
- lab safety skills
- teacher support
- troubleshooting advice

What's BIOLOGY Got To Do With It?

What's BIOLOGY Got To Do With It? DVD

Engage your students with these videos from the Glencoe Science Video Library.

Includes:

- applications of biology concepts in real-life situations
- videos that reinforce biology concepts through problem-based learning

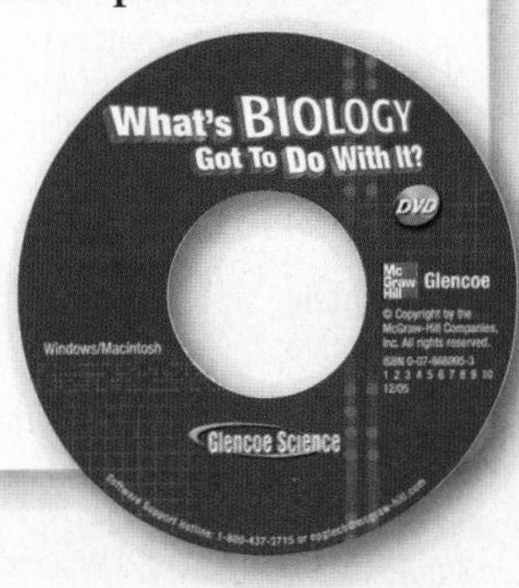

Virtual Labs

Virtual Labs CD-ROM Program

The Virtual Labs CD-ROM contains a collection of labs that allow students to complete labs that would be impractical to complete in a classroom lab setting.

Research Bibliography

In the bottom wrap of the Teacher Edition, you will find Research Citations that highlight research that supports teaching strategies used in the TE. The research is cited at point-of-use in the TE, but the full citations are listed here. Use these resources for additional professional development and discovery about various educational strategies to enhance the effectiveness of your teaching.

Alexander, P.A. 1984. Training analogical reasoning skills in the gifted. Roeper Review 6: 191–193.

Allen, J. 1999. *Words, Words, Words: Teaching Vocabulary in Grades 4–12.* Portland, ME: Stenhouse.

Alvermann, D.E., and P.R. Boothby. 1986. Children's transfer of graphic organizer instruction. *Reading Psychology* 7: 87–100.

Anderson, J.R. 1995. *Learning and Memory: An Integrated Approach.* New York: Wiley.

Anderson, T.H., and B.B. Armbruster. 1986. *The Value of Taking Notes During Lectures.* Cambridge, MA: Bolt, Beranek, & Newman.

Armbruster, B.B., T.H. Anderson, and J. Ostertag. 1987. Does text structure/summarization instruction facilitate learning from expository text? *Reading Research Quarterly* 22: 331–346.

Baumann, J.F., and E.J. Kameenui. 1991. Research on vocabulary instruction: Ode to Voltaire. In J. Flood, et al. *Handbook on Teaching the English Language Arts.* New York: MacMillan.

Blachowicz, C.L.Z. 1986. Making connections: alternatives to the vocabulary notebook. *Journal of Reading* 29: 643–649.

Brandford, J.D., et al. 2000. *How people learn: brain, mind, experience, and school.* Washington, DC: National Academy Press.

Bredekamp, S., and C. Copple. 1997. *Developmentally appropriate practice in early childhood programs.* Washington, DC: National Association for the Education of Young Children.

Buehl, D. 2001. *Classroom strategies for interactive learning.* Newark, DE: International Reading Association.

Carr, E., and D. Ogle. 1987. K–W–L plus: a strategy for comprehension and summarization. *Journal of Reading* 30: 626–631.

Carrasquillo, A.L., and V. Rodriguez. 1996. *Language and Minority Students in the Mainstream Classroom.* Clevedon, UK: Multilingual Matters.

Chambers, A. 1996. *Tell me: children, reading, and talk.* Portland, ME: Stenhouse.

Charles, R.I., and F.K. Lester, Jr. 1984. An evaluation of a process oriented mathematical problem–solving instructional program in grades 5 and 7. *Journal for Research in Mathematics Education* 15: 15–34.

Chen, Z. 1996. Children's analogical problem solving: the effects of superficial, structural, and procedural similarities. *Journal of Experimental Child Psychology* 62: 410–431.

Chen, Z. 1999. Schema induction in children's analogical problem solving. *Journal of Educational Psychology* 91: 703–715.

Chi, M.T.H., P.J. Feltovich, and R. Glaser. 1981. Categorization and representation of physics problems by experts and novices. *Cognitive Science* 5: 121–152.

Cole, J.C., and J.S. McLeod. 1999. Children's writing ability: the impact of the pictorial stimulus. *Psychology in the Schools* 36: 359–370.

Cooper, H. 1989. *Homework.* White Plains, NY: Longman.

Cooper, H. 1989. Synthesis of research on homework. *Educational Leadership* 47: 85–91.

Cooper, H., et al. 1999. Relationship between five after–school activities and academic achievement. *Journal of Educational Psychology* 91: 369–378.

Cummins, J. 2000. *Language, power, and pedagogy: bilingual children in the crossfire.* Clevedon, UK: Multilingual Matters.

Dagher, Z.R. 1995. Does the use of analogies contribute to conceptual change? *Science and Education* 78: 601–614.

Darch, C.B., D.W. Camine, and E.J. Kameenui. 1986. The role of graphic organizers and social structure in content area instruction. *Journal of Reading Behavior* 18: 275–295.

Davey, B. 1986. Using textbook activity guides to help students learn from textbooks. *Journal of Reading* 29: 489–494.

Denner, P.R. 1986. *Comparison of the effects of episodic organizers and traditional note taking on story recall.* Boise: Idaho State University.

Dong, Y.R. 2002. Integrating language and content: How three biology teachers work with non–native English–speaking students. *International Journal of Bilingual Education and Bilingualism* 5: 40–57.

Dong, Y.R. 2004. *Teaching language and content to linguistically and culturally diverse students: principles, ideas, and materials.* Greenwich, CT: Information Age Publishing.

Duncker, K. 1945. On problem–solving. *Psychological Monographs* 58: 270.

Duschl, R.A. 2003. Assessment of inquiry. In J.M. Arkin and J.E. Coffey. *Everyday Assessment in the Science Classroom.* Arlington, VA: NSTA Press.

Eanet, M., and A. Manzo. 1976. R.E.A.P. — a strategy for improving reading/ writing study skills. *Journal for Reading* 19: 647–652.

Einstein, G.O., J. Morris, and S. Smith. 1985. Note taking, individual differences, and memory for lecture information. *Journal of Educational Psychology* 77: 522–532.

English, L.D. 1997. *Mathematical Reasoning: Analogies, Metaphors, and Images.* Mahwah, NJ: Lawrence Erlbaum.

Eyler, J., and D.E. Giles. 1999. *Where's the learning in service–learning?* San Francisco: Jossey–Bass.

Fielding, L.G., and P.D. Pearson. 1994. Synthesis of research: Reading comprehension: what works. *Educational Leadership* 51: 62–67.

Fisher, D., and N. Frey. 2004. *Improving adolescent literacy: strategies at work.* Upper Saddle River, NJ: Merrill Prentice Hall.

Fisher, D., and C.H. Kennedy. 2001. *Differentiated instruction for diverse middle school students: inclusive middle schools.* Baltimore, MD: Paul H. Brookes.

Flick, L. 1992. Where concepts meet percepts: stimulating analogical thought in children. *Science and Education* 75: 215–230.

Gagne, R.M., and M.P. Driscoll. 1988. *Essentials of learning for instruction.* Englewood Cliffs, NJ: Prentice Hall.

Gentner, D., and A.B. Markman.1994. Structural alignment in comparison: No difference without similarity. *Psychological Science* 5: 152–158.

Gerlic, I., and N. Jausovec. 1999. Multimedia: differences in cognitive processes observed with EEG. *Educational Technology Research and Development* 47: 5–14.

Gick, M.L., and K.J. Holyoak. 1980. Analogical problem solving. *Cognitive Psychology* 12: 306–355.

Gilbert, S., and S.W. Ireton. 2003. *Understanding models in earth and space science.* Arlington, VA: NSTA Press.

Gillet, J.W., and C.Temple. 1982. Understanding reading problems: assessment and instruction. Boston: Little, Brown.

Good, T.L., D.A. Grouws, and H. Ebmeier. 1983. *Active mathematics teaching.* New York: Longman.

Gorges, T.C., and S.N. Elliott. 1995. Homework: parent and student involvement and their effects on academic performance. *Canadian Journal of School Psychology* 11: 18–31.

Gottfried, G.M. 1998. Using metaphors as modifiers: children's production of metaphoric compounds. *Journal of Child Language* 24: 567–601.

Griffin, C., D.C. Simmons, and E.J. Kameenui. 1992. Investigating the effectiveness of graphic organizer instruction on the comprehension and recall of science content by students with learning disabilities. *Journal of Reading, Writing, and Learning Disabilities International* 4: 355–376.

Heibert, J., et al. 1997. *Making sense: teaching and learning mathematics with understanding.* Portsmouth, NH: Heinemann Prentice Research.

Hembree, R. and H. Marsh. 1993. Problem solving in early childhood: building foundations. In R.J. Jensen. *Research Ideas for the Classroom: Early Childhood Mathematics.* New York: McMillen.

Hitt, A., and S. Townsend. 2004. Models that matter. *The Science Teacher* 71: 29–32.

Hoffman, J. 1992. Critical reading/thinking across the curriculum: using I–charts to support learning. *Language Arts* 69: 121–127.

Holliday, W.G. 2004. Choosing science textbooks: connecting research to common sense. In E.W. Saul. *Crossing Borders in Literacy and Science Instruction Perspectives on Theory and Practice.* Newark, DE: International Reading Asssociation.

Horowitz, R. 1985. Text patterns. *Journal of Reading* 28: 448–454.

Horton, S.V., T.C. Lovitt, and D. Bergerud. 1990. The effectiveness of graphic organizers for three classifications of secondary students in content area classes. *Journal of Learning Disabilities* 23: 12–22.

Jitendra, A.K., M.M. Salmento, and L.A. Haydt. 1999. Adherence to important instructional design criteria. *Learning Disabilities Research and Practice* 14: 69–79.

Johnson, D.W., et al. 1984. *Circle of learning: cooperation in the classroom.* Alexandria, VA: Association of Supervision and Curriculum Development.

Jorgensen, C.M. 1988. Restructuring high schools for all students. Baltimore: Paul H. Brookes.

Kaput, J., and J.E. Sims–Knight. 1983. Errors in translations to algebraic equations: roots and implications. *Focus on Learning Problems in Mathematics* 5: 63–78.

Kintsch, W. 1979. On modeling comprehension. *Educational Psychologist* 1: 3–14.

Kirby, D., T. Liner, and R. Vinz. 1988. *Inside out: developmental strategies for teaching writing.* Portsmouth, NH: Heinemann–Boynton/Cook.

Kirkpatrick, J., W.G. Martin, and D. Schifter. 2003. *A research companion to principals and standards for school mathematics.* Reston, Virginia: National Council of Teachers of Mathematics.

Kloosterman, P. and P.H. Gainey. 1993. Students' thinking: middle grade methematics. In *Research ideas for the classroom: middle grades mathematics.* Reston, Virginia: National Council of Teachers of Mathematics.

Lampert, M., and P. Cobb. 2003. Communication and language. In J. Kilpatrick, W.G. Martin, and D. Schifter. *A research companion to principles and standards for school mathematics.* Reston, VA: National Council of Teachers of Mathematics.

Langer, J.A., and A. Applebee. 1987. *How writing shapes thinking.* Urbana, IL: National Council of Teachers of English.

Lewis. 1991. *The kid's guide to social action.* Free Spirit Publishing.

Manzo, A. 1969. The ReQuest procedure. *Journal of Reading* 13: 23–26.

Markman, A.B., and D. Gentner. 1993. Splitting the differences: a structural alignment view of similarity. *Journal of Memory and Learning* 32: 517–535.

Markman, A.B., and D. Gentner. 1993. Structural alignment during similarity comparisons. *Cognitive Psychology* 25: 431–467.

Martin, C.E., M.A. Martin, and C.G. O'Brien. 1984. Spawning ideas for writing in the content area. *Reading World* 11: 11–15.

Marzano, Pickering, and Pollack. 2001. *Classroom instruction that works: research based strategies for increasing student achievement.* ASCD.

Mason, L. 1994. Cognitive and metacognitive aspects in conceptual change by analogy. *Instructional Science* 22: 157–187.

Mason, L. 1995. *Analogy, meta–conceptual awareness and conceptual change: a classroom study.* Educational Studies 20: 267–291.

Mayer, R.E. 1979. Can advance organizers influence meaningful learning? *Review of Educational Research* 49: 371–383.

Mayer, R.E. 1989. Models of understanding. *Review of Educational Research* 59: 43–64.

McGinley, W., and P. Denner. 1987. Story impressions: a prereading/ writing activity. *Journal of Reading* 31: 248–253.

McKeown, M.G., et al. 1992. The contribution of prior knowledge and coherent text to tools for teaching content comprehension. *Reading Research Quarterly* 27: 79–93.

McLaughlin, E.M. 1991. Effects of graphic organizers and levels of text difficulty on less–proficient fifth–grade readers' comprehension of expository text. *Disseration Abstracts International* 51: 3028.

McTeague, F. 1996. The questions game. In A. Chambers. *Tell me: children, reading, and talk.* Portland, ME: Stenhouse.

Medin, D., R.L. Goldstone, and A.B. Markman. 1995. Comparison and choice: relationship between similarity processes and decision processes. *Psychonomic Bulletin & Review* 2: 1–19.

Mohan, B., C. Leung, and C. Davison. 2001. *English as a second language in the mainstream.* Harlow, UK: Longman.

Morgan, W., and M. Streb. 2001. Building citizenship: how student voice in service–learning develops civic values. *Social Science Quarterly* 82: 155–169.

Nagy, W. 1988. *Teaching vocabulary to improve reading comprehension.* Newark, DE: International Reading Association.

National Research Council. 2002. *Helping children learn mathematics.* Washington, DC: National Academy Press.

National Research Council. 2002. *How students learn: history, mathematics, and science in the classroom.* Washington DC: National Academy Press.

Newall, A., and P.S. Rosenbloom. 1981. Mechanisms of skill acquisition and the law of practice. In J.R. Anderson. *Cognitive skills and their acquisition.* Hillsdale, NJ: Erlbaum.

Newby, T.J., P.A. Ertmer, and D.A. Stepich. 1995. Instructional analogies and the learning of concepts. *Educational Technology Research and Development* 43: 5–18.

Newkirk, T. 1986. *To compose: teaching writing in the high school.* Portsmouth, NH: Heinemann.

Ogle, D. 1986. K–W–L: a teaching model that develops active reading of expository text. *Reading Teacher* 39: 563–570.

Paivio, A. 1969. Mental imagery in associative learning and memory. *Psychological Review* 76: 241–263.

Paivio, A. 1971. *Imagery and verbal processing.* New York: Holt, Rinehart & Winston.

Paivio, A. 1990. *Mental representations: a dual coding approach.* New York: Oxford University Press.

Research Bibliography

Palinscar, A.S., and A. Brown. 1986. Interactive teaching to promote independent learning from text. *Reading Teacher* 39: 771–777.

Pauk, W. 1974. *How to study in college.* Boston: Houghton Mifflin.

Pearson, P.D., and D. Johnson. 1978. *Teaching reading: tools for teaching content comprehension.* New York: Holt, Rinehart, and Winston.

Polya, G. 1957. *How to solve it: a new aspect of mathematical method.* Princeton, NJ: Princeton University Press.

Raphael, T. 1984. Teaching learners about sources of information for answering comprehension questions. *Journal of Reading* 27: 303–311.

Raphael, T., and P.D. Pearson. 1982. *The effect of metacognitive awareness training on children's question answering behavior.* Urbana, IL: Center for the Study of Reading.

Ratterman, M.J., and D. Gentner. 1998. More evidence for a relational shift in the development of analogy: children's performance on a causal–mapping task. *Cognitive Development* 13: 453–478.

Readance, J.E., T. Bean, and R.S. Baldwin. 1985. *Content–area reading: an integrated approach.* Dubuque, IA: Kendall/Hunt.

Reeves, C.A., and R. Reeves. 2003. Encouraging students to think about how they think. *Mathematics Teaching in the Middle School* 8: 378.

Ripoli, T. 1999. Why this made me think of that. *Thinking and Reasoning* 4: 15–43.

Robinson, D.H., and D.A. Kiewra. 1996. Visual argument: graphic organizers are superior to outlines in improving learning from text. *Journal of Educational Psychology* 87: 455–467.

Rosenberg, M.S. 1989. The effects of daily homework assignment in the acquisition of basic skills by students with learning disabilities. *Journal of Learning Disabilities* 22: 314–323.

Rosenshine, B., and Meister, C.C. 1994. Reciprocal teaching: A review of the research. *Review of Educational Research* 64: 479–530.

Rosenshine, B., C. Meister, and S. Chapman. 1996. Teaching students to generate questions: A review of the intervention studies. *Review of Educational Research* 66: 181–221.

Ross, B.H. 1987. This is like that: the use of earlier problems and the separation of similarity effects. *Journal of Experimental Psychology* 13: 629–639.

Siegel, M., et al. 1996. Using reading to construct mathematical meaning. In P.C. Elliot. *Communication in mathematics: K–12 and beyond.* Reston, VA: National Council of Teachers of Mathematics.

Simpson, M.L., et al. 1988. An initial validation of study strategy system. *Journal of Reading Behavior* 20: 149–180.

Snow, M.A., M. Met, and F. Genesee. 1989. A conceptual framework for the integration of language and content in second/foreign language instruction. *TESOL Quarterly* 23: 201–217.

Solomon, I. 1995. Analogical transfer and "functional fixedness" in the science classroom. *Journal of Educational Research* 87: 371–377.

Sowell, E.J. 1989. Effects of manipulative materials in mathematics instruction. *Journal for Research in Mathematics Education* 20:498–505.

Stanic, G.M.A., and J. Kilpatrick. 1989. Historical perspective on problem solving in the mathematics curriculum. In R.I. Charles and E.A. Silver. *The teaching and assessing of mathematical problem solving.* Reston, VA: National Council of Teachers of Mathematics.

Stauffer, R. 1969. *Directing reading maturity as a cognitive process.* New York: Harper & Row.

Steen, L.A., and S.L. Forman. 1995. Mathematics for work and life. In I. Carl. *Prospects for school mathematics: seventy–five years of progress.* Reston, VA: National Council of Teachers of Mathematics.

Sternberg, R.J. 1979. *The development of human intelligence.* New Haven, CT: Yale University, Department of Psychology.

Sternberg, R.J. 1977. *Intelligence, information processing and analogical reasoning: the componential analysis of human abilities.* Hillsdale, NJ: Erlbaum.

Sternberg, R.J. 1978. *Toward a unified componential theory of human reasoning.* New Haven, CT: Yale University, Department of Psychology.

Sutton, J., and A. Krueger. 2002. *EDThoughts: what we know about mathematics teaching and learning.* Aurora, Colorado: Mid–Continent Research for Education and Learning.

Suydam, M.N. 1980. Untangling clues from research on problem solving. In S. Krulik and R.E. Reys. *Problem solving in school mathematics: 1908 yearbook.* Reston, VA: National Council of Teachers of Mathematics.

Swain, M. 1996. Integrating language and content in immersion classrooms: Research perspectives. *The Canadian Modern Language Review* 52: 529–548.

Swick, Kevin J., et al. 2002. *Service Learning and Character Education: Walking the Talk.* Corporation for National and Community Service.

Taba, H. 1967. *Teacher's handbook for elementary social studies.* Reading, MA: Addison–Wesley.

Tomlinson, C.A. 2001. *How to differentiate instruction in mixed–ability classroom.* Alexandria, Virginia: Association for Supervision and Curriculum Development.

Tomlinson, C. A., et al. 2003. Differentiating instruction in response to student readiness, interest, and learning profile in academically diverse classroom: A review of literature. *Journal for the Education of the Gifted* 27: 119–145.

Trafton, P.R. 1984. Toward more effective, efficient instruction in mathematics. *Elementary School Journal* 84: 514–528.

Van Dijk, T.A. 1980. *Macrostructures.* Hillsdale, NJ: Lawrence Erlbaum.

Vygotsky, L. 1962. *Thought and language.* Cambridge, MA: MIT Press.

Wenglinsky, H. 2000. *How teaching matters: bringing the classroom back into discussions of teacher quality.* Princeton, NJ: Educational Testing Service.

Winograd, P. 1984. Strategic difficulties in summarizing texts. *Reading Research Quarterly* 19: 404–425.

Wood, T., and T. Turner–Vorbeck. 2001. Extending the conception of mathematics teaching. In T. Wood, B.S. Nelson, and J. Warfield. *Beyond classical pedagogy: teaching elementary school mathematics.* Mahwah, NJ: Lawrence Eribaum Associates.

Zeldin, S., and S. Tarlov. 1997. Service learning as a vehicle for youth development. In J. Schine. *Service learning*: ninety-sixth yearbook of the national society for the study of education. Chicago: University of Chicago Press.

Setting the Standard for National Science Literacy

Unifying Concepts and Processes

UCP.1 Systems, order, and organization

UCP.2 Evidence, models, and explanation

UCP.3 Change, constancy, and measurement

UCP.4 Evolution and equilibrium

UCP.5 Form and function, Science as Inquiry

Science as Inquiry

A.1 Abilities necessary to do scientific inquiry

A.2 Understandings about scientific inquiry

Physical Science

B.1 Structure of atoms

B.2 Structure and properties of matter

B.3 Chemical reactions

B.4 Motions and forces

B.5 Conservation of energy and increase in disorder

B.6 Interactions of energy and matter

Life Science

C.1 The cell

C.2 Molecular basis of heredity

C.3 Biological evolution

C.4 Interdependence of organisms

C.5 Matter, energy, and organization in living systems

C.6 Behavior of organisms

Earth and Space Sciences

D.1 Energy in the earth system

D.2 Geochemical cycles

D.3 Origin and evolution of the earth system

D.4 Origin and evolution of the universe

Science and Technology

E.1 Abilities of technological design

E.2 Understandings about science and technology

Science in Personal and Social Perspectives

F.1 Personal and community health

F.2 Population growth

F.3 Natural resources

F.4 Environmental quality

F.5 Natural and human-induced hazards

F.6 Science and technology in local, national, and global challenges

History and Nature of Science

G.1 Science as a human endeavor

G.2 Nature of scientific knowledge

G.3 Historical perspectives

Pacing Guide

Planning Your School Year
Glencoe Biology provides a complete selection of core concepts that are presented to effectively meet the needs of all students. The following Pacing Guide offers general suggestions for pacing your students through the book. Three different class levels and two different schedule types are provided to assist you in

- designing a biology course that meets the needs of your individual students and classes;
- setting the pace at which the content is covered;
- determining what material should be given the most emphasis.

For the following pacing guides, a regular period is defined as one 45-minute class period, and a block period is defined as one 90-minute class period. The total number of days in each level of pacing is fewer than the typical 180-day school year to allow for flexibility in planning due to testing, school cancellations, or shortened class periods.

Basic Biology Course – For this option, teachers should spend more time on the core areas and then choose one of the groups to finish the school year.

Core Areas		
Chapter	Regular Periods	Block Periods
1	8	4
2	6	3
3	5	2.5
4	9	4.5
5	7	3.5
6	9	4.5
7	6	3
8	6	3
9	8	4
10	7	3.5
11	9	4.5
12	8	4
13	7	3.5
14	6	3
15	8	4
16	8	4
17	9	4.5
plus one of the groups below		
Units 5 & 6		
18	4	2
19	7	3.5
20	5	2.5
21	7	3.5
22	5	2.5
23	5	2.5
Units 7 & 8		
24	5	2.5
25	6	3
26	5	2.5
27	3	1.5
28	3	1.5
29	4	2
30	4	2
31	4	2
Unit 9		
32	5	2.5
33	6	3
34	5	2.5
35	6	3
36	6	3
37	6	3

General Biology Course – This option offers a more accelerated pace and covers more material than the basic course.

Core Areas		
Chapter	Regular Periods	Block Periods
1	6	3
2	8	4
3	7	3.5
4	5	2.5
5	6	3
6	8	4
7	8	4
8	6	3
9	6	3
10	5	2.5
11	6	3
12	8	4
13	5	2.5
14	4	2
15	7	3.5
16	5	2.5
17	7	3.5
18	4	2
19	6	3
20	5	2.5
21	7	3.5
22	5	2.5
23	5	2.5
plus one of the groups below		
Unit 7		
24	5	2.5
25	5	2.5
26	5	2.5
27	3	1.5
Unit 8		
28	4	2
29	4	2
30	5	2.5
31	5	2.5
Unit 9 (part 1)		
32	6	3
33	7	3.5
34	5	2.5
Unit 9 (part 2)		
35	5	2.5
36	6	3
37	7	3.5

Honors Biology Course – This option is designed to take students through the content at the depth and pace appropriate for an honors class.

Core Areas		
Chapter	Regular Periods	Block Periods
1	3	1.5
2	4	2
3	5	2.5
4	5	2.5
5	3	1.5
6	9	4.5
7	8	4
8	9	4.5
9	5	2.5
10	8	4
11	6	3
12	7	3.5
13	7	3.5
14	4	2
15	8	4
16	1	0.5
17	2	1
18	8	4
19	5	2.5
20	2	1
21	4	2
22	4	2
23	4	2
24	4	2
25	5	2.5
26	4	2
27	2	1
28	4	3
29	3	1.5
30	2	1
31	2	1
plus one of the groups below		
Unit 9 (part 1)		
32	4	2
33	4	2
34	5	2.5
Unit 9 (part 2)		
35	4	2
36	4	2
37	5	2.5

Safety in the Laboratory

The Need for Safety: Creating a Safety Culture

Creating a culture of safety requires the development of a safety ethic based on the understanding of teacher responsibilities, student responsibilities, and the creation of a safe science environment. A safety ethic as an entity is difficult to define. It is a target rather than a thing. It is exhibited through our actions and what we strive to achieve.

It is impossible to anticipate all the safety issues that teachers might face within their science curriculum. The study of biology brings with it a unique set of safety concerns for the student and teacher. Teachers are not expected to be superhuman in their efforts. Rather, they are expected to be reasonable and prudent within their training and teaching experiences when anticipating safety concerns and adjusting accordingly. Such a safety ethic should include habits of observing carefully and critically within the biology lessons students will study. Common sense and the safety ethic in conjunction with a teacher's experience are the keys to keeping teachers and students safe.

Teacher Responsibilities

There is extensive agreement within the profession that the "hands-on, minds-on" approach to teaching and learning science, described within the NSES, is more effective for everyone. However, this curriculum results in serious safety challenges for uninformed teachers and students. This situation is further exacerbated in old and/or poorly equipped or maintained facilities.

According to Gerlovich, et al. (2004), as a teacher, the only way you can be certain that your students are safe when they are involved in inquiry-based active science learning is to assure that you address the following five concerns.

- ✓ First, you must be vigilant in *what activities you select* for student involvement.
- ✓ Second, you must be certain that *students are instructed in and understand the hazards* associated with these labs/activities.
- ✓ Third, you must verify that they are *properly supervised* throughout these activities.
- ✓ Fourth, you must be certain that *all equipment is in operating order* and accessible during emergencies.
- ✓ Fifth, it is imperative that facilities are *properly maintained.*

In each of the biology labs, you are provided specific activity **Safety Precautions** to assist you in addressing safety concerns. It is your responsibility to communicate this information clearly and emphatically to your students prior to performing labs. It is the students' responsibility to reflect their understanding of them in writing, using the *Lab Safety Form*.

The student responses must be sufficiently clear and accurate so that you can recognize that he/she is restating the most important safety details in his or her own words. You can then approve the student's safety responses by initialing or signing in the appropriate space on the form. Be sure to keep the form on file. Only at this point can you be confident that the students can safely proceed with the lab/activity.

Following this plan will not only protect students, it will also protect you by documenting that you have met all of your duties—instruction, supervision, and maintenance.

Only basic safety guidelines have been provided within this text. The purpose of the safety segment of this material is to encourage you to be cautious in all of your work with students. It is your responsibility to model and instill a safety ethic in all scientific investigations and create a classroom safety culture for everyone.

In addition to these guidelines, *Safety Symbols* have been provided in many of the student labs and activities. Understanding and applying the safety precautions communicated by these symbols along with the *Lab Safety Form* should combine to help prevent injury to students and you as teacher.

Field Experiences

It is the teacher's responsibility to understand the unique safety issues relating to in-the-field experiences. Prior to the field trip, the field-experience site should be pre-evaluated for safety hazards (for example: poison ivy, ticks, terrain, etc.) and applicability to the educational goals. Special attention should be paid to unique clothing and protective equipment needed by the students (helmets, goggles, gloves, etc.) for the site being studied. Students should be informed of any hazards associated with the site. The adult/student ratio should be limited to 1:10. If students with special needs are present, each represents two students in that ratio.

Each student's parent or guardian should complete a school-authorized field trip permission form indicating approval of their child's participation. The accompanying adults should be informed of the purpose of the trip, be familiarized with the site, and cautioned about any potential hazards on the site. You should be aware of any student medical problems (hay fever, allergies, etc.) that may exist and be prepared to address those. A question concerning student health issues should be included in the permission form so that parents have the opportunity to indicate issues related to their child.

A buddy system for the students should be established and the responsibilities of each student explained. Pre-arranged meeting sites should be established and shared with adults and students. It is recommended teachers have a means of communication (cell phone, two-way radio) in case of emergency while off school grounds.

For much more comprehensive science safety information, including applicable laws, codes, and professional standards as well as comprehensive, customizable safety audits, chemical management systems, safety videos, safety research studies, and hundreds of applicable Web links, teachers may wish to investigate the following interactive CD-ROM.

The Total Science System (CD-ROM) © 2005
JaKel, Inc. Waukee, IA
http://www.netins.net/showcase/jakel
515-225-6317
jakel@netins.net

Chemical Storage and Disposal

General Guidelines

The following are guidelines commonly used. It is the responsibility of each teacher to be informed of school, city, county, state, and federal regulations for the handling, storage and disposal of chemicals. Teachers who use chemicals should consult the book entitled *Prudent Practices in the Laboratory* (National Academy Press, 1995) from the National Research Council. Current laws in your area would supersede the information in this book.

1. Separate chemicals by reaction type. Strong acids should be stored together. Likewise, strong bases should be stored together and should be separated from acids. Oxidants should be stored away from easily oxidized materials, and so on.
2. Be sure all chemicals are stored in labeled containers indicating contents, concentration, source, date purchased (or prepared), any precautions for handling and storage, and expiration date.
3. Dispose of any outdated or waste chemicals properly according to accepted disposal procedures.
4. Do not store chemicals above eye level.
5. Wood shelving is preferable to metal. All shelving should be firmly attached to the wall and should have anti-roll edges.
6. Store only those chemicals that you plan to use.
7. Hazardous chemicals require special storage containers and conditions. Be sure to know which chemicals those are and the accepted practices for your area. Some substances must be stored outside the building.
8. When working with chemicals or preparing solutions, observe the same general safety precautions that you would expect from students. These include wearing an apron and goggles during lab preparation, activity, and cleanup. Wear gloves and use the fume hood when necessary.
9. If you are a new teacher in a particular laboratory, it is your responsibility to survey the chemicals stored there to be sure they are stored properly. Consult chemical storage and disposal information from local, state, and federal governments.

DISCLAIMER

McGraw-Hill Education makes no claims to the completeness of this discussion of laboratory safety and chemical storage. The material presented is not all-inclusive, nor does it address all of the hazards associated with handling, storing, and disposing of chemicals, or with laboratory management.

Laboratory Preparation

Preparation of Solutions

It is most important to use safe laboratory techniques when handling chemicals. Many substances may appear harmless but are, in fact, toxic, corrosive, or very reactive. Always check with the supplier. Chemicals should never be ingested. Be sure to use proper techniques to smell solutions or other agents. Always wear safety goggles, gloves, and an apron. Observe the following precautions.

1. *Poisonous/corrosive liquid and/or vapor*—use in the fume hood; Examples: acetic acid, nitric acid, hydrochloric acid, ammonium hydroxide
2. *Poisonous and corrosive to eyes, lungs, and skin;* Examples: acids, limewater, iron(III) chloride, bases, silver nitrate, iodine, potassium permanganate
3. *Poisonous if swallowed, inhaled, or absorbed through the skin;* Examples: glacial acetic acid, copper compounds, barium chloride, lead compounds, chromium compounds, lithium compounds, cobalt(II) chloride, silver compounds
4. Always add acids to water, never the reverse.
5. When sulfuric acid and sodium hydroxide are added to water, a large amount of heat is released. Sodium metal reacts violently with water. Use extra care when handling any of these substances.

Alcohol testing solution: Wear goggles, gloves, and an apron. In a fume hood, add 20 g of potassium dichromate powder to a glass beaker. Pour 20 mL concentrated H_2SO_4 into the beaker and stir with a glass stirring rod to dissolve the powder. Slowly and carefully pour the solution into 60 mL distilled water in a glass beaker and continue to stir. The solution becomes VERY HOT. Allow it to cool. Powder may precipitate out after cooling. Pour only the liquid solution into dropper bottles for student use. The solution has a shelf life of one year.

Baking soda (sodium bicarbonate) solution: To prepare a 0.25% solution, dissolve 0.5 g baking soda (sodium hydrogen carbonate) in 200 mL of water.

Benedict's solution: Dissolve 173 g sodium citrate and 100 g sodium carbonate in 700 mL water over a hot plate. Filter. Dissolve 17.3 g copper sulfate in 100 mL water. Slowly add to the first solution. Add water to a total volume of 1 L.

Bromothymol blue: Add 0.5 g bromothymol blue powder to 500 mL distilled water to make a BTB stock solution. Dilute 40 mL BTB stock solution to 2 L with distilled water. Solution should be bright blue. If not, add one drop of NaOH at a time, swirling to mix. Check color.

Cola, dilute solution: Add 1 part cola to 1 part distilled water.

Congo red: Add 0.1 g Congo red powder to 50 mL distilled water.

Cough medicine, dilute: Add 2 mL of cough medicine (syrup) to 98 mL distilled water. Stir before use.

Ethyl alcohol, dilute: Add 2 mL ethyl alcohol to 98 mL distilled water. Stir.

Fertilizer solution: To make a 1% fertilizer solution, mix 1 g 5-10-5 fertilizer with 99 mL water. For a 0.1% serial dilution, mix 1 mL 1% solution with 9 mL water. For a 0.01% serial dilution, mix 1 mL 0.1% solution with 9 mL water.

Gelatin solution: Soften 1 g gelatin in 20 mL water; then add 80 mL hot, not boiling, water to dissolve. Cool to room temperature before using.

Glucose solution: For 1% glucose solution, dissolve 1 g of glucose in 99 mL water.

Gum arabic solution: Dissolve 1 g gum arabic in 100 mL warm water. Cool to room temperature before use.

Hydrochloric acid (HCl) solution: To make a 10% solution, add 27 mL concentrated hydrochloric acid to 73 mL water while stirring. To make a 0.1M solution, add 1 mL concentrated hydrochloric acid to 100 mL water while stirring.

Iodine solution/Iodine stain: Dilute 1 part Lugol's solution with 15 parts water.

Lugol's solution: Dissolve 10 g potassium iodide in 100 mL distilled water; then add and dissolve 5 g iodine. Store in dark bottle. Keeps indefinitely.

Methylene blue stain: Dissolve 1.5 g methylene blue in 100 mL ethyl alcohol. Dilute by adding 10 mL of solution to 90 mL water.

Methylcellulose solution: Add 20 g methylcellulose to 40 mL of boiling distilled water. Let stand for 30 min, then add 40 mL distilled water. Stir until uniform. Solution will be very thick.

Pancreatic solution: Blend a pig or sheep pancreas with 150 mL 30% ethyl alcohol. Allow the solution to stand for 24 h, shaking occasionally. Strain the solution through cheesecloth and then filter. Neutralize with KOH until you get near the end point, then use 0.5% sodium carbonate.

Potassium chloride (KCl) solution: To make a 0.5 M solution, dissolve 3.73 g of potassium chloride in 60 mL of distilled water, then add distilled water to make 100 mL final volume.

Salt (NaCl) solution: For a 3.5% salt solution that simulates the concentration of ocean water, dissolve 35 g salt in 965 mL water. For a 1% solution, dissolve 1 g of salt in 99 mL of water. For a 3% solution, dissolve 3 g of salt in 97 mL of water. For a 5% solution, dissolve 5 g of salt in 95 mL of water. For a 6% solution, dissolve 6 g of salt in 94 mL of water.

Silver nitrate solution: Add 4 g silver nitrate to 250 mL distilled water.

Sodium hydroxide (NaOH) solution: To make a 1% solution, dissolve 1 g NaOH in 99 mL of water. For a 0.04% serial dilution, mix 4 mL 1% solution with 96 mL water.

Solutions of various pHs: To make acidic solutions, add 50 mL 0.1M HCl to 450 mL distilled water. Test the pH level and continue diluting the solution until the desired pH levels are obtained. Do the same with NaOH to make a variety of basic solutions.

Starch solution: Make a 1% solution by stirring a slurry of 1 g cornstarch and 50 mL cold water into 1 L boiling water. Cool before using.

Sterile pond water: Filter pond water and place it in flat pans. Boil for 15 min. Allow to cool before using.

Sucrose solution: For a 1% sucrose solution, dissolve 1 g sucrose in 99 mL water. For a 2% sucrose solution, dissolve 2 g sucrose in 98 mL water. For a 5% sucrose solution, dissolve 5 g sucrose with 95 mL water. For a 10% sucrose solution, dissolve 10 g of sucrose in 90 mL water. For a 20% sucrose solution, dissolve 20 g of sucrose in 80 mL of water. For a 30% sucrose solution, dissolve 30 g of sucrose in 70 mL of water. For a 40% sucrose solution, dissolve 40 g of sucrose in 60 mL of water.

Sugar solution: Add 1 tablespoon of sugar to 1 cup of warm water in a deep jar or flask. Stir to dissolve.

Tetrazolium solution: Dissolve 1 g of 2,3,5-triphenyl tetrazolium chloride in 100 mL of water. Store in dark glass bottle.

Tobacco solution: Grind tobacco from one cigarette into a fine powder. Mix the powder with 100 mL of a 1% glucose solution.

Urine (artificial) solutions: Normal: Add 1 tsp. of salt and 4 drops of yellow food coloring to 500 mL of tap water. Stir to dissolve. Abnormal: Add 1 tsp. of salt, 2 tsp. of glucose or honey, and 4 drops of yellow food coloring to 500 mL of tap water. Stir to dissolve.

Yeast culture: Add 1/5 package dry baker's yeast to 200 mL distilled water.

Laboratory Materials

This table of equipment and inexpensive, easily accessible materials can help you prepare for your biology classes for the year. Refer to the Chapter Organizer in front of each chapter for a list of equipment and materials used for each laboratory activity in the chapter.

Consumables		Labs		
Item	Quantity (8 set-ups per class)	Launch Lab	MiniLab	BioLab
aged tap water	4240 mL		10 mL (p. 748, 912)	500 mL (p. 753), 10 mL (p. 925)
aluminum foil	several rolls		2×2 cm (p. 220)	20×20 cm (p. 235, 259, 593)
antibiotic discs	40			1–5 per dish (p. 533)
apple	8		1 (p. 159)	
autoclave disposable bag	8			1 (p. 533)
beans (three sizes)	480 (160 each size)			60 (20 each size) (p. 443)
beef broth	800 mL			100 mL (p. 409)
beef liver	8 g			1 g (p. 173)
black paper	10 sheets	3×3 cm (p. 417)		1 sheet (p. 925)
bread	32 slices		2 slices (p. 583)	2 slices (p. 593)
cardboard (pieces or boxes)	8 sheets/8 boxes			1 sheet (p. 871), 1 shoebox (p. 925)
celery stalk (cross section)	1 stalk,thinly sliced			1 (p. 634)
cellulose dialysis tubing	16			2 (p. 209)
cheesecloth (30×30 cm squares)	32			4 (p. 351)
clay (colored sticks)	32	2 (different colors) (p. 269)	2 (different colors) (p. 1052)	
colored markers	8 sets			1 set (p. 871)
conifer cones	8–40		1–5 (p. 666)	
conifer leaf samples	16–40		2–5 (p. 620)	
contact lens cleaning tablet (containing papain)	8			1 (p. 351)
cooked egg white	1 egg		1 small piece (p. 728)	
corn kernels	400 g			50 g (p. 351)
cotton swabs	generous supply including long handle swabs		1 (p. 361)	1 per dish (p. 533), 1 per cup (p. 593), 1 (p. 653)
crackers (3 kinds)	8 each kind			1 each kind (p. 1039)

Consumables		Labs		
Item	Quantity (8 set-ups per class)	Launch Lab	MiniLab	BioLab
dishwashing liquid	8 mL			1 mL (p. 653)
disinfectant	clean up			clean up (p. 533)
disks	8–40			1–5 (p. 533)
distilled water	± 4 L	100 mL (p. 217)	10 mL (p. 154), 5 mL (p. 1023)	1 L (p. 173), 1 L (p. 209, 653), 3 mL (p. 653)
dried beans	generous supply			supply (p. 871)
dry yeast packet	8		1 (p. 580)	
dye (stain)	1 mL		1 drop (p. 634)	
eudicot flowers	several samples			sample (p. 681)
felt pieces	samples			several (p. 871)
filter paper	40		1 (p. 748)	1 (p. 925), 3 (p. 1039)
flowers	cut flowers at various times	several (p. 661)	several (p. 672)	several (p. 23)
food substances (with labels)	32 different		4 different (p. 154)	
gelatin (plain powdered)	8 packets			1 packet (p. 593)
glue	8 bottle/stick			1 bottle/stick (p. 871)
graph paper	32 sheets		1 sheet (p. 1002)	1 sheet (p. 653, 925, 983)
hardboiled egg white	8	1 (p. 1019)		
ice	supply at different times			ice bath (p. 173, 351, 381)
labeled food items	32	4 (p. 147)		
leaf litter sample	8 samples		sample (p. 127)	
lemon juice	600 mL		75 mL (p. 159)	
lily flower	8		1 (p. 361)	
marigold or radish seeds	1008			126 (p. 107)
marking pen	8			1 (p. 533)
masking tape	320 cm		30 cm (p. 464)	10 cm (p. 107)
materials to produce stimulus in protozoa	unknown			unknown (p. 567)
meat tenderizer (homogenization medium)	800–1200 mL			100–150 mL (p. 351)
monocot flowers	several samples			sample (p. 681)
nitrate test kit	1–8		1 (p. 48)	

Laboratory Materials

Consumables		Labs		
Item	**Quantity (8 set-ups per class)**	**Launch Lab**	**MiniLab**	**BioLab**
nontoxic dye	8 mL			1 mL (p. 381)
onion epidermis	1 onion		1 cm square (p. 203)	
paper	ream			1 sheet (p. 475, 983, 1097)
paper cups (small)	24			2 (p. 1097)
paper plates (small)	8			1 (p. 925)
paper towels	generous supply	clean up (p. 725)	1 (p. 159, 634, 912)	3 (p. 843), clean up (p. 925)
peanuts (with hulls)	8	1 (p. 3)		
pear tissue	1 pear		small piece (p. 634)	
pH test strip (indicator)	1 roll			several strips (p. 1097)
pipe cleaners	32	4 (p. 269)		
plant fertilizer	8 g			1 g (p. 653)
plant leaves (variety)	80		10 (p. 605)	
plastic bags (large)	16			2 (p. 653)
plastic wrap	generous supply (several colors of cellophane)		2 sheets (p. 255, 1082)	20×20 cm (p. 235), sheet (p. 593, 925)
pond mud	Large supply			large sample (p. 83)
pond water	10 L		10 mL (p. 223, 1082)	500 mL (p. 83)
poster board	10 sheets	1/4 sheet (p. 1075)		1 sheet (p. 653)
potato slices	2 small potatoes		1 (p. 634)	several (p. 173)
potting soil	several bags			6 pots full (p. 107), 2 pots full (p. 287)
prepared agarose gel	match to number of plates available			electrophoresis plate (p. 381)
prepared gelatin (in small cup)	4 cups			1/2 cupful (p. 593)
printed maze	8 ±		1 (p. 19)	
raw beef liver	small chunk			small piece (p. 173)
raw chicken wing treated with bleach	8 wings	1 whole wing (p. 935)	1 whole wing (p. 938)	
red paper	10 sheets	3×3 cm (p. 417)		
salt	10 g		1 g (p. 583)	
sample-loading dye (electrophoresis)	10 mL			1mL (p. 381)

Consumables		Labs		
Item	Quantity (8 set-ups per class)	Launch Lab	MiniLab	BioLab
sand	generous supply			50 cc (p. 843), unknown quantity (p. 871)
seeds, various sizes (alternative material)	generous supply		alternative material: 10 (p. 488)	alternative material (p. 443)
skinned chicken wing	8		1 (p. 945)	
soil	generous supply		several containers full (p. 396), sample (p. 1082)	sample (p. 783), 100 cc (p. 843), unknown quantity (p. 871)
spring water	4010 mL		1 mL (p. 748)	500 mL (p. 753)
sterile nutrient agar	8 Petri dishes			1 Petri dish (p. 533)
straw (plastic or paper)	8		1 (p. 220)	
sugar	32 g		3 g (p. 580)	1 g (p. 593)
sunscreen products	10 mL each of several products		1 drop (p. 255)	1 mL (p. 259)
sun sensitive paper	1 sheet		1 piece (p. 255)	
tape	several rolls		10 cm (p. 365)	unknown (p. 925)
toothpicks	several boxes			unknown (p. 871)
vegetable oil	40 mL		5 mL (p. 1023)	
water	10 L plus water for clean up, water baths, etc.	30 mL (p. 1019)	water bath (p. 154), 75 mL (p. 159), 2 drops (p. 203), unknown (p. 396, 738), 100 mL (p. 580), 250 mL (p. 583), 2 drops (p. 634), 125 mL (p. 1023)	unknown (p. 23), water bath (p. 351, 381), 250 mL (p. 843)
water, soapy	for hand washing and clean up		unknown (p. 938, 1082)	
water from a saltwater aquarium	1600 mL	± 200 mL (p. 791)		
water samples from various sources	8 each source		1 each (p. 48)	
wooden sticks (various sizes)	dozens			several (p. 871)
yeast extract dextrose (YED) agar plates	80			10 (p. 259)

Laboratory Materials

Non-Consumables			
Item	Launch Lab	MiniLab	BioLab
acrylic (1 m^2 piece)		p. 965	
aluminum foil or plastic wrap			p. 593
aquarium			p. 717
art supplies (pencils, chalks in various colors)		p. 184, 468	p. 681
balance	p. 3	p. 605	p. 107, 1039
beads (three sizes)			p. 443
beaker		p. 220	p. 351, 783, 1039
beaker (250-mL)	p. 217	p. 159, 1023	
beaker (400-mL)			p. 173, 209
beaker (500-mL)			p. 753
binoculars		p. 866	p. 899
blender			p. 351
blood pressure chart		p. 996	
blood pressure cuff		p. 996	
bones (small) and bone fragments		p. 396	
book		p. 255	
books describing characteristics of organisms			p. 505
bunsen burner			p. 409, 533, 1039
calculator			p. 983
cereal box	p.147		
circular paper DNA sequence		p. 365	
closed door		p 464	
coat hangers			p.137
coins			p. 317
collection vials			p. 783
colored plastic ribbon			p.137
compound microscope	p. 515, 540, 1047	p. 203, 500, 519, 564, 634, 1093	p. 567
container	p. 3	p. 396, 1082	p. 533, 843
cooler		p. 127	
copies of small world maps		p. 468	
cup		p. 127	p. 593
deck of cards	p. 359		
diagrams of skeletal remains	p. 391		

Non-Consumables			
Item	Launch Lab	MiniLab	BioLab
dish (clear)		p. 580	
dish cloth		p. 1082	
dishpan			p. 209
dissecting kit		p. 938	
dissecting pan	p. 661, 725	p. 938, 945	
dissection scissors		p. 938, 945	
DNA model building kit		p. 331	
DNA model building kit		p. 334	
dollar bill		p. 1082	
droppers			p. 173, 209, 753, 1039
echinoderm reference book			p. 809
electrophoresis chamber			p. 381
envelopes containing paper bones and clues			p. 475
Erlenmeyer flasks			p. 235, 409
Erlenmeyer flasks (250 mL)		p. 580	
examples of cladograms			p. 505
field guide for local birds		p. 866	
field guide for trees		p. 666	
field guide of area species (plant, animal, and fungus)			p.137
field guide of arthropods			p. 783
field guide of North American mammals			p. 899
field guide of trees			p. 623
field guides for birds and reptiles			p. 871
field journal			p. 137, 809, 899
foam container			p. 381
forceps		p. 127	p. 137, 443, 533, 925
funnel			p. 209, 783, 1039
glass or plastic clear gallon jars			p. 83
glass probe	p. 791		
glass rod		p. 580	
glass spooling hook			p. 351
globe		p. 66	
gloves		p. 912, 938, 945	

Laboratory Materials

Non-Consumables			
Item	**Launch Lab**	**MiniLab**	**BioLab**
gooseneck lamp			p. 783
graduated cylinder	p. 217	p. 154	p. 593, 1039
graduated cylinder (10 mL)			p. 173, 209, 235
graduated cylinder (50 mL)			p. 173
high-wattage lightbulb and lamp			p. 843
hot plate		p. 154	p. 173
impressions of three unknown bones			p. 953
incubator	p. 1019		
Internet access		p. 1060	p. 809, 1067
jar		p. 127	
knife	p. 1019	p. 159	p. 173
labeled and unlabeled ultrasound images of fetuses			p. 1067
labeled diagram of earthworm cross section		p. 702	
labeled diagram of hydra cross section		p. 702	
labeled drawing of a lily flower		p. 361	
lamp with incandescent bulb		p. 66	
lamp with reflector and 150 W bulb			p. 235
light microscope	p. 243		p. 753
light source			p. 653, 925
magnifying lens	p. 3, 31, 631, 661, 691, 725	p. 361, 429, 620, 693, 728, 748, 765	p. 137, 623, 753, 783, 953
marbles	p. 359		
metric ruler	p. 3, 661	p. 284, 429, 620, 666	p. 235, 623, 653, 783, 843, 953
microcentrifuge tubes and rack			p. 381
micropipette and tips			p. 381
microprojector		p. 184	
microscope	p. 181	p. 223, 702	
mortar and pestle			p. 1039
net			p. 137
objects (nonliving)		p. 8	
observation dish		p. 728	
paintbrush		p. 650, 912	
pan (square or rectangular)			p. 173

Non-Consumables			
Item	Launch Lab	MiniLab	BioLab
paper		p. 464	
paper cutouts	p. 269		
Pasteur pipets			p. 1097
pencil		p. 464	p.137, 475, 983, 1097
pencil eraser		p. 634	
permanent marker		p. 255	p. 107
petition or sign-up sheet with 50 names		p. 1082	
petri dish	p. 791	p. 693, 748	p. 533, 717, 753, 925
photo or illustration of desert ecosystem	p. 483		
photographs of mammals	p. 879		
photographs of various organisms			p. 505
photos of a rusted nail		p. 1082	
photos of each of the three groups of fishes	p. 819		
photos of skeletal remains	p. 391		
photos or videos of animal behavior	p. 907		
ping pong ball		p. 965	
plastic bottle caps in various colors		p. 975	
plastic centrifuge tube (30-50 mL)			p. 351
plastic plate		p. 605	
plastic pots (9 cm)			p. 107
plastic tubing			p. 409
pop beads	p. 269		
power source			p. 381
reference materials	p. 851		
resource materials about health choices			p. 1011
ring stand			p. 409, 783
rocks		p. 396	p. 871
rubber band			p. 351
ruler			p. 107, 381, 475
scalpel		p. 938	
science textbook		p. 1082	
scissors	p. 417	p. 365	p. 23, 209, 871, 925

Laboratory Materials

Non-Consumables			
Item	Launch Lab	MiniLab	BioLab
self-sealing bag	p. 935	p. 583, 938	
set of clues			p. 953
shallow tray for pots			p. 107
shells (small) and shell fragments		p. 396	
shoe		p. 488	
shoelaces		p 464	
short-nosed pliers			p. 443
small flowerpots or other growing containers			p. 287
small gardening trowel			p. 107, 287
spray bottle		p. 583	p. 593, 653
spoon		p. 127	
staining and destaining containers			p. 381
stakes (1m)			p.137
stereomicroscope	p. 691, 791	p. 693, 748, 765	p. 717, 753
sterile pipettes			p. 259
sterile spreaders			p. 259
stethoscope		p. 996	
stirring rod	p. 217	p. 154	p. 351
stopper		p. 220, 1023	p. 409
stopwatch or watch with second hand		p. 19, 464, 748, 975, 1002	p. 173, 235, 351, 443, 1039
straight paper DNA sequence		p. 365	
string			p. 137, 209, 409, 953
table of gene-pair crossover frequency		p. 284	
table of inherited human facial characteristics			p. 317
test tubes	p. 1019	p. 154, 220, 1023	p. 209, 351, 1039, 1097
test tubes (15 mL)			p. 235
test tubes (18 mm × 150 mm)			p. 173
test-tube rack		p. 154, 220	p. 173, 209, 259, 1039, 1097
thermometer	p. 217	p. 66	p. 173, 533, 593, 843
tongs		p. 159	p. 173
tray		p. 912	p. 443
tweezers	p. 661		p. 717
used cutting board		p. 1082	

Non-Consumables			
Item	Launch Lab	MiniLab	BioLab
UV lamp			p. 259
vase			p. 23
wading boots			p. 717
watch glasses			p. 1039
watering can or bottle			p. 107, 287
wax pencil			p. 209
wire mesh			p. 783

Living Organisms		Labs		
Item	Quantity (8 set-ups per class)	Launch Lab	MiniLab	BioLab
arthropod (live)	1		1 (p. 765)	
bacteria cultures	8 set ups			1 (p. 83, 533)
black worms (live)	16		1 (p. 748)	1 (p. 753)
dilution of UV sensitive yeast	1 culture			1 culture (p. 259)
earthworm (live)	16	1 (p. 725)	1 (p. 912)	
fern plant (frond)	8	1 (p. 661)		
fishes (live)	8–32	3 photos (p. 819)	1–4 (p. 823)	
freshwater algae samples (slide)	8 (minimum)		1 (p. 223)	
fruit flies (mixed sexes)	24	3 (p. 31)		
isopods	24–40			3–5 (p. 925)
land snails	8			1 (p. 753)
live green algae cultures	24		3 (p. 558)	
live sea star	8	1 (p. 791)		
living brine shrimp	24		3 (p. 693)	
living hydra	24		3 (p. 693)	
living pond organisms	many			several (p. 83)
mold	several samples			sample (p. 593)
moss	8	1 (p. 661)		
objects (living)	many		several (p. 8)	
planaria	16		1 (p. 728)	1 (p. 753)
potted dwarf-pea plant seedlings	24–32			3–4 (p. 653)
potted plant	8	1 (p. 631)		
preserved specimen of pill bugs	8	1 (p. 761)		

Laboratory Materials

Living Organisms		Labs		
Item	Quantity (8 set-ups per class)	Launch Lab	MiniLab	BioLab
protozoa cultures	several			several (p. 567)
Venus flytrap plant	1–8		1 (p. 650)	
vinegar eels	8			1 (p. 753)

Chemicals		Labs		
Item	Quantity (8 set-ups per class)	Launch Lab	MiniLab	BioLab
anhydrous Benedict's reagent	2.5 mL			3 drops (p. 209)
anhydrous calcium chloride	320 g	40 g (p. 217)		
bile salt	8 g		1 g (p. 1023)	
biuret reagent	2.5 mL			3 drops (p. 209)
DNA samples	several sources			several (p. 381)
Epsom salts	320 g	40 g (p. 217)		
ethanol (70%)	1 L			100 mL (p. 533)
ethanol (95%)	1 L			12 mL (p. 351), 90 mL (p. 783)
gibberillic acid in various concentrations	supply			unknown (p. 653)
homogenization medium	800–1200 mL			100–150 mL (p. 351)
iodine stain	2.5 mL		3 drops (p. 203)	
isopropyl alcohol (95%) — alternative	100 mL			12 mL (p. 351)
phenol red (alternative)	25 mL		24–30 drops (p. 1023)	
pheolphthalein	25 mL		24–30 drops (p. 1023)	
restriction enzyme	2 mL			5 drops (p. 381)
testing indicator	3 mL			3 drops (p. 1097)
zinc oxide	1 mL		1 drop (p. 255)	

Solutions		Labs		
Item	Quantity (8 set-ups per class)	Launch Lab	MiniLab	BioLab
albumin solution	400 mL			50 mL (p. 209)
amylase solution	24 mL			3 mL (p. 1039)
baking soda solution (0.25%)	1 box			unknown (p. 235)
Benedict's solution	40 mL		5 mL (p. 154)	

Solutions		Labs		
Item	Quantity (8 set-ups per class)	Launch Lab	MiniLab	BioLab
bromthymol blue (BTB) solution	800 mL		100 mL (p. 220)	
buffer solutions (pH 5, pH 6, pH 7, pH 8)	generous quantity			unknown (p. 173)
glucose solution	400 mL			50 mL (p. 209)
HCl solution	80 mL	10 mL (p. 1019)		
hydrogen peroxide (3%)	several liters			unknown (p. 173)
iodine solution	30 mL			3 drops (p. 209), several mL (p. 103)
NaCl solution (salt water)	410 mL		2 drops (p. 203)	50 mL (p. 209)
NaOH solution	200 mL		10 mL (p. 1023)	10 mL (p. 1097)
pancreatic solution	40 mL		5 mL (p. 1023)	
pepsin solution	40 mL	5 mL (p. 1019)		
silver nitrate solution	2.5 mL			3 drops (p. 209)
starch solution	400 mL			50 mL (p. 209)
sugar solution	600 mL		75 mL (p. 159)	

Preserved Specimens			
Item	Launch Lab	MiniLab	BioLab
animal skeletons			p. 953
aquatic plant material		p. 220	p. 235
arthropod specimens		p. 765	
crayfish specimens	p. 761		
dried mount of a fan coral	p. 691		
dried mount of a species of red algae	p. 691		
fish specimens	p. 819		
fungi samples	p. 575		
male and female conifer cones	p. 661		
mammal specimens	p. 879		
mammal teeth and skulls		p. 884	
monarch butterfly specimens		p. 429	
plant specimens	p. 603		
prepared slide of cross section of a hydra		p. 702	
prepared slide of cross section of an earthworm		p. 702	

Preserved Specimens			
Item	Launch Lab	MiniLab	BioLab
sand dollar specimen		p. 793	
sea cucumber specimen		p. 793	
sea star specimen		p. 793	
sea urchin specimen		p. 793	
skeletal parts	p. 391		
slides of algae cells		p. 223	
slides of animal cells	p. 515		
slides of bacteria	p. 515	p. 500, 519	
slides of cancerous human liver cells		p. 1093	
slides of cells	p. 181	p. 184	
slides of egg cells	p. 1047		
slides of healthy human liver cells		p. 1093	
slides of human cells	p. 243		
slides of onion root tip cells	p. 243		
slides of plant cells		p. 223	
slides of protist cells	p. 243		
slides of sperm cells	p. 1047		
slides of various protists	p. 540		
slides of various slime molds		p. 564	
teeth	p. 391		
viceroy butterfly		p. 429	

Suppliers

Equipment Suppliers

American Science & Surplus
P.O. Box 1030
Skokie, IL 60076
(847) 647-0011
www.sciplus.com

Arbor Scientific
P.O. Box 2750
Ann Arbor, MI 48106-2750
(734) 477-9370
www.arborsci.com

Bio-Rad Laboratories
2000 Alfred Nobel Dr.
Life Science Group
Hercules, CA 94547
(800) 876-3425
www.biorad.com

Carolina Biological Supply Co.
2700 York Road
Burlington, NC 27215
(800) 334-5551
www.carolina.com

Chem Scientific, LLC
1250 Washington St.
Norwood, MA 02062
(888) 527-5827
www.chemscientific.com

Edmund Scientifics
60 Pearce Ave.
Tonawanda, NY 14150-6711
(800) 728-6999
www.scientificsonline.com

Fisher Science Education
4500 Turnberry
Hanover Park, IL 60133
(800) 955-1177
www.fisheredu.com

Flinn Scientific
P.O. Box 219
770 N. Raddant Rd.
Batavia, IL 60510
(800) 452-1261
www.flinnsci.com

Frey Scientific
P.O. Box 8101
100 Paragon Parkway
Mansfield, OH 44903
(800) 225-3739
www.freyscientific.com

Nasco Science
901 Janesville Avenue
P.O. Box 901
Fort Atkinson, WI 53538-0901
(800) 558-9595
www.enasco.com

Nebraska Scientific
3823 Leavenworth St.
Omaha, NE 68105-1180
(800) 228-7117
www.nebraskascientific.com

Pasco Scientific
10101 Foothills Blvd.
Roseville, CA 95747
(800) 772-8700
www.pasco.com

Sargent-Welch/VWR Scientific Products
P.O. Box 5229
Buffalo Grove, IL 60089-5229
(800) 727-4368
www.sargentwelch.com

Science Kit and Boreal Laboratories
777 East Park Dr.
P.O. Box 5003
Tonawanda, NY 14150
(800) 828-7777
www.sciencekit.com

VWR CanLab
2360 Argentina Rd.
Mississauga, Ontario L5N5Z7
(800) 932-5000
www.vwrcanlab.com

Ward's Natural Science Establishment, Inc.
5100 W. Henrietta Road
P.O. Box 92912
Rochester, NY 14692-9012
(800) 962-2660
www.wardsci.com

Audiovisual Distributors

Bullfrog Films
P.O. Box 149
Oley, PA 19547
(800) 543-FROG
www.bullfrogfilms.com

Coronet/MTI Film & Video
2349 Chaffee Dr.
St. Louis, MO 63146
(800) 221-1274
www.phoenixlearninggroup.com

Discovery Channel School
P.O. Box 6027
Florence, KY 41022-6448
(877) 900-8830
school.discovery.com

Films for the Humanities and Sciences
P.O. Box 2053
Princeton, NJ 08543
(800) 257-5126
www.films.com

Flinn Scientific
P.O. Box 219
770 N. Raddant Rd.
Batavia, IL 60510
(800) 452-1261
www.flinnsci.com

National Geographic School Publishing
1145 17th Street, N.W,
Washington, DC 20036
(800) 368-2728
www.ngschoolpub.org

Scholastic, Inc.
555 Broadway
New York, NY 10012-3999
(800) 724-6527
www.scholastic.com

Videodiscovery
920 N. 34th Street
Suit 300
Seattle, WA 98103
www.videodiscovery.com

Software Distributors

Educational Activities, Inc.
P.O. Box 87
Baldwin, NY 11510
(800) 645-3739
www.edact.com

IBM Education
4111 Northside Parkway
Atlanta, GA 30327-2150
(800) 426-8322
www.solutions.ibm.com/k12

J. Weston Walch, Publisher
40 Walch Drive
Portland, ME 04104-0658
(800) 341-6094
www.walch.com

Scholastic, Inc
555 Broadway
New York, NY 10012-3999
(800) 325-6149
www.scholastic.com

Sunburst Technology
15550 Executive Drive
Elgin, IL 60123
(888) 492-8817
www.sunburst.com

Contents

Your book is divided into units and chapters that are organized around Themes, Big Ideas, and Main Ideas of biology.

THEMES are overarching concepts used throughout the entire book that help you tie what you learn together. They help you see the connections among major ideas and concepts.

BIG Idea appear in each chapter and help you focus on topics within the themes. The Big Ideas are broken down even further into Main Ideas.

MAIN Idea draw you into more specific details about biology. All the Main Ideas of a chapter add up to the chapter's Big Idea.

THEMES
Change
Diversity
Energy
Homeostasis
Scientific Inquiry

BIG Idea
One per chapter

MAIN Idea
One per section

Student Guide

Unit 1

Contents

Labs

Launch Lab

Start off each chapter with hands-on introduction to the subject matter.

Inquiry Launch Lab

DATA ANALYSIS LAB

Build your analysis skills using actual data from real scientific sources.

DATA ANALYSIS LAB

Build your analysis skills using actual data from real scientific sources.

MiniLab

Practice scientific methods and hone your lab skills with these quick activities.

MiniLab

Practice scientific methods and hone your lab skills with these quick activities.

? Inquiry MiniLab

BIOLAB

Apply the skills you developed in Launch Labs, MiniLabs, and Data Analysis Labs in these chapter-culminating, real-world labs.

? Inquiry BioLab

Real-World Biology Features

Explore today's world of biology. Discover the hot topics in biology, delve into new technologies, uncover the discoveries impacting biology, and investigate careers in biology.

BioDiscoveries

Discover pivotal advancements that have influenced the biological sciences.

CUTTING-EDGE BIOLOGY

Challenge your brain with recent cutting edge developments in biology.

Biology & Society

Examine biology in the news and sharpen your debating skills on complex issues in biology.

In the Field

Get an inside look at careers in biology.

Careers

CAREERS IN BIOLOGY

Investigate a day in the life of people working in the field of biology.

Concepts in Motion

Concepts in Motion Animations

Analyze complex science topics with animations of the Visualizing features.

Concepts in Motion Interactive Tables

Check your understanding by viewing interactive versions of tables in your text.

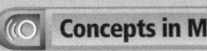

Concepts in Motion Animations

Enhance and enrich your knowledge of biology concepts through simple and 3D animations of visuals.

FOLDABLES®

by Dinah Zike

Folding Instructions

The following pages offer step-by-step instructions to make the Foldables study guides.

Layered-Look Book

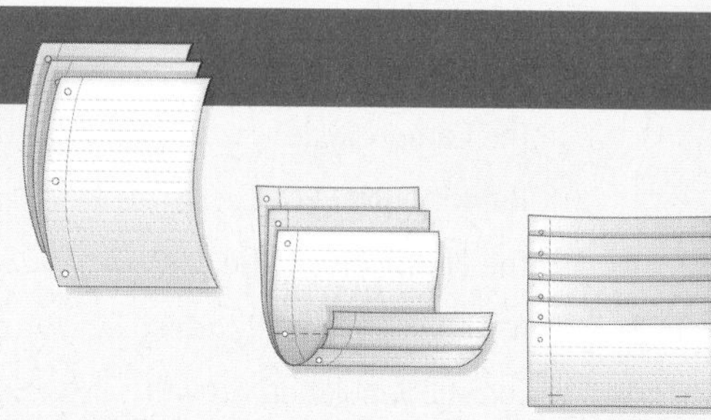

1. Collect three sheets of paper and layer them about ½ inch apart vertically. Keep the edges level.
2. Fold up the bottom edges of the paper to form six equal tabs.
3. Fold the papers and crease well to hold the tabs in place. Staple along the fold. Label each tab.

Trifold Book

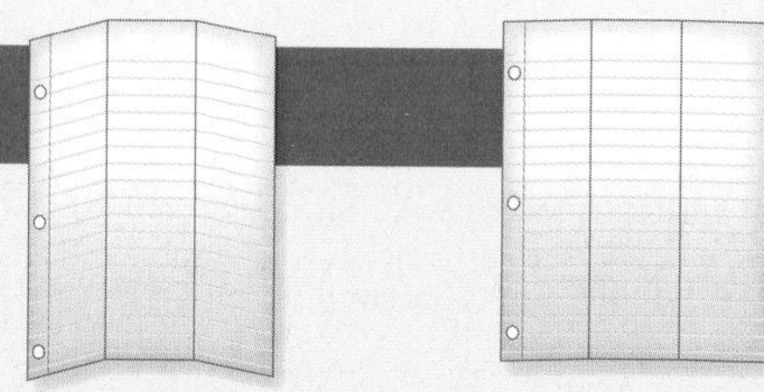

1. Fold a vertical sheet of paper into thirds.
2. Unfold and label each row.

Three-Tab Book

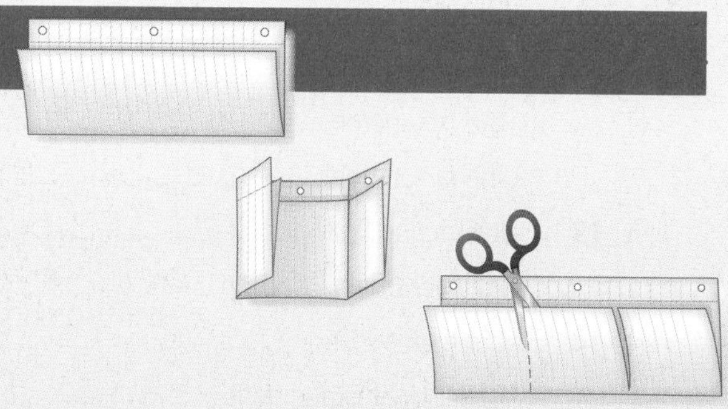

1. Fold a vertical sheet of paper from side to side. Make the front edge about 2 cm shorter than the back edge.
2. Turn lengthwise and fold into thirds.
3. Unfold and cut only the top layer along both folds to make three tabs. Label each tab.

Two- and Four-Tab Books

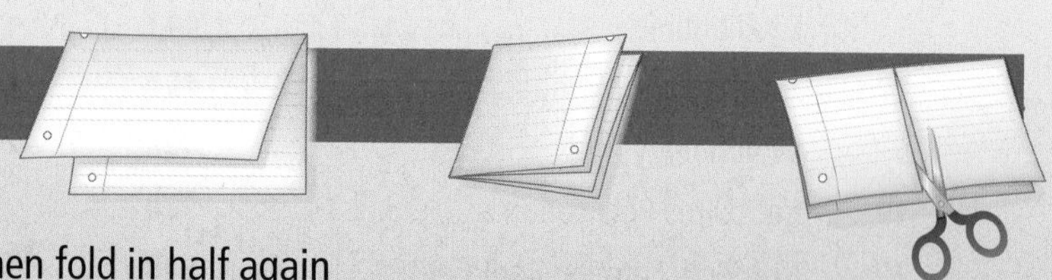

1. Fold a sheet of paper in half.
2. Fold in half again. If making a four-tab book, then fold in half again to make three folds.
3. Unfold and cut only the top layer along the folds to make two or four tabs. Label each tab.

Four-Door Book

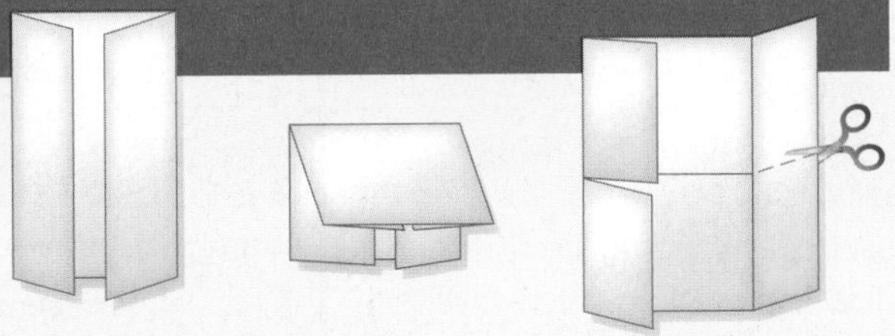

1. Find the middle of a horizontal sheet of paper. Fold both edges to the middle and crease the folds.
2. Fold the folded paper in half, from top to bottom.
3. Unfold and cut along the fold lines of the top layers to make four tabs. Label each tab.

Concept-Map Book

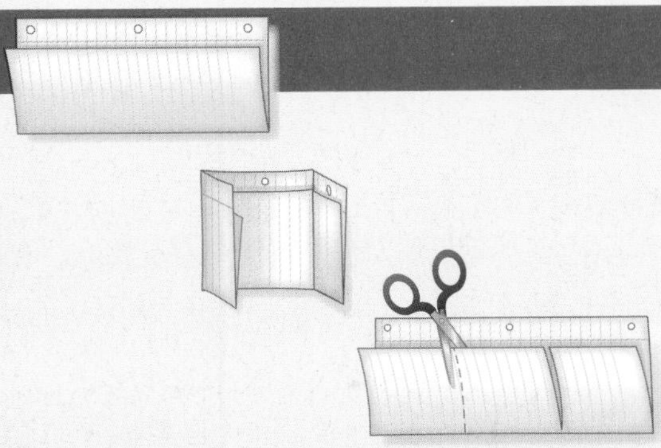

1. Fold a vertical sheet of paper from top to bottom. Make the top edge about 2 cm shorter than the bottom edge.
2. Turn lengthwise and fold into thirds.
3. Unfold and cut only the top layer along both folds to make three tabs. Label the top and each tab

Vocabulary Book

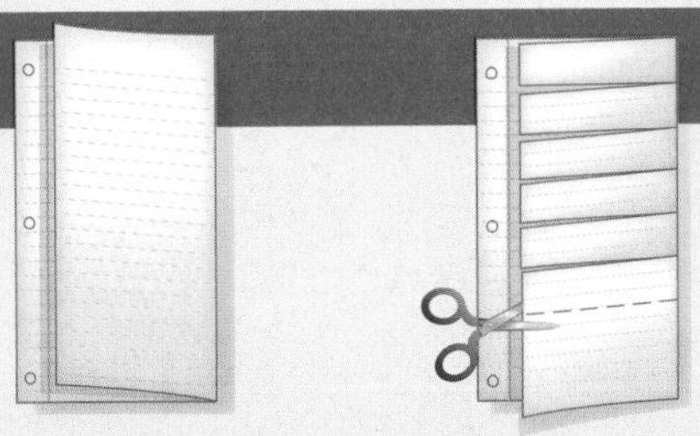

1. Fold a vertical sheet of notebook paper in half.
2. Cut along every third line of only the top layer to form tabs. Label each tab.

Folded Chart

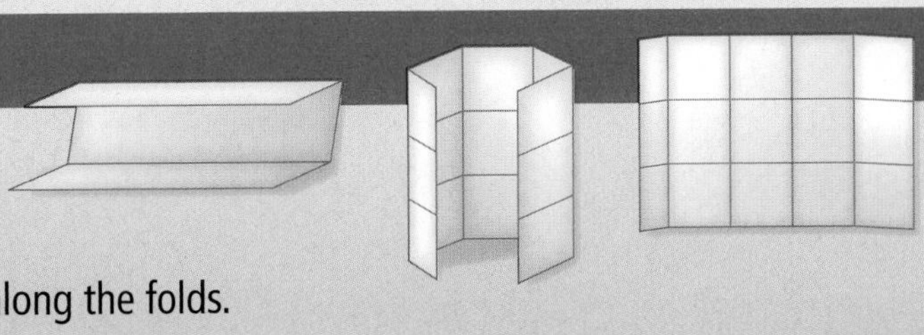

1. Fold a sheet of paper lengthwise into thirds.
2. Fold the paper widthwise into fifths.
3. Unfold, lay the paper lengthwise, and draw lines along the folds. Label the table.

SCIENCE SAFARI

1. 9 units, 37 chapters
2. pages 72 and 124
3. on the front end sheet and in Investigation and Experimentation handbook
4. page 82
5. The Math Skills Handbook
6. the Study Guide page
7. diversity
8. accept any Word Origin margin feature
9. answers may include: audio, video, quizzes, animations, interactive tables, personal tutors
10. see page 74 for the Main Idea
11. pages 462 and 463

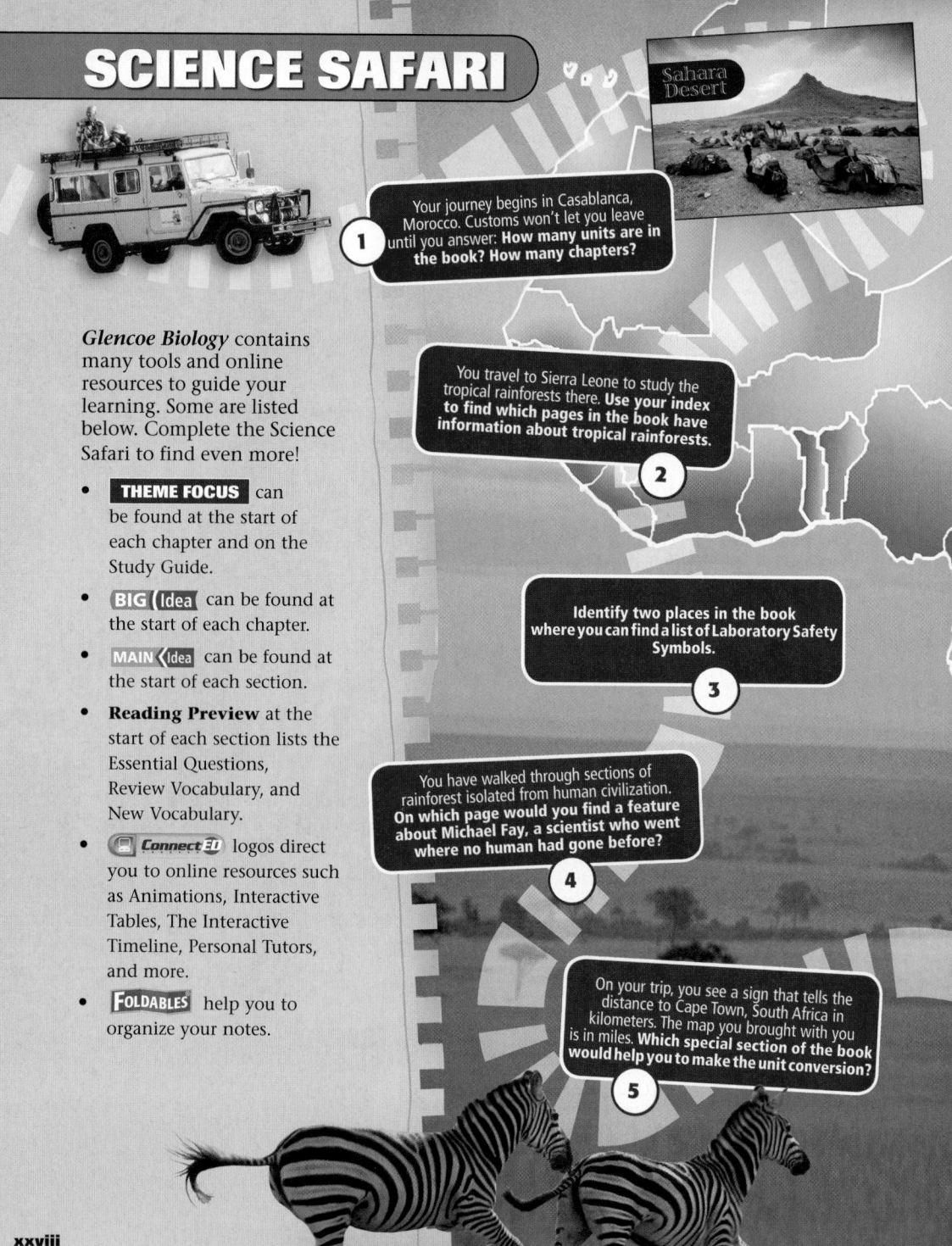

SCIENCE SAFARI

Glencoe Biology contains many tools and online resources to guide your learning. Some are listed below. Complete the Science Safari to find even more!

- **THEME FOCUS** can be found at the start of each chapter and on the Study Guide.
- **BIG Idea** can be found at the start of each chapter.
- **MAIN Idea** can be found at the start of each section.
- **Reading Preview** at the start of each section lists the Essential Questions, Review Vocabulary, and New Vocabulary.
- **ConnectED** logos direct you to online resources such as Animations, Interactive Tables, The Interactive Timeline, Personal Tutors, and more.
- **FOLDABLES** help you to organize your notes.

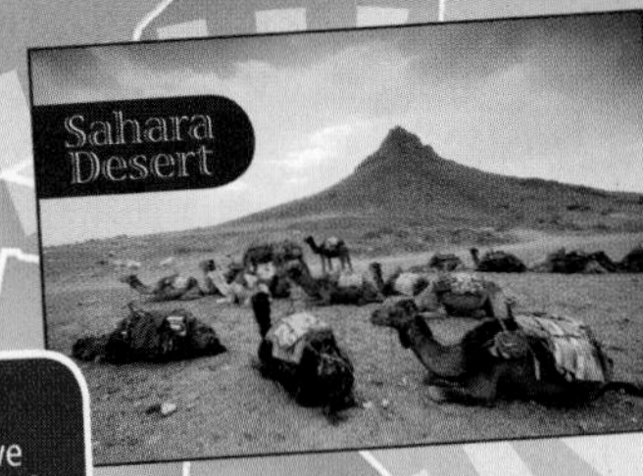

1 Your journey begins in Casablanca, Morocco. Customs won't let you leave until you answer: **How many units are in the book? How many chapters?**

2 You travel to Sierra Leone to study the tropical rainforests there. **Use your index to find which pages in the book have information about tropical rainforests.**

3 **Identify two places in the book where you can find a list of Laboratory Safety Symbols.**

4 You have walked through sections of rainforest isolated from human civilization. **On which page would you find a feature about Michael Fay, a scientist who went where no human had gone before?**

5 On your trip, you see a sign that tells the distance to Cape Town, South Africa in kilometers. The map you brought with you is in miles. **Which special section of the book would help you to make the unit conversion?**

xxviii

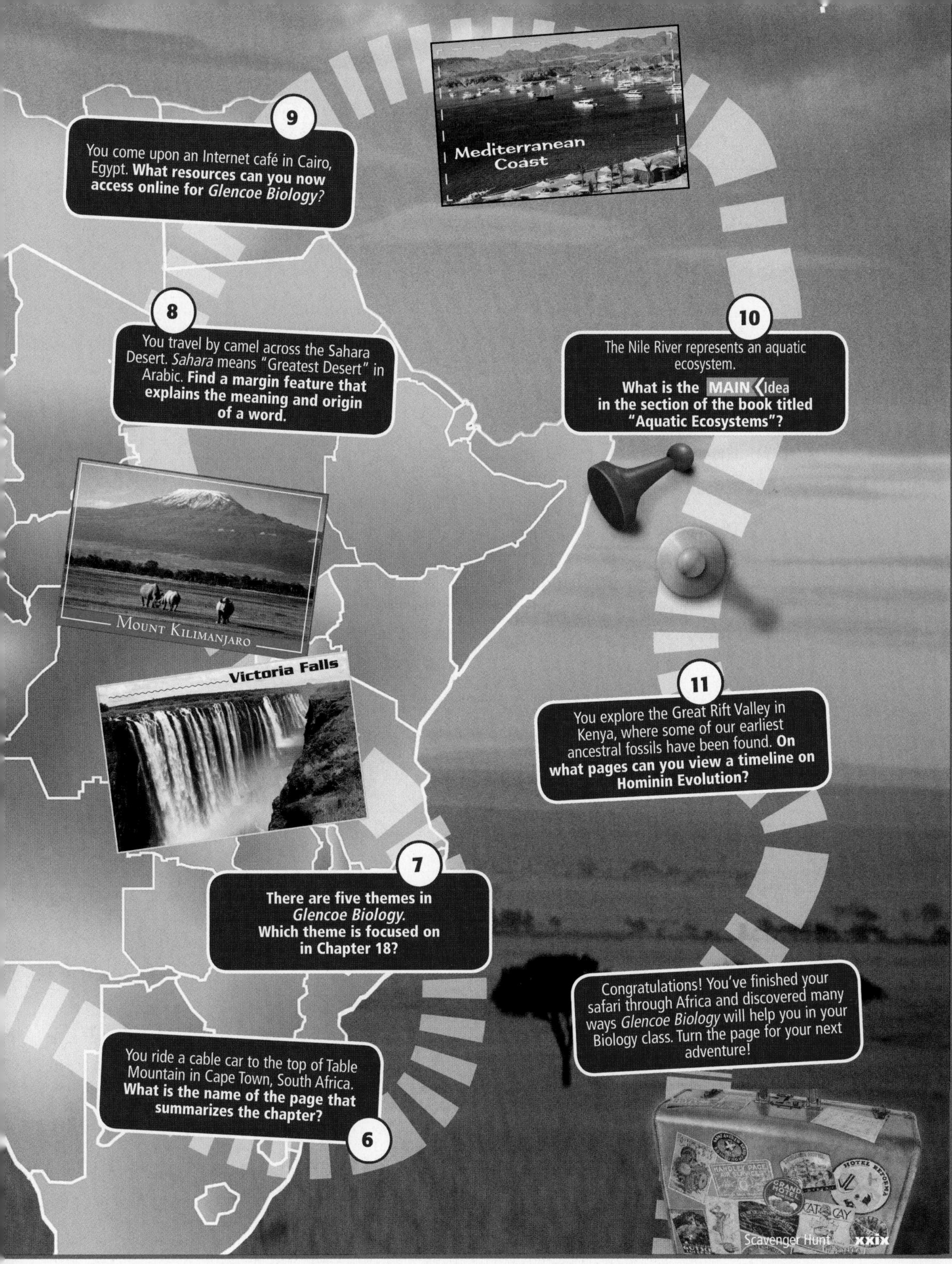

9 You come upon an Internet café in Cairo, Egypt. **What resources can you now access online for *Glencoe Biology*?**

Mediterranean Coast

8 You travel by camel across the Sahara Desert. *Sahara* means "Greatest Desert" in Arabic. **Find a margin feature that explains the meaning and origin of a word.**

10 The Nile River represents an aquatic ecosystem. **What is the MAIN Idea in the section of the book titled "Aquatic Ecosystems"?**

Mount Kilimanjaro

Victoria Falls

11 You explore the Great Rift Valley in Kenya, where some of our earliest ancestral fossils have been found. **On what pages can you view a timeline on Hominin Evolution?**

7 **There are five themes in *Glencoe Biology*. Which theme is focused on in Chapter 18?**

Congratulations! You've finished your safari through Africa and discovered many ways *Glencoe Biology* will help you in your Biology class. Turn the page for your next adventure!

6 You ride a cable car to the top of Table Mountain in Cape Town, South Africa. **What is the name of the page that summarizes the chapter?**

Scavenger Hunt **xxix**

Chapter 1 Organizer:
The Study of Life

LabManager™
Customize any lab with the LabManager™ CD-ROM.

Essential Questions	National Science Standards	Materials and Planning: Estimated times include cleanup and disposal, but do not include teacher prep time. For cleanup and disposal guidelines, see page 39T.	Est. Time (min)
Section 1 1. What is biology? 2. What are possible benefits from studying biology? 3. What are the characteristics of living things?	UCP.2; A.1, A.2; C.1, C.3, C.4, C.5, C.6; E.1, E.2; F.3, F.4, F.6; G.1, G.2, G.3	**Launch Lab,** p. 2: container of unshelled peanuts, measuring devices	25
		Demonstration, p. 4: various items, such as a model of a biomolecule, a potted plant, a skull or skeleton, a terrarium	5
		Demonstration, p. 7: various objects that are living, nonliving, or dead	10
		MiniLab 1, p. 8: various objects (both living and nonliving)	25
		Demonstration, p. 8: *Pieris rapae* caterpillars, frogs, tadpoles	10 per day
		Demonstration, p. 9: plant (*Mimosa pudica* recommended)	10 per day
Section 2 1. What are the characteristics of scientific inquiry? 2. What are the differences between science and pseudoscience? 3. Why is scientific literacy important?	UCP.2; A.1, A.2; B.2; E.1, E.2; F.3, F.4, F.6; G.1, G.2	**Activity,** p. 13: horoscopes for the same zodiac sign from 12 different days	10
		Demonstration, p. 14: various items to measure, metric measuring tools	10
Section 3 1. What are the differences between an observation and an inference? 2. What are the differences among a control, independent variable, and dependent variable? 3. What are the scientific methods a biologist uses for research? 4. Why are the metric system and SI important?	UCP.2; A.1, A.2; B.2; E.1, E.2; G.1, G.2	**Demonstration,** p. 16: various living organisms, clear containers	30
		MiniLab 2, p. 19: printed maze, timing device	25
		Design Your Own BioLab, p. 23: fresh-cut flowers, water, vases, scissors	140

Suggested Time for Each Lesson

Class	Chapter Opener	Section 1	Section 2	Section 3	Assessment
Basic	45 min	90 min	90 min	90 min	45 min
General	25 min	55 min	55 min	90 min	45 min
Honors	—	30 min	25 min	75 min	15 min

ConnectED

connectED.mcgraw-hill.com

Access interactive learning opportunities and teaching resources using these icons located throughout your StudentWorks™ Plus Online and eTeacherEdition Online.

Chapter 1 Section Resources	Additional Chapter 1 Resources	Technology
FAST FILE Unit 1 Resources: Launch Lab Worksheet* MiniLab Worksheet* Study Guide (English/Spanish)* Section Quick Check **Reading Essentials 1.1** **Science Notebook 1.1***	**FAST FILE Unit 1 Resources:** Chapter Diagnostic Test Concept Mapping* Real-World Biology Enrichment Chapter Tests A, B, and C **Transparencies:** Bellringer Transparencies* Biology Concepts Transparencies* **Lab Resources:** Laboratory Manual* Probeware Lab Manual* Forensics Lab Manual* Pre-AP Lab Manual* Open Inquiry in Biology* Guided Inquiry in Biology*	**Teaching Tools:** eTeacherEdition Online Classroom Presentation Toolkit CD-ROM* LabManager™ CD-ROM* Video Lab DVD* Virtual Lab CD-ROM* What's BIOLOGY Got To Do With It? StudentWorks™ Plus Online* **Chapter Assessment Tools:** Classroom Presentation Toolkit CD-ROM* *ExamView® Assessment Suite* CD-ROM **Web-Based Resources:** • StudentWorks™ Plus Online • eTeacherEdition Online • Animations* • The Interactive Time Line* • Interactive Tables* • Online Quizzes • Online Test Practice • Standardized Test Practice • Virtual Labs* • Multilingual eGlossary* • Vocabulary eGames* • Vocabulary eFlashcards • WebQuests • Personal Tutors
FAST FILE Unit 1 Resources: Study Guide (English/Spanish)* Section Quick Check **Reading Essentials 1.2** **Science Notebook 1.2***		
FAST FILE Unit 1 Resources: MiniLab Worksheet* BioLab Worksheet* Study Guide (English/Spanish)* Section Quick Check **Reading Essentials 1.3** **Science Notebook 1.3***		

While all resources listed are appropriate for English learners, the * indicates resources with a strong visual or hands-on component for EL.

Teaching strategies and activities have been coded for differentiated instruction.

AL Activities for students working above grade level	**OL** Activities for students working on grade level	**BL** Activities for students working below grade level	**EL** Activities for English learners (also ELL)	**COOP LEARN** Activities designed for small cooperative group work

CHAPTER 1

Launch Lab
Why is observation important?

Inquiry Launch Lab

For a lab worksheet, use your eTeacherEdition Online.

RUBRIC A rubric for evaluating Launch Labs is found on your eTeacherEdition Online.

Est. Time 25 min

Alternative Materials This lab could be completed using any objects that show variation.

Safety Precautions Determine if any students have peanut allergies before beginning.

Procedure

1. Read and complete the lab safety form.
2. Pick an unshelled **peanut** from the **container of peanuts.** Carefully observe the peanut using your senses and available tools. Record your observations.
3. Do not change or mark the peanut. Return it to the container.
4. After the peanuts are mixed, locate your peanut based on your recorded observations.

CHAPTER 1
The Study of Life

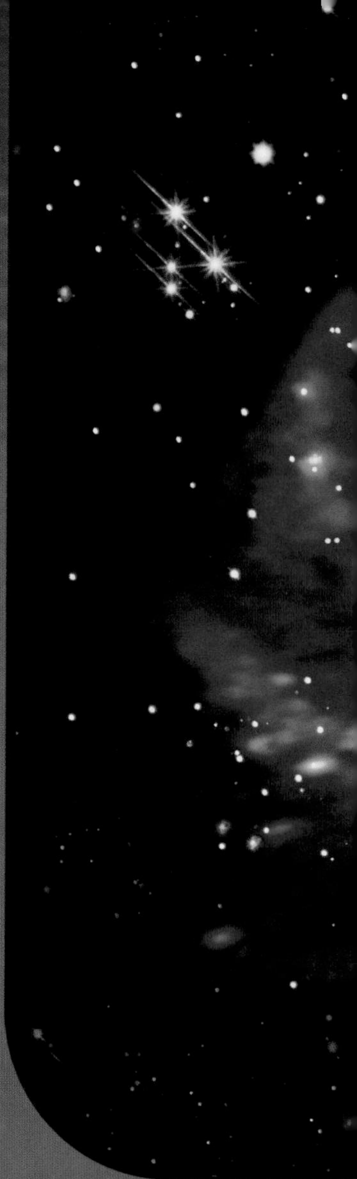

ConnectED
Your one-stop online resource
connectED.mcgraw-hill.com

- Video
- Audio
- Review
- Inquiry
- WebQuest
- Assessment
- Concepts in Motion
- Multilingual eGlossary

Launch Lab
Why is observation important?

Scientists use a planned, organized approach to solving problems. A key element of this approach is gathering information through detailed observations. Scientists extend their ability to observe by using scientific tools and techniques.

For a lab worksheet, use your StudentWorks™ Plus Online.

Inquiry Launch Lab

FOLDABLES®

Make a layered-look book using the titles shown. Use it to organize your notes on the roles of biologists.

Analysis

1. **List** the obervations that were the most helpful in identifying your peanut. Which were the least helpful? Answers will vary based on the specimen examined. Students may find that quantitative observations, such as mass and length, are most helpful in peanut identification. Color and shape might be least helpful in peanut identification unless these characteristics are unusual for the specimen identified.
2. **Classify** your observations into groups. Observations are either quantitative (based on direct measurement) or qualitative (describing some nonmeasured quality of an object).
3. **Justify** why it was important to record detailed observations in this lab. Infer why observations are important in biology. Detailed observations made it easier to identify the peanut in a group of similar objects. Biologists describe living things as they study them. Detailed observations create a record that can be used for future study.

Cleanup and Disposal
Have students wash their hands thoroughly after handling peanuts. Remind them that even small amounts of peanut residue could trigger an attack in a person who is severely allergic to nuts.

THEME FOCUS Scientific Inquiry
The essential characteristic of science is scientific inquiry.

BIG Idea Biology is the study of life.

Section 1 • Introduction to Biology
Section 2 • The Nature of Science
Section 3 • Methods of Science

THEMES

Scientific Inquiry Biology is based on scientific inquiry.

Diversity The study of biology covers a wide variety of topics and research areas.

Energy All living things require energy to perform life processes.

Homeostasis All living things have structures and functions that help them maintain homeostasis.

Change Some biologists study evolution—the change in species over time.

Introduce the Chapter

Biology

ASK STUDENTS: ***What does the illustration on this page tell you about the science of biology?*** Answers will vary. Interpretations might discuss Earth's uniqueness in the universe (contains life), the study of populations of organisms (human population), and the cellular components of those organisms. Encourage students to share different ideas about what biology is and how it relates to the image.

BIG Idea

Outline Copy the Big Idea onto the board. Have students outline the chapter by writing the Big Idea for the chapter and the Main Ideas and main bold heads for each section. Have students write questions under each main head and then fill in any answers they discover as they read. Sample outline:

Chapter 1 Big Idea: Biology is the study of life.
Section 1 Main Idea: All living things share the characteristics of life.

- A. The Science of Life
    1. What is biology?
    2. What do biologists do?
    3. What are the characteristics of life?

Section 1

MAIN Idea

BL OL AL Living Things
Have students read the Main Idea on this page.
ASK STUDENTS: ***What characteristics that are shared by all living things have you observed?*** Possible answers: All living things reproduce, grow, and use energy.

W Writing Support

BL OL Journal Writing
ASK STUDENTS: ***How does biology relate directly to your own life?*** Answers will vary, but students should note that they are alive and that biology is the study of living things. Other responses might include that a baseball player's leather mitt is made from the hide of cows; a hiker encounters wildflowers; and a swimmer has increased heart and breathing rates when swimming. Have students write a one-paragraph scenario explaining how biology relates to them personally. Encourage creativity as well as illustrations. Allow interested students to share their paragraphs in class.

Caption Question Fig. 1
Answers will vary, but may include: What kind of play behavior is exhibited in juvenile males? What kinds of tools are made by chimpanzees? How is aggressive behavior displayed in chimps?

Section 1

Reading Preview

Essential Questions

- What is biology?
- What are possible benefits of studying biology?
- What are the characteristics of living things?

Review Vocabulary

environment: the living and nonliving things that surround an organism and with which the organism interacts

New Vocabulary

biology
organism
organization
growth
development
reproduction
species
stimulus
response
homeostasis
adaptation

g Multilingual eGlossary

Introduction to Biology

MAIN Idea **All living things share the characteristics of life.**

Real-World Reading Link Think of as many living things as you can. What do oak trees, cheetahs, grass, snakes, planaria, and sharks have in common? What makes them unique? How do we know?

The Science of Life

W Before Jane Goodall, pictured in **Figure 1**, arrived in Gombe Stream National Park in Tanzania, Africa, in 1960 to study chimpanzees, the world of chimpanzees was a mystery. Jane's curiosity, determination, and patience over a long period of time resulted in the chimpanzee troop's acceptance of her presence so that she was able to observe their behavior closely.

When people study living things or pose questions about how living things interact with the environment, they are learning about **biology**, the study of life. Biology comes from the Greek word *bio*, meaning *life*, and from *logos*, meaning *study*.

In biology, you will study the origins and history of life and once-living things, the structures of living things, how living things interact with one another, and how living things function. This will help you understand how humans have a vital role in preserving the natural environment and sustaining life on Earth.

Have you ever hiked in a forest and wondered why different trees have leaves with different shapes? Maybe you have watched an ant quickly cross the sidewalk toward a breadcrumb and wondered how the ant knew that the breadcrumb was there. When you ask these questions, you are observing, and you are asking questions about life.

Figure 1 Jane Goodall conducted field research for many years to observe chimpanzee behavior.
Predict ***the types of questions you would ask if you observed chimpanzee behavior.***

Demonstration

BL OL What is biology? Place items such as a potted plant, a model of a biomolecule such as DNA, a model of a cell, a skull or skeleton, and a terrarium in the front of the room.
ASK STUDENTS: ***Describe how all these things relate to your study of biology in this class.*** Answers will vary. Guide students to an understanding that biology is the study of all living things. Est. time: 5 min

What do biologists do?

Imagine being the first person to look into a microscope and discover cells. What do you think it was like to find the first dinosaur fossils that indicated feathers? Who studies how organisms, including the marbled stargazer fish in **Figure 2,** obtain food? Will the AIDS virus be defeated? Is there life on other planets or anywhere else in the universe? Biologists are people who study biology. They make discoveries and seek explanations by performing laboratory and field investigations. Throughout this textbook, you will discover what biologists in the real world do and you will learn about careers in biology.

Study the diversity of life Jane Goodall, shown in **Figure 1,** traveled to Africa for the first time in the summer of 1960 to study chimpanzees in their natural environment. By studying chimps in the wild, Goodall witnessed behaviors that had not been observed before. For example, she saw chimps pulling leaves off twigs and using the twigs to retrieve termites from a mound. Before this observation, scientists thought only humans used tools. From her detailed notes, sketches, and maps of chimpanzees' daily travels, Goodall learned how chimpanzees grow and develop and how they gather food. Through Goodall's research we better understand chimpanzees and how to protect them.

Research disease Mary-Claire King studies chimpanzees from a different perspective. King studies chimpanzee genetics, and in 1973, she established that the genomes of chimpanzees and humans are 99 percent identical. This discovery has changed the field of biology. King's understanding of genetics has led to more research that helps us understand how diseases work and how to treat them.

Many biologists research diseases. Questions such as "What causes the disease?", "How does the body fight the disease?", and "How does the disease spread?" often guide biologists' research. Biologists have developed vaccines for smallpox, chicken pox, and diphtheria, and currently, some biologists are researching the development of a vaccine for HIV. Biologists worldwide are researching new treatments for such things as lowering cholesterol levels, fighting obesity, reducing the risk of heart attacks, and preventing Alzheimer's disease.

R **Develop technologies** When you hear the word *technology,* you might think of high-speed computers, cell phones, and DVD players. However, technology has a broader definition. Technology is defined as the application of scientific knowledge to solve human needs and to extend human capabilities. **Figure 3** shows how "bionic" hand technology can help someone who has lost an arm.

■ **Figure 2** The marbled stargazer fish lives beneath the ocean floor off the coast of Indonesia. It explodes upward from beneath the sand to grab its food.

Observe *How does this fish hide from its food?*

FOLDABLES®
Incorporate information from this section into your Foldable.

■ **Figure 3** A prosthetic "bionic" hand is new technology that can help extend human capabilities.

FOLDABLES®

✱RUBRIC A rubric for evaluating Foldables is found on your eTeacherEdition Online.

Going Further Have students each choose one of the roles of biologists and research the specific qualifications for that role. Have them add this information on the back of that tab of their Foldables.

Critical Thinking

AL **Predict**

ASK STUDENTS: ***What might be some strategies that biologists use to prevent the extinction of animals?*** Biologists attempt to preserve habitats from being lost, save species by doing reproductive research, and inform politicians so legislation can be passed to protect endangered species.

R Reading Strategy

BL OL

Active Comprehension Have a student volunteer read aloud the text under the heading *Develop technologies.*

ASK STUDENTS: ***What more would you like to know about the application of biology to technology?*** Answers will vary. Write student questions on the board.

AL Have students research answers to the questions on the board. Ask students to share what they learn with the class.

■ **Caption Question Fig. 2** Its color allows it to blend into the sand and sediment.

Differentiated Instruction

Hearing Impaired/Visually Impaired At the beginning of the school year, sit down with students who have visual or hearing impairments and discuss the best way to facilitate small group work. It is important that all students are aware of and sensitive to any special needs of their classmates. Find out what makes the students most comfortable and what type of help to elicit from peers in cooperative learning situations.

For more tips, see pages 14T–15T.

Writing Support

EL BL OL COOP LEARN

Creative Writing Have students work in small groups to write a brief skit depicting what a biologist does. Have each group present its skit and have the other students describe what the group is depicting.

D Develop Concepts

EL BL OL

Activate Prior Knowledge

SAY TO STUDENTS: ***List some examples of living things.*** Students might list butterflies, snakes, hermit crabs, fish, toads, various plants, mushrooms, bacteria, algae, etc. ***What do all of these living things have in common?*** Students might note that all of these living things grow and are able to reproduce. Brainstorm other characteristics of living things, using Table 1 as a reference.

Skill Practice

EL BL OL AL COOP LEARN

Concept Map Have groups of students design concept maps depicting the relationships among the eight characteristics of life. Use large butcher-block paper and have each student use a different-color marker to contribute equally to the maps. Be sure the students use linking words to show the relationships. Concept maps will vary. Some relationships students might identify in their concept maps include the relationship between using energy and maintaining homeostasis and the relationship among reproduction, growth, and development.

■ **Figure 4** Joanne Chory, a plant biologist, researches how plants respond to light.

■ **Figure 5** *Streptococcus pyogenes* is a unicellular organism. It can infect the throat, sinuses, or middle ear.

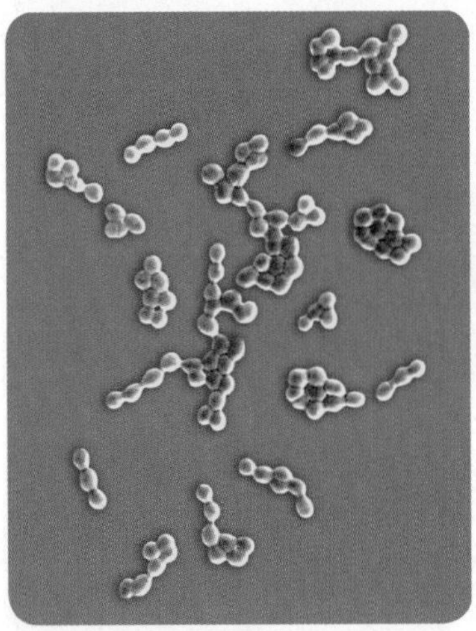

SEM Magnification: 7300×

Other examples of technology include the work of Charles Drew, a doctor who pioneered methods to separate blood plasma from blood cells and safely store and transport blood plasma for transfusions. His research led to blood banks that saved soldiers during World War II and helps countless patients today.

Biologists today continue to discover new ways to improve and save lives. For example, the field of bioengineering applies knowledge gained from studying the function of living systems to the design of mechanical devices such as artificial limbs. In addition, biologists in the field of biotechnology research cells, DNA, and living systems to discover new medicines and medical treatments.

Improve agriculture Some biologists study the possibilities of genetically engineering plants to grow in poor soils or to resist insects, fungal infections, or frost damage. Other biologists research agricultural issues to improve food production to feed the world's growing human population.

Joanne Chory, a plant biologist shown in **Figure 4,** studies mustard plants' sensitivity to light and their responses when exposed to different light sources, different times of exposure, and other conditions. Because of her work with plant growth hormones and light, agriculturists might be able to increase the amount of food produced from crops or to grow crops in areas where they normally would not grow.

Preserve the environment Environmental biologists seek to prevent the extinction of animals and plants by developing ways to protect them. Some biologists study the reproductive strategies of endangered species while they are in captivity. Other biologists work in nature preserves that provide safe places for endangered species to live, reproduce, and have protection against poachers.

Lee Anne Martinez is an ecologist who worked to protect the environment where outdoor toilets are common. She helped people in rural Africa construct composting toilets that use no water. The composted waste from the toilets can be added to soil to improve it for agricultural use.

The Characteristics of Life D

Have you ever tried to define the word *alive?* If you were to watch a grizzly bear catch a salmon from a river, you obviously would conclude that the bear and salmon are both alive. Is fire alive? Fire moves, increases in size, has energy, and seems to reproduce, but how does fire differ from the bear and salmon?

Over time and after many observations, biologists concluded that all living things have certain characteristics, as listed in **Table 1.** An **organism** is anything that has or once had all these characteristics.

Made of one or more cells Have you ever had strep throat? It probably was caused by a group A streptococcal bacteria, such as the *Streptococcus pyogenes* shown in **Figure 5.** A bacterium is unicellular—it has just one cell—yet it displays all the characteristics of life just like a skin cell on your body or a cell in a plant's leaf. Humans and plants are multicellular—they have many cells.

Research Citation

Skill Practice Educational research indicates the value of providing ample opportunities for students to practice skills as described on this page. This practice will reinforce understanding of main ideas and improve student achievement. (Good, et al., 1983)

Research bibliography on pages 32T–34T

Content Background

Real-World Connection One of the characteristics of life is reproduction. One goal of Joanne Chory's work is to feed the growing human population. At the end of the year 2005, the world's population was 6.4 billion and was growing at an annual rate of 1.2 percent. This means that about 76 million people are added to the population each year.

S

Table 1 Characteristics of Living Organisms — Concepts in Motion Interactive Table

Characteristic of Life	Example	Description
Made of one or more cells	Magnification: 160× 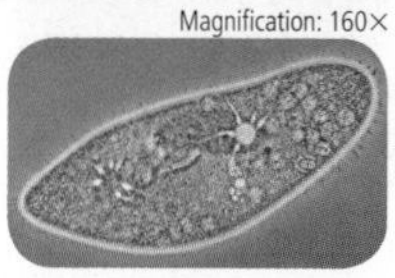	All organisms are made of one or more cells. The cell is the basic unit of life. Some organisms, such as the *Paramecium sp.*, are unicellular.
Displays organization		The levels of organization in biological systems begin with atoms and molecules and increase in complexity. Each organized structure in an organism has a specific function. The structure of an anteater's snout relates to one of its functions—a container for the anteater's long tongue.
Grows and develops	 	Growth results in an increase in mass. Development results in different abilities. A bullfrog tadpole grows and develops into an adult bullfrog.
Reproduces		Organisms reproduce and pass along traits from one generation to the next. For a species like the koala to continue to exist, reproduction must occur.
Responds to stimuli		Reactions to internal and external stimuli are called responses. This cheetah responds to the need for food by chasing a gazelle. The gazelle responds by running away.
Requires energy		Energy is required for all life processes. Many organisms, like this mouse, must take in food. Other organisms make their own food.
Maintains homeostasis		All organisms keep internal conditions stable by a process called homeostasis. For example, humans perspire to prevent their body temperature from rising too high.
Adaptations evolve over time		Adaptations are inherited changes that occur over time that help the species survive. Tropical orchids have roots that are adapted to life in a soil-less environment.

Demonstration

Living, Nonliving, or Dead Hold up various items and have students consider whether each item is living, nonliving, or dead. Have students explain what helped them determine whether the example was living. Potted plant (living), baker's yeast (living), pupa in a jar (living), glass of water (nonliving, though it might have living things in it), fresh cut flowers (living), pumpkin seeds (living), turtle shell (dead), cut hair (dead), cut fingernails (dead), tea leaves (dead), chicken sandwich (dead), rubber-band (dead), tree with no leaves on it in winter (living), book (dead), rock (nonliving). Have students determine whether any of these examples were once living.
Est time: 10 min

Concepts in Motion

Interactive Table

Develop Concepts

BL OL AL

Clarify a Misconception

ASK STUDENTS: ***How do you know if an organism is living?*** Answers will vary, but students should draw from Table 1. They might conclude that living things must display all these characteristics in order to be declared living. The exception to the rule is that organisms, such as a mule, which is a hybrid between two species (a donkey and a horse), cannot reproduce. In these cases, males and females don't produce viable germ cells.

S Skill Practice

EL BL **Visual Literacy** Have students cut a paper into eight squares. On the front of each square, have students write one of the characteristics of life listed in Table 1. Then have students illustrate the characteristic on the back of the square.

Develop Concepts

BL OL **Activity** Take students on a tour of the school and have them look for evidence of organization. Take them to the media center and have groups of students look for five ways in which organization is evident. Then take students outside and have them look for evidence of organization. Have them sketch their observations in a lab notebook. Possible answer: Trees show organizational structure because they all have roots, trunks, branches, and leaves that grow in a similar pattern.

R Reading Strategy

EL BL OL COOP LEARN

Brainstorm Have students read new vocabulary terms found on this page and the following page. In groups, have students brainstorm ideas that come to mind when they see each term. Record the ideas on the board. Then, have students add to their list as they read the text.

MiniLab 1

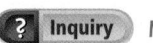

Inquiry MiniLab

For a lab worksheet, use your eTeacherEdition Online.

RUBRIC A rubric for evaluating MiniLabs is found on your eTeacherEdition Online.

Est. Time 25 min

Additional Materials possible objects: sponge (natural and synthetic), plant, moss, mushroom, rock, bark

Safety Precautions Approve lab safety forms before work begins.

Teaching Strategy Provide time for students to share their predictions before completing the analysis questions.

Analysis

1. Answers will vary depending on what students predicted and observed.
2. Possible answer: Some objects are nonliving, but they are made from materials that were once living.

Figure 6 In less than a month, these robin chicks grow and develop from helpless chicks to birds capable of flying.
***Infer** how the robins have developed in other ways.*

Cells are the basic units of structure and function in all living things. For example, each heart cell has a structure that enables it to contribute to the heart's function—continually pumping blood throughout the body. Likewise, each cell in a tree's roots has a structure that enables it to help anchor the tree in the ground and to take in water and dissolved minerals from the surrounding soil.

Displays organization Think of all the people in your high school building each day. Students, faculty, counselors, administrators, building service personnel, and food service personnel are organized based on the different tasks they perform and the characteristics they share. For example, the students are designated freshmen, sophomores, juniors, and seniors based on age and coursework.

R Living things also display **organization,** which means they are arranged in an orderly way. The *Paramecium* in **Table 1** is made up of one cell, yet that cell is a collection of organized structures that carries on life functions. Each of those structures is composed of atoms and molecules. The many cells that make up the robin chicks in **Figure 6** also contain structures made of atoms and molecules. However, in multicellular organisms, specialized cells are organized into groups that work together called tissues. These tissues are organized into organs, which carry on functions such as digestion and reproduction. Organ systems work together to support an organism.

MiniLab 1

Observe Characteristics of Life

Inquiry MiniLab

Is it living or nonliving? In this lab, you will observe several objects to determine if they are living or nonliving.

Procedure

1. Read and complete the lab safety form.
2. Create a data table with four columns titled *Object, Prediction, Characteristic of Life,* and *Evidence.*
3. Your teacher will provide several objects for observation. List each **object** in your table. Predict whether each object is living or nonliving.
4. Carefully observe each object. Discuss with your lab partner what characteristics of life it might exhibit.
5. Use **Table 1** to determine whether each object is living or nonliving. List the evidence in your data table.

Analysis

1. **Compare and contrast** your predictions and observations.
2. **Explain** why it was difficult to classify some objects as living or nonliving.

Caption Question Fig. 6 Possible answer: The robin chicks also developed the ability to see and the ability to navigate.

Demonstration

Growth and Development To demonstrate growth and development, obtain *Pieris rapae* caterpillars from a biological supplier and let them metamorphose into butterflies or moths in class. Bring in tadpoles and frogs and have students observe their behavior during different stages of their life cycles. Est. time: 10 min per day over several weeks

Grows and develops Most organisms begin as one cell. **Growth** results in the addition of mass to an organism and, in many organisms, the formation of new cells and new structures. Even a bacterium grows. Think about how you have grown throughout your life.

Robin chicks, like those in **Figure 6,** cannot fly for the first few weeks of their lives. Like most organisms, robins develop structures that give them specific abilities, such as flying. **Development** is the process of natural changes that take place during the life of an organism.

Reproduces Most living things are the result of **reproduction**—the production of offspring. Reproduction is not an essential characteristic for individual organisms. Many pets are spayed or neutered to prevent unwanted births. Obviously, these pets can still live even though they cannot reproduce. However, if a species is to continue to exist, then members of that species must reproduce. A **species** is a group of organisms that can breed with one another and produce fertile offspring. If the individuals of a species do not reproduce, then when the last individual of that species dies, the species becomes extinct.

D **Responds to stimuli** An organism's external environment includes all things that surround it, such as air, water, soil, rocks, and other organisms. An organism's internal environment is all things inside it. Anything that is part of either environment and causes some sort of reaction by the organism is called a **stimulus** (plural, stimuli). The reaction to a stimulus is a **response.** For example, if a shark smells blood in the ocean, it will respond quickly by moving toward the blood and attacking any organism present. Plants also respond to their environments, but they do so more slowly than most other organisms. If you have a houseplant and you place it near a sunny window, it will grow toward the window in response to the light. How does the Venus flytrap in **Figure 7** respond to stimuli?

Being able to respond to the environment is critical for an organism's safety and survival. If an organism is unable to respond to danger or to react to potential enemies, it might not live long enough to reproduce.

CAREERS IN BIOLOGY

Biology Teacher An enthusiasm for biology is one of the many reasons people become biology teachers. Other than courses in biological sciences, prospective biology teachers might take classroom management, teaching methods, and other courses needed to develop teaching skills.

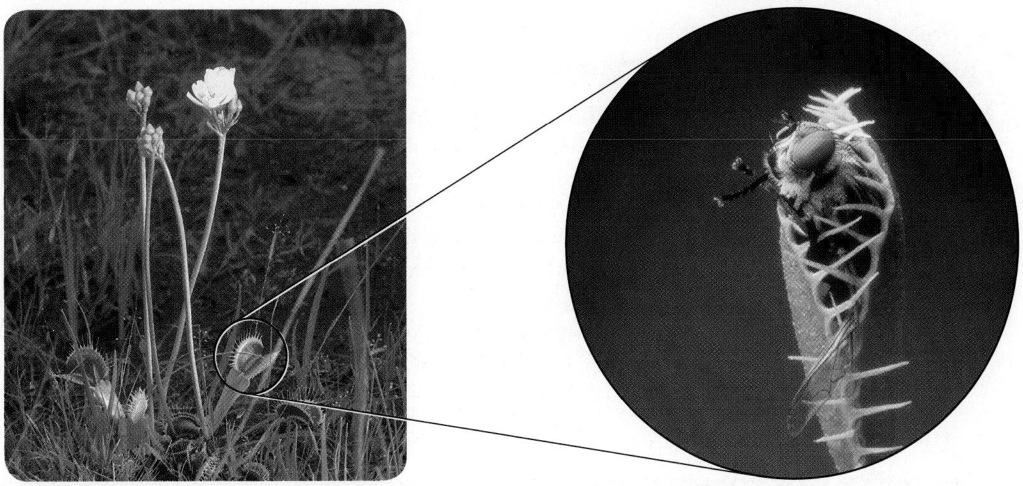

■ **Figure 7** In nature, this Venus flytrap grows in soils that lack certain nutrients. The plant captures and digests insects and takes in needed nutrients.
Explain ***how this plant responds to stimuli to obtain food.***

Demonstration

Response in Plants In order to demonstrate responses in plants, place a plant near a sunny window or obtain a light and place the plant near the light. Have students make observations over a period of days to see what happens to the plant. Try to obtain a sensitive plant such as *Mimosa pudica* that will respond to touch as well as to light. Est. time: 10 min daily over the course of a week

D Develop Concepts

BL OL AL Scaffolding

ASK STUDENTS: ***If a person puts on a coat in the winter, is this evidence of a response or an adaptation? Explain.*** response; it is a short-term reaction to a stimulus

How is reproduction linked to adaptation? Adaptation is the genetic passing of beneficial traits to offspring through reproduction.

Describe how response and adaptation differ. Response is a reaction to a stimuli and adaptation is an inherited characteristic that results from changes to a species over time in response to an environmental factor.

Develop Concepts

EL BL OL COOP LEARN

Activity Have students find pictures of organisms responding to stimuli, using energy, growing, developing, and reproducing. Have the students paste one picture on each sheet of paper. Organize students into pairs, and have students hold up a picture and ask their partners, "Which characteristic of life is being depicted? What is your evidence?" The partners must respond and provide evidence.

■ **Caption Question Fig. 7** The open leaves close around the insect.

GOING GREEN At the beginning of the school year, you might purchase supplies and books that arrive in corrugated cardboard boxes. Find out if your school recycles cardboard, and if not, contact a local recycler. Include students and other teachers in your plan.

R Reading Strategy

EL BL OL AL

Active Comprehension After they read the text under the head *Maintains homeostasis,* have students play a game of "homeostasis charades." Have one student act out a way an organism's homeostasis can be disrupted. For example, the student could act out an athlete who becomes overheated. Ask the class to guess what condition is being acted out and how the body can maintain homeostasis when this occurs.

Writing Support

BL OL **Creative Writing** Have students prepare a poem, song, or story depicting the characteristics of life of an organism they choose. Have students illustrate their writing. Answers need to demonstrate that students understand how their organisms display the characteristics of life.

■ **Figure 8** The structure of a drip-tip leaf is an adaptation to rainy environments.

Requires energy Living things need sources of energy to fuel their life functions. Living things get their energy from food. Most plants and some unicellular organisms use light energy from the Sun to make their own food and fuel their activities. Other unicellular organisms can transform the energy in chemical compounds to make their food.

Organisms that cannot make their own food, such as animals and fungi, get energy by consuming other organisms. Some of the energy that an organism takes in is used for growth, development, and maintaining homeostasis. However, most of the energy is transformed into thermal energy and is radiated to the environment as heat.

Maintains homeostasis Regulation of an organism's internal conditions to maintain life is called **homeostasis** (hoh mee oh STAY sus). Homeostasis occurs in all living things. If anything happens within or to an organism that affects its normal state, processes to restore the normal state begin. If homeostasis is not restored, death might occur.

Connection to Earth Science When athletes travel to a location that is at a higher altitude than where they live, they generally arrive long before the competition so that their bodies have time to adjust to the thinner air. At higher altitudes, air has fewer molecules of gases, including oxygen, per unit of volume. Therefore, there is less oxygen available for an athlete's red blood cells to deliver to the cells and tissues, which disrupts his or her body's homeostasis. To restore homeostasis, the athlete's body produces more red blood cells. Having more red blood cells results in an adequate amount of oxygen delivered to the athlete's cells. R

Adaptations evolve over time Many trees in rain forests have leaves with drip tips, like the one shown in **Figure 8.** Water runs off more easily and quickly from leaves with drip tips. Harmful molds and mildews will not grow on dry leaves. This means a plant with dry leaves is healthier and has a better chance to survive. Drip tips are an adaptation to the rain forest environment. An **adaptation** is any inherited characteristic that results from changes to a species over time. Adaptations like rain forest trees with drip tips enable species to survive and, therefore, they are better able to pass their genes to their offspring.

Formative Assessment

Evaluation Have students list all eight characteristics of life and give an example of each. Use Table 1 to check answers.

Remediation Have each student retrieve their cards from the Visual Literacy activity on page 7. Have pairs of students quiz one another to identify the characteristic of life presented on the cards.

Section 1 Assessment

Section Summary

- Biologists study the structure and function of living things, their history, their interactions with the environment, and many other aspects of life.
- All organisms have characteristics that scientists use to determine whether the organisms are alive. All living organisms share these certain characteristics.

Understand Main Ideas

1. MAIN Idea **Describe** four characteristics used to identify whether something is alive.
2. **Explain** why cells are considered the basic units of living things.
3. **Define** biology and state some of the benefits of studying it.
4. **Differentiate** between response and adaptation.

Think Critically

5. MATH in Biology Survey students in your school—biology students and nonbiology students—and adults. Have participants choose characteristics of life from a list of various characteristics and rank their choices from most important to least important. Record, tabulate, average, and graph your results. Prepare a report that summarizes your findings.

Section 1 Assessment

1. Answers should include four of these characteristics: made of one or more cells, displays organization, grows and develops, reproduces, responds to stimuli, requires energy, maintains homeostasis, and adaptations evolve over time.
2. Cells are the smallest units known to exhibit all the characteristics of life.
3. Answers will vary. Possible answers include: understanding the origins and history of life; learning about the structures of living things, how living things interact with one another, and how living things function; understanding the role humans have in preserving the natural environment and maintaining life on Earth.
4. A response is a reaction to a stimulus. An adaptation is an inherited characteristic that results from changes to a species over time in response to an environmental factor.
5. Reports will depend on the sample surveyed.

Assessment Online Quiz

Reading Preview

Essential Questions

- What are the characteristics of scientific inquiry?
- What are the differences between science and pseudoscience?
- Why is scientific literacy important?

Review Vocabulary

investigation: a careful search or examination to uncover facts

New Vocabulary

science
theory
law
peer review
ethics

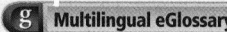

g Multilingual eGlossary

The Nature of Science

MAIN Idea **Science is a process based on inquiry that develops explanations.**

Real-World Reading Link If you see a headline that reads "Alien baby found in campsite," how do you know whether you should believe it or not? How do you know when to trust claims made in an advertisement on television or the Internet, or in a newspaper or magazine? What makes something science-based?

D What is science?

You probably have taken science class since you were in elementary school. But have you ever compared science to music, art, or math? **Science** is a body of knowledge based on the study of the natural world. There is science in almost everything we do. The nature, or essential characteristic, of science is scientific inquiry—the development of explanations. Scientific inquiry is both a creative process and a process rooted in unbiased observations and experimentation.

When many people think of a scientist, they think of someone in a white lab coat working in a laboratory. Scientists work all over the world in many locations, such as the volcanologist shown in **Figure 9.**

When enough evidence from many related investigations supports an idea, scientists consider that idea a **theory**—an explanation of a natural phenomenon supported by many observations and experiments over time. In biology, two of the most highly regarded theories are the cell theory and the theory of evolution. Both theories are based on countless observations and investigations, have extensive supporting evidence, and enable biologists to make accurate predictions.

A scientific **law** describes relationships under certain conditions in nature. For example, the law of conservation of matter indicates that before and after a change the same amount of matter exists. The law does not explain why this occurs, but it describes the relationship between matter before a change and matter after a change. It is important to note that because they are fundamentally different, theories do not become laws and laws do not become theories.

Figure 9 This volcanologist is collecting samples near molten lava flowing from Mount Etna. Lava temperatures can reach 750°C.

Research Citation

Check Understanding Educational research indicates that teachers' assessment of students' understanding should be an ongoing process. By clarifying misconceptions as suggested on this page, you can identify problem areas and provide a sense of confidence as students move forward through the chapter. (Heibert, et. al, 1997)

Research bibliography on pages 32T–34T

Differentiated Instruction

Below Level The reading strategy described on the next page works well with students who perform below level. These students will benefit when provided with models of what they are to do. They can pattern their reading after the examples you have shown them, improving their comprehension.

For more tips, see pages 14T–15T.

Section 2

MAIN Idea

BL OL AL Pose Questions Students will learn that a testable question is one in which the answer can be supported or not supported. **ASK STUDENTS:** ***What are some examples of testable questions?*** Possible answers: What impact will acid rain have on corn? How does exercising four times a week alter your cholesterol level? ***What are some examples of questions that are not testable?*** What is the meaning of life? Is this a good oil portrait? Why do some dogs like to sleep on their backs?

D Develop Concepts

BL OL

Clarify a Misconception

ASK STUDENTS: ***Have you ever read your horoscope in the newspaper? How was it determined? Was it based on sound scientific methods?*** Explain that astrology is a pseudoscience. **ASK STUDENTS:** ***How can you tell the difference between science and pseudoscience?*** Science only deals with things that are testable. If any part of a study or practice relies on untestable information, then it cannot be scientific. Tell students that this section will help them gain an understanding of science.

Critical Thinking

EL AL COOP LEARN Evaluate In pairs, have students locate examples of pseudoscience in magazines, in the newspaper, on television, or in other sources familiar to them. Ask students to explain how their examples are pseudoscience. Answers will vary.

R Reading Strategy

EL BL Model Help students internalize the process of comprehension by reading aloud the text under the headings *Expands knowledge* and *Challenges accepted theories.* Stress the meaning of these two important characteristics of science as you read, stopping frequently to verbalize your own methods of comprehension. For example, you might stop when you come to a difficult word and talk through how you determine its meaning from the context. Share your own visualization or connection as you read to model the process of reading. Modeling helps students understand how good readers construct meaning from the text.

W Writing Support

OL Narrative Writing Have students research other health issues in professional athletes. Ask students to write an article detailing what other health risks athletes might face and some possible preventative measures.

Reading Check Because athletes exercise and might do other things that are part of a healthy lifestyle.

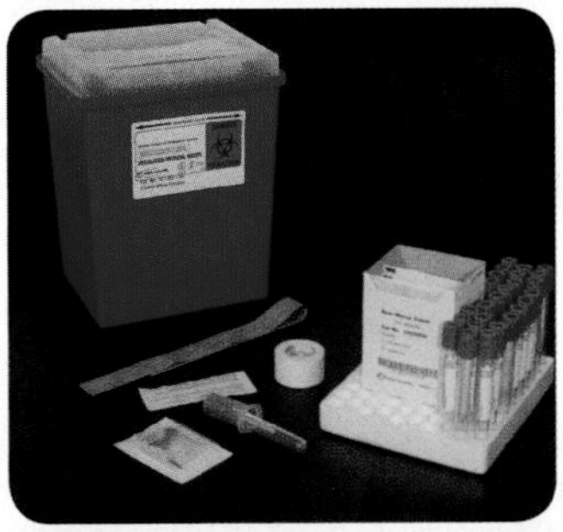

Blood draw kit

Tape measure

Caliper

■ **Figure 10** Dr. Buell and her team used supplies like these to collect data for her study. Blood was collected and tested by using sterile needles and syringes. Her team used a tape measure to measure waist circumference, and they used a caliper to determine body mass composition.

Makes observations and draws conclusions Dr. Jackie Buell is a scientist who conducts research at The Ohio State University in Columbus, Ohio. One of Dr. Buell's focuses is sports nutrition. Do you think a marathon runner, a college football player, and a golfer all need the same types of food and the same number of calories every day? Through the work of many scientists, we know how to calculate the number of calories a person needs every day. We also know what types of nutrients, vitamins, and minerals are needed, as well as other information about nutrition.

Subject selection Dr. Buell conducted a study on college football linemen to help further the understanding of sports nutrition. Dr. Buell investigated the presence of a condition called metabolic syndrome. A person with metabolic syndrome has risk factors such as abdominal obesity and elevated blood pressure. These risk factors are known to lead to heart disease, stroke, and diabetes.

Why do you think Dr. Buell studied college athletes? Many people assume that all athletes are healthy because they exercise and do many of the things doctors recommend for a healthy lifestyle. For this reason, an athlete with metabolic syndrome might not be aware that they are at risk for things such as heart disease or stroke.

Dr. Buell's research, however, showed that 34 of the 70 college linemen studied were at risk for metabolic syndrome. This information can be used to treat the athletes in the study. It can also be used to increase awareness. Athletes and doctors might be more likely to take health concerns in athletes more seriously. In addition, athletes can be given access to information regarding diet and exercise to help them decrease their risk factors.

Reading Check **Explain** why some people think all athletes are healthy.

Data collection What sort of data do you think Dr. Buell and her team gathered to study metabolic syndrome in her subjects? First, they measured the subjects' height, mass, blood pressure, upper-body skin folds, and waist circumference. Dr. Buell and her team also collected blood samples, family health histories, and information about exercise routines and nutrition habits. They used tools like the ones shown in **Figure 10** to collect the data.

Once all of these data were collected, they were analyzed to determine which athletes were at risk. Dr. Buell identified five risk factors for metabolic syndrome in her study. For one of the data sets, blood work, athletes that were found to have three, four, or all five risk factors were determined to have metabolic syndrome. Dr. Buell used this evidence to conclude that college athletes, specifically college football linemen, should not be assumed to be in good health simply because they are athletes.

Expands knowledge How can you know what information is science-based? Most scientific fields are guided by research that results in a constant reevaluation of what is known. This reevaluation often leads to new knowledge that scientists then evaluate. The search for new knowledge is the driving force that moves science forward.

Content Background

Real-World Connection Although Darwin first published his famous theory of evolution by natural selection in 1859, more than 100 years passed before scientists provided strong evidence to support this theory in wild animal populations. Rosemary and Peter Grant arrived in the Galápagos Islands in 1973 to study the finch populations. Three years later, a severe drought brought on by an El Niño wiped out 85 percent of the medium-sized ground finches on the Island of Daphne Major. Those individuals that survived had larger beaks and body sizes. The next generation of finches also exhibited larger beaks and body sizes, providing evidence that natural selection occurs in nature. The Grants' findings were published in *Science*. This is one of the most widely cited publications in evolutionary biology.

Pseudosciences are those areas of study that try to imitate science, often driven by cultural or commercial goals. Astrology, horoscopes, psychic reading, tarot card reading, face reading, and palmistry are pseudosciences. They do not provide science-based explanations about the natural world.

In pseudoscience, little research is done. If research is done, then often it is simply to justify existing knowledge rather than to extend the knowledge base. Pseudoscientific ideas generally do not ask new questions or welcome more research.

Scientists have done the research to identify metabolic syndrome. They know why the risk factors associated with it can lead to heart disease and other health concerns. Dr. Buell applied this information to athletes, specifically college football linemen. She expanded knowledge by showing that athletes, those often assumed to be healthy, might have metabolic syndrome. What do you think scientists might study next?

Challenges accepted theories Scientists welcome debate about one another's ideas. They regularly attend conferences and meetings where they discuss new developments and findings. Often, disagreements occur among scientists. When disagreements occur, more research is done to find which ideas are supported.

Sciences advance by accommodating new information as it is discovered. As we have discussed, athletes are often assumed to be at low risk for cardiovascular disease and other health concerns because they exercise regularly and often live what is considered to be a healthy lifestyle. However, Dr. Buell challenged this idea. Her research showed that there was a high incidence of metabolic syndrome in the athletes studied, putting them at risk for cardio vascular disease, diabetes, and stroke.

Questions results Observations or data that are not consistent with current scientific understanding are of interest to scientists. These inconsistencies often lead to further investigations. For example, early biologists grouped bats with birds because both had wings. Further study showed that bat wings are more similar to mammalian limbs than they are to bird wings, as shown in **Figure 11.** This led to an examination of the anatomy, genes, and proteins of rats and bats. The relationship was confirmed, and scientists established that bats were more closely related to mammals than birds. In pseudoscience, observations or data that are not consistent with beliefs are discarded or ignored.

Reading Check **Describe** how observations or data that are not consistent with current scientific understanding should be treated.

CAREERS IN BIOLOGY

Science Writer Communicating scientific information to the public is one of the goals of a science writer. He or she might write news stories, manuals, or press releases, or edit and summarize the written materials of scientists.

D

S

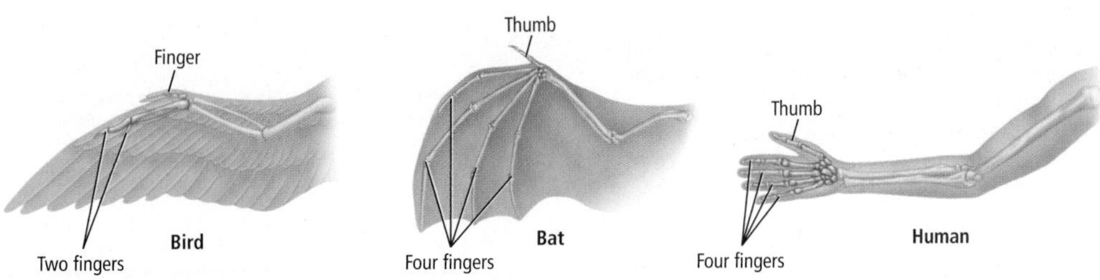

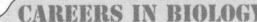

■ **Figure 11** The structure of a bat's wing is more like that of a human arm than a bird's wing.

S Skill Practice

BL OL AL Visual Literacy
Before students read the text on this page, have them examine Figure 11.

ASK STUDENTS: ***What can you infer from this figure?*** Bats are more closely related to humans than to birds.

D Develop Concepts

BL OL AL Discuss Explain to students that scientists should be skeptics. Lead a discussion about skepticism.

ASK STUDENTS: ***Is skepticism a neutral or a negative position?*** Being skeptical means you are open to ideas and you question what you hear and read. It is not a negative outlook, but a neutral outlook that seeks evidence.

Reading Check Students should indicate that these data and observations lead to further investigation.

Activity

BL OL AL Debunk Astrology Bring in newspaper horoscopes for the same zodiac sign from twelve different days. Do not identify the sign. Number each horoscope. Make photocopies and distribute to each group of students. Have students select the horoscope which best "fits" them. Ask the students to explain why the horoscope fits them, provide evidence, and justify their rationale. Then, explain that the horoscopes are all for the same sign, just different days. Students should learn that there is no scientific basis for astrology. Est. time: 10 min

DATA ANALYSIS LAB 1

About the Lab

- Some students will need assistance plotting the graph.

Think Critically

1. Division II (with 27 total)
2. Division II with 55.5%
3.

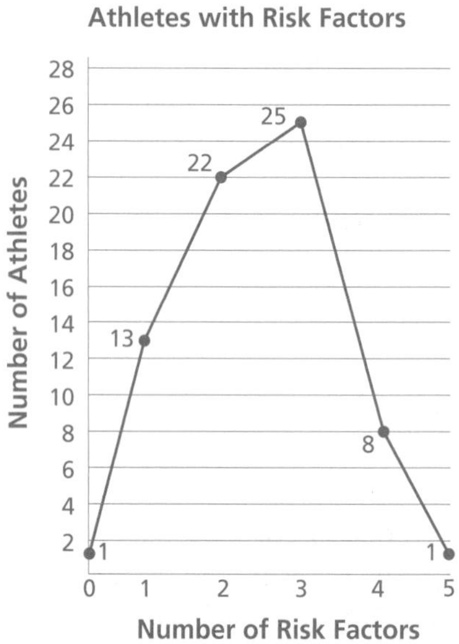

4. Answers may vary but should include losing weight, eating healthy, and monitoring their risk factors.

Reading Check to check experimental procedures and the accuracy of results to legitimize findings

VOCABULARY

ACADEMIC VOCABULARY

Unbiased
to be objective, impartial, or fair
The judges were unbiased in choosing the winner.

Tests claims Biologists use standard experimental procedures in their research. They make claims and draw conclusions based on a large amount of data and observations obtained from unbiased investigations and carefully controlled experimentation. Bias can occur when a scientist unfairly influences the results or conclusions of an investigation or experiment. Pseudoscientists often make claims that cannot be tested. These claims are often mixtures of fact and opinion and are heavily biased.

Dr. Buell made claims based on 14 data points for all the athletes in the study. The data were analyzed before any conclusions were drawn. The use of data to test and support claims is one way to differentiate science from pseudoscience.

Undergoes peer review Finally, before Dr. Buell's study was made public, it was reviewed by peers—scientists who are working in the same field of study. **Peer review** is a process by which the procedures and results of an experiment are evaluated by other scientists who are in the same field or who are conducting similar research. Peer review gives credibility to research papers and prevents false information from being printed in scientific journals.

When scientists publish their work, they make it available for other scientists to examine. You can examine data from Dr. Buell's study in Data Analysis Lab 1.

Reading Check **Infer** why scientists utilize peer reviews.

DATA ANALYSIS LAB 1

Based on Real Data*

Make and Use Graphs

How can graphs help us interpret data? The table shows the number risk factors for metabolic syndrome college linemen exhibited. The more factors a player exhibited, the greater the chance they had metabolic syndrome. The data are separated into players that play at a college identified as Division I, II, or III, according to the NCAA.

Think Critically

1. **Identify** which division had the largest sample size.
2. **Determine** which division had the largest percentage of participants with three or more risk factors.
3. **Construct** a line graph that shows the number of risk factors and the number of athletes that possess these risk factors.
4. **Extrapolate** If you were a doctor treating these athletes, what would your advice to them be?

Number of Risk Factors for Metabolic Syndrome

Number of Risk Factors	Division			
	I	II	III	Total
0	0	1	0	1
1	3	5	5	13
2	10	6	6	22
3	7	8	10	25
4	2	6	0	8
5	0	1	0	1

*Data obtained from: Buell, Jackie L., et al. 2008. Presence of Metabolic Syndrome in Football Linemen. *Journal of Athletic Training* 43(6):608-616

Differentiated Instruction

English Learners Students with limited English language proficiency might need additional support when reading the text. Provide these students with a graphic organizer to complete as they read the assigned material. This will help them organize information and identify important concepts.

For more tips, see pages 14T–15T.

Science in Everyday Life

There is widespread fascination with science. Popular television programs about crime are based on forensics, which applies science to matters of legal interest. The media is filled with information on flu epidemics, the latest medical advances, discoveries of new species, and technologies that improve or extend human lives. Clearly, science is not limited to the laboratory. The results of research go far beyond reports in scientific journals and meetings.

Science literacy In order to evaluate the vast amount of information available in print, online, and on television, and to participate in the fast-paced world of the twenty-first century, each of us must be scientifically literate. A person who is scientifically literate combines a basic understanding of science and its processes with reasoning and thinking skills.

Many of the issues our world faces every day relate to biology. Drugs, alcohol, tobacco, AIDS, mental illness, cancer, heart disease, and eating disorders provide subjects for biological research worldwide. Environmental issues such as global warming, pollution, deforestation, the use of fossil fuels, nuclear power, genetically modified foods, and conserving biodiversity are issues that you and future generations will face. Also, genetic engineering, cloning—producing genetically identical individuals, genetic screening—searching for genetic disorders in people, euthanasia (yoo thuh NAY zhuh)—permitting a death for reasons of mercy, and cryonics (kri AH niks)—freezing a dead person or animal with the hope of reviving it in the future—all involve **ethics,** which is a set of moral principles or values. Ethical issues must be addressed by society based on the values it holds important.

Scientists provide information about the continued expansion of science and technology. As a scientifically literate individual, you will be an educated consumer who can participate in discussions about important issues and support policies that reflect your views. You might also serve on a jury where DNA evidence, like that shown in **Figure 12,** is presented. You will need to understand the evidence, comprehend its implications, and decide the outcome of the trial.

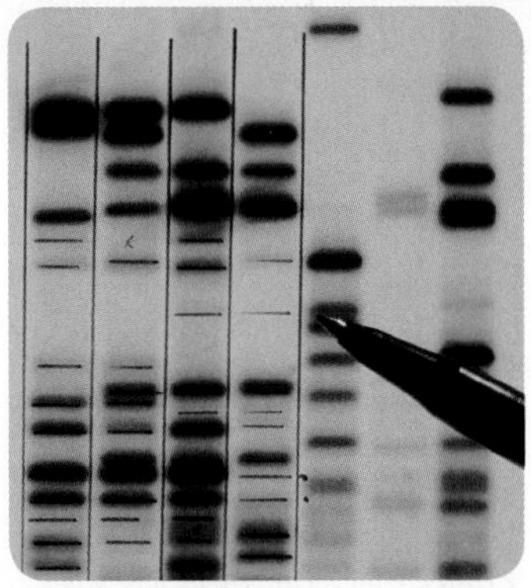

Figure 12 DNA analysis might exclude an alleged thief because his or her DNA does not match the DNA from the crime scene.

Section 2 Assessment

Section Summary

- Science is the study of the natural world and is rooted in scientific inquiry.
- Pseudoscience is not based on standard scientific research.
- Scientific literacy is important for everyday life.
- Ethics are moral principals that guide society and influnce science.

Understand Main Ideas

1. MAIN Idea **Describe** the characteristics of scientific inquiry.
2. **Define** *scientific theory.*
3. **Compare and contrast** science with pseudoscience.
4. **Defend** the importance of scientific literacy to a classmate who doesn't want to learn about science.

Think Critically

5. **Organize** the characteristics of science in a concept map.

WRITING in **Biology**

6. Write an article for the school newspaper that explains the nature of science. Use examples from Dr. Buell's research.

Develop Concepts

BL OL AL

Community Connection

Have students examine local newspapers for articles on health related issues. Ask students to evaluate the articles based on the following criteria:

1. scientific accuracy
2. amount of background knowledge needed to understand the issue
3. amount of research that went into the scientific finding

Formative Assessment

Evaluation Have students make a Venn diagram comparing and contrasting science with pseudoscience. Charts will vary. Students should point out that science is based on facts and pseudoscience is based on beliefs. Both are based on observations and try to explain the world.

Remediation Provide students with examples of pseudoscience and science. Then have them explain the differences. possible example of science: the discovery of the antobiotic effects of fungi such as penicillin; possible example of pseudoscience: astrological claims The students should then adjust their Venn diagrams accordingly.

Section 2 Assessment

1. Scientific inquiry is characterized by asking testable questions and using evidence to propose answers to those questions.
2. A scientific theory is an explanation based on many observations and experiments over time.
3. Science is based on evidence from valid investigations that can be reproduced. Pseudoscience uses scientific jargon, but it is not based on evidence from scientific investigations.
4. Students should indicate that scientific literacy is important for filtering through all the scientific and medical information that is available to them. Scientific literacy also helps them be critical thinkers.
5. Concept maps will vary but should show that science relies on evidence, expands knowledge, challenges accepted theories, questions results, and tests claims.
6. Answers will vary. Articles should explain that science relies on evidence, expands knowledge, challenges accepted ideas, minimizes bias, and includes peer review. Articles should cite examples from Dr. Buell's research.

Assessment Online Quiz

Section 3

MAIN Idea

BL OL AL

The Scientific Method

SAY TO STUDENTS: ***Think back to your experience with science before taking this class. Describe methods you used to conduct research.*** Possible answers include setting up experiments, posing hypotheses, making observations, collecting data, making conclusions. Inform students that in this section they will be seeing some of these same methods but may come to a new understanding of how biologists view the way research should be conducted.

Develop Concepts

BL OL

Clarify a Misconception

Many students believe the scientific method is a linear process. **ASK STUDENTS:** ***How is a scientific investigation done?*** Most likely, students will recite the following: make observations, state a hypothesis, design and conduct an experiment, gather results, report conclusions. Scientific investigations can involve various scientific methods, but they are not necessarily completed in a set order. Scientific investigations are fluid in nature and designed around a testable question.

EL On the board, draw arrows showing how scientific investigations are fluid and designed to progress from a testable question.

Section 3

Reading Preview

Essential Questions

- What are the differences between an observation and an inference?
- What are the differences among a control, independent variable, and dependent variable?
- What are the scientific methods a biologist uses for research?
- Why are the metric system and SI important?

Review Vocabulary

theory: an explanation of a natural phenomenon supported by many observations and experiments over time

New Vocabulary

observation
inference
scientific method
hypothesis
experiment
control group
experimental group
independent variable
dependent variable
constant
data
metric system
SI

g Multilingual eGlossary

Methods of Science

MAIN Idea **Biologists use specific methods when conducting research.**

Real-World Reading Link What do you do to find answers to questions? Do you ask other people, read, investigate, or observe? Are your methods haphazard or methodical? Over time, scientists have established standard procedures to find answers to questions.

Ask a Question

Imagine that you saw an unfamiliar bird in your neighborhood. You might develop a plan to observe the bird for a period of time. Scientific inquiry begins with **observation,** a direct method of gathering information in an orderly way. Often, observation involves recording information. In the example of your newly discovered bird, you might take photographs or draw a picture of it. You might write detailed notes about its behavior, including when and what it ate.

Science inquiry involves asking questions and processing information from a variety of reliable sources. The process of combining what you know with what you have learned to draw logical conclusions is called inferring; the conclusions themselves are called **inferences**. For instance, if you saw a photo of a bird similar to the unfamiliar bird in your neighborhood, you might infer that your bird and the bird in the photo are related. **Figure 13** illustrates how a field guide might be helpful in making inferences.

Scientific methods Biologists work in different places to answer their questions. For example, some biologists work in laboratories, perhaps developing new medicines, while others work outdoors in natural settings. No matter where they work, biologists all use similar methods to gather information and to answer questions. These methods sometimes are referred to as **scientific methods,** illustrated in **Figure 14.** Even though scientists do not use scientific methods in the same way each time they conduct an experiment, they observe and infer throughout the entire process.

■ **Figure 13** Scientists might use a field guide to help them identify or draw conclusions about things they observe in nature, such as this peregrine falcon.

Demonstration

BL OL COOP LEARN **Observe and Infer** Organize students into groups of three. Place a living organism in a clear container with airholes on the table for each group to observe. Possible organisms include a goldfish, a cricket, an earthworm, a mealworm, a gerbil, a hissing cockroach, a lizard, a crayfish, or a hermit crab. Have students make a list of observations about their organism. Each group should share their lists with the rest of the class.

ASK STUDENTS: ***How many of you listed inferences as observations?*** Students will invariably list inferences as observations. Be sure that their observations are ones that they directly observed and did not infer. Est. time: 30 min

Visualizing Scientific Methods

Figure 14
The way that scientists answer questions is through an organized series of events called scientific methods. There are no wrong answers to questions, only answers that provide scientists with more information about those questions. Questions and collected information help scientists form hypotheses. As experiments are conducted, hypotheses might or might not be supported.

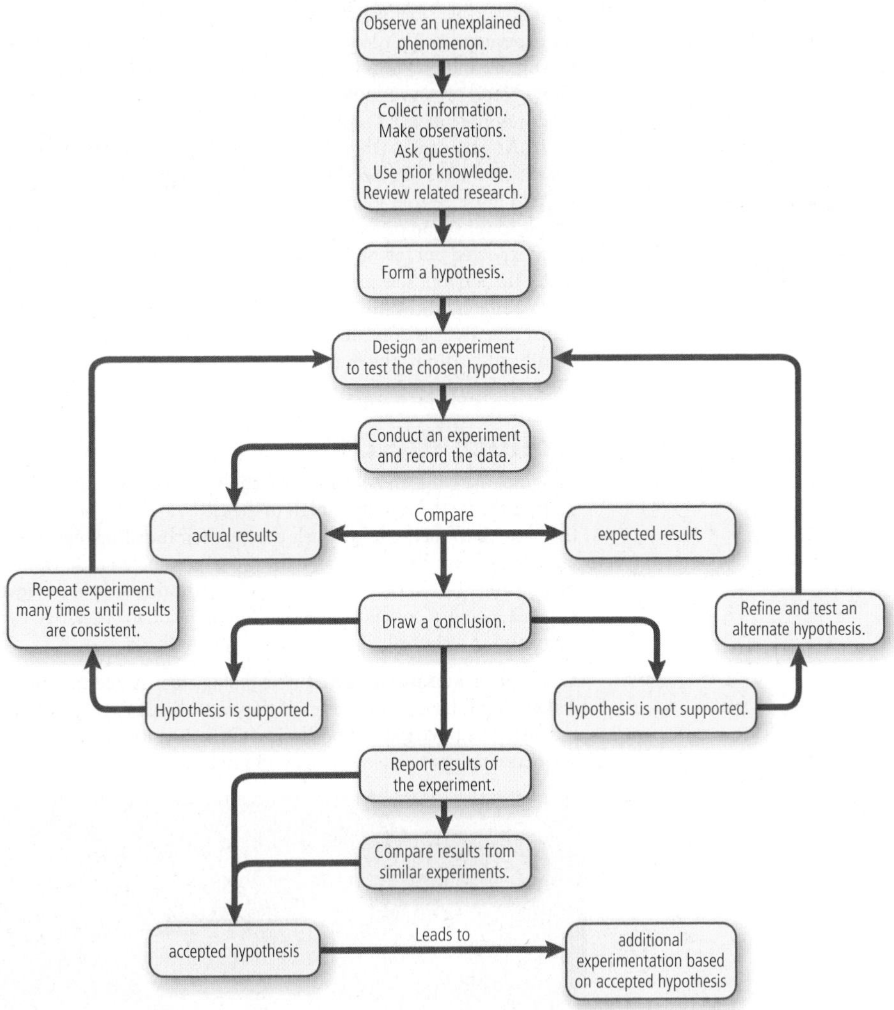

Concepts in Motion Animation

Visualizing Scientific Methods

Purpose

Students will learn about science inquiry as well as the nature of scientific knowledge.
A.1, A.2, G.2

Writing Support

BL OL Persuasive Writing
Have students examine Figure 14 and prepare a persuasive essay about how science methods are different from methods used to study art, history, or religion.

Skill Practice

EL BL OL Visual Literacy
Have students prepare a small book that depicts the scientific methods shown in Figure 14. The left-hand pages of the book should have the name of a scientific method, and the right-hand pages should have some sort of pictorial representation of the method.

Concepts in Motion
Animation

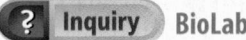

Inquiry BioLab

The lab at the end of the chapter can be used at this point in the lesson.

Content Background

Teacher FYI The scientific method depicted on posters at teacher supply stores and in older textbooks is the way science is reported in journals—not the way science is actually conducted. It is important to emphasize that science often proceeds in a cyclical manner with one question raising another and one observation leading to another, as one experiment leads to another. The linear step-by-step process is often used to describe an experiment in journals; however, scientists do not always take a linear pathway when conducting an experiment. Creativity and curiosity are integral components of the process, as are correcting missteps, revising hypotheses, and reaching dead ends.

R Reading Strategy

BL OL COOP LEARN

Make Connections Have pairs of students read the paragraph containing the term *serendipity.* Ask them to describe any experiences they have had with serendipity, using details so their partners can visualize the situation.

Critical Thinking

BL OL AL COOP LEARN

Design a Controlled Experiment Have students work in groups to design a controlled experiment that they could carry out in the classroom using common everyday organisms, such as crickets, mealworms, or earthworms. Each experiment needs a control group, an independent variable, and a dependent variable. Experiments will vary. Make sure the experiments contain all the necessary components and safety measures.

Critical Thinking

AL **Analyze** Bring copies of scientific journals to class. Have students review articles on biological research and prepare an analysis of the methods used in the research.

Skill Practice

EL BL OL COOP LEARN

Classify Present students with a list containing objects for measuring. Have students work in pairs or groups to classify each object as needing to be measured using meters, grams, or seconds.

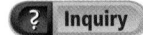

Inquiry Launch Lab

Assess Content Development
Assess how understanding has developed when students revisit the Launch Lab analysis questions.

Video BrainPOP

Inquiry Launch Lab

Review **Based on what you've read about observing and inferring, how would you now answer the analysis questions?**

Inquiry Virtual Lab

Video BrainPOP

Form a Hypothesis

Imagination, curiosity, creativity, and logic are key elements of the way biologists approach their research. In 1969, the U.S. Air Force asked Dr. Ronald Wiley to investigate how to enhance a pilot's ability to endure the effects of an increase in gravity (*g*-force) while traveling at high speed in an F-16 aircraft. It was known that isometrics, which is a form of exercise in which muscles are held in a contracted position, raised blood pressure. Wiley formed the hypothesis that the use of isometric exercise to raise blood pressure during maneuvers might increase tolerance to *g*-force and prevent blackouts. A **hypothesis** (hi PAH thuh sus) is a testable explanation of a situation.

Before Wiley formed his hypothesis, he made inferences based on his experience as a physiologist, what he read, discussions with Air Force personnel, and previous investigations. He did find that increasing a pilot's blood pressure could help the pilot withstand *g*-forces. But he also made an unexpected discovery.

During his study, Dr. Wiley discovered that isometric exercise decreased the resting blood pressure of the pilots. As a result, weight lifting and muscle-strengthening exercises are recommended today to help people lower blood pressure. Serendipity is the occurrence of accidental or unexpected but fortunate results. There are other examples of serendipity throughout science. R

When a hypothesis is supported by data from additional investigations, usually it is considered valid and is accepted by the scientific community. If not, the hypothesis is revised, and additional investigations are conducted.

Collect the Data

Imagine that while in Alaska on vacation, you noticed various kinds of gulls. You saw them nesting high in the cliffs, and you wondered how they maintain their energy levels during their breeding season. A group of biologists wondered the same thing and conducted a controlled experiment using gulls known as black-legged kittiwakes shown in **Figure 15.** When a biologist conducts an **experiment,** he or she investigates a phenomenon in a controlled setting to test a hypothesis.

Controlled experiments The biologists inferred that the kittiwakes would have more energy if they were given extra feedings while nesting. The biologists' hypothesis was that the kittiwakes would use the extra energy to lay more eggs and raise more chicks.

■ **Figure 15** This colony of black-legged kittiwakes along the Alaskan coast includes nesting pairs.

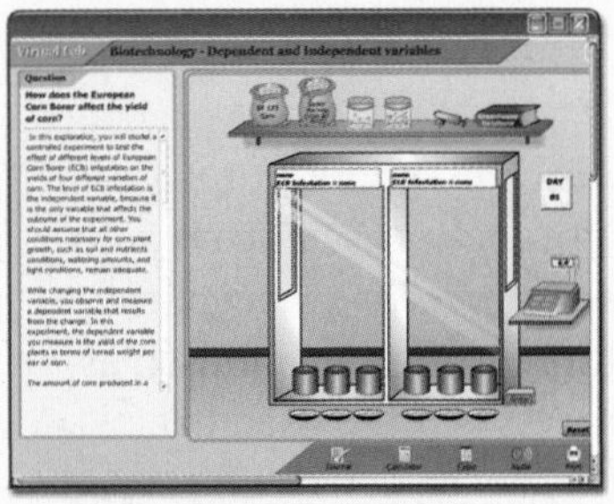

Inquiry **Virtual Lab** Students will test the effect of different levels of European Corn Borer (ECB) infestation on the yield of four varieties of corn crops.

"They know enough who know how to learn."
—HENRY BROOKS ADAMS

Biologists found nesting pairs of kittiwakes that were similar to each other and set up an experiment. A **control group** in an experiment is used for comparison. The kittiwakes not given the supplemental feedings were the control group. The **experimental group** is the group exposed to the factor being tested. The kittiwakes getting the supplemental feedings were the experimental group.

Experimental design When scientists design a controlled experiment, only one factor can change at a time. It is called the **independent variable** because it is the tested factor and it might affect the outcome of the experiment. In the kittiwakes experiment, the supplemental feeding was the independent variable. During an experiment, scientists measure a second factor called the **dependent variable.** It results from or depends on changes to the independent variable. The change in the kittiwakes' energy levels, as measured in reproductive output, was the dependent variable. A **constant** is a factor that remains fixed during an experiment while the independent and dependent variables change.

Data gathering As scientists test their hypotheses, they gather **data**—information gained from observations. The data can be quantitative or qualitative.

Data collected as numbers are called quantitative data. Numerical data can be measurements of time, temperature, length, mass, area, volume, or density.

Qualitative data are descriptions of what our senses detect. Often, qualitative data are interpreted differently because everyone does not sense things in the same way. However, many times it is the only collectible data.

Investigations Biologists conduct other kinds of scientific inquiry. They can investigate the behavior of organisms or spend their careers discovering and identifying new species. Some biologists use computers to model the natural behavior of organisms and systems. In investigations such as these, the procedure involves observation and collection of data rather than controlled manipulation of variables.

Metric system To make communication easier, most scientists use the metric system when collecting data and performing experiments. The **metric system** uses units with divisions that are powers of ten. The General Conference of Weights and Measures established the unit standards of the metric system in 1960. The system is called the International System of Units, commonly known as **SI.** In biology, the SI units you will use most often are meter (to measure length), gram (to measure mass), liter (to measure volume), and second (to measure time).

MiniLab 2

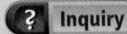

? Inquiry MiniLab

Manipulate Variables

How does a biologist establish experimental conditions? In a controlled experiment, a biologist develops an experimental procedure designed to investigate a question or problem. By manipulating variables and observing results, a biologist learns about relationships among factors in the experiment.

Procedure

1. Read and complete the lab safety form.
2. Create a data table with the columns labeled *Control, Independent Variable, Constants, Hypothesis,* and *Dependent Variable.*
3. Obtain a **printed maze.** Seated at your desk, have a classmate time how long it takes you to complete the maze. Record this time on the chart. This is the control in the experiment.
4. Choose a way to alter experimental conditions while completing the same maze. Record this as the independent variable.
5. In the column labeled *Constants,* list factors that will stay the same each time the experiment is performed.
6. Form a hypothesis about how the independent variable will affect the time it takes to complete the maze.
7. After your teacher approves your plan, carry out the experiment. Record the time required to complete the maze as the dependent variable.
8. Repeat Steps 3–7 as time allows.
9. Graph the data. Use the graph to analyze the relationship between the independent and dependent variables.

Analysis

1. **Explain** the importance of the control in this experiment.
2. **Error Analysis** By completing the maze more than once, you introduced another variable, which likely affected the time required to complete the maze. Would eliminating this variable solve the problem? Explain.

MiniLab 2

? Inquiry MiniLab

For a lab worksheet, use your eTeacherEdition Online.

RUBRIC A rubric for evaluating MiniLabs is found on your eTeacherEdition Online.

Est. Time 25 min

Additional Materials Printable mazes can be found on the Internet or in puzzle books, such as *Mazes, Mazes, Mazes* by Jody Taylor and *The Giant Book of Mazes* by Jeffrey A. O'Hare.

Safety Precaution Approve lab safety forms before work begins.

Teaching Strategies

- Prior to the lab, make sure students can use the terms *independent variable, dependent variable, constant,* and *control.*
- Discuss possible independent variables for this experiment. Instruct students to get your approval before conducting their planned experiment.

Analysis

1. The control provides a basis for comparison. In this experiment, the time required to complete the maze under various conditions was compared with the time it took to complete the maze while seated at a desk.
2. You gained knowledge about the maze while completing it the first time, which likely reduced the time required to complete the maze the second time. While this variable could be eliminated by using a different maze with the same level of difficulty, using a different maze also introduces another variable into the experiment.

LabManager™

Customize this lab with the LabManager™ CD-ROM.

Demonstration

BL OL Measure Gather various items to measure. Demonstrate the metric system to students by determining the mass of items in grams, measuring items in meters and milliliters, and timing events in seconds. Suggested items include students' height, the mass of a turtle or gerbil, the volume of a liquid, and timing two students as they walk down the hall and back.

ASK STUDENTS: ***Why is a common measurement system vital for the work of scientists?*** to facilitate replication of the work, to ease interpretation of results

Est. time: 10 min

S Skill Practice

BL OL AL Visual Literacy Draw students' attention to Figure 16. **ASK STUDENTS:** ***If the anole's mass was 2.4 g on April 11 and 2.7 g on April 29, what percent change was there during the 18-day period?*** 12 percent

Develop Concepts

BL OL AL COOP LEARN

Activity Have the class work together to design a short survey with questions such as "What is your favorite film?", "What famous person, dead or alive, would you like to have lunch with?", etc. Have students answer the survey questions and cut the paper into strips with one question and answer per strip. Organize students into groups, and have each group analyze the class data worth of strips. For example, group one analyzes the class data for question 1, and so on. Have each group figure out how to visually display the results on poster board using a table or a graph to present the data.

W Writing Support

OL Summary Writing After students have read the text under the headings *Collect the Data, Analyze the Data,* and *Report Conclusions,* have them write a paragraph about each of these processes, summarizing the important ideas from the text. Use the summaries to evaluate whether students understand the methods of science.

■ **Caption Question Fig. 16** 2.8 g

Reading Check The type of data collected and how it is collected are determined by the hypothesis that is being tested. Interpretation happens when the scientist determines whether the data support the hypothesis.

VOCABULARY

SCIENCE USAGE V. COMMON USAGE

Conclusion

Science usage: judgment, decision, or opinion formed after an investigation
The researcher formed the conclusion that the hypothesis was not supported.

Common usage: the end or last part
The audience left at the conclusion of the movie.

Analyze the Data

After analyzing the data from an investigation, a biologist usually asks, "Has my hypothesis been supported?" He or she then might ask, "Are more data needed?" or "Are different procedures needed?" Often, the investigation must be repeated many times to obtain consistent results.

As biologists look for explanations, patterns generally are noted that help to explain the data. A simple way to display the data is in a table or on a graph, such as the ones in **Figure 16,** which describe the change in mass over time of a lizard called an anole. The graph of the data makes the pattern easier to grasp. In this case, there is a regular pattern. Notice that the mass increases over a three-day period and then levels off for three days before increasing again. For more review about making graphs, refer to the Skillbuilder Handbook, pp. 1129–1132.

Because biologists often work in teams, meetings are held to discuss ongoing investigations, to analyze the data, and to interpret the results. The teams continue to examine their research plan to be certain they avoid bias, repeat their trials, and collect a large enough sample size. Analysis of the data might lead to a conclusion that the hypothesis has been supported. It also could lead to additional hypotheses, to further experimentation, or to general explanations of nature. Even when a hypothesis has not been supported, it is valuable.

Report Conclusions

Biologists report their findings and conclusions in scientific journals. Before a scientist can publish in a journal, the work is reviewed by peers. The reviewers examine the paper for originality, competence of the scientific method used, and accuracy. They might find fault with the reasoning or procedure, or suggest other explanations or conclusions. If the reviewers agree on the merit of the paper, then the paper is published for review by the public and use by other scientists. W

Reading Check Infer How does the hypothesis guide data collection and interpretation?

S

■ **Figure 16** After plotting the data points from the table on graph paper, draw a line that fits the pattern of the data rather than connects the dots.
Extrapolate ***What do you think the mass of the anole will be at 21 days?***

Anole

Change in Mass of Anole

Date	Mass (g)
April 11	2.4
April 14	2.5
April 17	2.5
April 20	2.6
April 23	2.6
April 26	2.7
April 29	2.7

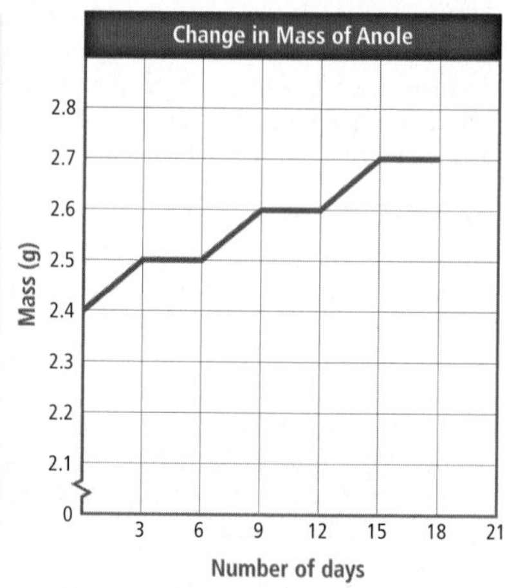

Content Background

Real-World Connection Bioinformatics is the use of computer technology to study biological systems. More than ever before, there is a huge amount of biological data. With the human genome project alone, 3 billion base pairs must be stored on the computer and can be more easily analyzed because of the technology existing today. Many biologists still use their laboratory notebooks; however, for those biologists working with microarrays, genechips, and nanotechnology, the computer is essential for collecting, analyzing, and storing their work.

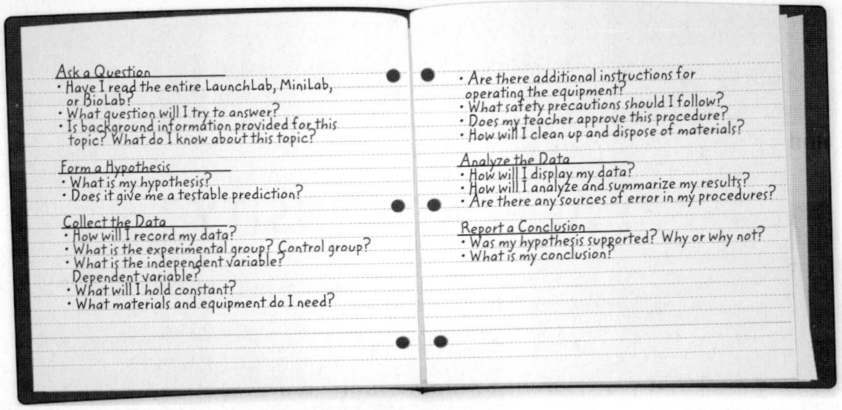

■ **Figure 17** To ask meaningful questions, form hypotheses, and conduct careful experiments, develop research plans based on scientific methods. Use your lab report to list your procedure, record your data, and report your conclusions.

Student Scientific Inquiry

You will be given many opportunities during your study of biology to do your own investigations and experiments. You might also receive a lab assignment that spells out a series of steps to follow or you might design your own procedure. Whether you are planning a lab report or an entire procedure and its lab report, be sure to ask yourself questions like those in **Figure 17.** For additional help with setting up experiments and using equipment, go to Investigation and Experimentation in the Student Handbook of this textbook.

Lab safety During biology labs, you will be alerted of possible safety hazards by warning statements and safety symbols. A safety symbol is a logo designed to alert you about a specific danger. Always refer to the safety symbols chart at the front of this book before beginning any field investigation or lab activity. Carefully read the meaning of each lab's safety symbols. Also, learn the location in the classroom of all safety equipment and how and when to use it. You are responsible for being safe at all times to protect yourself and your classmates.

D

Video

What's BIOLOGY Got To Do WIth It?

Section 3 Assessment

Section Summary

- Careful observation involves an orderly way of gathering information.
- Controlled experiments involve a control group and an experimental group.
- SI units include meters, grams, and liters.

Understand Main Ideas

1. MAIN Idea **Describe** how a biologist's research can proceed from an idea to a published article.
2. **State** why an observation cannot be an inference.
3. **Explain** why the metric system and SI are important.
4. **Differentiate** between controls, independent variables, and dependent variables.

Think Critically

5. **Design** a controlled experiment to determine whether earthworms are more attracted to perfume or to vinegar.

MATH in Biology

6. One kilogram equals 1000 grams. One milligram equals 0.001 grams. How many milligrams are in one kilogram?

D Develop Concepts

EL BL OL Lab Safety Give students a handout with pictures of different safety symbols without the labels. Have students cut out each one, glue it onto an index card, and write the name of the safety symbol on the back of the card. Instruct pairs of students to quiz each other on the meanings of the symbols.

Formative Assessment

Evaluation Ask students to compare and contrast an independent variable with a dependent variable. An independent variable is the factor that affects the outcome of the experiment. It is not affected by the experiment. Time is often an independent variable. The dependent variable results from changes to the independent variable in the experiment.

Remediation If students do not show a clear understanding of the differences between independent and dependent variables, have them read out loud with a partner the text under the heading *Experimental design.* Have the partner ask questions such as "What is the difference between the independent and dependent variable in an experiment?"

Section 3 Assessment

1. The biologist can use the idea to form a hypothesis, use an experiment to test the hypothesis, analyze the data from the experiment, and publish the analysis.
2. An observation is a direct method of gathering data, and an inference is an assumption that can be made from gathered data.
3. The metric system and SI are important because they give scientists a common system of measurement to use. Using common units to record measurements makse it easier to repeat experiments and communicate results.
4. A control group is one that is used for comparison. It does not have the independent variable applied to it. The independent variable is the tested factor in an experiment, while the dependent variable results from or depends on changes to the independent variable.
5. Answers will vary. Experimental designs should show an understanding of how to use a control group and an independent variable, as well as how to measure a dependent variable.
6. 1 million

Assessment **Online Quiz**

Purpose

Students will understand about science inquiry and science as a human endeavor.
A.2, C.1, E.2, G.1, G3

Anticipatory Guide

ASK STUDENTS: ***What is the study of biology?*** Biology is the study of living organisms and life processes. ***Why do people study it?*** People study biology to better understand the natural world. ***What is technology?*** Technology is the application of scientific knowledge of materials and processes to benefit people. ***Why is technology important in biology?*** Answers may include discoveries such as: microscopes make it easier to study forms of life; computers make it easier to track data; technology can help immensely in the field of medicine

Background

Osteoporosis is a condition that is often associated with elderly people, especially women. However, technologies such as the DXA machine have allowed doctors to diagnose this condition earlier and more accurately. The DXA machine can target areas such as the spine, hips, and wrists—areas where calcium is most likely to be leached from bones. Targeting these areas is important because an overall bone scan takes an average bone density and might come up as normal when the patient might still be at risk. Getting a reading specific to these areas can allow doctors an earlier and more accurate diagnosis.

CUTTING-EDGE BIOLOGY

MEASURING BONE DENSITY

You have probably been told that you need to drink milk or eat dairy products to get calcium, but do you know why? Your body uses calcium to build strong (dense) bones and teeth. Your body also uses calcium to help your heart beat and your nervous system and muscular system function properly.

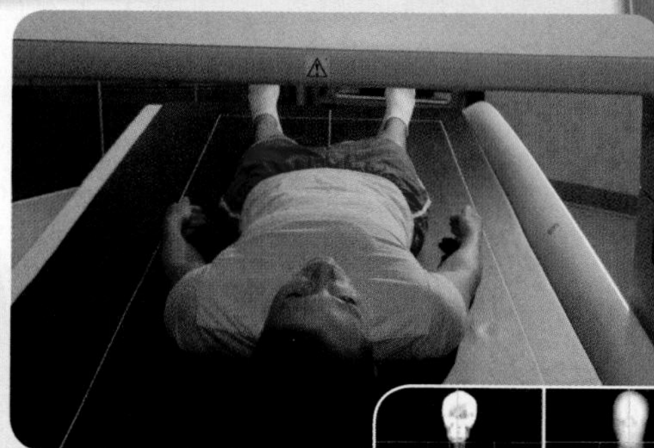

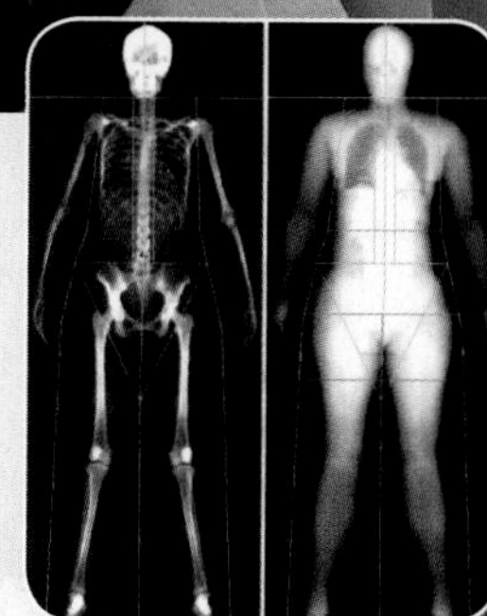

Above: The DXA has a moveable arm that scans the length of the patient's body.
Right: The DXA scan shows both body composition and bone density.

How are calcium and bone density related? If you don't get enough calcium in your diet, your body will pull calcium from your bones and teeth, where it is stored naturally. About 85-90% of bone mass is acquired in adolescence. It is important to consume enough calcium when you are in your teens to ensure that you have strong, dense bones later in life. People cannot feel their bones getting weaker. This is another reason that adequate calcium intake is important at any age.

When calcium is depleted you are more susceptible to broken bones, cavities, and osteoporosis. Osteoporosis is a condition that is characterized by the loss of bone density. When bones are less dense they are brittle and full of air pockets, and they can break more easily.

How do you measure bone density? A scanner called dual energy X ray absorptiometry (DXA) measures bone mineral density so that doctors can get an accurate picture of how much calcium is present in the bones. Dense bones have more calcium in them and are stronger than low-density bones.

How does the DXA machine work? The X rays are similar to visible light rays but have a much shorter wavelength. They reflect differently off tissues with different densities. On a traditional X ray, all bone appears white and soft tissue might not appear at all, or might appear a shade of gray.

The DXA machine uses X rays with several wavelengths that reflect differently off different densities of bone. This allows doctors to detect bone density in patients. The DXA machine can also download information to a computer program where the data can be compiled and presented to the patient in the form of a graph and image.

Doctors and scientists use the data provided by the DXA to help patients prevent or treat low bone density and osteoporosis. For some patients who are at risk for osteoporosis, regular DXA scans can track bone loss.

WRITING in Biology

Define technology Research a technology in the medical research field other than DXA. Present information about the technology you researched in a poster or pamphlet.

WRITING in Biology

RUBRIC Use the modifiable rubric found on your eTeacherEdition Online to assess writing assignments.

Activity Organize the class into groups. Instruct each group to create a chart of some ways biology can enhance your understanding of the world, and why it is important to study this. Tell groups to be sure to list specific applications of each field of biology and what technologies might arise from this field that could advance society. Have the class discuss their results. Example: The study of botany is important because it helps people understand how plants and pests interact. People need to study this to grow better crops. Pesticide alternatives are a potential technological advancement.

WebQuest

BIOLAB

Design Your Own

HOW CAN YOU KEEP CUT FLOWERS FRESH?

Background: When first cut from the garden, a bouquet of flowers looks healthy and has a pleasant aroma. Over time, the flowers droop and lose their petals. Leaves and stems below the water line begin to decay.

Question: *What steps can I take to extend the freshness of cut flowers?*

Possible Materials

Choose materials that would be appropriate for this lab.

fresh cut flowers	water
vases	scissors

Safety Precautions

Plan and Perform the Experiment

1. Read and complete the lab safety form.
2. Research strategies for extending the life of cut flowers. During your research, look for possible reasons why a specific strategy might be effective.
3. Form a hypothesis based on your research. It must be possible to test the hypothesis by gathering and analyzing specific data.
4. Design an experiment to test the hypothesis. Remember, the experiment must include an independent and dependent variable. Identify a control sample. List all factors that will be held constant.
5. Design and construct a data table.
6. Make sure your teacher approves your plan before you proceed.
7. Implement the experimental design. Organize the data you collect using a graph or chart.
8. **Cleanup and Disposal** Properly dispose of plant material. Wash hands thoroughly after handling plant material. Clean and return all lab equipment to the designated locations.

Analyze and Conclude

1. **Describe** the strategy tested by your hypothesis. Why did you choose this strategy to examine?
2. **Explain** how you established the control sample.
3. **Interpret Data** What trends or patterns do the data show?
4. **Analyze** What is the relationship between your independent and dependent variables?
5. **Draw Conclusions** Based on your data, describe one way to extend the freshness of cut flowers.
6. **Error Analysis** Critique your experimental design. Is it possible that any other variables were introduced? Explain. How could these variables be controlled?

WRITING in Biology

Brochure Compare the strategy for extending the freshness of cut flowers your group examined with strategies tested by other groups. Based on class results, create a brochure with the title "Make Cut Flowers Stay Beautiful Longer." Include tips for extending the life of cut flowers. Share the brochure with community members who might benefit from this information.

Analyze and Conclude

1. Answers will vary. Students may choose a strategy based on availability of materials, ease of implementing an experimental design, or area of interest.
2. Answers will vary. The control sample should be the one which provides a basis for comparison for all experimental trials.
3. Answers will vary. Students should compare the length of time flowers in the experimental trials remain fresh with the length of time flowers in the control group remain fresh.
4. Answers will vary. Changes in the independent variable will cause changes in the dependent variable.
5. Answers will vary based on the strategy addressed by the hypothesis.
6. Answers will vary, but may include variables such as water temperature, sunlight, and glucose levels that influenced flower freshness prior to students acquiring them for the experiment. Ideas on how to control these variables will vary. Sample idea: Instead of relying on sunlight, use timed artificial lighting for the experiment.

BIOLAB

Design Your Own

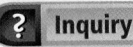

Inquiry BioLab

For a lab worksheet, use your eTeacherEdition Online.

RUBRIC A rubric for evaluating BioLabs is found on your eTeacherEdition Online.

Est. Time 140 min

Content Background When flowers are cut underwater using a sharp knife or scissors, air is prevented from entering the stem and damage to the stem is reduced. Flowers placed in clean vases sterilized with bleach are exposed to limited bacteria and algae that can block water uptake and decrease flower life. Both commercial and homemade preservative solutions extend flower life by providing needed sugars as well as substances that reduce bacteria and algae growth.

Safety Precautions Approve lab safety forms before work begins. Based on their research, students may choose to use bleach or citric acid. Enforce appropriate safety standards when these chemicals are used.

Teaching Strategies

- Review the definition and role of the independent variable, dependent variable, control sample, and experimental constants prior to the design phase of the lab.
- Refer to specific knowledge gained from the Launch Lab and MiniLabs as you assist students in developing an experimental design.

Alternative Teaching Demo Have the class agree on one hypothesis to test. Set up a single set of control and experimental samples, and have the entire class collect and analyze the data.

Chapter 1

Study Guide

ConnectED

Students can use the following to review the chapter.

Review

Vocabulary eGames
Vocabulary eFlashcards
Vocabulary PuzzleMaker

Assessment

Online Quizzes
Online Test Practice
Standardized Test Practice

Use the *ExamView®* *Assessment Suite* CD-ROM to:

- create multiple versions of tests
- create modified tests with one mouse click
- edit existing questions and add your own questions
- build tests aligned with state standards using built-in state curriculum tags
- change English tests to Spanish with one mouse click
- track students' progress using the Teacher Management System

Chapter 1 Study Guide

THEME FOCUS Scientific Inquiry Biologists use scientific methods to perform experiments and investigations in their study of life.

BIG Idea Biology is the study of life.

Section 1 Introduction to Biology

biology (p. 4)
organism (p. 6)
organization (p. 8)
development (p. 9)
growth (p. 9)
reproduction (p. 9)
response (p. 9)
species (p. 9)
stimulus (p. 9)
adaptation (p. 10)
homeostasis (p. 10)

MAIN Idea All living things share the characteristics of life.

- Biologists study the structure and function of living things, their history, their interactions with the environment, and many other aspects of life.
- All organisms have characteristics that scientists use to determine whether the organisms are alive. All living organisms share these certain characteristics.

Section 2 The Nature of Science

science (p. 11)
law (p. 11)
theory (p. 11)
peer review (p. 14)
ethics (p. 15)

MAIN Idea Science is a process based on inquiry that develops explanations.

- Science is the study of the natural world and is rooted in scientific inquiry.
- Pseudoscience is not based on standard scientific research.
- Scientific literacy is important for everyday life.
- Ethics are moral principles that guide society and influence science.

Section 3 Methods of Science

inference (p. 16)
observation (p. 16)
scientific method (p. 16)
experiment (p. 18)
hypothesis (p. 18)
constant (p. 19)
control group (p. 19)
data (p. 19)
dependent variable (p. 19)
experimental group (p. 19)
independent variable (p. 19)
metric system (p. 19)
SI (p. 19)

MAIN Idea Biologists use specific methods when conducting research.

- Careful observation involves an orderly way of gathering information.
- Controlled experiments involve a control group and an experimental group.
- SI units include meters, grams, and liters.

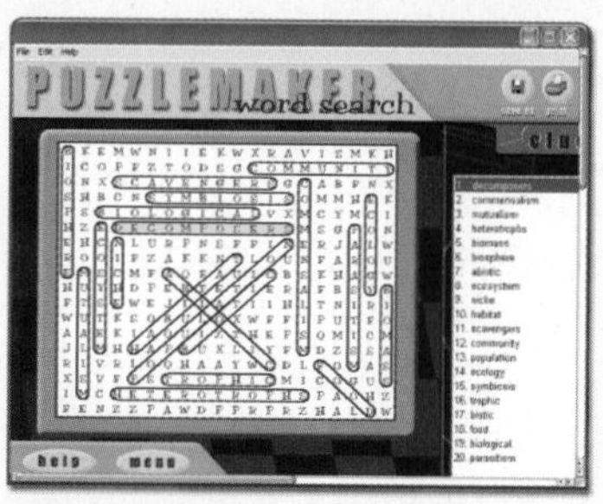

Review **Vocabulary PuzzleMaker**
For additional practice with vocabulary, have students access the Vocabulary PuzzleMaker online.

Review **Vocabulary eGames**

Section 1

Vocabulary Review

Replace the underlined phrase with the correct vocabulary term from the Study Guide page.

1. The production of offspring is a characteristic of life that enables the continuation of a species.
2. The internal control of mechanisms allows for an organism's systems to remain in balance.
3. The study of life involves learning about the natural world.

Understand Main Ideas

Use the graph below to answer question 4.

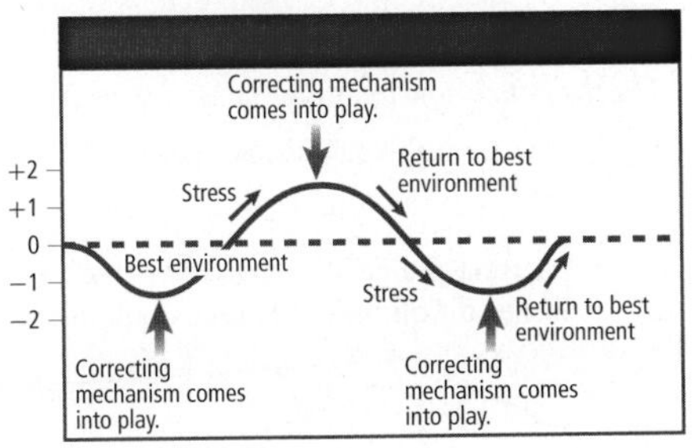

4. Which characteristic of life should be the title of this graph?
   A. Cellular Basis
   B. Growth
   C. Homeostasis
   D. Reproduction
5. Which best describes adaptation?
   A. reproducing as a species
   B. a short-term change in behavior in response to a stimuli
   C. inherited changes in response to environmental factors
   D. change in size as an organism ages

Constructed Response

6. **Open Ended** What is the role of energy in living organisms? Is it a more or less important role than other characteristics of life? Defend your response.

Think Critically

7. MAIN Idea Evaluate how the contributions made by Goodall, Chory, and Drew reinforce our understanding of the characteristics of life.
8. **Compare and contrast** a response and an adaptation. Use examples from your everyday world in your answer.

Section 2

Vocabulary Review

Identify the correct vocabulary term from the Study Guide page that corresponds to each phrase.

9. the set of moral principles or values that guide decisions about scientific and medical topics
10. a well-tested explanation that brings together many observations in science such as evolution, plate tectonics, biogenesis

Understand Main Ideas

11. Which best describes a scientific theory?
    A. a possible explanation of an event
    B. a set of moral values or principles
    C. a description of the relationship between objects
    D. an explanation supported by many experiments over time
12. Which is true about scientific inquiry?
    A. It poses questions about astrology.
    B. It can be done only by one person.
    C. It is resistant to change and not open to criticism.
    D. It is testable.

Constructed Response

13. **Short Answer** Differentiate between pseudoscience and science.

Think Critically

14. MAIN Idea Evaluate the statement: "Scientists just perform experiments to prove what they already believe."

Chapter 1

Assessment

Section 1

Vocabulary Review

1. reproduction
2. homeostasis
3. biology

Understand Main Ideas

4. C
5. C

Constructed Response

6. Energy is a critical characteristic of life because it drives everything an organism does. Without an energy source, the organism is incapable of reproducing, responding, maintaining homeostasis, and growing.

Think Critically

7. Each scientist studies unique aspects of the characteristics of life. Goodall spent years learning about the growth, development, and behavior of chimpanzees. Drew spent his entire career working at the cellular level trying to learn how to store blood efficiently and effectively. Chory studies plants' sensitivity to light and how growth is affected.
8. Response is a short-term reaction to a stimulus in the environment. Adaptation is a long-term inherited change that enables the organism to live more favorably in the environment.

Section 2

Vocabulary Review

9. ethics
10. theory

Understand Main Ideas

11. D
12. D

Constructed Response

13. Science is testable, open to revision, changes and evolves as new information comes along, is subject to peer review, and readily welcomes new ideas that can be investigated. Pseudoscience is often based on the supernatural, rarely changes its original idea or beliefs, often promotes itself via one group or person, and is not testable.

Think Critically

14. Science is characterized by unbiased investigations and experiments. Doing an experiment to prove a person's existing belief is an example of pseudoscience.

Assessment Online Test Practice

Section 3

Vocabulary Review

15. Data are collected from observations that are made.
16. A control group is not given or exposed to the factor being tested, while the experimental group is given or exposed to the factor being tested.
17. The independent variable is the tested factor in an experiment, while the dependent variable results from or depends on changes to the independent variable.

Understand Main Ideas

18. A
19. C

Constructed Response

20. Supplemental feeding decreases the chicks' FMR
21. Answers will vary. Students should indicate that a common system of measurement makes it easier to reproduce experiments and communicate results.

Think Critically

22. Guide students by helping them design questions for which the answers can be measured statistically. Answers can be rated and turned into numeric values in order to graph.

Summative Assessment

23. Answers will vary. Answers should include an area of biology, such as zoology, genetics, or ecology. Students should indicate what they already know and what they would like to know. Accept reasonable responses.
24. kilometer
25. Letters will vary.

DBQ Document-Based Questions

U.S. Geological Survey. *Seabirds, forage fish, and marine ecosystems*. http://www.absc.usgs.gov/research/seabird_foragefish/foragefish/index.html

26. 20 m
27. kachemak

Chapter 1 Assessment

Section 3

Vocabulary Review

Explain the differences between the terms in the following sets.

15. observation, data

16. control group, experimental group

17. independent variable, dependent variable

Understand Main Ideas

18. Which describes this statement, "The frog is 4 cm long"?

A. quantitative data
B. inference
C. control group
D. qualitative data

19. Which is a testable explanation?

A. dependent variable
B. independent variable
C. hypothesis
D. observation

Constructed Response

Use the table below to answer question 20.

Mean Body Mass and Field Metabolic Rate (FMR) of Black-Legged Kittiwakes

	Number	Mean body mass (g)	FMR
Fed females	14	426.8	2.04
Control females	14	351.1	3.08
Fed males	16	475.4	2.31
Control males	18	397.6	2.85

20. Short Answer Examine the data shown above. Describe the effects of feedings on the energy expenditure, FMR, of male and female kittiwakes.

Think Critically

21. Short Answer Defend the metric system to a scientist who does not want to use it.

22. MAIN Idea Design a survey to investigate students' opinions about current movies. Use 10 questions and survey 50 students. Graph the data. Report the findings to the class.

Summative Assessment

23. BIG Idea Biology is the study of life. Write a paragraph about one area of biology that interests you. Include information about what the area is, what you already know about it, and what you would like to know.

24. MATH in Biology Which metric unit of measurement would you use to measure the distance from your home to your school?

25. WRITING in Biology Prepare a letter to the editor of your school newspaper that encourages citizens to be scientifically literate about topics such as cancer, the environment, ethical issues, AIDS, smoking, lung diseases, cloning, genetic diseases, and eating disorders.

DBQ Document Based Questions

Use the data below to answer questions 26 and 27.

Data obtained from: U.S. Geological Survey. *Seabirds, forage fish, and marine ecosystems.* http://www.absc.usgs.gov/research/seabird_foragefish/foragefish/index.html

Relative Fish Biomass of Three Seabird Colonies in Lower Cook Inlet

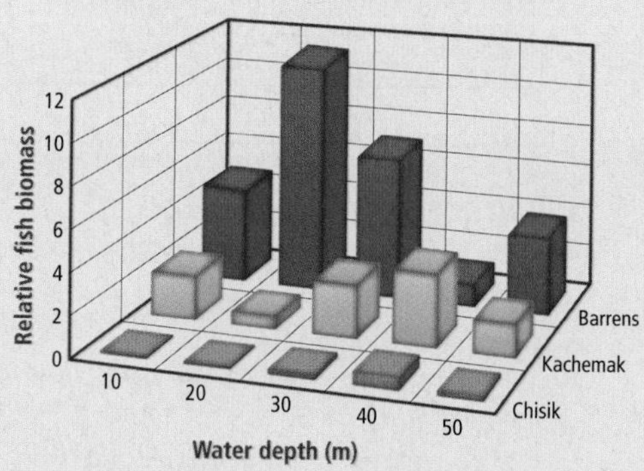

26. Identify the water depth with the highest relative fish biomass.

27. Determine which seabird colony has access to the highest fish biomass at a depth of 40 m.

Standardized Test Practice

Multiple Choice

1. Many scientific discoveries begin with direct observations. Which could be a direct observation?
   - A. Ants communicate by airborne chemicals.
   - B. Birds navigate by using magnetic fields.
   - C. Butterflies eat nectar from flowers.
   - D. Fish feel vibrations through special sensors.

Use this experimental description and data table to answer question 2.

A student reads that some seeds must be exposed to cold before they germinate. She wants to test seeds from one kind of plant to see if they germinate better after freezing. The student put the seeds in the freezer, took samples out at certain times, and tried to germinate them. Then she recorded her results in the table.

Germination Rate for Seeds Stored in a Freezer

Time in Freezer at −15°C	Germination Rate
30 days	48%
60 days	56%
90 days	66%
120 days	52%

2. According to the results of this experiment, how many days should seeds be stored in the freezer before planting for best germination?
   - A. 30
   - B. 60
   - C. 90
   - D. 120

Short Answer

3. Appraise one benefit to scientists of using SI units as standard units of measurement.

Extended Response

Use this drawing to answer question 4.

4. Look at the drawing and write five specific questions about the organisms shown that a biologist might try to investigate.

5. Compare and contrast a scientific hypothesis and a scientific theory.

Essay Question

A researcher experimented with adhesives and glues to find new and stronger adhesives. In 1968, he discovered an adhesive that was very weak rather than strong. The adhesive would stick to paper but it could be removed easily without leaving a trace of adhesive. Because he was trying to find stronger adhesives, the results of that experiment were considered a failure. Several years later, he had the idea of coating paper with the weak adhesive. This meant that notes could be stuck to paper and easily removed at a later time. Today, these removable notes are used by millions of people.

Using the information in the paragraph above, answer the following question in essay format.

6. The original adhesive experiment was considered a failure. Appraise the importance of evaluating the results of an experiment with an open mind.

NEED EXTRA HELP?						
If You Missed Question . . .	1	2	3	4	5	6
Review Section . . .	1.3	1.3	1.3	1.1	1.3	1.2

Standardized Test Practice

Multiple Choice

1. C
2. C

Short Answer

3. Answers can vary. One possible answer is that scientists all over the world speak many languages. If scientists everywhere use the same units of measurement, they can compare the measurements easily and accurately.

Extended Response

4. Answers can vary. Possible questions include the following: Where do these animals live? What do they eat? Do these animals eat each other? How do they live together? What happens if one group disappears?
5. Both a hypothesis and a theory are kinds of explanations. A hypothesis is a tentative and testable explanation for a specific scientific question. A hypothesis is often stated before a research experiment is done. A theory is an explanation for some natural phenomenon that has been repeatedly tested and confirmed by research.

Essay Question

6. Answers can vary. For instance, students might discuss how unexpected results could lead to a big advancement in understanding or lead to more questions and more experiments.

Ecology

Preview the Unit

Have students preview the chapters in this unit and make a concept map or graphic organizer relating the Themes, Big Ideas, and Main Ideas. Students' maps should show a hierarchy between Big Ideas and Main Ideas and the interconnectedness of the Themes.

Chapter 2
Principles of Ecology
BIG Idea Energy is required to cycle materials through living and nonliving systems.

Chapter 3
Communities, Biomes, and Ecosystems
BIG Idea Limiting factors and ranges of tolerance are factors that determine where terrestrial biomes and aquatic ecosystems exist.

Chapter 4
Population Ecology
BIG Idea Population growth is a critical factor in a species' ability to maintain homeostasis within its environment.

Chapter 5
Biodiversity and Conservation
BIG Idea Community and ecosystem homeostasis depend on a complex set of interactions among biologically diverse individuals.

WebQuest
Careers in Biology

UNIT 1 Ecology

THEMES

Scientific Inquiry Scientists use methods of inquiry to understand the natural world.

Diversity Adaptations to conditions in various biomes results in diversity.

Energy Energy created by photosynthesis sustains life at all levels.

Homeostasis Organisms use the resources in their environments to maintain homeostasis.

Change A climax community develops through the process of succession.

WebQuest **CAREERS IN BIOLOGY**

Wildlife biologists perform scientific research to study how species interact with each other and the environment, as the oystercatcher researchers are doing in this photograph. They protect and conserve wildlife species and also help maintain and increase wildlife populations.

5-Minute UNIT LAUNCH

Facets of Meaning Have students use the word *gradual* in a sentence.
ASK STUDENTS: ***What does it mean for a population to grow gradually?*** It takes some time to increase significantly. ***What does it mean for a forest to develop gradually?*** It changes slowly over time, sometimes taking more than a century. Have them make a list in their journals of ways the word is used in this unit.

Video
What's BIOLOGY Got To Do With It?
A professor discusses scientific methods and shark research.

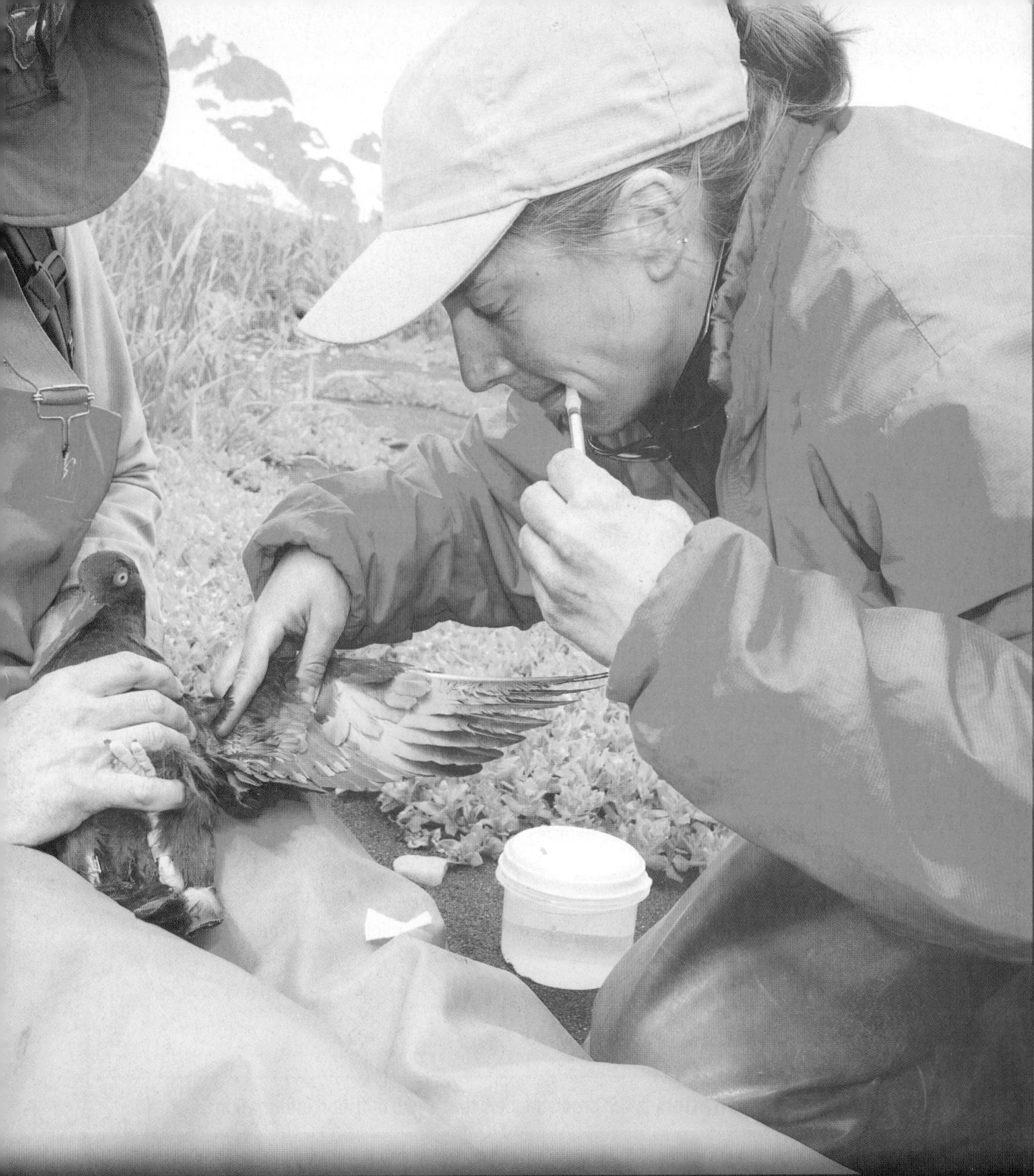

Misconceptions

In each section, *Clarify a Misconception* provides you with the information to dispel a common student misconception. A question will help you elicit the misconception and an explanation will help you correct it.

Below is a preview of misconceptions from each chapter in this unit.

Before studying Chapter 2, students might think that the same molecules of water cycle endlessly through the water cycle. Chapter 2 will explain that not all intact water molecules cycle through living things, but that photosynthesis and respiration break down the water molecules and use the hydrogen and oxygen to make other molecules (p. 46).

Before studying Chapter 3, students might think that deserts are always hot. Chapter 3 will explain that a desert is defined by precipitation, not temperature, and that Antarctica is actually a desert (p. 70).

Before studying Chapter 4, students might think that populations increase indefinitely. Chapter 4 will explain that all populations eventually become limited in size because resources are limited (p. 94).

Before studying Chapter 5, students might think that all members of a population die when their environment is disturbed. Chapter 5 will explain that, in most cases, populations are reduced but do not become extinct, and others might increase because they can withstand or even thrive under the new conditions (p. 126).

SERVICE LEARNING/COMMUNITY SERVICE

Parks Development Students can volunteer to work in state or local metropolitan parks and state historical sites doing a variety of activities, such as removing exotic plants, trail building or maintenance, or planting wildflower seeds. Making decisions about their volunteer activities empowers students (Morgan and Streb, 2001).

Research bibliography on pages 32T–34T

Chapter 2 Organizer:
Principles of Ecology

LabManager™
Customize any lab with the LabManager™ CD-ROM.

Essential Questions	National Science Standards	Materials and Planning Estimated times include cleanup and disposal, but do not include teacher prep time. For cleanup and disposal guidelines, see page 39T.	Est. Time (min)
Section 1 1. What is the difference between abiotic factors and biotic factors? 2. What are the interactions between the levels of biological communities? 3. What is the difference between an organism's habitat and its niche?	UCP.1–3; A.1, A.2; C.4, C.5, C.6; F.1, F.3, F.5; G.1,G.2, G.3	**Launch Lab,** p. 30: container housing several fruit flies	15 per day
		Demonstration, p. 38: fallen log or branch with fungi	5
Section 2 1. What are the producers and consumers in an ecosystem? 2. How does energy flow through an ecosystem? 3. What are food chains, food webs, and ecological pyramid models?	UCP.1–3; A.1, A.2; B.6; C.4, C.5, C.6; D.1; F.3, F.4, F.5; G.1,G.2, G.3	**Demonstration,** p. 42: sod or grass, water with algae in a beaker or jar	5
		MiniLab 1, p. 42: paper, pencils	30
		Demonstration, p. 43: algae, mosquito larvae, minnows or photos of these items	10
Section 3 1. How do nutrients move through the biotic and abiotic parts of an ecosystem? 2. Why are nutrients important to living organisms? 3. What are the biogeochemical cycles of nutrients and how are they alike?	UCP.1–3; A.1, A.2; B.3, B.6; C.4, C.5, C.6; D.1, D.2; F.3, F.4, F.5; G.1,G.2, G.3	**Demonstration,** p. 45: product labels that show nutrition information	10
		Demonstration, p. 48: fertilizer container with information label	5
		MiniLab 2, p. 48: water samples from different sources, nitrate test kit	30
		Design Your Own BioLab, p. 51: materials appropriate for the experiment	60

Suggested Time for Each Lesson

Class	Chapter Opener	Section 1	Section 2	Section 3	Assessment
Basic	45 min	90 min	45 min	45 min	45 min
General	25 min	100 min	100 min	90 min	45 min
Honors	5 min	90 min	20 min	45 min	20 min

ConnectED

connectED.mcgraw-hill.com

Access interactive learning opportunities and teaching resources using these icons located throughout your StudentWorks™ Plus Online and eTeacherEdition Online.

Chapter 2 Section Resources	Additional Chapter 2 Resources	Technology
FAST FILE Unit 1 Resources: Launch Lab Worksheet* Study Guide (English/Spanish)* Section Quick Check **Reading Essentials 2.1** **Science Notebook 2.1*** **FAST FILE Unit 1 Resources:** MiniLab Worksheet* Study Guide (English/Spanish)* Section Quick Check **Reading Essentials 2.2** **Science Notebook 2.2*** **FAST FILE Unit 1 Resources:** MiniLab Worksheet* BioLab Worksheet* Study Guide (English/Spanish)* Section Quick Check **Reading Essentials 2.3** **Science Notebook 2.3***	**FAST FILE Unit 1 Resources:** Chapter Diagnostic Test Concept Mapping* Real-World Biology Enrichment Chapter Tests A, B, and C **Transparencies:** Bellringer Transparencies* Biology Concepts Transparencies* **Lab Resources:** Laboratory Manual* Probeware Lab Manual* Forensics Lab Manual* Pre-AP Lab Manual* Open Inquiry in Biology* Guided Inquiry in Biology*	**Teaching Tools:** eTeacherEdition Online Classroom Presentation Toolkit CD-ROM* LabManager™ CD-ROM* Video Lab DVD* Virtual Lab CD-ROM* What's BIOLOGY Got To Do With It? StudentWorks™ Plus Online* **Chapter Assessment Tools:** Classroom Presentation Toolkit CD-ROM* *ExamView® Assessment Suite* CD-ROM **Web-Based Resources:** • StudentWorks™ Plus Online • eTeacherEdition Online • Animations* • The Interactive Time Line* • Interactive Tables* • Online Quizzes • Online Test Practice • Standardized Test Practice • Virtual Labs* • Multilingual eGlossary* • Vocabulary eGames* • Vocabulary eFlashcards • WebQuests • Personal Tutors

While all resources listed are appropriate for English learners, the * indicates resources with a strong visual or hands-on component for EL.

Teaching strategies and activities have been coded for differentiated instruction.

AL Activities for students working above grade level	**OL** Activities for students working on grade level	**BL** Activities for students working below grade level	**EL** Activities for English learners (also ELL)	**COOP LEARN** Activities designed for small cooperative group work

CHAPTER 2

Launch Lab
Problems in *Drosphilia* world?

Inquiry Launch Lab

For a lab worksheet, use your eTeacherEdition Online.

RUBRIC A rubric for evaluating Launch Labs is found on your eTeacherEdition Online.

Est. Time 15 min per day

Teaching Strategies

- Cultures of wild-type fruit flies and instant media (food) can be purchased from commercial science supply houses.
- Follow supplier's directions to avoid releasing fruit flies in the classroom.
- Place the media in a large clear plastic or glass container, such as a flask or quart jar. Use a wad of cotton to loosely plug the mouth of flasks. Use a rubber band to hold a piece of gauze tightly over the mouth of the jar. Add the flies. Do not replenish the container or move the flies at all during the week.

Procedure

1. Read and complete the lab safety form.
2. Prepare a data table to record your observations.
3. Your teacher has prepared a **container housing several fruit flies** (*Drosphilia melanogaster*) with food for the flies in the bottom. Observe how many fruit flies are present.
4. Observe the fruit flies over a period of one week and record any changes.

CHAPTER 2
Principles of Ecology

ConnectED

Your one-stop online resource
connectED.mcgraw-hill.com

- Video
- Audio
- Review
- Inquiry
- WebQuest
- Assessment
- Concepts in Motion
- Multilingual eGlossary

Launch Lab
Problems in *Drosophila* world?

What we understand to be the world is many smaller worlds combined to form one large world. Within the large world, there are groups of creatures interacting with each other and their environment. In this lab, you will observe an example of a small part of the world.

For a lab worksheet, use your StudentWorks™ Plus Online.

Inquiry Launch Lab

FOLDABLES®

Make a three-tab book using the labels shown. Use it to organize your notes about the water and carbon cycles.

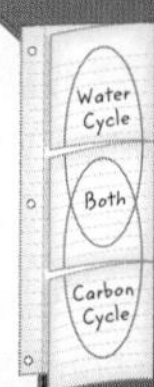

Analysis

1. **Summarize** the results of your observations. Many flies die as the food runs out. The environment looks polluted as waste and dead flies accumulate.
2. **Evaluate** whether or not this would be a reasonable way to study a real population. No; materials in the natural world are replenished through ecological cycles that are missing in the fruit-fly jars.

THEME FOCUS Energy
Energy from the Sun flows through all levels of biological organization and cycles.

BIG Idea Energy is required to cycle materials through living and nonliving systems.

THEMES

Scientific Inquiry The study of ecology includes the biosphere and everything contained in it.

Diversity Diversity within the biosphere provides opportunities for natural selection and evolution of new species.

Energy Autotrophs create the base of food webs by providing nutrients to heterotrophs.

Homeostasis Cycles within the biosphere, such as the water and carbon cycles, work together to main homeostasis.

Change Adaptations can evolve in response to environmental conditions.

Introduce the Chapter

Organism Interactions
SAY TO STUDENTS: ***The ecosystem shown in the photos is from the Pacific Northwest of the United States.***
ASK STUDENTS: ***Where does the energy to keep the organisms alive originally come from?*** the Sun ***How do the organisms in the photo get energy?*** from the food they eat or make This chapter will explain the relationships between organisms and the way in which energy and material flows through ecosystems.

BIG Idea

Information Search Organize students into pairs and assign approximately the same number of pages from the chapter to each group. Have each pair scan the headings and figure captions of their assigned pages to find new concepts. Have students share their information with the class in the order it appears in the chapter.
ASK STUDENTS: ***What are the main ideas that appear in the chapter?*** The main ideas emphasized are the relationships among organisms, the transfer of energy in an ecosystem, the diversity of organisms in an ecosystem, and homeostasis.

Section 1

MAIN Idea

BL OL AL

Organism Interactions

SAY TO STUDENTS: ***All living things require a supporting environment, including other living things. No organism lives in isolation.***

ASK STUDENTS: ***What evidence do you have that living things require each other?*** Possible answers: Plants require animals such as butterflies and bees for pollination. Animals eat other animals and plants for survival.

Reading Strategy

BL OL AL

Monitor Comprehension

SAY TO STUDENTS: ***Ask yourselves questions as you read. If you finish a paragraph and you have a question that has not been answered, reread the text where the question may be answered. If you still cannot answer it, write down the question and ask me or another student to help you answer it. This will help you and others in the class understand the concepts.*** It may be useful to walk through the room and prompt students with questions while they read.

S Skill Practice

BL OL AL **Visual Literacy**

Have students study Figure 1.

ASK STUDENTS: ***Which time line entry do you consider the most significant to ecological discoveries and why?*** Answers will vary, but encourage students to explain their reasoning.

Section 1

Reading Preview

Essential Questions

- What is the difference between abiotic factors and biotic factors?
- What are the interactions between the levels of biological communities?
- What is the difference between an organism's habitat and its niche?

Review Vocabulary

species: group of organisms that can interbreed and produce fertile offspring in nature

New Vocabulary

ecology
biosphere
biotic factor
abiotic factor
population
biological community
ecosystem
biome
habitat
niche
predation
symbiosis
mutualism
commensalism
parasitism

g Multilingual eGlossary

Organisms and Their Relationships

MAIN Idea **Biotic and abiotic factors interact in complex ways in communities and ecosystems.**

Real-World Reading Link On whom do you depend for your basic needs such as food, shelter, and clothing? Humans are not the only organisms that depend on others for their needs. All living things are interdependent. Their relationships are important to their survival.

Ecology

Scientists can gain valuable insight about the interactions between organisms and their environments and between different species of organisms by observing them in their natural environments. Each organism, regardless of where it lives, depends on nonliving factors found in its environment and on other organisms living in the same environment for survival. For example, green plants provide a source of food for many organisms as well as a place to live. The animals that eat the plants provide a source of food for other animals. The interactions and interdependence of organisms with each other and their environments are not unique. The same type of dependency occurs whether the environment is a barren desert, a tropical rain forest, or a grassy meadow. **Ecology** is the scientific discipline in which the relationships among living organisms and the interaction the organisms have with their environments are studied.

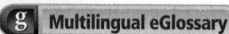

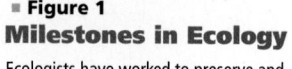

■ **Figure 1**
Milestones in Ecology
Ecologists have worked to preserve and protect natural resources.

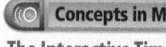

Concepts in Motion
The Interactive Timeline S

1900 — 1960 — 1970

1905 Theodore Roosevelt urges the U.S. Congress to set aside over 70 million hectares of land to protect the natural resources found on them.

1962 Rachel Carson publishes a best-selling book warning of the environmental danger of pollution and pesticides.

1967 The government of Rwanda and international conservation groups begin efforts to protect mountain gorillas, due in a large part to the work of Dian Fossey.

1971 Marjorie Carr stops the construction of the Cross Florida Barge Canal because of the environmental damage the project would cause.

Research Citation

Question Educational research indicates that the questioning technique described on this page will help students extend their thinking. Students are challenged to think critically and increase interaction with other students. (Heibert et al., 1997)

Research bibliography on pages 32T–34T

■ **Figure 2** Ecologists work in the field and in laboratories. This ecologist is enduring harsh conditions to examine a seal.

The study of organisms and their environments is not new. The word *ecology* was first introduced in 1866 by Ernst Haeckel, a German biologist. Since that time, there have been many significant milestones in ecology, as shown in **Figure 1.**

Scientists who study ecology are called ecologists. Ecologists observe, experiment, and model using a variety of tools and methods. For example, ecologists, like the one shown in **Figure 2,** perform tests in organisms' environments. Results from these tests might give clues as to why organisms are able to survive in the water, why organisms become ill or die from drinking the water, or what organisms could live in or near the water. Ecologists also observe organisms to understand the interactions among them.

Science models are a way of creating a visual representation of a hypothesis to test in a lab setting. A model allows a scientist to simulate a process or system. Studying organisms in the field can be difficult because there often are too many variables to study at one time. Models allow ecologists to control the number of variables present and to slowly introduce new variables in order to fully understand the effect of each variable.

Reading Check Describe a collection of organisms and their environment that an ecologist might study in your community.

VOCABULARY
WORD ORIGIN
Ecology
comes from the Greek words *oikos,* meaning *house,* and *ology,* meaning *to study*

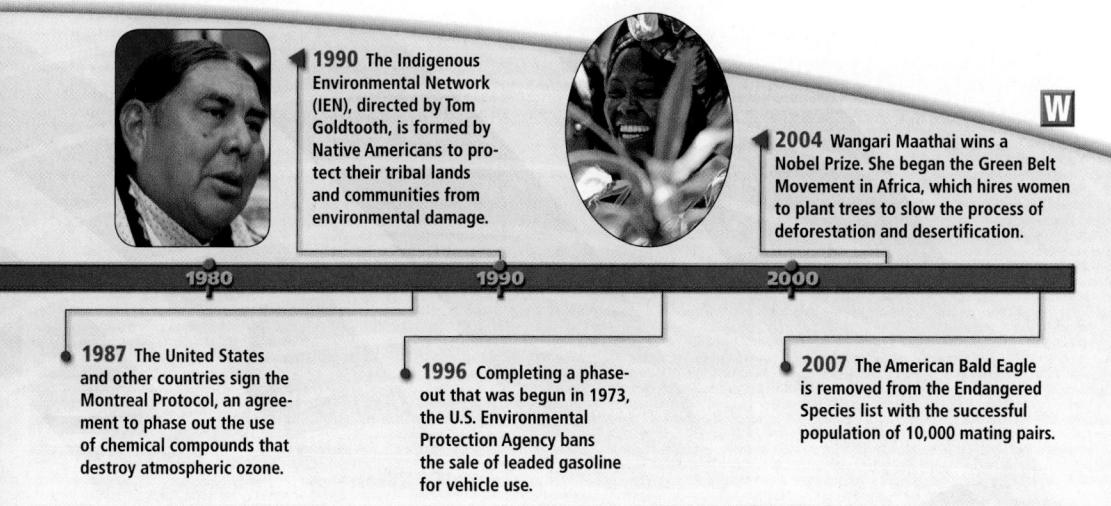

1990 The Indigenous Environmental Network (IEN), directed by Tom Goldtooth, is formed by Native Americans to protect their tribal lands and communities from environmental damage.

2004 Wangari Maathai wins a Nobel Prize. She began the Green Belt Movement in Africa, which hires women to plant trees to slow the process of deforestation and desertification.

1980 — 1990 — 2000

1987 The United States and other countries sign the Montreal Protocol, an agreement to phase out the use of chemical compounds that destroy atmospheric ozone.

1996 Completing a phase-out that was begun in 1973, the U.S. Environmental Protection Agency bans the sale of leaded gasoline for vehicle use.

2007 The American Bald Eagle is removed from the Endangered Species list with the successful population of 10,000 mating pairs.

Reading Check Answers will depend on which organisms students describe. Remind students that ecology involves all organisms, not just animals. Bacteria, plants, protists, and fungi are all important to most ecosystems.

S Skill Practice

BL OL AL Visual Literacy Tell students to study Figure 2. Then have them read this page.
ASK STUDENTS: ***What are some locations where you might find ecologists collecting data, and what tools might they use in these locations?*** Answers will vary, but can include taking water temperature with thermometers at a lake, using a net, or using an identification guide to study birds in a forest.

W Writing Support

BL OL AL Journal Writing
Have students respond to the following writing prompt: What I think of when I hear the word *ecology*. Responses will vary, but might include catastrophes such as forest fires or chemical spills. Allow students to share their journal entries in class.

W Writing Support

BL OL AL Informal Writing
Have students write a short essay explaining how the work of Wangari Maathai helps both the environment and impoverished women and children in Africa.

Concepts in Motion
The Interactive Time Line

Develop Concepts

EL BL OL
Activate Prior Knowledge
ASK STUDENTS: ***What types of organisms have you ever observed or collected that live near your home?*** Students may list butterflies, beetles, birds, squirrels, etc.
ASK STUDENTS: ***What are some interesting characteristics of these organisms?*** Answers will vary.

D Develop Concepts

BL OL AL Use Analogies

ASK STUDENTS: ***If Earth were the size of an apple, what part of the apple would represent the biosphere?*** the peel of the apple

Writing Support

AL Summary Writing Have students identify and write about the precautions they consider necessary for travel in a spacecraft destined to go beyond the Moon. Encourage students to identify the limits of the conditions inside and outside the craft that would allow travel.

Reading Strategy

BL OL AL SQ3R This five-step process helps promote active reading. Have students first **S**urvey a portion of text, focusing on the headings. Have students then write **Q**uestions about key concepts. Next, have students **R**ead the text, making notes related to the questions. Then, have students **R**ecite the vocabulary and **R**eview for meaning.

Figure 3 This color-enhanced satellite photo of Earth taken from space shows a large portion of the biosphere.

The Biosphere

Because ecologists study organisms and their environments, their studies take place in the biosphere. The **biosphere** (BI uh sfihr) is the portion of Earth that supports life. The photo of Earth taken from space shown in **Figure 3** shows why the meaning of the term *biosphere* should be easy to remember. The term *bio* means "life," and a sphere is a geometric shape that looks like a ball. When you look at Earth from this vantage point, you can see how it is considered to be "a ball of life."

Although "ball of life" is the literal meaning of the word *biosphere,* this is somewhat misleading. The biosphere includes only the portion of Earth that includes life. The biosphere forms a thin layer around Earth. It extends several kilometers above Earth's surface into the atmosphere and extends several kilometers below the ocean's surface to the deep-ocean vents. It includes landmasses, bodies of freshwater and saltwater, and all locations below Earth's surface that support life.

Figure 4 shows a glimpse into the vast amount of diversity contained within Earth's biosphere. From rainforests to deserts to coral reefs, diverse organisms populate diverse locations. The biosphere's diverse locations contain organisms that are able to survive in the unique conditions found in their particular environment. Ecologists study these organisms, their adaptations, and the factors in their environment. These factors are divided into two large groups—the living factors and the nonliving factors.

D

Reading Check **Define** the term *biosphere.*

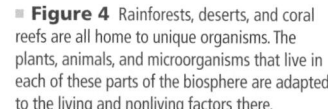

Figure 4 Rainforests, deserts, and coral reefs are all home to unique organisms. The plants, animals, and microorganisms that live in each of these parts of the biosphere are adapted to the living and nonliving factors there.

Reading Check The biosphere is the portion of Earth that supports life.

■ **Figure 5** The salmon swimming upstream are biotic factors in the stream community. Other organisms in the water, such as frogs and algae, also are biotic factors. **Explain** *how organisms are dependent on other organisms.*

Biotic factors The living factors in an organism's environment are called the **biotic** (by AH tihk) **factors.** Consider the biotic factors in the habitat of salmon shown in **Figure 5.** These biotic factors include all of the organisms that live in the water, such as other fish, algae, frogs, and microscopic organisms. In addition, organisms that live on the land adjacent to the water might be biotic factors for the salmon. Migratory animals, such as birds that pass through the area, also are biotic factors. The interactions among organisms are necessary for the health of all species in the same geographic location. For example, the salmon need other members of their species to reproduce. Salmon also depend on other organisms for food and, in turn, are a food source for other organisms.

Abiotic factors The nonliving factors in an organism's environment are called **abiotic** (ay bi AH tihk) **factors.** The abiotic factors for different organisms vary across the biosphere, but organisms that live in the same geographic area might share the same abiotic factors. These factors might include temperature, air or water currents, sunlight, soil type, rainfall, or available nutrients. Organisms depend on abiotic factors for survival. For example, the abiotic factors important to a particular plant might be the amount of rainfall, the amount of sunlight, the type of soil, the range of temperature, and the nutrients available in the soil. The abiotic factors for the salmon in **Figure 5** might be the temperature range of the water, the pH of the water, and the salt concentration of the water. **C**

Organisms are adapted to surviving in the abiotic factors that are present in their natural environments. If an organism moves to another location with a different set of abiotic factors, the organism might die if it cannot adjust quickly to its new surroundings. For example, if a lush green plant that normally grows in a swampy area is transplanted to a dry desert, the plant likely will die because it cannot adjust to abiotic factors present in the desert. **D**

Reading Check **Compare and contrast** abiotic and biotic factors for a plant or animal in your community.

CAREERS IN BIOLOGY

Ecologist The field of ecology is vast. Ecologists study the organisms in the world and the environments in which they live. Many ecologists specialize in a particular area such as marine ecology.

C Critical Thinking

BL OL AL

Analyze an Argument

Have students evaluate the following argument: Oxygen is the only abiotic factor that allows life to survive in the classroom, so as long as there is enough oxygen, all life will survive. Although oxygen is one abiotic factor, temperature, humidity, and air pressure are all important for life in the classroom.

D Develop Concepts

BL OL AL **Activity** Accompany students from the classroom to the school grounds. Have them identify the biotic and abiotic factors they observe. Alternatively, you could hold up magazine photographs of different environments and have students identify the biotic and abiotic factors they observe in each photograph.

EL Before beginning the exercise, define abiotic and biotic factors. Show students pictures of abiotic factors and biotic factors. Then organize students into small groups. Give each group pictures and have them classify them as showing abiotic or biotic factors.

Reading Check Answers will vary based on community location and student selections, but should accurately note the similarities and differences between abiotic and biotic factors. Be sure students understand that both abiotic and biotic factors are necessary for the survival of every organism.

■ **Caption Question Fig. 5** Sample answer: Organisms often depend on other organisms for food and reproduction.

D Develop Concepts

AL Extension Have students read the text under the head *Levels of Organization.*

SAY TO STUDENTS: ***Another name for the levels of organization is biological hierarchy. This hierarchy actually begins at the atomic level, with electrons, protons, and neutrons.***

ASK STUDENTS: ***What are the levels of biological hierarchy between subatomic particles and organism?*** atom, molecule, organelle, cell, tissue, organ, organ system, organism

S Skill Practice

EL BL OL

Use Graphic Organizers Have students fold a sheet of paper in half horizontally. Then have students make six equal tabs by cutting five slits in the top layer of the paper. Ask students to label each tab with the levels of organization and write the definition of each level of hierarchy under the appropriate tab. On the back of the paper, have students sketch an example of each level of organization. The examples should be different from the examples given in the text.

Develop Concepts

BL OL AL

Scaffolding

ASK STUDENTS: ***What is the lowest level of organization that most ecologists study?*** individual organism ***What name is given to several organisms of the same species interacting together?*** population ***What factors are included in an ecosystem that are not included in a community?*** abiotic factors ***Describe how ecosystems and biomes differ.*** Biomes include several ecosystems interacting over a large area. ***Which level of biological organization is the most complex?*** biosphere

? Inquiry Virtual Lab

Video BrainPOP

D

Levels of Organization

The biosphere is too large and complex for most ecological studies. To study relationships within the biosphere, ecologists look at different levels of organization or smaller pieces of the biosphere. The levels increase in complexity as the numbers and interactions between organisms increase. The levels of organization are

- organism;
- population;
- biological community;
- ecosystem;
- biome;
- biosphere.

Refer to **Figure 6** as you read about each level.

Study Tip

Question Session Study the levels of organization illustrated in **Figure 6** with a partner. Question each other about the topic to deepen your knowledge.

Organisms, populations, and biological communities

The lowest level of organization is the individual organism itself. In **Figure 6,** the organism is represented by a single fish. Individual organisms of a single species that share the same geographic location at the same time make up a **population.** The school of fish represents a population of organisms. Individual organisms often compete for the same resources, and if resources are plentiful, the population can grow. However, usually there are factors that prevent populations from becoming extremely large. For example, when the population has grown beyond what the available resources can support, the population size begins to decline until it reaches the number of individuals that the available resources can support.

The next level of organization is the biological community. A **biological community** is a group of interacting populations that occupy the same geographic area at the same time. Organisms might or might not compete for the same resources in a biological community. The collection of plant and animal populations, including the school of fish, represents a biological community.

? Inquiry Launch Lab

Review Based on what you've read about populations, how would you now answer the analysis questions?

Ecosystems, biomes, and the biosphere The next level of organization after a biological community is an ecosystem. An **ecosystem** is a biological community and all of the abiotic factors that affect it. As you can see in **Figure 6,** an ecosystem might contain an even larger collection of organisms than a biological community. In addition, it contains the abiotic factors present, such as water temperature and light availability. Although **Figure 6** represents an ecosystem as a large area, an ecosystem also can be small, such as an aquarium or tiny puddle. The boundaries of an ecosystem are somewhat flexible and can change, and ecosystems even might overlap.

The next level of organization is the biome. A **biome** is a large group of ecosystems that share the same climate and have similar types of communities. The biome shown in **Figure 6** is a marine biome. All of the biomes on Earth combine to form the highest level of organization—the biosphere.

S

Reading Check **Infer** what other types of biomes might be found in the biosphere if the one shown in **Figure 6** is called a marine biome.

Reading Check Other biomes might be terrestrial, atmospheric, and subterranean.

? Inquiry Launch Lab

Assess Content Development

Assess how understanding has developed when students revisit the Launch Lab analysis questions.

Differentiated Instruction

Below Level The scaffolding technique described on this page can benefit students working below level. This method of questioning will guide students through their thought processes.

For more tips, see page 14T–15T.

Visualizing Levels of Organization

S Figure 6
In order to study relationships within the biosphere, it is divided into smaller levels of organization. The simplest level of organization is the organism, with increasing organization shown in the population, biological community, ecosystem, and biome until reaching the most complex level of biosphere.

Biosphere The highest level of organization is the biosphere, which is the layer of Earth—from high in the atmosphere to deep in the ocean—that supports life.

Biome A biome is a group of ecosystems, such as the coral reefs off the coast of the Florida Keys, that share the same climate and have similar types of communities.

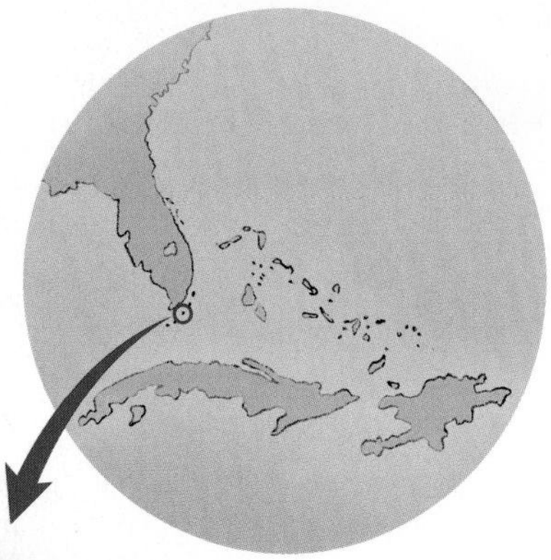

Ecosystem A biological community, such as the coral reef, and all of the abiotic factors, such as the sea water, that affect it make up an ecosystem.

Biological Community All of the populations of species—fishes, coral, and marine plants—that live in the same place at the same time make up a biological community.

Population A group of organisms of the same species that interbreed and live in the same place at the same time, such as the school of striped fish, is a population.

Organism An individual living thing, such as one striped fish, is an organism.

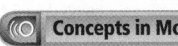

Concepts in Motion Animation

Visualizing Levels of Organization

Purpose
Students will identify levels of the biological hierarchy from individual organism to the biosphere. UCP.1, C.4, C.5

S Skill Practice
BL OL AL COOP LEARN

Visual Literacy Organize students into groups. Have each group develop a presentation that demonstrates how the levels of organization in Figure 6 are related. For example, students might present the information as a triangle, with *Organism* at the point at the top, *Biosphere* along the bottom, and the other levels listed between. This illustrates that each level involves more organisms than the one above it.

Concepts in Motion **Animation**

Video **BrainPOP**

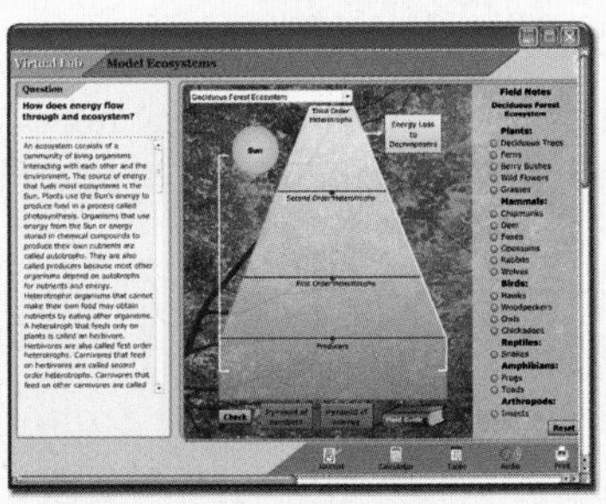

? Inquiry **Virtual Lab** In this lab, students will explore and analyze five simplified model ecosystems.

"The aim of education should be to teach us rather how to think, than what to think—rather to improve our minds, so as to enable us to think for ourselves, than to load the memory with thoughts of other men."

–Bill Beattie

S Skill Practice

EL OL AL COOP LEARN

Visual Literacy Have students read the text under the heading *Ecosystem Interactions* and review Figure 7. Assign students to work in pairs to sketch a different scene containing a biological habitat of their choice. Have them include at least six organisms that live in the habitat. Tell students to list the niche of each organism on the back of their drawings.

BL Help students list four organisms that live in the habitat.

R Reading Strategy

EL AL COOP LEARN

Brainstorm Arrange students in groups of two or three.

SAY TO STUDENTS: ***Read the new vocabulary under the heading* Ecosystem Interactions. *Brainstorm ideas for the meaning of each word.*** Write all ideas on the board for students to see. Tell students to write down the words *habitat* and *niche* and write what they consider to be the best analogy for each word beside it. For example, students' habitat might be a school. Their niche would be learners.

D Develop Concepts

BL OL AL **Discuss** The concepts of habitat and niche are often confused with each other.

ASK STUDENTS: ***How is a habitat different from a niche?*** The niche is a characteristic of a species and the niche involves the role an individual organism plays in the community. A habitat is the physical area in which the organism lives. ***What is an example of a habitat and an individual's niche in that habitat?*** Answers will vary, but should distinguish between an organism and its habitat.

Figure 7 These trees are the habitat for the community of organisms that live there.

Ecosystem Interactions

S

The interactions between organisms are important in an ecosystem. A community of organisms increases the chances for survival of any one species by using the available resources in different ways. If you look closely at a tree in the forest, like the one shown in **Figure 7,** you will find a community of different birds using the resources of the tree in different ways. For example, one bird species might eat insects on the leaves while another species of bird eats the insects found on the bark. The chance of survival for the birds increases because they are using different resources.

R The trees shown in **Figure 7** also are habitats. A **habitat** is an area where an organism lives. A habitat might be a single tree for an organism that spends its life on one tree. If the organism moves from tree to tree, its habitat would be a grove of trees.

Organisms not only have a habitat—they have a niche as well. A **niche** (NIHCH) is the role or position that an organism has in its environment. An organism's niche is how it meets its needs for food, shelter, and reproduction. The niche might be described in terms of requirements for living space, temperature, moisture, or in terms of appropriate mating or reproduction conditions. D

Reading Check **Compare and contrast** a habitat and a niche.

Community Interactions

Organisms that live together in a biological community constantly interact. These interactions, along with the abiotic factors, shape an ecosystem. Interactions include competition for basic needs such as food, shelter, and mates, as well as relationships in which organisms depend on each other for survival.

Competition Competition occurs when more than one organism uses a resource at the same time. Resources are necessary for life and might include food, water, space, and light. For example, during a drought, as shown in **Figure 8,** water might be scarce for many organisms. The strong organisms directly compete with the weak organisms for survival. Usually the strong survive and the weak die. Some organisms might move to another location where water is available. At times when water is plentiful, all organisms share the resources and competition is not as fierce.

Predation Many species get their food by eating other organisms. The act of one organism pursuing and consuming another organism for food is **predation** (prih DAY shun). The organism that pursues another organism is the predator, and the organism that is pursued is the prey. If you have watched a cat catch a bird or mouse, you have witnessed a predator catch its prey.

Figure 8 During droughts, animals compete for water; when water is plentiful, organisms share this resource.

Reading Check A habitat is an area. A niche is the role an organism plays in its environment.

Demonstration

BL OL **Illustrate a Niche** Show the class a fallen log or branch with bracket fungus or other fungi on it.

ASK STUDENTS: ***How is the fungus using the branch?*** The log or branch is a habitat for the fungus. ***What is one example the niche of the fungus?*** The fungus is a decomposer, taking its nutrients from the wood. Est. time: 5 min

Some insects also prey on other insects. Ladybugs and praying mantises are two examples of insects that are predators. Insect predators, such as these two, also are called beneficial insects because they are used by organic gardeners for insect control. Instead of using insecticides, organic gardeners use beneficial insects to control other insect populations.

Animals are not the only organisms that are predators. The Venus flytrap, a plant native to some regions of North and South Carolina, has modified leaves that form small traps for insects and other small animals. The plant emits a sweet, sticky substance that attracts insects. When the insect lands on the leaf, the leaf trap snaps shut. Then, the plant secretes a substance that digests the insect over several days.

Symbiotic relationships Some species survive because of relationships they have developed with other species. The close relationship that exists when two or more species live together is **symbiosis** (sihm bee OH sus). There are three different kinds of symbiosis: mutualism, commensalism, and parasitism.

Mutualism The relationship between two or more organisms that live closely together and benefit from each other is **mutualism** (MYEW chuh wuh lih zum). Lichens, shown in **Figure 9,** display an example of a mutualistic relationship between fungi and algae. The tree merely provides a habitat for lichens, allowing it to receive ample sunlight. The algae provide food for the fungi, and the fungi provide a habitat for the algae. The close association of these two organisms provides two basic needs for the organisms—food and shelter.

Figure 9 Algae and fungi form lichens through a mutualistic relationship.
Explain *why lichens are an example of a mutualistic relationship.*

DATA ANALYSIS LAB 1

Based on Real Data*

Analyze the Data

Does temperature affect growth rates of protozoans? Researchers studied the effect of temperature on the growth rates of protozoans. They hypothesized that increasing temperature would increase the growth rate of the protozoans.

Data and Observations

The graph shows the effect of temperature on the growth rate of *Colpidium* and *Paramecium*.

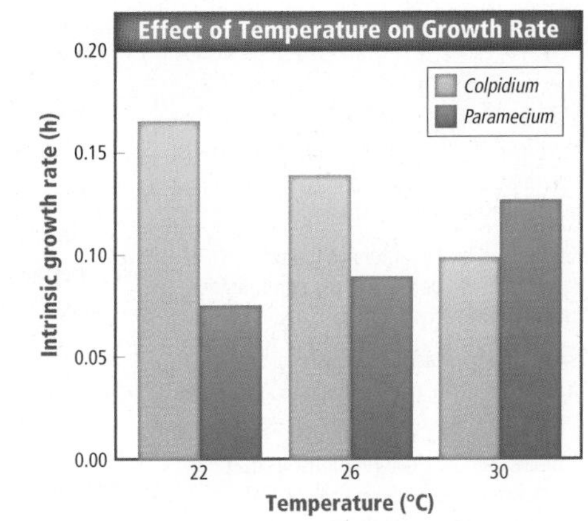

Think Critically

1. **Describe** the differences in population growth for the two species.
2. **Evaluate** what would be the next probable step in the researcher's investigation.

*Data obtained from: Jiang, L. and Kulczycki, A. 2004. Competition, predation, and species responses to environmental change. *Oikos* 106: 217–224.

DATA ANALYSIS LAB 1

About the Lab

- Some students will need help in reading the graph. Explain that the *x*-axis shows the three experimental temperatures and the *y*-axis the growth rate of the protozoans, in hours.
- Also see Beisner, B. E., E. McCauley and F. J. Wrona. 1996. Temperature-mediated dynamics of planktonic food chains: the effect of an invertebrate carnivore. *Freshwater Biol.* 35: 219–232. Also Hairston, N. G. and S. L. Kellermann. 1965. Competition between varieties 2 and 3 of *Paramecium aurelia*: the influence of temperature in a food-limited system. *Ecology* 46:134–139.

Think Critically

1. *Colpidium* grows faster than *Paramecium* at 22°C and 26°C, but *Paramecium* grows faster at 30°C.
2. Sample answer: Test the growth rates for both at 34°C.

Inquiry BioLab

The lab at the end of the chapter can be used at this point in the lesson.

Caption Question Fig. 9 In a mutualistic relationship, both species benefit from the relationship. The algae provide food for the fungi and the fungi provide a habitat for the algae.

Content Background

Real-World Connection The number of symbiotic relationships is enormous. Studies indicate that there might be as many as 50 million species that have some type of symbiotic relationship, instead of the 1.5 million presently known. For example, yeasts, one of the best-studied of all groups of microbes, have many more symbiotic species than the 1,000 presently named. At least 200 species of yeasts were recently found in the guts of beetle species.

D Develop Concepts

BL OL AL

Clarify a Misconception
Many students think parasites always kill their hosts.
ASK STUDENTS: ***What parasites of humans cause disease, but usually do not cause death?*** Students may know of some parasites, such as ticks and lice. Explain that even many harmful parasites, such as tapeworms, often don't cause death.

Formative Assessment

Evaluation Have students differentiate between the three categories of symbiosis and give an example of each. The three categories are mutualism, commensalism, and parasitism. Examples will vary.

Remediation Give each student three index cards. Have them write the types of symbiosis explained in this section on one side and make a visual cue on the other side. One helpful way for students to visualize is to use plus and minus signs. For example, with mutualism, both organisms benefit, so it can be represented with +/+. Parasitism: +/–, and commensalism: +/0 (0 can represent no effect.) Then allow students to trade cards with the code side up and identify the type of symbiosis. Have students use the cards to quiz each other on these relationships.

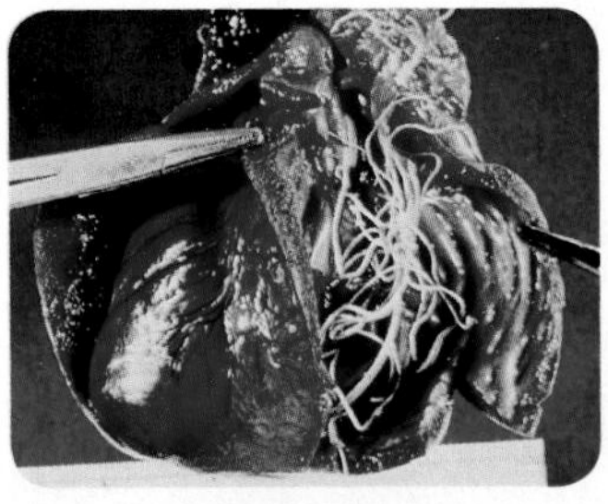

■ **Figure 10** This heart from a dog is infected with internal parasites called heartworms. Internal parasites depend on a host to supply their nutrients and habitat.

Commensalism Look back at **Figure 9.** This time, think about the relationship between the lichens and the tree. The lichens benefit from the relationship by gaining more exposure to sunlight, but they do not harm the tree. This type of relationship is commensalism. **Commensalism** (kuh MEN suh lih zum) is a relationship in which one organism benefits and the other organism is neither helped nor harmed.

The relationship between clownfish and sea anemones is another example of commensalism. Clownfish are small, tropical marine fish. Clownfish swim among the stinging tentacles of sea anemones without harm. The sea anemones protect the fish from predators while the clownfish eat bits of food missed by the sea anemones. This is likely a commensal relationship because the clownfish receives food and protection while the sea anemones are not harmed, nor do they receive any apparent benefit from this relationship.

D **Parasitism** A symbiotic relationship in which one organism benefits at the expense of another organism is **parasitism** (PER us suh tih zum). Parasites can be external, such as ticks and fleas, or internal, such as bacteria, tapeworms, and roundworms. The heartworms in **Figure 10** show how destructive parasites can be. Pet dogs in many areas of the United States are treated to prevent heartworm infestation. Usually the heartworm (the parasite) does not kill the host, but it might harm or weaken it. In parasitism, if the host dies, the parasite also would die unless it quickly finds another host.

Another type of parasitism is brood parasitism. Brown-headed cowbirds demonstrate brood parasitism because they rely on other bird species to build their nests and incubate their eggs. A brown-headed cowbird lays its eggs in another bird's nest and abandons the eggs. The host bird incubates and feeds the young cowbirds. Often the baby cowbirds push the host's eggs or young from the nest, resulting in the survival of only the cowbirds. In some areas, the brown-headed cowbirds have significantly lowered the population of songbirds through this type of parasitism.

Section 1 Assessment

Section Summary

- Ecology is the branch of biology in which interrelationships between organisms and their environments are studied.
- Abiotic and biotic factors shape an ecosystem and determine the communities that will be successful in it.
- Levels of organization in ecological studies include organism, population, biological community, ecosystem, biome, and biosphere.
- Symbiosis is the close relationship that exists when two or more species live together. There are three types of symbiotic relationships.

Understand Main Ideas

1. MAIN Idea **Compare and contrast** biotic and abiotic factors.
2. **Describe** the levels of organization of an organism that lives in your biome.
3. **Describe** at least two populations that share your home.
4. **Differentiate** between the habitat and niche of an organism that is found in your community.

Think Critically

5. **Design** an experiment that determines the symbiotic relationship between a sloth, which is a slow-moving mammal, and a species of green algae that lives in the sloth's fur.

WRITING in Biology

6. Write a short story that demonstrates the dependence of all organisms on other organisms.

Section 1 Assessment

1. Biotic factors are alive. Abiotic factors are not alive.
2. Answers will vary according to location and student choices. All answers should include the following levels: organism, population, biological community, ecosystem, biome, biosphere.
3. Answers will vary. Sample answer: my family and my dogs.
4. Answers will vary depending on student choices. All answers should clearly distinguish between a habitat (which is an area) and a niche (which is a role).
5. Experiments will vary. Students may try to determine if the green algae provides the sloth with camouflage or the sloth provides the green algae with a habitat.
6. WRITING in Biology
Stories will vary, but students should note a broad range of organisms from all kingdoms.
RUBRIC Use the modifiable rubric found on your eTeacherEdition Online to assess writing assignments.

Assessment Online Quiz

Reading Preview

Essential Questions

- What are the producers and consumers in an ecosystem?
- How does energy flow through an ecosystem?
- What are food chains, food webs, and ecological pyramid models?

Review Vocabulary

energy: the ability to cause change; energy cannot be created or destroyed, only transformed

New Vocabulary

autotroph R
heterotroph
herbivore
carnivore
omnivore
detritivore
trophic level
food chain
food web
biomass

g Multilingual eGlossary

Flow of Energy in an Ecosystem

MAIN Idea Autotrophs capture energy, making it available for all members of a food web.

Real-World Reading Link When you eat a banana, you are supplying your body with energy. You might be surprised to learn that the Sun is the original source of energy for your body. How did the Sun's energy get into the banana?

Energy in an Ecosystem

One way to study the interactions of organisms within an ecosystem is to follow the energy that flows through an ecosystem. Organisms differ in how they obtain energy, and they are classified as autotrophs or heterotrophs based on how they obtain their energy in an ecosystem.

Autotrophs All of the green plants and other organisms that produce their own food in an ecosystem are primary producers called autotrophs. An **autotroph** (AW tuh trohf) is an organism that collects energy from sunlight or inorganic substances to produce food. Organisms that contain chlorophyll absorb energy during photosynthesis and use it to convert the inorganic substances carbon dioxide and water to organic molecules. In places where sunlight is unavailable, some bacteria use hydrogen sulfide and carbon dioxide to make organic molecules to use as food. Autotrophs are the foundation of all ecosystems because they make energy available for all other organisms in an ecosystem.

Heterotrophs A **heterotroph** (HE tuh roh trohf) is an organism that gets its energy requirements by consuming other organisms. Therefore, heterotrophs also are called consumers. A heterotroph that eats only plants is an **herbivore** (HUR buh vor) such as a cow, a rabbit, or grasshopper. Heterotrophs that prey on other heterotrophs, such as wolves, lions, and lynxes, shown in **Figure 11,** are called **carnivores** (KAR nuh vorz). C

Figure 11 This lynx is a heterotroph that is about to consume another heterotroph, a rabbit. **Identify** *an additional classification for each of these animals.*

Section 2

MAIN Idea BL OL AL

Organisms Need Energy

ASK STUDENTS: ***What is the process by which autotrophs convert light energy into chemical energy?*** photosynthesis In Section 2, students will learn how energy flows in one direction through an ecosystem. Have students read carefully to learn the reason why energy cannot be recycled through a system.

R Reading Strategy

OL AL **Activate Background Vocabulary**

SAY TO STUDENTS: ***Four of the vocabulary words for this section end in the suffix* –vore.** This suffix comes from the Latin word *vora,* meaning "eat" or "devour." **ASK STUDENTS:** ***How can this help you understand the meaning of these words?*** Each has something to do with eating. Lead a discussion in which students try to work out the meanings of each of the new vocabulary terms.

C Critical Thinking

AL **Evaluate** Have students evaluate the benefits of being an autotroph. Autotrophs can produce their own food, so they do not rely on other organisms for food sources.

Caption Question Fig. 11 carnivore and herbivore

Differentiated Instruction

Hearing Impaired When students with hearing difficulties are in the classroom, be sure that the lighting is adequate. Good lighting will allow students to see your lips and facial expressions clearly, which will help with their understanding.

For more tips, see pages 14T–15T.

GOING GREEN To cut energy costs of travel to school, carpool, use public transportation, walk, or ride a bicycle. Encourage your students to do the same—even for just one day each week.

MiniLab 1

Inquiry MiniLab

For a lab worksheet, use your eTeacherEdition Online.

RUBRIC A rubric for evaluating MiniLabs is found on your eTeacherEdition Online.

Est. Time 30 min

Safety Precautions Approve lab safety forms before work begins.

Teaching Strategy Students could work on this lab individually or in small groups.

Analysis

1. Herbivores: grey squirrels, grasshoppers, meadow voles, crayfishes; carnivores: none; omnivores: raccoons, red foxes, muskrats; detrivores: crayfishes
2. Sample answer: Removing the white oak from the system would force other animals, such as meadow voles, to eat the red clover, so there would be less clover for the muskrats to eat. Furthermore, raccoons would no longer have white oak to eat, so they may increase their consumption of muskrats.

LabManager™

Customize this lab with the LabManager™ CD-ROM.

Figure 12 This fungus is obtaining food energy from the dead log. Fungi are decomposers that recycle materials found in dead organisms.

Explain *why decomposers are important in an ecosystem.*

In addition to herbivores and carnivores, there are organisms that eat both plants and animals, called **omnivores** (AHM nih vorz). Bears, humans, and mockingbirds are examples of omnivores.

The **detritivores** (duh TRYD uh vorz), which eat fragments of dead matter in an ecosystem, return nutrients to the soil, air, and water where the nutrients can be reused by organisms. Detritivores include worms and many aquatic insects that live on stream bottoms. They feed on small pieces of dead plants and animals. Decomposers, similar to detritivores, break down dead organisms by releasing digestive enzymes. Fungi, such as those in **Figure 12,** and bacteria are decomposers.

All heterotrophs perform some decomposition when consuming another organism. Decomposers are the primary method and tool used to break down organic compounds and make nutrients available to producers for reuse. Without the presence and activities of detritivores and decomposers, organic material would not break down and the nutrients would no longer be available to other organisms.

Reading Check **Compare and contrast** the four different types of heterotrophs.

Models of Energy Flow

Ecologists use food chains and food webs to model the energy flow through an ecosystem. Like any model, food chains and food webs are simplified representations of the flow of energy. Each step in a food chain or food web is called a **trophic** (TROH fihk) **level.** Autotrophs make up the first trophic level in all ecosystems. Heterotrophs make up the remaining levels. With the exception of the first trophic level, organisms at each trophic level get their energy from the trophic level before it.

MiniLab 1

Inquiry MiniLab

Construct a Food Web

How is energy passed from organism to organism in an ecosystem? A food chain shows a single path for energy flow in an ecosystem. The overlapping relationships between food chains are shown in a food web.

Procedure

1. Read and complete the lab safety form.
2. Use the following information to construct a food web in a meadow ecosystem:
   - Red foxes feed on raccoons, crayfishes, grasshoppers, red clover, meadow voles, and gray squirrels.
   - Red clover is eaten by grasshoppers, muskrats, red foxes, and meadow voles.
   - Meadow voles, gray squirrels, and raccoons all eat parts of the white oak tree.
   - Crayfishes feed on green algae and detritus, and they are eaten by muskrats and red foxes.
   - Raccoons feed on muskrats, meadow voles, gray squirrels, and white oak trees.

Analysis

1. **Identify** all of the herbivores, carnivores, omnivores, and detritivores in the food web.
2. **Describe** how the muskrats would be affected if disease kills the white oak trees.

Caption Question Fig. 12 Decomposers are important to ecosystems because they break down dead organisms and detritus so that producers can reuse the nutrients stored there.

Reading Check Herbivores eat only plants/autotrophs; carnivores eat other heterotrophs; omnivores eat both autotrophs and heterotrophs; detritivores consume dead organic material.

Demonstration

BL OL AL Autotrophs Bring in a piece of sod or grow some grass in a pot. Pet grass can also be purchased at pet stores. Also, place a jar or beaker containing pond water with algae at the front of the room.

ASK STUDENTS: ***What do the grass and the algae have in common?*** Answers will vary. Sample answer: Grass and some algae are green. Moreover, they are both autotrophic organisms that carry on photosynthesis. Discuss with students how these producers provide energy for different ecosystems. Est. time: 5 min

Food chains A **food chain** is a simple model that shows how energy flows through an ecosystem. **Figure 13** shows a typical grassland food chain. Arrows represent the one-way energy flow which typically starts with autotrophs and moves to heterotrophs. The flower uses energy from the Sun to make its own food. The grasshopper receives energy from eating the flower. The mouse obtains energy from eating the grasshopper. Finally, the snake gains energy from eating the mouse. Each organism uses a portion of the energy it obtains from the organism it eats for cellular processes to build new cells and tissues. The remaining energy is released into the surrounding environment and no longer is available to these organisms. **D**

Food webs Feeding relationships usually are more complex than a single food chain because most organisms feed on more than one species. Birds, for instance, eat a variety of seeds, fruits, and insects. The model most often used to represent the feeding relationships in an ecosystem is a food web. A **food web** is a model representing the many interconnected food chains and pathways in which energy flows through a group of organisms. **Figure 14** shows a food web illustrating the feeding relationships in a desert community.

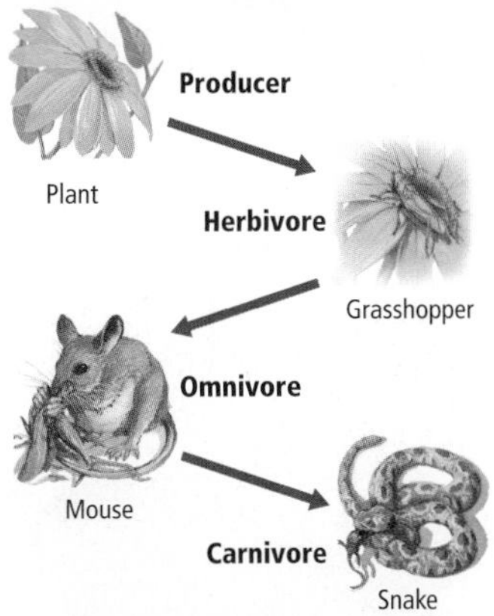

■ **Figure 13** A food chain is a simplified model representing the transfer of energy from organism to organism.

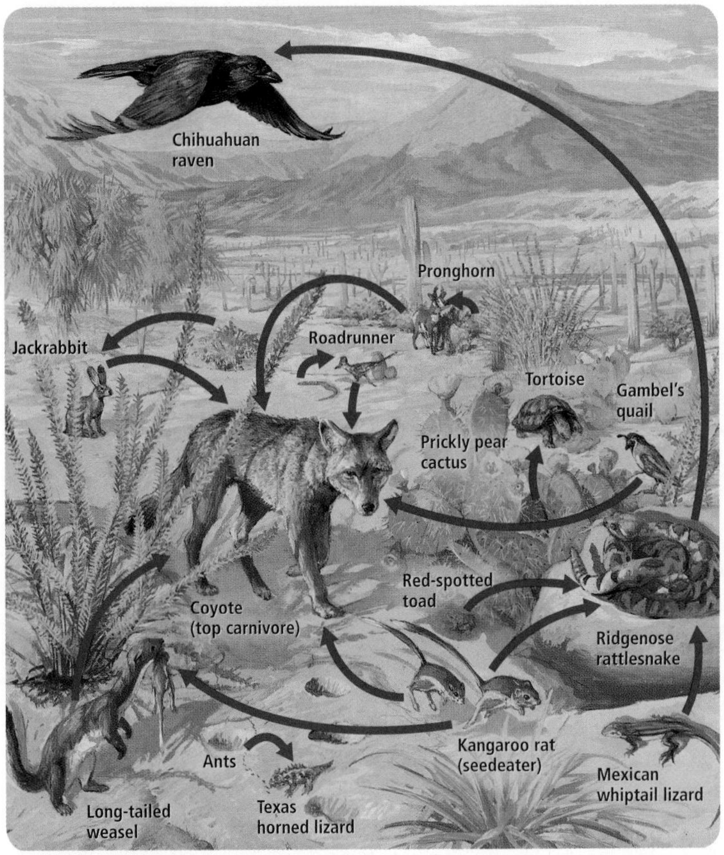

■ **Figure 14** A food web is a model of the many ways in which energy flows through organisms.

Concepts in Motion
Animation

Develop Concepts

BL OL AL Discuss

SAY TO STUDENTS: ***In the previous section, you learned about predatory relationships.*** **ASK STUDENTS:** ***What kind of animal is a predator?*** Students may say that predators are carnivores. A few might be less specific and say consumers. If students say all consumers are predators, point out that herbivores and scavengers are consumers that are not predatory. ***Can an animal be a predator and not be a carnivore?*** Yes, some omnivores might be predatory at least part of the time.

D Develop Concepts

OL Clarify a Misconception

ASK STUDENTS: ***Does a food chain have an end?*** Answers will vary. Explain the important conservation law of physics: that both matter and/or energy are neither created nor destroyed over time—they merely change form, and their sum remains the same. Students will learn more about recycling of nutrients in the next section.

BL Show students examples of food chains and food webs before asking the question.

Concepts in Motion
Animation

Demonstration

Food Chains Using available living materials such as algae, mosquito larvae, and minnows, or using photos that have been cut from magazines, show students a food chain that contains at least three links. Est. time: 10 min

S Skill Practice

OL AL Visual Literacy

ASK STUDENTS: ***How do the three ecological pyramid models in Figure 15 compare?*** All three models show how matter and energy move through an ecosystem.

BL In small groups, have students fill in a Venn diagram using the three ecological pyramids.

W Writing Support

EL BL OL COOP LEARN

Summary Writing After reading and discussing the section, have students work in small groups to brainstorm 5–10 important terms from the section. Then, have them say a sentence using each term while one student writes down each sentence.

Formative Assessment

Evaluation

ASK STUDENTS: ***Compare and contrast a food chain and a food web.*** Food chains show how energy moves through an ecosystem. A food web shows how food chains interact.

Remediation Model food chains and food webs with students. Organize students into teams of four. Each team of four represents a different food chain. Once the chains are established, invite the teams to form a food web in which everyone is connected to at least one other person.

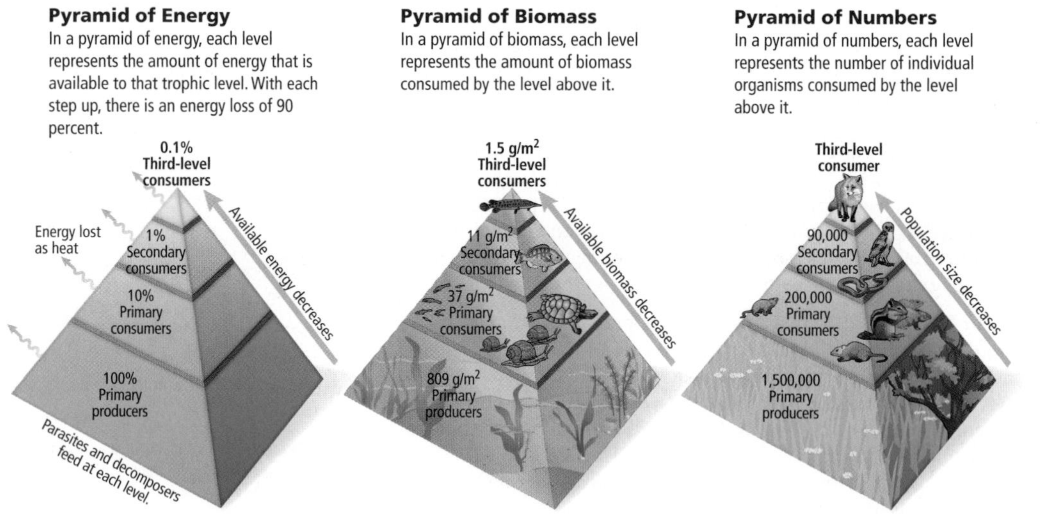

■ **Figure 15** Ecological pyramids are models used to represent trophic levels in ecosystems.

S

Ecological pyramids Another model that ecologists use to show how energy flows through ecosystems is the ecological pyramid. An ecological pyramid is a diagram that can show the relative amounts of energy, biomass, or numbers of organisms at each trophic level in an ecosystem.

Notice in **Figure 15** that in a pyramid of energy, only 10 percent of all energy is transferred to the level above it. This occurs because most of the energy contained in the organisms at each level is consumed by cellular processes or released to the environment as heat. Usually, the amount of **biomass**—the total mass of living matter at each trophic level—decreases at each trophic level. As shown in the pyramid of numbers, the relative number of organisms at each trophic level also decreases because there is less energy available to support organisms. W

Section 2 Assessment

Section Summary

- Autotrophs capture energy from the Sun or use energy from certain chemical substances to make food.
- Heterotrophs include herbivores, carnivores, omnivores, and detritivores.
- A trophic level is a step in a food chain or food web.
- Food chains, food webs, and ecological pyramids are models used to show how energy moves through ecosystems.

Understand Main Ideas

1. MAIN Idea **Compare and contrast** autotrophs and heterotrophs.
2. **Illustrate** the flow of energy through a simple food chain that ends with a lion as the final consumer.
3. **Classify** a pet dog as an autotroph or heterotroph and as an herbivore, carnivore, or omnivore. Explain.
4. **Evaluate** the impact on living organisms if the Sun began to produce less energy and then finally burned out.

Think Critically

5. **Create** a simple food web of organisms in your community.

MATH in Biology

6. Draw an energy pyramid for a food chain made up of grass, a caterpillar, tiger beetle, lizard, snake, and a roadrunner. Assume that 100 percent of the energy is available for the grass. At each stage, show how much energy is lost and how much is available to the next trophic level.

Section 2 Assessment

1. Autotrophs and heterotrophs both require energy, but autotrophs collect energy from sunlight or from inorganic substances to produce food. Heterotrophs get energy by consuming other organisms.
2. Sample answer: grass → zebra → lion
3. A family dog is a heterotroph. A dog is also an omnivore because commercial dog food contains both animal and plant products.
4. Sample answer: As the Sun produced less and less energy, the producers would have less and less energy to capture. Consumers would have fewer producers to eat, and the available producers would be small. Carnivores would have fewer consumers to eat. When the Sun burned out, the system would stop.
5. Answers will vary, but all food webs should include producers, herbivores, carnivores, and detrivores.
6. The pyramid should show grass (100 percent available energy) at the lowest level, followed by caterpillar (10 percent available energy), tiger beetle (1 percent available energy), lizard (0.1 percent available energy), snake (0.01 percent available energy), and roadrunner (0.001 percent available energy) at the top.

Assessment Online Quiz

Section 3

Reading Preview

Essential Questions
- How do nutrients move through biotic and abiotic parts of an ecosystem?
- Why are nutrients important to living organisms?
- What are the biogeochemical cycles of nutrients and how are they alike?

Review Vocabulary
cycle: a series of events that occur in a regular repeating pattern

New Vocabulary
matter
nutrient
biogeochemical cycle
nitrogen fixation
denitrification

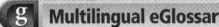

g Multilingual eGlossary

Cycling of Matter

MAIN Idea Essential nutrients are cycled through biogeochemical processes.

Real-World Reading Link Do you recycle your empty soda cans? If so, then you know that materials such as glass, aluminum, and paper can be reused. Natural processes in the environment cycle nutrients to make them available for use by other organisms.

D Cycles in the Biosphere

Energy is transformed into usable forms to support the functions of an ecosystem. A constant supply of usable energy is needed, but matter must be cycled through the biosphere.

The law of conservation of mass states that matter is not created or destroyed. Therefore, natural processes cycle matter through the biosphere. **Matter**—anything that takes up space and has mass—provides the nutrients needed for organisms to function. A **nutrient** is a chemical substance that an organism must obtain from its environment to sustain life and to undergo life processes. The bodies of all organisms are built from water and nutrients such as carbon, nitrogen, and phosphorus.

The cycling of nutrients in the biosphere involves both matter in living organisms and physical processes found in the environment such as weathering. Weathering breaks down large rocks into particles that become part of the soil used by plants and other organisms. The exchange of matter through the biosphere is called the **biogeochemical cycle.** As the name suggests, these cycles involve living organisms (*bio*), geological processes (*geo*), and chemical processes (*chemical*).

Connection to Chemistry In most ecosystems, plants obtain nutrients, in the form of elements and compounds, from the air, soil, or water. Plants convert some elements and compounds into organic molecules that they use. The nutrients flow through organisms in an ecosystem, such as the ecosystem shown in **Figure 16.** The green grass captures substances from the air, soil, and water, and then converts them into usable nutrients. The grass provides nutrients for the cow. If an organism eats the cow, the nutrients found in the cow are passed on to the next consumer. The nutrients are passed from producer—the green grass—to consumers. Decomposers return the nutrients to the cycle at every level.

Reading Check Explain why it is important to living organisms that nutrients are cycled.

Figure 16 Nutrients are cycled through the biosphere through organisms. In this example, the grasses are the producers and begin the cycle by capturing energy from the Sun.
***Explain** how nutrients continue to be cycled through the biosphere in this photo.*

Reading Check Cycling makes nutrients available for other organisms to use.

Caption Question Fig. 16 Nutrients continue to be recycled by wastes from the cows as well as when humans or predators eat the cattle.

Demonstration

Nutrients Show product labels from a variety of cereal boxes, soup cans, and other food. Point out on the labels where the nutrient content of the food is listed, and indicate which nutrients are biological, such as carbohydrates and protein, and which are biogeochemicals, such as calcium and phosphorus. Est. time: 10 min

Section 3

MAIN Idea

BL OL AL Nutrient Cycle

SAY TO STUDENTS: ***In the last section, you learned that energy flows in one direction through an ecosystem and much of the energy becomes unavailable at each trophic level. This is not true of essential nutrients.***
ASK STUDENTS: ***What would happen if matter was bound in living matter and never recycled?*** Nutrients would eventually be depleted and life would cease. ***What does it mean to say that matter is recycled?*** Matter moves from one living thing to another, or to the abiotic parts of the biosphere and back into the biotic parts.

D Develop Concepts

EL BL OL COOP LEARN

Use Models Have students read Section 3 in small groups and make models of the cycles presented. They can draw pictures on paper or construct three-dimensional models using various types of materials.

Writing Support

BL OL Summary Writing
Have students write one or two paragraphs to summarize each nutrient cycle. Tell them to use the new vocabulary terms in their summaries.
AL Have students use an analogy, such as clothes stored, worn, and laundered, for the cycle.

D Develop Concepts

BL OL Discuss Have students discuss what they know about the water cycle. Introduce and explain the concept of transpiration.

D Develop Concepts

AL Clarify a Misconception

Many students think that the same molecules of water cycle endlessly through the water cycle.

ASK STUDENTS: ***How many times can an intact molecule of water cycle in the abiotic parts of the water cycle?*** forever; infinitely ***How many times do the same water molecules cycle through the biotic parts of the water cycle?*** Intact water molecules don't cycle through living things, with the exception of some water that could be brought from the roots of plants and lost directly through stomata in transpiration. Photosynthesis and respiration break down the water molecules taken in and use the oxygen and hydrogen to make other molecules. Help students understand that water molecules form in the atmosphere and that water does not always move quickly in the cycle or in the sequence shown on the page. For example, snow falling on a glacier might freeze and be locked into the glacier for hundreds of years.

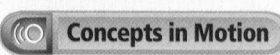

Concepts in Motion Animation

Video BrainPOP

Review Personal Tutor

Listen to a teacher explain biogeochemical cycles.

CAREERS IN BIOLOGY

Hydrologist A hydrologist studies water processes, such as the distribution in nature, the water flow in a dam or river, or the water flow of a sewer or of a city drinking-water system.

Review Personal Tutor

Video BrainPOP

D The water cycle Organisms cannot live without water. Hydrologists study water found underground, in the atmosphere, and on Earth's surface in the form of lakes, streams, rivers, glaciers, ice caps, and oceans. Follow along with **Figure 17** to trace processes that cycle water through the biosphere.

Connection to Earth Science Water is constantly evaporating into the atmosphere from bodies of water, soil, and organisms. Water in the atmosphere is called water vapor. Water vapor rises and begins to cool in the atmosphere. Clouds form when the cooling water vapor condenses into droplets around dust particles in the atmosphere. Water falls from clouds as precipitation in the form of rain, sleet, snow, or hail, transferring water to Earth's surface. As shown in **Figure 17,** groundwater and runoff from land surfaces flow into streams, rivers, lakes, and oceans, where they evaporate into the atmosphere to continue through the water cycle. Approximately 90 percent of water vapor evaporates from oceans, lakes, and rivers; about 10 percent evaporates from the surfaces of plants through a process called transpiration.

All living organisms rely on freshwater. Even ocean-dwelling organisms rely on freshwater flowing to oceans to prevent high saline content and to maintain ocean volume. Freshwater constitutes only about 3 percent of all water on Earth. Water available for living organisms is about 31 percent of all freshwater. The remaining 69 percent of all freshwater is frozen and found in ice caps and glaciers, which makes it unavailable for use by living organisms. D

Reading Check **Identify** three processes in the water cycle.

Concepts in Motion Animation

■ **Figure 17** The water cycle is the natural process by which water is continuously cycled through the biosphere.
Identify ***the largest reservoirs of water on Earth.***

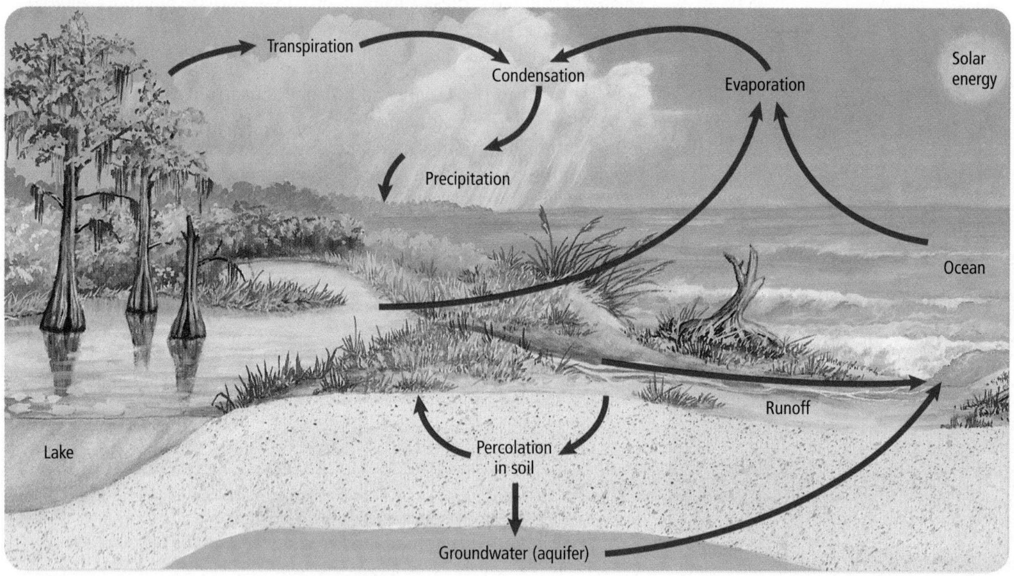

■ **Caption Question Fig. 17** The largest reserves of water are the oceans.

Reading Check Three processes in the water cycle are evaporation, condensation, and precipitation. Other answers might be transpiration and percolation.

Differentiated Instruction

English Learners Students with limited English language proficiency could have problems understanding the main ideas of a lesson. Provide these students with an overview in the form of a KWL chart, Venn diagram, or other graphic organizer.

For more tips, see pages 14T–15T.

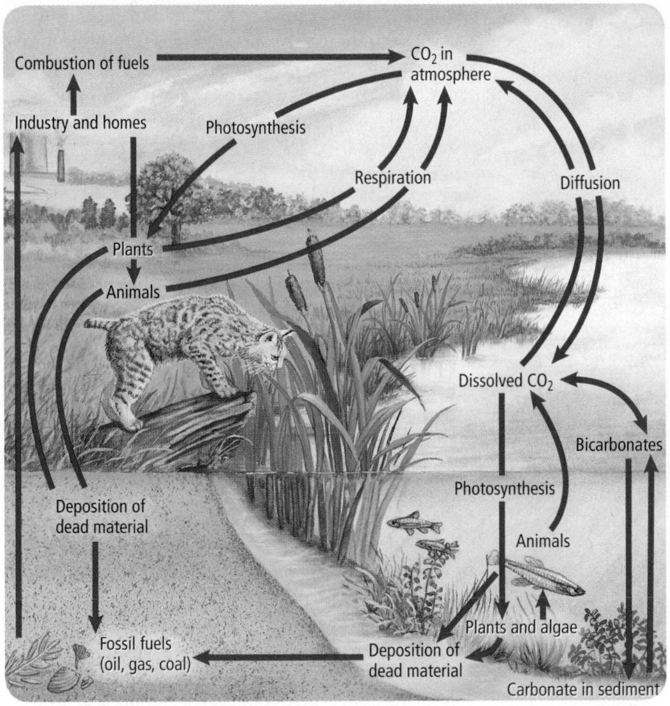

■ **Figure 18** The diagram shows how carbon and oxygen cycle through the environment.
Describe ***how carbon moves from the abiotic to the biotic parts of the ecosystem.***

Concepts in Motion
Animation

S

The carbon and oxygen cycles All living things are composed of molecules that contain carbon. Atoms of carbon form the framework for important molecules such as proteins, carbohydrates, and fats. Oxygen is another element that is important to many life processes. Carbon and oxygen often make up molecules essential for life, including carbon dioxide and simple sugars.

Look at the cycles illustrated in **Figure 18.** During a process called photosynthesis, green plants and algae convert carbon dioxide and water into carbohydrates and release oxygen back into the air. These carbohydrates are used as a source of energy for all organisms in the food web. Carbon dioxide is recycled when autotrophs and heterotrophs release it back into the air during cellular respiration. Carbon and oxygen recycle relatively quickly through living organisms.

Carbon enters a long-term cycle when organic matter is buried underground and converted to peat, coal, oil, or gas deposits. The carbon might remain as fossil fuel for millions of years. Carbon is released from fossil fuels when they are burned, which adds carbon dioxide to the atmosphere.

In addition to combining to form fossil fuels, carbon and oxygen can combine with calcium and create calcium carbonate ($CaCO_3$).The white cliffs shown in **Figure 19** are made of calcium carbonate. Calcium carbonate is found in the shells of plankton and animals such as coral, clams, and oysters. These organisms fall to the ocean floor, creating vast deposits of limestone rock. Carbon and oxygen remain trapped **C** in these deposits until the rocks are exposed to weathering and erosion and carbon and oxygen are released.

FOLDABLES® Incorporate information from this section into your Foldable.

■ **Figure 19** The white cliffs in Dover, England, are composed almost entirely of calcium carbonate, or chalk. The carbon and oxygen found in these cliffs are in the long-term part of the cycle for carbon and oxygen.

■ **Caption Question Fig. 18** Carbon moves from the abiotic parts of the ecosystem to the biotic parts of the ecosystem when producers convert carbon dioxide into food.

Concepts in Motion
Animation

FOLDABLES®

RUBRIC A rubric for evaluating Foldables is found on your eTeacherEdition Online.
Going Further Have students draw a Venn diagram on the back of their Foldables to compare the nitrogen cycle and the phosphorus cycle. Diagrams will vary, but might include overlapping zones such as "absorbed into organisms" and "returned to the environment when organism decomposes."

S Skill Practice
BL OL AL Visual Literacy
SAY TO STUDENTS: ***Look closely at Figure 18 and read the caption.***
ASK STUDENTS: ***Where in the carbon-oxygen cycle do you see carbon and oxygen intertwined?*** Carbon and oxygen are found together in CO_2, carbonate rock, fossil fuels, and in living material. Stress the fact that life on Earth, as it is presently understood, could not have evolved without the presence of carbon and oxygen.

C Critical Thinking
BL OL AL Predict
ASK STUDENTS: ***Based on your understanding of the carbon cycle, predict what might happen if large areas of tropical rain forest continue to be cleared.*** Carbon dioxide would continue to build up in the atmosphere without the plants that use the CO_2 for photosynthesis.

Concepts in Motion

Animation

MiniLab 2

Inquiry MiniLab

For a lab worksheet, use your eTeacherEdition Online.

RUBRIC A rubric for evaluating MiniLabs is found on your eTeacherEdition Online.

Est. Time 30 min

Safety Precaution Approve lab safety forms before work begins.

Teaching Strategies

- Water samples and a nitrate test kit can be purchased from biological supply companies.
- This could also be done as a demonstration to save time and materials.
- Encourage students to think about how household practices, such as fertilizing the lawn, contribute to nitrate pollution.

Analysis

1. The samples probably contained different amounts of nitrate because different water sources are going to contain different levels of contamination.
2. Sample answer: agricultural activities and lawn maintenance
3. Sample answer: An increase in algae could cause an algal bloom, which can cause human health problems.

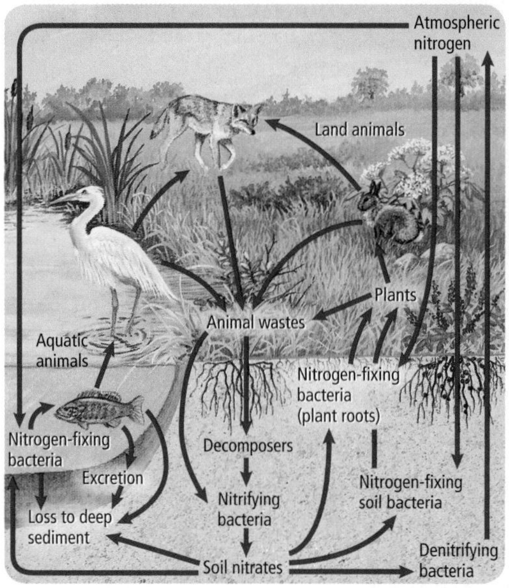

Figure 20 Nitrogen is used and reused as it is cycled continuously through the biosphere.

Concepts in Motion Animation

The nitrogen cycle Nitrogen is an element found in proteins. The largest concentration of nitrogen is found in the atmosphere. Plants and animals cannot use nitrogen directly from the atmosphere. Nitrogen gas is captured from the air by species of bacteria that live in water, the soil, or grow on the roots of some plants. The process of capture and conversion of nitrogen into a form that is usable by plants is called **nitrogen fixation.** Some nitrogen is also fixed during electrical storms when the energy from lightning bolts changes nitrogen gas to nitrates. Nitrogen is also added to soil when chemical fertilizers are applied to lawns, crops, or other areas.

Nitrogen enters the food web when plants absorb nitrogen compounds from the soil and convert them into proteins, as illustrated in **Figure 20.** Consumers get nitrogen by eating plants or animals that contain nitrogen. They reuse the nitrogen and make their own proteins. Because the supply of nitrogen in a food web depends on the amount of nitrogen that is fixed, nitrogen is often a factor that limits the growth of producers.

Nitrogen is returned to the soil in several ways, also shown in **Figure 20.** When an animal urinates, nitrogen returns to the water or soil and is reused by plants. When organisms die, decomposers transform the nitrogen in proteins and other compounds into ammonia. Organisms in the soil convert ammonia into nitrogen compounds that can be used by plants. Finally, in a process called **denitrification,** some soil bacteria convert fixed nitrogen compounds back into nitrogen gas, which returns it to the atmosphere.

MiniLab 2

Test for Nitrates

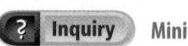

Inquiry MiniLab

How much nitrate is found in various water sources? One ion containing nitrogen found in water can be easily tested—nitrate. Nitrate is a common form of inorganic nitrogen that is used easily by plants.

Procedure

1. Read and complete the lab safety form.
2. Prepare a data table to record your observations.
3. Obtain the **water samples** from different sources that are provided by your teacher.
4. Using a **nitrate test kit,** test the amount of nitrate in each water sample.
5. Dispose of your samples as directed by your teacher.

Analysis

1. **Determine** whether the samples contain differing amounts of nitrate. Explain.
2. **Identify** what types of human activities might increase the amount of nitrate in the water.
3. **Infer** what problems a high nitrate level could cause, considering that nitrates also increase the growth rate of algae in waterways.

Demonstration

Mineral Cycles Display an empty fertilizer carton or bag. Show students the label that lists the amount of each mineral. Instruct students how to read the contents of the fertilizer. Point out the amount of nitrogen, phosphorus, and potassium in the fertilizer. Tell students that applying large quantities of fertilizer to an area adds excess biochemicals to the food web. Est. time: 5 min

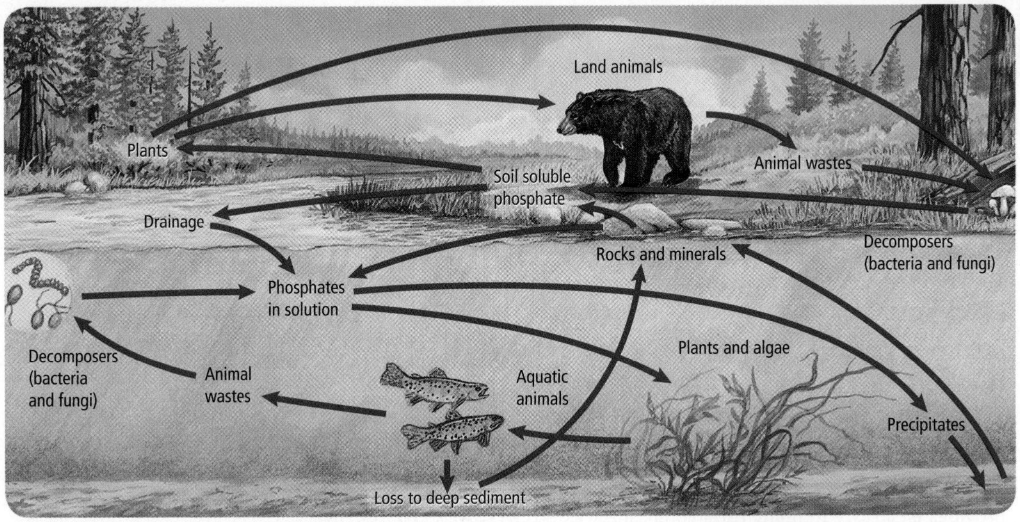

■ **Figure 21** The phosphorus cycle has a short-term cycle and a long-term cycle.

Concepts in Motion
Animation

The phosphorus cycle Phosphorus is an element that is essential for the growth and development of organisms. **Figure 21** illustrates the two cycles of phosphorus—a short-term and long-term cycle. In the short-term cycle, phosphorus in phosphates in solution, is cycled from the soil to producers and then from the producers to consumers. When organisms die or produce waste products, decomposers return the phosphorus to the soil where it can be used again. Phosphorus moves from the short-term cycle to the long-term cycle through precipitation and sedimentation to form rocks. In the long-term cycle, weathering or erosion of rocks that contain phosphorus slowly adds phosphorus to the R cycle. Phosphorus, in the form of phosphates, might be present only in small amounts in soil and water. Therefore, phosphorus is a factor that limits the growth of producers.

Section 3 Assessment

Section Summary

- Biogeochemical cycles include the exchange of important nutrients between the abiotic and biotic parts of an ecosystem.
- The carbon and oxygen cycles are closely intertwined.
- Nitrogen gas is limited in its ability to enter biotic portions of the environment.
- Phosphorus and carbon have short-term and long-term cycles.

Understand Main Ideas

1. MAIN Idea **Name** four important biogeochemical processes that cycle nutrients.
2. **Compare and contrast** two of the cycles of matter.
3. **Explain** the importance of nutrients to an organism of your choice.
4. **Describe** how phosphorus moves through the biotic and abiotic parts of an ecosystem.

Think Critically

5. **Design** an experiment to test the amount of fertilizer to use on a lawn for the best results. Fertilizers usually contain nitrogen, phosphorus, and potassium. The numbers on the label represent the amount of each nutrient in the fertilizer. How would you experiment to determine the correct quantity of fertilizer?

Concepts in Motion
Animation

R Reading Strategy

EL BL OL **Modeling** The nitrogen cycle on the previous page and the phosphorus cycle on this page are often difficult for students to comprehend. Read these two pages aloud or call on students to read individual paragraphs aloud. Stop frequently to check for understanding. Share your own visualization or connections while reading to demystify the concepts. Modeling helps students understand how to construct meaning from the text.

Formative Assessment

Evaluation Have students draw the steps of the carbon, nitrogen, and phosphorus cycles. Have them label each step of each cycle. See Figures 18, 20, and 21 in this section for reference.

Remediation Have students work in pairs to draw each step of each cycle on an index card. When they are finished, have students shuffle the cards together and put the steps for each cycle in sequence.

Section 3 Assessment

1. water, carbon, nitrogen, and phosphorus
2. Answers will vary, but should clearly demonstrate how cycles are related and how they differ.
3. Answers will vary, but should illustrate all the ways organisms can obtain nutrients.
4. In the biotic cycle, phosphorus is cycled from the soil to producers and then from producers to consumers. When an organism dies, decomposers return the phosphorus to the soil. In the abiotic cycle, phosphorus erodes from rocks that contain phosphorus. The phosphorus goes into the soil and groundwater. The phosphorus forms sediments, which form new rock.
5. Sample experiment: Under controlled conditions, add varying amounts of the fertilizer to areas of grass. The ideal amount of fertilizer to add will be the amount that helped a patch of grass grow best.

Assessment **Online Quiz**

Purpose

Students will describe ways in which damming a river impacts the ecosystem. Students will evaluate the pros and cons of damming a river in terms of the biological, economic, and recreational impacts on the area.
C.4, F.3, F.5, F.6

Anticipatory Guide

ASK STUDENTS: ***Why do people build dams?*** Sample answers: for flood control, or hydroelectric power ***What are some positive side effects of building a dam?*** the creation of lakes and recreation areas around the lakes, flood control, and hydroelectric power In this feature, students will learn how damming a river impacts the ecosystem as well as the economic gains that can result from a dam.

Background

The Glen Canyon Dam project has not been without controversy. Some say that it was the building of the Glen Canyon Dam that kicked off the original environmental movement back in the early 1960s because of how it would affect the Colorado River.

Biology & Society

To Dam or Not to Dam

The Glen Canyon area is a popular location for whitewater rafting, fishing, hiking, and kayaking. The Glen Canyon area is also the location of a controversial dam, the Glen Canyon Dam. It was built between 1956 and 1963 in Arizona on the Colorado River. The dam holds and releases water from Lake Powell.

Economic benefits The Glen Canyon Dam provides electricity to many rural communities. It also provides water to California, New Mexico, Arizona, and Nevada. Lake Powell, which is one of the most visited tourist destinations of the southwest, provides jobs for many of the local residents. Millions of tourists visit Lake Powell each year for activities such as hiking, boating, fishing, and swimming.

■ The Glen Canyon Dam provides opportunities for recreation to millions of tourists every year. However, it also impacts the Colorado River ecosystem.

Impact on flora and fauna The construction of the dam has brought economic benefits to the area, but it also has negatively impacted the Colorado River ecosystem. The habitat of native fish has changed as a result of the dam. Three species of fish—the roundtail chub, the bonytail chub, and the Colorado squawfish—have become endangered. The Lake Powell shoreline now is dominated by a nonnative, semidesert scrub known as saltcedar or tamarisk. The saltcedar outcompetes native vegetation such as the sandbar willow, Gooding's willow, and Fremont cottonwood. Saltcedar collects salt in its tissues over time. This salt eventually is released into the soil, making it unsuitable for many native plants.

Impact on temperature Before the dam was built, the water temperature of the Colorado River ranged from near freezing in the winter to a warm 29°C in the summer. Since the dam was built, the temperature of the water released downstream remains steady at 7–10°C. This temperature is fine for the nonnative trout that are bred for recreational activities; however, the native species do not fare as well.

The Bureau of Reclamation has proposed placing a temperature control device on the Glen Canyon Dam that would regulate the water temperature. Environmentalists suggest that this solution might not solve the problems for the native species because the native species need the fluctuating temperatures that were once part of the river system.

The Glen Canyon Dam has negatively impacted the ecosystem of the Colorado River area, but it has benefited the area economically. How do the costs weigh against the benefits? Biologists face real-world issues like these every day.

DEBATE in Biology

Collaborate Form teams to debate whether the recreational and economic opportunities outweigh the costs of damming the Colorado River. Conduct additional research prior to the debate.

DEBATE in Biology

Collaborate This is an example of a real-world situation that has both positive and negative effects. If a dam is necessary, careful planning—including ecological modeling and impact studies—can minimize its damage to the ecosystem. Have students research both sides of the issue and come to class prepared to debate either side. After students debate the issue, have the class vote on which side was the most persuasive. Discuss the results as a class.

WebQuest

BIOLAB

Design Your Own

FIELD INVESTIGATION: EXPLORE HABITAT SIZE AND SPECIES DIVERSITY

Background: Ecologists know that a major key to maintaining not only individual species but also a robust diversity of species is preserving the proper habitat for those species.

Question: *What effect does increasing the size of a habitat have on the species diversity within that habitat?*

Materials

Choose materials that would be appropriate for the experiment you plan.

Safety Precautions

WARNING: *Follow all safety rules regarding travel to and from the study site. Be alert on site and avoid contact with stinging or biting animals and poisonous plants.*

Plan and Perform the Experiment

1. Read and complete the lab safety form.
2. Form a hypothesis that you can test to answer the above question.
3. Record your procedure. List the materials you will use to test your hypothesis.
4. Make sure your experiment allows for the collection of quantitative data, which are data that can be expressed in units of measure.
5. Design and construct appropriate data tables.
6. Make sure your teacher approves your plan before you proceed.
7. Carry out the procedure at an appropriate field site.

Analyze and Conclude

1. **Graph Data** Prepare a graph of your data and the combined class data if they are available.
2. **Analyze** Do any patterns emerge as you analyze your group and class data and graphs? Explain.
3. **Conclude** Based on your data, was your initial hypothesis correct?
4. **Error Analysis** Compare your observations and conclusions with your classmates. Did your observations and conclusions match? If not, what could explain the differences? How could you verify your results?
5. **Determine** Did the populations and diversity change proportionally as the habitat was expanded? As the habitat expanded, did it become more or less suitable for supporting life?
6. **Hypothesize** Would you expect the same results if you performed this experiment in other habitats? Explain.
7. **Think Critically** Would you expect the same results 10 years from now? 20 years from now? Explain your answer.

APPLY YOUR SKILL

Presentation Diagram and explain at least one food chain that might exist in the habitat you explored in this lab.

BIOLAB

Design Your Own

? Inquiry BioLab

For a lab worksheet, use your eTeacherEdition Online.

RUBRIC A rubric for evaluating BioLabs is found on your eTeacherEdition Online.

Est. Time 60 min

Content Background
Ecologists try to answer questions similar to those asked in this lab: How much habitat is enough for an organism? Can the organism thrive given only islands of habitat within human habitation, or must its habitat be continuous? What other resources and populations must be present to support the organism?

Safety Precautions Approve lab safety forms before work begins. If traveling to a site off school grounds, establish safety and travel rules. Visit the site before taking the students there to determine any possible safety concerns.

Teaching Strategies
- Have lab teams prepare appropriate data tables before traveling to the study site.
- One experimental approach is to have students investigate the effect of doubling the size of the investigational area on species diversity.

Alternative Teaching Demo
Have students brainstorm what might happen to species diversity as their habitat size is incrementally decreased; then have them draw pictures of a habitat decreasing in size to provide a visual example.

Analyze and Conclude

1. Have each lab team graph their data and then use the data from all lab teams to prepare a class data table and graph.
2. Often, as the habitat grows larger, the number of different species increases.
3. Accept any reasonable conclusion that is based on data collected.
4. Answers will vary. Encourage students to share ideas about improving the lab. Lab teams in close proximity to each other may note greatly varied data. Life on Earth is not a homogenous layer. It is found in clumps. Thus, even the clumps of life found in the small neighboring study quadrants of this lab may be vastly different.
5. Answers will depend on the data collected. Generally, as the habitat expands so does the population and diversity, a direct proportion. A habitat will generally become more suitable for life as it expands.
6. Observations and results gathered from one type of habitat in one locale may not hold true for other types of habitats and situations in other locations.
7. Answers will vary. For example, if the area undergoes a lot of development, the results may vary substantially.

Chapter 2

Study Guide

ConnectED

Students can use the following to review the chapter.

Review

Vocabulary eGames
Vocabulary eFlashcards
Vocabulary PuzzleMaker

Assessment

Online Quizzes
Online Test Practice
Standardized Test Practice

Use the *ExamView® Assessment Suite* CD-ROM to:

- create multiple versions of tests
- create modified tests with one mouse click
- edit existing questions and add your own questions
- build tests aligned with state standards using built-in state curriculum tags
- change English tests to Spanish with one mouse click
- track students' progress using the Teacher Management System

Chapter 2 Study Guide

THEME FOCUS Energy Autotrophs convert energy from the Sun into chemical energy during photosynthesis. Autotrophic energy forms the basis of food webs and ecological pyramids.

BIG Idea **Energy is required to cycle materials through living and nonliving systems.**

Section 1 Organisms and Their Relationships

ecology (p. 32)
biosphere (p. 34)
biotic factor (p. 35)
abiotic factor (p. 35)
population (p. 36)
biological community (p. 36)
ecosystem (p. 36)
biome (p. 36)
habitat (p. 38)
niche (p. 38)
predation (p. 38)
symbiosis (p. 39)
mutualism (p. 39)
commensalism (p. 40)
parasitism (p. 40)

MAIN Idea **Biotic and abiotic factors interact in complex ways in communities and ecosystems.**

- Ecology is the branch of biology in which interrelationships between organisms and their environments are studied.
- Abiotic and biotic factors shape an ecosystem and determine the communities that will be successful in it.
- Levels of organization in ecological studies include organism, population, biological community, ecosystem, biome, and biosphere.
- Symbiosis is the close relationship that exists when two or more species live together. There are three types of symbiotic relationships.

Section 2 Flow of Energy in an Ecosystem

autotroph (p. 41)
heterotroph (p. 41)
herbivore (p. 41)
carnivore (p. 41)
omnivore (p. 42)
detritivore (p. 42)
trophic level (p. 42)
food chain (p. 43)
food web (p. 43)
biomass (p. 44)

MAIN Idea **Autotrophs capture energy, making it available for all members of a food web.**

- Autotrophs capture energy from the Sun or use energy from certain chemical substances to make food.
- Heterotrophs include herbivores, carnivores, omnivores, and detritivores.
- A trophic level is a step in a food chain or food web.
- Food chains, food webs, and ecological pyramids are models used to show how energy moves through ecosystems.

Section 3 Cycling of Matter

matter (p. 45)
nutrient (p. 45)
biogeochemical cycle (p. 45)
nitrogen fixation (p. 48)
denitrification (p. 48)

MAIN Idea **Essential nutrients are cycled through biogeochemical processes.**

- Biogeochemical cycles include the exchange of important nutrients between the abiotic and biotic parts of an ecosystem.
- The carbon and oxygen cycles are closely intertwined.
- Nitrogen gas is limited in its ability to enter biotic portions of the environment.
- Phosphorus and carbon have short-term and long-term cycles.

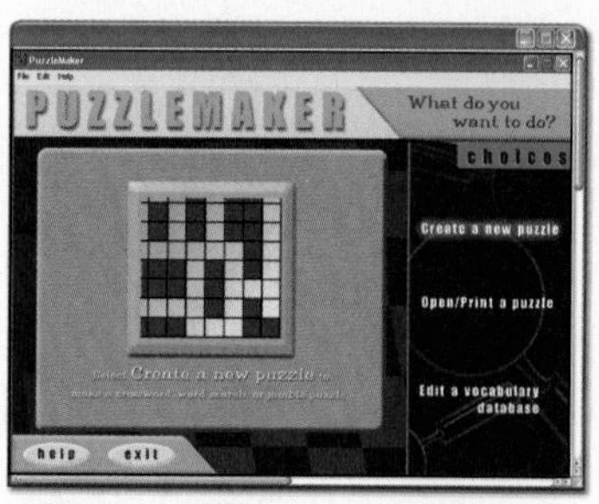

Review Vocabulary PuzzleMaker

For additional practice with vocabulary, have students access the Vocabulary PuzzleMaker online.

Review Vocabulary eGames

Section 1

Vocabulary Review

Replace each underlined word with the correct vocabulary term from the Study Guide page.

1. A niche is the place in which an organism lives.
2. The presence of interbreeding individuals in one place at a given time is called a biological community.
3. A group of biological communities that interact with the physical environment is the biosphere.

Understand Main Ideas

4. Which of these levels of organization includes all the other levels?
   A. community **C.** individual
   B. ecosystem **D.** population
5. Which would be an abiotic factor for a tree in the forest?
   A. a caterpillar eating its leaves
   B. wind blowing through its branches
   C. a bird nesting in its branches
   D. fungus growing on its roots

Use the photo below to answer questions 6 and 7.

6. The insect in the photo above is gathering pollen and nectar for food, but at the same time is aiding in the plant's reproduction. What does this relationship demonstrate?
   A. predation **C.** mutualism
   B. commensalism **D.** parasitism
7. What term best describes the bee's role of gathering pollen?
   A. niche **C.** parasite
   B. predator **D.** habitat

Use the illustration below to answer question 8.

8. Which type of heterotroph best describes this snake?
   A. herbivore **C.** omnivore
   B. carnivore **D.** detritivore

Constructed Response

9. **Short Answer** Explain the difference between a habitat and a niche.
10. MAIN Idea Describe how abiotic factors affect biotic factors in your environment. Give specific examples.
11. **CAREERS IN BIOLOGY** Summarize why most ecologists do not study the biosphere level of organization.

Think Critically

12. **Identify** an example of a predator-prey relationship, a competitive relationship, and a symbiotic relationship in an ecosystem near where you live.
13. **Explain** why it is advantageous for organisms such as fungi and algae to form mutualistic relationships.

Section 2

Vocabulary Review

Explain how the terms in each set below are related.

14. heterotroph, omnivore, carnivore
15. food chain, food web, trophic level
16. decomposer, heterotroph, carnivore
17. autotroph, food chain, heterotroph

Chapter 2 Assessment

Section 1

Vocabulary Review

1. habitat
2. population
3. ecosystem

Understand Main Ideas

4. B
5. B
6. C
7. A
8. B

Constructed Response

9. A habitat is an area where an organism lives. A niche is a role an organism plays in the habitat.
10. Abiotic factors such as temperature and weather will control biotic factors such as vegetation growth and water availability.
11. There are extreme difficulties in studying the entire biosphere. It is easier and more economical to study populations, communities, or ecosystems on a local level.

Think Critically

12. Student answers will vary depending upon the examples they choose. Sample response: A predator-prey relationship exists between starlings that eat worms. The starlings may compete among themselves for the worms. Lice may be parasitic on the skin of the starlings.
13. Each organism benefits from the other, because each organism provides something the other cannot get on its own.

Section 2

Vocabulary Review

14. Terms describe organisms that cannot make their own food.
15. Terms describe relationships in the flow of energy in an ecosystem.
16. Terms describe organisms that consume other organisms or the remains of decaying organisms.
17. Terms describe parts of a food web.

Assessment Online Test Practice

Understand Main Ideas
18. B
19. A
20. A
21. D
22. D

Constructed Response
23. Answers will vary upon location, but should include organisms for that area. Autotrophs form the base of all food webs and without them food webs would collapse.
24. Food webs are more complex than food chains; they are better models for showing energy flow in communities or ecosystems because they can show more detail.
25. 990 calories

Think Critically
26. Posters will vary depending upon the area of the country where you live. Accept all reasonable food web interactions.

Section 3

Vocabulary Review
27. nutrient
28. nitrogen fixation
29. biogeochemical cycle

Understand Main Ideas
30. D
31. B

Understand Main Ideas

18. How does energy first enter a pond ecosystem?
A. through growth of algae
B. through light from the Sun
C. through decay of dead fish
D. through runoff from fields

19. Which statement is true about energy in an ecosystem?
A. Energy for most ecosystems originates from the Sun.
B. Energy most often is released as light from an ecosystem.
C. Energy flows from heterotrophs to autotrophs.
D. Energy levels increase toward the top of the food chain.

Use the illustration below to answer questions 20 and 21.

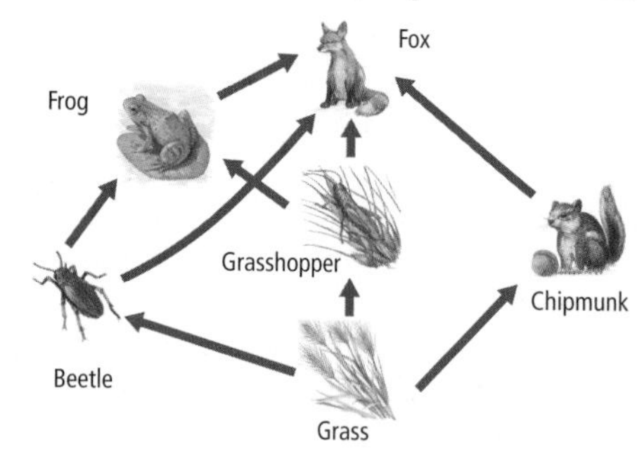

20. What does the illustration represent?
A. a food web
B. a food chain
C. an ecological pyramid
D. a pyramid of energy

21. Which organism in the illustration is an autotroph?
A. frog
B. grasshopper
C. fox
D. grass

22. Which is a detritivore?
A. cat
B. mouse
C. sunflower
D. crayfish

Constructed Response

23. MAIN Idea Create a food web that occurs in your community. Explain the importance of the autotrophs in the food web.

24. THEME FOCUS Energy Describe why food webs usually are better models for explaining energy flow than food chains.

25. Short Answer Determine approximately how much total energy is lost from a three-step food chain if 1000 calories enter at the autotroph level.

Think Critically

26. Apply Information Create a poster of a food web that might exist in an ecosystem that differs from your community. Include as many organisms as possible in the food web.

Section 3

Vocabulary Review

Each of the following sentences is false. Make each sentence true by replacing the italicized word with a vocabulary term from the Study Guide page.

27. Because nitrogen is required for growth, it is considered an essential *nitrate.*

28. Converting nitrogen from a gas to a useable form by bacteria is *denitrification.*

29. The movement of chemicals on a global scale from abiotic through biotic parts of the environment is a *lithospheric process.*

Understand Main Ideas

30. What is the name of the process in which bacteria and lightning convert nitrogen into compounds that are useful to plants?
A. ammonification
B. denitrification
C. nitrate cycling
D. nitrogen fixation

Use the following diagram to answer question 31.

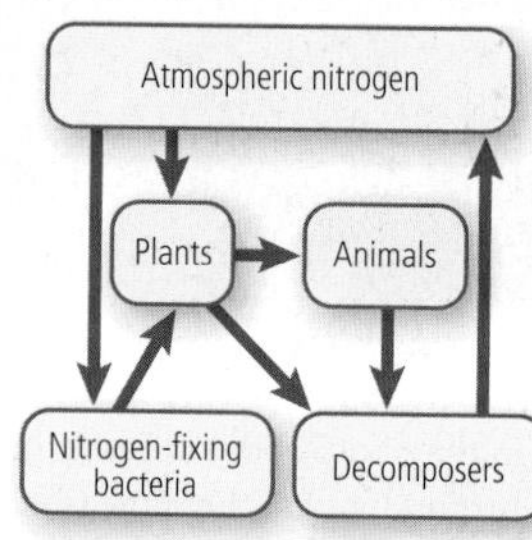

31. Where is the largest concentration of nitrogen found?
A. animals
B. atmosphere
C. bacteria
D. plants

Chapter 2 Assessment

32. What are the two major life processes that involve carbon and oxygen?
A. coal formation and photosynthesis
B. photosynthesis and respiration
C. fuel combustion and open burning
D. death and decay

33. Which process locks phosphorus in a long-term cycle?
A. organic materials buried at the bottom of oceans
B. phosphates released into the soil
C. animals and plants eliminating wastes
D. rain eroding mountains

Constructed Response

34. Short Answer Clarify what is meant by the following statement: Grass is just as important as mice in the diet of a carnivore such as a fox.

35. Short Answer The law of conservation of matter states that matter cannot be created or destroyed. How does this law relate to the cycling of carbon in an ecosystem?

36. MAIN Idea Explain the role of decomposers in the nitrogen cycle.

Think Critically

Use the illustration below to answer question 37 and 38.

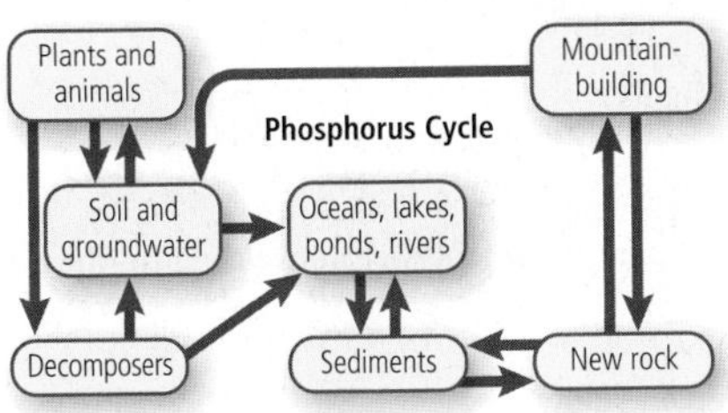

37. Interpret Scientific Illustrations Predict the effect of additional mountain building in the Rocky Mountains on the levels of phosphorus in the surrounding valleys.

38. Explain how decomposers supply phosphorus to soil, groundwater, oceans, lakes, ponds, and rivers.

Summative Assessment

39. BIG Idea Choose a specific organism from a food web in the chapter. Hypothesize how the energy from the Sun directly and indirectly affects its activities and life.

40. WRITING in Biology Write a poem that includes vocabulary terms and concepts from the chapter.

41. Summarize What is the difference between a heterotroph and an autotroph?

DBQ Document-Based Questions

The following information pertains to an ancient sand dune in Florida that is now landlocked—Lake Wales Ridge. Read the passage and answer the following questions.

Data obtained from: Mohlenbrock, R. H. 2004–2005. Florida high. *Natural History* 113: 46–47.

The federally listed animals that live on the ridge are the blue-tailed mole skink, the Florida scrub jay, and the sand skink (which seems to "swim" through loose sand of the scrub). Other animals on the ridge are the eastern indigo snake (which can grow to more than eight feet long, making it the longest nonvenomous snake species in North America), the Florida black bear, the Florida gopher frog, the Florida mouse, the Florida pine snake, the Florida sandhill crane, the Florida scrub lizard, the gopher tortoise, Sherman's fox squirrel, and the short-tailed snake.

The gopher tortoise is particularly important because its burrows, sometimes as long as thirty feet, serve as homes for several of the rare species as well as many other more common organisms. The burrows also provide temporary havens when fires sweep through the area, or when temperatures reach high or low extremes.

42. Construct a simple food web using at least five of the organisms listed.

43. Explain how the burrows are used during fires and why they are effective.

32. B
33. A

Constructed Response

34. It is true that the fox depends on mice for food. However, the mice depend on producers for food. Without the grass, there could be no mice and, therefore, no foxes.

35. Carbon can be converted into different chemical compounds and used first by one organism and then by another before entering the atmosphere for recycling, but the carbon atoms are never created nor destroyed.

36. The decomposers break down tissues and wastes and release nitrogen-containing compounds that are converted to other nitrogen-containing compounds or nitrogen gas.

Think Critically

37. Available phosphorus levels would increase. These increases could allow greater plant growth and higher animal productivity.

38. Decomposers break down organisms, which allows the phosphorus in the organisms to go back into the ecosystem.

Summative Assessment

39. Answers will vary, but the answer should include the name of an organism and determine how photosynthesis impacts the energy received from previous layers of the food web

WRITING in Biology

RUBRIC Use the modifiable rubric found on your eTeacherEdition Online to assess writing assignments.

40. Poems will vary. To receive full credit, students should properly use at least three vocabulary words and explain one of the principles presented in the chapter.

41. Autotrophs produce their own food, heterotrophs must get their food from other organisms.

DBQ Document-Based Questions

Mohlenbrock, R. H. 2004–2005. Florida high. *Natural History* 113: 46–47.

42. Students should produce a food web with the maximum number of possible connections.

43. Organisms hide in the burrows to escape fires. They are effective because they are underground shelters that are out of the way of the fire.

Assessment Online Test Practice

Standardized Test Practice

Multiple Choice

1. C
2. B
3. C
4. D
5. A
6. B
7. B
8. A
9. B

Short Answer

10. Answers can vary. Possible answers include the following. Biotic factors: organisms that may be a food source for the worm; organisms that compete with the worm for nutrients. Abiotic factors: amount of water in the soil; temperature of the soil.
11. Answers can vary. Possible answers include the following.
    - A. Nitrogen cycle: nitrogen-fixing bacteria in the soil convert nitrogen from the air into a form available to the plants.
    - B. Oxygen cycle: the worm uses oxygen for respiration.
    - C. Carbon cycle: as plant and animal matter in the soil decompose, carbon dioxide gas is released into the atmosphere.
12. In everyday use, "theory" often means just an idea or an unsupported explanation for something. For scientists, a theory is a way to summarize an idea that is based on many observations and experiments
13. Answers might vary. One possible answer is that scientific knowledge is constantly changing as new discoveries are made. New discoveries may change the way scientists make observations and interpretations, thus expanding scientific knowledge. Scientific knowledge will continue to grow because humans are curious and they do not know everything.

Standardized Test Practice

Cumulative

Multiple Choice

1. Which would be considered an ecosystem?
   - A. bacteria living in a deep ocean vent
   - B. biotic factors in a forest
   - C. living and nonliving things in a pond
   - D. populations of zebras and lions

Use the illustration below to answer questions 2 and 3.

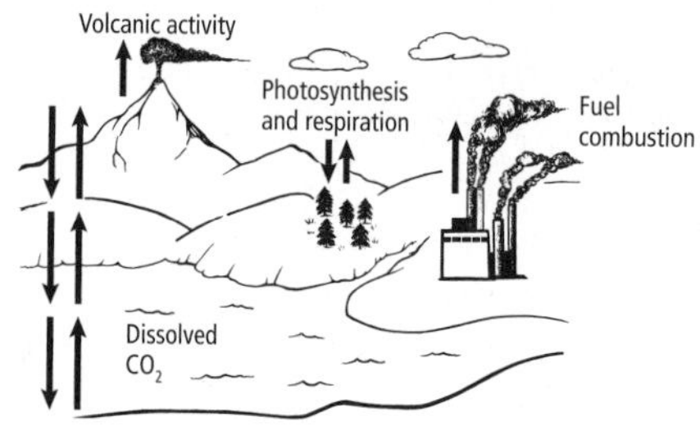

2. Which part of the diagram above relates to carbon leaving a long-term cycle?
   - A. dissolved CO_2
   - B. fuel combustion
   - C. photosynthesis and respiration
   - D. volcanic activity

3. Which part of the diagram above relates to carbon moving from an abiotic to a biotic part of the ecosystem?
   - A. dissolved CO_2
   - B. fuel combustion
   - C. photosynthesis and respiration
   - D. volcanic activity

4. Which is a scientific explanation of a natural phenomenon supported by many observations and experiments?
   - A. factor
   - B. hypothesis
   - C. result
   - D. theory

5. The mole is the SI unit for which quantity?
   - A. number of particles in a substance
   - B. compounds that make up a substance
   - C. number of elements in a substance
   - D. total mass of a substance

6. Suppose two leaf-eating species of animals live in a habitat where there is a severe drought and many plants die as a result. Which term describes the kind of relationship the two species probably will have?
   - A. commensalism
   - B. competition
   - C. mutualism
   - D. predation

Use the illustration below to answer questions 7–9.

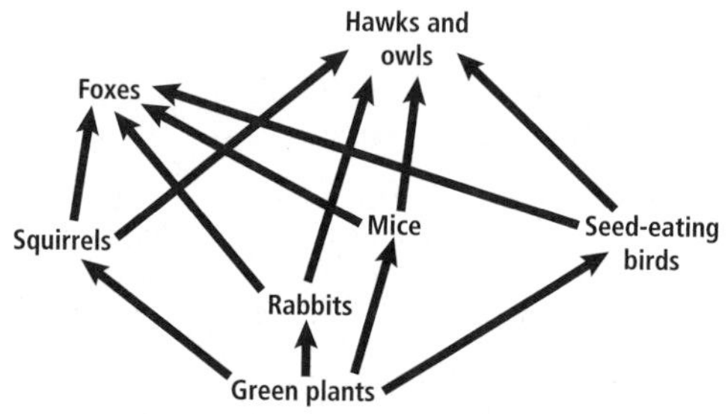

7. Which part of the food web above contains the greatest biomass?
   - A. foxes
   - B. green plants
   - C. mice
   - D. rabbits

8. Which part of the food web above contains the least biomass?
   - A. foxes
   - B. green plants
   - C. mice
   - D. rabbits

9. What happens to the energy that the fox uses for maintaining its body temperature?
   - A. It is taken up by decomposers that consume the fox.
   - B. It moves into the surrounding environment.
   - C. It stays in the fox through the metabolism of food.
   - D. It travels to the next trophic level when the fox is eaten.

Short Answer

Use the illustration below to answer questions 10 and 11.

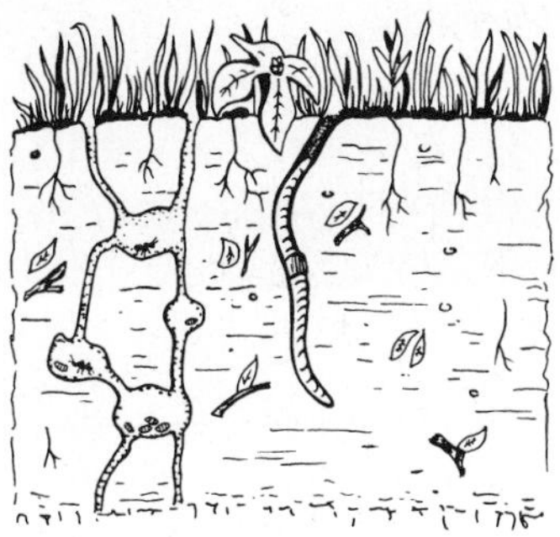

10. What are two biotic factors and two abiotic factors that affect a worm found in a situation similar to what is shown in the diagram?

11. Explain the portions of the following biogeochemical cycles that are related to the diagram above.
   A. nitrogen cycle
   B. oxygen cycle
   C. carbon cycle

12. Distinguish between the everyday use of the term *theory* and its true scientific meaning.

13. Evaluate how scientific knowledge changes and how the amount of scientific knowledge grows. Suggest a reason why it probably will continue to grow.

14. Describe how a forest ecosystem might be different without the presence of decomposers and detritivores.

15. Suppose that some unknown organisms are discovered in the deep underground of Earth. Give two examples of questions that biologists might try to answer by researching these organisms.

Extended Response

Use this drawing to answer questions 16 and 17.

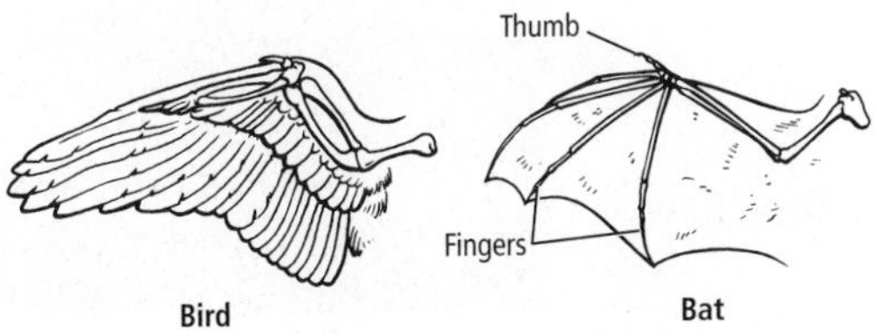

16. Someone tells you that bats and birds are closely related because they both have wings. Evaluate how this diagram could be used to critique the idea that bats and birds are not closely related.

17. Suppose you form a hypothesis that bats and birds are not closely related and you want to confirm this by comparing the way bats and birds fly. Design an experiment to test this hypothesis.

Essay Question

Various substances or elements on Earth move through long-term and short-term biogeochemical cycles as they become part of different aspects of the biosphere. The amount of a substance that is involved in a long-term cycle has an effect on the availability of that substance for use by humans and other organisms on Earth.

Using the information in the paragraph above, answer the following question in essay format.

18. Choose a substance or element that you know is involved in both long-term and short-term biogeochemical cycles. In a well-organized essay, describe how it moves through both types of cycles, and how these cycles affect its availability to humans and other organisms.

NEED EXTRA HELP?																		
If You Missed Question . . .	1	2	3	4	5	6	7	8	9	10	11	12	13	14	15	16	17	18
Review Section . . .	2.2	2.3	2.3, 2.1	1.2	1.2	2.1	2.2	2.2	2.2	2.1	2.3	1.2	1.2	2.2	1.3	1.2	1.3	2.3

14. Eventually all the organisms in the forest would die. Without decomposer organisms to break down dead matter and return nutrients to the soil, plants and other organisms could not live. Eventually, most of the available nutrients would be tied up in the dead organisms and would be no longer available to living organisms.

15. Answers can vary. Biologists could try to answer questions about how the organisms live, where they live, how they interact with each other, how they interact with their environment, and where they originated.

Extended Response

16. The drawing clearly shows that the structure of a bat wing and a bird wing are different and therefore not closely related. A bat's wing is structurally more similar to a human arm. The multiple bones in the outer part of a bat's wing are similar to the multiple bones in the fingers of the human hand. In a bird's wing, the outer bones are few in number.

17. Answers can vary. For example, one experiment is to make movies of bats and birds in flight. Then, compare characteristics, such as the range of wing movement and frequency of wing motion, by doing graphic analysis of the movie frames.

Essay Question

18. Answers can vary, depending on which substance students choose to write. For example, water is a possible topic. Water cycles through a short-term cycle when it evaporates from bodies of water, forms clouds, and falls back to Earth in the form of precipitation. It can also enter a long-term cycle if it is frozen in glaciers or percolates into inaccessible areas underground. Water that is part of a long-term cycle is not available to humans for drinking, bathing, fishing, and so on. The only freshwater that is useful to humans is involved in short-term cycles through the biosphere.

Chapter 3 Organizer:
Communities, Biomes, and Ecosystems

LabManager™
Customize any lab with the LabManager™ CD-ROM.

Essential Questions	National Science Standards	Materials and Planning Estimated times include cleanup and disposal, but do not include teacher prep time. For cleanup and disposal guidelines, see page 39T.	Est. Time (min)
Section 1 1. How do unfavorable abiotic and biotic factors affect species? 2. How do ranges of tolerance affect the distribution of organisms? 3. What are the stages of primary and secondary succession?	UCP.1, UCP.3, UCP.4; A.1, A.2; C.4, C.5; D.3; F.5; G.3	**Launch Lab,** p. 58: textbook, pencil, paper	10
		Demonstration, p. 60: thermometer, barometer, other weather instruments	5
		Demonstration, p. 61: 10 beans, 4 plastic pots, sand, distilled water, salt solutions	5 per day
Section 2 1. How is latitude related to the three major climate zones? 2. What are the major abiotic factors that determine the location of a terrestrial biome? 3. How are the terrestrial biomes distinguished based on climate and biotic factors?	UCP.1–3; A.1, A.2; C.4, C.5, C.6; F.3, F.4; G.1, G.2, G.3	**MiniLab 1,** p. 66: lamp with an incandescent bulb, globe, thermometer	25
		Demonstration, p. 69: soil test kit, soil samples, vinegar, soap solution	10
		Demonstration, p. 70: various plants from desert and grassland biomes	10
		Activity, p. 71: butcher paper, colored pencils	40
Section 3 1. What are the major abiotic factors that determine the aquatic ecosystems? 2. What are transitional aquatic ecosystems and why are they important? 3. What are the zones of marine ecosystems?	UCP.1–3; A.1, A.2; C.4, C.5, C.6; F.3, F.4; G.1, G.2, G.3	**Demonstration,** p. 74: state map	5
		Demonstration, p. 76: beaker of water with ice cubes	5
		MiniLab 2, p. 77: textbook, pencil, paper	20
		Demonstration, p. 77: preserved organisms from littoral zones	5
		Design Your Own BioLab, p. 83: glass or clear plastic gallon jars, pond water, pond mud, appropriate cultures and select living organisms, other appropriate materials	40–135

Suggested Time for Each Lesson

Class	Chapter Opener	Section 1	Section 2	Section 3	Assessment
Basic	45 min	90 min	—	45 min	45 min
General	25 min	100 min	100 min	45 min	45 min
Honors	5 min	20 min	90 min	90 min	20 min

ConnectED

connectED.mcgraw-hill.com

Access interactive learning opportunities and teaching resources using these icons located throughout your StudentWorks™ Plus Online and eTeacherEdition Online.

Chapter 3 Section Resources

FAST FILE Unit 1 Resources:
Launch Lab Worksheet*
Study Guide (English/Spanish)*
Section Quick Check

Reading Essentials 3.1
Science Notebook 3.1*

FAST FILE Unit 1 Resources:
MiniLab Worksheet*
Study Guide (English/Spanish)*
Section Quick Check

Reading Essentials 3.1
Science Notebook 3.1*

FAST FILE Unit 1 Resources:
MiniLab Worksheet*
BioLab Worksheet*
Study Guide (English/Spanish)*
Section Quick Check

Reading Essentials 3.3
Science Notebook 3.3*

Additional Chapter 3 Resources

FAST FILE Unit 1 Resources:
Chapter Diagnostic Test
Concept Mapping*
Real-World Biology
Enrichment
Chapter Tests A, B, and C

Transparencies:
Bellringer Transparencies*
Biology Concepts Transparencies*

Lab Resources:
Laboratory Manual*
Probeware Lab Manual*
Forensics Lab Manual*
Pre-AP Lab Manual*
Open Inquiry in Biology*
Guided Inquiry in Biology*

Technology

Teaching Tools:
eTeacherEdition Online
Classroom Presentation Toolkit CD-ROM*
LabManager™ CD-ROM*
Video Lab DVD*
Virtual Lab CD-ROM*
What's BIOLOGY Got To Do With It?
StudentWorks™ Plus Online*

Chapter Assessment Tools:
Classroom Presentation Toolkit CD-ROM*
ExamView® Assessment Suite CD-ROM

Web-Based Resources:
- StudentWorks™ Plus Online
- eTeacherEdition Online
- Animations*
- The Interactive Time Line*
- Interactive Tables*
- Online Quizzes
- Online Test Practice
- Standardized Test Practice
- Virtual Labs*
- Multilingual eGlossary*
- Vocabulary eGames*
- Vocabulary eFlashcards
- WebQuests
- Personal Tutors

While all resources listed are appropriate for English learners, the * indicates resources with a strong visual or hands-on component for EL.

Teaching strategies and activities have been coded for differentiated instruction.

AL Activities for students working above grade level	**OL** Activities for students working on grade level	**BL** Activities for students working below grade level	**EL** Activities for English learners (also ELL)	**COOP LEARN** Activities designed for small cooperative group work

CHAPTER 3

Launch Lab
What is my biological address?

Inquiry Launch Lab

For a lab worksheet, use your eTeacherEdition Online.

RUBRIC A rubric for evaluating Launch Labs is found on your eTeacherEdition Online.

Est. Time 10 min

Safety Precautions Approve lab safety forms before work begins.

Teaching Strategies
- Begin by reviewing and defining these appropriate concepts and terms: biosphere, biome, ecosystem, and community.
- Consider comparing a student's postal address to their biological address. Progress from smallest unit to largest unit:

Postal Address	Biological Address
Mary Smith	Mary Smith
Hertown	Community
Nebraska	Ecosystem
United States	Biome
Planet Earth	Biosphere

Procedure

1. Consider the following question: What do the terms community and ecosystem mean to you?
2. Describe the biological community and an ecosystem to which you belong.

Analysis

1. **Compare** Did your classmates all identify the same community and ecosystem? How would you describe, in general, the plants and animals in your area to someone from another country? Answers will vary, but should include reference to the students' findings as compared to their classmates. Answers should propose specific examples of plants and animals to someone from another country.
2. **Examine** Communities and ecosystems are constantly changing through a process known as succession. What changes do you think your biological community has undergone in the last 100 to 150 years? Answers will vary, but should include a summary of the succession in the local community. Students should talk about the sizes of plants and trees and the amount of plants and trees.

CHAPTER 3

Communities, Biomes, and Ecosystems

ConnectED

Your one-stop online resource
connectED.mcgraw-hill.com

- Video
- Audio
- Review
- Inquiry
- WebQuest
- Assessment
- Concepts in Motion
- Multilingual eGlossary

Launch Lab
What is my biological address?

Just as you have a postal address, you also have a biological "address." As a living organism, you are part of interwoven ecological units that vary in size from as large as the whole biosphere to the place you occupy right now.

For a lab worksheet, use your StudentWorks™ Plus Online.

Inquiry Launch Lab

FOLDABLES®

Make a shutter fold book using the labels shown. Use it to organize your notes on succession.

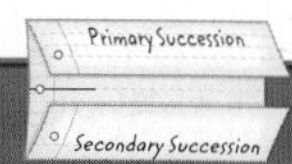

THEME FOCUS Change
Constantly changing communities of plants and animals drive succession.

BIG Idea Limiting factors and ranges of tolerance are factors that determine where terrestrial biomes and aquatic ecosystems exist.

Section 1 • Community Ecology
Section 2 • Terrestrial Biomes
Section 3 • Aquatic Ecosystems

THEMES

Scientific Inquiry Biologists study interactions between organisms and their environment.

Diversity Each biome has a unique range of diverse organisms and ecosystems.

Energy The Sun is the source of energy in each ecosystem.

Homeostasis The size of populations within an ecosystem is balanced by limiting factors.

Change Ecological succession is the result of changing abiotic and biotic factors.

Introduce the Chapter

Reef Ecology

ASK STUDENTS: ***What do the photos on this page tell you about barrier reefs?*** Student responses will vary, but might include that reefs are found in shallow water, they are marine environments, and many species live there.

TELL STUDENTS: ***Reefs are found in shallow, tropical waters in many parts of the world. There are probably more different species living in reef environments than in any other ecosystem, with the exception of the tropical rain forest.***

BIG Idea

Directed Reading Have students create a chart with columns titled *What I know, What I think I know, What I think I'll learn,* and *What I learned.* Direct students to the Big Idea, then have them preview each section of the chapter, fill out the first two columns to identify misconceptions, and complete the third column to set a purpose. After they read each section, have students fill out the last column. After reading each section, have students list the Main Idea on the back of the paper.

GOING GREEN Check with your school or department about ordering recycled paper. Encourage students to buy recycled paper as well.

Section 1

MAIN Idea

BL OL AL Limiting Factors
ASK STUDENTS: ***What are some abiotic factors that limit plant growth?*** water, temperature, chemical nutrients ***What are some biotic factors that limit plant growth?*** population density and life span of herbivores

Develop Concepts

AL Activate Prior Knowledge
ASK STUDENTS: ***What are some changes you associate with the change of seasons?*** Answers may include changes in length of day, temperatures, and precipitation patterns. ***Why do these changes occur?*** the tilt of Earth's axis, lower temperature, Earth's annual rotation, amount of rainfall, humidity, or sunlight

Writing Support

BL Informal Writing Have the class brainstorm a list of abnormal weather patterns for their region. Then have students write a letter to a friend concerning an abnormal weather pattern they have experienced. Select two letters to read to the class and have students identify the abiotic factors that contributed to the abnormal weather.

Section 1

Reading Preview

Essential Questions

- How do unfavorable abiotic and biotic factors affect species?
- How do ranges of tolerance affect the distribution of organisms?
- What are the stages of primary and secondary succession?

Review Vocabulary

abiotic factor: the nonliving part of an organism's environment

New Vocabulary

community
limiting factor
tolerance
ecological succession
primary succession
climax community
secondary succession

g Multilingual eGlossary

Community Ecology

MAIN Idea All living organisms are limited by factors in the environment.

Real-World Reading Link Wherever you live, you probably are used to the conditions of your environment. If it is cold outdoors, you might wear a coat, hat, and gloves. Bears have adaptations such as their warm fur coat to the cold so they do not need these types of clothes.

Communities

When you describe your community, you probably include your family, the students in your school, and the people who live nearby. A biological **community** is a group of interacting populations that occupy the same area at the same time. Therefore, your community also includes plants, other animals, bacteria, and fungi. Not every community includes the same variety of organisms. An urban community is different from a rural community, and a desert community is different from a polar community.

You have learned that organisms depend on one another for survival. You also learned about abiotic factors and how they affect individual organisms. How might abiotic factors affect communities? Consider soil, which is an abiotic factor. If soil becomes too acidic, some species might die or become extinct. This might affect food sources for other organisms, resulting in a change in the community.

Organisms adapt to the conditions in which they live. For example, a wolf's heavy fur coat enables it to survive in harsh winter climates, and a cactus's ability to retain water enables it to tolerate the dry conditions of a desert. Depending on which factors are present, and in what quantities, organisms can survive in some ecosystems but not in others. For example, the plants in the desert oasis shown in **Figure 1** decrease in number away from the water source.

Figure 1 Notice that populations of organisms live within a relatively small area surrounding the oasis.

Demonstration

Weather Instruments Hold up and describe the purposes of a large wall thermometer, a barometer, and any other weather instruments you have. Students will learn that these instruments are used to measure various abiotic factors that can limit the distribution of human populations.
Est. time: 5 min

Differentiated Instruction

Below Level Providing structure will help students who are performing below level succeed. Review concepts from previous lessons, summarize main ideas, and model activities that students will be expected to perform.

For more tips, see pages 14T–15T.

Limiting factors Any abiotic factor or biotic factor that restricts the numbers, reproduction, or distribution of organisms is called a **limiting factor.** Abiotic limiting factors include sunlight, climate, temperature, water, nutrients, fire, soil chemistry, and space. Biotic limiting factors include living things, such as other plant and animal species. Factors that restrict the growth of one population might enable another to thrive. For example, in the oasis shown in **Figure 1,** water is a limiting factor for all of the organisms. Temperature also might be a limiting factor. Desert species must be able to withstand the heat of the Sun and the cold temperatures of desert nights.

Range of tolerance For any environmental factor, there is an upper limit and lower limit that define the conditions in which an organism can survive. For example, steelhead trout live in cool, clear coastal rivers and streams from California to Alaska. The ideal range of water temperature for steelhead trout is between 13°C and 21°C, as illustrated in **Figure 2.** However, steelhead trout can survive water temperatures from 9°C to 25°C. At these temperatures, steelhead trout experience physiological stress, such as inability to grow or reproduce. **D** They will die if the water temperature goes beyond the upper and lower limits.

Have you ever had to tolerate a hot day or a boring activity? The ability of any organism to survive when subjected to abiotic factors or biotic factors is called **tolerance.** Consider **Figure 2** again. Steelhead trout tolerate a specific range of temperatures. That is, the range of tolerance of water temperature for steelhead is 9°C to 25°C. Notice that the greatest number of steelhead live in the optimum zone in which the temperature is best for survival. Between the optimum zone and the tolerance limits lies the zone of physiological stress. At these temperatures, there are fewer fish. Beyond the upper tolerance limit of 25°C and the lower tolerance limit of 9°C, there are no steelhead trout. Therefore, **C** water temperature is a limiting factor for steelhead when water temperature is outside the range of tolerance.

Reading Check **Describe** the relationship between a limiting factor and a range of tolerance.

CAREERS IN BIOLOGY

Conservation Biologist Among other duties, a conservation biologist might tag and track animals in a community. Understanding the biotic and abiotic factors of the community can help explain changes in populations.

S

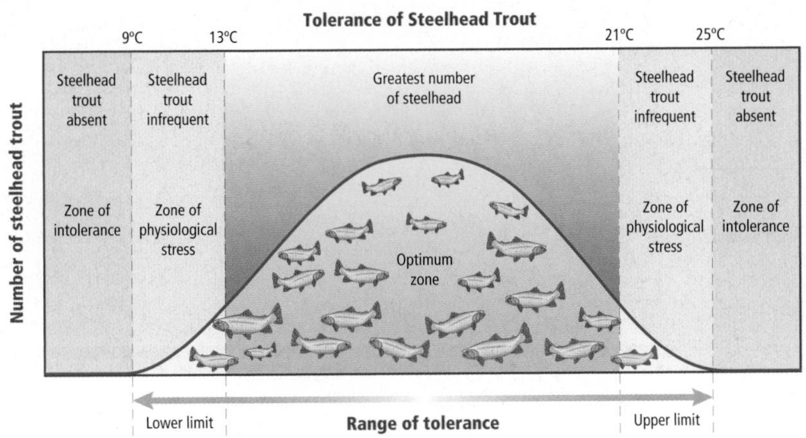

Figure 2 Steelhead trout are limited by the temperature of the water in which they live.
***Infer** which other abiotic factors might limit the survival of steelhead trout.*

S Skill Practice

BL Visual Literacy Have students examine Figure 2.
ASK STUDENTS: ***What is the optimum temperature range for steelhead trout?*** between 13°C and 21°C

D Develop Concepts

AL Discuss Generate a discussion with students about the limits of tolerance of some particular plants and animals in your area. Determine which ones have a wider tolerance range for precipitation or temperature.
ASK STUDENTS: ***Why are the limits of tolerance for many factors wider for humans than for most other organisms?*** Humans have the ability to alter the environment in ways that allow them to adapt to a wider range of variations than most species.

C Critical Thinking

OL Infer Have students use their understanding of the vocabulary terms *tolerance* and *limiting factor* to infer how they are related to each other. Tolerance is the ability to survive any particular limiting factor.

Caption Question Fig. 2 In addition to temperature, steelhead trout might be limited by dissolved oxygen content, depth of water, and types of minerals present.

Reading Check A range of tolerance is often defined by the limiting factors that affect a species.

Demonstration

Determine Tolerance Plant ten beans or other seeds in each of four plastic pots that contain sand. Water the first pot with distilled water; the second with a 1% salt solution; the third with a 10% salt solution; and the fourth with a 30% salt solution. Show the pots to the students each day for two weeks. Have students determine the tolerance the seedlings have to salt by counting how many seeds germinate and the growth rate of seedlings in each pot. Est. time: 5 min each day

![FOLDABLES®]

RUBRIC A rubric for evaluating Foldables is found on your eTeacherEdition Online.

Going Further

SAY TO STUDENTS: ***On the back of your Foldable, draw a four-part grid and explain how a community can be destroyed by answering the questions*** **what, where, when,** ***and*** **why.** ***Use the 1988 forest fire in Yellowstone National Park as an example, or you can select your own.***

D Develop Concepts

OL AL Integrate Geology

SAY TO STUDENTS: ***The geology of an area might make it more susceptible to disturbance. For instance, hillsides erode more quickly than level areas if all other variables are the same. Human activities might also contribute to succession.***

ASK STUDENTS: ***What would be the effect of overgrazing a grassland or clear cutting a forest?*** Both activities would disturb the plant community, resulting in ecological succession.

C Critical Thinking

AL Analyze

ASK STUDENTS: ***Why are pioneer species often able to adapt to a greater range of tolerance than some other later species?*** In a community, many species tend to buffer the range of some factors. Pioneer species lack such a buffer and must survive extreme ranges in factors such as heat and humidity.

Concepts in Motion

Animation

FOLDABLES® Incorporate information from this section into your Foldable.

Ecological Succession

Ecosystems are constantly changing. They might be modified in small ways, such as a tree falling in the forest, or in large ways, such as a forest fire. They also might alter the communities that exist in the ecosystem. Forest fires can be good and even necessary for the forest community. Forest fires return nutrients to the soil. Some plants, such as fireweed, have seeds that will not sprout until they are heated by fire. Some ecosystems depend on fires to get rid of debris. If fires are prevented, debris builds up to the point where the next fire might burn the shrubs and trees completely. A forest fire might change the habitat so drastically that some species no longer can survive, but other species might thrive in the new, charred conditions.

The change in an ecosystem that happens when one community replaces another as a result of changing abiotic and biotic factors is **ecological succession.** There are two types of ecological succession—primary succession and secondary succession. **D**

VOCABULARY

SCIENCE USAGE V. COMMON USAGE

Primary

Science usage: first in rank, importance, value, or order

A doctor's primary concern should be the patient.

Common usage: the early years of formal education

Elementary grades, up to high school, are considered to comprise a student's primary education.

Primary succession On a solidified lava flow or exposed rocks on a cliff, no soil is present. If you took samples of each and looked at them under a microscope, the only biological organisms you would observe would be bacteria and perhaps fungal spores or pollen grains that drifted there on air currents. The establishment of a community in an area of exposed rock that does not have any topsoil is **primary succession,** which is illustrated in **Figure 3.** Primary succession usually occurs very slowly at first.

Almost all plants require soil for growth. But, how is soil formed? Usually lichens, a mutualistic combination of a fungus and algae, begin to grow on the rock. Because lichens, along with some mosses, are among the first organisms to appear, they are called pioneer species. Pioneer species help to create soil by secreting acids that help to break down rocks. **C**

Figure 3 The formation of soil is the first step in primary succession. Once soil formation starts, there is progressive succession toward a climax community.

Concepts in Motion

Animation

Inquiry

Video Lab

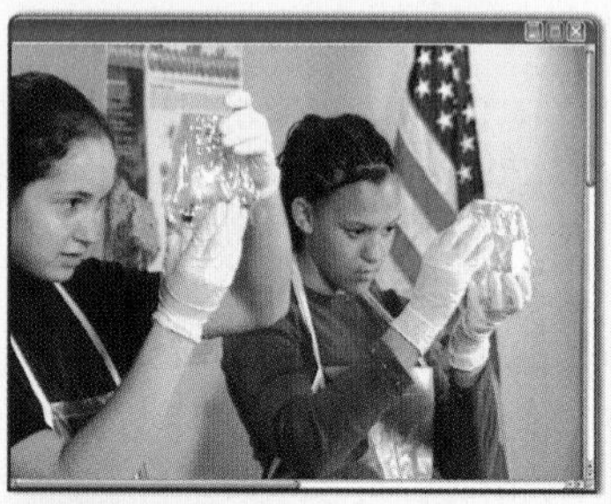

Inquiry **Video Lab** Students will observe the stages of succession in a model of an ecosystem.

As pioneer organisms die, their decaying organic materials, along with bits of sediment from the rocks, make up the first stage of soil development. At this point, small weedy plants, including ferns, and other organisms such as fungi and insects, become established. As these organisms die, additional soil is created. Seeds, transported by animals, water, or wind, begin to grow in the newly formed soil. Eventually, enough soil is present so that shrubs and trees can grow.

A mature community can eventually develop from bare rock, as illustrated in **Figure 3.** The stable, mature community that results when there is little change in the composition of species is a **climax community.** Scientists today realize that disturbances, such as climate change, are ongoing in communities; therefore, a true climax community is unlikely to occur.

D

Secondary succession Disturbances such as fire, flood, or a windstorm can disrupt a community. After a disturbance, new species of plants and animals might occupy the habitat. Over time, there is a natural tendency for the species belonging to the mature community to return. **Secondary succession** is the orderly and predictable change that takes place after a community of organisms has been removed but the soil has remained intact. Pioneer species—mainly plants that begin to grow in the disturbed area—are the first species to start secondary succession.

DATA ANALYSIS LAB 1

Based on Real Data*

Interpret the Data

How do soil invertebrates affect secondary succession in a grassland environment? An experiment was performed by adding soil invertebrates to controlled grassland communities. The growth of various plants was measured at four months, six months, and 12 months. Growth was measured by recording shoot biomass—the mass of the grass stems.

Data and Observations

The bars on the graph indicate the change in the biomass of the plants over time.

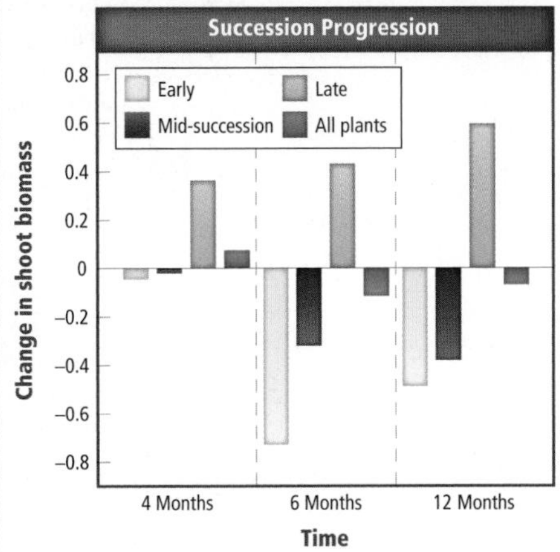

Think Critically

1. **Infer** what a negative value of change in shoot biomass indicates.
2. **Generalize** which communities were most positively affected and which were most negatively affected by the addition of soil invertebrates.

*Data obtained from: De Deyn, G.B. et al. 2003. Soil invertebrate fauna enhances grassland succession and diversity. *Nature* 422: 711–713.

DATA ANALYSIS LAB 1

About the Lab

- Point out to students that an understanding of how invertebrates affect succession might improve the restoration and conservation of species diversity in threatened ecosystems.
- Also see Olff and Ritchie. 1998. Effects of herbivores on grassland plant diversity. *Trends in Ecology and Evolution* 13: 261–265.

Think Critically

1. A negative value of change in shoot mass indicates that the amount of shoot mass has decreased over time.
2. The late-succession plants were the most positively affected plants, and the early succession plants were the most negatively affected by the addition of soil organisms.

D Develop Concepts

AL Clarify a Misconception

ASK STUDENTS: ***Where do climax communities exist?*** Answers will vary. Students might think that climax communities are communities that don't change and that these are common in the environment. A climax community has traditionally been defined as one in which succession has stopped, and which displays stability in the numbers and types of species present. Based on an increased understanding of global climate changes and disturbances, scientists think that a true climax community might not currently exist. In most applications, the term *climax community* refers to a stable, mature community.

Content Background

Real-World Connection Chaparral is a shrubby fire-dependent ecosystem found in California. Sprouting species of chaparral catch on fire more easily than woodland and forest communities. When fire is suppressed, succession in chaparral is not a series of different vegetation, but a gradual buildup of woody species. Succession after fire in desert chaparral is slow, and the mature community is composed of large shrub specimens with clusters of shorter plants.

R Reading Strategy

EL BL OL Build Vocabulary Have students explain the difference between *primary succession* and *secondary succession* and provide examples of each. Primary succession is the new growth from rock base (speciation on a volcano); secondary succession is regrowth after a disturbance (new plant growth after a fire).

Formative Assessment

Evaluation

ASK STUDENTS: ***What happens when organisms and populations enter their zones of physiological stress?*** Organisms might show physical changes or die. Populations might show a change in age distribution or decreased numbers.

Remediation Using a wet paper towel and marbles, show how the towel holds some marbles, then begins to tear as more are added, and finally breaks when too many marbles are added. Relate this to tolerance zones in biological systems.

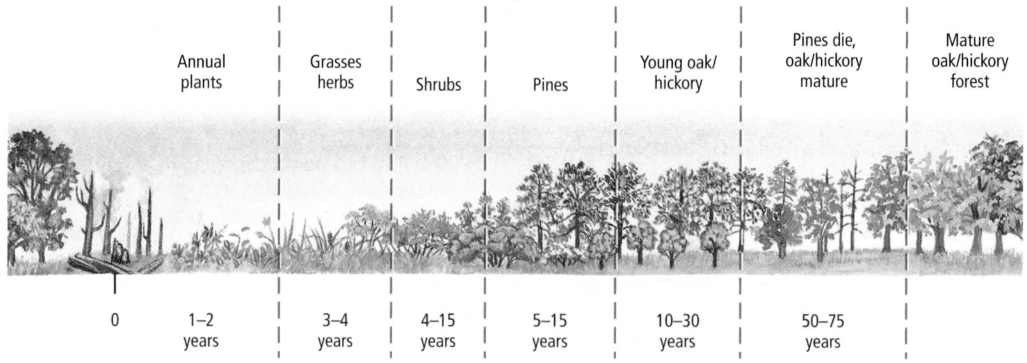

■ **Figure 4** After a fire, a forest might appear devastated. However, a series of changes ultimately leads back to a mature community.

During secondary succession, as in primary succession, the community of organisms changes over a period of time. **Figure 4** shows how species composition changes after a forest fire. Secondary succession usually occurs faster than primary succession because soil already exists and some species still will be present (although there might be fewer of them). Also, undisturbed areas nearby can be sources of seeds and animals.

Succession's end point Ecological succession is a complex process that involves many factors. The end point of succession after a disturbance cannot be predicted. Natural communities are constantly changing at different rates, and the process of succession is very slow. Human activities also affect the species that might be present. Because of these factors, it is difficult to determine if succession has reached a climax community in many areas on Earth.

Section 1 Assessment

Section Summary

- Abiotic and biotic limiting factors restrict the growth of a population within a community.
- Organisms have a range of tolerance for each limiting factor that they encounter.
- Primary succession occurs on areas of exposed rock or bare sand (no soil).
- Communities progress until there is little change in the composition of species.
- Secondary succession occurs as a result of a disturbance in a mature community.

Understand Main Ideas

1. MAIN Idea **Identify** how temperature is a limiting factor for polar bears.
2. **Predict** how unfavorable abiotic and biotic factors affect a species.
3. **Describe** how ranges of tolerance affect the distribution of a species.
4. **Classify** the stage of succession of a field that is becoming overgrown with shrubs after a few years of disuse.

Think Critically

5. **Interpret Figure 2** and predict the general growth trend for steelhead trout in a stream that is 22°C.

MATH in Biology

6. Graph the following data to determine the range of tolerance for catfish. The first number in each pair of data is temperature in degrees Celsius, and the second number is the number of catfish found in the stream: (0, 0); (5, 0); (10, 2); (15, 15); (20, 13); (25, 3); (30, 0); (35, 0).

Section 1 Assessment

1. Temperature defines a polar bear's community and ecosystem. The bear's food sources and its physiology are adapted to the cold temperatures.
2. Unfavorable factors might restrict the population numbers and ability to reproduce. Some factors that are unfavorable to one species might be favorable to another.
3. Fewer organisms will be found in their zone of physiological intolerance than in their tolerance zone.
4. secondary succession
5. The steelhead trout will grow more slowly in their zone of physiological stress.
6. Catfish can tolerate a temperature range from 10°C–25°C.

Assessment Online Quiz

Section 2

Reading Preview

Essential Questions

- How is latitude related to the three major climate zones?
- What are the major abiotic factors that determine the location of a terrestrial biome?
- How are the terrestrial biomes distinguished based on climate and biotic factors?

Review Vocabulary

biome: a large group of ecosystems that share the same climate and have similar types of plant communities

New Vocabulary

weather
latitude
climate
tundra
boreal forest
temperate forest
woodland
grassland
desert
tropical savanna
tropical seasonal forest
tropical rain forest

g Multilingual eGlossary

Terrestrial Biomes

MAIN Idea **Ecosystems on land are grouped into biomes primarily based on the plant communities within them.**

Real-World Reading Link If you live in the eastern part of the United States, you might live in an area surrounded by deciduous forests. If you live in the central part of the United States, there might be a grassy prairie nearby. Plant communities are specific to particular ecosystems.

Effects of Latitude and Climate

Regardless of where you live, you are affected by weather and climate. During a newscast, a meteorologist will make forecasts about the upcoming weather. **Weather** is the condition of the atmosphere at a specific place and time. What causes the variation in the weather patterns that you experience? What are the effects of these weather patterns on organisms that live in different areas on Earth? One of the keys to understanding communities is to be aware of latitude and climatic conditions.

Connection to Earth Science **Latitude** The distance of any point on the surface of Earth north or south from the equator is **latitude.** Latitudes range from 0° at the equator to 90° at the poles. Light from the Sun strikes Earth more directly at the equator than at the poles, as illustrated in **Figure 5.** As a result, Earth's surface is heated differently in different areas. Ecologists refer to these areas as polar, temperate, and tropical zones.

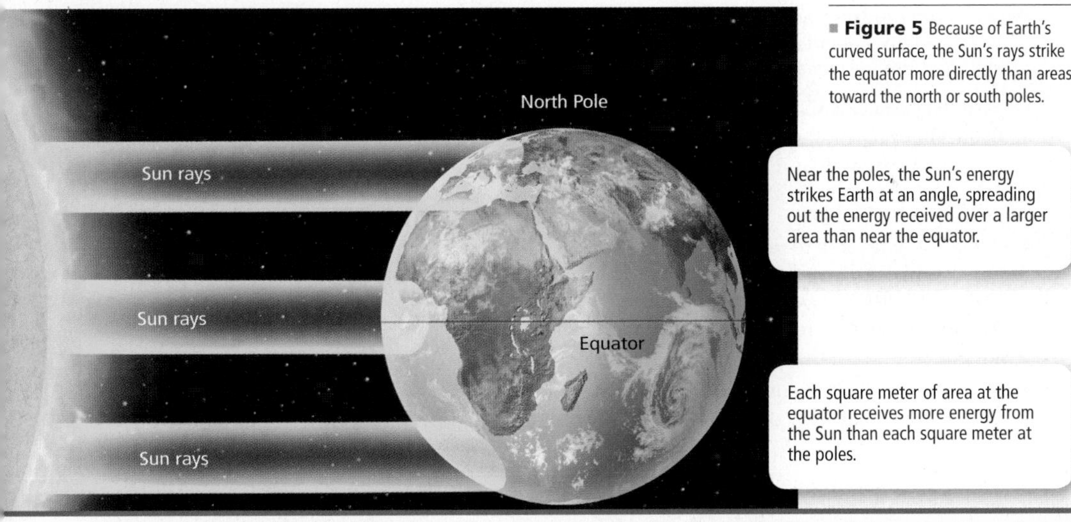
North Pole
Sun rays
Sun rays
Equator
Sun rays
Near the poles, the Sun's energy strikes Earth at an angle, spreading out the energy received over a larger area than near the equator.
Each square meter of area at the equator receives more energy from the Sun than each square meter at the poles.

Figure 5 Because of Earth's curved surface, the Sun's rays strike the equator more directly than areas toward the north or south poles.

Section 2

MAIN Idea

BL OL AL Land Biomes
SAY TO STUDENTS: ***As you study this section, pay particular attention to the types of plants found in each land biome.***
ASK STUDENTS: ***Why do you think the plants might be different in each major area?*** Different plants grow best under different climatic conditions. As the temperature and precipitation changes, the types of plants that grow in the area also will change.

Writing Support

BL OL AL Creative Writing
Assign a research project to each student. Have students research how climate varies across the United States and then write a story, song, play, or poem that details important information found in their research. Allow students to present their projects to the class.

Critical Thinking

OL AL Hypothesize
ASK STUDENTS: ***Why might the species in one biome be more diverse than the species in another?*** More species will be found in biomes where there are few limiting factors. The fewer limiting factors a biome has, the greater number of species that will be able to live there.

Research Citation

Build Vocabulary Educational research indicates that reading comprehension will improve when students are given explicit strategies for building vocabulary. Modeling practices such as using context clues can help students when they encounter unfamiliar terms.
(Nagy, 1997)

Research bibliography on pages 32T–34T

MiniLab 1

? Inquiry MiniLab

For a lab worksheet, use your eTeacherEdition Online.

✻RUBRIC A rubric for evaluating Launch Labs is found on your eTeacherEdition Online.

Est. Time 25 min

Additional Materials lamp with incandescent bulb (fluorescent bulbs do not generate enough heat)

Safety Precaution Approve lab safety forms before work begins.

Teaching Strategies

- Have students position the bulb of the lamp at a right angle 25–30 cm from the equator of the globe. You may need to adjust the distance of the lamp from the globe for best results.
- Link this lab to the concepts of biomes and the ecosystems and communities that exist within them.

Cleanup and Disposal
Remind students to return all items to their previous storage locations.

Analysis

1. Evaluate diagrams individually. Students should show warmer climates near the equator and cooler climates toward the north and south poles.
2. As you move north or south away from the equator, where the Sun's rays produce the warmest temperatures, the heat waves strike Earth at an increasingly oblique angle, resulting in less heat.

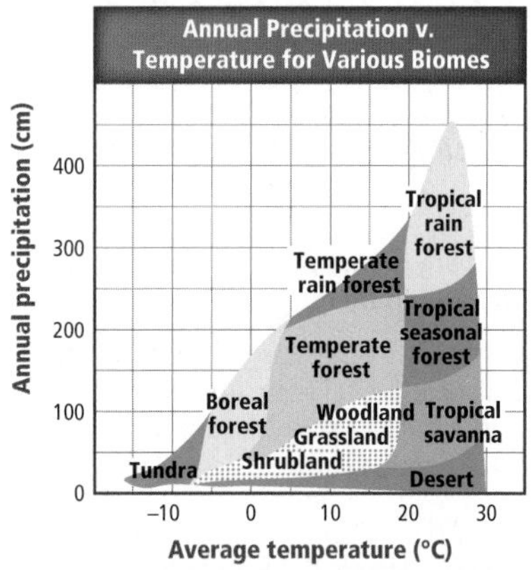

■ **Figure 6** Temperature and precipitation are two major factors that influence the kind of vegetation that can exist in an area.
***Analyze** which biome you would expect in an area that receives 200 cm of precipitation annually if the average annual temperature is 10°C.*

Review Personal Tutor

Video BrainPOP

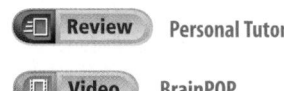

Climate The average weather conditions in an area, including temperature and precipitation, describe the area's **climate.** An area's latitude has a large effect on its climate. If latitude were the only abiotic factor involved in climate, biomes would be spread in equal bands encircling Earth. However, other factors such as elevation, continental landmasses, and ocean currents also affect climate. The graph in **Figure 6** shows how temperature and precipitation influence the communities that develop in an area. You can investigate the relationship between temperature and latitude in **Minilab 1.**

A biome is a large group of ecosystems that share the same climate and have similar types of communities. It is a group of plant and animal communities that have adapted to a region's climate. A biome's ecosystems occur over a large area and have similar plant communities. Even a small difference in temperature or precipitation can affect the composition of a biome. Refer to **Figure 7** to learn how Earth's ocean currents and prevailing winds affect climate. Also illustrated in **Figure 7** are two ways humans might be affecting climate—through the hole in the ozone layer and through global warming. Global warming is in part a result of the greenhouse effect.

Major Land Biomes

Biomes are classified primarily according to the characteristics of their plants. Biomes also are characterized by temperature and precipitation. Animal species are an important characteristic of biomes as well. This section describes each of the major land biomes.

MiniLab 1

Formulate a Climate Model

? Inquiry MiniLab

How are temperature and latitude related? At the equator the climate is very warm. However, as you change latitude and move north or south of the equator, temperatures also change. This results in different latitudinal climate belts around the world.

Procedure

1. Read and complete the lab safety form.
2. Position a **lamp** so that it shines directly on the equator of a **globe.**
3. Predict how the temperature readings will change as you move a **thermometer** north or south, away from the equator.
4. Prepare a data table to record your observations.
5. Use the thermometer to take temperature readings at different latitudes as instructed by your teacher. **WARNING:** ***The lamp and bulb will be very hot.***
6. Record temperature readings in your data table.

Analysis

1. **Model** climate belts by using your data to draw a diagram.
2. **Cause and Effect** Why do the temperature readings change as you move north or south of the equator?

■ **Caption Question Fig. 6** temperate forest

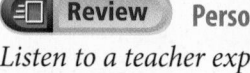

Review **Personal Tutor**
Listen to a teacher explain the greenhouse effect.

Video **BrainPOP**

Visualizing Global Effects on Climate

Figure 7
Some parts of Earth receive more heat from the Sun. Earth's winds and ocean currents contribute to climate and balance the heat on Earth. Many scientists think human impacts on the atmosphere upset this balance.

Winds on Earth

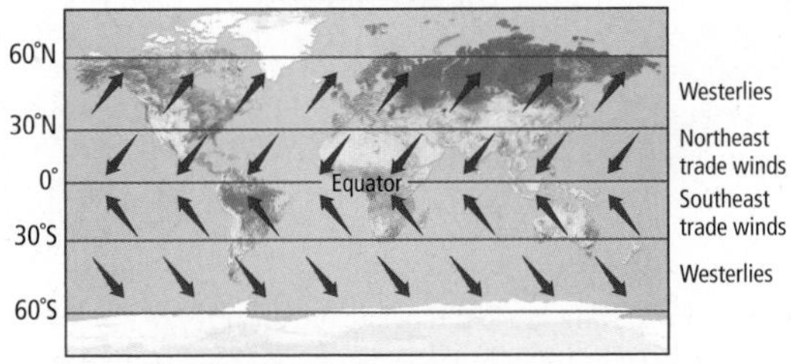

Winds are created from temperature imbalances. Distinct global wind systems transport cold air to warm areas and warm air to cold areas.

Earth's Ocean Currents

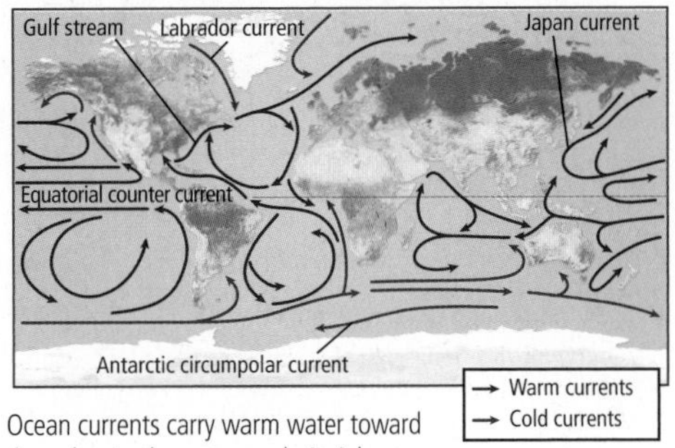

Ocean currents carry warm water toward the poles. As the water cools, it sinks toward the ocean floor and moves toward tropical regions.

Greenhouse Effect

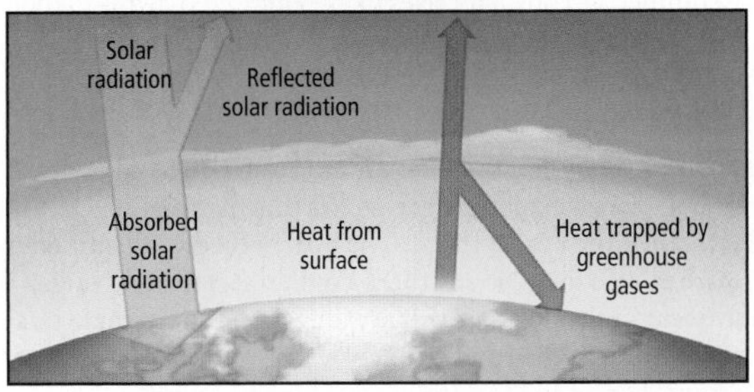

Earth's surface is warmed by the greenhouse effect. Certain gases in Earth's atmosphere, including naturally occurring water vapor, reduce the amount of energy Earth radiates into space. Other important greenhouse gases are carbon dioxide and methane.

Human Impact on the Atmosphere

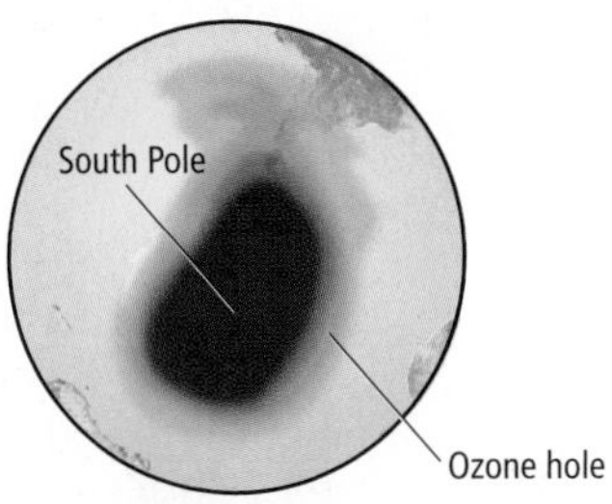

The ozone layer is a protective layer in the atmosphere that absorbs most of the harmful UV radiation from the Sun. Atmospheric studies have indicated that chlorofluorocarbons (CFCs) contribute to a seasonal reduction in ozone concentration over Antarctica, forming the Antarctic ozone hole.

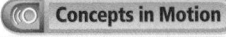

Concepts in Motion Animation

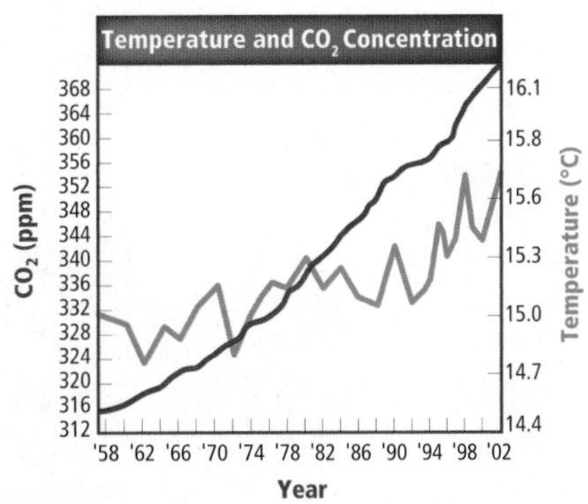

The measured increase of carbon dioxide (CO_2) in the atmosphere is mainly due to the burning of fossil fuels. As carbon dioxide levels have increased, the average global temperature has increased.

Visualizing Global Effects on Climate

Purpose

Students will learn about winds, currents, and other activities that affect global climate.
UCP.2, UCP.3, F.4, F.5

Develop Concepts

OL Scaffolding

ASK STUDENTS: ***What are some important greenhouse gasses?*** carbon dioxide and methane ***How are temperature and carbon dioxide levels related on the graph?*** As carbon dioxide levels have increased, the temperature has also increased. ***Relate the information in the graph to the greenhouse effect.*** As carbon dioxide (greenhouse gas) levels have increased, the greenhouse effect has also increased, causing the global temperature to increase.

AL Have students research other greenhouse gases to see if they have increased or decreased in the past 30 years. Have them present their research to the class.

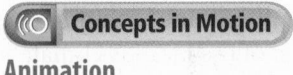

Concepts in Motion

Animation

Differentiated Instruction

Physically Disabled Include all students in group activities such as the MiniLab described on the previous page. If necessary, modify activities so that students with physical disabilities are able to participate.

For more tips, see pages 14T–15T.

Develop Concepts

BL OL AL

Clarify a Misconception

Show students a picture of lemmings.

ASK STUDENTS: ***Have you ever seen an image of lemmings jumping off cliffs or rushing into the ocean?*** Some students might have seen videos of this. ***Why do you think lemmings do that?*** A common misconception is that large numbers of lemmings will jump from cliffs or drown in the ocean when their populations increase suddenly. In reality, lemmings migrate to new areas when their populations explode. Some might accidentally fall into the ocean, but there is no mass suicidal rush to reduce population size.

Skill Practice

BL OL AL **Make a Chart** Have students make a four-column chart comparing and contrasting the main characteristics of the land biomes discussed in this section. Have them list biome types in the first column of the chart, information about the biome's location in the second column, a description of the biome's climate in the third column, and information about organisms that live in the biome in the fourth column. Charts should compare biomes on the basis of geographic location, temperature, vegetation, and animal species.

W Writing Support

OL **Technical Writing** Have students write driving instructions from their area to the nearest tundra. Provide world maps and have students indicate major landmarks along the route between the two areas.

Figure 8 Tundra
Average precipitation: 15–25 cm per year
Temperature range: –70°C–12°C
Plant species: short grasses, shrubs
Animal species: caribou, polar bears, birds, insects, wolves, arctic hares, musk ox
Geographic location: south of the polar ice caps in the Northern Hemisphere
Abiotic factors: soggy summers; permafrost; cold and dark much of the year

Tundra Extending in a band below the polar ice caps across northern Europe, North America, and Siberia in Asia is the tundra. The **tundra** is a treeless biome with a layer of permanently frozen soil below the surface called permafrost. Although the ground thaws to a depth of a few centimeters in the summer, its constant cycles of freezing and thawing do not allow tree roots to grow. Some animals and shallow-rooted plants that have adapted to tundra conditions are illustrated in **Figure 8.** W

Boreal forest South of the tundra is a broad band of dense evergreen forest extending across North America, Europe, and Asia, called the boreal forest. The **boreal forest,** illustrated in **Figure 9,** also is called northern coniferous forest, or taiga. Summers in the boreal forest are longer and somewhat warmer than in the tundra, enabling the ground to remain warmer than in the tundra. Boreal forests, therefore, lack a permafrost layer.

Figure 9 Boreal forest
Average precipitation: 30–84 cm per year
Temperature range: –54°C–21°C
Plant species: spruce and fir trees, deciduous trees, small shrubs
Animal species: birds, moose, beavers, deer, wolverines, lynx
Geographic location: northern part of North America, Europe, and Asia
Abiotic factors: summers are short and moist; winters are long, cold, and dry

Content Background

Teacher FYI A strip of boreal forest, also called northern coniferous forest or taiga, lies along the edge of North America from the north part of California to Alaska. This narrow strip of land is never wider than 161 km, but contains some of the world's tallest trees. Some spruce, hemlock, and fir trees in this region are up to 75 m tall. Taigas are also found in northern Europe and in Asia.

Figure 10 Temperate forest
Average precipitation: 75–150 cm per year
Temperature range: –30°C–30°C
Plant species: oak, beech, and maple trees, shrubs
Animal species: squirrels, rabbits, skunks, birds, deer, foxes, black bears, frogs, snakes
Geographic location: south of the boreal forests in eastern North America, eastern Asia, Australia, and Europe
Abiotic factors: well-defined seasons; summers are hot, and winters are cold

Temperate forest Temperate forests cover much of southeastern Canada, the eastern United States, most of Europe, and parts of Asia and Australia. As shown in **Figure 10,** the **temperate forest** is composed mostly of broad-leaved, deciduous (dih SIH juh wus) trees—trees that shed their leaves in autumn. The falling red, orange, and gold leaves return nutrients to the soil. All four seasons occur in temperate forests. In spring, warm temperatures and precipitation restart the growth cycles of plants and trees.

Temperate woodland and shrubland Open **woodlands** and mixed shrub communities are found in areas with less annual rainfall than in temperate forests. The woodland biome occurs in areas surrounding the Mediterranean Sea, on the western coasts of North and South America, in South Africa, and Australia. Areas that are dominated by shrubs, such as in California, are called the chaparral. **Figure 11** illustrates woodland and shrub communities.

Figure 11 Temperate woodland and shrubland
Average precipitation: 38–100 cm per year
Temperature range: 10°C–40°C
Plant species: evergreen shrubs, corn oak
Animal species: foxes, jackrabbits, birds, bobcats, coyotes, lizards, snakes, butterflies
Geographic location: surrounds the Mediterranean Sea, western coasts of North and South America, South Africa, and Australia
Abiotic factors: summers are very hot and dry; winters are cool and wet

Demonstration

BL OL AL Soil pH Obtain a soil test kit (available from garden centers or biological supply houses) and test three or four samples of soil from the school grounds. Compare the pH of the soil with such common items as vinegar (acidic) and soap solution (basic). Students will learn the significance of pH on plant growth. Discuss the effects of acid precipitation on a biome. Est. time: 10 min

Develop Concepts

EL BL OL Use Models Have students make three-dimensional models or dioramas of biomes by using shoeboxes and common objects. Have students vote on which model is the most realistic, the most colorful, the most unusual, and the best overall. Award certificates for the best model in each category.

Writing Support

EL BL OL AL

Journal Writing Have students collect leaves from as many different deciduous trees and shrubs as can be found in their area. Remind students to respect private property. Instruct students to dry the leaves between newspaper pages and press the leaves using a stack of heavy books. Alternatively, students could draw or photograph deciduous leaves. Have students mount the pressed leaves or pictures on pages in their journal and identify each leaf using a field guide. Tell students to list the common and scientific names for each leaf and provide an account of the climate, such as average annual temperature and precipitation, where the leaves were found.

Critical Thinking

BL OL AL Consider

ASK STUDENTS: ***Why are black bears not usually found in large groups?*** Black bears generally are solitary animals with large territories. Black bears must consume large amounts of food to prepare for their winter hibernation. If they were in large groups, there likely would not be enough food to support them for long.

Develop Concepts

BL OL AL Activity If possible, collect samples of soil from different biomes such as boreal forests, temperate forests, temperate woodlands, and shrublands. Alternatively, you could bring in photographs of soils. Have students identify the biomes from which the soils were taken based on color, texture, and other properties of the soil.

C Critical Thinking

AL Evaluate Grasses and many shrubs often have a meristem growing under the soil surface. Tell students that the meristem of a plant is the region of rapidly dividing cells. As the cells in meristems mature, they can develop into many different kinds of plant cells.

ASK STUDENTS: ***How might the meristem be an adaptation to fire?*** Fire can burn the grasses to ground level, but they quickly grow back from the meristem, which is the undifferentiated plant tissue from which new cells are formed. This adaptation allows grasses to take advantage of the nutrients available after the fire.

D Develop Concepts

AL Clarify a Misconception

ASK STUDENTS: ***Can a desert be cold?*** Yes; by definition, a desert is an area where evaporation exceeds precipitation. Students might think that deserts are always hot. Point out that most of Antarctica is desert because there is very little annual precipitation. Also, nighttime temperatures in most temperate deserts, such as the Sonoran and Chihuahuan Deserts in the United States, might drop to below freezing. The Gobi Desert in Asia and the Great Basin in the United States are high deserts that sometimes have bitterly cold winter temperatures due to their high altitudes.

Figure 12 Temperate grassland
Average precipitation: 50–89 cm per year
Temperature range: –40°C–38°C
Plant species: grasses, herbs, flowers
Animal species: gazelles, bison, horses, lions, deer, mice, coyotes, foxes, wolves, birds, snakes, grasshoppers, spiders
Geographic location: North America, South America, Asia, Africa, and Australia
Abiotic factors: summers are hot, winters are cold, moderate rainfall, fires possible

Temperate grassland A biome that is characterized by fertile soils that are able to support a thick cover of grasses is called **grassland,** illustrated in **Figure 12.** Drought, grazing animals, and fires keep grasslands from becoming forests. Due to their underground stems and buds, perennial grasses and herbs are not eliminated by the fires that destroy most shrubs and trees. Temperate grasslands are found in the middle latitudes of North America, South America, Asia, Africa, and Australia. Grasslands are called steppes in Asia; prairies in North America; pampas and llanos in South America; savannas in Africa; and rangelands in Australia. C

D **Desert** Deserts exist on every continent except Europe. A **desert** is any area in which the annual rate of evaporation exceeds the rate of precipitation. You might imagine a desert as a desolate place full of sand dunes, but many deserts do not match that description. As shown in **Figure 13,** deserts can be home to a wide variety of plants and animals.

Figure 13 Desert
Average precipitation: 2–26 cm per year
Temperature range: high: 20°C–49°C, low: –18°C–10°C
Plant species: cacti, Joshua trees, succulents
Animal species: lizards, bobcats, birds, tortoises, rats, antelope, desert toads
Geographic location: every continent except Europe
Abiotic factors: varying temperatures, low rainfall

Demonstration

Plant Adaptations Show students various cacti, grasses, and other plants from desert and grassland biomes. Compare the various leaf adaptations between plant types and the climates of the biomes in which they occur. To make the demonstration even more effective, consider making a terrarium for each biome with the plants as you compare them. Est. time: 10 min

Figure 14 Tropical savanna
Average precipitation: 50–130 cm per year
Temperature range: 20°C–30°C
Plant species: grasses and scattered trees
Animal species: lions, hyenas, cheetahs, elephants, giraffes, zebras, birds, insects
Geographic location: Africa, South America, and Australia
Abiotic factors: summers are hot and rainy, winters are cool and dry

Tropical savanna A **tropical savanna** is characterized by grasses and scattered trees in climates that receive less precipitation than some other tropical areas. Tropical savanna biomes occur in Africa, South America, and Australia. The plants and animals shown in **Figure 14** are common to tropical savannas.

Tropical seasonal forest **Figure 15** illustrates a tropical seasonal forest. **Tropical seasonal forests,** also called tropical dry forests, grow in areas of Africa, Asia, Australia, and South and Central America. In one way, the tropical seasonal forest resembles the temperate deciduous forest because during the dry season, almost all of the trees drop their leaves to conserve water.

Reading Check **Compare and contrast** tropical savannas and tropical seasonal forests.

Figure 15 Tropical seasonal forest
Average precipitation: >200 cm per year
Temperature range: 20°C–25°C
Plant species: deciduous and evergreen trees, orchids, mosses
Animal species: elephants, tigers, monkeys, koalas, rabbits, frogs, spiders
Geographic location: Africa, Asia, Australia, and South and Central America
Abiotic factors: rainfall is seasonal

Develop Concepts

EL BL OL AL Activity Have each student make a collage poster that describes their favorite terrestrial biome. Posters should contain no words, only photographs and drawings. When you have collected all of the posters, have the class try to identify the biomes depicted from the visual details. Then have students group the posters by biomes.

Develop Concepts

BL OL AL COOP LEARN

Activity Write the names of the terrestrial biomes on note cards. Give one card to each student and tell him or her not to show his or her card. Organize students into pairs and have students ask each other yes/no questions such as, "Are large herds of grazers found there?" or "Is there much precipitation there?", etc. After each student guesses his or her partner's biome correctly, have partners exchange cards and find new partners. Have students continue in this fashion for five rounds.

Skill Practice

BL OL Visual Literacy Have students read the captions for Figures 8–16. Ask students questions that relate to the captions. As an example, you might ask: On average, how much precipitation annually falls in a tropical rain forest? 200–1000 cm

Reading Check A tropical savanna has grasses and scattered trees, whereas a tropical seasonal forest has deciduous and evergreen trees. A tropical savanna receives 50–130 cm of rain per year, while a tropical seasonal forest receives > 200 cm of rain per year.

Activity

EL BL OL Precipitation Have students use the figure captions in this section to find the average annual precipitation of each biome. Then have them make a bar graph using a strip of butcher paper at least 3 m long. Instruct students to use a different color pencil to represent each biome on the graph. The y-axis should show the total amount of precipitation, and the x-axis should show the names of the biomes.
Est. time: 40 min

W Writing Support

BL OL AL Creative Writing

Have students research a threatened or endangered animal that lives in the tropical rain forest and write a short poem about it. In addition to creativity, student pieces should mention how environments are changing and how this affects the species.

D Develop Concepts

OL AL Scaffolding

ASK STUDENTS: ***What term is given to assemblages of land plants and animals that have the same climate?*** terrestrial biomes ***Identify species that might be found in tropical rain forests.*** mosses, ferns, exotic flowers, brightly colored birds, insects, monkeys, snakes ***Why are these species successful in this particular biome?*** Plant and animal species in the tropical rain forest flourish with warm temperatures and significant rainfall. The abundance of resources produces many niches that are inhabited by a large number of species. ***Predict what might happen to the tropical rain forests if a dramatic climate change caused colder temperatures and less precipitation.*** Temperature and precipitation changes could damage the delicate balance in the biome, possibly causing widespread extinctions and population decreases beyond the tolerance limits.

Reading Strategy

BL OL COOP LEARN

Discussion Groups After students examine Figures 8–16, ask students to name their favorite animals. Place students in groups based on similar responses. Have students discuss what limiting factors might affect the population of these animals.

■ **Figure 16** Tropical rain forest
Average precipitation: 200–1000 cm per year
Temperature range: 24°C–27°C
Plant species: broadleaf evergreens, bamboo, ferns, orchids
Animal species: chimpanzees, Bengal tigers, elephants, orangutans, bats, toucans, sloths, cobra snakes
Geographic location: Central and South America, southern Asia, west central Africa, and northeastern Australia
Abiotic factors: humid all year, hot and wet

Tropical rain forest Warm temperatures and large amounts of rainfall throughout the year characterize the **tropical rain forest** biome illustrated in **Figure 16.** Tropical rain forests are found in much of Central and South America, southern Asia, west central Africa, and northeastern Australia. The tropical rain forest is the most diverse of all land biomes. Tall, broad-leaved trees with branches heavy with mosses, ferns, and orchids make up the canopy of the tropical rain forest. Shorter trees, shrubs, and plants, such as ferns and creeping plants, make up another layer, or understory, of tropical rain forests.

Other Terrestrial Areas

You might have noticed that the list of terrestrial biomes does not include some important areas. Many ecologists omit mountains from the list. Mountains are found throughout the world and do not fit the definition of a biome because their climate characteristics and plant and animal life vary depending on elevation. Polar regions also are not considered true biomes because they are ice masses and not true land areas with soil.

Mountains If you go up a mountain, you might notice that abiotic conditions, such as temperature and precipitation, change with increasing elevation. These variations allow many communities to exist on a mountain. As **Figure 17** illustrates, biotic communities also change with increasing altitude, and the tops of tall mountains may support communities that resemble those of the tundra.

? Inquiry Virtual Lab

Study Tip

Summaries Review the terrestrial biomes featured in this section. Choose one or two biomes and write two sentences that summarize the information.

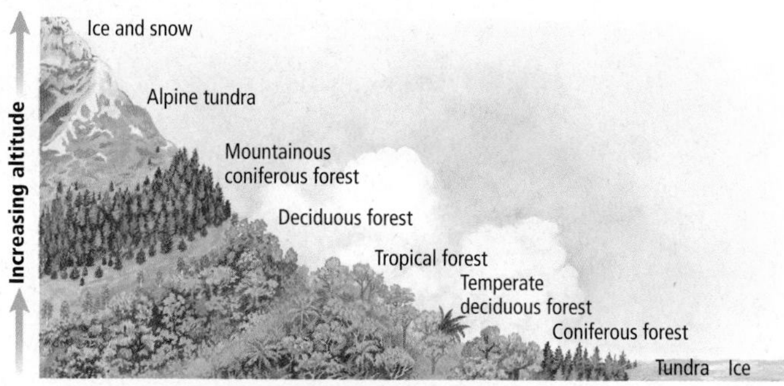

■ **Figure 17** As you climb a mountain or increase in latitude, the temperature drops and the climate changes.
Describe *the relationship between altitude and latitude.*

■ **Caption Question Fig. 17** As altitude increases, the biotic communities appear as if the latitude is also increasing.

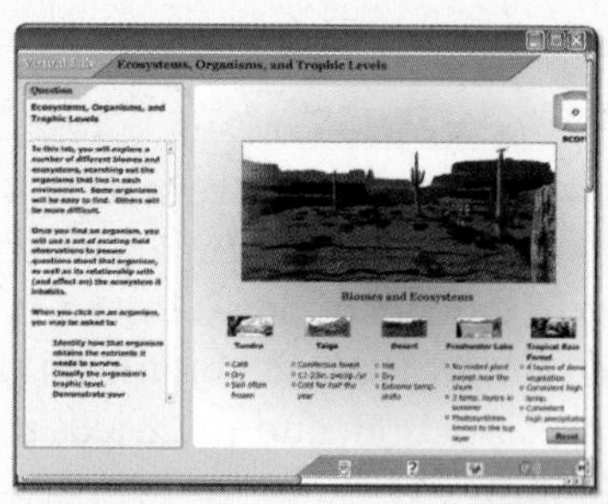

? Inquiry **Virtual Lab** In this lab, students will learn about ecosystems, organisms, and trophic levels.

■ **Figure 18** A surprising number of species inhabit the polar regions, including these penguins in Antarctica.

Polar regions Polar regions border the tundra at high latitudes, and these regions are cold all year. The coldest temperature ever recorded, –89°C, was in Antarctica, the continent that lies in the southern polar region. In the northern polar region lies the ice-covered Arctic Ocean and Greenland. Covered by a thick layer of ice, the polar regions might seem incapable of sustaining life. However, as shown in **Figure 18**, colonies of penguins live in Antarctica. Additionally, whales and seals patrol the coasts, preying on penguins, fish, or shrimplike invertebrates called krill. The arctic polar region supports even more species, including polar bears and arctic foxes. Human societies have also inhabited this region throughout history. Although the average winter temperature is about –30°C, the arctic summer in some areas is warm enough for vegetables to be grown. C

CAREERS IN BIOLOGY

Climatologist Unlike meteorologists, who study current weather conditions, climatologists study long-term climate patterns and determine how climate changes affect ecosystems.

Section 2 Assessment

Section Summary

- Latitude affects terrestrial biomes according to the angle at which sunlight strikes Earth.
- Latitude, elevation, ocean currents, and other abiotic factors determine climate.
- Two major abiotic factors define terrestrial biomes.
- There are nine major terrestrial biomes. There are two additional terrestrial regions that do not fit into these categories.

Understand Main Ideas

1. MAIN Idea **Describe** the nine major terrestrial biomes.
2. **Describe** the abiotic factors that determine a terrestrial biome.
3. **Summarize** variations in climate among three major zones as you travel south from the equator toward the South Pole.
4. **Indicate** the differences between temperate grasslands and tropical savannas.
5. **Compare and contrast** the climate and biotic factors of tropical seasonal forests and temperate forests.

Think Critically

6. **Hypothesize** why the tropical rain forests have the greatest diversity of living things.

WRITING in **Biology**

7. Tropical forests are being felled at a rate of 17 million hectares per year, which represents almost two percent of the forest area. Use this information to write a pamphlet describing how much rain forest area exists and when it might be gone.

C Critical Thinking

BL OL AL Evaluate

ASK STUDENTS: ***What changes can you predict for the polar regions if global warming continues at its present rate?*** Glaciers will continue to retreat. Ice shelves will collapse. Some top predators could become endangered or extinct. Sea level will likely increase. Discuss students' predictions.

Skill Practice

BL OL Use Maps Review with students the locations of the continents. Choose one student at a time to point out and name a continent. Then have students use the map key to name each of the major land biomes that occurs on that continent. Have another student identify the latitude and longitude of your location on a world map or globe.

Formative Assessment

Evaluation Call on individual students to identify the characteristics of each biome that you choose at random. Student responses will vary, but if you identify "boreal forest," students should say something like "long, cold winters with short, mild summers."

Remediation Give each student a world map with the terrestrial biomes outlined. Have students review the biome descriptions, then identify the biomes on the map, color-code them, and label the climate, plants, and animals found in each biome.

Section 2 Assessment

1. Students should list the following biomes: tundra, boreal forest, temperate forest, temperate grassland, temperate woodland and shrubland, desert, savanna, tropical dry forest, and tropical rain forest. Make sure their descriptions match the information given in the text.
2. Abiotic factors include temperature and precipitation.
3. The equatorial zone is generally warm all year with high precipitation and humidity; the temperate zone has warm to hot summers with mild winters and seasonal precipitation; and polar areas are frigid with brief, cold summers.
4. Temperate grasslands are warm to hot in the summer, with seasonal precipitation. Tropical savannahs are warm year-round with much more rainfall during the wet season.
5. A tropical seasonal forest has a different rain pattern and is warmer than a temperate forest, but both have deciduous trees.
6. Students' answers should indicate that a warm climate and abundant precipitation provides more niches for organisms.
7. 850 million hectares; 50 y

Section 3

MAIN Idea

BL OL AL Aquatic Ecosystems
ASK STUDENTS: ***What are some abiotic factors that you might use to describe a body of water such as a pond, river, or ocean?*** Answers will vary but may include rate of flow, depth, and salinity. ***What are some biotic factors that would be different in each aquatic environment?*** Answers will vary, but students should indicate that different kinds of fish, birds, insects, and algae live in each different environment.

R Reading Strategy

EL BL OL Two-Column Notes
Before students read, have them skim Section 3 and list the major headings on the left-hand side of a piece of paper. As they read, have them write key words and phrases from the text under that head on the right-hand side of the paper.

D Develop Concepts

BL OL AL Integrate History
From hollowed-out log canoes, skin-covered kayaks, and reed rafts to sailing ships and ocean liners, humans have depended on various types of watercraft to travel short or long distances over water. Human cultures are strongly tied to the aquatic ecosystems near them. Discuss with students how their community interacts with local aquatic ecosystems.

Section 3

Reading Preview

Essential Questions

- What are the major abiotic factors that determine the aquatic ecosystems?
- What are transitional aquatic ecosystems and why are they important?
- What are the zones of marine ecosystems?

Review Vocabulary

salinity: a measure of the amount of salt in a body of water

New Vocabulary

sediment
littoral zone
limnetic zone
plankton
profundal zone
wetlands
estuary
intertidal zone
photic zone
aphotic zone
benthic zone
abyssal zone

g Multilingual eGlossary

Aquatic Ecosystems

R **MAIN Idea** **Aquatic ecosystems are grouped based on abiotic factors such as water flow, depth, distance from shore, salinity, and latitude.**

Real-World Reading Link Think about the body of water that is closest to where you live. What are its characteristics? How deep is it? Is it freshwater or salt water? For centuries, bodies of water have been central to cultures around the world.

D The Water on Earth

When you think about water on Earth, you might recall a vacation at the ocean or a geography lesson in which you located Earth's oceans and seas. You probably have heard about other large bodies of water, such as the Amazon river and the Great Salt Lake. A globe of Earth is mainly blue in color because the planet is largely covered with water. Ecologists recognize the importance of water because of the biological communities that water supports. In this section, you will read about freshwater, transitional, and marine aquatic ecosystems. You also will read about the abiotic factors that affect these ecosystems.

Freshwater Ecosystems

The major freshwater ecosystems include ponds, lakes, streams, rivers, and wetlands. Plants and animals in these ecosystems are adapted to the low salt content in freshwater and are unable to survive in areas of high salt concentration. Only about 2.5 percent of the water on Earth is freshwater, as illustrated by the circle graph on the left in **Figure 19.** The graph on the right in **Figure 19** shows that of that 2.5 percent, 68.9 percent is contained in glaciers, 30.8 percent is groundwater, and only 0.3 percent is found in lakes, ponds, rivers, streams, and wetlands. Interestingly, almost all of the freshwater species live in this 0.3 percent.

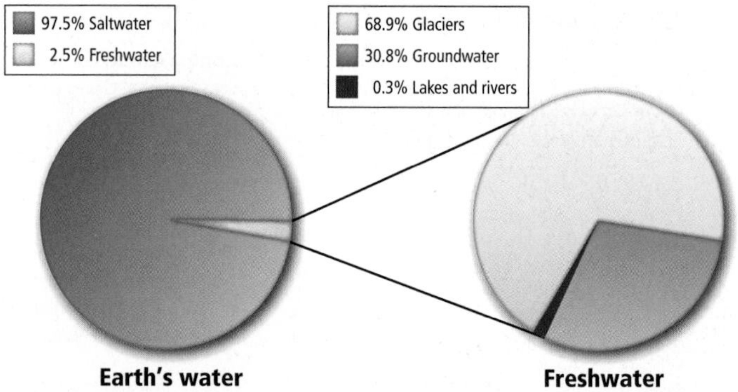

■ **Figure 19** The vast majority of Earth's water is salt water. Most of the freshwater supply is locked in glaciers.

Demonstration

Map Aquatic Ecosystems Use a map of your state to locate various bodies of water, including lakes, rivers, or marine coastal areas. Point out the relative size of the freshwater bodies compared to saltwater sources, and have students relate the findings on the map to the percentages of freshwater and salt water on Earth shown in Figure 19.
Est. time: 5 min

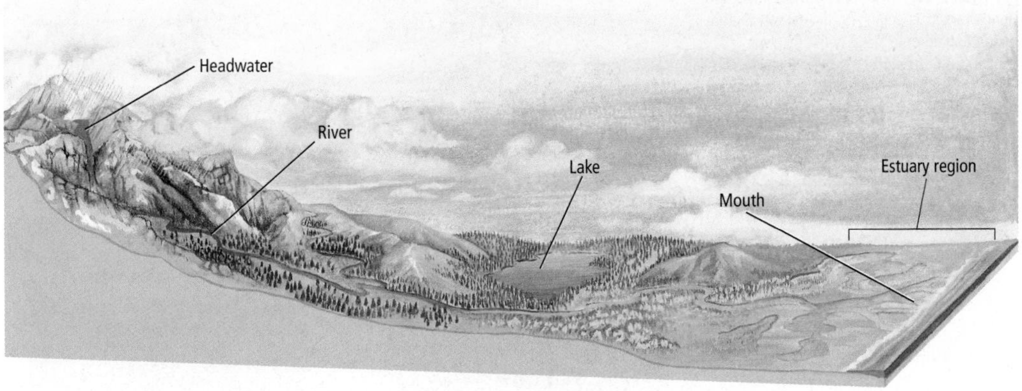

■ **Figure 20** Mountain streams have clear, cold water that is highly oxygenated and supports the larvae of many insects and the coldwater fish that feed on them. Rivers become increasingly wider, deeper, and slower. At the mouth, many rivers divide into many channels where wetlands or estuaries form.

Rivers and streams The water in rivers and streams flows in one direction, beginning at a source called a headwater and traveling to the mouth, where the flowing water empties into a larger body of water, as illustrated in **Figure 20.** Rivers and streams also might start from underground springs or from snowmelt. The slope of the landscape determines the direction and speed of the water flow. When the slope is steep, water flows quickly, causing a lot of sediment to be picked up and carried by the water. **Sediment** is material that is deposited by S water, wind, or glaciers. As the slope levels, the speed of the water flow decreases and sediments are deposited in the form of silt, mud, and sand.

The characteristics of rivers and streams change during the journey from the source to the mouth. Interactions between wind and the water stir up the water's surface, which adds a significant amount of oxygen to the water. Interactions between land and water result in erosion, in nutrient availability, and in changing the path of the river or stream.

The currents and turbulence of fast-moving rivers and streams prevent much accumulation of organic materials and sediment. For this reason, there are usually fewer species living in rapid waters similar to that in **Figure 21.** An important characteristic of life in rivers and streams is the ability to withstand the constant water current. Plants that root themselves into the streambed are common in areas where water is C slowed by rocks or sandbars. Young fish hide in these plants and feed on the drifting microscopic organisms and aquatic insects.

In slow-moving water, insect larvae are the primary food source for many fish, including American eel, brown bullhead catfish, and trout. Other organisms, such as crabs and worms, are sometimes present in calm water. Animals that live in slow-moving water include newts, tadpoles, and frogs.

Reading Check **Describe** key abiotic factors that define rivers and streams.

■ **Figure 21** The turbulent churning action of fast-moving rivers and streams does not allow for many plants to take root or for other species to inhabit these waters.

Develop Concepts

BL OL AL COOP LEARN Activity
Set up several microscopes with slides of living protozoa and algae collected from a stream, river, lake, or pond. If you are not able to collect organisms, prepared slides can be ordered from a biological supply house. Provide field guides and have students work in groups to identify the organisms on the slides.

S Skill Practice

BL Sequence Call on a student at random to give the sequence of water flow from a high mountain spring to the ocean. The sequence is from the spring to a stream. The stream flows into a river, which eventually flows into the ocean.

C Critical Thinking

BL OL AL Evaluate
ASK STUDENTS: ***What are some reasons that mountain springs and streams are usually clearer, colder, and more oxygenated than rivers?*** At their source, streams have not flowed far enough to pick up much silt. In high altitudes, mountain streams usually are fed by cold meltwater from snow. Cold, fast-flowing water holds more oxygen than warm, slowly flowing water.

Inquiry BioLab
The lab at the end of the chapter can be used at this point in the lesson.

Reading Check Abiotic factors that define rivers and streams include flow rate, sediment level and the amount of dissolved oxygen.

Differentiated Instruction

Gifted Provide opportunities for gifted students to manage or design a lab activity or assignment. These types of activities will help students develop leadership skills.

For more tips, see pages 14T–15T.

D Develop Concepts

OL AL

Clarify a Misconception

ASK STUDENTS: ***Would you expect to find the same species inhabiting several different types of freshwater bodies?*** No; although some species are cosmopolitan, most are found in only one environment, such as a pond or river. Point out that species are not distributed evenly in these ecosystems, but are found where the abiotic factors they prefer are optimal.

S Skill Practice

BL Observe and Infer Point out that the seasonal change that occurs in some lakes is called turnover. **ASK STUDENTS:** ***Why do you think this name has been given to this process?*** Inorganic material from the bottom comes to the top layers and oxygen is provided to the bottom layers of the lake.

R Reading Strategy

AL Content-Specific Words Review the origins of the terms *oligotrophic* and *eutrophic* given in the vocabulary feature on this page. **ASK STUDENTS:** ***Why are these words used to describe lakes?*** Lakes are classified based on their nutrient availability. ***Do you think most human-made lakes are oligotrophic or eutrophic? Explain your answer.*** eutrophic; because most humanmade lakes are made by damming rivers, causing the river's sediments to be trapped in the lake.

Caption Question Fig. 22 A lake in the tropics will not freeze, so life can be more diverse.

Figure 22 The temperature of lakes and ponds varies depending on the season. During spring and autumn, deep water receives oxygen from the surface water and surface water receives inorganic nutrients from the deep water.
Compare *the type of life that might live in a shallow lake in the tropics to one in the mid-latitudes.*

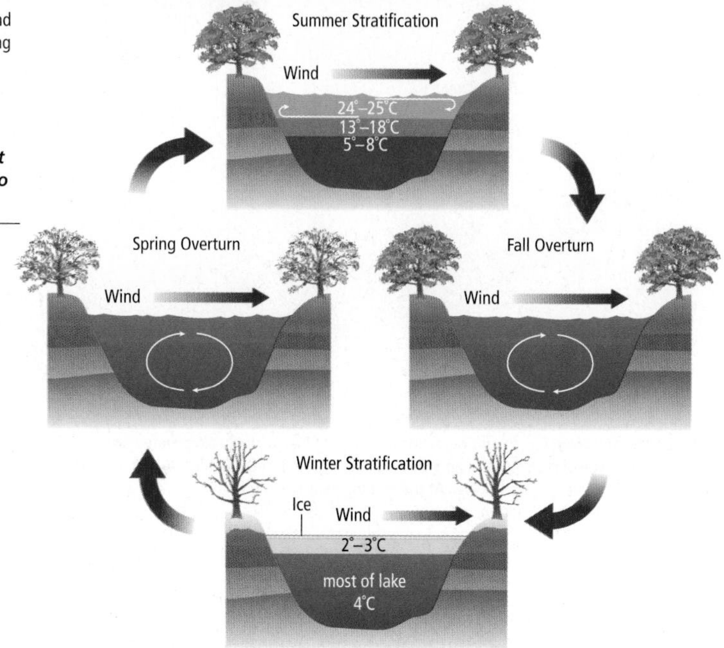

D Lakes and ponds An inland body of standing water is called a lake or a pond. It can be as small as a few square meters or as large as thousands of square meters. Some ponds might be filled with water for only a few weeks or months each year, whereas some lakes have existed for thousands of years. **Figure 22** illustrates how in temperate regions the temperature of lakes and ponds varies depending on the season.

During the winter, most of the water in a lake or pond is the same temperature. In the summer, the warmer water on top is less dense than the colder water at the bottom. During the spring and fall, as the water warms or cools, turnover occurs. The top and bottom layers of water mix, often due to winds, and this results in a uniform water temperature. This mixing circulates oxygen and brings nutrients from the bottom to the surface. S

Nutrient-poor lakes, called oligotrophic (uh lih goh TROH fihk) lakes, often are found high in the mountains. Few plant and animal species are present as a result of small amounts of organic matter and nutrients. Nutrient-rich lakes, called eutrophic (yoo TROH fihk) lakes, usually are found at lower altitudes. Many plant and animal species are present as a result of organic matter and plentiful nutrients, some of which come from agricultural and urban activities.

R

VOCABULARY

WORD ORIGIN

Eutrophic/oligotrophic
eu– prefix; from Greek, meaning *well*
oligo– prefix; from Greek, meaning *few*
–***trophic***; from Greek, meaning *nourish*

Lakes and ponds are divided into three zones based on the amount of sunlight that penetrates the water. The area closest to the shore is the **littoral** *(LIH tuh rul)* **zone.** The water in this zone is shallow, which allows sunlight to reach the bottom. Many producers, such as aquatic plants and algae, live in these shallow waters. The abundance of light and producers make the littoral zone an area of high photosynthesis. Many consumers also inhabit this zone, including frogs, turtles, worms, crustaceans, insect larvae, and fish.

Demonstration

BL OL AL Lakes in Winter Show students a beaker of water with ice cubes floating in it. Discuss with students that one of the unique properties of water is that it expands when it freezes. This indicates that the density of ice is less than water. Point out that many bodies of water, such as lakes and rivers, would freeze solid in winter if ice did not float and provide an insulating layer. Lead students to understand that if a lake or river froze solid, most of the organisms in it would die over the winter. Then tell students that some lakes in the far north freeze solid in the winter.
ASK STUDENTS: ***What adaptations do you think organisms living in these lakes might have?*** Possible answers: the ability to hibernate or a life cycle that occurs over the course of a year or less Est. time: 5 min

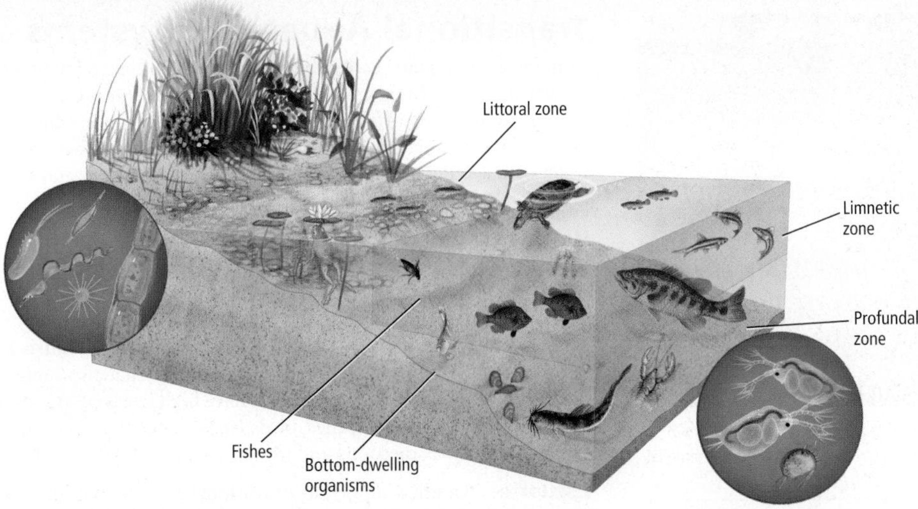

The **limnetic** (lihm NEH tihk) **zone** is the open water area that is well lit and is dominated by plankton. **Plankton** are free-floating photosynthetic autotrophs that live in freshwater or marine ecosystems. Many species of freshwater fish live in the limnetic zone because food, such as plankton, is readily available.

Minimal light is able to penetrate through the limnetic zone into the deepest areas of a large lake, which is called the **profundal** (pruh FUN dul) **zone.** The profundal zone is therefore much colder and lower in oxygen than the other two zones. A limited number of species live in this harsh environment. **Figure 23** identifies the zones and biodiversity of lakes and ponds.

■ **Figure 23** Most of a lake's biodiversity is found in the littoral and limnetic zones. However, many species of bottom dwellers depend on nutrients and materials that drift down from above.

S

MiniLab 2

Prepare a Scientific Argument

Inquiry MiniLab

Should an environment be disturbed? One of the greatest challenges that we face as a species is balancing the needs of an ever-growing human global population with the needs of wildlife and the quality of the global environment. Imagine this scenario: The county commissioners are considering a proposal to build a road through the local pond and wetlands. This road will provide much-needed access to areas of work, and will help boost the economy of a struggling town. This will mean that the pond and surrounding wetlands must be drained and filled. Many people support the proposal, while many people oppose it. How will a compromise be reached?

Procedure

1. Prepare a comparison table in which you can list pros and cons.
2. Identify the pros and cons for draining the pond and building the road, for keeping the pond and not building the road, or for building the road elsewhere.

Analysis

1. **Design** a plan to support one course of action. What steps could you take to achieve your goal? Be prepared to share and defend your plan to the rest of the class.
2. **Think critically** about why decisions involving the environment are difficult to make.

Demonstration

OL AL Littoral Zone Make a collection of preserved organisms from the littoral zone of a lake or pond. Include larval stages of insects, snails, and floating aquatic plants. Organisms can be purchased from biological supply houses. **ASK STUDENTS:** ***What is the importance of having populations of these small animals and algae in the littoral zone of a lake or pond?*** They provide food for the larger animals such as fish, snakes, and turtles that inhabit the lake or pond.

Est. time: 5 min

S Skill Practice

BL OL Visual Literacy Using the examples in Figure 23, call on students randomly to identify the zone of a lake where they would be most likely to find different organisms. for example, lily pads in the littoral zone; fish in the limnetic zone; crayfish in the profundal zone

MiniLab 2

Inquiry MiniLab

For a lab worksheet, use your eTeacherEdition Online.

RUBRIC A rubric for evaluating MiniLabs is found on your eTeacherEdition Online.

Est. Time 20 min

Teaching Strategies

- Direct students to include any alternatives or compromises.
- Take this activity further by having the entire class develop a single course of action and a plan to accomplish that action.

Analysis

1. Evaluate plans individually. Students should mention that thorough research and presentation of facts is key. Be sure students have a strong defense of their plan.
2. Decisions regarding the environment are complicated by the many factors that must be considered. There are no easy decisions to be made when it comes to the environment.

LabManager™

Customize this lab with the LabManager™ CD-ROM.

W Writing Support

BL OL AL Persuasive Writing

Have students use research materials to write a short paper that argues for or against the restoration of wetlands in Florida, Louisiana, and other states. Papers supporting the restoration should mention the environmental importance of wetlands. Papers against the restoration should mention the expense of restoration and the economic importance of developing wetland areas.

S Skill Practice

BL OL AL Observe and Infer

Prepare a saltwater solution by adding 10 g of salt and a few drops of food coloring to 100 mL of water in a 150-mL beaker. Have students place 50 mL of distilled or tap water in a 100-mL beaker. Once the water has stopped moving, have students slowly add several drops of the saltwater solution to the freshwater using a dropper. **ASK STUDENTS:** ***What do you observe about the solutions?*** The saltwater solution initially sinks before dissolving into the freshwater. ***If the procedure had been reversed, what do you predict would have happened?*** The freshwater would have floated on the salt water. Relate the results to a transitional aquatic ecosystem.

Skill Practice

BL OL Compare and Contrast

Have students use the illustrations in this section to compare and contrast the freshwater and marine ecosystems that are described. Instruct them to emphasize differences in the abiotic factors, but point out the similarities in the overall ecosystem functions.

Figure 24 Bogs are a type of wetland characterized by moist, decaying plant material and dominated by mosses.

Transitional Aquatic Ecosystems

In many areas, aquatic ecosystems do not look like a stream or a pond or even an ocean. In fact, many aquatic environments are a combination of two or more different environments. These areas, which ecologists call transitional aquatic ecosystems, can be areas where land and water or salt water and freshwater intermingle. Wetlands and estuaries are common examples of transitional aquatic ecosystems.

Wetlands Areas of land such as marshes, swamps, and bogs that are saturated with water and that support aquatic plants are called **wetlands.** Plant species that grow in the moist, humid conditions of wetlands include duckweed, pond lilies, cattails, sedges, mangroves, cypress, and willows. Bogs, like the cedar bog shown in **Figure 24,** are wet and spongy areas of decomposing vegetation that also support many species of organisms. Wetlands have high levels of species diversity. Many amphibians, reptiles, birds (such as ducks and herons), and mammals (such as raccoons and mink) live in wetlands. W

Estuaries Another important transitional ecosystem is an estuary, shown in **Figure 25.** Estuaries are among the most diverse ecosystems, rivaled only by tropical rain forests and coral reefs. An **estuary** (ES chuh wer ee) is an ecosystem that is formed where freshwater from a river or stream merges with salt water from the ocean. Estuaries are places of transition, from freshwater to saltwater and from land to sea, that are inhabited by a wide variety of species. Algae, seaweeds, and marsh grasses are the dominant producers. However, many animals, including a variety of worms, oysters, and crabs, depend on detritus for food. Detritus (dih TRY tus) is comprised of tiny pieces of organic material.

Mangrove trees also can be found in tropical estuaries, such as the Everglades National Park in Florida, where they sometimes form swamps. Many species of marine fishes and invertebrates, such as shrimp, use estuaries as nurseries for their young. Waterfowl, such as ducks and geese, depend on estuary ecosystems for nesting, feeding, and migration rest areas. S

VOCABULARY
ACADEMIC VOCABULARY
Comprise
to be made up of
Your community is comprised of your family, your classmates, and people who live nearby.

Figure 25 Salt-tolerant plants above the low-tide line dominate estuaries formed in temperate areas.
***Infer** how an estuary would differ in a tropical area.*

Caption Question Fig. 25 In a tropical area, an estuary would have mangrove trees as the dominant salt-tolerant plants.

> *"The objective of education is to prepare the young to educate themselves throughout their lives."*
>
> –Robert Maynard Hutchins

Salt marshes are transitional ecosystems similar to estuaries. Salt-tolerant grasses dominate above the low-tide line, and seagrasses grow in submerged areas of salt marshes. Salt marshes support different species of animals, such as shrimp and shellfish.

Marine Ecosystems

Connection to Earth Science Earth is sometimes called "the water planet." As such, marine ecosystems have a significant impact on the planet. For example, through photosynthesis, marine algae consume carbon dioxide from the atmosphere and produce over 50 percent of the atmosphere's oxygen. Additionally, the evaporation of water from oceans eventually provides the majority of precipitation—rain and snow. Like ponds and lakes, oceans are separated into distinct zones.

R **Intertidal zone** The **intertidal** (ihn tur TY dul) **zone** is a narrow band where the ocean meets land. Organisms that live in this zone must be adapted to the constant changes that occur as daily tides and waves alternately submerge and expose the shore. The intertidal zone is further divided into vertical zones, as illustrated in **Figure 26.** The area of the spray zone is dry most of the time. It is only during high tides that this part of the shoreline is sprayed with salt water, and few plants and animals are able to live in this environment. The high-tide zone is under water only during high tides. However, this area receives more water than the spray zone, so more plants and animals are able to live there. The mid-tide zone undergoes severe disruption twice a day as the tides cover and uncover the shoreline with water. Organisms in this area must be adapted to long periods of air and water. The low-tide zone is covered with water unless the tide is unusually low and is the most populated area of the intertidal zone. D

Reading Check **Describe** environmental variation in intertidal zones.

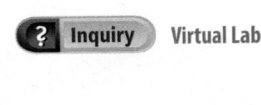

Inquiry Virtual Lab

W

Figure 26 The intertidal zone is further divided into zones where different communities exist.
Compare and contrast** the zones illustrated in* ***Figures 23** and **26.

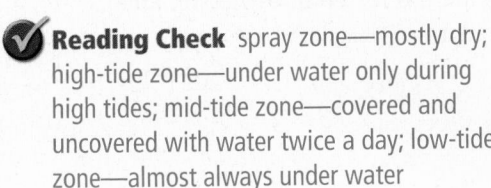

W Writing Support

BL OL AL Technical Writing
Have students prepare a trifold tourist brochure for a marine ecosystem. Instruct students to include descriptions of the abiotic factors encountered (such as water temperature and salinity), species likely to be seen, and photos cut from magazines or hand-drawn illustrations.

R Reading Strategy

OL Activate Background Vocabulary
ASK STUDENTS: ***Three vocabulary terms in this section and two other terms include the word zone. What comes to mind when you hear or see the word zone?*** Student responses will vary but should include an indication of an area. ***Infer the meanings of the five zone words.*** *Intertidal zone,* for example, implies the area between the tides.

D Develop Concepts

BL Integrate Geology
SAY TO STUDENTS: ***Geology determines the features along coastal ecosystems.***
ASK STUDENTS: ***What descriptions are used to define intertidal zones along coasts?*** Responses will vary, but should include a sandy beach, a pebble beach, and a rocky coast.

Caption Question Fig. 26 The zones of both lakes and oceans are determined by depth and distance from shore. For the intertidal zone, depth determines exposure to the tide.

Reading Check spray zone—mostly dry; high-tide zone—under water only during high tides; mid-tide zone—covered and uncovered with water twice a day; low-tide zone—almost always under water

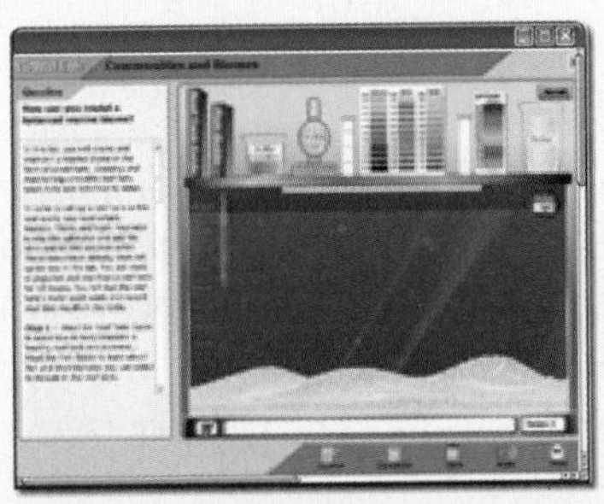

Inquiry Virtual Lab Students will populate a saltwater aquarium and monitor the conditions to ensure a healthy marine biome.

Develop Concepts

BL OL AL Classroom Debate Some people support the use of the ocean as a dumping ground for human wastes. They suggest that the ocean volume minimizes the effects of the waste. Other people suggest that the ocean should be considered a support system for life on Earth. Have students defend their viewpoints using scientific data.

D Develop Concepts

BL OL Activity Draw a square on the board and divide it into four smaller squares. In each section place one of the following terms: *benthic zone, aphotic zone, photic zone,* and *abyssal zone.* Call on students at random to add descriptions for each of the ocean's zones.

Develop Concepts

BL Activity Place several beakers of water with different temperatures around the room: one with ice cubes, one at room temperature, and one containing hot water. Place a thermometer in each beaker. Drop a single drop of food coloring into each of the beakers. Tell students not to disturb the water, but to record their observations, including the temperature of the water. Have them move from beaker to beaker until they have had a chance to observe all of them. The water moves at different rates—slower in cold water and faster in warm water.

OL AL ASK STUDENTS: ***Why does warm water move faster than cold water?*** The molecules in warm water have more kinetic energy than the molecules in cold water. ***How does this information apply to currents in the photic and aphotic zones?*** Currents in the photic zone will move faster than currents in the aphotic zone because water in the photic zone is warmer.

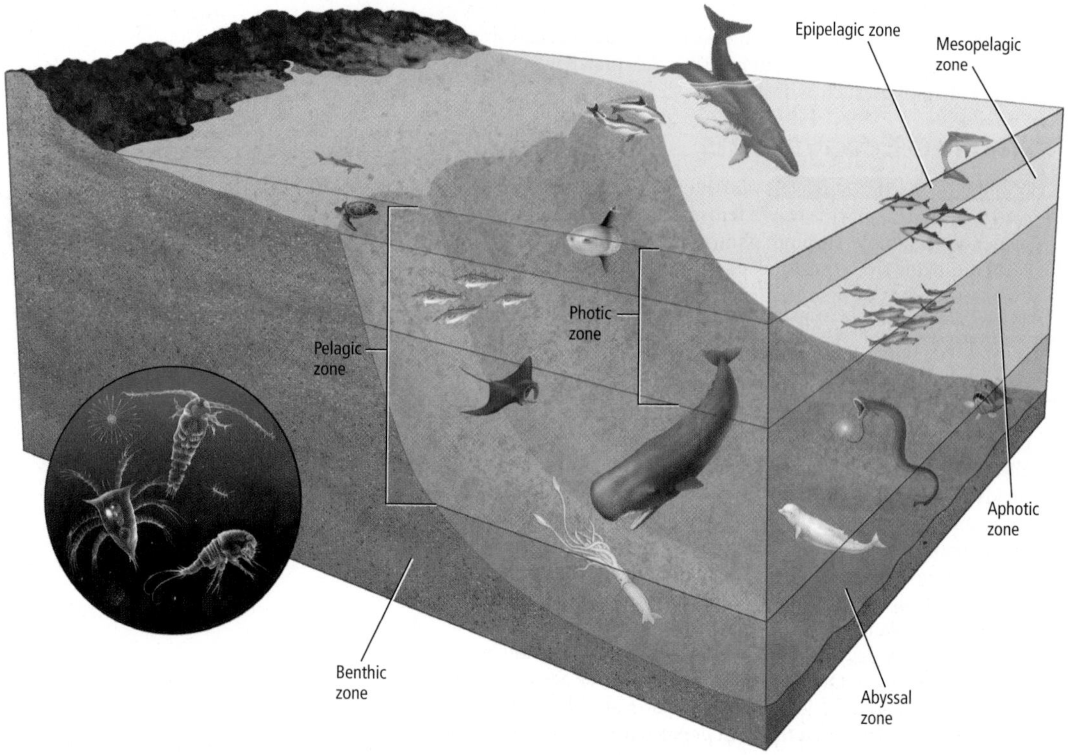

Figure 27 Producers are found in the photic zone. Consumers live in the pelagic, abyssal, and benthic zones.

Open ocean ecosystems As illustrated in **Figure 27,** the zones in the open ocean include the pelagic (puh LAY jihk) zone, abyssal (uh BIH sul) zone, and benthic zone. The area to a depth of about 200 m of the pelagic zone is the **photic zone,** also called the euphotic zone. The photic zone is shallow enough that sunlight is able to penetrate. As depth increases, light decreases. Autotrophic organisms in the photic zone include surface seaweeds and plankton. Animals in the photic zone include many species of fish, sea turtles, jellyfish, whales, and dolphins. Many of these animals feed on plankton, but others feed on larger species. The photic zone is subdivided into the epipelagic zone and the mesopelagic zone, as shown in **Figure 27.**

Below the photic zone lies the **aphotic zone,** an area where sunlight is unable to penetrate. This region of the pelagic zone remains in constant darkness and generally is cold, but there is thermal layering with a mixing of warm and cold ocean currents. Organisms that depend on light energy to survive cannot live in the aphotic zone.

The **benthic zone** is the area along the ocean floor that consists of sand, silt, and dead organisms. In shallow benthic zones, sunlight can penetrate to the bottom of the ocean floor. As depth increases, light and temperature decrease. Species diversity tends to decrease with depth, except in areas with hydrothermal vents, where shrimp, crabs, and many species of tubeworms are found. Many species of fishes, octopuses, and squids live in the benthic zone. D

VOCABULARY

WORD ORIGIN

Photic
comes from the Greek word *photos,* meaning *light.*

Research Citation

Hands-On Activities Educational research indicates that students perform better in classrooms where they are given opportunities for hands-on activities. Students' attitudes and understanding improve when they are interested in the lesson and understand how they can apply what they are learning. (Wenglinsky, 2000)

Research bibliography on pages 32T–34T

The deepest region of the ocean is called the **abyssal zone.** Water in this area is very cold. Most organisms in this zone rely on food materials that drift down from the zones above. However, on the seafloor along the boundaries of Earth's plates, hydrothermal vents spew large amounts of hot water, hydrogen sulfide, and other minerals. Scientists have found bacterial communities existing in these locations that can use the sulfide molecules for energy. These organisms are at the bottom of a food chain that includes invertebrates, such as clams and crabs, and vertebrates, such as fishes.

Coastal ocean and coral reefs One of the world's largest coral reefs is off the southern coast of Florida. Coral reefs are among the most diverse ecosystems. They are widely distributed in warm shallow marine waters. Coral reefs form natural barriers along continents that protect shorelines from erosion. The dominant organisms in coral reefs are corals. When you think of coral, you might picture a hard, stony structure, but this is only the framework secreted by tiny animal polyps. Corals are soft-bodied invertebrates that live in the stonelike structures.

Most coral polyps have a symbiotic relationship with algae called zooxanthellae (zoo uh zan THEL uh). These algae provide corals with food, and in turn, the coral provides protection and access to light for the algae. Corals also feed by extending tentacles to obtain plankton from the water. Other coral reef animals include species of microorganisms, sea slugs, octopuses, sea urchins, sea stars, and fishes. **Figure 28** shows only a small portion of the diversity of Florida's coral reef.

Like all ecosystems, coral reefs are sensitive to changes in the environment. Changes that are the result of naturally occurring events, such as increased sediment from a tsunami, can cause the death of a reef. Human activities, such as land development and harvesting for calcium carbonate, also can damage or kill a coral reef. Today, ecologists monitor reefs and reef environments to help protect these delicate ecosystems.

Figure 28 Coral reefs off the southern tip of Florida are among the world's largest and most diverse reefs.

D

Section 3 Assessment

Section Summary

- Freshwater ecosystems include ponds, lakes, streams, rivers, and wetlands.
- Wetlands and estuaries are transitional aquatic ecosystems.
- Marine ecosystems are divided into zones that are classified according to abiotic factors.
- Estuaries and coral reefs are among the most diverse of all ecosystems.

Understand Main Ideas

1. MAIN Idea **List** the abiotic factors that are used to classify aquatic ecosystems.
2. **Apply** what you know about ponds. Do you think the same organisms that would live in a seasonal pond would live in a pond that existed year-round? Explain.
3. **Describe** an ecological function of an estuary.
4. **Describe** the zones of the open ocean.

Think Critically

5. **Infer** how autotrophs in the abyssal zone of the ocean are different from those of the photic zone.

MATH in Biology

6. In November 2004, the floodgates of Glen Canyon Dam opened in an attempt to improve the Colorado River habitat. The release topped 1161 m^3/s—four times the usual daytime flow. Based on this information, about how much water normally flows through the dam on a daily basis?

D Develop Concepts

OL Activity Pass a piece of coral around the classroom.

ASK STUDENTS: ***How is this different from what would be found on a coral reef?*** It is dead. There are no living polyps. Then pass around some beach sand containing small shells.

ASK STUDENTS: ***Describe the environment where these objects were found.*** Coastal zones often have sandy beaches with shells. Discuss both ecosystems with students.

Formative Assessment

Evaluation Describe aquatic ecosystems by giving one or two features or abiotic factors and randomly call on students to name the aquatic ecosystem. Return to the same aquatic system several times by giving different features or abiotic factors as clues.

Remediation Assign pairs of students to make a chart that shows each aquatic ecosystem, its abiotic characteristics, and its common biotic characteristics using information from the chapter.

Section 3 Assessment

1. depth, amount of sunlight that penetrates the water, and salinity
2. The species would be very different in a seasonal pond. For instance, long-lived fish could not survive in a pond that dried up every year. Other species, such as insects and plants, might be able to survive in both seasonal ponds and ponds that exist year round.
3. Estuaries are breeding grounds and nurseries for many species.
4. photic zone: light penetrates; aphotic zone: no light, mixed water temperatures; abyssal zone: where water is deepest and coldest; benthic zone: along ocean floor
5. Autotrophs in the abyssal zone are chemosynthetic bacteria, and those in the photic zone are photosynthetic algae.
6. 290.25 m^3/s

Assessment Online Quiz

In the Field

Purpose
Students will understand the importance of preserving untouched ecosystems.
UCP.5, C.4

Anticipatory Guide
Refer students to a map of Africa.
ASK STUDENTS: ***What do you think are environmental conditions and geography in central Africa?*** hot, thickly forested, mountainous in areas, swampy in areas, relatively unpopulated
SAY TO STUDENTS: ***This is one of the few places on Earth where biologists can study organisms that are basically unaffected by human activities.***

Background
Conservation biologists think human activities, including logging, resource extraction, agriculture, and animal poaching, will change the Megatransect study area in the future. Acknowledging the need for preservation, leaders in Gabon have designated certain forested areas as "protected." However, protected forests are not necessarily off-limits to loggers. The government has granted permits to several logging companies to cut trees in protected areas of Gabon, and logging is occurring in those areas today. The governments of Gabon and the Republic of the Congo have agreed to work toward designating 10 percent of their forests as national parks. Logging would not be allowed in these areas. The proposal for Gabon's first national park was based partly on data collected by the Megatransect project.

In the Field

Career: Wildlife Conservation Biologist

The Last Wild Place On Earth

Imagine you are hiking through a dense forest, thick with undergrowth and trailing vines. There are no roads or even footpaths. Sound like a nightmare? To wildlife conservation biologist Dr. Michael Fay, it's paradise.

Megatransect Fay is a conservation biologist who studies how human activities affect ecosystems. While working in central Africa, Fay realized that a vast, intact forest corridor untouched by human activities ran from the center of the continent to the Atlantic Ocean. Fay envisioned walking the length of this corridor to study what he called "the last wild place on Earth." He named this historic project Megatransect.

Through the heart of Africa Megatransect began in 1999. During the 15-month journey, Fay's team covered 3200 km on foot, traveling through the republics of Congo, Cameroon, and Gabon. Thirteen national parks have been created in Gabon as a result of Fay's work.

Megatransect data at work
Megatransect data are helping to define human impact in measurable terms. Using satellite and field data, conservation biologists have designed a global map called the Human Footprint, which describes the extent of human influence in central Africa.

The success of Megatransect led to the funding of Megaflyover, a 110,000-km journey over Africa in a small airplane. Fay began his eight-month flight in 2004. The plane was mounted with a high-resolution digital camera that was matched with a Global Positioning Satellite (GPS) in an attempt to build on data collected during Megatransect.

West Central Africa

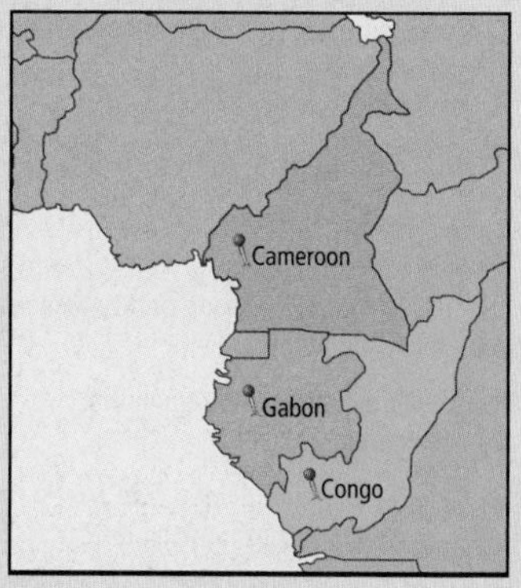

CAREERS in Biology

Oral Report Research to learn more about Fay's work. Develop an oral presentation describing the skills and knowledge that made the Megatransect project a success.

Activity
SAY TO STUDENTS: ***The Human Footprint illustrates the extent of human activity throughout the world. Study the Human Footprint from reliable links on the Internet and describe patterns you observe. Compare data from central Africa to other world areas. How can the Human Footprint help conservation biologists in their efforts to promote preservation of wild areas?*** The Human Footprint can help people visualize the effects of human activities.

WebQuest

BIOLAB

Design Your Own

FIELD INVESTIGATION: A POND IN A JAR

Background: Ecologists study parts of the biosphere. Each part is a unit containing many complex interactions between living things, such as food chains and food webs and the physical environment, the water cycle, and the mineral cycle. Smaller parts of the biosphere, such as communities and ecosystems, are the most practical for ecologists to explore and investigate.

Question: *What can we learn from studying a miniaturized biological ecosystem?*

Materials

glass or clear plastic gallon jars
pond water
pond mud
appropriate cultures and select living organisms
Choose any other materials that would be appropriate to this lab.

Safety Precautions

WARNING: *Use care when handling jars of pond water.*

Plan and Perform the Experiment

1. Read and complete the lab safety form.
2. Prepare an observation table as instructed.
3. Brainstorm and plan the step-by-step miniaturization of a pond community. Make sure your teacher has approved your plan before you proceed.
4. Decide on a particular aspect of your miniature community to evaluate and design an appropriate experiment. For example, you might test the effect of sunlight on your ecosystem.
5. Carry out your experiment.

Analyze and Conclude

1. **Explain** why you conducted your experiment slowly in a step-by-step manner. What might have happened if you poured everything into the jar all at once?
2. **Identify** the independent variable and the dependent variable.
3. **Design an experiment** Did your experiment have a control? Explain.
4. **Analyze and conclude** how your community differs from a pond community found in nature.
5. **Error analysis** How effective was your design? Explain possible sources of errors.

WRITING in Biology

Communicate Write a short story in which you describe what it would be like to be a microscopic animal living in your pond-in-a-jar.

BIOLAB

Design Your Own

Inquiry BioLab

For a lab worksheet, use your eTeacherEdition Online.

RUBRIC A rubric for evaluating BioLabs is found on your eTeacherEdition Online.

Est. Time 40–135 min

Content Background Students will design a miniature community in a jar. The phases of the design will help students recognize the layers and facets of an ecosystem.

Safety Precaution Approve lab safety forms before work begins.

Teaching Strategies

- An aquatic ecosystem is ideal because most students probably are familiar with ponds, and many of the organisms that thrive in a pond are microscopic to very small.
- If students establish the jars, seal the top of the experimental jar to test the soundness of the design by putting stress on the system. (Ecosystems in well-designed jars sealed in this manner have been known to thrive for years.)

Alternative Teaching Demo

Go through the design process with the class and have an example of a previously established ecosystem to observe.

Analyze and Conclude

1. Each component of the community must have time to become established in order to support the next phase of organisms being added.
2. Answers will depend on the students' experiment designs. The dependent variable most likely will be the viability of the ecosystem. The independent variable could be plant life, sunlight, or some other manipulated variable. Make sure students have only one independent variable.
3. The jar not sealed serves as a control to the experimental sealed jar.
4. Possible answer: My pond community is smaller and contains only microorganisms.
5. If the design was sound, the pond will thrive. If the design was flawed, the pond will visibly decline. Regardless of the outcome, have students suggest ways to improve the design.

WRITING in Biology

RUBRIC Use the modifiable rubric found on your eTeacherEdition Online to assess writing assignments.

Study Guide

ConnectED

Students can use the following to review the chapter.

Review

Vocabulary eGames
Vocabulary eFlashcards
Vocabulary PuzzleMaker

Assessment

Online Quizzes
Online Test Practice
Standardized Test Practice

Use the *ExamView® Assessment Suite* CD-ROM to:

- create multiple versions of tests
- create modified tests with one mouse click
- edit existing questions and add your own questions
- build tests aligned with state standards using built-in state curriculum tags
- change English tests to Spanish with one mouse click
- track students' progress using the Teacher Management System

Chapter 3 Study Guide

THEME FOCUS Change Specific organisms are present during different stages of succession.

BIG Idea Limiting factors and ranges of tolerance are factors that determine where terrestrial biomes and aquatic ecosystems exist.

Section 1 Community Ecology

community (p. 60)
limiting factor (p. 61)
tolerance (p. 61)
ecological succession (p. 62)
primary succession (p. 62)
climax community (p. 63)
secondary succession (p. 63)

MAIN Idea All living organisms are limited by factors in the environment.

- Abiotic and biotic limiting factors restrict the growth of a population within a community.
- Organisms have a range of tolerance for each limiting factor that they encounter.
- Primary succession occurs on areas of exposed rock or bare sand (no soil).
- Communities progress until there is little change in the composition of species.
- Secondary succession occurs as a result of a disturbance in a mature community.

Section 2 Terrestrial Biomes

weather (p. 65)
latitude (p. 65)
climate (p. 66)
tundra (p. 68)
boreal forest (p. 68)
temperate forest (p. 69)
woodland (p. 69)
grassland (p. 70)
desert (p. 70)
tropical savanna (p. 71)
tropical seasonal forest (p. 71)
tropical rain forest (p. 72)

MAIN Idea Ecosystems on land are grouped into biomes primarily based on the plant communities within them.

- Latitude affects terrestrial biomes according to the angle at which sunlight strikes Earth.
- Latitude, elevation, ocean currents, and other abiotic factors determine climate.
- Two major abiotic factors define terrestrial biomes.
- There are nine major terrestrial biomes. There are two additional terrestrial regions that do not fit into these major categories.

Section 3 Aquatic Ecosystems

sediment (p. 75)
littoral zone (p. 76)
limnetic zone (p. 77)
plankton (p. 77)
profundal zone (p. 77)
wetlands (p. 78)
estuary (p. 78)
intertidal zone (p. 79)
photic zone (p. 80)
aphotic zone (p. 80)
benthic zone (p. 80)
abyssal zone (p. 81)

MAIN Idea Aquatic ecosystems are grouped based on abiotic factors such as water flow, depth, distance from shore, salinity, and latitude.

- Freshwater ecosystems include ponds, lakes, streams, rivers, and wetlands.
- Wetlands and estuaries are transitional aquatic ecosystems.
- Marine ecosystems are divided into zones that are classified according to abiotic factors.
- Estuaries and coral reefs are among the most diverse of all ecosystems.

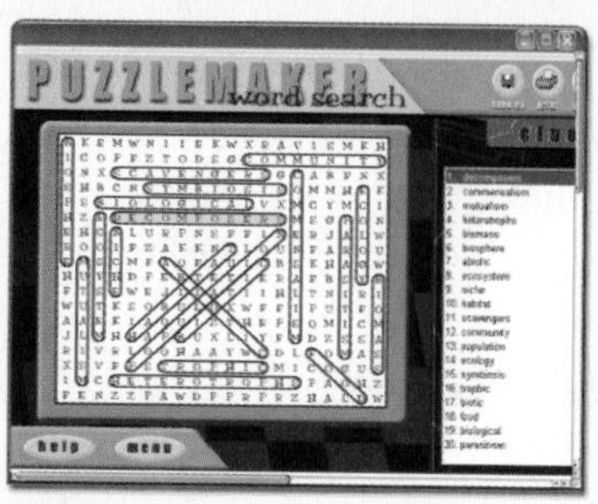

Review Vocabulary PuzzleMaker

For additional practice with vocabulary, have students access the Vocabulary PuzzleMaker online.

Review Vocabulary eGames

Section 1

Vocabulary Review

Choose the correct italicized term to complete each sentence.

1. An area of forest that experiences very little change in species composition is a *climax community/primary succession.*
2. The amount of oxygen in a fish tank is a *tolerance zone/limiting factor* that affects the number of fish that can live in the tank.
3. *Ecological succession/Secondary succession* describes the events that take place on a hillside that has experienced a destructive mudslide.

Understand Main Ideas

4. Lack of iron in the photic zone of the open ocean restricts the size of plankton populations. Iron is what kind of factor for marine plankton?
   A. distribution
   B. tolerance
   C. limiting
   D. biotic

For questions 5-7, use the generalized graph below that describes an organism's tolerance to a particular factor.

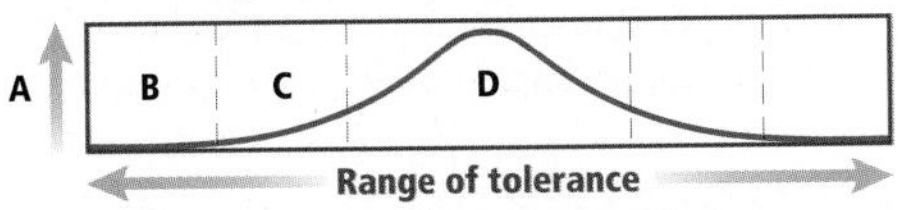

5. According to the graph, which letter represents the zone of intolerance for the factor in question?
   A. A **C.** C
   B. B **D.** D
6. What does the letter "D" represent in the graph?
   A. zone of intolerance
   B. zone of physiological stress
   C. optimum range
   D. upper limit
7. Which letter in the graph represents the zone of physiological stress?
   A. A **C.** C
   B. B **D.** D
8. Which place would you most likely find pioneer species growing?
   A. climax forest **C.** disturbed grassland
   B. coral reef **D.** newly formed volcano

Constructed Response

9. **CAREERS IN BIOLOGY** A state park and wildlife department stocks several bodies of water, including rivers and lakes, with rainbow trout. The trout survive but do not reproduce. In terms of tolerance, discuss what might be happening.

Use the image below to answer question 10.

10. **Short Answer** Describe how the successional stages would differ from primary succession.
11. **MAIN Idea** Explain why the concepts of limiting factors and tolerance are important in ecology.

Think Critically

12. **THEME FOCUS Change** Infer whether species diversity increases or decreases after a fire on a grassland. Explain your response.
13. **Generalize** the difference between a successional stage and a climax community.

Section 2

Vocabulary Review

Choose the vocabulary term from the Study Guide page that best fits each definition below.

14. the condition of the atmosphere
15. the average conditions in an area
16. a biome characterized by evaporation exceeding precipitation

Chapter 3

Assessment

Section 1

Vocabulary Review

1. climax community
2. limiting factor
3. Secondary succession

Understand Main Ideas

4. C
5. B
6. C
7. C
8. D

Constructed Response

9. The trout are in their zone of physiological stress due to some limiting factor, such as temperature.
10. Answers will vary, but the student should indicate that the successional stages would occur more rapidly and begin with a different set of organisms.
11. Limiting factors restrict the reproduction, existence, numbers, or distribution of populations. Ranges of tolerance provide additional information about how limiting factors act on populations.

Think Critically

12. Diversity increases when the habitat is disturbed and first building toward succession because species of more than one community are likely to be present.
13. A successional community has steadily changing plant and animal populations, but a climax community has a homeostatic balance between plant and animal populations.

Section 2

Vocabulary Review

14. weather
15. climate
16. desert

Understand Main Ideas
17. B
18. A
19. D
20. C
21. D

Constructed Response
22. Students should describe a tropical rain forest, tropical seasonal forest, or savanna.
23. Regional warming is causing the breakup of Antarctica's ice shelves. As temperature increases, icebergs prevent the adult penguins from getting enough food to feed their young.

Think Critically
24. Plant communities can be studied more easily, and they tend to exist in similar biomes. Animals in one biome may be very different from those in the same biome in a distant location.
25. temperate grassland

Section 3

Vocabulary Review
26. estuary
27. photic zone
28. intertidal zone

Understand Main Ideas

17. Which best describes the distribution of communities on a tall mountain?
A. Evergreen forests exist up to the tree line and no vegetation is found above the tree line.
B. Several communities might be stratified according to altitude and might end in an ice field at the top of the highest mountains.
C. As altitude increases, tall trees are replaced by shorter trees, and ultimately are replaced by grasses.
D. Tundra-like communities exist at the top of the highest mountains, and deserts are found at the lower elevations.

Use the diagram below to answer question 18.

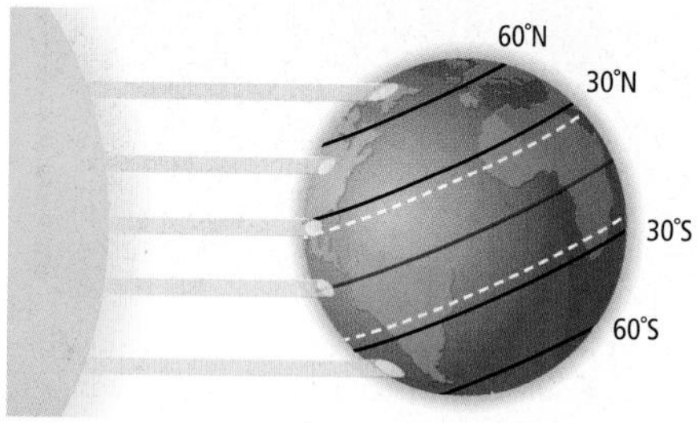

18. Which area receives the least amount of solar energy per unit of surface area?
A. north of 60°N and south of 60°S
B. south of 30°N and north of 30°N
C. between the Tropic of Cancer and the Tropic of Capricorn
D. north and south temperate zones

19. What is the name for large geographic areas with similar climax communities?
A. assemblages
B. communities
C. successions
D. biomes

20. Which biome occurs in the United States and once contained huge herds of grazing herbivores?
A. boreal forest
B. temperate forest
C. grassland
D. savanna

21. Which land biome contains the greatest species diversity?
A. tundra
B. grassland
C. desert
D. tropical rain forest

Constructed Response

Use the image below to answer question 22.

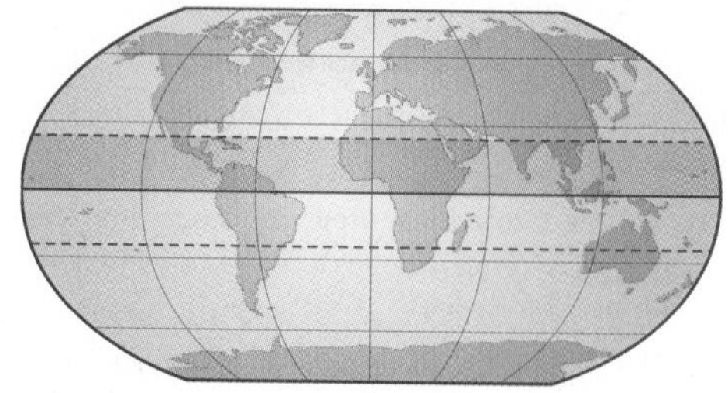

22. Open Ended Describe a biome that might be found in the shaded area shown above.

23. Open Ended In December 2004, a huge iceberg caused a large number of penguin chicks to die of starvation. Ice shelves broke apart in areas where the air temperature increased. The parents of the penguins were cut off from their food source. How is this an example of temperature as a limiting factor?

Think Critically

24. MAIN Idea Suggest why land biomes are classified according to their plant characteristics rather than according to the animals that inhabit them.

25. Classify a biome that is warm to hot in the summer and cool or cold in the winter and that receives approximately 50–89 cm of precipitation annually.

Section 3

Vocabulary Review

Replace the underlined words with the correct terms from the Study Guide page.

26. A(n) area where freshwater and salt water meet provides habitat for a diversity of organisms.

27. The well-lit portion of the ocean is the area where all of the photosynthetic organisms live.

28. The shoreline of the ocean contains communities that are layered depending on how long they are submerged by tides.

Understand Main Ideas

29. Where is the largest percentage of water located?
A. groundwater **C.** oceans
B. rivers **D.** glaciers

Use the diagram below to answer question 30.

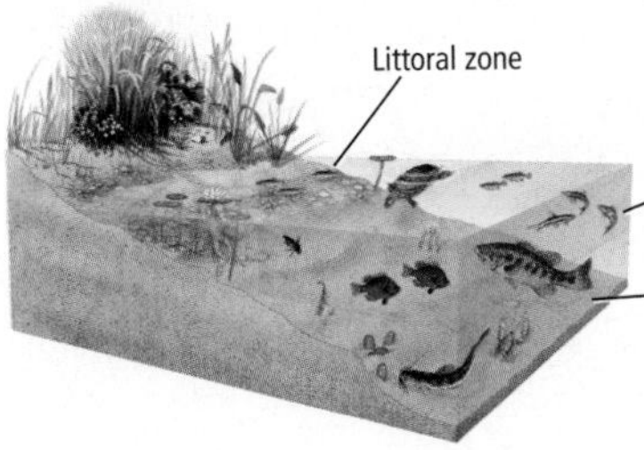

30. In which area of the lake is there likely to be the greatest diversity of plankton?
A. littoral zone **C.** profundal zone
B. limnetic zone **D.** aphotic zone

31. Which best describes the intertidal zone on a rocky shore?
A. The dominant low-energy community is likely to be an estuary.
B. The communities are adapted to shifting sands due to incoming waves.
C. The communities are stratified from the high-tide line to the low-tide line.
D. The organisms in the community constantly require dissolved oxygen.

Constructed Response

32. Short Answer How is light a limiting factor in oceans?

33. Short Answer Describe characteristics of an estuary.

34. Open Ended Describe adaptations of an organism living in the abyssal zone of the ocean.

Think Critically

35. Predict the consequences a drought would have on a river such as the Mississippi River.

36. MAIN Idea Compare the intertidal zone with the photic zone in terms of tidal effect.

Summative Assessment

37. BIG Idea Explain the importance of limiting factors and ranges of tolerance for a specific biome or ecosystem.

38. WRITING in Biology Choose a biome other than the one in which you live. Write an essay explaining what you think you would like and what you think you would dislike about living in your chosen biome.

DBQ Document-Based Questions

"Leaf mass per area (LMA) measures the leaf dry-mass investment per unit of light-intercepting leaf area deployed. Species with high LMA have a thicker leaf blade or denser tissue, or both."

"Plant ecologists have emphasized broad relationships between leaf traits and climate for at least a century. In particular, a general tendency for species inhabiting arid and semi-arid regions to have leathery, high-LMA leaves has been reported. Building high-LMA leaves needs more investment per unit leaf area. Construction cost per unit leaf mass varies relatively little between species: leaves with high protein content (typically low-LMA leaves) tend to have low concentrations of other expensive compounds such as lipids or lignin, and high concentrations of cheap constituents such as minerals. Leaf traits associated with high LMA (for example, thick leaf blade; small, thick-walled cells) have been interpreted as adaptations that allow continued leaf function (or at least postpone leaf death) under very dry conditions, at least in evergreen species."

Data obtained from: Wright, I.J. et al. The worldwide leaf economics spectrum. *Nature* 428:821–828.

39. From the information presented, would you expect leaves on trees in the tropical rain forest to contain large quantities of lipids? Explain your answer in terms of energy investment.

40. Hypothesize how high-LMA leaves are adapted for dry conditions.

Understand Main Ideas

29. C
30. B
31. C

Constructed Response

32. Photosynthetic autotrophs depend on light for their energy. As light decreases, the numbers of photosynthetic plankton and other autotrophs decrease.

33. Estuaries are low-energy environments where freshwater and saltwater mix. Many food chains begin with detritus. The diversity is extremely high due to the mixing of environments.

34. Answers will vary, but students might indicate that they would have adaptations to survive extreme pressures, bioluminescence to attract prey, or the ability to detect dead organisms that drift down from layers above.

Think Critically

35. The river's level would drop, and its flow and oxygen levels would decrease. Some species, such as insect larvae, might be pushed into their zone of physiological stress, while others, such as catfish and carp, might be able to tolerate the changes without noticeable effect.

36. Tides have a much greater effect on the intertidal zone as land is alternately exposed and submerged in this high-energy environment. The photic zone extends to a depth of about 200 meters regardless of the tide.

Summative Assessment

37. Answers will vary depending on biome or ecosystem chosen. Answers should include reference to climate, including air or water temperatures and weather, which determine what type of vegetation will grow, thereby determining the types of animals. Limiting factors such as amount of potable water and food sources should also be referenced.

WRITING in Biology

RUBRIC Use the modifiable rubric found on your eTeacherEdition Online to assess writing assignments.

38. Answers will depend on the biome chosen and whether the student thinks they would like or dislike living in the biome. Students should mention abiotic and biotic factors.

DBQ Document-Based Questions

Ian J. Wright, Peter B. Reich. 2004. The worldwide leaf economics spectrum. *Nature* 428: 821–828.

39. No. Too much energy investment would be required in a leaf that is not evergreen.

40. High-LMA leaves incorporate larger amounts of high-energy compounds, such as lignin and lipids. To get a return on energy investment, the leaves must be constructed to live longer.

Assessment Online Test Practice

Standardized Test Practice

Multiple Choice

1. A
2. D
3. A
4. B
5. D
6. C
7. C
8. C

Short Answer

9. Answers may vary. Possible answers include the following.
   A. Both: ground freezes completely at certain times of the year; not much precipitation.
   B. Boreal forest: trees and shrubs can grow in the soil; short summers and cold winters.
   C. Tundra: layer of permafrost a few centimeters below the surface; only shallow-rooted plants can grow.
10. A pioneer species breaks down rock, thereby creating soil that allows plants to grow. Eventually, other animals and plants can survive in the area.
11. Answers will vary. One possible answer is humans have organs—such as the stomach, brain, and lungs—that perform specific activities. Also humans have organ systems that perform particular functions, such as digestion, respiration, movement, and circulation. The activities of the organs and the organ systems are coordinated to maintain homeostasis.
12. This is a symbiotic relationship, specifically mutualism, because both organisms benefit from the interaction.
13. Animals in the photic zone are those that feed on photosynthesizing plants or other organisms that consume producers. There are no producers in the aphotic zone, so only animals can live there that do not depend on living producers or on light.
14. Answers can vary. Possible answers include the following.
   A. Gardener can add nitrogen-containing fertilizer to the soil.
   B. Gardener can grow plants, such as legumes, that are nitrogen fixing.

Standardized Test Practice

Cumulative

Multiple Choice

1. If science can be characterized as discovery, then technology can be characterized as which?
   A. application
   B. information
   C. manufacturing
   D. reasoning

Use the illustration below to answer questions 2 and 3.

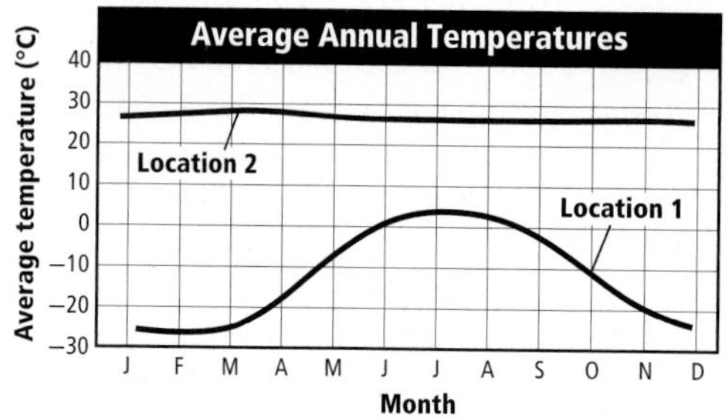

2. Based on the graph above, which term describes Location 2?
   A. oceanic
   B. polar
   C. temperate
   D. tropical

3. Suppose that in Location 2 there is very little rainfall during the year. What would be the name of that biome in this region?
   A. desert
   B. tundra
   C. temperate forest
   D. tropical rain forest

4. Which process is associated with long-term cycling of matter through the biosphere?
   A. breakdown of organic material by decomposers
   B. formation and weathering of minerals in rocks
   C. formation of compounds used for food by living organisms
   D. movement of fresh water from the land into bodies of water through run-off

Use the illustration below to answer question 5.

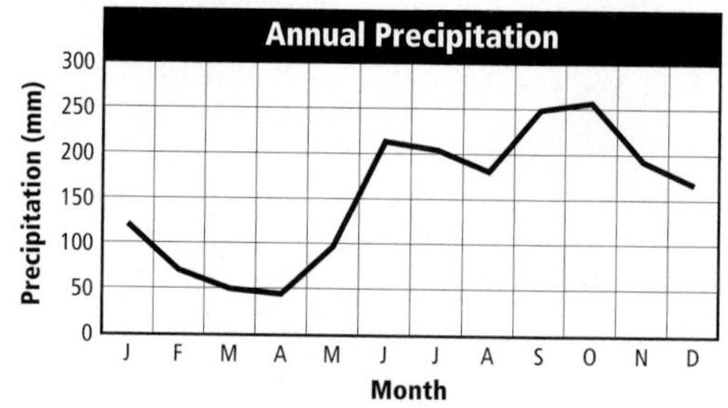

5. Look at the information in the graph. From what kind of biome are these data probably taken?
   A. desert
   B. tundra
   C. temperate forest
   D. tropical rain forest

6. Which system of measurement is the basis for many of the SI units?
   A. binary
   B. English
   C. metric
   D. number

7. Which of these organisms is a decomposer?
   A. a bacterium that makes food from inorganic compounds
   B. a clam that takes in water and filters food
   C. a fungus that gets nutrients from dead logs
   D. a plant that makes food using sunlight

8. Which distinguishes scientific ideas from popular opinions?
   A. Popular opinions are always rational and logical.
   B. Popular opinions depend on research and evidence.
   C. Scientific ideas are always testable and repeatable.
   D. Scientific ideas depend on anecdotes and hearsay.

Short Answer

9. How is a tundra similar to and different from a boreal forest? Use a Venn diagram to organize information about the similarities and differences of these biomes.

10. What is the role of a pioneer species in primary succession?

11. Give two examples of how the human body shows the living characteristic of organization.

12. Suppose a certain insect species lives only in a specific species of tree. It feeds off the sap of the tree and produces a chemical that protects the tree from certain fungi. What kind of relationship is this?

13. Why would you expect to find different animals in the photic and aphotic zones of the ocean?

14. Suppose a gardener learns that the soil in a garden has low nitrogen content. Describe two ways to increase the nitrogen available for plants in the garden.

15. Explain how the establishment of a climax community through primary succession differs from the establishment of a climax community that occurs through secondary succession.

16. Why is the ability to adapt an important characteristic of living things?

Extended Response

Use the illustration below to answer question 17.

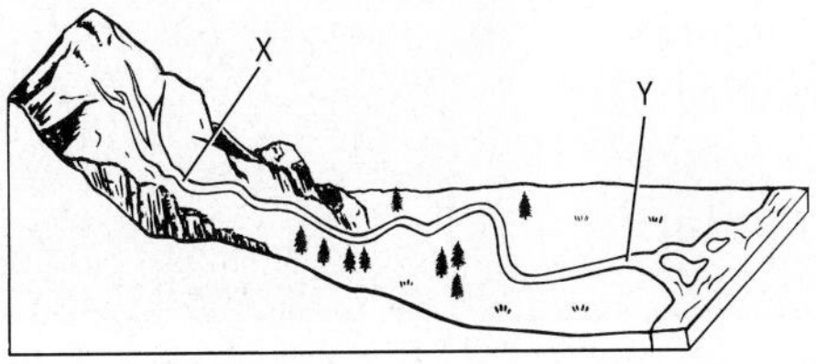

17. Based on the information in the illustration above, what can you infer about the major differences between the freshwater ecosystems at Point X and Point Y?

18. Suppose a nonnative species is introduced into an ecosystem. What is one kind of community interaction you might expect from the other organisms in that ecosystem?

Essay Question

Suppose there is a dense temperate forest where people do not live. After a few hot, dry months, forest fires have started to spread through the forest area. There is no threat of the fires reaching areas inhabited by humans. Some people are trying to get the government to intervene to control the fires, while others say the fires should be allowed to run their natural course.

Using the information in the paragraph above, answer the following question in essay format.

19. Explain which side of this debate you would support. Provide evidence based on what you know about change in ecosystems.

NEED EXTRA HELP?

If You Missed Question . . .	1	2	3	4	5	6	7	8	9	10	11	12	13	14	15	16	17	18	19
Review Section . . .	3.2	3.2	3.2	2.3	3.3	1.2	2.2	1.3	3.2	3.1	1.1	2.1	3.3	2.3	3.1	1.1	3.3	3.3	3.1, 3.2

15. Primary succession: A climax community can be established only after rock is broken down into soil, species move in, and equilibrium is established.
    Secondary succession: A climax community can be established more quickly because soil is already present, allowing organisms and seeds to move in from surrounding areas.
16. Being able to adapt enables a species to survive and pass genes to offspring.

Extended Response

17. Possible answers: At point X, the water is probably carrying more sediment than at point Y, since it is moving faster. Some kinds of floating plants can live in the water. The water at point X is fast moving, so it probably has a higher exchange of gases. This affects which organisms can survive. The slow-moving water at point Y allows for more plants to take root in the stream than at point X. It also allows for more animal populations to be established there, because they do not have to withstand such fast currents. At point Y, the water *may* begin to mix with ocean water, possibly causing it to have a higher salinity.
18. Because the non-native species did not evolve in the same area, it might lack the ability to survive certain aspects of the ecosystem. The relationship might be one of predation, as other native organisms eat the organism. On the other hand, native organisms did not evolve along with the non-native one, so they may lack defenses to deal with the nonnative organism, or a way to prey upon it. The non-native organism might out compete the native organisms and replace them in the ecosystem.

Essay Question

19. Answers can vary. One side could argue that forest fires are part of the natural "life" of forests. If forests are partly destroyed by fire, then secondary succession takes place and eventually a climax community is established. From that viewpoint, the forest fires should be allowed to occur naturally without human intervention. The other side could argue that human intervention makes the occurrence of forest fires much less devastating than the fires would be naturally. Fires destroy natural habitats and kill many animals. Also, there may be endangered species or other factors to consider. Therefore, humans should intervene to stop the fires.

Chapter 4 Organizer:
Population Ecology

LabManager™
Customize any lab with the LabManager™ CD-ROM.

Essential Questions	National Science Standards	Materials and Planning	
		Estimated times include cleanup and disposal, but do not include teacher prep time. For cleanup and disposal guidelines, see page 39T.	Est. Time (min)
Section 1 1. What are the characteristics of populations and how they are distributed? 2. What are the differences between density-independent and density-dependent limiting factors? 3. What are the similarities between the different models used to quantify the growth of a population? 4. How does carrying capacity affect reproductive rates?	UCP.1–3; A.1, A.2; C.4, C.5; F.2, F.4, F.5, F.6; G.1,G.2	**Launch Lab,** p. 90: textbook	20–25
		Demonstration, p. 92: magazine photos of populations	5–10
Section 2 1. What aspects affect human population growth? 2. What are the trends in human population growth? 3. What are the age structures of representative nongrowing, slowly growing, and rapidly growing countries? 4. What might be the consequences of continued population growth?	UCP.1–3; A.1, A.2; C.4, C.5, C.6; F.4, F.5; G.1,G.3	**MiniLab 1,** p. 101: textbook	20
		Demonstration, p. 104: information about age structures for several developed and developing countries	10
		BioLab, p. 107: marigold seeds or radish seeds, 9-cm plastic pots, clean potting soil, rulers, shallow tray for pots, small garden trowels, masking tape, permanent markers, balance (accurate to 0.1 gram), watering can	150, 15 per week

Suggested Time for Each Lesson

Class	Chapter Opener	Section 1	Section 2	Assessment
Basic	90 min	135 min	135 min	45 min
General	45 min	60 min	75 min	45 min
Honors	25 min	90 min	65 min	45 min

ConnectED

connectED.mcgraw-hill.com

Access interactive learning opportunities and teaching resources using these icons located throughout your StudentWorks™ Plus Online and eTeacherEdition Online.

Chapter 4 Section Resources

FAST FILE Unit 1 Resources:
Launch Lab Worksheet*
Study Guide (English/Spanish)*
Section Quick Check

Reading Essentials 4.1
Science Notebook 4.1*

FAST FILE Unit 1 Resources:
MiniLab Worksheet*
BioLab Worksheet*
Study Guide (English/Spanish)*
Section Quick Check

Reading Essentials 4.2
Science Notebook 4.2*

Additional Chapter 4 Resources

FAST FILE Unit 1 Resources:
Chapter Diagnostic Test
Concept Mapping*
Real-World Biology
Enrichment
Chapter Tests A, B, and C

Transparencies:
Bellringer Transparencies*
Biology Concepts Transparencies*

Lab Resources:
Laboratory Manual*
Probeware Lab Manual*
Forensics Lab Manual*
Pre-AP Lab Manual*
Open Inquiry in Biology*
Guided Inquiry in Biology*

Technology

Teaching Tools:
eTeacherEdition Online
Classroom Presentation Toolkit CD-ROM*
LabManager™ CD-ROM*
Video Lab DVD*
Virtual Lab CD-ROM*
What's BIOLOGY Got To Do With It?
StudentWorks™ Plus Online*

Chapter Assessment Tools:
Classroom Presentation Toolkit CD-ROM*
ExamView® Assessment Suite CD-ROM

Web-Based Resources:
- StudentWorks™ Plus Online
- eTeacherEdition Online
- Animations*
- The Interactive Time Line*
- Interactive Tables*
- Online Quizzes
- Online Test Practice
- Standardized Test Practice
- Virtual Labs*
- Multilingual eGlossary*
- Vocabulary eGames*
- Vocabulary eFlashcards
- WebQuests
- Personal Tutors

While all resources listed are appropriate for English learners, the * indicates resources with a strong visual or hands-on component for EL.

Teaching strategies and activities have been coded for differentiated instruction.

AL Activities for students working above grade level	**OL** Activities for students working on grade level	**BL** Activities for students working below grade level	**EL** Activities for English learners (also ELL)	**COOP LEARN** Activities designed for small cooperative group work

CHAPTER 4

Launch Lab
A population of one?

Inquiry Launch Lab

For a lab worksheet, use your eTeacherEdition Online.

RUBRIC A rubric for evaluating Launch Labs is found on your eTeacherEdition Online.

Est. Time 20–25 min

Safety Precaution Approve lab safety forms before work begins.

Teaching Strategies
- Using the textbook definitions, discuss the terms with the class and develop a class definition and example for each term.
- When possible, use local organisms as examples.

Procedure
1. Read and complete the lab safety form.
2. In your assigned group, brainstorm and predict the meaning of the following terms: *population, population density, natality, mortality, emigration, immigration,* and *carrying capacity.*

Analysis
1. **Infer** whether it is possible to have a population of one. Explain your answer. An individual can constitute a population. Populations are described by geographic distribution, density, and growth rate. All three characteristics can be applied to an individual.
2. **Analyze** your definitions and determine whether a relationship exists between the terms. Explain. Answers will vary. Accept any answer where a relationship is supported.

CHAPTER 4

Population Ecology

ConnectED

Your one-stop online resource
connectED.mcgraw-hill.com

Video
Audio
Review
Inquiry
WebQuest
Assessment
Concepts in Motion
Multilingual eGlossary

Launch Lab
A population of one?

Ecologists study populations of living things. They also study how populations interact with each other and with the abiotic factors in the environment. But what exactly is a population? Are the deer shown on these pages a population? Is a single deer a population?

For a lab worksheet, use your StudentWorks™ Plus Online.

Inquiry Launch Lab

FOLDABLES®

Make a three-tab book using the labels shown. Use it to organize your notes on populations.

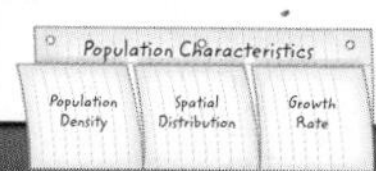

Differentiated Instruction

Above Level When working with students who perform above level, introduce new concepts by building on prior knowledge. Connecting new material to both academic and experiential knowledge that the students already have helps them to understand the relevance of what they are learning.

For more tips, see pages 14T–15T.

THEME FOCUS Homeostasis
Many factors influence homeostasis within a population.

BIG Idea Population growth is a critical factor in a species' ability to maintain homeostasis within its environment.

Section 1 • Population Dynamics
Section 2 • Human Population

THEMES

Scientific Inquiry Scientists study population characteristics to better understand growth and distribution of organisms.

Diversity Populations have different distributions and densities depending on the species represented in the population.

Energy Organisms in a population compete for energy sources, such as food and sunlight.

Homeostasis Homeostasis within a population is controlled by density-dependent and density-independent limiting factors.

Change Human population varies little overall, but can change greatly within small populations.

Introduce the Chapter

Populations

ASK STUDENTS: ***How do the deer in the larger photo represent part of a population?*** The deer are members of the same species that inhabit a particular area at a given time.

SAY TO STUDENTS: ***Just as the deer represent a population that interacts with its environment, so do the other organisms shown in the smaller photos. From studying different populations, scientists have learned some important principles that all populations share.***

BIG Idea

Recognize Cause and Effect

Divide the class into two groups. Ask the students in one group to compile a list of how populations can change. Three possible answers exist (increase, decrease, remain the same). Have the other group make a list of environmental factors that can cause a population to change. When students have finished, ask a student from the first group to read one way a population can change. Then have a student from the other group identify factors on their list that could be responsible for this change. Continue until the students in the first group have gone through their list. Tell students to make changes to their lists as they read the chapter. Sample answer: Students in the first group might list an increase in size as an example of how a population can change. Factors that the second group might list include an increased food supply, less competition from other populations, or improved climate conditions.

Section 1

MAIN Idea

BL OL AL

Population Dynamics

ASK STUDENTS: ***What are some observations you can make about populations of insects over the course of a year?*** Students might say that the populations of flies or mosquitoes go up in spring and summer and decline in fall. ***Do they die out completely in winter?*** A few individuals in each population find places to go over winter, and some migrate. Explain that density and growth rate are two population characteristics. Another characteristic is spatial distribution.

R Reading Strategy

EL **Vocabulary Chart** Ask students to look at the new vocabulary terms in this section and discuss what they know about them. Have students create a two-column chart with the terms in the left column. As they read, have them write the definitions in the right column.

D Develop Concepts

BL OL AL **Integrate Math** Tell students that the density of a population is calculated by dividing the number of organisms in the population by the area the population occupies.

ASK STUDENTS: ***Suppose that 15,000 black bass, 275 turtles, and 148,070 minnows live in a 1-hectare pond. A hectare is 100,000 m^2. What is the density of each population per square meter?*** 0.15 black bass/m^2, 0.0028 turtles/m^2, and 1.48 minnows/m^2

Section 1

Reading Preview

Essential Questions

- What are the characteristics of populations and how they are distributed?
- What are the differences between density-independent and density-dependent limiting factors?
- What are the similarities between the different models used to quantify the growth of a population?
- How does carrying capacity affect reproductive rates?

Review Vocabulary

population: the members of a single species that share the same geographic location at the same time

New Vocabulary

R

population density
dispersion
density-independent factor
density-dependent factor
population growth rate
emigration
immigration
carrying capacity

g Multilingual eGlossary

Population Dynamics

MAIN Idea Populations of species are described by density, spatial distribution, and growth rate.

Real-World Reading Link Have you ever observed a beehive or an ant farm? The population had certain characteristics that could be used to describe it. Ecologists study population characteristics that are used to describe all populations of organisms.

Population Characteristics

All species occur in groups called populations. There are certain characteristics that all populations have, such as population density, spatial distribution, and growth rate. These characteristics are used to classify all populations of organisms, including bacteria, animals, and plants.

D **Population density** One characteristic of a population is its **population density,** which is the number of organisms per unit area. For example, the population density of cattle egrets, shown with the water buffalo in **Figure 1,** is greater near the buffalo than farther away. Near the water buffalo, there might be three birds per square meter. Fifty meters from the water buffalo, the density of birds might be zero.

Spatial distribution Another characteristic of a population is called **dispersion**—the pattern of spacing of a population within an area. **Figure 2** shows the three main types of dispersion—uniform, clumped groups, and random. Black bears are typically dispersed in a uniform arrangement. American bison are dispersed in clumped groups or herds. White-tailed deer are dispersed randomly with unpredictable spacing. One of the primary factors in the pattern of dispersion for all organisms is the availability of resources such as food.

■ **Figure 1** The population density of the cattle egrets is greater near the water buffalo.
***Suggest** the type of dispersion you would expect these birds to have.*

■ **Caption Question Fig. 1** The birds exhibit a clumped dispersal pattern.

Demonstration

BL OL **Dispersal Comparison** Display photos obtained from magazines to provide examples of the concept of dispersal. Hold up a photo that shows a population.

SAY TO STUDENTS: ***Describe the dispersal of this population.*** Answers will vary. Est. time: 5–10 min

Visualizing Population Characteristics

Figure 2
Population density describes how many individual organisms live in a given area. Dispersion describes how the individuals are spaced within that area. Population range describes a species' distribution.

Black Bear

Dispersion: American black bear males usually are dispersed uniformly within territories as large as several hundred square kilometers. Females have smaller territories that overlap those of males.

Density: one bear per several hundred square kilometers

Black Bear Distribution (in purple)

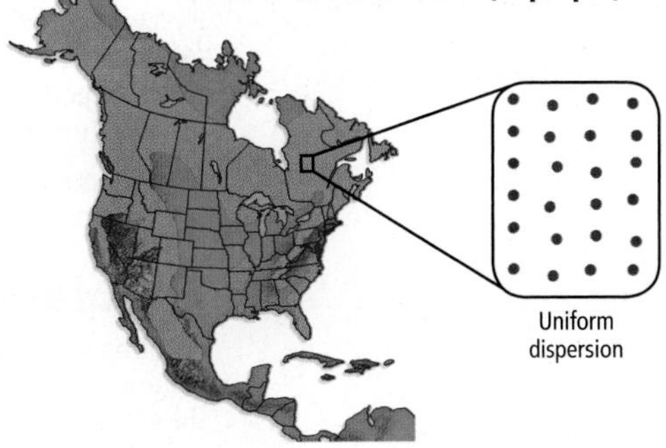

American Bison

Dispersion: American bison are found in clumped groups called herds.

Density: four bison/km^2 in Northern Yellowstone in 2000

Bison Distribution (historic range prior to 1865 in orange)

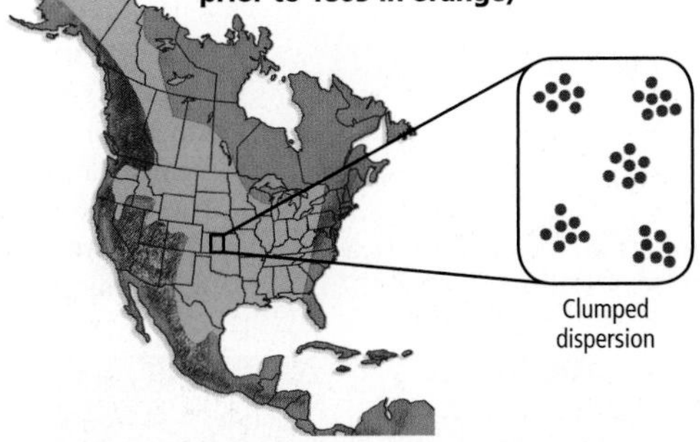

White-tailed Deer

Dispersion: White-tailed deer are dispersed randomly throughout appropriate habitats.

Density: 10 deer/km^2 in some areas of the northeastern United States

White-tailed Deer Distribution (in blue)

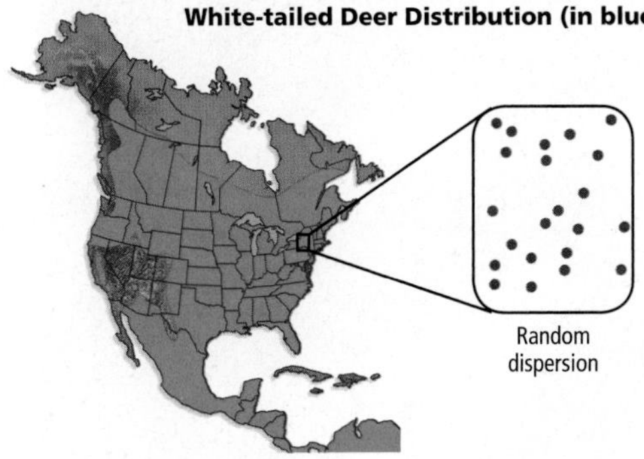

Concepts in Motion Animation

> *"What office is there which involves more responsibility, which requires more qualifications, and which ought, therefore, to be more honorable, than that of teaching?"*
>
> —Harriet Martineau

Visualizing Population Characteristics

Purpose

Students will compare and contrast three ways that populations might be dispersed in the environment.
UCP.1, C.5

Skill Practice

BL OL AL Observe and Infer
Explain that species of smaller fishes often form clumped groups known as schools. Species of larger fishes usually do not form schools.

ASK STUDENTS: ***What advantage do smaller fish gain by forming clumped groups, or schools?*** It is hypothesized that schooling behavior confuses predators and provides additional safety for individuals within the center of the school.

Critical Thinking

AL Infer
ASK STUDENTS: ***Which type of population distribution allows you to predict more accurately how many individuals reside in a given area?***
If a population has uniform distribution, one has a better idea of how many can be found in a given geographic area. This is not true for clumped groups and random aggregates.

Concepts in Motion
Animation

W Writing Support

BL OL AL COOP LEARN

Persuasive Writing Have students work in pairs and write an advertisement to attract the early American settlers to expand their population range by heading west. Ask for volunteers to read their ads. As they do, have the class identify any abiotic and biotic factors that are mentioned in these ads. Students might mention that the soil (abiotic factor) in the west is ideal for growing crops or that the wildlife (biotic factor) is plentiful.

D Develop Concepts

BL OL **Clarify a Misconception** Students might fail to realize the impact of limited resources and think that populations can increase indefinitely.

ASK STUDENTS: ***Imagine you are at a birthday party. How many people could come before there was not enough cake for everyone?*** Tell students, eventually the cake-to-person ratio would be too low, and someone would not get cake. Just like the birthday cake, there are a limited number of resources in your city, your state, your country, and the world. Point out that all populations eventually become limited in size by one or more limiting factors in their environment. Lead a discussion of the differences between density-independent and density-dependent limiting factors that eventually halt the growth of various populations, including those of humans around the world.

Develop Concepts

EL OL AL COOP LEARN

Integrate Geography Have pairs of students research and present information about the population ranges of the state mammal, bird, fish, flower, and tree. Tell students to include the common name and the species name on their distribution maps.

VOCABULARY

SCIENCE USAGE V. COMMON USAGE

Distribution

Science usage: the area where something is located or where a species lives and reproduces
The white-tailed deer has a wide distribution that covers much of the United States.

Common usage: the handing out or delivery of items to a number of people
The distribution of report cards to students occurred today.

W **Population ranges** No population, not even the human population, occupies all habitats in the biosphere. Some species, such as the Hawaiian honeycreeper shown in **Figure 3,** have a very limited population range, or distribution. This songbird is found only on some of the islands of Hawaii. Other species, such as the peregrine falcon shown in **Figure 3,** have a vast distribution. Peregrine falcons are found on all continents except Antarctica. Note the distribution of the animals in **Figure 2.**

You might have learned that organisms adapt to the biotic and abiotic factors in their environment. A species might not be able to expand its population range because it cannot survive the abiotic conditions found in the expanded region. A change in temperature range, humidity level, annual rainfall, or sunlight might make a new geographic area uninhabitable for the species. In addition, biotic factors, such as predators, competitors, and parasites, present threats that might make the new location difficult for survival.

Reading Check **Describe** two reasons why a species might not be able to expand its range.

D

Population-Limiting Factors

Limiting factors are biotic or abiotic factors that keep a population from continuing to increase indefinitely. Decreasing a limiting factor, such as the available food supply, often changes the number of individuals that are able to survive in a given area. In other words, if the food supply increases a larger population might result, and if the food supply decreases a smaller population might result.

Density-independent factors There are two categories of limiting factors—density-independent factors and density-dependent factors. Any factor in the environment that does not depend on the number of members in a population per unit area is a **density-independent factor.** These factors usually are abiotic and include natural phenomena such as weather events. Weather events that limit populations include drought or flooding, extreme heat or cold, tornadoes, and hurricanes.

Figure 3 The Hawaiian honeycreeper lives only on some of the Hawaii islands. The peregrine falcon is found worldwide.

Hawaiian honeycreeper

Peregrine falcon

Reading Check Abiotic factors that prohibit survival or biotic factors, such as competitors, can prevent a species from expanding its range.

Crown fire damage

Managed ground fire damage

■ **Figure 4** A crown fire is a density-independent factor that can limit population growth. However, small ground fires can promote growth of pines in a pine forest community.
Explain ***why these two situations involving fire have different results on the pine tree populations.***

S

Figure 4 shows an example of the effects that fire can have on a population. Fire has damaged this ponderosa pine forest community. Sometimes the extreme heat from a crown fire, which is a fire that advances to the tops of the trees, can destroy many mature ponderosa pine trees—a dominant species in forests of the western United States. In this example, the fire limits the population of ponderosa trees by killing many of the trees. However, smaller but more frequent ground fires have the opposite effect on the population. By thinning lower growing plants that use up nutrients, a healthier population of mature ponderosa pines is produced.

Populations can be limited by the unintended results of human alterations of the landscape. For example, over the last 100 years, human activities on the Colorado River, such as building dams, water diversions, and water barriers, have significantly reduced the amount of water flow and changed the water temperature of the river. In addition, the introduction of nonnative fish species altered the biotic factors in the river. Because of the changes in the river, the number of small fish called humpback chub was reduced. During the 1960s, the number of humpback chub dropped so low that they were in danger of disappearing from the Colorado River altogether. D

Air, land, and water pollution are the result of human activities that also can limit populations. Pollution reduces the available resources by making some of the resources toxic.

W **Density-dependent factors** Any factor in the environment that depends on the number of members in a population per unit area is a **density-dependent factor.** Density-dependent factors are often biotic factors such as predation, disease, parasites, and competition. A study of density-dependent factors was done on the wolf–moose populations in northern Michigan on Isle Royale, located in Lake Superior.

CAREERS IN BIOLOGY

Population Biologist A population biologist studies the characteristics of populations, such as growth, size, distribution, or genetics. They use their findings to predict the future of populations and determine what can be done to lessen the negative impacts.

Research Citation

Concept Ladder Educational research indicates that students should be required to generate their own questions as a way to extend their thinking. Supplement the scaffolding strategy described on page 97 by having students complete a concept ladder as they read. Students will generate their own questions as a way to guide their reading and understanding of the text. (Gillet and Temple, 1982)

Research bibliography on pages 32T–34T

S Skill Practice

BL OL Visual Literacy As students study Figure 4, have them compare and contrast the differences between the two fires. Crown fires tend to be hotter and more damaging to both plant and animal populations because they often burn uncontrollably for some time, destroying thousands of hectares of habitats. Controlled fires, often called ground fires, burn with less intensity and at a lower level than the canopy. With controlled fires, usually only the dead material on the ground is burned.

D Develop Concepts

AL Independent Research Have students determine the current policies of the Bureau of Land Management for regulating the Colorado River. Students should also investigate why the Colorado River has so many regulations compared to most other rivers in the U.S. Students should find that there are various standards for the river such as pesticide use, salinity, and flow rate, and rules regulating boating and fishing. Have students determine the present policies of a similar scenario in their home state.

W Writing Support

BL OL AL Informal Writing Have students write a paragraph comparing density-dependent and density-independent factors that can limit human populations. Student paragraphs will differ, but should identify and describe various factors of each type and how they influence human populations. Students should recognize that the impact of these factors depends on the region of the world in which the population lives.

■ **Caption Question Fig. 4** Crown fires tend to kill the pines, but ground fires remove understory growth and keep pines well spaced.

S Skill Practice

AL Visual Literacy Have students refer to Figure 5.

ASK STUDENTS: ***What was the approximate ratio of moose to wolves in 1965?*** 21:1 ***In 1980?*** 16:1 ***In 1995?*** 160:1 ***In 2000?*** 30:1

W Writing Support

BL OL Informal Writing Parvovirus is a highly contagious virus that can kill dogs and wolves. Have students imagine that they visited Isle Royale in Lake Superior. Have them write a letter to a friend describing the density-dependent factors between parvovirus and wolves and between wolves and moose. Students should explain that the virus limits the population of wolves and the wolves limit the population of moose. Without limits, both wolf and moose populations could expand and damage their environments.

AL Extension Have students explain the density-dependent factors among parvovirus, wolves, and moose. What would happen to the population without limits? How would this impact the environment?

FOLDABLES®

RUBRIC A rubric for evaluating Foldables is found on your eTeacherEdition Online.

Going Further On the back of their Foldables, have students describe the rapid life history pattern of an insect and compare it to the slower life history pattern of a mammal.

Caption Question Fig. 5 The wolf population decreased during years preceding 1995.

■ **Figure 5** The long-term study of the wolf and moose populations on Isle Royale shows the relationship between the number of predators and prey over time.
Infer *what might have caused the increase in the number of moose in 1995.*

S

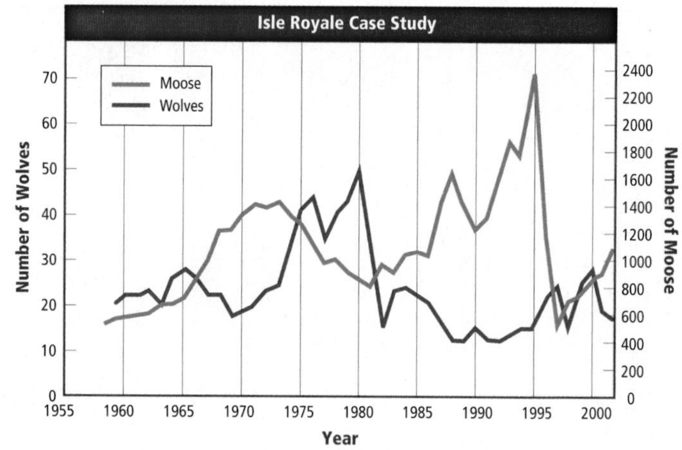

FOLDABLES® Incorporate information from this section into your Foldable.

Inquiry Virtual Lab

Prior to the winter of 1947–48, apparently there were no wolves on Isle Royale. During that winter, a single pair of wolves crossed the ice on Lake Superior, reaching the island. During the next ten years, the population of wolves reached about twenty individuals. **Figure 5** shows some of the results from the long-term study conducted by population biologists. Notice that the rise and fall of the numbers of each group was dependent on the other group. For example, follow the wolves' line on the graph. As the number of wolves decreased, the number of moose increased. W

Disease Another density-dependent factor is disease. Outbreaks of disease tend to occur when population size has increased and population density is high. When population density is high, disease is transmitted easily from one individual to another because contact between individuals is more frequent. Therefore, the disease spreads easily and quickly through a population. This is just as true for human populations as it is for populations of protists, plants, and other species of animals.

Competition Competition between organisms also increases when density increases. When the population increases to a size so that resources such as food or space become limited, individuals in the population must compete for the available resources. Competition can occur within a species or between two different species that use the same resources. Competition for insufficient resources might result in a decrease in population density in an area due to starvation or to individuals leaving the area in search of additional resources. As the population size decreases, competition becomes less severe.

The lemmings shown in **Figure 6** are an example of a population that often undergoes competition for resources. Lemmings are small mammals that live in the tundra biome. When food is plentiful, their population increases exponentially. As food becomes limited, many lemmings begin to starve and their population size decreases significantly.

Parasites Populations also can be limited by parasites, in a way similar to disease, as population density increases. The presence of parasites is a density-dependent factor that can negatively affect population growth at higher densities.

■ **Figure 6** Lemmings are mammals that produce offspring in large numbers when food is plentiful. When the food supply diminishes, lemmings starve and many die.

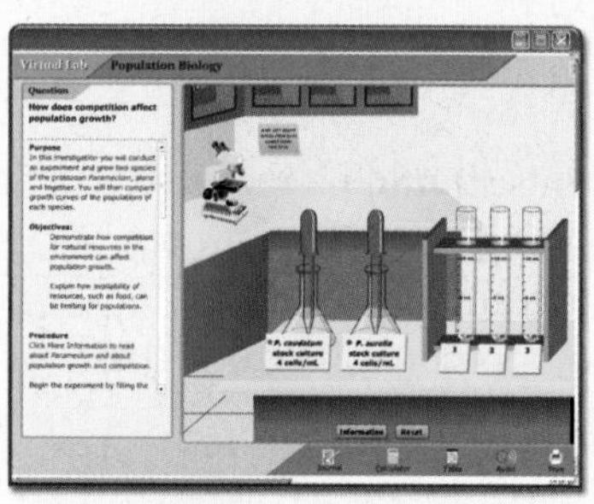

Inquiry Virtual Lab In this investigation, students will conduct an experiment and grow two species of the protozoan *Paramecium*.

Population growth rate An important characteristic of any population is its growth rate. The **population growth rate** (PGR) explains how fast a given population grows. One of the characteristics of the population ecologists must know, or at least estimate, is natality. The natality of a population is the birthrate, or the number of individuals born in a given time period. Ecologists also must know the mortality—the number of deaths that occur in the population during a given time period.

The number of individuals emigrating or immigrating also is important. **Emigration** (em uh GRAY shun) is the term ecologists use to describe the number of individuals moving away from a population. **Immigration** (ih muh GRAY shun) is the term ecologists use to describe the number of individuals moving into a population. In most instances, emigration is about equal to immigration. Therefore, natality and mortality usually are most important in determining the population growth rate.

Some populations tend to remain approximately the same size from year to year. Other populations vary in size depending on conditions within their habitats. To better understand why populations grow in different ways, you should understand two mathematical models for population growth—the exponential growth model and the logistic growth model.

Exponential growth model Look at **Figure 7** to see how a population of mice would grow if there were no limits placed on it by the environment. Assume that two adult mice breed and produce a litter of young. Also assume the two offspring are able to reproduce in one month. If all of the offspring survive to breed, the population grows slowly at first. This slow growth period is defined as the lag phase. The rate of population growth soon begins to increase rapidly because the total number of organisms that are able to reproduce has increased. After only two years, the experimental mouse population would reach more than three million mice.

Connection to Math Notice in **Figure 7** that once the mice begin to reproduce rapidly, the graph becomes J-shaped. A J-shaped growth curve illustrates exponential growth. Exponential growth, also called geometric growth, occurs when the growth rate is proportional to the size of the population. All populations grow exponentially until some limiting factor slows the population's growth. It is important to recognize that even in the lag phase, the use of available resources is exponential. Because of this, the resources soon become limited and population growth slows.

Logistic growth model Many populations grow like the model shown in **Figure 8** rather than the model shown in **Figure 7.** Notice that the graphs look exactly the same through some of the time period. However, the second graph curves into an S-shape. An S-shaped curve is typical of logistic growth. Logistic growth occurs when the population's growth slows or stops following exponential growth, at the population's carrying capacity. A population stops increasing when the number of births is less than the number of deaths or when emigration exceeds immigration.

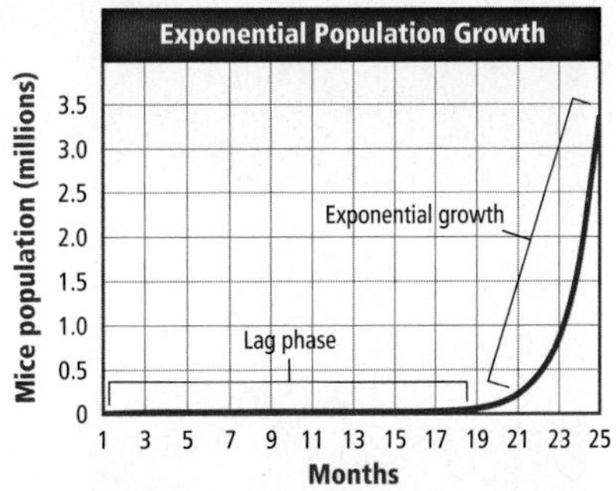

■ **Figure 7** If two mice were allowed to reproduce unhindered, the population would grow slowly at first but would accelerate quickly.
***Infer** why mice or other populations do not continue to grow exponentially.*

Concepts in Motion Animation

■ **Figure 8** When a population exhibits growth that results in an S-shaped graph, it exhibits logistic growth. The population levels off at a limit called the carrying capacity.

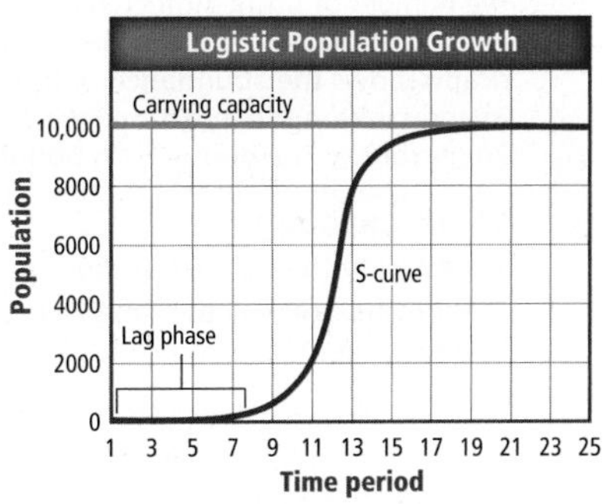

Inquiry BioLab

The lab at the end of the chapter can be used at this point in the lesson.

Develop Concepts

BL OL AL Scaffolding

ASK STUDENTS: ***What are three characteristics used to describe populations?*** spatial distribution, population density, and growth rate ***What is the difference between uniform and random distributions?*** Uniform distribution appears equally spaced, and random distributions can have organisms closely spaced in some areas and more distantly spaced in others. ***How would you classify a biotic factor, such as food availability, that limits its population size?*** It would be a density-dependent factor. ***How do you distinguish between the shapes of an exponential growth curve and a logistic growth curve?*** Exponential growth curves are J-shaped, and logistic growth curves are S-shaped. ***Can you describe what is happening to a population in the exponential phase of growth?*** It is growing rapidly.

Concepts in Motion

Animation

■ **Caption Question Fig. 7** All populations are eventually limited by one or more factors in their environment.

Activity

OL AL Compare Growth Rates

SAY TO STUDENTS: ***An employer offers two equal jobs of one hour each for fourteen days. The first pays $10/h. The second pays only 1 cent the first day, but the rate doubles each day.***

ASK STUDENTS: ***Which job would you rather have?*** Plot the results of both pay rates on the board. The first shows linear growth resulting in a sum of $140.00. The second shows exponential growth resulting in a sum of $163.83. Ask the students to plot the data. Then, lead a discussion of the differences between the rates and explain that the problem associated with exponential growth is that in populations, there are always limits. Est. time: 15 min

■ **Figure 9** Locusts, which are an example of r-strategists, produce many offspring in their short lifetimes.
Infer *what specific factors might fluctuate in a locust's environment.*

Carrying capacity In **Figure 8** on the previous page, notice that logistic growth levels off at the line on the graph identified as the carrying capacity. The maximum number of individuals in a species that an environment can support for the long term is the **carrying capacity.** Carrying capacity is limited by the energy, water, oxygen, and nutrients available. When populations develop in an environment with plentiful resources, there are more births than deaths. The population soon reaches or passes the carrying capacity. As a population nears the carrying capacity, resources become limited. If a population exceeds the carrying capacity, deaths outnumber births because adequate resources are not available to support all of the individuals. The population then falls below the carrying capacity as individuals die. The concept of carrying capacity is used to explain why many populations tend to stabilize. S

Reproductive patterns The graph in **Figure 8** shows the number of individuals increasing until the carrying capacity is reached. However, there are several additional factors that must be considered for real populations. Species of organisms vary in the number of births per reproduction cycle, in the age that reproduction begins, and in the life span of the organism. Both plants and animals are placed into groups based on their reproductive factors.

Members of one of the groups are called the *r*-strategists. The rate strategy, or *r*-strategy, is an adaptation for living in an environment where fluctuation in biotic or abiotic factors occur. Fluctuating factors might be availability of food or changing temperatures. An *r*-strategist is generally a small organism such as a fruit fly, a mouse, or the locusts shown in **Figure 9.** *R*-strategists usually have short life spans and produce many offspring. W

DATA ANALYSIS LAB 1

Based on Real Data*

Recognize Cause and Effect

Do parasites affect the size of a host population? In 1994, the first signs of a serious eye disease caused by the bacterium *Mycoplasma gallisepticum* were observed in house finches that were eating in backyard bird feeders. Volunteers collected data beginning three different years on the number of finches infected with the parasite and the total number of finches present. The graph shows the abundance of house finches in areas where the infection rate was at least 20 percent of the house finch population.

Data and Observations

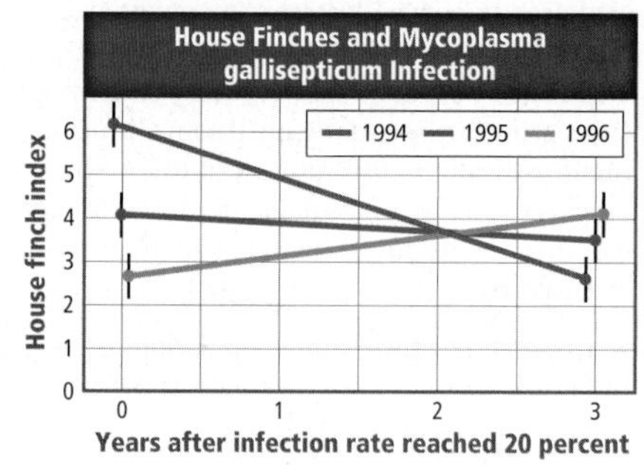

Think Critically

1. **Compare** the data from the three areas.
2. **Hypothesize** why the house finch abundance stabilized in 1995 and 1996.
3. **Infer** whether the parasite, *Mycoplasma gallisepticum,* is effective in limiting the size of house finch populations. Explain.

*Data obtained from: Gregory, R., et al. 2000. Parasites take control. *Nature* 406: 33–34.

S Skill Practice

EL BL OL AL Sequence Have students sequence the phases of growth. The slowly growing phase is the lag phase, followed by the rapidly growing exponential phase, and eventually ending in the logistic phase near the carrying capacity.

W Writing Support

BL OL Creative Writing Have students imagine that they are houseflies. Assign them to write a short comic strip, with illustrations, explaining what it is like to be an *r*-strategist from a fly's viewpoint. Stories should indicate a "boom-or-bust" lifestyle.

DATA ANALYSIS LAB 1

About the Lab

- Discuss the graph as a class. Model for students how data is read from a graph.
- Some students might have difficulty reading the graph. You might need to help them individually or assign them a peer tutor.
- Also see Peter J. Hudson, et al., 1998. *Prevention of population cycles by parasite removal, Science* 282 (5397):2256–2258.

Think Critically

1. In 1994, the population size decreased rapidly after infection. In 1995 and 1996, the population did not change much after the infection rate reached 20 percent.
2. As the populations decline to a particular density, the parasite's effect decreases because it is not as easily transmitted when the population is smaller.
3. Yes, the parasite appears to limit the population size of house finches in a density-dependent manner.

■ **Caption Question Fig. 9** Abiotic or biotic factors such as food availability or temperature may fluctuate.

■ **Figure 10** Elephants are *k*-strategists that produce few offspring, but they invest a lot of care in the raising of their offspring.

The reproductive strategy of an *r*-strategist is to produce as many offspring as possible in a short time period in order to take advantage of some environmental factor. They typically expend little or no energy in raising their young to adulthood. Populations of *r*-strategists usually are controlled by density-independent factors, and they usually do not maintain a population near the carrying capacity.

Just as some environments fluctuate, others are fairly predictable. The elephants in **Figure 10** experience a carrying capacity that changes little from year to year. The carrying-capacity strategy, or *k*-strategy, is an adaptation for living in these environments. A *k*-strategist generally is a larger organism that has a long life span, produces few offspring, and whose population reaches equilibrium at the carrying capacity. The reproductive strategy of a *k*-strategist is to produce only a few offspring that have a better chance of living to reproductive age because of the energy, resources, and time invested in the care for the young. Populations of *k*-strategists usually are controlled by density-dependent factors.

VOCABULARY
ACADEMIC VOCABULARY
Fluctuate
to vary or change measured levels or from one thing to another in an unpredictable way
The speed of a car fluctuates when you are driving on narrow, winding roads.

R

Section 1 Assessment

Section Summary

- There are population characteristics that are common to all populations of organisms, including plants, animals, and bacteria.
- Populations tend to be distributed randomly, uniformly, or in clumps.
- Population limiting factors are either density-independent or density-dependent.
- Populations tend to stabilize near the carrying capacity of their environment.

Understand Main Ideas

1. MAIN Idea **Compare and contrast** spatial distribution, population density, and population growth rate.
2. **Summarize** the concepts of carrying capacity and limiting factors and their effects on reproductive patterns.
3. **Sketch** diagrams showing population dispersion patterns.
4. **Analyze** the impact a nonnative species might have on a native species in terms of population dynamics.

Thinking Critically

5. **Design** an experiment that you could perform to determine which population growth model applies to fruit fly populations.

WRITING in Biology

6. Write a newspaper article describing how a weather event, such as drought, has affected a population of animals in your community.

R Reading Strategy

BL OL AL Brainstorm Have students prepare a table comparing and contrasting *r*-strategists and *k*-strategists. List the factors that they should compare and contrast: size of individual, life span, and production and care of offspring.

ASK STUDENTS: ***Hypothesize why populations of r-strategists are usually controlled by density-independent factors, whereas populations of k-strategists are usually controlled by density-dependent factors.*** Populations of *r*-strategists rarely reach the carrying capacity when density-dependent factors are important. In contrast, populations of *k*-strategists reach equilibrium at the carrying capacity.

Formative Assessment

Evaluation Have students hypothesize what might happen to a population that has reached its carrying capacity if a competing species emigrated from the environment. The population would likely increase and reach a new carrying capacity.

Remediation Place lightweight objects into a student's arms, slowly at first to represent the lag phase of population growth. Then, do it faster to represent exponential growth. Explain that when objects begin falling out of the student's arms, carrying capacity has been reached.

Section 1 Assessment

1. Spatial distribution describes the dispersal pattern displayed by a population in its habitat. Population density refers to the numbers of individuals living in a given area. Population growth rate refers to how fast a given population is growing.
2. The carrying capacity represents the maximum number of individuals in a population that the environment can support over time. Limiting factors control the numbers of individuals in a population, sometimes maintaining it at or near the carrying capacity.
3. Answers will vary but should show all three dispersal patterns.
4. Nonnative species might out-compete the native species or might prey upon them.
5. Student experimental designs will vary, but should begin with a small number of fruit flies in a small area such as a 500-mL flask with a given amount of food. The population should then be counted until it declines and the data plotted on a graph.
6. Articles will differ, but should state that a weather event such as a drought is a density-independent factor.

Assessment Online Quiz

Section 2

MAIN Idea

BL OL AL Human Population

SAY TO STUDENTS: ***Your perception of human population growth might be different if you lived in one of the world's largest cities such as Mexico City with a population of 17 million, or in a small town such as Dellview, North Carolina, with a population of 16.*** **ASK STUDENTS:** ***No matter where you live, would you say that the total population is growing faster today or that it grew faster 50 years ago?*** The rate of growth was faster 50 years ago, but the total number of people being added to the population each day is greater today.

R Reading Strategy

EL Active Comprehension

Have students examine the titles, subtitles, captions, illustrations, figures, and bold text in this section. Then, as a class, brainstorm questions that might be answered in this section. Start a question for the students and guide them to complete it. Write their questions on the board. Underline key phrases in the questions. Then, have students read the section and determine if any of the questions have been answered. Record answers as appropriate.

S Skill Practice

EL BL OL Visual Literacy

Have students examine Figure 11. **ASK STUDENTS:** ***Does this graph illustrate exponential or logistic population growth?*** This graph shows exponential growth. If students have difficulty answering this question, have them review Figures 7 and 8.

Section 2

Reading Preview

Essential Questions

- What aspects affect human population growth?
- What are the trends in human population growth?
- What are the age structures of representative nongrowing, slowly growing, and rapidly growing countries?
- What might be the consequences of continued population growth?

Review Vocabulary

carrying capacity: the maximum number of individuals in a species that an environment can support for the long term

New Vocabulary

demography
demographic transition
zero population growth (ZPG)
age structure

g Multilingual eGlossary

R Human Population

MAIN Idea Human population growth changes over time.

Real-World Reading Link Has someone you know recently had a baby? The odds of babies surviving to adulthood are greater than ever before in most countries today.

Human Population Growth

The study of human population size, density, distribution, movement, and birth and death rates is **demography** (de MAH gra fee). The graph in **Figure 11** shows demographers' estimated human population on Earth for several thousand years.

Notice that the graph in **Figure 11** shows a relatively stable number of individuals over thousands of years—until recently. Notice also the recovery of the human population after the outbreak of the bubonic plague in the 1300s when an estimated one-third of the population of Europe died. Perhaps the most significant feature in this graph is the increase in human population in recent times. In 1804, the population of Earth was an estimated one billion people. Earth reached a milestone in 1999, when our planet's population was recorded at six billion people. With the current growth rate at just over 80 million people per year we are expected to reach a population of seven billion by 2012, and nine billion by 2050.

S **Figure 11** The human population on Earth was relatively constant until recent times, when the human population began to grow at an exponential rate.

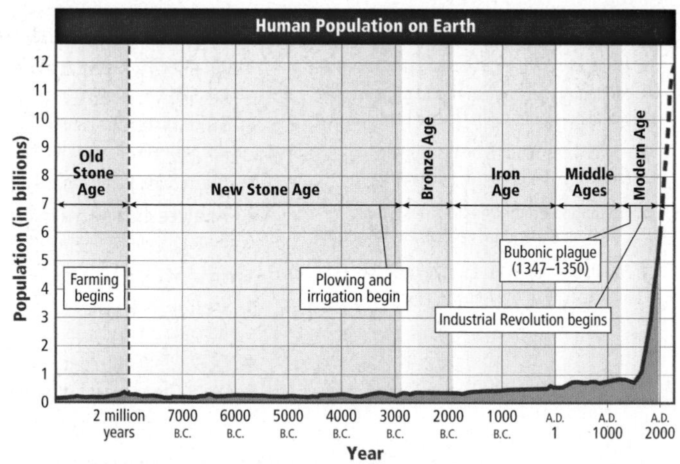

Research Citation

Main Ideas Educational research indicates that students should be instructed to identify the main ideas of a lesson. Their performance will improve when they are asked to understand not only isolated facts, but also the larger context in which they can be applied. (National Research Council, 2005)

Research bibliography on pages 32T–34T

Technological advances For thousands of years, environmental conditions kept the size of the human population at a relatively constant number below the environment's carrying capacity. Humans have learned to alter the environment in ways that appear to have changed its carrying capacity. Agriculture and domestication of animals have increased the human food supply. Technological advances and medicine have improved the chances of human survival by reducing the number of deaths from parasites and disease. In addition, improvements in shelter have made humans less vulnerable to climatic impact.

Reading Check **Explain** why an improvement in shelter increased the survival rate of the human population.

Human population growth rate Although the human population is still growing, the rate of its growth has slowed. **Figure 12** shows the percent increase in human population from the late 1940s through 2009. The graph also includes the projected population increase through 2050. Notice the sharp dip in human population growth in the 1960s. This was due primarily to a famine in China in which about 60 million people died. The graph also shows that human population growth reached its peak at over 2.2 percent in 1963. By 2009, the percent increase in human population growth had dropped to less than 1.2 percent. Population models predict the overall population growth rate to be below 0.6 percent by 2050. The decline in human population growth is due primarily to diseases such as AIDS and voluntary population control.

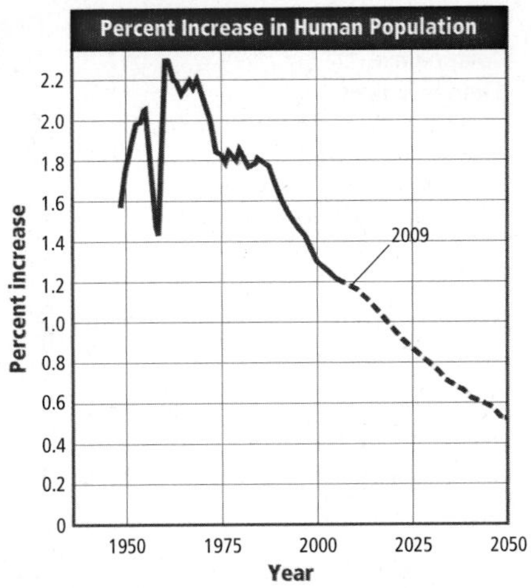

■ **Figure 12** This graph shows the percent increase in the global human population using data from the late 1940s through 2009 and the projected percent increase to 2050.
Determine *the approximate population increase in the year 2025.*

D

MiniLab 1

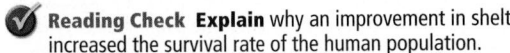

Evaluate Factors

Inquiry MiniLab

What factors affect the growth of a human population? Technological advances have resulted in a rapid growth in human population. However, human population growth is not equal in all countries.

Procedure

1. The graph shows one factor affecting human population growth. Use the data to predict how this factor will affect the population in each country between now and the year 2050.
2. Brainstorm a list of factors, events, or conditions that affect the growth of human populations in these countries. Predict the effect of each factor on the population growth rate.

Analysis

Think Critically In your opinion, what factors or groups of factors have the greatest impact on population growth? Justify your answer.

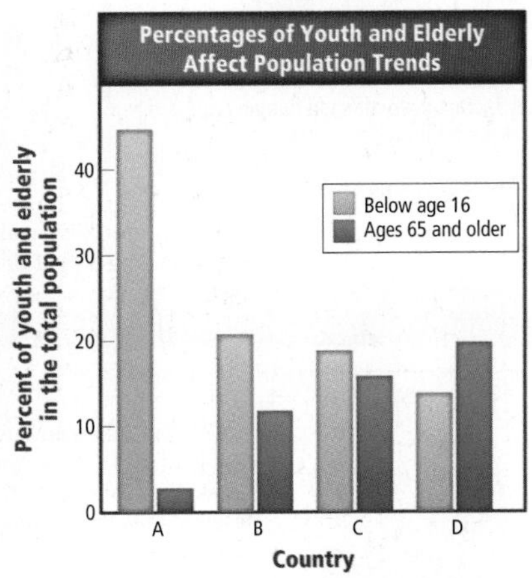

Reading Check Adequate shelter provides defense against extremes of the environment such as temperature, precipitation, and wind. In addition, shelter provides defense against biotic factors in the environment such as venomous snakes, mosquitoes, other insects that harbor parasites, and large predators such as wolves and bears. All of these have the potential to shorten the life span of individuals, thereby affecting the human population as a whole.

■ **Caption Question** **Fig. 12** 0.85%

D Develop Concepts

BL OL AL

Clarify a Misconception Some students might think that humans are exempt from the principles that affect all other species.

ASK STUDENTS: ***What do the graphs in Figure 11 and Figure 12 indicate about the growth of the human population?*** The biological principles that govern population growth are the same for all species.

MiniLab 1

Inquiry MiniLab

For a lab worksheet, use your eTeacherEdition Online.

RUBRIC A rubric for evaluating MiniLabs is found on your eTeacherEdition Online.

Est. Time 20 min

Teaching Strategies

- Discuss ranking predictions. Help students understand that countries with large proportions of young people are most likely to have the greatest population growth.
- Extend the activity by having students research current world population data to check their predictions and identify additional factors affecting population growth.

Analysis

Answers will vary, but should include the age structure of a population, as well as the population's health and longevity due to factors such as advancements in medicine, in agriculture, and in sanitation.

LabManager™

Customize this lab with the LabManager™ CD-ROM.

C Critical Thinking

AL Contrast

ASK STUDENTS: ***What are the differences in the current living conditions among countries that have not yet experienced demographic transition and those that have?*** Those that have experienced transition have generally better services and living conditions.

Critical Thinking

BL OL Speculate

ASK STUDENTS: ***What factor would cause a country to have a negative growth rate?*** The birthrate would be lower than the death rate.

Inquiry Launch Lab

Assess Content Development

Assess how understanding has developed when students revisit the Launch Lab analysis questions.

S Skill Practice

EL BL OL AL Visual Literacy

Have students examine Figure 13.

ASK STUDENTS: ***What are the factors shown in this time line that have affected human population growth? Which factors are density-dependent? Which factors are density-independent? Explain the reason for your choices.*** The global climate change (69,000 B.C.), the Industrial Revolution (1800), World War II (1939–1945), and improved medical care and sanitation (1954) are density-independent factors because they do not depend on the number of individuals in the population. In contrast, the bubonic plague (1347–1351), the Spanish Flu (1918), and AIDS (2004) are density-dependent factors because diseases are more likely to spread when the density of the population increases.

VOCABULARY

WORD ORIGIN

Demography

demo– from the Greek word *demos;* meaning *people*

–ography from the French word *graphie;* meaning *writing*

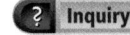

Inquiry Launch Lab

Review Based on what you've read about populations, how would you now answer the analysis questions?

Trends in Human Population Growth

The graph in **Figure 12** is somewhat deceptive. Population trends can be altered by events such as disease and war. **Figure 13** shows a few historical events that have changed population trends. **Figure 12** could also easily be misinterpreted because human population growth is not the same in all countries. However, population growth trends are often similar in countries that have similar economies.

For example, one trend that has developed during the previous century is a change in the population growth rate in industrially developed countries such as the United States. An industrially developed country is advanced in industrial and technological capabilities and has a population with a high standard of living. In its early history, the United States had a high birthrate and a high death rate. It was not uncommon for people to have large families and for individuals to die by their early forties. Many children also died before reaching adulthood. Presently, the birthrate in the United States has decreased dramatically and the life expectancy is greater than seventy years. This change in a population from high birth and death rates to low birth and death rates is called a **demographic transition.**

Connection to Math How do population growth rates (PGR) compare in industrially developed countries and developing countries? As an example, we will compare the 2008 populations for the United States and Honduras, a small country in Central America. The calculation for PGR is C

$$\frac{\text{birthrate} - \text{deathrate} + \text{migration rate}}{10} = \text{PGR (\%)}$$

In our example, we'll have to divide the final answer by 10 to get a percentage because the rates are calculated per 1000.

The United States has birthrate 14.1 (per 1000), death rate 8.3 (per 1000), and migration rate 2.9 (per 1000). This gives a PGR of 0.87 percent for the United States. Honduras has birthrate 26.9 (per 1000), death rate 5.4 (per 1000), and migration rate -1.3 (per 1000). This gives a PGR of 2.02 percent for Honduras.

S

Figure 13

History of Human Population Trends

Many factors have affected human population growth throughout history.

Concepts in Motion The Interactive Timeline

1347–1351 The bubonic plague kills one-third of Europe's population and 75 million people throughout the world.

1800 The Industrial Revolution leads to a dramatic population explosion.

69,000 B.C. Researchers think that as few as 15,000 to 40,000 people survived global climate changes that resulted from the eruption of the Toba supervolcano.

1798 The first essay on human population is written by Thomas Malthus, who predicted exponential population growth leading to famine, poverty, and war.

Content Background

Teacher FYI In 1960, there were only five countries in which the population growth rates had dipped to replacement level or below. That number has continued to increase so that by 2000 the number of countries had reached 64. Total fertility varies very little among the 64 countries, but there is considerable variation in the patterns of partnership and reproductive behaviors among them. If this trend continues, population predictions may have to be adjusted downward significantly from their present highest estimates.

S

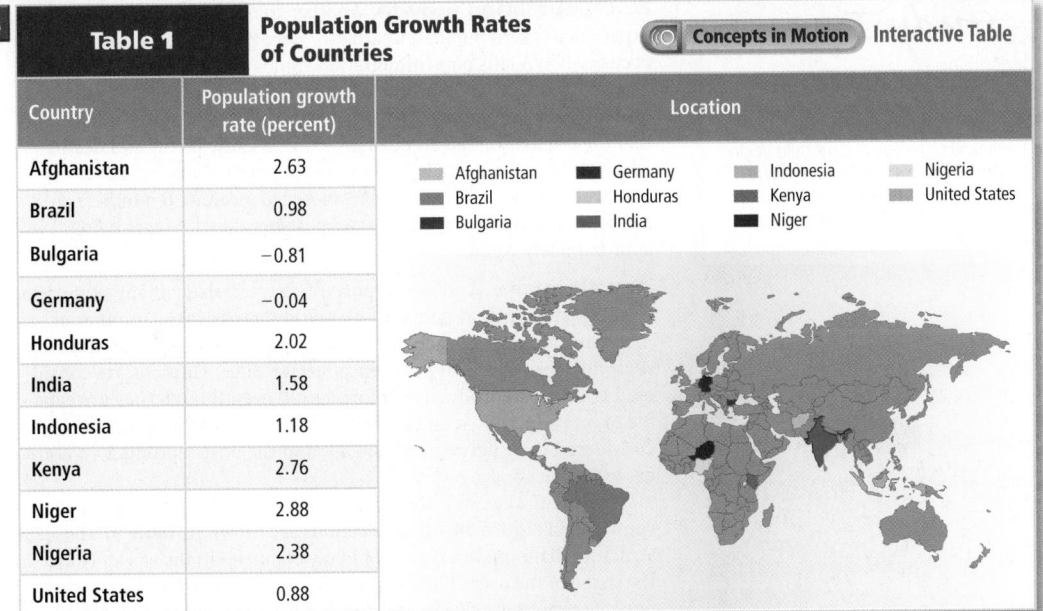

Table 1 Population Growth Rates of Countries

Concepts in Motion Interactive Table

Country	Population growth rate (percent)
Afghanistan	2.63
Brazil	0.98
Bulgaria	−0.81
Germany	−0.04
Honduras	2.02
India	1.58
Indonesia	1.18
Kenya	2.76
Niger	2.88
Nigeria	2.38
United States	0.88

Location

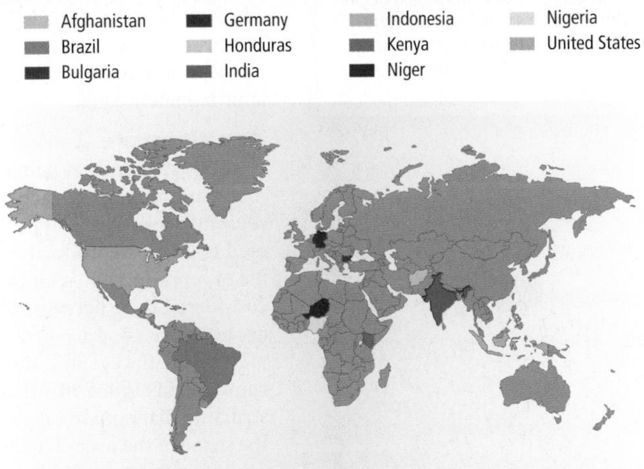

Developing countries will add more people to the world population as compared to the amount of people added in the industrially developed countries. For example, between now and 2050, the developing country Niger—shown in **Table 1**—will be one of the fastest growing countries. Its population is expected to expand from 13 to 53 million people. The industrially developed country Bulgaria is expected to have a population decline from seven to five million people in the same time period. W

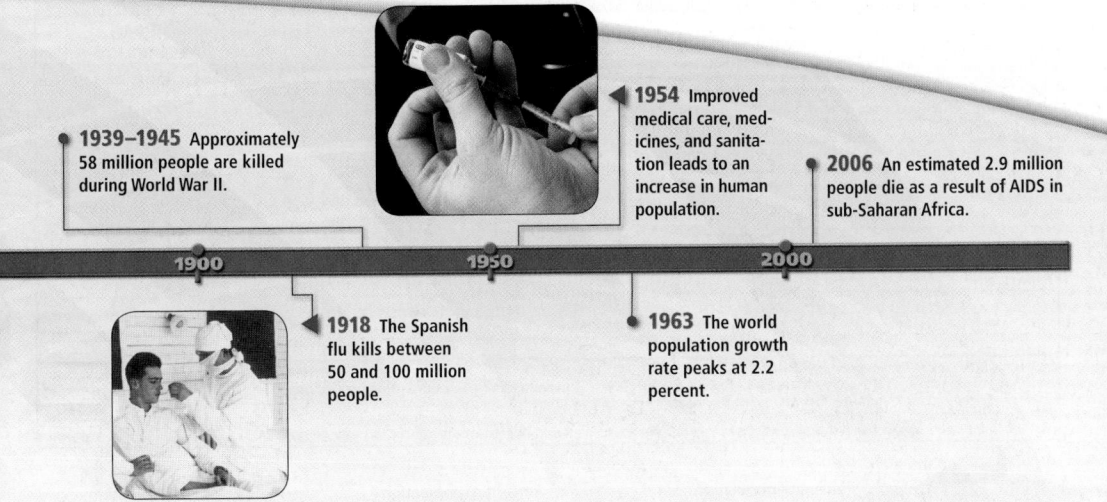

1939–1945 Approximately 58 million people are killed during World War II.

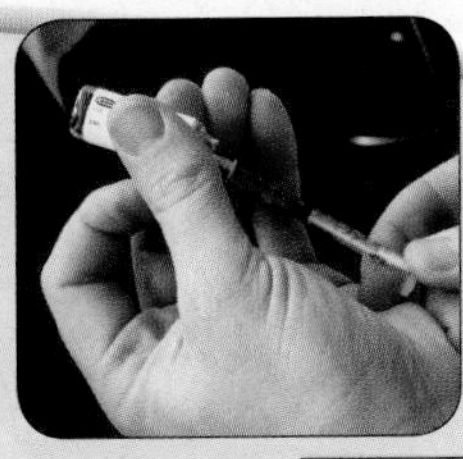

1954 Improved medical care, medicines, and sanitation leads to an increase in human population.

2006 An estimated 2.9 million people die as a result of AIDS in sub-Saharan Africa.

1900 — 1950 — 2000

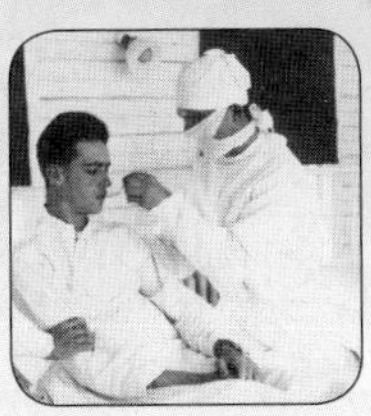

1918 The Spanish flu kills between 50 and 100 million people.

1963 The world population growth rate peaks at 2.2 percent.

Differentiated Instruction

Below Level When beginning assignments like the summary writing described on this page, provide students performing below grade level with a rubric that has clear guidelines. Students will know the goals of the project and can follow the guidelines as they complete the assignment.

For more tips, see pages 14T–15T.

Concepts in Motion

The Interactive Timeline
Interactive Table

S Skill Practice

BL OL Visual Literacy

ASK STUDENTS: ***From Table 1, would you expect there to be more developed countries in the northern hemisphere or in the southern hemisphere?*** There are more developed countries in the northern hemisphere.

AL Ask students to explain their answers.

W Writing Support

OL AL COOP LEARN

Summary Writing Assign pairs of students to research the demographics of one of the world's countries. Be sure to assign at least the United States, Honduras, Niger, Bulgaria, Kenya, Germany, and Afghanistan. Once students complete their study, have them produce summaries of the information they gathered, including tables, graphs, and maps as appropriate.

GOING GREEN Start a compost pile or bin on school grounds. Enlist the support and assistance of building administrators, engineers, and other teachers. The compost produced could be used as a soil amendment on school grounds. Information about how to start composting can be found through your local agricultural research station, local universities, and online. Involve students in the project.

W Writing Support

BL OL AL Persuasive Writing

Have students write a paragraph that explains their opinion about whether ZPG is an important concept for human populations. Student responses will vary. Accept those opinions that offer support.

D Develop Concepts

BL OL COOP LEARN Activity

Reproduce additional age structure charts from the Internet. Before assigning this activity, discuss a sample graph with the class. Have students work in pairs to determine whether the countries appear to show negative growth, rapid growth, or slow growth. When students have made their choices, lead a discussion about the usefulness of the charts.

S Skill Practice

BL OL AL Visual Literacy

ASK STUDENTS: ***Examine Figure 14. What do you observe about Kenya's growth?*** The base is very wide, so it is growing rapidly. ***Why does a chart like Germany's show negative growth?*** Most people of the population are in later-reproductive and post-reproductive stages. ***Comparing the top halves of the three charts, what can you determine about growth rates?*** Growth rates slow as a greater proportion of the population is in the upper part of the chart.

Reading Check Kenya has a large proportion of pre-reproductive and reproductive individuals. The U.S. has a smaller proportion of these two groups, and Germany has an even smaller proportion.

Video BrainPOP

Study Tip

Interactive Reading As you read, write three questions on sticky notes about human population dynamics. The questions should begin with *why, how, where,* or *when.* Use the notes to ask a partner questions about the content in the chapter.

Video BrainPOP

Zero population growth Another trend that populations can experience is zero population growth. **Zero population growth** (ZPG) occurs when births plus immigration equals deaths plus emigration. One estimate is that the world will reach ZPG between 2020 with 6.64 billion people and 2029 with 6.90 billion people. This will mean that the population has stopped growing, because births and deaths occur at the same rate. Once the world population reaches ZPG, the age structure eventually should be more balanced with numbers at pre-reproductive, reproductive, and post-reproductive ages being approximately equal. W

Age structure Another important characteristic of any population is its age structure. A population's **age structure** is the number of males and females in each of three age groups: pre-reproductive stage, reproductive stage, and post-reproductive stage. Humans are considered to be pre-reproductive before age 20 even though they are capable of reproduction at an earlier age. The reproductive years are considered to be between 20 and 44, and the post-reproductive years are after age 44.

Analyze the age structure diagrams for three different representative countries in **Figure 14—**their locations are shown in **Table 1.** The age structure diagrams are typical of many countries in the world. Notice the shape of the overall diagram for a country that is rapidly growing, one that is growing slowly, and one that has reached negative growth. The age structure for the world's human population looks more like that of a rapidly growing country. D

Reading Check Compare and contrast the age structures of the countries shown in **Figure 14.**

Figure 14 The relative numbers of individuals in pre-reproductive, reproductive, and post-reproductive years are shown for three representative countries.

S

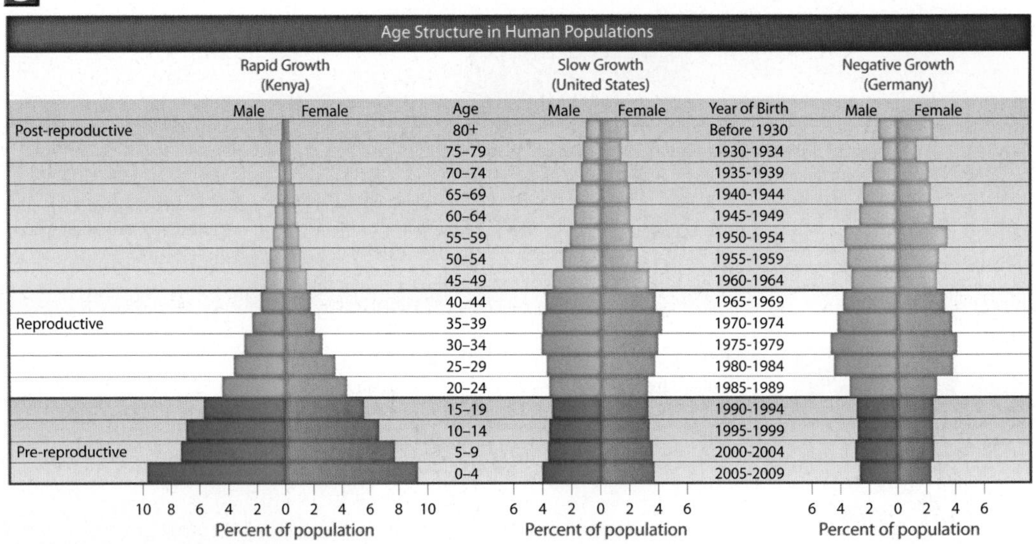

Demonstration

BL OL AL Contrasting Age Structures Collect information about age structures for several countries, using an internet search engine. Include both industrialized and developing countries. As you discuss the concept of age structure, plot the age structures on the board or use an overhead projector to enlarge them on a screen. (Figure 14 is available as a Biology Concepts transparency.) Have students discuss similarities and differences. Est. time: 10 min

Human carrying capacity Calculating population growth rates is not just a mathematical exercise. Scientists are concerned about the human population reaching or exceeding the carrying capacity. As you learned in Section 1, all populations have carrying capacities, and the human population is no exception. Many scientists suggest that human population growth needs to be reduced. In many countries, voluntary population control is occurring through family planning. Unfortunately, if the human population continues to grow —as most populations do—and areas become overcrowded, disease and starvation will occur. However, technology has allowed humans to increase Earth's carrying capacity, at least temporarily. It might be possible for technology and planning to keep the human population at or below its carrying capacity.

Another important factor in keeping the human population at or below the carrying capacity is the amount of resources from the biosphere that are used by each person. Currently, individuals in industrially developed countries use far more resources than those individuals in developing countries, as shown in **Figure 15**. This graph shows the estimated amount of land required to support a person through his or her life, including land used for production of food, forest products and housing, and the additional forest land required to absorb the carbon dioxide produced by the burning of fossil fuels. Countries such as India are becoming more industrialized, and they have a high growth rate. These countries are adding more people and are increasing their use of resources. At some point, the land needed to sustain each person on Earth might exceed the amount of land that is available.

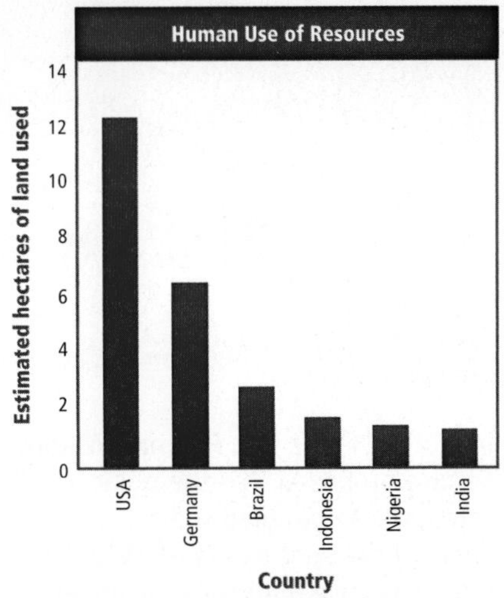

■ **Figure 15** The amount of resources used per person varies around the world. Refer to **Table 1** for the locations of these countries.

Critical Thinking

AL Decide

ASK STUDENTS: ***Why will disease and starvation become larger problems if the population continues to increase?*** Disease is a density-dependent factor that increases in importance with population growth. Food and land that are suitable for agricultural use will eventually be a limiting factor for the population.

Formative Assessment

Evaluation Have students write a paragraph explaining why it is important for humans to maintain a population at or below the carrying capacity. Student paragraphs should include such factors as reducing starvation and using other resources at sustainable levels.

Remediation If a student's paragraph fails to explain the factors important in maintaining carrying capacity, pair him or her with a peer tutor and redirect them to the original discussion of limiting factors and carrying capacity in the first section and the two paragraphs on this page. After the pair has studied the material again, ask two or three multiple-choice questions to reassess the knowledge of the student struggling with the content.

Section 2 Assessment

Section Summary

- Human population growth rates vary in industrially developing countries and industrialized countries.
- Zero population growth occurs when the birthrate and immigration rate of a population equals the death rate and the emigration rate.
- The age structure of the human population is a contributing factor to population growth in some countries.
- Earth has an undefined carrying capacity for the human population.

Understand Main Ideas

1. MAIN Idea **Describe** the change in human population growth over time.
2. **Describe** the differences between the age structure graphs of nongrowing, slowly growing, and rapidly growing countries.
3. **Assess** the consequences of exponential population growth of any population.
4. **Summarize** why the human population began to grow exponentially in the Modern Age.

Think Critically

5. **Predict** the short-term and long-term effects of a newly emerging disease on industrially developing and developed countries.

MATH in Biology

6. Construct an age-structure diagram using the following percentages: 0–19 years: 44.7; 20–44 years: 52.9; 45 years and over: 2. 4. Which type of growth is this country experiencing?

Section 2 Assessment

1. The human population underwent a very long lag phase followed by an exponential growth in modern times.
2. A nongrowing population would look like a rectangle, a slow-growing population would look like a rectangle with a bulge in the middle, and a rapidly growing population would look like a triangle with its base at the bottom.
3. An exponentially growing population is likely to place stress on its environment.
4. Factors that contributed to this exponential growth included the advent of the industrial age; improvements in sanitation, medical care, and medicines; and increased food production.
5. In each case, the disease could be expected to cause many deaths, but an even greater number in a developing country. In terms of human population growth for Earth, it probably wouldn't make much difference in the long term.
6. The diagram would look triangular. The country is experiencing rapid growth.

Assessment Online Quiz

Purpose
Students will understand real-world applications of biology.
E.2

Anticipatory Guide
ASK STUDENTS: ***Does anyone know what GIS is?*** Geographic Information System is a way of capturing and analyzing large amounts of data. ***Why might this be important?*** because it allows for the analysis of massive amounts of data ***Can you think of fields of biology that can benefit from GIS and bioinformatics?*** All fields that need to analyze data can benefit, including medicine, genomic applications, agriculture, and so on.

Background
Polar bears breed in the spring. The males actively seek out females by following their tracks on sea ice. They remain with the female for a short time, then leave in search of another female. As sea ice continues to melt earlier each year, breeding will be increasingly difficult for polar bears.

CUTTING-EDGE BIOLOGY

POLAR BEAR ECOLOGY

In late 2006, the U.S. Fish and Wildlife Service proposed that the polar bear be listed as a threatened species under the Endangered Species Act of 1973. Since then, scientists have undertaken a novel approach to studying the ecological needs of the world's largest terrestrial predator—not by tracking the bears themselves but by tracking the receding ice habitat in which the bears reside, which is vital to their survival.

Scott Bergen, an ecologist with the Wildlife Conservation Society, will work with other scientists utilizing satellites and meteorological data to predict where sea ice will remain in the near future. Conservation efforts will focus on these locations.

Bear necessities Polar bears only live in the circumpolar north, which includes the countries of the United States (Alaska), Canada, Russia, Denmark (Greenland), and Norway. The sea ice that forms each winter creates passages in which the bears travel, as well as creating an optimal environment for hunting. Polar bears rely on seasonal sea ice to stalk their favorite prey—ringed and bearded seals. As the sea ice dwindles, so does the polar bears' ability to effectively hunt these fast-swimming marine mammals.

The cold, hard facts Scientists plan to combine daily satellite and meteorological data from the past 30 years, including global climate change projections, to extrapolate where conservation efforts to save the species would be most successful. The data will also be used to create a Geographical Information Systems (GIS) map.

Approximately 60 percent of the polar bear population reside in Canada.

Using the GIS map, scientists think they will be able to determine short-term seasonal effects as well as large-scale phenomena (like the Arctic and North Atlantic oscillations) and their effect on the Arctic's megafauna. A scientist with the project contends, "The survival of some polar bear populations depends on the decisions we make within the next year."

WRITING in Biology

Persuasive Letter Research what criteria must be met to have a species added to the Endangered Species list. Then choose a species and write a persuasive letter to emphasize the importance that the species be added to the list.

WRITING in Biology

RUBRIC Use the modifiable rubric found on your eTeacherEdition Online to assess writing assignments.

Activity
Prepare one homogeneous "population" for each group. Place a specific number of items into a self-sealing sandwich bag. Distribute masking tape for students to "mark" the population. Explain to students that they will be randomly sampling a population by capturing "animals," marking them, and then releasing them. They should use the numbers of recaught animals with marks to estimate the population. A high number of recaptures suggests a low population, whereas a low number suggests a higher population.

WebQuest

BIOLAB

DO PLANTS OF THE SAME SPECIES COMPETE WITH ONE ANOTHER?

Background: Ecologists often study plant competition by comparing the biomass of individual plants in plant populations. In this lab, you will study intraspecific competition—competition among plants of the same species. As with most ecological studies, you will need to collect data for several weeks.

Question: *Do plant populations of various densities grow differently due to competition?*

Materials

marigold seeds or radish seeds
9-cm plastic pots (6)
clean potting soil
rulers
shallow tray for pots
small garden trowels
masking tape
permanent markers
balance (accurate to 0.1 g)
watering can

Safety Precautions

Procedure

1. Read and complete the lab safety form.
2. Plant seeds in several pots as instructed by your teacher. Your goal should be to have pots with the following densities of plants: 2, 4, 8, 16, 32, and 64.
3. Place the pots in a shallow tray near a sunny window or under a grow light. Continue to keep the soil moist—not drenched—throughout the course of the experiment.
4. After the seeds have sprouted, weed out any extra plants so that you have the correct density.
5. Write a hypothesis about the effect plant density will have on the average biomass of each pot's population.
6. Construct a data table. Observe the plants once each week for a 5–6 week period. Record your observations.
7. At the end of the experiment, measure the biomass of the plants in each pot by cutting each plant at soil level and quickly weighing all the plants from the same pot together. Record your measurements. Calculate the average per-plant biomass of each pot.
8. **Cleanup and Disposal** Wash and return all reusable materials. Wash your hands after watering or working with the plants. Dispose of the plants at the end of the lab as instructed by your teacher.

Analyze and Conclude

1. **Graph Data** Prepare a graph showing the relationship between the average plant biomass and the density of plants. Draw a best-fit line for your data points. What was the effect of plant density on the average biomass of each pot's population? Does this graph support your hypothesis?
2. **Infer** Draw a second graph that compares the total biomass for each population to the number of plants in each population.
3. **Think Critically** Based on your results, infer how human population growth is affected by population density.
4. **Error Analysis** What sources of error might have affected your results?

SHARE YOUR DATA

Poster Session Create a poster using the graphs you produced as a result of your experiment. If a digital camera is available, take photos of each pot of plants to include on your poster. Add headings and legends for each graph and photograph that explain and summarize your findings. Display your poster in the classroom or a hallway of your school.

Analyze and Conclude

1. When graphed, data should show that the average mass per plant decreases as the density increases. If students calculate the slope of the best-fit line, they should see that it is a negative number.
2. This graph should show that the total biomass increases with density. If plotted logarithmically, the data likely will indicate that this increase is beginning to level off as density increases.
3. Human population growth will increase until it encounters limiting factors.
4. Sources of error include: miscounting of seeds or of harvested plants; mistakes in measuring the mass of the plants; letting plants sit for too long after they are cut, resulting in mass measuring errors; or letting one population have an advantage over another by not controlling access to resources.

BIOLAB

? Inquiry BioLab

For a lab worksheet, use your eTeacherEdition Online.

RUBRIC A rubric for evaluating BioLabs is found on your eTeacherEdition Online.

Est. Time 150 min, 15 min per week

Content Background Often biomass is measured as the mass of the dried plant. In a field situation, all plants in a measured area can be cut at ground level, dried, and then measured. However, the fresh weight can also be measured as is done in this experiment. When calculating biomass using freshly cut plants, the plants must be measured soon after they are cut since they very quickly lose water. Therefore, students should cut only the plants in one pot at a time for measurement.

Alternative Materials used cottage cheese cartons or other 10-cm containers with holes for drainage (for flower pots), basil seeds, zinnia seeds, or seed of other quick growing plants (NOTE: If you use larger seeds, increase the size of the pots used to 16 or 20 cm.)

Teaching Strategy Provide planting instruction sheets for students that give guidance concerning the following: how to prepare pots for planting, how many extra seeds are needed to help insure the correct number of seedlings per pot (expect about 80–90 percent to sprout), how to space seeds so that they are uniformly distributed, and how to plant the seeds in soil.

Alternative Teaching Demo The lab can also be run as a classroom experiment. If this is done, make sure that there is a replicate pot for each setup.

Chapter 4

Study Guide

ConnectED

Students can use the following to review the chapter.

Review

Vocabulary eGames
Vocabulary eFlashcards
Vocabulary PuzzleMaker

Assessment

Online Quizzes
Online Test Practice
Standardized Test Practice

Use the *ExamView®* *Assessment Suite* CD-ROM to:

- create multiple versions of tests
- create modified tests with one mouse click
- edit existing questions and add your own questions
- build tests aligned with state standards using built-in state curriculum tags
- change English tests to Spanish with one mouse click
- track students' progress using the Teacher Management System

Chapter 4 Study Guide

THEME FOCUS Homeostasis Carrying capacity, competition, disease, and other factors limit the size of populations and lead to homeostasis within the community.

BIG Idea **Population growth is a critical factor in a species' ability to maintain homeostasis within its environment.**

Section 1 Population Dynamics

population density (p. 92)
dispersion (p. 92)
density-independent factor (p. 94)
density-dependent factor (p. 95)
population growth rate (p. 97)
emigration (p. 97)
immigration (p. 97)
carrying capacity (p. 98)

MAIN Idea **Populations of species are described by density, spatial distribution, and growth rate.**

- There are population characteristics that are common to all populations of organisms, including plants, animals, and bacteria.
- Populations tend to be distributed randomly, uniformly, or in clumps.
- Population limiting factors are either density-independent or density-dependent.
- Populations tend to stabilize near the carrying capacity of their environment.

Section 2 Human Population

demography (p. 100)
demographic transition (p. 102)
zero population growth (ZPG) (p. 104)
age structure (p. 104)

MAIN Idea **Human population growth changes over time.**

- Human population growth rates vary in industrially developing countries and industrialized countries.
- Zero population growth occurs when the birthrate and immigration rate of a population equals the death rate and the emigration rate.
- The age structure of the human population is a contributing factor to population growth in some countries.
- Earth has an undefined carrying capacity for the human population.

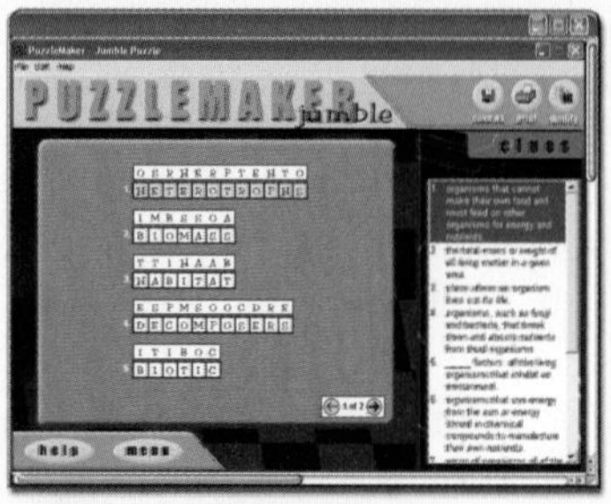

Review **Vocabulary PuzzleMaker**

For additional practice with vocabulary, have students access the Vocabulary PuzzleMaker online.

Review **Vocabulary eGames**

Section 1

Vocabulary Review

Replace the underlined words with the correct vocabulary term from the Study Guide page.

1. The number added to a population by movement can considerably increase a population's size.
2. Drought is a density-dependent factor.
3. Were it not for the long-term limit, a population would continue to grow exponentially.

Understand Main Ideas

Use the illustration to answer questions 4–6.

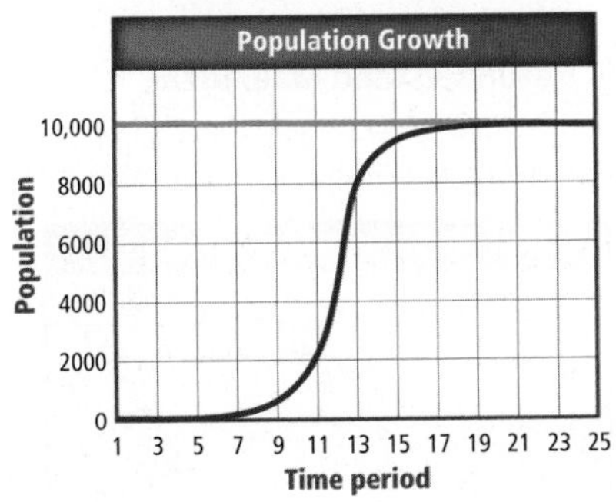

4. Which population growth model does this graph illustrate?
   A. exponential growth
   B. lag phase
   C. logistic growth
   D. straight-line growth
5. What is the horizontal line on this graph called?
   A. carrying capacity **C.** geometric growth
   B. exponential growth **D.** straight-line growth
6. What do the time periods 1–7 represent?
   A. acceleration phase **C.** exponential growth
   B. carrying capacity **D.** lag phase
7. If angelfish produce hundreds of young several times a year, which statement below is true?
   A. Angelfish have a *k*-strategy reproductive pattern.
   B. Angelfish have an *r*-strategy reproductive pattern.
   C. Angelfish probably have a low mortality rate.
   D. Angelfish provide a lot of care for their young.
8. If an aquarium holds 80 L of water and contains 170 guppies, what is the approximate density of the guppy population?
   A. 1 guppy/L **C.** 3 guppies/L
   B. 2 guppies/L **D.** 4 guppies/L
9. Which is a density-independent factor?
   A. a severe drought
   B. an intestinal parasite
   C. a fatal virus
   D. severe overcrowding

Use the photo below to answer questions 10 and 11.

10. Why is the life span of this finch with an eye disease most likely reduced?
    A. The bird cannot mate.
    B. The bird cannot find food or water.
    C. The bird spreads the disease to others.
    D. The bird cannot survive a temperature change.
11. Which is a possible reason for the relatively quick spread of the shown disease?
    A. an abiotic factor
    B. a decreased food supply
    C. increased population density
    D. increased immunity
12. What is the dispersion pattern of herding animals, birds that flock together, and fish that form schools?
    A. clumped **C.** uniform
    B. random **D.** unpredictable

Constructed Response

13. **Short Answer** Female Atlantic right whales can reproduce at ten years of age and live more than fifty years. They can produce a calf every three to five years. Assuming that a right whale begins to reproduce at age ten, produces a calf every four years, and gives birth to its last calf at age fifty, how many whales will this female produce in her lifetime?

Assessment Online Test Practice

Chapter 4

Assessment

Section 1

Vocabulary Review

1. Immigration
2. density-independent factor
3. carrying capacity

Understand Main Ideas

4. C
5. A
6. D
7. B
8. B
9. A
10. B
11. C
12. A

Constructed Response

13. 11

14. approximately 42 million people/million km^2 or 42 people/km^2
15. A *k*-strategist's population tends to slow when they near the carrying capacity. At this time, the resources become limiting.
16. Answers will vary. An example might be that a flood could kill a population of cacti by providing too much water, or a freeze could kill members of a tropical plant population such as lemons.
17. Answers will vary. An example might be a disease that kills enough of a population to slow its growth, or coyotes that prey upon a jackrabbit population in a desert.
18. As a population becomes larger, the density increases and the total resource base decreases.

Think Critically

19. It will be a logistic growth pattern.
20. The cow is a *k*-strategist because it produces only a few offspring and invests time, energy, and resources, ensuring that the offspring reach reproductive age.
21. random
22. minnow; beetle; bacteria

Section 2

Vocabulary Review

23. ZPG
24. age structure
25. demography

Understand Main Ideas

26. A
27. C

Chapter 4 Assessment

14. Short Answer What is the population density of Canada and the United States if they have a combined area of approximately 12.4 million square kilometers and a combined population of approximately 524 million?

15. Short Answer How does the carrying capacity affect *k*-strategists?

16. Open Ended Give two examples of how two different density-independent factors can limit a specific population.

17. Open Ended Give two examples of how two different density-dependent factors can limit a specific population.

18. Short Answer Explain how competition limits a population's growth.

Think Critically

19. Predict the shape of a population growth curve for a game park in which a male and a female rhinoceros are released.

Use the photo below to answer question 20.

20. Infer the reproductive strategy of the animal in the photo. Explain your answer.

21. MAIN Idea Opossums are solitary animals that usually meet in nature only to mate. What is their probable dispersion pattern?

22. Select from the following list the species that are r-strategists: minnow, giraffe, human, beetle, bacteria, eagle, and cougar.

Section 2

Vocabulary Review

Using the list of vocabulary words from the Study Guide, identify the term described by the scenario.

23. A population has an equal number of births and deaths.

24. Twenty percent of a population is in pre-reproductive years, 50 percent is in the reproductive years, and 30 percent is in the post-reproductive years.

25. The size, density, and birth and death rates of a human population are studied.

Understand Main Ideas

Use the graph below of the growth of the human population through history to answer questions 26 and 27.

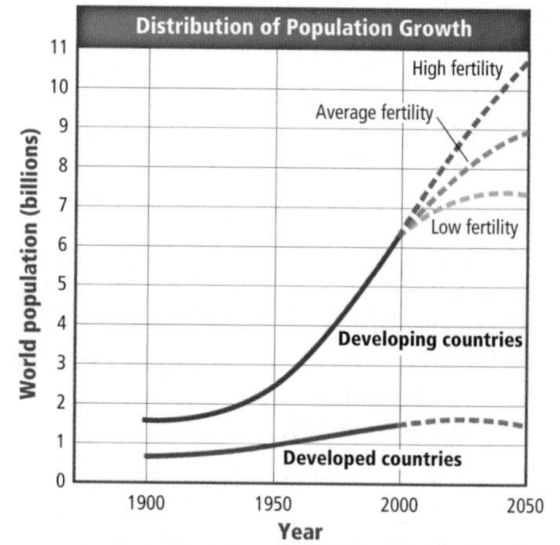

26. What is the projected population of developed countries by 2050?

A. 1.5 billion
B. 7.3 billion
C. 9 billion
D. 10.5 billion

27. What is the approximate population difference between developing countries that have low fertility rates and developing countries that have high fertility rates in 2050?

A. 1.5 billion
B. 1.7 billion
C. 3.2 billion
D. 9 billion

28. When did the human population begin to increase exponentially? Use **Figure 11** as a reference.
A. 2 million years ago **C.** 1800 B.C.
B. 6500 B.C. **D.** 1500 A.D.

29. Japan had a birthrate of eight and a death rate of nine in 2008. What was the PGR?
A. 0.01 percent **C.** −1 percent
B. 1 percent **D.** −10 percent

30. Georgia, a country in western Asia, had a birthrate of 11 and a death rate of 10 in 2008. What was the PGR of Georgia in that year?
A. 1 percent **C.** 1.1 percent
B. 0.11 percent **D.** 11 percent

Constructed Response

31. **Open Ended** Do you think the birthrate or the death rate is more important to human populations? Explain your answer.

32. **THEME FOCUS Homeostasis** Why might a population continue to grow when the number of births equals deaths?

33. **MAIN Idea** Study **Figure 11** and identify which phase of growth occurred between the Old Stone Age and the Middle Ages.

Think Critically

34. **Hypothesize** the shape of the age diagram for Switzerland, a developed country in Europe.

Use the graph below to answer question 35.

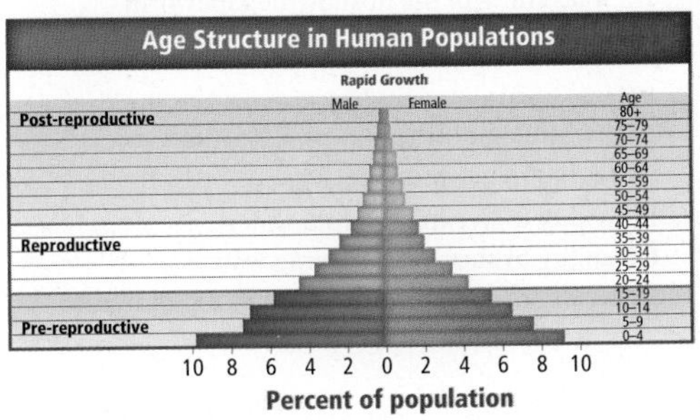

35. **Describe** the advantages and disadvantages of a population that has this type of age structure.

Summative Assessment

36. **BIG Idea** Create an imaginary community in which a particular population has been growing exponentially fast. What factors can you adjust to create a thriving, but steady, community?

37. **WRITING in Biology** Write a letter to the editor of your student newspaper expressing your views on the effect of human activities on a population of animals in your area.

DBQ Document-Based Questions

Northern right whales were once abundant in the northwestern Atlantic Ocean. By 1900, their numbers were almost depleted. Today, there are an estimated 300 individuals remaining.

Use the graph below to answer the following questions.

Data obtained from: Fujiwara, M., et al. 2001. Demography of the endangered North Atlantic right whale. *Nature* 414: 537-540.

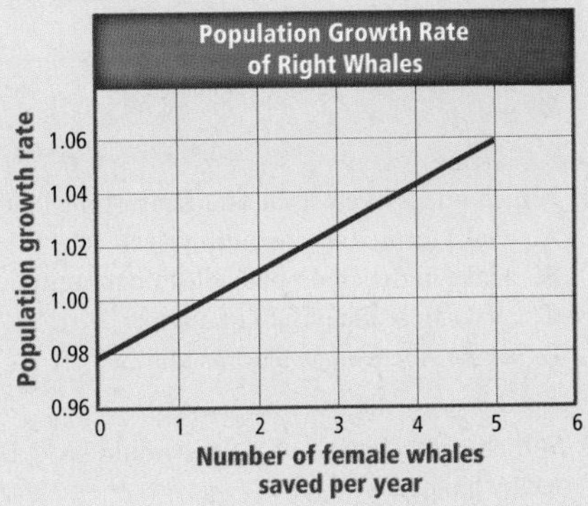

38. Predict the population growth rate if six female North Atlantic right whales were saved each year.

39. Saving females isn't the only factor to take into consideration when trying to restore the whale population. Write a hypothetical plan of action that takes into account two other factors that you think might help.

28. D
29. C
30. A

Constructed Response

31. Answers will vary. Accept any answer that is reasonably supported.
32. Immigration exceeds emigration, so the total number of people in the area continues to increase.
33. lag phase

Think Critically

34. The shape would be more rectangular or have a bulge in the middle.
35. This age structure is typical of a population that is rapidly growing. This rapid growth can pose several disadvantages if it is not accompanied by adequate resources. One advantage is that the large group of reproductive age people means the work force may be large.

Summative Assessment

36. Answers will vary, but should include references to limiting factors such as enough food, parasites and disease, space availability and limits to carrying capacity.
37. Letters will vary. Accept any response that the student supports with logical reasoning.

DBQ Document-Based Questions

Fujiwara, M., et al. 2001. Demography of the endangered North Atlantic right whale. *Nature* 414: 537-540.

38. 1.08
39. Answers will vary, but might include slowing fishing rates to increase resources available or limiting threats to the population by rerouting shipping lanes, etc.

Standardized Test Practice

Multiple Choice

1. A
2. D
3. B
4. A
5. D
6. D
7. B
8. C
9. A

Short Answer

10. After a sharp rise in the lynx population, the hare population drops quickly.
11. The lynx population would decrease rapidly and possibly die out if lynxes could not find other prey.
12. Answers will vary. Students could describe situations involving diseases, malnutrition, or destruction of the environment. Students should make a connection between lack of understanding and the harmful effects.
13. Both types of factors affect population growth. Density-dependent factors increase their effect as population size increases. Density-independent factors affect populations regardless of population size.
14. The organisms thrive in the optimum temperature zone. As the temperature exceeds the optimum temperature, the organisms begin to be physiologically stressed. As the temperatures continue to climb, organisms begin to die. Once the temperature reaches the zone that is outside the organisms tolerance range, all of the organisms have died.
15. Answers may vary. For instance, a forest fire can kill individuals, disrupt the habitat, and remove the food source for a population.
16. A population is all the organisms of one species in an area. The ecosystem includes several populations and the abiotic factors that affect the populations, such as temperature, availability of water, and type of soil.

Standardized Test Practice

Cumulative

Multiple Choice

1. Which is the main benefit of scientific debate for scientists?
   - **A.** challenging accepted theories
   - **B.** creating controversy
   - **C.** gaining research funding
   - **D.** publishing results

Use the graph below to answer question 2.

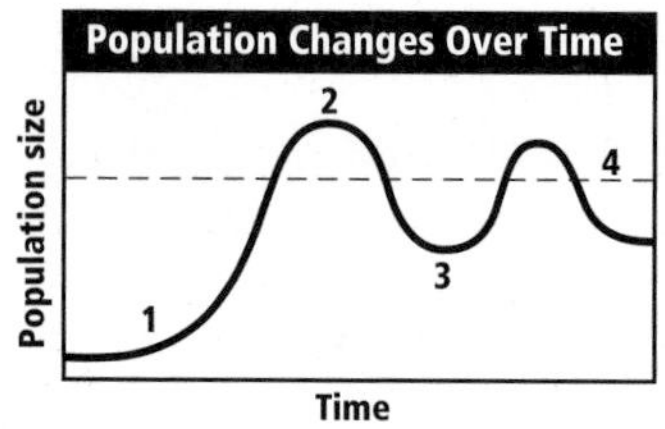

2. Which part of the graph indicates the carrying capacity of the habitat?
   - **A.** 1
   - **B.** 2
   - **C.** 3
   - **D.** 4

3. Which one is likely to be an oligotrophic lake?
   - **A.** a lake formed by a winding river
   - **B.** a lake in the crater of a volcanic mountain
   - **C.** a lake near the mouth of a river
   - **D.** a lake where algae blooms kill the fish

4. Which characteristic of a plant would NOT be studied by biologists?
   - **A.** beauty
   - **B.** chemical processes
   - **C.** growth rate
   - **D.** reproduction

5. Which statement describes the first changes in a forest that would follow a forest fire?
   - **A.** A climax community is established.
   - **B.** New plants grow from seeds that the wind carries to the area.
   - **C.** New soil forms.
   - **D.** Pioneer species are established.

Use this graph to answer question 6.

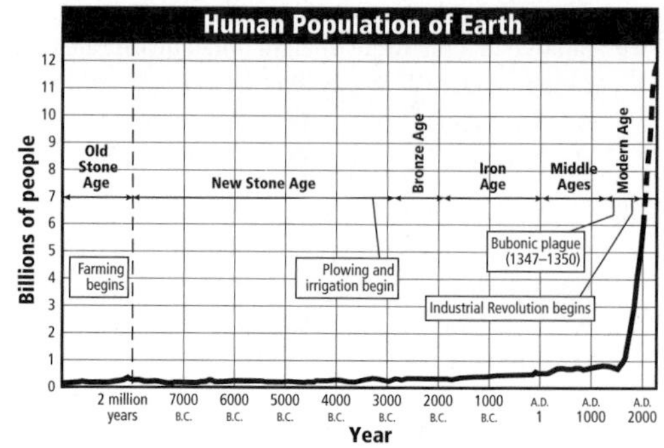

6. Which event appears to coincide with a gradual increase in human population?
   - **A.** bubonic plague
   - **B.** farming
   - **C.** Industrial Revolution
   - **D.** plowing and irrigation

7. Suppose an organism is host to a parasitic tapeworm. Which would be beneficial to the tapeworm?
   - **A.** death of the host from disease caused by the tapeworm
   - **B.** absorbing enough nutrients to sustain the tapeworm without harming the host
   - **C.** treatment of the host with antitapeworm drugs
   - **D.** weakening of the host by the tapeworm

8. Which adaptation would you expect to find in an organism living in an intertidal zone?
   - **A.** ability to live in total darkness
   - **B.** ability to live in very cold water
   - **C.** ability to survive in moving water
   - **D.** ability to survive without water for 24 hours

9. Which limiting factor is dependent on the density of the population?
   - **A.** contagious fatal virus
   - **B.** dumping toxic waste in a river
   - **C.** heavy rains and flooding
   - **D.** widespread forest fires

Short Answer

Use this graph to answer questions 10 and 11.

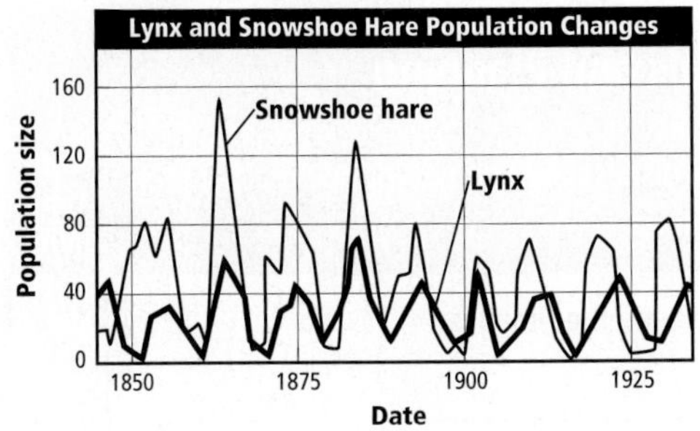

10. Assess what happened to the hare population after a sharp rise in the lynx population.

11. Lynxes hunt hares for food. Predict what would happen to the lynx population if a disease killed all of the hares.

12. Using your knowledge of current events or history, give an example of when ignorance about biology had a harmful effect on people.

13. Compare and contrast how density-dependent and density-independent factors regulate the growth of populations.

14. Describe what happens to organisms whose optimum temperature zone is between 21°C and 32°C when the temperature rises from 21°C to 50°C.

15. Give some examples of the ways that an environmental factor, such as a forest fire, can affect a population.

16. Explain how a population relates to an ecosystem.

Extended Response

Use these graphs to answer question 17.

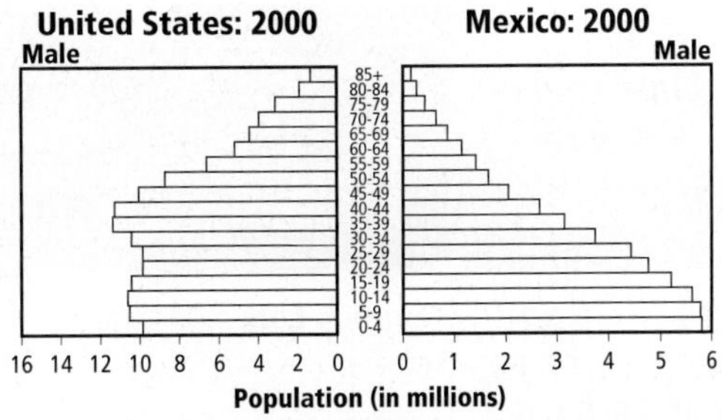

17. State what you think is the most significant area of difference between the two populations and justify your reasoning.

18. Many vertebrates that live in temperate forests hibernate in the winter. How do you think this adaptation helps with survival in this biome?

Essay Question

Author Carrie P. Snow once said, "Technology… is a queer thing. It brings you great gifts with one hand, and it stabs you in the back with the other."
C. P. Snow, New York Times, 15 March 1971

Using the information contained in the quotation above, answer the following question in essay format.

19. You are in charge of organizing a debate about whether technology is good or bad. Using your prior knowledge, choose a position and write a summary of the key points you would debate.

NEED EXTRA HELP?																			
If You Missed Question . . .	1	2	3	4	5	6	7	8	9	10	11	12	13	14	15	16	17	18	19
Review Section . . .	1.2	4.1	3.2	1.2	3.1	4.2	2.1	3.3	3.1	4.1	4.1	1.1	4.1	3.2	4.1	2.1	4.2	3.2	1.2

Extended Response

17. Answers will vary. The male population of the United States has a greater distribution of all age brackets than the male population of Mexico. Mexico has a greater number of males that are in their reproductive years and in their pre-reproductive years than it does in the post-reproductive years.

18. Temperate forests get cold in winter and many of the trees and plants lose their leaves. If animals hibernate through these months, instead of expending energy hunting and finding food, it may help them survive better. It is an adaptation that better suits the climate of a temperate forest.

Essay Question

19. Answers can vary. Debaters might present the idea that technology can be good or bad and give examples to support their position. One argument for technology is that it benefits many people. For example, the invention of X-ray machines led to health benefits for millions of people. Also, the invention of cell phones allows people to communicate easily and rapidly. One argument against technology is that it might have unforeseen and harmful consequences. The widespread use of DDT as an insecticide caused the death of many birds. The use of chlorofluorocarbon gases in spray cans caused damage to the ozone layer. Accept answers supported by logical reasoning.

Chapter 5 Organizer: Biodiversity and Conservation

LabManager™
Customize any lab with the LabManager™ CD-ROM.

Essential Questions	National Science Standards	Materials and Planning: Estimated times include cleanup and disposal, but do not include teacher prep time. For cleanup and disposal guidelines, see page 39T.	Est. Time (min)
Section 1 1. What are three types of biodiversity? 2. Why is biodiversity important? 3. What are the direct and indirect values of biodiversity?	UCP.1–3; A.1, A.2; C.4, C.5; F.1, F.2, F.3, F.4, F.5, F.6; G.1, G.2, G.3	**Launch Lab,** p. 114: magazine, book, internet images	20
		Demonstration, p. 116: photographs of animals and plants showing varying degrees of genetic diversity	10
		Demonstration, p. 118: several different varieties of apples	5
		MiniLab 1, p. 120: guest speaker from local conservancy or government agency	30–45
Section 2 1. What are the threats to biodiversity? 2. How is the current extinction rate different from the background extinction rate? 3. How can the decline of a single species affect an entire ecosystem?	UCP.1–3; A.1, A.2; C.4, C.5, C.6; F.1, F.2, F.3, F.4, F.5, F.6; G.1, G.2, G.3	**Demonstration,** p. 122: photos of extinct organisms that were part of mass extinctions and background extinctions	10
		Demonstration, p. 126: Two small aquariums (2–5 gallons each), clean pond water, fertilizer, algae, duckweed plants, small fish (such as guppies)	30
		MiniLab 2, p.127: lists of local ecological threats, leaf litter samples, field guides, forceps, jar, cups and spoon, cooler	30
Section 3 1. What are the two classes of natural resources? 2. What are the methods used to conserve biodiversity? 3. What are two techniques used to restore biodiversity?	UCP.1–3; A.1, A.2; C.4, C.5, C.6; E.1, E.2; F.2, F.3, F.4, F.5, F.6; G.1, G.2, G.3	**Demonstration,** p. 129: photos of farms with different crops, of forested areas that have been replanted, and of a person hunting deer	5–10
		Demonstration, p. 131: map of state and a national map that includes parks	10
		Demonstration, p. 134: one-gallon jar, pond or aquarium water, pond substrate, used motor oil	30
		BioLab, p. 137: coat hangers or 1-m stakes, field notebook, pencil, 50-m colored plastic ribbon, 60-m string, field guide of local plants, animals, and fungi	30–45

Suggested Time for Each Lesson

Class	Chapter Opener	Section 1	Section 2	Section 3	Assessment
Basic	45 min	90 min	45 min	90 min	45 min
General	25 min	65 min	45 min	90 min	45 min
Honors	20 min	20 min	70 min	20 min	20 min

ConnectED

connectED.mcgraw-hill.com

Access interactive learning opportunities and teaching resources using these icons located throughout your StudentWorks™ Plus Online and eTeacherEdition Online.

Chapter 5 Section Resources	Additional Chapter 5 Resources	Technology
FAST FILE Unit 1 Resources: Launch Lab Worksheet* MiniLab Worksheet* Study Guide (English/Spanish)* Section Quick Check **Reading Essentials 5.1** **Science Notebook 5.1*** **FAST FILE Unit 1 Resources:** MiniLab Worksheet* Study Guide (English/Spanish)* Section Quick Check **Reading Essentials 5.2** **Science Notebook 5.2*** **FAST FILE Unit 1 Resources:** BioLab Worksheet* Study Guide (English/Spanish)* Section Quick Check **Reading Essentials 5.3** **Science Notebook 5.3***	**FAST FILE Unit 1 Resources:** Chapter Diagnostic Test Concept Mapping* Real-World Biology Enrichment Chapter Tests A, B, and C **Transparencies:** Bellringer Transparencies* Biology Concepts Transparencies* **Lab Resources:** Laboratory Manual* Probeware Lab Manual* Forensics Lab Manual* Pre-AP Lab Manual* Open Inquiry in Biology* Guided Inquiry in Biology*	**Teaching Tools:** eTeacherEdition Online Classroom Presentation Toolkit CD-ROM* LabManager™ CD-ROM* Video Lab DVD* Virtual Lab CD-ROM* What's BIOLOGY Got To Do With It? StudentWorks™ Plus Online* **Chapter Assessment Tools:** Classroom Presentation Toolkit CD-ROM* *ExamView® Assessment Suite* CD-ROM **Web-Based Resources:** • StudentWorks™ Plus Online • eTeacherEdition Online • Animations* • The Interactive Time Line* • Interactive Tables* • Online Quizzes • Online Test Practice • Standardized Test Practice • Virtual Labs* • Multilingual eGlossary* • Vocabulary eGames* • Vocabulary eFlashcards • WebQuests • Personal Tutors

While all resources listed are appropriate for English learners, the * indicates resources with a strong visual or hands-on component for EL.

Teaching strategies and activities have been coded for differentiated instruction.

AL Activities for students working above grade level	**OL** Activities for students working on grade level	**BL** Activities for students working below grade level	**EL** Activities for English learners (also ELL)	**COOP LEARN** Activities designed for small cooperative group work

CHAPTER 5

Launch Lab

What Lives Here?

? Inquiry Launch Lab

For a lab worksheet, use your eTeacherEdition Online.

RUBRIC A rubric for evaluating Launch Labs is found on your eTeacherEdition Online.

Est. Time 20 min

Alternative Materials photographs of landscapes obtained by yourself or by students.

Teaching Strategy This activity can be taught using students' prior experiences, the photographs in this chapter, or images you obtain from magazines.

Procedure

1. Read and complete the lab safety form.
2. Choose three locations in your community that are familiar to you, such as a tree, a group of trees, a drainage ditch, a field, a dumpster, a park or a pond.
3. Rank the locations in descending order, greatest to least, according to the number of species of organisms you think you would find there.

Analysis

1. **Define** the term *biodiversity* in your own words. Accept any reasonable answer that describes biodiversity in terms of the tremendous variety of life that exists on Earth.
2. **Explain** how you chose to rank the locations in order. Answer will vary, but should reflect a correlation between species diversity and environments where abiotic and biotic factors can support a variety of life-forms.
3. **Describe** scientific methods you could use to find out how many species live in each habitat. Methods would include mapping a study area, making close observations, and recording the number of animals identified from each species.

CHAPTER 5

Biodiversity and Conservation

ConnectED

Your one-stop online resource
connectED.mcgraw-hill.com

- Video
- Audio
- Review
- Inquiry
- WebQuest
- Assessment
- Concepts in Motion
- Multilingual eGlossary

Launch Lab

What lives here?

Some landscapes support more organisms than others. In this lab, you will infer the relative numbers of species that can be found in each environment.

For a lab worksheet, use your StudentWorks™ Plus Online.

? Inquiry Launch Lab

FOLDABLES®

Make a three-tab foldable using the labels shown. Use it to organize your notes about biodiversity.

THEMES Focus on Diversity
The biosphere contains diverse communities and ecosystems.

BIG Idea Community and ecosystem homeostasis depend on a complex set of interactions among biologically diverse individuals.

Section 1 • Biodiversity
Section 2 • Threats to Biodiversity
Section 3 • Conserving Biodiversity

THEMES

Scientific Inquiry Biologists research methods of conservation to maintain wildlife populations.

Diversity Maintaining biodiversity is important to conserve the health of an ecosystem.

Energy Many renewable and nonrenewable resources are used for energy.

Homeostasis A disruption in biodiversity, such as species extinction, can cause disruption of ecosystem homeostasis.

Change Sudden change in an ecosystem, such as a forest fire, can decrease biodiversity.

Introduce the Chapter

Invasive Species

Use the photo to introduce students to the problem caused by invasive species.

SAY TO STUDENTS: ***The alga shown in the photo is popular with fish hobbyists because it is fast-growing, attractive, and hardy. This alga grows naturally in tropical seas, including the Caribbean. However, the alga has been introduced into other areas where it represents an invasive species.***

ASK STUDENTS: ***Why do you think this alga is causing problems in areas where it has been introduced?*** Abiotic and biotic factors limit its growth in tropical seas, but these factors are diminished or even absent outside its natural habitats.

BIG Idea

Check Comprehension

Ask students to monitor themselves as they read the chapter. Instruct them to slow down when they encounter new or difficult concepts, new vocabulary, or text that contains large amounts of information. If they do not understand the Big Idea or a Main Idea, they need to review what is unclear. In addition, have them write down questions as they study and bring any unanswered questions to class to be addressed during class discussions.

Section 1

MAIN Idea

BL OL AL **Biodiversity**

ASK STUDENTS: ***Why is it important that a large variety of species be maintained in the environment?*** Responses will vary, but may include such answers as, "Species depend on other species for food," or "The loss of just one species can affect many other species."

TELL STUDENTS: ***Biodiversity, the variety of life in an area, is important because it provides direct and indirect economic benefits and maintains a healthy biosphere.***

S **Skill Practice**

BL OL AL **Classify** Have students classify groups of dogs based on their genetic diversity. Point out that the differences they observe are the result of genetic variations. Humans have manipulated the genetic diversity within this species to produce the dog breeds we have today. However, all dogs are part of the species *Canis familiaris*.

ASK STUDENTS: ***Which dogs have greater genetic biodiversity: purebred dogs, such as poodles and Chihuahuas, or mixed breeds?*** As a general rule, mixed breeds and feral dogs have the greatest amount of genetic diversity.

■ **Caption Question Fig. 1** Other characteristics include number of spots and size of the beetles.

Section 1

Reading Preview

Essential Questions

- What are three types of biodiversity?
- Why is biodiversity important?
- What are the direct and indirect values of biodiversity?

Review Vocabulary

gene: functional unit that controls the expression of inherited traits and is passed from generation to generation

New Vocabulary

extinction
biodiversity
genetic diversity
species diversity
ecosystem diversity

g Multilingual eGlossary

Biodiversity

MAIN Idea **Biodiversity maintains a healthy biosphere and provides direct and indirect value to humans.**

Real-World Reading Link Stop for a moment and consider the effect of all the jackrabbits in a food web dying suddenly. What would happen to the other members of the food web? Is the disappearance of one species from Earth important? Will another species fill its niche?

What is biodiversity?

The loss of an entire species in a food web is not an imaginary situation. Entire species permanently disappear from the biosphere when the last member of the species dies in a process called **extinction.** As species become extinct, the variety of species in the biosphere decreases, which decreases the health of the biosphere. **Biodiversity** is the variety of life in an area that is determined by the number of different species in that area. Biodiversity increases the stability of an ecosystem and contributes to the health of the biosphere. There are three types of biodiversity to consider: genetic diversity, species diversity, and ecosystem diversity.

Genetic diversity The variety of genes or inheritable characteristics that are present in a population comprises its **genetic diversity. Figure 1** shows characteristics that are shared by Asian ladybird beetles, such as general body structure. The variety of colors demonstrates a form of genetic diversity. The beetles have other characteristics that differ, but they are not as apparent as their color. These characteristics might include resistance to a particular disease, the ability to recover from a disease, or the ability to obtain nutrients from a new food source should the old food source disappear. The beetles with these characteristics are more likely to survive and reproduce than beetles without these characteristics.

Genetic diversity within interbreeding populations increases the chances that some individuals will survive during changing environmental conditions or during an outbreak of disease. S

■ **Figure 1** These Asian ladybird beetles, *Harmonia axyridis*, demonstrate some visible genetic diversity because of their different colors.
Suggest ***some other characteristics that might vary among the beetles.***

Demonstration

Genetic Diversity Using photographs from *National Geographic* or similar magazines, have students determine whether the individual or group pictured is considered genetically diverse. Organisms with little genetic diversity include purebred animals or plants and organisms that are on the brink of extinction. Organisms with more genetic diversity include humans on a busy street, mixed-breed or feral animals, and large wild animal populations, such as insects. Est. time: 10 min

■ **Figure 2** Many species gather at this watering hole, making it a habitat rich in species diversity.

Species diversity The number of different species and the relative abundance of each species in a biological community is called **species diversity.** As you look at **Figure 2,** notice how many different species of organisms are in this one area. This habitat represents an area with a high level of species diversity because there are so many species present in one location. Species diversity, however, is not evenly distributed over the biosphere. As you move geographically from the polar regions to the equator, species diversity increases. For example, **Figure 3** shows the number of bird species from Alaska to Central America. Use the color key to see how diversity changes as you move toward the equator.

FOLDABLES® Incorporate information from this section into your Foldable.

D

Reading Check **Compare and contrast** genetic and species diversity.

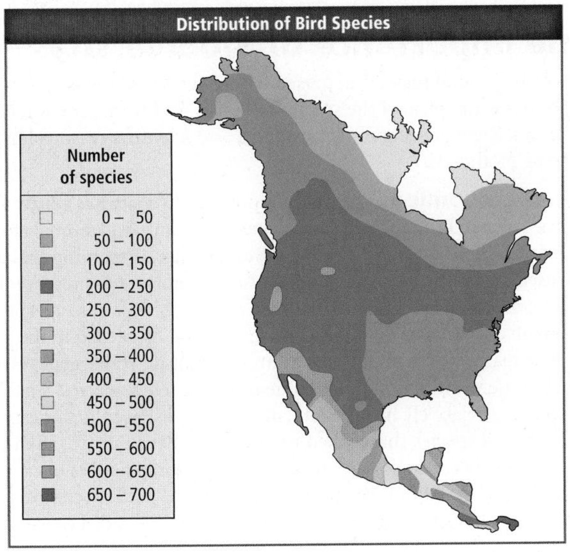

S

■ **Figure 3** This map shows the distribution of bird species in North and Central America. As you move toward the tropics, biodiversity increases.
Estimate ***the number of bird species where you live.***

Reading Check Genetic diversity refers to the variations within the gene pool of an individual species. Species diversity refers to the number of species in a given area.

■ **Caption Question** **Fig. 3** Answers will vary depending on location, but the numbers will most likely fall between 50 and 300 species.

D Develop Concepts

BL OL Activity To help students better understand the concept of species diversity, have them make a list of the species found in a classroom aquarium. Then have them go to an area near the school, such as a wooded or grassy area, and make a list of species found there. Field guides and source books are necessary for this exercise. Give students working below level a chart to complete.

EL Have students start by working in pairs and using a photograph to identify and list species. They can swap lists and fill in missing species. As a class, define *biodiversity* and then continue with the above activity.

ASK STUDENTS: ***How do the two lists compare? Does a bigger area necessarily have more biodiversity?*** No; Answers will depend on the outside area chosen. A creek or wooded area will have more biodiversity than a large lot of mowed grass.

S Skill Practice

BL OL AL Visual Literacy

Have students examine Figure 3.

ASK STUDENTS: ***What environmental factors might be involved in the increasing diversity of species as one moves from northern latitudes to the tropics?*** Responses will vary, but should include more moderate climate and greater availability of food.

FOLDABLES®

RUBRIC A rubric for evaluating Foldables is found on your eTeacherEdition Online.

Going Further On the back of their Foldables, have students draw a two-column chart to record ways in which biodiversity is directly and indirectly beneficial to the biosphere.

D Develop Concepts

BL OL Brainstorm

ASK STUDENTS: ***What are some species that produce direct economic benefit?*** Write student responses on the board. Students may indicate food crops such as corn, farm animals such as cattle, or plants such as rubber trees.

C Critical Thinking

OL AL Imagine

ASK STUDENTS: ***What criteria would you use to determine the direct economic benefit of a particular food crop?*** Responses will vary, but may include cost of production and number of people fed calculated on a unit basis such as per bushel or per ton. Point out that other economic benefits are derived from wages earned in the production of the crop.

R Reading Strategy

EL BL OL AL Anticipate

Before students read the text below the heading *The Importance of Biodiversity*, have them predict whether five to ten statements that you have developed from this section are true or false. After they read, have students validate or revise their answers based on the information in the text.

S Skill Practice

BL OL AL Make a Table Have students make a table with columns labeled *Importance of Biodiversity, Example,* and *How Important.* Have students fill in their tables. The third column should be an evaluation of value the student assigns. Practice value statements with students to help with the last column.

Reading Check Each ecosystem has unique organisms that interact with abiotic factors that support them.

Dall Sheep, *Ovis dalli,* in Alaska

Tropical birds in Peru

Figure 4 The biosphere contains many ecosystems with diverse abiotic factors that support a variety of organisms.

Ecosystem diversity The variety of ecosystems that are present in the biosphere is called **ecosystem diversity.** An ecosystem is made up of interacting populations and the abiotic factors that support them. The interactions of organisms affect the development of stable ecosystems. Different locations around the world have different abiotic factors that support different types of life. For example, an ecosystem in Alaska has a set of abiotic factors that supports Dall sheep, which are shown in **Figure 4.** An ecosystem in South America has a different set of abiotic factors that supports tropical birds, also shown in **Figure 4.** Like these ecosystems, most of the ecosystems on Earth support a diverse collection of organisms. D C

Vocabulary

Academic Vocabulary

Diverse
made of different qualities
The colors and shapes of flowers are very diverse.

Reading Check **Explain** why ecosystem diversity results in species diversity in a healthy biosphere.

R The Importance of Biodiversity

S There are several reasons to preserve biodiversity. Many humans work to preserve and protect the species on Earth for future generations. In addition, there are economic, aesthetic, and scientific reasons for preserving biodiversity.

Direct economic value Maintaining biodiversity has a direct economic value to humans. Humans depend on plants and animals to provide food, clothing, energy, medicine, and shelter. Preserving species that are used directly is important, but it also is important to preserve the genetic diversity in species that are not used directly. Those species serve as possible sources of desirable genes that might be needed in the future.

The reason there might be a future need for desirable genes is that most of the world's food crops come from just a few species. These plants have relatively little genetic diversity and share the same problems that all species share when genetic diversity is limited, such as lacking resistance to disease. In many cases, close relatives of crop species still grow wild in their native habitat. These wild species serve as reservoirs of desirable genetic traits that might be needed to improve domestic crop species.

Demonstration

Economic Importance of Biodiversity Bring in examples of several varieties of apples from a local grocery store. As you discuss the economic importance of biodiversity, point out that each variety of apple has a different purpose and provides added income for those who supply the crops. For instance, Arkansas Black apples are excellent for long-term storage, Golden Delicious apples are well suited for cooking, Gala and Fuji apples are best eaten fresh, and Winesap apples are good for making apple cider. Est. time: 5 min

Teosinte plant

Commercial corn plant

■ **Figure 5** The teosinte plant contains genes that are resistant to several viral diseases that affect commercial corn plants. These genes have been used to produce virus-resistant commercial corn varieties.

The distant relative of corn, teosinte, shown in **Figure 5,** is resistant to the viral diseases that damage commercial corn crops. Using this wild species, plant pathologists developed disease-resistant corn varieties. If this wild species had not been available, this genetic diversity would have been lost, and the ability to develop disease-resistant corn varieties would also have been lost.

In addition, biologists are beginning to learn how to transfer genes that control inherited characteristics from one species to the other. This process is sometimes referred to as genetic engineering. Crops have been produced that are resistant to some insects, that have increased nutritional value, and that are more resistant to spoilage. Most wild species of plants and animals have not been evaluated for useful genetic traits. The opportunity to benefit from these genes is lost forever if wild species of plants and animals become extinct. This increases the importance of species that currently have no perceived economic value because their economic value might increase in the future.

Reading Check **Explain** why preserving biodiversity is important for the human food supply.

D **Connection to Health** Many of the medicines that are used today are derived from plants or other organisms. You probably know that penicillin, a powerful antibiotic discovered in 1928 by Alexander Fleming, is derived from bread mold. Ancient Greeks, Native Americans, and others extracted salicin, a painkiller, from the willow tree. Today, a version of this drug is synthesized in laboratories and is known as aspirin. **Figure 6** shows a Madagascar periwinkle flower, which recently was found to yield an extract that is useful in treating some forms of leukemia. This extract has been used to develop drugs that have increased the survival rate for some leukemia patients from 20 percent to more than 95 percent.

Scientists continue to find new extracts from plants and other organisms that help in the treatment of human diseases. However, many species of organisms are yet to be identified, especially in remote regions of Earth, so their ability to provide extracts or useful genes is unknown.

S

■ **Figure 6** Medicines developed from an extract from Madagascar periwinkle, *Catharanthus roseus,* are used to treat forms of leukemia.
Summarize ***Why is it important to maintain biodiversity for medical reasons?***

Reading Check Humans do not depend upon many species for their food. However, these species depend on other species for their nutrients. In turn, these species depend on still other species. As a result, preserving biodiversity is important for the human food supply.

■ **Caption Question Fig. 6** Drugs used to treat many diseases including ovarian cancer and childhood leukemias have been developed from extracts of unusual plants in biologically diverse areas.

S Skill Practice

AL Visual Literacy

ASK STUDENTS: ***How do the two species pictured in Figure 5 compare?*** Domesticated corn is larger, but it has less genetic variation than wild teosinte.

Develop Concepts

BL OL AL Integrate History

Inform students that Fleming's discovery of penicillin was one of many accidental discoveries in the history of science. Fleming decided not to clean some petri dishes he had used because he was in a hurry to leave for a vacation. Upon his return, he noticed mold growing on some of the dishes. Fleming also observed that bacteria had not grown near the mold. This casual observation led to the discovery of penicillin.

D Develop Concepts

OL AL

Clarify a Misconception

Many students will think that the medicines described in Connection to Health are still manufactured directly from the plants from which the active ingredient was first derived.

ASK STUDENTS: ***How do you think penicillin and aspirin are made today?*** For the most part, these drugs and others similar to them are manufactured synthetically.

BL For students working below level, use scaffolded questions (i.e., Are medicines made directly from plants? Why? Why not? How are they made?).

W Writing Support

AL **COOP LEARN**

Technical Writing Have students work in pairs to prepare a technical summary describing how conservation efforts to improve watersheds for New York City improve the water supply. Efforts center on implementing extensive watershed management measures, including water quality monitoring and disease surveillance, land acquisition and comprehensive planning, and upgrading wastewater treatment plants.

■ **Caption Question** **Fig. 7** toxic waste dumps, fertilizer from farm runoff, sewage, diverting water or destroying wetlands

MiniLab 1

? Inquiry **MiniLab**

For a lab worksheet, use your eTeacherEdition Online.

RUBRIC A rubric for evaluating MiniLabs is found on your eTeacherEdition Online.

Est. Time 30–45 min

Safety Precaution Approve lab safety forms before work begins.

Teaching Strategy You might wish to invite a class speaker from a local conservation group or governmental agency to provide some background information about this topic.

Analysis

1. Answers will vary depending on the severity and target of the threat.
2. Answers should follow logical conclusions about what would happen if the plan were implemented.

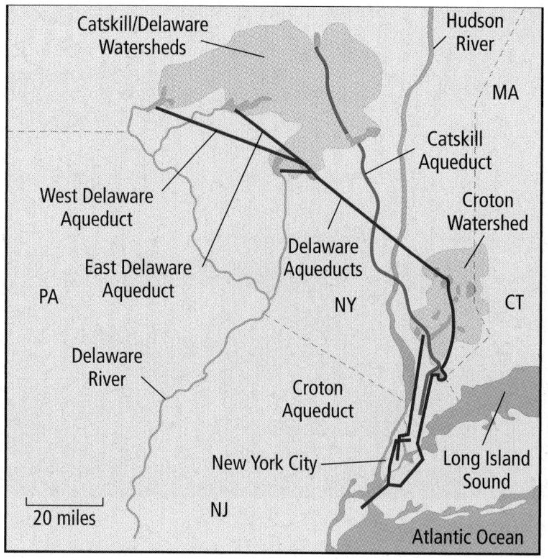

■ **Figure 7** New York City's drinking water is supplied by the Catskill and Delaware watersheds.
Infer ***What types of human activities could affect a watershed and decrease its water quality?***

Indirect economic value A healthy biosphere provides many services to humans and other organisms that live on Earth. For example, green plants provide oxygen to the atmosphere and remove carbon dioxide. Natural processes provide drinking water that is safe for human use. Substances are cycled through living organisms and nonliving processes, providing nutrients for all living organisms. As you will soon learn, healthy ecosystems provide protection against floods and drought, generate and preserve fertile soils, detoxify and decompose wastes, and regulate local climates.

It is difficult to attach an economic value to the services that a healthy biosphere provides. However, some scientists and economists have attempted to do just that. In the 1990s, New York City was faced with the decision of how to improve the quality of its drinking water. A large percentage of New York City's drinking water was supplied by watersheds, as shown in **Figure 7.** Watersheds are land areas where the water on them or the water underneath them drains to the same place. The Catskill and Delaware watersheds did not meet clean water standards and no longer could supply quality drinking water to the city.

The city was faced with two choices: build a new water filtration system for more than $6 billion or preserve and clean up the watersheds for approximately 1.5 billion dollars. The economic decision was clear in this case. A healthy ecosystem was less expensive to maintain than using technology to perform the same services. **W**

MiniLab 1

Investigate Threats to Biodiversity

? Inquiry **MiniLab**

What are the threats to natural habitats in your local area? Investigate these threats and brainstorm possible remedies with which you can educate others.

Procedure

1. Read and complete the lab safety form.
2. With your lab group, choose one factor that is threatening the biodiversity in your community and study how it has affected the climax community.
3. Brainstorm ways that this threat could be reversed.
4. Organize this information about threats and possible solutions with your classmates.

Analysis

1. **Evaluate** What are the most important pieces of information that the public needs to know about this threat?
2. **Infer** Imagine you have implemented one plan to reverse a threat you studied. Now it is 100 years later. What does the ecosystem look like? What changes have occurred? What species are there now?

Content Background

Cultural Diversity The aesthetic value of biodiversity has been criticized. Some argue that aesthetics do not necessarily increase biodiversity. For example, a well-kept lawn has low biodiversity. Also, aesthetics probably affect only a minority in industrialized countries. Many in developing countries do not have the luxury of considering aesthetics. Have a class discussion about cultural ideas of beauty, and provide specific examples (e.g., dog breeding).

■ **Figure 8** Emerald Bay in Lake Tahoe is an environment with many aesthetic qualities. Lake Tahoe was once pristine, but urbanization, increased runoff, and other forms of pollution have harmed the environment's health. Many groups are working together to keep Lake Tahoe healthy and beautiful.

This example shows that nature can provide services, such as water that is safe for human consumption, at less expense than using technology to provide the same service. Some scientists think the natural way should be the first choice for providing these services. Research indicates that when healthy ecosystems are preserved, the services the ecosystems provide will continue to be less expensive than performing the same services with technology.

Aesthetic and scientific values Two additional considerations for maintaining biodiversity and healthy ecosystems are the aesthetic and scientific values that they provide. It is difficult to attach a value to something that is beautiful, such as the ecosystem shown in **Figure 8**, or something that is interesting to study. However, scientists are finding ways to show the value in protecting and studying the environment.

W

Section 1 Assessment

Section Summary

- Biodiversity is important to the health of the biosphere.
- There are three types of biodiversity: genetic, species, and ecosystem.
- Biodiversity has aesthetic and scientific values, and direct and indirect economic value.
- It is important to maintain biodiversity to preserve the reservoir of genes that might be needed in the future.
- Healthy ecosystems can provide some services at a lesser expense than the use of technology.

Understand Main Ideas

1. MAIN Idea **Explain** why biodiversity is important to the biosphere.
2. **Summarize** the three types of biodiversity.
3. **Generalize** why maintaining biodiversity has a direct economic value to humans.
4. **Differentiate** between the direct and indirect economic value of biodiversity.
5. **Evaluate and discuss** the importance of maintaining biodiversity for future medical needs.

Think Critically

6. **Design a course of action** for the development of a building project in your community, such as a shopping mall, housing development, city park, or highway, that provides for the maintenance of biodiversity in the plan.

WRITING in Biology

7. Write a short report explaining the desirability of maintaining genetic diversity in domesticated animals, such as dogs, cats, pigs, cattle, and chickens. Include the advantages and disadvantages in your report.

W Writing Support

OL Summary Writing

Have students write a two-paragraph summary of this section. Instruct them to include all new vocabulary terms defined on this page in their summary.

BL Have students write a one-paragraph summary.

EL Have students orally use new vocabulary terms in sentences.

Formative Assessment

Evaluation Ask students to list and describe three types of biodiversity. genetic diversity–variety of alleles of genes present in the gene pool of a species; species biodiversity–number and abundance of species in a small area; ecosystem biodiversity–overall number of species in an ecosystem

Remediation Write the following five phrases on the board: *dogs in a neighborhood, tropical rain forest, microorganisms in a pond, vegetable garden,* and *students in school.*

ASK STUDENTS: ***Which type of biodiversity does each of these represent?*** dogs–genetic; tropical rain forest–ecosystem; pond–species; vegetable garden–species; students–genetic

Section 1 Assessment

1. Biodiversity maintains a healthy biosphere and provides both direct and indirect benefits to humans.
2. genetic diversity—variations in the gene pool of a species; species diversity—different species in a community; ecosystem diversity—variety of ecosystems in the biosphere
3. Humans depend on various species for food, medicines, clothing, and shelter.
4. direct economic value—apparent and often recognized immediately; indirect economic benefit—not obvious and/or realized after time
5. Scientists have analyzed only a fraction of species for the medicines they can provide. It is important to maintain biodiversity to preserve species that might prove valuable.
6. Students should address measures that will conserve biodiversity, such as replanting species of plants, and keeping water sources clean.
7. disadvantage—maintaining undesirable traits; advantage—increases chances of survival during times of environmental change

Assessment Online Quiz

Section 2

MAIN Idea

BL OL AL

Threats to Biodiversity

ASK STUDENTS: ***What happens when a new building project starts in an area that was previously undeveloped?*** Responses will vary, but some students will likely talk about new houses or office buildings, while others might talk about changes in the biotic community that was present. Point out that human activity always causes the existing biological community and ecosystem to change. The same changes that are positive for some species may be negative for others. Also, there are often unintended consequences associated with human activity.

R Reading Strategy

EL BL OL **Assessment Preview**

Before students read Section 2, have them read the section assessment questions on page 128.

SAY TO STUDENTS: ***Read this section with the section assessment questions in mind to help you identify the most important information.***

W Writing Support

BL OL AL **Narrative Writing**

Have students select one of the mass extinctions from Table 1. Tell them to research what scientists think was the cause of the extinction and write a summary. Below level research material should be available.

Concepts in Motion

Interactive Table

Section 2

Reading Preview

Essential Questions

- What are the threats to biodiversity?
- How is the current extinction rate different from the background extinction rate?
- How can the decline of a single species affect an entire ecosystem?

Review Vocabulary

food web: a model representing the many interconnected food chains and pathways in which energy and matter flow through a group of organisms

New Vocabulary

background extinction
mass extinction
natural resource
overexploitation
habitat fragmentation
edge effect
biological magnification
eutrophication
introduced species

Multilingual eGlossary

Threats to Biodiversity

R **MAIN Idea** **Some human activities reduce biodiversity in ecosystems, and current evidence suggests that reduced biodiversity might have serious long-term effects on the biosphere.**

Real-World Reading Link Have you ever built a structure with blocks and then tried to remove individual blocks without causing the entire structure to collapse? Similarly, if you remove one species from a food web, the food web can collapse.

Extinction Rates

Many species have become extinct, and paleontologists study fossils of those extinct species. The gradual process of species becoming extinct is known as **background extinction.** Stable ecosystems can be changed by the activity of other organisms, climate changes, or natural disasters. This natural process of extinction is not what concerns scientists. Instead, many worry about a recent increase in the rate of extinction. Some scientists predict that between one-third and two-thirds of all plant and animal species will become extinct during the second half of this century. Most of these extinctions will occur near the equator.

Some scientists estimate that the current rate of extinction is about 1000 times the normal background extinction rate. These scientists think that we are witnessing a period of mass extinction. **Mass extinction** is an event in which a large percentage of all living species become extinct in a relatively short period of time. The last mass extinction occurred about 65 million years ago, as illustrated in **Table 1,** when the last of the surviving dinosaurs became extinct.

W

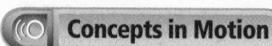

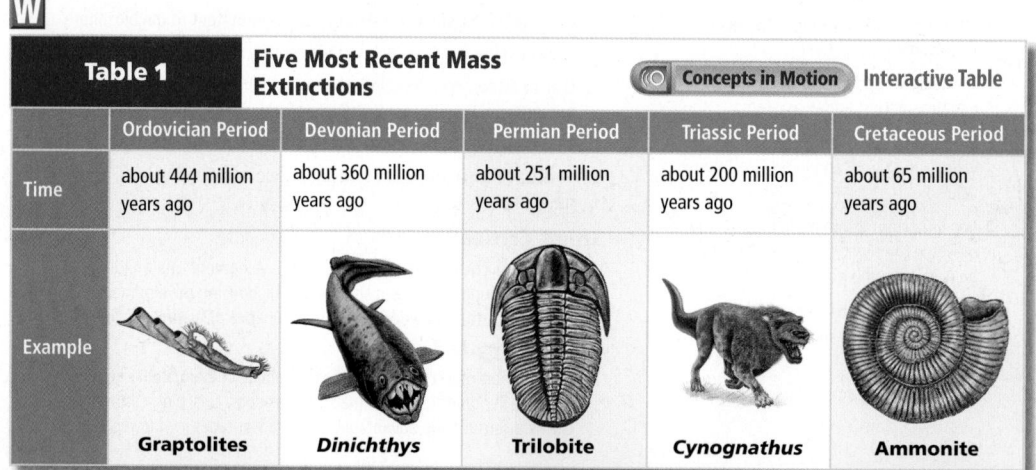

Table 1 **Five Most Recent Mass Extinctions** — Concepts in Motion Interactive Table

	Ordovician Period	Devonian Period	Permian Period	Triassic Period	Cretaceous Period
Time	about 444 million years ago	about 360 million years ago	about 251 million years ago	about 200 million years ago	about 65 million years ago
Example	 **Graptolites**	 ***Dinichthys***	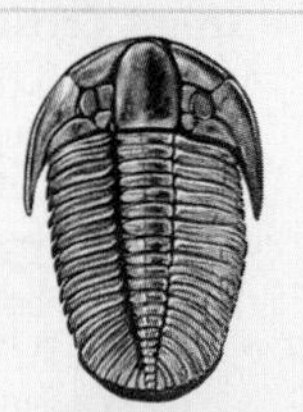 **Trilobite**	 ***Cynognathus***	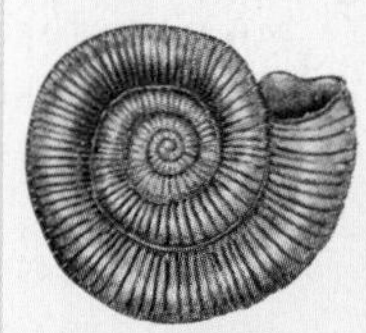 **Ammonite**

Demonstration

Extinction Rates Use photos from magazines showing various extinct organisms. Show students which organisms were part of a mass extinction (such as dinosaurs) and compare them to those that were part of a background extinction (such as *Eohippus* or other similar species). Est time: 10 min

Differentiated Instruction

Below Level Students performing below grade level may be easily distracted. When using the reading strategy described on this page, seat these students in an area that is free from distractions so that they can focus on the material.

For more tips, see pages 14T–15T.

Table 2 **Estimated Number of Extinctions Since 1600** Concepts in Motion Interactive Table

Group	Mainland	Island	Ocean	Total	Approximate Number of Known Species	Percent of Group Extinct
Mammals	30	51	4	85	4000	2.1
Birds	21	92	0	113	9000	1.3
Reptiles	1	20	0	21	6300	0.3
Amphibians*	2	0	0	2	4200	0.05
Fish	22	1	0	23	19,100	0.1
Invertebrates	49	48	1	98	1,000,000+	0.01
Flowering plants	245	139	0	384	250,000	0.2

*An alarming decrease of amphibian populations has occurred since the mid-1970s, and many species might be on the verge of extinction.

S

Connection to History The accelerated loss of species began several centuries ago. **Table 2** shows the estimated number of extinctions that have occurred by group since 1600. Many of the species' extinctions in the past have occurred on islands. For example, 60 percent of the mammals that have become extinct in the past 500 years lived on islands, and 81 percent of bird extinctions occurred on islands.

Species on islands are particularly vulnerable to extinction because of several factors. Many of these species evolved without the presence of natural predators. As a result, when a predator, such as a dog, cat, rat, or human, is introduced to the population, the native animals do not have the ability or skills to escape. When a nonnative species is introduced to a new population, it can be a carrier of a disease to which the native population has no resistance. The native population often dies off as a result. In addition, islands typically have relatively small population sizes and individual animals rarely travel between islands, both of which increases the vulnerability of island species to extinction.

Reading Check **Explain** why organisms found on islands are more vulnerable to extinction than other organisms.

VOCABULARY
WORD ORIGIN
Native
from the Latin word *nativus*, meaning to be born

Factors That Threaten Biodiversity

R Scientists point out that today's high rate of extinction differs from past mass extinctions. The current high rate of extinction is a result of the activities of a single species—*Homo sapiens*. After a mass extinction in the past, new species evolved and biodiversity recovered after several million years. This time, the recovery might be different. Humans are changing conditions on Earth faster than new traits can evolve in some species to cope with the new conditions. Evolving species might not have the natural resources they need. **Natural resources** are all materials and organisms found in the biosphere, including minerals, fossil fuels, nuclear fuels, plants, animals, soil, clean water, clean air, and solar energy.

Reading Check Organisms found on islands generally have a narrower range and a lower total population than species found on the mainland. Any introduced predators might be more efficient at hunting organisms that have not previously developed defenses against them while living on islands.

Concepts in Motion

Interactive Table

S Skill Practice

BL OL AL COOP LEARN

Analyze the Table Have students work in pairs to discuss the importance of the data presented in Table 2. Once students have discussed the data, use the table to begin a discussion of the apparent increase in extinctions above the background rate and what this might mean for the future.

Reading Strategy

EL Vocabulary Chart Have students create a three-column chart. Have them write the terms *extinction, eutrophication, habitat loss, pollution,* and *general threats to biodiversity* in the first column. Have them write the definition in the second column, and a pictorial clue to help remember the meaning in the third column.

R Reading Strategy

BL OL AL COOP LEARN

Directed Reading

SAY TO STUDENTS: ***Create a chart on your paper that contains at least three broad categories of factors that threaten biodiversity.*** Preview the text below the heading *Factors that Threaten Biodiversity* on the next several pages. Organize students into groups and have them brainstorm these factors and put them under broad headings such as *Overexploitation, Habitat, Pollution,* or *Others*. Have each group present one of their headings to the rest of the class and explain why they chose to include the specific factors under the broad heading. Point out that the categories actually overlap one another.

■ **Figure 9** The ocelot and all species of rhinos, including the white rhinoceros, are in danger of becoming extinct, due in part to overexploitation.

Ocelot

White rhinoceros

■ **Figure 10** Cleared land often is used for agricultural crops or as grazing land for livestock. Planting large expanses of crops reduces the biodiversity of the area.

Natural tropical rain forest

Cleared tropical rain forest

Overexploitation One of the factors that is increasing the current rate of extinction is the **overexploitation,** or excessive use, of species that have economic value. For example, the great herds of bison that once roamed the central plains of North America were hunted to the brink of extinction because their meat and hides could be sold commercially and because they were hunted for sport. At one time, it is estimated that there were 50 million bison. By 1889, there were less than 1000 bison left.

Passenger pigeons are another example of a species that has been overexploited. At one time, there were huge flocks of these birds that would darken the skies of North America during their migration. Unfortunately, they were overhunted and forced from their habitats. By the early 1900s, they had become extinct.

The ocelot, shown in **Figure 9,** is found from Texas to Argentina and is in danger of becoming extinct. The increasing loss of their habitat and the commercial value of their fur are reasons for their declining numbers. The white rhinoceros, also shown in **Figure 9,** is one of five species of rhinos, all of which are in danger of becoming extinct. They are hunted and killed for their horns, which are then sold for medicinal purposes. Historically, overexploitation was the primary cause of species extinction. However, the number one cause of species extinction today is the loss or destruction of habitat.

Reading Check **Explain** the term overexploitation as it relates to species extinction.

Habitat loss There are several ways that species can lose their habitats. If a habitat is destroyed or disrupted, the native species might have to relocate or they will die. For example, humans are clearing areas of tropical rain forests and are replacing the native plants with agricultural crops or grazing land.

Destruction of habitat The clearing of tropical rain forests, like what is shown in **Figure 10,** has a direct impact on global biodiversity. As mentioned earlier, the tropical latitudes contain much of the world's biodiversity in their native populations. In fact, estimates show that more than half of all species on Earth live in the tropical rain forests. The removal of so much of the natural forest will cause many species on Earth to become extinct as a result of habitat loss. W

W Writing Support

BL OL AL

Technical Writing Have each student prepare a brochure about a species that is threatened or endangered as a result of overexploitation or habitat destruction. Inform them that any species mentioned in the text cannot be used. The brochure should be made from a sheet of paper that has been folded into thirds vertically so that it has six panels—three on the front and three on the back. Tell students that one panel should be the title of the brochure and should include the author's name. One panel should have a photo or sketch of the species. Other panels should detail the geography of the species, history of the species, why it has become threatened or endangered, and what might be done to reverse the situation.

Develop Concepts

BL OL AL COOP LEARN

Biodiversity Alphabet Have students work in groups of three to create an alphabet of biodiversity. For each letter of the alphabet, have students list one organism and describe how it is used, for food, shelter, or clothing, or its role in the environment. Tell students to also list the country or continent where the organism is found. Have them place an asterisk next to the name of any organism that is being overexploited or whose habitat is being destroyed. For example, for the letter *L* students might list llama—pack animal—South America. Allow students to illustrate the list if they wish.

Reading Check Overexploitation involves taking more individuals from a species' population than the species can replace. In such overexploitation, genetic diversity may decrease as the species' population declines. Overexploitation may result from hunting, fishing, or poaching.

Content Background

Real-World Connection Humans affect all habitats on Earth. Humans have reduced the Earth's forests by approximately 50 percent. Human activity has destroyed the Gulf Coast wetlands so much that they have lost the ability to mitigate damage from natural disasters like hurricanes.

■ **Figure 11** A declining population of one species can affect an entire ecosystem. When the number of harbor seals and sea lions declined, killer whales ate more sea otters. The decline in sea otter population led to an increase in sea urchins, which eat kelp. This led to the ultimate decline in kelp forests.

S

Disruption of habitat Some habitats might not be destroyed, but they can be disrupted. For example, off the coast of Alaska, a chain of events occurred in the 1970s that demonstrates how the declining numbers of one member of a food web can affect the other members. As you can see from the chain of events shown in **Figure 11,** the decline of one species can affect an entire ecosystem. When one species plays such a large role in an ecosystem, that species is called a keystone species. A decline in various fish populations, possibly due to overfishing, has led to a decline in sea lion and harbor seal populations. Some scientists hypothesize that global warming also played a role in the decline. This started a chain reaction within the marine ecosystem that affected many species.

Reading Check **Name** the keystone species in the example in Figure 11.

Fragmentation of habitat The separation of an ecosystem into small pieces of land is called **habitat fragmentation.** Populations often stay within the confines of the small parcel because they are unable or unwilling to cross the human-made barriers. This causes several problems for the survival of various species.

First, the smaller the parcel of land, the fewer species it can support. Second, fragmentation reduces the opportunities for individuals in one area to reproduce with individuals from another area. For this reason, genetic diversity often decreases over time in habitat fragments. Smaller, separated, and less genetically diverse populations are less able to resist disease or respond to changing environmental conditions.

S Skill Practice

EL BL OL Visual Literacy

Have students examine Figure 11. **SAY TO STUDENTS:** ***If one member of the food web was removed at a time, how would its removal affect the rest of the organisms? Consider this question for each organism pictured in the figure.***

Develop Concepts

BL OL AL Scaffolding

ASK STUDENTS: ***What is species diversity?*** the number of species and their abundance in a community ***Predict what will happen to the economy as biodiversity continues to decrease.*** The economy will be disrupted. ***Classify the type of biodiversity value that would be placed on the beauty of a flower in its habitat.*** aesthetic value ***Explain the difference between background extinction and mass extinction.*** Background extinction is the normal rate of extinction, and mass extinction is an extinction event where a large percentage of all living species becomes extinct in a relatively short period of time. ***If a natural resource is overexploited, what might happen to its price on the market?*** Its price would increase. ***Which threat to biodiversity do you think is most detrimental? Why?*** Student responses will vary.

Reading Check Fish

Content Background

Real-World Connection Habitat disruption is especially dangerous for migratory birds. Scientists have helped propose and develop wildlife refuges at critical places along flyways. The establishment of wildlife refuges must be an international effort. In the western hemisphere, the Shorebird Reserve Network operates in both Central and South America.

Research Citation

Scaffolding Educational research indicates that scaffolding is a valuable strategy for helping students deepen their understanding of a text. By guiding them through the reading with a series of questions that build on each other, scaffolding requires that students become engaged in the reading and their own learning. (Jorgensen, 1998)

Research bibliography on pages 32T–34T

Critical Thinking

OL AL Infer

ASK STUDENTS: ***Why do you think some predators thrive along the boundaries of an ecosystem?*** Answers will vary, but could include greater ease of movement and better conditions for seeing at a distance.

Review Personal Tutor
Listen to a teacher explain edge effects.

Develop Concepts

BL OL AL

Clarify a Misconception

Students often think that all members of a species in a particular habitat die when their habitat is disturbed by an environmental factor such as acid precipitation.

ASK STUDENTS: ***When a fish kill occurs in a river, do all the fish die?*** No; some usually survive to reproduce. Point out that in most cases, populations are reduced but do not become extinct. Also, as some species decline in numbers, others may increase because they can withstand or even thrive under the new conditions.

AL ASK STUDENTS: ***Why don't all fish die? What is the effect on future generations?*** They don't all die because some fish might have variations that allow them to survive in the new conditions. Future generations might be better adapted to live in the new conditions.

Reading Check Compared to a larger parcel, a small piece of land has a larger proportion of its habitats subjected to edge effects.

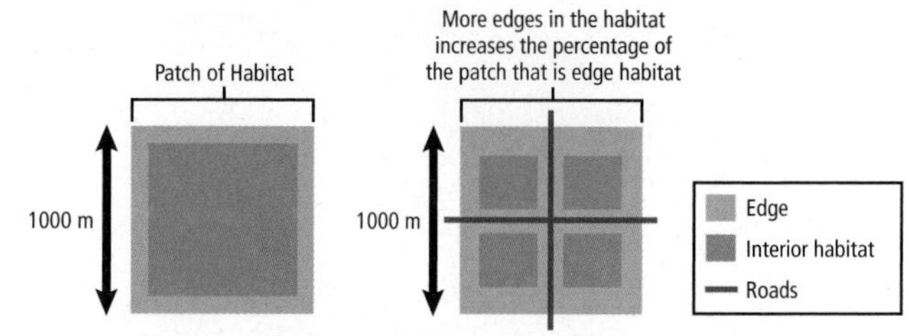

Figure 12 The smaller the habitat size, the greater percentage of the habitat that is subject to edge effects.

Review Personal Tutor

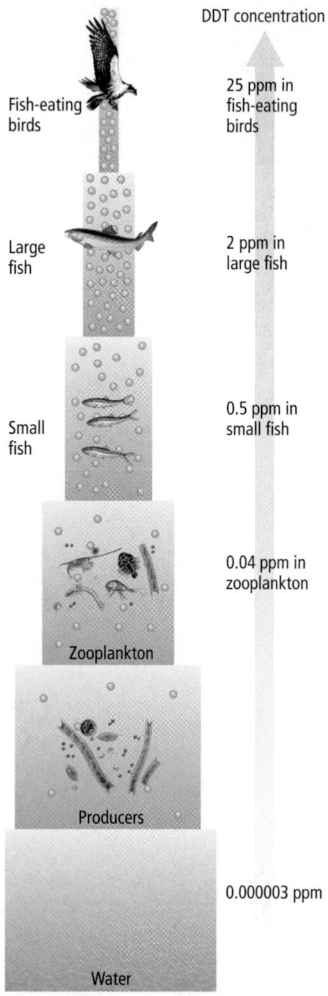

Figure 13 The concentration of toxic substances increases as the trophic level in a food chain increases.

Third, carving the large ecosystem into small parcels increases the number of edges, creating edge effects, as illustrated in **Figure 12.** **Edge effects** are different environmental conditions that occur along the boundaries of an ecosystem. For example, edges of a forest near a road have different abiotic factors, such as temperature, wind, and humidity, than does the interior of a forest. Typically, the temperature and wind will be higher and the humidity lower on the edges in a tropical forest. Species that thrive deep in the dense forest might perish on the edges of the ecosystem. Predators and parasites also thrive on the boundaries of ecosystems, which makes the species in these areas more vulnerable to attack. Edge effects do not always create a disadvantage for all species. Some species find these conditions favorable, and they thrive.

Reading Check **Explain** how a larger percentage of land is affected by edge effects when the piece of land is fragmented.

Pollution Pollution and atmospheric changes threaten biodiversity and global stability. Pollution changes the composition of air, soil, and water. There are many types of pollution. Substances—including many human-made chemicals that are not found in nature—are released into the environment. Pesticides, such as DDT (dichloro-diphenyl-trichloroethane), and industrial chemicals, such as PCBs (polychlorinated biphenyls), are examples of substances that are found in food webs. These substances are ingested by organisms when they drink water or eat other organisms that contain the toxic substances. Some substances are metabolized by an organism and excreted with other waste products. However, other substances, such as DDT and PCBs, accumulate in the tissues of organisms.

Carnivores at the higher trophic levels seem to be most affected by the accumulation of toxic substances because of a process called biological magnification. **Biological magnification** is the increasing concentration of toxic substances in organisms as trophic levels increase in a food chain or food web, as shown in **Figure 13.** The concentration of a toxic substance is relatively low when it enters the food web. The concentration of a toxic substance in individual organisms increases as it spreads to higher trophic levels.

Current research implies that these substances might disrupt normal processes in some organisms. For example, DDT might have played a role in the near extinction of the American bald eagle and the peregrine falcon. DDT is a pesticide that was used from the 1940s to the 1970s to control crop-eating and disease-carrying insects. DDT proved to be a highly effective pesticide, but evidence suggested that it caused the eggshells of fish-eating birds to be fragile and thin, which led to the death of the developing birds. Once these toxic effects were discovered, the use of DDT was banned in some parts of the world.

Demonstration

Eutrophication You can demonstrate eutrophication by setting up two small aquariums (2–5 gallons each) a couple of weeks before teaching this chapter. Label one *oligotrophic* and fill it with clean pond or stream water. Label the other *eutrophic* and fill it with the same water, but add half a teaspoon of 10-10-10 fertilizer. Place both aquaria in the light and add a small amount of algae, a few duckweed plants, and a couple of small fish, such as guppies. The aquarium labeled *eutrophic* should develop a bloom of algae and duckweed to a much greater extent than the oligotrophic aquarium. Est. time: 30 min

Acid precipitation Another pollutant that affects biodiversity is acid precipitation. When fossil fuels are burned, sulfur dioxide is released into the atmosphere. In addition, the burning of fossil fuels in automobile engines releases nitrogen oxides into the atmosphere. These compounds react with water and other substances in the air to form sulfuric acid and nitric acid. These acids eventually fall to the surface of Earth in rain, sleet, snow, or fog. Acid precipitation removes calcium, potassium, and other nutrients from the soil, depriving plants of these nutrients. It damages plant tissues and slows their growth, as shown in **Figure 14.** Sometimes, the acid concentration is so high in lakes, rivers, and streams that fish and other organisms die, also as shown in **Figure 14.**

Eutrophication Another form of water pollution, called eutrophication, destroys underwater habitats for fish and other species. **Eutrophication** (yoo troh fih KAY shun) occurs when fertilizers, animal waste, sewage, or other substances rich in nitrogen and phosphorus flow into waterways, causing extensive algae growth. The algae use up the oxygen supply during their rapid growth and after their deaths during the decaying process. Other organisms in the water suffocate. In some cases, algae also give off toxins that poison the water supply for other organisms. Eutrophication is a natural process, but human activities often accelerate the rate at which it occurs.

Forest damage

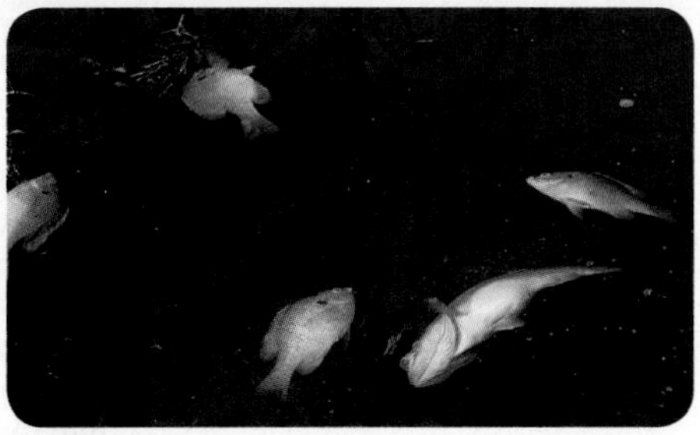

Fish kill

■ **Figure 14** Acid precipitation damages plant tissues and can kill fish if the acid concentration is high.
Infer *Which areas of the United States would most likely have acid precipitation problems?*

? Inquiry Virtual Lab S

MiniLab 2

? Inquiry MiniLab

Survey Leaf Litter Samples

How do you calculate biodiversity? Scientists calculate the biodiversity in a sample area and use that data to estimate the biodiversity in similar areas.

Procedure

1. Read and complete the lab safety form.
2. In the **leaf-litter sample** that your teacher has provided, count and record the species in a section that is visible to the eye. Look up any unknown species in a **field guide.**
3. Record your observations in a data table.
4. Calculate the index of diversity (IOD), using the following equation (unique species is different species observed; total individuals is the total of every individual observed):

$$\text{IOD} = \frac{\text{\# of unique species} \times \text{\# of samples}}{\text{\# of total individuals}}$$

Analysis

1. **Classify** which observed species are native and nonnative to your area.
2. **Infer** from your survey the effects, if any, that the nonnative species have on the native species. Are these nonnative species invasive? How do you know this?
3. **Hypothesize** whether the IOD has changed in your area over the last 200 years. Explain.

MiniLab 2

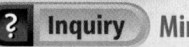

? Inquiry MiniLab

For a lab worksheet, use your eTeacherEdition Online.

RUBRIC A rubric for evaluating MiniLabs is found on your eTeacherEdition Online.

Est. Time 30 min

Additional Materials forceps, jar, cups and spoons, cooler for storage

Safety Precaution Approve lab safety forms before work begins.

Teaching Strategies

- Contact a local fish and wildlife service, forest service, or other environmental agency for supplemental materials.
- Explain the difference between the number of samples, the number of unique species, and the total number of individuals.

Analysis

1. Answers will vary, most will probably be native.
2. Answers will vary, some nonnative may be invasive.
3. Answers will vary, but the IOD has likely changed in the last 200 years as a result of human activities.

LabManager™

Customize this lab with the LabManager™ CD-ROM.

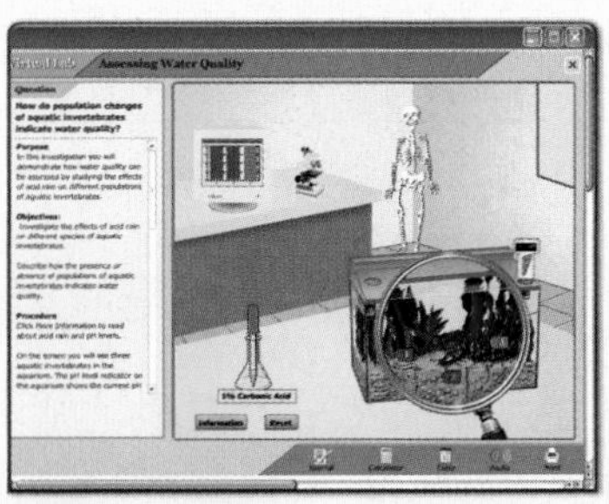

? Inquiry **Virtual Lab** Students will study the effects of acid rain on different populations of aquatic invertebrates.

■ **Caption Question Fig. 14** Densely populated cities with large numbers of cars have acid precipitation problems. Heavily industrialized areas are also at risk.

Inquiry Launch Lab

Assess Content Development
Assess how understanding has developed when students revisit the Launch Lab analysis questions.

Inquiry BioLab

The lab at the end of the chapter can be used at this point in the lesson.

Formative Assessment

Evaluation To evaluate the third objective for this section, have students answer the following questions by referring to Figure 11. **ASK STUDENTS:** ***What is the name given to a single species that plays an overarching role in an ecosystem?*** keystone species ***Why might the sea lion and harbor seal populations have decreased?*** Their food supply, fish, decreased. ***When sea lions died, which species did killer whales begin to consume at a greater level?*** sea otters ***When sea otters declined, which population increased?*** kelp

Remediation Have students predict what impact a change in one organism in a food web will have on the rest of the food web. Because organisms in a food web depend on each other, a change in one organism will have a direct impact on the other organisms.

Range Expansion of Imported Fire Ants From 1918–2005

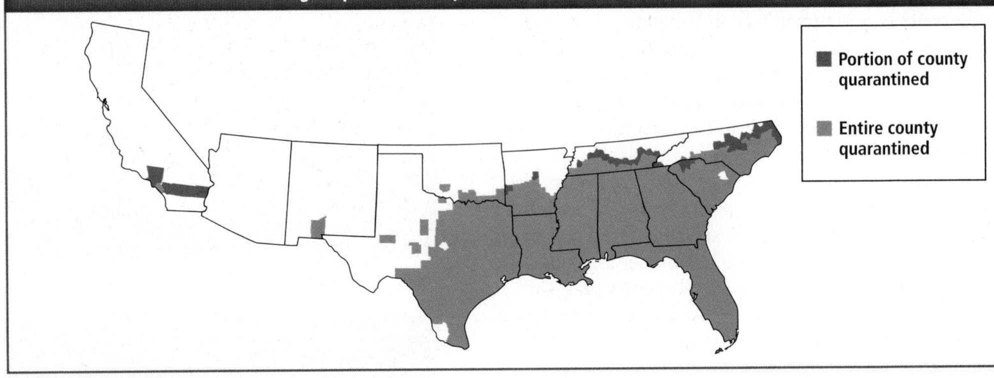

Figure 15 Fire ants were transported accidentally by ship to the port of Mobile in Alabama. The ants spread throughout the southern and southwestern United States.

Inquiry Launch Lab

Review Based on what you've read about biodiversity, how would you now answer the analysis question?

Introduced species Nonnative species that are either intentionally or unintentionally transported to a new habitat are known as **introduced species.** These species are not a threat to biodiversity in their native habitats. Predators, parasites, and competition between species keep the native ecosystem in balance. However, when these species are introduced into a new area, these controlling factors are not in place. Introduced species often reproduce in large numbers because of a lack of predators and become invasive species in their new habitat.

The imported fire ant is a species that was accidentally introduced to the United States through the port of Mobile, Alabama, in the 1920s by ships from South America. The fire ants spread throughout the southern and southwestern United States, as illustrated in **Figure 15.** Fire ants attack and feed on some wildlife, such as newborn deer and hatching or newly hatched ground-nesting birds.

Introduced species are a worldwide environmental problem. An estimated 40 percent of the extinctions that have occurred since 1750 are a result of introduced species, and billions of dollars are spent every year in an effort to clean up or control the damage caused by introduced species.

Section 2 Assessment

Section Summary

- Some scientists estimate that the current rate of species extinction is abnormally high.
- Species on islands are particularly vulnerable to extinction.
- Historically, overexploitation by humans has led to the extinction of some species.
- Human activities can result in a decrease in biodiversity.

Understand Main Ideas

1. MAIN Idea **Explain** three ways that humans threaten biodiversity.
2. **Summarize** what has caused a recent increase in the rate of extinction.
3. **Choose** one of the factors that threatens biodiversity and suggest one way in which biodiversity can be preserved in a real-life scenario.
4. **Summarize** how the overharvesting of a single species, such as baleen whales, can affect an entire ecosystem.

Think Critically

5. **Design** a planned community that preserves biodiversity and accommodates the human population. Work in small groups to accomplish this task.
6. **Survey** your community to identify at least five threats to biodiversity and suggest ways in which biodiversity can be preserved.

Section 2 Assessment

1. Possible answers include species extinction, depletion of natural resources, overexploitation, habitat destruction, habitat disruption, habitat fragmentation, and pollution.
2. Answers should emphasize that the recent increase in the rate of extinction is likely due to human activities related to habitat loss and poaching.
3. Answers should clearly indicate how the suggested change will preserve biodiversity.
4. Overharvesting the baleen whale would affect the entire ecosystem by changing the relationships among organisms in the food web.
5. Answers should include specific steps for creating a planned community. Steps must include suggestions on how biodiversity will be maintained while recognizing that human interference cannot be eliminated.
6. Students should explain how their particular suggestions will alleviate or even eliminate the identified threat.

Assessment Online Quiz

Conserving Biodiversity

Reading Preview

Essential Questions

- What are the two classes of natural resources?
- What are the methods used to conserve biodiversity?
- What are two techniques used to restore biodiversity?

Review Vocabulary

natural resources: materials and organisms found in the biosphere

New Vocabulary

renewable resource
nonrenewable resource
sustainable use
endemic
bioremediation
biological augmentation

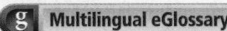

Multilingual eGlossary

MAIN Idea **People are using many approaches to slow the rate of extinctions and to preserve biodiversity.**

Real-World Reading Link Have you ever broken a decorative item and repaired it? You probably carefully searched for all of the pieces and then carefully glued them together again. Repairing a damaged ecosystem is a similar process. Scientists carefully search for all of the pieces of the ecosystem, repair the damages, and secure the location to protect the ecosystem from future damage.

R Natural Resources

S The biosphere currently supplies the basic needs for more than six billion humans in the form of natural resources. The human population continues to grow, and the growth is not evenly distributed throughout the world. An increase in human population growth increases the need for natural resources to supply the basic needs of the population.

The consumption rate of natural resources is also not evenly distributed. **Figure 16** shows the consumption of natural resources per person for selected countries. The natural resource consumption rate is much higher for people living in developed countries than for people living in developing countries. As developing countries become more industrialized and the standard of living increases, the rate of natural resource consumption also increases. Because of the rising human population growth and an increased rate of consumption of natural resources, a long-term plan for the use and conservation of natural resources is important.

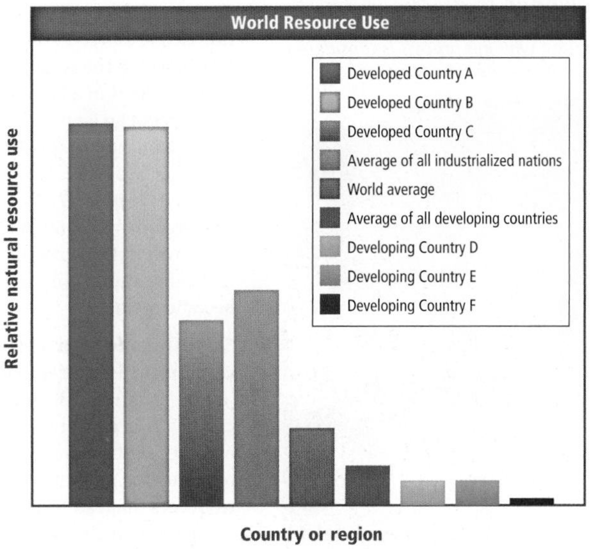

Figure 16 This graph shows the consumption of natural resources per person for selected countries based on the equivalent kilograms of oil.
***Explain** why the use of natural resources is high for Developed Country A and for Developed Country B, but is low for Developing Country E and for Developing Country F.*

Demonstration

Resource Conservation Use photos of farms that show different crops planted in different fields, forested areas that have been replanted, and a person hunting deer as examples of resources that are conserved by practice or by law. Explain that both methods conserve the resources for future use by others.
Est. time: 5–10 min

Caption Question Fig. 16 Answers may vary. Students might suggest that citizens from developed countries A and B use more combustible fuels in cars and consume more products that require oil in their manufacturing process than do citizens in developing countries.

Section 3

MAIN Idea

BL OL AL Conservation and Preservation

SAY TO STUDENTS: ***Conservation and preservation are the two main ways of slowing the decrease of biodiversity. What is the main difference between conservation and preservation?*** Conservation involves maintaining species and habitats as resources for use; preservation involves complete protection. *Preservation* = nonuse, and *conservation* = wise use(s)

R Reading Strategy

BL OL COOP LEARN

Discussion Triads Divide the class into three groups. Assign one of the following topics per group: natural resources, protecting ecosystems, and restoring ecosystems. Have students reread text that relates to their topics and explain the major points of the text in their own words. Have each group make a five-minute presentation using at least one visual aid.

S Skill Practice

BL OL AL COOP LEARN

Gather Data Have students work in groups of two or three to prepare a questionnaire to assess attitudes about conservation and preservation of natural resources, especially those that are important in your area. Tell students to collect data from other students in the school and adults in the community, such as parents and neighbors, and write a summary paper that can be presented to the class. For more significant data, develop the questionnaire as a class and have all students gather the same data. Each student can then write an individual summary report based on the entire database.

D Develop Concepts

OL AL

Clarify a Misconception

Many students think that nonrenewable resources are being depleted quickly.

ASK STUDENTS: ***When do you think we will have used all the coal, natural gas, and petroleum resources?*** At the current rate of use and without any additional finds, the estimated reserve for coal is about 500 y, natural gas about 57 y, and oil about 40 y. However, additional reserves are being found every year.

D Develop Concepts

EL COOP LEARN

Activity Pass out labeled pictures of renewable and nonrenewable resources. Organize students into two groups: those with renewable resources and those with nonrenewable resources. Tell the class to stand up. Now have students representing nonrenewable resources sit down to depict loss of resources.

D Develop Concepts

EL OL **Activity** Have students identify both a renewable and a nonrenewable resource that is economically important to their native country. Ask them to research what steps are being taken to preserve these resources. Compile a summary on the board. Identify any resources that are common to several countries.

S Skill Practice

EL BL OL AL **Make a Table**

SAY TO STUDENTS: *Make a table with three labeled columns:* **Renewable Resources, Nonrenewable Resources,** *and* **Uses of Resources.** *Complete the table.* After students have completed their tables, discuss which resources and uses they think are most important.

■ **Figure 17** This cleared forest is considered a nonrenewable resource because there is not enough of the forest intact to provide a habitat for the organisms that live there.

Renewable resources Plans for long-term use of natural resources must take into consideration the difference between the two groups of natural resources—renewable and nonrenewable resources. Those resources that are replaced by natural processes faster than they are consumed are called **renewable resources.** Solar energy is considered a renewable resource because the supply appears to be endless. Agricultural plants, animals, clean water, and clean air are considered renewable because they are normally replaced faster than they are consumed. However, the supply of these resources is not unlimited. If the demand exceeds the supply of any resource, the resource might become depleted.

D **Nonrenewable resources** Resources that are found on Earth in limited amounts or that are replaced by natural processes over extremely long periods of time are called **nonrenewable resources.** Fossil fuels and mineral deposits, such as radioactive uranium, are considered nonrenewable resources. Species are considered renewable resources until the last of a species dies. When extinction occurs, a species is nonrenewable because it is lost forever.

■ **Figure 18** Replacing resources preserves the health of the biosphere.
Explain *why this process is considered a sustainable use of a resource.*

Renewable versus nonrenewable resources The classification of a resource as renewable or nonrenewable depends on the context in which the resource is being discussed. A single tree or a small group of trees in a large forest ecosystem is renewable because replacement trees can be planted or can regrow from seeds present in the soil. Enough of the forest is still intact to serve as a habitat for the organisms that live there. However, when the entire forest is cleared, as shown in **Figure 17,** the forest is not considered a renewable resource. The organisms living in the forest have lost their habitat, and they most likely will not survive. In this example, it is possible that more than one natural resource is nonrenewable: the forest and any species that might become extinct. D D

Sustainable use One approach to using natural resources, called sustainable use, is demonstrated in **Figure 18.** Just as the name implies, **sustainable use** means using resources at a rate at which they can be replaced or recycled while preserving the long-term environmental health of the biosphere. Conservation of resources includes reducing the amount of resources that are consumed, recycling resources that can be recycled, and preserving ecosystems, as well as using them in a responsible manner. S

■ **Caption Question Fig. 18** Because people are planting and thus replacing resources as they are being used, they are sustaining the use of resources.

Differentiated Instruction

English Learners When assigning the Skill Practice exercise suggested on this page, pair students with limited English proficiency with students who are native speakers. English learners can learn from their partner how best to express their ideas in writing.

For more tips, see pages 14T–15T.

Protecting Biodiversity

In Section 2, you learned how human activities have affected many ecosystems. Many efforts are underway worldwide to slow the loss of biodiversity and to work toward sustainable use of natural resources.

Protected areas in the United States Conservation biologists recognize the importance of establishing protected areas where biodiversity can flourish. The United States established its first national park, Yellowstone National Park, in 1872 to protect the area's geological features. Many additional national parks and nature reserves have been established since 1872. **D**

International protected areas The United States is not the only country to establish national parks and nature reserves. Currently, about seven percent of the world's land is set aside as some type of reserve. Historically, these protected areas have been small islands of habitat surrounded by areas that contain human activity. Because the reserves are small, they are impacted heavily by human activity. The United Nations supports a system of Biosphere Reserves and World Heritage sites. Costa Rica has established megareserves. These reserves contain one or more zones that are protected from human activity by buffer zones, areas in which sustainable use of natural resources is permitted. This approach creates large managed areas for preserving biodiversity while providing natural resources to local populations.

Reading Check **Explain** the advantages of megareserves.

DATA ANALYSIS LAB 1

Based on Real Data*

Use Maps

How is the biodiversity of perching birds distributed in the Americas? The distribution of birds, like that of other species, is not even. Perching birds appear to be more concentrated in some areas of the Americas than others.

Data and Observations

Use the map to answer the following questions about the biodiversity of perching birds.

Distribution of Perching Birds

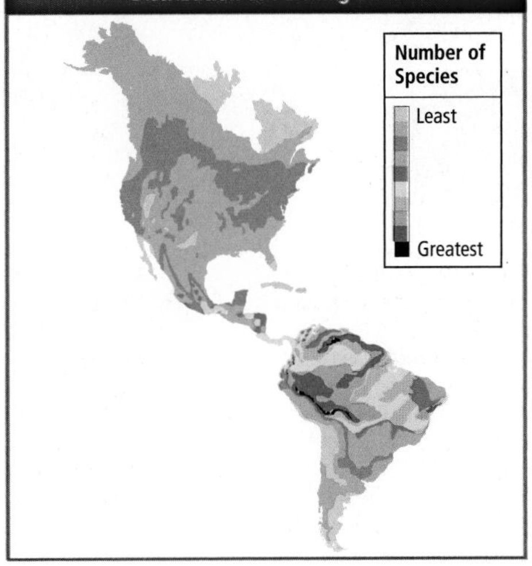

Think Critically

1. **Determine** the location of the highest concentration of perching birds.
2. **Generalize** the trend in the number of perching birds as you move from Canada to South America.
3. **Infer** Why does the number of perching birds change as you move toward the southern tip of South America?

*Data obtained from: Pimm, S.L. and Brown J.H. 2004. Domains of diversity. *Science* 304: 831–833.

D Develop Concepts

BL OL AL **Brainstorm**

ASK STUDENTS: ***What protected area is closest to our school?*** Answers will depend on location. ***Is this area protected by the state, or is it a nationally protected area?*** Answers will vary.

DATA ANALYSIS LAB 1

About the Lab

- The purpose of this Data Analysis Lab is to show the general pattern of biodiversity decrease in either direction away from the equator toward the poles.
- Also see Robert K. Colwell, et al. 2004. The mid-domain effect and species richness patterns. *The American Naturalist.* 163: 13 E1–E23.

Think Critically

1. the northern half of South America (Amazonia) and Central America
2. Biodiversity of perching birds increases from Canada to South America.
3. Responses will vary, but can include abiotic factors such as decreased temperature or biotic factors such as decreasing availability of food.

GOING GREEN Adjust your classroom computers to go into sleep or hibernation mode when not in use rather than using screen savers. This can reduce energy consumption by up to 70 percent.

Demonstration

Geography of Protected Areas Display a map for your state. As you discuss natural parks and other protected areas, point out those that occur within your state. You could also display a national map and point out national parks in other areas. You can obtain maps from local and state departments of fish and wildlife that show protected areas. Est. time: 10 min

> *"The task of modern education is not to cut down jungles, but to irrigate deserts."*
>
> –C. S. Lewis

Reading Check Megareserves provide natural resources for the local population while creating a large managed area for preserving biodiversity.

Visualizing Biodiversity Hot Spots

Purpose

Students will see that biodiversity hot spots are small and scattered, and that the concentration of unique species, and species diversity in general, are concentrated in these areas.
UCP.2, UCP.4, C.4

Writing Support

AL Formal Writing Have students choose one of the biodiversity hot spots to research, and then write an article about the threats to a particular species or group of species in that area. Combine the articles into a magazine to be printed for the whole class. Struggling students and students working at grade level can participate by creating ads for the magazine or compiling illustrations.

Concepts in Motion
Animation

Visualizing Biodiversity Hot Spots

Figure 19 Biodiversity hot spots, highlighted in red on the map, are ecosystems where endemic species are threatened. If these species become extinct, biodiversity will decrease.

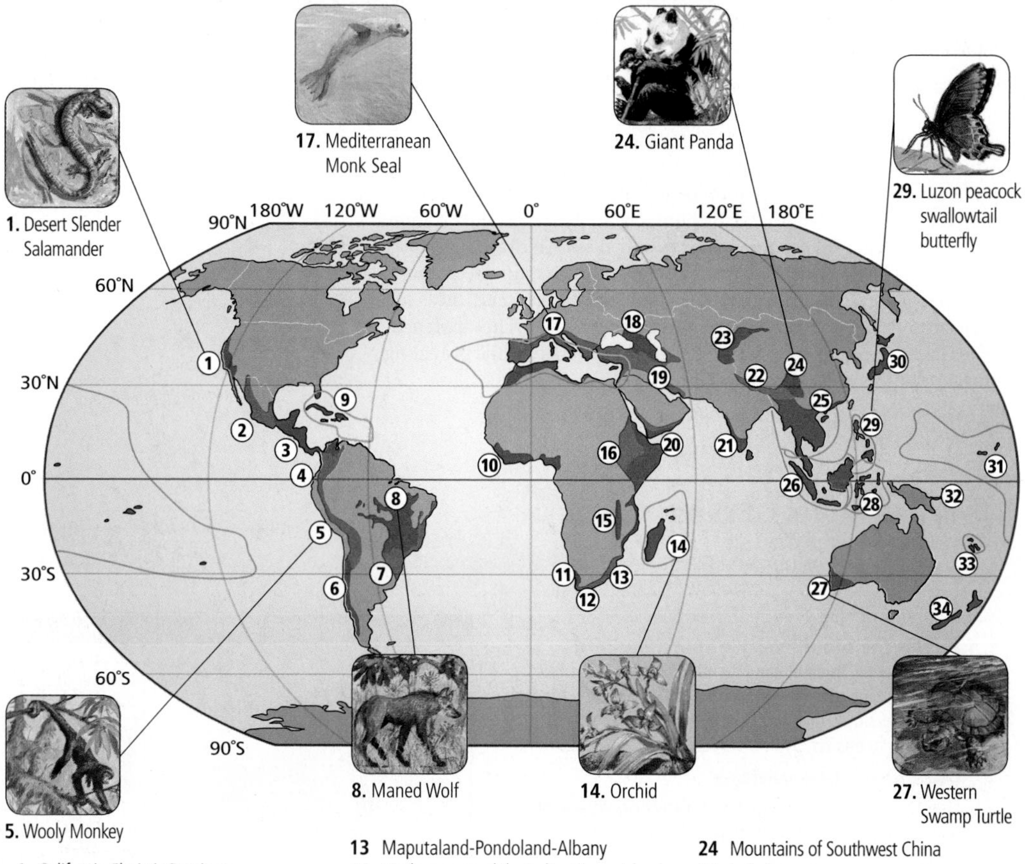

1 California Floristic Province	**13** Maputaland-Pondoland-Albany	**24** Mountains of Southwest China
2 Madrean Pine-Oak Woodlands	**14** Madagascar and the Indian Ocean Islands	**25** Indo-Burma
3 Mesomerica	**15** Coastal Forests of Eastern Africa	**26** Sundaland
4 Tumbes-Chocó-Magdalena	**16** Eastern Aforomontane	**27** Southwest Australia
5 Tropical Andes	**17** Mediterranean Basin	**28** Wallacea
6 Chilean Winter Rainfall-Valdivian Forests	**18** Caucasus	**29** Philippines
7 Atlantic Forest	**19** Irano-Anatolian	**30** Japan
8 Cerrado	**20** Horn of Africa	**31** Polynesia-Micronesia
9 Caribbean Islands	**21** Western Ghats and Sri Lanka	**32** East Melanesian Islands
10 Guinean Forests of West Africa	**22** Himalayans	**33** New Caledonia
11 Succulent Karoo	**23** Mountains of Central Asia	**34** New Zealand
12 Cape Floristic Region		

Concepts in Motion **Animation**

Biodiversity hot spots Conservation biologists have identified locations around the world that are characterized by exceptional levels of **endemic** species—species that are only found in that specific geographic area—and critical levels of habitat loss. To be called a hot spot, a region must meet two criteria. First, there must be at least 1500 species of vascular plants that are endemic, and the region must have lost at least 70 percent of its original habitat. The 34 internationally recognized hot spots are shown in **Figure 19.**

Approximately half of all plant and animal species are found in hot spots. These hot spots originally covered 17 percent of Earth's surface; however, only about a tenth of that habitat remains.

Biologists in favor of recovery efforts in these areas argue that focusing on a limited area would save the greatest number of species. Other biologists argue that concentrating funding on saving species in these hot spots does not address the serious problems that are occurring elsewhere. For example, saving a wetland area might save fewer species, but the wetland provides greater services by filtering water, regulating floods, and providing a nursery for fish. These biologists think that funding should be spent in areas around the world rather than focused on the biodiversity hotspots. **D**

Corridors between habitat fragments Conservation ecologists also are focusing on improving the survival of biodiversity by providing corridors, or passageways, between habitat fragments. Corridors, such as those shown in **Figure 20,** are used to connect smaller parcels of land. These corridors allow organisms from one area to move safely to the other area. This creates a larger piece of land that can sustain a wider variety of species and a wider variety of genetic variation. However, corridors do not completely solve the problem of habitat destruction. Diseases easily pass from one area to the next as infected animals move from one location to another. This approach also increases edge effect. One large habitat would have fewer edges, but often a large habitat is hard to preserve.

VOCABULARY

SCIENCE USAGE V. COMMON USAGE

Corridor

Science usage: a passageway between two habitat fragments

The deer uses the corridor to safely travel between the two habitat fragments.

Common usage: a passageway, as in a hotel, into which rooms open

The ice machine is in the hotel corridor by the elevators.

■ **Figure 20** Corridors between habitat fragments allow safe passage for animals.
Describe ***What are the advantages and disadvantages of corridors?***

Writing Support

BL OL AL COOP LEARN

Persuasive Writing Have students work in pairs to write a letter to the editor of the local newspaper advocating a proposed solution to some environmental problem that affects biodiversity at a local, national, or international level. Have students share the letters with their peers to get their comments and suggestions. Then have students edit their letters based on the comments and suggestions. Obtain proper permissions from school administrators, parents, and students before sending the best letters for possible publication in the newspaper.

D Develop Concepts

BL OL AL Discuss

SAY TO STUDENTS: ***Identify the biome with most of Earth's biodiversity hot spots.*** The biome with the most hot spots is a tropical rain forest. ***Are most of the biodiversity hot spots in developed countries or in developing countries?*** Most are in developing countries.

Develop Concepts

OL AL Build Models Have students study maps that show city parks and green belts and then build a model of a corridor that might be constructed to connect habitat fragments in your local area.

■ **Caption Question Fig. 20** Advantage—creates a larger piece of land that can sustain greater biodiversity. Disadvantage—Diseases can pass from one area to another.

Research Citation

Model Educational research indicates that the use of models will provide students with a more concrete understanding of difficult topics. The modeling activity on this page requires that students evaluate existing maps and extend this information to create their own model. This activity not only helps students visualize the concept, but it also helps them connect it to a real-world situation. (Hitt and Townsend, 2004)

Research bibliography on pages 32T–34T

S Skill Practice

BL OL AL Visual Literacy Point out that Figure 21 shows the recovery time for biological communities.

ASK STUDENTS: ***What are the two types of disasters plotted in this graph?*** natural and human-made ***Is recovery from human disasters generally on the shorter end of the spatial scale, or the longer end?*** The range is toward the upper half of the scale for both length of time and space. Discuss why human-caused disasters take longer for recovery.

D Develop Concepts

BL OL AL Discuss Review the definition of *bioremediation.*

ASK STUDENTS: ***What evidence would indicate that bioremediation of an oil spill was working?*** Responses will vary, but may include testing to determine if the amount of oil decreases or if populations of decontaminating or detoxifying organisms increase in the polluted area.

Caption Question Fig. 21 10 y

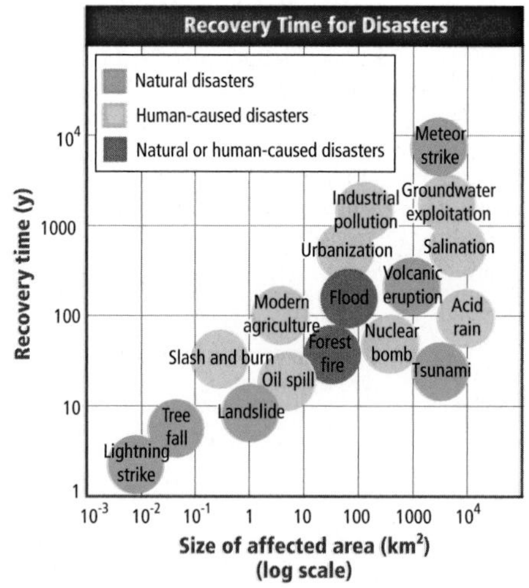

Figure 21 The recovery time for disasters is dependent upon the size of the area affected and on the type of disturbance.
Determine *the approximate recovery time for a landslide.*

S

Restoring Ecosystems

Sometimes, biodiversity is destroyed in an area such that it no longer provides the abiotic and biotic factors needed for a healthy ecosystem. For example, the soil from cleared tropical rain forests becomes unproductive for farming after a few years. After mining activities are completed, land might be abandoned in a condition that does not support biodiversity. Accidental oil spills and toxic chemical spills might pollute an area to such a degree that the native species cannot live there.

Given time, biological communities can recover from natural and human-made disasters, as illustrated in **Figure 21.** The size of the area affected and the type of disturbance are determining factors for recovery time. The length of time for recovery is not related directly to whether the disaster is natural or human-made. In general, the larger the affected area, the longer it takes for the biological community to recover. Ecologists use two methods to speed the recovery process of these damaged ecosystems: bioremediation and biological augmentation.

Bioremediation The use of living organisms, such as prokaryotes, fungi, or plants, to detoxify a polluted area is called **bioremediation.** In 1975, a leak from a fuel-storage facility in South Carolina released about 80,000 gallons of kerosene-based jet fuel. The fuel soaked into the sandy soil and contaminated the underground water table. Microorganisms that naturally are found in the soil break down these carbon-based fuels into carbon dioxide. Scientists found that by adding additional nutrients to the soil, the rate at which the microorganisms decontaminated the area increased. In a few years, the contamination in the area was greatly reduced. These microorganisms can be used in other ecosystems to remove toxins from soils that are contaminated by accidental oil or fuel spills. D

Some species of plants are being used to remove toxic substances, such as zinc, lead, nickel, and organic chemicals, from damaged soils, as shown in **Figure 22.** These plants are planted in contaminated soils, where they store the toxic metals in their tissues. The plants then are harvested, and the toxic metals are removed from the ecosystem. Bioremediation is relatively new, but there appears to be great promise in using organisms to detoxify some ecosystems that have been damaged.

Figure 22 Chemical waste from an industrial complex is being treated using reed beds. Bacteria and fungi in the reed beds transform a wide range of pollutants into harmless substances.

Demonstration

Bioremediation Fill a one-gallon jar with pond or aquarium water. Add about 2.5 cm of substrate from a nearby pond and let this settle for an hour. Then stir approximately one teaspoon of used motor oil into the water. Over two weeks, some of the microbes naturally present in the substrate will flourish and begin to consume the oil while others will die. Display the jar in class over time as it illustrates the phases of bioremediation. Est. time: 30 min

Biological augmentation Adding natural predators to a degraded ecosystem is called **biological augmentation.** For example, aphids—very small insects—eat vegetables and other plants, which can result in the destruction of farm crops. Aphids also can transmit plant diseases. Some farmers rely on ladybugs to control pests that eat their crops. Certain species of ladybugs eat aphids, as shown in **Figure 23,** and can be used to control aphid infestation. The ladybugs do not harm the crops, and the fields are kept free of aphids.

■ **Figure 23** Ladybugs can be introduced into an ecosystem to control aphid populations.

Legally Protecting Biodiversity

During the 1970s, a great deal of attention was focused on destruction of the environment and maintaining biodiversity. Laws were enacted in countries around the world, and many treaties between countries were signed in an effort to preserve the environment. In the United States, the Endangered Species Act was enacted in 1973. It was designed to legally protect the species that were becoming extinct or in danger of becoming extinct. An international treaty, the Convention on International Trade in Endangered Species of Wild Fauna and Flora (CITES), was signed in 1975. It outlawed the trade of endangered species and animal parts, such as ivory elephant tusks and rhinoceros horns. Since the 1970s, many more laws and treaties have been enacted and signed with the purpose of preserving biodiversity for future generations.

C

C Critical Thinking

BL OL AL Infer

ASK STUDENTS: ***Orchid enthusiasts enjoy collecting a variety of species from around the world, many of which are endangered in their natural habitats. The U.S. requires CITES certificates on imported orchid plants. What conditions do you think CITES certificates require for orchid species to be imported legally?*** CITES certificates are provided for species that have been grown under greenhouse conditions and ensure that specimens have not been collected in the wild. The CITES treaty covers animal species as well.

Formative Assessment

Evaluation To determine whether students have met the second objective of the section, ask why sustainable use is an example of a biodiversity conservation method and not a biodiversity preservation method Sustainable use conserves resources so that they are used at a rate at which they can be replaced or recycled. A preservation method would prohibit use of the resource.

Remediation Have students work in pairs to find the information in the text that provides the answers to the questions they missed. Then have them write a sentence identifying how each of the biodiversity conservation methods serves to increase or conserve biodiversity.

Section 3 Assessment

Section Summary

- One approach to using natural resources is sustainable use.
- There are many approaches used to conserve biodiversity in the world.
- Biodiversity hot spots contain a large number of endemic species that are threatened with extinction.
- Two techniques used to restore an ecosystem are bioremediation and biological augmentation.
- Since the 1970s, many forms of legislation have been passed to protect the environment.

Understand Main Ideas

1. MAIN Idea **Describe** three approaches used to slow down the rate of extinction or to preserve biodiversity.
2. **Define** the two classes of natural resources.
3. **Choose** a human-caused disaster from **Figure 21.** Discuss the methods that could be used to restore biodiversity.
4. **Compare** the advantages and disadvantages of large and small nature reserves.

Think Critically

5. **Create** a script of dialogue that could occur between a conservationist and a person who lives in a biodiversity hot spot. The local person wants to use the natural resources to provide a living for his or her family. The dialogue should include a compromise in which both sides are satisfied with the use of resources.

MATH in Biology

6. If Earth has 150,100,000 km^2 of land area, how much land area is included in the biodiversity hot spots?

Section 3 Assessment

1. Possible answers include sustainable use, establishment of protected areas, creation of corridors between habitat fragments, bioremediation, and passage of laws.
2. Renewable resources are those which are replaced by natural processes faster than they are consumed. Nonrenewable resources are those that are found in limited amounts or are replaced by natural processes over long periods of time.
3. Answers will vary. Possible answer: Oil spill – microorganisms that break down carbon-based fuels into CO_2 could be added.
4. Answers will vary. Large reserves are more difficult to maintain but are less affected by edge effect.
5. Answers will vary. Both sides should be presented.
6. Hot spots originally covered 15.7 percent of Earth's surface but now only cover one-tenth of that.
   $0.1 \times 0.157 = 0.0157$
   $150{,}100{,}000\ km^2 \times 0.0157 = 2{,}356{,}570\ km^2$

Assessment Online Quiz

In the Field

Purpose

Students will understand how human activities affect the stability of ecosystems.
A.1, A.2, C.4, C.6, E.2, F.4, F.5, F.6

Anticipatory Guide

Have students brainstorm human activities that affect rain forest ecosystems. Activities should include deforestation caused by commercial logging, mining, slash-and-burn agriculture, consumption of wood as a fuel source, and hunting specific animal species or gathering certain plant species at a greater rate than they are replenished naturally.
ASK STUDENTS: ***Do you think there is anything one person could do to reverse the negative environmental impacts caused by these activities?*** Answers will vary.
Introduce Wangari Maathai and briefly describe her background and contributions in Africa.

Background

Wangari Maathai was born in 1940. She attended universities in the United States, Germany, and Kenya. In the 1980s, Maathai introduced the idea of providing women with the resources to plant trees throughout Kenya, with the goal of conserving the environment and improving the quality of life for women in rural areas. Successful initiatives based on Kenya's Green Belt Movement have taken hold in Tanzania, Uganda, Malawi, Lesotho, Ethiopia, and Zimbabwe.

In the Field

Career: Conservationist

Wangari Maathai: Planting Seeds of Change

Living and working in her homeland of Kenya, Wangari Maathai was disturbed by the plight of women in rural areas of the country. Limited firewood, scarce water resources, and poor soil made it difficult for rural women to meet their families' needs. Maathai's solution? Plant trees, and teach other women to do the same.

Wangari Maathai

What began with planting trees in 1977 evolved into the Green Belt Movement, with Maathai as its energetic leader. This grassroots, non-governmental organization involves Kenyans in reducing the environmental and social effects of deforestation. While tree planting is the focal activity, the movement also promotes environmental consciousness, volunteerism, conservation of local biodiversity, community development, and self-empowerment, particularly for Kenyan women and girls. Maathai was awarded the Nobel Peace Prize in 2004 for her contribution to sustainable development, democracy, and peace.

Positive change in Kenya As a leader for environmental change in Kenya, Maathai's work has helped Kenyans achieve a deeper understanding of their role in environmental conservation. Today, there are more than 600 community networks throughout Kenya that oversee about 6000 tree nurseries. These nurseries are staffed primarily by Kenyan women, and provide an income source for their families and for rural communities. Individuals working within community networks have planted more than 30 million trees throughout the country. Degraded forested areas are experiencing regrowth, resulting in areas that can support plant and animal biodiversity. Soil erosion has slowed, and both soil fertility and water-holding capacity in planted areas has increased. By promoting the planting of fruit trees and other food plants, hunger has been reduced and nutrition has improved in rural households.

The impact of the Green Belt Movement, now more than 30 years old, has been phenomenal. Expanding beyond Kenya, Green Belt methods have been adopted in other African countries, including Tanzania, Uganda, Malawi, Lesotho, Ethiopia, and Zimbabwe.

COMMUNITY SERVICE

Action Plan How can you get involved with tree planting in your community? Develop an action plan that includes contacting local groups for information, designing the project, obtaining resources, and implementing the activity.

Discussion

Share the following quote by Wangari Maathai with students: "A degraded environment leads to a scramble for scarce resources and may culminate in poverty and even conflict." Lead a discussion in which students share what the quote means to them.
ASK STUDENTS: ***If resources that you rely on became scarce, how might this affect your life and behavior?*** Answers will vary. Students might suggest that fewer resouces would increase competition for those resources.

WebQuest

BIOLAB

FIELD INVESTIGATION: HOW CAN SURVEYING A PLOT OF LAND AROUND YOUR SCHOOL HELP YOU UNDERSTAND THE HEALTH OF YOUR ECOSYSTEM?

Background One of the jobs of a conservation biologist is to survey land and provide an analysis of the health of the ecosystem. Then, if problems are discovered, he or she would propose possible solutions, decide on a course of action, and implement the plan.

Question: *How can an ecosystem be restored to its natural state?*

Materials

wire coat hangers or 1-m stakes (61)
field notebook
field guide of area species (plant, animal, and fungus)
colored plastic ribbon (50 m)
string (600 m)
pencil

Safety Precautions

WARNING: ***Use care in observing wildlife; do not disturb the species.***

Procedure

1. Read and complete the lab safety form.
2. Determine a site to be studied. Make sure the site owner has given permission to conduct a survey on that site.
3. With four stakes, mark off a 15 m × 15 m area within that site.
4. Further divide the area into 1 m × 1 m squares with 57 remaining stakes and string. These will be your sampling areas.
5. Using the method you used in **MiniLab 2**, survey your site and calculate the index of diversity.
6. Research the history of your area. How has it changed since it was first settled?
7. Research and recommend appropriate methods to care for the plot of land you surveyed in an environmentally responsible manner, perhaps by restoring it to its original state.
8. Make a plan to implement your methods. What limitations might you encounter?
9. If possible, implement part of your plan.

Analyze and Conclude

1. **Predict** how your methods of care would impact your plot of land. Why is this important?
2. **Determine** Is there a key species you expect to be affected by your plan?
3. **Analyze** What are some possible negative consequences of your plan?
4. **Defend** Is there another possible conservation biology technique that could be used? Explain.
5. **Calculate** What might the index of diversity be if you made the changes you recommended?
6. **Interpret** Was an increase in biodiversity your goal? Why or why not?

SHARE YOUR DATA

Present As a class, create a presentation of your plan to give to school administration. The presentation should use multimedia to show the data you collected, the time, money, and resources needed to implement your plan, and a strong argument for implementing your plan.

BIOLAB

Inquiry BioLab

For a lab worksheet, use your eTeacherEdition Online.

RUBRIC A rubric for evaluating BioLabs is found on your eTeacherEdition Online.

Est. Time 30–45 min

Content Background Students conduct a field investigation that involves observing, classifying, and recording data to determine the index of diversity for a local site.

Additional Materials net, forceps, hand lens

Safety Precautions Approve lab safety forms before work begins. Since students will be in the field, make sure they dress appropriately by wearing long pants, shirts with sleeves, sturdy shoes, hats, and sunscreen. Get appropriate permission for field study in the area you will be visiting.

Teaching Strategy If students are having trouble identifying a species, have them draw the organism and/or record characteristics or take a digital or instant picture of it. They can look it up later in a field guide.

Alternative Teaching Demo If a field investigation is not possible in your area, provide students with a pond sample or a leaf litter sample to bring the lab indoors. Demonstrate the same techniques using pond water.

Analyze and Conclude

1. Answers will vary. The methods are important because they are intended to restore the biodiversity of the selected plot of land.
2. Answers will vary. A key species that might be affected is likely to be one that has been most threatened by local environmental changes.
3. Answers will vary. Possibilities include opposition by people who might be affected economically or the restriction of the selected plot for future public use.
4. Answers will vary depending on the area surveyed.
5. The IOD should show an increase.
6. Restoring the ecosystem to its natural state was the primary goal. This goal may or may not result in an increase in biodiversity.

Chapter 5

Study Guide

ConnectED

Students can use the following to review the chapter.

Review

Vocabulary eGames
Vocabulary eFlashcards
Vocabulary PuzzleMaker

Assessment

Online Quizzes
Online Test Practice
Standardized Test Practice

Use the *ExamView® Assessment Suite* CD-ROM to:

- create multiple versions of tests
- create modified tests with one mouse click
- edit existing questions and add your own questions
- build tests aligned with state standards using built-in state curriculum tags
- change English tests to Spanish with one mouse click
- track students' progress using the Teacher Management System

Chapter 5 Study Guide

THEME FOCUS Diversity The biosphere supports genetic diversity, species diversity, and ecosystem diversity, which humans are working to preserve through conservation efforts.

BIG Idea Community and ecosystem homeostasis depends on a complex set of interactions among biologically diverse individuals.

Section 1 Biodiversity

extinction (p. 116)
biodiversity (p. 116)
genetic diversity (p. 116)
species diversity (p. 117)
ecosystem diversity (p. 118)

MAIN Idea Biodiversity maintains a healthy biosphere and provides direct and indirect value to humans.

- Biodiversity is important to the health of the biosphere.
- There are three types of biodiversity: genetic, species, and ecosystem.
- Biodiversity has aesthetic and scientific values, and direct and indirect economic value.
- It is important to maintain biodiversity to preserve the reservoir of genes that might be needed in the future.
- Healthy ecosystems can provide some services at a lesser expense than the use of technology.

Section 2 Threats to Biodiversity

background extinction (p. 122)
mass extinction (p. 122)
natural resource (p. 123)
overexploitation (p. 124)
habitat fragmentation (p. 125)
edge effect (p. 126)
biological magnification (p. 126)
eutrophication (p. 127)
introduced species (p. 128)

MAIN Idea Some human activities reduce biodiversity in ecosystems, and current evidence suggests that reduced biodiversity might have serious long-term effects on the biosphere.

- Some scientists estimate that the current rate of species extinction is abnormally high.
- Species on islands are particularly vulnerable to extinction.
- Historically, overexploitation of some species by humans has led to their extinction.
- Human activities can result in a decrease in biodiversity.

Section 3 Conserving Biodiversity

renewable resource (p. 130)
nonrenewable resource (p. 130)
sustainable use (p. 130)
endemic (p. 133)
bioremediation (p. 134)
biological augmentation (p. 135)

MAIN Idea People are using many approaches to slow the rate of extinctions and to preserve biodiversity.

- One approach to using natural resources is sustainable use.
- There are many approaches used to conserve biodiversity in the world.
- Biodiversity hot spots contain a large number of endemic species that are threatened with extinction.
- Two techniques used to restore an ecosystem are bioremediation and biological augmentation.
- Since the 1970s, many forms of legislation have been passed to protect the environment.

Review Vocabulary PuzzleMaker

For additional practice with vocabulary, have students access the Vocabulary PuzzleMaker online.

Review Vocabulary eGames

Section 1

Vocabulary Review

Each of the following sentences is false. Make each sentence true by replacing the italicized word with a vocabulary term from the Study Guide page.

1. *Biodiversity* of a species occurs when the last member of the species dies.
2. *Genetic diversity* refers to the variety of ecosystems that are present in the biosphere.
3. *Ecosystem diversity* is the number of different species and the relative abundance of each species in a biological community.

Understand Main Ideas

4. In which location would you expect to find the greatest species diversity?
   - **A.** Canada
   - **B.** Costa Rica
   - **C.** Mexico
   - **D.** United States

Use the photo below to answer questions 5 and 12.

5. Which term best describes what the rabbits in the photo demonstrates?
   - **A.** ecosystem diversity
   - **B.** genetic diversity
   - **C.** species richness
   - **D.** species diversity
6. Refer to **Figure 3.** What is the species diversity in southern Florida?
   - **A.** 0–50 species
   - **B.** 50–100 species
   - **C.** 100–150 species
   - **D.** 150–200 species
7. Which represents an indirect economic value of biodiversity?
   - **A.** food
   - **B.** clothing
   - **C.** flood protection
   - **D.** medicines
8. Which term best describes this collection of locations: a forest, a freshwater lake, an estuary, and a prairie?
   - **A.** ecosystem diversity
   - **B.** extinction
   - **C.** genetic diversity
   - **D.** species diversity

Constructed Response

9. **Open Ended** Infer why there is more species diversity in southern Florida than there is in northern Alaska.
10. **THEME FOCUS Diversity** Explain why increased ecosystem diversity contributes to increased biodiversity in the biosphere.
11. **MAIN Idea** Describe three values that the biosphere provides.
12. **Short Answer** Explain how a trait such as the one demonstrated in the photo on the left helps the species survive.

Think Critically

13. **Explain** why it is difficult to attach a value to the aesthetic qualities of biodiversity.
14. **Describe** a service that an ecosystem provides in your community that should be protected to ensure that the quality of the service continues.

Section 2

Vocabulary Review

Explain the difference between each pair of terms below. Then explain how the terms are related.

15. background extinction, mass extinction
16. habitat fragmentation, edge effect
17. overexploitation, introduced species

Chapter 5 Assessment

Section 1

Vocabulary Review

1. Extinction
2. Ecosystem diversity
3. Species diversity

Understand Main Ideas

4. B
5. B
6. B
7. C
8. A

Constructed Response

9. The milder climate in southern Florida supports a wider range of habitats.
10. Each ecosystem supports a different variety of life.
11. economic, aesthetic, and scientific values
12. A variety of coat colors allows this rabbit species to survive in different types of environments.

Think Critically

13. What one person considers desirable might not be viewed in the same way by another person.
14. Possible answer: trees provide shade

Section 2

Vocabulary Review

15. Both terms refer to the elimination of a species from Earth's biosphere. Background extinction is a slow process that does not affect many species at the same time. Mass extinction is a relatively fast process that results in the elimination of a large number of species.
16. Both occur when an ecosystem is separated into smaller pieces. Habitat fragmentation is the actual process. Edge effect is the consequence whereby different environmental conditions are established along the edges of the fragmented habitats.
17. Both can result in a decrease in biodiversity of an ecosystem. Overexploitation is the excessive use of a species for its economic value. An introduced species is a nonnative species that is either intentionally or unintentionally transported to a new habitat.

Assessment Online Test Practice

Understand Main Ideas
18. B
19. C
20. B
21. A
22. A
23. C
24. C

Constructed Response
25. They are hunted and killed for their horns, which are used in Asian markets for medicinal purposes.

Think Critically
26. Possible answers include ways to reduce the runoff of fertilizers, animal wastes, and sewage into waterways.
27. The exotic pet would be an introduced species that can exploit the ecosystem at the expense of native species.

Section 3

Vocabulary Review
28. renewable resources
29. endemic
30. bioremediation
31. nonrenewable resources

Understand Main Ideas
32. A
33. D

Understand Main Ideas

18. Which group of organisms listed in **Table 2** has the greatest number of extinctions overall?
A. birds
B. flowering plants
C. invertebrates
D. mammals

19. Which group listed in **Table 2** has the greatest percentage of extinctions?
A. birds
B. fish
C. mammals
D. reptiles

Use the figure below to answer questions 20 and 21.

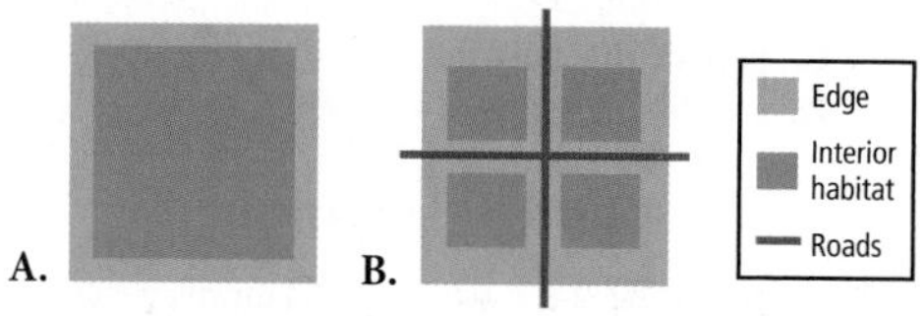

20. Which habitat has the greatest impact resulting from edge effects?
A. A
B. B
C. A and B equally
D. neither A nor B

21. Which habitat naturally supports the greater amount of biodiversity?
A. A
B. B
C. A and B equally
D. neither A nor B

22. Which is not a way in which species lose their habitats?
A. background extinction
B. destruction
C. disruption
D. pollution

23. Approximately how much greater is the current background extinction compared to the normal rate?
A. 1 time
B. 10 times
C. 1000 times
D. 10,000 times

24. Which condition triggered the chain of events off the coast of Alaska that caused the kelp forests to begin to disappear?
A. a decrease in the amount of plankton
B. an increase in the number of sea otters
C. overharvesting of plankton-eating whales
D. pollution caused by pesticides

Constructed Response

25. MAIN Idea Explain why rhinos are in danger of becoming extinct.

Think Critically

26. Recommend ways in which eutrophication can be reduced in waterways.

27. Explain why it is not a good idea to release exotic pets into a local ecosystem.

Section 3

Vocabulary Review

Answer each question with a vocabulary term from the Study Guide page.

28. What are resources called that are replaced by natural processes faster than they are consumed?

29. What are species called that are found in only one geographic location?

30. What is the name of the process of using living organisms to detoxify a location?

31. What are resources called that are found in limited amounts or are replaced by natural processes over extremely long periods of time?

Understand Main Ideas

32. Which term is a method that is used to restore biodiversity to a polluted or damaged area?
A. biological augmentation
B. biological corridor
C. renewable resource
D. sustainable use

Use the figure below to answer question 33.

33. Which is an advantage of the habitat corridor shown above?
A. Corridors increase the edge effect in the area.
B. Diseases are passed easily from one area to another.
C. Parasites are passed easily from one area to another.
D. Members of species can move safely from one area to another.

Use the graph below to answer questions 34 and 35.

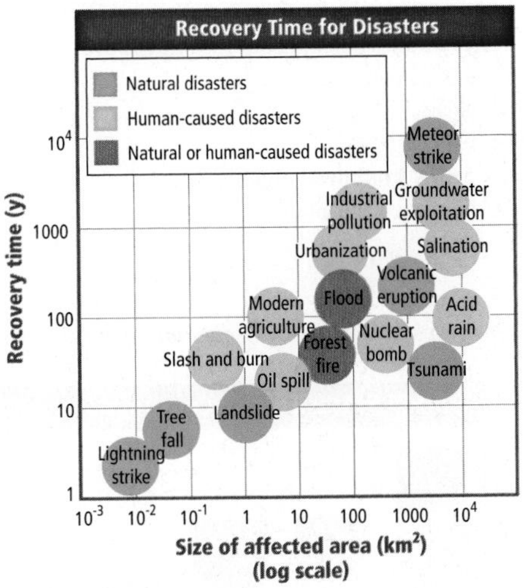

34. Which human-caused disaster requires the greatest recovery time?
A. groundwater exploitation
B. industrial pollution
C. nuclear bomb
D. oil spill

35. Which natural disaster requires the least amount of recovery time?
A. lightning strike **C.** tsunami
B. meteor strike **D.** volcanic eruption

Constructed Response

36. MAIN Idea Explain why reserves protect biodiversity.

37. CAREERS IN BIOLOGY Explain how an environmental microbiologist might use bioremediation to detoxify polluted areas.

Think Critically

38. **Evaluate** why it is important to develop a sustainable-use plan for the use of natural resources.

39. **Evaluate** how a sustainable-use plan for natural resources will change as the world population continues to grow and people living in developing countries increase their standards of living.

Summative Assessment

40. BIG Idea Consider how community and ecosystem homeostasis can be disrupted as a result of a decrease in biodiversity. Write your answer in an essay format.

41. WRITING in Biology Write a short essay about the importance of preserving biodiversity.

42. WRITING in Biology Choose an organism that is in danger of becoming extinct, and write a song or poem detailing the organism's situation.

43. Select an endangered plant or animal and investigate what factors are contributing to its near extinction. Evaluate the organism's chances for survival, taking into consideration genetic diversity, species diversity, and ecosystem diversity.

DBQ Document-Based Questions

Data obtained from: Wilson, E.O. 1980. Resolutions for the 80s. *Harvard Magazine* (January–February): 20.

The quote below was obtained from one of Pulitzer Prize winner Edward O. Wilson's journal articles.

"The worst that can happen—will happen—is not energy depletion, economic collapse, limited nuclear war, or conquest by a totalitarian government. As terrible as these catastrophes would be for us, they can be repaired within a few generations. The one process ongoing in the 1980s that will take millions of years to correct is the loss of genetic and species diversity by the destruction of natural habitats. This is the folly our descendants are least likely to forgive us."

44. How do you think biodiversity has changed since the 1980s?

45. Why do you think Wilson compares the loss of biodiversity with energy depletion, economic collapse, nuclear war, and conquest?

46. What does Wilson mean when he says, "This is the folly our descendants are least likely to forgive us"?

DBQ Document-Based Questions

Wilson, E. O. 1980. Resolutions for the 80s. *Harvard Magazine* (January–February): 20.

44. The decrease in biodiversity has been going on since the 1980s.

45. All these are catastrophic events that can affect anyone and everyone.

46. Our children and grandchildren may wonder why we did not take steps to prevent the loss of biodiversity.

34. A

35. A

Constructed Response

36. Reserves prevent overexploitation and reduce the chances of habitat destruction, pollution, or fragmentation.

37. Bioremediation involves the use of organisms to detoxify an area.

Think Critically

38. Sustainable use of natural resources means that they will be used at a rate at which they can be replenished or recycled.

39. Answers will vary, but they should indicate that increased population numbers and standards of living will put additional strain on renewable resources. As a result, more and more people will have to practice sustainable use.

Summative Assessment

WRITING in Biology

RUBRIC Use the modifiable rubric found on your eTeacher-Edition Online to assess writing assignments.

40. Possible answer: When a habitat is destroyed, biodiversity is decreased. The destruction of habitat may result in extinction of species. This would disrupt the food web, and therefore disrupt homeostasis.

41. Answers will vary, but should include three main points.

42. Answers will vary. Encourage creativity.

43. Students should use multiple current reference resources about endangered plant and animal species. Encourage students to use what they have learned about genetic diversity, species diversity, and ecosystem diversity to evaluate the organism's chances for survival.

Assessment Online Test Practice

Standardized Test Practice

Multiple Choice

1. C
2. A
3. D
4. D
5. C
6. D
7. D
8. C

Short Answer

9. Two possible answers: the scientist should revise the hypothesis or the scientist should repeat the experiment.
10. Experimenting: some observations cannot be tested experimentally.
11. The death rate is increasing and the birthrate is decreasing, or the death rate is increasing and the birthrate does not change.
12. Answers can vary. Possible answers include the following.
    A. Renewable resource: solar energy, because there is always more being produced—there appears to be an inexhaustible supply of solar energy
    B. Nonrenewable resource: mineral deposits, because once they are used, Earth processes cannot replace the deposits
13. The age-structure graph indicates whether a population is growing rapidly, growing slowly, not growing, or declining. The graph also shows the percentage of the population in specific age brackets.
14. If ginger is an invasive species, this means that it has no natural predators and probably reproduces quickly. It might choke out other native plant species, which can lead to extinction of those plant species. Because Hawaii consists of islands, it is particularly prone to extinctions when a nonnative species is introduced.

Standardized Test Practice

Cumulative

Multiple Choice

1. Which factor is most responsible for the lack of plants in polar regions?
A. heavy grazing by herbivores
B. little precipitation
C. no soil for plants to take root
D. not enough sunlight

Use the graph below to answer questions 2 and 3.

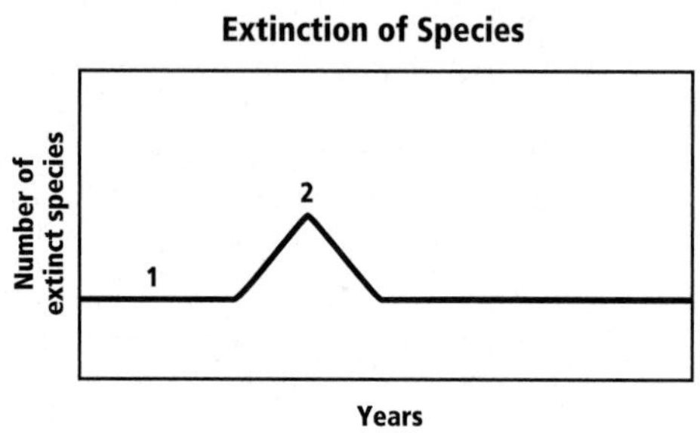

2. Which term best describes the section of the graph labeled *1*?
A. background extinction
B. habitat destruction
C. mass extinction
D. species overexploitation

3. The peak labeled *2* on the graph would not be caused by which event?
A. destruction of a native animal's habitat as humans populate an island
B. increasing industrialization and human influence over time
C. introduction of a nonnative animal into an island ecosystem
D. a fatal disease affecting a single population

4. Which factor is density-dependent?
A. climate
B. weather
C. barometric pressure
D. food competition

5. What would you expect to find in the profundal zone of a lake?
A. algae
B. plankton
C. debris from dead organisms
D. floating water plants

Use the graph below to answer questions 6 and 7.

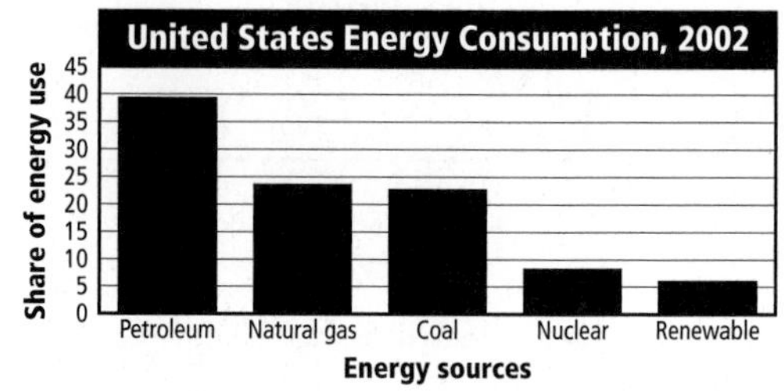

6. What percentage of the United States energy consumption in 2002 was fossil fuels?
A. 23
B. 24
C. 39
D. 86

7. What percentage of the United States energy consumption in 2002 was nonrenewable resources?
A. 8
B. 23
C. 39
D. 94

8. Which situation is an abiotic limiting factor for the habitat of coral organisms?
A. annual rainfall
B. soil chemistry
C. temperature throughout the year
D. zooanthellae in the reef

Short Answer

Use the diagram below to answer questions 9 and 10.

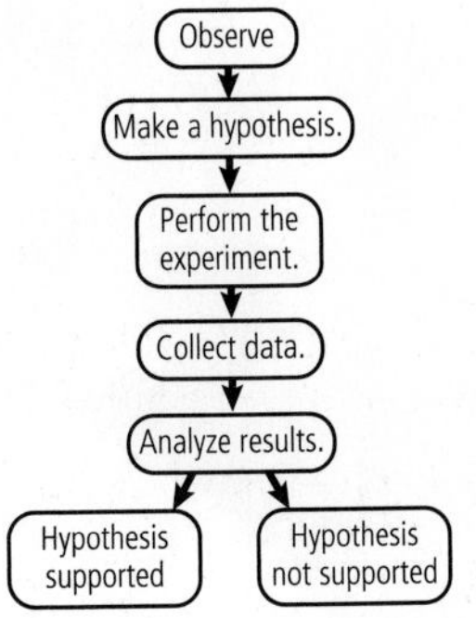

9. Explain what a scientist should do if the experimental data do not support his or her hypothesis.

10. Scientists do not always follow the same scientific method step-by-step. Name one step in the scientific method shown above that often is omitted. Justify your answer.

11. If a population is experiencing a decrease in size, how do the birth and death rates compare?

12. List an example of a renewable resource and a nonrenewable resource, and analyze why they are classified as such.

13. Explain the type of information that is displayed on an age-structure graph.

14. The ginger plant is considered an invasive species in Hawaii. Justify why park officials in Hawaii have to kill ginger plants.

Extended Response

Use the illustration below to answer question 15.

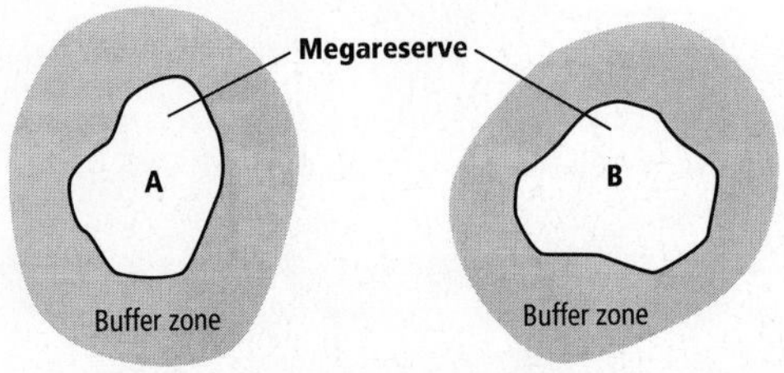

15. The map above shows two megareserves surrounded by buffer zones. Appraise a positive and negative point about these protected zones for a bird species living in Area A.

16. Explain why two species involved in a symbiotic relationship probably evolved around the same time.

Essay Question

The U.S. government takes a census of the population every ten years. The first census took place in 1790 and recorded 3.9 million people. In the 2000 census, the U.S. population was nearly a quarter of a billion people. The census also shows population trends, such as people moving from rural areas to cities.

Using the information in the paragraph above, answer the following question in an essay format.

17. The census provides a snapshot of the U.S. population every ten years. Many things can happen between census dates that affect the population. Describe some of the factors that could contribute to a radical change in the U.S. population between each census.

NEED EXTRA HELP?																	
If You Missed Question . . .	1	2	3	4	5	6	7	8	9	10	11	12	13	14	15	16	17
Review Section . . .	3.2	5.2	5.2	4.1	3.3	5.3	5.3	3.2	1.3	1.3	4.2	5.3	4.2	5.2	5.3	2.1	4.2

Extended Response

15. Answers can vary. A positive point is that megareserves are very large and surrounded by buffer zones where only the sustainable use of resources is allowed. Consequently, these reserves allow the bird species to survive better than in smaller reserves. A negative point is that the two reserves are protected areas separated by unprotected land, so the members of the bird species cannot travel safely between the protected areas.

16. Each organism in a mutualistic relationship has characteristics that are needed by both organisms. Other types of symbiotic relationships involve one organism that is more dependent on the other. These dependent organisms must have evolved along side their counterparts or they would not have survived.

Essay Question

17. Answers will vary. Natural disasters such as a hurricane can force populations to relocate; outbreak of disease can kill segments of a population; outbreak of war can kill segments of a population; a booming economy or troops returning from war can increase the birth rate; and people moving from agricultural areas to cities for jobs can shift the location of segments of a population.

UNIT 2

The Life of a Cell

Preview the Unit

Have students preview the chapters in this unit and make a concept map or graphic organizer relating the Themes, Big Ideas, and Main Ideas. Students' maps should show a hierarchy between Big Ideas and Main Ideas and the interconnectedness of the Themes.

Chapter 6
Chemistry in Biology
BIG Idea Atoms are the foundation of biological chemistry and the building blocks of all living organisms.

Chapter 7
Cellular Structure and Function
BIG Idea Cells are the structural and functional units of all living organisms.

Chapter 8
Cellular Energy
BIG Idea Photosynthesis converts the Sun's energy into chemical energy, while cellular respiration uses chemical energy to carry out life functions.

Chapter 9
Cellular Reproduction
BIG Idea Cells go through a life cycle that includes interphase, mitosis, and cytokinesis.

WebQuest
Careers in Biology

UNIT 2

The Cell

THEMES

Scientific Inquiry Scientific investigations have led to the discovery of the cell and its functions and to the manipulation of the cell's interior structures.

Diversity Cells contain many macromolecules and structures and rely on various functions and processes.

Energy Energy is stored in chemical bonds. Various cellular processes break those bonds to obtain the energy.

Homeostasis Active transport across the plasma membrane maintains homeostasis within the cell.

Change Cellular processes result in changes in a cell and its environment and produce new cells.

WebQuest **CAREERS IN BIOLOGY**

Forensic pathologists are medical specialists who investigate the cause and the manner of human death. Forensic pathologists work in the field and in a laboratory to analyze medical evidence such as skulls.

5-Minute UNIT LAUNCH

K-W-L Chart Have students make a list of what they know about cells. Next, have them skim Unit 2, taking notice of the photos of cells and the bold heads. Ask students what questions came up, and have them list what they now want to know about cells. Discuss the lists and create a K-W-L chart with their responses. After completing the unit, revisit the chart and reassess their knowledge by asking them what they learned about cells.

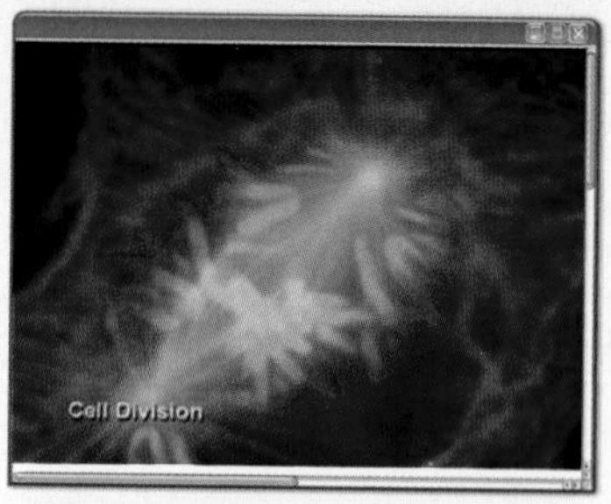

Video

What's BIOLOGY Got To Do With It?
This video examines how cancer drugs are used to control cell growth.

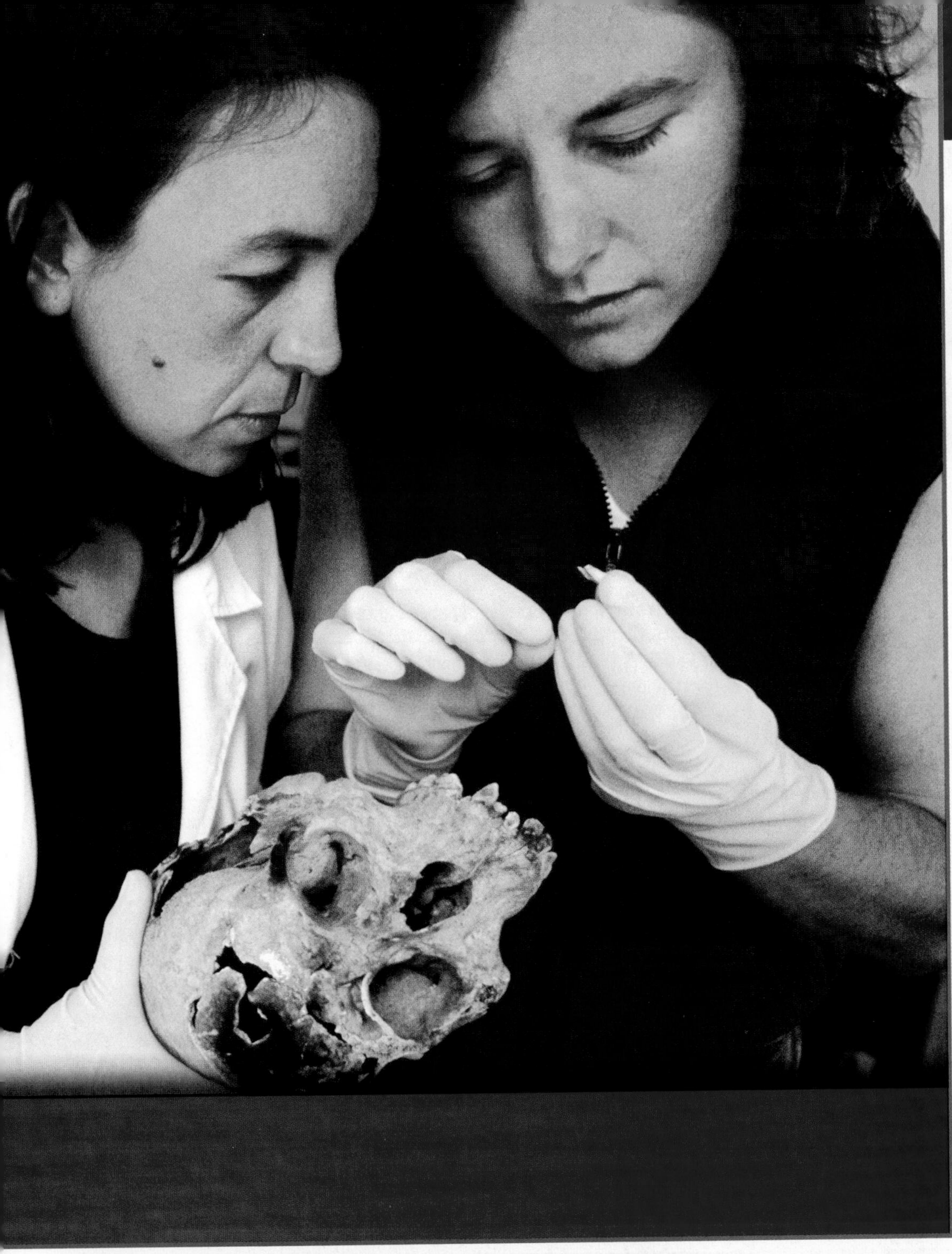

Misconceptions

In each section, *Clarify a Misconception* provides you with the information to dispel a common student misconception. A question will help you elicit the misconception and an explanation will help you correct it.

Below is a preview of misconceptions from each chapter in this unit.

Before studying Chapter 6, students might think that a chemical reaction occurs when compounds change state. Chapter 6 will explain that a chemical reaction occurs when a substance is changed into a different substance with different composition and properties (p. 156).

Before studying Chapter 7, students might think that a cell wall is impermeable like a classroom wall. Chapter 7 will explain that the cell wall is permeable, allowing exchange between the cell and its environment (p. 198).

Before studying Chapter 8, students might think the term *organic* means "natural," as in "natural foods." Chapter 8 will explain that *organic* refers to many compounds that contain carbon (p. 226).

Before studying Chapter 9, students might think that "bigger is better" at the cellular level. Chapter 9 will explain that substances are transported more efficiently in small cells than in large cells (p. 244).

SERVICE LEARNING/COMMUNITY SERVICE

Science Reading Tutors Students can set up a tutoring service with middle and elementary school science teachers to help younger students with their science reading and evaluation skills. Tutoring others strengthens students' own science reading skills (Eyler and Giles, 1999).

Research bibliography on pages 32T–34T

Chapter 6 Organizer:
Chemistry in Biology

LabManager™
Customize any lab with the LabManager™ CD-ROM.

Essential Questions	National Science Standards	Materials and Planning Estimated times include cleanup and disposal, but do not include teacher prep time. For cleanup and disposal guidelines, see page 39T.	Est. Time (min)
Section 1 1. What are atoms? 2. How are the particles that make up atoms diagrammed? 3. What are the similarities between covalent and ionic bonds? 4. How are van der Waals forces described?	UCP.1, UCP.2, UCP.3; A.1, A.2; B.1, B.2, B.3; C.5; G.1, G.2, G.3	**Launch Lab,** p.146: cereal box, other labeled food items, modeling clay, straws, gumdrops	20
		Demonstration, p. 153: Lewis dot diagrams	10
		MiniLab 1, p. 154: food substances, hot water bath, hot plate, 1000-mL beaker, four test tubes, graduated cylinder, distilled water, Benedict's solution, stirring rod, test tube holders, honey, milk, potato, butter, apple, sugar-free pudding	15
Section 2 1. What are the parts of a chemical reaction? 2. How can energy changes be related to chemical reactions? 3. What is the importance of enzymes in living organisms?	UCP.1, UCP.2, UCP.3, UCP.5; A.1, A.2; B.3; C.5; E.2; F.1; G.1, G.2	**Demonstration,** p. 156: pieces of paper, source of fire, scissors	5
		MiniLab 2, p. 159: boiling water, lemon juice, paper towel, 250-mL beakers, sugar solution, tongs, apple	20
Section 3 1. How does the structure of water make it a good solvent? 2. What are the similarities and differences between solutions and suspensions? 3. What are the differences between acids and bases?	UCP.1, UCP.2, UCP.3; A.1, A.2; B.1, B.2, B.3, B.4, B.6; C.5; G.1, G.2, G.3	**Demonstration,** p. 161: two clear plastic bottles, water, powdered food coloring, cooking oil	10
		Demonstration, p. 164: grated red cabbage, vinegar, lemon juice, soda, baking soda, detergent	10
Section 4 1. What is the role of carbon in living organisms? 2. What are the four major families of biological macromolecules? 3. What are the functions of each group of biological macromolecules?	UCP.1, UCP.2, UCP.3; A.1, A.2; B.1, B.2, B.3, B.6; C.5; E.1, E.2; F.1, F.5; G.1, G.2, G.3	**Demonstration,** p. 166: interlocking building blocks, molecular modeling kit	20
		Demonstration, p. 170: molecular modeling kit, beaded necklace	10
		BioLab, p. 173: 400-mL beaker, 50-mL graduated cylinder, 10-mL graduated cylinder, kitchen knife, hot plate, tongs or large forceps, test tube rack, square or rectangular pan, ice, stopwatch or timer, beef liver, nonmercury thermometer, dropper, 3% hydrogen peroxide, distilled water, potato slices, 18-mm × 150-mm test tubes, buffer solutions (pH 5, pH 6, pH 7, pH 8)	45

Suggested Time for Each Lesson

Class	Chapter Opener	Section 1	Section 2	Section 3	Section 4	Assessment
Basic	45 min	45 min	45 min	45 min	45 min	45 min
General	25 min	55 min	55 min	55 min	55 min	45 min
Honors	5 min	60 min	60 min	60 min	60 min	20 min

ConnectED

connectED.mcgraw-hill.com

Access interactive learning opportunities and teaching resources using these icons located throughout your StudentWorks™ Plus Online and eTeacherEdition Online.

Chapter 6 Section Resources

FAST FILE Unit 2 Resources:
Launch Lab Worksheet *
MiniLab Worksheet *
Study Guide (English/Spanish) *
Section Quick Check

Reading Essentials 6.1
Science Notebook 6.1 *

FAST FILE Unit 2 Resources:
MiniLab Worksheet *
Study Guide (English/Spanish) *
Section Quick Check

Reading Essentials 6.2
Science Notebook 6.2 *

FAST FILE Unit 2 Resources:
Study Guide (English/Spanish) *
Section Quick Check

Reading Essentials 6.3
Science Notebook 6.3 *

FAST FILE Unit 2 Resources:
BioLab Worksheet *
Study Guide (English/Spanish) *
Section Quick Check

Reading Essentials 6.4
Science Notebook 6.4 *

Additional Chapter 6 Resources

FAST FILE Unit 2 Resources:
Chapter Diagnostic Test
Concept Mapping *
Real-World Biology
Enrichment
Chapter Tests A, B, and C

Transparencies:
Bellringer Transparencies *
Biology Concepts Transparencies *

Lab Resources:
Laboratory Manual *
Probeware Lab Manual *
Forensics Lab Manual *
Pre-AP Lab Manual *
Open Inquiry in Biology *
Guided Inquiry in Biology *

Technology

Teaching Tools:
eTeacherEdition Online
Classroom Presentation Toolkit CD-ROM *
LabManager™ CD-ROM *
Video Lab DVD *
Virtual Lab CD-ROM *
What's BIOLOGY Got To Do With It?
StudentWorks™ Plus Online *

Chapter Assessment Tools:
Classroom Presentation Toolkit CD-ROM *
ExamView® Assessment Suite CD-ROM

Web-Based Resources:

- StudentWorks™ Plus Online
- eTeacherEdition Online
- Animations *
- The Interactive Time Line *
- Interactive Tables *
- Online Quizzes
- Online Test Practice
- Standardized Test Practice
- Virtual Labs *
- Multilingual eGlossary *
- Vocabulary eGames *
- Vocabulary eFlashcards
- WebQuests
- Personal Tutors

While all resources listed are appropriate for English learners, the * indicates resources with a strong visual or hands-on component for EL.

Teaching strategies and activities have been coded for differentiated instruction.

AL Activities for students working above grade level	**OL** Activities for students working on grade level	**BL** Activities for students working below grade level	**EL** Activities for English learners (also ELL)	**COOP LEARN** Activities designed for small cooperative group work

CHAPTER 6

Launch Lab
How does the nutrient content of foods compare?

? Inquiry Launch Lab

For a lab worksheet, use your eTeacherEdition Online.

RUBRIC A rubric for evaluating Launch Labs is found on your eTeacherEdition Online.

Est. Time 20 min

Alternative Materials packaging from other food items

Safety Precautions Approve lab safety forms before work begins. Caution students to never eat anything in a science classroom.

Teaching Strategies

- Provide molecular structures and formulas representing the six nutrients students will study. Compare their chemical compositions and identify common elements among nutrients.
- Help students understand that minerals are inorganic substances, whereas vitamins are organic substances derived from plants and animals. Provide examples of each.

CHAPTER 6
Chemistry in Biology

ConnectED
Your one-stop online resource
connectED.mcgraw-hill.com

- Video
- Audio
- Review
- Inquiry
- WebQuest
- Assessment
- Concepts in Motion
- Multilingual eGlossary

Launch Lab
How does the nutrient content of foods compare?

Your body's structures and functions depend on chemical elements including those found in proteins, carbohydrates, fats, vitamins, minerals, and water. In this lab, you will investigate nutrients that provide those elements.

For a lab worksheet, use your StudentWorks™ Plus Online.

? Inquiry Launch Lab

FOLDABLES®

Make a four-door book using the labels shown. Use it to organize your notes on enzyme activity.

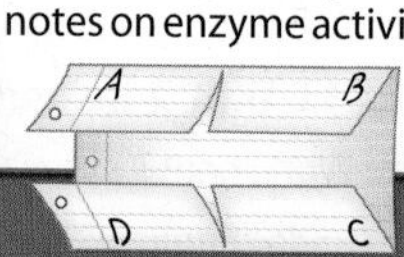

Procedure

1. Read and complete the lab safety form.
2. Construct a data table to record grams or percent of each nutrient. Include columns for Serving Size, Calories, and Calories from Fat.
3. Study and record data from the Nutrition Facts label on a **cereal box.**
4. Choose three additional **labeled food items.** Predict how the nutrients in these items compare with the nutrients in the cereal. Use the Nutrition Facts labels to record data.

Analysis

1. **Evaluate** What factors influenced your predictions of the nutrient contents? Were your predictions correct? Factors might include texture, composition, or taste, as well as prior knowledge of how the item is classified among food groups.
2. **Analyze** Which food item has the greatest amount of proteins per serving? The least? Answers will vary depending on the types of foods surveyed.

Cleanup and Disposal Remind students to return all food items and to wash hands thoroughly after completing the lab.

THEME FOCUS Energy
In every chemical reaction, there is a change in energy.

BIG Idea Atoms are the foundation of biological chemistry and the building blocks of all living organisms.

Section 1 • Atoms, Elements, and Compounds

Section 2 • Chemical Reactions

Section 3 • Water and Solutions

Section 4 • The Building Blocks of Life

THEMES

Scientific Inquiry It took nearly 200 years of scientific experimentation to prove that atoms exist.

Diversity The structure of the atom allows for the diversity of elements that exist on Earth.

Energy Energy is stored in chemical bonds between atoms.

Homeostasis In order to maintain homeostasis, the body must control levels of hydrogen ions.

Change A chemical equation shows how reactants change into products in a reaction.

Introduce the Chapter

Skin Have students look at the chapter opener photograph. **ASK STUDENTS:** ***What do you feel when you place your hand on your cheek?*** Students may reply that they feel soft skin. ***What is the skin made of?*** Students might indicate that skin is made of cells, tissues, or some other small structure. At the molecular level, skin is made of substances composed of atoms and molecules and billions of units of particular substances.

BIG Idea

Outline Have students outline the chapter, using the main ideas and section headings. Encourage students to keep the Big Idea in mind as they progress through the chapter and consider how essential the fundamentals of chemistry are to living organisms.
Sample outline:

1. Atoms are the building blocks of matter.
   A. Atoms are made up of protons, neutrons, and electrons.
2. Elements are pure substances that cannot be broken down by physical or chemical means.
   A. Isotopes are atoms of elements with a different number of neutrons.
   B. Radioactive isotopes are isotopes that give off radiation.
3. Compounds are formed when two or more elements combine.

Section 1

MAIN Idea

BL OL AL Units of Matter
ASK STUDENTS: ***What is the smallest unit of matter?*** atom Students might think that an element or chemical compound is the smallest unit of matter. Some might be aware of atoms, but might not know about subatomic particles. ***How are atoms and elements related?*** Elements are pure substances comprised of only one type of atom. ***Are living organisms comprised of these same elements?*** yes ***How is chemistry related to the growth and survival of living organisms?*** All biological processes are chemical reactions.

S Skill Practice
BL OL Compare and Contrast
SAY TO STUDENTS: ***List the similarities and differences among protons, electrons, and neutrons.*** Protons, electrons, and neutrons are similar because they are all components of an atom. However, they have different charges. Protons are positively charged, electrons are negatively charged, and neutrons have no charge (they are neutral). Protons and neutrons are similar because they both reside in the nucleus of an atom, whereas electrons are in constant motion around the nucleus.

S Skill Practice
BL OL AL Visual Literacy
Have students examine Figure 1 and note the location of each subatomic particle. Remind students why the locations of these particles are essential to their roles in the atom.
ASK STUDENTS: ***How does the location of the electrons in an atom allow them to be involved in bonding?*** Students should realize that electrons are involved in bonding because they are on the periphery of an atom.

Section 1

Reading Preview

Essential Questions
- What are atoms?
- How are the particles that make up atoms diagrammed?
- What are the similarities between covalent and ionic bonds?
- How are van der Waals forces described?

Review Vocabulary
substance: a form of matter that has a uniform and unchanging composition

New Vocabulary
atom
nucleus
proton
neutron
electron
element
isotope
compound
covalent bond
molecule
ion
ionic bond
van der Waals force

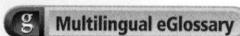

Multilingual eGlossary

Video BrainPOP

Atoms, Elements, and Compounds

MAIN Idea **Matter is composed of tiny particles called atoms.**

Real-World Reading Link Many scientists think that the universe began with a sudden, rapid expansion billions of years ago. They think that the building blocks that make up the amazing diversity of life we see today are a result of that expansion. The study of those building blocks is the science of chemistry.

Atoms

Chemistry is the study of matter, its composition, and properties. Matter is anything that has mass and takes up space. All of the organisms that you study in biology are made up of matter. **Atoms** are the building blocks of matter.

Connection to History In the fifth century B.C., Greek philosophers Leucippus and Democritus first proposed the idea that all matter is made up of tiny, indivisible particles. It wasn't until the 1800s that scientists began to collect experimental evidence to support the existence of atoms. As technology improved over the next two centuries, scientists proved not only that atoms exist but also that they are made up of even smaller particles.

The structure of an atom An atom is so small that billions of them could fit on the head of a pin. Yet, atoms are made up of even smaller particles called neutrons, protons, and electrons, as illustrated in **Figure 1.** Neutrons and protons are located at the center of the atom, which is called the **nucleus. Protons** are positively charged particles (p^+), and **neutrons** are particles that have no charge (n^0). **Electrons** are negatively charged particles (e^-) that are located outside the nucleus. Electrons constantly move around an atom's nucleus in energy levels. The basic structure of an atom is the result of the attraction between protons and electrons. Atoms contain an equal number of protons and electrons, so the overall charge of an atom is zero. S

S

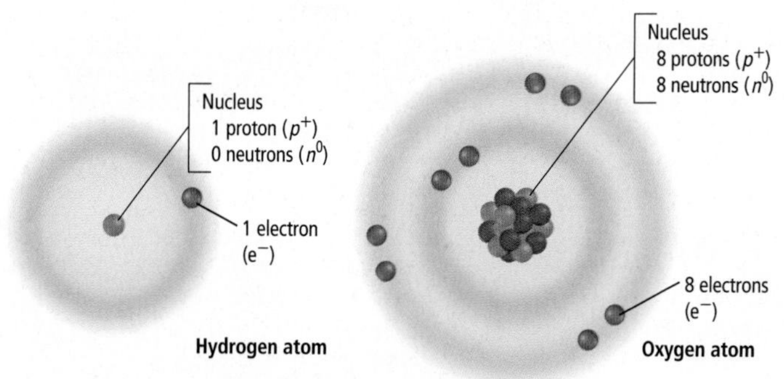

Figure 1 Hydrogen has only one proton and one electron. Oxygen has eight protons, eight neutrons, and eight electrons. The electrons move around the nucleus in two energy levels (shown as the darker shaded rings).
Infer *the charge of an atom if it contained more electrons than protons.*

Caption Question Fig. 1 It would have a negative charge.

Video BrainPOP

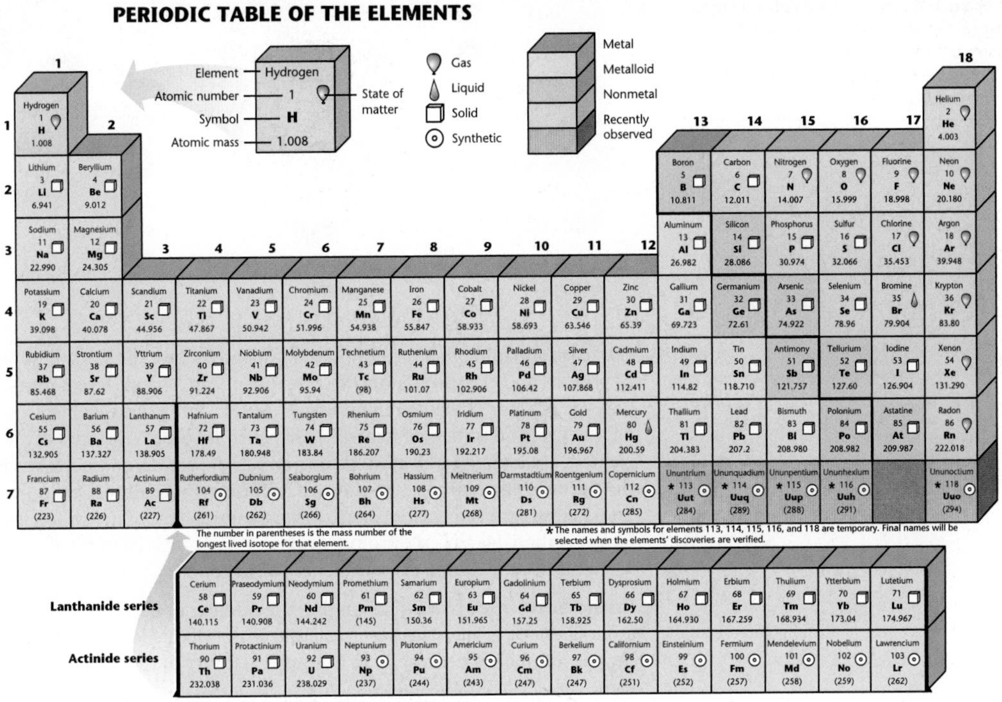

■ **Figure 2** The periodic table of the elements organizes all of the known elements. Examine the biologists' guide to the periodic table on the back cover of this book.

Elements

An **element** is a pure substance that cannot be broken down into other substances by physical or chemical means. Elements are made of only one type of atom. There are over 100 known elements, 92 of which occur naturally. Scientists have collected a large amount of information about the elements, such as the number of protons and electrons each element has and the atomic mass of each element. Also, each element has a unique name and symbol. All of these data, and more, are collected in an organized table called the periodic table of the elements.

The periodic table of the elements As shown in **Figure 2,** the periodic table is organized into horizontal rows, called periods, and vertical columns, called groups. Each individual block in the grid represents an element. The table is called periodic because elements in the same group have similar chemical and physical properties. This organization even allows scientists to predict elements that have not yet been discovered or isolated. As shown in **Figure 3,** elements found in living organisms also are found in Earth's crust.

■ **Figure 3** The elements in Earth's crust and living organisms vary in their abundance. Living things are composed primarily of three elements: carbon, hydrogen, and oxygen.
Interpret *what the most abundant element is that exists in living things.*

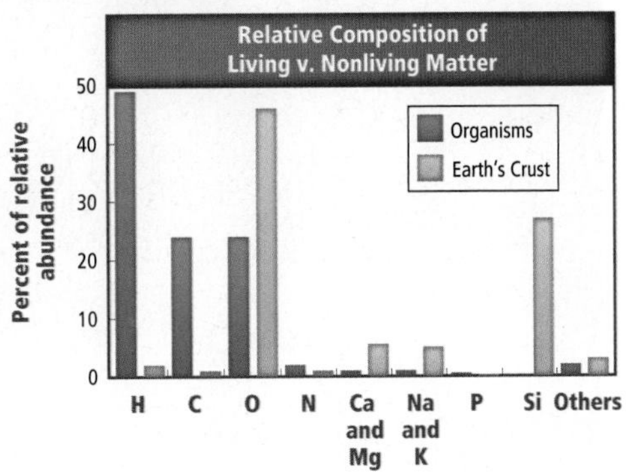

Develop Concepts

BL OL AL

Integrate Chemistry Inform students that the continual bonding and breaking apart of compounds is an essential process in living organisms. Remind students of examples such as photosynthesis, cellular respiration, and the digestion of food. Remind students that all compounds can be broken down into smaller particles and that these smaller particles—atoms—can recombine to form new compounds.

EL Have students examine models of compounds and the smaller particles.

Writing Support

AL Summary Writing Have students research the discovery of subatomic particles and describe the history of atomic research in a summary report. Have students include the impact of these discoveries on today's scientists.

■ **Caption Question Fig. 3**

hydrogen

S Skill Practice

BL OL Make a Graph

Have students make a graph that illustrates the radioactive decay of phosphorus-32 over a 12-week period. The half-life of P-32 is approximately two weeks. Instruct them to plot time in weeks on the x-axis and plot percent phosphorus-32 (zero to 100) on the y-axis.

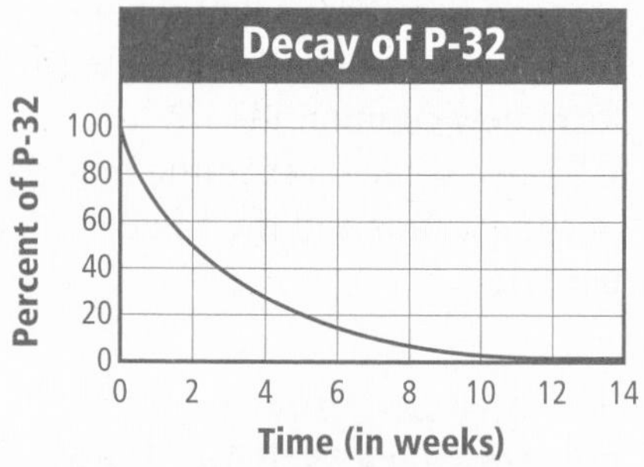

D Develop Concepts

OL AL Discuss

ASK STUDENTS: ***Have you ever heard about medical tests that require the use of radioisotopes? Which test? What isotope? What do you know about these tests?*** Answers will vary, but some students might mention radioactive dyes. Answers should include the time it takes the isotope to decay, the ability to bind the isotope to other molecules, or the ability of the isotope to remain independent so it can travel in the body to be recorded on film or computer before it is eliminated. Have students compare the process for determining the age of fossilized bones to the ones used in medical tests. Discuss benefits and risks of exposure to radioisotopes during diagnostic medical tests. Compare these to the use of isotopes in medical treatments for cancer.

Video BrainPOP

■ **Figure 4** Carbon-12 and carbon-13 occur naturally in living and nonliving things. All living things also contain a small amount of carbon-14. **Compare** ***the similarities and differences of isotopes.***

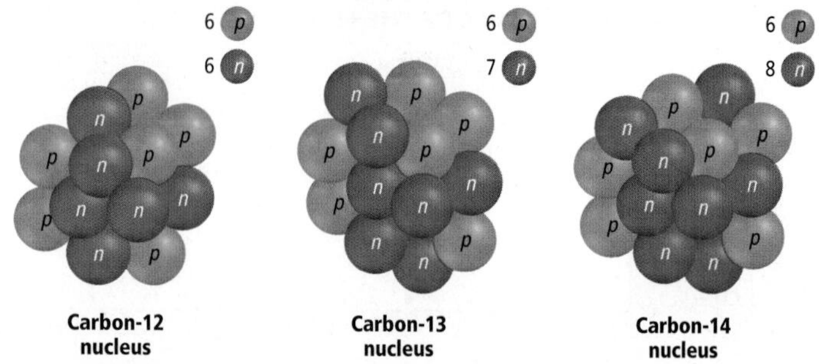

Video BrainPOP

Isotopes Although atoms of the same element have the same number of protons and electrons, atoms of an element can have different numbers of neutrons, as shown in **Figure 4.** Atoms of the same element that have different numbers of neutrons are called **isotopes.** Isotopes of an element are identified by adding the number of protons and neutrons in the nucleus. For example, the most abundant form of carbon, carbon-12, has six protons and six neutrons in its nucleus. One carbon isotope—carbon-14—has six protons and eight neutrons. Isotopes of elements have the same chemical characteristics.

Radioactive isotopes Changing the number of neutrons in an atom does not change the overall charge of the atom. However, changing the number of neutrons can affect the stability of the nucleus, in some cases causing the nucleus to decay, or break apart. When a nucleus breaks apart, it gives off radiation that can be detected. Isotopes that give off radiation are called radioactive isotopes. S

Carbon-14 is a radioactive isotope that is found in all living things. Scientists know the half-life, or the amount of time it takes for half of carbon-14 to decay, so they can calculate the age of an object by finding how much carbon-14 remains in the sample. Other radioactive isotopes have medical uses, as shown in **Figure 5.** D

Reading Check **State** the difference between an isotope and a radioactive isotope.

■ **Figure 5** Radioactive isotopes are used to help doctors diagnose disease, and locate and treat certain types of cancer.

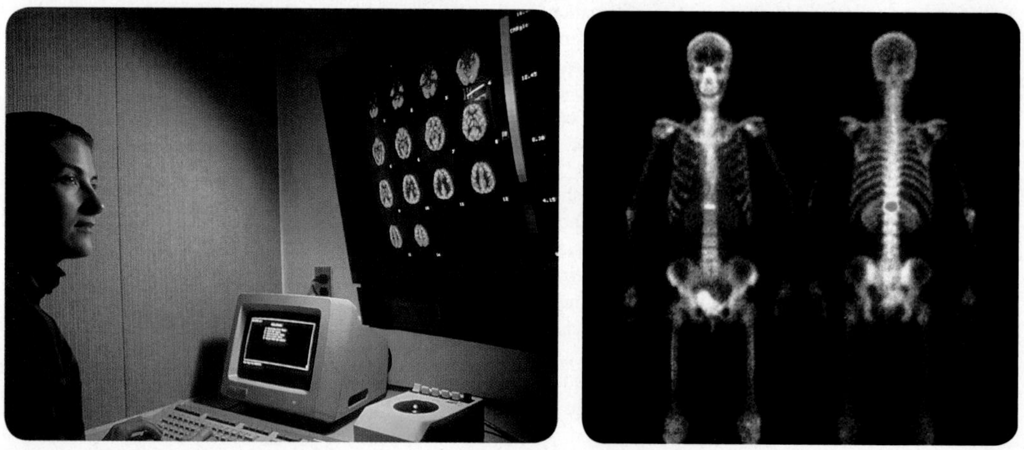

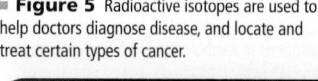

■ **Caption Question Fig. 4** The isotopes differ in their number of neutrons. They have the same number of protons.

Reading Check Radioactive isotopes are unstable and give off radiation.

> *"Education is a better safeguard of liberty than a standing army."*
>
> —Edward Everett

Brilliant fireworks displays depend on compounds such as the metal strontium.

Table salt is the compound NaCl.

Wetlands are sources of living things made of complex compounds and the simple compound methane (CH_4).

Compounds

Elements can combine to form more complex substances. A **compound** is a pure substance formed when two or more different elements combine. There are millions of known compounds and thousands more discovered each year. **Figure 6** shows a few of them. Each compound has a chemical formula made up of the chemical symbols from the periodic table. You might know that water is the compound H_2O. Sodium chloride (NaCl) is the compound commonly called table salt. The fuel people use in cars is a mixture of hydrocarbon compounds. Hydrocarbons have only hydrogen and carbon atoms. Methane (CH_4) is the simplest hydrocarbon. Bacteria in areas such as the wetlands shown in **Figure 6** release 76 percent of global methane from natural sources by decomposing plants and other organisms. They are made of compounds, too.

Compounds have several unique characteristics. First, compounds are always formed from a specific combination of elements in a fixed ratio. Water always is formed in a ratio of two hydrogen atoms and one oxygen atom, and each water molecule has the same structure. Second, compounds are chemically and physically different from the elements that comprise them. For example, water has different properties than hydrogen and oxygen.

Another characteristic of compounds is that they cannot be broken down into simpler compounds or elements by physical means, such as tearing or crushing. Compounds, however, can be broken down by chemical means into simpler compounds or into their original elements. Consider again the example of water. You cannot pass water **W** through a filter and separate the hydrogen from the oxygen, but a process called electrolysis, illustrated in **Figure 7**, can break water down **S** into hydrogen gas and oxygen gas.

■ **Figure 6** You and your world are made of compounds.

■ **Figure 7** Electrolysis of water produces hydrogen gas that can be used for hydrogen fuel cells.

W Writing Support

BL OL AL Narrative Writing Have students write and illustrate a paragraph explaining how compounds are formed. Tell students to include a description of how the unique characterisitics of compounds are created.

S Skill Practice

BL OL Concept Map Have students make a concept map diagramming the relationship between atoms, subatomic particles, and compounds. Maps should emphasize the hierarchical nature of the relationship.

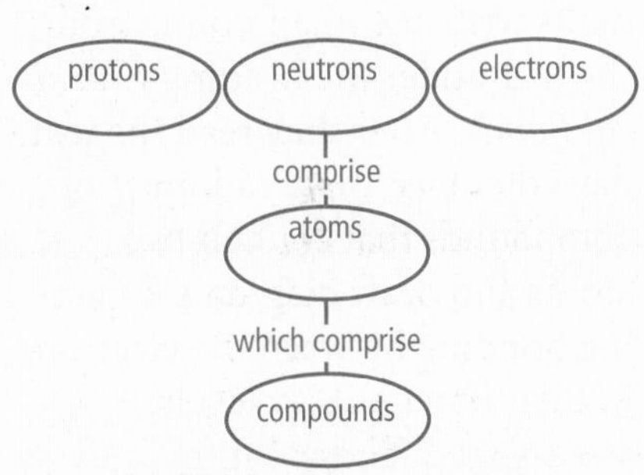

EL COOP LEARN Give students a blank concept map and a separate list of terms. Have students work in pairs to complete the map.

R Reading Strategy

EL BL OL SQ3R Have students **S**urvey the text under the heading *Chemical Bonds,* focusing on the vocabulary terms. Tell students to write at least three **Q**uestions about key concepts. For example, *What is the difference between covalent and ionic bonds?* Then have students **R**ead the text, taking notes related to the questions they wrote. Finally, have students **R**ecite vocabulary terms and **R**eview the text for the meanings.

C Critical Thinking

BL OL AL Evaluate Have students write the main points from the text under the heading *Chemical Bonds.* After they read the text, have them list three examples of compounds that contain two atoms and draw diagrams depicting bonding between the electrons in their outer energy levels. Examples are NaF, LiCl, and N_2.

D Develop Concepts

BL OL AL

Clarify a Misconception

Draw the chemical structure for carbon monoxide (CO) on the board, showing the covalent bond that is formed.

ASK STUDENTS: ***How do the electrons in the covalent bond know which atom they "belong" to?*** Students might think that each atom has its own electrons. Electrons are not specific to atoms; that is, electrons do not "belong" to any particular atom. All electrons are the same and can be transferred from one atom to another. Further, electrons are not shared equally in all covalent bonds. In some covalent bonds, one atom attracts an electron pair more than the other atom and causes the electron pair to be closer to one atom than to another.

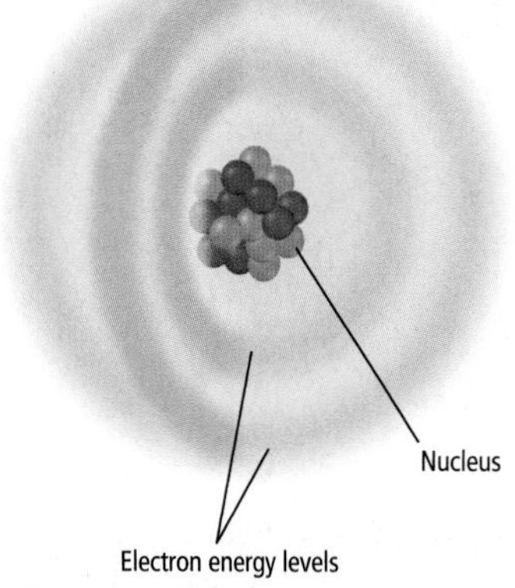

■ **Figure 8** Electrons are moving constantly within the energy levels surrounding the nucleus.

R Chemical Bonds

C Compounds such as water, salt, and methane are formed when two or more substances combine. The force that holds the substances together is called a chemical bond. Think back to the protons, neutrons, and electrons that make up an atom. The nucleus determines the chemical identity of an atom, and the electrons are involved directly in forming chemical bonds. Electrons travel around the nucleus of an atom in areas called energy levels, as illustrated in **Figure 8.** Each energy level has a specific number of electrons that it can hold at any time. The first energy level, which is the level closest to the nucleus, can hold up to two electrons. The second can hold up to eight electrons.

A partially filled energy level is not as stable as an energy level that is empty or completely filled. Atoms become more stable by losing electrons or attracting electrons from other atoms. This results in the formation of chemical bonds between atoms. It is the forming of chemical bonds that stores energy and the breaking of chemical bonds that provides energy for processes of growth, development, adaptation, and reproduction in living things. There are two main types of chemical bonds—covalent bonds and ionic bonds.

Covalent bonds When you were younger, you probably learned to share. If you had a book that your friend wanted to read as well, you could enjoy the story together. In this way, you both benefited from the book. Similarly, one type of chemical bond forms when atoms share electrons in their outer energy levels.

The chemical bond that forms when electrons are shared is called a **covalent bond. Figure 9** illustrates the covalent bonds between oxygen and hydrogen that form water. Each hydrogen (H) atom has one electron in its outermost energy level, and oxygen (O) has six. Because the outermost energy level of oxygen is the second level, which can hold up to eight electrons, oxygen has a strong tendency to fill the energy level by sharing the electrons from the two nearby hydrogen atoms. Hydrogen does not completely give up the electrons; it also has a strong tendency to share electrons with oxygen to fill its outermost energy level. Two covalent bonds form, which creates water.

Most compounds in living organisms have covalent bonds holding them together. Water and other substances with covalent bonds are called molecules. A **molecule** is a compound in which the atoms are held together by covalent bonds. Depending on the number of pairs of electrons that are shared, covalent bonds can be single, double, or triple, as shown in **Figure 10.** D

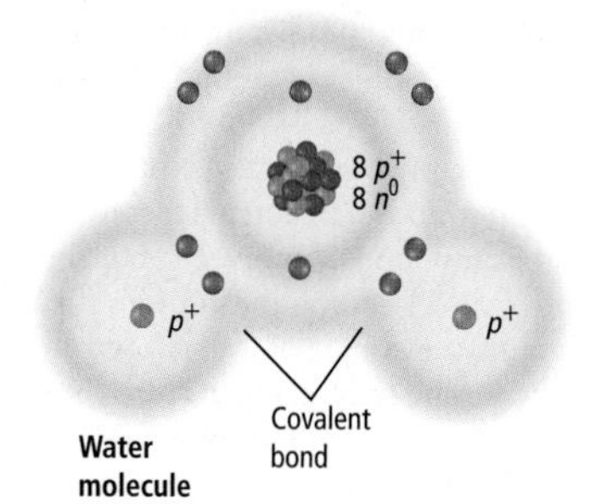

■ **Figure 9** In water (H_2O), two hydrogen atoms each share one electron with one oxygen atom. Because the oxygen atom needs two electrons to fill its outer energy level, it forms two covalent bonds, one with each hydrogen atom.

Content Background

Teacher FYI True nonpolar covalent bonds form only when diatomic molecules are formed from two identical atoms; otherwise polar covalent bonds form. When two identical atoms bond, the electrons are shared equally. When the atoms differ greatly, then the sharing is not equal and the bond becomes polar. The relative polarity of a bond can be quantified using the electronegativity (the ability of an atom to compete for electrons with the other atom to which it is bonded). In the periodic table, electronegativity decreases from top to bottom in a group and increases from left to right. The greater the difference in electronegativity, the greater the polarity of the bond.

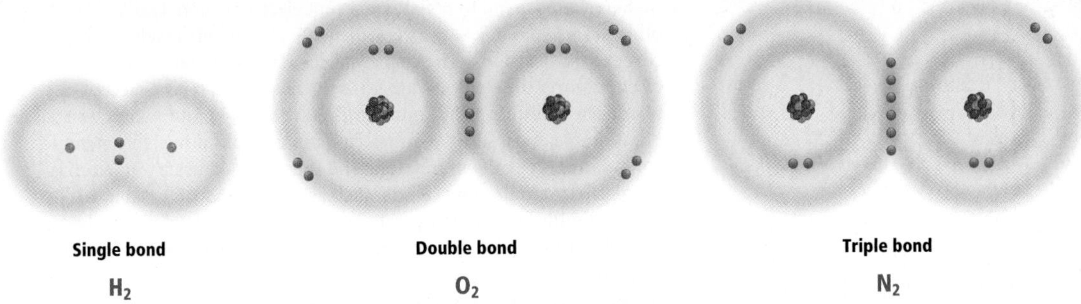

Ionic bonds Recall that atoms are neutral; they do not have an electric charge. Also recall that for an atom to be most stable, the outermost energy level should be either empty or completely filled. Some atoms tend to give up (donate) or obtain (accept) electrons to empty or fill the outer energy level to be stable. An atom that has lost or gained one or more electrons becomes an **ion** and carries an electric charge. For example, sodium has one electron in its outermost energy level. Sodium can become more stable if it gives up this one electron, leaving its outer energy level empty. When it gives away this one negative charge, the neutral sodium atom becomes a positively charged sodium ion (Na^+). Similarly, chlorine has seven electrons in its outer energy level and needs just one electron to fill it. When chlorine accepts an electron from a donor atom, such as sodium, chlorine becomes a negatively charged ion (Cl^-).

An **ionic bond** is an electrical attraction between two oppositely charged atoms or groups of atoms called ions. **Figure 11** shows how an ionic bond forms as a result of the electrical attraction between Na^+ and Cl^- to produce NaCl (sodium chloride). Substances formed by ionic bonds are called ionic compounds.

D **R** Ions in living things include sodium, potassium, calcium, chloride, and carbonate ions. They help maintain homeostasis as they travel in and out of cells. In addition, ions help transmit signals among cells that allow you to see, taste, hear, feel, and smell.

■ **Figure 10** A single bond has one pair of shared electrons, a double bond has two pairs, and a triple bond has three pairs.

Review Personal Tutor

■ **Figure 11** To form ions, sodium donates an electron and chlorine gains an electron. An ionic bond forms when the oppositely charged ions come close together.

Concepts in Motion

Animation

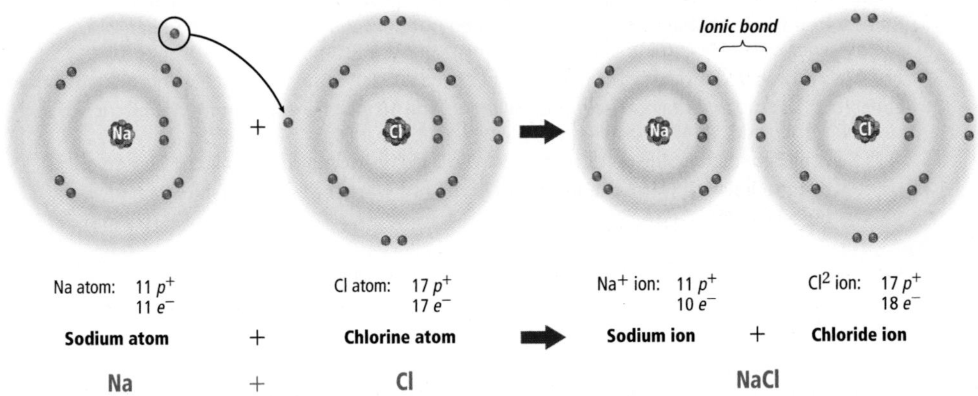

D Develop Concepts

BL OL AL Identify Describe the compound sodium hydroxide (NaOH) to students.

SAY TO STUDENTS: ***Identify the type of bond that holds the molecules together.*** Na^+ and OH^- ions form an ionic bond in NaOH.

R Reading Strategy

EL BL OL AL Illustrate Have students draw depictions of covalent and ionic bonds. Diagrams of covalent bonds should show electrons that are shared. Diagrams of ionic bonds should show electrons that are unequally distributed—one of the atoms in the bond will have more electrons around it than the other atom.

Develop Concepts

BL OL AL

Integrate Chemistry Start a discussion about everyday objects that contain compounds with ionic bonds. Bring examples to class. Have students hold up objects in which they think ionic bonds contribute to structure and strength. Ask students to determine which compounds are included in the object and which ionic bonds would be present. Some examples include calcium carbonate (in carpet, ceramics, glass), sodium carbonate (in detergent), and sodium fluoride (in toothpaste). Include all objects with metal and rust, such as paperclips, lamps, chairs, or wire. Have students brainstorm about the strength of the bonds in each example.

Review

Personal Tutor

Listen to a teacher explain bonds.

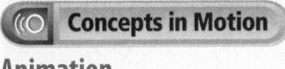

Concepts in Motion

Animation

Demonstration

Diagram Atoms To help students understand atomic structure, construct Lewis dot diagrams of different atoms (Cl, S, P, N, O, H, C). Lewis dot diagrams are used by scientists to illustrate the number of electrons on the outer orbital of an atom. Remind students that only the electrons in the outermost energy level of an atom participate in bond formation. Est. time: 10 min

Research Citation

Reading Strategies Educational research indicates the value of providing students with reading strategies like the one described on the previous page. Students' understanding of the text will improve when they are provided with strategies to develop self-questioning and higher-level thinking about the concepts. (McTeague, 1996)

Research bibliography on pages 32T–34T

MiniLab 1

Inquiry MiniLab

For a lab worksheet, use your eTeacherEdition Online.

RUBRIC A rubric for evaluating MiniLabs is found on your eTeacherEdition Online.

Est. Time 15 min

Additional Materials honey, milk, potato, butter, apple, sugar-free pudding, materials for handling heated glassware

Safety Precautions Approve lab safety forms before work begins. Prelab instructions should include review of a hot water bath preparation, instructions for handling heated glassware, and caution about Benedict's solution's tendency to stain skin and clothing and that it should be handled carefully.

Teaching Strategies

- Provide a variety of liquid food choices. Compile class results for discussion.
- Explain that Benedict's solution indicates the presence of simple sugars by turning from deep blue to yellow, orange, or red when added to food and heated.

Cleanup and Disposal Have students pour all solutions into a designated container, then dispose of them appropriately. Have students wash hands thoroughly after handling chemicals and glassware.

Analysis

1. Answers will be based on the foods tested. Students should find that the honey and apple contained glucose.
2. Students might find a positive result because some sugar-free foods contain natural fruit sugar.

VOCABULARY

WORD ORIGIN

Atom
comes from the Greek word *atomos,* meaning *not divisible*

Some atoms tend to donate or accept electrons more easily than other atoms do. Look at the periodic table of elements inside the back cover of this textbook. The elements identified as metals tend to donate electrons, and the elements identified as nonmetals tend to accept electrons. The resulting ionic compounds have some unique characteristics. For example, most dissolve in water. When dissolved in solution, ionic compounds break down into ions and these ions can carry an electric current. Most ionic compounds, such as sodium chloride (table salt), are crystalline at room temperature. Ionic compounds generally have higher melting points than do molecular compounds formed by covalent bonds.

Connection to Earth Science Although most ionic compounds are solid at room temperature, other ionic compounds are liquid at room temperature. Like their solid counterparts, ionic liquids are made up of positively and negatively charged ions. Ionic liquids have important potential in real-world applications as safe and environmentally friendly solvents that can possibly replace other harmful solvents. The key characteristic of ionic liquid solvents is that they typically do not evaporate and release chemicals into the atmosphere. Most ionic liquids are safe to handle and store, and they can be recycled after use. For these reasons, ionic liquids are attractive to industries that are dedicated to environmental responsibility.

Reading Check **Compare** ionic solids and liquids.

MiniLab 1

Test for Simple Sugars

Inquiry MiniLab

What common foods contain glucose? Glucose is a simple sugar that provides energy for cells. In this lab, you will use a reagent called Benedict's solution, which indicates the presence of –CHO (carbon, hydrogen, oxygen) groups. A color change determines the presence of glucose and other simple sugars in common foods.

Procedure

1. Read and complete the lab safety form.
2. Create a data table with columns labeled *Food Substance, Sugar Prediction, Observations,* and *Results.*
3. Choose four **food substances** from those provided by your teacher. Read the food labels and predict the presence of simple sugar in each food. Record your prediction.
4. Prepare a **hot water bath** with a temperature between 40°–50°C using a **hot plate** and **1000-mL beaker.**
5. Label four **test tubes.** Obtain a **graduated cylinder.** Add 10 mL of a different food substance to each test tube. Then add 10 mL of **distilled water.** Swirl gently to mix.
6. Add 5 mL of **Benedict's solution** to each tube. Use a clean **stirring rod** to mix the contents.
7. Using **test-tube holders,** warm the test tubes in the hot water bath for 2–3 min. Record your observations and results.

Analysis

1. **Interpret Data** Did any of the foods contain simple sugars? Explain.
2. **Think Critically** Could a food labeled "sugar-free" test positive using Benedict's solution as an indicator? Explain.

Differentiated Instruction

Hearing Impaired When conducting the MiniLab on this page, control the noise level in the classroom. This will allow students who are hearing impaired to communicate more easily with their group members and to hear any instructions that you give.

For more tips, see pages 14T–15T.

Reading Check Most ionic compounds are solid at room temperature. Ionic liquids are liquid at room temperature. Both are made of positively and negatively charged ions. Solids dissolve easily in water and can carry an electric current. Ionic liquids are safe to handle and don't evaporate or release chemicals into the atmosphere.

R van der Waals Forces

You have learned that positive ions and negative ions form based on the ability of an atom to attract electrons. If the nucleus of the atom has a weak attraction for the electron, it will donate the electron to an atom with a stronger attraction. Similarly, elements in a covalent bond do not always attract electrons equally. Recall also that the electrons in a molecule are in random motion around the nuclei. This movement of electrons can cause an unequal distribution of the electron cloud around the molecule, creating temporary areas of slightly positive and negative charges.

When molecules come close together, the attractive forces between these positive and negative regions pull on the molecules and hold them together. These attractions between the molecules are called **van der Waals forces,** named for Dutch physicist Johannes van der Waals, who first described the phenomenon. The strength of the attraction depends on the size of the molecule, its shape, and its ability to attract electrons. Although van der Waals forces are not as strong as covalent and ionic bonds, they play a key role in biological processes.

Scientists have determined that geckos can climb smooth surfaces because of van der Waals forces between the atoms in the hairlike structures on their toes, shown in **Figure 12,** and the atoms on the surface they are climbing.

van der Waals forces in water Consider how van der Waals forces work in a common substance—water. The areas of slight positive and negative charges around the water molecule are attracted to the opposite charge of other nearby water molecules. These forces hold the water molecules together. Without van der Waals forces, water molecules would not form droplets, and droplets would not form a surface of water. It is important to understand that van der Waals forces are the attractive forces between the water molecules, not the forces between the atoms that make up water.

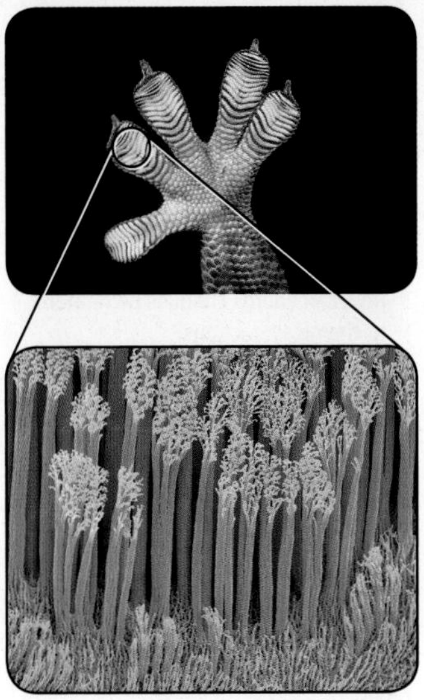

Figure 12 Geckos have millions of microscopic hairs on the bottoms of their feet that are about as long as two widths of a human hair. Each spreads into 1000 smaller pads.

Section 1 Assessment

Section Summary

- Elements are pure substances made up of only one kind of atom.
- Isotopes are forms of the same element that have a different number of neutrons.
- Compounds are substances with unique properties that are formed when elements combine.
- Elements can form covalent and ionic bonds.

Understand Main Ideas

1. MAIN Idea **Diagram** Sodium has 11 protons and 11 neutrons in its nucleus. Draw a sodium atom. Be sure to label the particles.
2. **Explain** why carbon monoxide (CO) is or is not an atom.
3. **Explain** Are all compounds molecules? Why or why not?
4. **Compare** van der Waals forces, ionic bonds, and covalent bonds.

Think Critically

5. **Explain** how the number of electrons in an energy level affects bond formation.

MATH in Biology

6. Beryllium has four protons in its nucleus. How many neutrons are in beryllium-9? Explain how you calculated your answer.

R Reading Strategy

EL BL OL AL

Directed Reading Before reading text under the heading *van der Waals Forces,* have students create a chart with columns titled *What I know now, What I think I know, What I think I'll learn,* and *What I learned.* Have students preview the text on van der Waals forces and fill out the first two columns. After the students read the section, have them complete the last column.

Formative Assessment

Evaluation In pairs, have students verbally describe covalent and ionic bonds to each other. When atoms share electrons, a covalent bond is formed. An ionic bond forms when two oppositely charged atoms or groups of atoms form a bond due to electrical attraction.

Remediation Have pairs of students compile a list of the similarities and differences between ionic and covalent bonds. Then, have them quiz each other on the different types of compounds and which types of bonds they contain. similarities: both bonds involve electrons; differences: covalent bonds occur when electrons between two atoms are shared, whereas ionic bonding occurs when there is an unequal distribution of electrons around each atom in the bond

Section 1 Assessment

1. The first energy level has two electrons, the second has eight, and the third has one electron.
2. Carbon monoxide is not an atom because it is made of two kinds of atoms. CO is a molecule.
3. No; CO is a compound formed by a bond between two atoms.
4. van der Waals forces hold molecules together. Ionic bonds are electrical attractions between two oppositely charged atoms. A covalent bond forms when electrons are shared.
5. Atoms donating or taking up only one or two electrons in their outer energy levels tend to form ionic bonds. Covalent bonds are usually formed when atoms need two or more electrons to fill an energy orbital.
6. five neutrons; the number of protons added to the number of neutrons gives the atomic number

Assessment Online Quiz

Section 2

MAIN Idea

BL OL AL Chemical Reactions **ASK STUDENTS:** ***What is the relationship between a chemical bond and a chemical reaction?*** Chemical bonds are created or broken by chemical reactions. Point out that the terms *chemical bond* and *chemical reactions* both include the word *chemical.* Encourage students to look for the relationships among the vocabulary terms in this section and in Section 1.

R Reading Strategy

EL OL SQ3R Have students **S**urvey the text under the heading *Reactants and Products,* focusing on the vocabulary terms. Ask students to write at least three **Q**uestions about key concepts, such as, *What is a chemical reaction?* Have students **R**ead the text, taking notes related to the questions they wrote. Finally, have students **R**ecite vocabulary terms and **R**eview the section for the meanings. Have English learners dictate their questions to the teacher to write on the board. Have students look for the answers as they read and practice the subsequent "R"s out loud with teacher input.

D Develop Concepts

BL OL AL

Clarify a Misconception

ASK STUDENTS: ***Is boiling water an example of a chemical reaction?*** no Students might think that a chemical reaction occurs when compounds change state. Remind students that chemical reactions occur only when bonds are broken or formed. When water boils, no changes occur in the bonds between the hydrogen atoms and the oxygen atom. Therefore, boiling water is a physical change, not a chemical reaction.

Section 2

Reading Preview

Essential Questions

- What are the parts of a chemical reaction?
- How can energy changes be related to chemical reactions?
- What is the importance of enzymes in living organisms?

Review Vocabulary

process: a series of steps or actions that produce an end product

New Vocabulary

chemical reaction
reactant
product
activation energy
catalyst
enzyme
substrate
active site

g Multilingual eGlossary

Chemical Reactions

MAIN Idea Chemical reactions allow living things to grow, develop, reproduce, and adapt.

Real-World Reading Link When you lie down for the night, you might think that your body is completely at rest. In fact, you are still digesting the food that you ate that day, the scrape on your elbow is healing, and your muscles and bones are growing and developing. All the things that happen inside your body are the result of chemical reactions.

R Reactants and Products

A new car with shining chrome and a clean appearance is appealing to many drivers. Over time, however, the car might get rusty and lose some of its appeal. Rust is a result of a chemical change called a chemical reaction. A **chemical reaction** is the process by which atoms or groups of atoms in substances are reorganized into different substances. Chemical bonds are broken and formed during chemical reactions. The rust on the chain in **Figure 13** is a compound called iron oxide (Fe_2O_3), and it was formed when oxygen (O_2) in the air reacted with iron (Fe).

It is important to know that substances can undergo changes that do not involve chemical reactions. For example, consider the water in **Figure 13.** The water is undergoing a physical change. A physical change alters a substance's appearance but not its composition. The water is water before and after the change.

How do you know when a chemical reaction has taken place? Although you might not be aware of all the reactions taking place inside your body, you know that the surface of the chain in **Figure 13** has changed. What was once silver and shiny is now dull and orange-brown. Other clues that a chemical reaction has taken place include the production of heat or light, and the formation of a new gas, liquid, or solid. D

Figure 13 After a chemical change, such as rusting, a new substance is formed. During a physical change, such as ice melting or water boiling, the chemical makeup of the water is not altered.

Chemical change

Physical change

Demonstration

Chemical v. Physical Change Illustrate the differences between physical changes and chemical reactions by using three pieces of paper. Bring a previously burned piece of paper to class, fold one of the pieces of paper, and cut a hole in the middle of another. Explain that chemical reactions occur when the bonds in one or more compounds are broken and new bonds are formed. Burning is a chemical change; folding and cutting are physical changes. Discuss the examples and give students a chance to defend any arguments that arise. Est. time: 5 min

Chemical equations When scientists write chemical reactions, they express each component of the reaction in a chemical equation. In written chemical equations, chemical formulas describe the substances in the reaction with arrows indicating the process of change.

Reactants and products A chemical equation shows the **reactants,** the starting substances, on the left side of the arrow. The **products,** the substances formed during the reaction, are on the right side of the arrow. The arrow can be read as "yields" or "react to form."

Reactants → Products

The following chemical equation can be written to describe the reaction that provides energy to the volleyball players in **Figure 14.**

$$C_6H_{12}O_6 + O_2 \rightarrow CO_2 + H_2O$$

Glucose and oxygen react to form carbon dioxide and water.

Balanced equations In chemical reactions, matter cannot be created or destroyed. This principle is called the law of conservation of mass. Accordingly, all chemical equations must show this balance of mass. This means that the number of atoms of each element on the reactant side must equal the number of atoms of the same element on the product side. Coefficients are used to make the number of atoms on each side of the arrow equal.

$$C_6H_{12}O_6 + 6O_2 \rightarrow 6CO_2 + 6H_2O$$

Multiply the coefficient by the subscript for each element. You can see in this example that there are six carbon atoms, twelve hydrogen atoms, and eighteen oxygen atoms on each side of the arrow. The equation confirms that the number of atoms on each side is equal, and therefore the equation is balanced.

S

Reading Check Explain why chemical equations must be balanced.

Energy of Reactions

Connection to Physics A sugar cookie is made with flour, sugar, and other ingredients mixed together, but it is not a cookie until it is baked. Something must start the change from dough to cookie. The key to starting a chemical reaction is energy. For the chemical reactions that transform the dough to a cookie, energy in the form of heat is needed. Similarly, most compounds in living things cannot undergo chemical reactions without energy.

Figure 14 The process that provides your body with energy involves the reaction of glucose with oxygen to form carbon dioxide and water.

VOCABULARY

ACADEMIC VOCABULARY

Coefficient
in a chemical equation, the number written in front of a reactant or a product
The number 6 in $6Fe_2O_3$ is a coefficient.

Develop Concepts

BL Clarify a Misconception
Write the following chemical equation on the board:

$$C_6H_{12}O_6 + 6O_2 \rightarrow 6CO_2 + 6H_2O.$$

ASK STUDENTS: ***Is a compound that cannot be seen still a part of a chemical reaction?*** yes
Students might not realize that even gaseous compounds, such as carbon dioxide, are essential parts of chemical equations. Whether it can be seen or not, matter is always conserved.
ASK STUDENTS: ***Is the heat or energy required to initiate a chemical reaction also conserved?*** yes

S Skill Practice

OL AL Balance Chemical Equations Have students practice balancing the following equations:

1. $K + B_2O_3 \rightarrow K_2O + B$

2. $HCl + NaOH \rightarrow NaCl + H_2O$

3. $CH_4 + O_2 \rightarrow CO_2 + H_2O$

4. $N_2 + H_2 \rightarrow NH_3$

5. $Al + S_8 \rightarrow Al_2S_3$

1. $6K + B_2O_3 \rightarrow 3K_2O + 2B$
2. $HCl + NaOH \rightarrow NaCl + H_2O$
3. $CH_4 + 2O_2 \rightarrow CO_2 + 2H_2O$
4. $N_2 + 3H_2 \rightarrow 2NH_3$
5. $16Al + 3S_8 \rightarrow 8Al_2S_3$

EL COOP LEARN Have students work in pairs to balance the equations.

Reading Check Chemical equations must be balanced because matter can neither be created nor destroyed.

Differentiated Instruction

Below Level Differentiate lessons when students with different ability levels are in the classroom. For example, the activity on balancing equations described on this page can be modified for students who perform below level by decreasing the number of equations they are required to balance.

For more tips, see pages 14T–15T.

Writing Support

EL BL OL AL Creative Writing Have students write a poem that describes the energy required to activate a chemical reaction (e.g., lighting the wick of a candle, lighting the fuse of a firework, lighting a bonfire, starting a car).

Critical Thinking

BL OL AL Relate Describe the conditions inside the cell that enable enzymes to be active. Enzymes are only active at a specific pH and temperature, thus an enzyme in a human cell, except for in lysosomes, would be active at body temperature (37°C, 98.6°F) and at a pH of approximately 7.0.

S Skill Practice

BL OL AL Visual Literacy Have one or several students volunteer to read aloud the text under the headings *Activation energy* and *Enzymes.* As the students read, direct the class to pay close attention to Figure 17 and consider how the figure depicts key concepts. Have students draw graphs showing the effect of a catalyst on the activation energy needed for a chemical reaction.

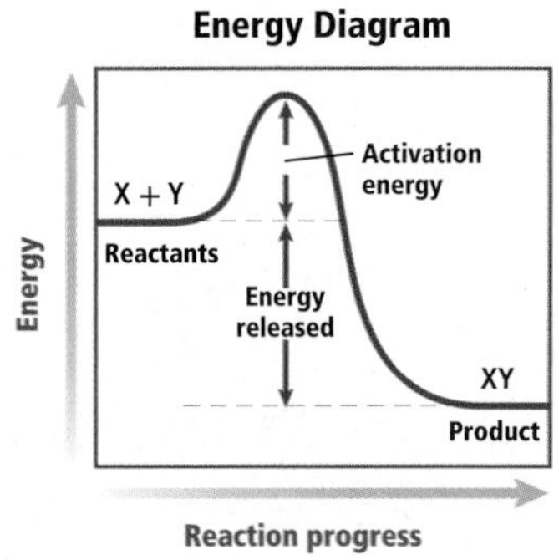

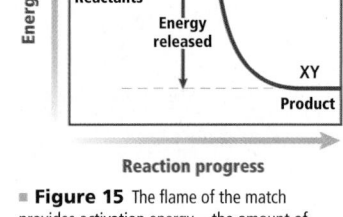

Figure 15 The flame of the match provides activation energy—the amount of energy needed to begin a reaction. The reaction gives off energy in the form of heat and light.

Inquiry Virtual Lab

Inquiry Video Lab

S Activation energy The minimum amount of energy needed for reactants to form products in a chemical reaction is called the **activation energy.** For example, you know that a candle will not burn until you light its wick. The flame provides the activation energy for the reaction of the substances in the candle wick with oxygen. In this case, once the reaction begins, no further input of energy is needed and the candle continues to burn on its own. **Figure 15** shows that for the reactants X and Y to form product XY, energy is required to start the reaction. The peak in the graph represents the amount of energy that must be added to the system to make the reaction occur. Some reactions rarely happen because they have a very high activation energy.

Energy change in chemical reactions Compare how energy changes during the reaction in **Figure 15** to how energy changes during the reaction in **Figure 16.** Both reactions require activation energy to get started. However, the reaction in **Figure 15** has lower energy in the product than in the reactants. This reaction is exothermic—it released energy in the form of heat. The reaction in **Figure 16** is endothermic—it absorbed heat energy. The energy of the products is higher than the energy of the reactants. In every chemical reaction, there is a change in energy caused by the making and breaking of chemical bonds as reactants form products. Exothermic reactions keep your internal body temperature at about 37°C.

Figure 16 In an endothermic reaction, the energy of the products is higher than the energy of the reactant.

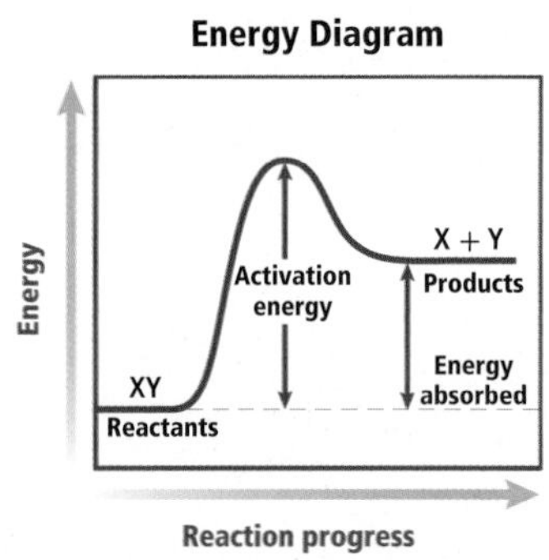

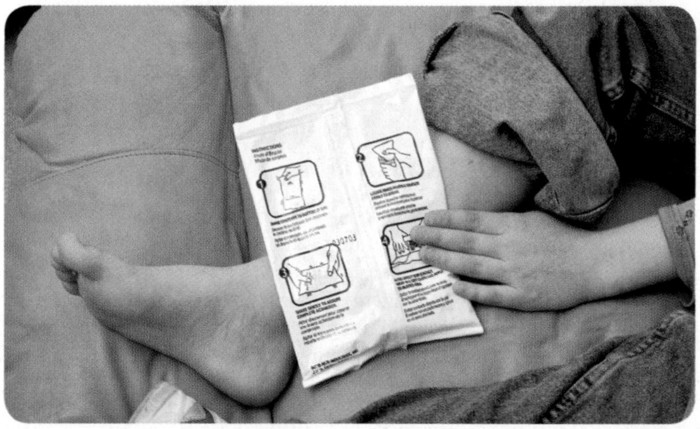

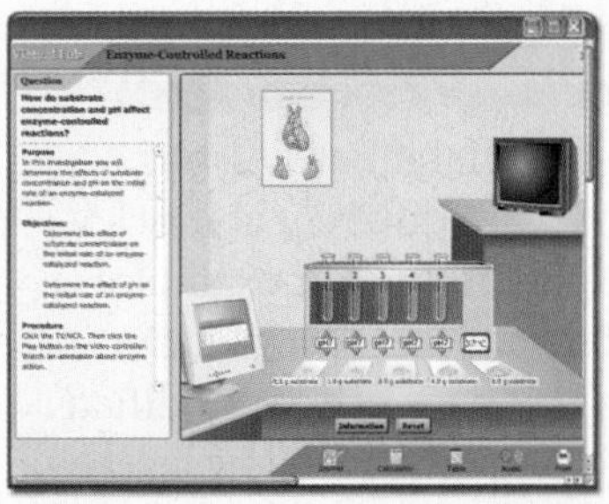

Inquiry Virtual Lab Students will determine how substrate concentration and pH affect the initial rate of an enzyme-catalyzed reaction.

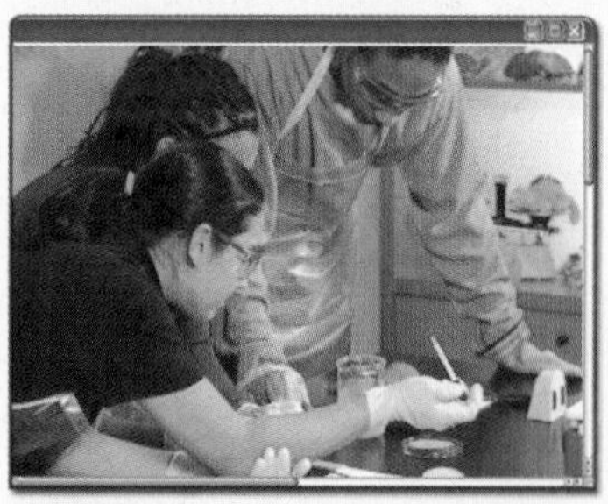

Inquiry Video Lab Students will determine whether temperature affects an enzyme reaction.

Enzymes

All living things are chemical factories driven by chemical reactions. However, these chemical reactions proceed very slowly when carried out in the laboratory because the activation energy is high. To be useful to living organisms, additional substances must be present where the chemical reactions occur to reduce the activation energy and allow the reaction to proceed quickly.

A **catalyst** is a substance that lowers the activation energy needed to start a chemical reaction. Although a catalyst is important in speeding up a chemical reaction, it does not increase how much product is made and it does not get used up in the reaction. Scientists use many types of catalysts to make reactions occur thousands of times faster than the reaction would be able to occur without the catalyst.

Special proteins called **enzymes** are the biological catalysts that speed up the rate of chemical reactions in biological processes. Enzymes are essential to life. Compare the progress of the reaction described in **Figure 17** to see the effect of an enzyme on a chemical reaction. Like all catalysts, the enzyme is not used up by the chemical reaction. Once it has participated in a chemical reaction, it can be used again.

An enzyme's name describes what it does. For example, amylase is an important enzyme found in saliva. Digestion of food begins in the mouth when amylase speeds the breakdown of amylose, one of the components of starch. Like amylase, most enzymes are specific to one reaction.

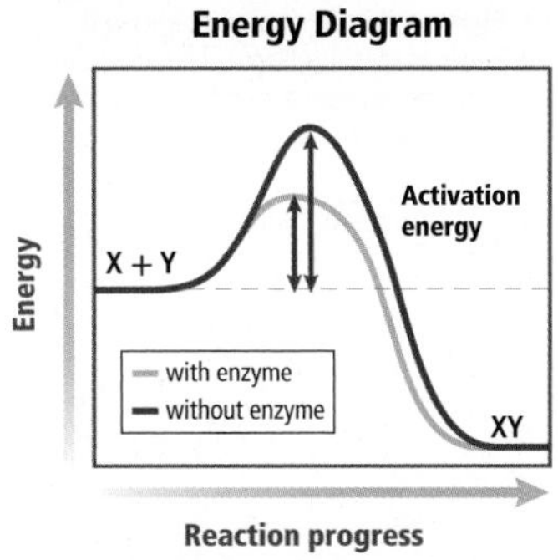

■ **Figure 17** When an enzyme acts as a biological catalyst, the reaction occurs at a rate that is useful to cells.

Compare ***the activation energy of the reaction without an enzyme to the activation energy of the reaction with an enzyme.***

D

MiniLab 2

Investigate Enzymatic Browning

? Inquiry MiniLab

What factors affect enzymatic browning? When sliced, an apple's soft tissue is exposed to oxygen, causing a chemical reaction called oxidation. Enzymes in the apple speed this reaction, producing darkened, discolored fruit. In this lab, you will investigate methods used to slow enzymatic browning.

Procedure

1. Read and complete the lab safety form.
2. Predict the relative amount of discoloration that each of the following apple wedges will show when exposed to air. Justify your predictions.
   Sample 1: Untreated apple wedge
   Sample 2: Apple wedge submerged in boiling water
   Sample 3: Apple wedge submerged in lemon juice
   Sample 4: Apple wedge submerged in sugar solution
3. Prepare 75 mL of each of the following: **boiling water, lemon juice,** and **sugar solution** in three **250-mL beakers.**
4. Slice an **apple** into four wedges. Immediately use **tongs** to submerge each wedge in a different liquid. Put one wedge aside.
5. Submerge the wedges for three minutes, then place them on a **paper towel,** skin-side down. Observe for 10 min, and then record the relative amount of discoloration of each apple wedge.

Analysis

1. **Analyze** how each treatment affected the chemical reaction that occurred on the fruit's soft tissue. Why were some of the treatments successful?
2. **Think critically** about what factors a restaurant owner who wants to serve fresh-cut fruit might consider when choosing a recipe and preparation method.

■ **Caption Question Fig. 17** The activiation energy decreases with the presence of the enzyme.

? Inquiry BioLab

The lab at the end of the chapter can be used at this point in the lesson.

D Develop Concepts

BL OL AL Scaffolding

ASK STUDENTS: ***What are enzymes?*** proteins with catalytic activity ***Why are enzymes important?*** to speed up reactions ***Name some biological processes that require enzymatic activity.*** possible answers: muscle contraction, DNA replication, cell division, digestion ***What effect does an enzyme have on a chemical reaction?*** It increases the rate of the reaction. ***How do enzymes maintain specificity?*** regions of the enzyme bind only certain substrates

MiniLab 2

? Inquiry MiniLab

For a lab worksheet, use your eTeacherEdition Online.

***RUBRIC** A rubric for evaluating MiniLabs is found on your eTeacherEdition Online.

Est. Time 20 min

Safety Precautions Approve lab safety forms before work begins. Caution students never to eat anything during science class.

Teaching Strategy Have apple slices that have turned brown to compare with students' slices.

Analysis

1. They slowed down, or prevented, the reaction of the soft tissue with oxygen.
2. The owner should choose a recipe that decreases the enzyme's ability to catalyze oxidation (i.e., lower pH with lemon juice). The addition of lemon juice or some other acid will prevent browning, keep the apples more rigid, and enhance appearance.

LabManager™

Customize this lab with the LabManager™ CD-ROM.

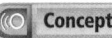

Concepts in Motion

Animation

FOLDABLES®

RUBRIC A rubric for evaluating Foldables is found on your eTeacherEdition Online.

Going Further On the back of their Foldables, have students list factors that alter the activity of an enzyme. Then have students add a few examples of known enzymes that affect human biological processes.

Formative Assessment

Evaluation Have students relate the specificity of an enzyme to the analogy of a lock and key. Enzymes interact only with substrates of a certain structure because the active site (where the substrate binds) is designed to allow only molecules of specific shapes and sizes to fit, much like a key fits only into a lock of a certain size and shape.

Remediation Have students outline the properties of enzymes. Responses should include the enzyme's ability to decrease activation energy, the need for optimal pH and temperature, and the enzyme substrate specificity.

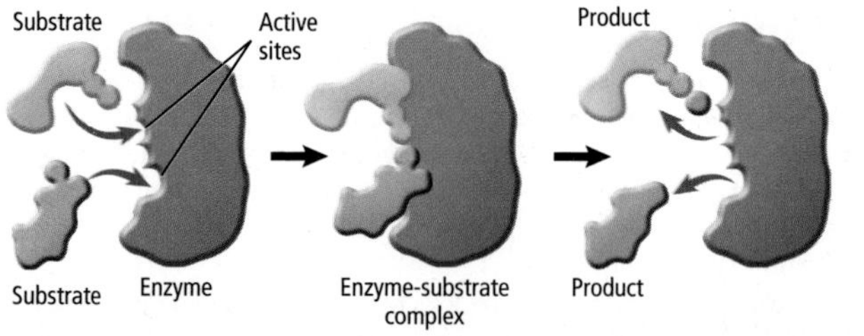

Figure 18 Substrates interact with enzymes at specific places called active sites. Only substrates with a specific shape can bind to the active site of an enzyme.

Concepts in Motion

Animation

FOLDABLES® Incorporate information from this section into your Foldable.

Follow **Figure 18** to learn how an enzyme works. The reactants that bind to the enzyme are called **substrates.** The specific location where a substrate binds on an enzyme is called the **active site.** The active site and the substrate have complementary shapes. This enables them to interact in a precise manner, similar to the way in which puzzle pieces fit together. As shown in **Figure 18,** only substrates with the same size and shape as the active site will bind to the enzyme.

Once the substrates bind to the active site, the active site changes shape and forms the enzyme-substrate complex. The enzyme-substrate complex helps chemical bonds in the reactants to be broken and new bonds to form—the substrates react to form products. The enzyme then releases the products.

Factors such as pH, temperature, and other substances affect enzyme activity. For example, most enzymes in human cells are most active at an optimal temperature close to 37°C. However, enzymes in other organisms, such as bacteria, can be active at other temperatures.

Enzymes affect many biological processes. When a person is bitten by a venomous snake, enzymes in the venom break down the membranes of that person's red blood cells. Hard green apples ripen because of the action of enzymes. Photosynthesis and cellular respiration provide energy for the cell with the help of enzymes. Just as worker bees are important for the survival of a beehive, enzymes are the chemical workers in cells.

Section 2 Assessment

Section Summary

- Balanced chemical equations must show an equal number of atoms for each element on both sides.
- Activation energy is the energy required to begin a reaction.
- Catalysts are substances that alter chemical reactions.
- Enzymes are biological catalysts.

Understand Main Ideas

1. MAIN Idea **Identify** the parts of this chemical reaction: A+B → AB.
2. **Diagram** the energy changes that can take place in a chemical reaction.
3. **Explain** why the number of atoms of reactants must equal the number of atoms of products formed.
4. **Describe** the importance of enzymes to living organisms.

Think Critically

MATH in Biology

5. For the following chemical reaction, label the reactants and products, and then balance the chemical equation. ____H_2O_2 → ____H_2O + ____O_2

WRITING in Biology

6. Draw a diagram of a roller coaster and write a paragraph relating the ride to activation energy and a chemical reaction.

Section 2 Assessment

1. A and B are reactants; AB is the product.
2. Diagrams should resemble Figures 15, 16, 17, which depict exothermic, endothermic, and catalyzed reactions.
3. Matter is neither created nor destroyed; it can only change forms.
4. Enzymes lower the activation energy needed to start a chemical reaction.
5. reactants: H_2O_2; products: H_2O and O_2; $2H_2O_2 \rightarrow 2H_2O + O_2$
6. Roller coaster must be brought to the top of the structure before it can speed downhill; chemical reactions need sufficient activation energy to begin.

WRITING in Biology

RUBRIC Use the modifiable rubric found on your eTeacherEdition Online to assess writing assignments.

Assessment Online Quiz

Reading Preview

Essential Questions

- How does the structure of water make it a good solvent?
- What are the similarities and differences between solutions and suspensions?
- What are the differences between acids and bases?

Review Vocabulary

physical property: characteristic of matter, such as color or melting point, that can be observed or measured without changing the composition of the substance

New Vocabulary

polar molecule
hydrogen bond
mixture
solution
solvent
solute
acid
base
pH
buffer

g Multilingual eGlossary

Water and Solutions

MAIN Idea The properties of water make it well suited to help maintain homeostasis in an organism.

Real-World Reading Link You probably know that the main color on a globe is blue. That's because water covers about 70 percent of Earth's surface, giving it the blue color you see from a distance. Now imagine zooming in to a single cell of an organism on Earth. Water accounts for approximately 70 percent of that cell's mass. It is one of the most important molecules for life.

D Water's Polarity

Earlier in this chapter, you discovered that water molecules are formed by covalent bonds that link two hydrogen (H) atoms to one oxygen (O) atom. Because electrons are more strongly attracted to the oxygen atom's nucleus, the electrons in the covalent bond with hydrogen are not shared equally. In water, the electrons spend more time near the oxygen atom's nucleus than they do near the hydrogen atoms' nuclei. **Figure 19** shows that there is an unequal distribution of electrons in a water molecule. This, along with the bent shape of water molecules, results in the oxygen end of the molecule having a slightly negative charge and the hydrogen ends of the molecule having a slightly positive charge. Molecules that have an unequal distribution of charges are called **polar molecules,** meaning that they have oppositely charged regions.

Polarity is the property of having two opposite poles, or ends. A magnet has polarity—there is a north pole and a south pole. When the two ends are brought close to each other, they attract each other. Similarly, when a charged region of a polar molecule comes close to the oppositely charged region of another polar molecule, a weak electrostatic attraction results. In water, the electrostatic attraction is called a hydrogen bond. A **hydrogen bond** is a weak interaction involving a hydrogen atom and a fluorine, oxygen, or nitrogen atom. Hydrogen bonding is a strong type of van der Waals force. **Figure 20** describes polarity and the other unique properties of water that make it important to living things.

S

Figure 19 Because water molecules have a bent shape and electrons are not shared equally between hydrogen and oxygen, hydrogen bonds form among the molecules. Due to the attraction among the atoms that make up water, the surface of water supports a water strider.

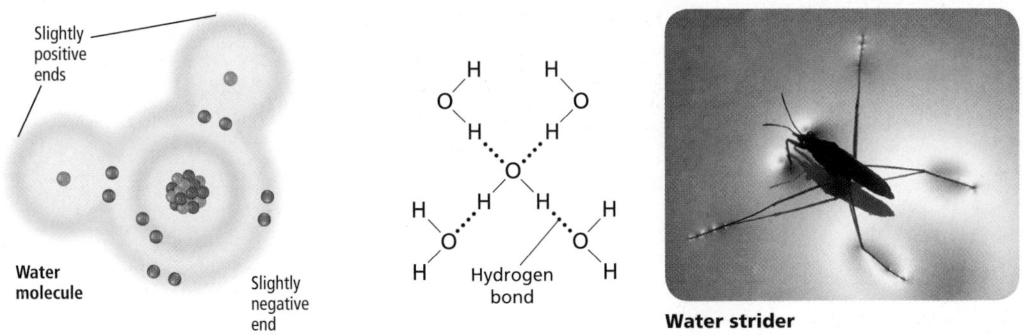

Demonstration

Water—The Universal Solvent Fill a clear plastic bottle with water. Add powdered food coloring to demonstrate the ability of water (as a polar molecule) to dissolve other polar molecules. Once the powder is dissolved, place half of the colored water in another clear plastic bottle and add oil. Point out that while water dissolves other polar compounds, nonpolar compounds, such as cooking oil, do not. Other examples can be used to illustrate the difference between mixtures and solutions. Est. time: 10 min

Section 3

MAIN Idea

BL OL AL

Water and Solutions Review the molecular structure of water with students.

ASK STUDENTS: ***What is the chemical equation for water?*** H_2O Remind students that the chemical equation denotes the number of atoms of each element in the compound. Water is two atoms of hydrogen and one oxygen atom.

D Develop Concepts

EL BL OL

Clarify a Misconception

Show students pictures of the three physical states of water (ice, vapor, and liquid). In addition, draw water molecules showing polarity on the board.

ASK STUDENTS: ***What is the chemical equation for ice? Vapor? Liquid water?*** H_2O Students might think that liquid water, vapor, and ice are chemically different. Although all three substances are physically different, they all have the same chemical composition. This is also true for other molecules.

S Skill Practice

BL OL **Visual Literacy** After reading the text under the heading *Water's Polarity,* instruct students to review the diagram in Figure 19, paying close attention to the shape of the water molecule.

ASK STUDENTS: ***How does Figure 19 help you understand what you just read?*** The bent structure of water makes the molecule polar and allows water to form bonds with numerous other molecules. Encourage students to think about the effect of the four unbonded electrons on the oxygen molecule on the shape of water.

AL Have students discuss the importance of water's polarity.

Visualizing Properties of Water

Purpose
Students will evaluate the properties of water.
C.5, F.3

Concepts in Motion
Animation

Develop Concepts
OL Activity Organize students into groups of two or three. Have each group pick one of the properties of water represented on this page and prepare a demonstration to present to the class.

Writing Support
OL AL Narrative Writing Tell students that water is vital to life on Earth. There are many literary references to water in poetry and prose. Have students research at least one literary reference to water that can relate to one of its properties learned in this lesson. Have students describe the literary reference in a short paragraph and explain how it relates to what they have learned about the properties of water. Students can choose to write their paragraph about a visual arts reference as well. Paragraphs will vary.

GOING GREEN Bottled water is popular for both adults and teens. Ask students to calculate how many plastic bottles they use each week. Have a class discussion about alternatives to purchasing bottled water or other drinks in plastic bottles. As a teacher, be an example and use reusable alternatives to plastic bottles in your classroom.

Visualizing Properties of Water

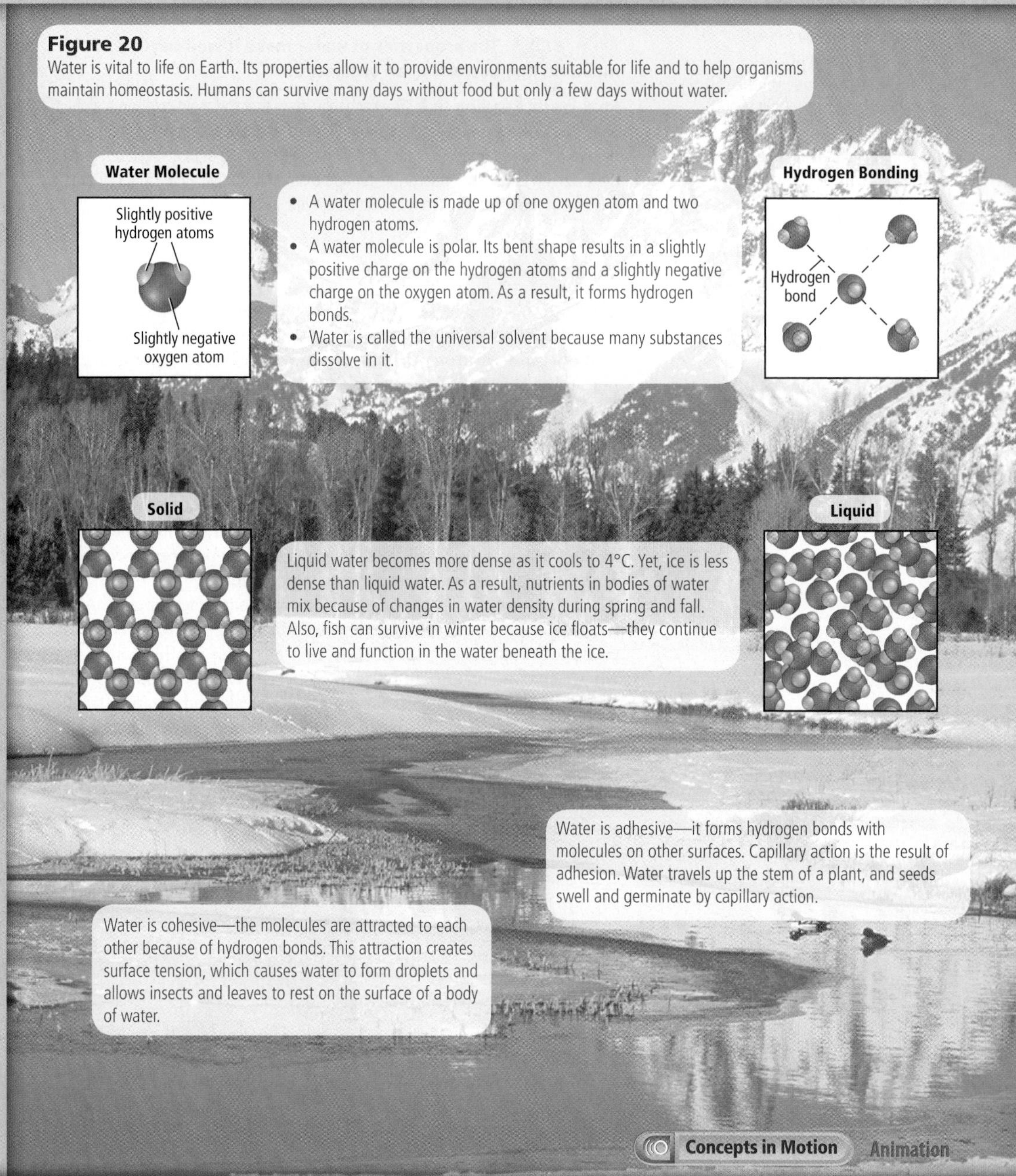

Water Molecule
Slightly positive hydrogen atoms
Slightly negative oxygen atom
• A water molecule is made up of one oxygen atom and two hydrogen atoms.
• A water molecule is polar. Its bent shape results in a slightly positive charge on the hydrogen atoms and a slightly negative charge on the oxygen atom. As a result, it forms hydrogen bonds.
• Water is called the universal solvent because many substances dissolve in it.
Hydrogen Bonding
Hydrogen bond
Solid
Liquid
Liquid water becomes more dense as it cools to 4°C. Yet, ice is less dense than liquid water. As a result, nutrients in bodies of water mix because of changes in water density during spring and fall. Also, fish can survive in winter because ice floats—they continue to live and function in the water beneath the ice.
Water is adhesive—it forms hydrogen bonds with molecules on other surfaces. Capillary action is the result of adhesion. Water travels up the stem of a plant, and seeds swell and germinate by capillary action.
Water is cohesive—the molecules are attracted to each other because of hydrogen bonds. This attraction creates surface tension, which causes water to form droplets and allows insects and leaves to rest on the surface of a body of water.
Concepts in Motion Animation

Figure 20
Water is vital to life on Earth. Its properties allow it to provide environments suitable for life and to help organisms maintain homeostasis. Humans can survive many days without food but only a few days without water.

R Mixtures with Water

S You are probably familiar with powdered drink products that dissolve in water to form a flavored beverage. When you add a powdered substance to water, it does not react with water to form a new product. You create a mixture. A **mixture** is a combination of two or more substances in which each substance retains its individual characteristics and properties.

Homogeneous mixtures When a mixture has a uniform composition throughout, it is called a homogeneous (hoh muh JEE nee us) mixture. A **solution** is another name for a homogeneous mixture. For example, in the powdered tea solution shown in **Figure 21,** tea is on top, tea is in the middle, and tea is at the bottom of the container. The water retains its properties and the drink mix retains its properties.

In a solution, there are two components: a solvent and a solute. A **solvent** is a substance in which another substance is dissolved. A **solute** is the substance that is dissolved in the solvent. In the case of the drink mix, water is the solvent and the powdered substance is the solute. A mixture of salt and water is another example of a solution because the solute (salt) dissolves completely in the solvent (water). Saliva moistens your mouth and begins the digestion of some of your food. Saliva is a solution that contains water, proteins, and salts. In addition, the air you breathe is a solution of gases.

Heterogeneous mixtures Think about the last time you ate a salad. Perhaps it contained lettuce and other vegetables, croutons, and salad dressing. Your salad was a heterogeneous mixture. In a heterogeneous mixture, the components remain distinct, that is, you can tell what they are individually. Compare the mixture of sand and water to the solution of salt and water next to it in **Figure 22.** Sand and water form a type of heterogeneous mixture called a suspension. Over time, the particles in a suspension settle to the bottom.

A colloid is a heterogeneous mixture in which the particles do not settle out like the sand settled from the water. You are probably familiar with many colloids, including fog, smoke, butter, mayonnaise, milk, S paint, and ink. Blood is a colloid made up of plasma, cells, and other substances.

Reading Check **Distinguish** between solutions and suspensions.

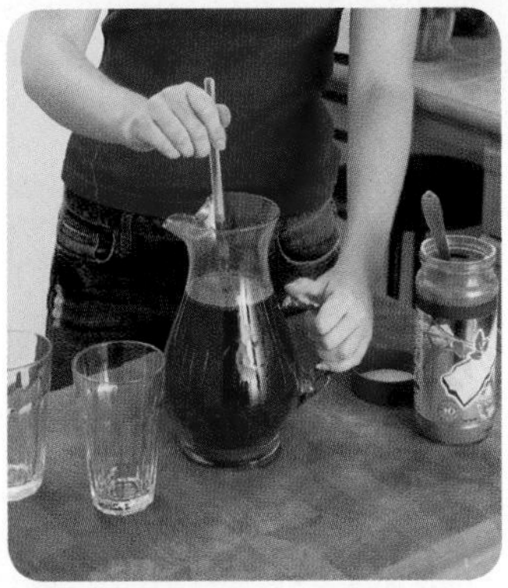

■ **Figure 21** Tea forms a homogeneous mixture in water. The particles of the solute (tea) are dissolved and spread throughout the solvent (water).

VOCABULARY

ACADEMIC VOCABULARY

Suspend
to keep from falling or sinking
A slender thread suspended the spider from the web.

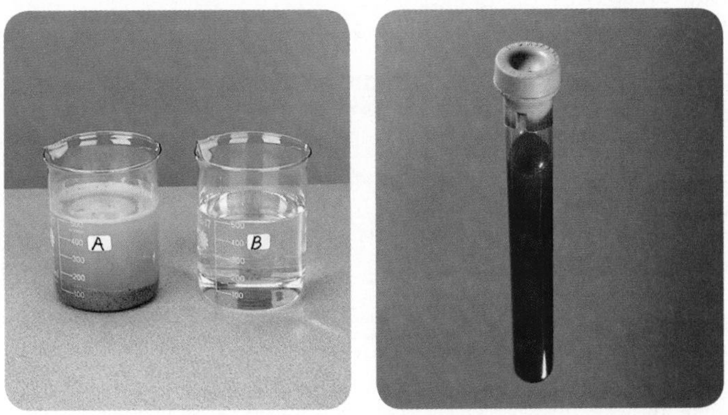

■ **Figure 22**
Left: Sand and water form a heterogeneous mixture; you can see both the liquid and the solid. The homogeneous mixture of salt and water is a liquid; you cannot see the salt.
Right: Blood is a heterogeneous mixture called a colloid.

Differentiated Instruction

Visually Impaired Students who are visually impaired may struggle with reading assignments. When requiring students to read the text for the note-taking strategy suggested on this page, provide these students with an audio version of the text, available on the StudentWorks™ Plus Online.

For more tips, see pages 14T–15T.

Reading Check A solution is a homogeneous mixture; a suspension is a heterogeneous mixture.

R Reading Strategy

BL OL Morphological Word Analysis Write the words *homogeneous* and *heterogeneous* on the board. Before reading the text under the heading *Mixtures with Water,* have students predict meanings for the terms. Have students do an Internet search for these terms and write down some of what they find. Tell students to brainstorm examples of each term. **AL** Have students discuss the meaning of these terms.

S Skill Practice

EL BL OL Take Notes Before reading text under the heading *Mixtures with Water,* have students create a T-chart to record their notes. On the left side, tell students to list the following major concepts: *polarity, polar molecules, hydrogen bond, mixture, solution, solvent, solute, suspension, colloid, acids, bases, pH,* and *buffer.* Have students read the text under the heading *Mixtures with Water.* Then have them work in pairs to write the explanation of each of the above concepts on the right side of their T-charts.

S Skill Practice

EL OL AL Classify Have students brainstorm examples of homogeneous and heterogeneous mixtures. List their ideas on the board. Possible examples of items are salad dressing, plasma, salt water, soda, and powdered beverages. On a piece of paper, have students make two columns labeled either *homogeneous mixtures* or *heterogeneous mixtures* and classify the items on the board into the appropriate column. Remind students that some items may appear in more than one column. Go through the list to make sure students have classified the items correctly.

Develop Concepts

OL AL Integrate Math Water makes up about 70 percent of the human body. Using the following body masses, have students calculate how much mass is contributed by water: 30 kg, 45 kg, 68 kg, 102 kg, 170 kg. 21 kg, 31.5 kg, 47.6 kg, 71.4 kg, 119 kg

BL Provide students with the formulas and allow them to use calculators.

DATA ANALYSIS LAB 1

About the Lab

- Some bacteria live in extreme conditions—high temperature, pH, sulfur, etc. These bacteria are often sources for enzymes that can be used by scientists for biological research.
- The *Taq* polymerase enzyme is used in the polymerase chain reaction (PCR) to amplify DNA.
- Also see Haki and Rakshit. 2003. Developments in industrially important thermostable enzymes: a review. *Bioresource Technology* 89 (1):17–34.

Think Critically

1. The range of pH values tested was 5–12, and the range of temperatures tested was 30°C to 90°C.
2. Highest activity is at pH 10 and 60°C.
3. Yes, because the enzyme had the highest activity at a high pH (basic) and at a high temperature.

■ **Figure 23** Substances that release H^+ in water are acids. Substances that release OH^- in water are bases.

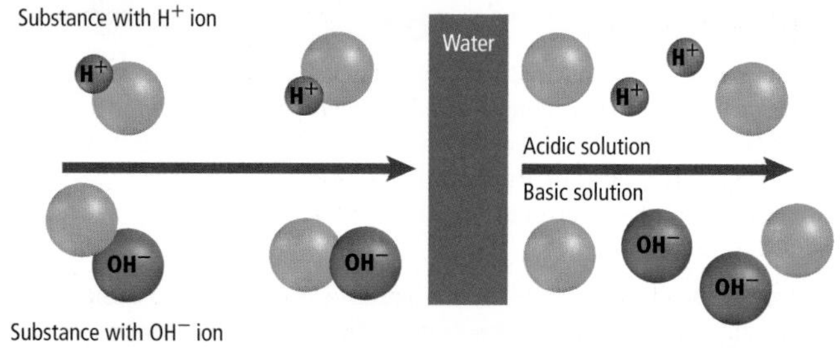

Acids and bases Many solutes readily dissolve in water because of water's polarity. This means that an organism, which might be as much as 70 percent water, can be a container for a variety of solutions. When a substance that contains hydrogen is dissolved in water, the substance might release a hydrogen ion (H^+) because it is attracted to the negatively charged oxygen atoms in water, as shown in **Figure 23.** Substances that release hydrogen ions when they are dissolved in water are called **acids.** The more hydrogen ions a substance releases, the more acidic the solution becomes.

Similarly, substances that release hydroxide ions (OH^-) when they are dissolved in water are called **bases.** Sodium hydroxide (NaOH) is a common base that breaks apart in water to release sodium ions (Na^+) and hydroxide ions (OH^-). The more hydroxide ions a substance releases, the more basic the solution becomes.

Acids and bases are key substances in biology. Many of the foods and beverages that we eat and drink are acidic, and the substances in the stomach that break down the food, called gastric juices, are highly acidic.

DATA ANALYSIS LAB 1

Based on Real Data*

Recognize Cause and Effect

How do pH and temperature affect protease activity? Proteases are enzymes that break down protein. Bacterial proteases often are used in detergents to help remove stains such as egg, grass, blood, and sweat from clothes.

Data and Observations

A protease from a newly isolated strain of bacteria was studied over a range of pH values and temperatures.

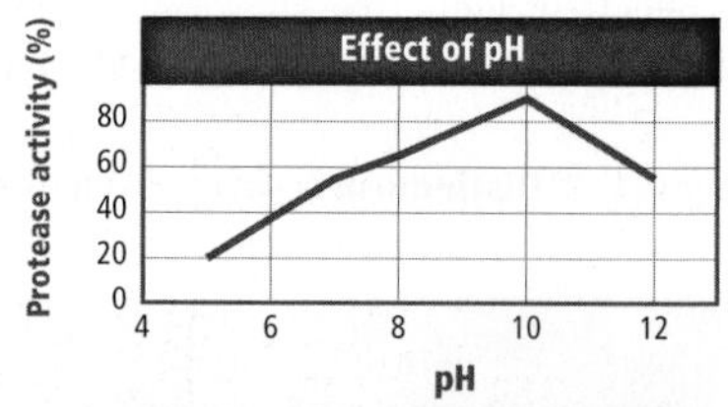

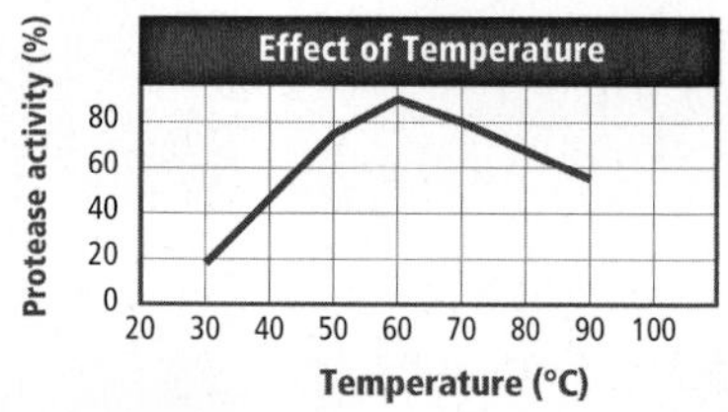

Think Critically

1. **Identify** the range of pH values and temperatures used in the experiment.
2. **Summarize** the results of the two graphs.
3. **Infer** If a laundry detergent is basic and requires hot water to be most effective, would this protease be useful? Explain.

*Data obtained from: Adinarayana, et al. 2003. Purification and partial characterization of thermostable serine alkaline protease from a newly isolated *Bacillus subtilis* PE-11. *AAPS PharmSciTech 4: article 56.*

Demonstration

Determine pH Cabbage juice can be used to test the pH of various substances. Before class, make the indicator by boiling a head of grated red cabbage. Add some of the cabbage juice to different products, such as vinegar, lemon juice, soda, baking soda, and detergent. Red cabbage contains pigments called anthocyanins that give it the red/purplish color. In an acidic solution, the anthocyanin is a red color. In a neutral solution, it is a purplish color. In a basic solution, it appears greenish-yellow. Make indicator paper with the cabbage juice and have students use dried-out indicator paper to test the pH themselves. Then this demonstration will become an activity. Est. time: 10 min

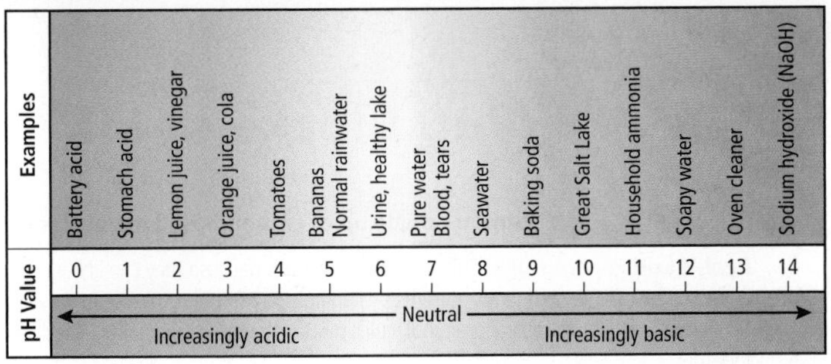

■ **Figure 24** The pH scale is used to indicate the relative strength of acids and bases—in other words, the amount of hydrogen ions (H^+) in a solution.

pH and buffers The amount of hydrogen ions or hydroxide ions in a solution determines the strength of an acid or base. Scientists have devised a convenient way to measure how acidic or basic a solution is. The measure of concentration of H^+ in a solution is called **pH.** As shown in **Figure 24,** pure water is neutral and has a pH value of 7.0. Acidic solutions have an abundance of H^+ and have pH values lower than 7. Basic solutions have more OH^- than H^+ and have pH values higher than 7.

Connection to Health The majority of biological processes carried out by cells occur between pH 6.5 and 7.5. In order to maintain homeostasis, it is important to control H^+ levels. If you've ever had an upset stomach, you might have taken an antacid to feel better. The antacid tablet is a buffer to help neutralize the stomach acid. **Buffers** are mixtures that can react with acids or bases to keep the pH within a particular range. In cells, buffers keep the pH in a cell within the 6.5 to 7.5 pH range. Your blood, for example, contains buffers that keep the pH about 7.4. C W

CAREERS IN BIOLOGY

Pool Technician Every recreational body of water, such as a recreational swimming pool, training spa, or medical therapy pool, must meet strict requirements for water quality. Pool technicians make sure these requirements are met by monitoring water pH, bacteria and algae levels, and water clarity.

Section 3 Assessment

Section Summary

- Water is a polar molecule.
- Solutions are homogeneous mixtures formed when a solute is dissolved in a solvent.
- Acids are substances that release hydrogen ions into solutions. Bases are substances that release hydroxide ions into solutions.
- pH is a measure of the concentration of hydrogen ions in a solution.

Understand Main Ideas

1. MAIN Idea **Describe** one way in which water helps maintain homeostasis in an organism.
2. **Relate** the structure of water to its ability to act as a solvent.
3. **Draw** a pH scale and label water (H_2O), hydrochloric acid (HCl), and sodium hydroxide (NaOH) in their general areas on the scale.
4. **Compare and contrast** solutions and suspensions. Give examples of each.

Think Critically

5. **Explain** how baking soda ($NaHCO_3$) is basic. Describe the effect of baking soda on the H^+ ion concentration of stomach contents with pH 4.
6. **Predict** If you add hydrochloric acid (HCl) to water, what effect would this have on the H^+ ion concentration? On the pH?

C Critical Thinking

BL OL AL Relate

SAY TO STUDENTS: ***Relate the importance of buffers to a live cell.*** Biological processes occur only within a narrow pH range. Therefore, buffers are vital because they prevent large fluctuations in the concentrations of hydrogen ions in a cell.

W Writing Support

BL OL AL Creative Writing

Have students write a song about the pH scale and what it is used to measure. You might also wish to encourage students to perform it for the class.

Formative Assessment

Evaluation

SAY TO STUDENTS: ***Relate the structure of water to its ability to dissolve other substances, including the phrase "like dissolves like".*** Water is polar, so the unequal distribution of electrons in the molecule allows for the formation of hydrogen bonds with other molecules.

Remediation Have students read the text under the heading *Water's Polarity* and draw the structure of water. Remind students that the unequal distribution of electrons allows water to dissolve other polar molecules. Have students draw the interaction between water and NaCl.

Section 3 Assessment

1. Water's ability to increase and decrease hydrogen ions helps maintain pH.
2. As a polar molecule, electrons in hydrogen atom bonds are closer to the oxygen atom, creating a negative charge that attracts positive atoms in solutes.
3. hydrochloric acid, below 7; sodium hydroxide, above 7; water, at 7
4. Solutions are homogeneous mixtures (salt water). Suspensions are heterogeneous mixtures (salad dressing made out of oil and vinegar).
5. The baking soda will buffer the H^+ ions. It has more OH^- than H^+ levels.
6. increase hydrogen ions and decrease the pH

✓ Assessment Online Quiz

Section 4

MAIN Idea

BL OL AL

The Building Blocks of Life

Draw the atomic structure of carbon on the board.

ASK STUDENTS: ***How many bonds can carbon form with other atoms?*** as many as four single bonds or two double bonds Review chemical bonding and the differences between covalent and ionic bonds with students before reading Section 4. Ask students working above level what the atomic structure looks like.

R Reading Strategy

BL OL Content-Specific Words

Have students use the word *organic* in a sentence. Students might mention organic vegetables. Ask a student to read aloud the text under the heading *Organic Chemistry.* Point out that some words used in everyday speech can have specific meanings in a scientific context.

ASK STUDENTS: ***What does it mean if something is organic?*** It contains carbon. Point out that all living things are organic.

S Skill Practice

BL OL Visual Literacy Have students study Figure 25. Encourage students to pay close attention to the electrons on the outermost shell of the carbon atom.

ASK STUDENTS: ***How does Figure 25 help you better understand the text under the heading* Organic Chemistry?** A carbon atom can form four covalent bonds with atoms of other elements and with other carbon atoms, and it can have shapes such as chains, rings, or branches. Remind students of the differences between covalent and ionic bonds and that the unique bonding properties of carbon allow it to sustain life.

Section 4

Reading Preview

Essential Questions

- What is the role of carbon in living organisms?
- What are the four major families of biological macromolecules?
- What are the functions of each group of biological macromolecules?

Review Vocabulary

organic compound: a carbon-based substance that is the basis of living matter

New Vocabulary

macromolecule
polymer
carbohydrate
lipid
protein
amino acid
nucleic acid
nucleotide

Multilingual eGlossary

The Building Blocks of Life

MAIN Idea **Organisms are made up of carbon-based molecules.**

Real-World Reading Link Children enjoy toy trains because they can link long lines of cars together and make patterns by joining cars of similar color or function. Similarly, in biology, there are large molecules made of many smaller units joined together.

Organic Chemistry

R The element carbon is a component of almost all biological molecules. For this reason, life on Earth often is considered carbon-based. Because carbon is an essential element, scientists have devoted an entire branch of chemistry, called organic chemistry, to the study of organic compounds, which are those compounds containing carbon.

As shown in **Figure 25,** carbon has four electrons in its outermost energy level. Recall that the second energy level can hold eight electrons, so one carbon atom can form four covalent bonds with other atoms. These covalent bonds enable the carbon atoms to bond to each other, which results in a variety of important organic compounds. These compounds can be in the shape of straight chains, branched chains, and rings, such as those illustrated in **Figure 25.** Together, carbon compounds lead to the diversity of life on Earth.

S

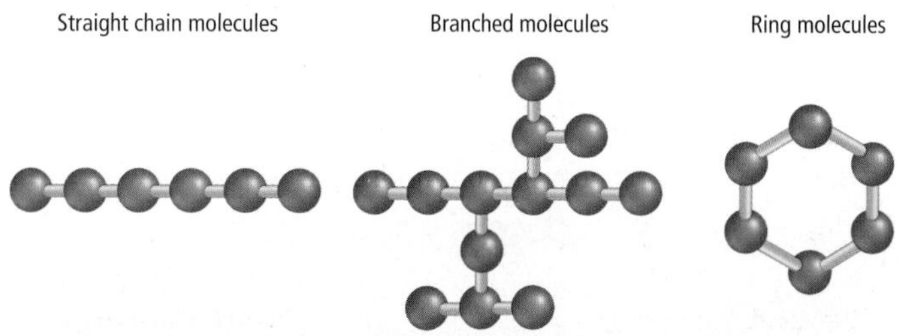

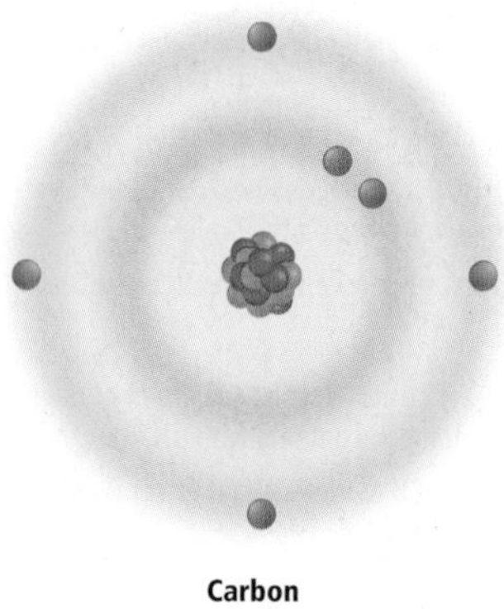

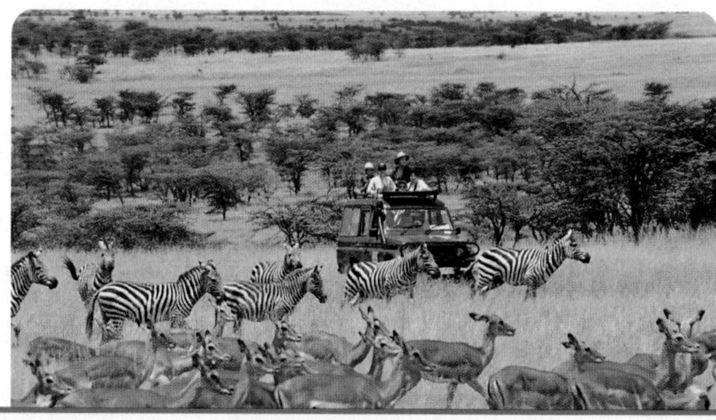

■ **Figure 25** The amazing diversity of life is based on the variety of carbon compounds. The half-filled outer energy level of carbon allows for the formation of straight chain, branched, and ring molecules.

Demonstration

Macromolecular Polymerization Using interlocking building blocks, demonstrate the repetitive nature of macromolecule assembly. Then, using a molecular modeling kit, assemble a nucleic acid, an amino acid, a simple sugar, and a lipid. Point out the differences in composition among the four macromolecules. For example, carbohydrates contain only carbon, hydrogen, and oxygen; however, amino acids contain carbon, nitrogen, hydrogen, and oxygen. Est. time: 20 min

Macromolecules

Carbon atoms can be joined to form carbon molecules. Similarly, most cells store small carbon compounds that serve as building blocks for large molecules. **Macromolecules** are large molecules that are formed by joining smaller organic molecules together. These large molecules are also called polymers. **Polymers** are molecules made from repeating units of identical or nearly identical compounds called monomers that are linked together by a series of covalent bonds. As shown in **Table 1,** biological macromolecules are organized into four major categories: carbohydrates, lipids, proteins, and nucleic acids.

Reading Check **Use an analogy** to describe macromolecules.

VOCABULARY
WORD ORIGIN
Polymer
poly– prefix; from Greek, meaning *many*
–meros from Greek, meaning *part*

Table 1 **Biological Macromolecules** — Concepts in Motion, Interactive Table

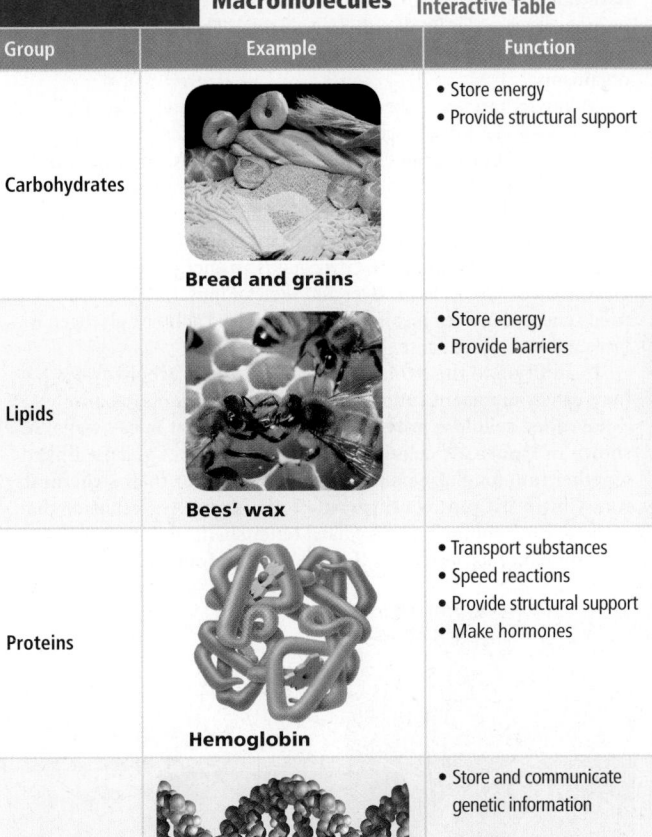

Group	Example	Function
Carbohydrates	 **Bread and grains**	• Store energy • Provide structural support
Lipids	 **Bees' wax**	• Store energy • Provide barriers
Proteins	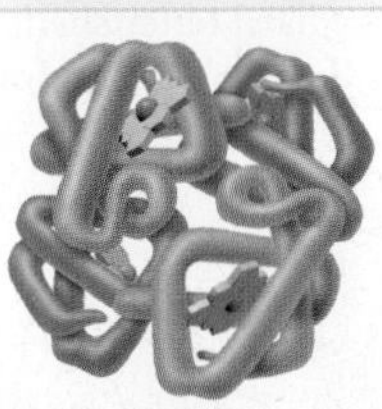 **Hemoglobin**	• Transport substances • Speed reactions • Provide structural support • Make hormones
Nucleic acids	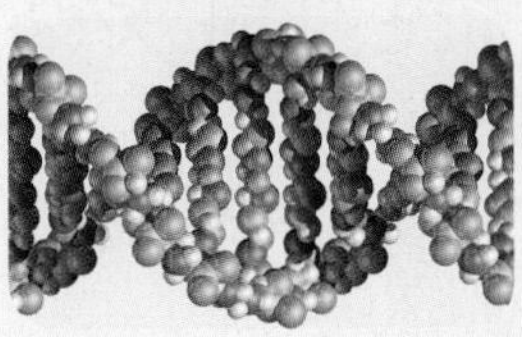 **DNA**	• Store and communicate genetic information

Study Tip

Double-Entry Notes Fold a piece of paper in half lengthwise and write the boldfaced subheadings that appear under the *Biological Macromolecules* heading on the left side. As you read the text, make a bulleted list of notes about the important ideas and terms.

Skill Practice

BL OL AL Make a Table Have students make and complete a table of the most abundant elements found in living organisms. **EL COOP LEARN** Students could complete the table in small groups.

Chemical/ Symbol	Atomic Number	Atomic Mass	Bonds Formed
Carbon-C	6	12	4
Hydrogen-H	1	1	1
Nitrogen-N	7	14	3
Oxygen-O	8	16	2
Phosphorus-P	15	31	5
Sulfur-S	16	32	2

Tell students to refer to this table when learning about the four classes of macromolecules in cells.

Concepts in Motion
Interactive Table

Differentiated Instruction

English Learners When asking students to complete the table described on this page, model each stage of the task. Provide an example of what information should be placed in each column to help students who are learning English understand the activity.

For more tips, see pages 14T–15T.

Reading Check Analogies might include a bicycle chain, beaded jewelry, a brick wall, etc.

D Develop Concepts

EL BL OL Activity Have students bring in nutrition content labels from food products, and identify which foods contain simple sugars and which ones contain complex carbohydrates. Examples of products containing simple sugars include candy bars and soda; examples of products with complex carbohydrates might include pastas, oatmeal, and frozen peas.

Review

Personal Tutor

Listen to a teacher explain monomers.

Develop Concepts

BL OL Clarify a Misconception Students may confuse organic molecules with organic foods. **ASK STUDENTS:** ***If a vegetable farmer grows crops without the use of chemical fertilizers and pesticides, is the produce considered organic?*** Remind students that the term *organic molecules* refers to compounds that contain carbon. However, *organic foods* is a term used to describe foods that are produced without chemicals, such as pesticides.

C Critical Thinking

BL OL AL Differentiate Starch, a polysaccharide, dissolves easily in water, whereas cellulose does not. Both molecules consist of polymers of glucose molecules. **ASK STUDENTS:** ***What structural difference between starch and cellulose accounts for their difference in solubility?*** Starch exists in either highly branched chains or long, twisted chains, while cellulose occurs in long, straight chains. The branched structure dissolves more readily than does the straight chain structure.

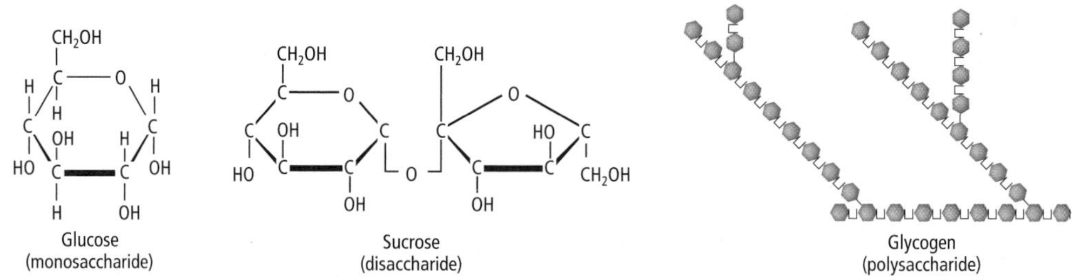

Figure 26 Glucose is a monosaccharide. Sucrose is a disaccharide composed of glucose and fructose monosaccharides. Glycogen is a branched polysaccharide made from glucose monomers.

Review **Personal Tutor**

Carbohydrates Compounds composed of carbon, hydrogen, and oxygen in a ratio of one oxygen and two hydrogen atoms for each carbon atom are called **carbohydrates.** A general formula for carbohydrates is written as $(CH_2O)_n$. Here the subscript n indicates the number of CH_2O units in a chain. Biologically important carbohydrates that have values of n ranging from three to seven are called simple sugars, or monosaccharides (mah nuh SA kuh ridz). The monosaccharide glucose, shown in **Figure 26,** plays a central role as an energy source for organisms.

Monosaccharides can be linked to form larger molecules. Two monosaccharides joined together form a disaccharide (di SA kuh rid). Like glucose, disaccharides serve as energy sources. Sucrose, also shown in **Figure 26,** which is table sugar, and lactose, which is a component of milk, are both disaccharides. Longer carbohydrate molecules are called polysaccharides. One important polysaccharide is glycogen, which is shown in **Figure 26.** Glycogen is an energy storage form of glucose that is found in the liver and skeletal muscle. When the body needs energy between meals or during physical activity, glycogen is broken down into glucose.

In addition to their roles as energy sources, carbohydrates have other important functions in biology. In plants, a carbohydrate called cellulose provides structural support in cell walls. As shown in **Figure 27,** cellulose is made of chains of glucose linked together into tough fibers that are well suited for their structural role. D Chitin (KI tun) is a nitrogen-containing polysaccharide that is the main component in the hard outer shells of shrimp, lobsters, and some insects, as well as the cell walls of some fungi. C

Figure 27 The cellulose in plant cells provides the structural support for trees to stand in a forest.

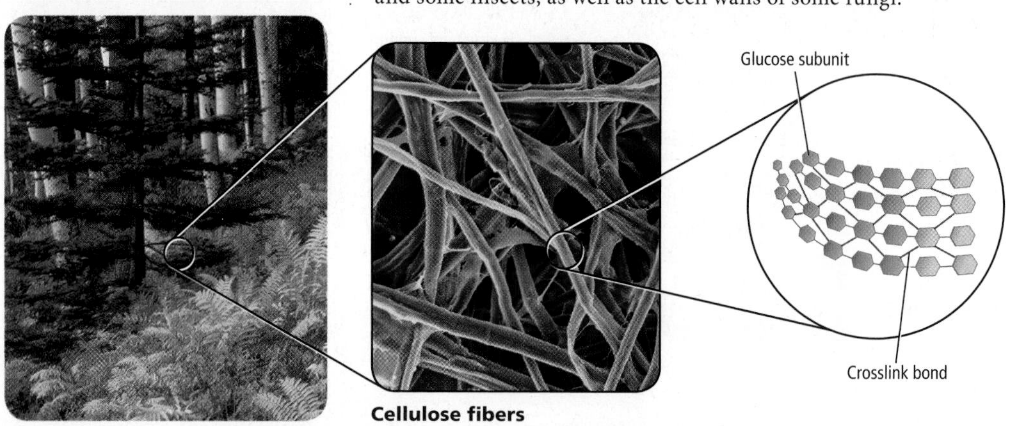

Content Background

Real-World Connection Over the past several years, there has been controversy regarding the effect of trans fats on cardiovascular health. To help foods stay fresh on the shelf or to get a solid fat product, such as margarine, food manufacturers hydrogenate polyunsaturated oils. To hydrogenate means to add hydrogen. In clinical studies, trans fatty acids, or hydrogenated fats, tend to raise total blood cholesterol levels and LDL ("bad") cholesterol and lower HDL ("good") cholesterol when used instead of cis fatty acids or natural oils. These changes in cholesterol levels increase the risk of heart disease.

Lipids Another important group of biological macromolecules is the lipid group. **Lipids** are molecules made mostly of carbon and hydrogen that make up the fats, oils, and waxes. Lipids are composed of fatty acids, glycerol, and other components. The primary function of lipids is to store energy. A lipid called a triglyceride (tri GLIH suh rid) is a fat if it is solid at room temperature and an oil if it is liquid at room temperature. In addition, triglycerides are stored in the fat cells of the body. Plant leaves are coated with lipids called waxes to prevent water loss, and the honeycomb in a beehive is made of beeswax.

R **Saturated and unsaturated fats** Organisms need lipids to function properly. The basic structure of a lipid includes fatty acid tails, as shown in **Figure 28.** Each tail is a chain of carbon atoms bonded to hydrogen and other carbon atoms by single or double bonds. Lipids that have tail chains with only single bonds between the carbon atoms are called saturated fats because no more hydrogens can bond to the tail. Lipids that have at least one double bond between carbon atoms in the tail chain can accommodate at least one more hydrogen and are called unsaturated fats. Fats with more than one double bond in the tail are called polyunsaturated fats.

Phospholipids A special lipid shown in **Figure 28,** called a phospholipid, is responsible for the structure and function of the cell membrane. Lipids are hydrophobic, which means they do not dissolve in water. This characteristic is important because it allows lipids to serve as barriers in biological membranes.

Steroids Another important category of lipids is the steroid group. Steroids include substances such as cholesterol and hormones. Despite its reputation as a "bad" lipid, cholesterol provides the starting point for other necessary lipids such as vitamin D and the hormones estrogen and testosterone.

DATA ANALYSIS LAB 2

Based on Real Data*

Interpret the Data

Does soluble fiber affect cholesterol levels? High amounts of a steroid called cholesterol in the blood are associated with the development of heart disease. Researchers study the effects of soluble fiber in the diet on cholesterol.

Data and Observations

This experiment evaluated the effects of three soluble fibers on cholesterol levels in the blood: pectin (PE), guar gum (GG), and psyllium (PSY). Cellulose was the control (CNT).

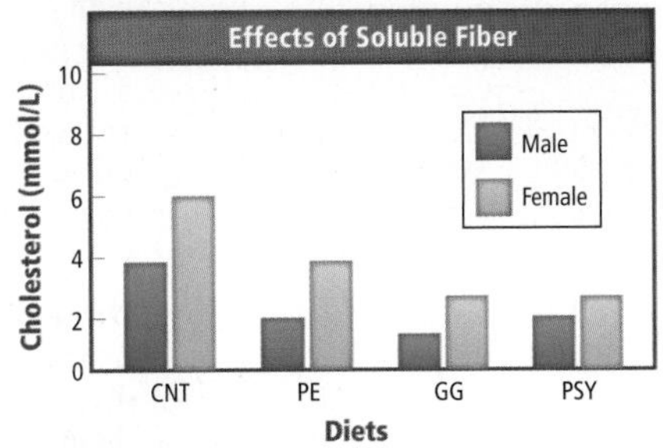

Think Critically

1. **Calculate** the percentage of change in cholesterol levels as compared to the control.
2. **Describe** the effects that soluble fiber appears to have on cholesterol levels in the blood.

*Data obtained from: Shen, et al. 1998. Dietary soluble fiber lowers plasma LDL cholesterol concentrations by altering lipoprotein metabaolism in female Guinea pigs. *Journal of Nutrition* 128: 1434-1441.

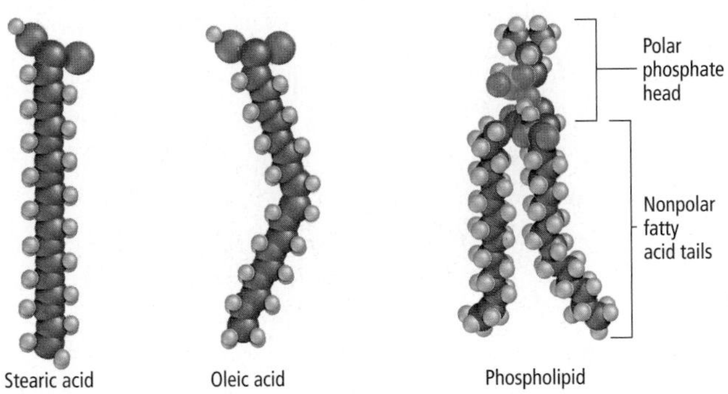

■ **Figure 28** Stearic acid has no double bonds between carbon atoms; oleic acid has one double bond. Phospholipids have a polar head and two nonpolar tails.

R Reading Strategy

BL OL AL

Supplemental Reading Have students research the terms *unsaturated fats* and *saturated fats* to learn the structural differences in the two types of fats and the relationship between these structural differences and human health. You can provide students with supplemental readings that you find online or in the library.

BL Provide students with resources geared to their level, and have them work in pairs.

AL Have students include the relationship between the information they find and the surge of products offered with "0 trans fat."

ASK STUDENTS: ***Why have products with 0 trans fat flooded the food market?***

DATA ANALYSIS LAB 2

About the Lab

- Observers have reported lower coronary heart disease in subjects who consume diets high in fiber.
- Fiber can be classified as a dietary source or a supplement.
- Fiber can be divided into water-soluble and insoluble forms.
- Some forms of dietary fiber, such as oat or rice bran, can reduce LDL levels modestly.
- Artis et al. 2006. The effects of a new soluble dietary fiber on weight gain and selected blood parameters in rats. *Metabolism* 55(2): 195–202.

Think Critically

1. pectin: 50 percent decrease in men, 33 percent in women; guar gum: 75 percent decrease in men, 50 percent in women; psyllium: 50 percent decrease in men and women
2. Soluble fiber appears to lower cholesterol levels.

Research Citation

Problem Solve Educational research indicates that student achievement will improve when they are provided with direct instruction on how to solve real-world problems. The Data Analysis Lab on this page provides an opportunity for students to practice problem-solving skills and better retain the concepts they have learned. (Charles and Lester, 1984)

Research bibliography on pages 32T–34T

Reading Strategy

EL BL OL AL

Anticipation Guide Before students read the text under the heading *Proteins,* have them predict the answers to the following true or false questions:
(1) proteins are organic molecules,
(2) proteins are made in cells,
(3) enzymes are proteins,
(4) amino acids are the building blocks of proteins. all true

Develop Concepts

BL OL AL

Clarify a Misconception

ASK STUDENTS: ***What types of food, other than meat, are rich sources of protein?*** eggs, milk, fish, cheese, beans, nuts Students might think that only meat contains protein. Remind students that proteins are major components of all cells.

EL Show students pictures of these and other foods and ask them to identify the ones that are rich sources of protein.

Writing Support

AL **Report Writing** Have students research one of the diseases caused by a lack of protein in the diet (eg., kwashiorkor, hemoglobinopathies, marasmus, diabetes) and write a report that includes symptoms, regions of the world where the disease is common, and ways in which the lack of dietary protein might be remedied. Have students report their findings to the class.

Concepts in Motion

Animation

Caption Question Fig. 29
water (H_2O)

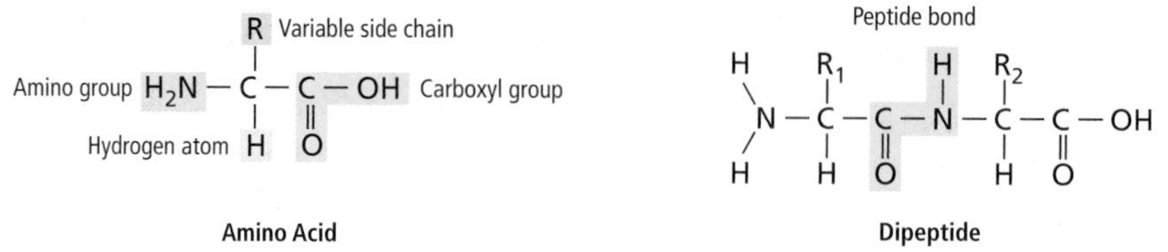

Figure 29
Left: The general structure of an amino acid has four groups around a central carbon.
Right: The peptide bond in a protein happens as a result of a chemical reaction.
Interpret *which other molecule is a product when a peptide bond forms.*

Concepts in Motion
Animation

Proteins Another primary building block of living things is protein. A **protein** is a compound made of small carbon compounds called amino acids. **Amino acids** are small compounds that are made of carbon, nitrogen, oxygen, hydrogen, and sometimes sulfur. All amino acids share the same general structure.

Amino acid structure Amino acids have a central carbon atom like the one shown in **Figure 29.** Recall that carbon can form four covalent bonds. One of those bonds is with hydrogen. The other three bonds are with an amino group ($-NH_2$), a carboxyl group ($-COOH$), and a variable group ($-R$). The variable group makes each amino acid different. There are 20 different variable groups, and proteins are made of different combinations of all 20 different amino acids. Several covalent bonds called peptide bonds join amino acids together to form proteins, which is also shown in **Figure 29.** A peptide bond forms between the amino group of one amino acid and the carboxyl group of another.

Three-dimensional protein structure Based on the variable groups contained in the different amino acids, proteins can have up to four levels of structure. The number of amino acids in a chain and the order in which the amino acids are joined define the protein's primary structure. After an amino acid chain is formed, it folds into a unique three-dimensional shape, which is the protein's secondary structure. **Figure 30** shows two basic secondary structures: the helix and the pleat. A protein might contain many helices, pleats, and folds. The tertiary structure of many proteins is globular, such as the hemoglobin protein shown in **Table 1,** but some proteins form long fibers. Some proteins form a fourth level of structure by combining with other proteins.

Protein function Proteins make up about 15 percent of your total body mass and are involved in nearly every function of your body. For example, your muscles, skin, and hair are made of proteins. Your cells contain about 10,000 different proteins that provide structural support, transport substances inside the cell and between cells, communicate signals within a cell and between cells, speed up chemical reactions, and control cell growth.

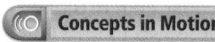

Figure 30 The shape of a protein depends on the interactions among the amino acids. Hydrogen bonds help the protein hold its shape.

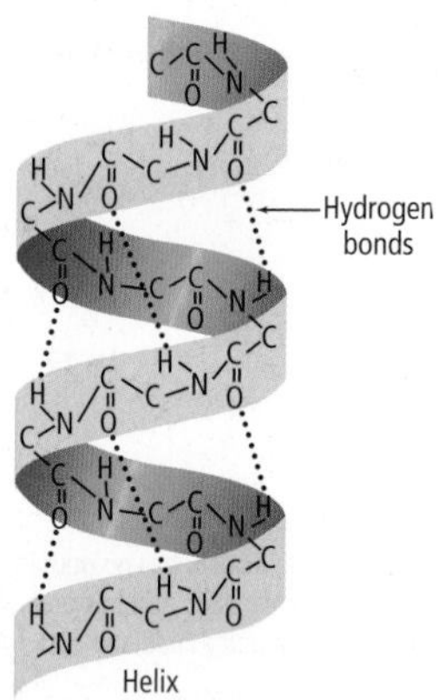

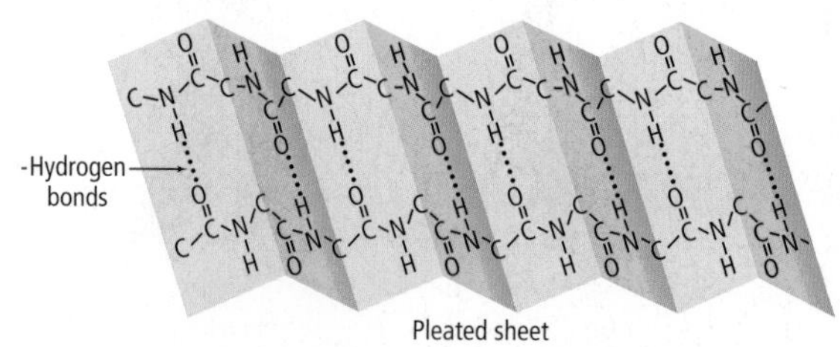

Demonstration

3-D Genetic Information Using a molecular modeling kit, build the structure of DNA and RNA. Emphasize that both macromolecules are composed of similar repeating units. DNA assembles to form a double-stranded helical structure, whereas RNA forms a linear structure. Use a beaded necklace to demonstrate amino acid assembly into proteins, emphasizing that each bead is an amino acid and the entire necklace is the peptide chain. Est. time: 10 min

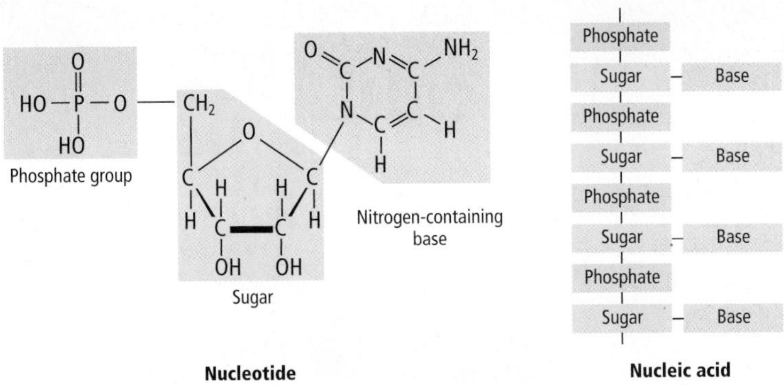

Figure 31
Left: DNA nucleotides contain the sugar deoxyribose. RNA nucleotides contain the sugar ribose.
Right: Nucleotides are joined together by bonds between their sugar group and phosphate group.

Nucleic acids The fourth group of biological macromolecules are nucleic acids. **Nucleic acids** are complex macromolecules that store and transmit genetic information. Nucleic acids are made of smaller repeating subunits composed of carbon, nitrogen, oxygen, phosphorus, and hydrogen atoms, called **nucleotides. Figure 31** shows the basic structure of a nucleotide and nucleic acid. There are six major nucleotides, all of which have three units—a phosphate, a nitrogenous base, and a ribose sugar.

There are two types of nucleic acids found in living organisms: deoxyribonucleic (dee AHK sih rib oh noo klay ihk) acid (DNA) and ribonucleic (rib oh noo KLAY ihk) acid (RNA). In nucleic acids such as DNA and RNA, the sugar of one nucleotide bonds to the phosphate of another nucleotide. The nitrogenous base that sticks out from the chain is available for hydrogen bonding with other bases in other nucleic acids.

A nucleotide with three phosphate groups is adenosine triphosphate (ATP). ATP is a storehouse of chemical energy that can be used by cells in a variety of reactions. It releases energy when the bond between the second and third phosphate group is broken. Less energy is released when the bond between the first and second phosphate group is broken. W D

Section 4 Assessment

Section Summary

- Carbon compounds are the basic building blocks of living organisms.
- Biological macromolecules are formed by joining small carbon compounds into polymers.
- There are four types of biological macromolecules.
- Peptide bonds join amino acids in proteins.
- Chains of nucleotides form nucleic acids.

Understand Main Ideas

1. MAIN Idea **Explain** If an unknown substance found on a meteorite is determined to contain no trace of carbon, can scientists conclude that there is life at the metorite's origin?
2. **Compare** the types of biological macromolecules and their functions.
3. **Determine** the components of carbohydrates and proteins.
4. **Discuss** the importance of amino acid order to a protein's function.

Think Critically

5. **Summarize** Given the large number of proteins in the body, explain why the shape of an enzyme is important to its function.
6. **Draw** two structures (one straight chain and one ring) of a carbohydrate with the chemical formula $(CH_2O)_6$.

W Writing Support

AL Narrative Writing Have students write a report on the history of DNA. Tell them to include information on how and when scientists discovered the structure, function, and cellular location of DNA. Then have students create a short documentary to be performed for the class. Encourage students to use available technology.

D Develop Concepts

EL BL OL AL Use Models Use a molecular modeling set to demonstrate how the order in which nucleic acids join together in DNA allows for genetic diversity.

Formative Assessment

Evaluation

ASK STUDENTS: ***What is the relationship between macromolecules and polymers?*** Macromolecules are large structures that are formed when small repeating units polymerize, or join together. ***What are the four categories of macromolecules?*** carbohydrates, lipids, proteins, and nucleic acids.

Remediation Have students read the text describing carbon compounds and list the elements for each category of macromolecule. For example, for carbohydrates, students will list the elements C, H, and O. Have students give as many examples of each macromolecule as possible.

Section 4 Assessment

1. no, because all known life-forms contain carbon
2. Carbohydrates store energy and provide support; lipids store energy, provide barriers; proteins transport substances, speed reactions, provide structural support, and make hormones; nucleic acids store and communicate genetic information.
3. carbohydrates: C, H, O; proteins: C, N, O, H, S
4. Protein properties stem from the order in which the amino acids assemble and determine how the peptides fold into a three-dimensional structure.
5. Every enzyme has an active site that binds only specific substrates. This active site is formed when the peptides fold into specific three-dimensional shapes.
6. Drawings should be variations of Figure 26.

Assessment Online Quiz

Purpose

Students will understand that artificial sweeteners have chemical structures similar to those of sugars. A.1, A.2, B.2, F.1, G.1, G.3

Anticipatory Guide

ASK STUDENTS: ***What do you know about artificial sweeteners?*** Students might know that many artificial sweeteners do not have calories. ***Why do you think artificial sweeteners taste sweet?*** Artificial sweeteners taste sweet because their chemical structures are similar to those of sugars. ***In what products have you seen artificial sweeteners used?*** diet sodas, baked goods, dairy products, toothpaste, mouthwash

Background

Saccharin, the first artificial sweetener used, was discovered in 1879 by a chemistry student at John Hopkins University. When the student left his experiments for a lunch break, he did not wash his hands. (Remind students that they should always wash their hands after finishing an experiment.) He noticed that the bread he was eating tasted extremely sweet. He figured that the sweetness must have come from a compound that he touched during the morning's experiments. The student then tasted the compounds with which he had been working until he came across saccharin. (Remind students that it is very dangerous to taste anything used in the laboratory.)

CUTTING-EDGE BIOLOGY

SWEETER THAN SUGAR

The reason why people love desserts is right on the tips of their tongues—literally. The taste buds in that location are the receptors that register sweetness most strongly. Many of the small bumps, called papillae, that you see on your tongue contain taste buds.

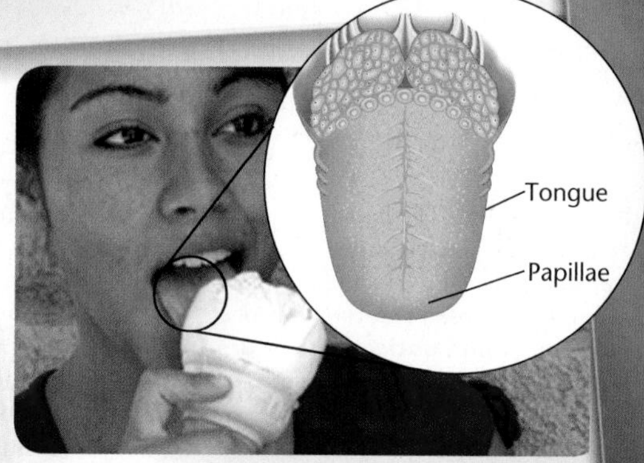

Taste buds on your tongue send impulses to your brain so that your brain can interpret how the food or drink tastes.

Registering Sweetness When you eat, the molecules from food temporarily bind themselves to protein molecules in the receptor cells of your tongue. As a result, the receptors send electrical impulses through your nerves to your brain. Your brain interprets the impulses as taste. Sometimes the taste is what you think of as sweet.

Natural vs. Artificial Sweeteners are substances added to foods to make them taste sweet. There are many natural sweeteners, such as table sugar and honey. An artificial sweetener is a man-made substance that has the same effect on taste buds as sugar does. Artificial sweeteners, such as saccharin, cyclamate, and aspartame, are hundreds of times sweeter than any naturally occurring sugar.

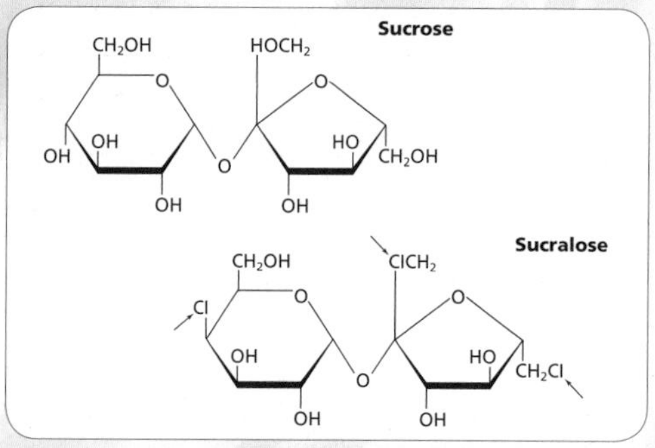

The difference between sucrose and sucralose is the substitution of three chlorine (Cl) atoms for three hydroxyl (OH) groups.

The molecules of these artificial sweeteners mimic the geometry and composition of natural sweeteners and are able to bind to the receptor cells in human taste buds.

One recently developed artificial sweetener, sucralose, has a chemical structure that is nearly identical to sucrose, or table sugar. The only difference is three hydroxyl (OH) groups in sucrose are replaced by chlorine atoms (Cl) in sucralose. This keeps the human body from metabolizing sucralose and makes it calorie-free.

Artificial sweeteners are used in many products, from diet sodas to children's medications. They provide the sweetness that people crave without the calories that natural sweeteners contain. Scientists continue to search for new sweeteners that are economical and healthful to customers.

WRITING in Biology

Marketing Campaign Research an artificial sweetener that has been approved by the FDA. Devise a marketing campaign to inform consumers about your chosen artificial sweetener. Your marketing campaign might include a press release, television or radio commercials, Web ads, social networking sites, or other methods of spreading information.

WRITING in Biology

RUBRIC Use the modifiable rubric found on your eTeacherEdition Online to assess writing assignments.

Activity To help students understand what a marketing campaign is, choose a popular product, such as a cell phone, and ask students to share where they have seen or heard information about that product. Today, marketing campaigns are far-ranging. In their marketing campaigns for an artificial sweetener, students might put a new twist on an old idea, perhaps constructing a billboard in an unusual place or with unusual 3-D components.

WebQuest

BIOLAB Design Your Own

WHAT FACTORS AFFECT AN ENZYME REACTION?

Background: The compound hydrogen peroxide, H_2O_2, is produced when organisms metabolize food, but hydrogen peroxide damages cell parts. Organisms combat the buildup of H_2O_2 by producing the enzyme peroxidase. Peroxidase speeds up the breakdown of hydrogen peroxide into water and oxygen.

Question: *What factors affect peroxidase activity?*

Possible Materials

400-mL beaker
kitchen knife
hot plate
test-tube rack
ice
beef liver
dropper
distilled water
50-mL graduated cylinder
10-mL graduated cylinder
tongs or large forceps
square or rectangular pan
stopwatch or timer
nonmercury thermometer
3% hydrogen peroxide
potato slices
18-mm × 150-mm test tubes
buffer solutions (pH 5, pH 6, pH 7, pH 8)

Safety Precautions

CAUTION: *Use only GFCI-protected circuits for electrical devices.*

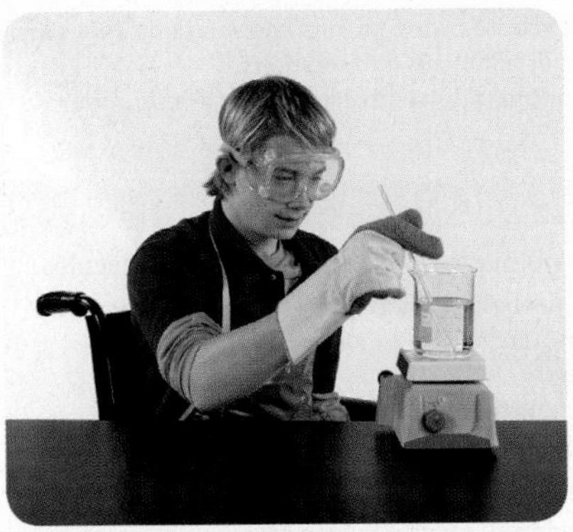

Plan and Perform the Experiment

1. Read and complete the lab safety form.
2. Choose a factor to test. Possible factors include temperature, pH, and substrate (H_2O_2) concentration.
3. Form a hypothesis about how the factor will affect the reaction rate of peroxidase.
4. Design an experiment to test your hypothesis. Create a procedure and identify the controls and variables.
5. Create a data table for recording your observations and measurements.
6. Make sure your teacher approves your plan before you proceed.
7. Conduct your approved experiment.
8. **Cleanup and Disposal** Clean up all equipment as instructed by your teacher and return everything to its proper place. Wash your hands thoroughly with soap and water.

Analyze and Conclude

1. **Describe** how the factor you tested affected the enzyme activity of peroxidase.
2. **Graph** your data, and then analyze and interpret your graph.
3. **Discuss** whether or not your data supported your hypothesis.
4. **Infer** why hydrogen peroxide is not the best choice for cleaning an open wound.
5. **Error Analysis** Identify any experimental errors or other errors in your data that might have affected the accuracy of your results.

SHARE YOUR DATA

Compare your data with the data collected by other groups in the class that tested the same factor. Infer reasons why your group's data might differ from the data collected by other groups.

Analyze and Conclude

1. An increase in temperature will speed up the reaction until the enzyme is deactivated around 70°C. The ideal pH range for the enzyme will be 6–8. An increased concentration of the substrate will increase the reaction until the enzyme is saturated with the substrate.
2. Graphs will depend on the factor being tested. A graph of temperature data will show a bell-shaped curve that tops out at about 35°C. A graph showing the effects of pH changes will also have a bell shape, and will top out around pH 7. A line graph of substrate concentration should show a steady increase before leveling off as the enzyme becomes saturated with the substrate.
3. Answers will depend on the factor tested and data collected.
4. Human cells have the enzyme peroxidase, which catalyzes the hydrogen peroxide into water and oxygen, limiting the chemical's antiseptic value.
5. Answers will vary but could include the introduction of more than one variable, or measurement errors.

BIOLAB Design Your Own

? Inquiry BioLab

For a lab worksheet, use your eTeacherEdition Online.

RUBRIC A rubric for evaluating BioLabs is found on your eTeacherEdition Online.

Est. Time 45 min

Content Background Enzymes catalyze specific reactions. An increase in temperature speeds enzyme reactions, but peroxidase is deactivated above 70°C. Peroxidase has an ideal pH range of pH 6–8. The substrate (hydrogen peroxide) concentration also affects the activity of an enzyme. At low concentrations, the activity is proportional to the amount of substrate, but as the substrate concentration increases, the enzyme becomes saturated and activity decreases or stops.

Safety Precautions Instruct students to handle all glassware with tongs. Caution students that hydrogen peroxide is an irritant. Flush any spills on the skin or eyes with water for 15 min.

Teaching Strategy Compare three different temperatures, four substrate concentrations, and four pHs, to show the effects of these variables on peroxidase activity. Be certain to include multiple points around the ideal ranges for these variables for this enzyme (e.g., for temperature, lower and higher than 70°C; for pH, 5-8; for substrate concentration, 0.5 –3% hydrogen peroxide).

Alternative Teaching Demo Demonstrate the effects of three temperatures (chilled, 70°C, and boiling) on an enzyme reaction by using slices of potato.

Cleanup and Disposal Peroxide of 3% concentration or less can be poured down the drain.

Chapter 6

Study Guide

ConnectED

Students can use the following to review the chapter.

Review

Vocabulary eGames
Vocabulary eFlashcards
Vocabulary PuzzleMaker

Assessment

Online Quizzes
Online Test Practice
Standardized Test Practice

Use the *ExamView®* *Assessment Suite* CD-ROM to:

- create multiple versions of tests
- create modified tests with one mouse click
- edit existing questions and add your own questions
- build tests aligned with state standards using built-in state curriculum tags
- change English tests to Spanish with one mouse click
- track students' progress using the Teacher Management System

Chapter 6 Study Guide

THEME FOCUS Energy In every chemical reaction, there is a change in energy caused by the making and breaking of chemical bonds as reactants form products.

BIG Idea Atoms are the foundation of biological chemistry and the building blocks of all living things.

Section 1 Atoms, Elements, and Compounds

atom (p. 148)
nucleus (p. 148)
proton (p. 148)
neutron (p. 148)
electron (p. 148)
element (p. 149)
isotope (p. 150)
compound (p. 151)
covalent bond (p. 152)
molecule (p. 152)
ion (p. 153)
ionic bond (p. 153)
van der Waals force (p. 155)

MAIN Idea **Matter is composed of tiny particles called atoms.**

- Atoms consist of protons, neutrons, and electrons.
- Elements are pure substances made up of only one kind of atom.
- Isotopes are forms of the same element that have a different number of neutrons.
- Compounds are substances with unique properties that are formed when elements combine.
- Elements can form covalent and ionic bonds.

Section 2 Chemical Reactions

chemical reaction (p. 156)
reactant (p. 157)
product (p. 157)
activation energy (p. 158)
catalyst (p. 159)
enzyme (p. 159)
substrate (p. 160)
active site (p. 160)

MAIN Idea **Chemical reactions allow living things to grow, develop, reproduce, and adapt.**

- Balanced chemical equations must show an equal number of atoms for each element on both sides.
- Activation energy is the energy required to begin a reaction.
- Catalysts are substances that alter chemical reactions.
- Enzymes are biological catalysts.

Section 3 Water and Solutions

polar molecule (p. 161)
hydrogen bond (p. 161)
mixture (p. 163)
solution (p. 163)
solvent (p. 163)
solute (p. 163)
acid (p. 164)
base (p. 164)
pH (p. 165)
buffer (p. 165)

MAIN Idea **The properties of water make it well suited to help maintain homeostasis in an organism.**

- Water is a polar molecule.
- Solutions are homogeneous mixtures formed when a solute is dissolved in a solvent.
- Acids are substances that release hydrogen ions into solutions. Bases are substances that release hydroxide ions into solutions.
- pH is a measure of the concentration of hydrogen ions in a solution.

Section 4 The Building Blocks of Life

macromolecule (p. 167)
polymer (p. 167)
carbohydrate (p. 168)
lipid (p. 169)
protein (p. 170)
amino acid (p. 170)
nucleic acid (p. 171)
nucleotide (p. 171)

MAIN Idea **Organisms are made up of carbon-based molecules.**

- Carbon compounds are the basic building blocks of living organisms.
- Biological macromolecules are formed by joining small carbon compounds into polymers.
- There are four types of biological macromolecules.
- Peptide bonds join amino acids in proteins.
- Chains of nucleotides form nucleic acids.

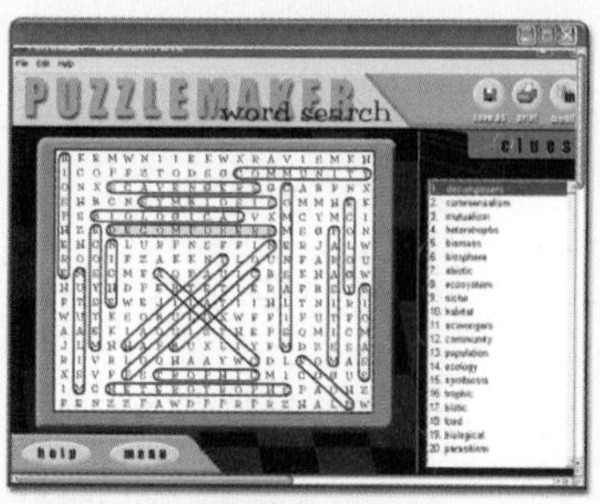

Review **Vocabulary PuzzleMaker**

For additional practice with vocabulary, have students access the Vocabulary PuzzleMaker online.

Review **Vocabulary eGames**

Section 1

Vocabulary Review

Describe the difference between the terms in each pair.

1. electron, proton

2. ionic bond, covalent bond

3. isotope, element

4. atom, ion

Understand Main Ideas

Use the photo below to answer question 5.

5. What does the image above show?
A. a covalent bond
B. a physical property
C. a chemical reaction
D. van der Waals forces

6. Which process changes a chlorine atom into a chloride ion?
A. electron gain **C.** proton gain
B. electron loss **D.** proton loss

7. MAIN Idea Which of these is a pure substance that cannot be broken down by a chemical reaction?
A. a compound **C.** an element
B. a mixture **D.** a neutron

8. How do the isotopes of hydrogen differ?
A. in the number of protons
B. in the number of electrons
C. in the number of energy levels
D. in the number of neutrons

Constructed Response

9. Short Answer What is a radioactive isotope? List uses of radioactive isotopes.

10. Short Answer What factor determines that an oxygen atom can form two covalent bonds while a carbon atom can form four?

11. Open Ended Why is it important for living organisms to have both strong bonds (covalent and ionic) and weak bonds (hydrogen and van der Waals forces)?

Think Critically

Use the graph below to answer question 12.

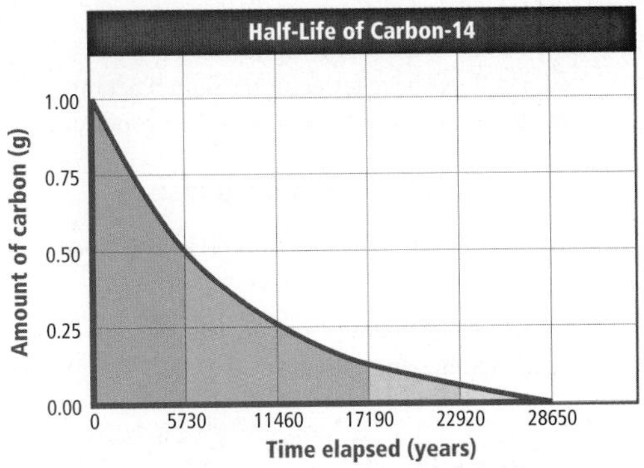

12. Analyze According to the data, what is the half-life of carbon-14? How can this information be used by scientists?

13. Explain The gecko is a reptile that climbs on smooth surfaces such as glass using van der Waals forces to adhere to the surfaces. How is this method of adhesion more advantageous than covalent interactions?

Section 2

Vocabulary Review

Match the term on the left with the correct definition on the right.

14. activation energy	**A.** a protein that speeds up a reaction
15. substrate	**B.** a substance formed by a chemical reaction
16. enzyme	**C.** the energy required to start a reaction
17. product	**D.** a substance that binds to an enzyme

Chapter 6 Assessment

Section 1

Vocabulary Review

1. Electrons are negatively charged and circulate in energy orbitals around the nucleus, whereas protons are positively charged particles that reside in the nucleus.
2. Ionic bonds are formed when one atom donates an electron to another atom, whereas covalent bonds are formed when two atoms share a pair of electrons.
3. An isotope is a form of an element that has a different number of neutrons.
4. An atom is neutral, whereas ions are either positively or negatively charged.

Understand Main Ideas

5. C
6. A
7. C
8. D

Constructed Response

9. A radioactive isotope is a form of an element that has a different number of neutrons and an unstable nucleus. It emits ionizing radiation to try to stabilize itself. This forms an unstable atom that emits particles as it disintegrates. Radioactive isotopes are used for chemotherapy, dating fossils, and in research to label cellular molecules (proteins, DNA, RNA, etc).
10. the number of electrons on the outermost energy orbital
11. Biological systems use strong bonds to make small molecules and weaker bonds to form higher-order structures (assemble a protein into its three-dimensional geometry).

Think Critically

12. 5730 years; scientists can use this information to date material that has carbon compounds in it.
13. van der Waals forces are more advantageous than covalent interactions because van der Waals forces are weak and will allow the gecko to move by repeatedly detaching and reattaching to the surface.

Section 2

Vocabulary Review

14. C
15. D
16. A
17. B

Understand Main Ideas

18. C
19. A
20. B

Constructed Response

21. They proceed at a rate that is different than the rate at which they would proceed without an enzyme.
22. Temperature, pH, and substrate concentration can all increase, decrease, or terminate enzyme activity.

Think Critically

23. Temperature increases the rate of both reactions within specific ranges.
24. Enzyme A would be more active in a living cell because the maximal activity is around 37°C.

Section 3

Vocabulary Review

25. A solution is a type of mixture.
26. A buffer is used to decrease the hydrogen ion concentration created when acids are dissolved in water. This lowers the pH.
27. The pH scale is used to measure the strength of acids (1–7) and bases (7–14).
28. A solute is dissolved by a solvent.
29. Polar molecules can form hydrogen bonds because of the unequal distribution of electrons.

Understand Main Ideas

30. A
31. C
32. A

Understand Main Ideas

18. **THEME FOCUS Energy** Which of the following is a substance that lowers the activation energy?
A. an ion **C.** a catalyst
B. a reactant **D.** a substrate

19. In which of the following are bonds broken and new bonds formed?
A. chemical reactions **C.** isotopes
B. elements **D.** polar molecules

20. Which statement is true of chemical equations?
A. Reactants are on the right.
B. Products are on the right.
C. Products have fewer atoms than reactants.
D. Reactants have fewer atoms than products.

Constructed Response

21. Short Answer What features do all reactions involving enzymes have in common?

22. Open Ended Identify and describe factors that can influence enzyme activity.

Think Critically

Use the graph to answer questions 23 and 24.

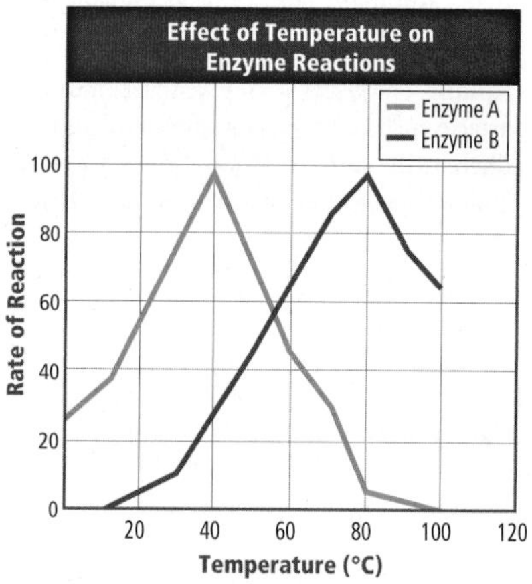

23. Describe the effect that temperature has on the rate of the reactions using the graph above.

24. MAIN Idea Which enzyme is more active in a human cell? Why?

Section 3

Vocabulary Review

State the relationship between the terms in each pair.

25. solution, mixture

26. pH, buffer

27. acid, base

28. solvent, solute

29. polar molecule, hydrogen bond

Understand Main Ideas

Use the figure below to answer question 30.

30. What does the image above show?
A. a heterogeneous mixture **C.** a solution
B. a homogeneous mixture **D.** a suspension

31. Which statement is not true about pure water?
A. It has a pH of 7.0.
B. It is composed of polar molecules.
C. It is composed of ionic bonds.
D. It is a good solvent.

32. Which is a substance that produces OH^- ions when it is dissolved in water?
A. a base **C.** a buffer
B. an acid **D.** salt

Constructed Response

33. MAIN Idea Why are hydrogen bonds so important for living organisms?

34. Short Answer Hydrochloric acid (HCl) is a strong acid. What ions are formed when HCl dissolves in water? What is the effect of HCl on the pH of water?

35. Open Ended Explain the importance of buffers to living organisms.

Constructed Response

33. Hydrogen bonds are important because they allow for higher-order structures to form (protein tertiary structure) and for molecules to communicate/interact.
34. H^+ and Cl^- are formed when HCl is dissolved in water. The pH of the solution will decrease because the H^+ ion concentration has increased.
35. Buffers help maintain cellular pH between 6.5 and 7.5, where most enzymatic reactions and cellular processes occur.

Think Critically

36. **Predict** two places in the body where buffers are used to limit sharp changes in pH.

37. **Draw** a diagram of table salt (NaCl) dissolved in water.

Section 4

Vocabulary Review

Complete the following sentences with vocabulary terms from the Study Guide page.

38. Carbohydrates, lipids, proteins, and nucleic acids are __________.

39. Proteins are made from __________ that are joined by __________.

40. __________ make up fats, oils, and waxes.

41. DNA and RNA are examples of __________.

Understand Main Ideas

42. Which two elements are always found in amino acids?
   - **A.** nitrogen and sulfur
   - **B.** carbon and oxygen
   - **C.** hydrogen and phosphorus
   - **D.** sulfur and oxygen

43. Which joins amino acids together?
   - **A.** peptide bonds
   - **B.** hydrogen bonds
   - **C.** van der Waals forces
   - **D.** ionic bonds

44. Which substance is not part of a nucleotide?
   - **A.** a phosphate
   - **B.** a base
   - **C.** a sugar
   - **D.** water

Constructed Response

45. **Open Ended** Why do cells contain both macromolecules and small carbon compounds?

46. **Open Ended** Why can't humans digest all carbohydrates?

Think Critically

47. MAIN Idea **Create** a table for the four main biological macromolecules that lists their component and functions.

Summative Assessment

48. BIG Idea Diagram the basic unit of matter, describe the parts, and relate them to each other.

49. WRITING in Biology Research and write a job description for a biochemist. Include the types of tasks that biochemists perform and materials that are used in their research.

DBQ Document-Based Questions

Starch is the major carbon storehouse in plants. Experiments were performed to determine if trehalose might regulate starch production in plants. Leaf disks were incubated for three hours in sorbitol (the control), sucrose, and trelahose solutions. Then, levels of starch and sucrose in the leaves were measured. Use the data to answer the questions below.

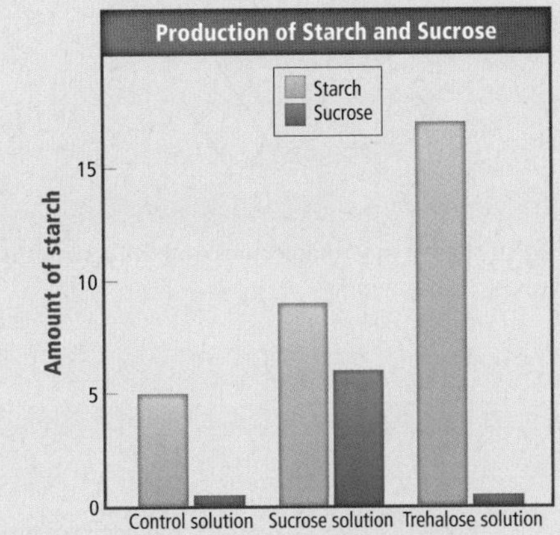

Data obtained from: Kolbe, et al. Trehalose 6-phosphate regulates starch synthesis via post translational redox activation of ADP-glucose pyrophophorylase. *Proceedings of the National Academy of Sciences of the USA* 102(31): 11118–11123.

50. Summarize the production of starch and sucrose in the three solutions.

51. What conclusion might the researchers have reached based on these data?

Think Critically

36. Possible answers will include the stomach, intestinal tract, blood, lungs, etc.

37. Drawings should depict polar water molecules surrounding Na^+ ions and Cl^- ions.

Section 4

Vocabulary Review

38. macromolecules
39. amino acids; peptide bonds
40. Lipids
41. nucleotides

Understand Main Ideas

42. B
43. A
44. D

Constructed Response

45. Cells contain both macromolecules and small carbon compounds because macromolecules are routinely broken down during cellular processes, and small carbon compounds are required to restore depleted macromolecules.

46. Humans do not have enzymes that can break down some complex, branched polysaccharides such as cellulose and chitin.

Think Critically

47.

Macromolecule	Building Block	Function	Example
Protein	Amino acids	Cellular processes	Enzymes
Carbohydrate	Monosaccharide	Energy	Steroids, fats
Nucleic acid	**Nucleotide**	Information storage Genetic code	DNA, RNA
Lipid	**Fatty acids**	Cell membranes	Glycogen starch

Summative Assessment

48. Diagrams should resemble Figure 1. The basic structure of an atom is the result of the attraction between protons and electrons.

49. Answers should include tasks and materials.

WRITING in Biology

RUBRIC Use the modifiable rubric found on your eTeacherEdition Online to assess writing assignments.

50. Leaves always showed more starch than sucrose in all three solutions.

51. Trehalose increases starch production in leaves and decreases sucrose almost entirely.

DBQ Document-Based Questions

Kolbe, et al. Trehalose 6-phosphate regulates starch synthesis via post translational redox activation of ADP-glucose pyrophophorylase. *Proceedings of the National Academy of Sciences of the USA* 2005 102(31): 11118–11123.

Standardized Test Practice

Multiple Choice

1. A
2. D
3. B
4. A
5. A
6. B
7. B
8. C

Short Answer

9. Without buffers, the cells could not stay in the correct pH range. This would affect homeostasis because many cellular reactions can occur only within a certain pH range.
10. Answers may vary. Possible answers include the following. Element: O_2—molecular oxygen has two atoms of the same type Compound: CH_4—methane is a molecule made of different atoms.
11. Because the water temperature has to be consistently warm throughout the year, it should be a tropical region. Because the depth cannot be too great and the water has to be saline, it should be a marine environment in shallow water, probably near the coast.
12. Answers can vary, but should reflect an understanding that species diversity depends on having an environment where many different species can live. For example, the warmer climate closer to the tropics may be more hospitable to a wide range of species—perhaps even similar species that are slightly different from one another—than the colder regions near the poles.
13. Answers may vary. Probably, the largest age groups are the pre-reproductive age group and the post-reproductive age group.
14. This ensures that enzymes act on specific compounds and are involved in specific reactions. Enzymes are specific for the reactions that they catalyze and this makes chemical processes in organisms go faster.

Standardized Test Practice

Cumulative

Multiple Choice

1. If a population of parrots has greater genetic diversity than a hummingbird population in the same region, which outcome could result?
   - **A.** The parrot population could have a greater resistance to disease than the hummingbird population.
   - **B.** Other parrot populations in different regions could become genetically similar to this one.
   - **C.** The parrot population could have a greater variety of abiotic factors with which to interact.
   - **D.** The parrot population could interact with a greater variety of other populations.

Use the diagram below to answer questions 2 and 3.

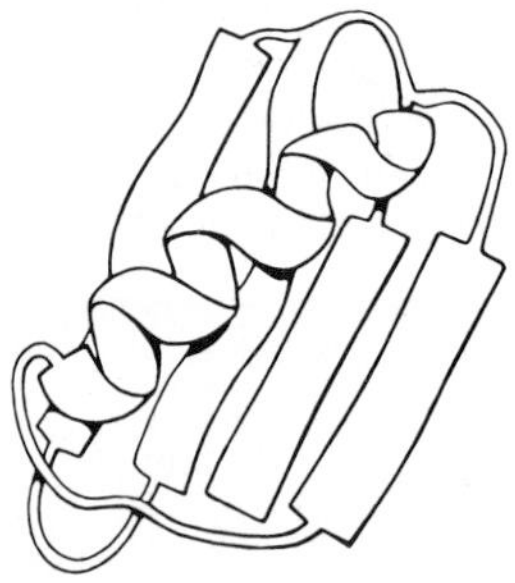

2. Which type of macromolecule can have a structure like the one shown?
   - **A.** a carbohydrate
   - **B.** a lipid
   - **C.** a nucleotide
   - **D.** a protein

3. Which molecular activity requires a folded structure?
   - **A.** behavior as a nonpolar compound
   - **B.** function of an active site
   - **C.** movement through cell membranes
   - **D.** role as energy storage for the cell

4. Which describes the effects of population increase and resource depletion?
   - **A.** increased competition
   - **B.** increased emigration
   - **C.** exponential population growth
   - **D.** straight-line population growth

5. Which property of populations might be described as random, clumped, or uniform?
   - **A.** density
   - **B.** dispersion
   - **C.** growth
   - **D.** size

6. Which is an example of biodiversity with direct economic value?
   - **A.** sparrow populations that have great genetic diversity
   - **B.** species of a water plant that makes a useful antibiotic
   - **C.** trees that create a barrier against hurricane winds
   - **D.** villagers who all use the same rice species for crops

Use the illustration below to answer question 7.

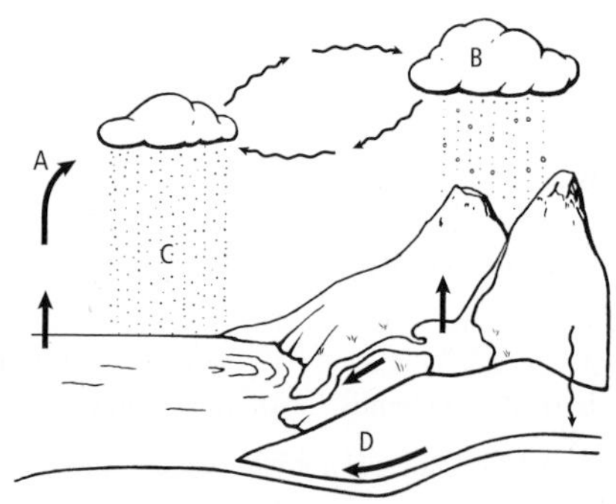

7. Which term describes the part of the cycle labeled *A*?
   - **A.** condensation
   - **B.** evaporation
   - **C.** runoff
   - **D.** precipitation

8. Which is a characteristic of exponential growth?
   - **A.** the graphical representation goes up and down
   - **B.** the graphical representation has a flat line
   - **C.** a growth rate that increases with time
   - **D.** a growth rate that stays constant in time

Short Answer

9. Assess what might happen if there were no buffers in human cells.

10. Choose an example of an element and a compound and then contrast them.

Use the chart below to answer question 11.

Factors Affecting Coral Survival	
Factor	**Optimal Range**
Water temperature	23°C to 25°C
Salinity	30 to 40 parts per million
Sedimentation	little or no sedimentation
Depth	up to 48 m

11. Using the data in the chart, describe which region of the world would be optimal for coral growth.

12. Provide a hypothesis to explain the increase in species diversity as you move from the polar regions to the tropics.

13. In a country with a very slow growth rate, predict which age groups are the largest in the population.

14. Why is it important that enzymes can bind only to specific substrates?

Extended Response

15. Suddenly, after very heavy rains, many fish in a local lake begin to die, yet algae in the water seem to be doing very well. You know that the lake receives runoff from local fields and roads. Form a hypothesis about why the fish are dying, and suggest how to stop the deaths.

16. When scientists first discovered atoms, they thought they were the smallest parts into which matter could be divided. Relate how later discoveries led scientists to revise this definition.

17. Identify and describe three types of symbiotic relationships and provide an example of each.

Essay Question

Many kinds of molecules found in living organisms are made of smaller monomers that are put together in different sequences, or in different patterns. For example, organisms use a small number of nucleotides to make nucleic acids. Thousands of different sequences of nucleotides in nucleic acids provide the basic coding for all the genetic information in living things.

Using the information in the paragraph above, answer the following question in essay format.

18. Describe how it is beneficial for organisms to use monomers to create complex macromolecules.

NEED EXTRA HELP?																		
If You Missed Question . . .	1	2	3	4	5	6	7	8	9	10	11	12	13	14	15	16	17	18
Review Section . . .	5.1	6.4	6.4	4.1	5.1	2.3	4.1	4.1	6.3	5.3	3.1, 3.3	5.1	4.2	6.2	5.2	6.1	2.1	6.4

Extended Response

15. Hypotheses and solutions can vary. For example, the problem may be caused by rapid eutrophication of the lake. Because heavy rains are washing more runoff into the lake, more fertilizers and chemicals are entering the water, promoting growth of algae. The algae can use up the oxygen in the lake as they grow and later decompose. Fish need oxygen, and they begin to die off without it. A solution would be to prevent the runoff into the lake, clean the algae from the lake, or put in pumps to help oxygenate the water for the fish.

16. Scientists have discovered smaller particles that make up atoms: electrons, protons, and neutrons. These parts can be broken away from the rest of the atom. For example, an atom loses nuclear particles during radioactive decay. Atoms also lose or share electrons when they form covalent or ionic bonds.

Essay Question

17. Mutualism is a symbiotic relationship in which two or more organisms live closely together and benefit each other. The fungus and algae that make up lichens are an example of mutualism.
Commensalism is a symbiotic relationship in which one organism gains from the relationship and the other does not benefit and is not harmed. A lichen growing on a tree is an example of commensalism.
Parasitism is a symbiotic relationship in which one organism benefits at the expense of the other. A tick on a dog is an example of parasitism.
Examples can vary.

18. Although polymers are large, complicated molecules, the monomers of which they are made are readily available in cells. In cells similar polymers are made of a limited number of monomers. For example a few monosaccharides are used to make various disaccharides, complex sugars, starch, and cellulose. Just a few bases are used to make RNA and DNA molecules. Consequently a variety of complex molecules can be synthesized more easily, because they share monomer parts with related complex molecules.

Chapter 7 Organizer:
Cellular Structure and Function

LabManager™
Customize any lab with the LabManager™ CD-ROM.

Essential Questions	National Science Standards	Materials and Planning	
		Estimated times include cleanup and disposal, but do not include teacher prep time. For cleanup and disposal guidelines, see page 39T.	Est. Time (min)
Section 1 1. How are the advances in microscope technology related to discoveries about cells? 2. What are the similarities and differences between compound light microscopes and electron microscopes? 3. What are the principles of the cell theory? 4. What are the differences between a prokaryotic cell and a eukaryotic cell?	UCP.1, UCP.5; A.1, A.2; C.1; E.1, E.2; G.1–3	**Launch Lab,** p. 180: specimen slides (living and nonliving things), microscopes	10–15
		Activity, p. 182: bubble wrap; honeycomb-shaped cereal	5
		MiniLab 1, p. 184: slides of microscopic organisms, microscopes, art supplies for student drawings	15–20
Section 2 1. How does a cell's plasma membrane function? 2. What are the roles of proteins, carbohydrates, and cholesterol in the plasma membrane?	UCP.1–3, UCP.5; A.1, A.2; B.2; C.1, C.5	**Demonstration,** p. 187: fish bowl, water, sealable sandwich bag, marbles	5
		Demonstration, p. 188: small aquarium, water, colored balls, stick, or ruler	5
Section 3 1. What are the structures of a typical eukaryotic cell, and what are their functions? 2. What are the similarities and differences between plant and animal cells?	UCP.1–3, UCP.5; A.1, A.2; C.1, C.5; G.1–3	**Demonstration,** p. 191: dismantled tennis shoe or hiking boot	5
		Activity, p. 192: slides of cells (*Elodea,* skin cells, leaf epidermis); microscopes	30
Section 4 1. What are the processes of diffusion, facilitated diffusion, and active transport? 2. What is the effect of a hypotonic, hypertonic, or isotonic solution on a cell? 3. How do large particles enter and exit cells?	UCP.1–3, UCP.5; A.1, A.2; B.6; C.1, C.5	**Demonstration,** p. 201: stamens, pollen, microscope slides, microscope	10
		MiniLab 2, p. 203: microscope slides, onion epidermis, iodine stain, salt water, microscope	20
		Demonstration, p. 205: cucumbers, spices, pickle recipe, jar, water	10
		BioLab; p. 209: cellulose tubing; beakers; string; scissors; distilled water; pan; solutions: starch, albumin, glucose, NaCl, iodine, silver nitrate; anhydrous Benedict's reagent; biuret reagent; graduated cylinder; test tubes; rack; funnel; wax pencil; droppers	75–100
		Demonstration, p. 203: cornstarch, cellophane, or cellulose tubing, iodine, water, beaker	10

Suggested Time for Each Lesson

Class	Chapter Opener	Section 1	Section 2	Section 3	Section 4	Assessment
Basic	45 min	90 min	45 min	45 min	—	45 min
General	25 min	100 min	55 min	90 min	45 min	45 min
Honors	5 min	45 min	20 min	155 min	90 min	45 min

ConnectED

connectED.mcgraw-hill.com

Access interactive learning opportunities and teaching resources using these icons located throughout your StudentWorks™ Plus Online and eTeacherEdition Online.

Chapter 7 Section Resources

FAST FILE Unit 2 Resources:
Launch Lab Worksheet*
MiniLab Worksheet*
Study Guide (English/Spanish)*
Section Quick Check

Reading Essentials 7.1
Science Notebook 7.1*

FAST FILE Unit 2 Resources:
Study Guide (English/Spanish)*
Section Quick Check

Reading Essentials 7.2
Science Notebook 7.2*

FAST FILE Unit 2 Resources:
Study Guide (English/Spanish)*
Section Quick Check

Reading Essentials 7.3
Science Notebook 7.3*

FAST FILE Unit 2 Resources:
MiniLab Worksheet*
BioLab Worksheet*
Study Guide (English/Spanish)*
Section Quick Check

Reading Essentials 7.4
Science Notebook 7.4*

Additional Chapter 7 Resources

FAST FILE Unit 2 Resources:
Chapter Diagnostic Test
Concept Mapping*
Real-World Biology
Enrichment
Chapter Tests A, B, and C

Transparencies:
Bellringer Transparencies*
Biology Concepts Transparencies*

Lab Resources:
Laboratory Manual*
Probeware Lab Manual*
Forensics Lab Manual*
Pre-AP Lab Manual*
Open Inquiry in Biology*
Guided Inquiry in Biology*

Technology

Teaching Tools:
eTeacherEdition Online
Classroom Presentation Toolkit CD-ROM*
LabManager™ CD-ROM*
Video Lab DVD*
Virtual Lab CD-ROM*
What's BIOLOGY Got To Do With It?
StudentWorks™ Plus Online*

Chapter Assessment Tools:
Classroom Presentation Toolkit CD-ROM*
ExamView® Assessment Suite CD-ROM

Web-Based Resources:

- StudentWorks™ Plus Online
- eTeacherEdition Online
- Animations*
- The Interactive Time Line*
- Interactive Tables*
- Online Quizzes
- Online Test Practice
- Standardized Test Practice
- Virtual Labs*
- Multilingual eGlossary*
- Vocabulary eGames*
- Vocabulary eFlashcards
- WebQuests
- Personal Tutors

While all resources listed are appropriate for English learners, the * indicates resources with a strong visual or hands-on component for EL.

Teaching strategies and activities have been coded for differentiated instruction.

AL Activities for students working above grade level	**OL** Activities for students working on grade level	**BL** Activities for students working below grade level	**EL** Activities for English learners (also ELL)	**COOP LEARN** Activities designed for small cooperative group work

CHAPTER 7

Launch Lab
What is a cell?

Inquiry Launch Lab

For a lab worksheet, use your eTeacherEdition Online.

RUBRIC A rubric for evaluating Launch Labs is found on your eTeacherEdition Online.

Est. Time 10–15 min

Alternative Materials Photomicrographs of specimens can be found online at various microscopy Web sites.

Safety Precautions Approve lab safety forms before work begins. Review proper microscope techniques so glass slides are not broken while students locate the sample and focus.

Teaching Strategies
- Have students work in small groups so they can help each other.
- Save time and materials by assigning lab teams certain slides. Have them report their findings to the class.

Procedure
1. Read and complete the lab safety form.
2. Construct a data table for recording your observations
3. Obtain **slides of various specimens.**
4. View the slides through a **microscope** at the power designated by your teacher.
5. As you view the slides, fill out the data table you constructed.

CHAPTER 7
Cellular Structure and Function

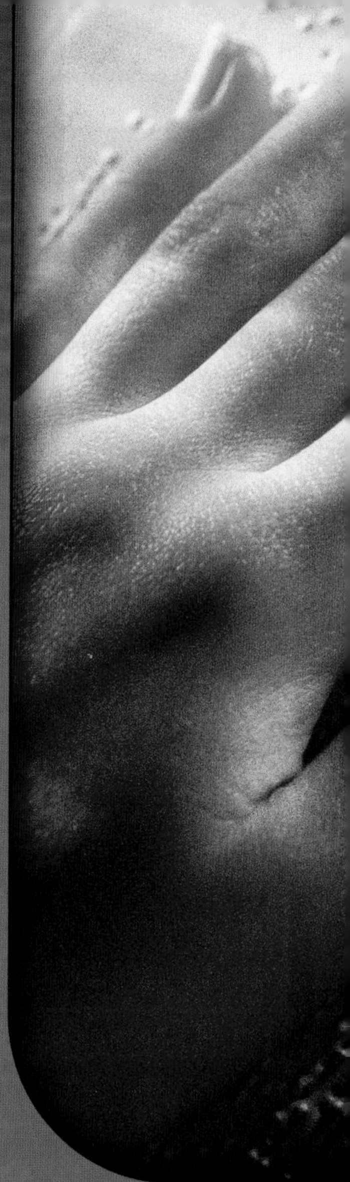

ConnectED

Your one-stop online resource
connectED.mcgraw-hill.com

- Video
- Audio
- Review
- Inquiry
- WebQuest
- Assessment
- Concepts in Motion
- Multilingual eGlossary

Launch Lab
What is a cell?

All things are made of atoms and molecules, but only in living things are the atoms and molecules organized into cells. In this lab, you will use a compound microscope to view slides of living things and nonliving things.

For a lab worksheet, use your StudentWorks™ Plus Online.

Inquiry Launch Lab

FOLDABLES®

Make a layered-look book using the titles shown. Use it to organize your notes on cellular transport.

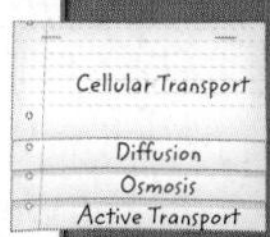

Analysis
1. **Describe** some of the ways to distinguish between the living things and the nonliving things. Accept all reasonable responses. Students should note that all the living samples had cells.
2. **Write** a definition of a cell based on your observations. Accept all reasonable responses. The formal definition of a cell is "the basic structural and functional unit of all living organisms."

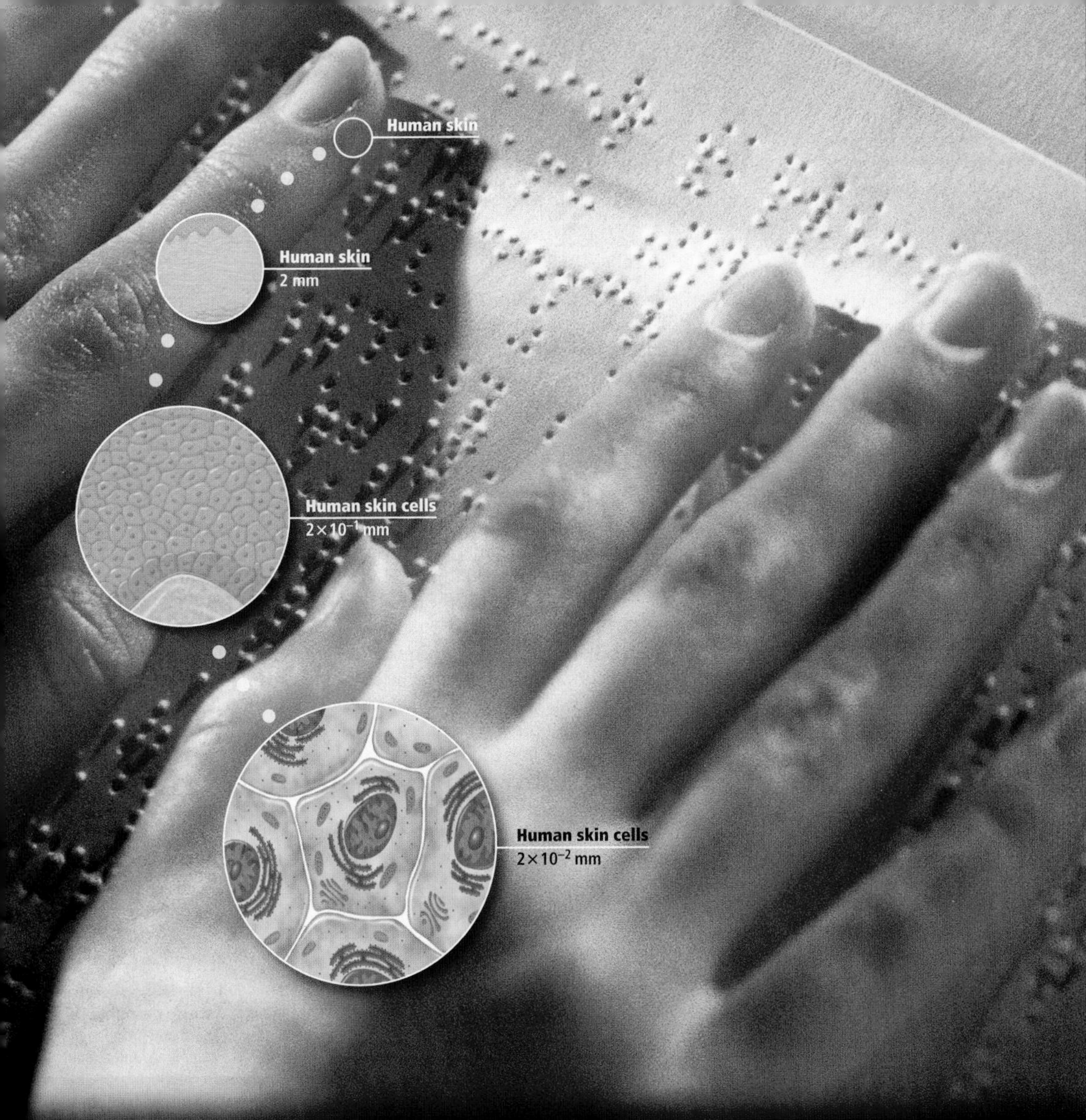

THEME FOCUS Scientific Inquiry
Scientific inquiry led to the invention of the microscope, which made many discoveries possible.

BIG Idea Cells are the structural and functional units of all living organisms.

Section 1 • Cell Discovery and Theory
Section 2 • The Plasma Membrane
Section 3 • Structures and Organelles
Section 4 • Cellular Transport

Introduce the Chapter

Microscopic Cells Have students examine the opening illustrations of cells that are not visible to the unaided eye. The biofact says the human body is made of about 10 trillion cells.

ASK STUDENTS: ***Why is a macroscopic organism made of microscopic cells?*** Possible answers may include division of labor, cell specialization, or cell size limitations.

BIG Idea

Outline Have students outline the chapter by writing the Big Idea for the chapter and Main Ideas for each section. Encourage students to take notes under the Main Ideas in their outline as they read the chapter.

Sample outline:
Big Idea: Cells are the structural and functional units of all living things.

I. Section 1 Main Idea: The invention of the microscope led to the discovery of cells.
   A. History of the cell theory
   B. Microscope technology
   C. Basic cell types

AL For further research, have students go online to find links to microscopy sites and analyze the different types of images according to microscope type.

THEMES

Scientific Inquiry Cells were discovered through scientific investigation.

Diversity Diversity exists within a cell due to the presence of various macromolecules, structures, functions, and processes.

Energy Mitochondria are responsible for converting fuel into usable energy for cells.

Homeostasis Active transport maintains homeostasis within a cell and its environment.

Change Cellular processes allow cells to respond to change in the environment.

Section 1

MAIN Idea

BL OL AL

Cell Discovery and Theory Place a small slice of natural bottle cork on a microprojector at the beginning of the section or show students a photomicrograph of cork.

SAY TO STUDENTS: ***Describe the shape of the cork and what you see in the cork cells.*** Answers may include a polygon shape or cube-like shape. There is nothing inside these cells (except possibly debris) because they are dead. Cork usually comes from the bark of a cork oak and is harvested and sold as bottle corks.

ASK STUDENTS: ***What is the function of cork in the cork oak tree?*** The cork provides a protective insulation layer for the tree. This barrier protects the tree from water loss, physical damage, and pathogens.

R Reading Strategy

EL BL COOP LEARN

Brainstorm Organize students into small groups and have them list what comes to mind when they think of the word *cell.* After five minutes, have the groups share their lists with the class. Write the ideas on the board and point out which ones will be covered in the section.

S Skill Practice

OL AL **Visual Literacy**

ASK STUDENTS: ***Looking at the time line, why do you think there often were long periods between significant discoveries about cells?*** Students should realize that discoveries about cells often were dependent on significant advances in technology or invention of new, unique microtechniques.

Activity

BL OL AL **Make a Comparison** Bring in several materials that are "cell-like" in their composition. Some examples might include bubble wrap or breakfast cereal shaped like honeycombs. Have students list on the board other examples (organic and inorganic) of cellular-type constructions and discuss how this structure is beneficial in each case. Est. time: 5 min

"The best teacher is the one who suggests rather than dogmatizes, and inspires his listener with the wish to teach himself."

—Edward G. Bulwer-Lytton

Section 1

Reading Preview

Essential Questions

- How are the advances in microscope technology related to discoveries about cells?
- What are the similarities and differences between compound light microscopes and electron microscopes?
- What are the principles of the cell theory?
- What are the differences between a prokaryotic cell and a eukaryotic cell?

Review Vocabulary

organization: the orderly structure shown by living things

New Vocabulary

cell
cell theory
plasma membrane
organelle
eukaryotic cell
nucleus
prokaryotic cell

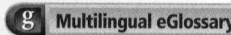

g Multilingual eGlossary

Cell Discovery and Theory

MAIN Idea **The invention of the microscope led to the discovery of cells.**

Real-World Reading Link The different parts of your body might seem to have nothing in common. Your heart, for example, pumps blood throughout your body, while your skin protects and helps cool you. However, your body parts have one thing in common—they are composed of cells.

R History of the Cell Theory

For centuries, scientists had no idea that the human body consists of trillions of cells. Cells are so small that their existence was unknown before the invention of the microscope. In 1665, as indicated in **Figure 1,** an English scientist named Robert Hooke made a simple microscope and looked at a piece of cork, the dead cells of oak bark. Hooke observed small, box-shaped structures, such as those shown in **Figure 2.** He called them cellulae (the Latin word meaning *small rooms*) because the boxlike cells of cork reminded him of the cells in which monks live at a monastery. It is from Hooke's work that we have the term *cell.* A **cell** is the basic structural and functional unit of all living organisms.

During the late 1600s, Dutch scientist Anton van Leeuwenhoek (LAY vun hook) designed his own microscope after he was inspired by a book written by Hooke. To his surprise, he saw living organisms in pond water, milk, and various other substances. The work of these scientists and others led to new branches of science and many new and exciting discoveries.

S

Figure 1
Microscopes in Focus
The invention of microscopes, improvements to the instruments, and new microscope techniques have led to the development of the cell theory and a better understanding of cells.

Concepts in Motion
The Interactive Timeline

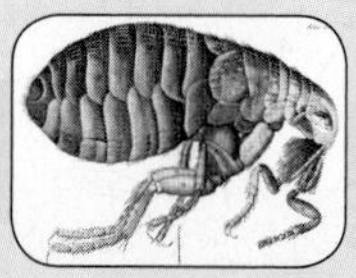

1500 **1600** **1700** **1800**

1590 Dutch lens grinders Hans and Zacharias Janssen invent the first compound microscope by placing two lenses in a tube.

1665 Robert Hooke observes cork and names the tiny chambers that he sees *cells.* He publishes drawings of cells, fleas, and other minute bodies in his book *Micrographia.*

1683 Dutch biologist Anton van Leeuwenhoek discovers single-celled, animal-like organisms, now called protozoans.

1830–1855 Scientists discover the cell nucleus (1833) and propose that both plants and animals are composed of cells (1839).

D **The cell theory** Scientists continued observing the living microscopic world using glass lenses. In 1838, German scientist Matthias Schleiden carefully studied plant tissues and concluded that all plants are composed of cells. A year later, another German scientist, Theodor Schwann, reported that animal tissues also consisted of individual cells. Prussian physician Rudolph Virchow proposed in 1855 that all cells are produced from the division of existing cells. The observations and conclusions of these scientists and others are summarized as the cell theory. The **cell theory** is one of the fundamental ideas of modern biology and includes the following three principles:

1. All living organisms are composed of one or more cells.
2. Cells are the basic unit of structure and organization of all living organisms.
3. Cells arise only from previously existing cells, with cells passing copies of their genetic material on to their daughter cells.

Reading Check **Explain** Can cells appear spontaneously without genetic material from previous cells?

Microscope Technology

The discovery of cells and the development of the cell theory would not have been possible without microscopes. Improvements made to microscopes have enabled scientists to study cells in detail, as described in **Figure 1.**

Turn back to the opening pages of this chapter and compare the illustrations of the skin shown there. Note that the detail increases as the magnification and resolution—the ability of the microscope to make individual components visible—increase. Hooke and van Leewenhoek would not have been able to see the individual structures within human skin cells with their microscopes. Developments in microscope technology have given scientists the ability to study cells in greater detail than early scientists ever thought possible.

LM Magnification: 100×

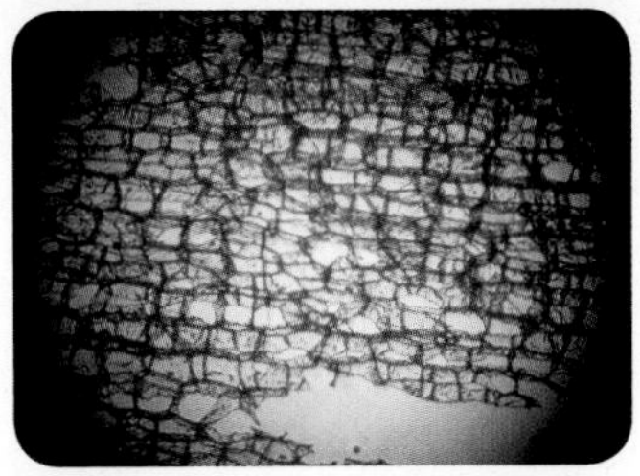

Figure 2 Robert Hooke used a basic light microscope to see what looked like empty chambers in a cork sample.
Infer *what you think Hooke would have seen if these were living cells.*

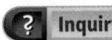

Inquiry Launch Lab

Based on what you've read about cells, how would you now answer the analysis questions?

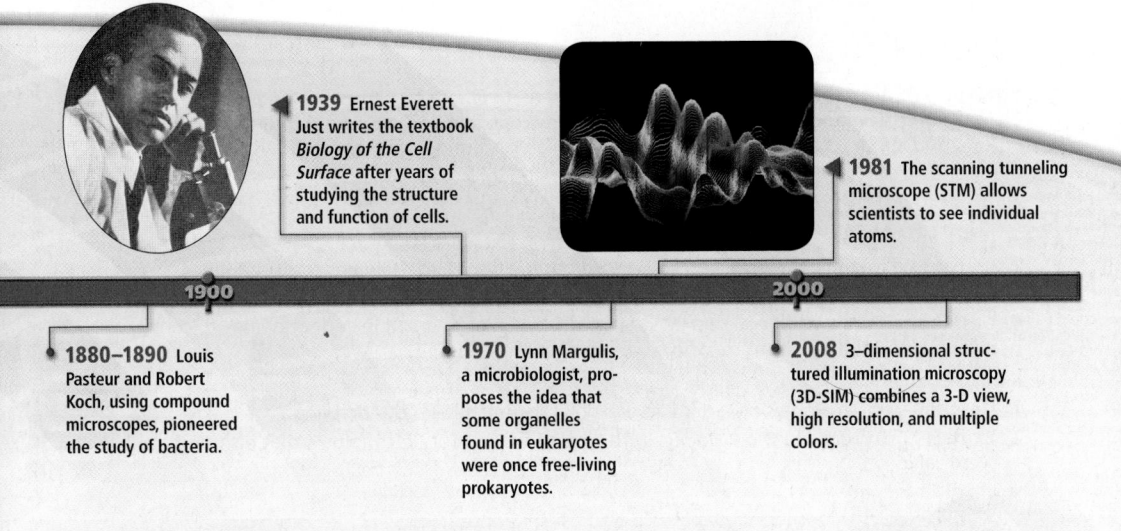

1939 Ernest Everett Just writes the textbook *Biology of the Cell Surface* after years of studying the structure and function of cells.

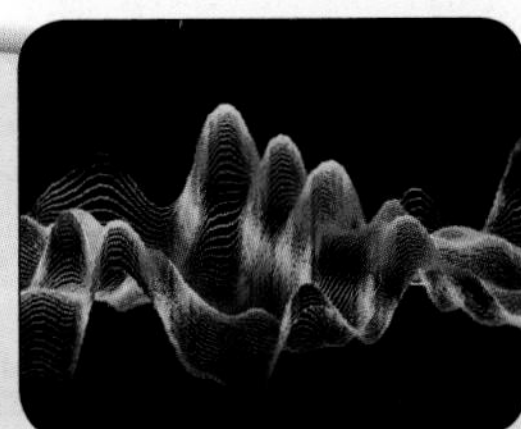

1981 The scanning tunneling microscope (STM) allows scientists to see individual atoms.

1900 — 2000

1880–1890 Louis Pasteur and Robert Koch, using compound microscopes, pioneered the study of bacteria.

1970 Lynn Margulis, a microbiologist, proposes the idea that some organelles found in eukaryotes were once free-living prokaryotes.

2008 3-dimensional structured illumination microscopy (3D-SIM) combines a 3-D view, high resolution, and multiple colors.

Demonstration

Resolution Without the students being able to see your actions, draw two dots on the board that are extremely close together, but not touching. Ask students from the middle of the classroom to tell you whether you have drawn one or two dots. They should see one dot. Explain that the reason the students see them as one dot is the resolution of the eye from that distance. A closer examination allows the eye to resolve that there actually are two dots. Est. time: 5 min

Writing Support

BL OL Narrative Writing

Bring in various materials—living (or once alive) and nonliving. Examples could include leaves, rocks, wood, wool, etc. Have students examine at least one of the materials and decide whether the material is made of cells. Have them write a descriptive paragraph about how they came to their conclusion.

D Develop Concepts

OL AL

Activate Prior Knowledge

ASK STUDENTS: ***What steps are involved in developing a scientific theory?*** Observe, ask a question, form a hypothesis, collect data, publish results, and, if necessary, develop a new hypothesis. Once a hypothesis has been supported by a large body of evidence, the hypothesis can become a theory—a largely accepted explanation for an observation. Have students use what they already know about cells to develop their own hypothesis about a question involving cells.

Inquiry Launch Lab

Assess Content Development

Assess how understanding has developed when students revisit the Launch Lab analysis questions.

Concepts in Motion

The Interactive Time Line

Reading Check no

Caption Question Figure 2
various structures of different shapes and sizes that we now know to be organelles

D Develop Concepts

BL OL Display Have students collect pictures of compound light microscopes and various types of electron microscopes. Have them also collect diagrams of how each microscope type works. Prepare a "microscopes" bulletin board.

AL Have students evaluate the type of microscope and its advantages and disadvantages.

MiniLab 1

? Inquiry MiniLab

For a lab worksheet, use your eTeacherEdition Online.

RUBRIC A rubric for evaluating MiniLabs is found on your eTeacherEdition Online.

Est. Time 15–20 min

Alternative Materials slides of cells (other than cork), microprojector

Safety Precautions Approve lab safety forms before work begins.

Teaching Strategies

- Discuss ways that scientists communicate their observations. Refer to Hooke's book *Micrographia* and relate it to today's scientific journals.
- Discuss the importance of using images and figures to describe scientific findings.

Analysis

1. Accept any reasonable answer that illustrates an understanding of cells and the cell theory.
2. Answers might vary. Accept reasonable responses. Using light and electron microscopes, the student could show that Hooke's observations are still vaid.

CAREERS IN BIOLOGY

Technology Representative Companies that manufacture scientific equipment employ representatives to demonstrate and explain their products to the scientific community. A technology representative is an expert in these new technology products and brings this expertise to scientists who might use the products in the laboratory.

Compound light microscopes The modern compound light microscope consists of a series of glass lenses and uses visible light to produce a magnified image. Each lens in the series magnifies the image of the previous lens. For example, when two lenses each individually magnify 10 times, the total magnification is 100 times (10 × 10). Scientists often stain cells with dyes to see them better when using a light microscope because cells are so tiny, thin, and translucent. Over the years, scientists have developed various techniques and modifications for light microscopes, but the properties of visible light will always limit resolution with these microscopes. Objects cause light to scatter, which blurs images. The maximum magnification without blurring is around 1000×. D

Electron microscopes As they began to study cells, scientists needed greater magnification to see the details of tiny parts of cells. During the second World War, in the 1940s, they developed the electron microscope. Instead of lenses, the electron microscope uses magnets to aim a beam of electrons at thin slices of cells. This type of electron microscope is called a transmission electron microscope (TEM) because electrons are passed, or transmitted, through a specimen to a fluorescent screen. Thick parts of the specimen absorb more electrons than thin parts, forming a black-and-white shaded image of the specimen. Transmission electron microscopes can magnify up to 500,000×, but the specimen must be dead, sliced very thin, and stained with heavy metals.

Over the past 65 years, many modifications have been made to the original electron microscopes. For example, the scanning electron microscope (SEM) is one modification that directs electrons over the surface of the specimen, producing a three-dimensional image. One disadvantage of using a TEM and an SEM is that only nonliving cells and tissues can be observed. Photomicrographs made with electron microscopes can be found online.

MiniLab 1

Discover Cells

? Inquiry MiniLab

How can you describe a new discovery? Imagine that you are a scientist looking through the eyepiece of some newfangled instrument called a microscope and you see a field of similarly shaped objects. You might recognize that the shapes that you see are not merely coincidence and random objects. Your whole idea of the nature of matter is changing as you view these objects.

Procedure

1. Read and complete the lab safety form.
2. Prepare a data table in which you will record observations and drawings for three slides.
3. View the **slide images** that your teacher projects for the class.
4. Describe and draw what you see. Be sure to include enough detail in your drawings to convey the information to other scientists who have not observed cells.

Analysis

1. **Describe** what analogies or terms could explain the images in your drawings.
2. **Explain** how you could show Hooke, with twenty-first-century technology, that his findings were valid.

Content Background

Real-World Connection Max Knoll and Ernst Ruska constructed the first electron microscope in 1931, but the immense power of the EM was not realized until the 1950s when ultramicrotomes were built to prepare extremely thin sections for viewing. For the TEM, specimens usually are embedded in a hard matrix such as epoxy or acrylic resin, cut to around 25–100 nm with a diamond knife. Slicing the specimen is like cutting a bread loaf. The thin section is loaded on a grid and stained with a dense element such as lead. For SEM, specimens must be covered with a dense element and dehydrated. One of the constant concerns about TEM or SEM work is that specimen preparation can introduce artifacts from the preparation techniques that do not exist in the living cell.

Another type of microscope, the scanning tunneling electron microscope (STM), involves bringing the charged tip of a probe extremely close to the specimen so that the electrons "tunnel" through the small gap between the specimen and the tip. This instrument has enabled scientists to create three-dimensional computer images of objects as small as atoms. Unlike TEM and SEM, STM can be used with live specimens. **Figure 3** shows DNA, the cell's genetic material, magnified with a scanning tunneling electron microscope.

The atomic force microscope (AFM) measures various forces between the tip of a probe and the cell surface. To learn more about AFM, read the *Cutting Edge Biology* feature at the end of this chapter.

Basic Cell Types

You have learned, according to the cell theory, that cells are the basic units of all living organisms. By observing your own body and the living things around you, you might infer that cells must exist in various shapes and sizes. You also might infer that cells differ based on the functions they perform for an organism. However, all cells have at least one physical trait in common: they all have a structure called a plasma membrane. A **plasma membrane**, labeled in **Figure 4,** is a special boundary that helps control what enters and leaves the cell. Each of your skin cells has a plasma membrane, as do the cells of a rattlesnake. This critical structure is described in detail in the next section.

Cells generally have a number of functions in common. For example, most cells have genetic material in some form that provides instructions for making substances that the cell needs. Cells also break down molecules to generate energy. Scientists have grouped cells into two broad categories. These categories are prokaryotic (pro kar ee AW tik) cells and eukaryotic (yew kar ee AW tik) cells. **Figure 4** shows TEM photomicrographs of these two cell types. The images of the prokaryotic cell and eukaryotic cell have been enlarged so that you can compare the cell structures. Eukaryotic cells generally are one to one hundred times larger than prokaryotic cells.

Reading Check **Compare** the sizes of prokaryotic cells and eukaryotic cells.

False-Color STM Magnification: 2,000,000×

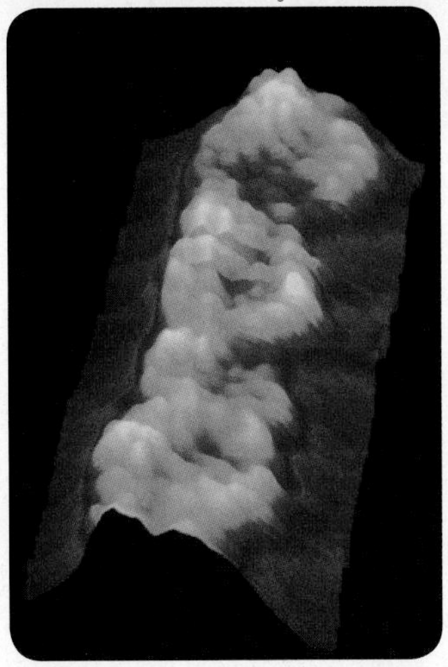

DNA

■ **Figure 3** The scanning tunneling microscope (STM) provides images, such as this DNA molecule, in which cracks and depressions appear darker and raised areas appear lighter.
***Name** an application for which an STM might be used.*

Inquiry Video Lab

■ **Figure 4** The prokaryotic cell on the left is smaller and appears less complex than the eukaryotic cell on the right. The prokaryotic cell has been enlarged for the purpose of comparing each cell's internal sturctures.

Color-Enhanced TEM Magnification: 15,000×

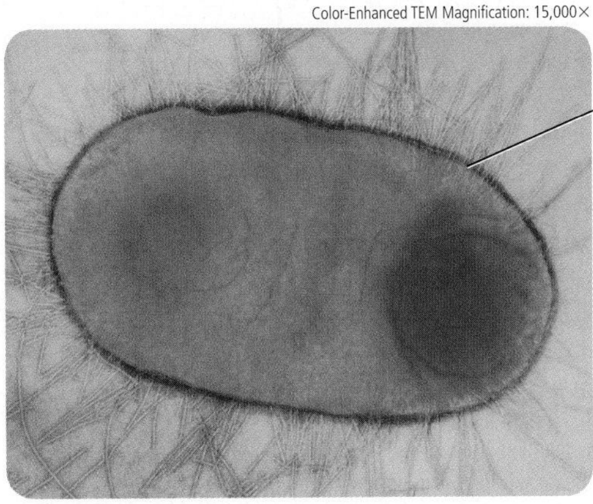

Prokaryotic cell

Color-Enhanced Magnification: unavailable

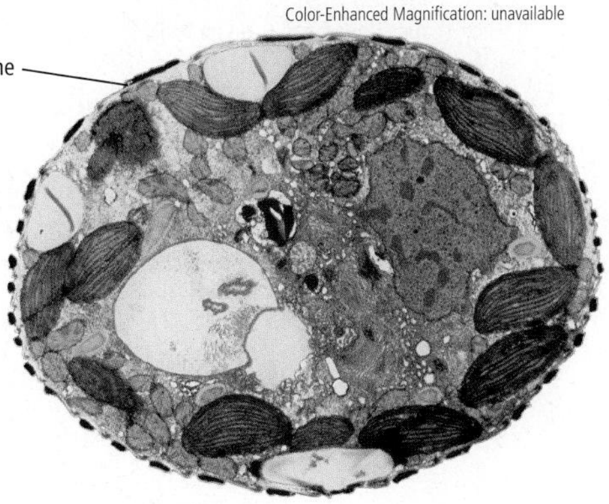

Eukaryotic cell

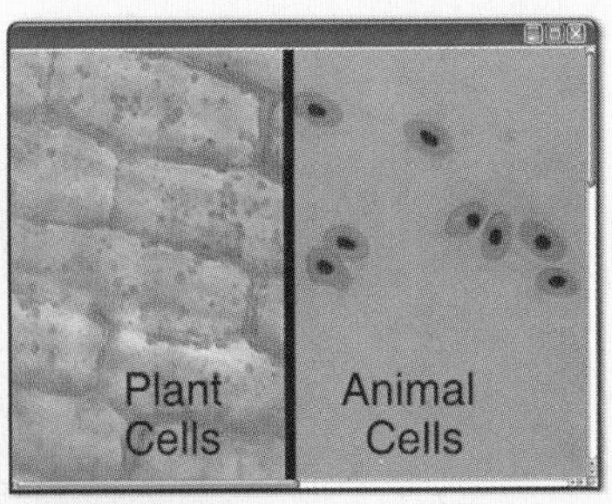

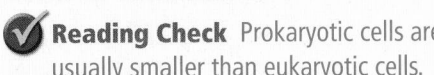

Inquiry **Video Lab** Students will observe and compare different cell types in this video lab.

■ **Caption Question** **Fig. 3** to study molecule shapes or surface characteristics

Reading Check Prokaryotic cells are usually smaller than eukaryotic cells.

Develop Concepts

BL OL

Clarify a Misconception

ASK STUDENTS: ***What determines the quality of a microscope image?*** Resolution of the microscope—not magnification—mainly determines the quality. Show students a blurry image (due to poor resolution) and then show them the result of magnifying this blurry image. A magnified blurry image is still blurry.

Skill Practice

BL OL AL Observe and Infer Have students view slides or micrographs of at least one prokaryotic cell, such as a bacterium, and eukaryotic cells, such as *Euglena* or skin cells.

ASK STUDENTS: ***What differences do you observe between the two cells?*** Students should observe that the eukaryotic cells are larger and have organelles. They might observe the movement of the *Euglena* and various structures within the *Euglena* cell, such as the red eyespot, the flagella, and chloroplasts depending on the slides viewed. Contrast these two basic cell types while discussing prokaryotic and eukaryotic cells.

Skill Practice

OL AL Use Math Skills Have students calculate how many cells could line up end-to-end in 1 cm if each cell is 100 μm in length. 100 cells This would represent a large eukaryotic cell. Many bacteria are only 1 μm in length.

Inquiry BioLab

The lab at the end of the chapter can be used at this point in the lesson.

Critical Thinking

BL OL AL Infer

ASK STUDENTS: ***How have eukaryotic cells contributed to the evolution of multicellular higher organisms?*** Eukaryotic cells enabled the development of specialized cells such as skin, skeletal, muscle, and nerve cells.

Formative Assessment

Evaluation Prepare a quiz comparing a light microscope with an electron microscope. Have students take the quiz and then correct the quiz with a partner. Have students use the textbook to look up any questions they missed and explain to each other the correct answer.

Remediation Have students who are having difficulty comparing the light microscope and electron microscope make flash cards. Have them write a characteristic of a light or electron microscope on one side of the card. On the other side, have them write which type of microscope it is. Then have them quiz each other using the cards.

Video BrainPOP

Video BrainPOP

VOCABULARY

WORD ORIGIN

Eukaryote
Prokaryote
eu– prefix; from Greek, meaning *true*
pro– prefix; from Greek, meaning *before*
–kary from Greek, meaning *nucleus*

Refer again to **Figure 4** and compare the types of cells to see why scientists place them into two broad categories that are based on internal structures. Both have a plasma membrane, but one cell contains many distinct internal structures called **organelles**—specialized structures that carry out specific cell functions.

Eukaryotic cells contain a nucleus and other organelles that are bound by membranes, also referred to as membrane-bound organelles. The **nucleus** is a distinct central organelle that contains the cell's genetic material in the form of DNA. Organelles enable cell functions to take place in different parts of the cell at the same time. Most organisms are made up of eukaryotic cells and are called eukaryotes. However, some unicellular organisms, such as some algae and yeast, also are eukaryotes.

Prokaryotic cells are defined as cells without a nucleus or other membrane-bound organelles. As you can see in **Figure 4,** prokaryotic cells are simpler than eukaryotic cells. Most unicellular organisms, such as bacteria, are prokaryotic cells. Thus, they are called prokaryotes. Many scientists think that prokaryotes are similar to the first organisms that lived on Earth.

Origin of cell diversity Scientists continue to investigate why there are two basic types of cells. The answer might be that eukaryotic cells evolved from prokaryotic cells millions of years ago. According to the endosymbiont theory, a symbiotic relationship involves one prokaryotic cell living inside of another and both cells benefiting from the relationship.

Imagine how organisms would be different if the eukaryotic form had not evolved. Because eukaryotic cells are larger and have distinct organelles, these cells have developed specific functions. Having specific functions has led to cell diversity, and thus more diverse organisms that can adapt better to their environments. Life-forms more complex than bacteria might not have evolved without eukaryotic cells.

Section 1 Assessment

Section Summary

- Microscopes have been used as tools for scientific study since the late 1500s.
- Scientists use different types of microscopes to study cells.
- The cell theory summarizes three principles.
- There are two broad groups of cell types: prokaryotic cells and eukaryotic cells.

Understand Main Ideas

1. MAIN Idea **Explain** how the development and improvement of microscopes changed the study of living organisms.
2. **Compare and contrast** a compound light microscope and an electron microscope.
3. **Summarize** the cell theory.
4. **Differentiate** the plasma membrane and the organelles.

Think Critically

5. **Describe** how you would determine whether the cells of a newly discovered organism were prokaryotic or eukaryotic.

MATH in Biology

6. If the overall magnification of a series of two lenses is 30×, and one lens magnifies 5×, what is the magnification of the other lens? Calculate the total magnification if the 5× lens is replaced by a 7× lens.

Section 1 Assessment

1. With more sophisticated tools, scientists have been able to learn much more detail about the cell and its structures.
2. Light microscopes use visible light and glass lenses. Electron microscopes use beams of electrons and magnets, and an STM can be used to view live specimens.
3. Cells are the basic structures of all life; all living things are made of cells; cells arise only from other living cells.
4. The plasma membrane helps control what goes in and out of cells. Organelles carry out specialized functions in the cell.
5. Using an electron microscope, you could determine whether or not they had distinct internal structures. If so, it would be a eukaryotic cell. If not, it would be a prokaryotic cell.
6. 30/5 = 6×. The magnification would increase to 42× (6 times 7×).

Assessment Online Quiz

Reading Preview

Essential Questions

- How does a cell's plasma membrane function?
- What are the roles of proteins, carbohydrates, and cholesterol in the plasma membrane?

Review Vocabulary

ion: an atom or group of atoms with a positive or negative electric charge

New Vocabulary

selective permeability
phospholipid bilayer
transport protein
fluid mosaic model

g Multilingual eGlossary

The Plasma Membrane

MAIN Idea The plasma membrane helps to maintain a cell's homeostasis.

Real-World Reading Link When you approach your school, you might pass through a gate in a fence that surrounds the school grounds. The fence prevents people who should not be there from entering, and the gate allows students, staff, and parents to enter. Similarly, prokaryotic cells and eukaryotic cells have structures that maintain control of their internal environments.

D Function of the Plasma Membrane

Recall that the process of maintaining balance in an organism's internal environment is called homeostasis. Homeostasis is essential to the survival of a cell. One of the structures that is primarily responsible for homeostasis is the plasma membrane. The plasma membrane is a thin, flexible boundary between a cell and its environment that allows nutrients into the cell and allows waste and other products to leave the cell. All prokaryotic cells and eukaryotic cells have a plasma membrane to separate them from the watery environments in which they exist.

A key property of the plasma membrane is **selective permeability** (pur mee uh BIH luh tee), by which a membrane allows some substances to pass through while keeping others out. Consider a fish net as an analogy of selective permeability. The net shown in **Figure 5** has holes that allow water and other substances in the water to pass through, but not the fish. Depending on the size of the holes in the net, some kinds of fish might pass through, while others are caught. The diagram in **Figure 5** illustrates selective permeability of the plasma membrane. The arrows show that substances enter and leave the cell through the plasma membrane. Control of how, when, and how much of these substances enter and leave a cell relies on the structure of the plasma membrane. W

Reading Check **Define** the term *selective permeability.*

Figure 5
Left: The fish net selectively captures fish while allowing water and other debris to pass through.
Right: Similarly, the plasma membrane selects substances entering and leaving the cell.

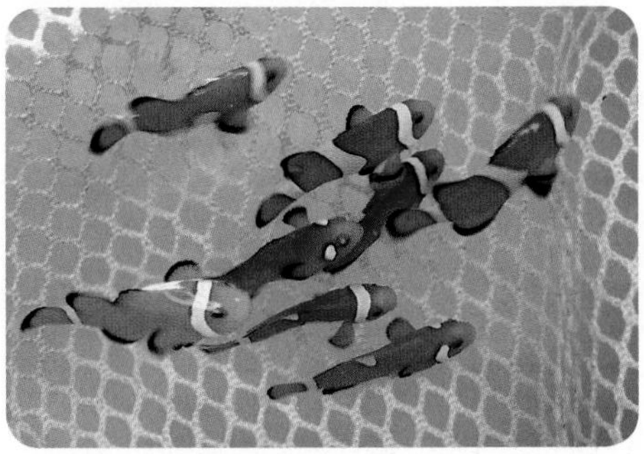

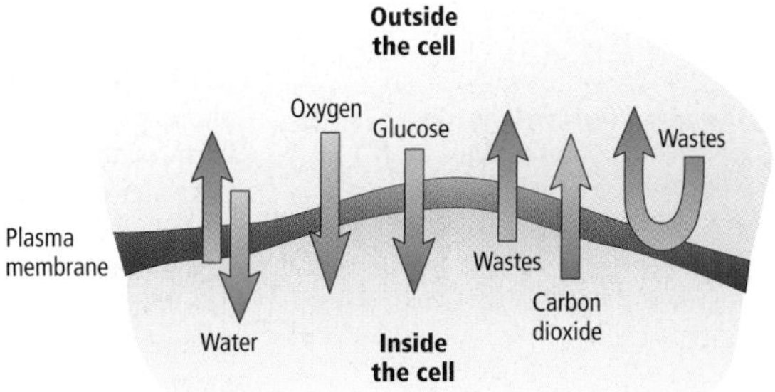

Section 2

MAIN Idea

BL OL AL

The Plasma Membrane

Show students a filter for a coffee pot. Place coffee grounds, sand, or other substances in the filter and then pour water through into a container. Explain that a filter allows water to pass through but traps unwanted particles and keeps them from entering the container. Relate this to a cell's permeable membrane that allows some substances to pass through and keeps other substances away from the cellular material inside the cell.

D Develop Concepts

BL OL

Clarify a Misconception

ASK STUDENTS: ***What kind of substances can go out of cells?*** Students may not realize that substances also go out of a cell. Explain that specific substances such as water, oxygen, and glucose pass in through the selectively permeable membrane, and carbon dioxide and other wastes pass out through the membrane.

W Writing Support

OL AL COOP LEARN

Narrative Writing Have students write their own analogy for a cell's selective permeability. Have them trade papers with a partner and evaluate the strengths and weaknesses of each other's analogies.

Reading Check Selective permeability is a property that allows some substances to pass through a membrane while keeping others out.

Demonstration

BL OL AL **Plasma Membrane** Place a sealable sandwich bag filled with marbles into a fish bowl filled with water.
ASK STUDENTS: ***In what way does this sandwich bag represent a cell?*** Answers may include that cells are separate entities from their environments, and most cells exist in a watery environment. Both the sandwich bag and the plasma membrane act to contain the contents inside. Point out that the plasma membrane and the sandwich bag display selective permeability, allowing some substances to pass through while keeping others out. Est. time: 5 min

S Skill Practice

BL OL Visual Literacy

Review the bilayer structure of the membrane illustrated in Figure 6. Explain that this structure is important because it directly affects the homeostasis of the cell. Emphasize how the hydrophobic and hydrophilic characteristics of the two layers work together.

C Critical Thinking

OL AL Predict Vitamin C (ascorbic acid) is a charged molecule. **ASK STUDENTS:** ***Do you think vitamin C can enter cells?*** No. Although vitamin C is water soluble, it cannot diffuse through the plasma membrane because it is a charged, polar molecule.

D Develop Concepts

EL BL OL AL COOP LEARN

Use a Model Provide materials, such as packing peanuts of various sizes, colored yarn, or colored paper, that can be used to make a model of a plasma membrane. Have students work in groups of two or three to build their models. Models should include the phospholipids, proteins, and cholesterol in the membrane. Have each group describe their model to the class.

Caption Question Fig. 6 They must be moved across the plasma membrane by transport proteins.

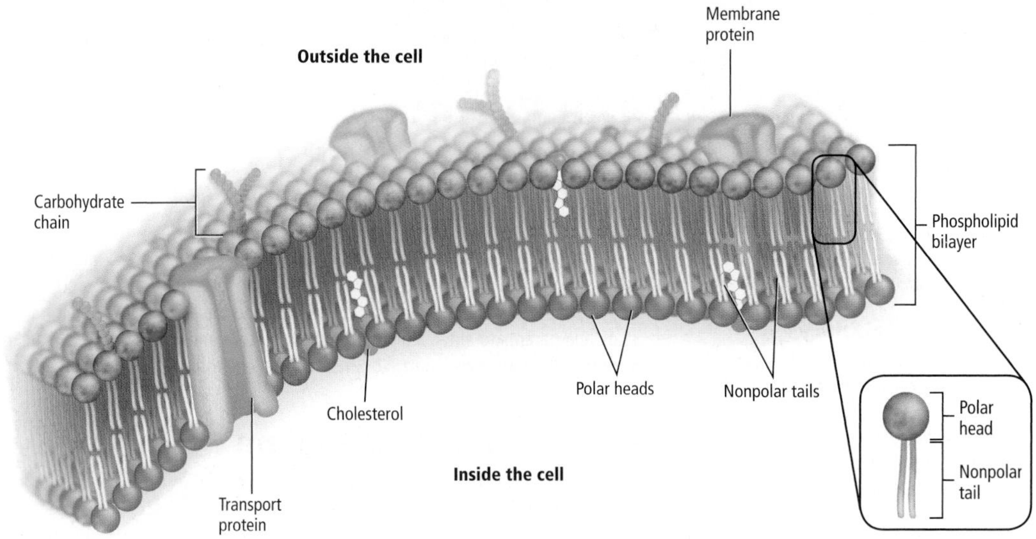

Figure 6 The phospholipid bilayer looks like a sandwich, with the polar heads facing the outside and the nonpolar tails facing the inside.
***Infer** how hydrophobic substances cross a plasma membrane.*

S

VOCABULARY
SCIENCE USAGE V. COMMON USAGE
Polar
Science usage: having an unequal distribution of charge
The positive end of a polar molecule attracts the negative end of a polar molecule.

Common usage: relating to a geographic pole or region
The polar ice cap in Greenland is, on average, 1.6 km thick.

Structure of the Plasma Membrane

Connection to Chemistry Most of the molecules in the plasma membrane are lipids. Lipids are large molecules that are composed of glycerol and three fatty acids. If a phosphate group replaces a fatty acid, a phospholipid forms. A phospholipid (fahs foh LIH pid) is a molecule that has a glycerol backbone, two fatty acid chains, and a phosphate-containing group. The plasma membrane is composed of a **phospholipid bilayer,** in which two layers of phospholipids are arranged tail-to-tail, as shown in **Figure 6.** In the plasma membrane, phospholipids arrange themselves in a way that allows the plasma membrane to exist in the watery environment.

The phospholipid bilayer Notice in **Figure 6** that each phospholipid is diagrammed as a head with two tails. The phosphate group in each phospholipid makes the head polar. The polar head is attracted to water because water also is polar. The two fatty acid tails are nonpolar and are repelled by water.

The two layers of phospholipid molecules resemble a sandwich, with the fatty acid tails forming the interior of the plasma membrane and the phospholipid heads facing the watery environments found inside and outside the cell, as shown in **Figure 6.** This bilayer structure is critical for the formation and function of the plasma membrane. The phospholipids are arranged in such a way that the polar heads can be closest to the water molecules and the nonpolar tails can be farthest away from the water molecules. C

When many phospholipid molecules come together in this manner, a barrier is created that is polar at its surfaces and nonpolar in the middle. Water-soluble substances will not move easily through the plasma membrane because they are stopped by the nonpolar middle. Therefore, the plasma membrane can separate the environment inside the cell from the environment outside the cell. D

Demonstration

Phospholipid Membrane Fill a 5- or 10-gallon aquarium half full with water and add enough floating balls to cover the top of the water surface. Make sure all of these balls are the same color. They will represent the phospholipids in the membrane. Add a different-colored ball or two to represent proteins floating in the membrane. Using a stick or ruler, move the different-colored balls and have students watch the movement of the other balls. Point out that proteins float in a sea of phospholipids. Be sure the students understand that in a real membrane there are two rows of phospholipids.
Est. time: 5 min

Other components of the plasma membrane Moving with and among the phospholipids in the plasma membrane are cholesterol, proteins, and carbohydrates. When found on the outer surface of the plasma membrane, proteins called receptors transmit signals to the inside of the cell. Proteins at the inner surface anchor the plasma membrane to the cell's internal support structure, giving the cell its shape. Other proteins span the entire membrane and create tunnels through which certain substances enter and leave the cell. These **transport proteins** move needed substances or waste materials through the plasma membrane and therefore contribute to the selective permeability of the plasma membrane.

Reading Check **Describe** the benefit of the bilayer structure of the plasma membrane.

Locate the cholesterol molecules in **Figure 6.** Nonpolar cholesterol is repelled by water and is positioned among the phospholipids. Cholesterol helps to prevent the fatty-acid tails of the phospholipid bilayer from sticking together, which contributes to the fluidity of the plasma membrane. Although avoiding a high-cholesterol diet is recommended, cholesterol plays a critical role in plasma membrane structure and it is an important substance for maintaining homeostasis in a cell.

Other substances in the membrane, such as carbohydrates attached to proteins, stick out from the plasma membrane to define the cell's characteristics and help cells identify chemical signals. For example, carbohydrates in the membrane might help disease-fighting cells recognize and attack a potentially harmful cell.

Study Tip

Question Session Work with a partner and ask each other questions about the plasma membrane. Discuss each other's answers. Ask as many questions as you think of while taking turns.

C

DATA ANALYSIS LAB 1

Based on Real Data*

Interpret the Diagram

How are protein channels involved in the death of nerve cells after a stroke? A stroke occurs when a blood clot blocks the flow of oxygen-containing blood in a portion of the brain. Nerve cells in the brain that release glutamate are sensitive to the lack of oxygen and release a flood of glutamate when oxygen is low. During the glutamate flood, the calcium pump is destroyed. This affects the movement of calcium ions into and out of nerve cells. When cells contain excess calcium, homeostasis is disrupted.

Think Critically

1. **Interpret** how the glutamate flood destroys the calcium pump.
2. **Predict** what would happen if Ca^{2+} levels were lowered in the nerve cell during a stroke.

*Data obtained from: Choi, D.W. 2005. Neurodegeneration: cellular defences destroyed. *Nature* 433: 696–698.

Data and Observations

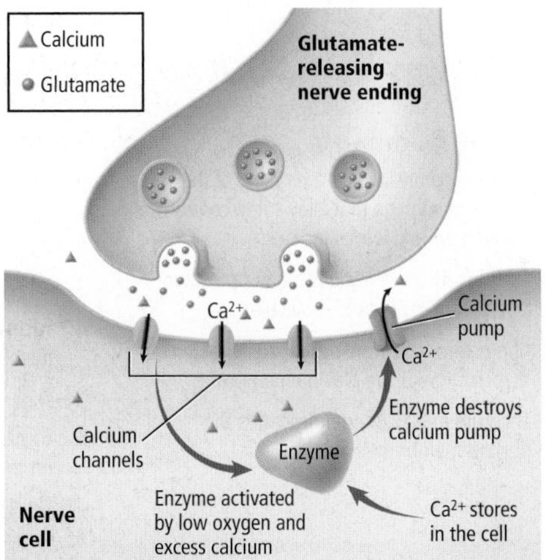

C Critical Thinking

OL AL Analyze Have students evaluate the following argument: High levels of cholesterol lead to reduced blood flow and, therefore, cholesterol is bad for overall health. Although high levels of cholesterol can lead to reduced blood flow, some cholesterol is needed by the body because it plays an important role in stabilizing the plasma membrane.

DATA ANALYSIS LAB 1

About the Lab

- Calcium concentration is extremely important in the homeostasis and proper functioning of nerve cells. Calcium channels are concentrated at the end (axon) of nerve cells. Normally, when a stimulation reaches the axon of the nerve cell, it causes calcium channels to open, and this eventually leads to the release of neurotransmitters.
- Also see Bano, et al. 2005. Cleavage of the Plasma Membrane Na^+/Ca^{2+} Exchanger in Excitotoxicity. *Cell* 120:275–285. Kiedrowski, et al. 2004. Differential Contribution of Plasmalemmal Na^+/Ca^{2+} Exchange Isoforms to Sodium-Dependent Calcium Influx and NMDA Excitotoxicity in Depolarized Neurons. *Journal of Neurochemistry.* 90(1):117–118.

Think Critically

1. causes excess calcium to flow into cells, which stimulates the release of an enzyme that destroys the calcium pump
2. Lowering calcium levels in the cell when a stroke is occurring would prevent an excess of calcium from building up in the cell and would therefore prevent cell death.

Differentiated Instruction

English Learners To help students with limited English proficiency build their vocabulary, write key words on the board or on a transparency as you discuss them.

For more tips, see pages 14T–15T.

Reading Check Two layers allow for a more effective barrier.

R Reading Strategy

BL OL Build Vocabulary

Explain the terms *fluid* and *mosaic*.

- Fluids consist of particles that can change position without separating. Have students provide examples of fluids.
- A mosaic is a picture or pattern made of small pieces of different colors and shapes. Show students pictures of mosaics found in art books.

Formative Assessment

Evaluation Have students draw a diagram of the structure of the plasma membrane, indicating a bilayer of phospholipids with proteins and cholesterol. Have students compare their diagram with Figure 7.

Remediation Have students make a concept map using the following terms: *plasma membrane, phospholipids, bilayer, polar, nonpolar, cholesterol,* and *proteins.* Have students present and explain their concept maps to the class.

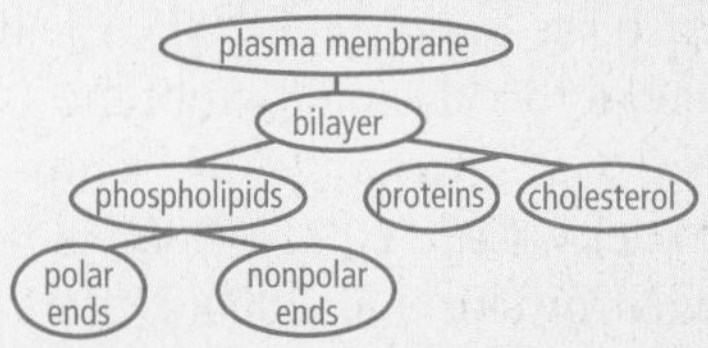

Concepts in Motion
Animation

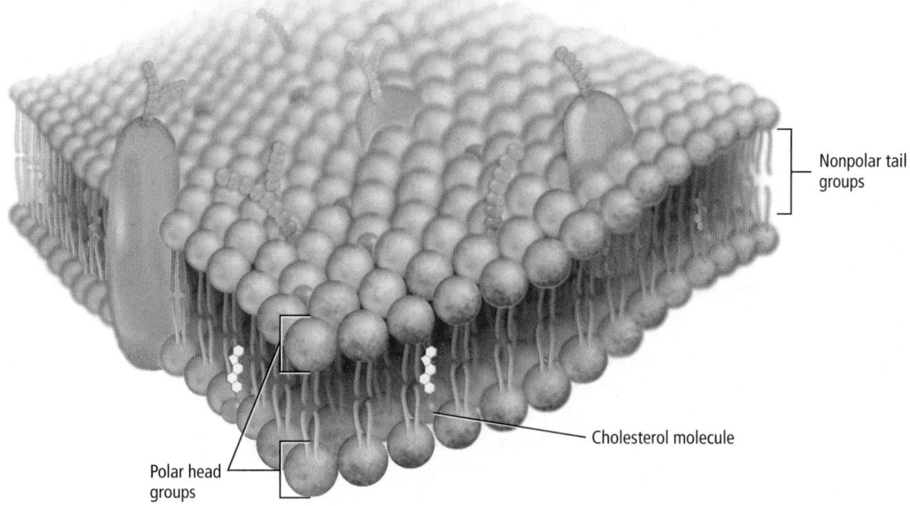

Figure 7 The fluid mosaic model refers to a plasma membrane with substances that can move around within the membrane.

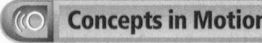

Concepts in Motion
Animation

Together, the phospholipids in the bilayer create a "sea" in which other molecules can float, like apples floating in a barrel of water. This "sea" concept is the basis for the **fluid mosaic model** of the plasma membrane. The phospholipids can move sideways within the membrane, just as apples move around in water. At the same time, other components in the membrane, such as proteins, also move among the phospholipids. Because there are different substances in the plasma membrane, a pattern, or mosaic, is created on the surface. You can see this pattern in **Figure 7.** The components of the plasma membrane are in constant motion, sliding past one another. R

Section 2 Assessment

Section Summary

- Selective permeability is a property of the plasma membrane that allows it to control what enters and leaves the cell.
- The plasma membrane is made up of two layers of phospholipid molecules.
- Cholesterol and transport proteins aid in the function of the plasma membrane.
- The fluid mosaic model describes the plasma membrane.

Understand Main Ideas

1. MAIN Idea **Describe** how the plasma membrane helps maintain homeostasis in a cell.
2. **Explain** how the inside of a cell remains separate from its environment.
3. **Diagram** the plasma membrane and label each component.
4. **Identify** the molecules in the plasma membrane that provide basic membrane structure, cell identity, and membrane fluidity.

Think Critically

5. **Explain** what effect more cholesterol in the plasma membrane will have on the membrane.

WRITING in Biology

6. Using what you know about the term *mosaic,* write a paragraph describing another biological mosaic.

Section 2 Assessment

1. It controls the substances that enter and exit the cell.
2. The phospholipid bilayer forming the plasma membrane provides a barrier from the environment around the cell.
3. Diagrams should include the correct orientation of the phospholipids, proteins, carbohydrates, and cholesterol in the membrane.
4. basic membrane structure: phospholipids; cell identity: proteins and carbohydrates; membrane fluidity: cholesterol
5. Increasing the level of cholesterol in the membrane would make the membrane more fluid.
6. Accept all reasonable answers. Responses might include fallen leaves in autumn or a variety of shells on the beach.

WRITING in Biology

RUBRIC Use the modifiable rubric found on your eTeacherEdition Online to assess writing assignments.

Assessment Online Quiz

Reading Preview

Essential Questions

- What are the structures of a typical eukaryotic cell, and what are their functions?
- What are the similarities and differences between plant and animal cells?

Review Vocabulary

enzyme: a protein that speeds up the rate of a chemical reaction

New Vocabulary

cytoplasm
cytoskeleton
ribosome
nucleolus
endoplasmic reticulum
Golgi apparatus
vacuole
lysosome
centriole
mitochondrion
chloroplast
cell wall
cilium
flagellum

g Multilingual eGlossary

Structures and Organelles

MAIN Idea Eukaryotic cells contain organelles that allow the specialization and the separation of functions within the cell.

Real-World Reading Link Suppose you start a company to manufacture hiking boots. Each pair of boots could be made individually by one person, but it would be more efficient to use an assembly line. Similarly, eukaryotic cells have specialized structures that perform specific tasks, much like a factory.

Cytoplasm and Cytoskeleton

You just have investigated the part of a cell that functions as the boundary between the inside and outside environments. The environment inside the plasma membrane is a semifluid material called **cytoplasm.** In a prokaryotic cell, all of the chemical processes of the cell, such as breaking down sugar to generate the energy used for other functions, take place directly in the cytoplasm. Eukaryotic cells perform these processes within organelles in their cytoplasm. At one time, scientists thought that cell organelles floated in a sea of cytoplasm.

More recently, cell biologists have discovered that organelles do not float freely in a cell, but are supported by a structure within the cytoplasm similar to the structure shown in **Figure 8.** The **cytoskeleton** is a supporting network of long, thin protein fibers that form a framework for the cell and provide an anchor for the organelles inside the cells. The cytoskeleton also has a function in cell movement and other cellular activities.

The cytoskeleton is made of substructures called microtubules and microfilaments. Microtubules are long, hollow protein cylinders that form a rigid skeleton for the cell and assist in moving substances within the cell. Microfilaments are thin protein threads that help give the cell shape and enable the entire cell or parts of the cell to move. Microtubules and microfilaments rapidly assemble and disassemble and slide past one another. This allows cells and organelles to move.

Figure 8 Microtubules and microfilaments make up the cytoskeleton.

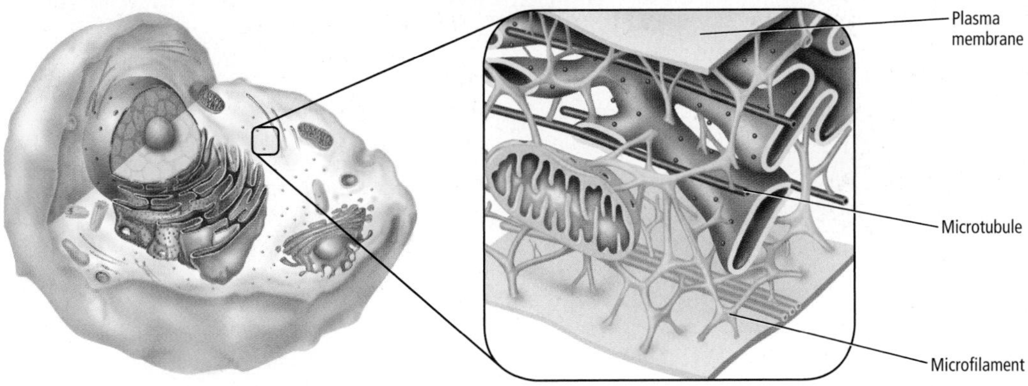

Demonstration

Factory Assembly Bring in a tennis shoe or hiking boot and have students identify the different parts of the shoe, such as sole, upper, lining, and laces. Talk about the manufacturing of shoes from design to shipment. Elicit from students the various components of manufacturing (such as master design, raw materials, assembly line for parts such as soles and laces, packaging, and delivery) and how the shoe or boot comes together if each task is done accurately. Remind students to keep this analogy in mind as they read about cells and their components. Est. time: 5 min

Section 3

MAIN Idea

BL OL AL

Structures and Organelles

ASK STUDENTS: ***Why might eukaryotic cells have developed specialized structures to carry out various functions?*** Use this discussion to introduce cell organelles. By separating various functions into cell organelles, eukaryotic cells can specialize certain internal regions to various functions, some of which can happen at the same time. Enzymes and other potentially harmful molecules can be separated into vesicles and kept from other parts of the cells. Use protists as examples of eukaryotic cells and encourage students to think of the life requirements of these cells in terms of the development of organelles.

Reading Strategy

EL BL Review and Preview Divide the class into dominant language groups. While English language students work independently, preview the main ideas and vocabulary with the other groups, allowing them to confer and collaborate with one another in their respective primary languages. Continue with the lesson in English, then regroup and review the key concepts and resolve any concepts that remain unclear.

Develop Concepts

BL OL Use Models Various models of cells are available from scientific supply companies. These models can help students understand that cells are three-dimensional. Have students build their own 3-D models of cells using clay, candy, or styrofoam.

Purpose

Students will compare and contrast plant, animal, and bacterial cells.
UCP.1–3, UCP 5; A.1, A.2; C.1, C.5

Skill Practice

BL OL Use Graphic Organizers Have each student make a Venn diagram showing which cell structures are found only in plant cells, which are found only in animal cells, which are found only in prokaryotic cells, and which are found in all three.

Concepts in Motion

Animation

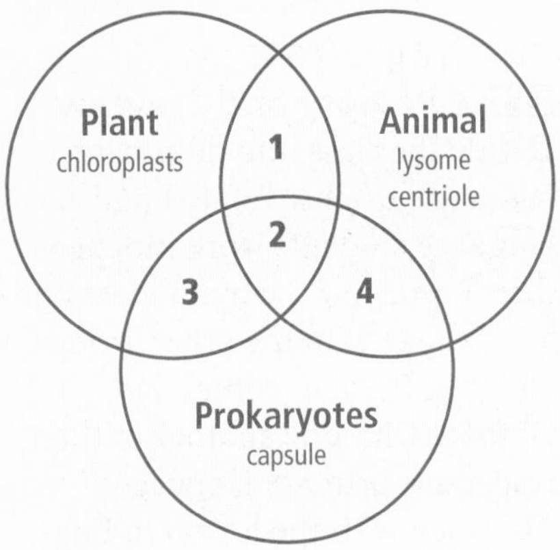

1. **Plant and Animal**
   cytoskeleton
   nucleus
   endoplasmic reticulum
   Golgi apparatus
   vacuole
   mitochondria
2. **All Three**
   genetic material
   plasma membrane
   ribosomes
   cytoplasm
3. **Plant and Prokaryotes**
   cell wall
4. **Animal and Prokaryotes**
   cilia
   flagella

Visualizing Cells

Figure 9

Compare the illustrations of a plant cell, animal cell, and prokaryotic cell. Some organelles are found only in plant cells; others are found only in animal cells. Prokaryotic cells do not have membrane-bound organelles.

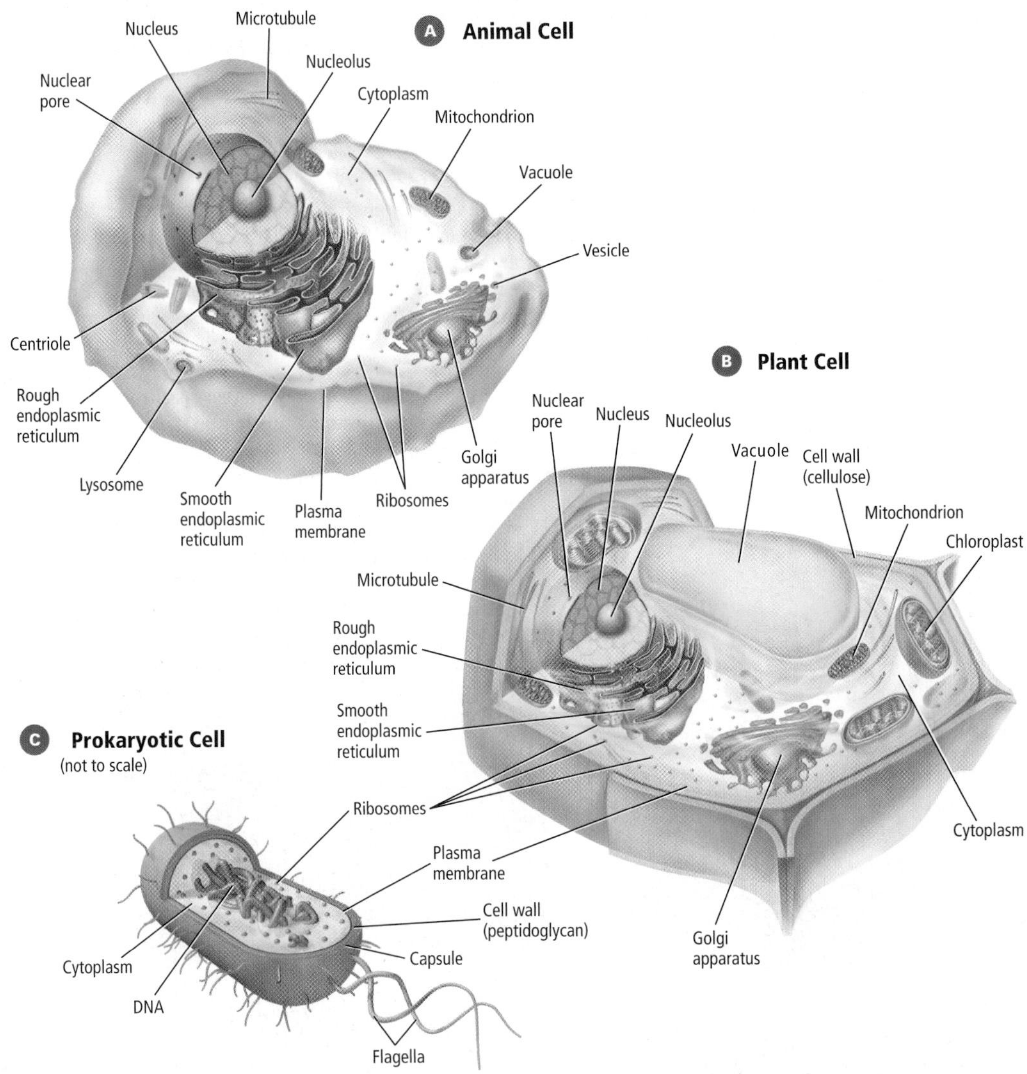

Concepts in Motion **Animation**

Activity

OL AL Identify Cells Prepare a series of microscopes with slides of various cells, such as stained cheek cells, *Elodea* cells, skin cells, or an epidermal peel from a leaf. Provide a variety of animal and plant cells. Alternatively, show students photomicrographs of the specimens. Photomicrographs can be found online. Have students view the unidentified slides or photos and write down whether the cell is an animal cell or a plant cell and how they knew. Then have students draw at least one of the cells and label the organelles they see. Est. time: 30 min

Cell Structures

In a factory, there are separate areas set up for performing different tasks. Eukaryotic cells also have separate areas for tasks. Membrane-bound organelles make it possible for different chemical processes to take place at the same time in different parts of the cytoplasm. Organelles carry out essential cell processes, such as protein synthesis, energy transformation, digestion of food, excretion of wastes, and cell division. Each organelle has a unique structure and function. You can compare organelles to a factory's offices, assembly lines, and other important areas that keep the factory running. As you read about the different organelles, refer to the diagrams of plant and animal cells in **Figure 9** to see the organelles of each type.

The nucleus Just as a factory needs a manager, a cell needs an organelle to direct the cell processes. The nucleus, shown in **Figure 10,** is the cell's managing structure. It contains most of the cell's DNA, which stores information used to make proteins for cell growth, function, and reproduction.

The nucleus is surrounded by a double membrane called the nuclear envelope. The nuclear envelope is similar to the plasma membrane, except the nuclear membrane has nuclear pores that allow larger-sized substances to move in and out of the nucleus. Chromatin, which is a complex DNA attached to protein, is spread throughout the nucleus.

Reading Check **Describe** the role of the nucleus.

Ribosomes One of the functions of a cell is to produce proteins. The organelles that help manufacture proteins are called **ribosomes.** Ribosomes are made of two components—RNA and protein—and are not bound by a membrane like other organelles are. Within the nucleus is the site of ribosome production called the **nucleolus,** shown in **Figure 10.**

Cells have many ribosomes that produce a variety of proteins that are used by the cell or are moved out and used by other cells. Some ribosomes float freely in the cytoplasm, while others are bound to another organelle called the endoplasmic reticulum. Free-floating ribosomes produce proteins for use within the cytoplasm of the cell. Bound ribosomes produce proteins that will be bound within membranes or used by other cells.

VOCABULARY
WORD ORIGIN
Cytoplasm
Cytoskeleton
cyte– prefix; from Greek, meaning *cell*

Video BrainPOP

W

S

■ **Figure 10** The nucleus of a cell is a three-dimensional shape. The photomicrograph shows a cross section of a nucleus.
***Infer** why all of the cross sections of a nucleus are not identical.*

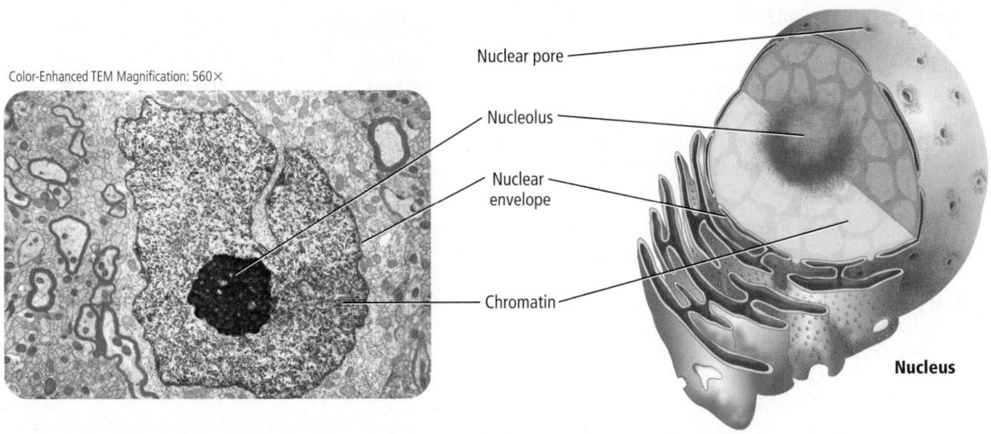

W Writing Support

BL OL AL COOP LEARN

Creative Writing In groups of three or four, have students write and enact a play about the role of the nucleus. For example, one student can play the nucleus, directing the other students who are playing organelles to do specific tasks. Encourage students to dramatize what might happen if the nucleus became damaged or was removed.

S Skill Practice

BL OL AL **Visual Literacy**

SAY TO STUDENTS: ***Study the information in Figure 10 and explain why it is helpful to have an illustration along with the electron micrograph.*** Illustrations can make the structural interpretation of the electron micrograph clearer and illustrate what scientists see when they look at various pictures of the organelle with the electron microscope. Point out that many of the figures in this section depict organelles as seen by an electron micrograph as well as an illustration.

Video BrainPOP

Reading Check The nucleus controls cell function.

■ **Caption Question Fig. 10** different structures floating in the nucleus might appear in different cross sections

C Critical Thinking

OL AL Analyze

ASK STUDENTS: ***What is the function of the rough endoplasmic reticulum?*** transporting proteins to the outside of the cell ***What types of human cells would contain a large amount of rough endoplasmic reticulum?*** cells that are involved in manufacturing large amounts of proteins for secretion, such as liver cells, and the cells in the pancreas involved in manufacturing and secreting insulin

DATA ANALYSIS LAB 2

About the Lab

- Researchers think that the budding of a vesicle from the ER and its route to the Golgi apparatus might not be separate and disconnected activities. This research and other similar studies imply that the ER-to-Golgi traffic is a programmed event.
- Also see Barrowman J., et al. 2003. The Yip 1p/ Yif 1p complex is required for the fusion competence of ER-derived vesicles. *Journal of Biological Chemistry.* 278: 19878–19884.

Think Critically

1. The two complexes are targeting complex and unknown targeting complex.
2. Vesicle transport might be directed through the cytoplasm by microtubules.

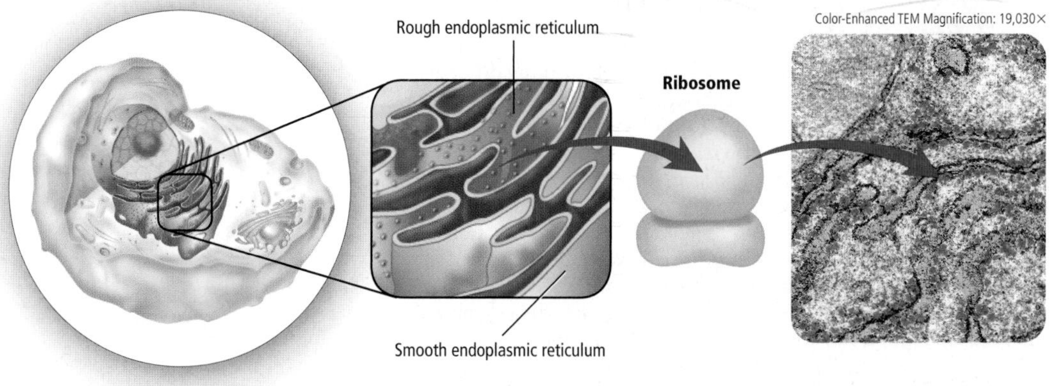

■ **Figure 11** Ribosomes are simple structures made of RNA and protein that may be attached to the surface of the rough endoplasmic reticulum. They look like bumps on the endoplasmic reticulum.

C

? Inquiry Virtual Lab

Endoplasmic reticulum The **endoplasmic reticulum** (en duh PLAZ mihk • rih TIHK yuh lum), also called ER, is a membrane system of folded sacs and interconnected channels that serves as the site for protein and lipid synthesis. The pleats and folds of the ER provide a large amount of surface area where cellular functions can take place. The area of ER where ribosomes are attached is called rough endoplasmic reticulum. Notice in **Figure 11** that the rough ER appears to have bumps on it. These bumps are the attached ribosomes that will produce proteins for export to other cells.

Figure 11 also shows that there are areas of the ER that do not have ribosomes attached. The area of ER where no ribosomes are attached is called smooth endoplasmic reticulum. Although the smooth ER has no ribosomes, it does perform important functions for the cell. For example, the smooth ER provides a membrane surface where a variety of complex carbohydrates and lipids, including phospholipids, are synthesized. Smooth ER in the liver detoxifies harmful substances.

DATA ANALYSIS LAB 2

Based on Real Lab Data*

Interpret the Data

How is vesicle traffic from the ER to the Golgi apparatus regulated? Some proteins are synthesized by ribosomes on the endoplasmic reticulum (ER). The proteins are processed in the ER, and vesicles containing these proteins pinch off and migrate to the Golgi apparatus. Scientists currently are studying the molecules that are involved in fusing these vesicles to the Golgi apparatus.

Think Critically

1. **Interpret the diagram** by naming two complexes on the Golgi apparatus that might be involved in vesicle fusion.
2. **Hypothesize** an explanation for vesicle transport based on what you have read about cytoplasm and the cytoskeleton.

Data and Observations

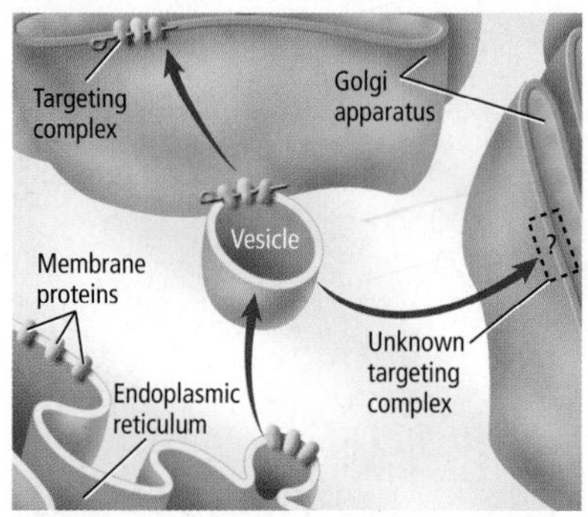

*Data obtained from: Brittle, E. E., and Waters, M. G. 2000. ER-to-golgi traffic—this bud's for you. *Science* 289: 403–404.

Differentiated Instruction

Visually Impaired Students with impaired vision can benefit from the information in the Venn diagram on page 192. To help these students, verbally describe the information that is being presented in this diagram.

For more tips, see pages 14T–15T.

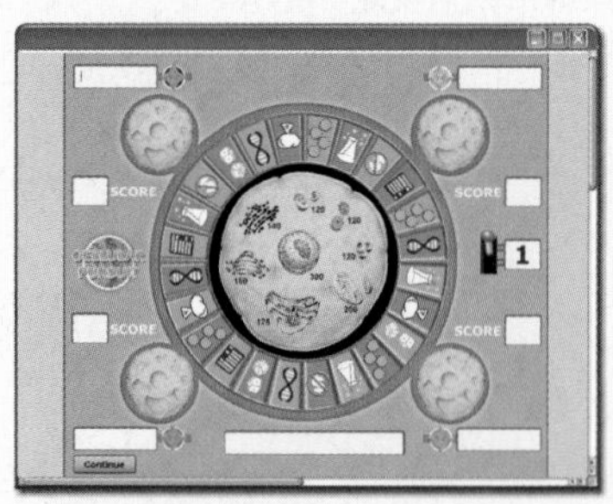

? Inquiry **Virtual Lab** Students will take a spin on the wheel of cells in Cellular Pursuit.

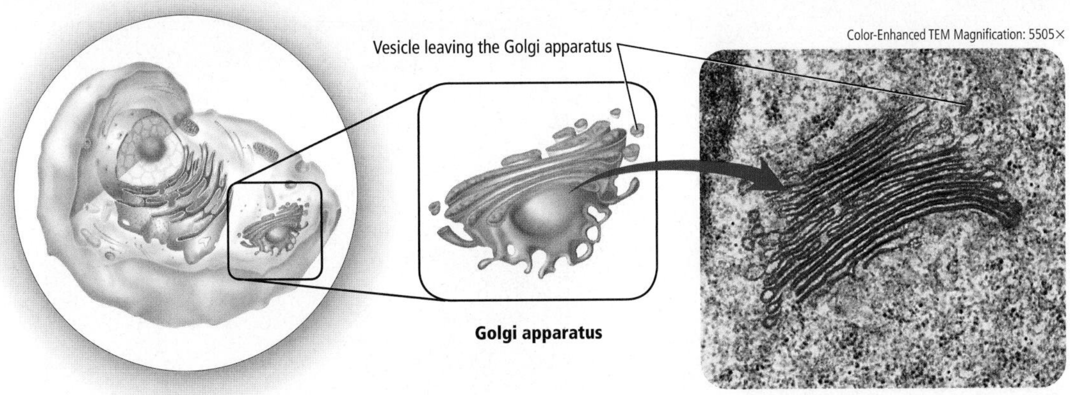

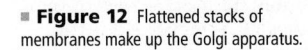

■ **Figure 12** Flattened stacks of membranes make up the Golgi apparatus.

Golgi apparatus After hiking boots are made in a factory, they must be organized into pairs, boxed, and shipped. Similarly, after proteins are made in the endoplasmic reticulum, some might be transferred to the Golgi (GAWL jee) apparatus, illustrated in **Figure 12.** The **Golgi apparatus** is a flattened stack of membranes that modifies, sorts, and packages proteins into sacs called vesicles. Vesicles then can fuse with the cell's plasma membrane to release proteins to the environment outside the cell. Observe the vesicle in **Figure 12.** W

Vacuoles A factory needs a place to store materials and waste products. Similarly, cells have membrane-bound vesicles called vacuoles for temporary storage of materials within the cytoplasm. A **vacuole,** such as the plant vacuole shown in **Figure 13,** is a sac used to store food, enzymes, and other materials needed by a cell. Some vacuoles store waste products. Interestingly, animal cells usually do not contain vacuoles. If animal cells do have vacuoles, they are much smaller than those in plant cells. D

■ **Figure 13** Plant cells have large membrane-bound storage compartments called vacuoles.

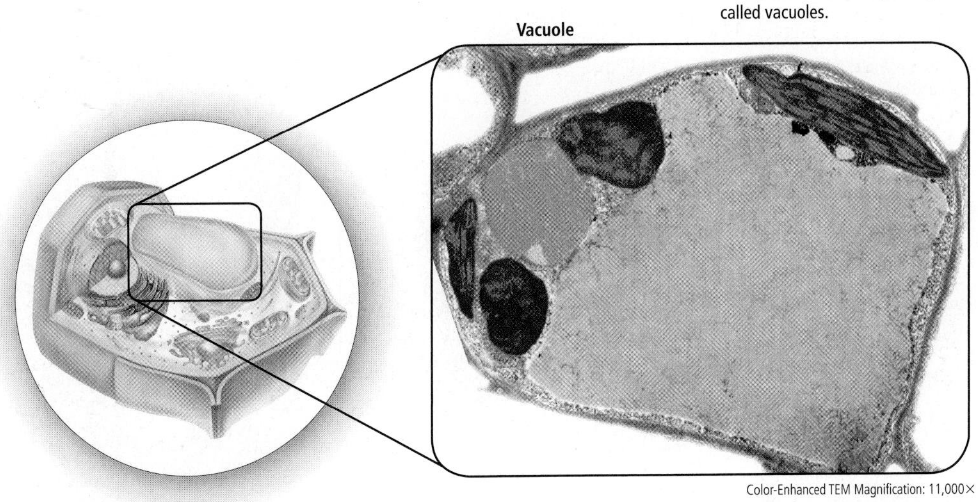

Reading Strategy

BL OL Illustrate Have students review the section to this point and create a cartoon describing the function of the nucleus, ribosomes, ER, Golgi, and vacuoles. Cartoons should indicate that the nucleus directs the manufacture of protein at the ribosomes and ER, then it is packed into units in the Golgi apparatus, and vacuoles collect waste.

W Writing Support

BL OL AL Narrative Writing Have students prepare a short biography about the life and work of Camillo Golgi, for whom the Golgi apparatus is named.

D Develop Concepts

BL OL AL Activity Have students view a microscope slide of a thin section of a small piece of red beet tissue and observe the vacuoles. The vacuoles contain the red pigment betacyanin and are relatively large and easy to see through a high-power objective.

Content Background

Real-World Connection Like lysosomes, peroxisomes are membrane-bound compartments that contain enzymes. Peroxisomes in the liver help detoxify various harmful substances. Unlike lysosomes, peroxisomes do not bud off of the Golgi apparatus but are formed by incorporating lipids from the ER and proteins from the cytoplasm. Peroxisomes are self-replicating and may split into two when they reach a particular size. One of the enzymes peroxisomes contain is an enzyme to destroy hydrogen peroxide (H_2O_2), a by-product of many enzyme-mediated cellular reactions. Hydrogen peroxide, while an important component of some peroxisome reactions, is toxic to the cell in certain quantities. The enzyme catalase breaks down hydrogen peroxide in the peroxisome before it can damage the cell.

C Critical Thinking

OL AL Infer

ASK STUDENTS: ***What are lysosomes?*** vesicles that digest excess, worn-out or harmful substances in cell vacuoles ***In the immune system, how might lysosomes be important to cells that attack foreign organisms such as bacteria?*** Immune cells use lysosomes to digest bacteria and viruses that invade a cell. ***How are lysosomes helpful during the process of metamorphosis?*** Lysosomes are used in metamorphosis to digest cells that will be replaced by cells organized into different types of tissues.

S Skill Practice

BL OL AL COOP LEARN

Visual Literacy Have students carefully study the illustrations in Figure 15. Place students in groups of two or three and pro-vide them with short pieces of small drinking or stirring straws. Have students create models of centrioles made of microtubules similar to those shown in Figure 15.

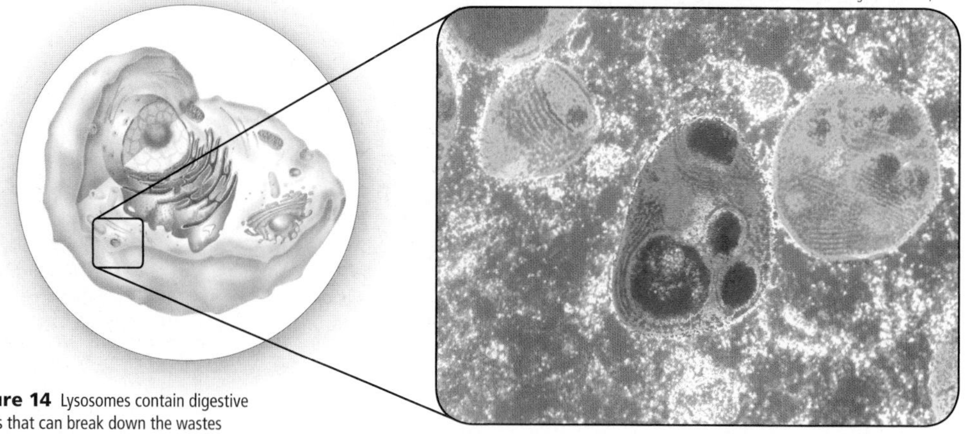

■ **Figure 14** Lysosomes contain digestive enzymes that can break down the wastes contained in vacuoles.

Lysosomes Factories and cells also need cleanup crews. In a cell, there are **lysosomes,** shown in **Figure 14,** which are vesicles that contain substances that digest excess or worn-out organelles and food particles. Lysosomes also digest bacteria and viruses that have entered the cell. The membrane surrounding a lysosome prevents the digestive enzymes inside from destroying the cell. Lysosomes can fuse with vacuoles and dispense their enzymes into the vacuoles. These enzymes digest the wastes inside.

C

Centrioles Previously in this section, you read about microtubules and the cytoskeleton. Groups of microtubules form another structure called a centriole (SEN tree ol). **Centrioles,** shown in **Figure 15,** are organelles made of microtubules that function during cell division. Centrioles are located in the cytoplasm of animal cells and most protists and usually are near the nucleus.

S

■ **Figure 15** Centrioles are made of microtubules and play a role in cell division.

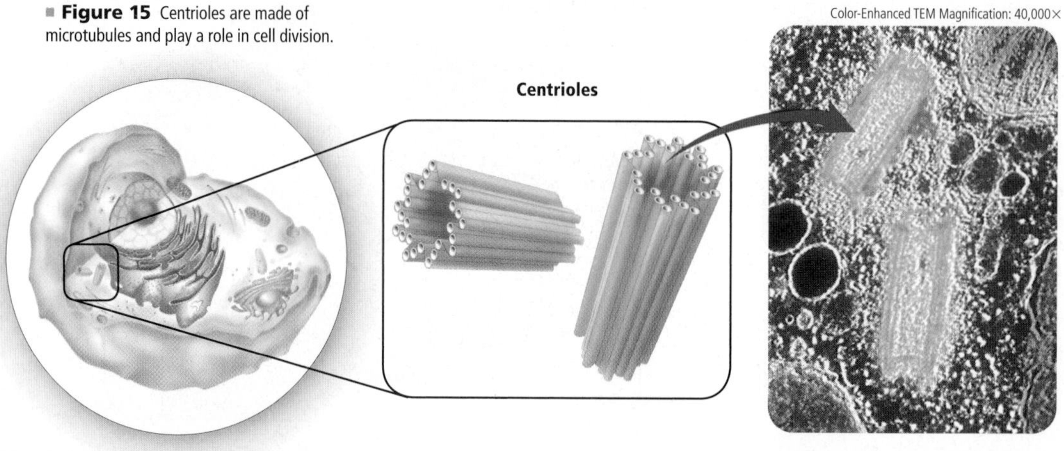

Content Background

Teacher FYI Lysosomes, sometimes called "suicide sacs," are phospholipid sacs of hydrolytic enzymes capable of digesting nucleic acids, polysaccharides, fats, and proteins. The inside of the lysosome is acidic, providing the best environment for the enzymes to work. Lysosomes are important in recycling the cell's organic material as well as intracellular digestion of large molecules. Lysosomes also are involved in programmed cell death. People with Tay-Sachs disease, an inherited disorder of the nervous system, are missing one or more of the lysosomal hydrolytic enzymes that "clean out" the cells.

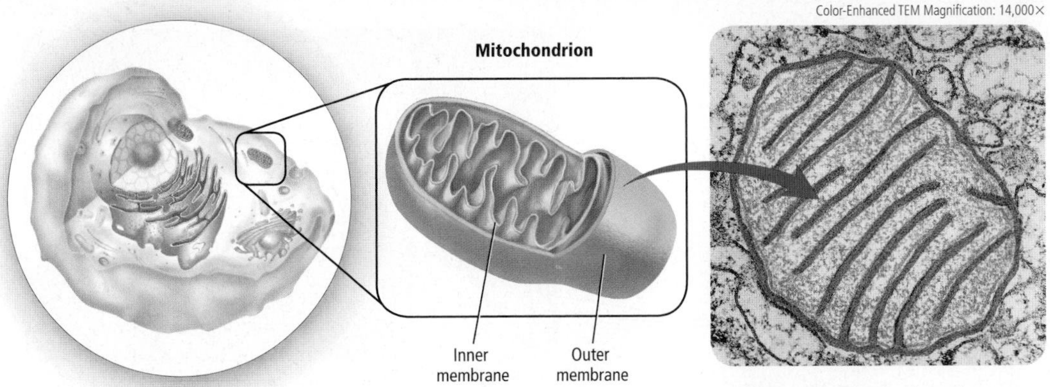

■ **Figure 16** Mitochondria make energy available to the cell.
Describe ***the membrane structure of a mitochondrion.***

Mitochondria Imagine now that a boot factory has its own generator that produces the electricity it needs. Cells also have energy generators called **mitochondria** (mi tuh KAHN dree uh; singular, mitochondrion), which convert fuel particles (mainly sugars) into usable energy. **Figure 16** shows that a mitochondrion has an outer membrane and a highly folded inner membrane that provides a large surface area for breaking the bonds in sugar molecules. The energy **D** produced from that breakage is stored in the bonds of other molecules and later used by the cell. For this reason, mitochondria often are referred to as the "powerhouses" of cells.

Chloroplasts Factory machines need electricity that is generated by burning fossil fuels or by collecting energy from alternative sources, such as the Sun. Plant cells have their own way of using solar energy. In addition to mitochondria, plants and some other eukaryotic cells contain **chloroplasts,** which are organelles that capture light energy and convert it to chemical energy through a process called photosynthesis. Examine **Figure 17** and notice that inside the inner membrane are many small, disk-shaped compartments called thylakoids. It is there that the energy from sunlight is trapped by a pigment called chlorophyll. Chlorophyll gives leaves and stems their green color.

Chloroplasts belong to a group of plant organelles called plastids, some of which are used for storage. Some plastids store starches or lipids. Others, such as chromoplasts, contain red, orange, or yellow pigments that trap light energy and give color to plant structures such as flowers and leaves.

■ **Figure 17** In plants, chloroplasts capture and convert light energy to chemical energy.

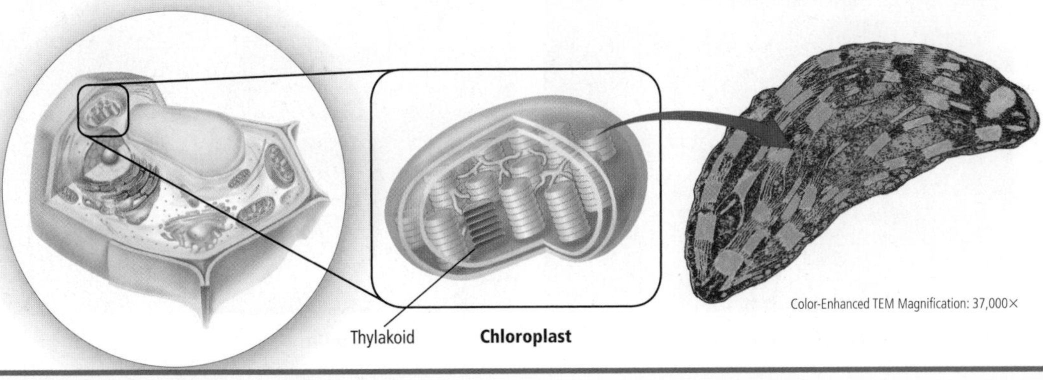

D Develop Concepts

OL AL Analogy To demonstrate to students how folding can greatly increase surface area, bring in a box of facial tissues. Have students calculate the total surface area of the folded tissues in the box and compare with the surface area of the box itself. Remind students how to calculate surface area—calculate length × height for each face of the box, then add the answers together to find the total surface area of the box. For instance, if the box is 22 cm × 11 cm × 8 cm, the box surface area is (22 cm × 11 cm × 2) + (11 cm × 8 cm × 2) + (21 cm × 8 cm × 2) = 996 cm^2. For the tissues, (20 cm × 18 cm × 2) × 240 (the number of tissues in the box) = 172,800 cm^2. The difference in the amount of surface area in the same space is a result of folding. By folding the inside membrane in the mitochondria, there is a tremendous increase in membrane surface area for respiratory reactions.

Develop Concepts

BL OL AL

Clarify a Misconception

ASK STUDENTS: ***Do plant cells have mitochondria?*** Yes. Students often think that animal cells have mitochondria and plant cells have only chloroplasts. Plant cells also have mitochondria. Chemical energy formed in the chloroplasts is used by the mitochondria for cellular energy.

■ **Caption Question Fig. 16** The inner membrane is highly folded to provide significant surface area for the mitochondrial reactions to take place.

Content Background

Real-World Connection Mitochondrial diseases are due to problems in the energy metabolism carried out by the mitochondria. More than 1000 proteins are encoded by the DNA found in the mitochondria. Rare illnesses can result from a deficiency of one or more of these proteins. Depending on which cells are affected, symptoms can include loss of motor control, muscle weakness, intestinal disorders, cardiac disease, liver disease, and various neurological disorders. Some scientists also think that some diseases often associated with aging, such as Alzheimer's and Parkinson's diseases, are associated with a decrease in activity in the mitochondria.

C Critical Thinking

OL AL Infer Students should know that plant cells have cell walls but animal cells do not.
ASK STUDENTS: ***How do plants benefit from cell walls?*** Answers may include that cell walls are rigid, which helps plant cells have shape and structure.

D Develop Concepts

BL OL

Clarify a Misconception
ASK STUDENTS: ***How is a cell wall different from our classroom wall?*** Point out that cell walls are permeable but a classroom wall is impermeable. Students may think the cell wall is impermeable like the classroom wall. Remind students that everything that enters and leaves a plant cell must be able to pass through the cell wall. Cell walls have channels that perforate the cell's wall, allowing easier exchange between the cell and its environment.

Caption Question Fig. 19 Cells with cilia may line the surfaces on which substances are moved.

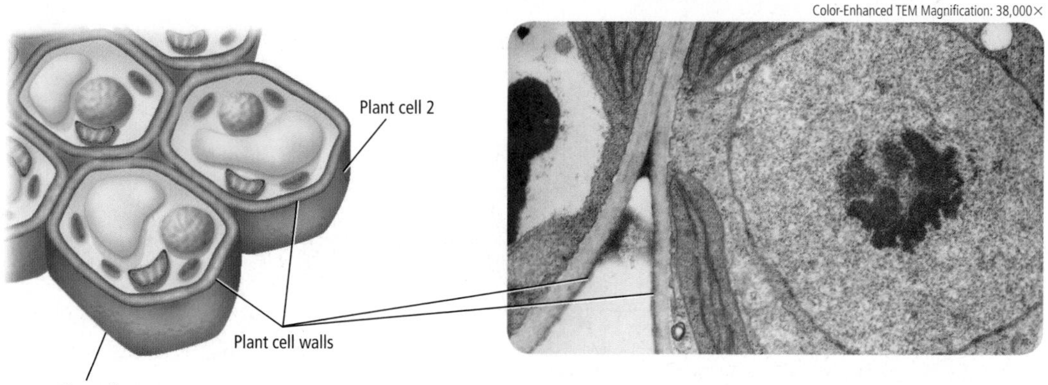

Figure 18 The illustration shows plant cells and their cell walls. Compare this to the transmission electron micrograph showing the cell walls of adjacent plant cells.

Cell wall Another structure associated with plant cells is the cell wall, shown in **Figure 18.** The **cell wall** is a thick, rigid, mesh of fibers that surrounds the outside of the plasma membrane, protects the cell, and gives it support. Rigid cell walls allow plants to stand at various heights—from blades of grass to California redwood trees. Plant cell walls are made of a carbohydrate called cellulose, which gives the cell walls their inflexible characteristics. **Table 1** summarizes cell walls and various other cell structures.

Cilia and flagella Some eukaryotic cell surfaces have structures called cilia and flagella that project outside the plasma membrane. As shown in **Figure 19, cilia** (singular, cilium) are short, numerous projections that look like hairs. The motion of cilia is similar to the motion of oars in a rowboat. **Flagella** (singular, flagellum) are longer and less numerous than cilia. These projections move with a whiplike motion. Cilia and flagella are composed of microtubules arranged in a 9 + 2 configuration, in which nine pairs of microtubules surround two single microtubules. Typically, a cell has one or two flagella.

Prokaryotic cilia and flagella contain cytoplasm and are enclosed by the plasma membrane. These structures are made of complex proteins. While both structures are used for cell movement, cilia are also found on stationary cells.

Figure 19 The hairlike structures in the photomicrograph are cilia, and the tail-like structures are flagella. Both structures function in cell movement.
Infer *where in the body of an animal you would predict cilia might be found.*

Cilia on the surface of a *Paramecium*

Bacteria with flagella

Research Citation

Big Ideas Educational research indicates that activities requiring students to identify main ideas, such as those at the beginning of each section of this chapter, are beneficial. They allow students to see how the facts they learn are applied to a larger context.
(National Research Council, 2002)

Research bibliography on pages 32T–34T

Table 1 **Summary of Cell Structures** Concepts in Motion Interactive Table

Cell Structure	Example	Function	Cell Type
Cell wall		An inflexible barrier that provides support and protects the plant cell	Plant cells, fungi cells, and some prokaryotes
Centrioles		Organelles that occur in pairs and are important for cell division	Animal cells and most protist cells
Chloroplast	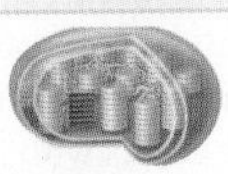	A double-membrane organelle with thylakoids containing chlorophyll; where photosynthesis takes place	Plant cells and some protist cells
Cilia		Projections from cell surfaces that aid in locomotion and feeding; also used to sweep substances along surfaces	Some animal cells, protist cells, and prokaryotes
Cytoskeleton		A framework for the cell within the cytoplasm	All eukaryotic cells
Endoplasmic reticulum	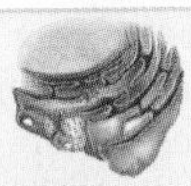	A highly folded membrane that is the site of protein synthesis	All eukaryotic cells
Flagella	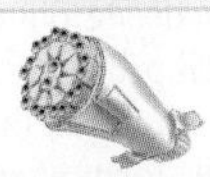	Projections that aid in locomotion and feeding	Some animal cells, prokaryotes, and some plant cells
Golgi apparatus	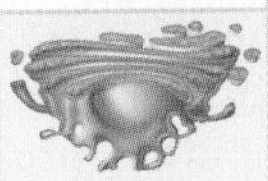	A flattened stack of tubular membranes that modifies proteins and packages them for distribution outside the cell	All eukaryotic cells
Lysosome		A vesicle that contains digestive enzymes for the breakdown of excess or worn-out cellular substances	Animal cells and rare in plant cells
Mitochondrion	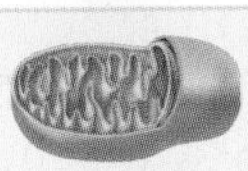	A membrane-bound organelle that makes energy available to the rest of the cell	All eukaryotic cells
Nucleus		The control center of the cell that contains coded directions for the production of proteins and cell division	All eukaryotic cells
Plasma membrane	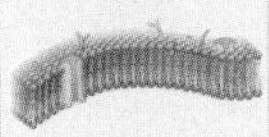	A flexible boundary that controls the movement of substances into and out of the cell	All cells
Ribosome		Organelle that is the site of protein synthesis	All cells
Vacuole		A membrane-bound vesicle for the temporary storage of materials	Plant cells–one large; rarely animal cells–a few small

Develop Concepts

OL AL Scaffolding

ASK STUDENTS: ***Name the location of protein synthesis.*** on the ribosome ***Relate DNA to protein synthesis.*** DNA contains the code for which protein is to be synthesized on the ribosome. ***Generalize how DNA in the nucleus can guide protein synthesis on the ribosome in the cytoplasm.*** DNA coding information is transferred to an RNA molecule that leaves the nucleus. Together, RNA and ribosomes manufacture proteins. ***Analyze why it would be an advantage to a protein-secreting cell to have ribosomes on the endoplasmic reticulum.*** The endoplasmic reticulum is involved in transporting materials around the cell and to the Golgi apparatus for transport out of the cell. Placing the ribosomes on the ER allows proteins to be manufactured and easily transported. ***What would happen to a cell if the number of ribosomes was reduced?*** Protein manufacture rates likely would decrease.

Concepts in Motion

Interactive Table

Research Citation

Anticipatory Guides Educational research indicates that asking students to make predictions and using anticipation guides can help students gain more understanding of a text. These activities can help activate background knowledge and build interest in the lesson.

(Readence, Bean, and Baldwin, 1985)

Research bibliography on pages 32T–34T

GOING GREEN Use found materials—things that would normally be thrown away—to make a model. Divide students into groups and assign each group two organelles from Table 1. Have the students bring in materials to construct the models of the organelles. Suggested items include empty cereal boxes, packing pellets, clean yogurt containers, paper cups and yarn.

Develop Concepts

BL OL AL COOP LEARN

Activity Host a quiz show with students as the contestants. Divide the class into two teams and have each team write the questions for the opposing team to answer. Students may write their answers on desk-size white-boards, if available, or sheets of paper. Have them compete to be first to hold up the correct answer.

Formative Assessment

Evaluation On the board, list the organelles that were introduced in the section and have students write what they know about the organelles.

Remediation Have students review the materials on organelles in this section. Call on individual students and ask them to silently act out the part of an organelle. Have the class try to guess the identity of the organelle and then review its function(s) and characteristics.

CAREERS IN BIOLOGY

Science Communications Specialist Many publishers of scientific material hire communications specialists to write about research and its importance to the general public. This often is accomplished through press releases, ads, pamphlets, and targeted mailings.

Comparing Cells

Table 1 summarizes the structures of eukaryotic plant cells and animal cells. Notice that plant cells contain chlorophyll; they can capture and transform energy from the Sun into a usable form of chemical energy. This is one of the main characteristics that distinguishes plants from animals. In addition, recall that animal cells usually do not contain vacuoles. If they do, vacuoles in animal cells are much smaller than vacuoles in plant cells. Also, animal cells do not have cell walls. Cell walls give plant cells protection and support.

Organelles at Work

With a basic understanding of the structures found within a cell, it becomes easier to envision how those structures work together to perform cell functions. Take, for example, the synthesis of proteins.

Protein synthesis begins in the nucleus with the information contained in the DNA. Genetic information is copied and transferred to another genetic molecule called RNA. Then RNA and ribosomes, which have been manufactured in the nucleolus, leave the nucleus through the pores of the nuclear membrane. Together, RNA and ribosomes manufacture proteins. Each protein made on the rough ER has a particular function; it might become a protein that forms a part of the plasma membrane, a protein that is released from the cell, or a protein transported to other organelles. Other ribosomes will float freely in the cytoplasm and also make proteins.

Most of the proteins made on the surface of the ER are sent to the Golgi apparatus. The Golgi apparatus packages the proteins in vesicles and transports them to other organelles or out of the cell. Other organelles use the proteins to carry out cell processes. For example, lysosomes use proteins, enzymes in particular, to digest food and waste. Mitochondria use enzymes to produce a usable form of energy for the cell.

After reading about the organelles in a cell, it becomes clear why people equate the cell to a factory. Each organelle has its job to do, and the health of the cell depends on all of the components working together.

Section 3 Assessment

Section Summary

- Eukaryotic cells contain membrane-bound organelles in the cytoplasm that perform cell functions.
- Ribosomes are the sites of protein synthesis.
- Mitochondria are the powerhouses of cells.
- Plant and animal cells contain many of the same organelles, while other organelles are unique to either plant cells or animal cells.

Understand Main Ideas

1. MAIN Idea **Identify** the role of the nucleus in a eukaryotic cell.
2. **Summarize** the role of the endoplasmic reticulum.
3. **Create** a flowchart comparing the parts of a cell to an automobile production line.
4. **Compare and contrast** structures of plant and animal cells.

Think Critically

5. **Hypothesize** how lysosomes would be involved in changing a caterpillar into a butterfly.

WRITING in **Biology**

6. Categorize the structures and organelles in **Table 1** into lists based on cell type and then draw a concept map illustrating your organization.

Section 3 Assessment

1. The nucleus contains DNA and controls the manufacturing of proteins.
2. The rough endoplasmic reticulum has ribosomes that produce proteins for export to other cells. Smooth endoplasmic reticulum is involved in the synthesis of complex carbohydrates and lipids.
3. Charts should demonstrate an understanding of the role of each of the cell organelles.
4. Plant cells do not have lysosomes, centrioles, or cilia, but have all of the other organelles that animal cells have. Animal cells do not have chloroplasts, cell walls, and rarely have vacuoles that plant cells have.
5. Answers will vary but might include: the lysosomes may be involved in the digestion of the caterpillar tissues so that the butterfly can develop.
6. Evaluate student lists and concept maps. Accept all reasonable answers.

✓ Assessment Online Quiz

Reading Preview

Essential Questions

- What are the processes of diffusion, facilitated diffusion, and active transport?
- What is the effect of a hypotonic, hypertonic, or isotonic solution on a cell?
- How do large particles enter and exit cells?

Review Vocabulary

homeostasis: the regulation of the internal environment of a cell or organism to maintain conditions suitable for life

New Vocabulary

diffusion
dynamic equilibrium
facilitated diffusion
osmosis
isotonic solution
hypotonic solution
hypertonic solution
active transport
endocytosis
exocytosis

g Multilingual eGlossary

R Cellular Transport

MAIN Idea Cellular transport moves substances within the cell and moves substances into and out of the cell.

Real-World Reading Link Imagine studying in your room while cookies are baking in the kitchen. You probably did not notice when the cookies were put into the oven because you could not smell them. But, as the cookies baked, the movement of the aroma from the kitchen to your room happened through a process called diffusion.

D Diffusion

Connection to Chemistry As the aroma of baking cookies makes its way to you, the particles are moving and colliding with each other in the air. This happens because the particles in gases, liquids, and solids are in random motion. Similarly, substances dissolved in water move constantly in random motion called Brownian motion. This random motion causes **diffusion,** which is the net movement of particles from an area where there are many particles of the substance to an area where there are fewer particles of the substance. The amount of a substance in a particular area is called concentration. Therefore, substances diffuse from areas of high concentration to low concentration. **Figure 20** illustrates the process of diffusion. Additional energy input is not required for diffusion because the particles already are in motion.

For example, if you drop red and blue ink into a container of water at opposite ends of the container, which is similar to the watery environment of a cell, the process of diffusion begins, as shown in **Figure 20(A).** In a short period of time, the ink particles have mixed as a result of diffusion to the point where a purple-colored blended area is visible. **Figure 20(B)** shows the initial result of this diffusion.

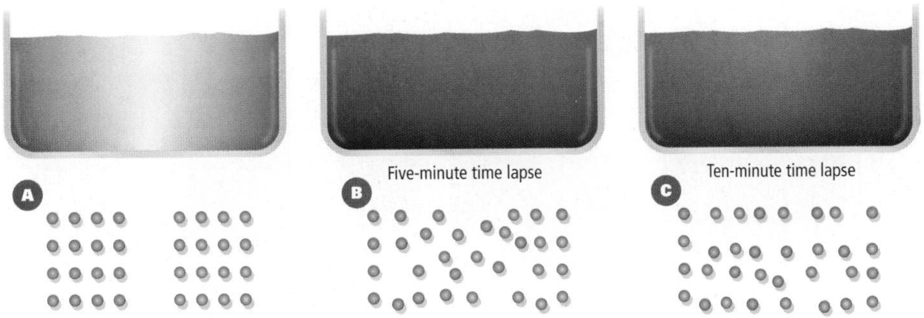

■ **Figure 20** Diffusion causes the inks to move from high-ink concentration to low-ink concentration until the colors become evenly blended in the water.

Differentiated Instruction

Gifted Gifted students will benefit from seeing the connections between what they are learning in class and real-world events. Bring in supplemental materials and discuss current events that will allow them to see these connections.

For more tips, see pages 14T–15T.

Demonstration

Brownian Motion Using the stamens from a flower such as a lily, suspend some pollen grains in water on a glass slide. (Florists may provide "old" flowers as teacher aids.) Warm the slide slightly, then place on a microscope. Have students look in the microscope and observe the moving pollen grains. Est. time: 10 min

Section 4

MAIN Idea

BL OL AL Cellular Transport

ASK STUDENTS: ***How can you tell when breakfast is cooking in the morning?*** Some students may say they can smell food such as bacon cooking. ***How did these smells reach your nose?*** Molecules from the cooking food travel through the air to the nose. Use this situation to bring up the idea of diffusion of molecules from an area of high concentration to an area of low concentration.

R Reading Strategy

BL OL AL

Assessment Preview Before students read Section 4, have them read the Section Assessment questions. By reading the questions ahead of time, students can better identify important information as they read the text.

D Develop Concepts

BL OL

Clarify a Misconception

ASK STUDENTS: ***What processes allow substances to enter a cell?*** Students may answer diffusion. Explain that diffusion is only one of the processes whereby molecules enter the cell. Tell students that as they read this section, they will learn about active transport and endocytosis as other ways by which materials get into cells. Diffusion is a very slow process; faster ways to let material into the cell are essential.

Develop Concepts

OL AL Integrate Health

Point out that kidney dialysis machines use the principle of diffusion to cleanse the blood. When a person is on dialysis, the blood leaves the body through a tube that enters the dialysis machine. There, waste products diffuse out of their blood into the fluid of the machine. The cleansed blood then is returned to the person's body.

D Develop Concepts

BL Clarify a Misconception

ASK STUDENTS: ***Do substances diffuse in response to a stimulus?*** Substances do not diffuse because they are "prodded" by a stimulus. Diffusion occurs as a result of a concentration gradient and random motion. Students may use terminology that suggests a purpose to diffusion. Stress that diffusion is simply movement from high concentration toward lower concentration—it is not a response to a stimulus.

FOLDABLES®

RUBRIC A rubric for evaluating Foldables is found on your eTeacherEdition Online.

Going Further

SAY TO STUDENTS: ***On the back of your Foldable, draw a three-column chart. Label the columns* Hypotonic, Hypertonic, *and* Isotonic. *Record what you have learned about how osmosis affects cells in each type of solution.***

Concepts in Motion

Animation

Reading Check Sodium ions can enter cells through passive transport proteins, diffusing from high concentration to low concentration.

VOCABULARY

ACADEMIC VOCABULARY

Concentration
the amount of a component in a given area or volume
The concentration of salt in the aquarium was too high, causing the fishes to die.

Given more time, the ink particles continue to mix and, in this case, continue to form the uniform purple mixture shown in **Figure 20(C).** Mixing continues until the concentrations of red ink and blue ink are the same in all areas. The final result is the purple solution. After this point, the particles continue to move randomly, but no further change in concentration will occur. This condition, in which there is continuous movement but no overall change, is called **dynamic equilibrium.**

One of the key characteristics of diffusion is the rate at which diffusion takes place. Three main factors affect the rate of diffusion: concentration, temperature, and pressure. When concentration is high, diffusion occurs more quickly because there are more particles that collide. Similarly, when temperature or pressure increases, the number of collisions increases, thus increasing the rate of diffusion. Recall that at higher temperatures particles move faster, and at higher pressure the particles are closer together. In both cases, more collisions occur and diffusion is faster. The size and charge of a substance also affects the rate of diffusion.

FOLDABLES® Incorporate information from this section into your Foldable.

Diffusion across the plasma membrane In addition to water, cells need certain ions and small molecules, such as chloride ions and sugars, to perform cellular functions. Water can diffuse across the plasma membrane, as shown in **Figure 21(A),** but most other substances cannot. Another form of transport, called **facilitated diffusion,** uses transport proteins to move other ions and small molecules across the plasma membrane. By this method, substances move into the cell through a water-filled transport protein, called a channel protein, that opens and closes to allow the substance to diffuse through the plasma membrane, as shown in **Figure 21(B).** Another type of transport protein, called a carrier protein, also can help substances diffuse across the plasma membrane. Carrier proteins change shape as the diffusion process continues to help move the particle through the membrane, as illustrated in **Figure 21(C).** D

Diffusion of water and facilitated diffusion of other substances require no additional input of energy because the particles are moving from an area of high concentration to an area of lower concentration. This is also known as passive transport. You will learn later in this section about a form of cellular transport that does require energy input.

Reading Check **Describe** how sodium (Na^+) ions get into cells.

Figure 21 Although water moves freely through the plasma membrane, other substances cannot pass through the phospholipid bilayer on their own. Such substances enter the cell by facilitated transport.

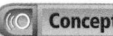

Concepts in Motion

Animation

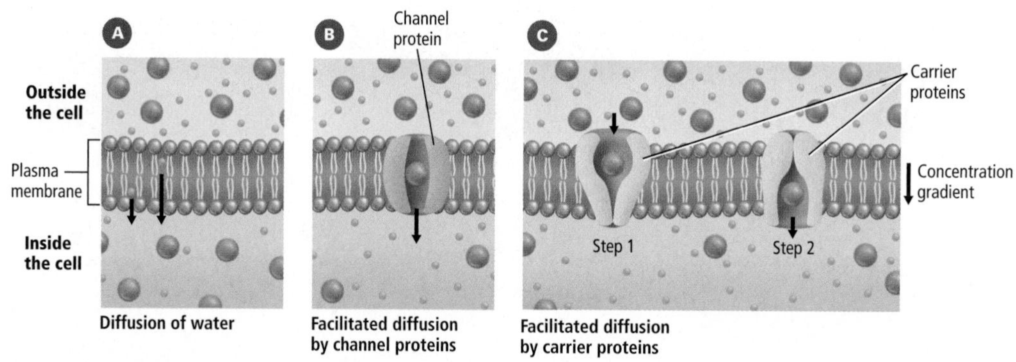

Activity

EL BL OL Student Diffusion Have students line up around the edges of the classroom. For the next five minutes, ask students to slowly walk forward until they are ready to bump into something. Right before they bump into something, ask them to turn at any angle and continue until they almost bump into something else. Have them turn at any angle and continue until you call time. After about five minutes, students should end up dispersed around the classroom, demonstrating the process of diffusion, ending with a dynamic equilibrium of students dispersed throughout the room. With a large group of students, it may take a few more minutes to disperse them throughout the classroom. Est. time: 10 min

Osmosis: Diffusion of Water

Water is a substance that passes freely into and out of a cell through the plasma membrane. The diffusion of water across a selectively permeable membrane is called **osmosis** (ahs MOH sus). Regulating the movement of water across the plasma membrane is an important factor in maintaining homeostasis within the cell.

How osmosis works Recall that in a solution, a substance called the solute is dissolved in a solvent. Water is the solvent in a cell and its environment. Concentration is a measure of the amount of solute dissolved in a solvent. The concentration of a solution decreases when the amount of solvent increases.

Examine **Figure 22,** showing a U-shaped tube containing solutions with different sugar concentrations separated by a selectively permeable membrane. What will happen if the solvent (water) can pass through the membrane but the solute (sugar) cannot?

Water molecules diffuse toward the side with the greater sugar concentration—the right side. As water moves to the right, the concentration of the sugar solution decreases. The water continues to diffuse until dynamic equilibrium occurs—the concentration of the solutions is the same on both sides. Notice in **Figure 22** that the result is an increase in solution level on the right side. During dynamic equilibrium, water molecules continue to diffuse back and forth across the membrane. But, the concentrations on each side no longer change.

Reading Check **Compare and contrast** diffusion and osmosis.

MiniLab 2

Inquiry MiniLab

Investigate Osmosis

What will happen to cells placed in a strong salt solution? Regulating the flow and amount of water into and out of a cell is critical to the survival of that cell. Osmosis is one method used to regulate a cell's water content.

Procedure

1. Read and complete the lab safety form.
2. Prepare a control **slide** using **onion epidermis, water,** and **iodine stain** as directed by your teacher.
3. Prepare a test slide using onion epidermis, **salt water,** and iodine stain as directed by your teacher.
4. Predict the effect, if any, that the salt solution will have on the onion cells in the test slide.
5. View the control slide using a **compound microscope** under low power and sketch several onion cells.
6. View the test slide under the same magnification and sketch your observations.

Analysis

1. **Analyze and conclude** whether your prediction was correct or incorrect. Explain.
2. **Explain** Use the process of osmosis to explain what you observe.

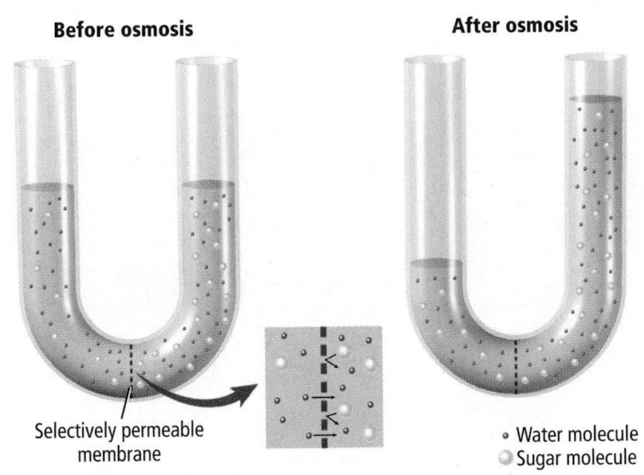

■ **Figure 22** Before osmosis, the sugar concentration is greater on the right side. After osmosis, the concentrations are the same on both sides.
Name *the term for this phenomenon.*

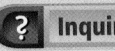

MiniLab 2

Inquiry MiniLab

For a lab worksheet, use your eTeacherEdition Online.

RUBRIC A rubric for evaluating MiniLabs is found on your eTeacherEdition Online.

Est. Time 20 min

Safety Precautions Approve lab safety forms before work begins.

Teaching Strategy Use this lab as a starting point to talk about various staining techniques.

Analysis

1. Accept all reasonable answers.
2. On the control slide, no change is seen because the concentration of water molecules inside the cell and outside the cell is nearly the same. As a result, there is no strong flow of water molecules into or out of the cells. However, on the test slide, the number of water molecules outside the cells in the strong salt solution is far lower than the number of water molecules inside the cells. Consequently, a great deal of water begins to diffuse out of the cell due to osmosis and the cell contents begin to shrink away from the cell walls.

LabManager™

Customize this lab with the LabManager™ CD-ROM.

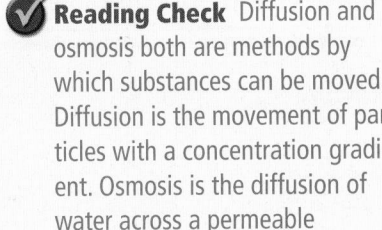

Demonstration

Diffusion Seal a dilute solution of cornstarch inside of a piece of cellophane or cellulose tubing from a biological supply company (a sandwich bag will also work). Place it in a beaker containing a dilute solution of iodine in water (yellowish in color). Allow the cellophane or cellulose tubing to sit in the beaker during the whole class period. The cellophane or cellulose container represents a selectively permeable plasma membrane. The iodine solution will diffuse in and react with the starch, turning the water inside dark purple. The starch molecules cannot diffuse out, so the solution outside will remain yellow. Est. time: 5 min at the beginning of class and 5 min at the end of class

Reading Check Diffusion and osmosis both are methods by which substances can be moved. Diffusion is the movement of particles with a concentration gradient. Osmosis is the diffusion of water across a permeable membrane.

■ **Caption Question** **Fig. 22** dynamic equilibrium

C Critical Thinking

BL OL AL Predict Place three raw eggs in a dilute solution of vinegar or 0.05% HCl. Change the solution of acid several times until the shell dissolves. Carefully transfer one egg to a 250-mL beaker containing distilled water (hypotonic), one to a container of corn syrup (hypertonic), and one to a container of 0.9% NaCl (isotonic). Leave the eggs overnight and observe them the next day.

SAY TO STUDENTS: ***Predict what will happen to each of the eggs in their respective solutions.*** egg in the distilled water will swell and possibly burst (hypotonic), egg in the heavy corn syrup water will shrink (hypertonic), and egg in the 0.9% NaCl will remain about the same (isotonic)

W Writing Support

OL AL Creative Writing Have students write a poem about a cell that is first in an isotonic solution and then in a hypotonic solution. The cell may be either a plant or animal cell.

Concepts in Motion

Animation

GOING GREEN Place an iceberg lettuce leaf in fresh water and another in a solution of 3 parts water and 1 part vinegar. This solution represents acid rain. The next day, have students examine the leaves using a microscope. Ask them to explain how the cells are different in each treatment.

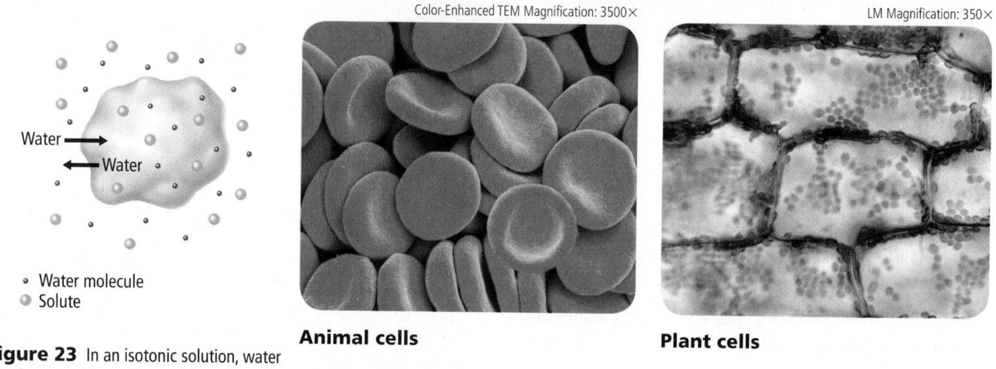

■ **Figure 23** In an isotonic solution, water molecules move into and out of the cell at the same rate, and cells retain their normal shape. The animal cell and the plant cell have their normal shapes in an isotonic solution.

Concepts in Motion

Animation

Cells in an isotonic solution When a cell is in a solution that has the same concentration of water and solutes—ions, sugars, proteins, and other substances—as its cytoplasm, the cell is said to be in an **isotonic solution.** *Iso-* comes from the Greek word meaning *equal.* Water still moves through the plasma membrane, but water enters and leaves the cell at the same rate. The cell is at equilibrium with the solution, and there is no net movement of water. The cells retain their normal shape, as shown in **Figure 23.** Most cells in organisms are in isotonic solutions, such as blood. C

Cells in a hypotonic solution If a cell is in a solution that has a lower concentration of solute, the cell is said to be in a **hypotonic solution.** *Hypo-* comes from the Greek word meaning *under.* There is more water outside of the cell than inside. As a result of osmosis, the net movement of water through the plasma membrane is into the cell, as illustrated in **Figure 24.** Pressure generated as water flows through the plasma membrane is called osmotic pressure. In an animal cell, as water moves into the cell, the pressure increases and the plasma membrane swells. If the solution is extremely hypotonic, the plasma membrane might be unable to withstand this pressure and the cell might burst.

Because they have a rigid cell wall that supports them, plant cells do not burst when in a hypotonic solution. As the pressure inside a cell increases, the plant's central vacuole fills with water, pushing the plasma membrane against the cell wall, shown in the plant cells in **Figure 24.** Instead of bursting, the plant cell becomes firmer. Grocers use this process to keep produce looking fresh by misting fruits and vegetables with water. W

■ **Figure 24** In a hypotonic solution, water enters a cell by osmosis, causing the cell to swell. Animal cells may continue to swell until they burst. Plant cells swell beyond their normal size as internal pressure increases.

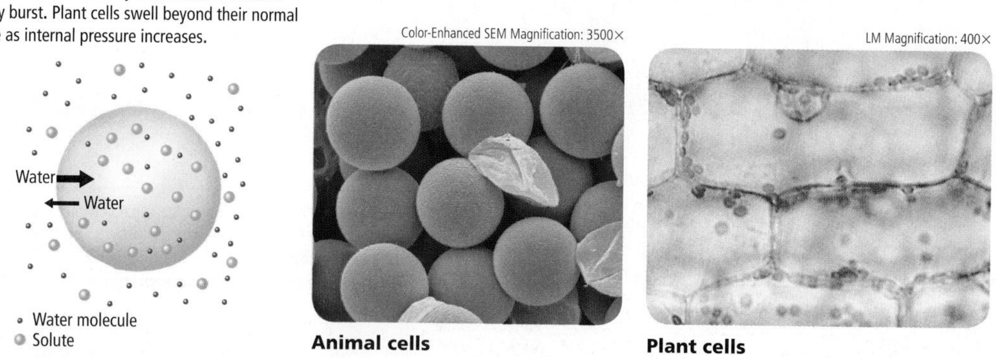

Content Background

Real-World Connection When cells of a *Mimosa pudica* leaf are touched, cells in the lower portion of the leaf base rapidly lose potassium ions. As potassium ions leave the cell, water follows, and the cells shrink and cause the leaflets of the plant to close. These plants can be purchased at a nursery and used to demonstrate this sensitive plant's reaction to being touched.

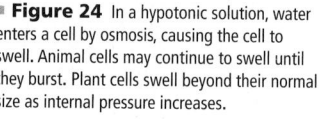

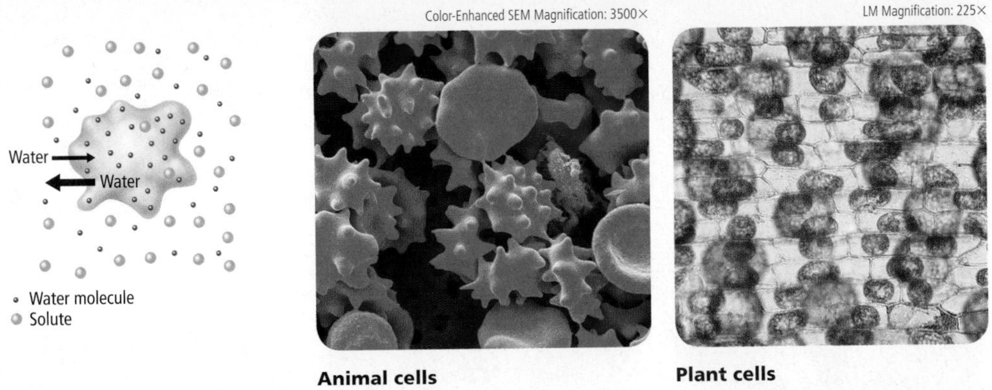

■ **Figure 25** In a hypertonic solution, water leaves a cell by osmosis, causing the cell to shrink. Animal cells shrivel up as they lose water. As plant cells lose internal pressure, the plasma membrane shrinks away from the cell wall.

Cells in a hypertonic solution When a cell is placed in a **hypertonic solution,** the concentration of the solute outside of the cell is higher than it is inside. *Hyper-* comes from the Greek word meaning *above.* During osmosis, the net movement of water is out of the cell, as illustrated in **Figure 25.** Animal cells in a hypertonic solution shrivel because of decreased pressure in the cells. Plant cells in a hypertonic solution lose water, mainly from the central vacuole. The plasma membrane shrinks away from the cell wall. Loss of water in a plant cell causes wilting.

Reading Check **Compare and contrast** the three types of solutions.

Active Transport

Sometimes substances must move from a region of lower concentration to a region of higher concentration against the passive movement from higher to lower concentration. This movement of substances across the plasma membrane against a concentration gradient requires energy; therefore, it is called **active transport. Figure 26** illustrates how active transport occurs with the aid of carrier proteins, commonly called pumps. Some pumps move one type of substance in only one direction, while others move two substances either across the membrane in the same direction or in opposite directions. Because of active transport, the cell maintains the proper balance of substances it needs. Active transport helps maintain homeostasis.

W

■ **Figure 26** Carrier proteins pick up and move substances across the plasma membrane against the concentration gradient and into the cell.
Explain *why active transport requires energy.*

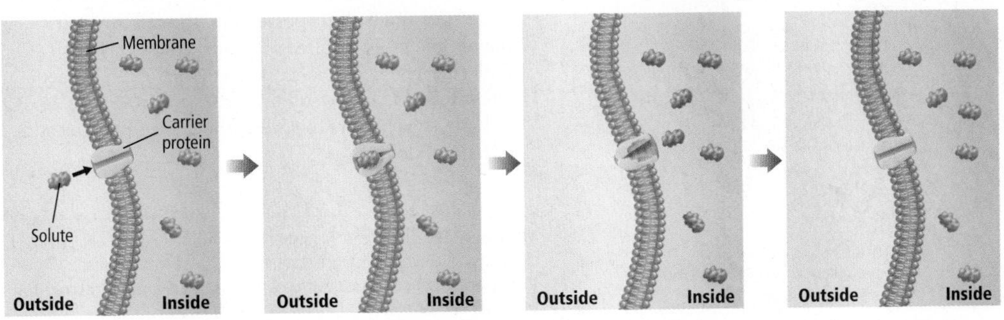

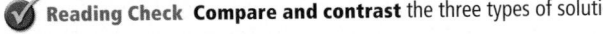

W Writing Support

OL AL Informal Writing Have students write a brief analogy that compares active transport in a cell with bus transport in a city located in a hilly area.

Critical Thinking

AL OL Evaluate Have students evaluate the benefit of sports drinks—flavored electrolyte solutions that athletes drink during or after exercise instead of water. Answers should include a discussion of how exercise causes an individual to sweat, losing salts as well as water. If the person drinks only water, the lost electrolytes are not replaced.
ASK STUDENTS: ***Is there any danger in consuming sports drinks even when you have not exercised?*** Yes; can add too much sodium or sugar to the diet

Reading Check isotonic—a solution with the same concentration of solutes as inside a cell; hypotonic—a solution that has a lower concentration of solute outside than inside a cell; hypertonic—a solution that has a higher concentration of solute outside than inside a cell

■ **Caption Question Fig. 26**
In active transport, the movement of substances is against the concentration gradient and requires a "boost," much like energy is required to move an object uphill.

Demonstration

Make Pickles Bring a simple pickle recipe into class and begin to make a small batch of pickles in front of the class. Explain that heavy salting draws the water out of the cucumber cells. Point out that the cucumber slices must remain in the salt solution for several hours. Next, using an already salt-soaked batch, place the slices in a dilute solution of vinegar and spices. Students should understand that this solution is hypotonic; meaning that it will allow the cucumbers to take up the vinegar and spices to flavor the cucumber slices, turning them into pickles. Est. time: 10 min

Develop Concepts

OL AL Scaffolding

ASK STUDENTS: ***In what ways can materials move across a cell membrane?*** diffusion, facilitated diffusion, osmosis, active transport, endocytosis, and exocytosis ***What is the difference between osmosis, diffusion, and facilitated diffusion?*** Osmosis is the diffusion of water. In diffusion, materials move through the plasma membrane, whereas facilitated diffusion is the movement of ions of molecules through a channel protein. ***Why are channel proteins needed?*** Charged polar molecules cannot diffuse through the phospholipid bilayer but can diffuse through a channel protein. ***How do materials move against the concentration gradient?*** Active transport, which requires energy, moves substances against the concentration gradient.

W Writing Support

BL OL Narrative Writing

Have students write a paragraph explaining the role that the sodium-potassium ATPase pump plays in moving sugar molecules into cells.

Concepts in Motion

Animation

Review

Personal Tutor

Listen to a teacher explain the sodium/potassium pump.

Caption Question Fig. 28

Passive transport moves materials with the diffusion gradient and does not require energy expenditure for the cell. Active transport can move materials against the diffusion gradient and requires energy expenditure for the cell.

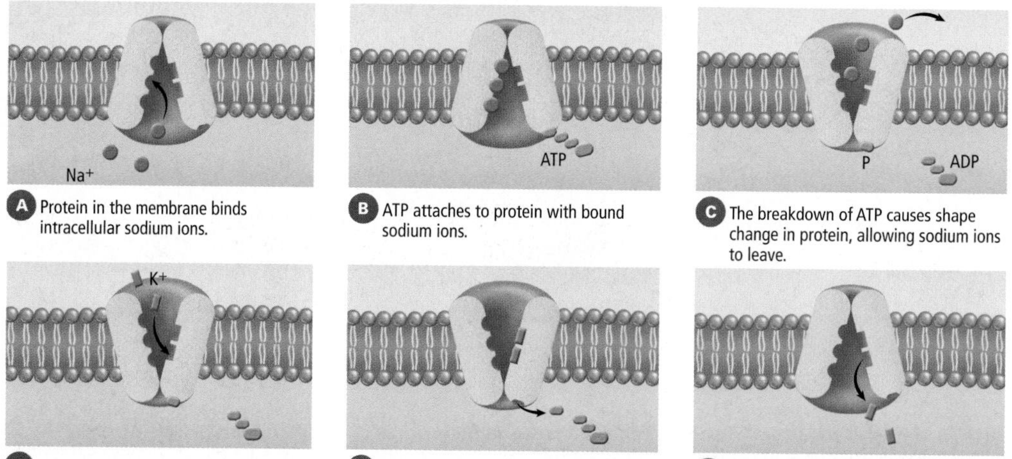

A Protein in the membrane binds intracellular sodium ions.

B ATP attaches to protein with bound sodium ions.

C The breakdown of ATP causes shape change in protein, allowing sodium ions to leave.

D Extracellular potassium ions bind to exposed sites.

E Binding of potassium causes release of phosphate from protein.

F Phosphate release changes protein back to its original shape, and potassium ions move into the cell.

Figure 27 Some cells use elaborate pumping systems, such as the Na^+/K^+ ATPase pump shown here, to help move substances through the plasma membrane.

Concepts in Motion Animation

Review Personal Tutor

Na^+/K^+ ATPase pump One common active transport pump is called the sodium-potassium ATPase pump. This pump is found in the plasma membrane of animal cells. The pump maintains the level of sodium ions (Na^+) and potassium ions (K^+) inside and outside the cell. This protein pump is an enzyme that catalyzes the breakdown of an energy-storing molecule. The pump uses the energy to transport three sodium ions out of the cell while moving two potassium ions into the cell. The high level of sodium on the outside of the cell creates a concentration gradient. Follow the steps in **Figure 27** to see the action of the Na^+/K^+ ATPase pump.

The activity of the Na^+/K^+ ATPase pump can result in yet another form of cellular transport. Substances, such as sugar molecules, must come into the cell from the outside, where the concentration of the substance is lower than it is inside. This requires energy. Recall, however, that the Na^+/K^+ ATPase pump moves Na^+ out of the cell, which creates a low concentration of Na^+ inside the cell. In a process called coupled transport, the Na^+ ions that have been pumped out of the cell can couple with sugar molecules and be transported into the cell through a membrane protein called a coupled channel. The sugar molecule, coupled to a Na^+ ion, enters the cell by facilitated diffusion of the sodium, as shown in **Figure 28.** As a result, sugar enters the cell without spending any additional cellular energy. W

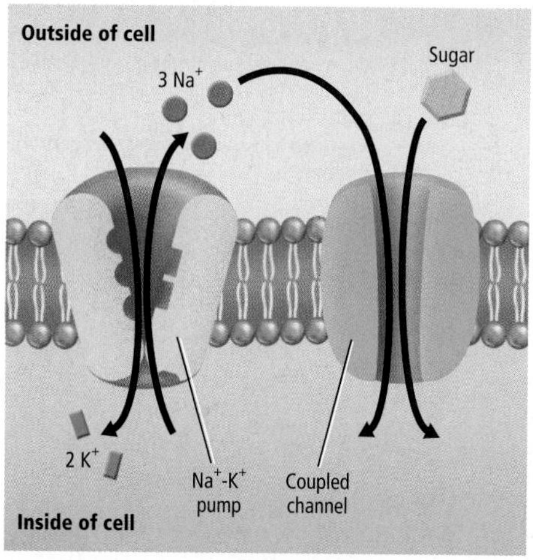

Figure 28 Substances "piggy-back" their way into or out of a cell by coupling with another substance that uses an active transport pump. **Compare and contrast** ***active and passive transport across the plasma membrane.***

Content Background

Real-World Connection Receptor-mediated endocytosis involves a specific receptor molecule located in pits on the plasma membrane. These receptors cause the plasma membrane surrounding the receptor to undergo endocytosis and become an internal transport vesicle. Molecules that are taken into cells in this manner include cholesterol, transferrin (an iron-binding protein), insulin, and other protein hormones. The inherited condition hypercholesterolemia (high blood cholesterol) occurs when receptors are unable to bind to the cholesterol and the cholesterol stays in the blood instead of entering the cells.

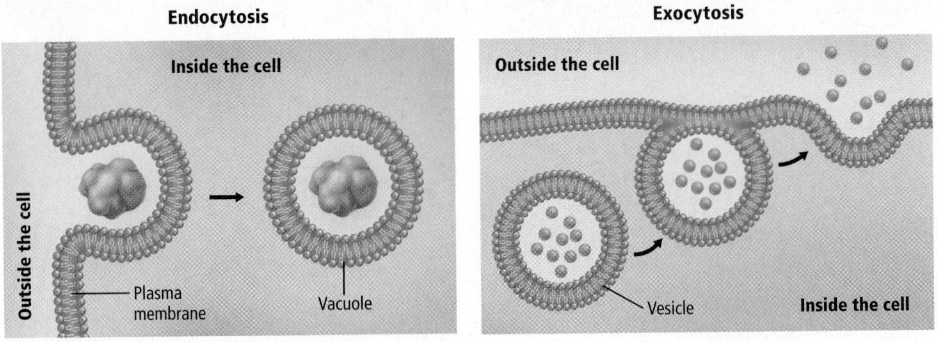

■ **Figure 29**
Left: Large substances can enter a cell by endocytosis.
Right: Substances can be deposited outside the cell by exocytosis.

S

Transport of Large Particles

Some substances are too large to move through the plasma membrane by diffusion or transport proteins and must get inside the cell by a different process. **Endocytosis** is the process by which a cell surrounds a substance in the outside environment, enclosing the substance in a portion of the plasma membrane. The membrane then pinches off and leaves the substance inside the cell. The substance shown on the left in **Figure 29** is engulfed and enclosed by a portion of the cell's plasma membrane. The membrane then pinches off inside of the cell, and the resulting vacuole, with its contents, moves to the inside of the cell.

Exocytosis is the secretion of materials at the plasma membrane. The illustration on the right in **Figure 29** shows that exocytosis is the reverse of endocytosis. Cells use exocytosis to expel wastes and to secrete substances, such as hormones, produced by the cell. Both endocytosis and exocytosis require the input of energy. Cells maintain homeostasis by moving substances into and out of the cell. Some transport processes require additional energy input, while others do not. Together, the different types of transport allow a cell to interact with its environment while maintaining homeostasis.

Section 4 Assessment

Section Summary

- Cells maintain homeostasis using passive and active transport.
- Concentration, temperature, and pressure affect the rate of diffusion.
- Cells must maintain homeostasis in all types of solutions, including isotonic, hypotonic, and hypertonic.
- Some large molecules are moved into and out of the cell using endocytosis and exocytosis.

Understand Main Ideas

1. MAIN Idea **List and describe** the types of cellular transport.
2. **Describe** how the plasma membrane controls what goes into and comes out of a cell.
3. **Sketch** a before and an after diagram of an animal cell placed in a hypotonic solution.
4. **Contrast** how facilitated diffusion is different from active transport.

Think Critically

5. **Describe** Some organisms that normally live in pond water contain water pumps. These pumps continually pump water out of the cell. Describe a scenario that might reverse the action of the pump.
6. **Summarize** the role of the phospholipid bilayer in cellular transport in living cells.

S Skill Practice

BL OL AL Visual Literacy

Have students examine Figure 29 and make a Venn diagram comparing and contrasting the processes of endocytosis and exocytosis.

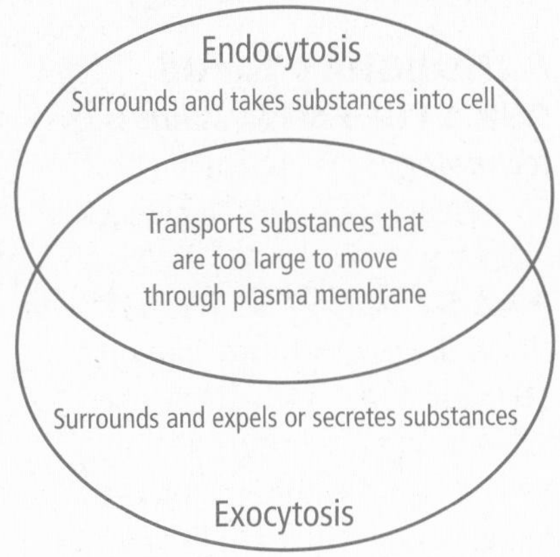

Formative Assessment

Evaluation Quiz students on the different types of cellular transport. Ask them to list and compare the various modes of cellular transport. Answers should include diffusion, osmosis, active transport, endocytosis, and exocytosis.

Remediation Have students write a sentence defining each of the vocabulary words that refer to methods of cellular transport.

Section 4 Assessment

1. Lists and descriptions should include diffusion, osmosis, active transport, endocytosis, and exocytosis.
2. The plasma membrane is selectively permeable. Cellular transport methods also move substances into and out of a cell.
3. Drawings should demonstrate that the animal cell will swell and burst.
4. Facilitated diffusion moves substances with the gradient and does not require cellular energy to transport a molecule across the plasma membrane. Active transport requires energy because it moves substances against the gradient.
5. Placing the protist in a hypertonic solution may reverse the pump.
6. Answers may vary but may be similar to the following: Phospholipid bilayers provide a fluid structure surrounding the cell. It provides a selectively permeable fluid barrier that allows substances through by diffusion, facilitated diffusion, and active transport.

CUTTING-EDGE BIOLOGY

Purpose
Students will relate nanotechnology to biology through real-world applications.
E.2, F.6.

Anticipatory Guide
ASK STUDENTS: ***What is technology?*** the application of scientific research to society's needs and problems

ASK STUDENTS: ***What do you think the prefix* nano- *means?*** possible answers: very small, one-billionth part of something, as in *nanosecond* As students read the feature they will learn how nanotechnology can lead to more advancements in medicine.

Background
Nanosurgery using lasers requires a refinement of existing technology. Lasers already are used for many medical techniques. They can be used in surgery in place of a surgical knife to make incisions with little loss of blood. Lasers also are used to reshape the corneas of eyes to improve vision.

CUTTING-EDGE BIOLOGY

EXPLORING NANOTECHNOLOGY

Imagine that cancer cells could be detected and destroyed one by one, or that a new drug could be tested on a single cell to evaluate its clinical performance. Advances in technologies that allow scientists to focus on individual cells might make these scenarios a reality in the near future.

Nanotechnology (na no tek NAW luh jee) is the branch of science that deals with the development and use of devices on the nanometer scale. A nanometer (nm) is one billionth of a meter (10^{-9} m). To put this scale into perspective, consider that most human cells are between 10,000 and 20,000 nm in diameter. Nanotechnology is a fast-growing branch of science that likely will leave its mark on everything from electronics to medicine.

Atomic force microscopes At the National Institute of Advanced Industrial Science and Technology in Hyogo, Japan, researchers are using nanotechnology in the form of an atomic force microscope (AFM) to operate on single cells. The microscope is actually used as a "nanoneedle." The AFM creates a visual image of a cell using a microscopic sensor that scans the cell. Then the probe of the AFM, sharpened into a needle tip that is approximately 200 nm in diameter, can be inserted into the cell without damaging the cell membrane.

Some scientists envision many applications for this technique. The nanoneedle might help scientists study how a cell responds to a new drug or how the chemistry of a diseased cell differs from that of a healthy cell. Another application for the nanoneedle might be to insert DNA strands directly into the nucleus of a cell to test new gene therapy techniques that might correct genetic disorders.

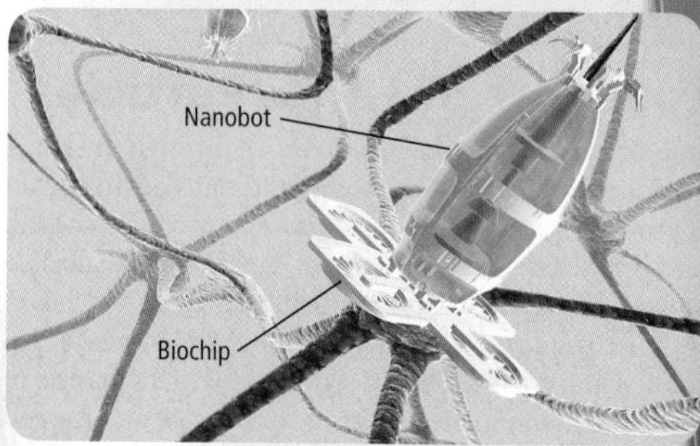

This computer-generated image shows a nanobot armed with a biochip. Someday, a biochip, which is an electronic device that contains organic materials, might repair a damaged nerve cell.

Lasers Nanotechnology applications, perhaps in the form of nanosurgery, could be used to investigate how cells work or to destroy individual cancer cells without harming nearby healthy cells. Researchers at Harvard University have developed a laser technique that allows them to manipulate a specific component of the cell's internal parts without causing damage to the cell membrane or other cell structures. Imagine having the capability to perform extremely delicate surgery on a cellular level!

In the future, nanotechnology might be our first line of defense to treat cancer. It also might become the standard technique to test new drugs or even become a favored treatment used in gene therapy.

WRITING in Biology
Review Write an overview of one technology related to medicine and healthcare that you find interesting. Describe its advantages and challenges. You may include a presentation with your overview.

WRITING in Biology
RUBRIC Use the modifiable rubric found on your eTeacherEdition Online to assess writing assignments.

Follow-Up Discussion
After the students prepare their reviews, have several students share their reviews with the class. How did they see nanotechnology impacting health care? How is nanotechnology different from what is currently available? What advantages does nanotechnology offer the scientific community? What advantages does nanotechnology offer the doctor and patient? Were any disadvantages or ethical concerns from the nanotechnology uncovered? What did the students learn by doing their research?

WebQuest

BIOLAB

WHICH SUBSTANCES WILL PASS THROUGH A SELECTIVELY PERMEABLE MEMBRANE?

Background: All membranes in cells are selectively permeable. In this lab, you will examine the movement of some biologically important molecules through a dialysis membrane that is analogous to the plasma membrane. Because a dialysis membrane has tiny pores, it is permeable only for tiny molecules.

Question: *Which substances pass through a dialysis membrane?*

Materials

cellulose dialysis tubing (2)
400-mL beakers (2)
string
scissors
distilled water
small plastic dishpan
starch solution
albumin solution
glucose solution
NaCl solution
iodine solution (tests starch)
anhydrous Benedict's reagent (tests glucose)
silver nitrate solution (tests NaCl)
biuret reagent (tests albumin)
10-mL graduated cylinder
test tubes (2)
test-tube rack
funnel
wax pencil
eye droppers

Safety Precautions

Procedure

1. Read and complete the lab safety form.
2. Construct a data table as instructed by your teacher. Predict which substances will pass through the dialysis membrane.
3. Collect two lengths of dialysis tubing, two 400-mL beakers, and the two solutions that you have been assigned to test.
4. Label the beakers with the type of solution that you place in the dialysis tubing.
5. With a partner, prepare and fill one length of dialysis tubing with one solution. Rinse the outside of the bag thoroughly. Place the filled tubing bag into a beaker that contains distilled water.
6. Repeat Step 5 using the second solution.
7. After 45 minutes, transfer some of the water from each beaker into separate test tubes.
8. Add a few drops of the appropriate test reagent to the water.
9. Record your results and determine whether your prediction was correct. Compare your results with those of other groups in your class and record the results for the two solutions that you did not test.
10. **Cleanup and Disposal** Wash and return all reusable materials. Dispose of test solutions and used dialysis tubing as directed by your teacher. Wash your hands thoroughly after using any chemical reagent.

Analyze and Conclude

1. **Evaluate** Did your test molecules pass through the dialysis tubing? Explain.
2. **Think Critically** What characteristics of a plasma membrane give it more control over the movement of molecules than the dialysis membrane has?
3. **Error Analysis** How could failing to rinse the dialysis tube bags with distilled water prior to placing them in the beaker cause a false positive test for the presence of a dissolved molecule? What other sources of error might lead to inaccurate results?

POSTER SESSION

Communicate A disease called cystic fibrosis occurs when plasma membranes lack a molecule that helps transport chloride ions. Research this disease and present your finding to your class using a poster.

BIOLAB

? Inquiry BioLab

For a lab worksheet, use your eTeacherEdition Online.

RUBRIC A rubric for evaluating BioLabs is found on your eTeacherEdition Online.

Est. Time 75 min

Content Background

Dialysis membranes are used in the laboratory to separate proteins and nucleic acids from small molecules that may be present as contaminants. They also are used in artificial kidneys for dialysis. Clinitest test tablets or strips are used to test for glucose in the urine. The test for albumin uses biuret reagent, which reacts with the peptide bonds of proteins to produce a pink-to-purple color change depending on the number of peptide bonds. The chloride ion can be detected by adding silver nitrate ($AgNO_3$), which will produce a milky-white precipitate. Adding iodine will create a blue-black color.

Alternative Materials Jars or cups of the appropriate size may be substituted for the beakers.

Safety Precaution Approve lab safety forms before work begins.

Teaching Strategies

- Before class, prepare a set of control samples showing a positive reaction for each of the molecules tested.
- Cut the dialysis tubing prior to lab and have it soaking in distilled water ready for use. You probably will want to demonstrate how to prepare the bags and fill them using a funnel.

Alternative Teaching Demo

You may prepare just one set of bags for each molecule in solution and test samples as a class demo.

Analyze and Conclude

1. Phospholipid, enzyme, DNA, and fat molecules are all too large to pass through the membrane. Oxygen and fructose should pass through easily.
2. Carrier proteins and protein pumps help move molecules in a cell. The phospholipid bilayer can engulf very large molecules or groups of molecules in vacuoles to move them into and out of the cell.
3. If bags are not rinsed thoroughly after filling them with a solution, some of the solution might remain on the outside of the bag and would be present in the beaker without passing through the dialysis membrane. Accept all reasonable analyses.

Chapter 7

Study Guide

ConnectED

Students can use the following to review the chapter.

Review

Vocabulary eGames
Vocabulary eFlashcards
Vocabulary PuzzleMaker

Assessment

Online Quizzes
Online Test Practice
Standardized Test Practice

Use the *ExamView® Assessment Suite* CD-ROM to:

- create multiple versions of tests
- create modified tests with one mouse click
- edit existing questions and add your own questions
- build tests aligned with state standards using built-in state curriculum tags
- change English tests to Spanish with one mouse click
- track students' progress using the Teacher Management System

Chapter 7 Study Guide

THEME FOCUS Scientific Inquiry It was through scientific inquiry that the microscope, cells, and protozoans were discovered. These discoveries led to new branches of science.

BIG Idea Cells are the structural and functional units of all living things.

Section 1 Cell Discovery and Theory

cell (p. 182)
cell theory (p. 183)
plasma membrane (p. 185)
eukaryotic cell (p. 186)
nucleus (p. 186)
organelle (p. 186)
prokaryotic cell (p. 186)

MAIN Idea **The invention of the microscope led to the discovery of cells.**

- Microscopes have been used as tools for scientific study since the late 1500s.
- Scientists use different types of microscopes to study cells.
- The cell theory summarizes three principles.
- There are two broad groups of cell types: prokaryotic cells and eukaryotic cells.
- Eukaryotic cells each contain a nucleus and organelles.

Section 2 Plasma Membrane

selective permeability (p. 187)
phospholipid bilayer (p. 188)
transport protein (p. 189)
fluid mosaic model (p. 190)

MAIN Idea **The plasma membrane helps to maintain a cell's homeostasis.**

- Selective permeability is the property of the plasma membrane that allows it to control what enters and leaves the cell.
- The plasma membrane is made up of two layers of phospholipid molecules.
- Cholesterol and transport proteins aid in the function of the plasma membrane.
- The fluid mosaic model describes the plasma membrane.

Section 3 Structures and Organelles

cytoplasm (p. 191)
cytoskeleton (p. 191)
nucleolus (p. 193)
ribosome (p. 193)
endoplasmic reticulum (p. 194)
Golgi apparatus (p. 195)
vacuole (p. 195)
centriole (p. 196)
lysosome (p. 196)
chloroplast (p. 197)
mitochondrion (p. 197)
cell wall (p. 198)
cilium (p. 198)
flagellum (p. 198)

MAIN Idea **Eukaryotic cells contain organelles that allow the specialization and the separation of functions within the cell.**

- Eukaryotic cells contain membrane-bound organelles in the cytoplasm that perform cell functions.
- Ribosomes are the sites of protein synthesis.
- Mitochondria are the powerhouses of cells.
- Plant and animal cells contain many of the same organelles, while other organelles are unique to either plant cells or animal cells.

Section 4 Cellular Transport

diffusion (p. 201)
dynamic equilibrium (p. 202)
facilitated diffusion (p. 202)
osmosis (p. 203)
hypotonic solution (p. 204)
isotonic solution (p. 204)
active transport (p. 205)
hypertonic solution (p. 205)
endocytosis (p. 207)
exocytosis (p. 207)

MAIN Idea **Cellular transport moves substances within the cell and moves substances into and out of the cell.**

- Cells maintain homeostasis using passive and active transport.
- Concentration, temperature, and pressure affect the rate of diffusion.
- Cells must maintain homeostasis in all types of solutions, including isotonic, hypotonic, and hypertonic.
- Some large molecules are moved into and out of the cell using endocytosis and exocytosis.

Review **Vocabulary PuzzleMaker**

For additional practice with vocabulary, have students access the Vocabulary PuzzleMaker online.

Review **Vocabulary eGames**

Section 1

Vocabulary Review

Each of the following sentences is false. Make each sentence true by replacing the italicized word with a vocabulary term from the Study Guide page.

1. The *nucleus* is a structure that surrounds a cell and helps control what enters and exits the cell.
2. A(n) *prokaryote* has membrane-bound organelles.
3. *Organelles* are basic units of all organisms.

Understand Main Ideas

4. If a microscope has a series of three lenses that magnify individually 5×, 5×, and 7×, what is the total magnification of the microscope?
   A. 25× **C.** 17×
   B. 35× **D.** 175×
5. Which is not part of the cell theory?
   A. The basic unit of life is the cell.
   B. Cells came from preexisting cells.
   C. All living organisms are composed of cells.
   D. Cells contain membrane-bound organelles.

Use the photo to answer question 6.

Color-Enhanced TEM Magnification: 15,000×

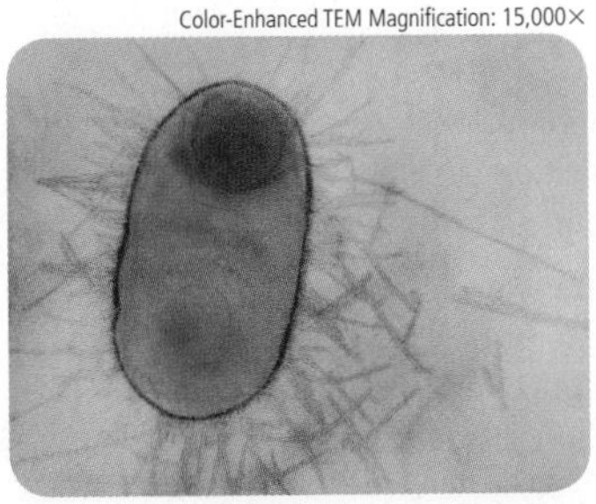

6. The photomicrograph shows which kind of cell?
   A. prokaryotic cell **C.** animal cell
   B. eukaryotic cell **D.** plant cell

Constructed Response

7. MAIN Idea Explain how the development of the microscope changed how scientists studied living organisms.
8. **Short Answer** Compare and contrast prokaryotic cells and eukaryotic cells.

Think Critically

9. **THEME FOCUS Scientific Inquiry** Why might a microscopist, who specializes in the use of microscopes to examine specimens, use a light microscope instead of an electron microscope?
10. **Analyze** A material is found in an asteroid that might be a cell. What criteria must the material meet to be considered a cell?

Section 2

Vocabulary Review

Complete the sentences below using vocabulary terms from the Study Guide page.

11. A ________ is the basic structure that makes up the plasma membrane.
12. ________ proteins move needed substances or waste materials through the plasma membrane.
13. ________ is the property that allows only some substances in and out of a cell.

Understand Main Ideas

14. Which of the following orientations of phospholipids best represents the phospholipid bilayer of the plasma membrane?

A. 
C. 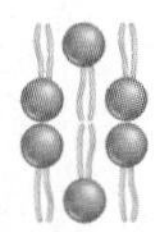
B. 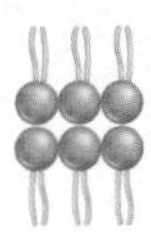
D. 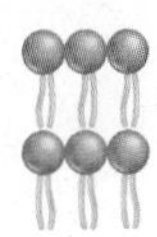

15. Which situation would increase the fluidity of a phospholipid bilayer?
   A. decreasing the temperature
   B. increasing the number of proteins
   C. increasing the number of cholesterol molecules
   D. increasing the number of unsaturated fatty acids

Chapter 7 Assessment

Section 1

Vocabulary Review

1. plasma membrane
2. eukaryotic cell
3. cells

Understand Main Ideas

4. D
5. D
6. A

Constructed Response

7. Microscopes enable scientists to observe and study things that are smaller than those visible to the unaided eye. Technologically advanced microscopes give views of microscopic surfaces and structures at the atomic level, which has made it possible to gather detailed information on the structure and function of organisms.
8. Prokaryotic cells and eukaryotic cells are both basic structural units of organisms. Prokaryotic cells do not have specialized internal structures; eukaryotic cells do.

Think Critically

9. Light microscopes have a large range of magnification capability at high resolutions and do not require that the specimen be damaged or destroyed.
10. Answers will vary but should describe that the material has a cell wall and/or a cell membrane and conforms to the principles of cell theory.

Section 2

Vocabulary Review

11. phospholipid
12. transport
13. Selective permeability

Understand Main Ideas

14. A
15. C

Assessment Online Test Practice

Constructed Response

16. The plasma membrane controls what enters and leaves a cell, maintaining homeostasis.
17. A mosaic is a type of artwork in which the overall image is made from many small units of other materials, such as tiles or even other images. The term *fluid mosaic model* is used to describe the surface of a cell because it is composed of many subunits that are capable of moving to make the whole.
18. In the plasma membrane, the hydrophilic, polar headgroups are on the outside, allowing them to interact with the watery environment outside the cell. The hydrophobic, nonpolar tails are on the inside of the membrane and do not interact with the outside environment.

Think Critically

19. The cell could no longer maintain homeostasis and would eventually die.
20. Without cholesterol, the cell's plasma membrane would be less fluid, possibly not allowing important substances to pass across the membrane.

Section 3

Vocabulary Review

21. vacuole
22. nucleolus
23. mitochondrion
24. Golgi apparatus

Understand Main Ideas

25. C
26. B
27. B

Constructed Response

28. The cytoskeleton can be seen only with a high-resolution microscope, which is a recent invention.

Constructed Response

16. MAIN Idea Explain how the plasma membrane maintains homeostasis within a cell.

17. **Open Ended** Explain what a mosaic is and then explain why the term *fluid mosaic model* is used to describe the plasma membrane.

18. **Short Answer** How does the orientation of the phospholipids in the bilayer allow a cell to interact with its internal and external environments?

Think Critically

19. **Hypothesize** how a cell would be affected if it lost the ability to be selectively permeable.

20. **Predict** What might happen to a cell if it no longer could produce cholesterol?

Section 3

Vocabulary Review

Fill in each blank with the vocabulary term from the Study Guide page that matches the function definition.

21. __________ stores wastes
22. __________ produces ribosomes
23. __________ generates energy for a cell
24. __________ sorts proteins into vesicles

Understand Main Ideas

Use the diagram below to answer questions 25 and 26.

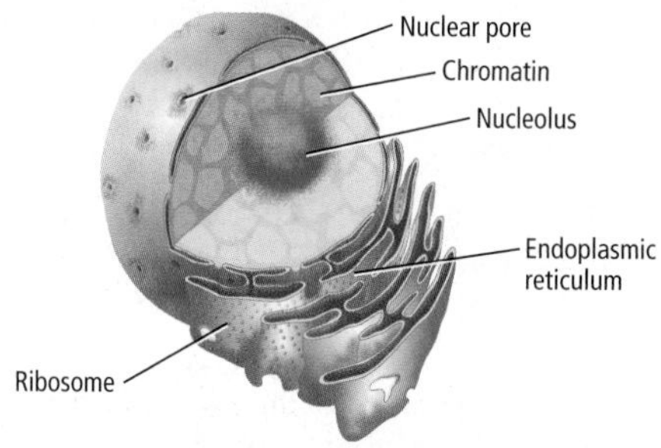

25. Which structure synthesizes proteins that will be used by the cell?
    A. chromatin
    B. nucleolus
    C. ribosome
    D. endoplasmic reticulum

26. Which is the site of protein synthesis?
    A. nuclear pore
    B. endoplasmic reticulum
    C. chromatin
    D. nucleolus

27. In which structure would you expect to find a cell wall?
    A. human skin cell
    B. cell from an oak tree
    C. blood cell from a cat
    D. liver cell from a mouse

Constructed Response

28. **Short Answer** Describe why the cytoskeleton within the cytoplasm was a recent discovery.

29. **Short Answer** Compare the structures and functions of the mitochondrion and chloroplast below.

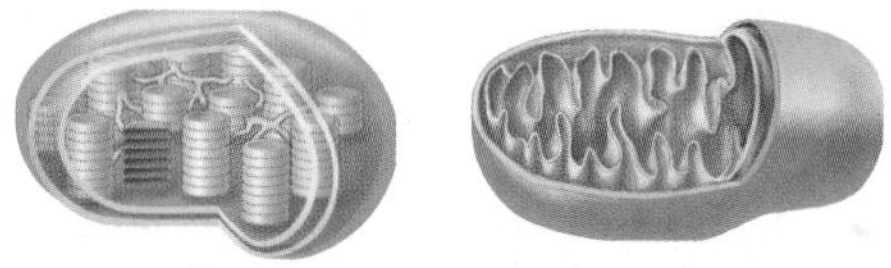

30. MAIN Idea Suggest a reason why packets of proteins collected in a vacuole might merge with lysosomes.

Think Critically

31. **Identify** a specific example in which the cell wall structure has aided the survival of a plant in its natural habitat.

32. **Infer** why plant cells that transport water against the force of gravity contain many more mitochondria than other plant cells do.

Section 4

Vocabulary Review

Explain the difference in the terms in each pair below. Then explain how the terms are related.

33. active transport, facilitated diffusion
34. endocytosis, exocytosis
35. hypertonic solution, hypotonic solution

---

29. Mitochondria convert the energy stored in food molecules to a different energy-storing substance (ATP) that can be used by the cell. Chloroplasts capture light energy and convert it to chemical energy. Both Organelles rely on vast surface area to function correctly.
30. If the packets contain waste products, merging with lysosomes would destroy the contents.

Think Critically

31. Examples will vary. The cell wall in tree cells supports the tree so it can grow above other plants where sunlight is not blocked from its leaves.
32. Plant cells need more energy to transport water against the force of gravity. Additional mitochondria provide the energy.

Understand Main Ideas

36. Which is not a factor that affects the rate of diffusion?
A. conductivity **C.** pressure
B. concentration **D.** temperature

37. Which type of transport requires energy input from the cell?
A. active transport
B. facilitated diffusion
C. osmosis
D. simple diffusion

Constructed Response

38. Short Answer Why is active transport an energy-utilizing process?

39. Short Answer Some protists that live in a hypotonic pond environment have cell membrane adaptations that slow water uptake. What adaptations might this protist living in the hypertonic Great Salt Lake have?

LM Magnification: 75×

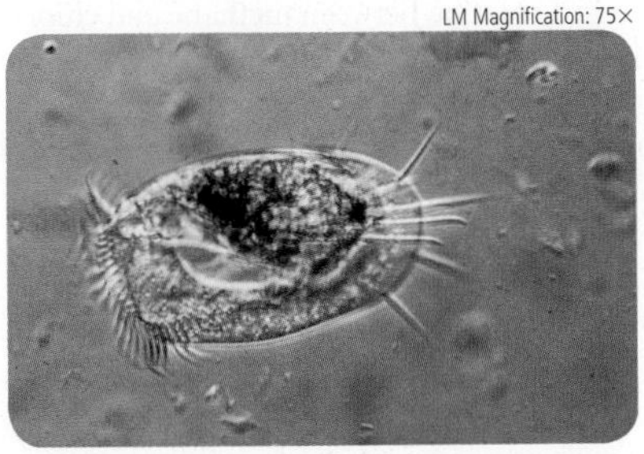

40. MAIN Idea Summarize how cellular transport helps maintain homeostasis within a cell.

Think Critically

41. Hypothesize how oxygen crosses the plasma membrane if the concentration of oxygen is lower inside the cell than it is outside the cell.

42. Analyze Farming and watering that are done in very dry regions of the world leave salts that accumulate in the soil as water evaporates. Based on what you know about concentration gradients, why does increasing soil salinity have adverse effects on plant cells?

Summative Assessment

43. BIG Idea Cells are the structural and functional units of living things. Create an analogy where "smaller parts" provide structure and function for a "whole." Relate it to cells and living things by giving specific examples.

44. Use what you have learned about osmosis and cellular transport to design an apparatus that would enable a freshwater fish to survive in a saltwater habitat.

45. WRITING in Biology Create a poem that describes the functions of at least five cell organelles.

DBQ Document-Based Questions

The graph below describes the relationship between the amount of glucose entering a cell and the rate at which the glucose enters the cell with the help of carrier proteins. Use this graph to answer questions 46 and 47.

Data obtained from: Raven, P.H., and Johnson, G.B. 2002. *Biology*, 6th ed.: 99.

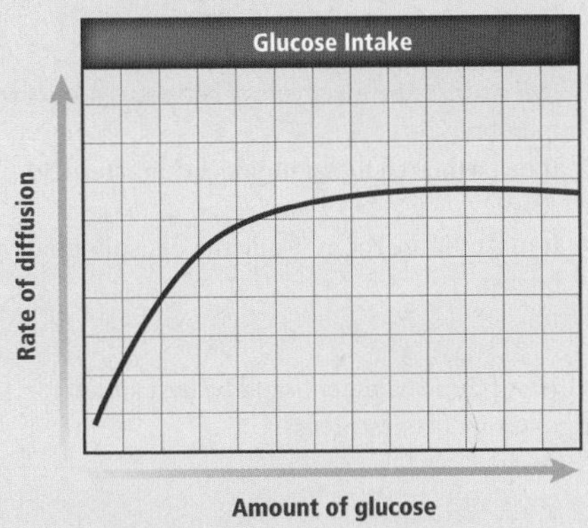

46. Summarize the relationship between the amount of glucose and the rate of diffusion.

47. Infer why the rate of diffusion tapers off with higher amounts of glucose. Make an illustration to explain your answer.

Section 4

Vocabulary Review

33. Active transport requires energy input; facilitated diffusion does not. Both are methods of moving materials into and out of a cell.
34. In endocytosis, a cell surrounds and takes in substances. In exocytosis, a cell expels substances. Both involve movement of substances into and out of the cell.
35. In a hypertonic solution, the concentration of dissolved substances outside the cell is higher than inside. In a hypotonic solution, the concentration is higher inside. Both can lead to the movement of molecules across the cell membrane.

Understand Main Ideas

36. A
37. A

Constructed Response

38. In active transport, substances are moving against a concentration gradient, which requires energy.
39. Cells in a hypertonic environment tend to lose water, so a protist in the Great Salt Lake would probably adapt to taking in water more quickly to counteract the outflow.
40. Cells require substances to come in and move out. The various forms of cellular transport bring the needed substances in and export wastes and other substances. These activities contribute to homeostasis.

Think Critically

41. Oxygen must enter the cell by active transport.
42. Increasing salinity could place the plant cells in a hypertonic environment, dehydrating the cells and disrupting homeostasis.

Summative Assessment

43. Answers will vary. Students may say that cells are to living things as humans are to civilizations. Humans have different jobs to make a civilization run well, just as cells are specialized to perform certain functions for an organism.
44. Students would have to design an apparatus that would prevent osmosis from occuring.
45. Answers will vary. Be sure five organelles are described.

DBQ Document-Based Questions

Raven, P. H. and Johnson, G. B. 2002. *Biology*, 6th edition. McGraw Hill Higher Education, New York: 99.

46. As the amount of glucose increases, the diffusion rate increases until a maximum rate is reached, as shown by the graph line.
47. The rate of diffusion levels off because the carrier proteins cannot carry more glucose; there are no more carriers available to transport the glucose.

Assessment Online Test Practice

Standardized Test Practice

Multiple Choice

1. B 5. C 9. D
2. B 6. C
3. D 7. C
4. C 8. D

Short Answer

10. Possible answers are shown in the boxes.

Nucleus contains genetic information that manages protein synthesis.

↓ **Ribosomes in cytoplasm** leave the nucleus and manufacture proteins for use by the same cell in its cytoplasm.

↓ **Ribosomes on endoplasmic reticulum** leave the nucleus and manufacture proteins that will be exported and used by other cells.

↓ **Golgi apparatus** packages proteins in vesicle, to be transported within the cell or outside the cell.

11. Carbohydrates are important for energy storage and structural support. Lipids also store energy and are a major component of cellular membranes. Lipids also function as steroids and provide waterproof coatings for small cells. Proteins transport substances, catalyze reactions, and also serve as hormones. The main functions of nucleic acids are to store and communicate genetic information.
12. Water has a negative area (around the O atom) and positive areas (around the H atoms). These areas with different charges can form weak bonds with other polar, charged molecules and enable them to dissolve in solutions.
13. The Cl atom has seven electrons in its outer orbit. It is an electron acceptor because it needs one electron to fill its outer energy level. It takes one electron from the K atom, which only has one electron in its outer energy level. Thus, the outer shell of this ion now has eight electrons. The ions are held together by an ionic bond.
14. Selective permeability allows the cell to control what enters and exits the cell. This means that the right amount of certain compounds needed to do the cell's work enter the cell, and waste materials leave the cell—even if the concentration gradient would not seem to promote the movement of these materials.
15. Answers can vary, but should reflect an understanding that sustainable use requires using less than is replaced by natural processes. For example: Shrimp are a renewable natural resource. If people catch just enough shrimp so that the shrimp population can thrive, this is a sustainable use of the resource.
16. Because they contain no membrane-bound organelles, they must have evolved earliest. Most later-evolved cells contain membrane-bound organelles, which is a sign of greater complexity in an organism.

Standardized Test Practice

Cumulative

Multiple Choice

Use the illustration below to answer questions 1 and 2.

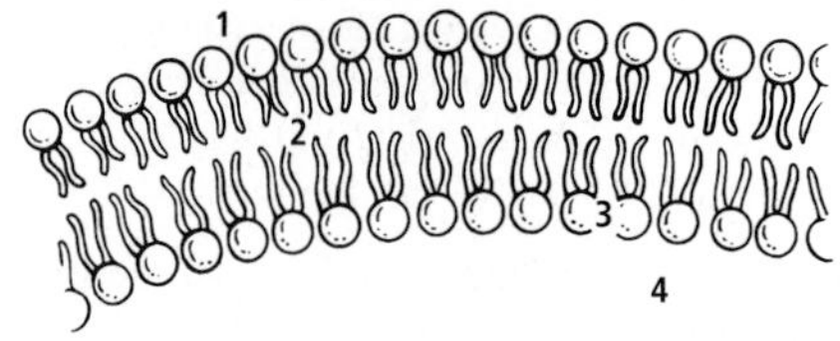

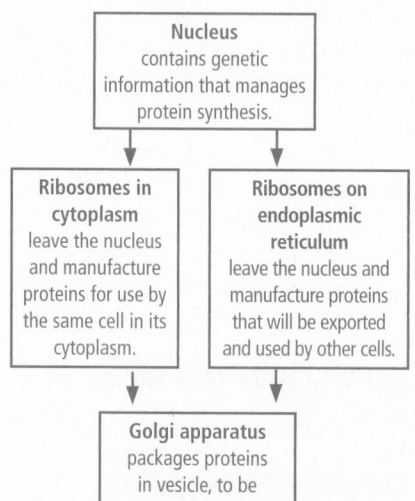

1. Which number in the illustration represents the location where you would expect to find water-insoluble substances?
   A. 1
   B. 2
   C. 3
   D. 4

2. Which is the effect of having the polar and nonpolar ends of phospholipid molecules oriented as they are in the illustration?
   A. It allows transport proteins to move easily through the membrane.
   B. It controls the movement of substances across the membrane.
   C. It helps the cell to maintain its characteristic shape.
   D. It makes more room inside the phospholipid bilayer.

3. Which of these habitats would be best suited for a population of *r*-strategists?
   A. desert
   B. grassland
   C. deciduous forest
   D. tropical rain forest

4. Which adaptation helps plants survive in a tundra biome?
   A. deciduous leaves that fall off as winter approaches
   B. leaves that store water
   C. roots that grow only a few centimeters deep
   D. underground stems that are protected from grazing animals

5. Which is a nonrenewable resource?
   A. clean water from freshwater sources
   B. energy provided by the Sun
   C. an animal species that has become extinct
   D. a type of fish that is caught in the ocean

6. In which type of cell would you find a chloroplast?
   A. prokaryote
   B. animal
   C. plant
   D. fungus

Use this incomplete equation to answer questions 7 and 8.

$$CH_4 + 4Cl_2 \rightarrow \_\_HCl + \_\_CCl_4$$

7. The chemical equation above shows what can happen in a reaction between methane and chlorine gas. The coefficients have been left out in the product side of the equation. Which is the correct coefficient for HCl?
   A. 1
   B. 2
   C. 4
   D. 8

8. Which is the minimum number of chlorine (Cl) atoms needed for the reaction shown in the equation?
   A. 1
   B. 2
   C. 4
   D. 8

9. Why is *Caulerpa taxifolia* considered an invasive species in some coastal areas of North America?
   A. It is dangerous to humans.
   B. It is nonnative to the area.
   C. It grows slowly and invades over time.
   D. It outcompetes native species for resources.

Short Answer

10. Use a flowchart to organize information about cell organelles and protein synthesis. For each step, analyze the role of the organelle in protein synthesis.

11. Compare and contrast the functions of carbohydrates, lipids, proteins, and nucleic acids.

12. State why the polarity of water molecules makes water a good solvent.

Use the figure below to answer question 13.

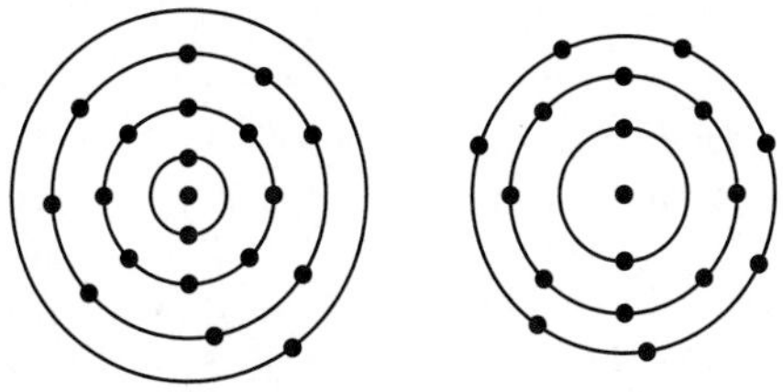

K
Atomic number 19

Cl
Atomic number 17

13. Use the figure to describe how the ionic compound potassium chloride (KCl) is formed.

14. What might happen if cell membranes were not selectively permeable?

15. Choose a specific natural resource and develop a plan for the sustainable use of that resource.

16. What can you infer about the evolution of bacterial cells from studying their structure?

Extended Response

The illustration below shows a single animal cell in an isotonic solution. Use the illustration to answer question 17.

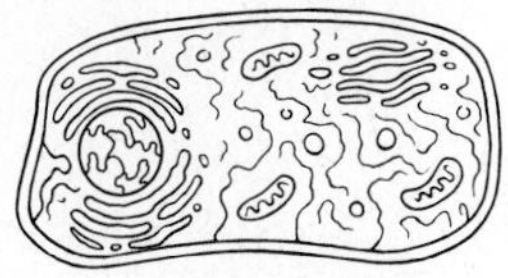

17. Describe what would happen to this cell in a hypertonic solution and in a hypotonic solution.

18. Explain why direct economic value is not the only important consideration of biodiversity.

19. Analyze why an electron microscope can produce higher magnification than a light microscope can.

20. Assess why transport proteins are needed to move certain substances across a cell membrane.

Essay Question

Recently, some international trade agreements have allowed scientists and companies to patent the discoveries they make about organisms and their genetic material. For instance, it is possible to patent seeds that have genes for disease resistance and plants that can be used in medicine or industry. Owners of patents now have greater control over the use of these organisms.

Using the information in the paragraph above, answer the following question in essay format.

21. Based on what you know about biodiversity, identify some pros and cons of a patent system. Write an essay exploring the pros and cons of patenting discoveries about organisms.

NEED EXTRA HELP?																					
If You Missed Question . . .	1	2	3	4	5	6	7	8	9	10	11	12	13	14	15	16	17	18	19	20	21
Review Section . . .	7.2	7.2	4.1	3.1	5.3	7.3	6.2	6.8	5.2	7.3	6.4	6.3	6.1	7.2	5.3	7.1	7.4	5.1	7.1	7.4	5.2

Extended Response

17. In a hypertonic solution, water will move out of the cell because the concentration of solute outside is higher, and the cell will shrivel. In a hypotonic solution, water will move into the cell because the concentration of solute is lower outside the cell, and the cell will swell or burst.

18. One reason is that economic values are not always known. The value of organisms in a diverse ecosystem may not be known, so it is shortsighted to consider only the economic value of things that are known. Moreover, there could be long-term indirect economic values—things that are unpredictable but have significant outcomes. Also, placing a value on biodiversity is difficult, and just considering economic values of biodiversity is not wise.

19. A light microscope depends on light bouncing off of a sample in order to produce an image. Therefore, there is a limit to the magnification that a light microscope can provide because the resolution of an image is not good after a certain magnification. An electron microscope, on the other hand, creates an image based on the number of electrons that pass through a sample. This allows for greater magnification. It also allows for imaging of three-dimensional samples.

20. Transport proteins are useful for materials that are water soluble, and therefore would not make it past the polar part of the phospholipid bilayer. They are also important in active transport where materials are moved against the concentration gradient.

Essay Question

21. Answers should focus on the positive and negative effects of patenting discoveries about organisms and how this would affect biodiversity. Positive effects could include the following: species might be protected better if there are patents involving their parts; knowledge about the uses of certain organisms could be shared in an organized way; people who invest a great deal of money into learning about the benefits of certain organisms would then be able to make money from their uses.

Some negative effects could include the following: ability to draw on biodiversity might be limited to people who have enough money to pay for patented materials; if parts of organisms, such as seeds, are patented, it might be hard for farmers to afford them; certain people might be left out and might not experience benefits after organisms are patented; a loss of biodiversity could result if only patented organisms were maintained from generation to generation.

Chapter 8 Organizer: Cellular Energy

LabManager™
Customize any lab with the LabManager™ CD-ROM.

Essential Questions	National Science Standards	Materials and Planning: Estimated times include cleanup and disposal, but do not include teacher prep time. For cleanup and disposal guidelines, see page 39T.	Est. Time (min)
Section 1 1. What are the two laws of thermodynamics? 2. What is the difference between an anabolic pathway and a catabolic pathway? 3. How does ATP work in a cell?	UCP.1–3; A.1, A.2; B.3, B.6; C.5; G.1, G.3	**Launch Lab,** p. 216: water, graduated cylinder, 250-mL beaker, thermometer, anhydrous calcium chloride, stirring rod, Epsom salts	20
		Demonstration, p. 220: molecular model set	20
		MiniLab 1, p. 220: beakers, straws, test tubes, stoppers, rack, bright light, aquatic plant such as *Elodea,* bromothymol blue solution, aluminum foil	10 min per day
Section 2 1. What are the two phases of photosynthesis? 2. What is the function of a chloroplast during the light reactions? 3. How can electron transport be described and diagramed?	UCP.1–3, UCP.5; A.1, A.2; B.3, B.6; C.5; G.1, G.3	**MiniLab 2,** p. 223: slides of plant and algae cells, microscope, pond water, freshwater algae samples, blank microscope slides, coverslips	15
		Demonstration, p. 224: test tubes, phenol red solution, straws, *Elodea* sprigs, light source	25
Section 3 1. What are the stages of cellular respiration? 2. What is the role of electron carriers in each stage of cellular respiration? 3. What are the similarities between alcoholic fermentation and lactic acid fermentation?	UCP.1–3, UCP.5; A.1, A.2; B.3, B.6; C.5; G.1	**Activity,** p. 228: clothespins	10
		Demonstration, p. 231: baker's yeast, water, sugar, flask, balloon	10
		Design Your Own BioLab, p. 235: materials appropriate for the students' lab designs, aquatic plant material, erlenmeyer flasks, test tubes, graduated cylinder, metric ruler, colored cellophane, aluminum foil, 150-watt lamp with reflector, baking soda solution, watch with a second hand	45

Suggested Time for Each Lesson

Class	Chapter Opener	Section 1	Section 2	Section 3	Assessment
Basic	45 min	90 min	45 min	45 min	45 min
General	25 min	90 min	55 min	55 min	45 min
Honors	5 min	40 min	155 min	160 min	45 min

ConnectED

connectED.mcgraw-hill.com

Access interactive learning opportunities and teaching resources using these icons located throughout your StudentWorks™ Plus Online and eTeacherEdition Online.

Chapter 8 Section Resources	Additional Chapter 8 Resources	Technology
FAST FILE Unit 2 Resources: Launch Lab Worksheet* MiniLab Worksheet* Study Guide (English/Spanish)* Section Quick Check **Reading Essentials 8.1** **Science Notebook 8.1*** **FAST FILE Unit 2 Resources:** MiniLab Worksheet* Study Guide (English/Spanish)* Section Quick Check **Reading Essentials 8.2** **Science Notebook 8.2*** **FAST FILE Unit 2 Resources:** BioLab Worksheet* Study Guide (English/Spanish)* Section Quick Check **Reading Essentials 8.3** **Science Notebook 8.3***	**FAST FILE Unit 2 Resources:** Chapter Diagnostic Test Concept Mapping* Real-World Biology Enrichment Chapter Tests A, B, and C **Transparencies:** Bellringer Transparencies* Biology Concepts Transparencies* **Lab Resources:** Laboratory Manual* Probeware Lab Manual* Forensics Lab Manual* Pre-AP Lab Manual* Open Inquiry in Biology* Guided Inquiry in Biology*	**Teaching Tools:** eTeacherEdition Online Classroom Presentation Toolkit CD-ROM* LabManager™ CD-ROM* Video Lab DVD* Virtual Lab CD-ROM* What's BIOLOGY Got To Do With It? StudentWorks™ Plus Online* **Chapter Assessment Tools:** Classroom Presentation Toolkit CD-ROM* *ExamView® Assessment Suite* CD-ROM **Web-Based Resources:** • StudentWorks™ Plus Online • eTeacherEdition Online • Animations* • The Interactive Time Line* • Interactive Tables* • Online Quizzes • Online Test Practice • Standardized Test Practice • Virtual Labs* • Multilingual eGlossary* • Vocabulary eGames* • Vocabulary eFlashcards • WebQuests • Personal Tutors

While all resources listed are appropriate for English learners, the * indicates resources with a strong visual or hands-on component for EL.

Teaching strategies and activities have been coded for differentiated instruction.

AL Activities for students working above grade level	OL Activities for students working on grade level	BL Activities for students working below grade level	EL Activities for English learners (also ELL)	COOP LEARN Activities designed for small cooperative group work

CHAPTER 8

Launch Lab
How is energy transformed?

Inquiry Launch Lab

For a lab worksheet, use your eTeacherEdition Online.

RUBRIC A rubric for evaluating Launch Labs is found on your eTeacherEdition Online.

Est. Time 20 min

Safety Precautions Approve lab safety forms before work begins. Have students wear goggles and aprons during the lab.

Teaching Strategies

- Anhydrous calcium chloride is available where swimming pool supplies are sold. Be sure to use only the anhydrous form—the hydrate will not work.
- Reinforce the following definitions and concepts prior to the lab: energy, specific forms of energy, transformation of energy among forms, and conservation of energy.

Procedure

1. Read and complete the lab safety form.
2. Measure 100 mL of **water** using a **graduated cylinder;** pour into a **250-mL beaker.** Use a **thermometer** to record the water temperature.
3. Measure 40 g of **anhydrous calcium chloride** ($CaCl_2$). Use a **stirring rod** to dissolve $CaCl_2$ in the water. Record the solution temperature every 15 seconds for 3 minutes.
4. Repeat steps 2 and 3 using 40 g of **Epsom salts** instead of $CaCl_2$.

CHAPTER 8
Cellular Energy

ConnectED
Your one-stop online resource
connectED.mcgraw-hill.com

Video
Audio
Review
Inquiry
WebQuest
Assessment
Concepts in Motion
Multilingual eGlossary

Launch Lab
How is energy transformed?

The flow of energy in living systems is driven by a variety of chemical reactions and chemical processes. Energy is transformed from the Sun's radiant energy to chemical energy to other forms of energy along the way. In this lab, you will observe two processes in which energy is transformed.

For a lab worksheet, use your StudentWorks™ Plus Online.

Inquiry Launch Lab

FOLDABLES®

Make a pocket book using the titles shown. Use it to organize your notes on stages of cellular respiration.

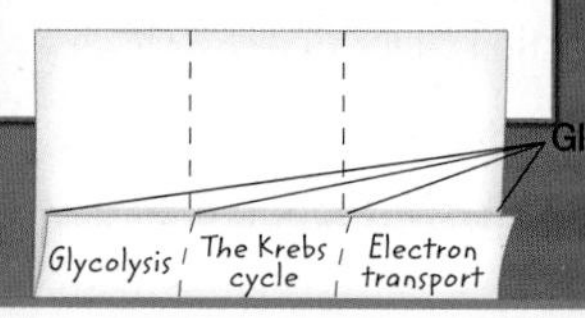

5. Graph your data using a different color for each process.

Analysis

1. **Describe** the graph of your data. Graphs should show that the temperature of the solution increased after the $CaCl_2$ was added. The temperature of the solution with Epsom salts decreased over time.
2. **Predict** what energy transformations occurred in the two processes. Energy transformation occurred when the anhydrous calcium solution was added because thermal energy was released. When Epsom salts were added, thermal energy was absorbed.

THEME FOCUS Energy
The Sun is the source of nearly all of the energy on Earth.

BIG Idea Photosynthesis converts the Sun's energy into chemical energy, while cellular respiration uses chemical energy to carry out life functions.

THEMES

Scientific Inquiry Scientific investigations are underway to research additional functions of mitochondria other than energy production.

Diversity There are variations in the process that converts light energy to chemical energy.

Energy Cellular processes break chemical bonds to use energy that is stored in them.

Homeostasis Many cellular processes that help maintain homeostasis require energy input.

Change The change of light energy to chemical energy via photosynthesis makes most of life possible.

Introduce the Chapter

Energy Transfer

ASK STUDENTS: ***What do you think of when you hear the word energy?*** Answers might include electric power or physical strength and endurance. Point out that energy exists in many forms and can be interconverted between these forms. Have students name forms of energy and write them on the board. ***What are some examples of energy conversion?*** Answers can include turning on a battery-powered radio or burning wood. ***Why is energy important for life?*** Answers will vary, but remind students about the different tasks that cells perform (replicating DNA, translating proteins, synthesizing carbohydrates).

BIG Idea

Picture Exploration Before reading the text in this section, have students look at the figures. **ASK STUDENTS:** ***What do you think you will learn from studying this section?*** how plants, animals, and other organisms obtain and use energy ***What is the source of this energy?*** the Sun ***What kinds of energy do the figures in this section illustrate?*** light energy and chemical energy

GOING GREEN Ask students to use clean rags instead of paper towels for lab cleanup. Have on hand washcloth-sized clean rags cut from old t-shirts and towels. These rags can be washed and reused. Hang a piece of string across the back of the classroom where students can hang their rags to dry.

Section 1

MAIN Idea

BL OL AL Energy Conversion
ASK STUDENTS: ***Name processes cells perform that require energy. How do cells obtain the energy needed to carry out daily functions?*** Students might think that the only form of energy for all types of cells is from food. Students will learn that while some organisms obtain energy by consuming other organisms (food), other organisms (plants) obtain energy by converting light energy into chemical energy.

D Develop Concepts
EL BL OL AL

Clarify a Misconception
ASK STUDENTS: ***What comes to mind when you hear the word work?*** Have students give examples. Point out that the word *work* has several meanings. Because energy is defined as the ability to do work or cause change, students may think of "work" only as a physical process involving movement. Write all of the forms of energy on the board (light, chemical, elastic, mechanical, heat, etc.) and point out that energy can take many forms. Have students give examples of each form of energy.

R Reading Strategy
BL OL COOP LEARN

Brainstorm Have students read the list of vocabulary terms for this section. Have students work in small groups to brainstorm ideas that come to mind when they see each term.
EL Have students make a three-column chart. Have them write the vocabulary words in the left column, draw or write what they think the word means in the middle column, and write the definition in the third column after reading the section.

Section 1

Reading Preview

Essential Questions
- What are the two laws of thermodynamics?
- What is the difference between an anabolic pathway and a catabolic pathway?
- How does ATP work in a cell?

Review Vocabulary
trophic level: each step in a food chain or a food web

New Vocabulary
energy
thermodynamics **R**
metabolism
photosynthesis
cellular respiration
adenosine triphosphate (ATP)

Multilingual eGlossary

How Organisms Obtain Energy

MAIN Idea All living organisms use energy to carry out all biological processes.

Real-World Reading Link New York City is sometimes called "the city that never sleeps." Much like the nonstop movement of a big city, living cells are sites of constant activity.

D Transformation of Energy

Many chemical reactions and processes in your cells are ongoing, even when you might not think that you are using any energy. Macromolecules are assembled and broken down, substances are transported across cell membranes, and genetic instructions are transmitted. All of these cellular activities require **energy**—the ability to do work. **Figure 1** shows some of the major advancements in the study of cellular energy. **Thermodynamics** is the study of the flow and transformation of energy in the universe.

Laws of thermodynamics The first law of thermodynamics is the law of conservation of energy, which states that energy can be converted from one form to another, but it cannot be created nor destroyed. For example, the stored energy in food is converted to chemical energy when you eat and to mechanical energy when you run or kick a ball.

Figure 1
Understand Cellular Energy
Scientific discoveries have led to a greater understanding of photosynthesis and cellular respiration.

Concepts in Motion
The Interactive Timeline

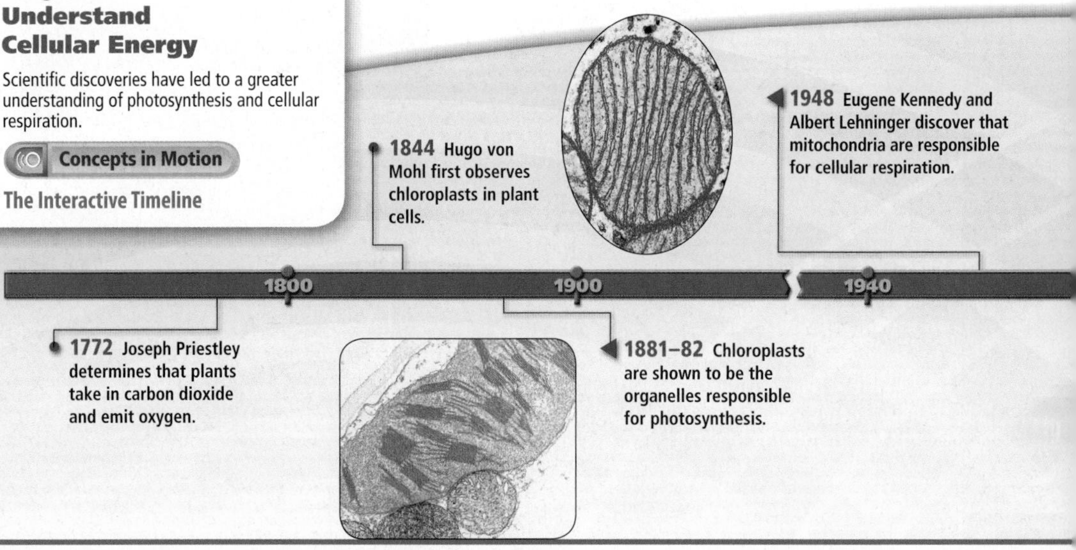

1844 Hugo von Mohl first observes chloroplasts in plant cells.
1948 Eugene Kennedy and Albert Lehninger discover that mitochondria are responsible for cellular respiration.
1800
1900
1940
1772 Joseph Priestley determines that plants take in carbon dioxide and emit oxygen.
1881–82 Chloroplasts are shown to be the organelles responsible for photosynthesis.

■ **Figure 2** Almost all the energy in living organisms originates from the Sun, and energy flows from autotrophs to heterotrophs.
Relate *the laws of thermodynamics to the organisms in the figure.*

S

The second law of thermodynamics states that energy cannot be converted without the loss of usable energy. The energy that is "lost" is generally converted to thermal energy. Entropy (EN truh pee) is the measure of disorder, or unusable energy, in a system. Therefore, the second law of thermodynamics can also be stated as "entropy increases." One example of the second law of thermodynamics is evident in food chains. Recall that in a food chain, the amount of usable energy that is available to the next trophic level decreases.

Autotrophs and heterotrophs All organisms need energy to live. Directly or indirectly, nearly all the energy for life comes from the Sun. Some organisms make their own food, while others must obtain it from other organisms. Autotrophs are organisms that make their own food. Some autotrophs, called chemoautotrophs, use inorganic substances such as hydrogen sulfide as a source of energy. Other autotrophs, such as the plant in **Figure 2,** convert light energy from the Sun into chemical energy. Autotrophs that convert energy from the Sun are called photoautotrophs. Heterotrophs, such as the aphid and the ladybug in **Figure 2,** are organisms that need to ingest food to obtain energy.

D
W

VOCABULARY
WORD ORIGIN
Autotroph
comes from the Greek word *autotrophos,* meaning *supplying one's own food*

1980 Exploring the mitochondria of fruit flies and mice, Jaime Miquel provides the first evidence that mitochondrial breakdown causes aging.

2002 Josephine S. Modica-Napolitano proposes that differences in healthy and cancerous mitochondria could lead to early cancer detection and new cancer treatments.

1960 — 1980 — 2000

1993 Fossils of the earliest known prokaryotic cells are unearthed. These cells carried out photosynthesis.

2009 Research shows that defects in mitochondria may be linked to diseases such as Parkinson's and Alzheimer's.

S Skill Practice

OL Visual Literacy

Have students pay close attention to the energy source used by each organism shown in Figure 2.
SAY TO STUDENTS: ***Make a list of five heterotrophs not shown in the figure. Research what type of food they eat—autotrophs, other heterotrophs, or both.***

D Develop Concepts

OL AL Scaffolding

ASK STUDENTS: ***What is energy?*** the ability to do work ***Can energy be created?*** No; energy exists in many forms. ***List some energy forms.*** thermal/heat, mechanical, elastic, chemical, light ***Analyze why living things need energy.*** to grow, move, reproduce, etc. ***How do humans obtain energy?*** Humans obtain energy by eating and digesting food.

W Writing Support

BL OL AL Creative Writing

Have students write a short poem describing the flow of energy from autotrophs to heterotrophs. Encourage students to describe the central role of the Sun as an energy source.

Concepts in Motion
The Interactive Timeline

Differentiated Instruction

Hearing Impaired When conducting MiniLab 1 on page 220, control the noise level in the classroom. This will allow students with hearing difficulties to communicate more easily with their group members and to hear any instructions that you give.

For more tips, see pages 14T–15T.

■ **Caption Question Fig. 2** Energy is neither created nor destroyed by the organisms in the food chain; it is converted to usable forms. In the conversion of energy, some energy is converted to an unusable form—thermal energy—thus increasing the entropy of the system.

? Inquiry Launch Lab

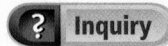

Assess Content Development
Assess how understanding has developed when students revisit the Launch Lab analysis questions.

MiniLab 1

? Inquiry MiniLab

For a lab worksheet, use your eTeacherEdition Online.

RUBRIC A rubric for evaluating MiniLabs is found on your eTeacherEdition Online.

Est. Time 10 min per day for two days

Safety Precautions Approve lab safety forms before work begins.

Teaching Strategy Ensure that students understand that BTB returns to blue when CO_2 is used up during photosynthesis.

Analysis

Expected results of color changes:

Tube Contents	Treatment	Initial Color	Final Color
BTB, CO_2, *Elodea*	Dark	Yellow	Yellow
BTB, CO_2, *Elodea*	Light	Yellow	Blue

1. The tube wrapped in aluminum foil (control) demonstrates that carbon dioxide is used by the plant only when in the light and is therefore able to perform photosynthesis.
2. In photosynthesis, plants take in CO_2 and convert it, using light energy, to sugars and oxygen. Plants and animals both perform cellular respiration, which uses oxygen to burn carbohydrates, producing carbon dioxide. The two processes are interdependent.

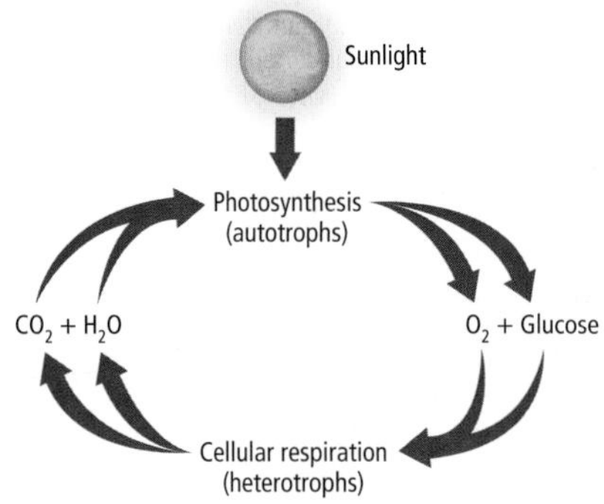

■ **Figure 3** In an ecosystem, photosynthesis and cellular respiration form a cycle.
Identify *the anabolic and catabolic pathways in the figure.*

? Inquiry Launch Lab

Review Based on what you have read about energy transformations, how would you now answer the analysis questions?

Metabolism

All of the chemical reactions in a cell are referred to as the cell's **metabolism.** A series of chemical reactions in which the product of one reaction is the substrate for the next reaction is called a metabolic pathway. Metabolic pathways include two broad types: catabolic (ka tuh BAH lik) pathways and anabolic (a nuh BAH lik) pathways. Catabolic pathways release energy by breaking down larger molecules into smaller molecules. Anabolic pathways use the energy released by catabolic pathways to build larger molecules from smaller molecules. The relationship of anabolic and catabolic pathways results in the continual flow of energy within an organism.

Energy continually flows between the metabolic reactions of organisms in an ecosystem. **Photosynthesis** is the anabolic pathway in which light energy from the Sun is converted to chemical energy for use by the cell. In this reaction, autotrophs use light energy, carbon dioxide, and water to form glucose and oxygen. The energy stored in the glucose produced by photosynthesis can be transferred to other organisms when the molecules are consumed as food.

Cellular respiration is the catabolic pathway in which organic molecules are broken down to release energy for use by a cell. In cellular respiration, oxygen is used to break down organic molecules, resulting in the production of carbon dioxide and water. Notice the cyclical nature of these processes in **Figure 3,** where the products of one reaction are the reactants for the other reaction.

MiniLab 1

Relate Photosynthesis to Cellular Respiration

? Inquiry MiniLab

How do photosynthesis and cellular respiration work together in an ecosystem? Use a chemical indicator to examine how carbon dioxide is transferred in photosynthesis and cellular respiration.

Procedure

1. Read and complete the lab safety form.
2. Prepare a data table to record the contents, treatment, initial color, and final color for two experimental test tubes.
3. Pour 100 mL of **bromothymol blue (BTB) solution** into a **beaker.** Using a **straw,** exhale gently into the solution until it just turns yellow. **WARNING:** ***Do not exhale so much that the solution bubbles over or that you get a headache. Do not suck on the straw.***
4. Fill two large **test tubes** three-quarters full with the yellow BTB solution.
5. Cover one test tube entirely with **aluminum foil.** Place a 6-cm sprig of an **aquatic plant** into both of the tubes, tightly insert the **stoppers** into the tubes, and place them in a **rack** in bright light overnight.
6. Record your observations in your data table.

Analysis

1. **Describe** the purpose of the tube covered with aluminum foil.
2. **Explain** how your results demonstrate that photosynthesis and cellular respiration depend on one another.

■ **Caption Question Fig. 3** The anabolic pathway goes from photosynthesis in autotrophs to heterotrophs. The catabolic pathway goes from cellular respiration in heterotrophs to autotrophs.

Demonstration

Model Using a molecular model set, build the three-phosphate group structures of ATP. Pass the model around the class so that students can have a three-dimensional view. Alternatively, if enough components of a molecular model set are available, organize students into small groups and have them construct the phosphate group model. Est. time: 20 min

ATP: The Unit of Cellular Energy

Connection to Chemistry Energy exists in many forms, including light energy, mechanical energy, thermal energy, and chemical energy. In living organisms, chemical energy is stored in biological molecules and can be converted to other forms of energy when needed. For example, the chemical energy in biological molecules is converted to mechanical energy when muscles contract. **Adenosine triphosphate** (uh DEN uh seen • tri FAHS fayt)—ATP—is the most important biological molecule that provides chemical energy.

ATP structure ATP is a multipurpose storehouse of chemical energy that can be used by cells in a variety of reactions. Although other carrier molecules transport energy within cells, ATP is the most abundant energy-carrier molecule in cells and is found in all types of organisms. As shown in **Figure 4,** ATP is a nucleotide made of an adenine base, a ribose sugar, and three phosphate groups.

ATP function ATP releases energy when the bond between the second and third phosphate groups is broken, forming a molecule called adenosine diphosphate (ADP) and a free phosphate group, as shown in **Figure 4.** Energy is stored in the phosphate bond formed when ADP receives a phosphate group and becomes ATP. As shown in **Figure 4,** ATP and ADP can be interchanged by the addition or removal of a phosphate group. Sometimes ADP becomes adenosine monophosphate (AMP) by losing an additional phosphate group. There is less energy released in this reaction, so most of the energy reactions in the cell involve ATP and ADP.

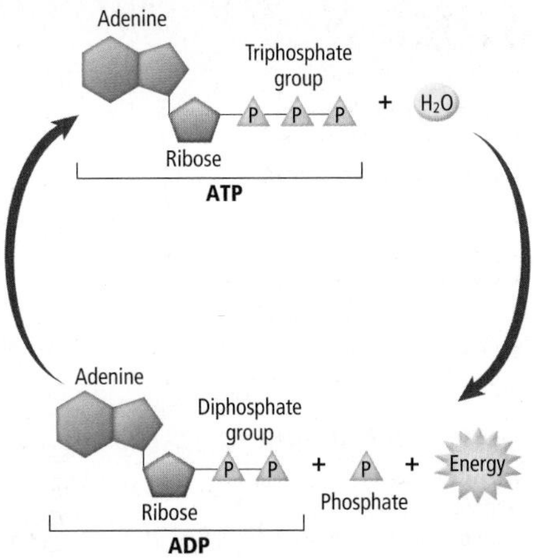

■ **Figure 4** The breakdown of ATP releases energy for powering cellular activities in organisms.

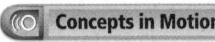

Concepts in Motion Animation

C

Concepts in Motion Animation

C Critical Thinking

BL OL AL Relate

ASK STUDENTS: ***How is the function of ATP in a cell like that of a battery in a car?*** Batteries convert stored chemical energy to mechanical energy that enables cars to move. In a cell, when ATP is broken down to ADP, the stored chemical energy is converted to other forms of energy that the cell can use.

Formative Assessment

Evaluation

ASK STUDENTS: ***What is the main difference between autotrophs and heterotrophs?*** Autotrophs make their own food for energy; heterotrophs obtain food energy by eating other organisms.

Remediation Have a student volunteer to reread aloud the text under the heading *Autotrophs and heterotrophs.* Then have students identify each of the following statements as true or false:
1. Heterotrophs are dependent on autotrophs. 2. Autotrophs depend on heterotrophs for food. 3. Autotrophs make their own food.
4. Heterotrophs make food using light energy. 1—T, 2—F, 3—T, 4—F

Section 1 Assessment

Section Summary

- The laws of thermodynamics control the flow and transformation of energy in organisms.
- Some organisms produce their own food, whereas others obtain energy from the food they ingest.
- Cells store and release energy through coupled anabolic and catabolic reactions.
- The energy released from the breakdown of ATP drives cellular activities.

Understand Main Ideas

1. MAIN Idea **Identify** the major source of energy for living organisms.
2. **Describe** an example of the first law of thermodynamics.
3. **Compare and contrast** anabolic and catabolic pathways.
4. **Explain** how ATP stores and releases energy.

Think Critically

WRITING in Biology

5. Write an essay describing the laws of thermodynamics. Use examples related to biology to support your ideas.
6. **Create** an analogy to describe the relationship between photosynthesis and cellular respiration.

Section 1 Assessment

1. sunlight
2. Stored energy in food is converted to chemical energy and then to mechanical energy when muscles move to do work.
3. Catabolic pathways break down large molecules into small molecules. Anabolic pathways build large molecules from small molecules.
4. ATP is formed from ADP; energy is stored in phosphate bonds and is released when ATP is hydrolyzed to ADP.
5. First law: energy cannot be created or destroyed; in photosynthesis, light energy is converted to chemical energy (glucose). Second law: systems naturally change from orderly to disorderly.
6. Sample analogy: chemical energy in a battery being converted to sound energy in a radio.

WRITING in Biology

RUBRIC Use the modifiable rubric found on your eTeacherEdition Online to assess writing assignments.

Assessment Online Quiz

Section 2

MAIN Idea

BL OL AL The Sun's Energy

ASK STUDENTS: ***What is the benefit of photosynthesis for humans?*** Photosynthetic reactions produce oxygen, which humans breathe, and food energy in plants, which humans eat. ***How does photosynthesis benefit plants?*** Photosynthesis enables plants to produce carbon molecules, which are storehouses for energy.

D Develop Concepts

EL BL OL AL

Clarify a Misconception Display pictures of soil, water, minerals, and the sky to represent air. **ASK STUDENTS:** ***Do air, soil, water, or minerals provide energy for photosynthesis?*** No. The only source of energy for photosynthesis is light energy. Remind students that green plants use carbon dioxide and water in photosynthesis, but the energy that drives the process comes from light, usually sunlight.

Skill Practice

EL BL OL COOP LEARN

Visual Literacy Have students work in pairs to examine the figures in this section. Have them discuss what they see in the figures and make a list of the information they can determine from the figures. Once students have read the section, have them add additional information to the notes they took based only on the illustrations. **AL** Have students explain the process of photosynthesis based on information in the figures.

Reading Preview

Essential Questions

- What are the two phases of photosynthesis?
- What is the function of a chloroplast during the light reactions?
- How can electron transport be described and diagramed?

Review Vocabulary

carbohydrate: an organic compound containing only carbon, hydrogen, and oxygen, usually in a 1:2:1 ratio

New Vocabulary

thylakoid
granum
stroma
pigment
NADP+
Calvin cycle
rubisco

g Multilingual eGlossary

Photosynthesis

MAIN Idea Light energy is trapped and converted into chemical energy during photosynthesis.

Real-World Reading Link Energy is transformed all around us every day. Batteries convert chemical energy into electric energy, and radios convert electric energy into the energy carried by sound waves. Similarly, some autotrophs convert light energy into chemical energy through photosynthesis.

Overview of Photosynthesis

D Most autotrophs, including plants, make organic compounds, such as sugars, by a process called photosynthesis. Recall that photosynthesis is a process in which light energy is converted into chemical energy. The overall chemical equation for photosynthesis is shown below.

$$6CO_2 + 6H_2O \xrightarrow{\text{light}} C_6H_{12}O_6 + 6O_2$$

Photosynthesis occurs in two phases. The locations of these phases are shown in **Figure 5.** In phase one, the light-dependent reactions, light energy is absorbed and then converted into chemical energy in the form of ATP and NADPH. In phase two, the light-independent reactions, the ATP and NADPH that were formed in phase one are used to make glucose. Once glucose is produced, it can be joined to other simple sugars to form larger molecules. These larger molecules are complex carbohydrates, such as starch. Recall that carbohydrates are composed of repeating units of small organic molecules. The end products of photosynthesis also can be used to make other organic molecules, such as proteins, lipids, and nucleic acids.

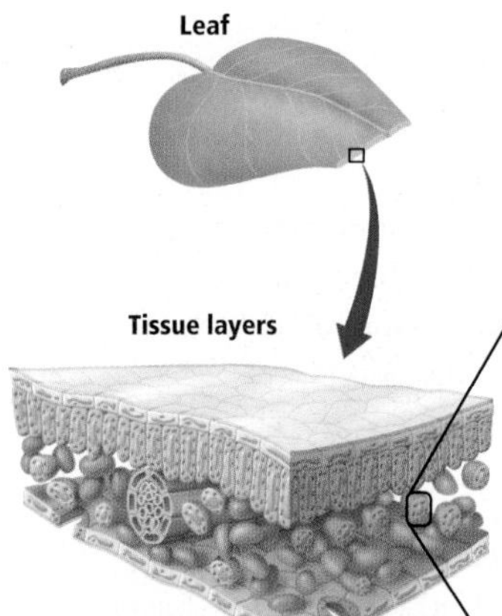

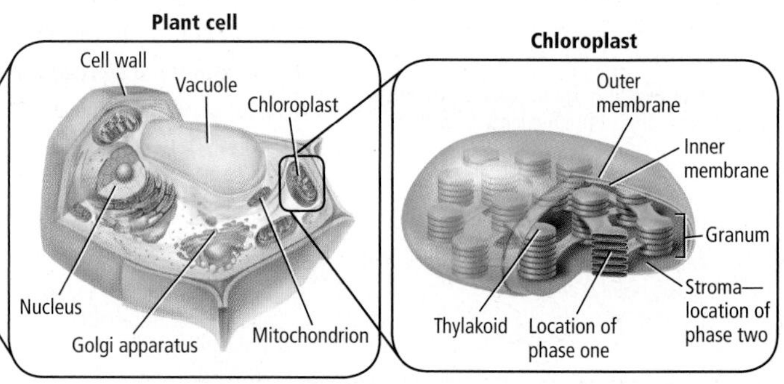

■ **Figure 5** Photosynthesis occurs inside pigmented organelles called chloroplasts.

"Education is a social process. Education is growth. Education is not a preparation for life; education is life itself."

–John Dewey

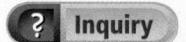

? Inquiry BioLab

The lab at the end of the chapter can be used at this point in the lesson.

Phase One: Light Reactions

The absorption of light is the first step in photosynthesis. Plants have special organelles to capture light energy. Once the energy is captured, two energy storage molecules, NADPH and ATP, are produced to be used in the light-independent reactions.

Chloroplasts Large organelles, called chloroplasts, capture light energy in photosynthetic organisms. In plants, chloroplasts are found mainly in the cells of leaves. As shown in **Figure 5,** chloroplasts are disk-shaped organelles that contain two main compartments essential to photosynthesis. The first compartment is called the thylakoid (THI la koyd). **Thylakoids** are flattened, saclike membranes that are arranged in stacks. These stacks are called **grana** (singular, granum). Light-dependent reactions take place within the thylakoids. The second important compartment is called the **stroma**, the fluid-filled space that is outside the grana. This is the location of the light-independent reactions in phase two of photosynthesis.

Pigments Light-absorbing colored molecules called **pigments** are found in the thylakoid membranes of chloroplasts. Different pigments absorb specific wavelengths of light, as illustrated in **Figure 6.**

The major light-absorbing pigments in plants are chlorophylls. There are several types of chlorophylls, but the most common two are chlorophyll *a* and chlorophyll *b*. The structure of chlorophyll can differ from one molecule to another, enabling distinct chlorophyll molecules to absorb light at unique areas of the visible spectrum. In general, chlorophylls absorb most strongly in the violet-blue region of the visible light spectrum and reflect light in the green region of the spectrum. This is why plant parts that contain chlorophyll appear green to the human eye.

Reading Check **Distinguish** between thylakoids and stroma.

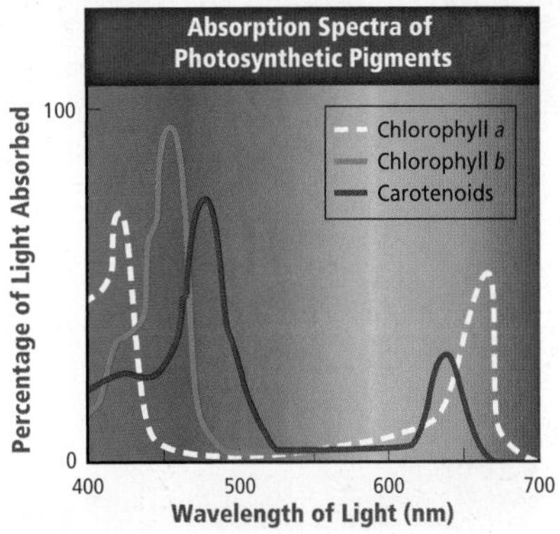

Figure 6 Colorful pigments found in the leaves of trees differ in their ability to absorb specific wavelengths of light.
Hypothesize ***the effect on light absorption if a plant did not have chlorophyll*** **b.**

MiniLab 2

Observe Chloroplasts

Inquiry MiniLab

What do chloroplasts look like? Most ecosystems and organisms in the world depend on tiny organelles called chloroplasts. Discover what chloroplasts look like in this investigation.

Procedure

1. Read and complete the lab safety form.
2. Observe the **slides of plant and algae cells** with a **microscope.**
3. Identify the chloroplasts in the cells that you observe.
4. Make a data table to record your observations, and sketch the chloroplasts in the cells.

Analysis

1. **Compare and contrast** the physical features of the chloroplasts that you observed in the different cells.
2. **Hypothesize** why plant leaves vary in color.

Research Citation

Problem Solve Educational research indicates that student achievement will improve when they are provided with direct instruction on how to solve real-world problems. The MiniLab on this page provides an opportunity for students to practice problem-solving skills and to better retain the concepts they have learned. (Charles and Lester, 1984)

Research bibliography on pages 32T–34T

Caption Question Fig. 6 Without chlorophyll *b,* the plant would absorb less light. This might cause a reduction in the rate of photosynthesis.

Reading Check Thylakoids are membranes where light-dependent reactions occur. Stroma is the space outside the grana where light-independent reactions occur.

MiniLab 2

Inquiry MiniLab

For a lab worksheet, use your eTeacherEdition Online.

RUBRIC A rubric for evaluating MiniLabs is found on your eTeacherEdition Online.

Est. Time 15 min

Additional Materials pond water, freshwater algae samples, blank microscope slides and coverslips

Safety Precaution Approve lab safety forms before work begins.

Teaching Strategies

- Chloroplasts are easily observed inside algae cells when viewed under the highest power of a microscope.
- Prepare slides of plant-leaf samples by making diagonal cuts on the tip of a leaf with a scalpel and placing the thin slices on a blank slide and cover with a coverslip.
- Encourage students to focus on one layer at a time in multilayered leaves.

Cleanup and Disposal Discard pond water or return it with all algae samples back to their ecosystems.

Analysis

1. Chloroplasts vary in size and shape from spherical or oval to irregular. Chloroplasts vary from light to dark green and can contain different amounts of chlorophyll.
2. There are different types of chlorophyll, which have different colors, and there are other pigments that also contribute to photosynthesis.

LabManager™

Customize this lab with the LabManager™ CD-ROM.

R Reading Strategy

EL OL AL **SQ3R** Have students **S**urvey the text under the heading *Electron transport,* focusing on the vocabulary words. Have students write at least three **Q**uestions about key concepts. Sample question: Why is $NADP^+$ important for electron transport in photosynthesis? Have students **R**ead the *Electron Transport* paragraph, taking notes related to the questions they wrote. Finally, have students **R**ecite the vocabulary terms and **R**eview the text for the meanings.

W Writing Support

BL OL COOP LEARN

Creative Writing Organize students in groups of five and have each group write a skit that summarizes the light dependent phase of photosynthesis. Skits should include the roles of pigments such as chlorophylls and carotenoids as well as depict electron transport and the conversion of light energy to chemical energy. Have students perform their skits.

C Critical Thinking

OL AL **Compare** Have students use an analogy to relate the photosynthetic reactions in plants to an activity they perform daily. For example, photosynthesis can be related to listening to a radio. The parts in the radio capture radio-wave energy just as chloroplasts capture light energy. The energy in the radio is used to produce sound, and light energy in the plant is used to produce food.

Reading Check The breakdown of water provides electrons for electron transport and hydrogen ions.

Figure 7 When chlorophyll breaks down in the leaves of some trees, the other pigments become visible.

VOCABULARY

ACADEMIC VOCABULARY

Transport
to carry something from one place to another
$NADP^+$ molecules transport electrons during photosynthesis.

In addition to chlorophylls, most photosynthetic organisms contain accessory pigments that allow plants to trap additional light energy from other areas of the visible spectrum. One such group of accessory pigments is the carotenoids (kuh ROH tuh noydz). Carotenoids, such as β-carotene (beta-carotene), absorb light mainly in the blue and green regions of the spectrum, while reflecting most light in the yellow, orange, and red regions. Carotenoids produce the colors of carrots and sweet potatoes.

Chlorophylls are more abundant than other pigments in leaves, and thus hide the colors of the other pigments. However, autumn in certain parts of the United States can bring out shades of yellow, red, and orange as the leaves turn colors, as shown in **Figure 7.** As trees prepare to lose their leaves before winter, the chlorophyll molecules break down, revealing the colors of the other pigments.

R **Electron transport** The structure of the thylakoid membrane is the key to efficient energy transfer during electron transport. Thylakoid membranes have a large surface area, which provides the space needed to hold large numbers of electron-transporting molecules and two types of protein complexes called photosystems. Photosystem I and photosystem II contain light-absorbing pigments and proteins that play important roles in the light reactions. Follow along in **Figure 8** as you continue to read about electron transport.

- First, the light energy excites electrons in photosystem II. The light energy also causes a water molecule to split, releasing an electron into the electron transport system, a hydrogen ion (H^+)—also called a proton—into the thylakoid space, and oxygen (O_2) as a waste product. This breakdown of water is essential for photosynthesis to occur.
- The excited electrons move from photosystem II to an electron-acceptor molecule in the thylakoid membrane.
- Next, the electron-acceptor molecule transfers the electrons along a series of electron-carriers to photosystem I.
- In the presence of light, photosystem I transfers the electrons to a protein called ferrodoxin. The electrons lost by photosystem I are replaced by electrons shuttled from photosystem II.
- Finally, ferrodoxin transfers the electrons to the electron carrier **$NADP^+$**, forming the energy-storage molecule NADPH.

Chemiosmosis ATP is produced in conjunction with electron transport by the process of chemiosmosis—the mechanism by which ATP is produced as a result of the flow of electrons down a concentration gradient. The breakdown of water is essential not only for providing the electrons that initiate the electron transport chain, but also for providing the protons (H^+) necessary to drive ATP synthesis during chemiosmosis. The H^+ released during electron transport accumulate in the interior of the thylakoid. As a result of a high concentration of H^+ in the thylakoid interior and a low concentration of H^+ in the stroma, H^+ protons diffuse down their concentration gradient out of the thylakoid interior into the stroma through ion channels spanning the membrane, as shown in **Figure 8.** These channels are enzymes called ATP synthases. As H^+ moves through W ATP synthases, ATP is formed in the stroma. C

Reading Check **Summarize** the function of water during chemiosmosis in photosynthesis.

Demonstration

Photosynthesis Half fill several pairs of test tubes with phenol red solution. This pH indicator is red at pH 7 or higher (alkaline) and pale yellow at less than pH 7 (acid). Use straws to blow air, which contains CO_2, into one of each pair of tubes until the phenol red turns yellow. Add a sprig of *Elodea* to the tubes containing the yellow solution, but not to the red solution. Place the test tubes under a desk lamp or other light for 15–20 min. The yellow solution should turn red again and tiny oxygen bubbles should form in the tubes containing the *Elodea* as the plant begins to take in CO_2 and photosynthesize.
Est. time: 25 min

Visualizing Electron Transport

Figure 8

Activated electrons are passed from one molecule to another along the thylakoid membrane in a chloroplast. The energy from electrons is used to form a proton gradient. As protons move down the gradient, a phosphate is added to ADP, forming ATP.

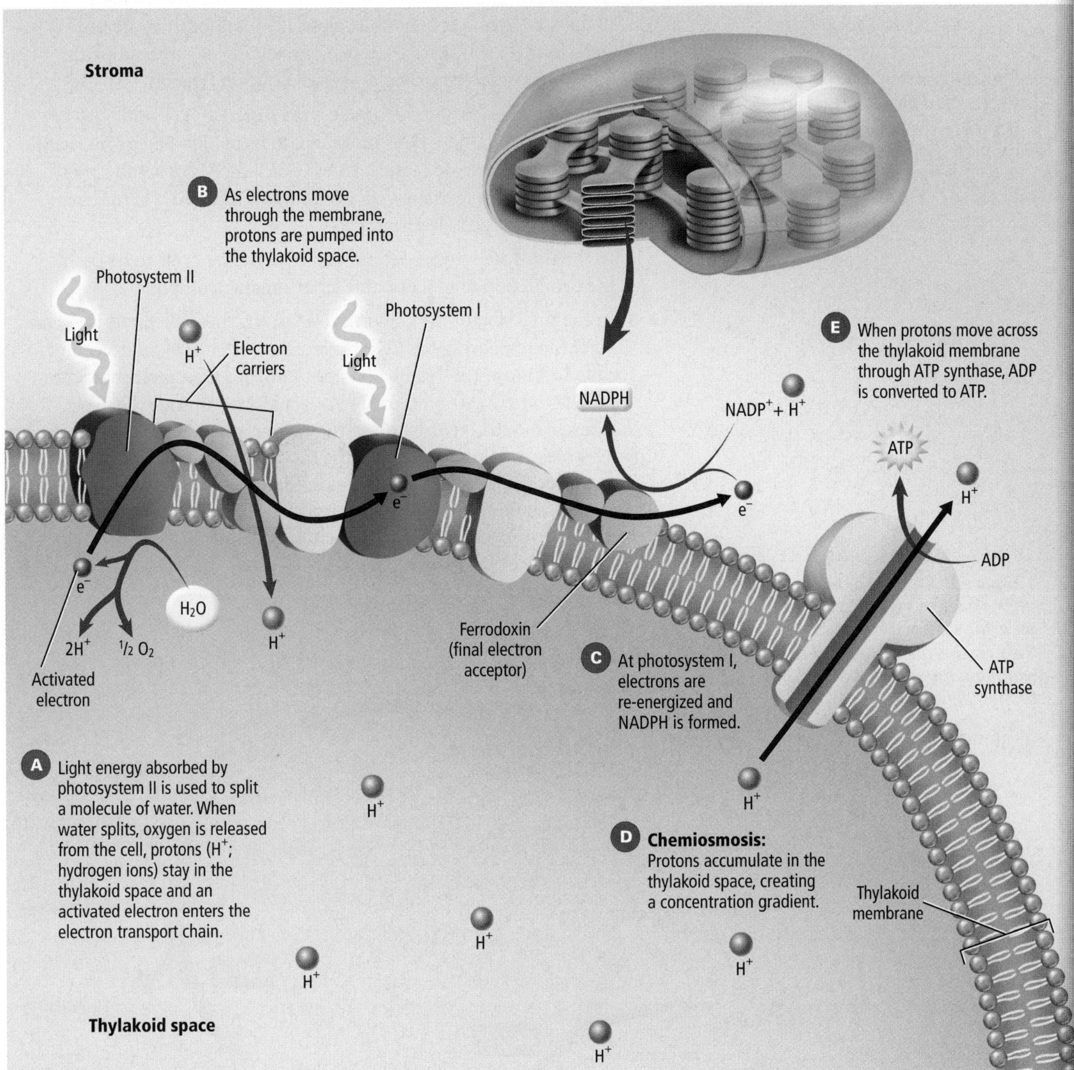

Concepts in Motion **Animation**

Visualizing Electron Transport

Purpose

Students will understand how electrons are passed from one molecule to another in the thylakoid membrane.
C.1, C.5, C.6

Develop Concepts

Activity Have students use library resources to research a cellular process that utilizes energy. Encourage students to find out how many molecules of ATP are utilized (or produced) in the process.

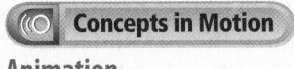

Concepts in Motion **Animation**

Content Background

Real-World Connection The impact of deforestation and burning fossil fuels on the environment is a serious concern in many tropical areas of the world, where huge forests are being cut down. These forests are important because they produce oxygen and reduce the amount of carbon dioxide in the air. Carbon dioxide is a gas that is increasing in the atmosphere because of industrial pollution and exhaust from automobiles. Carbon dioxide is one of the greenhouse gases in the atmosphere that traps heat from the Sun. Too much carbon dioxide could change the planet's climate.

D Develop Concepts

BL OL AL

Clarify a Misconception

ASK STUDENTS: ***What comes to mind when you hear the term*** **organic?** Students might think that *organic* means "natural," as in "natural foods." Remind students that when used in chemistry or biological sciences, *organic* refers to compounds that contain carbon. Although carbon dioxide by itself is inorganic, it contributes carbon for forming organic compounds. Organic compounds are found in living things and in the remains of living things.

R Reading Strategy

EL BL OL **Directed Reading**

Before reading the text under the heading *Phase Two: The Calvin Cycle,* have students create a chart with columns titled *What I know now, What I think I'll learn,* and *What I learned.* Have students preview the text on the Calvin cycle and fill out the first column. When students fill out the second column, encourage them to pay close attention to the structures of the molecules formed during the Calvin cycle in Figure 9. After the students read the text on this page, have them fill out the last column.

Concepts in Motion

Animation

R D

Phase Two: The Calvin Cycle

Although NADPH and ATP provide cells with large amounts of energy, these molecules are not stable enough to store chemical energy for long periods of time. Thus, there is a second phase of photosynthesis called the **Calvin cycle,** in which energy is stored in organic molecules such as glucose. The reactions of the Calvin cycle are also referred to as the light-independent reactions. Follow along in **Figure 9** as you learn the steps of the Calvin cycle.

- In the first step of the Calvin cycle, called carbon fixation, six carbon dioxide (CO_2) molecules combine with six 5-carbon compounds to form twelve 3-carbon molecules called 3-phosphoglycerate (fahs foh GLI suh rayt) (3-PGA). The joining of carbon dioxide with other organic molecules is called carbon fixation.
- In the second step, the chemical energy stored in ATP and NADPH is transferred to the 3-PGA molecules to form high-energy molecules called glyceraldehyde 3-phosphates (G3P). ATP supplies the phosphate groups for forming G3P molecules, while NADPH supplies hydrogen ions and electrons.
- In the third step, two G3P molecules leave the cycle to be used for the production of glucose and other organic compounds.
- In the final step of the Calvin cycle, an enzyme called **rubisco** converts the remaining ten G3P molecules into 5-carbon molecules called ribulose 1, 5-bisphosphates (RuBP). These molecules combine with new carbon dioxide molecules to continue the cycle.

Because rubisco converts inorganic carbon dioxide molecules into organic molecules that can be used by the cell, it is considered one of the most important biological enzymes. Plants use the sugars formed during the Calvin cycle both as a source of energy and as building blocks for complex carbohydrates, including cellulose, which provides structural support for plants.

CAREERS IN BIOLOGY

Phytochemist A biologist who studies the chemical products of plants is a phytochemist. Phytochemists might work in medical research to find new treatments for diseases.

■ **Figure 9** The Calvin cycle joins carbon dioxide with organic molecules inside the stroma of the chloroplast.
Determine ***the compound in which energy is stored at the end of the Calvin cycle.***

Concepts in Motion

Animation

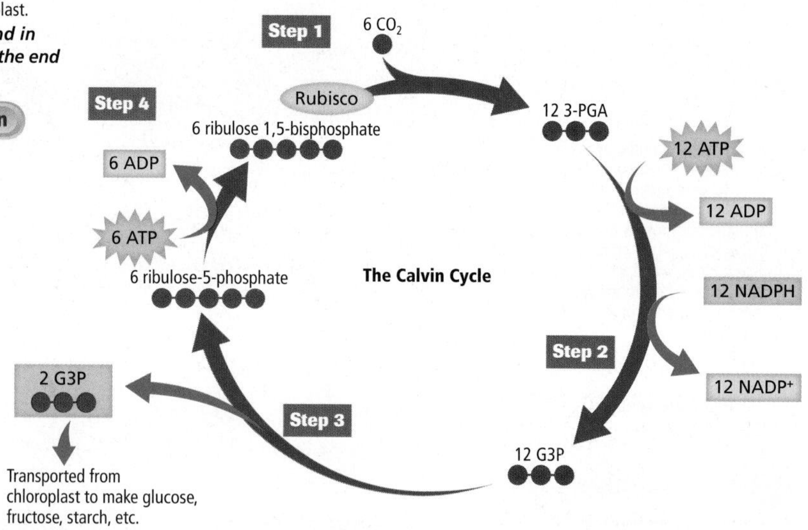

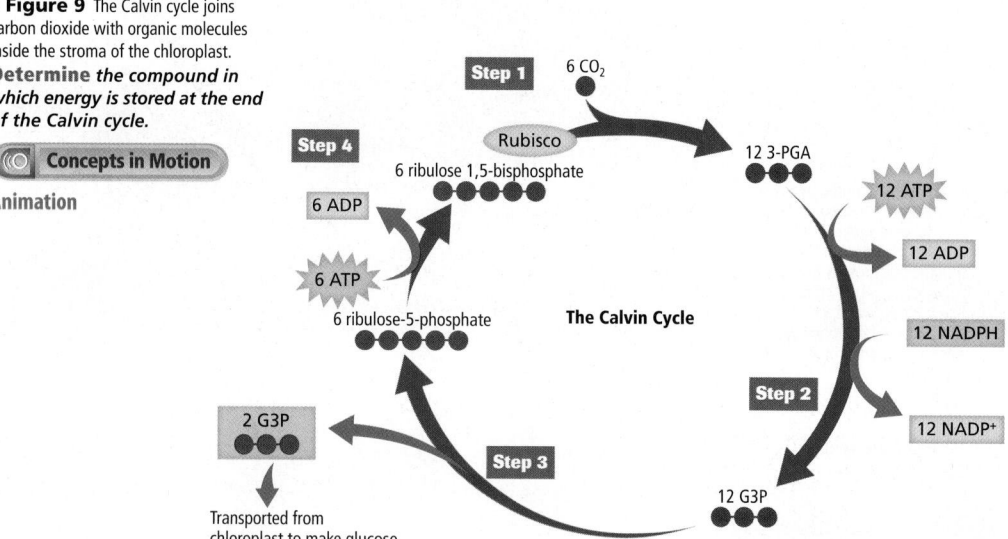

■ **Caption Question Fig. 9** in glucose and other organic molecules (fructose, starch); also accept G3P

Differentiated Instruction

English Learners When asking students to complete the chart as part of the Reading Strategy described on this page, model each stage of the task for English learners. Provide an example of what information should be placed in each column so that they are sure to understand.

For more tips, see pages 14T–15T.

Alternative Pathways

The environment in which an organism lives can impact the organism's ability to carry out photosynthesis. Environments in which the amount of water or carbon dioxide available is insufficient can decrease the ability of a photosynthetic organism to convert light energy into chemical energy. For example, plants in hot, dry environments are subject to excessive water loss that can lead to decreased photosynthesis. Many plants in extreme climates have alternative photosynthesis pathways to maximize energy conversion.

C_4 plants One adaptive pathway that helps plants maintain photosynthesis while minimizing water loss is called the C_4 pathway. The C_4 pathway occurs in plants such as sugarcane and corn. These plants are called C_4 plants because they fix carbon dioxide into four-carbon compounds instead of three-carbon molecules during the Calvin cycle. C_4 plants also have significant structural modifications in the arrangement of cells in the leaves. In general, C_4 plants keep their stomata (plant cell pores) closed during hot days, while the four carbon compounds are transferred to special cells where CO_2 enters the Calvin cycle. This allows for sufficient carbon dioxide uptake, while simultaneously minimizing water loss.

CAM plants Another adaptive pathway used by some plants to maximize photosynthetic activity is called crassulacean (KRAH soo lay shun) acid metabolism (CAM photosynthesis). The CAM pathway occurs in water-conserving plants that live in deserts, salt marshes, and other environments where access to water is limited. CAM plants, such as cacti, orchids, and the pineapple in **Figure 10,** allow carbon dioxide to enter the leaves only at night, when the atmosphere is cooler and more humid. At night, these plants fix carbon dioxide into organic compounds. During the day, carbon dioxide is released from these compounds and enters the Calvin cycle. This pathway also allows for sufficient carbon dioxide uptake while minimizing water loss.

■ **Figure 10** This pineapple plant is an example of a CAM plant.

Critical Thinking

AL Predict

ASK STUDENTS: ***What is the goal of photosynthesis?*** to convert solar energy to chemical energy in the bonds of glucose ***Has that been accomplished in the light reaction?*** no ***Where will this conversion be accomplished?*** in the Calvin cycle

Formative Assessment

Evaluation

ASK STUDENTS: ***What is the chemical equation for photosynthesis?*** $CO_2 + H_2O$ (in the presence of light energy) $\rightarrow$ glucose $+ O_2$ Have students relate the source of these reactants and the cellular organelles where the reactions take place.

Remediation Have students write a statement that explains photosynthesis. Have them take turns reading their statements aloud. Clarify any misunderstandings that students might have about the process.

Section 2 Assessment

Section Summary

- Plants contain chloroplasts with light-absorbing pigments that convert light energy into chemical energy.
- Photosynthesis is a two-phase process that consists of light reactions and the Calvin cycle.
- In the light reactions, autotrophs trap and convert light energy into chemical energy in the form of NADPH and ATP.
- In the Calvin cycle, chemical energy in ATP and NADPH is used to synthesize carbohydrates such as glucose.

Understand Main Ideas

1. MAIN Idea **Summarize** how chemical energy is formed from light energy during photosynthesis.
2. **Relate** the structure of a chloroplast to the phases of photosynthesis.
3. **Explain** why water is essential for the light reactions.
4. **Summarize** the steps in the Calvin cycle.
5. **Diagram** and explain electron transport.

Think Critically

6. **Predict** how environmental factors such as light intensity and carbon dioxide levels can affect rates of photosynthesis.

WRITING in Biology

7. Research the effects of global warming on photosynthesis. Write an article summarizing your findings.

Section 2 Assessment

1. Light energy is converted to ATP and NADPH, which are then converted to glucose.
2. Chloroplasts contain thylakoids, sites of light-dependent reactions, and stroma, sites of light-independent reactions.
3. Water produces hydrogen ions for ATP synthase and ATP production.
4. Six carbon dioxide molecules with six 5-carbon molecules split to form 12 3-carbon compounds. Aided by ATP hydrolysis, two of the 12 make sucrose; the other ten are converted into 5-carbon molecules for another cycle.
5. Diagrams should show electrons moving on thylakoid membrane. Explanations should describe how water provides electrons and hydrogen ions and follow them through the electron transport chain.
6. Increased light and CO_2 increase photosynthesis rates.
7. Increase in carbon dioxide levels by burning fossil fuels should increase substrate available for photosynthesis if there were enough trees and other vegetation available.

Assessment Online Quiz

Section 3

MAIN Idea

BL OL AL Energy From Food Ask for a student volunteer to explain the differences between autotrophs and heterotrophs. **ASK STUDENTS:** ***How do most autotrophs produce food?*** through photosynthesis; Some autotrophs living in the deep sea produce food through chemosynthesis. ***Can anyone predict how heterotrophs obtain energy?*** through cellular respiration, which converts chemical energy in food into cellular energy

D Develop Concepts

BL OL AL

Clarify a Misconception
ASK STUDENTS: ***Is air the same as oxygen?*** No. The terms *air* and *oxygen* are not interchangeable. ***How is air different from oxygen?*** Air is a mixture of many gases, including oxygen, nitrogen, and carbon dioxide. Students might also think that cellular respiration occurs only in lung cells or gill cells. Remind students that cellular respiration occurs in all cells and should not be confused with *respiration,* as in the exchange of materials between the lungs and the atmosphere, or *breathing,* the act of inhaling and exhaling.

Section 3

Reading Preview

Essential Questions

- What are the stages of cellular respiration?
- What is the role of electron carriers in each stage of cellular respiration?
- What are the similarities between alcoholic fermentation and lactic acid fermentation?

Review Vocabulary

cyanobacterium: a type of bacterium that is a photosynthetic autotroph

New Vocabulary

anaerobic process
aerobic respiration
aerobic process
glycolysis
Krebs cycle
fermentation

g Multilingual eGlossary

Cellular Respiration

MAIN Idea Living organisms obtain energy by breaking down organic molecules during cellular respiration.

Real-World Reading Link Monarch butterflies must constantly feed on nectar from flowers to provide energy to sustain themselves during their winter migration to parts of Mexico and California each year. Similarly, humans and other living organisms need reliable food sources to supply energy to survive and grow.

D Overview of Cellular Respiration

Recall that organisms obtain energy in a process called cellular respiration. The function of cellular respiration is to harvest electrons from carbon compounds, such as glucose, and use that energy to make ATP. ATP is used to provide energy for cells to do work. The overall chemical equation for cellular respiration is shown below. Notice the equation for cellular respiration is the opposite of the equation for photosynthesis.

$$C_6H_{12}O_6 + 6O_2 \rightarrow 6CO_2 + 6H_2O + \text{Energy}$$

Cellular respiration occurs in two main parts: glycolysis and aerobic respiration. The first stage, glycolysis, is an anaerobic process. **Anaerobic processes** do not require oxygen. **Aerobic respiration** includes the Krebs cycle and electron transport and is an aerobic process. **Aerobic processes** require oxygen. Cellular respiration with aerobic respiration is summarized in **Figure 11.**

Figure 11 Cellular respiration occurs in the mitochondria, the energy powerhouse organelles of a cell.

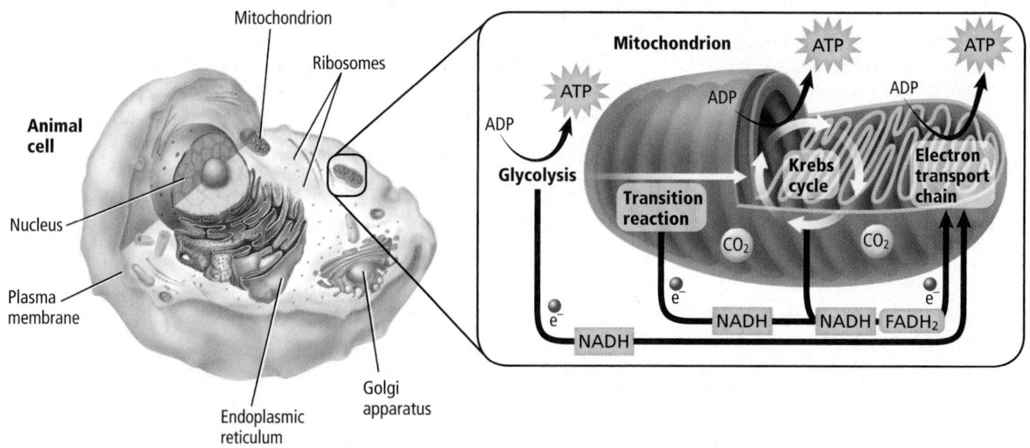

Activity

BL OL AL Energy Expenditure Give each student a clothespin. Have them open and close the pins repeatedly for 1 min, then ask how their fingers feel. Point out that squeezing a clothespin, like other biological processes, requires energy. The energy needed is provided by the breakdown of sugars in food to form ATP, a process called cellular respiration. Cellular respiration requires oxygen, but after some time cells are unable to provide the needed amount of oxygen, and lactic acid fermentation occurs. When lactic acid builds up in muscle cells during exercise, the muscles feel sore and fatigued. Est. time: 10 min

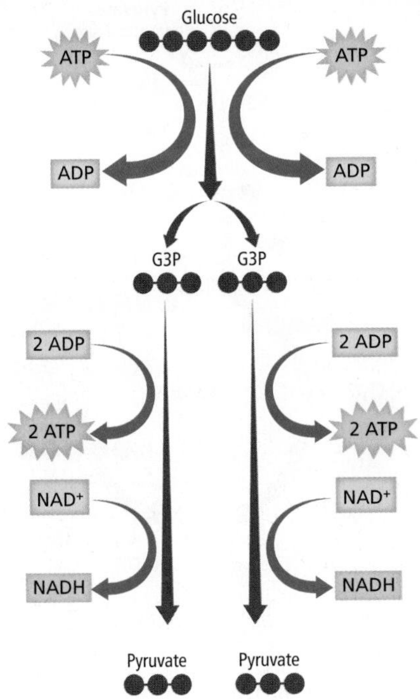

■ **Figure 12** Glucose is broken down during glycolysis inside the cytoplasm of cells.
Summarize ***the reactants and products of glycolysis.***

Review Personal Tutor

R Glycolysis

Glucose is broken down in the cytoplasm through the process of **glycolysis.** Two molecules of ATP and two molecules of NADH are formed for each molecule of glucose that is broken down. Follow along with **Figure 12** as you read about the steps of glycolysis.

First, two phosphate groups, derived from two molecules of ATP, are joined to glucose. Notice that some energy, two ATP, is required to start the reactions that will produce energy for the cell. The 6-carbon molecule is then broken down into two 3-carbon compounds. Next, two phosphates are added and electrons and hydrogen ions (H^+) combine with two NAD^+ molecules to form two NADH molecules. NAD^+ is similar to NADP, an electron carrier used during photosynthesis. Last, the two 3-carbon compounds are converted into two molecules W of pyruvate. At the same time, four molecules of ATP are produced.

Reading Check **Explain** why there is a net yield of two, not four, ATP molecules in glycolysis.

Krebs Cycle

Glycolysis has a net result of two ATP and two pyruvate molecules. Most of the energy from the glucose is still contained in the pyruvate. In the presence of oxygen, pyruvate is transported into the mitochondrial matrix, where it is eventually converted to carbon dioxide. The series of reactions in which pyruvate is broken down into carbon dioxide is called the **Krebs cycle**, or the tricarboxylic acid (TCA) cycle. This cycle also is referred to as the citric acid cycle.

VOCABULARY

WORD ORIGIN

Glycolysis
comes from the Greek words *glykys*, meaning *sweet* and *lysis*, meaning *to rupture or break*

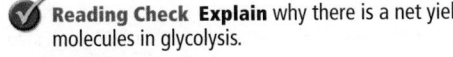

FOLDABLES®
Incorporate information from this section into your Foldable.

Reading Check Glycolysis begins with the input of two molecules of ATP.

■ **Caption Question Fig. 12** The reactants are: one molecule of glucose, two ATP, two NAD^+, and four ADP. The products are: two ADP, two NADH, four ATP, and two pyruvates.

Review Personal Tutor

Listen to a teacher explain glycolysis, the Krebs cycle, and electron transport.

R Reading Strategy

AL Morphological Word Analysis

Before reading the text under the heading *Glycolysis,* have students look at the Word Origin margin feature on glycolysis. Have students predict how the meanings of *glykys* and *lysis* relate to the overall goal of cellular respiration. Sugars break down to release energy.

W Writing Support

BL OL AL Summary Writing

Have students write a summary of the steps involved in glycolysis. In preparing their summary, have them use the information in Figure 12 as well as the information in the text. Summaries should include the terms *ATP, NAD$^+$, NADH, phosphate groups,* and *carbon compounds.*

EL Have students work in small groups to discuss the information in Figure 12 and in the text regarding glycolysis. Then have each group make a list of the steps in the glycolysis process.

FOLDABLES®

RUBRIC A rubric for evaluating Foldables is found on your eTeacherEdition Online.

Going Further

SAY TO STUDENTS: ***On the back of your Foldable, write a comparison of the electron transport chain in the mitochondria of the cells of heterotrophs to the electron transport chain in the thylakoids of chloroplasts in the cells of autotrophs.***

Concepts in Motion

Animation

S Skill Practice

EL BL OL Visual Literacy

Have students preview the diagram in Figure 13. Point out that the illustration shows a cycle. **ASK STUDENTS:** ***What other cycles have you learned about in science?*** Possible answers include: life cycle, cell cycle, water cycle. Point out that these terms all include the word *cycle.* Review the definition of the word *cycle.*

AL ***Why are cycles important in biological systems?*** They recycle (or reuse) materials.

R Reading Strategy

AL Active Comprehension

Have students read the text under the heading *Steps of the Krebs cycle.* **ASK STUDENTS:** ***What more would you like to know about the Krebs cycle?*** Encourage students to compare and contrast photosynthetic reactions occurring in autotrophs with reactions like the Krebs cycle that occurs in heterotrophs.

D Develop Concepts

AL Activity Organize students into two groups—a Krebs cycle group and a Calvin cycle group. Have students review the Krebs cycle and the Calvin cycle. Encourage students to gather supplemental information about Krebs and Calvin in the library. Have the groups create a bulletin board comparing and contrasting the two processes.

■ **Figure 13** Pyruvate is broken down into carbon dioxide during the Krebs cycle inside the mitochondria of cells. **S**

Trace ***Follow the path of carbon molecules that enter and leave the Krebs cycle.***

Concepts in Motion

Animation

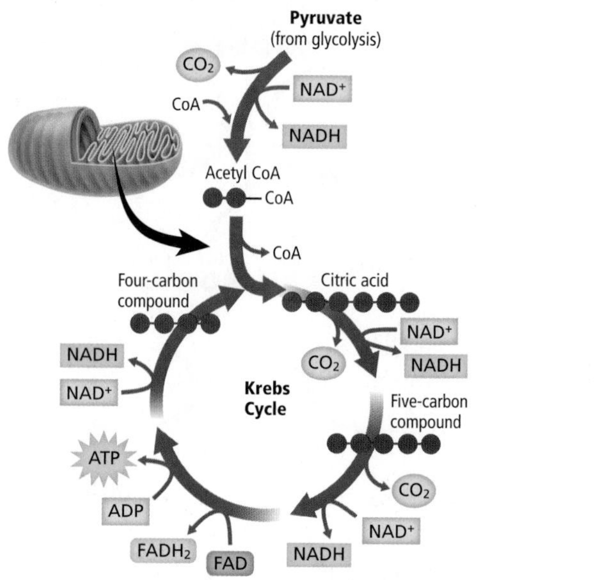

Study Tip

Clarifying Statement Work with a partner to read the text and discuss unfamiliar words and difficult concepts. Write a clarifying statement to summarize the Krebs cycle.

R **Steps of the Krebs cycle** Prior to the Krebs cycle, pyruvate first reacts with coenzyme A (CoA) to form a 2-carbon intermediate called acetyl CoA. At the same time, carbon dioxide is released and NAD^+ is converted to NADH. Acetyl CoA then moves to the mitochondrial matrix. The reaction results in the production of two carbon dioxide molecules and two NADH molecules. Follow along in **Figure 13** as you continue reading about the steps of the Krebs cycle.

- The Krebs cycle begins with acetyl CoA combining with a 4-carbon compound to form a 6-carbon compound known as citric acid.
- Citric acid is then broken down in the next series of steps, releasing two molecules of carbon dioxide and generating one ATP, three NADH, and one $FADH_2$. FAD is another electron carrier similar to NAD^+ and $NADP^+$.
- Finally, acetyl CoA and citric acid are generated and the cycle continues.

Recall that two molecules of pyruvate are formed during glycolysis, resulting in two "turns" of the Krebs cycle for each glucose molecule. The net yield from the Krebs cycle is six carbon dioxide molecules, two ATP, eight NADH, and two $FADH_2$. Ten NADH and two $FADH_2$ move on to play a significant role in the next stage of aerobic respiration. **D**

CAREERS IN BIOLOGY

Bioenergeticist A researcher who studies energy transfers in cells is a bioenergeticist. Some bioenergeticists study mitochondria and their relationship to aging and disease.

Electron Transport

In aerobic respiration, electron transport is the final step in the breakdown of glucose. It also is the point at which most of the ATP is produced. High-energy electrons and hydrogen ions from NADH and $FADH_2$ produced in the Krebs cycle are used to convert ADP to ATP.

Research Citation

Reading Strategies Educational research indicates the value of providing students with reading strategies such as the one described on this page. Students' understanding of the text will improve when they are provided with strategies to develop self-questioning and higher-level thinking about the concepts. (McTeague, 1996)

Research bibliography on pages 32T–34T

■ **Caption Question Fig. 13** from pyruvate to citric acid to a five-carbon compound to a four-carbon compound

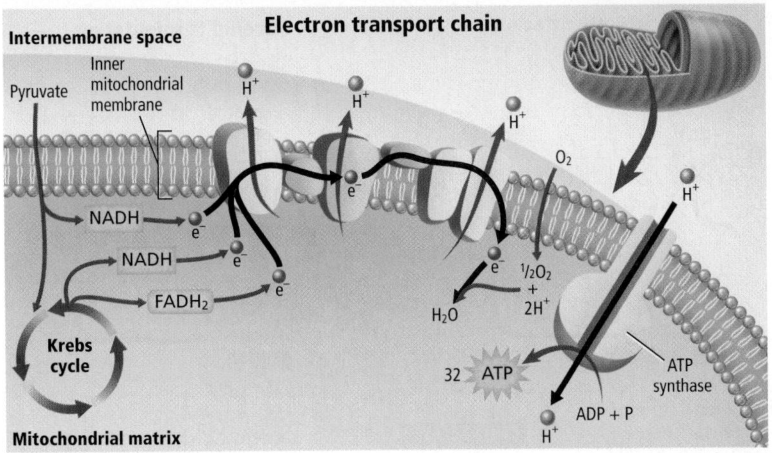

■ **Figure 14** Electron transport occurs along the mitochondrial membrane.
Compare and contrast *electron transport in cellular respiration and photosynthesis.*

D As shown in **Figure 14,** electrons move along the mitochondrial membrane from one protein to another. As NADH and $FADH_2$ release electrons, the energy carriers are converted to NAD^+ and FAD, and H^+ ions are released into the mitochondrial matrix. The H^+ ions are pumped into the mitochondrial matrix across the inner mitochondrial membrane. H^+ ions then diffuse down their concentration gradient back across the membrane and into the matrix through ATP synthase molecules in chemiosmosis. Electron transport and chemiosmosis in cellular respiration are similar to these processes in photosynthesis. Oxygen is the final electron acceptor in the electron transport system in cellular respiration. Protons and electrons are transferred to oxygen to form water.

Overall, electron transport produces 32 ATP. Each NADH molecule produces three ATP and each group of three $FADH_2$ produces two ATP. In **W** eukaryotes, one molecule of glucose yields 36 ATP under ideal conditions.

Prokaryotic cellular respiration Some prokaryotes also undergo aerobic respiration. Because prokaryotes do not have mitochondria, there are differences in the process. The main difference involves the use of the prokaryotic cellular membrane as the location of electron transport. In eukaryotic cells, pyruvate is transported to the mitochondria. In prokaryotes, this movement is unnecessary, saving the prokaryotic cell two ATP, and increasing the net total of ATP produced to 38.

Anaerobic Respiration

Some cells can function for a short time when oxygen levels are low. Some prokaryotes are anaerobic organisms—they grow and reproduce without oxygen. In some cases these cells continue to produce ATP through glycolysis. However, there are problems with solely relying on glycolysis for energy. Glycolysis provides only two net ATP for each molecule of glucose, and a cell has a limited amount of NAD^+. Glycolysis will stop when all the NAD^+ is used up if there is not a process to replenish NAD^+. The anaerobic pathway that follows glycolysis is anaerobic respiration, or fermentation. **Fermentation** occurs in the cytoplasm and regenerates the cell's supply of NAD^+ while producing a small amount of ATP. The two main types of fermentation are lactic acid fermentation and alcohol fermentation.

VOCABULARY
SCIENCE USAGE V. COMMON USAGE
Concentration
Science usage: the relative amount of a substance dissolved in another substance
The concentration of hydrogen ions is greater on one side of the membrane than on the other.

Common usage: the directing of close, undivided attention
The student's concentration was focused on the exam.

D Develop Concepts

BL OL AL Integrate Chemistry Remind students that electrons are negatively charged particles that orbit the nucleus of the atom. Students might have difficulty understanding that the outer electrons can move from one molecule or atom to another. Encourage students to keep in mind that electrons are negatively charged and that the movement of these particles through the electron transport chain depends on the presence of positive charges that attract them.

W Writing Support

BL OL AL Narrative Writing Have students write a paragraph summarizing the electron transport chain. Tell them to include the purpose of the electron transport chain, where the reactions are occurring in the cell, and important molecules that take part in the process.

■ **Caption Question Fig. 14** Electron transport occurs along the mitochondrial membrane in cellular respiration and along the thylakoid membrane in photosynthesis.

Demonstration

Alcohol Fermentation At the beginning of class, mix baker's yeast, water, and sugar in a flask. Stretch a balloon snugly over the mouth of the flask. As carbon dioxide is produced, the balloon will expand. Point out to students that when making bread containing yeast, the dough rises due to the increased production of carbon dioxide gas.
Est. time: 10 min

Develop Concepts

BL OL AL Review Review the major concepts of photosynthesis. **ASK STUDENTS:** ***What is photosynthesis?*** conversion of light energy into chemical energy ***What are the two phases of photosynthesis?*** light-dependent and light-independent reactions ***Where do these reactions take place?*** Light-dependent reactions take place in the thylakoids, and light-independent reactions occur in the stroma. ***What is the major product of light-dependent reactions?*** ATP ***What is the major product of light-independent reactions?*** monosaccharides

DATA ANALYSIS LAB 1

About the Lab

- One of the symptoms of a viral infection is lethargy. The invading virus can decrease the amount of ATP produced by a cell. Decreases in ATP production can compromise the body's ability to mount an immune response.
- Also see Forsyth, et al. 1999. Therapeutic effects of oral NADH on the symptoms of patients with chronic fatigue syndrome. *Annals of Allergy, Asthma, and Immunology* 82: 185–191.

Think Critically

1. The virus increased lactic acid production after four hours.
2. After 8 h, the virus increased lactic acid production by approximately 75% and decreased ATP production by approximately 28%.
3. because of decreased ATP synthesis

Caption Question Fig. 15 Lactic acid fermentation replenishes the supply of NAD^+ by converting pyruvate to lactic acid. Alcohol fermentation converts pyruvate to ethanol and carbon dioxide to replenish NAD^+. Both occur without oxygen.

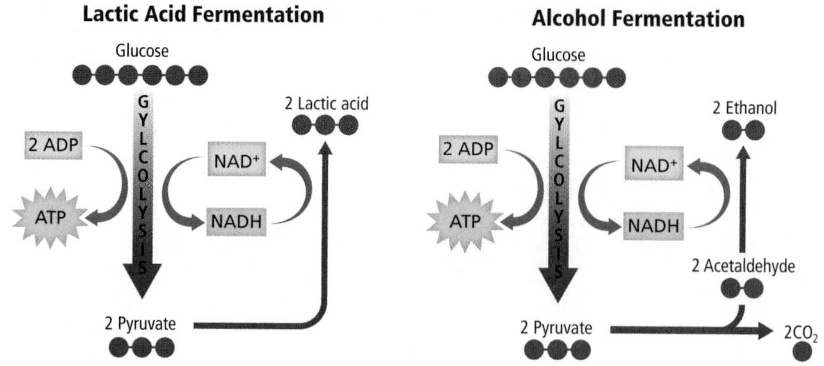

Figure 15 When oxygen is absent or in limited supply, fermentation can occur.
Compare and contrast *lactic acid fermentation and alcohol fermentation.*

Inquiry Virtual Lab

Connection to Health **Lactic acid fermentation** In lactic acid fermentation, enzymes convert the pyruvate made during glycolysis to lactic acid, as shown in **Figure 15.** This involves the transfer of high-energy electrons and protons from NADH. Skeletal muscles produce lactic acid when the body cannot supply enough oxygen, such as during periods of strenuous exercise. When lactic acid builds up in muscle cells, muscles become fatigued and might feel sore. Lactic acid also is produced by several microorganisms that often are used to produce many foods, including cheese, yogurt, and sour cream.

Alcohol fermentation Alcohol fermentation occurs in yeast and some bacteria. **Figure 15** shows the chemical reaction that occurs during alcohol fermentation when pyruvate is converted to ethyl alcohol and carbon dioxide. Similar to lactic acid fermentation, NADH donates electrons during this reaction and NAD^+ is regenerated.

DATA ANALYSIS LAB 1

Based On Real Data*

Interpret the Data

How does viral infection affect cellular respiration? Infection by viruses can significantly affect cellular respiration and the ability of cells to produce ATP. To test the effect of viral infection on the stages of cellular respiration, cells were infected with a virus, and the amount of lactic acid and ATP produced were measured.

Think Critically

1. **Analyze** how the virus affected lactic acid production in the cells.
2. **Calculate** After 8 hours, by what percentage was the lactic acid higher in the virus group than in the control group? By what percentage was ATP production decreased?

Data and Observations

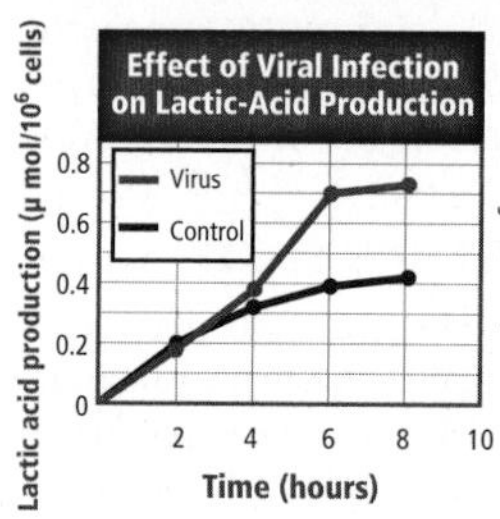

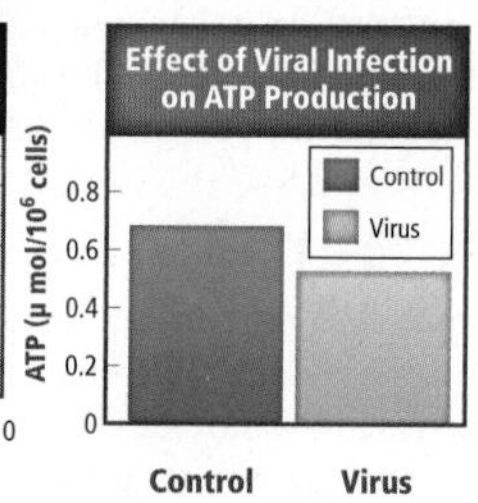

3. **Infer** why having a virus such as the flu might make a person feel tired.

Data obtained from: El-Bacha, T., et al. 2004. Mayaro virus infection alters glucose metabolism in cultured cells through activation of the enzyme 6-phosphofructo 1-kinase. *Molecular and Cellular Biochemistry* 266: 191–198.

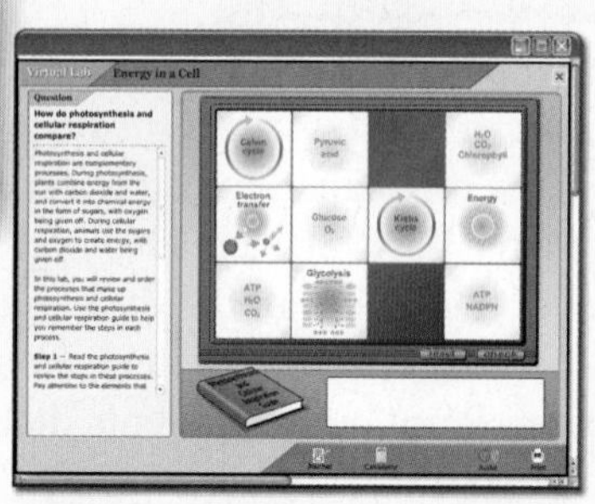

Inquiry Virtual Lab Students will compare the phases of photosynthesis and cellular respiration.

Differentiated Instruction

Below Level Differentiate lessons when students with different ability levels are in the classroom. For example, the question on calculating described in the Data Analysis Lab can be modified for students who perform below level by having them determine percentage only for lactic acid production.

For more tips, see pages 14T–15T.

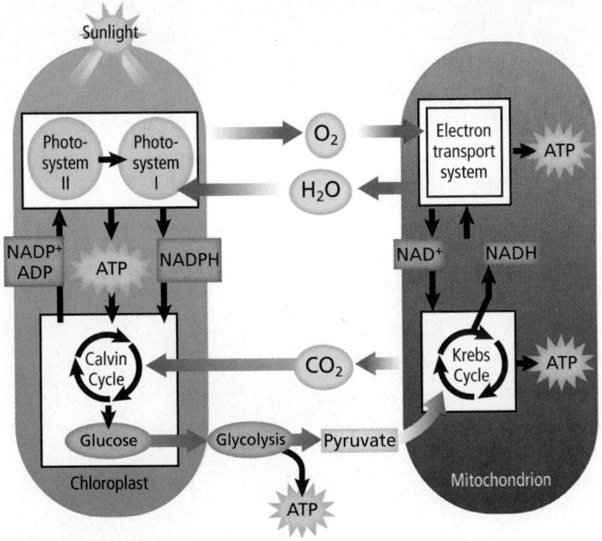

■ **Figure 16** Photosynthesis and cellular respiration form a cycle in which the products of one metabolic pathway form the reactants of the other metabolic pathway.

Photosynthesis and Cellular Respiration

As you have learned, photosynthesis and cellular respiration are two important processes that cells use to obtain energy. They are metabolic pathways that produce and break down simple carbohydrates. **Figure 16** shows how these two processes are related. Recall that the products of photosynthesis are oxygen and glucose, the reactants needed for cellular respiration. The products of cellular respiration, which are carbon dioxide and water, are the reactants for photosynthesis.

Video BrainPOP

Section 3 Assessment

Section Summary

- Many living organisms use cellular respiration to break down glucose.
- NADH and $FADH_2$ are important electron carriers for cellular respiration.
- In the absence of oxygen, cells can sustain glycolysis by fermentation.

Understand Main Ideas

1. MAIN Idea **Summarize** the stages of cellular respiration.
2. **Identify** how many carbons from one glucose molecule enter one round of the Krebs cycle.
3. **Explain** how high-energy electrons are used in electron transport.
4. **Describe** the role of fermentation in maintaining ATP and NAD^+ levels.

Think Critically

MATH in Biology

5. How many ATP, NADH, and $FADH_2$ are produced in each step of cellular respiration? How is the number of ATP produced different from the net ATP available?
6. **Compare and contrast** the two types of fermentation.

Critical Thinking

AL Theorize

ASK STUDENTS: ***If you drink a soft drink containing 33 grams of sugar (sucrose), why don't you gain the weight of the sugar?*** The body will store only a fraction of the 33 grams, while breaking down the rest. The sugar will be broken down to ultimately form CO_2 by aerobic respiration. The hydrogen atoms found in the sucrose molecules will unite with oxygen gas to produce water. Most of the water produced will be eliminated by breathing and urination. However, some will be retained in the cell. If the sugar is not needed for cellular respiration, it will be converted to polymeric storage molecules, such as glycogen and lipids.

Formative Assessment

Evaluation

ASK STUDENTS: ***What type of energy is sunlight converted to during photosynthesis?*** chemical energy ***What type of energy is stored in glucose in food?*** chemical energy ***What type of energy is glucose converted to?*** cellular chemical energy in the form of ATP Remind students that chemical energy can exist in multiple forms.

Remediation Have students create a two-column chart that lists the characteristics of photosynthesis on one side and important concepts about cellular respiration on the other side.

Video BrainPOP

Section 3 Assessment

1. Glycolysis splits the glucose into two smaller sugars; the Krebs cycle supplies electrons for electron transport; electron transport produces most of the ATP obtained from cellular respiration.
2. Three carbons (pyruvate) from the original 6-carbon glucose molecule are processed. The other three (as pyruvate) enter a separate Krebs cycle.
3. Electron pairs are transferred from NADH and $FADH_2$ to convert ADP into ATP.
4. During fermentation, NADH donates electrons for regeneration.
5. First stage (glycolysis): 4 molecules ATP, 2 molecules NADH; second stage (Krebs cycle): 2 ATP, 8 NADH, 2 $FADH_2$; third stage (electron transport): 32 ATP. Two electrons are required to initiate glycolysis, therefore the net production of ATP from glycolysis is two.
6. Lactic acid fermentation replenishes the supply of NAD^+ by converting pyruvate to lactic acid. Alcohol fermentation converts pyruvate to ethanol and carbon dioxide to replenish NAD^+. Both occur without oxygen.

Assessment Online Quiz

CUTTING-EDGE BIOLOGY

Purpose
Students will understand how scientists use mitochondrial DNA as a tool for learning about prehuman ancestors.
A.2, C.2, C.3, E.2

Anticipatory Guide
ASK STUDENTS: ***What are the mitochondria of the cell?*** Mitochondria are the powerhouses of the cell; they produce energy. ***What role do the mitochondria play?*** Mitochondria are the location of complex biological processes, such as the Kreb's cycle and the electron transport chain. ***How might mitochondria help determine where humans originated?*** Answers will vary but should reflect scientific reasoning.

Background
DNA (deoxyribonucleic acid) is the genetic material. Though the DNA for most functions of the cell is contained in the cell's nucleus, mitochondria have their own circular DNA. Mitochondrial DNA (mtDNA) is DNA that is unique from the nuclear DNA and passed only through the female line because an offspring's mitochondria come from the mother's egg. Also, Y-chromosome DNA is used for determining inheritance through the male line. Since both mtDNA and Y-chromosome DNA have a predictable rate of mutation, they can be used as a genetic time line of sorts.

CUTTING-EDGE BIOLOGY

Tracking Human Evolution

DNA evidence has been used to solve mysteries that were decades, or even centuries old—but imagine trying to unravel a mystery that is millions of years old. This is exactly what scientists are doing when they use DNA analysis to track human evolution.

EM Magnification: 150,000×

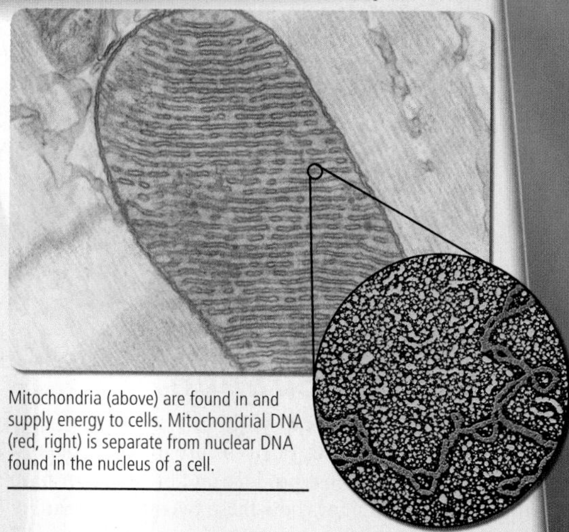

Mitochondria (above) are found in and supply energy to cells. Mitochondrial DNA (red, right) is separate from nuclear DNA found in the nucleus of a cell.

Mitochondrial DNA You might wonder what mitochondria have to do with DNA analysis and human evolution. Mitochondria often are called the powerhouses of the cell. They are the organelles in which cells release the energy stored in food. Mitochondria have their own DNA, which is much smaller than nuclear DNA and more abundant due to its presence outside the nucleus and the number of mitochondria in most cells. Mitochondrial DNA (mtDNA) is easier to detect and extract than nuclear DNA, making it a useful tool for unlocking some of science's toughest mysteries.

One particular characteristic of mtDNA makes it especially useful for tracking human evolution. Mitochondria are inherited through maternal lineage. When a sperm and egg combine at fertilization, the nuclear DNA of the two gametes combine, but the mitochondria in the offspring are supplied solely by the egg. Therefore, mtDNA can be used as a marker to trace motherhood from generation to generation.

Tracing evolution Scientists use DNA analysis to trace the path of prehuman creatures, called hominids, as they spread around the world. The genomic DNA that is found in the nuclei of cells often is degraded or present in miniscule amounts in these ancient samples. However, scientists discovered that mtDNA is found abundantly and can be used for their analysis.

Mutations in mtDNA occur in relatively predictable patterns, and those patterns are studied and compared by scientists. By comparing mutations in mtDNA, scientists can trace mtDNA inheritance. Based on these studies of mtDNA, scientists have determined that the most recent maternal common ancestor of people living on Earth today is "Mitochondrial Eve." Mitochondrial Eve is thought to be a woman who lived in Africa approximately 200,000 years ago.

Based on the theory of Mitochondrial Eve, an international study is being conducted to trace the migration and ancestry of early humans. The project uses mtDNA sequences in females, but uses sequences from the Y chromosome to trace ancestry in males.

WRITING in Biology
Research Paper Research mtDNA. Choose one aspect of the current research with mtDNA and write a research paper about it.

WRITING in Biology

RUBRIC Use the modifiable rubric found on your eTeacherEdition Online to assess writing assignments.

Discussion Discuss how mutations in mtDNA and Y-chromosome DNA can be used as a genetic timer, since random mutations occur in each at a relatively steady rate. Also discuss how mtDNA mutations are easy to trace because they go directly from mother to child.

BIOLAB

Design Your Own

DO DIFFERENT WAVELENGTHS OF LIGHT AFFECT THE RATE OF PHOTOSYNTHESIS?

Background: **Photosynthesizing organisms need light to complete photosynthesis. White light is composed of the different colors of light found in the visible light spectrum, and each color of light has a specific wavelength. During this lab, you will design an experiment to test the effect of different light wavelengths on the rate of photosynthesis.**

Question: *How do different wavelengths of light affect photosynthesis rates?*

Possible Materials

Choose materials that would be appropriate for this lab.

aquatic plant material
Erlenmeyer flasks
test tubes (15 mL)
graduated cylinder (10 mL)
metric ruler
colored cellophane (assorted colors)
aluminum foil
lamp with reflector and 150 W bulb
baking soda solution (0.25%)
watch with a second hand

Safety Precautions

Plan and Perform the Experiment

1. Read and complete the lab safety form.
2. Predict how different wavelengths of light will affect the rate of photosynthesis in your plant.
3. Design an experiment to test your prediction. Write a list of steps that you will follow, and identify the controls and variables that you will use.
4. Explain how you will generate light with different wavelengths, supply the plant with carbon dioxide, and measure the oxygen production of the plant.
5. Create a data table for recording your observations and measurements.
6. Make sure your teacher approves your plan before you begin.
7. Conduct your experiment as approved.
8. **Cleanup and Disposal** Clean up all equipment as instructed by your teacher, and return everything to its proper place. Dispose of plant material as instructed by your teacher. Wash your hands thoroughly with soap and water.

Analyze and Conclude

1. **Identify** the controls and variables in your experiment.
2. **Explain** how you measured the rate of photosynthesis.
3. **Graph** your data.
4. **Describe** how the rate of photosynthesis is affected by different wavelengths of light based on your data.
5. **Discuss** whether or not your data supported your prediction.
6. **Error Analysis** Identify possible sources of error in your experimental design, procedure, and data collection.
7. **Suggest** how you would reduce these sources of error if you repeated the experiment.

COMMUNICATE

Peer Review Post your data and graph at the front of the room. Review data posted by other students. Discuss and use comments from other students to improve your own methods.

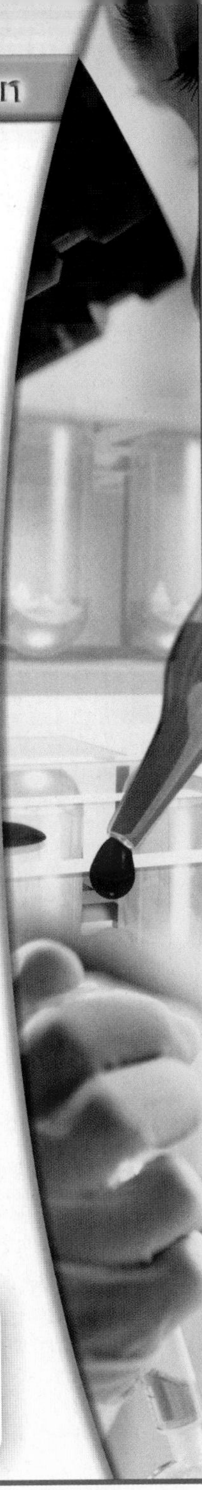

Analyze and Conclude

1. Controls may include equal volumes of water and of sodium bicarbonate solution, and white light. Variables may include the wavelengths of light from colored cellophane.
2. Answers will depend on how students measure oxygen production. Photosynthesis rate is measured by measuring oxygen production.
3. Graphs should show greatest photosynthesis in red and violet light and little or none in other wavelengths.
4. Photosynthesis rate will be greatest in red and violet light. There should be little or none in blue, green, yellow, and orange light.
5. Answers will depend on data and students' predictions.
6. Stirring plants in the beaker or leaving a portion of plant out of the water affects oxygen production. Other errors might include not completely covering the lightbulb with cellophane or leaving air at the top of the test tube.
7. Take care in handling.

BIOLAB

Design Your Own

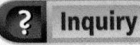

Inquiry BioLab

For a lab worksheet, use your eTeacherEdition Online.

RUBRIC A rubric for evaluating BioLabs is found on your eTeacherEdition Online.

Est. Time 45 min

Content Background Green aquatic plants and algae carry out photosynthesis under water, producing dissolved oxygen. Most photosynthesizing organisms use chlorophyll *a*, which absorbs light most effectively in the violet and red portions of the spectrum, and least effectively in blue, green, yellow, or orange light.

Alternative Materials 100-mL beakers, masking tape, balance, dissolved oxygen kit, reaction chamber, other green aquatic plants, classroom clock

Safety Precautions Approve lab safety forms before work begins. Be certain students' hands and work areas are dry when handling electrical equipment.

Teaching Strategies

- Place the aquatic plant material in a large bowl under a lamp for about 10 minutes to reduce time for photosynthesis to begin.
- Covering bulb with cellophane of specific colors filters different wavelengths of light.

Alternative Teaching Demo Place a flask or test tube with a sprig beneath lamps covered with colored cellophane. Have student volunteers measure the oxygen produced by exposure to the different light wavelengths.

Cleanup and Disposal Return plant materials to an aquarium.

Chapter 8

Study Guide

ConnectED

Students can use the following to review the chapter.

Review

- Vocabulary eGames
- Vocabulary eFlashcards
- Vocabulary PuzzleMaker

Assessment

- Online Quizzes
- Online Test Practice
- Standardized Test Practice

Use the *ExamView® Assessment Suite* CD-ROM to:

- create multiple versions of tests
- create modified tests with one mouse click
- edit existing questions and add your own questions
- build tests aligned with state standards using built-in state curriculum tags
- change English tests to Spanish with one mouse click
- track students' progress using the Teacher Management System

Chapter 8 Study Guide

THEME FOCUS Energy The Sun is the source of nearly all of the energy on Earth, and it is converted to chemical energy at the cellular level through photosynthesis.

BIG Idea **Photosynthesis converts the Sun's energy into chemical energy, while cellular respiration uses chemical energy to carry out life functions.**

Section 1 How Organisms Obtain Energy

energy (p. 218)
thermodynamics (p. 218)
metabolism (p. 220)
photosynthesis (p. 220)
cellular respiration (p. 220)
adenosine triphosphate (ATP) (p. 221)

MAIN Idea **All living organisms use energy to carry out all biological processes.**

- The laws of thermodynamics control the flow and transformation of energy in organisms.
- Some organisms produce their own food, whereas others obtain energy from the food they ingest.
- Cells store and release energy through coupled anabolic and catabolic reactions.
- The energy released from the breakdown of ATP drives cellular activities.

Section 2 Photosynthesis

thylakoid (p. 223)
granum (p. 223)
stroma (p. 223)
pigment (p. 223)
$NADP^+$ (p. 224)
Calvin cycle (p. 226)
rubisco (p. 226)

MAIN Idea **Light energy is trapped and converted into chemical energy during photosynthesis.**

- Plants contain chloroplasts with light-absorbing pigments that convert light energy into chemical energy.
- Photosynthesis is a two-phase process that consists of light reactions and the Calvin cycle.
- In the light reactions, autotrophs trap and convert light energy into chemical energy in the form of NADPH and ATP.
- In the Calvin cycle, chemical energy in ATP and NADPH is used to synthesize carbohydrates such as glucose.

Section 3 Cellular Respiration

anaerobic process (p. 228)
aerobic respiration (p. 228)
aerobic process (p. 228)
glycolysis (p. 229)
Krebs cycle (p. 229)
fermentation (p. 231)

MAIN Idea **Living organisms obtain energy by breaking down organic molecules during cellular respiration.**

- Many living organisms use cellular respiration to break down glucose.
- The stages of cellular respiration are glycolysis, the Krebs cycle, and electron transport.
- NADH and $FADH_2$ are important electron carriers for cellular respiration.
- In the absence of oxygen, cells can sustain glycolysis by fermentation.

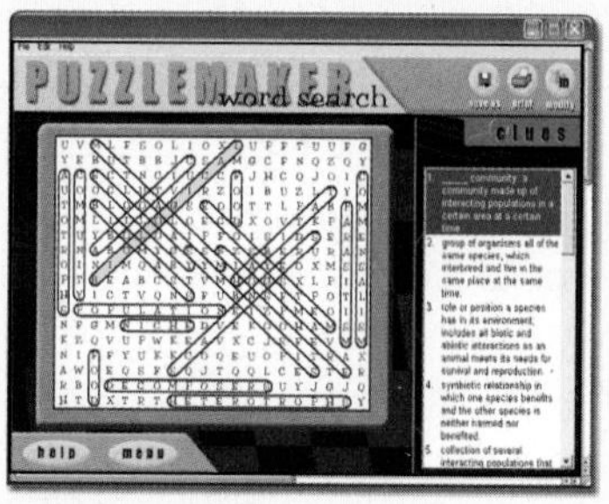

Review **Vocabulary PuzzleMaker**

For additional practice with vocabulary, have students access the Vocabulary PuzzleMaker online.

Review **Vocabulary eGames**

Section 1

Vocabulary Review

Each of the following sentences is false. Make each sentence true by replacing the italicized word with a vocabulary term from the Study Guide page.

1. *Metabolism* is the energy currency of the cell.
2. The study of the flow and transformation of energy is called *energy.*
3. *Bioenergetics* can exist in many forms.
4. Chemical reactions that convert energy within a cell are refered to as *autotrophs.*
5. Light energy is converted into chemical energy during the process of *sunlight.*

Understand Main Ideas

6. Which is not a characteristic of energy?
   A. cannot be created nor destroyed
   B. is the capacity to do work
   C. exists in forms such as chemical, light, and mechanical
   D. changes spontaneously from disorder to order
7. Which organism depends on an external source of organic compounds?
   A. autotroph
   B. heterotroph
   C. chemoautotroph
   D. photoautotroph

Use the figure below to answer question 8.

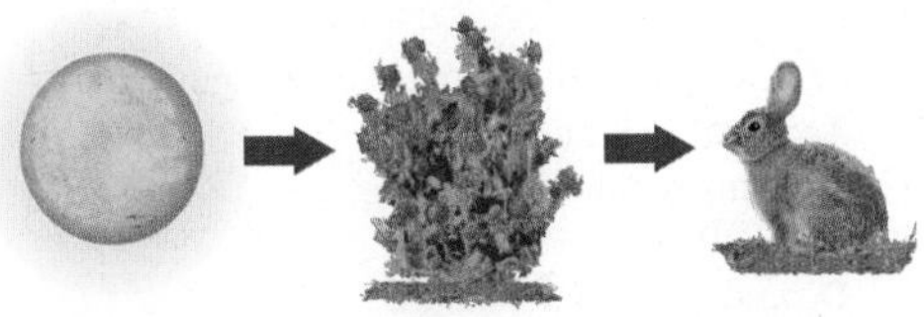

8. **THEME FOCUS Energy** Which part of this food chain provides energy to just one other part?
   A. the chemoautotroph
   B. the heterotroph
   C. the Sun
   D. the photoautotroph
9. What do cells store and release as the main source of chemical energy?
   A. ATP
   B. ADP
   C. $NADP^+$
   D. NADPH

Constructed Response

10. **MAIN Idea** How do autotrophs and heterotrophs differ in the way in which they obtain energy?
11. **Open Ended** Use an analogy to describe the role of ATP in living organisms.

Think Critically

12. **Describe** how energy is released from ATP.
13. **Relate** anabolic and catabolic reactions. Create an analogy for the relationship between photosynthesis and cellular respiration.

Section 2

Vocabulary Review

Write the vocabulary term from the Study Guide page for each definition.

14. the location of the light reactions
15. a stack of thylakoids
16. a colored molecule that absorbs light
17. a process in which energy is stored in organic molecules

Understand Main Ideas

Use the equation below to answer question 18.

$$6CO_2 + 6H_2O \xrightarrow{\text{energy}} C_6H_{12}O_6 + ?$$

18. What waste product of photosynthesis is released to the environment?
   A. carbon dioxide
   B. water
   C. oxygen
   D. ammonia

Chapter 8 Assessment

Section 1

Vocabulary Review

1. Adenosine triphosphate (ATP)
2. thermodynamics
3. Energy
4. metabolism
5. photosynthesis

Understand Main Ideas

6. D
7. B
8. D
9. A

Constructed Response

10. Autotrophs get energy by absorbing light energy from the Sun, whereas heterotrophs get energy from the chemical energy stored in food.
11. Possible analogy: In living cells, ATP is like the gasoline that is used to keep an automobile running.

Think Critically

12. Energy is released from ATP when it is broken down (hydrolyzed) into ADP and a phosphate group.
13. Anabolic pathways store energy by building molecules. Catabolic pathways release energy by breaking down molecules. Analogies will vary but should show the relationship of products and reactants.

Section 2

Vocabulary Review

14. thylakoid
15. granum
16. pigment
17. Calvin cycle

Understand Main Ideas

18. C

19. A
20. B
21. B

Constructed Response

22. Light-dependent reactions—sunlight is absorbed by chlorophyll, producing ATP and NADPH. Light-independent reactions (or Calvin cycle)—ATP and NADPH are used to fuel the conversion of carbon dioxide into sucrose.
23. Hydrogen ion generation is essential for ATP production because it provides energy for conversion of ADP to ATP by ATP synthase.
24. The Calvin cycle depends on light-dependent reactions to provide the energy (ATP and NADPH) needed for sucrose production.

Think Critically

25. Oxygen is released into the atmosphere during the synthesis of sucrose and is not a product formed for use by the autotroph.
26. Deforestation will decrease the number of trees available for photosynthesis, thereby decreasing oxygen released into the atmosphere and ultimately the amount of oxygen available for cellular respiration.
27. C_4 pathway: fixes carbon dioxide into four-carbon molecules instead of three-carbon molecules in the Calvin cycle; plants have modifications in arrangements of leaf cells; helps plants maintain photosynthesis while minimizing water loss; CAM photosynthesis: carbon dioxide enters only at night when carbon dioxide is fixed into organic compounds; during the day, CO_2 is released from these compounds and enters the Calvin cycle; allows for sufficient CO_2 uptake while minimizing water loss. Both pathways help plants survive extreme climates.

Chapter 8 Assessment

19. Which is the internal membrane of the chloroplast that is organized into flattened membranous sacs?
A. thylakoids
B. mitochondria
C. theca
D. stroma

Use the figure below to answer question 20.

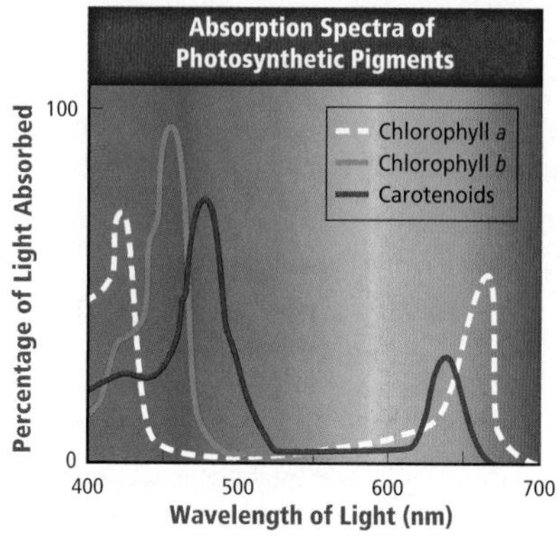

20. Of which wavelength of light do carotenoids absorb the greatest percentage?
A. 400
B. 500
C. 600
D. 700

21. Which supplies energy used to synthesize carbohydrates during the Calvin cycle?
A. CO_2 and ATP
B. ATP and NADPH
C. NADPH and H_2O
D. H_2O and O_2

Constructed Response

22. MAIN Idea Summarize the phases of photosynthesis. Describe where each phase occurs in the chloroplast.

23. Short Answer Why is hydrogen ion generation essential for ATP production during photosynthesis?

24. Short Answer Explain why the Calvin cycle depends on light reactions.

Think Critically

25. Explain the following statement: The oxygen generated by photosynthesis is simply a by-product formed during the production of ATP and carbohydrates.

26. Predict the effect of the loss of forests on cellular respiration in other organisms.

27. Describe two alternative photosynthesis pathways found in plants. Suggest how these adaptations might help plants.

Section 3

Vocabulary Review

Define each vocabulary term in a complete sentence.

28. Krebs cycle
29. anaerobic process
30. fermentation
31. aerobic
32. glycolysis

Understand Main Ideas

Use the figure below to answer questions 33 and 34.

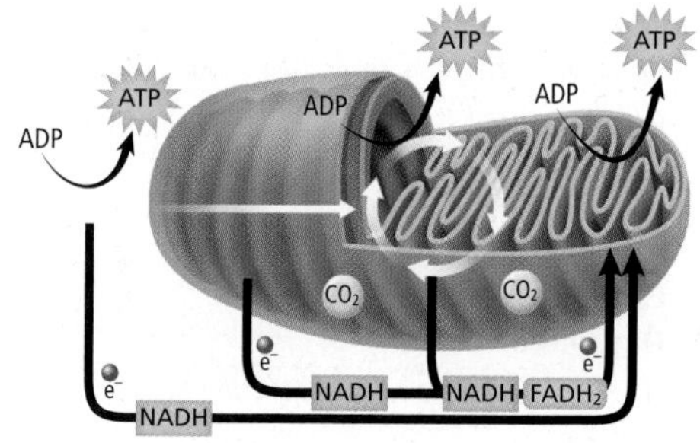

33. Which organelle is illustrated in the figure?
A. Golgi apparatus
B. mitochondrion
C. nucleus
D. endoplasmic reticulum

34. Which process does not occur in the organelle illustrated above?
A. glycolysis
B. Krebs cycle
C. conversion of pyruvate to acetyl CoA
D. electron transport

Section 3

Vocabulary Review

28. Pyruvate is broken down into carbon dioxide during the tricarboxylic acid cycle (TCA), or Krebs cycle.
29. Anaerobic processes occur in the absence of oxygen.
30. The two types of fermentation are lactic-acid fermentation and alcohol fermentation.
31. Oxygen is required for aerobic processes.
32. Glucose is broken down during the process of glycolysis.

Understand Main Ideas

33. B
34. A

Assessment Online Test Practice

35. Which is not a stage of cellular respiration?
   A. glycolysis
   B. Krebs cycle
   C. electron transport chain
   D. lactic acid fermentation

36. What is produced when the electrons leave the electron transport chain in cellular respiration and bind to the final electron acceptor for the chain?
   A. H_2O
   B. O_2
   C. CO_2
   D. CO

37. In which molecule is most of the energy of glucose stored at the end of glycolysis?
   A. pyruvate
   B. acetyl CoA
   C. ATP
   D. NADH

Constructed Response

38. **Short Answer** Discuss the roles of NADH and $FADH_2$ in cellular respiration.

39. **Short Answer** In cellular respiration, where do the electrons in the electron transport chain originate? What is the final destination of the electrons?

40. **Short Answer** Why do your muscles hurt for some time after a large amount of strenuous exercise?

Think Critically

41. **Explain** The end products of cellular respiration are CO_2 and H_2O. Where do the oxygen atoms in the CO_2 originate? Where does the oxygen atom in H_2O originate?

42. MAIN Idea What is the advantage of aerobic metabolism over anaerobic metabolism in energy production in living organisms?

43. **Compare and contrast** electron transport in photosynthesis and cellular respiration.

Summative Assessment

44. BIG Idea What are the chemical equations for photosynthesis and cellular respiration? Analyze the relationship between photosynthesis and cellular respiration using the equations for both processes.

45. WRITING in Biology Write an article using what you know about the relationship between photosynthesis and cellular respiration to explain the importance of plants in an ecosystem.

DBQ Document-Based Questions

Cadmium is a heavy metal that is toxic to humans, plants, and animals. It is often found as a contaminant in soil. Use the data below to answer questions about the effect of cadmium on photosynthesis in tomato plants.

Data obtained from: Chaffei, C., et al. 2004. Cadmium toxicity induced changes in nitrogen management in *Lycopersicon esculentum* leading to a metabolic safeguard through an amino acid storage strategy. *Plant and Cell Physiology* 45(11): 1681–1693.

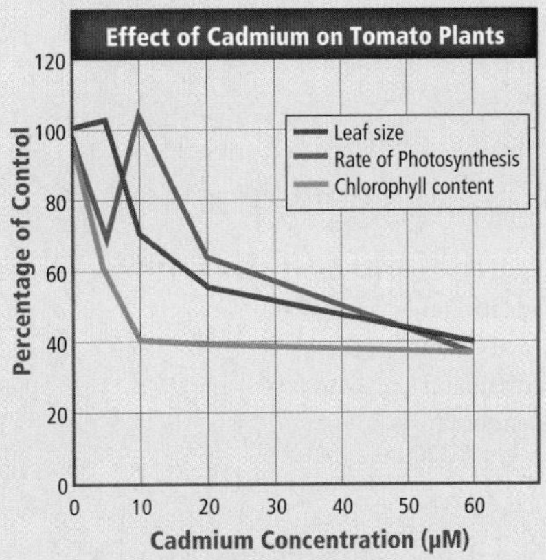

46. What was the effect of cadmium on leaf size, chlorophyll content, and photosynthesis rate?

47. At what concentration of cadmium was the largest effect on leaf size observed? On chlorophyll content? On photosynthesis rate?

48. Predict the effects on cellular respiration if an animal eats contaminated tomatoes.

35. D
36. A
37. C

Constructed Response

38. Oxidation of NADH and $FADH_2$ provides electrons used in the electron transport chain, which provides the energy needed to transport hydrogen ions and, ultimately, make ATP.
39. The electrons in the electron transport chain come from NADH and $FADH_2$. The final destination of the electrons is to combine with hydrogen ions and oxygen to form water.
40. Muscles are sore after exercise because lactic acid is produced by the fermentation of pyruvate, which occurs when oxygen levels are low.

Think Critically

41. The oxygen atoms in carbon dioxide come from glucose, and the oxygen in water comes from the atmosphere.
42. Aerobic metabolism is more efficient in forming ATP because the Krebs cycle and the electron transport chain (both of which require oxygen) produce 32 molecules of ATP. Only 2 molecules of ATP are produced by glycolysis.
43. Photosynthesis: electrons move on thylakoid membrane; cellular respiration: electrons move along mitochondrial membrane.

Summative Assessment

44. Answers should include the equations for photosynthesis and cellular respiration, and should explain that the processes are opposite of each other. Photosynthesis converts CO_2 and H_2O to sugars; cellular respiration converts those sugars into CO_2 and H_2O.
45. Articles should emphasize the transfer of energy, beginning with sunlight.

DBQ Document-Based Questions

Chaffei, C., et al. 2004. Cadmium toxicity induced changes in nitrogen management in *Lycopersicon esculentum* leading to a metabolic safeguard through an amino acid storage strategy. *Plant Cell Physiology* 45(11): 1681–1693.

46. Increasing concentrations of cadmium decreased leaf size, chlorophyll content, and the rate of photosynthesis.
47. The highest concentration had the greatest effect on all three variables tested.
48. Since the light-dependent reaction and the electron transport chain are very similar, cellular respiration may decrease.

WRITING in Biology

RUBRIC Use the modifiable rubric found on your eTeacherEdition Online to assess writing assignments.

Assessment Online Test Practice

Standardized Test Practice

Multiple Choice

1. A 5. B 9. D
2. A 6. D
3. B 7. C
4. B 8. C

Short Answer

10. Thylakoid: Light-dependent reactions, Phase one
    Stroma: Calvin cycle, Phase two
11. Similar: Both are permeable, allowing substances in and out of the cell. Different: Cell wall is not selectively permeable, like a cell membrane; it is just porous. Cell wall has a more rigid structure, since it is made from cellulose, and not from a "fluid mosaic" like a phospholipid bilayer of a cell membrane.
12. Energy is stored in the phosphate bonds in an ATP molecule, like a loaded spring. When a phosphate group is removed, energy is released as ADP is formed.
13. Answers can vary, depending on which components the student chooses. Possible answers include:
    Phospholipid bilayer: creates a barrier between inside and outside the cell, as water-soluble substances cannot move easily across it
    Transport proteins: allow certain substances to enter and leave the cell, even against a concentration gradient
    Cholesterol molecules: contribute to the cell membrane's structure, so the cell maintains a shape.
14. A solution, or homogeneous mixture, is formed. The salt is the solute and the water is the solvent.
15. Cells in the leaves would have the greatest number of chloroplasts, but all green parts of the plant would contain some chloroplasts. The leaves are the parts of the plants where photosynthesis

Standardized Test Practice

Cumulative

Multiple Choice

1. Suppose that the most common form of element X is X-97. The isotope X-99 has more of which?
   A. neutrons
   B. protons
   C. orbiting electrons
   D. overall charge

Use the graph below to answer question 2.

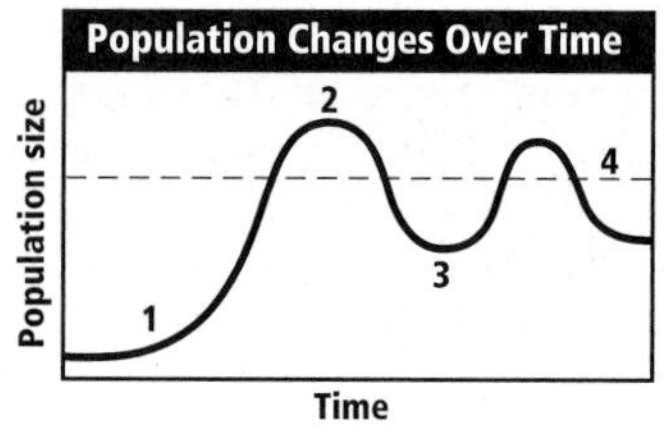

2. Which part of the graph indicates exponential growth?
   A. 1
   B. 2
   C. 3
   D. 4

3. Which type of transport does NOT require the input of additional energy?
   A. active transport
   B. diffusion
   C. endocytosis
   D. exocytosis

4. Which step occurs during the Calvin cycle?
   A. formation of ATP
   B. formation of six-carbon sugars
   C. release of oxygen gas
   D. transport of electrons by $NADP^+$

5. Which describes extinctions caused by deforestation in tropical rain forests?
   A. ecosystem pollution
   B. habitat destruction
   C. introduced species
   D. species overexploitation

Use the diagram below to answer question 6.

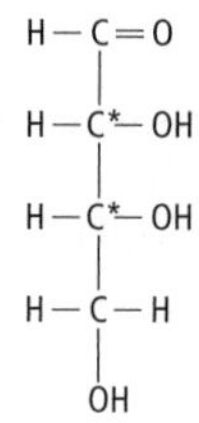

6. Based on the diagram, which is the correct molecular formula if the molecule shown above has six carbons?
   A. $C_6H_8O_4$
   B. $C_6H_{10}O_6$
   C. $C_6H_{12}O_4$
   D. $C_6H_{12}O_6$

7. Which energy transformation can occur only in autotrophs?
   A. chemical energy into mechanical energy
   B. electrical energy into thermal energy
   C. light energy into chemical energy
   D. mechanical energy into thermal energy

8. Which statement does the cell theory support?
   A. Cells can form from proteins in the environment.
   B. Cells contain membrane-bound organelles.
   C. Life-forms are made of one or more cells.
   D. Organelles are the smallest form of life.

9. Which part of the scientific method evaluates the procedures used in an experiment?
   A. forming a hypothesis
   B. publishing results
   C. making an observation
   D. peer review

Short Answer

Use the illustration below to answer question 10.

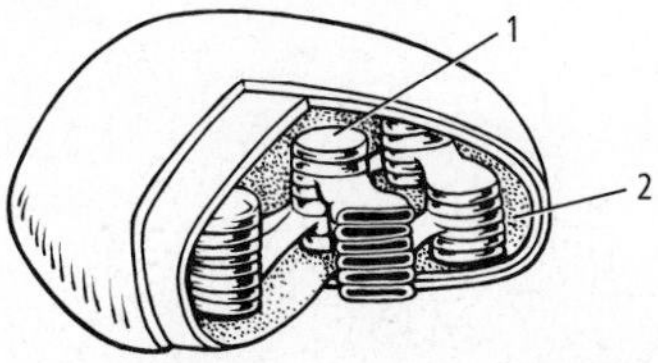

10. The diagram above shows a chloroplast. Name the two parts shown in the diagram and state which phase of photosynthesis occurs in each part.

11. Compare and contrast the structure of a cell wall and the structure of a cell membrane.

12. Relate the bonds between phosphate groups in ATP to the release of energy when a molecule of ATP is changed to ADP.

13. Name three components of a cell's plasma membrane and explain why each component is important for the function of the cell.

14. What kind of mixture is formed by stirring a small amount of table salt into water until the salt all dissolves? Identify the components of this mixture.

15. In which parts of a plant would you expect to find cells with the most chloroplasts? Explain your answer.

16. Long-distance runners often talk about training to raise their anaerobic threshold. The anaerobic threshold is the point at which certain muscles do not have enough oxygen to perform aerobic respiration and begin to perform anaerobic respiration. Hypothesize why you think it is important for competitive runners to raise their anaerobic threshold.

Extended Response

Use the graph below to answer question 17.

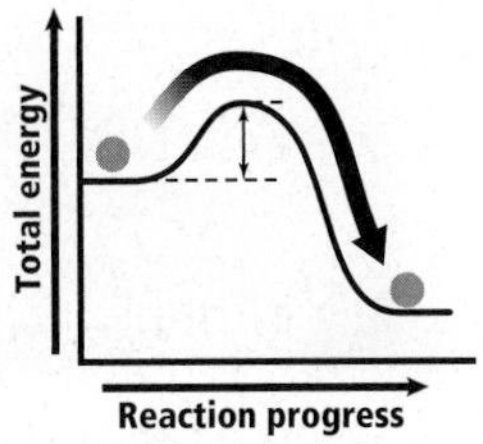

17. The graph shows the effect of an enzyme involved in the breakdown of proteins in the digestive system. Hypothesize how protein digestion would be different in a person who does not have this enzyme.

18. Which organelle would you expect to find in large numbers in cells that pump stomach acid out against a concentration gradient? Give a reason for your answer.

Essay Question

The human body constantly interacts with the environment, taking in some substances and releasing others. Many substances taken in by humans have a specific role in maintaining basic cellular processes such as respiration, ion transport, and synthesis of various macromolecules. Likewise, many of the substances released by the body are waste products of cellular processes.

Using the information in the paragraph above, answer the following question in essay format.

19. Write an essay that explains how humans take in substances that are important for cellular respiration, and how they release the waste products from this process.

NEED EXTRA HELP?																			
If You Missed Question . . .	1	2	3	4	5	6	7	8	9	10	11	12	13	14	15	16	17	18	19
Review Section . . .	6.1	4.1	7.4	8.2	5.2	6.4	8.1	7.1	1.3	8.2	7.3	8.1	7.2	6.3	7.3	8.3	6.2	7.2, 7.4	8.3

produces the sugars that are used by the whole plant.

16. By raising their anaerobic threshold, runners can get more energy out of their muscles by aerobic respiration. This also allows them to avoid feeling fatigue, pain, or soreness caused by the buildup of lactic acid during anaerobic respiration.

Extended Response

17. More energy would be required to start the reaction involving breakdown of proteins and make the reaction proceed quickly. Protein digestion would take more time. As a result, the person would probably not be able to digest proteins as quickly or as completely.

18. Cells that pump acid against a concentration gradient require a lot of energy for the process. Those cells would likely contain more mitochondria than cells that perform functions requiring less energy. Mitochondria are the organelles that release chemical energy in cells.

Essay Question

19. Humans take in oxygen that is needed for cellular respiration by inhaling. Carbon dioxide is a product of cellular respiration that is released from the body by exhalation. Water is another product of cellular respiration. Some of that water is used for other body processes, and the excess is released by sweating and exhaling.

Chapter 9 Organizer:
Cellular Reproduction

LabManager™
Customize any lab with the LabManager™ CD-ROM.

Essential Questions	National Science Standards	Materials and Planning	
		Estimated times include cleanup and disposal, but do not include teacher prep time. For cleanup and disposal guidelines, see page 39T.	Est. Time (min)
Section 1 1. Why are cells relatively small? 2. What are the primary stages of the cell cycle? 3. What are the stages of interphase?	UCP.1–3; A.1, A.2; B.2; C.1, C.5; G.1, G.2	**Launch Lab,** p. 242: light microscope, slides of human cells, onion root tip cells, other prepared slides of cells.	15
		Demonstration, p. 244: prepared gelatin dessert, square pan, dark dye, ruler, containers	15
		MiniLab 1, p. 245: pencil and paper	20
Section 2 1. What are the events of each stage of mitosis? 2. What is the process of cytokinesis?	UCP.1, UCP.2; A.1, A.2; B.3; C.1, C.5; G.1, G.2	**Demonstration,** p. 249: clear plastic boxes, plastic utensils, rubber bands	5
		Demonstration, p. 251: two-wire insulated wire (lamp cord)	15
Section 3 1. What is the role of cyclin proteins in controlling the cell cycle? 2. How does cancer relate to the cell cycle? 3. What is the role of apoptosis? 4. What are the two types of stem cells and what are their potential uses?	UCP.1, UCP.2; A.1, A.2; C.1, C.6; E.1, E.2; F.1, F.4, F.5, F.6; G.1, G.2	**MiniLab 2,** p. 255: sunscreen products, two sheets of plastic wrap, permanent marker, book, sun-sensitive paper	30
		BioLab, p. 259: sterile pipettes, aluminum foil, test-tube rack, sterile spreaders, dilution of UV-sensitive yeast, yeast extract dextrose (YED), agar plates, sun screens with various amounts of SPF	60

Suggested Time for Each Lesson

Class	Chapter Opener	Section 1	Section 2	Section 3	Assessment
Basic	45 min	90 min	90 min	90 min	45 min
General	25 min	55 min	55 min	90 min	45 min
Honors	5 min	20 min	130 min	25 min	45 min

ConnectED

connectED.mcgraw-hill.com

Access interactive learning opportunities and teaching resources using these icons located throughout your StudentWorks™ Plus Online and eTeacherEdition Online.

Chapter 9 Section Resources

FAST FILE Unit 2 Resources:
Launch Lab Worksheet*
MiniLab Worksheet*
Study Guide (English/Spanish)*
Section Quick Check

Reading Essentials 9.1
Science Notebook 9.1*

FAST FILE Unit 2 Resources:
Study Guide (English/Spanish)*
Section Quick Check

Reading Essentials 9.2
Science Notebook 9.2*

FAST FILE Unit 2 Resources:
MiniLab Worksheet*
BioLab Worksheet*
Study Guide (English/Spanish)*
Section Quick Check

Reading Essentials 9.3
Science Notebook 9.3*

Additional Chapter 9 Resources

FAST FILE Unit 2 Resources:
Chapter Diagnostic Test
Concept Mapping*
Real-World Biology
Enrichment
Chapter Tests A, B, and C

Transparencies:
Bellringer Transparencies*
Biology Concepts Transparencies*

Lab Resources:
Laboratory Manual*
Probeware Lab Manual*
Forensics Lab Manual*
Pre-AP Lab Manual*
Open Inquiry in Biology*
Guided Inquiry in Biology*

Technology

Teaching Tools:
eTeacherEdition Online
Classroom Presentation Toolkit CD-ROM*
LabManager™ CD-ROM*
Video Lab DVD*
Virtual Lab CD-ROM*
What's BIOLOGY Got To Do With It?
StudentWorks™ Plus Online*

Chapter Assessment Tools:
Classroom Presentation Toolkit CD-ROM*
ExamView® Assessment Suite CD-ROM

Web-Based Resources:

- StudentWorks™ Plus Online
- eTeacherEdition Online
- Animations*
- The Interactive Time Line*
- Interactive Tables*
- Online Quizzes
- Online Test Practice
- Standardized Test Practice
- Virtual Labs*
- Multilingual eGlossary*
- Vocabulary eGames*
- Vocabulary eFlashcards
- WebQuests
- Personal Tutors

While all resources listed are appropriate for English learners, the * indicates resources with a strong visual or hands-on component for EL.

Teaching strategies and activities have been coded for differentiated instruction.

AL Activities for students working above grade level	**OL** Activities for students working on grade level	**BL** Activities for students working below grade level	**EL** Activities for English learners (also ELL)	**COOP LEARN** Activities designed for small cooperative group work

CHAPTER 9

Launch Lab
From where do healthy cells come?

Inquiry Launch Lab

For a lab worksheet, use your eTeacherEdition Online.

RUBRIC A rubric for evaluating Launch Labs is found on your eTeacherEdition Online.

Est. Time 15 min

Safety Precautions Approve lab safety forms before work begins. Have students wash their hands thoroughly after handling slides. Never prepare slides using human blood.

Teaching Strategies

- Show students images of unhealthy cells, such as cancer cells, and normal, healthy cells.
- Have students observe mitosis in onion root tip cells.

Procedure

1. Read and complete the lab safety form.
2. Observe prepared **slides of human cells** under the microscope.
3. Observe **onion root tip cells** under the microscope.
4. Observe other cells on the **prepared slides** your teacher will give you.
5. Draw diagrams of the sample cells you observed. Identify and label any of the structures you recognize.

Analysis

1. **Compare and contrast** the different cells that you observed. Answers will vary depending upon the types of cells viewed. Plant cells will be rectangular in shape; protist cells might have variable shapes, and animal cells might be round or rectangular.
2. **Hypothesize** why the cells you observed had different appearances and structures. How could you identify diseased cells? Cells had different appearances and structures because they come from different organisms and perform different functions within the organism. Diseased cells will not have the same appearance as normal cells.

CHAPTER 9
Cellular Reproduction

ConnectED
Your one-stop online resource
connectED.mcgraw-hill.com

- Video
- Audio
- Review
- Inquiry
- WebQuest
- Assessment
- Concepts in Motion
- Multilingual eGlossary

Launch Lab
From where do healthy cells come?

All living things are composed of cells. The only way an organism can grow or heal itself is by cellular reproduction. Healthy cells perform vital life functions and they reproduce to form more cells. In this lab you wili investigate the appearance of different cell types.

For a lab worksheet, use your StudentWorks™ Plus Online.

Inquiry Launch Lab

FOLDABLES®

Make a layered-look book using the titles shown. Use it to organize your notes on phases of mitosis.

Differentiated Instruction

Behavior Disorders When performing the Launch Lab described on this page, be sure that students with behavior disorders know what is expected of them. Establish clear rules from the beginning so that these students know appropriate behaviors for the lab.

For more tips, see pages 14T–15T.

Root tip cells undergoing mitosis
Stained LM Magnification: 160×

Onion root tip
Stained LM Magnification: 50×

THEME FOCUS Change
Cells go through several changes as they grow and reproduce.

BIG Idea Cells go through a life cycle that includes interphase, mitosis, and cytokinesis.

Section 1 • Cellular Growth
Section 2 • Mitosis and Cytokinesis
Section 3 • Cell Cycle Regulation

THEMES

Scientific Inquiry Scientific investigations have led to better understanding of cellular activity during each stage of mitosis.

Diversity The various cells in the body differentiate from stem cells.

Energy Energy stored in chemical bonds is used during cellular processes, such as mitosis.

Homeostasis Transportation of materials through the plasma membrane maintains homeostasis within the cell.

Change Multiple changes and mutations within a cell can eventually lead to cancer.

Introduce the Chapter

Cell Division Students are usually quite interested in cellular reproduction. You might want to explain that onion root tips contain fast-growing cells. **ASK STUDENTS:** ***The onion root tips shown in the chapter opener grew from one cell. How did the onion tips grow in size?*** their cells divided ***What must happen to the genetic material in the original cell if it is going to be passed on to new cells as cells divide?*** It must be replicated. Use these questions and descriptions to lead into cell division covered in this chapter.

BIG Idea

Concept Map Have students make a concept map using the terms *cell cycle, mitosis, interphase, cytokinesis, anaphase, metaphase, prophase,* and *telophase.*

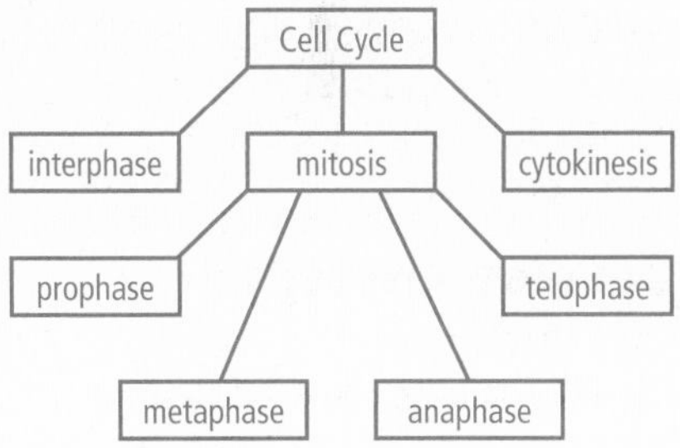

Section 1

MAIN Idea

BL OL AL Cellular Growth
SAY TO STUDENTS: ***Describe the components of the cell theory.*** All living organisms are composed of one or more cells. Cells are the smallest unit of living organisms. Cells arise only from previously existing cells. Use a review of the cell theory to reinforce the idea that cells have an organized way of reproducing, which students will learn about in this chapter.

Develop Concepts

BL OL Review Review cell structure with students, especially chromosomes, microtubules, microfilaments, cell membrane, cell wall, nucleus, and nucleolus.

S Skill Practice

BL OL AL Visual Literacy
Read this page aloud or have students read it silently. Have students study Figure 1.
ASK STUDENTS: ***How does the diagram help explain the limits of cell size?*** The ratio of surface area to volume decreases as the cell grows larger.

Develop Concepts

BL OL AL

Clarify a Misconception
ASK STUDENTS: ***Do large cells perform tasks more efficiently than small cells?*** No. Students may think that bigger is better at the cellular level; however, small cells transport substances more efficiently than large cells. Diffusion is a slow process; the larger the cell, the less efficient transport within it becomes.

Section 1

Reading Preview

Essential Questions
- Why are cells relatively small?
- What are the primary stages of the cell cycle?
- What are the stages of interphase?

Review Vocabulary
selective permeability: process in which a membrane allows some substances to pass through while keeping others out

New Vocabulary
cell cycle
interphase
mitosis
cytokinesis
chromosome
chromatin

Multilingual eGlossary

Cellular Growth

MAIN Idea Cells grow until they reach their size limit, then they either stop growing or divide.

Real-World Reading Link If you've ever played a doubles match in tennis, you probably felt that you and your partner could effectively cover your half of the court. However, if the court were much larger, perhaps you could no longer reach your shots. For the best game, the tennis court must be kept at regulation size. Cell size also must be limited to ensure that the needs of the cell are met.

Cell Size Limitations

Most cells are less than 100 μm (100×10^{-6} m) in diameter, which is smaller than the period at the end of this sentence. Why are most cells so small? This section investigates several factors that influence cell size.

Ratio of surface area to volume The key factor that limits the size of a cell is the ratio of its surface area to its volume. The surface area of the cell refers to the area covered by the plasma membrane. The plasma membrane is the structure through which all nutrients and waste products must pass. The volume refers to the space taken up by the inner contents of the cell, including the organelles in the cytoplasm and the nucleus.

Connection to Math To illustrate the ratio of surface area to volume, consider the small cube in **Figure 1,** which has sides of one micrometer (μm) in length. This is approximately the size of a bacterial cell. To calculate the surface area of the cube, multiply length times width times the number of sides (1 μm × 1 μm × 6 sides), which equals 6 μm^2. To calculate the volume of the cell, multiply length times width times height (1 μm × 1 μm × 1 μm), which equals 1 μm^3. The ratio of surface area to volume is 6:1.

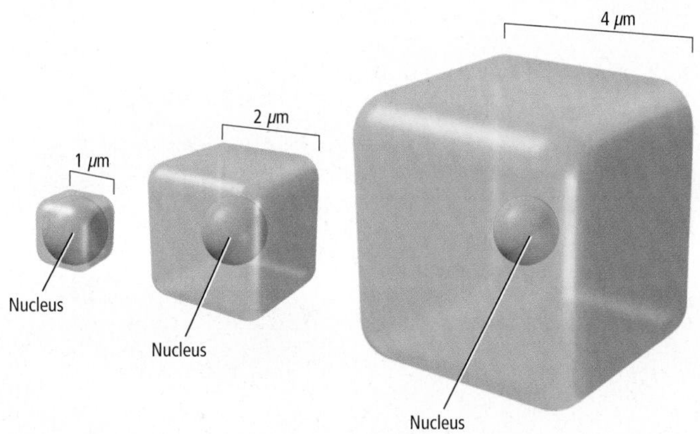

S

■ **Figure 1** The ratio of surface area to volume decreases as a cell gets bigger. The smallest cube shown has a ratio of 6 (1 μm × 1 μm × 6 sides) to 1 (1 μm × 1 μm × 1 μm), while the largest cube has a ratio of 96 (4 μm × 4 μm × 6 sides) to 64 (4 μm × 4 μm × 4 μm), or 3:2.

Demonstration

Diffusion Rate Prepare a light-colored gelatin dessert in a square pan. Cut cubes of different sizes—1 cm^3, 2 cm^3, etc. Place the gelatin cubes in a container of dark dye and allow to sit for most of the class period. Then remove the gelatin squares, cut in half, and measure how far the ink has traveled into the gelatin. Measure how close the ink is to the center of each size "cell." Point out that the ink reaches the middle in a small cell faster than in a large cell. Est. time: 15 min
AL Have students perform this demonstration as a lab activity and calculate the distance of diffusion for each cube.
ASK STUDENTS: ***Are the diffusion distances the same? How does this correlate to cell size?*** Yes; the ink is farther from the center in a larger cell.

If the cubic cell grows to 2 μm per side, as represented in **Figure 1,** the surface area becomes 24 μm^2 and the volume is 8 μm^3. The ratio of surface area to volume is now 3:1, which is less than it was when the cell was smaller. If the cell continues to grow, the ratio of surface area to volume will continue to decrease, as shown by the third cube in **Figure 1.** As the cell grows, its volume increases much more rapidly than the surface area. This means that the cell might have difficulty supplying nutrients and expelling enough waste products. By remaining small, cells have a higher ratio of surface area to volume and can sustain themselves more easily.

Reading Check **Explain** why a high ratio of surface area to volume benefits a cell.

Transport of substances Another task that can be managed more easily in a small cell than in a large cell is the movement of substances. Recall that the plasma membrane controls cellular transport because it is selectively permeable. Once inside the cell, substances move by diffusion or by motor proteins pulling them along the cytoskeleton. Diffusion over large distances is slow and inefficient because it relies on random movement of molecules and ions. Similarly, the cytoskeleton transportation network, shown in **Figure 2,** becomes less efficient for a cell if the distance to travel becomes too large. Small cell size maximizes the ability of diffusion and motor proteins to transport nutrients and waste products. Small cells maintain more efficient transport systems.

LM Magnification: 150×

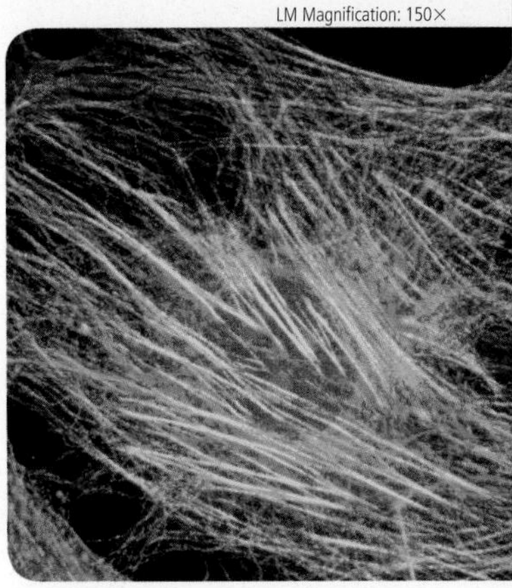

Figure 2 In order for the cytoskeleton to be an efficient transportation railway, the distances that substances have to travel within a cell must be limited.

MiniLab 1

Investigate Cell Size

Inquiry MiniLab

Could a cell grow large enough to engulf your school? What would happen if the size of an elephant were doubled? At the organism level, an elephant cannot grow significantly larger, because its legs would not support the increase in mass. Do the same principles and limitations apply at the cellular level? Do the math!

Procedure

1. Read and complete the lab safety form.
2. Prepare a data table for surface area and volume data calculated for five hypothetical cells. Assume the cell is a cube. (Dimensions given are for one face of a cube.)
   Cell 1: 0.00002 m (the average diameter of most eukaryotic cells)
   Cell 2: 0.001 m (the diameter of a squid's giant nerve cell)
   Cell 3: 2.5 cm
   Cell 4: 30 cm
   Cell 5: 15 m
3. Calculate the surface area for each cell using the formula: length × width × number of sides (6).
4. Calculate the volume for each cell using the formula: length × width × height.

Analysis

1. **Cause and Effect** Based on your calculations, confirm why cells do not become very large.
2. **Infer** Are large organisms, such as redwood trees and elephants, large because they contain extra large cells or just more standard-sized cells? Explain.

MiniLab 1

Inquiry MiniLab

For a lab worksheet, use your eTeacherEdition Online.

RUBRIC A rubric for evaluating MiniLabs is found on your eTeacherEdition Online.

Est. Time 20 min

Safety Precautions Approve lab safety forms before work begins.

Teaching Strategies

- Students could work individually, in small groups with each group doing calculations for all cells, or in small groups with each group doing calculations for one hypothetical cell and then reporting the results to the class.
- Emphasize that the dimensions given for each hypothetical cell are for one side of one face of a cube.
- Have students prepare a data table prior to beginning their calculations.

Analysis

1. physically: cells become too heavy; metabolically: limited surface area doesn't allow substances in and waste out at a high enough rate
2. more standard-sized cells

Demonstration

BL OL AL Ratio of Surface Area to Volume Hold up four small boxes. Put the boxes together (sides touching) to form a cube. Explain that the volume of the boxes when they are separate is equal to their volume when they are together as a cube. **ASK STUDENTS:** ***Which has the greater surface area—four small boxes or one large box?*** four small boxes Est. time: 5 min

Reading Check It makes transporting nutrients throughout the cell and removing waste products easier and more efficient.

S Skill Practice

EL BL OL AL Visual Literacy Have students look at Figure 3. Point out that the diagram illustrates a cycle.

ASK STUDENTS: ***What have you learned about cycles? What happens when events occur in a cycle?*** Students may conclude that biological cycles are ongoing and don't have a beginning or ending place. Remind students that the cell cycle does not repeat for a specific cell, but it does repeat for cells in general. Once a cell divides, the original cell no longer exists; it has been replaced by two identical daughter cells that will each continue in the cell cycle. Have students make their own diagram of the cell cycle as they read the text under the heading *The Cell Cycle.*

C Critical Thinking

OL AL Predict Tell students to imagine that a photographer took a photo every minute during an event. Have them predict how the pictures could be used to determine how long each portion of the event lasted. The more pictures of a particular portion, the longer that portion lasted. ***How can this apply to the cell cycle?*** By making "snapshot" observations of dividing cells at regular intervals, it can be determined how long a cell remains at various stages of the cell cycle.

■ **Caption Question Fig. 3** The cell spends less time dividing cytoplasm than growing, performing functions, and dividing nuclear material.

Video BrainPOP

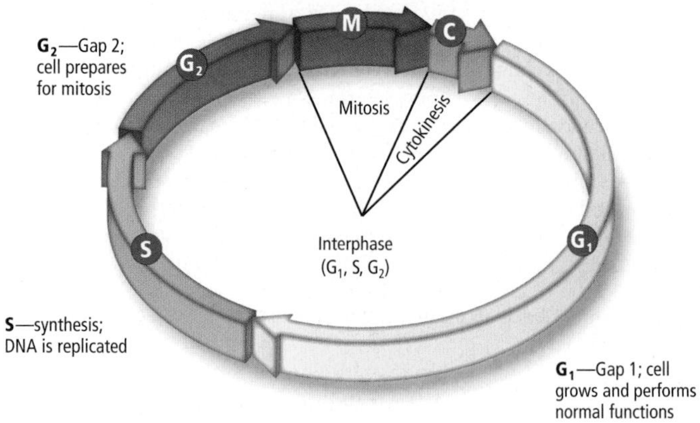

■ **Figure 3** The cell cycle involves three stages—interphase, mitosis, and cytokinesis. Interphase is divided into three substages.
Hypothesize ***why cytokinesis represents the smallest amount of time that a cell spends in the cell cycle.***

S

Cellular communications The need for signaling proteins to move throughout the cell also limits cell size. In other words, cell size affects the ability of the cell to communicate instructions for cellular functions. If the cell becomes too large, it becomes almost impossible for cellular communications, many of which involve movement of substances and signals to various organelles, to take place efficiently. For example, the signals that trigger protein synthesis might not reach the ribosome fast enough for protein synthesis to occur to sustain the cell.

Video BrainPOP

The Cell Cycle

Once a cell reaches its size limit, something must happen—either it will stop growing or it will divide. Most cells will eventually divide. Cell division not only prevents the cell from becoming too large, but it is also the way the cell reproduces. Cellular reproduction allows you to grow and heal certain injuries. Cells reproduce by a cycle of growing and dividing called the **cell cycle.** Each time a cell goes through one complete cycle, it becomes two cells. When the cell cycle is repeated continuously, the result is a continuous production of new cells. A general overview of the cell cycle is presented in **Figure 3.**

There are three main stages of the cell cycle. **Interphase** is the stage during which the cell grows, carries out cellular functions, and replicates, or makes copies of its DNA in preparation for the next stage of the cycle. Interphase is divided into three substages, as indicated by the segment arrows in **Figure 3.** **Mitosis** (mi TOH sus) is the stage of the cell cycle during which the cell's nucleus and nuclear material divide. Mitosis is divided into four substages. Near the end of mitosis, a process called cytokinesis begins. **Cytokinesis** (si toh kih NEE sis) is the method by which a cell's cytoplasm divides, creating a new cell. You will read more about mitosis and cytokinesis in Section 2.

The duration of the cell cycle varies, depending on the cell that is dividing. Some eukaryotic cells might complete the cycle in as few as eight minutes, while other cells might take up to one year. For most normal, actively dividing animal cells, the cell cycle takes approximately 12–24 hours. When you consider all that takes place during the cell cycle, you might find it amazing that most of your cells complete the cell cycle in about a day.

VOCABULARY
WORD ORIGIN
Cytokinesis
cyto- prefix; from the Greek word *kytos,* meaning *hollow vessel*
-kinesis from the Greek word *kinetikos,* meaning *putting in motion*

C

Content Background

Teacher FYI Nerve, muscle, and other highly specialized cells do not leave the G_1 phase of the cell cycle and therefore do not replicate in the human body under normal conditions. For example, brain nerve cells stop producing just a few months after birth. So if there is damage to the brain, it is a permanent injury and is not repairable by the process of mitosis.

The stages of interphase During interphase, the cell grows, develops into a mature, functioning cell, duplicates its DNA, and prepares for division. Interphase is divided into three stages, as shown in **Figure 3:** G_1, S, and G_2, also called Gap 1, synthesis, and Gap 2.

The first stage of interphase, G_1, is the period immediately after a cell divides. During G_1, a cell is growing, carrying out normal cell functions, and preparing to replicate DNA. Some cells, such as muscle and nerve cells, exit the cell cycle at this point and do not divide again.

The second stage of interphase, S, is the period when a cell copies its DNA in preparation for cell division. **Chromosomes** (KROH muh sohmz) are the structures that contain the genetic material that is passed from generation to generation of cells. **Chromatin** (KROH muh tun) is the relaxed form of DNA in the cell's nucleus. As shown in **Figure 4,** when a specific dye is applied to a cell in interphase, the nucleus stains with a speckled appearance. This speckled appearance is due to individual strands of chromatin that are not visible under a light microscope without the dye.

The G_2 stage follows the S stage and is the period when the cell prepares for the division of its nucleus. A protein that makes microtubules for cell division is synthesized at this time. During G_2, the cell also takes inventory and makes sure it is ready to continue with mitosis. When these activities are completed, the cell begins the next stage of the cell R cycle—mitosis.

Stained LM Magnification: 400×

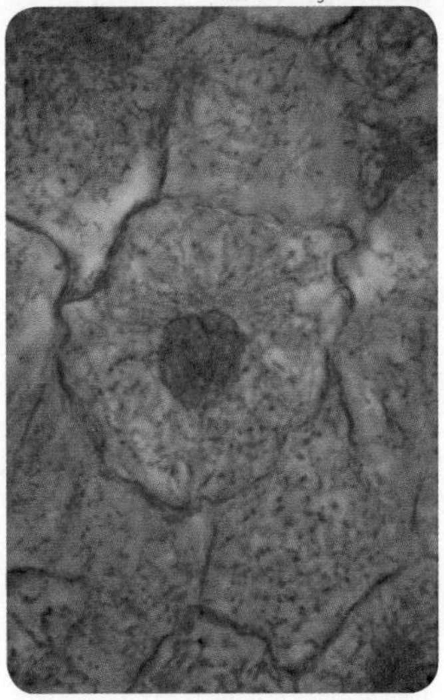

Figure 4 The grainy appearance of this nucleus from a rat liver cell is due to chromatin, the relaxed material that condenses to form chromosomes.

Mitosis and cytokinesis The stages of mitosis and cytokinesis follow interphase. In mitosis, the cell's nuclear material divides and separates into opposite ends of the cell. In cytokinesis, the cell divides into two daughter cells with identical nuclei. These important stages of the cell cycle are described in Section 2.

Prokaryotic cell division The cell cycle is the method by which eukaryotic cells reproduce themselves. Prokaryotic cells, which you have learned are simpler cells, reproduce by a method called binary fission.

Section 1 Assessment

Section Summary

- The ratio of surface area to volume describes the size of the plasma membrane relative to the volume of the cell.
- Cells are limited in size, with most cells having a diameter of less than 100 µm.
- The cell cycle is the process of cellular reproduction.
- A cell spends the majority of its lifetime in interphase.

Understand Main Ideas

1. MAIN Idea **Relate** cell size to cell functions, and explain why cell size is limited.
2. **Summarize** the primary stages of the cell cycle.
3. **Describe** what happens to DNA during the S stage of interphase.
4. **Create** a diagram of the stages of the cell cycle and describe what happens in each.

Think Critically

5. **Hypothesize** what the result would be if a large cell managed to divide, despite the fact that it had grown beyond an optimum size.

MATH in Biology

6. If a cube representing a cell is 100 µm on a side, calculate the surface area-to-volume ratio, and explain why this is or is not a good size for a cell.

R Reading Strategy

BL OL COOP LEARN

Question a Partner Organize students into pairs. Have Student A query Student B about what occurs in G_1. After Student A answers, have Student B query Student A about what occurs in G_2, and so on. Have students cover the cell cycle and phases of interphase.

Writing Support

BL OL **Narrative Writing** Have students write a paragraph containing the words *chromosome, sister chromatids,* and *centromere*. Students' paragraphs should demonstrate the correct usage of each of these terms.

AL Have students also include the terms *chromatin, condensation,* and *homologous chromosomes* in their paragraphs.

Formative Assessment

Evaluation Give students the measurements to calculate the surface area of a cell and the volume of a cell.

ASK STUDENTS: ***Why can't cells continually grow larger and still survive?*** The ratio of surface area to volume limits size.

Remediation Give students wood blocks of various sizes. Have students who are proficient in math help others calculate the ratio of surface area to volume. Volume can be calculated by measuring water displacement.

Section 1 Assessment

1. Transportation of nutrients and wastes across the plasma membrane and control of cell contents by the nucleus become difficult when the cell increases in size.
2. interphase, mitosis, and cytokinesis
3. DNA is replicated during the S stage.
4. Cell cycle diagrams should show interphase as the longest stage, and descriptions should include nuclear division and cytokinesis.
5. When a large cell divides into two cells, the surface area to volume ratio decreases and increases the cell's possibility to survive.
6. 60,000 µm^2:1,000,000 µm^3, or 6:100. A cell with this ratio might have difficulty transporting nutrients and wastes.

Section 2

MAIN Idea
BL OL AL
Mitosis and Cytokinesis
Lead students in a discussion about how to determine when one stage of the cell cycle ends and another begins.
ASK STUDENTS: ***How do scientists determine the stages of the cell cycle change?*** The stages flow one into another. The stages are used to conveniently categorize the main events that occur. Use this discussion to lead into the study of mitosis, which has stages that are categorized but actually overlap.

D Develop Concepts
BL OL AL
Clarify a Misconception
ASK STUDENTS: ***Does mitosis in a live cell occur in distinct stages?*** no ***Why do we study distinct stages?*** Students often get the idea that the stages of mitosis "leap" from one to another rather than flowing in a continuous process. If supplies are available, show a video of mitosis that demonstrates the actual flow of the stages.

R Reading Strategy
EL BL OL **SQ3R** As students read the text under the heading *The Stages of Mitosis,* have them follow the five-step SQ3R: First **S**urvey the headings, then write **Q**uestions about the stages. Next they should **R**ead the section, making notes that relate to the questions, **R**ecite the vocabulary, and **R**eview for meaning.

Section 2

Reading Preview

Essential Questions
- What are the events of each stage of mitosis?
- What is the process of cytokinesis?

Review Vocabulary
life cycle: the sequence of growth and development stages that an organism goes through during its life

New Vocabulary
prophase
sister chromatid
centromere
spindle apparatus
metaphase
anaphase
telophase

g Multilingual eGlossary

Mitosis and Cytokinesis

MAIN Idea Eukaryotic cells reproduce by mitosis, the process of nuclear division, and cytokinesis, the process of cytoplasm division.

Real-World Reading Link Many familiar events are cyclic in nature. The course of a day, the changing of seasons year after year, and the passing of comets in space are some examples of cyclic events. Cells also have a cycle of growth and reproduction.

D Mitosis

You learned in the last section that cells cycle through interphase, mitosis, and cytokinesis. During mitosis, the cell's replicated genetic material separates and the cell prepares to split into two cells. The key activity of mitosis is the accurate separation of the cell's replicated DNA. This enables the cell's genetic information to pass into the new cells intact, resulting in two daughter cells that are genetically identical. In multicellular organisms, the process of mitosis increases the number of cells as a young organism grows to its adult size. Organisms also use mitosis to replace damaged cells. Recall the last time you were accidentally cut. The body's process of healing the cut involves generating new skin cells. These new cells are produced by your existing skin cells. Under the scab, the existing skin cells divided by mitosis and cytokinesis to create new skin cells that filled the gap in the skin caused by the injury.

R The Stages of Mitosis

Like interphase, mitosis is divided into stages: prophase, metaphase, anaphase, and telophase.

Prophase The first stage and longest phase of mitosis is called **prophase.** In this stage, the cell's chromatin tightens, or condenses, into chromosomes. In prophase, the chromosomes are shaped like an X, as shown in **Figure 5.** At this point, each chromosome is a single structure that contains the genetic material that was replicated in interphase. Each half of this X is called a sister chromatid. **Sister chromatids** are structures that contain identical copies of DNA. The structure at the center of the chromosome where the sister chromatids are attached is called the **centromere.** This structure is important because it ensures that a complete copy of the replicated DNA will become part of the daughter cells at the end of the cell cycle. Locate prophase in the cell cycle illustrated in **Figure 6,** and note the position of the sister chromatids. As you continue to read about the stages of mitosis, refer back to **Figure 6** to follow the chromatids through the cell cycle.

Figure 5 Chromosomes in prophase are actually sister chromatids that are attached at the centromere.

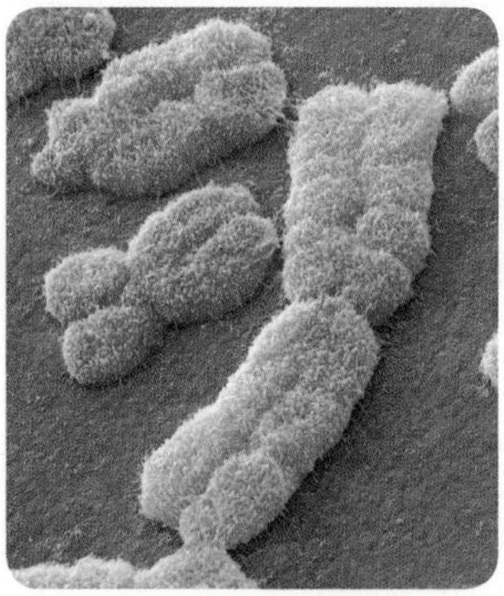

Color-Enhanced SEM magnification: 6875×

Reading Check **Compare** the key activity of interphase with the key activity of mitosis.

Differentiated Instruction

English Learners Students with limited English language proficiency may struggle with the SQ3R reading activity described on this page. Allow these students to read the text in their first language before reading it in English.

For more tips, see pages 14T–15T.

Reading Check interphase: cell grows and duplicates DNA; mitosis: nucleus divides

Visualizing the Cell Cycle

D Figure 6

The cell cycle begins with interphase. Mitosis follows, occurring in four stages—prophase, metaphase, anaphase, and telophase. Mitosis is followed by cytokinesis, then the cell cycle repeats with each new cell.

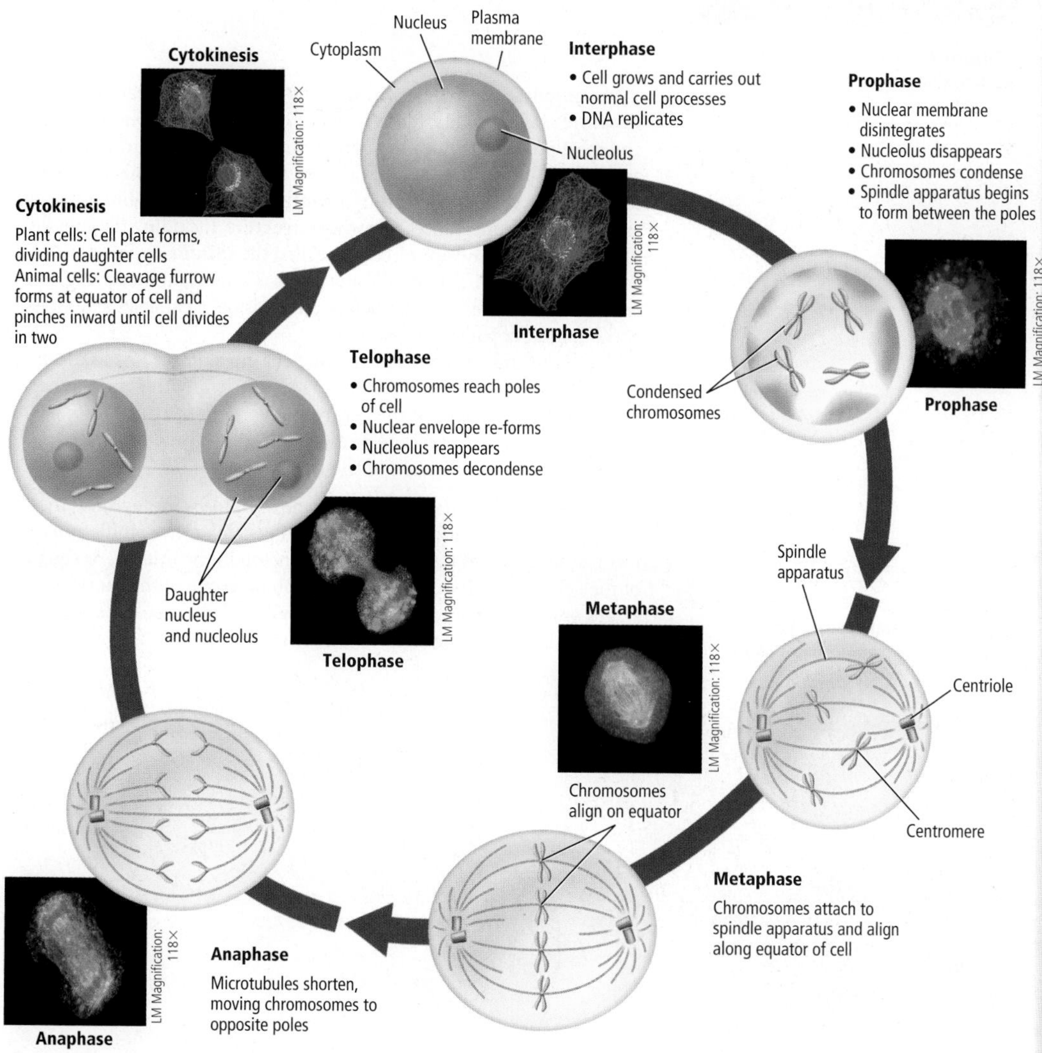

• Nucleolus disappears

Animal cells: Cleavage furrow forms at equator of cell and pinches inward until cell divides in two

Concepts in Motion Animation

Demonstration

Mitosis Stages Make three-dimensional cells to demonstrate the four stages of mitosis. Use clear plastic boxes. Use plastic utensils, such as plastic knives, or colored popsicle sticks to represent chromosomes and use rubber bands to represent centromeres. Use fishing line to hang the utensils inside the clear plastic "cells." Make a cell to represent prophase, metaphase, anaphase, and telophase. You may want to hang the "cells" around the room so students can refer to this three-dimensional view of mitosis as they continue to read the chapter. Est. time: 5 min

Visualizing the Cell Cycle

Purpose

Students will diagram and distinguish the various stages of mitosis. C.1, C.2

D Develop Concepts

EL BL OL AL Use Models Have students make a two- or three-dimensional model of one of the stages of mitosis. Some suggested materials might include socks, pipe cleaners, yarn, colored macaroni, licorice, or clay for chromosomes. Ring-shaped candy or rubber bands can be used for centromeres. A box could be used for a three-dimensional model by cutting out one side for viewing. Allow students to work independently or in pairs.

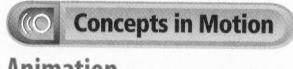

Concepts in Motion Animation

Develop Concepts

BL OL AL Scaffolding

SAY TO STUDENTS: ***Identify the stages of mitosis.*** prophase, metaphase, anaphase, telophase ***Describe the features of prophase.*** Cromatin condenses into chromosomes. Point out that chromosomes become visible during this phase as they shorten and condense. ***Infer why two sister chromatids attached by a centromere are important to cell function.*** This ensures that an exact copy of DNA will be in each of the new daughter cells.

C Critical Thinking

OL AL Differentiate

ASK STUDENTS: ***What are two differences between plant and animal cell division and cytokinesis?*** Plant cells do not have centrioles. Animal cells develop a cell furrow for cytokinesis, and plant cells develop a new cell wall between the two new cells.

Develop Concepts

BL OL AL

Clarify a Misconception

Students sometimes think that mitosis occurs in all cells of the body throughout life. Some tissues, such as muscle and nervous tissues, divide little if at all. Others, such as red blood cells, do not continue to divide once they are formed.

FOLDABLES®

RUBRIC A rubric for evaluating Foldables is found on your eTeacherEdition Online.

Going Further Have students make a two-column chart on the back of their Foldables to compare and contrast how unicellular and multicellular organisms undergo mitosis.

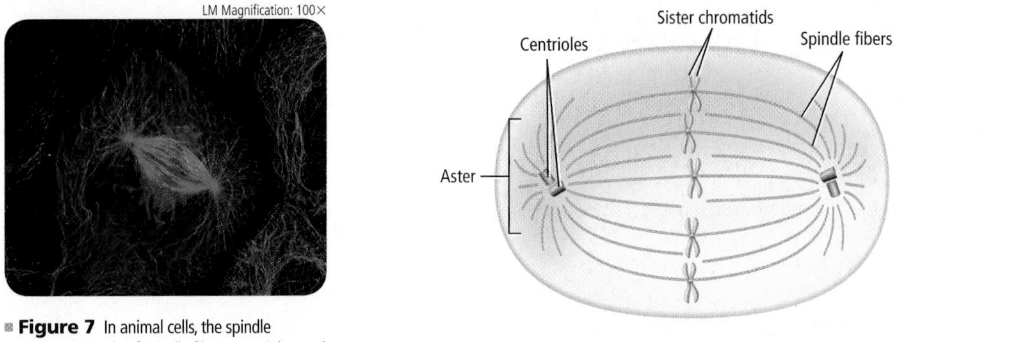

■ **Figure 7** In animal cells, the spindle apparatus is made of spindle fibers, centrioles, and aster fibers.

FOLDABLES® Incorporate information from this section into your Foldable.

As prophase continues, the nucleolus seems to disappear. Microtubule structures called spindle fibers form in the cytoplasm. In animal cells and most protist cells, another pair of microtubule structures called centrioles migrates to the ends, or poles, of the cell. Coming out of the centrioles are yet another type of microtubule called aster fibers, which have a starlike appearance. The whole structure, including the spindle fibers, centrioles, and aster fibers, is called the **spindle apparatus** and is shown in **Figure 7.** The spindle apparatus is important in moving and organizing the chromosomes before cell division. Centrioles are not part of the spindle apparatus in plant cells.

Near the end of prophase, the nuclear envelope seems to disappear. The spindle fibers attach to the sister chromatids of each chromosome on both sides of the centromere and then attach to opposite poles of the cell. This arrangement ensures that each new cell receives one complete copy of the DNA. C

Metaphase During the second stage of mitosis, **metaphase,** the sister chromatids are pulled by motor proteins along the spindle apparatus toward the center of the cell and they line up in the middle, or equator, of the cell, as shown in **Figure 8.** Metaphase is one of the shortest stages of mitosis, but when completed successfully, it ensures that the new cells have accurate copies of the chromosomes.

■ **Figure 8** In metaphase, the chromosomes align along the equator of the cell.
Infer *why the chromosomes align along the equator.*

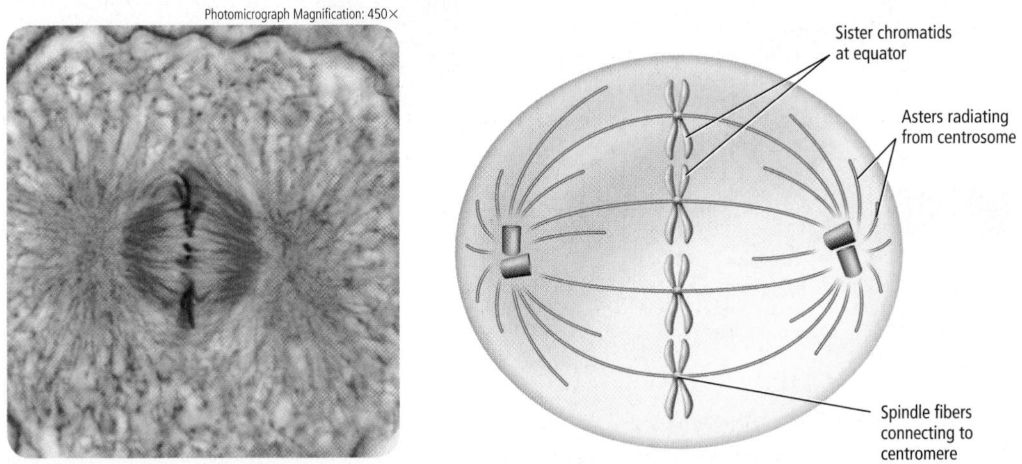

■ **Caption Question Fig. 8** Chromosomes align at the equator so they can separate equally. Because they are aligned, equal numbers of chromosomes go to both new cells during anaphase.

Research Citation

Clarify Misconceptions Educational research indicates that teachers should check students' progress and understanding throughout a lesson. The methods described on the previous page allow students to reflect on their learning and for you to make necessary adjustments. (Lampert and Cobb, 2003)

Research bibliography on pages 32T–34T

LM Magnification: 450×

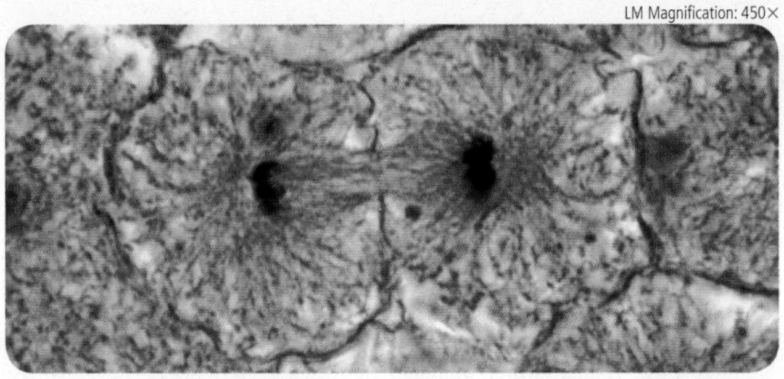

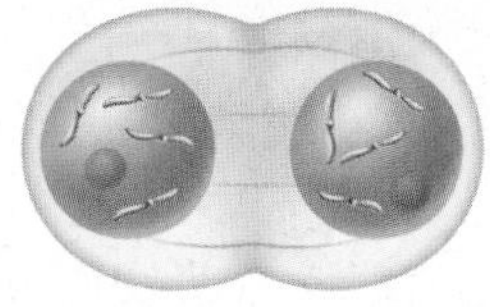

Anaphase The chromatids are pulled apart during **anaphase,** the third stage of mitosis. In anaphase, the microtubules of the spindle apparatus begin to shorten. This shortening pulls at the centromere of each sister chromatid, causing the sister chromatids to separate into two identical chromosomes. All of the sister chromatids separate simultaneously, although the exact mechanism that controls this is unknown. At the end of anaphase, the microtubules, with the help of motor proteins, move the chromosomes toward the poles of the cell.

■ **Figure 9** By the end of telophase, the cell has completed the work of duplicating the genetic material and dividing it into two "packages," but the cell has not completely divided.

Telophase The last stage of mitosis is called telophase. **Telophase** is the stage of mitosis during which the chromosomes arrive at the poles of the cell and begin to relax, or decondense. As shown in **Figure 9,** two new nuclear membranes begin to form and the nucleoli reappear. The spindle apparatus disassembles and some of the microtubules are recycled by the cell to build various parts of the cytoskeleton. Although the four stages of mitosis are now complete and the nuclear material is divided, the process of cell division is not yet complete.

DATA ANALYSIS LAB 1

Based on Real Data*

Predict the Results

What happens to the microtubules? Scientists performed experiments tracking chromosomes along microtubules during mitosis. They hypothesized that the microtubules are broken down, releasing microtubule subunits as the chromosomes are moved toward the poles of the cell. The microtubules were labeled with a yellow fluorescent dye, and using a laser, the microtubules were marked midway between the poles and the chromosomes by eliminating the fluorescence in the targeting region as shown in the diagram.

Data and Observations

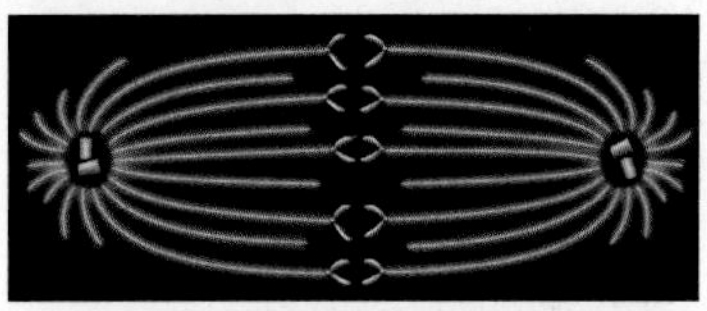

Fluorescent-labeled microtubules

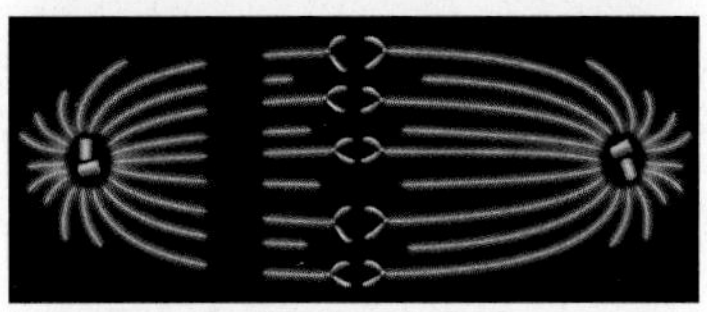

Laser-marked microtubules

Think Critically

1. **Explain** the purpose of the fluorescent dye.
2. **Predict** how the cell might appear later in anaphase by drawing a diagram.

*Data obtained from: Maddox, P., et al. 2003. Direct observation of microtubule dynamics at kinetochores in *Xenopus* extract spindles: implications for spindle mechanics. *The Journal of Cell Biology* 162: 377-382. Maddox, et al. 2004. Controlled ablations of microtubules using picosecond laser. *Biophysics Journal* 87: 4203-4212.

Writing Support

BL OL AL Creative Writing

Have students look up the prefixes *inter-*, *pro-*, *meta-*, *ana-*, and *telo-* and write a poem, song, or lyric that explains why these particular prefixes are appropriate for the stages of mitosis and the cell cycle. The prefix *inter-*, which means "between," is relevant to the term *interphase* because it is the time between cell divisions; *pro-*, which means "prior to" or "earlier than," describes prophase because it is the first stage of mitosis; *meta-*, which means "later than," describes metaphase because it is the second, or later, stage of mitosis; *ana-*, which means "upward" or "backward," describes anaphase because during this stage sister chromatids pull apart; *telo-*, which means "end," describes telophase because it is the last stage of mitosis.

DATA ANALYSIS LAB 1

About the Lab

- Also see Tanaka et al. 2005. Molecular mechanisms of kinetochore capture by spindle microtubules. *Nature* 434: 987–994.
- Also see Khodjakov et al. 2002. De novo formation of centrosomes in vertebrate cells arrested during S phase. *Journal of Cell Biology* 158:1171–1181.

Think Critically

1. The fluorescent dye made the microtubules visible.
2. Drawings should illustrate that the microtubule pieces attached to the chromosomes are shortened.

Demonstration

BL OL Sister Chromatids Purchase some two-wire insulated wire (commonly called lamp cord) at a hardware store. Cut a piece of wire about two feet long. Cut up between the two wires from both ends, leaving about four inches in the middle uncut. Show this to students and tell them it represents the sister chromatids during metaphase.

ASK STUDENTS: ***What happens during anaphase in this model?*** The two cords, representing chromatids, would become completely separated. Est. time: 15 min

S Skill Practice

EL BL OL Visual Literacy

After they study Figure 10, have students build two-dimensional models on a sheet of construction paper of cytokinesis in animal and plant cells. Have them use yarn for the animal cell membrane and toothpicks for the plant cell wall. You may choose to use this activity in combination with a model of mitosis to help students understand how the two processes are related.

Formative Assessment

Evaluation Project Figure 6 (show page 249 from eTeacher-Edition Online) or have students watch the animation. Quiz students on the stages of mitosis.

Remediation Prepare copies of drawings of the phases of mitosis. Cut apart the drawings and mix them up. Put students in pairs and give each pair a set of puzzle pieces. Have them arrange the pieces in the correct order.

Color-Enhanced SEM Magnification: 125×

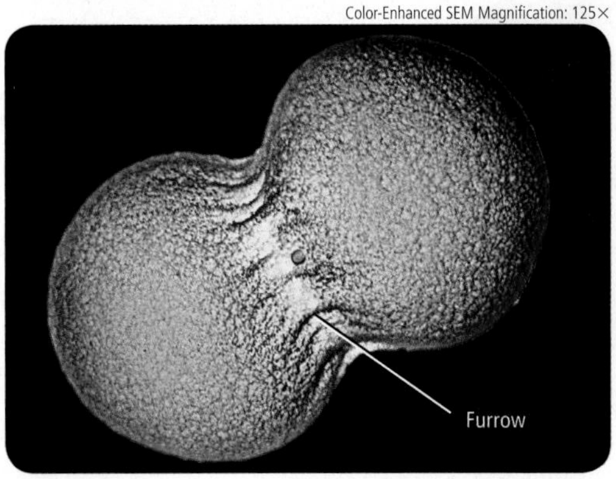

Animal cell

Stained LM Magnification: 1200×

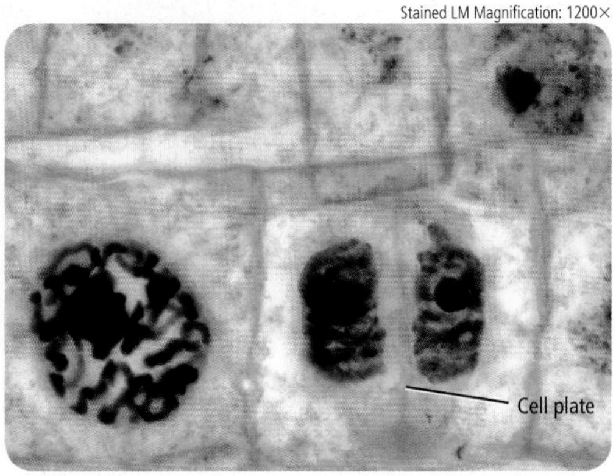

Plant cells

Figure 10
Left: In animal cells, cytokinesis begins with a furrow that pinches the cell and eventually splits the two cells apart.
Right: Plant cells build a cell plate that divides the cell into the two daughter cells.

Cytokinesis

Toward the end of mitosis, the cell begins another process called cytokinesis that will divide the cytoplasm. This results in two cells, each with identical nuclei. In animal cells, cytokinesis is accomplished by using microfilaments to constrict, or pinch, the cytoplasm, as shown in **Figure 10.** The area where constriction occurs is called the furrow.

Recall that plant cells have a rigid cell wall covering their plasma membrane. Instead of pinching in half, a new structure called a cell plate forms between the two daughter nuclei, as illustrated in **Figure 10.** Cell walls then form on either side of the cell plate. Once this new wall is complete, there are two genetically identical cells.

Prokaryotic cells, which divide by binary fission, finish cell division in a different way. When prokaryotic DNA is duplicated, both copies attach to the plasma membrane. As the plasma membrane grows, the attached DNA molecules are pulled apart. The cell completes fission, producing two new prokaryotic cells.

Section 2 Assessment

Section Summary

- Mitosis is the process by which the duplicated DNA is divided.
- The stages of mitosis include prophase, metaphase, anaphase, and telophase.
- Cytokinesis is the process of cytoplasm division that results in genetically identical daughter cells.

Understand Main Ideas

1. MAIN Idea **Explain** why mitosis alone does not produce daughter cells.
2. **Describe** the events of each stage of mitosis.
3. **Diagram** and label a chromosome in prophase.
4. **Identify** the stage of mitosis in which a cell spends the most time.
5. **Contrast** cytokinesis in a plant cell and an animal cell.

Think Critically

6. **Hypothesize** what might happen if a drug that stopped microtubule movement but did not affect cytokinesis was applied to a cell.

MATH in Biology

7. If a plant cell completes the cell cycle in 24 hours, how many cells will be produced in a week?

Section 2 Assessment

1. Mitosis is the process by which nuclear material is duplicated. A cell must undergo cytokinesis in order for cell division to be complete.
2. Prophase: nuclear membranes disintegrate and chromosomes condense; metaphase: chromosomes attach to spindle and line up along the equator; anaphase: chromosomes move to the opposite poles; telophase: nuclear envelope reforms and chromosomes decondense
3. The diagram should look like an "X" with the centromere and individual chromatids labeled.
4. prophase
5. Cytokinesis is due to microtubules pinching the cell into two in animal cells. In plant cells, a cell plate forms between the two cells.
6. Answers will vary. Accept all logical hypotheses, such as, if the movement of microtubules was stopped chromosomes would not be separated properly into the two daughter cells..
7. 128 cells

Assessment Online Quiz

Section 3

Reading Preview

Essential Questions

- What is the role of cyclin proteins in controlling the cell cycle?
- How does cancer relate to the cell cycle?
- What is the role of apoptosis?
- What are the two types of stem cells and what are their potential uses?

Review Vocabulary

nucleotide: subunit that makes up DNA and RNA molecules

New Vocabulary

cyclin
cyclin-dependent kinase
cancer
carcinogen
apoptosis
stem cell

g Multilingual eGlossary

Cell Cycle Regulation

MAIN Idea **The normal cell cycle is regulated by cyclin proteins.**

Real-World Reading Link No matter how many new homes a builder builds, even if building the same design, the crew always relies on blueprint instructions. Similarly, cells have specific instructions for completing the cell cycle.

Normal Cell Cycle

The timing and rate of cell division are important to the health of an organism. The rate of cell division varies depending on the type of cell. A mechanism involving proteins and enzymes controls the cell cycle.

The role of cyclins To start most cars, it takes a key turning in the ignition to signal the engine to start. Similarly, the cell cycle in eukaryotic cells is driven by a combination of two substances that signal the cellular reproduction processes. Proteins called **cyclins** bind to enzymes called **cyclin-dependent kinases** (CDKs) in the stages of interphase and mitosis to start the various activities that take place in the cell cycle. Different cyclin/CDK combinations control different activities at different stages in the cell cycle. **Figure 11** illustrates where some of the important combinations are active.

In the G_1 stage of interphase, the combination of cyclin with CDK signals the start of the cell cycle. Different cyclin/CDK combinations signal other activities, including DNA replication, protein synthesis, and nuclear division throughout the cell cycle. The same cyclin/CDK combination also signals the end of the cell cycle.

S

■ **Figure 11** Signaling molecules made of a cyclin bound to a CDK kick off the cell cycle and drive it through mitosis. Checkpoints monitor the cell cycle for errors and can stop the cycle if an error occurs.

Review Personal Tutor

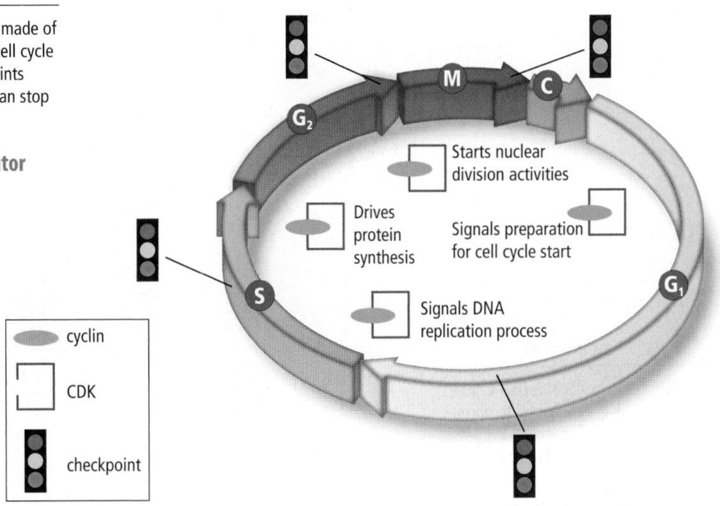

Section 3

MAIN Idea

BL OL AL

Cell Cycle Regulation Point out that the average human cell has a cell cycle of about 20 h. **ASK STUDENTS:** ***How many cells would be present at the end of the day? At the end of a week?*** one day—2 cells, one week—2^8 cells, or 256 cells ***Do you think all cells in the body reproduce at the same rate?*** Allow an open discussion but lead students to the answer by asking leading questions such as the following. ***Do you think your brain cells continue to divide at the same rate as your skin cells?*** Different cells in the body have cell cycles that vary in length. Some cells, such as skin, hair, and nail cells have a shorter cell cycle, and others such as bone tissue cells and nerve cells have longer cell cycles.

S Skill Practice

BL OL AL **Visual Literacy**

Have students examine Figure 11. **ASK STUDENTS:** ***What does a stoplight signal mean to you?*** Possible answers: stop, go, slow down As students discuss the meaning of a stoplight, guide them to the conclusion that the stoplight regulates (not only stops) the traffic through a particular area. It is set to alternate between green for go, yellow for slow, and red for stop. In a similar way, proteins and enzymes act as controls for the cell cycle.

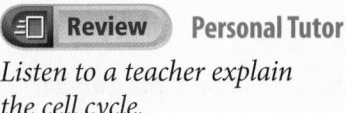

Review Personal Tutor

Listen to a teacher explain the cell cycle.

Research Citation

Make Connections Educational research indicates that students will be better able to solve problems that are relevant to situations they may have experienced in their own lives. The discussion about cancer described on page 254 exemplifies how you can draw on students' own experiences to help their comprehension. (Steen and Forman, 1995)

Research bibliography on pages 32T–34T

"A teacher affects eternity; he can never tell where his influence stops."

–Henry Brooks Adams

Critical Thinking

BL OL AL Observe and Infer

Write the following data on the board. Have students compare the cell cycle of normal chicken stomach cells and cancerous chicken stomach cells:

Normal stomach cells

Interphase	120 min
Prophase	60 min
Metaphase	10 min
Anaphase	3 min
Telophase	12 min

Cancerous stomach cells

Interphase	16 min
Prophase	15 min
Metaphase	2 min
Anaphase	1 min
Telophase	3 min

SAY TO STUDENTS: ***Compare the two cycles and summarize how they differ.*** The cancer cell cycle is much faster than the normal cycle. Point out that, although the cancer cell cycle is faster, the relative time requirements are similar in both normal and cancer cells. However, interphase is relatively shorter in cancer cells.

R Reading Strategy

BL OL AL Make Connections

ASK STUDENTS: ***How many of you have had a family member or friend who has had cancer?*** Have students read the text under the heading *Abnormal Cell Cycle: Cancer.* After reading, have them write a paragraph describing how the text helped them better understand the disease.

Inquiry BioLab

The lab at the end of the chapter can be used at this point in the lesson.

CAREERS IN BIOLOGY

Pharmaceutical QC Technician
Just as the cell cycle has built-in quality control checkpoints, so do biological product manufacturing processes. A QC (quality control) technician in a pharmaceutical manufacturing company uses various science and math skills to monitor processes and ensure product quality.

Quality control checkpoints Recall the process of starting a car. Many manufacturers use a unique microchip in the key to ensure that only a specific key will start each car. This is a checkpoint against theft. The cell cycle also has built-in checkpoints that monitor the cycle and can stop it if something goes wrong. For example, a checkpoint near the end of the G_1 stage monitors for DNA damage and can stop the cycle before entering the S stage of interphase. There are other quality control checkpoints during the S stage and after DNA replication in the G_2 stage. Spindle checkpoints also have been identified in mitosis. If a failure of the spindle fibers is detected, the cycle can be stopped before cytokinesis. **Figure 11** shows the location of key checkpoints in the cell cycle.

R

Abnormal Cell Cycle: Cancer

Connection to Health Although the cell cycle has a system of quality control checkpoints, it is a complex process that sometimes fails. When cells do not respond to the normal cell cycle control mechanisms, a condition called cancer can result. **Cancer** is the uncontrolled growth and division of cells—a failure in the regulation of the cell cycle. When unchecked, cancer cells can kill an organism by crowding out normal cells, resulting in the loss of tissue function. Cancer cells spend less time in interphase than do normal cells, which means cancer cells grow and divide unrestrained as long as they are supplied with essential nutrients. **Figure 12** shows how cancer cells can intrude on normal cells.

Video
What's BIOLOGY Got To Do With It?

Inquiry
Virtual Lab

Causes of cancer Cancer does not just occur in a weak organism. In fact, cancer occurs in many healthy, active, and young organisms. The changes that occur in the regulation of cell growth and division of cancer cells are due to mutations or changes in the segments of DNA that control the production of proteins, including proteins that regulate the cell cycle. Often, the genetic change or damage that occurs is repaired by various repair systems. But if the repair systems fail, cancer can result. Various environmental factors can affect the occurrence of cancer cells. Substances and agents that are known to cause cancer are called **carcinogens** (kar SIH nuh junz).

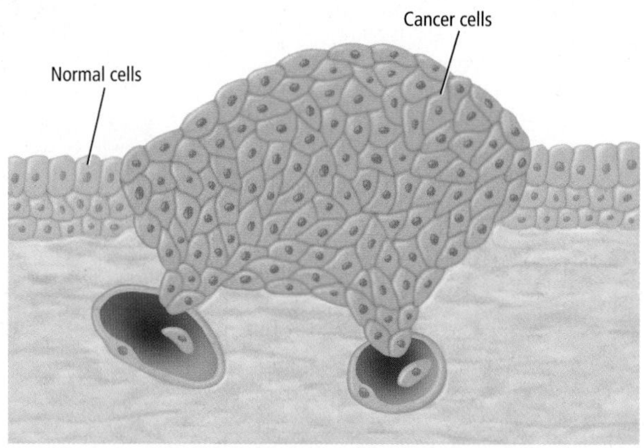

Figure 12 Cancer cells often have an abnormal, irregular shape compared to normal cells. In this image some cancer cells are entering vessels, which might carry them to another part of the body. This is one way cancer can spread from one body part to another.

Differentiated Instruction

Below Level When performing tasks like the Critical Thinking activity on this page, students who perform below their grade level may be more easily distracted than others. Seat them in an area that is free from distractions.

For more tips, see pages 14T–15T.

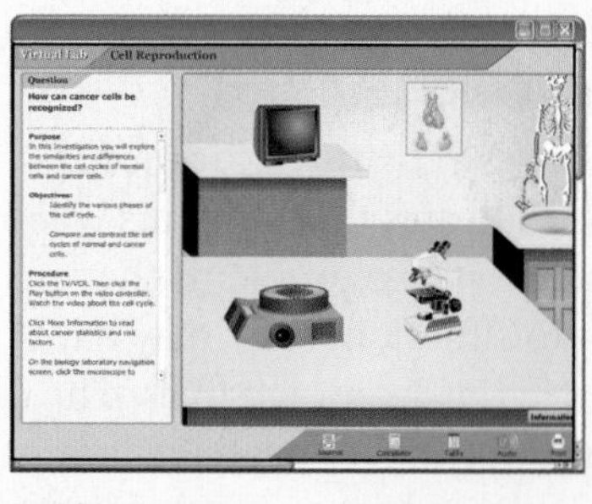

Inquiry Virtual Lab In this investigation, the student will explore the similarities and differences between cell cycles of normal cells and cell cycles of cancer cells.

Although not all cancers can be prevented, avoiding known carcinogens can help reduce the risk of cancer. A governmental agency called the Food and Drug Administration (FDA) works to make sure that the things you eat and drink are safe. The FDA requires labels and warnings for products that might be carcinogens. Industrial laws help protect people from exposure to cancer-causing chemicals in the workplace. Avoiding tobacco of all kinds, even secondhand smoke and smokeless tobacco, can reduce the risk of cancer.

Some radiation, such as ultraviolet radiation from the Sun, is impossible to avoid completely. There is a connection between the amount of ultraviolet radiation to which a person is exposed and the risk of developing skin cancer. Therefore, sunscreen is recommended for everyone who is exposed to the Sun. Other forms of radiation, such as X-rays, are used for medical purposes, such as to view a broken bone or to check for cavities in teeth. To protect against exposure, you might have worn a heavy lead apron when an X-ray was taken.

Reading Check **Identify** carcinogens to which you are regularly exposed.

Cancer genetics More than one change in DNA is required to change an abnormal cell into a cancer cell. Over time, there might be many changes in DNA. This might explain why the risk of cancer increases with age. An individual who inherits one or more changes from a parent is at a higher risk for developing cancer than someone who does not inherit these changes.

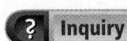

Inquiry Launch Lab

Review Based on what you've read about the abnormal cell cycle and its results, how would you now answer the analysis questions?

VOCABULARY

SCIENCE USAGE V. COMMON USAGE

Inheritance

Science usage: the passing of genetic traits from parent to offspring via DNA

A person's body structure and facial appearance are the result of genetic inheritance.

Common usage: assets acquired from a deceased person that can be given to surviving family members

The house was Jim's inheritance from his uncle.

MiniLab 2

Compare Sunscreens

Inquiry MiniLab

Do sunscreens really block sunlight? Sunscreens contain a variety of different compounds that absorb UVB from sunlight. UVB is linked to mutations in DNA that can lead to skin cancer. Find out how effective at blocking sunlight various sunscreens are.

Procedure

1. Read and complete the lab safety form.
2. Choose one of the **sunscreen products** provided by your teacher. Record the active ingredients and the Sun protection factor (SPF) on a data sheet.
3. Obtain **two sheets of plastic wrap.** On one sheet use a **permanent marker** to draw two widely spaced circles. Place a drop of sunscreen in the middle of one circle and a drop of **zinc oxide** in the middle of the other.
4. Lay the second sheet on top of both circles. Spread the drops by pressing with a **book.**
5. Take a covered piece of **Sun-sensitive paper** and your two pieces of plastic wrap to a sunny area. Quickly uncover the paper, lay the two pieces of plastic wrap on top, and place in the sunlight.
6. After the paper is fully exposed (1–5 minutes), remove it from the sunlight and develop according to instructions.

Analysis

1. **Think Critically** Why did you compare the sunscreens to zinc oxide?
2. **Draw Conclusions** After examining the developed Sun-sensitive papers from your class, which sunscreens do you think would be most likely to prevent DNA mutations?

GOING GREEN Sun-sensitive paper is not reusable. Instead, purchase reusable sun-sensitive beads made of recycled materials on which to lay the plastic wrap. The beads change in gradations of color depending on how much sun they are exposed to.

Reading Check Some examples are sunlight, secondhand smoke, automobile exhaust, radon, and air pollution.

Inquiry Launch Lab

Assess Content Development

Assess how understanding has developed when students revisit the Launch Lab analysis questions.

MiniLab 2

Inquiry MiniLab

For a lab worksheet, use your eTeacherEdition Online.

RUBRIC A rubric for evaluating MiniLabs is found on your eTeacherEdition Online.

Est. Time 30 min

Alternative Materials Acetate overhead transparencies can be substituted for the plastic wrap.

Safety Precaution Approve lab safety forms before work begins.

Teaching Strategies

- Provide sunscreens with various SPF numbers and active ingredients.
- Provide information about the various UV blocking chemicals found in sunscreens and the meaning of the SPF numbers.

Cleanup and Disposal Have students return the containers of sunscreen. If transparencies are used, they need to be washed and returned.

Analysis

1. Zinc oxide completely blocks sunlight, so it is a control to which the results of other sunscreens can be compared.
2. Sunscreens with higher SPF numbers should block more light. There may be differences between sunscreens that have the same SPF number but different active ingredients.

LabManager™

Customize this lab with the LabManager™ CD-ROM.

D Develop Concepts
BL OL

Clarify a Misconception
Students often think cells "just die" when they get old. Tell students that apoptosis, which is considered a natural, programmed death, is only one way by which cells die. Point out that another way cells die is by necrosis, which is cell death due to injury or illness of the tissue.

C Critical Thinking
BL OL AL **Predict**
ASK STUDENTS: ***What do you think would happen if the apoptosis cell pathways were turned on in a tissue inappropriately?*** Death of normal tissue and possibly severe illness or death of the organism would result.

R Reading Strategy
EL BL OL AL COOP LEARN

Anticipatory Guide Before they read the text under the heading *Stem Cells,* have students work in pairs to list what they know about stem cells and what they would like to know about stem cells. Discuss their questions as a class and write them on the board. After students have read the three paragraphs under the heading *Stem Cells,* discuss as a class which questions were answered in the text and which ones were not. Assign the questions that were not answered as research project topics to groups of students (one question per group).

Caption Question Figure 13
Introducing stem cells near the damaged nerve might allow the stem cells to become nerve cells.

D Apoptosis

Not every cell is destined to survive. Some cells go through a process called **apoptosis** (a pup TOH sus), or programmed cell death. Cells going through apoptosis actually shrink and shrivel in a controlled process. All animal cells appear to have a "death program" that can be activated.

One example of apoptosis occurs during the development of the human hand and foot. When the hands and feet begin to develop, cells occupy the spaces between the fingers and toes. Normally, this tissue undergoes apoptosis, with the cells shriveling and dying at the appropriate time so that the webbing is not present in the mature organism. An example of apoptosis in plants is the localized death of cells that results in leaves falling from trees during autumn. Apoptosis also occurs in cells that are damaged beyond repair, including cells with DNA damage that could lead to cancer. Apoptosis can help to protect organisms from developing cancerous growths. C

VOCABULARY
ACADEMIC VOCABULARY
Mature
to have reached full natural growth or development
After mitosis, the two new cells must mature before they divide.

R Stem Cells

The majority of cells in a multicellular organism are designed for a specialized function. Some cells might be part of your skin, and other cells might be part of your heart. In 1998, scientists discovered a way to isolate a unique type of cell in humans called the stem cell. **Stem cells** are unspecialized cells that can develop into specialized cells under the right conditions, as illustrated in **Figure 13.** Stem cells can remain in an organism for many years while undergoing cell division. There are two basic types of stem cells: embryonic stem cells and adult stem cells.

Embryonic stem cells After a sperm fertilizes an egg, the resulting mass of cells divides repeatedly until there are about 100–150 cells. These cells have not become specialized and are called embryonic stem cells. If separated, each of these cells has the capability of developing into a wide variety of specialized cells. If the embryo continues to divide, the cells specialize into various tissues, organs, and organ systems. Embryonic stem cell research is controversial because of ethical concerns about the source of the cells.

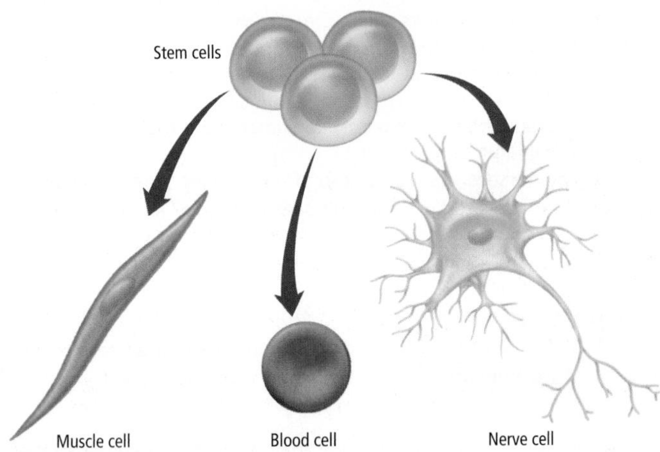

Figure 13 Because stem cells are not locked into becoming one particular type of cell, they might be the key to curing many medical conditions and genetic defects.
Explain *how stem cells could be used to cure nerve damage.*

Content Background

Teacher FYI Apoptosis, besides triggering cell death, also often signals phagocytosis of a dying cell. Apoptosis protects the body from triggering inflammation. If a dying cell isn't taken up by a phagocyte, cell contents can spill into the surrounding tissue, triggering inflammation and, potentially, autoimmune diseases such as lupus or diabetes. Healthy cells, on the other hand, can actively fend off macrophages.

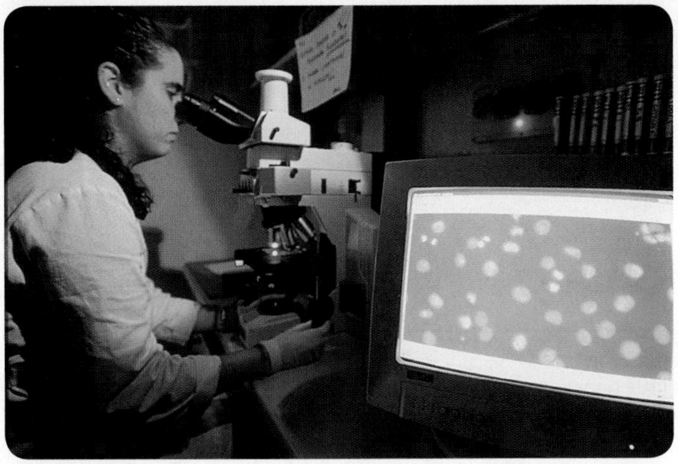

■ **Figure 14** Research with adult stem cells has led to advances in treatments for numerous injuries and diseases.

Adult stem cells The second type of stem cells—adult stem cells—is found in various tissues in the body and might be used to maintain and repair the same kind of tissue in which they are found. The term "adult stem cells" might be somewhat misleading because even a newborn has adult stem cells. Like embryonic stem cells, certain kinds of adult stem cells also might be able to develop into different kinds of cells, providing new treatments for many diseases and conditions. In 1999, researchers at Harvard Medical School used nervous system stem cells to restore lost brain tissue in mice. In 2008, researchers used adult stem cells along with an enzyme called PKA to create new bone tissue for repair in mice. Research with adult stem cells, like that shown in **Figure 14,** is much less controversial because the adult stem cells can be obtained with the consent of their donors.

D W

D Develop Concepts

BL OL AL COOP LEARN Activity Have pairs of students research the use of stem cells and the ethical concerns surrounding stem cell research. Have them hold a "congressional" hearing and debate whether the use of stem cells should be controlled. Refer students to the Skillbuilder Handbook for debate tips. You can use these criteria for assessment as well.

W Writing Support

AL Formal Writing Have students research some of the recent experiments being done with stem cells. Have each student select one disease that might be helped by this research and prepare an abstract of the research and its potential results.

Section 3 Assessment

Section Summary

- The cell cycle of eukaryotic cells is regulated by cyclins.
- Checkpoints occur during most of the stages of the cell cycle to ensure that the cell divides accurately.
- Cancer is the uncontrolled growth and division of cells.
- Apoptosis is a programmed cell death.
- Stem cells are unspecialized cells that can develop into specialized cells with the proper signals.

Understand Main Ideas

1. MAIN Idea **Describe** how cyclins control the cell cycle.
2. **Explain** how the cancer cell cycle is different from a normal cell cycle.
3. **Identify** three carcinogens.
4. **Contrast** apoptosis and cancer.
5. **Describe** a possible application for stem cells.
6. **Explain** the difference between embryonic stem cells and adult stem cells.

Think Critically

7. **Hypothesize** what might happen if apoptosis did not occur in cells that have significant DNA damage.

WRITING in **Biology**

8. Write a public service announcement about carcinogens. Choose a specific type of cancer, and write about the carcinogens linked to it.

Formative Assessment

Evaluation Have students compare a normal cell cycle and a cancer cell cycle by making a diagram of cell division stages to illustrate the differences. Have them label the differences.

Remediation Prepare a diagram similar to the one in Figure 3, but without labels. Have students label the phases of the cell cycle. At each phase, have them explain how a cancer cell at this point in the cycle differs from a normal cell at the same point in the cycle.

Section 3 Assessment

1. Certain cyclin proteins regulate mitosis and the cell cycle by allowing or stopping cell cycle processes.
2. It is shorter; cancer cells divide in an unrestrained way.
3. possible answers: cigarette smoke, ultraviolet radiation, asbestos
4. In apoptosis a cell undergoes programmed cell death; cancer cells can grow and divide unrestrained as long as they are supplied with essential nutrients.
5. Answers may include cures for medical conditions and genetic defects.
6. Embryonic stem cells, found in developing embryos, can develop into many kinds of cells. Adult stem cells are found in developed tissues.
7. People would probably have higher rates of cancer and genetic diseases.
8. Answers will vary. Announcements should include information about the carcinogen selected.

WRITING in **Biology**

RUBRIC Use the modifiable rubric found on your eTeacherEdition Online to assess writing assignments.

Biology & Society

Purpose
Students will examine how stem cells are different from regular cells. Students will create a book that depicts stem cell research.
A.2, C.1, E.2, F.6

Anticipatory Guide
ASK STUDENTS: ***Do you know anyone who is paralyzed because of a neck or back injury or who has Parkinson's disease?*** Students will have individual responses. ***How does this relate to stem cell research?*** Research may lead to treatment or a cure.

Background
Students might inquire about the difference between embryonic stem cell research and adult stem cell research. Embryonic stem cell research is controversial because harvesting the cells destroys the embryo. Adult stem cells are taken from tissues of a growing or adult human without harming or destroying the tissue. Embryonic stem cells can differentiate into any of the 220 cell types in the body, whereas adult stem cells have not yet been found to differentiate into all cell types.

Biology & Society

Stem Cells: Paralysis Cured?

A race car driver is paralyzed in a crash. A teen is paralyzed after diving into shallow water. Until recently, these individuals would have little hope of regaining the full use of their bodies, but new research on adult stem cells shows promise for reversing paralysis.

How can stem cells be used? Scientists are trying to find ways to grow stem cells in cell cultures and manipulate them to generate specific cell types. For example, stem cells might be used to repair cardiac tissue after a heart attack, to restore vision in diseased or injured eyes, to treat diseases such as diabetes, or to repair spinal cells to reverse paralysis. Current stem cell research in Ecuador involves bone marrow cells (BMCs). BMCs are adult stem cells being used to grow blood vessels. Re-establishing blood flow and oxygen to tissues aids in the healing process and provides therapy options for patients.

Stem cells and paralysis In Portugal, Dr. Carlos Lima and his team of researchers found that tissue taken from the nasal cavity is a rich source of adult stem cells. These stem cells become nerve cells when transplanted into the site of a spinal cord injury. The new nerve cells replace the cells that were damaged.

More than forty patients with paralysis due to accidents have undergone the Portuguese procedure. All patients have regained some sensation in paralyzed body areas. Most have regained some motor control. With intensive physical therapy, about ten percent of the patients now can walk with the aid of supportive devices, such as walkers and braces. This is promising news to the many individuals facing illnesses or injuries that have robbed them of the full use of their bodies.

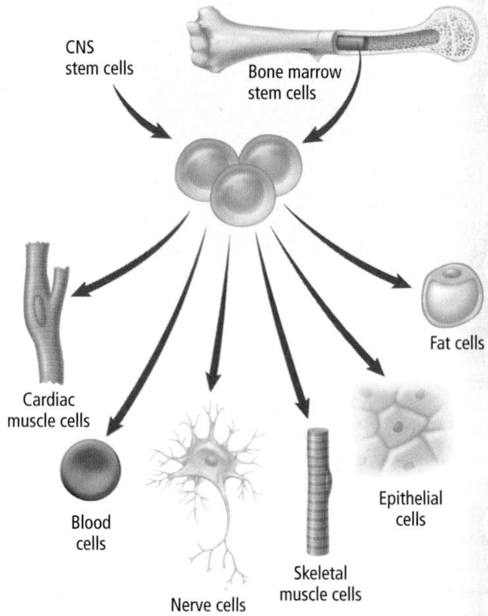

Stem cells from bone marrow or the central nervous system can be manipulated to generate many cell types that can be transplanted to treat illness or repair damage.

Stem cells and the future Scientists are eager to do the research necessary to make adult stem cell treatments a regular part of health care. Paralysis might not have to be permanent; stem cells could provide the cure.

WRITING in Biology

Pamphlet Create an illustrated pamphlet depicting the benefits of adult stem cell research. Research adult stem cells in order to include the research methodology, treatment, examples, cell physiology, and history of adult stem cell research.

WRITING in Biology

RUBRIC Use the modifiable rubric found on your eTeacherEdition Online to assess writing assignments.

Follow-Up Discussion
After students create their pamphlets, have them share with the class their most amazing discovery and explain how their knowledge of the topic changed as a result of being engaged in this project. Have them share whether they would consider becoming involved in the political process to protect the rights of scientists who conduct stem cell research.

WebQuest

BIOLAB

DOES SUNLIGHT AFFECT MITOSIS IN YEAST?

Background: Ultraviolet (UV) radiation is a component of sunlight that can damage DNA and interrupt the cell cycle.

Question: *Can sunscreens prevent damage to UV-sensitive yeast?*

Materials

sterile pipettes (10)
aluminum foil
test-tube rack
sterile spreaders or sterile cotton swabs (10)
dilution of UV-sensitive yeast
yeast extract dextrose (YED) agar plates (10)
sunscreens with various amounts of SPF

Safety Precautions

Procedure

1. Read and complete the lab safety form.
2. Obtain a test tube containing a diluted broth culture of the UV-sensitive yeast.
3. Formulate a hypothesis, then choose a sunscreen and predict how it will affect the yeast when exposed to sunlight.
4. Label ten YED agar plates with your group name. Label two plates as control. The control plates will not be placed in the sunlight. Label four of the experimental plates as "no sunscreen" and four as "sunscreen."
5. Spread a 0.1 mL sample of the yeast dilution on all ten YED agar plates. Wrap the control plates in foil and give them to your teacher for incubation.
6. With direction from your teacher, decide how long to expose each of the experimental plates and label each plate accordingly. Prepare a table in which to collect your data.
7. Wrap the "no sunscreen" plates in foil. Apply sunscreen to the lids of the four sunscreen plates and wrap them in foil.
8. Remove only enough aluminum foil from each of the experimental plates to expose the dish lids. Expose the plates for the planned times. Re-cover the plates after exposure and give them to your teacher for incubation.
9. After incubation, count and record the number of yeast colonies on each plate.
10. **Cleanup and Disposal** Wash and return all reusable materials. Dispose of the YED plates as instructed by your teacher. Disinfect your work area. Wash your hands thoroughly with soap and water.

Analyze and Conclude

1. **Estimate** Assume that each yeast colony on a YED plate grew from one yeast cell in the dilution. Use the number of yeast colonies on your control plate to determine the percent of yeast that survived on each exposed plate.
2. **Graph Data** Draw a graph with the percent survival on the *y*-axis and the exposure time on the *x*-axis. Use a different color to graph the data from the plates with and without sunscreen.
3. **Evaluate** Was your hypothesis supported by your data? Explain.
4. **Error Analysis** Describe several possible sources of error.

APPLY YOUR SKILL

Brainstorm Work with classmates to research and locate information and ideas about how UV-sensitive yeast could be used as a biological monitor to detect increases in the amounts of UV light reaching Earth's surface.

Analyze and Conclude

1. If there was an average of 100 colonies on the control plates and 50 colonies on the exposed plate, the survival rate would be 50 percent.
2. Student graphs should indicate that the survival rate was greater on the plates with the sunscreen than without the sunscreen.
3. Answers will vary but should take into account the protective effect of the sunscreen.
4. Possible sources include contamination by fungal spores and bacteria in the air and on the skin; errors in counting; prior exposure of colony to sunlight.

BIOLAB

Inquiry BioLab

For a lab worksheet, use your eTeacherEdition Online.

RUBRIC A rubric for evaluating BioLabs is found on your eTeacherEdition Online.

Est. Time 60 min

Content Background Ultraviolet (UV) radiation in sunlight is classified according to its wavelength as: UVA (380–315 nm), UVB (315–280 nm), and UVC (less than 280 nm). The shorter the wavelength, the more damage to DNA it can cause. Also, the more exposure a person has to sunlight, the more likely the radiation is to cause a mutation in genes that control the cell cycle, leading to cancer. Sunscreens contain chemicals that absorb UV radiation.

Alternative Materials A UV lamp can be substituted for sunlight. If so, be sure students protect their eyes from the UV radiation.

Safety Precautions Approve lab safety forms before work begins. Have students wear protective clothing and sunglasses in bright sunlight.

Teaching Strategies

- Make up the YED plates at least 24 h prior to the lab.
- Provide students with a short description of DNA, genes, and mutations.

Alternative Teaching Demo Students could prepare a hypothesis and the experiment could be a demonstration.

Chapter 9

Study Guide

ConnectED

Students can use the following to review the chapter.

Review

Vocabulary eGames
Vocabulary eFlashcards
Vocabulary PuzzleMaker

Assessment

Online Quizzes
Online Test Practice
Standardized Test Practice

Use the *ExamView®* *Assessment Suite* CD-ROM to:

- create multiple versions of tests
- create modified tests with one mouse click
- edit existing questions and add your own questions
- build tests aligned with state standards using built-in state curriculum tags
- change English tests to Spanish with one mouse click
- track students' progress using the Teacher Management System

Chapter 9 Study Guide

THEME FOCUS Change Stem cells undergo many changes to differentiate into one of many types of specialized cells.

BIG Idea **Cells go through a life cycle that includes interphase, mitosis, and cytokinesis.**

Section 1 Cellular Growth

cell cycle (p. 246)
interphase (p. 246)
mitosis (p. 246)
cytokinesis (p. 246)
chromosome (p. 247)
chromatin (p. 247)

MAIN Idea **Cells grow until they reach their size limit, then they either stop growing or divide.**

- The ratio of surface area to volume describes the size of the plasma membrane relative to the volume of the cell.
- Cells are limited in size, with most cells having a diameter of less than 100 µm.
- The cell cycle is the process of cellular reproduction.
- A cell spends the majority of its lifetime in interphase.

Section 2 Mitosis and Cytokinesis

prophase (p. 248)
sister chromatid (p. 248)
centromere (p. 248)
spindle apparatus (p. 250)
metaphase (p. 250)
anaphase (p. 251)
telophase (p. 251)

MAIN Idea **Eukaryotic cells reproduce by mitosis, the process of nuclear division, and cytokinesis, the process of cytoplasm division.**

- Mitosis is the process by which the duplicated DNA is divided.
- The stages of mitosis include prophase, metaphase, anaphase, and telophase.
- Cytokinesis is the process of cytoplasm division that results in genetically identical daughter cells.

Section 3 Cell Cycle Regulation

cyclin (p. 253)
cyclin-dependent kinase (p. 253)
cancer (p. 254)
carcinogen (p. 254)
apoptosis (p. 256)
stem cell (p. 256)

MAIN Idea **The normal cell cycle is regulated by cyclin proteins.**

- The cell cycle of eukaryotic cells is regulated by cyclins.
- Checkpoints occur during most of the stages of the cell cycle to ensure that the cell divides accurately.
- Cancer is the uncontrolled growth and division of cells.
- Apoptosis is a programmed cell death.
- Stem cells are unspecialized cells that can develop into specialized cells with the proper signals.

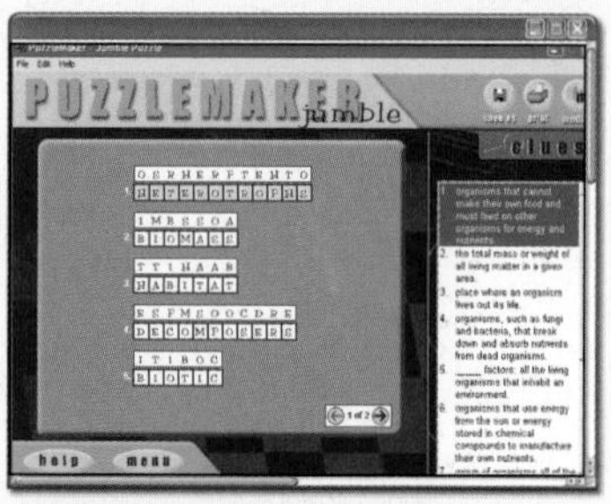

Review **Vocabulary PuzzleMaker**

For additional practice with vocabulary, have students access the Vocabulary PuzzleMaker online.

Review Vocabulary eGames

Section 1

Vocabulary Review

Match the correct vocabulary term from the Study Guide page to the following definitions.

1. the period in which the cell is not dividing
2. the process of nuclear division
3. the sequence of events in the life of a eukaryotic cell

Understand Main Ideas

4. Which is a reason why cells remain small?
   A. Large cells have difficulty diffusing nutrients rapidly enough.
   B. As cells grow, their ratio of surface area to volume increases.
   C. Transportation of wastes becomes a problem for large cells.
   D. All of the above.

Use the hypothetical cell shown below to answer question 5.

2 cm

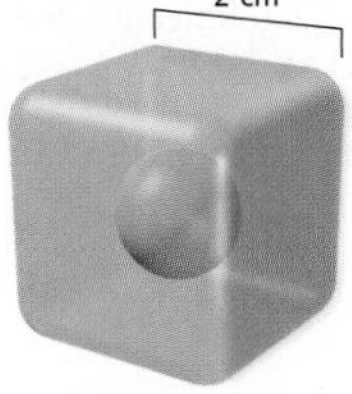

5. What is the ratio of surface area to volume?
   A. 2:1 **C.** 4:1
   B. 3:1 **D.** 6:1
6. Of the surface area-to-volume ratio, what does the surface area represent in a cell?
   A. nucleus
   B. plasma membrane
   C. mitochondria
   D. cytoplasm
7. Which describes the activities of a cell that include cellular growth and cell division?
   A. chromatin **C.** mitosis
   B. cytoplasm **D.** cell cycle
8. As a cell's volume increases, what happens to the proportional amount of surface area?
   A. increases
   B. decreases
   C. stays the same
   D. reaches its limit

Constructed Response

9. MAIN Idea Why are cellular transport and cellular communication factors that limit cell size?
10. **Short Answer** Summarize the relationship between surface area and volume as a cell grows.
11. **Short Answer** What types of activities are going on in a cell during interphase?

Think Critically

12. **Criticize** this statement: Interphase is a "resting period" for the cell before it begins mitosis.
13. **Explain** the relationship of DNA, a chromosome, and chromatin.

Section 2

Vocabulary Review

Complete the concept map using vocabulary terms from the Study Guide page.

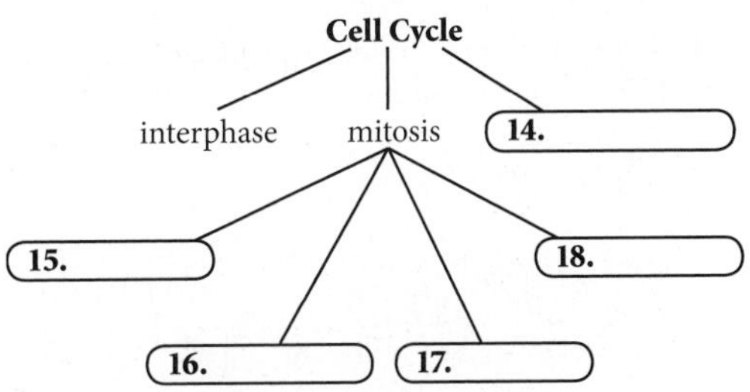

Understand Main Ideas

19. Starting with one cell that underwent six divisions, how many cells would result?
   A. 13 **C.** 48
   B. 32 **D.** 64

Chapter 9 Assessment

Section 1

Vocabulary Review

1. interphase
2. mitosis
3. cell cycle

Understand Main Ideas

4. D
5. B
6. B
7. D
8. B

Constructed Response

9. Both are essential for cell survival. As the cell grows larger, it is harder for the nucleus to make proteins fast enough to control the cell and transport molecules around the cell.
10. As the cell grows, the ratio of surface area to volume decreases.
11. The cell is actively synthesizing proteins and carrying out its normal functions. It duplicates DNA and prepares for division.

Think Critically

12. During interphase, the cell is not "resting" but rather is producing proteins and carrying out the cell's normal functions.
13. A chromosome is composed of DNA. Chromatin is the relaxed form of a chromosome.

Section 2

Vocabulary Review

14. cytokinesis
15. prophase
16. metaphase
17. anaphase
18. telophase

Understand Main Ideas

19. D

20. C
21. B
22. A

Constructed Response

23. during the G_2 stage of interphase, prophase, and metaphase
24. On the top row of cells, starting on the left, the first cell is in interphase, the second cell is in prophase, the third cell is in anaphase, the fourth cell is in metaphase, and the fifth cell is in telophase.
25. During telophase, the chromosomes have reached the poles of the cell, the nuclear membrane reforms, the nucleolus reappears and chromosomes recondense.

Think Critically

26. The cell is a plant cell.
27. 1/4 of 24 h, or 6 h

Section 3

Vocabulary Review

28. Cancer cells undergo uncontrolled, unrestrained growth and division because their genes have been changed.
29. Apoptosis is a cellular response to DNA damage that results in cell death.
30. Carcinogens are substances that cause cancer.

Understand Main Ideas

31. B
32. C

The following graph shows a cell over the course of its cell cycle. Use this graph to answer questions 20 and 21.

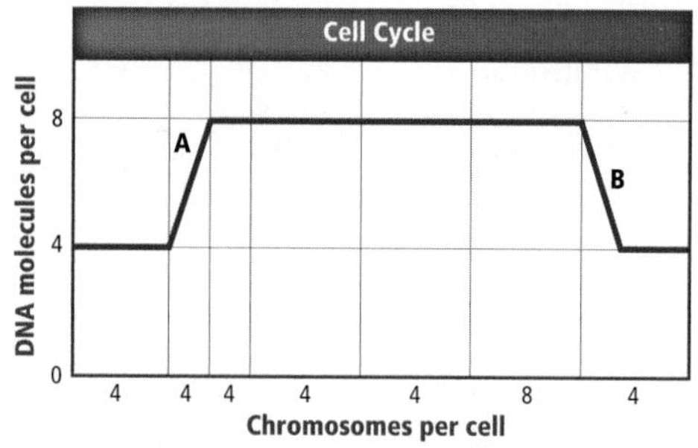

20. What stage occurred in the area labeled A?
A. prophase
B. G_1 stage
C. S stage
D. G_2 stage

21. What process occurred in the area labeled B?
A. interphase
B. cytokinesis
C. mitosis
D. metabolism

22. The cancer drug vinblastine interferes with synthesis of microtubules. In mitosis, this would interfere with what?
A. spindle formation
B. DNA replication
C. carbohydrate synthesis
D. disappearance of the nuclear envelope

Constructed Response

23. MAIN Idea During the cell cycle, when would a chromosome consist of two identical sister chromatids?

24. Short Answer In the following image of a section of onion root tip, identify a cell in each of the following stages: interphase, prophase, metaphase, anaphase, and telophase.

Stained LM Magnification: 130×

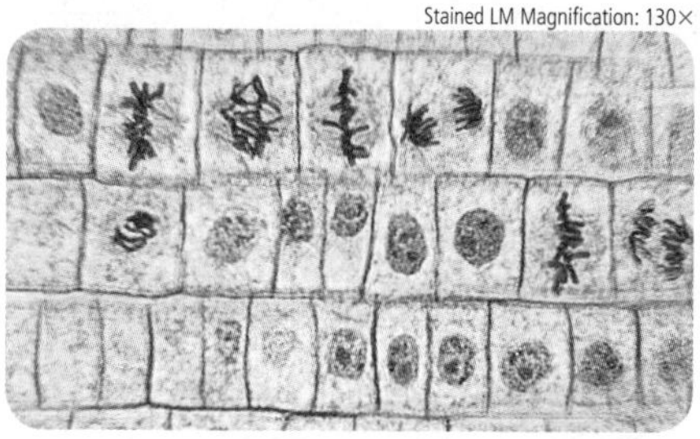

25. Short Answer Describe the events that occur in telophase.

Think Critically

26. Evaluate While looking through a microscope, you see a cell plate forming. This cell is most likely what type of cell?

27. MATH in Biology A biologist examines a series of cells and counts 90 cells in interphase, 13 cells in prophase, 12 cells in metaphase, 3 cells in anaphase, and 2 cells in telophase. If a complete cycle for this type of cell requires 24 hours, what is the average duration of mitosis?

Section 3

Vocabulary Review

The sentences below include term(s) that have been used incorrectly. Replace the incorrect term(s) with vocabulary terms from the Study Guide page to make the sentences true.

28. Stem cells undergo uncontrolled, unrestrained growth and division because their genes have been changed.

29. Cancer is a cell response to DNA damage that results in cell death.

30. Cyclins are substances that cause cancer.

Understand Main Ideas

31. What is the role of cyclins in a cell?
A. to control the movement of microtubules
B. to signal for the cell to divide
C. to stimulate the breakdown of the nuclear membrane
D. to cause the nucleolus to disappear

32. What substances form the cyclin-cyclin dependent kinase combinations that control the stages in the cell cycle?
A. fats and proteins
B. carbohydrates and proteins
C. proteins and enzymes
D. fats and enzymes

33. Which is a characteristic of cancer cells?
   A. controlled cell division
   B. contain multiple genetic changes
   C. cytokinesis stage is skipped
   D. cell cyclins function normally

34. Which describes apoptosis?
   A. occurs in all cells
   B. is a programmed cell death
   C. disrupts the normal development of an organism
   D. is a response to hormones

35. Why have some stem cell researchers experienced roadblocks in their studies?
   A. Stem cells cannot be found.
   B. There are ethical concerns about obtaining stem cells.
   C. There are no known uses for stem cells.
   D. Stem cells do not become specialized cells.

Constructed Response

Refer to the diagram to answer question 36.

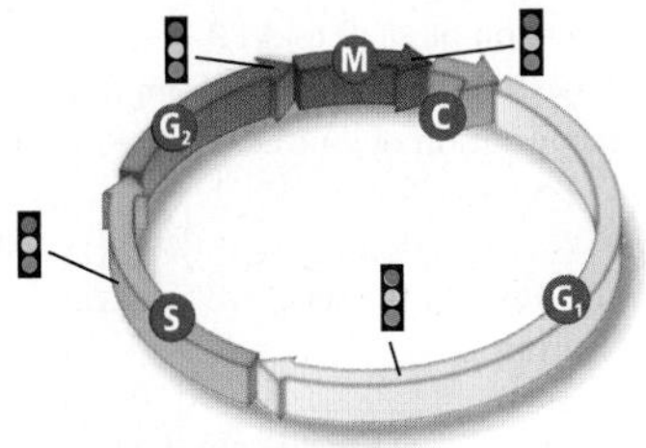

36. **THEME FOCUS Change** Explain the relationship between cancer cells and the cell cycle.

37. **Short Answer** Distinguish between mitosis and apoptosis.

Think Critically

38. **Describe** how stem cells might be used to help a patient who has a damaged spinal cord.

39. **MAIN Idea** **Explain** how the lack of cyclins would affect the cell cycle.

40. **Apply** Hundreds of millions of dollars are spent annually in the U.S. on the research and treatment of cancer, with much less being spent on cancer prevention. Compose a plan that would increase cancer prevention knowledge.

Summative Assessment

41. **BIG Idea** Besides reproduction, what factors cause cells to complete the cycle of interphase, mitosis, and cytokinesis?

42. **WRITING in Biology** Write a skit using props and people to demonstrate mitosis.

43. Research chemicals that are carcinogens and write about how these chemicals can damage DNA.

DBQ Document-Based Questions

Dr. Chang and co-workers evaluated the risk of pancreatic cancer by studying its occurrence in a population group. Their data included age at diagnosis. The graph below shows cancer diagnosis rates for African-American men and women.

Data obtained from: Chang, K. J. et al. 2005. Risk of pancreatic adenocarcinoma. *Cancer* 103: 349-357.

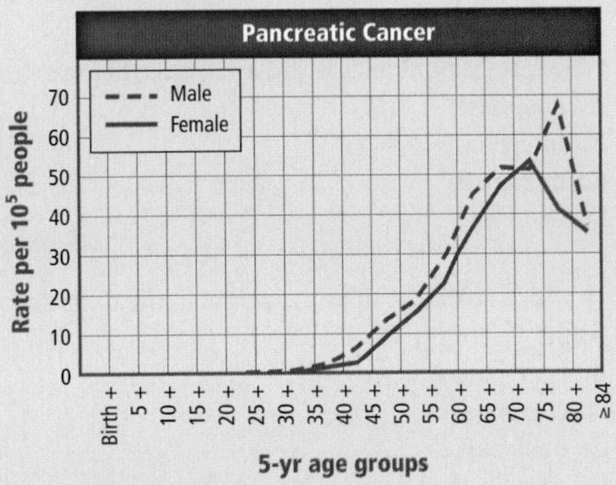

44. Summarize the relationship between the occurrence of cancer and age.

45. Considering what you know about cancer and the cell cycle, explain why incidences of cancer increase with age.

46. Compare the ages of men and women who are diagnosed with cancer.

47. At what age does diagnosis of pancreatic cancer decline?

33. B
34. B
35. B

Constructed Response

36. They have unrestrained cell division and spend little time in interphase.
37. Mitosis produces new cells, whereas apoptosis causes cell death.

Think Critically

38. They may help nerves in the spinal cord regrow and enable paralyzed people to walk again.
39. The lack of cyclins would completely stop the cell cycle process; cyclins combine with cyclin-dependent kinase enzymes.
40. Answers will vary, but may include avoiding carcinogens such as radiation.

Summative Assessment

41. Cells grow too large to be able to effectively complete cellular processes such as communication and transportation.

WRITING in Biology

RUBRIC Use the modifiable rubric found on your eTeacher-Edition Online to assess writing assignments.

42. Answers will vary, but the skit should demonstrate an understanding of mitosis.
43. Answers will vary, but should include specific carcinogens and their effect on DNA.

DBQ Document-Based Questions

Chang, K. J., et al. 2005. Risk of pancreatic adenocarcinoma.
Cancer 103: 349–357.

44. As age increases, the occurence rate of cancer increases until age 75–79 in females and age 80–84 in males, and then it declines.
45. As one ages, more cells accumulate mutations in their genes.
46. Sample answer: Men are generally diagnosed younger, and their diagnosis rates are higher than women's after age 70.
47. For women, age 70. For men, age 77

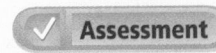

Assessment Online Test Practice

Standardized Test Practice

Multiple Choice

1. C 5. D 9. A
2. A 6. A 10. D
3. D 7. B
4. C 8. D

Short Answer

11. During interphase, the cell grows, carries out cellular functions, and prepares for mitosis to occur. These activities indicate that interphase is not a resting period.
12. At this checkpoint, the cell verifies that all the necessary tasks have occurred prior to mitosis and that the cell is ready for mitosis.
13. Mitosis requires many more steps—taking much longer to occur than cytokinesis.
14. It could be possible if the organism is a plant that has the ability to get energy from other organisms as well. (Answer may include the example of a carnivorous plant, such as a Venus flytrap, but this is not necessary.)
15. Ink: water-soluble ink would make a homogenous mixture, or solution, because the ink dissolves evenly throughout the water. Water-insoluble ink would make a heterogeneous mixture because the ink would not dissolve and would be unevenly mixed with the water. Pebbles: a heterogeneous mixture because the pebbles would not dissolve and would be unevenly mixed with the water. Salt: a homogenous mixture, or solution, because the salt dissolves evenly throughout the water.
16. ATP synthase pumps H^+ ions across the thylakoid membrane. Rubisco converts GAP molecules into RuBP molecules.
17. The volume of a cell increases much more rapidly than the surface area as the cell becomes larger. This causes the ratio of surface area to volume to decrease as a cell becomes larger.

Standardized Test Practice

Cumulative

Multiple Choice

1. Carbon (C) has four electrons in its outer energy level, and fluorine (F) has seven. Which compound would carbon and fluorine most likely form?
   A. CF_2
   B. CF_3
   C. CF_4
   D. CF_5

Use the diagram below to answer questions 2 and 3.

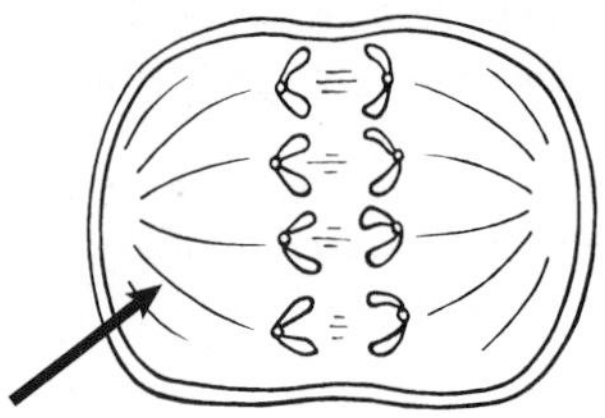

2. Which stage of mitosis is shown in this diagram?
   A. anaphase
   B. interphase
   C. metaphase
   D. telophase

3. To which structure does the arrow in the diagram point?
   A. centromere
   B. chromosome
   C. nucleolus
   D. spindle

4. Which stage of photosynthesis requires water to complete the chemical reaction?
   A. action of ATP synthase on ADP
   B. conversion of GAP molecules into RuBP
   C. conversion of $NADP^+$ to NADPH
   D. transfer of chemical energy to form GAP molecules

5. Which carbon-containing compound is the product of glycolysis?
   A. acetyl CoA
   B. glucose
   C. lactic acid
   D. pyruvate

Use the diagram below to answer question 6.

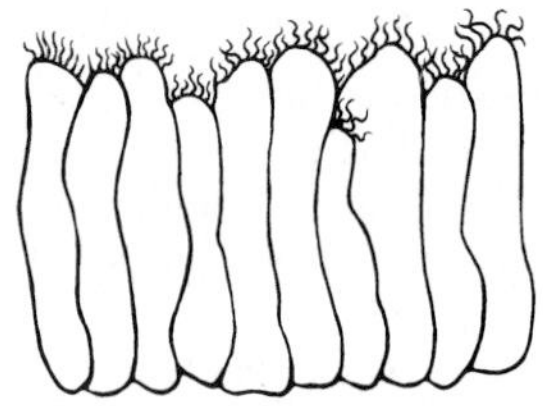

6. What are the structures projecting from the cells in the diagram?
   A. cilia
   B. flagella
   C. microfilaments
   D. villi

7. Which cellular process stores energy?
   A. the breaking of lipid chains
   B. the conversion of ADP to ATP
   C. the synthesization of proteins from RNA codons
   D. the transportation of ions across the membrane

8. Which contributes to the selective permeability of cell membranes?
   A. carbohydrates
   B. ions
   C. minerals
   D. proteins

9. If data from repeated experiments support a hypothesis, which would happen next?
   A. A conclusion would be established.
   B. The data would become a law.
   C. The hypothesis would be rejected.
   D. The hypothesis would be revised.

10. Which type of heterotroph is a mouse?
    A. carnivore
    B. detrivore
    C. herbivore
    D. omnivore

Short Answer

Use the diagram below to answer questions 11–13.

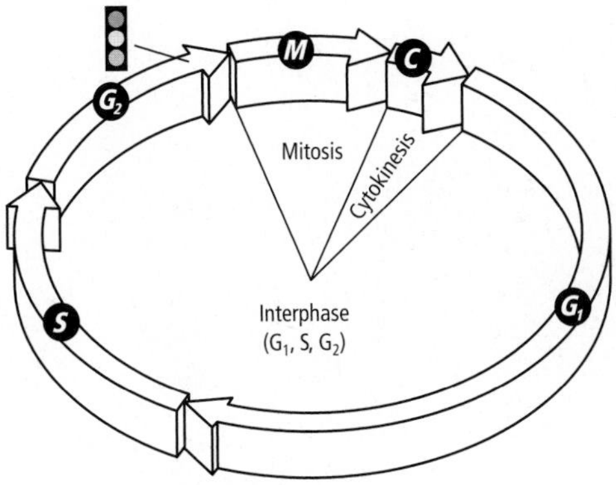

11. In the past, interphase often was called the "resting" phase of the cell cycle. Explain why this is inaccurate.

12. Explain what the cell does at the checkpoint indicated by the stoplight in the diagram.

13. Use the diagram to compare the relative rates at which mitosis and cytokinesis occur.

14. Hypothesize how an organism could be both a heterotroph and an autotroph.

15. Suppose you had ink, pebbles, and table salt. Describe what kind of mixture each one of these would make if mixed with water. Explain your answers.

16. Name two enzymes involved in photosynthesis, and describe their roles.

17. Infer how the ratio of surface area to volume changes as a cell grows larger.

Extended Response

Use the diagram below to answer questions 18 and 19.

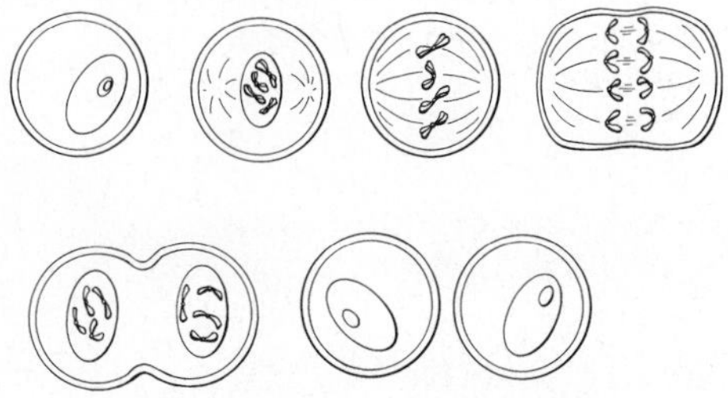

18. Analyze the diagram and describe the importance of the spindle fibers to chromatids during prophase.

19. Describe the function of the centromere and predict what might happen if cells did NOT have centromeres.

Essay Question

The same organelles are found in many different types of cells in an animal's body. However, there are differences in the number of organelles present, depending on the function of the different cells. For instance, the cells that require a great amount of energy to carry out their work would contain more mitochondria.

Using the information in the paragraph above, answer the following question in essay format.

20. How do you think two types of animal cells would differ in terms of the kinds of organelles they contain? Write a hypothesis about the cellular differences between two types of animal cells and then design an experiment to test your hypothesis.

NEED EXTRA HELP?																				
If You Missed Question . . .	1	2	3	4	5	6	7	8	9	10	11	12	13	14	15	16	17	18	19	20
Review Section . . .	6.1	9.2	9.2	8.2	8.3	7.3	8.1	7.2	1.3	2.1	9.1	9.1	8.2	8.1	6.3	8.2	9.1	9.2	9.2	7.3

Extended Response

18. The spindle fibers attach to the chromatids and pull them to their respective poles. Without the spindle fibers, the chromatids would not go to the correct poles.

19. The centromere is the location where the sister chromatids are connected. Without a central point, the chromatids might be pulled apart unevenly. This would cause the cell's genetic material to be divided unevenly and the daughter cells to be dysfunctional.

Essay Question

20. Answers will vary, depending on the types of cells selected for the essay. The answer should, however, reflect an understanding of the roles played by different organelles, even if the hypothesis does not reflect a complete understanding of cells found in animals. An example hypothesis: Muscle cells would contain more mitochondria than blood cells because they are involved in using energy for moving the body all the time. This could be tested by getting samples of the two kinds of cells and observing them under the microscope to see which kind of cell contains a greater number of mitochondria.

UNIT 3

Genetics

Preview the Unit

Have students preview the chapters in this unit and make a concept map or graphic organizer relating the Themes, Big Ideas, and Main Ideas. Students' maps should show a hierarchy between Big Ideas and Main Ideas and the interconnectedness of the Themes.

Chapter 10
Sexual Reproduction and Genetics
BIG Idea Reproductive cells, which pass on genetic traits from the parents to the child, are produced by the process of meiosis.

Chapter 11
Complex Inheritance and Human Heredity
BIG Idea Human inheritance does not always follow Mendel's laws.

Chapter 12
Molecular Genetics
BIG Idea DNA is the genetic material that contains a code for proteins.

Chapter 13
Genetics and Biotechnology
BIG Idea Genetic technology improves human health and quality of life.

WebQuest
Careers in Biology

UNIT 3
Genetics

THEMES

Scientific Inquiry Molecular discoveries have led to a better understanding of genetic inheritance.

Diversity Decoding the human genome helps scientists understand the range of diversity of all organisms.

Energy Cells require energy to reproduce and carry out life functions.

Homeostasis Cell division and genetic inheritance maintain species homeostasis.

Change Genetic mutations can be passed on to the next generations through inheritance.

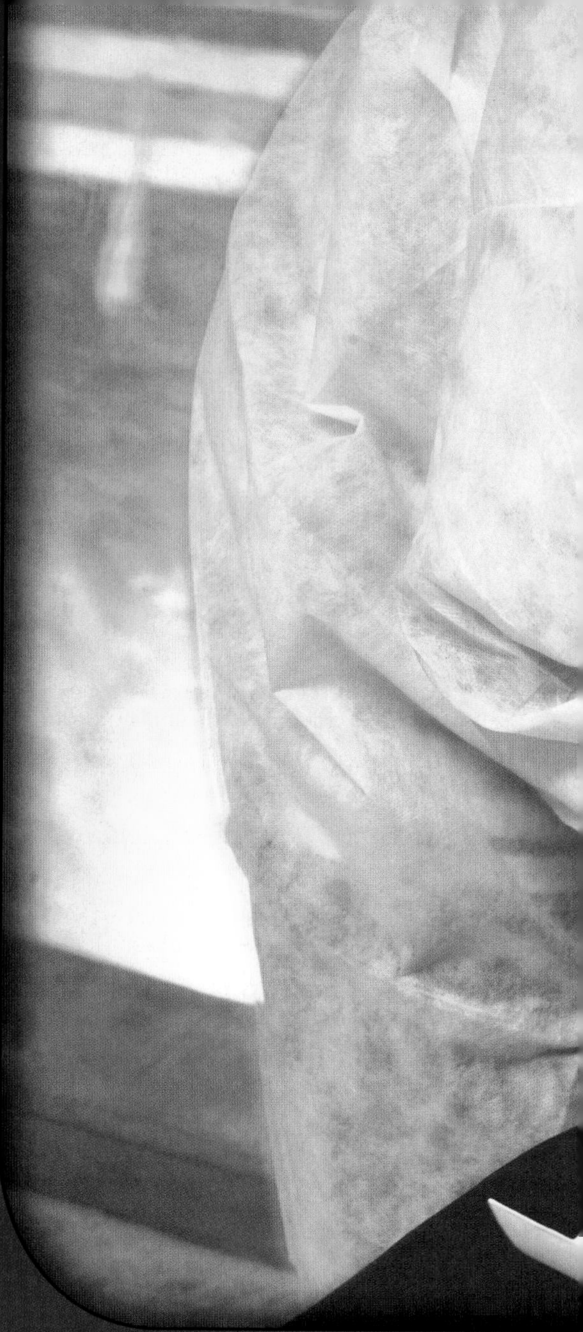

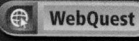

WebQuest **CAREERS IN BIOLOGY**

Geneticists are scientists who study heredity, genes, and variation in organisms. Geneticists, such as the ones shown here extracting genetic material from a mummy's arm, work to uncover the building blocks of life.

5-Minute UNIT LAUNCH

Connect to Students' Lives Have students spend a few minutes making a list of any features about themselves they think are inherited. Have students share their lists and generate a class list on the board. Discuss the lists and point out that most features, physical and mental, have an inherited component. During this unit, students will learn about the possible mechanisms of genetic inheritance.

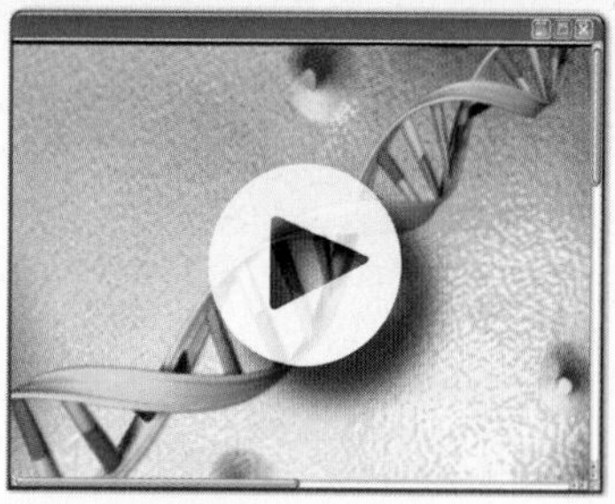

Video

What's BIOLOGY Got To Do With It?
A lawyer and a scientist explain DNA and its use in court cases.

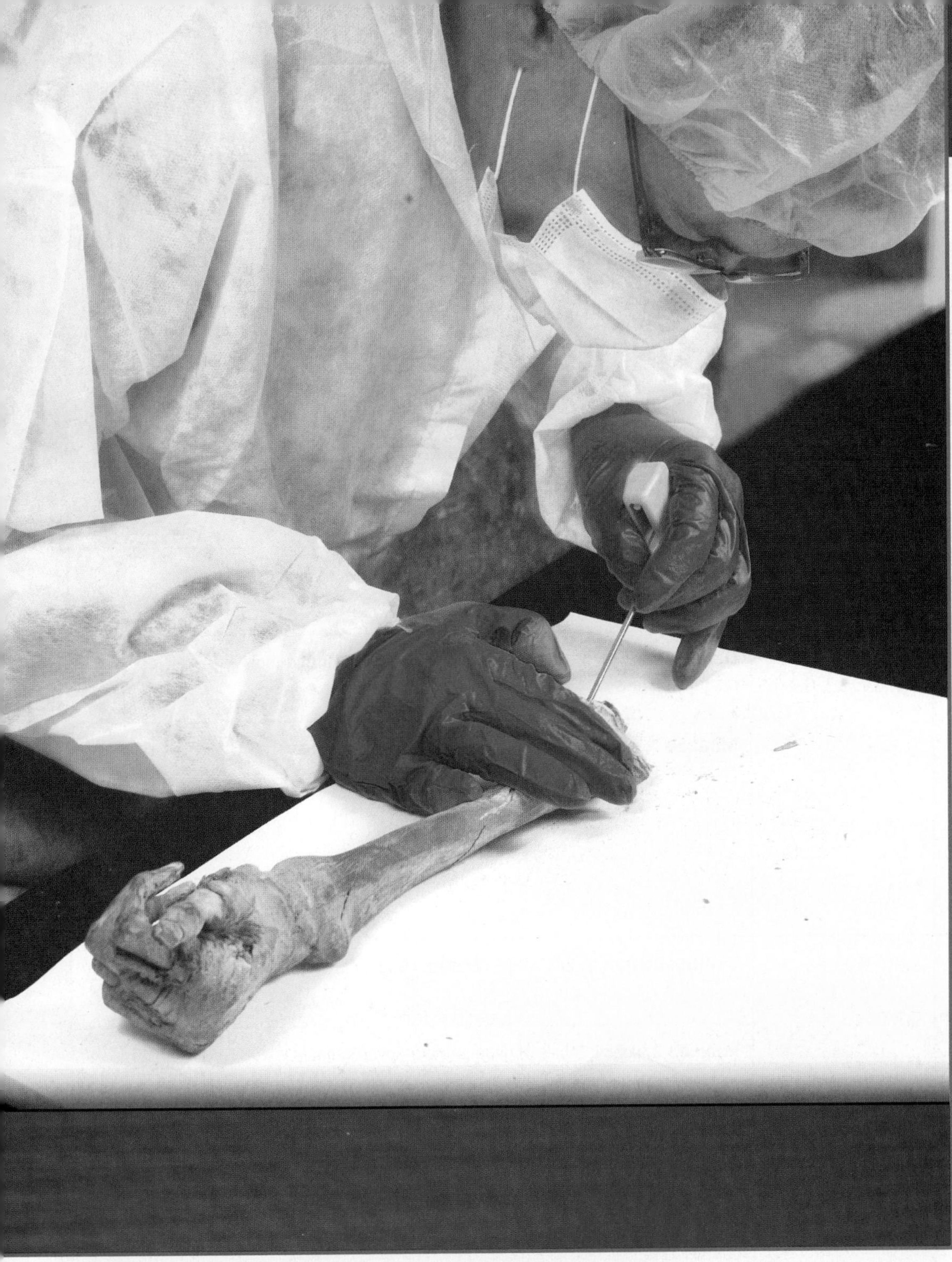

Misconceptions

In each section, *Clarify a Misconception* provides you with the information to dispel a common student misconception. A question will help you elicit the misconception, and an explanation will help you correct it.

Below is a preview of misconceptions from each chapter in this unit.

Before studying Chapter 10, students might think that more complex organisms will have more chromosomes than less complex organisms. Chapter 10 will explain that there is no known correlation between number of chromosomes and complexity (p. 270).

Before studying Chapter 11, students might think that shared traits mean that they inherited more genes from one parent than from the other. Chapter 11 will explain that an offspring inherits equal amounts of genetic material from each parent (p. 296).

Before studying Chapter 12, students might think that different types of cells, such as muscle cells and neurons, have different types of DNA. Chapter 12 will explain that every body cell contains the same genes but different cell types have different types of genes turned on and turned off (p. 344).

Before studying Chapter 13, students might think that pure breeds are "better" or more advantaged than mixed breeds. Chapter 13 will explain that pure breeds might actually be at a disadvantage due to lack of genetic diversity (p. 361).

SERVICE LEARNING/COMMUNITY SERVICE

Genetic Disorders Have students contact a program that conducts activities for people with genetic disorders, such as the Special Olympics. The students can volunteer to help with one of the activities. These students will be exposed to the human face of genetic disorders and the impact of the disorders on individuals and their families. Students can share with the class what they learned about interacting with people who are different from themselves, how they learned to work as a team, or how their experience helped them prepare for a job or a career (Zeldin and Tarlov, 1997).

Research bibliography on pages 32T–34T

Chapter 10 Organizer:
Sexual Reproduction and Genetics

Essential Questions	National Science Standards	Materials and Planning: Estimated times include cleanup and disposal, but do not include teacher prep time. For cleanup and disposal guidelines, see page 39T.	Est. Time (min)
Section 1 1. How does the reduction in chromosome number occur during meiosis? 2. What are the stages of meiosis? 3. What is the importance of meiosis in providing genetic variation?	UCP.1–3; A.1, A.2; C.1, C,2; E.1, E.2; F.6; G.1, G.2	**Launch Lab,** p. 268: clay, pop beads, pipe cleaners	20
		Demonstration, p. 272: two pairs of tennis shoes, two pairs of sandals	10
		Activity, p. 275: bags of kidney beans or white beans	20
Section 2 1. What is the significance of Mendel's experiments to the study of genetics? 2. What is the law of segregation and law of independent assortment? 3. What are the possible offspring from a cross using a Punnett square?	UCP.1–3, UCP.5; A.1, A.2; G.1, G.2, G.3	**Demonstration,** p. 279: lily or other large flower, cutting tool, magnifying lens	15
		MiniLab 1, p. 281: pictures of free and attached earlobes	25
Section 3 1. How does the process of meiosis produce genetic recombination? 2. How can gene linkage be used to create chromosome maps? 3. Why is polyploidy important to the field of agriculture?	UCP.1–3, UCP.5; A.1, A.2; C.1, C,2; G.1, G.2	**Demonstration,** p. 283: strips of colored paper with light and dark shades	15
		MiniLab 2, p. 284: tables of gene-pair crossover frequency	25
		Design Your Own BioLab, p. 287: two groups of plant seeds, potting soil, small flowerpots or other growing containers, watering can or bottle, small gardening trowel	45

Suggested Time for Each Lesson

Class	Chapter Opener	Section 1	Section 2	Section 3	Assessment
Basic	45 min	90 min	45 min	90 min	45 min
General	25 min	55 min	45 min	55 min	45 min
Honors	5 min	115 min	115 min	60 min	65 min

ConnectED

connectED.mcgraw-hill.com

Access interactive learning opportunities and teaching resources using these icons located throughout your StudentWorks™ Plus Online and eTeacherEdition Online.

Chapter 10 Section Resources	Additional Chapter 10 Resources	Technology
FAST FILE Unit 3 Resources: Launch Lab Worksheet* Study Guide (English/Spanish)* Section Quick Check **Reading Essentials 10.1** **Science Notebook 10.1*** **FAST FILE Unit 3 Resources:** MiniLab Worksheet* Study Guide (English/Spanish)* Section Quick Check **Reading Essentials 10.2** **Science Notebook 10.2*** **FAST FILE Unit 3 Resources:** MiniLab Worksheet* BioLab Worksheet* Study Guide (English/Spanish)* Section Quick Check **Reading Essentials 10.3** **Science Notebook 10.3***	**FAST FILE Unit 3 Resources:** Chapter Diagnostic Test Concept Mapping* Real-World Biology Enrichment Chapter Tests A, B, and C **Transparencies:** Bellringer Transparencies* Biology Concepts Transparencies* **Lab Resources:** Laboratory Manual* Probeware Lab Manual* Forensics Lab Manual* Pre-AP Lab Manual* Open Inquiry in Biology* Guided Inquiry in Biology*	**Teaching Tools:** eTeacherEdition Online Classroom Presentation Toolkit CD-ROM* LabManager™ CD-ROM* Video Lab DVD* Virtual Lab CD-ROM* What's BIOLOGY Got To Do With It? StudentWorks™ Plus Online* **Chapter Assessment Tools:** Classroom Presentation Toolkit CD-ROM* *ExamView® Assessment Suite* CD-ROM **Web-Based Resources:** • StudentWorks™ Plus Online • eTeacherEdition Online • Animations* • The Interactive Time Line* • Interactive Tables* • Online Quizzes • Online Test Practice • Standardized Test Practice • Virtual Labs* • Multilingual eGlossary* • Vocabulary eGames* • Vocabulary eFlashcards • WebQuests • Personal Tutors

While all resources listed are appropriate for English learners, the * indicates resources with a strong visual or hands-on component for EL.

Teaching strategies and activities have been coded for differentiated instruction.

AL Activities for students working above grade level	**OL** Activities for students working on grade level	**BL** Activities for students working below grade level	**EL** Activities for English learners (also ELL)	**COOP LEARN** Activities designed for small cooperative group work

CHAPTER 10

Launch Lab
What would happen without meosis?

Inquiry Launch Lab

For a lab worksheet, use your eTeacherEdition Online.

RUBRIC A rubric for evaluating Launch Labs is found on your eTeacherEdition Online.

Est. Time 20 min

Additional Materials Provide each student with enough clay, pop beads, paper cutouts, or pipe cleaners to make four chromosomes.

Teaching Strategy Make sure students realize that the procedure here (mitosis and then fertilization) is not the way in which organisms sexually reproduce. Organisms must reduce the chromosome number through meiosis.

Procedure

1. Read and complete the lab safety form.
2. Construct a data table with the headings *Cycle Number, Stage,* and *Chromosome Number.*
3. Fill in your data table for steps 4-5.
4. Model a cell with a pair of chromosomes.
5. Demonstrate mitosis.
6. Fuse one of your cells with another student's cell.
7. Repeat steps 4-5 two more times, recording the second and third cycles.

Analysis

1. **Summarize** how the chromosome number in your model changes with each cycle of mitosis and fusion. After each cycle of mitosis and fusion, the chromosome number in the cell doubles.
2. **Infer** what must occur when cells fuse in order for the chromosome number to remain constant. In order to maintain the chromosome number, a reduction in the number of chromosomes needs to occur in the cell prior to fertilization.

Sample Data

Cycle Number	Stage	Chromosome Number
1	Mitosis	2
1	Interphase	2
1	Fertilization	4
2	Mitosis	4
2	Interphase	4
2	Fertilization	8
3	Mitosis	8
3	Interphase	8
3	Fertilization	16

CHAPTER 10
Sexual Reproduction and Genetics

ConnectED

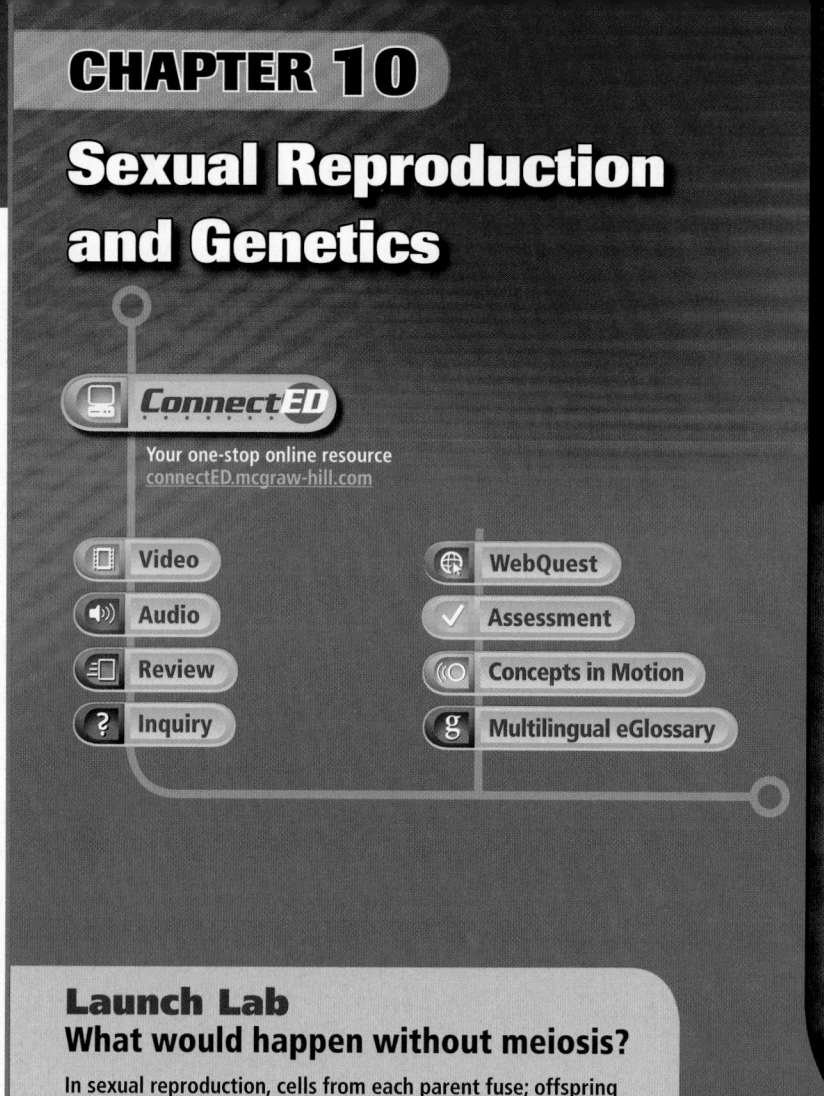

Your one-stop online resource
connectED.mcgraw-hill.com

- Video
- Audio
- Review
- Inquiry
- WebQuest
- Assessment
- Concepts in Motion
- Multilingual eGlossary

Launch Lab
What would happen without meiosis?

In sexual reproduction, cells from each parent fuse; offspring have the same chromosome number as the parents. Explore what would happen to the chromosome number if mitosis were the only type of cell division.

For a lab worksheet, use your StudentWorks™ Plus Online.

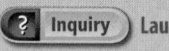

Inquiry Launch Lab

FOLDABLES®

Make a circle foldable using the titles shown. Use it to organize your notes on meiosis.

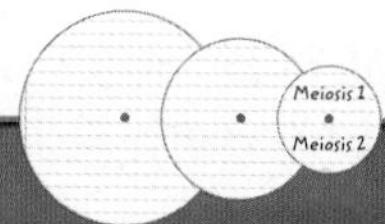

THEME FOCUS Diversity
The process of meiosis leads to genetic diversity.

BIG Idea Reproductive cells, which pass on genetic traits from the parents to the child, are produced by the process of meiosis.

Section 1 • Meiosis
Section 2 • Mendelian Genetics
Section 3 • Gene Linkage and Polyploidy

Introduce the Chapter

Elephant Life Cycle

ASK STUDENTS: ***Based on the life cycle illustrated on this page, if the chromosome number is to remain the same from generation to generation, how many sets of chromosomes must sex cells have before they combine?*** The number of chromosomes in sex cells must be half of the original body cell, so that when they combine, the chromosome number will not change.

BIG Idea

Demonstration Form a jumbled pile of socks. Include two pairs of each different type of sock in two different colors. For example, tube socks with a yellow band and tube socks with a blue band, a yellow pair of ankle crew socks and a blue pair of ankle crew socks, etc.
ASK STUDENTS: ***If your socks came out of the dryer all jumbled up, what features could you use to sort them into pairs?***
Possible answer: The socks could be sorted by color, shape, size, and type of material. Explain that the chromosomes in an animal's body also occur in pairs. During the metaphase I stage of meiosis, similar pairs of chromosomes line up along the equatorial plane.

THEMES

Scientific Inquiry Mendel's studies of pea plants were the beginning of the field of genetics.

Diversity Genetic recombination leads to huge genetic diversity possibilities.

Energy Cells use energy as they go through cell divisions in mitosis and meiosis.

Homeostasis Haploid cells all have the same number of chromosomes at the end of meiosis.

Change The number of chromosomes changes to half the original number by the end of meiosis.

Section 1

MAIN Idea

BL OL AL

Activate Prior Knowledge

List the following terms on the board: *chromosome, microtubules, spindle fibers, nucleus,* and *nucleolus.*

ASK STUDENTS: ***How are these cell parts involved in mitosis?*** Chromosomes are structures made of DNA and protein, and contain segments called genes. Spindle fibers are involved in moving chromosomes to the poles of the cell. The nucleus is the portion of a eukaryotic cell that contains the chromosomes. The nucleolus is a portion of the nucleus that manufactures ribosomes.

EL Have students illustrate the terms and then match each term to these statements: 1. contains the chromosomes; 2. made of DNA and protein and contains genes; 3. makes ribosomes; 4. moves chromosomes to poles of cell. 1 = nucleus; 2 = chromosomes; 3 = nucleolus; 4 = spindle fibers

D Develop Concepts

BL OL AL

Clarify a Misconception

ASK STUDENTS: ***Do you think an organism with 1200 chromosomes would be more complex than one with 46 chromosomes?*** Answers will vary, but the correct answer is no. Some students think that the number of chromosomes an organism has is a reflection of the complexity of the organism. There is no known connection between the number of chromosomes and complexity. For example, ferns have 1200 chromosomes while humans have just 46.

Section 1

Reading Preview

Essential Questions

- How does the reduction in chromosome number occur during meiosis?
- What are the stages of meiosis?
- What is the importance of meiosis in providing genetic variation?

Review Vocabulary

chromosome: cellular structure that contains DNA

New Vocabulary

gene
homologous chromosome
gamete
haploid
fertilization
diploid
meiosis
crossing over

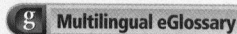

g Multilingual eGlossary

Meiosis

MAIN Idea **Meiosis produces haploid gametes.**

Real-World Reading Link Look around your biology class. You might notice that the students in your class do not look the same. They might be different heights and have different eye color, hair color, and other features. This variety of characteristics is a result of two sex cells combining during sexual reproduction.

D Chromosomes and Chromosome Number

Each student in your biology class has characteristics passed on to them by their parents. Each characteristic, such as hair color, height, or eye color, is called a trait. The instructions for each trait are located on chromosomes, which are found in the nucleus of cells. The DNA on chromosomes is arranged in segments called **genes** that control the production of proteins. Each chromosome consists of hundreds of genes, each gene playing an important role in determining the characteristics and functions of the cell.

Homologous chromosomes Human body cells have 46 chromosomes. Each parent contributes 23 chromosomes, resulting in 23 pairs of chromosomes. The chromosomes that make up a pair, one chromosome from each parent, are called **homologous chromosomes.** As shown in **Figure 1,** homologous chromosomes in body cells have the same length and the same centromere position, and they carry genes that control the same inherited traits. For instance, the gene for earlobe type will be located at the same position on both homologous chromosomes. Although these genes each code for earlobe type, they might not code for the exact same type of earlobe.

■ **Figure 1** Homologous chromosomes carry genes for any given trait at the same location. The genes that code for earlobe type might not code for the exact same type of earlobe.

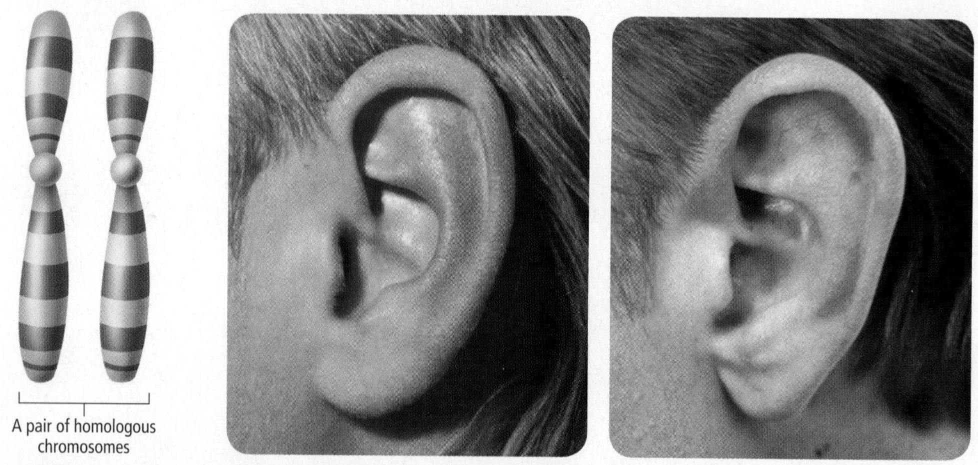

Content Background

Giant Chromosomes of Drosophila In the salivary glands of Drosophila larva, the chromosomes go through ten rounds of replication without going through cell division. The sister chromatids do not separate and consist of 2^{10} or 1024 DNA molecules hooked together. When these cells are stained, dense dark bands alternate with lighter bands. Each chromosome has a distinct banding pattern. These chromosomes, called polytene chromosomes, are useful in genetic research and chromosome mapping. These chromosomes have also been used to study the relationship between chromosome structure and gene activity.

Haploid and diploid cells In order to maintain the same chromosome number from generation to generation, an organism produces **gametes,** which are sex cells that have half the number of chromosomes. Although the number of chromosomes varies from one species to another, in humans each gamete contains 23 chromosomes. The symbol n can be used to represent the number of chromosomes in a gamete. A cell with n number of chromosomes is called a **haploid** cell. Haploid comes from the Greek word *haploos,* meaning *single.*

The process by which one haploid gamete combines with another haploid gamete is called **fertilization.** As a result of fertilization, the cell now will contain a total of $2n$ chromosomes—n chromosomes from the female parent plus n chromosomes from the male parent. A cell that contains $2n$ number of chromosomes is called a **diploid** cell.

Notice that n also describes the number of pairs of chromosomes in an organism. When two human gametes combine, 23 pairs of homologous chromosomes are formed.

R Meiosis I

Gametes are formed during a process called **meiosis,** which is a type of cell division that reduces the number of chromosomes; therefore, it is referred to as a reduction division. Meiosis occurs in the reproductive structures of organisms that reproduce sexually. While mitosis maintains the chromosome number, meiosis reduces the chromosome number by half through the separation of homologous chromosomes. A cell with $2n$ number of chromosomes will have gametes with n number of chromosomes after meiosis, as illustrated in **Figure 2.** Meiosis involves two consecutive cell divisions called meiosis I and meiosis II.

FOLDABLES® Incorporate information from this section into your Foldable.

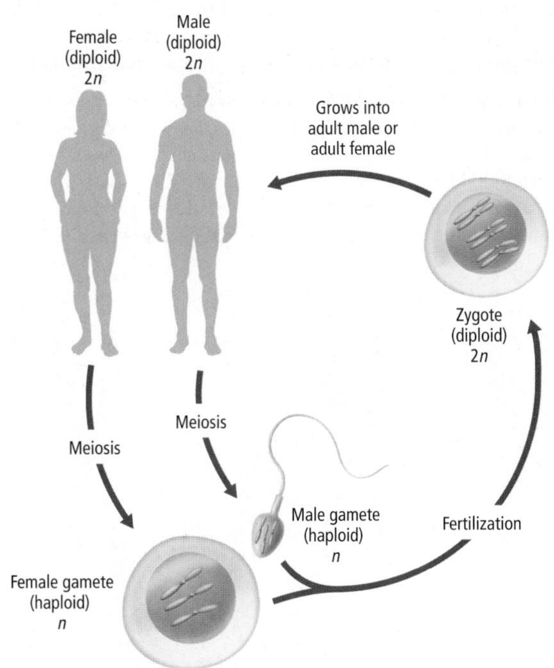

S

Figure 2 The sexual life cycle in animals involves meiosis, which produces gametes. When gametes combine in fertilization, the number of chromosomes is restored.
Describe *what happens to the number of chromosomes during meiosis.*

R Reading Strategy

EL BL OL SQ3R Have students do the five-step SQ3R as they read through the steps of Meiosis I and II. They should first **S**urvey the section focusing on the headings, then write **Q**uestions about the key concepts. Next, they should **R**ead the section, make notes that relate to the questions, **R**ecite the vocabulary, and **R**eview for meaning.

S Skill Practice

OL AL Make a Diagram Have students draw the general reproduction cycle of a cell that has six chromosomes. Have students indicate the stages in the life cycle that are $2n$ and the stages that are n. Answers should be similar to the life cycle shown in Figure 2.

FOLDABLES®

RUBRIC A rubric for evaluating Foldables is found on your eTeacherEdition Online.

Going Further

SAY TO STUDENTS: ***On the back of this Foldable, write the phase of mitosis that is similar to each stage of meiosis and compare and contrast mitosis and meiosis.***

Caption Question Fig. 2 The number of chromosomes is halved during meiosis.

Differentiated Instruction

English Learners English learners may need more guidance when starting activities. These students will benefit when instructions are stated in a step-by-step manner and written on the board.

For more tips, see pages 14T–15T.

Critical Thinking

BL OL AL Predict

ASK STUDENTS: ***Where in a frog could you find 2n or diploid number of chromosomes?*** all nonsex cells ***Where could you find n or haploid chromosomes?*** sperm or egg cells

D Develop Concepts

BL OL AL Scaffolding

ASK STUDENTS: ***What type of cell division produces sex cells?*** meiosis ***How many chromosomes will there be in the gametes of an organism with 18 body-cell chromosomes?*** 9 ***Compare the daughter cells of mitosis and meiosis.*** The daughter cells of mitosis are identical; the daughter cells of meiosis are not identical due to independent assortment and crossing over. ***What would happen if the sister chromatids of one pair did not separate during anaphase II?*** One gamete would end up with one extra chromosome and one gamete would end up with one less chromosome. Point out that this is one way in which Down syndrome (trisomy of chromosome 21) can occur.

Writing Support

OL Informal Writing Have students write a letter from a cell's point of view about the changes that happen to its chromosomes during meiosis. Have them include the words *anaphase, telophase, chromatids,* and *random.* Possible answer: Chromosome pairs align in a random fashion, and the pairs split during anaphase I. Each member of the pair consists of two chromatids. As a result, one of each pair is found at the poles during telophase I.

■ **Caption Question Fig. 4** the bottom right segment of the chromosome on the left and the bottom left segment of the chromosome on the right

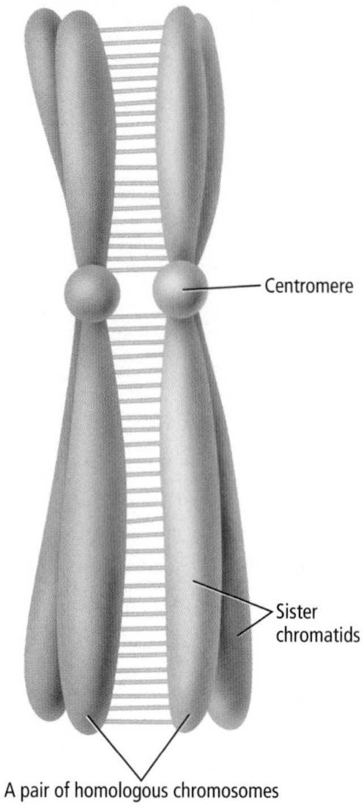

■ **Figure 3** The homologous chromosomes are physically bound together during synapsis in prophase I.

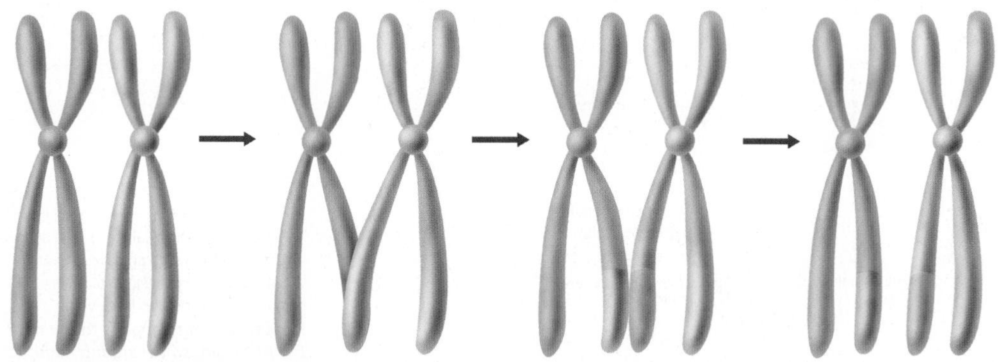

■ **Figure 4** The results of crossing over are new combinations of genes.
Determine ***which chromatids exchanged genetic material.***

Interphase Recall that the cell cycle includes interphase prior to mitosis. Cells that undergo meiosis also go through interphase as part of the cell cycle. Cells in interphase carry out various metabolic processes, including the replication of DNA and the synthesis of proteins.

Prophase I As a cell enters prophase I, the replicated chromosomes become visible. As in mitosis, the replicated chromosomes consist of two sister chromatids. As the homologous chromosomes condense, they begin to form pairs in a process called synapsis. The homologous chromosomes are held tightly together along their lengths, as illustrated in **Figure 3.** Notice that in **Figure 4** the pink and green chromosomes have exchanged segments. This exchange occurs during synapsis. **Crossing over** is a process during which chromosomal segments are exchanged between a pair of homologous chromosomes.

As prophase I continues, centrioles move to the cell's opposite poles. Spindle fibers form and bind to the sister chromatids at the centromere.

Metaphase I In the next phase of meiosis, the pairs of homologous chromosomes line up at the equator of the cell, as illustrated in **Figure 5.** In meiosis, the spindle fibers attach to the centromere of each homologous chromosome. Recall that during metaphase in mitosis, the individual chromosomes, which consist of two sister chromatids, line up at the cell's equator. During metaphase I of meiosis, the homologous chromosomes line up as pairs at the cell's equator. This is an important distinction between mitosis and meiosis.

Anaphase I During anaphase I, the homologous chromosomes separate, which is also illustrated in **Figure 5.** Each member of the pair is guided by spindle fibers and moves toward opposite poles of the cell. The chromosome number is reduced from $2n$ to n when the homologous chromosomes separate. Recall that in mitosis, the sister chromatids split during anaphase. During anaphase I of meiosis, however, each homologous chromosome still consists of two sister chromatids. D

Telophase I The homologous chromosomes, consisting of two sister chromatids, reach the cell's opposite poles. Each pole contains only one member of the original pair of homologous chromosomes. Notice in **Figure 5** that each chromosome still consists of two sister chromatids joined at the centromere. The sister chromatids might not be identical because crossing over might have occurred during synapsis in prophase I.

Demonstration

OL AL Meiosis Bring in two pairs of tennis shoes and two pairs of sandals. Each pair represents a pair of chromatids. Place one shoe of each pair on the floor.
ASK STUDENTS: ***What happens to the chromosomes (represented by the shoes) before the cell goes into prophase I?*** The chromosomes double. Place the other member of the pair next to its matching shoe. ***What happens to the chromosomes during metaphase I?*** The pairs line up. Line up the two pairs of tennis shoes together and line up the other four shoes together. Continue with the meiotic stages until you have four pairs consisting of one tennis shoe and one sandal. Est. time: 10 min

Visualizing Meiosis

D Figure 5

Follow along the stages of meiosis I and meiosis II, beginning with interphase at the left.

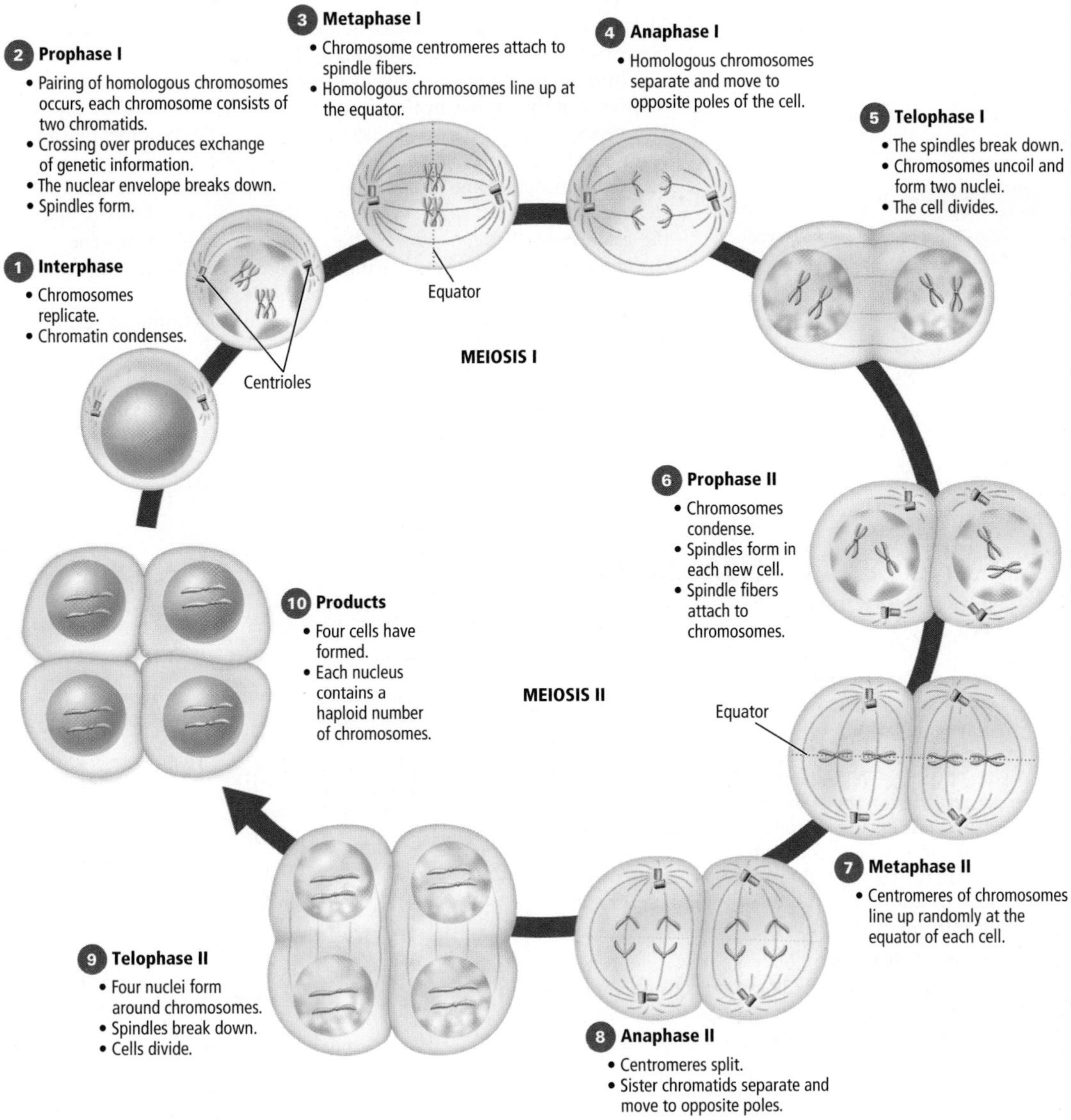

• Spindles form.

• The spindles break down.

• Spindles form in each new cell.

10 Products
• Four cells have formed.

• Four nuclei form around chromosomes.
• Spindles break down.

Concepts in Motion Animation

Research Citation

Hands-On Activities Educational research indicates that activities such as the meiosis activity described on this page provide valuable hands-on experience for students. These experiences can result in a higher level of interest and achievement.

(Wood and Turner-Vorbeck, 2001)

Research bibliography on pages 32T–34T

Visualizing Meiosis

Purpose

Students will understand the stages of meiosis and the important characteristics of each phase. A.2, C.1, C.2, C.5, G.2

D Develop Concepts

EL BL OL COOP LEARN

Activity Divide students into eight small groups. Assign each group one of the eight stages of meiosis for a cell that has a $2n$ chromosome number of 10. Have available yarn pieces in two colors (representing mother and father) cut to different lengths. Students should use a different length for each pair of chromosomes. Have students determine how many pieces of yarn of each length they need to represent their cell and then glue the yarn onto construction paper. Once each group is finished with their assigned stage, have groups line up to where the stages are presented in order. A spokesperson for each group can summarize what is happening in their assigned stage.

AL Have each group do all eight stages.

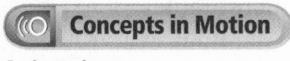

Concepts in Motion

Animation

During telophase I, cytokinesis usually occurs, forming a furrow by pinching in animal cells and by forming a cell plate in plant cells. Following cytokinesis, the cells may go into interphase again before the second set of divisions. However, the DNA is not replicated again during this interphase. In some species, the chromosomes uncoil, the nuclear membrane reappears, and nuclei re-form during telophase I. **D**

Meiosis II

Meiosis is only halfway completed at the end of meiosis I. During prophase II, a second set of phases begins as the spindle apparatus forms and the chromosomes condense. During metaphase II, the chromosomes are positioned at the equator by the spindle fibers, as shown in **Figure 5.** During metaphase of mitosis, a diploid number of chromosomes line up at the equator. During metaphase II of meiosis, however, a haploid number of chromosomes line up at the equator. During anaphase II, the sister chromatids are pulled apart at the centromere by the spindle fibers, and the sister chromatids move toward the opposite poles of the cell. The chromosomes reach the poles during telophase II, and the nuclear membrane and nuclei reform. At the end of meiosis II, cytokinesis occurs, resulting in four haploid cells, each with n number of chromosomes, as illustrated in **Figure 5.**

Reading Check **Infer** Why are the two phases of meiosis important for gamete formation?

CAREERS IN BIOLOGY

Medical Geneticist A medical geneticist researches how diseases are inherited, how to diagnose genetic conditions, and treatments for genetic diseases.

Inquiry Launch Lab

Review Based on what you have read about meiosis, how would you now answer the analysis questions?

DATA ANALYSIS LAB 1

Based on Real Data*

Draw Conclusions

How do motor proteins affect cell division? Many scientists think that motor proteins play an important role in the movement of chromosomes in both mitosis and meiosis. To test this hypothesis, researchers have produced yeast that cannot make the motor protein called Kar3p. They also have produced yeast that cannot make the motor protein called Cik1p, which many think moderates the function of Kar3p. The results of their experiment are shown in the graph to the right.

Think Critically

1. **Evaluate** whether Cik1p seems to be important for yeast meiosis. Explain.
2. **Assess** whether Kar3p seems to be necessary for yeast meiosis. Explain.
3. **Conclude** whether all motor proteins seem to play a vital role in meiosis. Explain.

Data and Observations

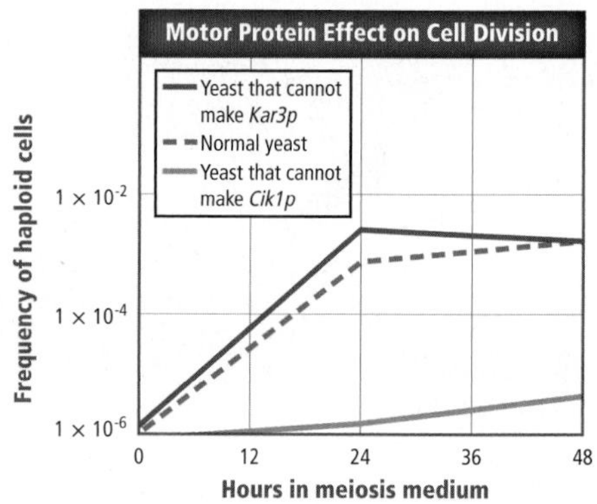

*Data obtained from: Shanks, et al. 2001. The Kar3-Interacting protein Cik1p plays a critical role in passage through meiosis I in *Saccharomyces cerevisiae*. *Genetics* 159: 939-951.

Inquiry Launch Lab

Assess Content Development
Assess how understanding has developed when students revisit the Launch Lab analysis questions.

D Develop Concepts

BL OL AL

Clarify a Misconception

ASK STUDENTS: *How many sets of chromosomes does each new cell contain after meiosis I?* one Students often have difficulty with the concept of chromosome reduction division occurring only during meiosis I. Emphasize that reduction division occurs only in meiosis I and that meiosis II is not a reduction division.

DATA ANALYSIS LAB 1

About the Lab

- Yeast cells without a functioning Kar3 gene arrest in prophase I. The protein product of Cik1 appears to play a role in homologous chromosome recombination in yeast cells and the formation of gametes. These proteins are thought to play a role in controlling the activity of the Kar3 gene. The Kar3 gene is thought to be important in the depolymerization of microtubules.
- Also see Manning, et al. 1999. Differential regulation of the Kar3p kinesin-related protein by two associated proteins, Cik1p and Vik1p. *Journal of Cell Biology* 144: 1219–1233.

Think Critically

1. Yes. The yeast that cannot make Cik1p produces far fewer haploid cells.
2. No. Cells without ability to make Kar3p still make haploid cells.
3. No. Of the two major proteins tested, Kar3p does not appear to play a role in meiosis.

Reading Check Answers will vary but should include the necessity of the chromosome number dividing by two in preparation for fertilization.

The Importance of Meiosis

Table 1 shows a comparison of mitosis and meiosis. Recall that mitosis consists of only one set of division phases and produces two identical diploid daughter cells. Meiosis, however, consists of two sets of divisions and produces four haploid daughter cells that are not identical. Meiosis is important because it results in genetic variation.

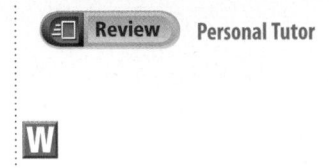

Review Personal Tutor

Table 1 **Mitosis and Meiosis** — **Concepts in Motion** Interactive Table

Mitosis	Meiosis
One division occurs during mitosis.	Two sets of divisions occur during meiosis: meiosis I and meiosis II.
DNA replication occurs during interphase.	DNA replication occurs once before meiosis I.
Synapsis of homologous chromosomes does not occur.	Synapsis of homologous chromosomes occurs during prophase I.
Two identical cells are formed per cell cycle.	Four haploid cells (*n*) are formed per cell cycle.
The daughter cells are genetically identical.	The daughter cells are not genetically identical because of crossing over.
Mitosis occurs only in body cells.	Meiosis occurs only in reproductive cells.
Mitosis is involved in growth and repair.	Meiosis is involved in the production of gametes and providing genetic variation in organisms.

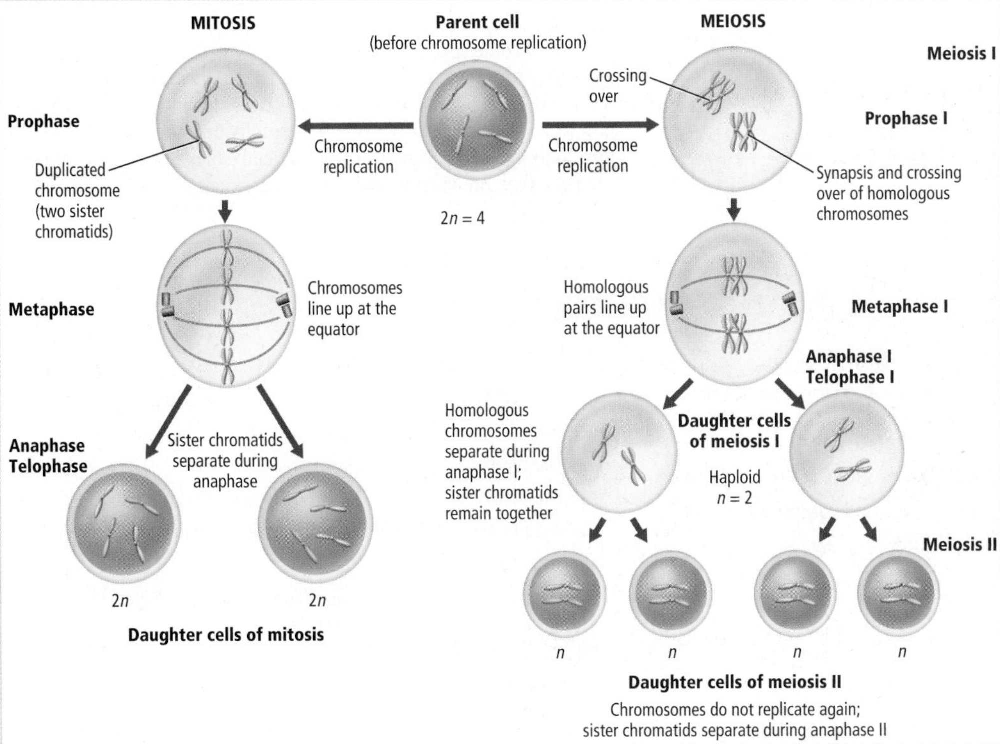

S Skill Practice

BL OL AL Visual Literacy Have students use one of the items from Table 1, such as daughter cells, to create an illustration that demonstrates the difference between mitosis and meiosis.

Review

Personal Tutor

Listen to a teacher explain variation.

Concepts in Motion

Interactive Table

W Writing Support

BL OL AL Creative Writing

Propose to students the fictional idea that scientists have proposed to end the process of meiosis. Have students write a position paper that either supports the scientists' idea or opposes it.

Skill Practice

BL OL AL Make a Table Have students make a chart of the events that occur during meiosis. Have them label the columns with the phases of meiosis and the rows with the cell parts: *nucleus, nucleolus, chromosomes* and *spindle fibers.* Then have them draw and label the phases of meiosis.

Activity

BL OL AL COOP LEARN Variation To demonstrate variation within offspring, bring in a bag of kidney beans or white beans, which are seeds. Divide students into groups and give each group about 20–30 beans. Have students accurately measure the length of the beans in mm. Have students prepare a bar graph of the length of the beans. Students will see that even among beans that look similar, there is a variety of lengths. Other features such as mass or width could also be measured. Interested students could germinate the beans to see if size has anything to do with viability.
Est. time: 20 min

D Develop Concepts

OL BL

Clarify a Misconception

Students often having difficulty distinguishing between sexual and asexual reproduction and the origins of variation.

ASK STUDENTS: ***What is the source of variations among puppies in a litter?*** Some students may attribute variation, such as size, only to environmental factors, such as amount of food available. Discuss alleles, independent assortment, crossing over, and environmental factors. Remind students that reproduction involving eggs, sperm, or pollen is sexual reproduction and produces a new "mix" of genes in the offspring; asexual reproduction does not.

Formative Assessment

Evaluation Using slides or pictures of various meiotic stages, show students the stages out of order. Have students identify the stage and write down how they knew it was that particular stage. Have them check their answers.

Remediation Have students make flash cards for the various phases of meiosis. Have students draw the phase on one side of the card, and on the other side have them write the phase and the features that identify it.

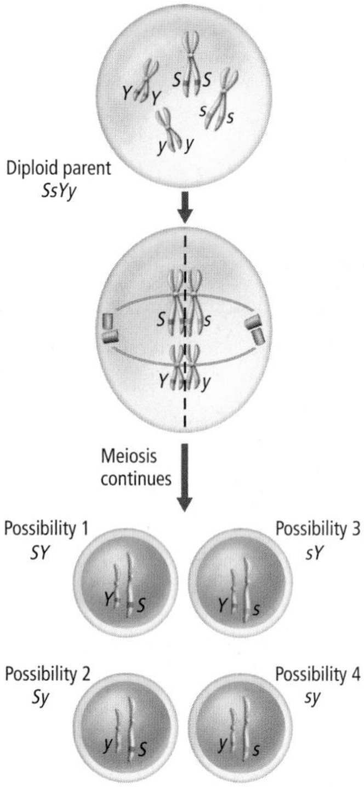

Figure 6 The order in which the homologous pairs line up explains how a variety of sex cells can be produced.

Meiosis provides variation Recall that pairs of homologous chromosomes line up at the equator during prophase I. How the chromosomes line up at the equator is a random process that results in gametes with different combinations of chromosomes, such as the ones in **Figure 6.** Depending on how the chromosomes line up at the equator, four gametes with four different combinations of chromosomes can result.

Notice that the first possibility shows which chromosomes were on the same side of the equator and therefore traveled together. Different combinations of chromosomes were lined up on the same side of the equator to produce the gametes in the second possibility. Genetic variation also is produced during crossing over and during fertilization, when gametes randomly combine.

Sexual Reproduction v. Asexual Reproduction

Some organisms reproduce by asexual reproduction, while others reproduce by sexual reproduction. The life cycles of still other organisms might involve both asexual and sexual reproduction. During asexual reproduction, the organism inherits all of its chromosomes from a single parent. Therefore, the new individual is genetically identical to its parent. Bacteria reproduce asexually, whereas most protists reproduce both asexually and sexually, depending on environmental conditions. Most plants and many of the more simple animals can reproduce both asexually and sexually, compared to more advanced animals that reproduce only sexually.

Why do some species reproduce sexually while others reproduce asexually? Recent studies with fruit flies have shown that the rate of accumulation of beneficial mutations is faster when species reproduce sexually than when they reproduce asexually. In other words, when reproduction occurs sexually, the beneficial genes multiply faster over time than they do when reproduction is asexual. D

Section 1 Assessment

Section Summary

- DNA replication takes place only once during meiosis, and it results in four haploid gametes.
- Meiosis consists of two sets of divisions.
- Meiosis produces genetic variation in gametes.

Understand Main Ideas

1. MAIN Idea **Analyze** how meiosis produces haploid gametes.
2. **Indicate** how metaphase I is different from metaphase in mitosis.
3. **Describe** how synapsis occurs.
4. **Diagram** a cell with four chromosomes going through meiosis.
5. **Assess** how meiosis contributes to genetic variation, while mitosis does not.

Think Critically

6. **Compare and contrast** mitosis and meiosis, using **Figure 5** and **Table 1,** by creating a Venn diagram.

WRITING in Biology

7. Imagine you are a chromosome going through meiosis. Describe what happens to you and the other chromosomes.

Section 1 Assessment

1. Through reduction division, each gamete contains half the numbers of chromosomes.
2. Metaphase I: homologous pairs line up; Metaphase of mitosis: individual chromosomes of two sister chromatids line up.
3. Homologous chromosomes are physically bound together during synapsis in prophase I.
4. Diagrams should demonstrate understanding of how chromosomes line up in meiosis I and II. Diagrams should show four chromosomes in each of the two daughter cells at the end of meiosis I and two chromosomes in each of the four daughter cells at the end of meiosis II.
5. During meiosis, the independent assortment of the pairs of chromosomes and crossing over provide a large amount of genetic variation. Mitosis produces identical cells.
6. Diagrams should reflect similarities and differences.
7. Answers will vary but should be narrative in nature and describe the processes involved in meiosis and the possible outcomes of the process.

Assessment Online Quiz

Reading Preview

Essential Questions

- What is the significance of Mendel's experiments to the study of genetics?
- What is the law of segregation and the law of independent assortment?
- What are the possible offspring from a cross using a Punnett square?

Review Vocabulary

segregation: the separation of allelic genes that typically occurs during meiosis

New Vocabulary

genetics
allele
dominant
recessive
homozygous
heterozygous
genotype
phenotype
law of segregation
hybrid
law of independent assortment

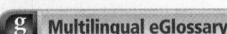

Multilingual eGlossary

■ **Figure 7** Gregor Mendel is known as the father of genetics.

Mendelian Genetics

MAIN Idea Mendel explained how a dominant allele can mask the presence of a recessive allele.

Real-World Reading Link There are many different breeds of dogs, such as Labrador retrievers, dachshunds, German shepherds, and poodles. You might like a certain breed of dog because of its height, coat color, and general appearance. These traits are passed from generation to generation.

How Genetics Began

In 1866, Gregor Mendel, an Austrian monk and a plant breeder, published his findings on the method of inheritance in garden pea plants. The passing of traits to the next generation is called inheritance, or heredity. Mendel, shown in **Figure 7,** was successful in sorting out the mystery of inheritance because of the organism he chose for his study—the pea plant. Pea plants are true-breeding, meaning that they consistently produce offspring with only one form of a trait.

Pea plants usually reproduce by self-fertilization. A common occurrence in many flowering plants, self-fertilization occurs when a male gamete within a flower combines with a female gamete in the same flower. Mendel also discovered that pea plants could easily be cross-pollinated by hand. Mendel performed cross-pollination by transferring a male gamete from the flower of one pea plant to the female reproductive organ in a flower of another pea plant.

Connection to History Mendel rigorously followed various traits in the pea plants he bred. He analyzed the results of his experiments and formed hypotheses concerning how the traits were inherited. The study of **genetics,** which is the science of heredity, began with Mendel, who is regarded as the father of genetics.

Reading Check **Infer** why it is important that Mendel's experiments used a true-breeding plant. **D**

The Inheritance of Traits

Mendel noticed that certain varieties of garden pea plants produced specific forms of a trait, generation after generation. For instance, he noticed that some varieties always produced green seeds and others always produced yellow seeds. In order to understand how these traits are inherited, Mendel performed cross-pollination by transferring male gametes from the flower of a true-breeding green-seed plant to the female organ of a flower from a true-breeding yellow-seed plant. To prevent self-fertilization, Mendel removed the male organs from the flower of the yellow-seed plant. Mendel called the green-seed plant and the yellow-seed plant the parent generation—also known as the P generation.

Section 2

MAIN Idea

BL OL AL Genetic Traits
ASK STUDENTS: ***Do all dogs look alike? What types of features indicate a particular breed?*** Dog breeds vary in many ways: color, size, shape, length and color of hairs, hair patterns, etc. ***Are these features inherited?*** The features are inherited by all of the dogs of that particular breed. ***Can you tell individuals within a breed apart?*** Individuals of a particular breed can be recognized by their unique characteristics. ***What does this tell you about the inheritance of these features?*** The inheritance of these traits varies within the breed. Remind students that all dogs belong to the same species, *Canis familiaris,* but there are different breeds within the species.

D Develop Concepts

EL BL OL Activity Have students plant seeds to represent Mendel's experiments. Use Wisconsin Fast plants in the genus *Brassia,* which flower in about 14 days. Seeds can be purchased from biological supply companies. Have students take note of the traits in the plants grown from these seeds.

Reading Check The use of true-breeding plants allowed Mendel to easily segregate the genes passed from generation to generation.

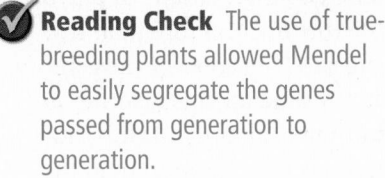

Content Background

Teacher FYI Johann Mendel was born in 1822 in the village of Heizendorf, Austria (then Moravia), the son of a peasant farmer. Mendel entered the monastery in what is now Brno, the Czech Republic, in 1843. Once there, he changed his name to Gregor. The monastery sent Mendel to the University of Vienna to study physics, math, chemistry, botany, paleontology, and plant physiology. Mendel acquired a copy of Darwin's *On the Origin of Species* translated into German. He studied plant pollination, which proved to play a significant role later in his genetic discoveries.

W Writing Strategy

OL AL Formal Writing Have students write an article for an 1860s newspaper announcing that Mendel has discovered the methods and mathematics of inheritance.

Critical Thinking

BL OL Analyze

ASK STUDENTS: ***Which generation (P, F_1, or F_2) is each of the following: your grandparents, your parents, and you?*** Your grandparents are P, your parents are F_1, and you are F_2.

D Develop Concepts

BL OL

Clarify a Misconception

ASK STUDENTS: ***Which do you think are better or more desirable—dominant genes or recessive genes?*** neither Students might be confused about the meanings of *dominant* and *recessive,* thinking *recessive* means small and weak and *dominant* means strong and overpowering. Students may also think that dominant genes are more desirable than recessive genes and believe that recessive genes are bad or harmful. Explain that certain dominant genes can cause disorders. Use the example of polydactyly (born with more than five fingers). The allele of the gene responsible for this disorder is dominant in humans. It is, however, far less common than the recessive form. ***Why is this so?*** Most people are homozygous for the recessive allele.

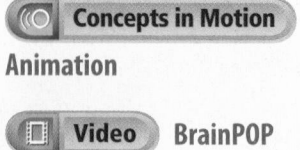

Concepts in Motion

Animation

Video BrainPOP

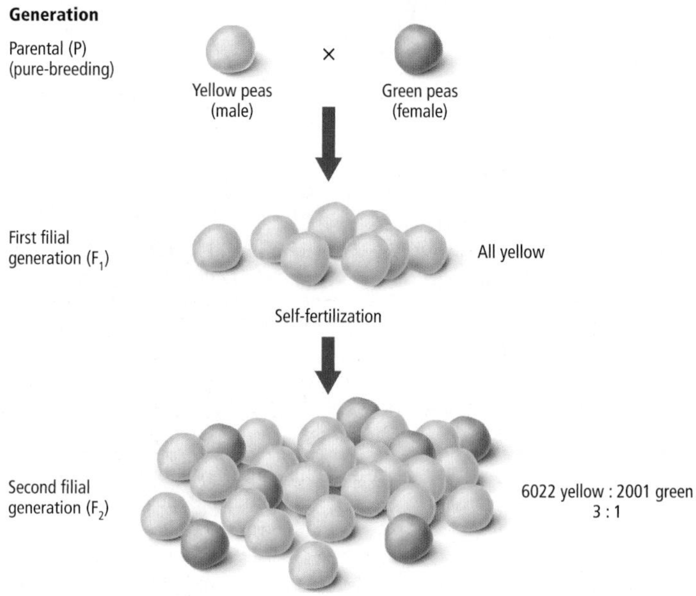

Figure 8 The results of Mendel's cross involving true-breeding pea plants with yellow seeds and green seeds are shown here. **Explain** ***why the seeds in the F_1 generation were all yellow.***

Concepts in Motion

Animation

W

F_1 and F_2 generations When Mendel grew the seeds from the cross between the green-seed and yellow-seed plants, all of the resulting offspring had yellow seeds. The offspring of this P cross are called the first filial (F_1) generation. The green-seed trait seemed to have disappeared in the F_1 generation, and Mendel decided to investigate whether the trait was no longer present or whether it was hidden, or masked.

Mendel planted the F_1 generation of yellow seeds, allowed the plants to grow and self-fertilize, and then examined the seeds from this cross. The results of the second filial (F_2) generation—the offspring from the F_1 cross—are shown in **Figure 8.** Of the seeds Mendel collected, 6022 were yellow and 2001 were green, which almost is a perfect 3:1 ratio of yellow to green seeds.

Mendel studied seven different traits—seed or pea color, flower color, seed pod color, seed shape or texture, seed pod shape, stem length, and flower position—and found that the F_2 generation plants from these crosses also showed a 3:1 ratio.

Video BrainPOP

Genes in pairs Mendel concluded that there must be two forms of the seed trait in the pea plants—yellow-seed and green-seed—and that each was controlled by a factor, which now is called an allele. An **allele** is defined as an alternative form of a single gene passed from generation to generation. Therefore, the gene for yellow seeds and the gene for green seeds are each different forms of a single gene.

Mendel concluded that the 3:1 ratio observed during his experiments could be explained if the alleles were paired in each of the plants. He called the form of the trait that appeared in the F_1 generation **dominant** and the form of the trait that was masked in the F_1 generation **recessive.** In the cross between yellow-seed plants and green-seed plants, the yellow seed was the dominant form of the trait and the green seed was the recessive form of the trait. D

CAREERS IN BIOLOGY

Genetics Laboratory Technician
A technician in a genetics laboratory assists a researcher by conducting experiments and helping to maintain the lab.

Caption Question Fig. 8 The yellow seed was the dominant form of the trait. All the seeds in the F_1 generation received one copy of the dominant gene.

Research Citation

Models Educational research indicates that students will benefit from the use of models. Models help students who are visual learners by giving them a concrete example of a difficult concept. (Hitt and Townsend, 2004)

Research bibliography on pages 32T–34T

Dominance When he allowed the F_1 generation to self-fertilize, Mendel showed that the recessive allele for green seeds had not disappeared but was masked. Mendel concluded that the green-seed form of the trait did not show up in the F_1 generation because the yellow-seed form of the trait is dominant and masks the allele for the green-seed form of the trait.

When modeling inheritance, the dominant allele is represented by a capital letter, and the recessive allele is represented by a lowercase letter. An organism with two of the same alleles for a particular trait is **homozygous** (ho muh ZI gus) for that trait. Homozygous, yellow-seed plants are *YY* and green-seed plants are *yy*. An organism with two different alleles for a particular trait is **heterozygous** (heh tuh roh ZY gus) for that trait, in this case *Yy*. When alleles are present in the heterozygous state, the dominant trait will be observed.

Genotype and phenotype A yellow-seed plant could be homozygous or heterozygous for the trait form. The outward appearance of an organism does not always indicate which pair of alleles is present. The organism's allele pairs are called its **genotype.** In the case of plants with yellow seeds, their genotypes could be *YY* or *Yy*. The observable characteristic or outward expression of an allele pair is called the **phenotype.** The phenotype of pea plants with the genotype *yy* will be green seeds.

Mendel's law of segregation Mendel used homozygous yellow-seed and green-seed plants in his P cross. In **Figure 9(A),** the top drawing shows that each gamete from the yellow-seed plant contains one *Y*. Recall that the chromosome number is divided in half during meiosis. The resulting gametes contain only one of the pair of seed-color alleles.

The bottom drawing in **Figure 9(A)** shows that each gamete from the green-seed plant contains one *y* allele. Mendel's **law of segregation** states that the two alleles for each trait separate during meiosis. During fertilization, two alleles for that trait unite.

The third drawing in **Figure 9(B)** shows the alleles uniting to produce the genotype *Yy* during fertilization. All resulting F_1 generation plants will have the genotype *Yy* and will have yellow seeds because yellow is dominant to green. These heterozygous organisms are called **hybrids**.

VOCABULARY
WORD ORIGIN
Homozygous and **Heterozygous** come from the Greek words *homos*, meaning *the same; hetero*, meaning *other* or *different;* and *zygon*, meaning *yoke*.

Figure 9 During gamete formation in the *YY* or *yy* plant, the two alleles separate, resulting in *Y* or *y* in the gametes. Gametes from each parent unite during fertilization.

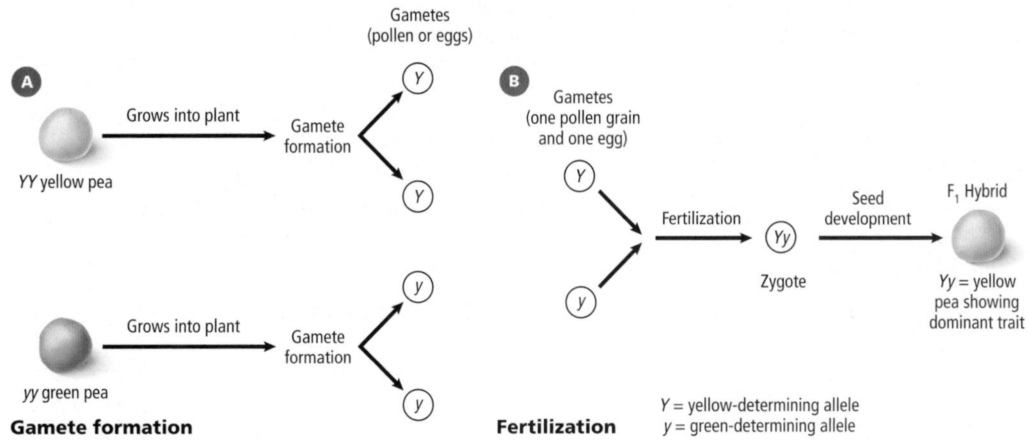

Demonstration

Cross Pollination Give groups of three to four students a lily or other large flower. Point out the stamen, anther, pollen, and pistil. Have them take the pistil out and cut it longitudinally. Have them use a magnifying lens to examine the ovules in the ovary at the bottom of the pistil. Explain that in cross pollination, pollen from one flower is used to fertilize the ovules in another flower. Stamens from fertilized flowers are removed to prevent self-fertilization. Est. time: 15 min

R Reading Strategy

BL OL AL

Content-Specific Words Students can eaily confuse the terms *genotype* and *phenotype.* Share with them the idea that genotypes are the *types* of *genes* a particular individual has. For example, B could represent a dominant gene for brown hair and b a recessive one. BB or Bb or bb would be possible genotypes. Phenotypes are the physical expression of the genes. (*Phen* means "to show" in Greek). The phenotype of an individual with BB or Bb genes would be brown hair.

S Skill Practice

OL **Visual Literacy** Have students study the information in Figure 9.

ASK STUDENTS: ***If* Y *represents yellow flowers in a plant and* y *represents white flowers, what is the phenotype of the genotype* YY?** yellow flowers ***What is the phenotype represented by* yy?** white flowers

D Develop Concepts

EL BL OL AL **Activity** Give students who are struggling with the law of segregation a number of lengths of colored yarn or pipe cleaners of two colors. Have them label the individuals of the pairs so they can keep track of them (such as 1a, 1b, 2a, 2b, etc.). Have them go through meiosis steps using the yarn chromosomes, emphasizing that when the pairs line up, any of the types of 1 (1a or 1b) can line up with any of the types of 2 (2a or 2b).

Inquiry BioLab

The lab at the end of the chapter can be used at this point in the lesson.

Reading Strategy

BL OL AL

Content-Specific Words

ASK STUDENTS: ***Why are some new cars called hybrids?*** They have two different motors: one powered by gasoline and the other by electricity. ***What does the word* hybrid *mean in biology?*** Point out that it has two different meanings in biology. In genetics, *hybrid* is commonly used to mean heterozygous. It is also used to indicate individuals of two species or strains that breed and produce offspring, such as hybrid corn.

Develop Concepts

BL OL COOP LEARN

Fix-Up Strategy Some students may have difficulty with the mathematical principles in this section. Have students keep track of questions on any parts they do not understand. Pair up students who understand the material with students having difficulty with math and have them work together on the math in this section.

Writing Support

BL OL COOP LEARN

Creative Writing Have students work in pairs to create a cartoon about the inheritance of more than one trait in pea plants. Encourage them to use text ballons and be creative, but the science must be accurate. They might also want to include information on Mendel's experiments.

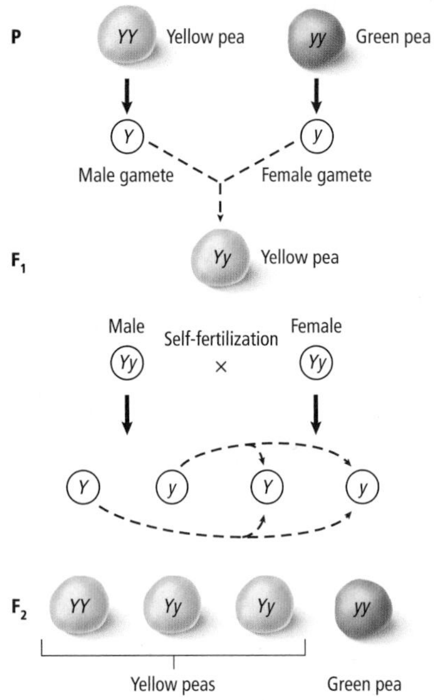

Figure 10 During the F_1 generation self-fertilization, the male gametes randomly fertilize the female gametes.

Monohybrid cross The diagram in **Figure 10** shows how Mendel continued his experiments by allowing the *Yy* plants to self-fertilize. A cross such as this one that involves hybrids for a single trait is called a monohybrid cross. The *Yy* plants produce two types of gametes—male and female—each with either the *Y* or *y* allele. The combining of these gametes is a random event. This random fertilization of male and female gametes results in the following genotypes—*YY, Yy, Yy*, or *yy*, as shown in **Figure 10.** Notice that the dominant *Y* allele is written first, whether it came from the male or female gamete. In Mendel's F_1 cross, there are three possible genotypes: *YY, Yy*, and *yy*; and the genotypic ratio is 1:2:1. The phenotypic ratio is 3:1—yellow seeds to green seeds.

Dihybrid cross Once Mendel established inheritance patterns of a single trait, he began to examine simultaneous inheritance of two or more traits in the same plant. In garden peas, round seeds *(R)* are dominant to wrinkled seeds *(r)*, and yellow seeds *(Y)* are dominant to green seeds *(y)*. If Mendel crossed homozygous yellow, round-seed pea plants with homozygous green, wrinkle-seed pea plants, the P cross could be represented by *YYRR* × *yyrr*. The F_1 generation genotype would be *YyRr*—yellow, round-seed plants. These F_1-generation plants are called dihybrids because they are heterozygous for both traits. R

Law of independent assortment Mendel allowed F_1 pea plants with the genotype *YyRr* to self-fertilize in a dihybrid cross. Mendel calculated the genotypic and phenotypic ratios of the offspring in both the F_1 and F_2 generations. From these results, he developed the **law of independent assortment,** which states that a random distribution of alleles occurs during gamete formation. Genes on separate chromosomes sort independently during meiosis.

As shown in **Figure 11,** the random assortment of alleles results in four possible gametes: *YR, Yr, yR* or *yr*, each of which is equally likely to occur. When a plant self-fertilizes, any of the four allele combinations could be present in the male gamete, and any of the four combinations could be present in the female gamete. The results of Mendel's dihybrid cross included nine different genotypes: *YYRR, YYRr, YYrr, YyRR, YyRr, Yyrr, yyRR, yyRr*, and *yyrr*. He counted and recorded four different phenotypes: 315 yellow round, 108 green round, 101 yellow wrinkled, and 32 green wrinkled. These results represent a phenotypic ratio of approximately 9:3:3:1. D W

Figure 11 The law of independent assortment is demonstrated in the dihybrid cross by the equal chance that each pair of alleles (*Yy* and *Rr*) can randomly combine with each other.

***Predict** how many possible gamete types are produced.*

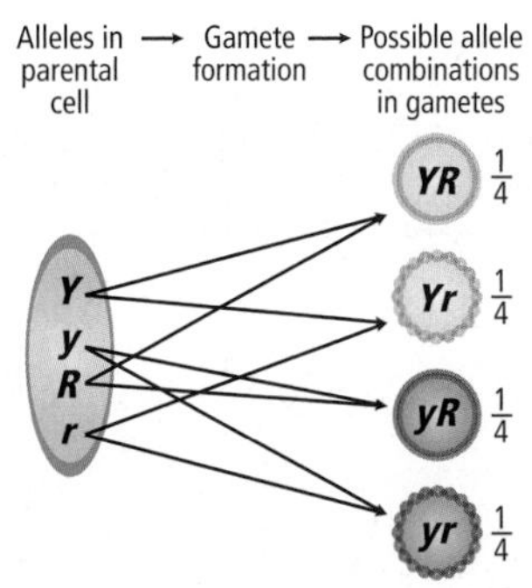

Reading Check **Evaluate** How can the random distribution of alleles result in a predictable ratio?

Punnett Squares

In the early 1900s, Dr. Reginald Punnett developed what is known as a Punnett square to predict the possible offspring of a cross between two known genotypes. Punnett squares make it easier to keep track of the possible genotypes involved in a cross.

"*Education is hanging around until you've caught on.*"

—Robert Frost

Caption Question **Fig. 11** Four

Reading Check Because there is an equal chance that each pair of alleles can randomly combine with each other, the outcome of a large sample size will be a predictable ratio.

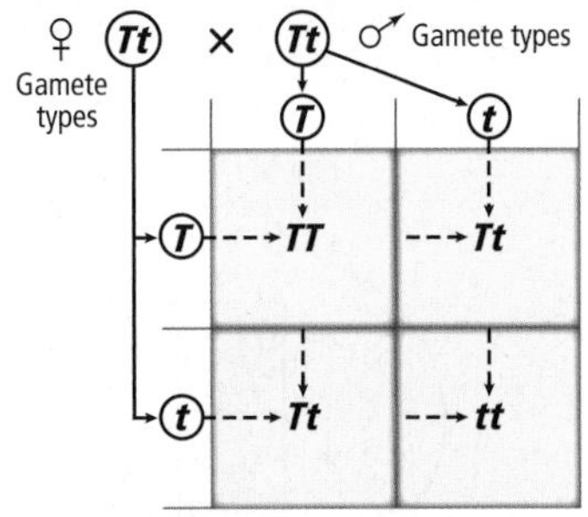

■ **Figure 12** The ability to roll one's tongue is a dominant trait. The Punnett square is a visual summary of the possible combinations of the alleles for the tongue-rolling trait.

Review Personal Tutor

Punnett square—monohybrid cross Can you roll your tongue like the person pictured in **Figure 12?** Tongue-rolling ability is a dominant trait, which can be represented by *T*. Suppose both parents can roll their tongues and are heterozygous (*Tt*) for the trait. What possible phenotypes could their children have?

Examine the Punnett square in **Figure 12.** The number of squares is determined by the number of different types of alleles—*T* or *t*—produced by each parent. In this case, the square is 2 squares × 2 squares because each parent produces two different types of gametes. Notice that the male gametes are written across the horizontal side and the female gametes are written on the vertical side of the Punnett square. The possible combinations of each male and female gamete are written on the inside of each corresponding square.

Inquiry Virtual Lab

MiniLab 1

Predict Probability in Genetics

Inquiry MiniLab

How can an offspring's traits be predicted? A Punnett square can help predict ratios of dominant traits to recessive traits in the genotype of offspring. This lab involves two parents who are both heterozygous for free earlobes (E), which is a dominant trait. The recessive trait is attached earlobes (e).

Procedure

1. Read and complete the lab safety form.
2. Determine the gamete genotype(s) for this trait that each parent contributes.
3. Draw a Punnett square that has the same number of columns and the same number of rows as the number of alleles contributed for this trait by the gametes of each parent.
4. Write the alphabetical letter for each allele from one parent just above each column, and write the alphabetical letter for each allele from the other parent just to the left of each row.
5. In the boxes within the table, write the genotype of the offspring resulting from each combination of male and female alleles.

Analysis

1. **Summarize** the possible offspring phenotypes that could occur.
2. **Evaluate** the phenotypic ratio of the possible offspring. What is the genotypic ratio of the possible offspring?

MiniLab 1

Inquiry MiniLab

For a lab worksheet, use your eTeacherEdition Online.

RUBRIC A rubric for evaluating MiniLabs is found on your eTeacherEdition Online.

Est. Time 25 min

Safety Precautions Approve lab safety forms before work begins.

Teaching Strategy For additional practice, have students complete Punnett squares and summarize the proportion of each genotype or phenotype present in the offspring.
monohybrid crosses: *AA* × *Aa*, *AA* × *aa*

Analysis

1. free earlobes and attached earlobes
2. phenotypes: 75 percent dominant (free earlobes), 25 percent recessive (attached earlobes); genotypes: 25 percent homozygous dominant, 50 percent heterozygous, 25 percent homozygous recessive

LabManager™

Customize this lab with the LabManager™ CD-ROM.

Differentiated Instruction

Visually Impaired When doing a demonstration, be sure that students with visual difficulties are able to benefit. Seat these students at the front of the class so that the demonstration is visible to them and describe what you are doing step-by-step.

For more tips, see pages 14T–15T.

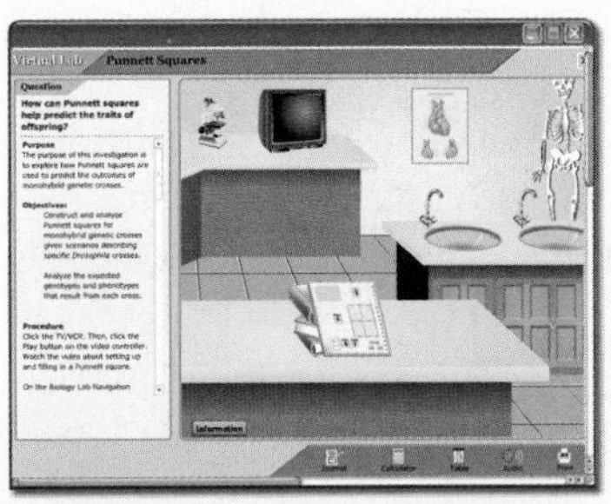

Inquiry **Virtual Lab** Students will use Punnett squares to predict the outcomes of monohybrid genetic crosses.

D Develop Concepts

EL BL OL AL Integrate Math Some students may have difficulty determining probability. Have these students practice with a coin. Being able to see the two sides of the coin may help them understand that the probability of throwing heads is 1:2. Then shift to a single die, predicting the probability of throwing a particular number. Counting the six sides of the die can help them understand the probability of throwing a particular number is 1:6. Shift to two dice, predicting the probability of throwing two of a particular number. Give the students some probability problems.

a) chance of throwing two heads from two coins $1/2 \times 1/2 = 1/4$

b) chance of throwing 2 sixes on two dice $1/6 \times 1/6 = 1/36$

Formative Assessment

Evaluation Prepare a quiz of both a monohybrid and dihybrid cross, asking students to perform a Punnett square on the crosses and summarize their results in both genotype and phenotype ratios.

Remediation Draw a large Punnett square on a piece of construction paper. Have students practice problems using colored popsicle sticks or colored yarn pieces.

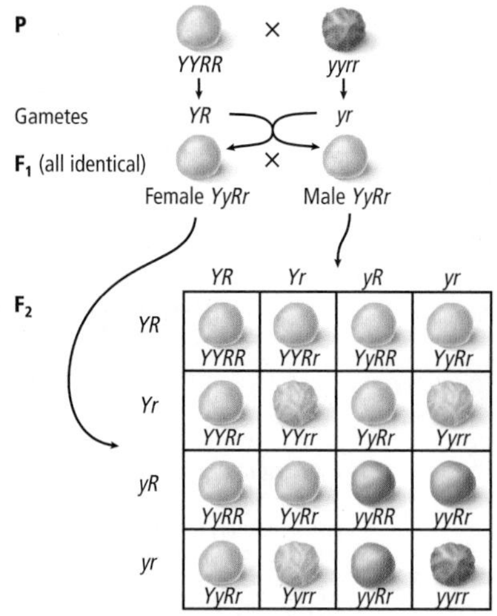

Type	Genotype	Phenotype	Number	Phenotypic Ratio
Parental	Y_R_	yellow round	315	9:16
Recombinant	yyR_	green round	108	3:16
Recombinant	Y_rr	yellow wrinkled	101	3:16
Parental	yyrr	green wrinkled	32	1:16

Figure 13 The dihybrid Punnett square visually presents the possible combinations of the possible alleles from each parent.

How many different genotypes are found in the Punnett square? One square has *TT*, two squares have *Tt*, and one square has *tt*. Therefore, the genotypic ratio of the possible offspring is 1:2:1. The phenotypic ratio of tongue rollers to non-tongue rollers is 3:1.

Punnett square—dihybrid cross Now examine the Punnett square in **Figure 13.** Notice that in the P cross, only two types of alleles are produced. However, in the dihybrid cross—when the F_1 generation is crossed—four types of alleles from the male gametes and four types of alleles from the female gametes can be produced. The resulting phenotypic ratio is 9:3:3:1—9 yellow round to 3 green round to 3 yellow wrinkled to 1 green wrinkled. Mendel's data closely matched the outcome predicted by the Punnett square.

Probability

The inheritance of genes can be compared to the probability of flipping a coin. The probability of the coin landing on heads is 1 out of 2, or 1/2. If the same coin is flipped twice, the probability of it landing on heads is 1/2 each time or $1/2 \times 1/2$, or 1/4 both times.

Actual data might not perfectly match the predicted ratios. You know that if you flip a coin you might not get heads 1 out of 2 times. Mendel's results were not exactly a 9:3:3:1 ratio. However, the larger the number of offspring involved in a cross, the more likely it will match the results predicted by the Punnett square. D

Section 2 Assessment

Section Summary

- The study of genetics began with Gregor Mendel, whose experiments with garden pea plants gave insight into the inheritance of traits.
- Mendel developed the law of segregation and the law of independent assortment.
- Punnett squares help predict the offspring of a cross.

Understand Main Ideas

1. MAIN Idea **Diagram** Use a Punnett square to explain how a dominant allele masks the presence of a recessive allele.
2. **Apply** the law of segregation and the law of independent assortment by giving an example of each.
3. **Use a Punnett square** In fruit flies, red eyes (*R*) are dominant to pink eyes (*r*). What is the phenotypic ratio of a cross between a heterozygous male and a pink-eyed female?

Think Critically

4. **Evaluate** the significance of Mendel's work to the field of genetics.

MATH in Biology

5. What is the probability of rolling a 2 on a six-sided die? What is the probability of rolling two 2s on two six-sided die? How is probability used in the study of genetics?

Section 2 Assessment

1. Punnett square should show possible combinations of dominant and recessive alleles. When at least one dominant allele is present in a pair, the phenotype of the dominant allele will be expressed.
2. Students should summarize, in their own words, the law of segregation and the law of independent assortment and give one example for each.
3. 1 red:1 pink
4. Mendel's work demonstrates how genes are passed from one generation to the next and how genotype affects phenotype. Mendel's work created the study of heredity and led to modern research in genetics.
5. 1/6; 1/36 ($1/6 \times 1/6$); to predict likely outcomes of crosses

Assessment Online Quiz

Reading Preview

Essential Questions

- How does the process of meiosis produce genetic recombination?
- How can gene linkage be used to create chromosome maps?
- Why is polyploidy important to the field of agriculture?

Review Vocabulary

protein: large, complex polymer essential to all life that provides structure for tissues and organs and helps carry out cell metabolism

New Vocabulary

genetic recombination
polyploidy

Multilingual eGlossary

Gene Linkage and Polyploidy

MAIN Idea **The crossing over of linked genes is a source of genetic variation.**

Real-World Reading Link You might have seen many varieties of roses at a garden center that range in color from red to pink to white. Plant breeders use scientists' knowledge of genes to vary certain characteristics in an effort to make their roses unique.

Genetic Recombination

Connection to Math The new combination of genes produced by crossing over and independent assortment is called **genetic recombination.** The possible combinations of genes due to independent assortment can be calculated using the formula 2^n, where n is the number of chromosome pairs. For example, pea plants have seven pairs of chromosomes. For seven pairs of chromosomes, the possible combinations are 2^7, or 128 combinations. Because any possible male gamete can fertilize any possible female gamete, the number of possible combinations after fertilization is 16,384 (128 × 128). In humans, the possible number of combinations after fertilization would be $2^{23} \times 2^{23}$, or more than 70 trillion. This number does not include the amount of genetic recombination produced by crossing over. **R**

Gene Linkage

Chromosomes contain multiple genes that code for proteins. Genes that are located close to each other on the same chromosome are said to be linked and usually travel together during gamete formation. Follow closely related genes A and B in **Figure 14** through the process of meiosis. The linkage of genes on a chromosome results in an exception to Mendel's law of independent assortment because linked genes usually do not segregate independently.

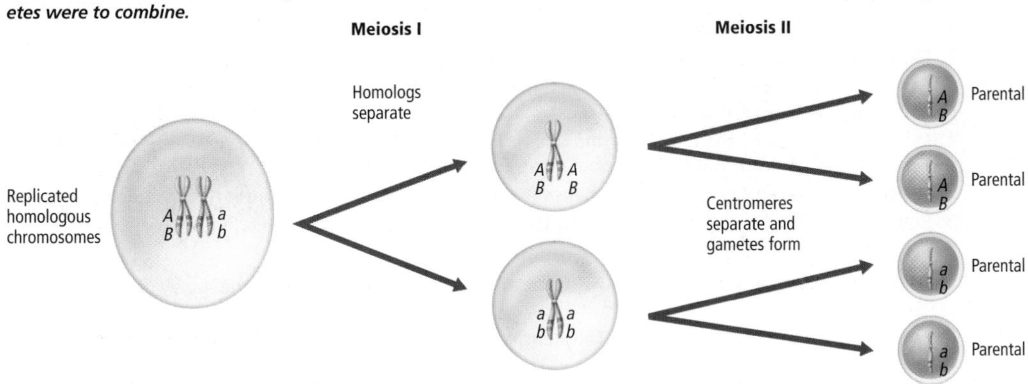

■ **Figure 14** Genes that are linked together on the same chromosome usually travel together in the gamete.
Calculate ***the number of possible combinations if two or three of these gametes were to combine.***

Demonstration

Chromatids Make linked chains from strips of colored paper. Use some colors that have light and dark shades, such as light blue and dark blue. Make two identical chains. Make a second set of chains matching the color sequence but using a different shade for some links. Hang the two sets of chains close together. Each chain represents a chromatid of a pair of chromosomes. Paper clip the identical chains together, representing the centromere. Exchange one of the dark colored strips on one chain with a light colored on another. Point out that this exchange of links represents crossing over among chromatids. Est. time: 15 min

MAIN Idea

EL BL OL AL Crossing Over Use two pairs of socks of different colors to represent a pair of chromosomes that will line up during meiosis. One pair could be striped socks and one pair tube socks to represent a pair of chromosomes (each consisting of two chromatids) that line up during metaphase I of meiosis. Place two yellow self-adhesive notes on each of three of the socks and one yellow note and a note of a different color on the fourth sock. The notes will allow students to follow sections of the chromosomes. Hold the socks so the note that is a different color is near one of the yellow notes. Ask one student volunteer to swap the notes.
ASK STUDENTS: ***What process does this exchange of sticky notes represent?*** crossing over

R Reading Strategy

BL OL AL COOP LEARN

Discussion Groups After reading the text under the heading *Genetic Recombination,* group students into teams of three.
SAY TO STUDENTS: ***Discuss why genetic recombination is important. Report your group's conclusion to the class.*** Students may relate genetic recombination to variation being important for natural selection and evolution.

■ **Caption Question Fig. 14** Calculation must use the formula 2^n

S Skill Practice

OL AL Visual Literacy Have students study Figure 15.

ASK STUDENTS: ***Is the crossover rate between y and v more or less than the crossover rate between y and w?*** more

MiniLab 2

Inquiry MiniLab

For a lab worksheet, use your eTeacherEdition Online.

RUBRIC A rubric for evaluating MiniLabs is found on your eTeacherEdition Online.

Est. Time 25 min

Additional Materials

Use the following table:

Gene Pair	Crossover Frequency	Gene Pair	Crossover Frequency
AB	5.5	BF	4.3
AC	6.4	CD	10.9
AD	4.5	CE	2.6
AE	9.0	CF	5.2
AF	1.2	DE	13.5
BC	0.9	DF	5.7
BD	10.0	EF	7.8
BE	3.5		

Teaching Strategies

- Model the logic process involved in this activity. Use these sample data: AB = 3, AC = 1, AD = 4, BC = 2, BD = 7, CD = 5.
- Sample data: D – 4.5 – A – 1.2 – F – 4.3 – B – 0.9 – C – 2.6 – E

Analysis

1. not without more information, such as relative location of a third gene
2. The more crossover frequencies known, the more information can be used to draw the map. Knowing crossover frequencies helps determine distances between genes.

LabManager™

Customize this lab with the LabManager™ CD-ROM.

■ **Figure 15** This chromosome map of the X chromosome of the fruit fly *Drosophila melanogaster* was created in 1913.

S

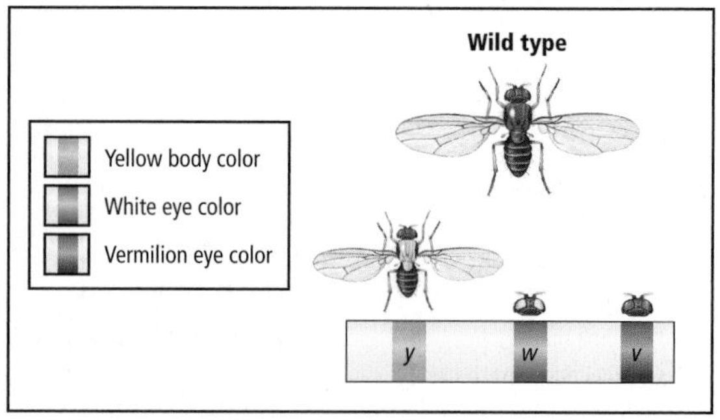

Gene linkage was first studied using the fruit fly *Drosophila melanogaster.* Thousands of crosses confirmed that linked genes usually traveled together during meiosis. However, some results revealed that linked genes do not always travel together during meiosis. Scientists concluded that linked genes can separate during crossing over.

Chromosome maps Crossing over occurs more frequently between genes that are far apart than those that are close together. A drawing called a chromosome map shows the sequence of genes on a chromosome and can be created by using crossover data. The very first chromosome maps were published in 1913 using data from thousands of fruit fly crosses. Chromosome map percentages are not actual chromosome distances, but they represent relative positions of the genes. **Figure 15** shows the first chromosome map created using fruit fly data. Notice that the higher the crossover frequency, the farther apart the two genes are.

MiniLab 2

Map Chromosomes

Inquiry MiniLab

Where are genes located on a chromosome? The distance between two genes on a chromosome is related to the crossover frequency between them. By comparing data for several gene pairs, a gene's relative location can be determined.

Procedure

1. Read and complete the lab safety form.
2. Obtain a table of the gene-pair crossover frequencies from your teacher.
3. Draw a line on a piece of paper and make marks every 1 cm. Each mark will represent a crossover frequency of 1 percent.
4. Label one mark near the middle of the line *A*. Find the crossover frequency between Genes A and B on the table, and use this data to label *B* the correct distance from A.
5. Use the crossover frequency between genes A and C and genes B and C to infer the position of gene C.
6. Repeat steps 4–5 for each gene, marking their positions on the line.

Analysis

1. **Evaluate** whether it is possible to know the location of a gene on a chromosome if only one other gene is used.
2. **Consider** why using more crossover frequencies would result in a more accurate chromosome map.

GOING GREEN Have recycling boxes or bins available for students in your classroom. Have bins for glass, paper, and plastic. Rinse glass and plastic containers and remove bottle caps. Glass and plastic can last thousands of years in a landfill. Paper is easily recycled.

Differentiated Instruction

Below Level Students who perform below level should receive timely feedback on their performance. Provide immediate reinforcement and suggestions on improvement so that students can see a clear connection to the quality of their work.

For more tips, see pages 14T–15T.

Strawberries (8*n*)

Coffee (4*n*)

■ **Figure 16** Various commercial plants, such as strawberries and coffee, are polyploids.

In a cross, the exchange of genes is directly related to the crossover frequency between them. This frequency correlates with the relative distance between the two genes. One map unit between two genes is equivalent to 1 percent of the crossing over occurring between them. Genes that are farther apart would have a greater D frequency of crossing over.

Polyploidy

Most species have diploid cells, but some have polyploid cells. **Polyploidy** is the occurrence of one or more extra sets of all chromosomes in an organism. A triploid organism, for instance, would be designated 3*n*, which means that it has three complete sets of chromosomes. Polyploidy rarely occurs in animals. In humans, polyploidy is always lethal.

Roughly one in three species of known flowering plants are polyploid. Polyploid plants are selected by plant growers for their desirable characteristics. Commercially grown bread wheat *(6n)*, oats *(6n)*, and sugar cane *(8n)* are polyploid crop plants. Polyploid plants, such as the ones shown in **Figure 16,** often have increased vigor and size. C

Section 3 Assessment

Section Summary

- Genetic recombination involves both crossing over and independent assortment.
- Early chromosome maps were created based on the linkage of genes on the chromosome.
- Polyploid organisms have one or more extra sets of all chromosomes.

Understand Main Ideas

1. MAIN Idea **Analyze** how crossing over is related to variation.
2. **Draw** Suppose genes *C* and *D* are linked on one chromosome and genes *c* and *d* are linked on another chromosome. Assuming that crossing over does not take place, sketch the daughter cells resulting from meiosis, showing the chromosomes and position of the genes.
3. **Describe** how polyploidy is used in the field of agriculture.

Think Critically

4. **Construct** a chromosome map for genes *A, B, C* and *D* using the following crossing over data: *A* to *D*=25 percent; *A* to *B*=30 percent; *C* to *D*=15 percent; *B* to *D*=5 percent; *B* to *C*=20 percent.
5. **Evaluate** what advantage polyploidy would give to a plant breeder.

WRITING in Biology

6. Write a short story describing a society with no genetic variation in humans.

D Develop Concepts

BL OL

Clarify a Misconception

ASK STUDENTS: ***Does crossing over occur more frequently among genes that are closer together?*** no Some students may have difficulty with this concept about crossing over. Explain that chromosome maps show that crossing over occurs most frequently among genes that are far apart.

C Critical Thinking

BL OL AL **Infer**

ASK STUDENTS: ***Why is polyploidy important to fruit growers?*** Polyploid plants may produce larger fruit that consumers are more likely to purchase.

Formative Assessment

Evaluation Draw two homologous chromosomes with linked genes labeled on each chromosome on the board. Refer to Figure 14 for assistance. Have students predict the possibility of two genes that are located next to each other on the chromosome crossing over. They are not likely to cross. The closer the genes are, the less likely they are to cross; it is an inversely related relationship.

Remediation Using different colored pipe cleaners demonstrate how chromosomes cross. Refer to Figure 4 for a model.

Section 3 Assessment

1. Genes are exchanged on chromosomes, creating variation.
2. Two daughter cells should have chromosomes with *C* and *D* on them and two daughter cells should have chromosomes with *c* and *d* on them.
3. to create flowers with larger blooms and fruits that are large or have other desirable traits
4. A – 10 – C – 15 – D – 5 – B.
5. It would allow the breeder to create plants with desirable and commercially valuable traits.
6. Answers will vary but should demonstrate an understanding of how steps in meiosis contribute to genetic variation.

WRITING in Biology

✻RUBRIC Use the modifiable rubric found on your eTeacherEdition Online to assess writing assignments.

✓ Assessment Online Quiz

BioDiscoveries

Purpose

Students will learn about Parkinson's disease, current treatments for the condition, and a potential treatment that uses stem cells. E.2, F.1, F.6

Anticipatory Guide

ASK STUDENTS: ***Does anyone know what Parkinson's disease is?*** Students might know that PD makes people shake and lose control of their muscles. ***What is a neuron?*** Explain that a *neuron* is a cell that carries nerve impulses throughout the body and is composed of a cell body, an axon, and dendrites. ***What is a neurotransmitter?*** Explain that a *neurotransmitter* is a chemical that diffuses across a synapse and binds to receptors on a neighboring neuron's dendrite, causing channels to open on the neighboring cell and the creation of a new action potential.

Background

Students might know actor Michael J. Fox from his roles in the *Back to the Future* movies, or as the voice of Stuart Little in three movies of the same name. The Michael J. Fox Foundation for Parkinson's Research has funded more than $143 million in research for ways to treat PD.

Students can also learn about the effects of PD by researching the life of Muhammad Ali, a world-famous boxer who held the title of heavyweight champion of the world three different times in the 1960s and 1970s. Ali was diagnosed with PD in the early 1980s, after he retired from boxing.

BioDiscoveries

A new treatment for Parkinson's Disease?

One morning, actor Michael J. Fox woke up to find his pinky finger twitching. At first he ignored this strange symptom. But a year later he was diagnosed with early-onset Parkinson's disease (PD), a debilitating illness that, among other symptoms, causes loss of control over the body's movements. On average, the disease strikes people around age 60; however, Fox was only 30 when he was diagnosed.

The Parkinson's Disease Foundation (PDF) along with other PD foundations, raise funds for PD research. A recent PDF-funded project studied a new treatment that might alleviate symptoms of the disease—with the help of an afflicted person's own skin cells.

What is PD? Parkinson's disease is an illness that kills or damages neurons in the brain. These neurons control muscle movement via a neurotransmitter called dopamine, which relays messages between neurons. In addition to problems controlling their muscles, people who have PD have trouble with muscle stiffness, balance, and coordination. The disease's symptoms are often subtle at first and worsen over time. Currently, there is no cure. Scientists do not know what causes PD. Some cases have been linked to mutated genes, the appearance of protein clumps in brain cells, and environmental factors.

Search for treatments Doctors usually treat PD symptoms with combinations of medications, brain surgery, and physical, speech, and other therapies. Recently, scientists investigated using stem cells, unspecialized cells that can develop into specialized cells under the right conditions, to replace brain neurons lost to PD. Scientists on the PDF-funded study are working to create stem cells from skin cells of PD patients.

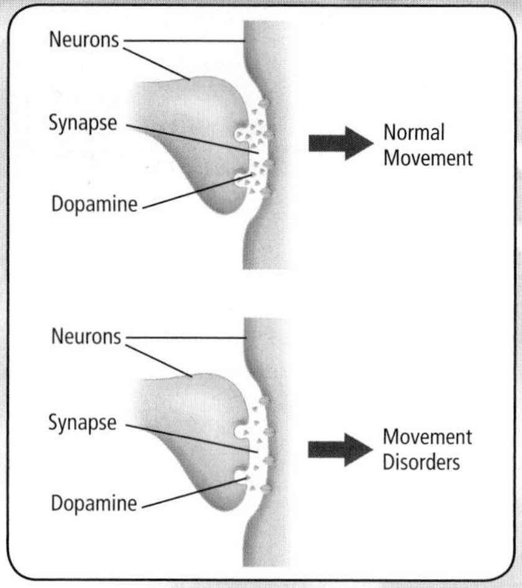

Lower levels of dopamine are an indicator of Parkinson's disease. Dopamine controls the movement of muscles.

These stem cells could be used to produce neurons that produce dopamine. Doctors could surgically introduce the newly created neurons into the brain. Because the stem cells came from the patient's own body, the immune system would not reject the cells, as sometimes happens with cells or organs donated by another person.

This stem-cell research is in its early stages with a pilot study that uses Rhesus monkeys as the patients. Scientists hope that their work will one day help alleviate the symptoms that make PD such a devastating illness.

COMMUNITY INVOLVEMENT

Volunteer Interview an administrator at a local agency who understands the needs of PD patients. Perhaps some people who have PD need help running errands or doing chores, such as yardwork. Compile a list of these needs to present to a local volunteer organization. If possible, volunteer to help people who have PD.

Community Involvement

Activity Students can learn more about how people cope with PD by typing the keywords "living with Parkinson's disease" into an online search engine. Students can also research the effects of PD by searching the databases of national health organizations such as the National Institutes of Health and the Centers for Disease Control and Prevention. Urge students to consider volunteering to help local people who have PD. Students who are interested in learning about how people live with PD might want to consult Fox's two books or his television special on the topic.

WebQuest

BIOLAB Design Your Own

HOW CAN THE PHENOTYPE OF OFFSPRING HELP DETERMINE PARENTAL GENOTYPE?

Background: **The traits of most plants have dominant and recessive alleles. Analysis of plants grown from seeds can be a good indicator of the expected genotypes of offspring as well as phenotypes and genotypes of the parent plants.**

Question: *Can the phenotypes and genotypes of parent organisms be determined from the phenotype of the offspring?*

Materials

Choose materials that would be appropriate for this lab.

two groups of plant seeds
potting soil
small flowerpots or other growing containers
watering can or bottle
small gardening trowel

Safety Precautions

Plan and Perform the Experiment

1. Read and complete the lab safety form.
2. Hypothesize whether the phenotype of offspring could be used to infer the genotypes of the parents.
3. Design an experiment to test your hypothesis.
4. Decide what data you need to collect.
5. Create a data table to record your observations.
6. Make certain your teacher has approved your experiment before you proceed.
7. Conduct your experiment.
8. **Cleanup and Disposal** Properly dispose of seeds or plants considered to be invasive species in your area. Never release invasive species into the environment.

Analyze and Conclude

1. **Collect and Organize Data** Count the number of seedlings of the different phenotypes in each group of plants. Prepare a graph of your data.
2. **Calculate** the ratio of different seedlings for each of your groups of seeds.
3. **Identify** two or more possible crosses that could have resulted in your observed ratio of seedlings.
4. **Analyze** Make a Punnett square for each cross you identified in question 3. Determine whether each possible cross could have resulted in the data you collected.
5. **Evaluate** how the combined data from the two seed groups affect the ratio of seedlings.
6. **Draw Conclusions** Based on the data from your two groups of seeds, list the genotype and phenotype of the parent plants.
7. **Error Analysis** Compare your calculated ratios to those of another student. Describe any differences. Combine your data with another group's data. Infer how increasing the number of seeds analyzed affects the outcome of the experiment.

COMMUNICATE

Poster Session Prepare a poster that describes the experiment you conducted and displays the data you collected. When posters are complete, have a poster session during which you examine each others' work and compare your results.

BIOLAB Design Your Own

Inquiry BioLab

For a lab worksheet, use your eTeacherEdition Online.

RUBRIC A rubric for evaluating BioLabs is found on your eTeacherEdition Online.

Content Background
Students will design an experiment to compare and contrast the phenotypes of plants grown from two separate groups of tobacco seeds. From the phenotypes of the two groups, students will use Punnett squares to infer the genotypes of the plants and the phenotypes of the parent parents.

Safety Precautions Approve lab safety forms before work begins.

Alternative Materials Other fast-growing seeds of which the genotypes and phenotypes can be guaranteed, greenhouse windows, temperature probe

Teaching Strategies

- Have students work in groups to design their experiments.
- Have students review the concepts they learned during previous labs to help them analyze and interpret the data.

Alternative Teaching Demo
Use photographs or drawings of plant species displaying dominant and recessive traits and offspring generated by hypothetical groups of seeds. Students can use Punnett squares to infer the genotypes of the offspring and the genotypes and phenotypes of the parents.

Analyze and Conclude

1. Students will observe the colors of the plants in each group and record the number of each colored plant from each group.
2. Answers will depend on the genotypes in the groups of seeds.
3. The ratio of green to white plants from a cross between two heterozygous parent plants will be approximately 3:1. The ratio of green to white plants from a cross between a heterozygous parent and a homozygous white parent plant will be approximately 1:1. If one parent plant is homozygous for the green, all the plants in that group will be green, and the phenotype and genotype of the second parent cannot be determined.
4. Answers will vary depending upon the data collected.
5. Answers will vary depending upon the data collected.
6. Answers will vary depending upon the data collected.
7. The more seeds, the more data can be collected for more accurate analysis.

Chapter 10

Study Guide

ConnectED

Students can use the following to review the chapter.

Review

Vocabulary eGames
Vocabulary eFlashcards
Vocabulary PuzzleMaker

Assessment

Online Quizzes
Online Test Practice
Standardized Test Practice

Use the *ExamView® Assessment Suite* CD-ROM to:

- create multiple versions of tests
- create modified tests with one mouse click
- edit existing questions and add your own questions
- build tests aligned with state standards using built-in state curriculum tags
- change English tests to Spanish with one mouse click
- track students' progress using the Teacher Management System

Chapter 10 Study Guide

THEME FOCUS Diversity The process of meiosis in humans creates 70 trillion genetic possibilities and the process of crossing over adds even more possibilities.

BIG Idea **Reproductive cells, which pass on genetic traits from the parents to the child, are produced by the process of meiosis.**

Section 1 Meiosis

gene (p. 270)
homologous chromosome (p. 270)
gamete (p. 271)
haploid (p. 271)
fertilization (p. 271)
diploid (p. 271)
meiosis (p. 271)
crossing over (p. 272)

MAIN Idea **Meiosis produces haploid gametes.**

- DNA replication takes place only once during meiosis, and it results in four haploid gametes.
- Meiosis consists of two sets of divisions.
- Meiosis produces genetic variation in gametes.

Section 2 Mendelian Genetics

genetics (p. 277)
allele (p. 278)
dominant (p. 278)
recessive (p. 278)
homozygous (p. 279)
heterozygous (p. 279)
genotype (p. 279)
phenotype (p. 279)
law of segregation (p. 279)
hybrid (p. 279)
law of independent assortment (p. 280)

MAIN Idea **Mendel explained how a dominant allele can mask the presence of a recessive allele.**

- The study of genetics began with Gregor Mendel, whose experiments with garden pea plants gave insight into the inheritance of traits.
- Mendel developed the law of segregation and the law of independent assortment.
- Punnett squares help predict the offspring of a cross.

Section 3 Gene Linkage and Polyploidy

genetic recombination (p. 283)
polyploidy (p. 285)

MAIN Idea **The crossing over of linked genes is a source of genetic variation.**

- Genetic recombination involves both crossing over and independent assortment.
- Early chromosome maps were created based on the linkage of genes on the chromosome.
- Polyploid organisms have one or more extra sets of all chromosomes.

Review **Vocabulary PuzzleMaker**

For additional practice with vocabulary, have students access the Vocabulary PuzzleMaker online.

Review **Vocabulary eGames**

Section 1

Vocabulary Review

Use what you know about the terms in the Study Guide to answer the following questions.

1. When two cells with *n* number of chromosomes fuse, what type of cell results?
2. During which process are gametes formed?
3. What process results in an exchange of genes between homologous chromosomes?

Understand Main Ideas

4. How many chromosomes would a cell have during metaphase I of meiosis if it has 12 chromosomes during interphase?
   A. 6 **C.** 24
   B. 12 **D.** 36

Use the diagram below to answer questions 5 and 6.

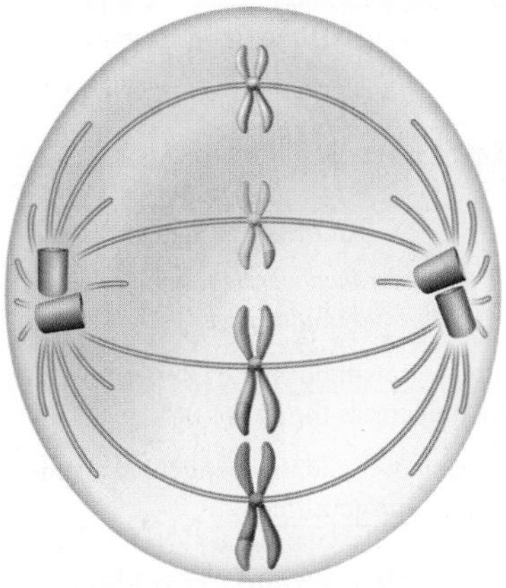

5. Which stage of meiosis is illustrated above?
   A. prophase I **C.** metaphase I
   B. prophase II **D.** metaphase II
6. What is the next step for the chromosomes illustrated above?
   A. They will experience replication.
   B. They will experience fertilization.
   C. Their number per cell will be halved.
   D. They will divide into sister chromatids.
7. Which is not a characteristic of homologous chromosomes?
   A. Homologous chromosomes have the same length.
   B. Homologous chromosomes have the same centromere position.
   C. Homologous chromosomes have the exact same type of allele at the same location.
   D. Homologous chromosomes pair up during meiosis I.

Constructed Response

8. MAIN Idea Relate the terms meiosis, gametes, and fertilization in one or two sentences.
9. **Open Ended** Plant cells do not have centrioles. Hypothesize why plant cells might not need centrioles for mitosis or meiosis.

Think Critically

10. **Analyze** A horse has 64 chromosomes and a donkey has 62. Using your knowledge of meiosis, evaluate why a cross between a horse and a donkey produces a mule, which usually is sterile.
11. **Hypothesize** In bees, the female queen bee is diploid but male bees are haploid. The fertilized eggs develop into female bees and the unfertilized eggs develop into males. How might gamete production in male bees differ from normal meiosis?

Section 2

Vocabulary Review

Explain the differences between the vocabulary terms in the following sets.

12. dominant, recessive
13. genotype, phenotype

Understand Main Ideas

14. If a black guinea pig (*Bb*) were crossed with a white guinea pig (*bb*) what would be the resulting phenotypic ratio?
    A. 0:1 black to white **C.** 1:1 black to white
    B. 1:0 black to white **D.** 3:1 black to white

Chapter 10

Assessment

Section 1

Vocabulary Review

1. diploid
2. meiosis
3. crossing over

Understand Main Ideas

4. B
5. D
6. D
7. C

Constructed Response

8. Gametes are the result of meiosis. During fertilization, gametes unite to restore the chromosome number of body cells.
9. Accept any logical hypotheses. It may be related to the firm square or rectangular shape of plant cells, naturally creating poles in the cell.

Think Critically

10. During metaphase I, the different chromosomes will not be able to find their homologous pair, so mules cannot normally make sex cells.
11. Students' answers may vary, but might include that sperm production does not occur through a typical meiosis with halving of the number of chromosomes.

Section 2

Vocabulary Review

12. A dominant gene paired with a recessive gene can hide the effect of the recessive gene.
13. Genotype expresses the type of genes an individual has, and phenotype shows the physical characteristics.

Understand Main Ideas

14. C

15. A
16. C

Constructed Response

17. The majority of the cats in the F_3 generation should have noncurly ears.
18. No, each fertilization is an independent event like each die toss. The probability is still 1:2.

Critical thinking

19. Some females with hair are homozygous and some are heterozygous.
20. 1/32

Section 3

Vocabulary

21. Polyploidy
22. genetic recombination

Understand Main Ideas

23. A
24. B

15. In garden peas, purple flowers (*P*) are dominant to white (*p*) flowers, and tall plants (*T*) are dominant to short plants (*t*). If a purple tall plant (*PpTt*) is crossed with a white short plant (*pptt*), what is the resulting phenotypic ratio?
 A. 1:1:1:1 purple tall to purple short to white tall to white short
 B. 3:2 purple tall to purple short
 C. 9:3:3:1 purple tall to purple short to white tall to white short
 D. all purple tall

Use the figure below to answer questions 16 and 17.

16. The unusual cat shown was crossed with a cat with noncurled ears. All the kittens born from that cross had noncurled ears. Later, when these offspring were crossed with each other, the phenotypic ratio was 3:1 noncurled to curled ears. What conclusions can be made about the inheritance of curled ears?
 A. Curled ears are a result of crossing over.
 B. It is a dominant trait.
 C. It is a recessive trait.
 D. More crosses need to be done to determine how the trait is inherited.

Constructed Response

17. MAIN Idea What might occur in the F_3 generation of the curly-eared cat shown above if the F_2 generation all reproduce with cats that have non-curly ears?

18. **Short Answer** If there are five boys and no girls born into a family, does that increase the likelihood that the sixth offspring will be a girl? Explain.

Think Critically

Use the figure below to answer question 19.

19. **Predict** There are two types of American rat terrier dogs—those without hair and those with hair, as shown in the figure. The presence of hair is a genetically determined trait. Some female rat terriers with hair produce only puppies with hair, whereas other females produce rat terrier puppies without hair. Explain how this can occur.

20. MATH in Biology What is the probability of a couple giving birth to five girls in a row?

Section 3

Vocabulary Review

Replace the underlined words with the correct vocabulary term from the Study Guide page.

21. Human growth hormone has been used in agriculture to increase the size of flowers.

22. Crossing over and independent assortment produce chromosomes.

Understand Main Ideas

23. Which does not contribute to genetic variation?
 A. chromosome number
 B. crossing over
 C. meiosis
 D. random mating

24. Which concept is considered an exception to Mendel's law of independent assortment?
 A. crossing over
 B. gene linkage
 C. polyploidy
 D. law of segregation

Assessment Online Test Practice

Use the figure below to answer questions 25 and 26.

25. A housefly, shown in the photo above, has six pairs of chromosomes. If two houseflies are crossed, how many possible types of fertilized eggs could result from the random lining up of the pairs?
A. 256 **C.** 4096
B. 1024 **D.** 16,384

26. For the housefly with its six pairs of chromosomes, how many possible combinations of gametes can be produced by the random lining up of pairs in meiosis?
A. 32 **C.** 64
B. 48 **D.** 120

Constructed Response

27. **THEME FOCUS Diversity** What three processes increase genetic variation?

28. Open Ended Hypothesize how a plant breeder might create a polyploid plant.

29. Short Answer How is chromosome gene linkage an exception to the law of independent assortment?

Think Critically

30. **CAREERS IN BIOLOGY** Horticulturists grow thousands of genetically identical plants by using cuttings. Cuttings do not involve sexual reproduction. Discuss the benefits and drawbacks of using cuttings to reproduce a certain type of plant.

31. **MAIN Idea** Crossing over provides genetic variation, eventually changing the gene pool in a population. Yet some sexually reproducing organisms do not seem to display recombination mechanisms. Why might it be advantageous for these organisms to reduce genetic recombination?

Summative Assessment

32. **BIG Idea** The process of meiosis produces gametes. What other actions result in variation and diversity in the offspring?

33. **WRITING in Biology** Imagine you are Gregor Mendel and create a journal entry for one of the days that you made a significant breakthrough. Describe your breakthrough and your next step.

34. In sheep, white wool is dominant and black wool is recessive. Suppose some sheep belonging to a certain flock are heterozygous for wool color. Write a plan indicating how a flock of pure-breeding white sheep could be developed.

35. In pigeons, the checker pattern of feathers (*P*) is dominant to the nonchecker pattern (*p*). Suppose a checker pigeon with the genotype *Pp* mates with a nonchecker pigeon. Use a Punnett square to predict the genotypic ratio of their offspring.

DBQ Document-Based Questions

The paragraphs below were obtained from Mendel's publication.

Data obtained from: Mendel, Gregor. 1866. *Experiments in Plant Hybridization.* Originally translated by Bateson, William, 1901: 2.

"The hybrids of such plants must, during the flowering period, be protected from the influence of all foreign pollen, or be easily capable of such protection."

36. Mendel made the above rule for his experimental plants. Summarize why this rule was important for the success of his experiments.

Ibid: 4

"The object of the experiment was to observe these variations in the case of each pair of differentiating characters, and to deduce the law according to which they appear in successive generations. The experiment resolves itself therefore into just as many separate experiments. There are constantly differentiating characters presented in the experimental plants."

37. Describe Mendel's purpose for conducting plant breeding experiments.

Assessment Online Test Practice

25. C
26. C

Constructed Response

27. meiosis, crossing over, and random fusion of sperm and egg
28. Accept any answer that is feasible.
29. Genes that are linked together on a chromosome travel together during meiosis and do not randomly assort during chromosome lining up in metaphase I.

Think Critically

30. Answers might include that the benefit is that the traits of the plants one desires will be passed on. A possible drawback is that if there is no variety in the plants, as new problems such as diseases develop, the plants may not be capable of surviving.
31. Accept any logical hypothesis.

Summative Assessment

32. Crossing over, mutations, the law of segregation, and the law of independent assortment are all ways that variation and diversity are produced in offspring.
33. Answers will vary, but should include a detailed description of the breakthrough and what the plans are for the next step in the process.
34. Plans should include a way to determine which white sheep are heterozygous; they should no longer be bred.
35. 1:1, checkered:non-checkered

DBQ Document-Based Questions

Data obtained from: Mendel, Gregor. 1866. *Experiments in Plant Hybridization*. Originally translated by Bateson, William, 1901: 2.

36. In order to control his crosses, Mendel needed to be able to ensure that his heterozygous plants were the result of his cross pollination, not some foreign material.
37. Mendel's purpose was to be able to hypothesize the mode of inheritance of characters in the pea plants.

Standardized Test Practice

Multiple Choice

1. A 5. A 9. C
2. A 6. C
3. D 7. D
4. B 8. B

Short Answer

10. Crossing over occurs between two different chromosomes but not between chromatids that are linked together. Also, it occurs between parts that are at the same location on their respective chromosomes. For example, there could be crossing over between B and H, between C and F, between D and E. Multiple answers are acceptable, as long as they fit the pattern for crossing over.
11. Crossing over can occur during synapsis, which occurs in prophase I. By this stage, the chromosomes have replicated, but they have not separated. When chromosomes come together, crossing over can occur.
12. A decrease in the CO_2 concentration would slow the process of the Calvin cycle in photosynthesis. Sugars would be produced more slowly, and the plants would grow more slowly.
13. Meiosis allows for a huge number of different combinations of genes in the sex cells of an organism, because the genes assort independently. Also, because the cells are haploid, when they combine with another sex cell (egg or sperm), there is an additional chance for variety to occur.
14. The chromosomes replicate and then become paired chromatids attached at the centromere.

Standardized Test Practice

Cumulative

Multiple Choice

1. A population will likely enter a long-term high growth rate when many individuals are which?
   A. below the main reproductive age
   B. just above the main reproductive age
   C. at the middle of the main reproductive age
   D. at the upper end of the main reproductive age

Use the illustration below to answer question 2.

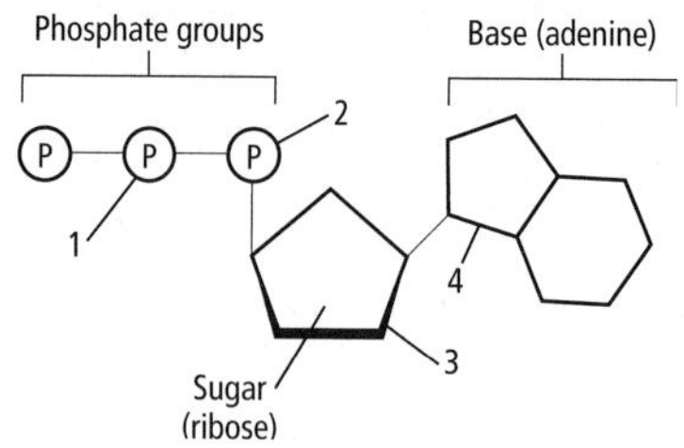

2. To release energy for use in the organism, the bond between which two groups in the ATP molecule must be broken?
   A. 1 and 2
   B. 2 and 3
   C. 2 and 4
   D. 3 and 4

3. Which process divides a cell's nucleus and nuclear material?
   A. cell cycle
   B. cytokinesis
   C. interphase
   D. mitosis

4. Which is the source of electrons in the electron transport chain stage of respiration?
   A. formation of acetyl CoA during the Krebs cycle
   B. creation of NADH and $FADH_2$ during the Krebs cycle
   C. fermentation of lactic acid
   D. breaking of bonds in glycolysis

5. Which would most likely cause lung cancer?
   A. exposure to asbestos particles
   B. exposure to fungus spores
   C. exposure to infrared radiation
   D. exposure to ultraviolet radiation

Use the illustration below to answer question 6.

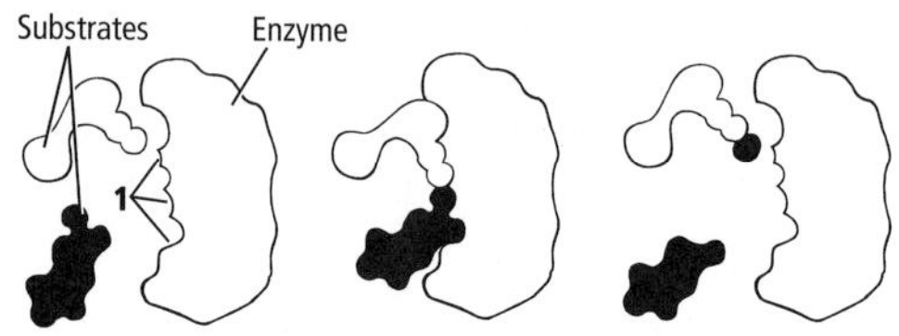

6. Which is the role of "1" in the activity of the enzyme?
   A. to make a reaction happen more slowly
   B. to make more reactants available to the substrate
   C. to provide a unique spot for substrate binding
   D. to raise the activation energy for the reaction

7. What causes the movement of calcium and sodium ions in and out of cardiac cells?
   A. charged particles in the phospholipid bilayer
   B. cholesterol molecules in the phospholipid bilayer
   C. diffusion channels in the cell membrane
   D. transport proteins in the cell membrane

8. In a cell undergoing meiosis, during which stage do the sister chromatids separate from each other?
   A. anaphase I
   B. anaphase II
   C. telophase I
   D. telophase II

9. Which is the standard SI unit for mass?
   A. candela
   B. kelvin
   C. kilogram
   D. meter

Short Answer

Use the diagram below to answer questions 10 and 11.

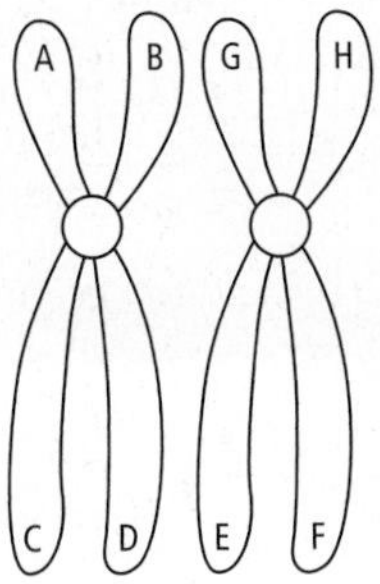

10. The diagram above shows a pair of chromosomes with different regions on the chromosomes labeled. Explain where crossing over could occur on this pair of chromosomes.

11. When is crossing over most likely to occur?

12. Suppose the concentration of CO_2 in a greenhouse decreases. Explain how the photosynthesis process could be affected by that change. Predict the overall effect on plants.

13. How does the process of meiosis promote genetic variation in a species?

14. Describe how the chromosomes change during the S phase.

15. Hypothesize why meiosis occurs in two stages—meiosis I and meiosis II.

16. Explain how factors in the environment can cause cancer to develop.

Extended Response

Use the diagram below to answer question 17.

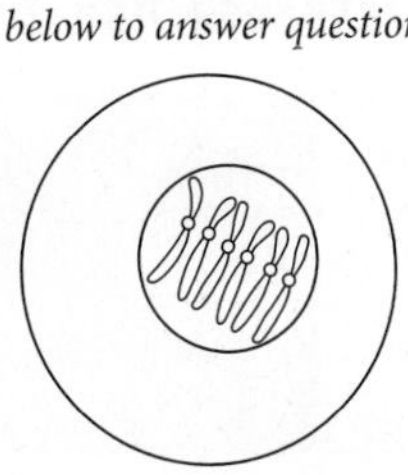

17. The diagram above shows the chromosomes found in the sex cells of a particular animal. Based on this diagram, describe what happens during fertilization in this species.

18. Assess what might happen if mitosis were NOT an extremely precise process.

Essay Question

Stem cells are cells that are not specialized for a particular function. Like other cells, stem cells contain all of the genetic material found in the organism. Stem cells, if given the correct signal, can become any type of specialized cell. There are two different types of stem cells. Embryonic stem cells are found in embryos, while adult stem cells are found in small quantities in mature tissues. The process of conducting research using stem cells, especially using embryonic stem cells, is controversial because of ethical concerns.

Using the information in the paragraph above, answer the following question in essay format.

19. Do you think medical researchers should be allowed to use stem cells as research material? Judge what you think are the benefits or risks of stem cell research.

NEED EXTRA HELP?																			
If You Missed Question . . .	1	2	3	4	5	6	7	8	9	10	11	12	13	14	15	16	17	18	19
Review Section . . .	4.2	8.2	9.1	8.3	9.3	6.2	7.2, 7.4	10.1	1.2	10.1	10.1	8.2	10.1, 10.3	9.2	10.2	9.3	10.1	9.2	9.2

15. Answers can vary. One possible answer is that two stages of meiosis are required because, first, the chromosomes divide to form a haploid number of chromosomes. Then, in meiosis II another division occurs to separate the chromatids. This allows the product of meiosis to be 4 haploid daughter cells. Without two separate stages, the number of chromatids in the daughter cells would be too great.
16. Many carcinogens are found in the environment, including UV radiation, x-rays, tobacco smoke, and chemicals.

Extended Response

17. The cell shown is haploid because it is a sex cell. It combines with another haploid cell (n=6) in fertilization to form a diploid gamete (n=12). The offspring has 12 chromosomes in its diploid form.
18. If mitosis were not reliably accurate, one or both of the resulting daughter cells might not function properly.

Essay Question

19. Answers will vary. Students should choose and state one side and provide support for their opinion. Students also may provide support for both benefits and risks.

Chapter 11 Organizer:
Complex Inheritance and Human Heredity

LabManager™
Customize any lab with the LabManager™ CD-ROM.

Essential Questions	National Science Standards	Materials and Planning: Estimated times include cleanup and disposal, but do not include teacher prep time. For cleanup and disposal guidelines, see page 39T.	Est. Time (min)
Section 1 1. How can genetic patterns be analyzed to determine dominant or recessive inheritance patterns? 2. What are examples of dominant and recessive disorders? 3. How can human pedigrees be constructed from genetic information?	UCP.1–3, UCP.5; A.1, A.2; C.2; F.1, F.5; G.1, G.2, G.3	**Launch Lab,** p. 294: textbook, pencil, paper	30
		Demonstration, p. 299: pictures or slides of various human genetic traits	10
		MiniLab 1, p. 300: textbook, pencil, paper	20
Section 2 1. What are the differences between various complex inheritance patterns? 2. How can sex-linked inheritance patterns be analyzed? 3. How can the environment influence the phenotype of an organism?	UCP.1–3, UCP.5; A.1, A.2; C.2; F.1, F.5; G.3	**Demonstration,** p. 303: microprojector or other projector, slides of normal blood cells and sickled cells	15
		Demonstration, p. 307: test for color blindness in children	10
		Demonstration, p. 309: mustard or *Brassica rapa* seeds, Petri plates, paper towel	5 min per day
Section 3 1. How are karyotypes used to study genetic disorders? 2. What is the role of telomeres? 3. How is nondisjunction related to Down syndrome and other abnormal chromosome numbers? 4. What are the benefits and risks of diagnostic fetal testing?	UCP.1–3, UCP.5; A.1, A.2; C.2; E.1; F.1, F.5; G.3	**Demonstraton,** p. 312: two pairs of socks, hook-and-loop tape	15
		MiniLab 2, p. 314: copies of data table	30
		BioLab, p. 317: coins, table of inherited human facial characteristics	35

Suggested Time for Each Lesson

Class	Chapter Opener	Section 1	Section 2	Section 3	Assessment
Basic	45 min	135 min	90 min	90 min	45 min
General	25 min	65 min	45 min	90 min	45 min
Honors	5 min	90 min	40 min	90 min	45 min

ConnectED

connectED.mcgraw-hill.com

Access interactive learning opportunities and teaching resources using these icons located throughout your StudentWorks™ Plus Online and eTeacherEdition Online.

Chapter 11 Section Resources	Additional Chapter 11 Resources	Technology
FAST FILE Unit 3 Resources: Launch Lab Worksheet* MiniLab Worksheet* Study Guide (English/Spanish)* Section Quick Check **Reading Essentials 11.1** **Science Notebook 11.1*** **FAST FILE Unit 3 Resources:** Study Guide (English/Spanish)* Section Quick Check **Reading Essentials 11.2** **Science Notebook 11.2*** **FAST FILE Unit 3 Resources:** MiniLab Worksheet* BioLab Worksheet* Study Guide (English/Spanish)* Section Quick Check **Reading Essentials 11.3** **Science Notebook 11.3***	**FAST FILE Unit 3 Resources:** Chapter Diagnostic Test Concept Mapping* Real-World Biology Enrichment Chapter Tests A, B, and C **Transparencies:** Bellringer Transparencies* Biology Concepts Transparencies* **Lab Resources:** Laboratory Manual* Probeware Lab Manual* Forensics Lab Manual* Pre-AP Lab Manual* Open Inquiry in Biology* Guided Inquiry in Biology*	**Teaching Tools:** eTeacherEdition Online Classroom Presentation Toolkit CD-ROM* LabManager™ CD-ROM* Video Lab DVD* Virtual Lab CD-ROM* What's BIOLOGY Got To Do With It? StudentWorks™ Plus Online* **Chapter Assessment Tools:** Classroom Presentation Toolkit CD-ROM* *ExamView® Assessment Suite* CD-ROM **Web-Based Resources:** • StudentWorks™ Plus Online • eTeacherEdition Online • Animations* • The Interactive Time Line* • Interactive Tables* • Online Quizzes • Online Test Practice • Standardized Test Practice • Virtual Labs* • Multilingual eGlossary* • Vocabulary eGames* • Vocabulary eFlashcards • WebQuests • Personal Tutors

While all resources listed are appropriate for English learners, the * indicates resources with a strong visual or hands-on component for EL.

Teaching strategies and activities have been coded for differentiated instruction.

AL Activities for students working above grade level	**OL** Activities for students working on grade level	**BL** Activities for students working below grade level	**EL** Activities for English learners (also ELL)	**COOP LEARN** Activities designed for small cooperative group work

CHAPTER 11

Launch Lab
What do you know about human inheritance?

Inquiry Launch Lab

For a lab worksheet, use your eTeacherEdition.

RUBRIC A rubric for evaluating Launch Labs is found on your eTeacherEdition.

Est. Time 30 min

Teaching Strategies
- Have students work individually or in small groups.
- Check answers to the genetics quiz below:
  - **A.** True. A sperm cell carries either a Y or an X chromosome. XY pairing produces a male; XX pairing produces a female.
  - **B.** True. Genetic traits not expressed in one generation may be expressed in later generations.
  - **C.** True. Because identical twins form from the same fertilized egg, they must be the same gender.

Procedure
1. Read the statements below carefully and determine whether they are true or false.
   Statements:
   - **A.** The father determines the gender of the child.
   - **B.** Individuals may transmit characteristics to their offspring which they themselves do not show.
   - **C.** Identical twins always are of the same gender.
2. Discuss your answers with your classmates and teacher.

CHAPTER 11
Complex Inheritance and Human Heredity

ConnectED

Your one-stop online resource
connectED.mcgraw-hill.com

- Video
- Audio
- Review
- Inquiry
- WebQuest
- Assessment
- Concepts in Motion
- Multilingual eGlossary

Launch Lab
What do you know about human inheritance?

As knowledge and understanding of human inheritance increases, long-standing ideas regarding the facts of human heredity must be reexamined. Any ideas disproven by new discoveries must be rejected.

For a lab worksheet, use your StudentWorks™ Plus Online.

Inquiry Launch Lab

FOLDABLES®

Make a vocabulary book and label each tab with the name of a different genetic disorder. Use it to organize your notes on genetic disorders.

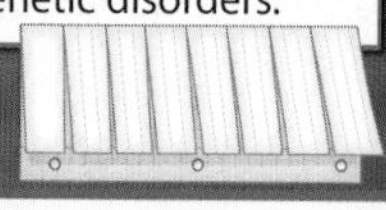

Analysis
1. **Assess** which question was missed most often by the entire class. Discuss reasons why. Answers will vary, but should give some insight into the knowledge, background, and experiences your students have regarding human heredity. Identify and correct any misconceptions.
2. **Analyze** why it is helpful to understand human heredity. Knowledge of human heredity is necessary to understand legal, social, and moral issues that involve inherited traits. Such knowledge could help people make certain health decisions.

THEME FOCUS Diversity
Complex forms of inheritance result in a wide diversity of characteristics.

BIG Idea Human inheritance does not always follow Mendel's laws.

Section 1 • Basic Patterns of Human Inheritance

Section 2 • Complex Patterns of Inheritance

Section 3 • Chromosomes and Human Heredity

Introduce the Chapter

Inheritance

ASK STUDENTS: ***What physical abilities should a good soccer player have?*** Answers may include good coordination, good running ability, and muscular strength. ***What physical features are not important for a good soccer player to have?*** Answers may include eye color, shape of nose, and curly or straight hair. List characteristics in two columns on the board as students share answers. Use this list to spark a discussion that can lead to human inheritance of physical features and the influence of environmental factors such as diet and exercise.

BIG Idea

Tongue-Rolling Ability

ASK STUDENTS: ***Can you roll your tongue? Discuss whether other members of your family have this trait.*** Tongue-rolling ability is dominant in humans. Use this example to discuss that traits are inherited. Tell students that in this chapter they will learn some other types of inheritance that were unknown by Mendel and are variations of Mendel's concept of dominance.

THEMES

Scientific Inquiry The discovery of DNA led to an understanding of the inheritance of traits from one generation to the next.

Diversity Complex inheritance patterns account for some of the vast genetic diversity in humans.

Energy Some genetic diseases, such as Tay-Sachs disease, affect metabolism.

Homeostasis Inheritance of genes from generation to generation helps maintain homeostasis among species.

Change Mutations in genes allow possible changes in inheritance to occur.

Section 1

MAIN Idea

BL OL AL COOP LEARN

Tracing Traits Remind students that the trait for the ability to roll one's tongue is dominant (*TT*). Then, ask student to imagine a family with three children. Two of the children cannot roll their tongues. **ASK STUDENTS:** ***What are the genotypes of the parents?*** Students should use Punnett squares to conclude that either one parent is heterozygous dominant (*Tt*) and the other parent is homozygous recessive (*tt*) or that both parents are heterozygous (*Tt*).

Develop Concepts

BL OL AL

Clarify a Misconception

ASK STUDENTS: ***If someone looks more like one parent than the other, did that person inherit more genes from that parent?*** no Some students might think that because children look more like one parent than the other, the child received more genetic material from one of the parents. Clarify that the child receives one set of chromosomes from one parent and the second set from the other parent. Review meiosis, the combination of chromosomes, and the concept of dominant and recessive traits.

Reading Strategy

EL BL OL

Find Supporting Details

Have students create a three-column chart. In the first column, have them write the name of each genetic disorder that they will read about in this chapter. After they read, have them write whether the disorder is dominant or recessive in the middle column. In the last column, have them write any symptoms of the disorder.

Section 1

Reading Preview

Essential Questions

- How can genetic patterns be analyzed to determine dominant or recessive inheritance patterns?
- What are examples of dominant and recessive disorders?
- How can human pedigrees be constructed from genetic information?

Review Vocabulary

genes: segments of DNA that control the production of proteins

New Vocabulary

carrier
pedigree

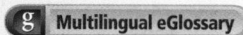

Multilingual eGlossary

Basic Patterns of Human Inheritance

MAIN Idea **The inheritance of a trait over several generations can be shown in a pedigree.**

Real-World Reading Link Knowing a purebred dog's ancestry can help the owner know health problems that are common to that dog. Similarly, tracing human inheritance can show how a trait was passed down from one generation to the next.

Recessive Genetic Disorders

Connection to History Gregor Mendel's work was ignored for more than 30 years. During the early 1900s, scientists began to take an interest in heredity, and Mendel's work was rediscovered. About this time, Dr. Archibald Garrod, an English physician, became interested in a disorder linked to an enzyme deficiency called alkaptonuria (al kap tuh NYUR ee uh), which results in black urine. It is caused by acid excretion into the urine. Dr. Garrod observed that the condition appeared at birth and continued throughout the patient's life, ultimately affecting bones and joints. He also noted that alkaptonuria ran in families. With the help of another scientist, he determined that alkaptonuria was a recessive genetic disorder.

Today, progress continues to help us understand genetic disorders. Review **Table 1,** and recall that a recessive trait is expressed when the individual is homozygous recessive for that trait. Therefore, those with at least one dominant allele will not express the recessive trait. An individual who is heterozygous for a recessive disorder is called a **carrier.** Review **Table 2** as you read about several recessive genetic disorders.

Table 1 Review of Terms — Concepts in Motion Interactive Table

Term	Example	Definition
Homozygous	True-breeding yellow-seed pea plants would be *YY*, and green-seed pea plants would be *yy*. 	An organism with two of the same alleles for a particular trait is said to be homozygous for that trait.
Heterozygous	A plant that is *Yy* would be a yellow-seed pea. 	An organism with two different alleles for a particular trait is said to be heterozygous for that trait. When alleles are present in the heterozygous state, the dominant trait will be observed.

Concepts in Motion
Interactive Table

Content Background

Teacher FYI Sir Archibald Garrod, a British physician, discovered a pattern of inheritance leading to alkaptonuria, a disorder in which urine turns black. Alkaptonuria also causes severe arthritis later in life. Garrod concluded that the dark urine is caused by an inherited biochemical abnormality. Considering that he worked in the early 1900s, Garrod's ideas were ahead of his time.

Table 2 Recessive Genetic Disorders in Humans

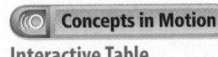

Concepts in Motion
Interactive Table

Disorder	Occurrence in the U.S.	Cause	Effect	Cure/Treatment
Cystic fibrosis	1 in 3500	The gene that codes for a membrane protein is defective.	• Excessive mucus production • Digestive and respiratory failure	• No cure • Daily cleaning of mucus from the lungs • Mucus-thinning drugs • Pancreatic enzyme supplements
Albinism	1 in 17,000	Genes do not produce normal amounts of the pigment melanin.	• No color in the skin, eyes and hair • Skin susceptible to UV damage • Vision problems	• No cure • Protect skin from the Sun and other environmental factors • Visual rehabilitation
Galactosemia	1 in 50,000 to 70,000	Absence of the gene that codes for the enzyme that breaks down galactose	• Mental disabilities • Enlarged liver • Kidney failure	• No cure • Restriction of lactose/galactose in the diet
Tay-Sachs disease	1 in 2500 (affects people of Jewish descent)	Absence of a necessary enzyme that breaks down fatty substances	• Buildup of fatty deposits in the brain • Mental disabilities	• No cure or treatment • Death by age 5

S

Cystic fibrosis One of the most common recessive genetic disorders among Caucasians is cystic fibrosis, which affects the mucus-producing glands, digestive enzymes, and sweat glands. Chloride ions are not absorbed into the cells of a person with cystic fibrosis but are excreted in the sweat. Without sufficient chloride ions in cells, water does not diffuse from cells. This causes a secretion of thick mucus that affects many areas of the body. The thick mucus clogs the ducts in the pancreas, interrupts digestion, and blocks the tiny respiratory pathways in the lungs. Patients with cystic fibrosis are at a higher risk of infection because of excess mucus in their lungs.

Treatment for cystic fibrosis currently includes physical therapy, medication, special diets, and the use of replacement digestive enzymes. Genetic tests are available to determine whether a person is a carrier, indicating they are carrying the recessive gene.

C

Albinism In humans, albinism is caused by altered genes, resulting in the absence of the skin pigment melanin in hair and eyes. Albinism is found in other animals as well. A person with albinism has white hair, very pale skin, and pink pupils. The absence of pigment in eyes can cause problems with vision. Although we all must protect our skin from the Sun's ultraviolet radiation, those with albinism need to be especially careful.

Tay-Sachs disease Tay-Sachs (TAY saks) disease is a recessive genetic disorder. Its gene is found on chromosome 15. Often identified by a cherry-red spot on the back of the eye, Tay-Sachs disease (TSD) seems to be predominant among Jews of eastern European descent.

FOLDABLES®
Incorporate information from this section into your Foldable.

Concepts in Motion
Interactive Table

S Skill Practice

EL BL OL AL COOP LEARN

Visual Literacy Organize students into pairs. Have partners look over Tables 2 and 3 and decide whether dominant or recessive disorders are more common. recessive

ASK STUDENTS: ***Why are recessive disorders more common than dominant disorders?*** When a disorder is dominant, only one allele must be inherited for the person to be affected. If the dominant trait interferes with survival, the individual is less likely to pass the gene to the next generation. When the disorder is recessive, carriers do not display the disorder. Many people carry recessive alleles without being affected by the disorder.

C Critical Thinking

BL OL AL **Predict** Draw a large Punnett square on the board. Perform a cross of two parents that are heterogenous for the gene.

ASK STUDENTS: ***What are the chances of two carriers of cystic fibrosis having a child with cystic fibrosis?*** one in four For caucasians, the odds of one carrier (1/23.6) marrying another carrier (1/23.6) is 1/500. The incidence of cystic fibrosis is about 1/2000 in Caucasians.

FOLDABLES®

RUBRIC A rubric for evaluating Foldables is found on your eTeacherEdition Online.

Going Further On the back of their Foldables, have students research and categorize the diseases investigated on the front tabs by dollar amounts spent to discover treatments or to find methods of prevention.

Content Background

Real-World Connection Singer Woodrow "Woody" Guthrie was born in Oklahoma in 1912. During the Dust Bowl of the 1930s, he gained fame singing on radio and writing political songs of protest. One of his most famous songs is "This Land Is Your Land." Later, the federal government paid him to compose songs. His health and behavior began to deteriorate, and he was misdiagnosed with such diseases as alcoholism and schizophrenia. In fact, he suffered from Huntington's disease, a dominant genetic disorder that had affected his mother. He died in October of 1967.

Writing Support
OL AL COOP LEARN

Summary Writing Have students work in small groups to research an inherited condition, such as sickle-cell disease or Tay-Sachs disease, that is more frequent in some populations than others. Have them write a summary of the condition and present it to the class.

Develop Concepts
EL BL OL AL COOP LEARN

Bulletin Board Have students collect articles from newspapers and magazines that relate to genetics. Have them work in groups to prepare a poster or a bulletin board covered with current articles about genetics.

W Writing Support
OL AL COOP LEARN

Technical Writing Have students investigate other dominant or recessive disorders that are not mentioned in the chapter. Some examples of these disorders include polydactylism, Marfan syndrome, galactosemia, and muscular dystrophy. Have them design and write a technical pamphlet describing the genetic disorder. The pamphlet should include symptoms, genetic causes, frequencies of occurrence, treatments, and at least one graph. Students can research various disorders on the Internet.

BL Supply students with appropriate research material and have them write a paragraph about a disorder.

Concepts in Motion
Interactive Table

VOCABULARY
ACADEMIC VOCABULARY
Decline
to gradually waste away; or a downward slope
His health declined because of the disease.

TSD is caused by the absence of the enzymes responsible for breaking down fatty acids called gangliosides. Normally, gangliosides are made and then dissolved as the brain develops. However, in a person affected by Tay-Sachs disease, the gangliosides accumulate in the brain, inflating brain nerve cells and causing mental deterioration.

Galactosemia Galactosemia (guh lak tuh SEE mee uh) is characterized by the inability of the body to digest galactose. During digestion, lactose from milk breaks down into galactose and glucose. Glucose is the sugar used by the body for energy and circulates in the blood. Galactose must be broken down into glucose by an enzyme named GALT. Persons who lack or have defective GALT cannot digest galactose. Persons with galactosemia should avoid milk products.

Dominant Genetic Disorders

Not all genetic disorders are caused by recessive inheritance. As described in **Table 3,** some disorders, such as the rare disorder Huntington's disease, are caused by dominant alleles. That means those who do not have the disorder are homozygous recessive for the trait.

Huntington's disease The dominant genetic disorder Huntington's disease affects the nervous system and occurs in one out of 10,000 people in the U.S. The symptoms of this disorder first appear in affected individuals between the ages of 30 and 50 years old. The symptoms include a gradual loss of brain function, uncontrollable movements, and emotional disturbances. Genetic tests are available to detect this dominant allele. However, no preventive treatment or cure for this disease exists.

Achondroplasia An individual with achondroplasia (a kahn droh PLAY zhee uh) has a small body size and limbs that are comparatively short. Achondroplasia is the most common form of dwarfism. A person with achondroplasia will have an adult height of about four feet and will have a normal life expectancy.

Interestingly, 75 percent of individuals with achondroplasia are born to parents of average size. When children with achondroplasia are born to parents of average size, the conclusion is that the condition occurred because of a new mutation or a genetic change.

Reading Check **Compare** the chances of inheriting a dominant disorder to the chances of inheriting a recessive disorder if you have one parent with the disease. W

Table 3 **Dominant Genetic Disorders in Humans** Concepts in Motion Interactive Table

Disorder	Occurrence in the U.S.	Cause	Effect	Cure/Treatment
Huntington's disease	1 in 10,000	A gene affecting neurological function is defective.	• Decline of mental and neurological functions • Ability to move deteriorates	• No cure or treatment
Achondroplasia	1 in 25,000	A gene that affects bone growth is abnormal.	• Short arms and legs • Large head	• No cure or treatment

Differentiated Instruction

Physically Disabled When students with physical disabilities are in class, do not expect less of them because of their disability. The same academic and social standards should be set for every student so that students with disabilities are not viewed as less capable than their peers.

For more tips, see pages 14T–15T.

Reading Check Recessive: 50% chance if parent without the disease is heterozygous, 0% chance if parent without the disease is homozygous dominant. Dominant: 50% chance if the parent with the disease is heterozygous, 100% chance if the parent with the disease is homozygous dominant.

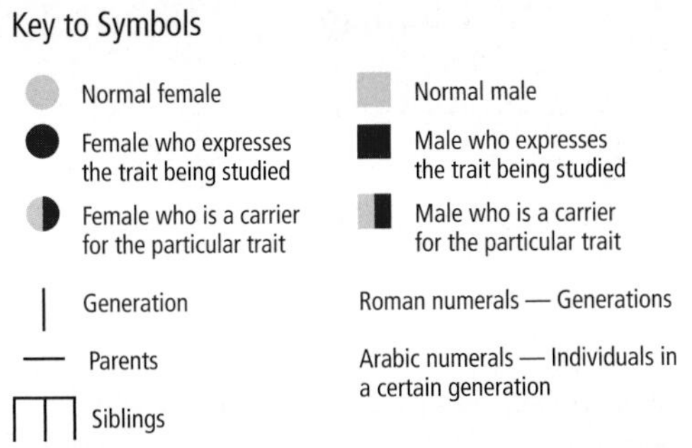

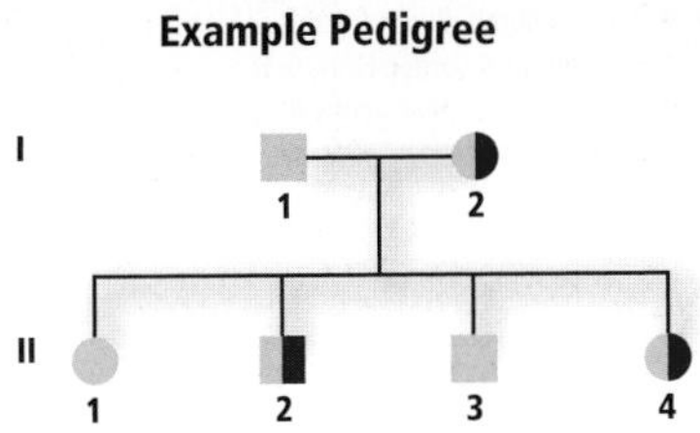

■ **Figure 1** A pedigree uses standard symbols to indicate what is known about the trait being studied.

Review Personal Tutor

Pedigrees

In organisms such as peas and fruit flies, scientists can perform crosses to study genetic relationships. In the case of humans, a scientist studies a family history using a **pedigree,** a diagram that traces the inheritance of a particular trait through several generations. A pedigree uses symbols to illustrate inheritance of the trait. Males are represented by squares, and females are represented by circles, as shown in **Figure 1.** One who expresses the trait being studied is represented by a dark, or filled, square or circle, depending on their gender. One who does not express the trait is represented by an unfilled square or circle.

A horizontal line between two symbols shows that these individuals are the parents of the offspring listed below them. Offspring are listed in descending birth order from left to right and are connected to each other and their parents.

A pedigree uses a numbering system in which Roman numerals represent generations, and individuals are numbered by birth order using Arabic numbers. For example, in **Figure 1,** individual II1 is a female who is the firstborn in generation II.

Analyzing Pedigrees

A pedigree illustrating Tay-Sachs disease is shown in **Figure 2.** Recall from **Table 2** that Tay-Sachs disease is a recessive genetic disorder caused by the lack of an enzyme involved in lipid metabolism. The missing enzyme causes lipids to build up in the central nervous system, which can lead to death.

Examine the pedigree in **Figure 2.** Note that two unaffected parents, I1 and I2, have an affected child—II3, indicating that each parent has one recessive allele—they both are heterozygous and carriers for the trait. The half-filled square and circle show that both parents are carriers.

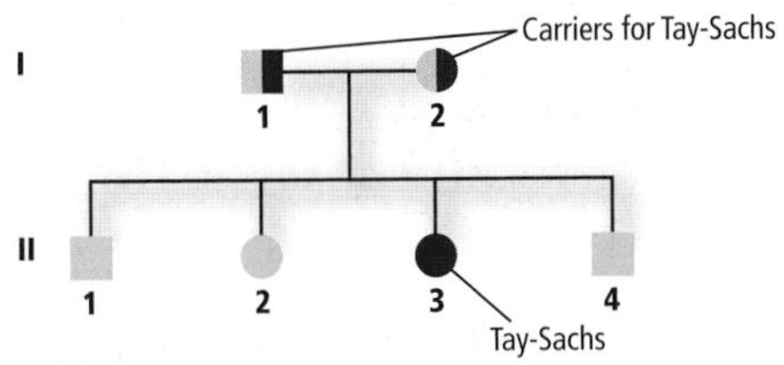

■ **Figure 2** This pedigree illustrates the inheritance of the recessive disorder Tay-Sachs disease. Note that two unaffected parents (I1 and I2) can have an affected child (II3).

D

Critical Thinking

BL OL AL Differentiate On the board, place two or three pedigrees that illustrate dominant or recessive inheritance, such as pedigrees showing the inheritance of cystic fibrosis, Huntington's disease, and Tay-Sachs disease. **ASK STUDENTS:** ***Which type of inheritance is shown in each pedigree?*** Have students write down how they determined which type of inheritance is demonstrated, then call on volunteers to share their answers orally.

Review Personal Tutor

Listen to a teacher explain pedigrees.

D Develop Concepts

BL OL AL Scaffolding
ASK STUDENTS: ***What symbols are used to represent a male and a female in a pedigree?*** square for male; circle for female ***For what purpose is a genetic pedigree used?*** It shows the inheritance of a particular trait across several generations. ***Describe the pedigree of a boy who has galactosemia if his father has galactosemia, his paternal grandparents are phenotypically normal, his mother and maternal grandparents are both phenotypically normal.*** Paternal grandparents were both carriers of the recessive allele. Either or both maternal grandparents carried the recessive allele. ***What information might be added from the family ancestry that could possibly help determine the mother's parents' genotypes?*** By knowing more about the family ancestry of the mother's parents, one might be able to determine whether one or both of them are carriers of galactosemia.

Demonstration

BL OL AL Human Genetic Traits Show students pictures that demonstrate various human genetic traits. Contact a local hospital's education specialist about borrowing a slideshow presentation that would be appropriate for this demonstration.
ASK STUDENTS: ***Is this trait dominant or recessive?*** Discuss dominant and recessive traits such as: widow's peak (dominant), PTC tasting (dominant), earlobe shape (attached is recessive), bent little finger (dominant), dimples (dominant), hair whorl (clockwise is dominant), and mid-digital hair (hair is dominant).
Est. time: 10 min

MiniLab 1

Inquiry MiniLab

For a lab worksheet, use your eTeacherEdition Online.

✱RUBRIC A rubric for evaluating MiniLabs is found on your eTeacherEdition Online.

Est. Time 20 min

Safety Precaution Approve lab safety forms before work begins.

Teaching Strategy Students could work individually or in small groups.

Analysis

1. With pedigrees, one can follow traits from one generaton to the next.
2. Families affected with unfavorable traits can be given advice about the chances of their future children possessing these traits. However, pedigree information obtained from only a few members of a family could be inaccurate, unreliable, or misleading.

LabManager™

Customize this lab with the LabManager™ CD-ROM.

S Skill Practice

BL OL AL COOP LEARN

Visual Literacy Have students form groups of two or three and compare Figures 2 and 3. **ASK STUDENTS:** ***What are the differences between the two types of inheritance?*** Dominant conditions often show up every generation. Individuals with one allele for a recessive condition would not be affected, but two individuals with one recessive allele each can have an affected child.

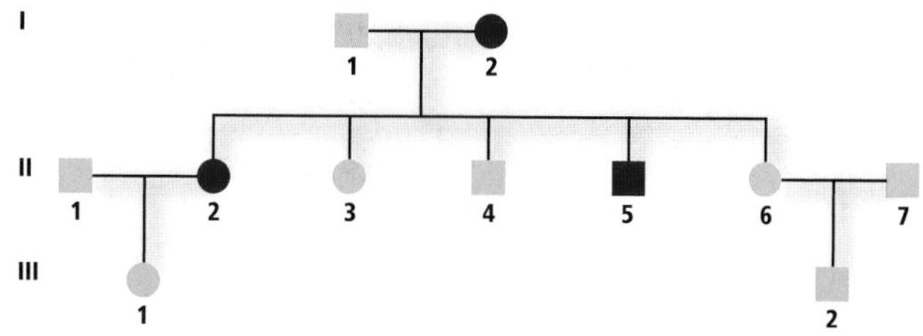

■ **Figure 3** This pedigree illustrates the inheritance of a dominant disorder. Note that affected parents can pass on their genes (II2, II5), but unaffected parents cannot have an affected child (III2).

S

The pedigree in **Figure 3** shows the inheritance of the dominant genetic disorder polydactyly (pah lee DAK tuh lee). People with this disorder have extra fingers and toes. Recall that with dominant inheritance the trait is expressed when at least one dominant allele is present. An individual with an unaffected parent and a parent with polydactyly could be either heterozygous or homozygous recessive for the trait. Each unaffected person would be homozygous recessive for the trait.

For example, in **Figure 3,** individual I2 has polydactyly, indicated by the dark circle. Because she shows the trait, she is either homozygous dominant or heterozygous. It can be inferred that she is heterozygous—having one dominant gene and one recessive gene—because offspring II3 and II4 do not have the disorder. Notice that II6 and II7, two unaffected parents, have an unaffected offspring—III2. What can be inferred about II2, based on the phenotype of her parents and her offspring?

MiniLab 1

Investigate Human Pedigrees

Inquiry MiniLab

Where are the branches on the family tree? Unlike some organisms, humans reproduce slowly and produce few offspring at one time. One method used to study human traits is pedigree analysis.

Procedure

1. Read and complete the lab safety form.
2. Imagine that you are a geneticist interviewing a person about his or her family concerning the hypothetical trait of hairy earlobes.
3. From the transcript below, construct a pedigree. Use appropriate symbols and format.
   "My name is Scott. My great grandfather Walter had hairy earlobes (HEs), but great grandma Elsie did not. Walter and Elsie had three children: Lola, Leo, and Duane. Leo, the oldest, has HEs, as does the middle child, Lola; but the youngest child, Duane, does not. Duane never married and has no children. Leo married Bertie, and they have one daughter, Patty. In Leo's family, he is the only one with HEs. Lola married John, and they have two children: Carolina and Luetta. John does not have HEs, but both of his daughters do."

Analysis

1. **Assess** In what ways do pedigrees simplify the analysis of inheritance?
2. **Think Critically** Using this lab as a frame of reference, how can we put to practical use our understanding of constructing and analyzing human pedigrees?

Content Background

Teacher FYI Tay Sachs disease is a fatal inherited disorder that most commonly affects infants. The babies appear healthy at birth but progressively deteriorate after a few months. They lack an enzyme (hexoaminindase A) to break down fatty substances that accumulate in nerve cells. Eventually these substances build up and destroy the nerve cells. Death usually occurs by the age of five.

Inferring genotypes Pedigrees are used to infer genotypes from the observation of phenotypes. By knowing physical traits, genealogists can determine what genes an individual is most likely to have. Phenotypes of entire families are analyzed in order to determine family genotypes, as symbolized in **Figure 3.**

Pedigrees help genetic counselors determine whether inheritance patterns are dominant or recessive. Once the inheritance pattern is determined, the genotypes of the individuals can largely be resolved through pedigree analysis. To analyze pedigrees, one particular trait is studied, and a determination is made as to whether that trait is dominant or recessive. Dominant traits are easier to recognize than recessive traits because dominant traits are exhibited in the phenotype.

A recessive trait will not be expressed unless the person is homozygous recessive for the trait. That means that a recessive allele is passed on by each parent. When recessive traits are expressed, the ancestry of the person expressing the trait is followed for several generations to determine which parents and grandparents were carriers of the recessive allele.

Predicting disorders If good records have been kept within families, disorders in future offspring can be predicted. However, more accuracy can be expected if several individuals within the family can be evaluated. The study of human genetics is difficult, because scientists are limited by time, ethics, and circumstances. For example, it takes decades for each generation to mature and then to have offspring when the study involves humans. Therefore, good record keeping, where it exists, helps scientists use pedigree analysis to study inheritance patterns, to determine phenotypes, and to ascertain genotypes within a family.

CAREERS IN BIOLOGY

Genealogist A genealogist studies or traces the descent of individuals or families. Many professional genealogists are board-certified and accredited.

C

Section 1 Assessment

Section Summary

- Genetic disorders can be caused by dominant or recessive alleles.
- Cystic fibrosis is a genetic disorder that affects mucus and sweat secretions.
- Individuals with albinism do not have melanin in their skin, hair, and eyes.
- Huntington's disease affects the nervous system.
- Achondroplasia sometimes is called dwarfism.
- Pedigrees are used to study human inheritance patterns.

Understand Main Ideas

1. MAIN Idea **Construct** a family pedigree of two unaffected parents with a child who suffers from cystic fibrosis.
2. **Explain** the type of inheritance associated with Huntington's disease and achondroplasia.
3. **Interpret** Can two parents with albinism have an unaffected child? Explain.
4. **Diagram** Suppose both parents can roll their tongues but their son cannot. Draw a pedigree showing this trait, and label each symbol with the appropriate genotype.

Think Critically

MATH in Biology

5. Phenylketonuria (PKU) is a recessive genetic disorder. If both parents are carriers, what is the probability of this couple having a child with PKU? What is the chance of this couple having two children with PKU?
6. **Determine** When a couple requests a test for the cystic fibrosis gene, what types of questions might the physician ask before ordering the tests?

C Critical Thinking

AL Consider Rare recessive disorders can occur in families after many generations.

ASK STUDENTS: ***How is this possible?*** The allele for a rare recessive disorder can remain hidden in the carrier state for many generations. Not until a family member with a recessive trait has offspring with another human who is a carrier will the recessive condition appear.

Formative Assessment

Evaluation

ASK STUDENTS: ***Name one type of condition that shows dominant inheritance and one that shows recessive inheritance.*** Answers will vary but should include examples from the chapter. ***List the effects (phenotypes) of each condition.***

Remediation Students having difficulty keeping track of the various types of genetic disorders can make flash cards for each disorder. Have them place the name of the disorder on one side and the type of inheritance and effects of the disorder on the other side. Students can use both sides of the card for studying.

Section 1 Assessment

1. The pedigree should show both parents as carriers (half-filled symbols) and the child infected with the disorder (a filled symbol).
2. dominant
3. Since albinism is recessive, the only type of offspring albino parents can have are albinos.
4. Both parents carry a recessive gene and have the genotype *Tt*. Their symbols should be half shaded. The boy is *tt*. His symbol should be shaded completely.
5. 1/4, 1/16 (1/4 × 1/4)
6. Answers may vary but might include: Why does the couple want to test for the cystic fibrosis gene? Is there a history of cystic fibrosis in either family?

Assessment Online Quiz

Section 2

MAIN Idea BL OL AL

Eye-Color Inheritance
ASK STUDENTS: ***What possible eye colors are there?*** Answers will likely include brown, green, and blue. Have students examine each other's eyes. ***What else do you notice about eye color?*** There are other shades, such as light blue, dark blue, and hazel; light, medium, and dark brown and black. Have students hypothesize whether eye color is inherited in a simple dominant/recessive manner. At this time the exact inheritance model of eye color has not been determined, but polygenic models have been made with a minimum of three pairs of genes.

R Reading Strategy

BL OL AL COOP LEARN

Brainstorm Have students read the new vocabulary terms on this page. Have students work in groups of three to brainstorm ways of remembering the definitions of these words.

C Critical Thinking

BL OL AL COOP LEARN

Compare Have students form pairs and examine Figure 4. **ASK STUDENTS:** ***Compare incomplete dominance and codominance to regular dominant/recessive inheritance.*** In codominance, each allele is expressed; in incomplete dominance, the resulting phenotype is an intermediate between the two homozygous phenotypes.

Section 2

Reading Preview

Essential Questions

- What are the differences between various complex inheritance patterns?
- How can sex-linked inheritance patterns be analyzed?
- How can the environment influence the phenotype of an organism?

Review Vocabulary

gamete: a mature sex cell (sperm or egg) with a haploid number of chromosomes

New Vocabulary

incomplete dominance
codominance
multiple alleles
epistasis
sex chromosome
autosome
sex-linked trait
polygenic trait

g Multilingual eGlossary

Complex Patterns of Inheritance

MAIN Idea Complex inheritance of traits does not follow inheritance patterns described by Mendel.

Real-World Reading Link Imagine that you have red-green color blindness. In bright light, red lights do not stand out against surroundings. At night, green lights look like white streetlights. To help those with red-green color blindness, traffic lights always follow the same pattern. Red-green color blindness, however, does not follow the same pattern of inheritance described by Mendel.

Incomplete Dominance

Recall that when an organism is heterozygous for a trait, its phenotype will be that of the dominant trait. For example, if the genotype of a pea plant is *Tt* and *T* is the genotype for the dominant trait *tall*, then its phenotype will be tall. When red-flowered snapdragons (C^RC^R) are crossed with white-flowered snapdragons (C^WC^W), the heterozygous offspring have pink flowers (C^RC^W), as shown in **Figure 4.** This is an R example of **incomplete dominance,** in which the heterozygous phenotype is an intermediate phenotype between the two homozygous phenotypes. When the heterozygous F_1 generation snapdragon plants are allowed to self-fertilize, as in **Figure 4,** the flowers are red, pink, and white in a 1:2:1 ratio, respectively.

Codominance

Recall that when an organism is heterozygous for a particular trait, the dominant phenotype is expressed. In a complex inheritance pattern called **codominance,** both alleles are expressed in the heterozygous condition. Sickle-cell disease provides a case study of codominant inheritance.

Review Personal Tutor

Figure 4 The color of snapdragon flowers is a result of incomplete dominance. When a plant with white flowers is crossed with a plant with red flowers, the offspring have pink flowers. Red, pink, and white offspring will result from self-fertilization of a plant with pink flowers.
C **Predict** *what would happen if you crossed a pink flower with a white flower.*

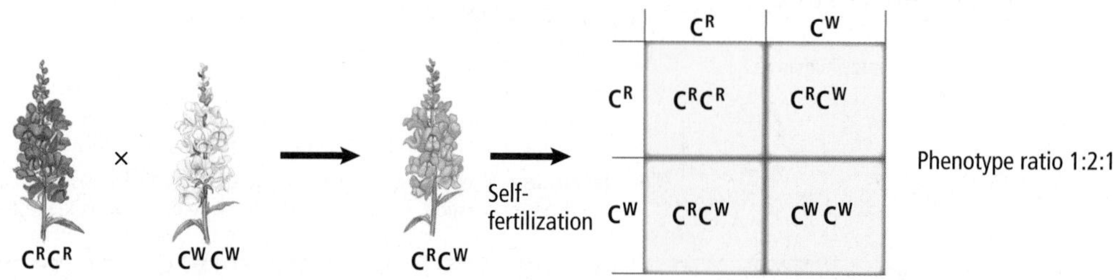

Review Personal Tutor

Listen to a teacher explain inheritance.

Caption Question Fig. 4 The offspring would be 1/2 pink and 1/2 white.

Color-Enhanced SEM Magnification: 10,000×

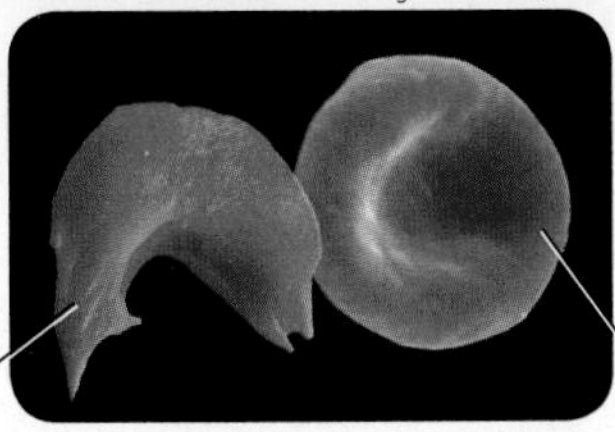

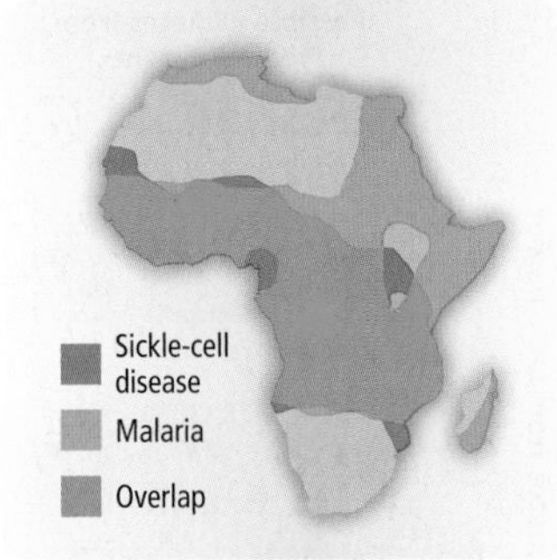

■ **Figure 5**
Left: Normal red blood cells are flat and disk-shaped. Sickle-shaped cells are elongated and C-shaped. They can clump, blocking circulation in small vessels.
Right: The sickle-cell allele increases resistance to malaria.

Sickle-cell disease The allele responsible for sickle-cell disease is particularly common in people of African descent, with about nine percent of African Americans having one form of the trait. Sickle-cell disease affects red blood cells and their ability to transport oxygen. The photograph in **Figure 5** shows the blood cells of an individual who is heterozygous for the sickle-cell trait. Changes in hemoglobin—the protein in red blood cells—cause those blood cells to change to a sickle, or C-shape. Sickle-shaped cells do not effectively transport oxygen because they block circulation in small blood vessels. Those who are heterozygous for the trait have both normal and sickle-shaped cells. These individuals can lead relatively normal lives, as the normal blood cells compensate for the sickle-shaped cells.

Sickle-cell disease and malaria Note in **Figure 5** the distribution of both sickle-cell disease and malaria in Africa. Some areas with sickle-cell disease overlap areas of widespread malaria. Why might such high levels of the sickle-cell allele exist in central Africa? Scientists have discovered that those who are heterozygous for the sickle-cell trait also have a higher resistance to malaria. The death rate due to malaria is lower where the sickle-cell trait is higher. Because less malaria exists in those areas, more people live to pass on the sickle-cell trait to offspring. Consequently, sickle-cell disease continues to increase in Africa.

D

DATA ANALYSIS LAB 1

Based on Real Data*

Interpret the Graph

What is the relationship between sickle-cell disease and other complications? Patients who have been diagnosed with sickle-cell disease face many symptoms, including respiratory failure and neurological problems. The graph shows the relationship between age and two different symptoms—pain and fever—during the two weeks preceding an episode of acute chest syndrome and hospitalization.

Think Critically

1. **State** which age group has the highest level of pain before being hospitalized.
2. **Describe** the relationship between age and fever before hospitalization.

Data and Observations

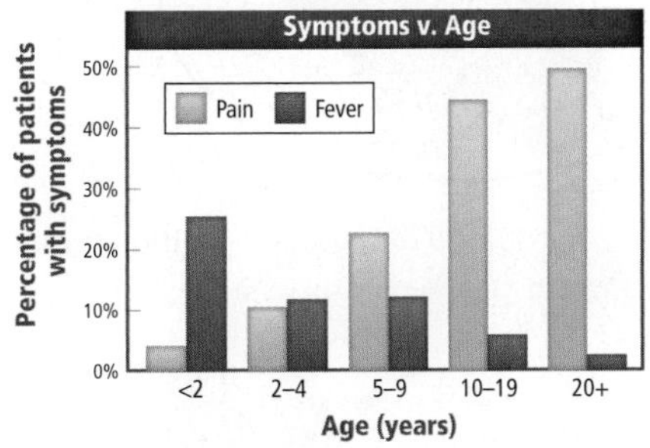

*Data obtained from: Walters, et al. 2002. Novel therapeutic approaches in sickle cell disease. *Hemotology* 17: 10-34.

Demonstration

Sickle-Cell Disease Using a microprojector, scanned photos, or images from the Internet, prepare a slideshow presentation showing a blood smear from a person without sickled cells and one showing sickle-cell disease. Emphasize that the cells are sickled when they reach areas of low oxygen in the body, such as in the hands and feet.
Est. time: 15 min

D Develop Concepts

EL BL OL AL

Demonstrate Codominance Display pictures of checkered chickens. Use the checkered chickens as another example of codominance. Black chickens breed with white chickens, resulting in chickens with both black and white feathers. Once you discuss this example, use a photo of a red shorthorn bull and a white shorthorn cow. When bred, they produce a both red and white hair mixed shorthorn offspring.
ASK STUDENTS: ***What type of inheritance does this demonstrate?*** codominance

DATA ANALYSIS LAB 1

About the Lab

- One of the main reasons people are hospitalized with sickle-cell disease is acute chest syndrome (ACS), characterized by fever, cough, chest pain, and shortness of breath. One study found that 29 percent of people with sickle-cell disease had at least one episode of ACS.
- Also see Stuart, M.J. and B.N. Setty. 2001. Acute chest syndrome of sickle cell disease: new light on an old problem. *Current Opinions in Hematology;* 8(2): 111–122.

Think Critically

1. 20+
2. Fever is highest in those under two years of age and lowest in those over 20. Generally fever reduces with age.

S Skill Practice

EL BL OL AL Visual Literacy

Have students make a table using information from Figure 6 and the text. They should label one column *Blood Type* and a second column *Possible Genotypes.*

Blood Type	Possible Genotypes
A	I^AI^A or I^Ai
B	I^BI^B or I^Bi
AB	I^AI^B
O	ii

Develop Concepts

BL OL AL

Clarify a Misconception

ASK STUDENTS: ***Is there such a thing as a universal blood donor?*** no Some students might think there is a universal donor for all blood groups. This is a misnomer. Because of complex immune reactions, researchers no longer use the term *universal donor.* Blood is typed and matched and given only to a matching blood type.

GOING GREEN Do you receive junk mail at school? Type the phrase "get rid of junk mail" into a search engine to find a variety of web sites that will assist you in clearing your mailbox of junk mail. Many of these sites provide their service for free.

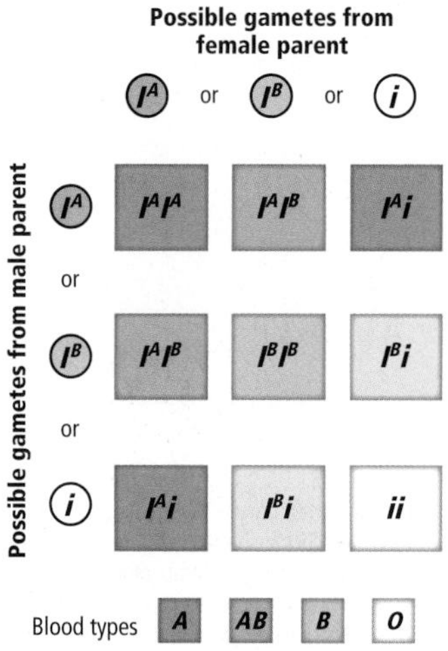

■ **Figure 6** There are three forms of alleles in the ABO blood group—I^A, I^B, and *i*.

S

■ **Figure 7** Rabbits have multiple alleles for coat color. The four alleles provide four basic variations in coat color.

Multiple Alleles

Not all traits are determined by two alleles. Some forms of inheritance are determined by more than two alleles referred to as **multiple alleles.** An example of such a trait is human blood group.

Blood groups in humans The ABO blood group, shown in **Figure 6,** has three forms of alleles, sometimes called AB markers: I^A is blood type A; I^B is blood type B; and *i* is blood type O. Type O is the absence of AB markers. Note that allele *i* is recessive to I^A and I^B. However, I^A and I^B are codominant; blood type AB results from both I^A and I^B alleles. Therefore, the ABO blood group is an example of both multiple alleles and codominance.

The Rh blood group includes Rh factors, inherited from each parent. Rh factors are either positive or negative (Rh+ or Rh–); Rh+ is dominant. The Rh factor is a blood protein named after the rhesus monkey because studies of the rhesus monkey led to discovery of that blood protein.

Coat color of rabbits Multiple alleles can demonstrate a hierarchy of dominance. In rabbits, four alleles code for coat color: *C*, c^{ch}, c^h, and *c*. Allele *C* is dominant to the other alleles and results in a full color coat. Allele *c* is recessive and results in an albino phenotype when the genotype is homozygous recessive. Allele c^{ch} is dominant to c^h, and allele c^h is dominant to *c* and the hierarchy of dominance can be written as $C > c^{ch} > c^h > c$. **Figure 7** shows the genotypes and phenotypes possible for rabbit-coat color. Full color is dominant over chinchilla, which is dominant over Himalayan, which is dominant over albino.

The presence of multiple alleles increases the possible number of genotypes and phenotypes. Without multiple-allele dominance, two alleles, such as *T* and *t*, produce only three possible genotypes—in this example *TT, Tt,* and *tt*—and two possible phenotypes. However, the four alleles for rabbit-coat color produce ten possible genotypes and four phenotypes, as shown in **Figure 7.** More variation in rabbit coat color comes from the interaction of the color gene with other genes.

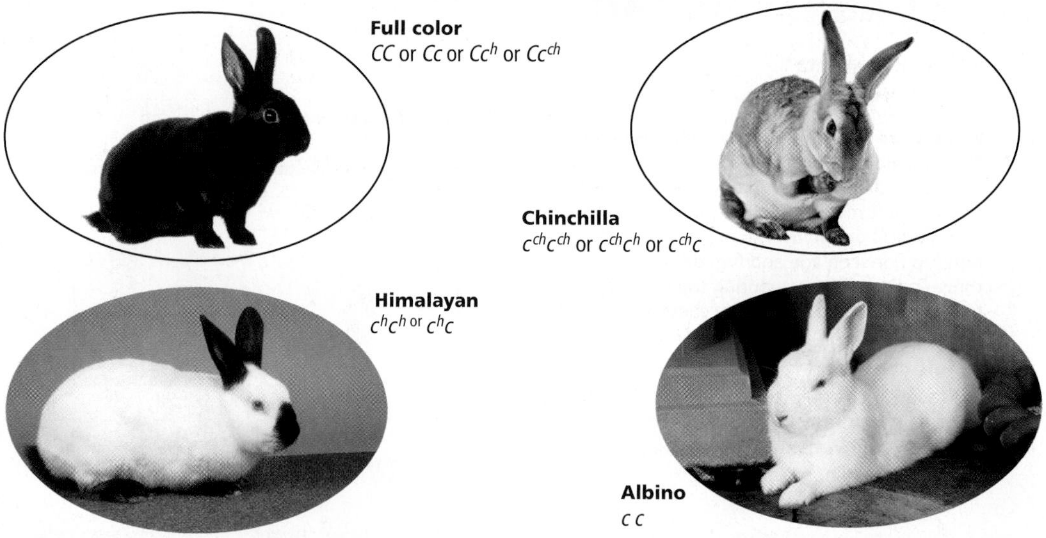

Differentiated Instruction

Below Level When students are performing the critical thinking activities, pair students who perform below level with peer tutors. These students can help them to understand any concepts that are confusing and help them to reach acceptable conclusions.

For more tips, see pages 14T–15T.

Epistasis

Coat color in Labrador retrievers can vary from yellow to black. This variety is the result of one allele hiding the effects of another allele, an interaction called **epistasis** (ih PIHS tuh sus). A Labrador's coat color is controlled by two sets of alleles. The dominant allele *E* determines whether the fur will have dark pigment. The fur of a dog with genotype *ee* will not have any pigment. The dominant B allele determines how dark the pigment will be. Study **Figure 8.** If the dog's genotype is *EEbb* or *Eebb,* the dog's fur will be chocolate brown. Genotypes *eebb, eeBb,* and *eeBB* will produce a yellow coat, because the *e* allele masks the effects of the dominant *B* allele.

■ **Figure 8** The results of epistasis in coat color in Labrador retrievers show an interaction of two genes, each with two alleles. Note that an underscore in the genotype allows for either a dominant or recessive gene.

Sex Determination

Each cell in your body, except for gametes, contains 46 chromosomes, or 23 pairs of chromosomes. One pair of these chromosomes, the **sex chromosomes,** determines an individual's gender. There are two types of sex chromosomes—X and Y. Individuals with two X chromosomes are female, and individuals with an X and a Y chromosome are male. The other 22 pairs of chromosomes are called **autosomes.** The offspring's gender is determined by the combination of sex chromosomes in the egg and sperm cell, as shown in **Figure 9.**

C

Color-Enhanced SEM Magnification: unavailable

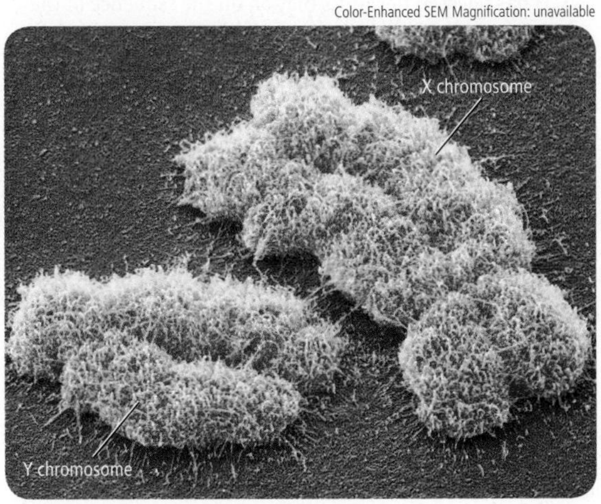

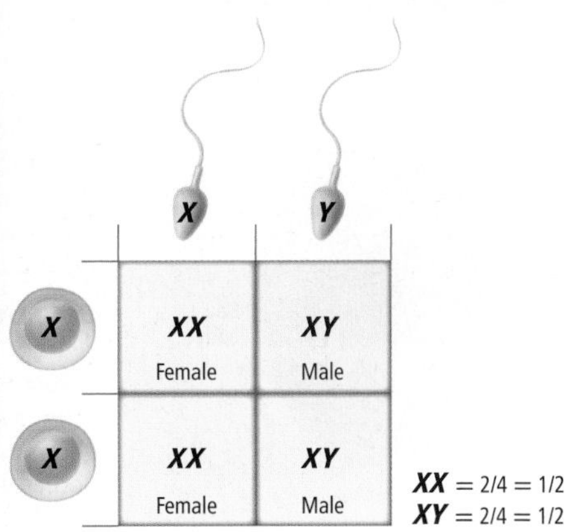

■ **Figure 9**
Left: The size and shape of the Y chromosome and the X chromosome are quite different from one another.
Right: The segregation of the sex chromosomes into gametes and the random combination of sperm and egg cells result in an approximately 1:1 ratio of males to females.

Develop Concepts
BL OL AL

Sex-Linked Inheritance

On the board, draw a Punnett square for a sex-linked inheritance such as color blindness. Be sure to stress the difference in writing these Punnett squares showing the X and Y chromosomes with linked genes. Emphasize to students that Punnett squares showing sex-linked inheritance must indicate both the X and the Y inheritance also.

? Inquiry BioLab

The lab at the end of the chapter can be used at this point in the lesson.

C Critical Thinking
BL OL AL **Evaluate**

ASK STUDENTS: ***During meiosis, what chromosome pairs up with the X chromosome?*** the Y or the X chromosome ***Why is there little crossover between the X and the Y when they are lined up?*** The X and the Y chromosome do not have the same alleles. Despite the fact that the X and Y chromosomes are different in size and the types of genes they contain, there is a small region where they match up during pairing in meiosis. Crossing over can occur only in this small region, and thus the frequency of crossover between the X and Y is lower than it is for other chromosome pairs.

Research Citation

Ample Practice Educational research indicates that students need to be provided with ample opportunities to practice a new skill in order to master the concept. When working with Punnett squares in this chapter, model how the charts are used, then provide time for students to practice using them individually so that you can assess their understanding. (Trafton, 1983)

Research bibliography on pages 32T–34T

D Develop Concepts

EL BL OL AL Scaffolding

ASK STUDENTS: ***How is gender determined genetically?*** by the father's sperm—whether it contributes an X or a Y chromosome ***Diagram the dosage difference between a female and male.*** Diagrams should show females have two large X chromosomes, males have one large X and one small Y chromosome. ***Explain how females compensate for the extra dosage of X chromosome compared to males.*** In females, one X chromosome randomly inactivates in every body cell. ***Infer how a calico cat inherits the colors of its coat.*** The coat color of a calico cat is the result of the random inactivation of one of the X chromosomes. In some cells, the X chromosome that was inherited from the mother is expressed, and in others, the X chromosome inherited from the father is expressed.

W Writing Support

AL Formal Writing Have students conduct research to find out about the life of Canadian biologist Murray Barr. Have them write a short biography of Barr and include his major scientific work.

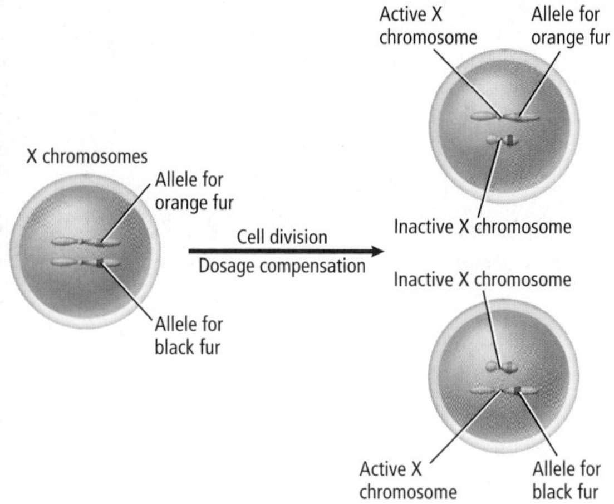

■ **Figure 10** The calico coat of this cat results from the random inactivation of the X chromosomes in body cells. One X chromosome codes for orange fur, and one X chromosome codes for black fur, as illustrated on the right.

■ **Figure 11** An inactivated X chromosome in a female body cell is called a Barr body, a dark body usually found near the nucleus.

Phase contrast LM Magnification: 1000×

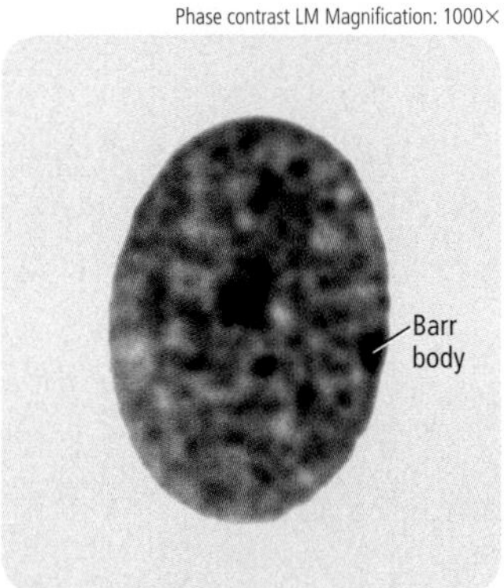

Dosage Compensation

Human females have 22 pairs of autosomes and one pair of X chromosomes. Males have 22 pairs of autosomes, along with one X and one Y chromosome. If you examine the X and Y chromosomes in **Figure 9,** you will notice that the X chromosome is larger than the Y chromosome. The X chromosome carries a variety of genes that are necessary for the development of both females and males. The Y chromosome mainly has genes that relate to the development of male characteristics.

Because females have two X chromosomes, it seems as though females get two doses of the X chromosome and males get only one dose. To balance the difference in the dose of X-related genes, one of the X chromosomes stops working in each of the female's body cells. This often is called dosage compensation or X-inactivation. Which X chromosome stops working in each body cell is a completely random event. Dosage compensation occurs in all mammals.

As a result of the Human Genome Project, the National Institutes of Health (NIH) has released new information on the sequence of the human X chromosome. Researchers now think that some genes on the inactivated X chromosome are more active than was previously thought. D

Chromosome inactivation The coat colors of the calico cat shown in **Figure 10** are caused by the random inactivation of a particular X chromosome. The resulting colors depend on the X chromosome that is activated. The orange patches are formed by the inactivation of the X chromosome carrying the allele for black coat color. Similarly, the black patches are a result of the inactivation of the X chromosome carrying the allele for orange coat color.

Barr bodies The inactivated X chromosomes can be observed in cells. In 1949, Canadian scientist Murray Barr observed inactivated X chromosomes in female calico cats. He noticed a condensed, darkly stained structure in the nucleus. The darkly stained, inactivated X chromosomes, such as the one shown in **Figure 11,** are called Barr bodies. It was discovered later that only females, including human females, have Barr bodies in their cell nuclei. W

Content Background

Teacher FYI Unlike the X chromosome, the Y chromosome is not "gene rich." Fewer than 100 genes have been mapped to the Y chromosome. Many of these genes contain instructions to make the baby a male. Without a functioning Y chromosome, the baby will develop similar to a female who has Turner syndrome (similar to an XO). In X inactivation, most of the X chromosome is inactivated in cells that have two X chromosomes. This occurs early in embryonic development. A gene called *XIST* produces RNA, which accumulates along the genes of one X chromosome, inactivating the majority of one X chromosome.

Sex-Linked Traits

Traits controlled by genes located on the X chromosome are called **sex-linked traits,** or X-linked traits. Because males have only one X chromosome, they are affected by recessive X-linked traits more often than are females. Females are less likely to express a recessive X-linked trait because the other X chromosome may mask the effect of the trait.

D Some traits that are located on autosomes may appear to be sex-linked, even though they are not. This occurs when an allele appears to be dominant in one gender but recessive in the other. For example, the allele for baldness is recessive in females but dominant in males, causing hair loss that follows a typical pattern called male-pattern baldness. A male would be bald if he were heterozygous for the trait, while a female would be bald only if she were homozygous recessive.

Red-green color blindness The trait for red-green color blindness is a recessive X-linked trait. About 8 percent of males in the United States have red-green color blindness. The photos in **Figure 12** show how a person with red-green color blindness might view colors compared to a person who does not have red-green color blindness.

Study the Punnett square shown in **Figure 12.** The mother is a carrier for color blindness because she has the recessive allele for color blindness on one of her X chromosomes. The father is not color blind because he does not have the recessive allele. The sex-linked trait is represented by writing the allele on the X chromosome. Notice that the only offspring that can possibly have red-green color blindness is a male child. As a result of it being an X-linked trait, red-green color blindness is very rare in females.

C

Figure 12 People with red-green color blindness view red and green as shades of gray.
Explain *why there are fewer females who have red-green color blindness than males.*

X^B = Normal
X^b = Red-green color blind
Y = Y chromosome

	X^B	Y
X^B	X^BX^B	X^BY
X^b	X^BX^b	X^bY

Caption Question Fig. 12 Since males have only one X chromosome, they are affected by recessive X-linked traits more often than females.

D Develop Concepts

EL BL OL AL Activity Have students gently scrape the inside of their cheek with a toothpick and rub the toothpick on a slide. Students should use caution with the sharp toothpicks. Add a drop of methylene blue and a coverslip. Female students should find a Barr body in their cells but males will not. Drop slides into a mild bleach solution before disposing of them.

Writing Support

OL AL Informal Writing
Have students research congenital generalized hypertrichosis and write an essay describing this sex-linked disorder.

C Critical Thinking

OL AL Infer The gene for male pattern baldness is on an autosome but is sex-influenced. The *B* allele is dominant in males but recessive in females.
ASK STUDENTS: ***What male genotypes will result in baldness?*** *BB* or *Bb* ***Will baldness result in a female with the genotype* Bb?** No ***What genotype will result in female baldness?*** *BB*

Demonstration

Color-Blind Test Children's color blindness tests are available from various companies. They are based on having the child match various colors and shades of yarn. Demonstrate this concept using one of the actual tests or using various shades of one color of yarn. Est. time: 10 min

Writing Support

BL OL AL Persuasive Writing Have students investigate the story of David, known as the "Boy in the Bubble." David, of Houston, Texas, suffered from the sex-linked disorder called severe combined immunodeficiency (SCID). He lived the majority of his life in a sterile "bubble." Have students write a persuasive essay explaining whether they feel David's medical treatment was or was not ethical.

S Skill Practice

BL OL Visual Literacy Have students study Figure 13 and describe the passage of the hemophilia gene from Queen Victoria through the generations to Alexis. Queen Victoria to Alice to Alexandra to Alexis

AL Have students draw a pedigree that includes Alexis if he had married a noncarrier and had two boys and two girls. Both boys would be fine, but both girls would be carriers.

D Develop Concepts

EL BL OL AL COOP LEARN

Activity In groups of three, have students draw an illustration that demonstrates the difference between autosomal and sex-linked inheritance. Diagrams should show dominant and recessive alleles in both types of inheritance and how X and Y chromosomes carry sex-linked traits and disorders.

■ **Caption Question Fig. 13** Alexis inherited his mother's X chromosome and displayed the disorder. His sisters might have been carriers, but they did not display the disorder.

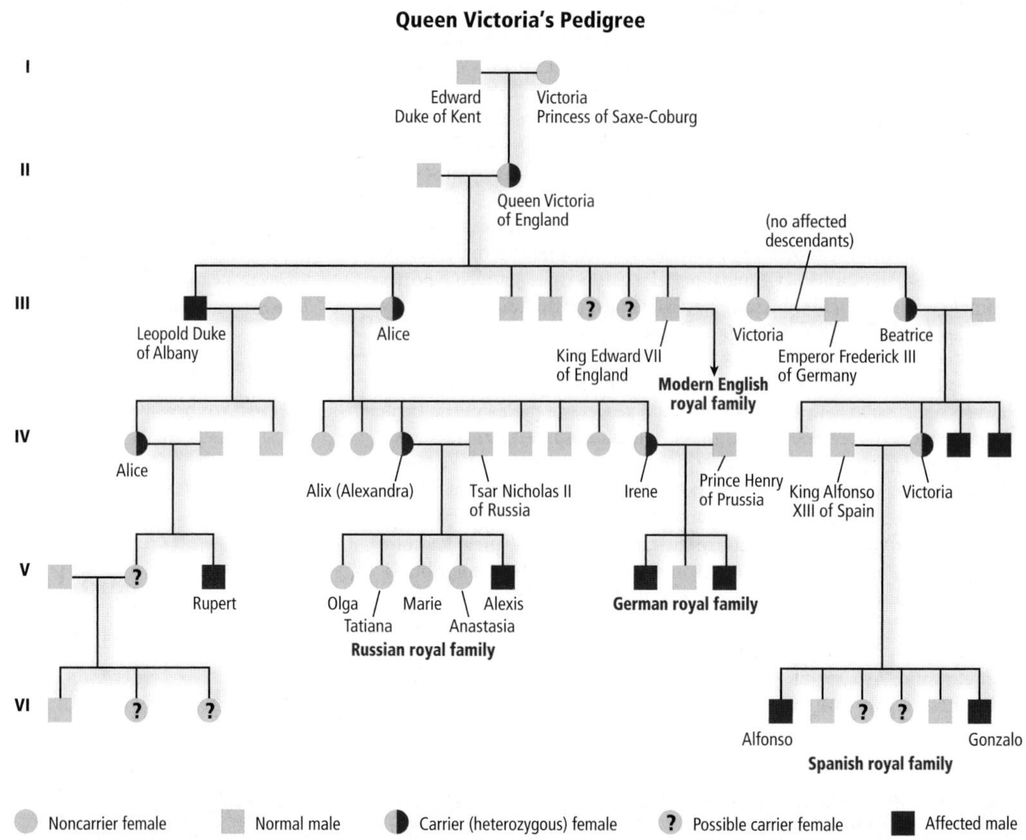

■ **Figure 13** The pedigree above shows the inheritance of hemophilia in the royal families of England, Germany, Spain, and Russia, starting with the children of Queen Victoria.
Determine *which of Alexandra's children inherited hemophilia.*

S

Inquiry Virtual Lab

Hemophilia Hemophilia, another recessive sex-linked disorder, is characterized by delayed clotting of the blood. Like red-green color blindness, this disorder is more common in males than in females.

A famous pedigree of hemophilia is one that arose in the family of Queen Victoria of England (1819-1901). Her son Leopold died of hemophilia, and her daughters Alice and Beatrice, as illustrated in the pedigree in **Figure 13,** were carriers for the disease. Alice and Beatrice passed on the hemophilia trait to the Russian, German, and Spanish royal families. Follow the generations in this pedigree to see how this trait was passed through Queen Victoria's family. Queen Victoria's granddaughter Alexandra, who was a carrier for this trait, married Tsar Nicholas II of Russia. Irene, another granddaughter, passed the trait on to the German royal family. Hemophilia was passed to the Spanish royal family through a third granddaughter, whose name also was Victoria.

Men with hemophilia usually died at an early age until the twentieth century when clotting factors were discovered and given to hemophiliacs. However, blood-borne viruses such as Hepatitis C and HIV were often contracted by hemophiliacs until the 1990s, when safer methods of blood transfusion were discovered.

D

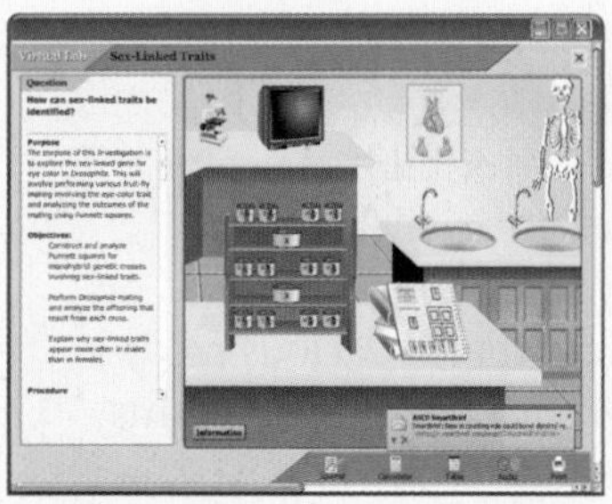

Inquiry Virtual Lab Students will explore the sex-linked gene for eye color in Drosophila by performing various fruit-fly matings.

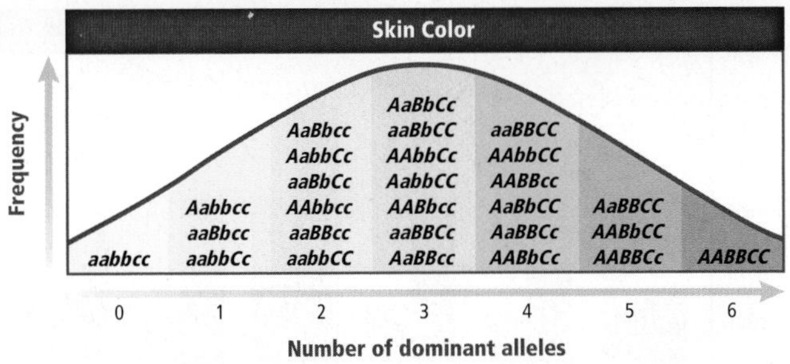

■ **Figure 14** This graph shows possible shades of skin color from three sets of alleles, although the trait is thought to involve more than three sets of alleles.
Predict *Would more gene pairs increase or decrease the number of possible phenotypes?*

Polygenic Traits

You have examined traits determined by a pair of genes. Many phenotypic traits, however, arise from the interaction of multiple pairs of genes. Such traits are called **polygenic traits.** Traits such as skin color, height, eye color, and fingerprint pattern are polygenic traits. One characteristic of polygenic traits is that, when the frequency of the number of dominant alleles is graphed, as shown in **Figure 14,** the result is a bell-shaped curve. This shows that more of the intermediate phenotypes exist than do the extreme phenotypes.

D

Reading Check **Infer** Why would a graph showing the frequency of the number of dominant alleles for polygenic traits be a bell-shaped curve?

Environmental Influences

The environment also has an effect on phenotype. For example, the tendency to develop heart disease can be inherited. However, environmental factors such as diet and exercise also can contribute to the occurrence and seriousness of the disease. Other ways in which environment influences phenotype are very familiar to you. You may not have thought of them in terms of phenotype, however. Sunlight, water, and temperature are environmental influences that commonly affect an organism's phenotype.

Sunlight and water Without enough sunlight, most flowering plants do not bear flowers. Many plants lose their leaves in response to water deficiency.

Temperature Most organisms experience phenotypic changes from extreme temperature changes. In extreme heat, for example, many plants suffer. Their leaves droop, flower buds shrivel, chlorophyll disappears, and roots stop growing. These are examples that probably do not surprise you, although you may have never thought of them as phenotypic changes. What other environmental factors affect the phenotypes of organisms? Temperature also influences the expression of genes. Notice the fur of the Siamese cat shown in **Figure 15.** The cat's tail, feet, ears, and nose are dark. These areas of the cat's body are cooler than the rest. The gene that codes for production of the color pigment in the Siamese cat's body functions only under cooler conditions. Therefore, the cooler regions are darker; and the warmer regions, where pigment production is inhibited by temperature, are lighter.

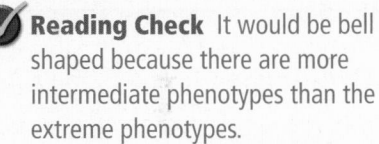

■ **Figure 15** Temperature affects the expression of color pigment in the fur of Siamese cats.

D Develop Concepts

EL BL OL AL Activity Pass around a sheet of paper and have students write their height on it. Make copies of the list and distribute it to students. Have students make a line graph from the height data. The line graph should be close to a bell-shaped curve if enough students are included. Point out that this is the characteristic pattern of a polygenic inheritance.

Develop Concepts

AL Research Send for a free classroom set of the curriculum supplement called *Human Genetic Variation,* which is available from the NIH Office of Science Education, 6100 Executive Blvd., Suite 5H01, Rockville, Maryland 20852. This supplement contains background and activities on human genetic variation. Have each student choose one topic covered in the supplement and present an oral report to the class.

Reading Check It would be bell shaped because there are more intermediate phenotypes than the extreme phenotypes.

■ **Caption Question Fig. 14** More gene pairs would increase the potential phenotypes.

Demonstration

Gene Expression Germinate 30 mustard seeds in petri dishes on moist paper towels. Germinate 15 in the dark and 15 with light exposure. Examine after seven days. *Brassica rapa* seeds, available from biological supply houses, will germinate in 24 h. The plants germinated in the dark will be white; those germinated in light will have green leaves. Set the plate germinated in the dark in the light for a few days to demonstrate the influence of environment on gene expression. Est. time: 5 min each day for 10 days

Inquiry Launch Lab

Assess Content Development
Assess how understanding has developed when students revisit the Launch Lab analysis questions.

Formative Assessment

Evaluation Have pairs of students prepare and solve several Punnett square or pedigree practice problems involving incomplete dominance, codominance, and sex-linked traits. Practice problems might include human blood groups and color blindness. Have the pairs exchange their problems and use each other's work to check the answers. If one pair produces an incorrect answer, have the other pair explain the correct answer.

Remediation Prepare a set of practice problems that illustrate each of the types of inheritance in this section. Have students who understand these complex patterns of inheritance work with students who are having difficulty understanding the concept.

■ **Figure 16** When a trait is found more often in both members of identical twins than in fraternal twins, the trait is presumed to have a significant inherited component.

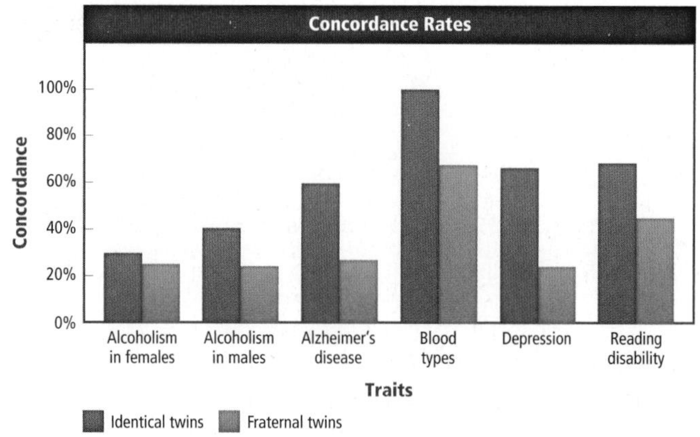

Inquiry Launch Lab

Review **Based on what you have read about human inheritance, how would you now answer the analysis questions?**

Twin Studies

Another way to study inheritance patterns is to focus on identical twins, which helps scientists separate genetic contributions from environmental contributions. Identical twins are genetically the same. If a trait is inherited, both identical twins will have the trait. Scientists conclude that traits that appear frequently in identical twins are at least partially controlled by heredity. Also, scientists presume that traits expressed differently in identical twins are strongly influenced by environment. The percentage of twins who both express a given trait is called a concordance rate. Examine **Figure 16** for some traits and their concordance rates. A large difference between fraternal twins and identical twins shows a strong genetic influence.

Section 2 Assessment

Section Summary

- Some traits are inherited through complex inheritance patterns, such as incomplete dominance, codominance, and multiple alleles.
- Gender is determined by X and Y chromosomes. Some traits are linked to the X chromosome.
- Polygenic traits involve more than one pair of alleles.
- Both genes and environment influence an organism's phenotype.
- Studies of inheritance patterns of large families and twins give insight into complex human inheritance.

Understand Main Ideas

1. MAIN Idea **Describe** two patterns of complex inheritance and explain how they are different from Mendelian patterns.
2. **Explain** What is epistasis, and how is it different from dominance?
3. **Determine** the genotypes of the parents if the father is blood type A, the mother is blood type B, the daughter is blood type O, one son is blood type AB, and the other son is blood type B.
4. **Analyze** how twin studies help to differentiate the effects of genetic and environmental influences.

Think Critically

5. **Evaluate** whether having sickle-cell disease would be advantageous or disadvantageous to a person living in central Africa.

MATH in Biology

6. What is the chance of producing a son with normal vision if the father is color-blind and the mother is homozygous normal for the trait? Explain.

Section 2 Assessment

1. incomplete dominance and codominance; Mendel described patterns of inheritance that were very simple.
2. Epistasis occurs when one allele masks or hides the expression of the other allele. It differs from dominance in that a recessive allele could potentially mask a dominant allele of another gene pair.
3. Both parents are heterozygous and carry a recessive type O (i) gene.
4. Identical twins are genetically alike, so traits that are alike are inherited and traits that are different are likely the result of environmental influences.
5. Sickle-cell disease can provide either an advantage and a disadvantage. In the heterozygous state, the person is resistant to malaria. In the homozygous sickle state, the person suffers from sickle-cell disease.
6. 100 percent (the father donates a Y chromosome and the mother an X chromosome with a normal vision gene)

Assessment Online Quiz

Reading Preview

Essential Questions

- How are karyotypes used to study genetic disorders?
- What is the role of telomeres?
- How is nondisjunction related to Down syndrome and other abnormal chromosome numbers?
- What are the benefits and risks of diagnostic fetal testing?

Review Vocabulary

mitosis: a process in the nucleus of a dividing cell, including prophase, metaphase, anaphase, and telophase

New Vocabulary

karyotype
telomere
nondisjunction

g Multilingual eGlossary

Chromosomes and Human Heredity

MAIN Idea **Chromosomes can be studied using karyotypes.**

Real-World Reading Link Have you ever lost one of the playing pieces belonging to a game? You might not have been able to play the game because the missing piece was important. Just as a misplaced game piece affects a game, a missing chromosome has a significant impact on the organism.

Karyotype Studies

The study of genetic material does not involve the study of genes alone. Scientists also study whole chromosomes by using images of chromosomes stained during metaphase. The staining bands identify or mark identical places on homologous chromosomes. During metaphase of mitosis, each chromosome has condensed greatly and consists of two sister chromatids. The pairs of homologous chromosomes are arranged in decreasing size to produce a micrograph called a **karyotype** (KER ee uh tipe). Karyotypes of a human male and a human female, each with 23 pairs of chromosomes, are shown in **Figure 17.** Notice that the 22 autosomes are matched together with one pair of nonmatching sex chromosomes. **D**

Telomeres

Scientists have found that chromosomes end in protective caps called **telomeres.** Telomere caps consist of DNA associated with proteins. The cap serves a protective function for the structure of the chromosome. Scientists have discovered that telomeres also might be involved in both aging and cancer. **W**

Figure 17 Karyotypes arrange the pairs of homologous chromosomes from increasing to decreasing size.
Distinguish *which two chromosomes are arranged separately from the other pairs.*

False-Color LM Magnification: 1400×   False-Color LM Magnification: 1400×

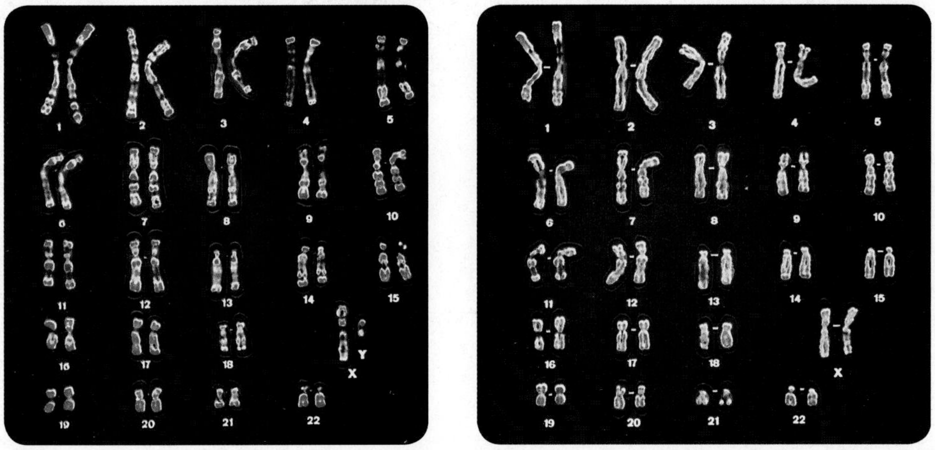

Caption Question Fig. 17 the X and Y chromosomes

Content Background

Teacher FYI Various stains, such as Giemsa dye, are used to band chromosomes. The staining results in dark and light regions. The number, intensity, and width of the band are reproducible characteristics and are used by geneticists to carefully prepare a medical karyotype. Computer programs can arrange the chromosomes into karyotypes.

Section 3

MAIN Idea

BL OL AL **Karyotypes** Show students a picture of a karyotype of a human male or female and one from another mammal.
ASK STUDENTS: ***What are the similarities and differences between the two karyotypes?*** Similarities: both show the chromosomes lined up in pairs, both show the chromosomes in a metaphase stage (consisting of two chromatids), and both are arranged from large to small chromosomes. Differences: the number of chromosomes; individuals of the two species may be different sexes.

D Develop Concepts
EL BL OL AL COOP LEARN
Activity Search the Internet for large copies of pictures of scattered male and female chromosomes. Give some pairs of students a male set and others a female set. Have students cut out the chromosomes and prepare a karyotype. They should be able to determine the sex of the individual.

W Writing Support
OL AL **Formal Writing** Have students research the hypothesized role of telomeres in cell aging and prepare a technical report on the possibility of telomeres being involved in aging that includes illustrations. Post the information on a bulletin board.

Visualizing Nondisjunction

Purpose

Students will illustrate how nondisjunction occurs either in meiosis I or meiosis II, causing Down syndrome.
C.1, C.2, F.1

Develop Concepts

OL COOP LEARN Research

Organize students into groups of three and have them research tests for detecting chromosomal abnormalities associated with Down syndrome. Have them create a visual report on their findings, which should also include the use of genetic counseling.

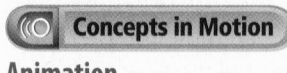

Concepts in Motion Animation

Visualizing Nondisjunction

Figure 18

Gametes with abnormal numbers of chromosomes can result from nondisjunction during meiosis. The orange chromosomes come from one parent, and the blue chromosomes come from the other parent.

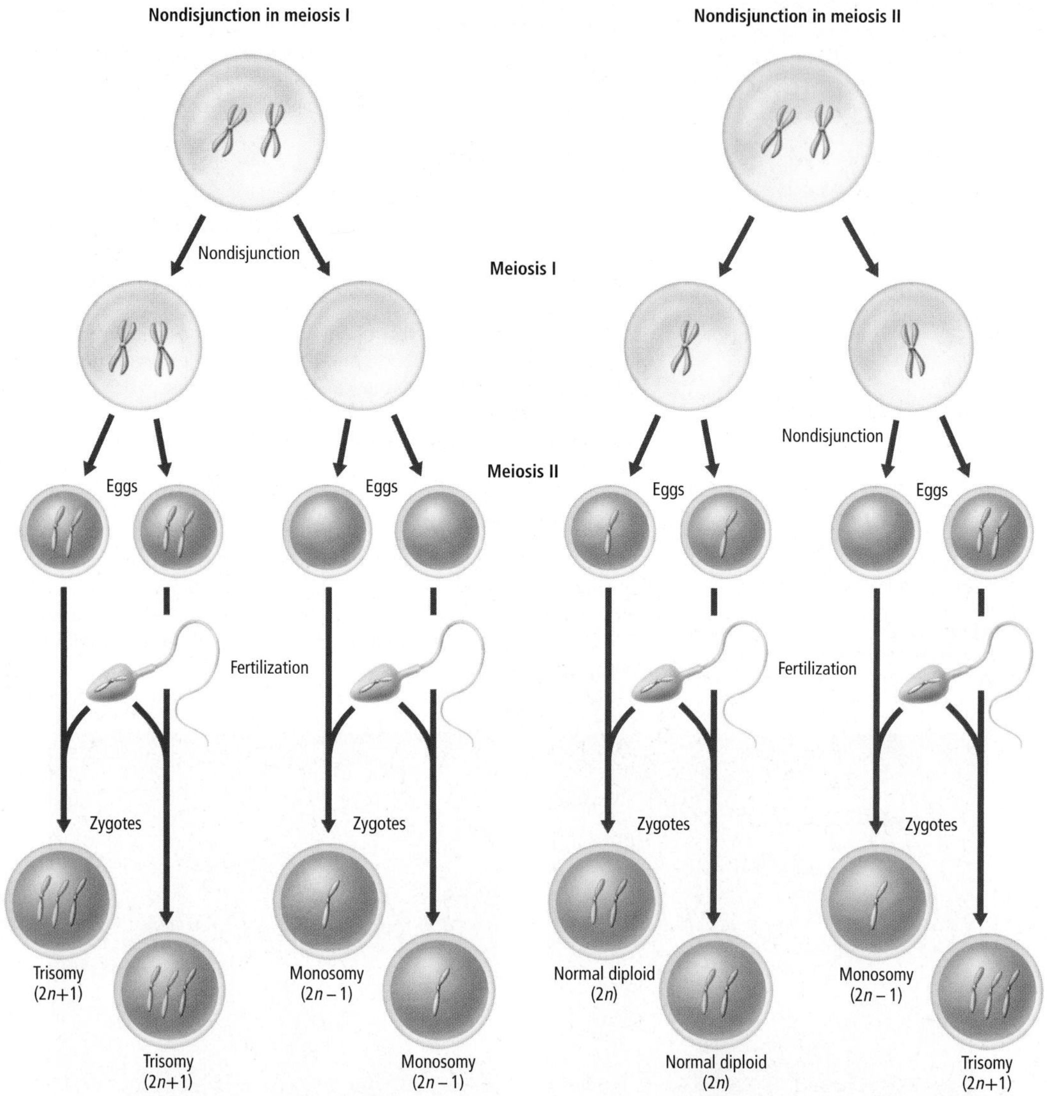

Concepts in Motion Animation

Demonstration

Sock Nondisjunction Use two pairs of socks to represent a pair of chromosomes (each consisting of two chromatids). Place a small piece of hook-and-loop tape on each sock to keep the pairs together as you hold them up to the class. The two pairs together represent a pair of chromosomes that line up during metaphase of meiosis I. Demonstrate nondisjunction during meiosis II as one of the pairs of socks fail to separate correctly. Two of the resulting four gametes have one sock chromatid each, one has two socks, and the fourth has none. Est. time: 15 min

R Nondisjunction

During cell division, the chromosomes separate, with one of each of the sister chromatids going to opposite poles of the cell. Therefore, each new cell has the correct number of chromosomes. Cell division during which sister chromatids fail to separate properly, which does happen occasionally, is called **nondisjunction.**

If nondisjunction occurs during meiosis I or meiosis II, as shown in **Figure 18,** the resulting gametes will not have the correct number of chromosomes. When one of these gametes fertilizes another gamete, the resulting offspring will not have the correct number of chromosomes. Notice that nondisjunction can result in extra copies of a certain chromosome or only one copy of a particular chromosome in the offspring. Having a set of three chromosomes of one kind is called trisomy (TRI so me). Having only one of a particular type of chromosome is called monosomy (MAH nuh so me). Nondisjunction can occur in any organism in which gametes are produced through meiosis. In humans, alterations of chromosome numbers are associated with serious human disorders, which are often are fatal.

Down syndrome One of the earliest known human chromosomal disorders is Down syndrome. It is the result of an extra chromosome 21. Therefore, Down syndrome often is called trisomy 21. Examine the karyotype of a child with Down syndrome, shown in **Figure 19.** Notice that she has three copies of chromosome 21. The characteristics of Down syndrome include distinctive facial features, as shown in **Figure 19,** short stature, heart defects, and mental disability. The frequency of children born with Down syndrome in the United States is approximately one out of 800. The frequency of Down syndrome increases with the age of the mother. Studies have shown that the risk of having a child with Down syndrome is about six percent in mothers W who are 45 and older.

CAREERS IN BIOLOGY

Research Scientist Research scientists know and research a particular field of science, such as genetic disorders. Most research scientists begin their work in their undergraduate studies and continue on to a Master's degree or Ph.D.

Figure 19 A person with Down syndrome has distinctive features and will have a karyotype that shows three copies of chromosome number 21.

False-Color LM Magnification: 1400×

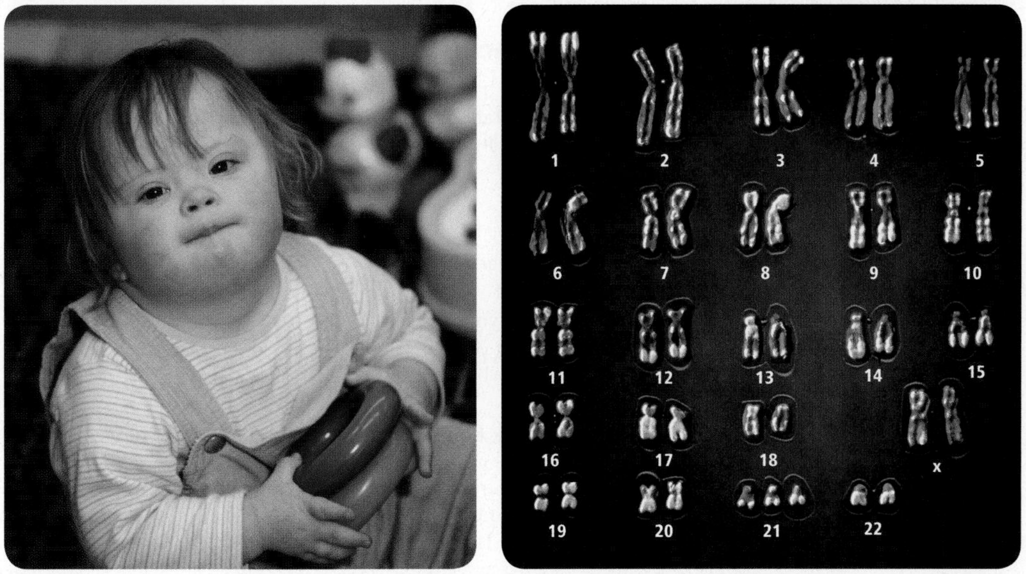

R Reading Strategy
EL BL OL AL

Anticipation Guide

Before students read the text below the heading *Nondisjunction*, have the following discussion. **ASK STUDENTS:** ***Do you know anyone with Down syndrome? What would you like to know about Down syndrome?*** Write the student questions on the board and then have students read the text. If any questions remain unanswered, have students research answers to those questions.

W Writing Support
BL OL AL **Informal Writing**

Give students the following scenario: A genetic test has just indicated that the child a couple is expecting will have Down syndrome. Have students write a letter from the physician explaining to the couple how Down syndrome occurred.

Critical Thinking
BL OL AL **Consider** The gametes from an individual with Klinefelter's syndrome are often sterile, but occasionally they can produce a functioning gamete. **ASK STUDENTS:** ***What problem do the chromosomes have during meiosis in an individual with Kleinfelter's?*** The two X chromosomes and one Y chromosome line up together, so improper pairing occurs during meiosis, making the presence of abnormal gametes more likely.

"Knowledge exists to be imparted."
–Ralph Waldo Emerson

Differentiated Instruction

Visually Impaired If you will be using any special equipment such as a projector during class, warn students who are visually impaired of any changes to the layout of the classroom. This warning will allow students to make any needed adjustments as they move around the room.

For more tips, see pages 14T–15T.

MiniLab 2

Inquiry MiniLab

For a lab worksheet, use your eTeacherEdition Online.

RUBRIC A rubric for evaluating MiniLabs is found on your eTeacherEdition Online.

Est. Time 30 min

Safety Precaution Approve lab safety forms before work begins.

Teaching Strategies

- Prepare and distribute copies of a data table, such as this one, with rows for as many subjects as needed.

Survey Subject	Hitchhiker's thumb Y/N
1	
2	

Analysis

1. Answers will vary. Sample answer: we looked for the ratio of subjects with a hitchhiker's thumb to subjects without a hitchhiker's thumb.
2. Students might suggest DNA analysis or compiling pedigrees to determine dominance. In small populations, traits can be more common even though they are recessive, which might cause students to misidentify them as dominant.

LabManager™

Customize this lab with the LabManager™ CD-ROM.

Table 4 **Nondisjunction in Sex Chromosomes** Concepts in Motion Interactive Table

Genotype	XX	XO	XXX	XY	XXY	XYY	OY
Example	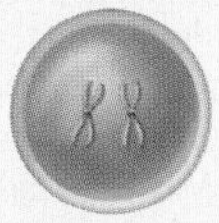	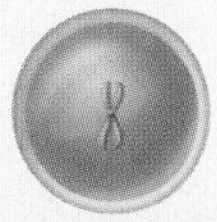	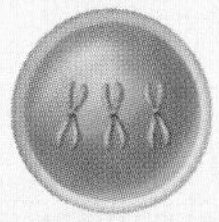	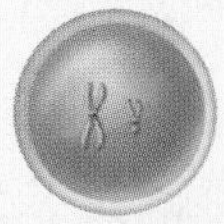	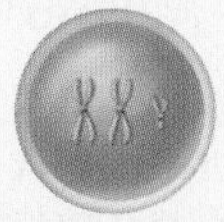	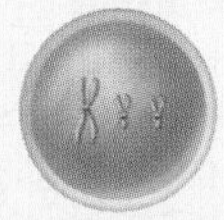	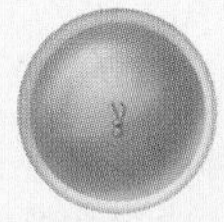
Phenotype	Normal female	Female with Turner's syndrome	Nearly normal female	Normal male	Male with Klinefelter's syndrome	Normal or nearly normal male	Results in death

S

Sex chromosomes Nondisjunction occurs in both autosomes and sex chromosomes. Some of the results of nondisjunction in human sex chromosomes are listed in **Table 4.** Note that an individual with Turner's syndrome has only one sex chromosome. This condition results from fertilization with a gamete that had no sex chromosome.

Fetal Testing

Couples who suspect they might be carriers for certain genetic disorders might want to have a fetal test performed. Older couples also might wish to know the chromosomal status of their developing baby, called the fetus. Various types of tests for observing both the mother and the baby are available.

MiniLab 2

Inquiry MiniLab

Explore the Methods of the Geneticist

How do geneticists learn about human heredity? Traditional methods used to investigate the genetics of plants, animals, and microbes are not suitable or possible to use on humans. A pedigree is one useful tool for investigating human inheritance. In this lab, you will explore yet another tool of the geneticist—population sampling.

Procedure

1. Read and complete the lab safety form.
2. Construct a data table as instructed by your teacher.
3. Survey your group for the hitchhiker's thumb trait.
4. Survey your group for other traits determined by your teacher.
5. Compile the class data, and analyze the traits that you investigated in the survey population. Determine which of the traits are dominant and which are recessive.

Analysis

1. **Interpret Data** What numerical clue did you look for to determine whether each trait surveyed was dominant or recessive?
2. **Think Critically** How could you check to see if you correctly identified dominant and recessive traits? Explain why you might have misidentified a trait.

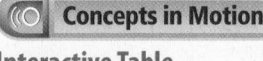

Concepts in Motion
Interactive Table

S Skill Practice

EL BL OL AL COOP LEARN

Visual Literacy Have students work in pairs to draw a series of meiosis stages illustrating one of the abnormal genotypes in Table 4. Have the groups exchange papers and infer which condition the meiosis pictures show.

Research Citation

Real-World Applications Research indicates that students gain a better understanding of concepts that are related to real-world problems. The MiniLab on this page demonstrates the relationship between pedigrees and inheritance, allowing students to relate this topic to the real world. (Steen and Forman, 1995)

Research bibliography on pages 32T–34T

Table 5	Fetal Tests	Concepts in Motion Interactive Table
Test	**Benefit**	**Risk**
Amniocentesis	• Diagnosis of chromosome abnormalities • Diagnosis of other defects	• Discomfort for expectant mother • Slight risk of infection • Risk of miscarriage
Chorionic villus sampling	• Diagnosis of chromosome abnormality • Diagnosis of certain genetic defects	• Risk of miscarriage • Risk of infection • Risk of newborn limb defects
Fetal blood sampling	• Diagnosis of genetic or chromosome abnormality • Checks for fetal blood problems and oxygen levels • Medications can be given to the fetus before birth	• Risk of bleeding from sample site • Risk of infection • Amniotic fluid might leak • Risk of fetal death

Connection to Health Many fetal tests can provide important information to the parents and the physician. **Table 5** describes the risks and benefits of some of the fetal tests that are available. Physicians must consider many factors when advising parents about such examinations. At least a small degree of risk is possible in any test or procedure. A physician would not want to advise tests that would endanger the mother or the fetus; therefore, when considering whether to recommend fetal testing, a physician would need to consider previous health problems of the mother and also the health of the fetus. If the physician and parents determine that any fetal test is needed, the health of both the mother and the fetus is closely monitored throughout the testing.

Section 3 Assessment

Section Summary

- Karyotypes are micrographs of chromosomes.
- Chromosomes terminate in a cap called a telomere.
- Nondisjunction results in gametes with an abnormal number of chromosomes.
- Down syndrome is a result of nondisjunction.
- Tests for assessing the possibility of genetic and chromosomal disorders are available.

Understand Main Ideas

1. MAIN Idea Explain how a scientist might use a karyotype to study genetic disorders.
2. **Summarize** the role of telomeres.
3. **Illustrate** Draw a sketch to show how nondisjunction occurs during meiosis.
4. **Analyze** Why might missing sections of the X or Y chromosome be a bigger problem in males than deletions would be in one of the X chromosomes in females?

Think Critically

5. **Create** a karyotype of a female organism in which $2n = 8$, showing trisomy of chromosome 3.
6. **Discuss** the benefits and risks of fetal testing.

WRITING in Biology

7. Conduct research on the consequences of nondisjunction other than trisomy 21. Write a paragraph about your findings.

Develop Concepts

BL OL AL

Clarify A Misconception

ASK STUDENTS: ***If a rare disorder appeared only once in a couple's family—affecting the male's great uncle or a first cousin, for example— should the couple have their developing baby tested for the disorder?*** Yes, if they choose to do so, because recessive genes can be expressed after several generations. Students might think that problems affecting relatives in the distant past have little chance of showing up in their offspring.

Concepts in Motion
Interactive Table

Formative Assessment

Evaluation Prepare a picture presentation that shows karyotypes of various disorders and pictures of telomeres.

SAY TO STUDENTS: ***Identify the disorders represented by the presentation and explain how you identified the disorder.***

Remediation Have students write review questions from this section on note cards and write the answers on the backs of the cards. Students having difficulty with the ideas in this section can use the cards to review concepts.

Section 3 Assessment

1. to determine the sex of the individual, whether the proper number of chromosomes are there, whether there is extra or missing chromosomal material
2. Telomeres protect chromosomes.
3. Sketches should demonstrate an understanding of nondisjunction.
4. Males only receive one X and one Y, so missing sections could contain genes that are vital. With females who have two X's, deletion in one X could be made up for by the other.
5. Answer should show understanding of karyotype and show that the individual has three copies of chromosome 3.
6. benefits = discovery of genetic problem; risk = harm to fetus
7. Paragraphs should show understanding of nondisjunction. Paragraphs should not describe Down syndrome.

WRITING in Biology

RUBRIC Use the modifiable rubric found on your eTeacherEdition Online to assess writing assignents.

Assessment Online Quiz

In the Field

Purpose
Students will understand that genetic counseling involves interpreting genetic tests and communicating the results to the client. Genetic counselors must have scientific and social skills.
C.4, E.2, G.1

Anticipatory Guide
Engage students in a discussion of uses for genetic counseling.
ASK STUDENTS: ***What are some different reasons for genetic testing?*** Answers may include testing to see if a person is a carrier for a genetic disorder. ***Why do you think this type of test is important?*** Answers will vary, but might include helping a couple determine whether to have a child based on the chance of a genetic disorder in their offspring.

Background
Genetic counselors have changed our world immensely. Genetic testing has become an important vehicle for disseminating information about genetic disorders and has at times been the center of controversy. Ensuring genetic test information is correct and discussing the ways in which this information can be used are of critical importance in order to keep the public's trust.

WRITING in Biology
RUBRIC Use the modifiable rubric found on your eTeacher-Edition Online to assess writing assignments.

In the Field

Career: Genetic Counselor
Genetic Testing and Support

Have you ever looked at your family tree? Do you know of any disorders or diseases that "run" in families? Genetic counselors specialize in uncovering, interpreting, and explaining this information.

Genetic counselors Genetic counselors apply their knowledge of genetics to provide information and support to people who are affected by genetic disorders. They specialize in evaluating genetic tests and indicating prevention, monitoring, and treatment options related to specific genetic conditions. Genetic counselors are also trained to deal with the emotional aspects associated with learning the results of a genetic test. They serve as patient advocates, referring individuals to community or state support services.

What does genetic testing involve? Tests are done to determine if any abnormalities are present in a particular gene or chromosome. Testing usually involves a sample of blood or tissue. In the case of prenatal genetic testing, a sample of amniotic fluid or tissue from around a fetus is taken.

It can be helpful to provide medical details about other people in your family, usually going back to your grandparents' generation, prior to meeting with a genetic counselor. Sometimes a family history gives doctors enough information to diagnose a genetic condition.

Who gets genetic testing? Sometimes a doctor recommends genetic testing. Other times, individuals seek it for themselves.

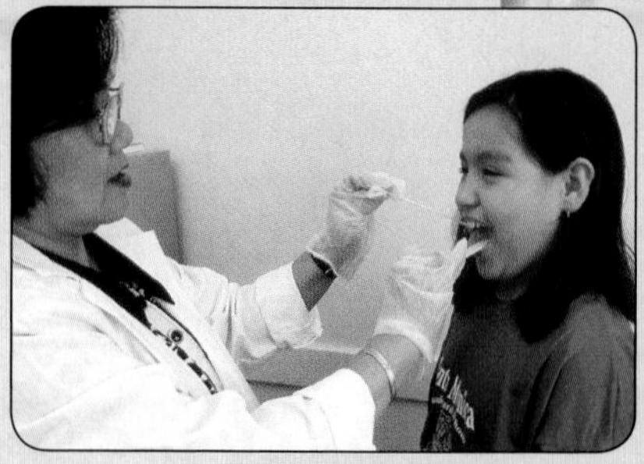

Sometimes a simple mouth swab is all that is needed to extract a genetic sample for testing.

Possible reasons for genetic testing include:
- a family history of genetic disorders;
- an unusual occurrence of certain types of cancer;
- having a child with learning difficulties or health problems, which might have a genetic cause;
- couples planning pregnancy who wish to determine if their child is at risk for a genetic condition.

Several hundred genetic tests are currently in use, with more being developed. While a doctor or health care specialist can order a genetic test, they often refer patients to genetic counselors who have received special training to interpret such tests, suggest available options, and provide supportive counseling.

WRITING in Biology

Debate Use the Skillbuilder Handbook to organize a debate about the use and potential implications of genetic testing. Write a summary of your notes and your argument before participating in the debate.

Discussion
Organize students into groups. Present to them the following questions to discuss, and have one member in each group write down the group's responses.
ASK STUDENTS: ***How does genetic testing affect a person who has a parent with a genetic disorder? If you had a parent with a genetic disorder, would you want to be tested for the disorder?*** Have the class regroup and discuss their responses in the remaining time. Discussion points will vary but should include the importance of understanding uncertainties in test results, and implications of being a carrier for a recessive disorder. Students should also discuss the impact of changing science and technology on the field of genetic counseling.

WebQuest

BIOLAB

WHAT'S IN A FACE? INVESTIGATE INHERITED HUMAN FACIAL CHARACTERISTICS

Background: **Most people know that they inherit their hair color and their eye color from their parents. However, there are many other head and facial traits that humans inherit. In this lab, you will investigate a number of different inherited facial structures that combine to compose a human face.**

Question: *What structures that comprise the human face are actually determined genetically?*

Materials

coins, 2 per team: heads=dominant trait, tails=recessive trait

table of inherited human facial characteristics provided by the teacher

Procedure

1. Read and complete the lab safety form.
2. Partner with a classmate.
3. One member of the team will represent the father, and one member will represent the mother. Decide which partner will represent the father and who will represent the mother.
4. Have the person representing the father flip a coin. If the coin lands *heads* facing up, the offspring is a female; if the coin lands *tails* facing up, the offspring is a male. Record the gender of the offspring.
5. Flip your coin at the same time as your partner. Flip the coins only once for each trait.
6. Continue to flip coins for each trait shown in the table. After each coin flip, record the trait of your offspring by placing a check in the appropriate box in the table.
7. Once the traits are determined, draw the offspring's facial features, give him or her a name, and be prepared to introduce the offspring to the rest of the class.

Analyze and Conclude

1. **Think Critically** Why did the partner representing the father flip the coin initially to determine the gender of the offspring?
2. **Calculate** What percent chance was there of producing male offspring? Female offspring? Explain.
3. **Recognize Cause and Effect** What are the possible genotypes of parents of the following three children: a boy with straight hair (hh), a daughter with wavy hair (Hh), and a son with curly hair (HH)?
4. **Observe and Infer** Which traits show codominance?
5. **Analyze and Conclude** Would you expect other student pairs in the class to have offspring exactly like yours? Explain.

WRITING in Biology

Research Imagine that you write a science column for a large newspaper. A reader has written to you asking for a job description for a genetic counselor. Research this question; then write a short newspaper column answering the question.

BIOLAB

Inquiry BioLab

For a lab worksheet, use your eTeacherEdition Online.

RUBRIC A rubric for evaluating BioLabs is found on your eTeacherEdition Online.

Est. Time 35 min

Content Background
Humans inherit many traits other than just eye color and hair color.

Safety Precaution Approve lab safety forms before work begins.

Teaching Strategies

- The table of inheritable traits is available in your eTeacherEdition Online.
- Have students compile their characteristics into a hand-drawn picture of their offspring, give the offspring a name, and introduce him/her to the class.
- Have students work in pairs.

Alternative Teaching Demo
Provide students with pictures of several members of a family. This may be members of a well-known family or your own family. Ask students to examine the pictures and determine why these people look related. What is similar about their faces?

Analyze and Conclude

1. The male determines the gender of the offspring in humans.
2. a 50 percent chance in each situation
3. To achieve this outcome, both parents must have wavy hair *(Hh).*
4. Answers will depend on the traits used.
5. The chances of two groups producing identical offspring are quite remote. It would require each coin flip for each group to be exactly the same for each trait.

WRITING in Biology

RUBRIC Use the modifiable rubric found on your eTeacherEdition Online to assess writing assignments.

Chapter 11

Study Guide

ConnectED

Students can use the following to review the chapter.

Review

Vocabulary eGames
Vocabulary eFlashcards
Vocabulary PuzzleMaker

Assessment

Online Quizzes
Online Test Practice
Standardized Test Practice

Use the *ExamView®* *Assessment Suite* CD-ROM to:

- create multiple versions of tests
- create modified tests with one mouse click
- edit existing questions and add your own questions
- build tests aligned with state standards using built-in state curriculum tags
- change English tests to Spanish with one mouse click
- track students' progress using the Teacher Management System

Chapter 11 Study Guide

THEME FOCUS Diversity Complex forms of inheritance, such as multiple alleles and codominance in the ABO blood group, result in a range of characteristics that contribute to the diversity and success of a species.

BIG Idea Human inheritance does not always follow Mendel's laws.

Section 1 Basic Patterns of Human Inheritance

carrier (p. 296)
pedigree (p. 299)

MAIN Idea The inheritance of a trait over several generations can be shown in a pedigree.

- Genetic disorders can be caused by dominant or recessive alleles.
- Cystic fibrosis is a genetic disorder that affects mucus and sweat secretions.
- Individuals with albinism do not have melanin in their skin, hair, and eyes.
- Huntington's disease affects the nervous system.
- Achondroplasia sometimes is called dwarfism.
- Pedigrees are used to study human inheritance patterns.

Section 2 Complex Patterns of Inheritance

incomplete dominance (p. 302)
codominance (p. 302)
multiple alleles (p. 304)
epistasis (p. 305)
sex chromosome (p. 305)
autosome (p. 305)
sex-linked trait (p. 307)
polygenic trait (p. 309)

MAIN Idea Complex inheritance of traits does not follow inheritance patterns described by Mendel.

- Some traits are inherited through complex inheritance patterns, such as incomplete dominance, codominance, and multiple alleles.
- Gender is determined by X and Y chromosomes. Some traits are linked to the X chromosome.
- Polygenic traits involve more than one pair of alleles.
- Both genes and environment influence an organism's phenotype.
- Studies of inheritance patterns of large families and twins give insight into complex human inheritance.

Section 3 Chromosomes and Human Heredity

karyotype (p. 311)
telomere (p. 311)
nondisjunction (p. 313)

MAIN Idea Chromosomes can be studied using karyotypes.

- Karyotypes are micrographs of chromosomes.
- Chromosomes terminate in a cap called a telomere.
- Nondisjunction results in gametes with an abnormal number of chromosomes.
- Down syndrome is a result of nondisjunction.
- Tests for assessing the possibility of genetic and chromosomal disorders are available.

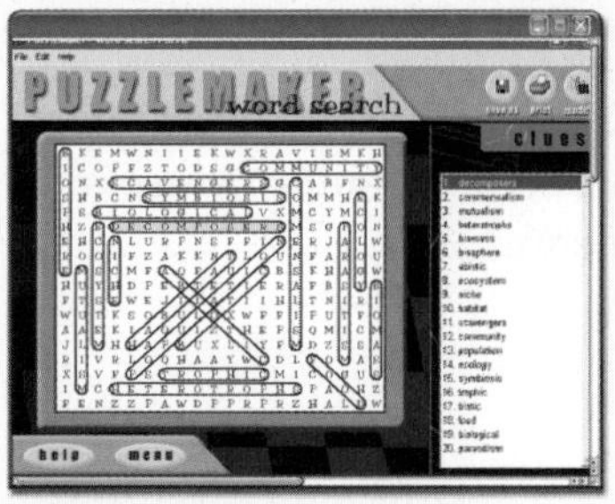

Review Vocabulary PuzzleMaker

For additional practice with vocabulary, have students access the Vocabulary PuzzleMaker online.

Review Vocabulary eGames

Section 1

Vocabulary Review

Use what you know about the vocabulary terms from the Study Guide page to answer the questions.

1. Which term describes a person who is heterozygous for a recessive disorder?

2. How is the inheritance pattern between parents and offspring represented diagrammatically?

Understand Main Ideas

3. Which condition is inherited as a dominant allele?
A. albinism
B. cystic fibrosis
C. Tay-Sachs disease
D. Huntington's disease

4. Which is not a characteristic of a person with cystic fibrosis?
A. chloride channel defect
B. digestive problems
C. lack of skin pigment
D. recurrent lung infections

Use the diagram below to answer questions 5 and 6.

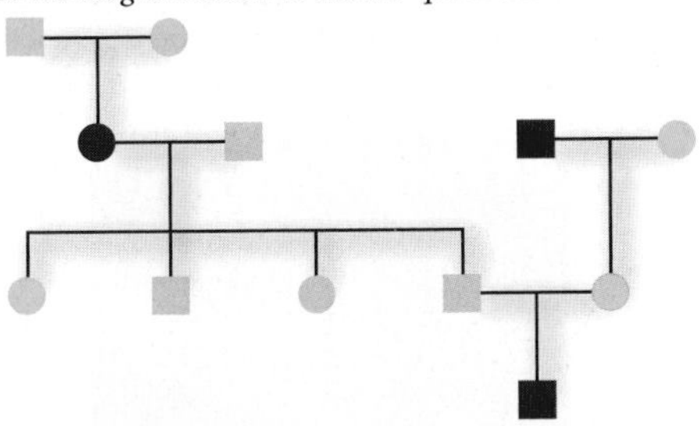

5. Which disorder could not follow the inheritance pattern shown?
A. cystic fibrosis
B. albinism
C. Tay-Sachs disease
D. Huntington's disease

6. MAIN Idea How many affected males and females are in the pedigree?
A. 1 male, 2 females
B. 2 males, 1 female
C. 1 male, 1 female
D. 2 males, 2 females

Constructed Response

Use the photo below to answer question 7.

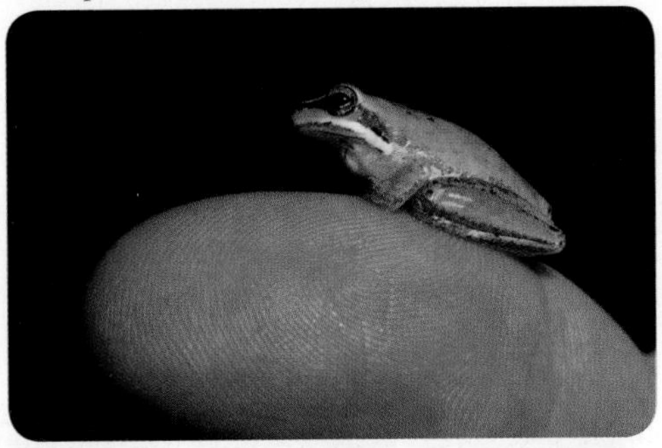

7. Open Ended Imagine that all animals have the same genetic disorders that humans have. What is the biological name of the genetic disorder that this dwarf tree frog would have? Describe the inheritance pattern of the genetic disorder.

8. Short Answer Predict the genotypes of the children of a father with Huntington's disease and an unaffected mother.

Think Critically

9. Draw a conclusion about the relationship of chloride ions to the excessively thick mucus in a patient suffering from cystic fibrosis.

Section 2

Vocabulary Review

Replace each underlined word with the correct vocabulary term from the Study Guide page.

10. <u>Codominance</u> is an inheritance pattern in which the heterozygous genotype results in an intermediate phenotype between the dominant and recessive phenotype.

11. A characteristic that has more than one pair of possible traits is said to be a(n) <u>epistasis</u>.

12. Genes found on the sex chromosomes are associated with <u>multiple alleles</u>.

Chapter 11 Assessment

Section 1

Vocabulary Review
1. carrier
2. pedigree

Understand Main Ideas
3. D
4. C
5. D
6. B

Constructed Response
7. achondroplasia, a dominant disorder caused by a mutation
8. Because Huntington's is a rare disorder, the male is likely Dd; the children each have a 50 percent chance of being *Dd* and a 50 percent chance of being *dd*.

Think Critically
9. Because chloride cannot leave the cell, water does not follow, so the mucus is thicker than normal.

Section 2

Vocabulary Review
10. Incomplete dominance
11. polygenic trait
12. sex-linked traits

Understand Main Ideas
13. A
14. B
15. C

Constructed Response
16. The recessive alleles on the *E* gene for no pigment can hide the dominant allele on the *B* gene for dark pigment.
17. No, this is an X chromosome sex-linked trait and males only receive one X chromosome.
18. phenotypes showing continuous variation, that is small differences between each phenotype

Think Critically
19. Humans have small families, long generation time, and cannot be studied in controlled experiments for ethical reasons.
20. There is a fairly large genetic component to the trait.

Section 3

Vocabulary Review
21. telomere
22. nondisjunction
23. karyotype

Understand Main Ideas
24. B
25. C
26. C

Understand Main Ideas

13. What determines gender in humans?
A. the X and Y chromosomes
B. chromosome 21
C. codominance
D. epistasis

14. MAIN Idea Which two terms best describe the inheritance of human blood types?
A. incomplete dominance and codominance
B. codominance and multiple alleles
C. incomplete dominance and multiple alleles
D. codominance and epistasis

Use the photos below to answer question 15.

15. **THEME FOCUS Diversity** In radishes, color is controlled by incomplete dominance. The figure above shows the phenotype for each color. What phenotypic ratios would you expect from crossing two heterozygous plants?
A. 2: 2 red: white
B. 1: 1: 1 red: purple: white
C. 1: 2: 1 red: purple: white
D. 3: 1 red: white

Constructed Response

16. Short Answer How does epistasis explain the differences in coat color in Labrador retrievers?

17. Short Answer Explain whether a male could be heterozygous for red-green color blindness.

18. Short Answer What types of phenotypes would one look for if a phenotype were a result of polygenic inheritance?

Think Critically

19. Evaluate why it might be difficult to perform genetic analysis in humans.

20. Summarize the meaning of the following information regarding trait inheritance: For a certain trait, identical twins have a concordance rate of 54 percent and fraternal twins have a rate of less than five percent.

Section 3

Vocabulary Review

Identify the vocabulary term from the Study Guide page described by each definition.

21. the protective ends of the chromosome

22. an error that occurs during cell division

23. a micrograph of stained chromosomes

Understand Main Ideas

24. MAIN Idea What could explain a human karyotype showing 47 chromosomes?
A. monosomy
B. trisomy
C. codominance
D. dominant traits

25. Why does nondisjunction occur?
A. Cytokinesis does not occur properly.
B. The nucleoli do not disappear.
C. The sister chromatids do not separate.
D. The chromosomes do not condense properly.

Use the photo below to answer question 26.

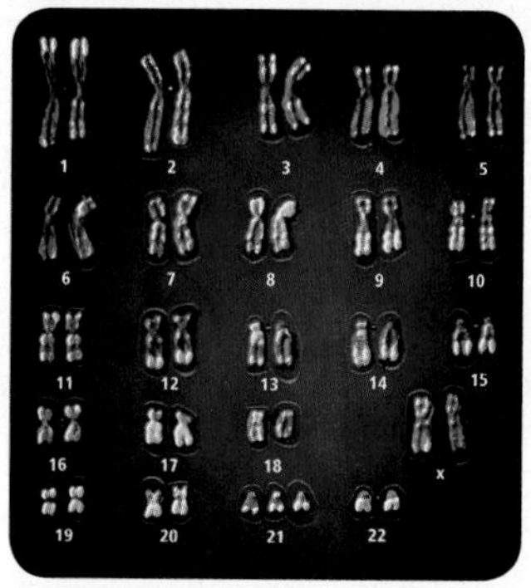

26. What disorder can be identified in the karyotype?
A. Turner's syndrome
B. Klinefelter's syndrome
C. Down syndrome
D. The karyotype shows no disorder.

27. Which statement concerning telomeres is not true?
A. They are found on the ends of chromosomes.
B. They consist of DNA and sugars.
C. They protect chromosomes.
D. They are involved with aging.

Constructed Response

Use the photo below to answer question 28.

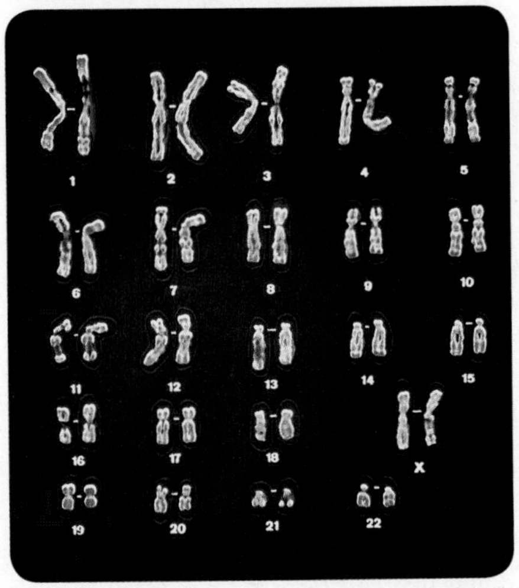

28. **Short Answer** Describe a fetal test that results in the karyotype shown above.

29. **Short Answer** What characteristics are associated with Down syndrome?

30. **Open Ended** Most cases of trisomy and monosomy in humans are fatal. Why might this be?

Think Critically

31. **Hypothesize** why chromosomes need telomeres.

32. **Explain** why a girl who has Turner's syndrome has red-green color blindness even though both of her parents have normal vision.

33. **Illustrate** what might have occurred to result in an extra chromosome in the following example: A technician is constructing a karyotype from male fetal cells. The technician discovers that the cells have one extra X chromosome.

Summative Assessment

34. **BIG Idea** Give a specific example of an inheritable trait that does not follow Mendel's laws of inheritance. Apply Mendel's laws to that trait, and infer how the resulting genotypes and phenotypes would be different from what actually exists.

35. Describe how hemophilia is inherited.

36. Describe the cause of Down syndrome.

37. **WRITING in Biology** Write a scenario for one of the genetic disorders described in **Table 2.** Then create a pedigree illustrating the scenario.

DBQ Document-Based Questions

Answer the questions below concerning the effect of environment on phenotype.

Data obtained from: Harnly, M.H. 1936. Genetics. *Journal of Experimental Zoology* 56: 363-379.

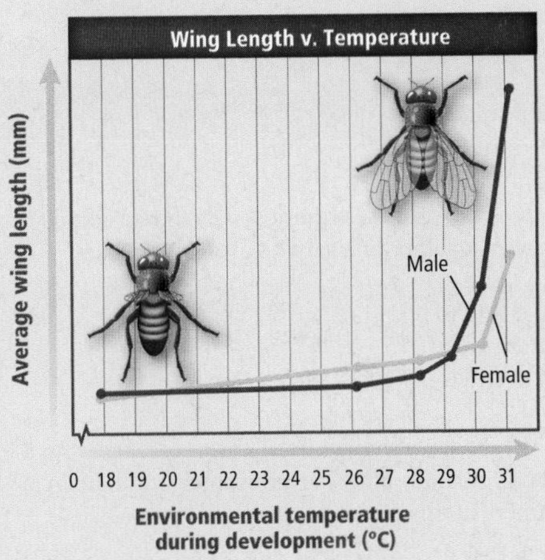

38. At which temperature is wing length the greatest?

39. Is male or female wing length more influenced by temperature? Explain.

40. What is the relationship between temperature and wing length for all flies?

DBQ Document-Based Questions

Harnly, M.H. 1936. Genetics. *Journal of Experimental Zoology* 56: 363–379.

38. 31°C
39. Males, they have a larger average wing length at 31°C than female.
40. As temperature increases during development wing length increases.

27. D

Constructed Response

28. Both amniocentesis and chronic villus sampling can generate karyotypes.
29. distinctive facial features, short stature, heart defects, mental disability
30. Not having normal number of chromosomes causes serious disorders.

Think Critically

31. Answer may vary, but may include protection of the chromosomes during cell division and against cellular enzymes.
32. Because females normally inactivate one X chromosome, a female with Turner Syndrome only has one X chromosome, which has the allele for color blindness.
33. Illustrations should show nondisjunction during meiosis.

Summative Assessment

34. Possible answer: The ABO blood group is an example of multiple alleles and codominance, not two alleles, one of which is dominant over the other. If the ABO blood group followed Mendel's laws, there would only be two alleles (such as A and B) resulting in 3 genotypes (AA, AB, BB) and 2 phenotypes (type A blood, type B blood). Since the inheritance of blood type is complex, there are 3 alleles, 9 genotypes, and 4 phenotypes.
35. Hemophilia is inherited as a sex-linked recessive trait.
36. nondisjunction
37. The scenario and pedigree should demonstrate an understanding of the chosen disorder.

WRITING in Biology

RUBRIC Use the modifiable rubric found on your eTeacher-Edition Online to assess writing assignments.

Standardized Test Practice

Multiple Choice

1. C 5. D 9. D
2. A 6. B
3. B 7. C
4. B 8. B

Short Answer

10. This Punnett square shows the outcome of the cross.

	Y	*y*
y	*Yy*	*yy*
y	*Yy*	*yy*

11. Homozygous plants make up 50% of the total. The plants with *yy* genotype are homozygous.

12. The onset of Huntington's disease is later than the age at which most people have children. So, although it is a fatal disease, it might not appear until after people have already reproduced.

13. When the cell cycle is disrupted, the amount of time spent in mitosis increases. Cells divide uncontrollably, and the resulting cancer cells accumulate to form a tumor.

14. The following steps are possible, but a student might answer in fewer steps by combining one or more of these listed.

A. During cell division in meiosis II, the sister chromatids start to separate.

B. The separation is not equal, causing a nondisjunction, in which one gamete gets an extra chromosome.

C. This gamete, with an extra chromosome in either the egg or sperm, is involved in fertilization.

D. The resulting embryo has three chromosomes in place of one of its chromosome pairs: a trisomy.

Standardized Test Practice

Cumulative

Multiple Choice

1. Which is affected when a cell has a low surface-area-to-volume ratio?
A. the ability of oxygen to diffuse into the cell
B. the amount of energy produced in the cell
C. the diffusion of proteins through the cells
D. the rate of protein synthesis in the cell

Use the diagram below to answer questions 2 to 4.

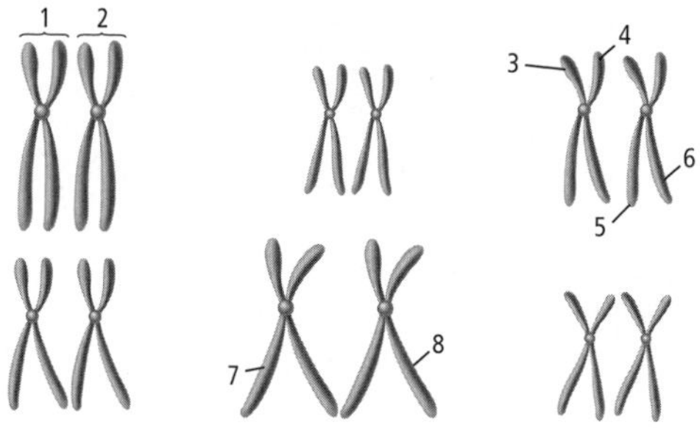

2. Which labeled structures represent a homologous pair?
A. 1 and 2
B. 3 and 4
C. 3 and 6
D. 7 and 8

3. Which parts of the chromosomes shown could appear together in a gamete of this organism?
A. 1 and 2
B. 3 and 6
C. 3 and 7
D. 5 and 6

4. If the diagram shows all the chromosomes from a body cell, how many chromosomes would be in a gamete of this organism at the end of meiosis I?
A. 3
B. 6
C. 9
D. 12

5. Which represents a polyploid organism?
A. 1/2 *n*
B. 1 1/2 *n*
C. 2 *n*
D. 3 *n*

Use the pedigree below to answer questions 6 and 7.

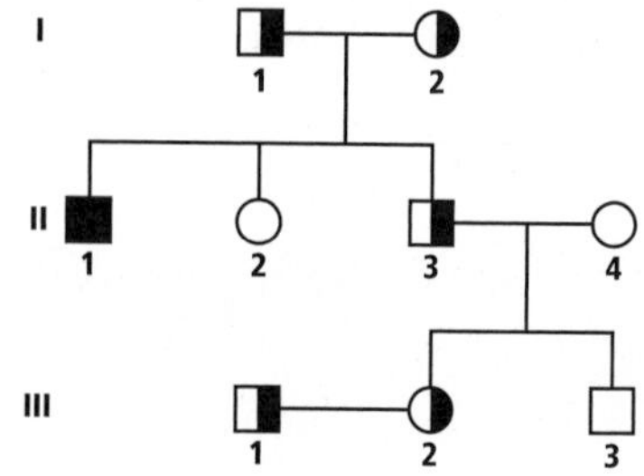

6. Which person could develop symptoms of the disease that is tracked in the pedigree?
A. I1
B. III1
C. II2
D. III2

7. According to the pedigree, who is a carrier and cannot have children with the disease?
A. I1
B. II1
C. II3
D. III1

8. Which condition would trigger mitosis?
A. Cells touch each other.
B. Cyclin builds up.
C. Environmental conditions are poor.
D. Growth factors are absent.

9. Shivering when you are cold raises your body temperature. This is an example of which characteristic of life?
A. Your body adapts over time.
B. Your body grows and develops.
C. Your body has one or more cells.
D. Your body maintains homeostasis.

Short Answer

10. In pea plants, yellow seed color is the dominant trait, and green seed color is the recessive trait. Use a Punnett square to show the results of a cross between a heterozygous yellow-seed plant and a green-seed plant.

11. Based on your Punnett square from question 10, what percentage of the offspring would have a homozygous genotype? Explain your answer.

12. Because Huntington's disease is a dominant genetic disorder, it might seem that it would be selected out of a population naturally. Write a hypothesis that states why the disease continues to occur.

13. Explain how a cancerous tumor results from a disruption of the cell cycle.

14. Write, in order, the steps that must occur for cell division to result in an organism with trisomy.

15. Which function in metabolism is performed by both the thylakoid membrane and the mitochondrial membrane? Give a reason why this function might or might not be important.

16. Suppose two parents have a mild form of a genetic disease, but their child is born with a very severe form of the same disease. What kind of inheritance pattern took place for this disease?

17. Describe an example of each of the following: species diversity, genetic diversity, and ecosystem diversity.

Extended Response

Use the diagram below to answer question 18.

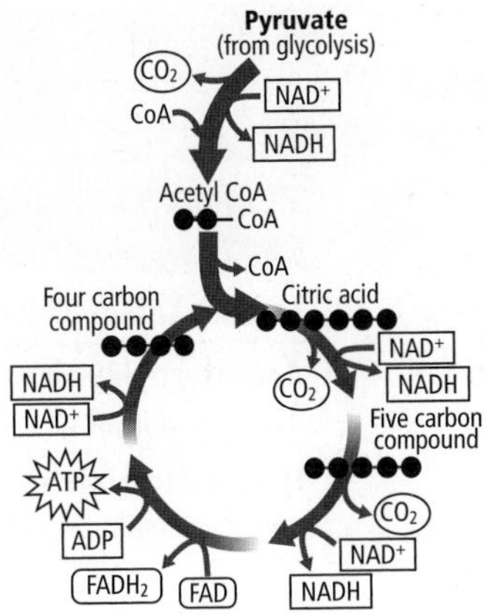

18. Identify the cycle in the figure and summarize the steps of the cycle.

19. Describe the function of microtubules, and predict what might happen if cells did NOT have microtubules.

Essay Question

The type of pea plants that Mendel investigated had either purple flowers or white flowers. One flower-color trait is dominant, and the other is recessive.

Using the information in the paragraph above, answer the following question in essay format.

20. Explain what crosses Mendel would have performed to determine which color is the dominant trait.

NEED EXTRA HELP?																				
If You Missed Question . . .	1	2	3	4	5	6	7	8	9	10	11	12	13	14	15	16	17	18	19	20
Review Section . . .	9.1	10.1	10.1	10.1	10.1	11.1	11.1	9.2	1.1	10.2	10.2	11.1	9.3	11.3	8.2, 8.3	11.2	2.2	8.3	7.3	10.2

15. Electron transport is performed by both membranes. That fact might be important because it could give evidence for similarities of structure or origin. On the other hand, the fact that the two membranes perform the same function might be coincidental.

16. The simplest explanation is that the disease is due to incomplete dominance of a pair of alleles. For example, the disease might be caused by a recessive gene *h* that is partially expressed in the presence of the dominant gene *H*. The genotypes of the parents would be *Hh*, giving them a mild form of the disease. The genotype of the child would be *hh*, giving the child a severe form of the disease.

17. Examples can vary, but they should demonstrate an understanding of how the three kinds of diversity are different. For example:
species diversity: in tropical rainforest region, there are a variety of populations of birds, flowering plants, etc;
genetic diversity: among the crows in a population, there are genes for different kind of coloration;
ecosystem diversity: as you move around Earth, you can find different types of ecosystems supporting different populations of living things

Extended Response

18. The diagram represents the Krebs cycle or tricarboxylic acid cycle. Pyruvate is converted to acetyl CoA, releasing CO_2 and NADH. Acetyl CoA joins with a 4-carbon compound to form citric acid. Citric acid is further processed, releasing CO_2, NADH, and $FADH_2$, and producing ATP. Citric acid is eventually converted back to a 4-carbon compound which joins the next acetyl group.

19. Microtubules provide structural support and are involved in transportation within a cell. They also help separate chromosomes in mitosis. Cells without microtubules might have decreased ability to transport materials or perform mitosis.

Essay Question

20. Mendel would have had to cross white and purple plants, then cross their offspring as well. Because either white or purple is recessive, it is possible to see which trait is least prevalent in the offspring of a cross of two heterozygous plants. The recessive trait would be least likely to show up in such a cross. Essay responses should explain these possible outcomes in detail to make clear how the recessive and dominant trait would be obvious.

Chapter 12 Organizer:
Molecular Genetics

LabManager™
Customize any lab with the LabManager™ CD-ROM.

Essential Questions	National Science Standards	Materials and Planning Estimated times include cleanup and disposal, but do not include teacher prep time. For cleanup and disposal guidelines, see page 39T.	Est. Time (min)
Section 1 1. Which experiments led to the discovery of DNA as the genetic material? 2. What is the basic structure of DNA? 3. What is the basic structure of the eukaryotic chromosomes?	UCP.1–3; A.1, A.2; B.2, B.3, C.2, C.3; E.2; G.1, G.2	**Launch Lab,** p. 324: textbook and other reference materials	20
		Activity, p. 329: three types of candy, including small candies, such as jelly beans of at least four different colors, construction paper, glue	30
		Demonstration, p. 330: small and large paper clips, two 4-cm X 8-cm polystyrene blocks, different-colored twist ties or pipe cleaners	10
		MiniLab 1, p. 331: DNA model building kits	30
Section 2 1. What is the role of enzymes in the replication of DNA? 2. How are leading and lagging strands synthesized differently? 3. How does DNA replication compare in eukaryotes and prokaryotes?	UCP.1, UCP.2; A.1, A.2; B.2, B.3, C.2; G.1, G.2	**Demonstration,** p. 334: zipper	5
		MiniLab 2, p. 334: DNA model from MiniLab 1	30
Section 3 1. How are messenger RNA, ribosomal RNA, and transfer RNA involved in the transcription and translation of genes? 2. What is the role of RNA polymerase in the synthesis of messenger RNA? 3. How is the code of DNA translated into messenger RNA and utilized to synthesize a protein?	UCP.1, UCP.2; A.1, A.2; B.2; C.2; G.1	**Demonstration,** p. 339: no materials required	10
Section 4 1. How are bacteria able to regulate their genes by two types of operons? 2. How do eukaryotes regulate the transcription of genes? 3. What are the various types of mutations?	UCP.1–4; A.1, A.2; B.2; C.2, C.3, C.4; E.1, E.2; F.1, F.4, F.5; G.1, G.2	**Demonstration,** p. 348: coiled and straight sections of telephone cord or shoelaces	10
		Activity, p. 350: straws in two different colors, polystyrene balls in four different colors, box of toothpicks, needle, thread	15
		BioLab, p. 351: corn kernels (50 g), beakers (2), blender, cheesecloth, rubber band, glass spooling hook, homogenization medium, plastic centrifuge tube, contact lens cleaning tablet containing papain, 95% ethanol, distilled water, test tube, container of ice, water bath at 60°C, stirring rod, timer or clock	50

Suggested Time for Each Lesson

Class	Chapter Opener	Section 1	Section 2	Section 3	Section 4	Assessment
Basic	45 min	90 min	90 min	45 min	45 min	45 min
General	25 min	90 min	90 min	45 min	65 min	45 min
Honors	5 min	40 min	25 min	135 min	65 min	45 min

ConnectED

connectED.mcgraw-hill.com

Access interactive learning opportunities and teaching resources using these icons located throughout your StudentWorks™ Plus Online and eTeacherEdition Online.

Chapter 12 Section Resources	Additional Chapter 12 Resources	Technology
FAST FILE Unit 3 Resources: Launch Lab Worksheet* MiniLab Worksheet* Study Guide (English/Spanish)* Section Quick Check **Reading Essentials 12.1** **Science Notebook 12.1*** **FAST FILE Unit 3 Resources:** MiniLab Worksheet* Study Guide (English/Spanish)* Section Quick Check **Reading Essentials 12.2** **Science Notebook 12.2*** **FAST FILE Unit 3 Resources:** Study Guide (English/Spanish)* Section Quick Check **Reading Essentials 12.3** **Science Notebook 12.3*** **FAST FILE Unit 3 Resources:** BioLab Worksheet* Study Guide (English/Spanish)* Section Quick Check **Reading Essentials 12.4** **Science Notebook 12.4***	**FAST FILE Unit 3 Resources:** Chapter Diagnostic Test Concept Mapping* Real-World Biology Enrichment Chapter Tests A, B, and C **Transparencies:** Bellringer Transparencies* Biology Concepts Transparencies* **Lab Resources:** Laboratory Manual* Probeware Lab Manual* Forensics Lab Manual* Pre-AP Lab Manual* Open Inquiry in Biology* Guided Inquiry in Biology*	**Teaching Tools:** eTeacherEdition Online Classroom Presentation Toolkit CD-ROM* LabManager™ CD-ROM* Video Lab DVD* Virtual Lab CD-ROM* What's BIOLOGY Got To Do With It? StudentWorks™ Plus Online* **Chapter Assessment Tools:** Classroom Presentation Toolkit CD-ROM* *ExamView® Assessment Suite* CD-ROM **Web-Based Resources:** • StudentWorks™ Plus Online • eTeacherEdition Online • Animations* • The Interactive Time Line* • Interactive Tables* • Online Quizzes • Online Test Practice • Standardized Test Practice • Virtual Labs* • Multilingual eGlossary* • Vocabulary eGames* • Vocabulary eFlashcards • WebQuests • Personal Tutors

While all resources listed are appropriate for English learners, the * indicates resources with a strong visual or hands-on component for EL.

Teaching strategies and activities have been coded for differentiated instruction.

AL Activities for students working above grade level	**OL** Activities for students working on grade level	**BL** Activities for students working below grade level	**EL** Activities for English learners (also ELL)	**COOP LEARN** Activities designed for small cooperative group work

CHAPTER 12

Launch Lab
Who discovered DNA?

? Inquiry Launch Lab

For a lab worksheet, use your eTeacherEdition Online.

RUBRIC A rubric for evaluating Launch Labs is found on your eTeacherEdition Online.

Est. Time 20 min

Safety Precaution Approve lab safety forms before work begins.

Teaching Strategies
- Have students work in small groups or pairs.
- Use the information and dates from student reports to prepare a class time line that can be displayed in the classroom.

Procedure
1. Work in groups of 3-4 to identify scientists and experiments that made important contributions to the understanding of genetics and DNA.
2. Preview the chapter in this **textbook.**
3. Make a time line showing when each important discovery mentioned in the text was made.

Analysis
1. **Compare** and contrast your group's time line with the other time lines in the class. Answers will vary, time lines should be similar because all students used the same source.
2. **Infer** how the results of the past experiments are important for each scientist that follows. Answers will vary, but students should see that each scientist's work is dependent upon the work of other scientists.

CHAPTER 12
Molecular Genetics

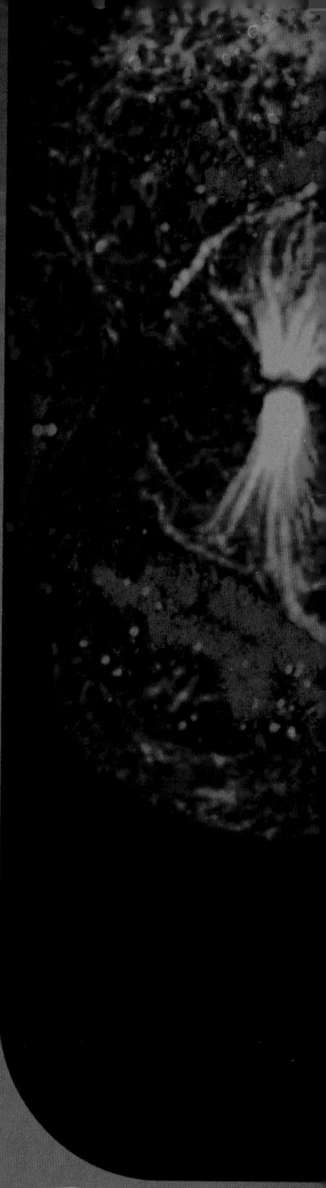

ConnectED
Your one-stop online resource
connectED.mcgraw-hill.com

- Video
- Audio
- Review
- Inquiry
- WebQuest
- Assessment
- Concepts in Motion
- Multilingual eGlossary

Launch Lab
Who discovered DNA?

The body of knowledge concerning genetics, DNA, and biotechnology has been accumulating for nearly one and a half centuries. In this lab you will make a time line of the discovery of DNA.

For a lab worksheet, use your StudentWorks™ Plus Online.

? Inquiry Launch Lab

FOLDABLES®

Make a two-tab book using the labels shown. Use it to organize your notes about transcription and translation.

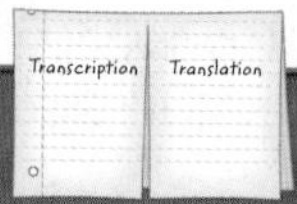

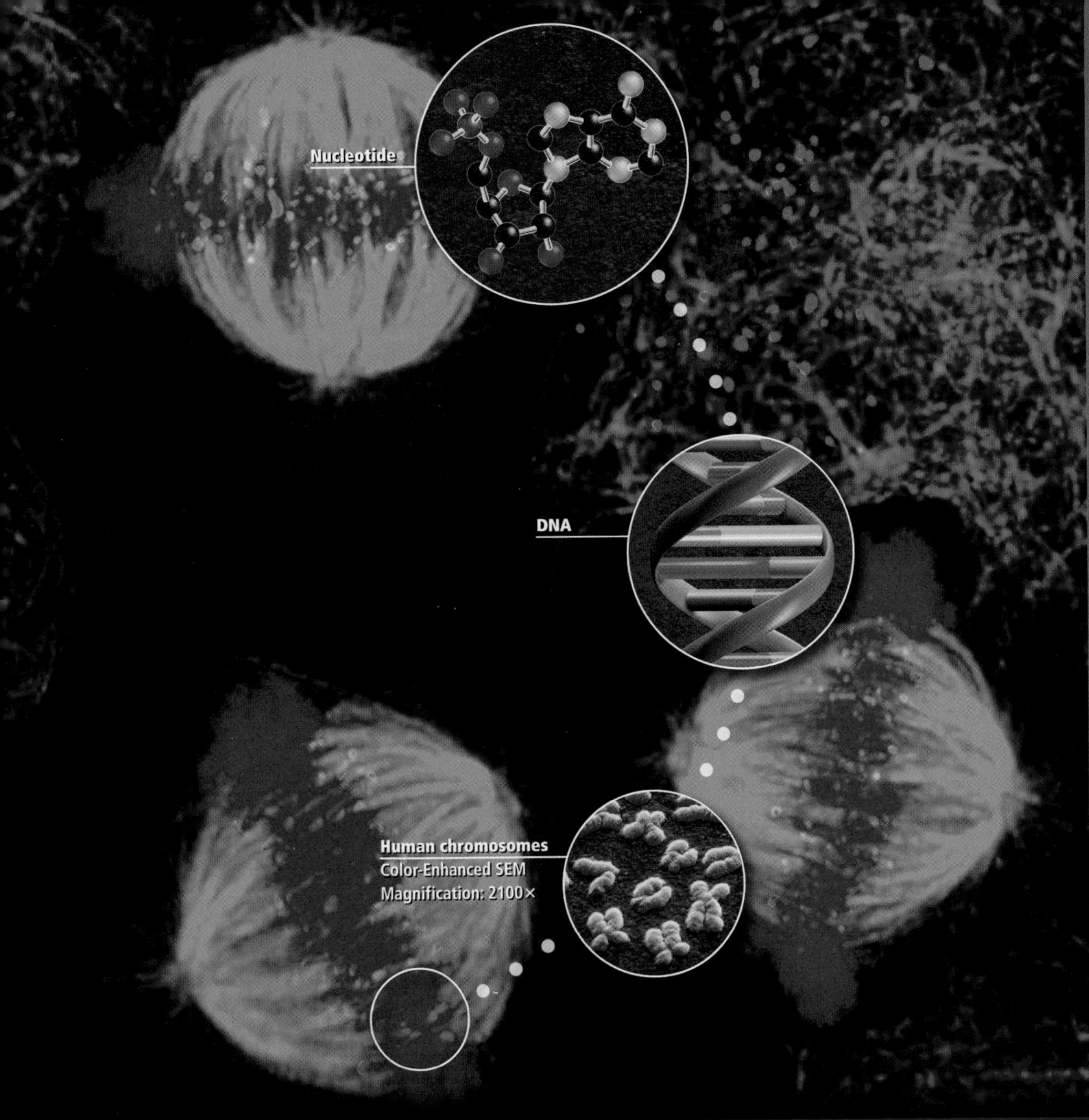

THEME FOCUS Scientific Inquiry

The discovery of the structure of DNA dramatically changed the field of biology.

BIG Idea DNA is the genetic material that contains a code for proteins.

Section 1 • DNA: The Genetic Material

Section 2 • Replication of DNA

Section 3 • DNA, RNA, and Protein

Section 4 • Gene Regulation and Mutation

Introduce the Chapter

Codes

ASK STUDENTS: ***Did you ever get a message from a friend that was in code?*** Some students will likely say yes. ***How did you figure out what the message said?*** Answers might include having a key or cracking the code to figure out the key. Use these questions to introduce how DNA serves as a code.

TELL STUDENTS: ***Like a secret code, DNA also involves the match of a code with a key, and the translation of the code results in something useful.***

BIG Idea

Outline Have students outline the chapter, writing first the Big Idea, then the Main Ideas and paragraph heads. Instruct students to continue the outline under the paragraph heads.

Sample outline:

I. Big Idea: DNA is the genetic material that contains a code for proteins.
   A. Main Idea: The discovery that DNA is the genetic code involved many experiments.
      1. Discovery of the Genetic Material
         a. Griffith
         b. Avery
         c. Hershey and Chase

THEMES

Scientific Inquiry Many experiments led to the discovery of DNA as the genetic code.

Diversity Mutations in DNA provide the possibility of extensive variation.

Energy Replication of DNA requires energy, as do all biosynthetic actions.

Homeostasis Mistakes within DNA are usually fixed before replication occurs.

Change Mutations within DNA can be passed on to future generations.

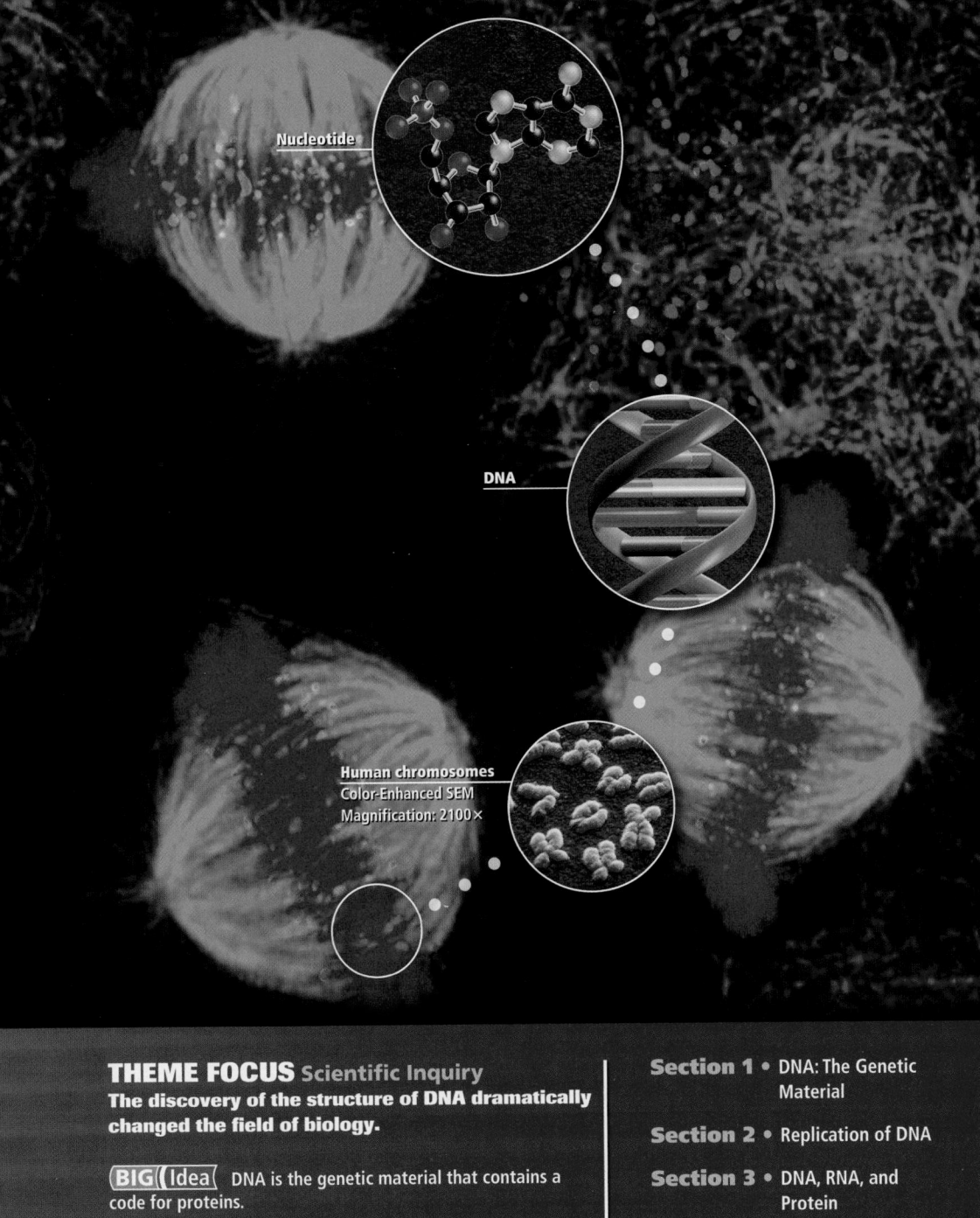

Section 1

MAIN Idea

BL OL AL Genes and Traits
ASK STUDENTS: ***What features do human beings share?*** Answers might include two legs, two arms, two eyes, and general body shape. ***What features are different among people?*** Answers might include eye color, hair color, particular shapes of features like nose and lips. Tell students that this chapter will begin to explain the molecular basis of what makes each person unique.

R Reading Strategy

EL BL OL AL Sequence Have students read about the experiments described in the text under the heading *Discovery of the Genetic Material.* Have them write a sequence of the experiments that led to the discovery of DNA on 3" x 5" cards, with the names of the people involved and a brief summary of what each experiment demonstrated.

Develop Concepts

EL BL OL Activity Have students begin collecting pictures of DNA and chromosomes in magazine and newspaper articles about genes to prepare a bulletin board on DNA.

Section 1

Reading Preview

Essential Questions

- Which experiments led to the discovery of DNA as the genetic material?
- What is the basic structure of DNA?
- What is the basic structure of eukaryotic chromosomes?

Review Vocabulary

nucleic acid: complex biomolecule that stores cellular information in the form of a code

New Vocabulary

double helix
nucleosome

g Multilingual eGlossary

DNA: The Genetic Material

MAIN Idea The discovery that DNA is the genetic code involved many experiments.

Real-World Reading Link Do you like to read mystery novels or watch people on television solve crimes? Detectives search for clues that will help them solve the mystery. Geneticists are detectives looking for clues in the mystery of inheritance.

R Discovery of the Genetic Material

Once Mendel's work was rediscovered in the 1900s, scientists began to search for the molecule involved in inheritance. Scientists knew that genetic information was carried on the chromosomes in eukaryotic cells, and that the two main components of chromosomes are DNA and protein. For many years, scientists tried to determine which of these macromolecules—nucleic acid (DNA) or proteins—was the source of genetic information.

Griffith The first major experiment that led to the discovery of DNA as the genetic material was performed by Frederick Griffith in 1928. Griffith studied two strains of the bacteria *Streptococcus pneumoniae,* which causes pneumonia. He found that one strain could be transformed, or changed, into the other form.

Of the two strains he studied, one had a sugar coat and one did not. Both strains are shown in **Figure 1.** The coated strain causes pneumonia and is called the smooth (S) strain. The noncoated strain does not cause pneumonia and is called the rough (R) strain because, without the coat, the bacteria colonies have rough edges.

Follow Griffith's study described in **Figure 2.** Notice the live S cells killed the mouse in the study. The live R cells did not kill the mouse, and the killed S cells did not kill the mouse. However, when Griffith made a mixture of live R cells and killed S cells and injected the mixture into a mouse, the mouse died. Griffith isolated live bacteria from the dead mouse. When these isolated bacteria were cultured, the smooth trait was visible, suggesting that a disease-causing factor was passed from the killed S bacteria to the live R bacteria. Griffith concluded that there had been a transformation from live R bacteria to live S bacteria. This experiment set the stage for the search to identify the transforming substance.

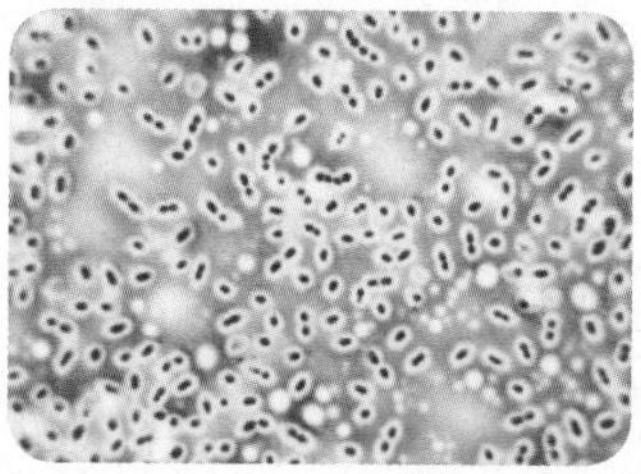

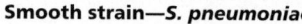

Smooth strain—*S. pneumoniae*

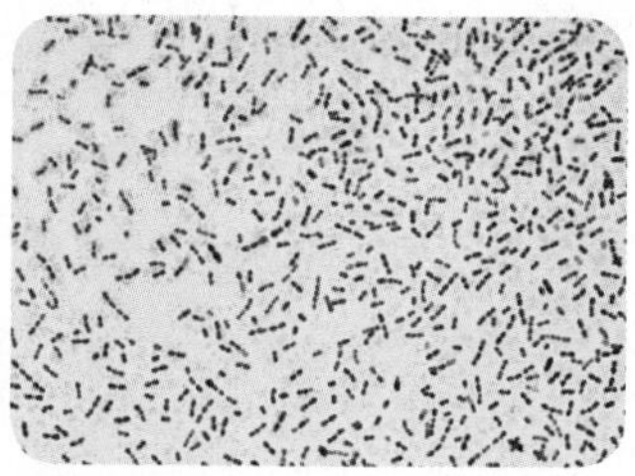

Rough strain—*S. pneumoniae*

Figure 1 The smooth (S) strain of *S. pneumoniae* can cause pneumonia, though the rough (R) strain is not disease-causing. The strains can be identified by the appearance of the colonies.

Research Citation

Critical Thinking Educational research indicates that students should be challenged to think critically about the material they are reading. The Critical Thinking discussion on p. 327 will help them to develop the valuable skills of identifying similarities and differences between ideas. (Ross, 1987)

Research bibliography on pages 32T–34T

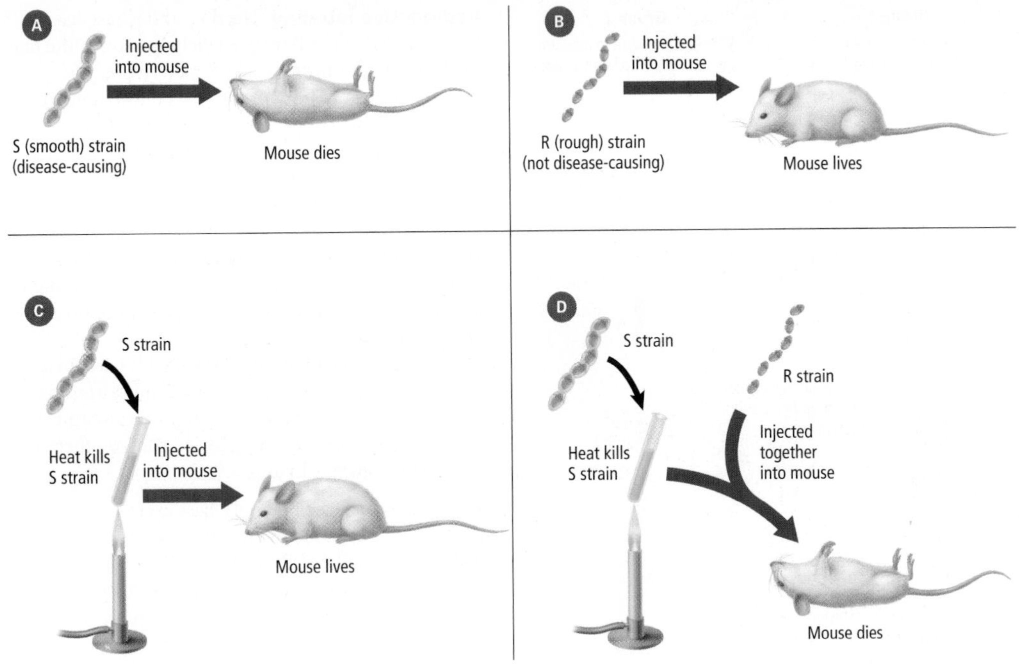

■ **Figure 2** Griffith's transformation experiment demonstrates the change of rough bacteria into smooth bacteria.
Explain ***why Griffith concluded there had been a change from live R bacteria to live S bacteria.***

S

Avery In 1944, Oswald Avery and his colleagues identified the molecule that transformed the R strain of bacteria into the S strain. Avery isolated different macromolecules, such as DNA, proteins, and lipids, from killed S cells. Then he exposed live R cells to the macromolecules separately. When the live R cells were exposed to the S strain DNA, they were transformed into S cells. Avery concluded that when the S cells in Griffith's experiments were killed, DNA was released. Some of the R bacteria incorporated this DNA into their cells, and this changed the bacteria into S cells. Avery's conclusions were not widely accepted by the scientific community, and many biologists continued to question and experiment to determine whether proteins or DNA were responsible for the transfer of genetic material.

W **C**

Reading Check **Explain** how Avery discovered the transforming factor.

Hershey and Chase In 1952, Alfred Hershey and Martha Chase published results of experiments that provided definitive evidence that DNA was the transforming factor. These experiments involved a bacteriophage (bak TIHR ee uh fayj), a type of virus that attacks bacteria. Two components made the experiment ideal for confirming that DNA is the genetic material. First, the bacteriophage used in the experiment was made of DNA and protein. Second, viruses cannot replicate themselves. They must inject their genetic material into a living cell to reproduce. Hershey and Chase labeled both parts of the virus to determine which part was injected into the bacteria and, thus, which part was the genetic material.

VOCABULARY
ACADEMIC VOCABULARY
Transform
to cause a change in type or kind
Avery used DNA to transform bacteria.

S Skill Practice

BL OL AL

Recognize Cause and Effect
ASK STUDENTS: ***What type of bacteria caused the mouse in Figure 2D to die?*** smooth bacteria ***Where did this type of bacteria come from?*** The bacteria were converted by a transforming substance from a rough to a smooth form of bacteria, which killed the mouse.

W Writing Support

OL AL Creative Writing
Have students write a poem, story, or play about the Griffith experiment. Tell them that their creative work should demonstrate an understanding of the scientific process and the methods of the Griffith experiment.

C Critical Thinking

OL AL Differentiate
ASK STUDENTS: ***How did Avery's experiment differ from Griffith's experiment?*** Griffith found that one strain of bacteria could be transformed to another and concluded that a transforming factor was involved. Avery tested to see which molecule changed the R strain into the S strain of bacteria. He found that DNA was the transforming molecule.

Content Background

Teacher FYI According to James Watson, one of the scientists who discovered the structure of DNA, the race to find the genetic material was split into two groups: those who thought the genetic material was protein and those who thought the genetic material was DNA. One of the main protein proponents was Nobel Prize-winning chemist Linus Pauling. Watson's background in virology made him well aware of the Hershey-Chase experiment, which helped convince him that the genetic material was DNA.

■ **Caption Question Fig. 2** The mouse died.

Reading Check When Avery exposed live R strain bacteria to DNA from killed S strain bacteria, the R cells were transformed to S cells.

C Critical Thinking

BL OL AL Conclude

ASK STUDENTS: ***What was the purpose of using radioactive labeled sulfur and phosphorus?*** This allowed the experimenters to track what happened to the protein, which was labeled with radioactive sulfur, and the DNA, which was labeled with radioactive phosphorus, throughout the experiment.

D Develop Concepts

BL OL AL COOP LEARN

Activity Organize students into groups of three or four and have them make a comic-style cartoon about the Hershey-Chase experiment. Text bubbles should contain conversations that explain the experimental procedure of radioactive labeling to trace molecules. Students can draw their final version of the cartoon in color on poster board or large sheets of paper. Hang cartoons around the classroom for other groups to examine.

Concepts in Motion

Interactive Table

Reading Check It showed that the genetic material in the form of DNA, not proteins, had entered the bacteria.

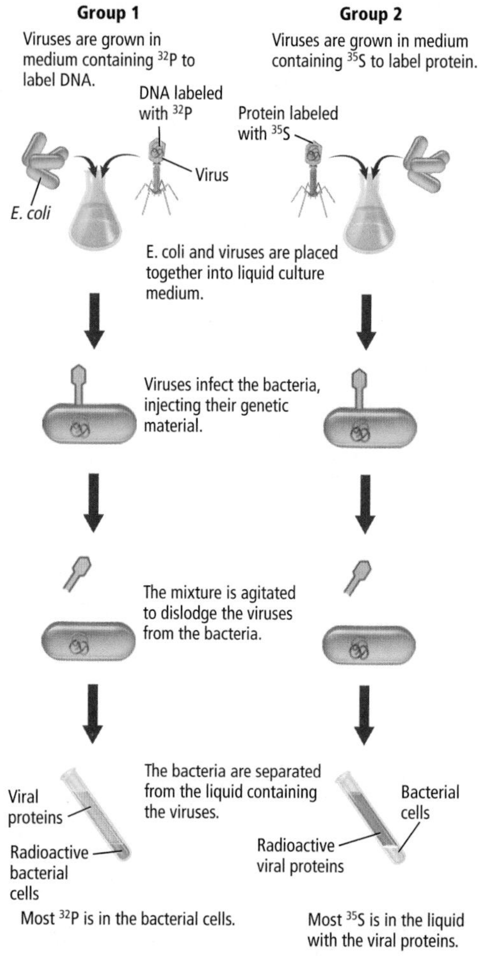

Figure 3 Hershey and Chase used radioactive labeling techniques to demonstrate that DNA is the genetic material in viruses.

Radioactive labeling Hershey and Chase used a technique called radioactive labeling to trace the fate of the DNA and protein as the bacteriophages infected bacteria and reproduced. Follow along in **Figure 3** as you continue learning about the Hershey-Chase experiment. They labeled one set of bacteriophages with radioactive phosphorus (^{32}P). Proteins do not contain phosphorous, so DNA and not protein in these viruses would be radioactive. Hershey and Chase labeled another set of bacteriophages with radioactive sulfur (^{35}S). Because proteins contain sulfur and DNA does not, proteins and not DNA would be radioactive. C

Hershey and Chase infected bacteria with viruses from the two groups. When viruses infect bacteria, they attach to the outside of the bacteria and inject their genetic material. The infected bacteria then were separated from the viruses.

Tracking DNA Hershey and Chase examined Group 1 labeled with ^{32}P and found that the labeled viral DNA had been injected into the bacteria. Viruses later released from the infected bacteria contained ^{32}P, further indicating that DNA was the carrier of genetic information.

When examining Group 2 labeled with ^{35}S, Hershey and Chase observed that the labeled proteins were found outside of the bacterial cells. Viral replication had occurred in the bacterial cells, indicating that the viruses' genetic material had entered the bacteria, but no label (^{35}S) was found. **Table 1** summarizes the results of the Hershey-Chase experiment.

Based on their results, Hershey and Chase concluded that the viral DNA was injected into the cell and provided the genetic information needed to produce new viruses. This experiment provided powerful evidence that DNA, not protein, was the genetic material that could be passed from generation to generation in viruses. D

Reading Check **Explain** why it is important that new viruses were produced in the bacteria.

Table 1 Summary of Hershey-Chase Results — Concepts in Motion Interactive Table

Group 1 (Viruses labeled with ^{32}P)		Group 2 (Viruses labeled with ^{35}S)	
Infected Bacteria	**Liquid with Viruses**	**Infected Bacteria**	**Liquid with Viruses**
• Labeled viral DNA (^{32}P) found in the bacteria • Viral replication occurred • New viruses contained ^{32}P	• No labeled DNA • No viral replication	• No labeled viral proteins (^{35}S) • Viral replication occurred • New viruses did not have a label	• Labeled proteins found • No viral replication

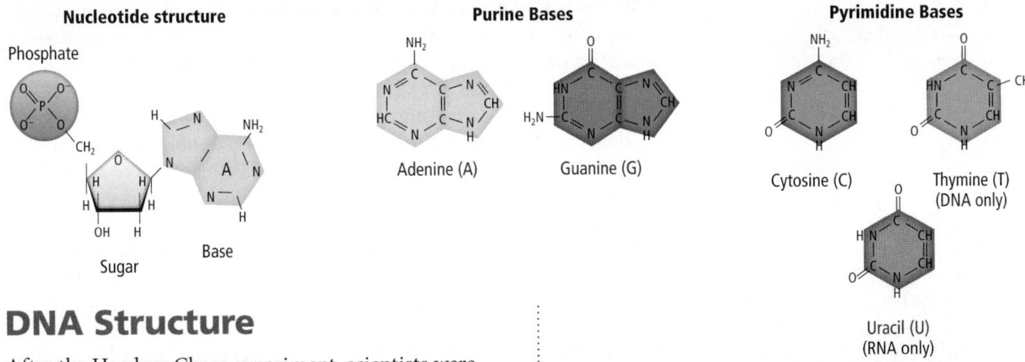

■ **Figure 4** Nucleotides are made of a phosphate, sugar, and a base. There are five different bases found in nucleotide subunits that make up DNA and RNA.
Identify ***the structural difference between purine and pyrimidine bases.***

DNA Structure

After the Hershey-Chase experiment, scientists were more confident that DNA was the genetic material. The clues had led to the identification of the genetic material, but the questions of how nucleotides came together to form DNA and how DNA could communicate information remained.

S **Nucleotides** In the 1920s, the biochemist P. A. Levene determined the basic structure of nucleotides that make up DNA. Nucleotides are the subunits of nucleic acids and consist of a five-carbon sugar, a phosphate group, and a nitrogenous base. The two nucleic acids found in living cells are DNA and RNA. DNA nucleotides contain the sugar deoxyribose (dee ahk sih RI bos), a phosphate, and one of four nitrogenous bases: adenine (A duh neen), guanine (GWAH neen), cytosine (SI tuh seen), or thymine (THI meen). RNA nucleotides contain the sugar ribose, a phosphate, and one of four nitrogenous bases: adenine, guanine, cytosine, or uracil (YOO ruh sihl). Notice in **Figure 4** that guanine (G) and adenine (A) are double-ringed bases. This type of base is called a purine base. Thymine (T), cytosine (C), and uracil (U) are single-ringed bases called pyrimidine **D** bases.

Chargaff Erwin Chargaff analyzed the amount of adenine, guanine, thymine, and cytosine in the DNA of various species. A portion of Chargaff's data, published in 1950, is shown in **Figure 5.** Chargaff found that the amount of guanine nearly equals the amount of cytosine, and the amount of adenine nearly equals the amount of thymine within a species. This finding is known as Chargaff's rule: C = G and T = A.

The structure question When four scientists joined the search for the DNA structure, the meaning and importance of Chargaff's data became clear. Rosalind Franklin, a British chemist; Maurice Wilkins, a British physicist; Francis Crick, a British physicist; and James Watson, an American biologist, provided information that was pivotal in answering the DNA structure question.

■ **Figure 5** Chargaff's data showed that though base composition varies from species to species, within a species C = G and A = T.

Chargaff's Data

	Base Composition (Mole Percent)			
Organism	A	T	G	C
Escherichia coli	26.0	23.9	24.9	25.2
Yeast	31.3	32.9	18.7	17.1
Herring	27.8	27.5	22.2	22.6
Rat	28.6	28.4	21.4	21.5
Human	30.9	29.4	19.9	19.8

S Skill Practice

BL OL AL Visual Literacy

Before students read the text under the heading *Nucleotides*, have them examine Figure 5 and see if they can determine any type of ratio relationship among the base amounts found by Chargaff. The amount of guanine almost equals the amount of cytosine, and thymine almost equals adenine.

ASK STUDENTS: ***Why are the percentages not exactly the same?*** experimental error

D Develop Concepts

EL BL OL AL COOP LEARN

Activity Organize students into groups of three, and give each group 20 strips of paper of four distinct colors, such as red, green, yellow, and blue. Have them write *T* on one color, *G* on one color, *A* on one color, and *C* on one color. Ask them to tape the strips end to end in any order they wish. See if any group came up with the same sequence, which is unlikely. Point out that these represent nucleotide units, the building blocks of DNA, making a polymer. This activity emphasizes the wide variety of coding that is possible, even using only 20 nucleotides.

ASK STUDENTS: ***How many possible combinations can the 20 colored strips form?*** The possible combinations of 4 colors, 20 strips long is 4^{20} or 1×10^{12}. Use this activity to demonstrate the wide variety of proteins that can be synthesized from a short DNA sequence.

■ **Caption Question Fig. 4** Purine bases have two rings, and pyrimidine bases have one ring.

Activity

BL OL AL Model DNA Have pairs of students make a candy model of DNA with three types of candies. One type of candy can represent the deoxyribose; another can represent phosphate groups. Small candies, such as jelly beans in four different colors, can represent A, T, C, or G. Have students attach their model to construction paper using glue and write a key to their candy representations. Est. time: 30 min

Writing Support

BL OL COOP LEARN

Creative Writing Organize students into groups of three, and have groups develop a poster about DNA. Poster topics may focus on such elements as the discovery of the structure of DNA in 1953, a biography of a key scientist and his or her contributions, or the importance of DNA to modern genetics, medicine, and biotechnology.

Inquiry Launch Lab

Assess Content Development

Assess how understanding has developed when students revisit the Launch Lab analysis questions.

D Develop Concepts

EL BL OL AL **Activity** Write the sequence of a strand of nucleotide bases on the board indicating the 3' and 5' ends. Have students write the complementary strand to go with this coding strand. Write the correct strand on the board aligned with the coding strand. C pairs with G and T pairs with A.

Reading Check Chargraff's data hinted that bases were specifically paired.

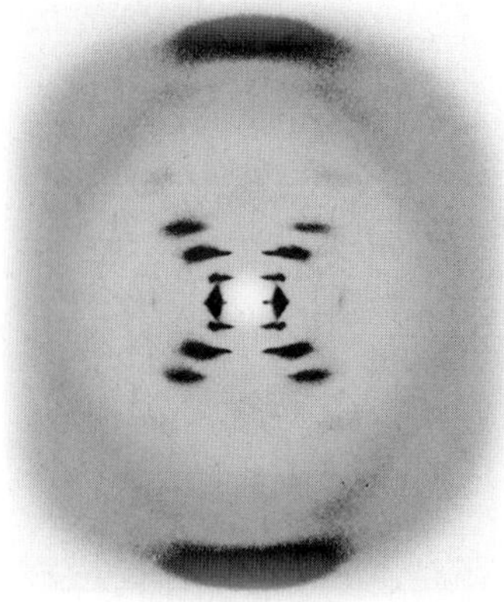

■ **Figure 6** Rosalind Franklin's Photo 51 and X-ray diffraction data helped Watson and Crick solve the structure of DNA. When analyzed and measured carefully, the pattern shows the characteristics of helix structure.

X-ray diffraction Wilkins was working at King's College in London, England, with a technique called X-ray diffraction, a technique that involved aiming X rays at the DNA molecule. In 1951, Franklin joined the staff at King's College. There she took the now famous Photo 51 and collected data eventually used by Watson and Crick. Photo 51, shown in **Figure 6,** indicated that DNA was a **double helix,** or twisted ladder shape, formed by two strands of nucleotides twisted around each other. The specific structure of the DNA double helix was determined later by Watson and Crick when they used Franklin's data and other mathematical data. DNA is the genetic material of all organisms, composed of two complementary, precisely paired strands of nucleotides wound in a double helix.

Watson and Crick Watson and Crick were working at Cambridge University in Cambridge, England, when they saw Franklin's X-ray diffraction picture. Using Chargaff's data and Franklin's data, Watson and Crick measured the width of the helix and the spacing of the bases. Together, they built a model of the double helix that conformed to the others' research. The model that they built is shown in **Figure 7.** Some important features of their proposed molecule include the following:

1. Two outside strands consist of alternating deoxyribose and phosphate.
2. Cytosine and guanine bases pair to each other by three hydrogen bonds.
3. Thymine and adenine bases pair to each other by two hydrogen bonds.

Inquiry Launch Lab

Review **Based on what you've read about the history of DNA experiments, how would you now answer the analysis questions?**

DNA structure DNA often is compared to a twisted ladder, with the rails of the ladder represented by the alternating deoxyribose and phosphate. The pairs of bases (cytosine–guanine or thymine–adenine) form the steps, or rungs, of the ladder. A purine base always binds to a pyrimidine base, ensuring a consistent distance between the two rails of the ladder. This proposed bonding of the bases also explains Chargaff's data, which suggested that the number of purine bases equaled the number of pyrimidine bases in a sample of DNA. Remember, cytosine and thymine are pyrimidine bases, adenine and guanine are purines, and C = G and A = T. Therefore, C + T = G + A, or purine bases equal pyrimidine bases. Complementary base pairing is used to describe the precise pairing of purine and pyrimidine bases between strands of nucleic acids. It is the characteristic of DNA replication through which the parent strand can determine the sequence of a new strand. D

Reading Check **Explain** why Chargaff's data was an important clue for putting together the structure of DNA.

■ **Figure 7** Using Chargaff's and Franklin's data, Watson and Crick, shown here, solved the puzzle of the structure of DNA.

Demonstration

Double Helix Construct a DNA model that demonstrates the double helix. Link two chains of ten paper clips together, alternating small and large paper clips (phosphate = small paper clip, deoxyribose = large paper clip). Insert the ends of each strand of clips into a 4-cm × 8-cm polystyrene block, about 5 cm apart. Insert the other ends of the strands into a similar polystyrene block. Use four different colors of either twist ties or colored pipe cleaners to represent the bases and connect the two strands across at the large paper clips. Hold the structure up and twist one of the blocks to demonstrate the double helix. Est. time: 10 min

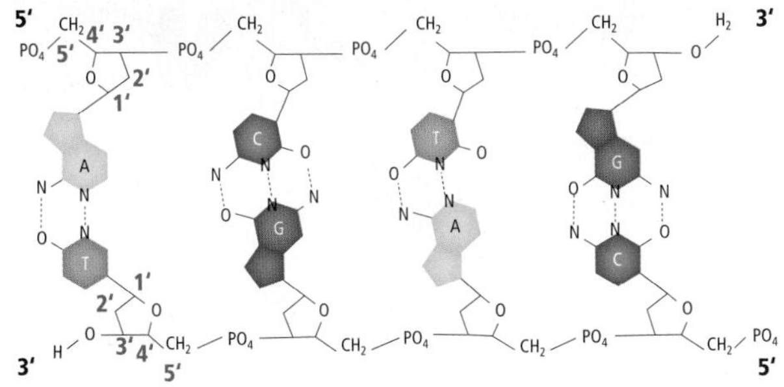

■ **Figure 8** Two strands of DNA running antiparallel make up the DNA helix.
Explain ***why the ends of the DNA strands are labeled 3' and 5'.***

Concepts in Motion

Animation

Orientation Another unique feature of the DNA molecule is the direction, or orientation, of the two strands. Carbon molecules can be numbered in organic molecules. **Figure 8** shows the orientation of the numbered carbons in the sugar molecules on each strand of DNA. On the top rail, the orientation of the sugar has the 5' (read "five-prime") carbon on the left, and on the end of that rail, the 3' (read "three-prime") carbon is on the right of the sugar-phosphate chain. The strand is said to be oriented 5' to 3'. The strand on the bottom runs in the opposite direction and is oriented 3' to 5'. This orientation of the two strands is called antiparallel. Another way to visualize antiparallel orientation is to take two pencils and position them so that the point of one pencil is next to the eraser of the other and vice versa.

The announcement In 1953, Watson and Crick surprised the scientific community by publishing a one-page letter in the journal *Nature* that suggested a structure for DNA and hypothesized a method of replication for the molecule deduced from the structure. In articles individually published in the same issue, Wilkins and Franklin presented evidence that supported the structure proposed by Watson and Crick. Still, the mysteries of how to prove DNA's replication and how it worked as a genetic code remained.

VOCABULARY

SCIENCE USAGE V. COMMON USAGE

Prime

Science usage: a mark located above and to the right of a character, used to identify a number or variable
Carbon molecules in organic molecules are numbered and labeled with a prime.

Common usage: first in value, excellence, or quality
The student found the prime seats in the stadium for watching the game.

MiniLab 1

Inquiry MiniLab

Model DNA Structure

What is the structure of the DNA molecule? Construct a model to better understand the structure of the DNA molecule.

Procedure

1. Read and complete the lab safety form.
2. Construct a model of a short segment of DNA using the materials provided by your teacher.
3. Identify which parts of the model correspond to the different parts of a DNA molecule.

Analysis

1. **Describe** the structure of your DNA molecule.
2. **Identify** the characteristics of DNA that you focused on when constructing your model.
3. **Infer** in what way your model is different from your classmates' models. How does this relate to differences in DNA among organisms?

MiniLab 1

Inquiry MiniLab

For a lab worksheet, use your eTeacherEdition Online.

RUBRIC A rubric for evaluating MiniLabs is found on your eTeacherEdition Online.

Est. Time 30 min

Safety Precaution Approve lab safety forms before work begins.

Teaching Strategies

- Couple the model-building with appropriate A/V materials on DNA, if available.
- Have each lab team show you their finished model and explain the structure of DNA to you.
- A time-saving alternative is to buy one kit and conduct this lab as a teacher-led demonstration.

Analysis

1. It appears to have side rails with rungs between them, and the rungs twist like a spiral staircase.
2. The sugar and phosphate groups represent the handrails; the bases represent the steps or rungs.
3. The rungs in different models contain a variety of bases that represent the genetic code. With the exception of identical twins or triplets, each organism has a unique genetic code.

LabManager™

Customize this lab with the LabManager™ CD-ROM.

Differentiated Instruction

English Learners Before beginning the MiniLab on this page, model each step for English learners. This reinforcement will reduce confusion.

For more tips, see pages 14T–15T.

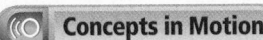

■ **Caption Question Fig. 8** because of the orientation of the carbon atoms in the sugar

Concepts in Motion

Animation

GOING GREEN Have students use items that would have normally become trash to build their models in MiniLab 1. These Items could include empty cereal boxes, clean plastic containers, paper towel rolls, and scrap paper.

D Develop Concepts

BL OL

Clarify a Misconception

ASK STUDENTS: ***What is the relationship among genes, DNA, and chromosomes?*** Genes are specific sequences of DNA in a chromosome, and they code for a protein. Some students might have difficulty understanding the concept of a gene and a chromosome. They might have a basic understanding of the idea of inheritance being associated with a gene, but might have difficulty understanding the relationship between DNA and genes and between genes and chromosomes.

Formative Assessment

Evaluation

ASK STUDENTS: ***Which experiments first showed what molecule carries the genetic information?*** Griffith and Avery experiments ***Which experiment first showed that DNA enabled the replication of viruses?*** Hershey and Chase experiment ***Which experiment demonstrated the ratio of the nucleotides in DNA?*** Chargaff experiment ***Which four individuals were involved in solving the structure of DNA?*** Watson, Crick, Wilkins, and Franklin

Remediation Obtain and distribute blank diagrams representing the experiments above. Have students label and explain each experiment.

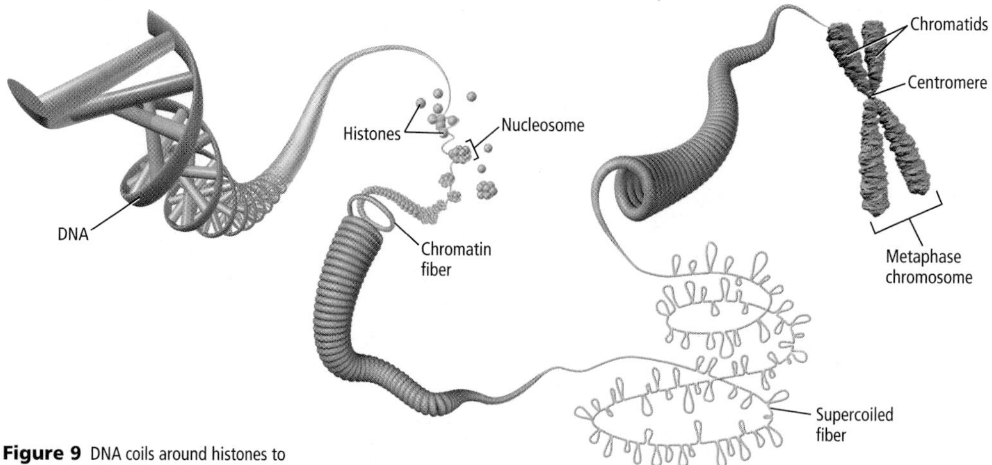

■ **Figure 9** DNA coils around histones to form nucleosomes, which coil to form chromatin fibers. The chromatin fibers supercoil to form chromosomes that are visible in the metaphase stage of mitosis.

Chromosome Structure

In prokaryotes, the DNA molecule is contained in the cytoplasm and consists mainly of a ring of DNA and associated proteins. Eukaryotic DNA is organized into individual chromosomes. The length of a human chromosome ranges from 51 million to 245 million base pairs. If a DNA strand 140 million nucleotides long was laid out in a straight line, it would be about five centimeters long. How does all of this DNA fit into a microscopic cell? In order to fit into the nucleus of a eukaryotic cell, the DNA tightly coils around a group of beadlike proteins called histones, as shown in **Figure 9.** The phosphate groups in DNA create a negative charge, which attracts the DNA to the positively charged histone proteins and forms a **nucleosome.** The nucleosomes then group together into chromatin fibers, which supercoil to make up the DNA structure recognized as a chromosome. D

Section 1 Assessment

Section Summary

- Griffith's bacterial experiment and Avery's explanation first indicated that DNA is the genetic material.
- The Hershey-Chase experiment provided evidence that DNA is the genetic material of viruses.
- Chargaff's rule states that in DNA the amount of cytosine equals the amount of guanine and the amount of thymine equals the amount of adenine.
- The work of Watson, Crick, Franklin, and Wilkins provided evidence of the double-helix structure of DNA.

Understand Main Ideas

1. MAIN Idea **Summarize** the experiments of Griffith and Avery that indicated that DNA is the genetic material.
2. **Describe** the data used by Watson and Crick to determine the structure of DNA.
3. **Draw** and label a segment of DNA showing its helix and complementary base pairing.
4. **Describe** the structure of eukaryotic chromosomes.

Think Critically

5. **Describe** two characteristics that DNA needs to fulfill its role as a genetic material.
6. **Evaluate** Hershey and Chase's decision to use radioactive phosphorus and sulfur for their experiments. Could they have used carbon or oxygen instead? Why or why not?

Section 1 Assessment

1. Griffith showed that bacteria could be transformed by the transfer of genetic material; Avery showed that DNA was the transforming factor.
2. Franklin's Photo 51 showed a helix shape. Her mathematical data showed distances between the strands. Chagraff's data suggested how bases pair.
3. Drawings should show C-G and A-T base pairing and the antiparallel orientation of the strands.
4. DNA coils around histones to form nucleosomes, which group together to form chromatin fibers, which supercoil to make the chromosome.
5. DNA must code for proteins and be able to replicate.
6. They used radioactive sulfur because sulfur is found only in proteins, and radioactive phosphorus because phosphorus is found only in DNA. They could not have used carbon or oxygen because those elements are found in both DNA and proteins.

Assessment Online Quiz

Reading Preview

Essential Questions

- What is the role of enzymes in the replication of DNA?
- How are leading and lagging strands synthesized differently?
- How does DNA replication compare in eukaryotes and prokaryotes?

Review Vocabulary

template: a molecule of DNA that is a pattern for synthesis of a new DNA molecule

New Vocabulary

semiconservative replication
DNA polymerase
Okazaki fragment

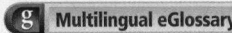

Multilingual eGlossary

Replication of DNA

MAIN Idea DNA replicates by making a strand that is complementary to each original strand.

Real-World Reading Link When copies are made using a photocopy machine, they are expected to be exact copies of the original. Making a copy would not be very efficient if it contained errors that were not in the original. Think about how your body might make copies of DNA.

R Semiconservative Replication

When Watson and Crick presented their model of DNA to the science community, they also suggested a possible method of replication called semiconservative replication. During **semiconservative replication,** parental strands of DNA separate, serve as templates, and produce DNA molecules that have one strand of parental DNA and one strand of new DNA. Recall that DNA replication occurs during interphase of mitosis and meiosis. An overview of semiconservative replication is in **Figure 10.** The process of semiconservative replication occurs in three main stages: unwinding, base pairing, and joining. C

Unwinding DNA helicase, an enzyme, is responsible for unwinding and unzipping the double helix. When the double helix is unzipped, the hydrogen bonds between the bases are broken, leaving single strands of DNA. Then, proteins called single-stranded binding proteins associate with the DNA to keep the strands separate during replication. As the helix unwinds, another enzyme, RNA primase, adds a short segment of RNA, called an RNA primer, on each DNA strand.

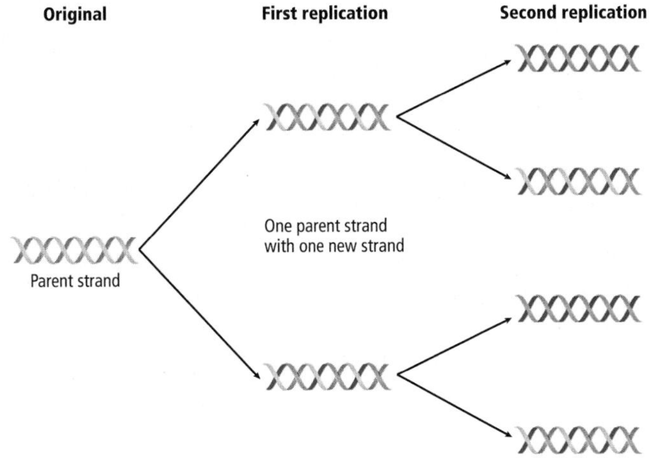

S

■ **Figure 10** In semiconservative replication, the parental DNA separates and serves as templates to produce two daughter DNA, which then can separate to produce four DNA.

Section 2

MAIN Idea

BL OL AL Making Copies

When Watson and Crick looked at the structure of DNA, they said, "...the specific pairing we have postulated immediately suggests a possible copying mechanism for the genetic material."

ASK STUDENTS: ***What pairing were these scientists referring to?*** the hydrogen bonds between the nucleotides: adenine to thymine and guanine to cytosine

R Reading Strategy

EL BL OL SQ3R Have students **S**urvey the text under the heading *Semiconservative Replication.* Next, have students write **Q**uestions about key points made in this section. Then have students **R**ead the section and make notes related to the questions. Finally, have students **R**ecite vocabulary and **R**eview for meaning.

C Critical Thinking

OL Hypothesize

ASK STUDENTS: ***What would be the result if DNA replication took place after mitosis occurred?*** Some of the daughter cells might have no DNA, some might not have copies of all chromosomes, and some might have double the amount of DNA. Those cells without DNA, lacking copies of all chromosomes, and with double the DNA would likely die.

S Skill Practice

BL OL AL Visual Literacy

Have students study the information in Figure 10. Based on what students have learned about DNA so far, have them predict how the process of semiconservative replication works.

Differentiated Instruction

Gifted The SQ3R Reading Strategy on this page can be extended for students working above grade level. Develop open-ended questions that require students to think critically about the reading instead of just read for information. Sample question: ***What might happen if DNA replication was not semiconservative?*** If one strand of DNA was not available as a template for making a new strand, as occurs during semiconservative replication, many errors in the new DNA could occur.

For more tips, see pages 14T–15T.

Writing Support

OL AL Narrative Writing

Have students write a paragraph explaining why the term *semiconservative* is a good name for the way by which DNA replicates. Paragraphs should describe how parent strands are used to build new DNA so that the new DNA is half "old" DNA.

MiniLab 2

Inquiry MiniLab

For a lab worksheet, use your eTeacherEdition Online.

RUBRIC A rubric for evaluating MiniLabs is found on your eTeacherEdition Online.

Est. Time 30 min

Safety Precaution Approve lab safety forms before work begins.

Teaching Strategy As an alternative, purchase a single kit and conduct this lab as a teacher-led demonstration.

Analysis

1. One strand (the parental strand) is from the original DNA molecule and makes up half of the new strand.
2. Nucleotides might not link up in the new strand. DNA ligase finishes the nucleotide-linking process.
3. during base pairing

Concepts in Motion Animation

Inquiry BioLab

The lab at the end of the chapter can be used at this point in the lesson.

MiniLab 2

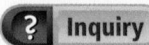

Inquiry MiniLab

Model DNA Replication

How does the DNA molecule replicate? Use a model to better understand the replication of the DNA molecule.

Procedure

1. Read and complete the lab safety form.
2. Use your DNA model from **MiniLab 1** and extra pieces to model the replication of your segment of DNA.
3. Use your model to demonstrate DNA replication for a classmate, and identify the enzymes involved in each step.

Analysis

1. **Explain** how your model of DNA replication shows semiconservative replication.
2. **Infer** how DNA replication in a cell would be affected by an absence of DNA ligase.
3. **Identify** where errors could occur in the replication process.

Base pairing The enzyme **DNA polymerase** catalyzes the addition of appropriate nucleotides to the new DNA strand. The nucleotides are added to the 3' end of the new strand, as illustrated in **Figure 11.** DNA polymerase continues adding new DNA nucleotides to the chain by adding to the 3' end of the new DNA strand. Recall that each base binds only to its complement—A binds to T and C binds to G. In this way, the templates allow identical copies of the original double-stranded DNA to be produced.

Notice in **Figure 11** that the two strands are made in a slightly different manner. One strand is called the leading strand and is elongated as the DNA unwinds. This strand is built continuously by the addition of nucleotides to the 3' end.

The other strand of DNA, called the lagging strand, elongates away from the replication fork. It is synthesized discontinuously into small segments, called **Okazaki fragments,** by the DNA polymerase in the 3' to 5' direction. These fragments are later connected by the enzyme DNA ligase. Each Okazaki fragment is about 100–200 nucleotides long in eukaryotes. Because one strand is synthesized continuously and the other is synthesized discontinuously, DNA replication is said to be semidiscontinuous as well as semiconservative.

Reading Check **Explain** how base pairing during replication ensures that the strands produced are identical to the original strand.

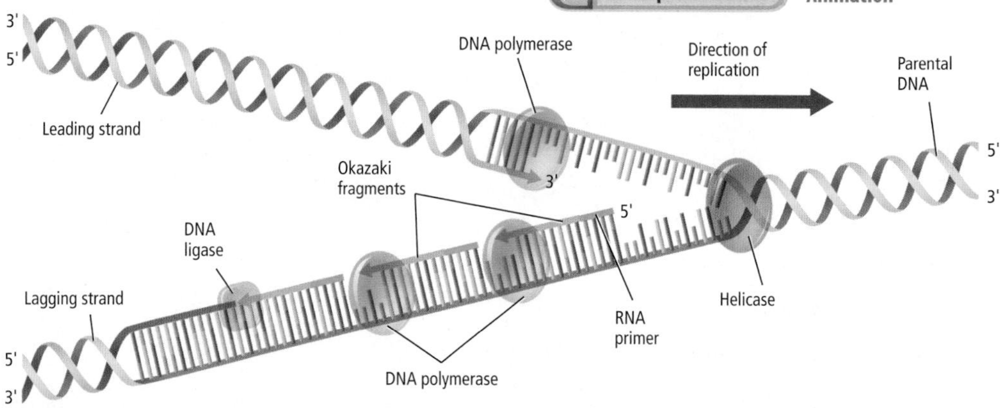

Figure 11 The DNA strands are separated during replication as each parent strand serves as a template for new strands.
Infer *why the lagging strand produces fragments instead of being synthesized continuously.*

Concepts in Motion Animation

Reading Check Each base binds only to its complement.

Caption Question Fig. 11
Because the lagging strand is in the opposite orientation (5′ to 3′) than the direction of replication, it must be synthesized in segments. Replication cannot occur in the lagging strand until the helix opens far enough to add another piece.

Demonstration

BL OL Unzip DNA Hold up a zipper and unzip it.
ASK STUDENTS: ***How does this model represent the unzipping of DNA? Analyze where it fails.*** The zipper can unzip in small sections like DNA. Its sliding device is like the DNA polymerase, but polymerase does not go in both directions, and a zipper isn't replicated when the sliding device moves.
Est. time: 5 min

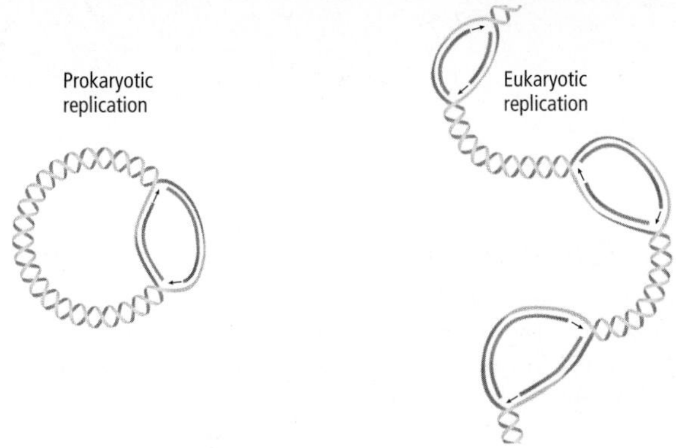

■ **Figure 12** Eukaryotes have many origins of replication. Bacteria have one origin of replication, with the DNA replicating in both directions when it unzips.

Joining Even though the leading strand is synthesized continuously, in eukaryotic DNA replication there often are many areas along the chromosome where replication begins. When the DNA polymerase comes to an RNA primer on the DNA, it removes the primer and fills in the place with DNA nucleotides. When the RNA primer has been replaced, DNA ligase links the two sections.

D

Comparing DNA Replication in Eukaryotes and Prokaryotes

Eukaryotic DNA unwinds in multiple areas as DNA is replicated. Each individual area of a chromosome replicates as a section, which can vary in length from 10,000 to one million base pairs. As a result, multiple areas of replication are occurring along the large eukaryotic chromosome at the same time. Multiple replication origins look like bubbles in the DNA strand, as shown in **Figure 12.**

In prokaryotes, the circular DNA strand is opened at one origin of replication, as shown in **Figure 12.** Notice in the figure that DNA replication occurs in two directions, just as it does in eukaryotes. Remember that prokaryotic DNA is typically shorter than eukaryotic DNA and remains in the cytoplasm, not packaged in a nucleus.

Section 2 Assessment

Section Summary

- The enzymes DNA helicase, RNA primase, DNA polymerase, and DNA ligase are involved in DNA replication.
- The leading strand is synthesized continuously, but the lagging strand is synthesized discontinuously, forming Okazaki fragments.
- Prokaryotic DNA opens at a single origin of replication, whereas eukaryotic DNA has multiple areas of replication.

Understand Main Ideas

1. MAIN Idea **Indicate** the sequence of the template strand if a nontemplate strand has the sequence 5' ATGGGGCGC 3'.
2. **Describe** the role of DNA helicase, DNA polymerase, and DNA ligase.
3. **Diagram** the way leading and lagging strands are synthesized.
4. **Explain** why DNA replication is more complex in eukaryotes than in bacteria.

Think Critically

MATH in Biology

5. If the bacteria *E. coli* synthesize DNA at a rate of 100,000 nucleotides per min and it takes 30 min to replicate the DNA, how many base pairs are in an *E. coli* chromosome?

D Develop Concepts

BL OL Clarify a Misconception

ASK STUDENTS: ***Explain the relationship of DNA replication to mitosis, meiosis, and reproduction.*** DNA must be replicated before the other steps can take place. Students do not always tie DNA replication to mitosis, meiosis, and reproduction. Point out that these processes rely on prior DNA replication to duplicate the chromosomes so that genes are passed to offspring cells.

Develop Concepts

BL OL AL Activity On the board, write a DNA sequence about 20 nucleotides long and the same DNA sequence with a portion unzipped as replication begins. Have students copy this and finish the replication in a third drawing by writing the complementary strand.

Formative Assessment

Evaluation Have students write a step-by-step summary of the replication of DNA. Have them exchange papers with a partner and have the partners evaluate the summary to determine whether any of the steps or important information is missing.

Remediation Have students write questions that they have about DNA and replication. Collect student questions and read them aloud. Have a student volunteer read aloud the relevant text in the book.

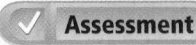

Section 2 Assessment

1. 3' TACCCCGCG 5'
2. DNA helicase is an enzyme that unwinds the DNA, DNA polymerase is an enzyme that builds the new DNA strand during replication, and DNA ligase hooks DNA Okazaki fragments together.
3. Diagrams should show that leading strands are synthesized continuously, while lagging strands are synthesized in fragments that are later connected.
4. The structure of the chromosome is much more complex and the chromosome is larger in eukaryotic cells. Eukaryotic cells have many origins of replication, whereas prokaryotes only have one.
5. 3,000,000 base pairs

Section 3

MAIN Idea

BL OL AL Protein Blueprint

ASK STUDENTS: ***Suppose you are going to build a house. What would you need to do first?*** An architect would first need to draw a house plan, or blueprint, that indicates the design of the house. Develop the analogy of an architect (cell) needing plans to build a house (a protein). ***Once the plans are drawn, what is next?*** The plans need to be read by the contractor and the area where the house is to be built needs to be staked out. Use this analogy with the mRNA (contractor) reading the plans of the DNA and carrying the message to the building site (ribosome). Materials (amino acids) will be brought in according to the plans by delivery trucks (tRNA). The whole process of building the house (protein) will cost a significant amount of money (energy) to the architect (cell).

W Writing Support

BL OL AL

Creative Writing As students read the text under the heading *Central Dogma,* have them think about the analogy of DNA as a cookbook recipe. Once they have read the text, organize students into pairs and have them write a recipe that develops this analogy further. One example might be making a cake (protein) with the recipe analogous to the DNA code, utensils analogous to RNAs, and ingredients analogous to amino acids. However, the difference is that recipes don't always have to follow the same sequence, whereas DNA, RNA, and protein must go in order.

Concepts in Motion

Interactive Table

Section 3

Reading Preview

Essential Questions

- How are messenger RNA, ribosomal RNA, and transfer RNA involved in the transcription and translation of genes?
- What is the role of RNA polymerase in the synthesis of messenger RNA?
- How is the code of DNA translated into messenger RNA and utilized to synthesize a protein?

Review Vocabulary

synthesis: the composition or combination of parts to form a whole

New Vocabulary

RNA
messenger RNA
ribosomal RNA
transfer RNA
transcription
RNA polymerase
intron
exon
codon
translation

g Multilingual eGlossary

DNA, RNA, and Protein

MAIN Idea DNA codes for RNA, which guides protein synthesis.

Real-World Reading Link Computer programmers write their programs in a particular language, or code. The computer is designed to read the code and perform a function. Like the programming code, DNA contains a code that signals the cell to perform a function.

W Central Dogma

One of the important features of DNA that remained unresolved beyond the work of Watson and Crick was how DNA served as a genetic code for the synthesis of proteins. Recall that proteins function as structural building blocks for the cells and as enzymes.

Geneticists now accept that the basic mechanism of reading and expressing genes is from DNA to RNA to protein. This chain of events occurs in all living things—from bacteria to humans. Scientists refer to this mechanism as the central dogma of biology: DNA codes for RNA, which guides the synthesis of proteins.

RNA RNA is a nucleic acid that is similar to DNA. However, **RNA** contains the sugar ribose, the base uracil replaces thymine, and usually is single stranded. Three major types of RNA are found in living cells. **Messenger RNA** (mRNA) molecules are long strands of RNA nucleotides that are formed complementary to one strand of DNA. They travel from the nucleus to the ribosome to direct the synthesis of a specific protein. **Ribosomal RNA** (rRNA) is the type of RNA that associates with proteins to form ribosomes in the cytoplasm. The third type of RNA, **transfer RNA** (tRNA) are smaller segments of RNA nucleotides that transport amino acids to the ribosome. **Table 2** compares the structures and functions of the three types of RNA.

Table 2 Comparison of Three Types of RNA — Concepts in Motion Interactive Table

Name	mRNA	rRNA	tRNA
Function	Carries genetic information from DNA in the nucleus to direct protein synthesis in the cytoplasm	Associates with protein to form the ribosome	Transports amino acids to the ribosome
Example	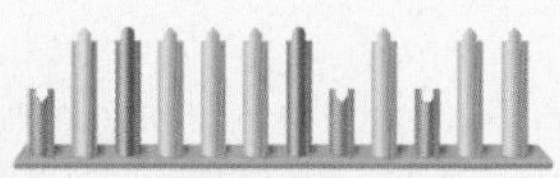	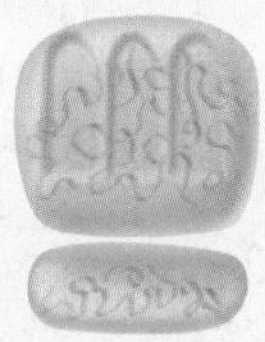	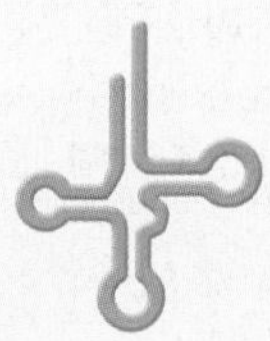

Content Background

Real-World Connection One exception to the central dogma is found in the enzyme reverse transcriptase, which was discovered in certain so-called retroviruses. These viruses include HIV, the virus that causes AIDS. The genetic material of a retrovirus is RNA rather than DNA. When a retrovirus invades a cell, the reverse transcriptase converts the RNA to DNA.

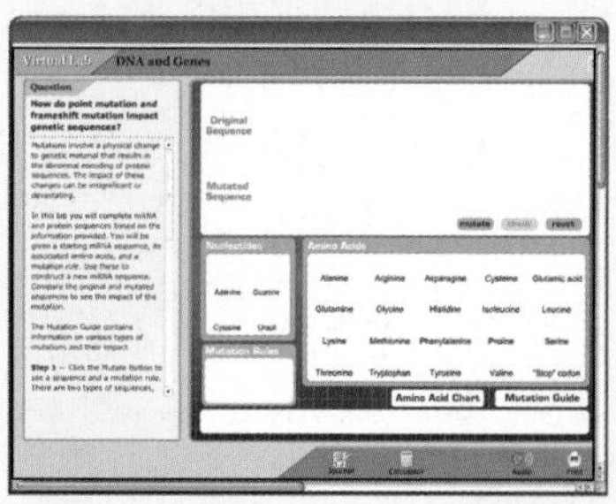

? Inquiry Virtual Lab Students will study the impact of mutation on mRNA strands.

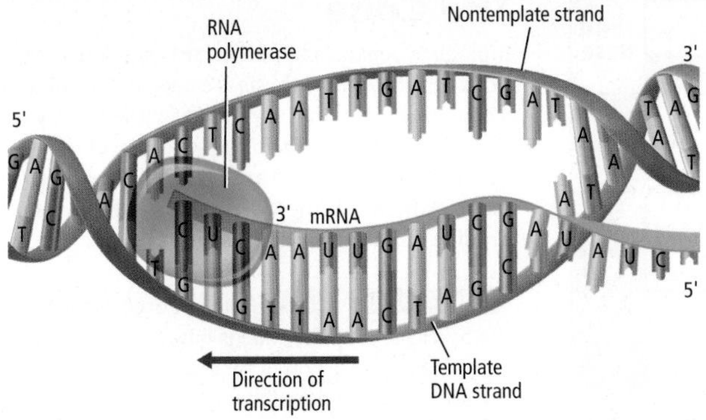

■ **Figure 13** RNA is grown in the 5′ to 3′ direction.
Identify ***which enzyme adds nucleotides to the growing RNA.***

Transcription The first step of the central dogma involves the synthesis of mRNA from DNA in a process called **transcription** (trans KRIHP shun). Through transcription, the DNA code is transferred to mRNA in the nucleus. The mRNA then can take the code into the cytoplasm for protein synthesis. Follow along with the process of transcription in **Figure 13.** The DNA is unzipped in the nucleus and **RNA polymerase,** an enzyme that regulates RNA synthesis, binds to a specific section where an mRNA will be synthesized. As the DNA strand unwinds, the RNA polymerase initiates mRNA synthesis and moves along one of the DNA strands in the 3' to 5' direction. The strand of DNA that is read by RNA polymerase is called the template strand, and mRNA is synthesized as a complement to the DNA nucleotides. The DNA strand not used as the template strand is called the nontemplate strand. The mRNA transcript is manufactured in a 5' to 3' direction, adding each new RNA nucleotide to the 3' end. Uracil is incorporated instead of thymine as the mRNA molecule is made. Eventually, the mRNA is released, and the RNA polymerase detaches from the DNA. The new mRNA then moves out of the nucleus through nuclear pores into the cytoplasm.

FOLDABLES® Incorporate information from this section into your Foldable.

D

Reading check **Explain** the direction in which the mRNA transcript is manufactured.

RNA processing When scientists compared the coding region of the DNA with mRNA that ultimately coded for a protein, they found that the mRNA code is significantly shorter than the DNA code. Upon closer examination, they discovered that the code on the DNA is interrupted periodically by sequences that are not in the final mRNA. These sequences are called intervening sequences, or **introns.** The coding sequences that remain in the final mRNA are called **exons.** In eukaryotes, the original mRNA made in the nucleus is sometimes called pre-mRNA and contains all of the DNA code. Before the pre-mRNA leaves the nucleus, the introns are removed from it. Other processing of the pre-mRNA includes adding a protective cap on the 5' end and adding a tail of many adenine nucleotides, called the poly-A tail, to the 3' end of the mRNA. Research shows that the cap aids in ribosome recognition, though the significance of the poly-A tail remains unknown. The mRNA that reaches the ribosome has been processed.

? Inquiry Video Lab

D Develop Concepts

BL OL

Clarify a Misconception

ASK STUDENTS: ***Is mRNA made from both sides or one side of the DNA?*** one side: the template strand Students often have difficulty with the idea that mRNA is made only from one side of the DNA. Emphasize the difference between the template strand and the nontemplate strand each time you write or talk about the DNA strands in transcription. Students should be able to explain that one side of the DNA is the template strand and the other side is the nontemplate strand.

FOLDABLES®

RUBRIC A rubric for evaluating Foldables is found on your eTeacherEdition Online.

Going Further On the back of their Foldables, have students draw a Venn diagram to compare and contrast translation and transcription.

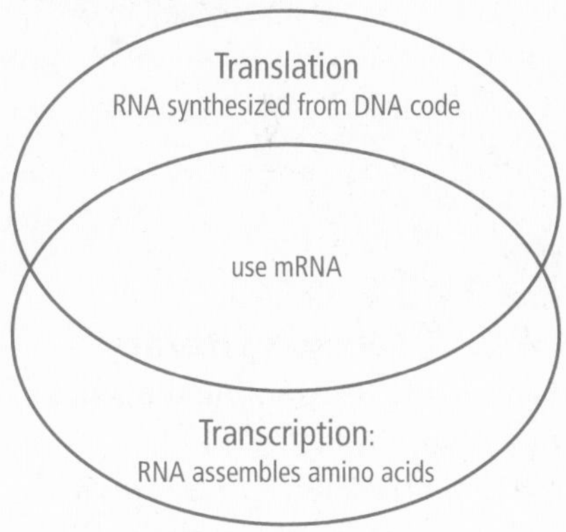

■ **Caption Question Fig. 13** RNA polymerase

Reading Check mRNA is built in a 5′ to 3′ direction.

Content Background

Teacher FYI RNA polymerase binds to an area of the DNA called the promoter, a sequence near the beginning of the gene. The area where the DNA is unwound by the RNA polymerase is called the transcription bubble. Within the bubble, the newly synthesized RNA remains paired with the DNA template. In those parts behind the bubble that have been transcribed, the DNA reforms a double helix and the RNA hangs out of the complex as a single strand.

Develop Concepts

BL OL

Clarify a Misconception

ASK STUDENTS: ***What accounts for the similarities among all human beings?*** Similar sequences of DNA make up genes. ***What accounts for individual differences?*** unique sequences of DNA that make up genes Students might understand that genetic differences account for individual traits but might not realize that genes also account for similarities among human beings. Common DNA sequences code for our general human features and differences in DNA sequences code for traits that make everyone unique.

C Critical Thinking

BL OL **Compare**

ASK STUDENTS: ***How does decoding DNA compare to reading music?*** Musical notes represent a code for a particular sound. The musician reading the notes knows what sound to play. DNA code represents amino acids and RNA, and ribosomes translate the code and assemble the amino acids into proteins. Each codon is like a note and the notes add up to make music.

S Skill Practice

BL OL AL **Visual Literacy**

Have students examine the code dictionary in Figure 14.

ASK STUDENTS: ***How many codons code for an amino acid?*** 61 ***How many codons code for "stop"?*** 3 ***What amino acid is coded by the codon AUG?*** methionine ***What is special about this particular codon (AUG)?*** It is the start codon (where the coding begins) for all mRNAs.

■ **Caption Question Fig. 14** AUG—UCU/UCC/UCA/UCG/AGU/AGC—CAU/CAC—UGG—UAA/UAG/UGA

First Base	Second Base				Third Base
	U	C	A	G	
U	UUU phenylalanine	UCU serine	UAU tyrosine	UGU cysteine	U
U	UUC phenylalanine	UCC serine	UAC tyrosine	UGC cysteine	C
U	UUA leucine	UCA serine	UAA *stop*	UGA *stop*	A
U	UUG leucine	UCG serine	UAG *stop*	UGG tryptophan	G
C	CUU leucine	CCU proline	CAU histidine	CGU arginine	U
C	CUC leucine	CCC proline	CAC histidine	CGC arginine	C
C	CUA leucine	CCA proline	CAA glutamine	CGA arginine	A
C	CUG leucine	CCG proline	CAG glutamine	CGG arginine	G
A	AUU isoleucine	ACU threonine	AAU asparagine	AGU serine	U
A	AUC isoleucine	ACC threonine	AAC asparagine	AGC serine	C
A	AUA isoleucine	ACA threonine	AAA lysine	AGA arginine	A
A	AUG *(start)* methionine	ACG threonine	AAG lysine	AGG arginine	G
G	GUU valine	GCU alanine	GAU aspartate	GGU glycine	U
G	GUC valine	GCC alanine	GAC aspartate	GGC glycine	C
G	GUA valine	GCA alanine	GAA glutamate	GGA glycine	A
G	GUG valine	GCG alanine	GAG glutamate	GGG glycine	G

■ **Figure 14** This "dictionary" of the genetic code is helpful for knowing which codons code for which amino acids.
Determine ***the possible sequences that would produce the amino acid chain: start—serine—histidine—tryptophan—stop.***

S

The Code

Biologists began to hypothesize that the instructions for protein synthesis are encoded in the DNA. They recognized that the only way the DNA varied among organisms was in the sequence of the bases. Scientists knew that 20 amino acids were used to make proteins, so they knew that the DNA must provide at least 20 different codes.

Connection to Math The hypothesis for how the bases formed the code is based on math and logic. If each base coded for one amino acid, then the four bases could code for four amino acids. If each pair of bases coded for one amino acid, then the four bases could only code for 16 (4×4 or 4^2) amino acids. However, if a group of three bases coded for one amino acid, there would be 64 (4^3) possible codes. This provides more than the 20 codes needed for the 20 amino acids, but is the smallest possible combination of bases to provide enough codes for the amino acids.

This reasoning meant that the code was not contained in the base pairs themselves, but must run along a single strand of the DNA. Experiments during the 1960s demonstrated that the DNA code was indeed a three-base code. The three-base code in DNA or mRNA is called a **codon.** Each of the three bases of a codon in the DNA is transcribed into the mRNA code. **Figure 14** shows a "dictionary" of the genetic code. Notice that all but three codons are specific for an amino acid; these three are stop codons. Codon AUG codes for the amino acid methionine and also functions as the start codon. C

Translation Once the mRNA is synthesized and processed, it moves to the ribosome. In eukaryotes, this means the mRNA must leave the nucleus and enter the cytoplasm. Once in the cytoplasm, the 5' end of the mRNA connects to the ribosome. This is where the code is read and translated to make a protein through a process called **translation.** Follow along in **Figure 15** as you learn about translation.

In translation, tRNA molecules act as the interpreters of the mRNA codon sequence. The tRNA is folded into a cloverleaf shape and is activated by an enzyme that attaches a specific amino acid to the 3' end. At the middle of the folded strand, there is a three-base coding sequence called the anticodon. Each anticodon is complementary to a codon on the mRNA. Though the code in DNA and RNA is read 5' to 3', the anticodon is read 3' to 5'.

Research Citation

Visual Literacy Educational research indicates that using graphic organizers like the one described on page 337 can help students with higher-order thinking skills such as making comparisons. By providing a visual representation of the information, teachers can address a variety of learning styles and needs. (Horowitz, 1985)

Research bibliography on pages 32T–34T

Differentiated Instruction

Physically Disabled When working with students with physical disabilities, know their strengths and abilities. When students are working in groups, assign tasks so that physically disabled students are given responsibilities that utilize their abilities so they can contribute in a meaningful way to their group's task.

For more tips see pages 14T–15T.

Visualizing Transcription and Translation

Figure 15

Transcription takes place in the nucleus. Translation occurs in the cytoplasm and results in the formation of polypeptides.

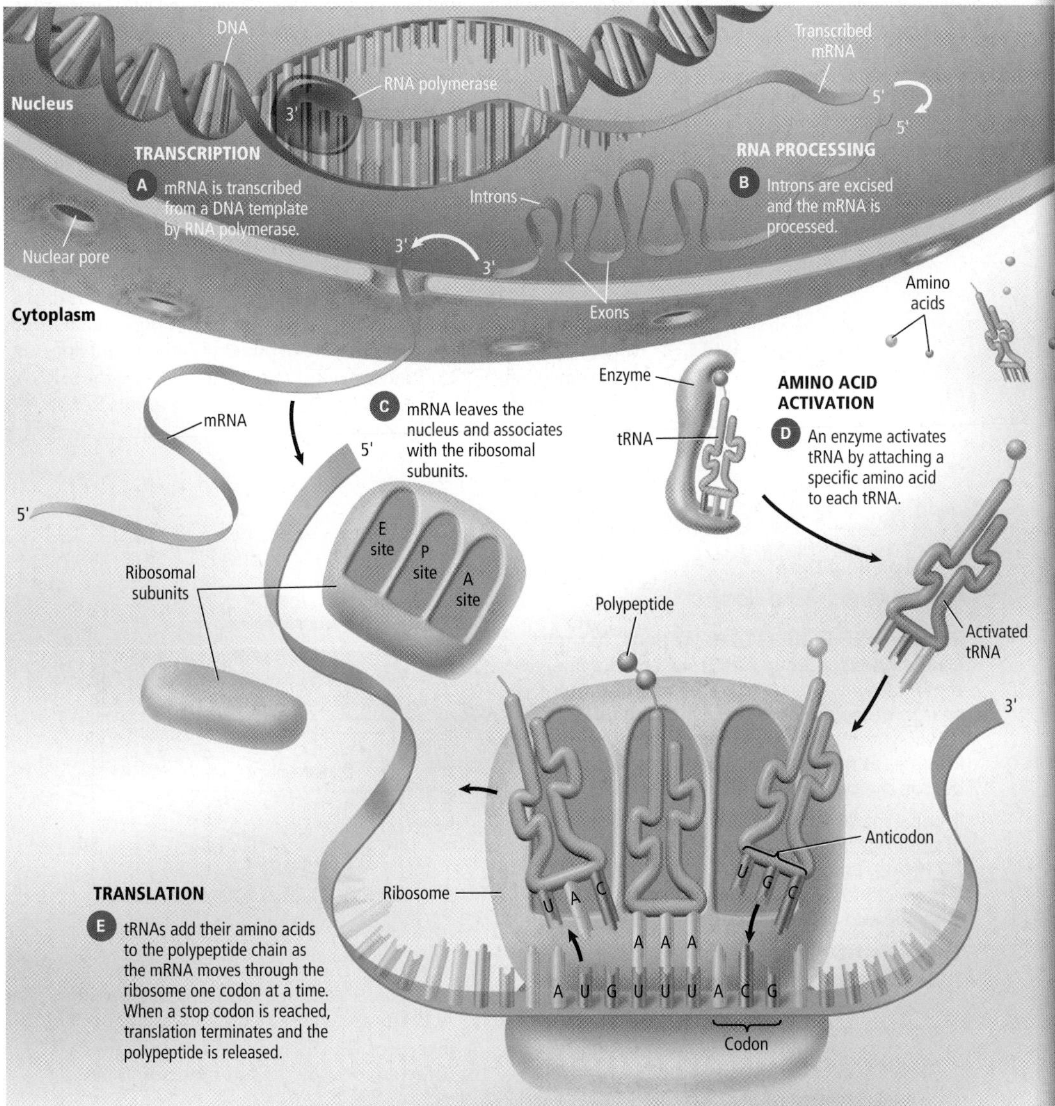

Concepts in Motion Animation

Visualizing Transcription and Translation

Purpose

Students will understand the process of DNA transcription and translation.
B.3, C.1, C.2

Develop Concepts

BL OL COOP LEARN Activity

Point out that the words *elm, elk,* and *eel* all differ by only one letter, yet their meanings are very different. In a similar manner, one letter in the DNA codon can make a major difference in the amino acid inserted into a protein. Have students form groups of three and come up with other similar word analogies for codons that differ by only one letter, similar to *elm, elk,* and *eel.*

Writing Support

BL OL Creative Writing Have students write a simple sentence in their notebooks. Then ask students to shift the letters. For example, "The fat cat ate the big rat" becomes "Hef atc ata tet heb igr att." Point out that the three-letter words model codons.

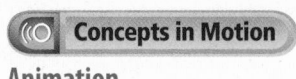

Concepts in Motion

Animation

Demonstration

Transcription and Translation On the board, draw the letters of the nucleotides of a piece of two-stranded DNA. Erase a portion of one side and redraw part of one side spaced apart to indicate unzipping. Add the RNA polymerase and begin making an mRNA on one of the sides (template). Show the RNA leaving the nucleus with an arrow and have students decode the mRNA into an amino acid polypeptide. Est. time: 10 min

Develop Concepts

BL OL AL Activity Draw a short section of DNA on the board, labeling one side the coding or template strand and the other side the complementary or noncoding strand. Ask students to decipher the code into a segment of amino acids.

D Develop Concepts

BL OL

Clarify a Misconception

ASK STUDENTS: ***Does protein synthesis "cost" the cell energy?*** yes Students may not understand that protein synthesis requires energy, as does all biosynthesis.

DATA ANALYSIS LAB 1

About the Lab

- Also see Liu, J., P. Feldman, and T. D. Chung. 2002. Real-time monitoring of *in vitro* transcription using molecular beacons. *Annals of Biochemistry* 300: 40–45.

Think Critically

1. Fluorescence levels increased the most over time in the bacterial and viral RNA not treated with rifampin.
2. RNA synthesis is inhibited.
3. *E. coli* and *M. smegmatis* are greatly affected by rifampin. Viral RNA is slightly affected.

Study Tip

Flowchart Draw a flowchart that connects the processes of DNA replication, transcription, and translation.

The role of the ribosome The ribosome consists of two subunits, as shown in **Figure 15.** These subunits are not associated when they are not involved in protein translation. When the mRNA leaves the nucleus, the two parts of the ribosome come together and attach to the mRNA to complete the ribosome. Once the mRNA is associated with the ribosome, a tRNA with the anticodon CAU carrying a methionine will move in and bind to the mRNA start codon—AUG—on the 5' end of the mRNA. The ribosome structure has a groove, called the P site, where the tRNA that is complementary to the mRNA moves in.

A second tRNA moves into a second groove in the ribosome, called the A site, and corresponds to the next codon of the mRNA. The next codon is UUU, so a tRNA with the anticodon AAA moves in, carrying the amino acid phenylalanine.

Part of the rRNA in the ribosome now acts as an enzyme catalyzing the formation of a bond between the new amino acid in the A site and the amino acid in the P site. As the two amino acids join, the tRNA in the P site is released to the third site, called the E site, where it exits the ribosome. The ribosome then moves so the tRNA found in Groove A is shifted to Site P, as shown in **Figure 15.** Now a new tRNA will enter the A site, complementing the next codon on the mRNA. This process will continue adding and linking amino acids in the sequence determined by the mRNA.

The ribosome continues to move along until the A site contains a stop codon. The stop codon signals the end of protein synthesis and does not complement any tRNA. Proteins called release factors cause the mRNA to be released from the last tRNA and the ribosome subunits to disassemble, ending protein synthesis. D

DATA ANALYSIS LAB 1

Based on Real Data*

Interpret the Data

How can a virus affect transcription? To study RNA synthesis, a group of scientists used a fluorescent molecular beacon to trace molecules. This beacon becomes fluorescent when it binds to newly synthesized RNA. The fluorescence increases as the RNA chain lengthens. Thus, the beacon can be used to follow RNA synthesis.

In this experiment, scientists added the antibiotic rifampin (rif) to RNA polymerase from a virus (T7 RNAP), *Escherchia coli (E. coli* RNAP*)*, and *Mycobacterium smegmatis (M. smegmatis* RNAP*)* and followed RNA synthesis.

Data and Observations

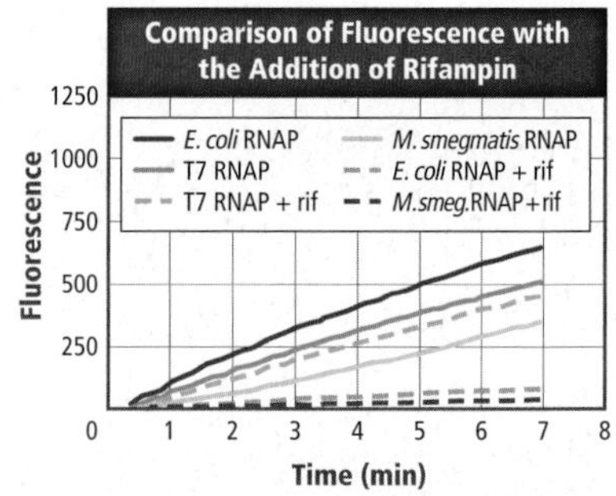

Think Critically

1. **Describe** the relationship between the fluorescence level and time in each experiment not exposed to rifampin.
2. **Infer** what the relationship between fluorescence level and time indicates is happening in each case where rifampin was added.
3. **Interpret** which organism's RNA synthesis is affected most by the antibiotic rifampin.

*Data obtained from: Marras, Salvatore A.E., et al. 2004. Real-time measurement of *in vitro* transcription. *Nucleic Acids Research* 32.9.e: 72.

Content Background

Cultural Diversity The discovery of the individual three-letter codes involved experiments by British scientists Francis Crick and Sydney Brenner, German plant physiologist Heinrich Matthaei and biochemist Marshall Nirenberg, and American geneticist Philip Leder. Crick and Brenner used mutants with deletions or additions of one, two, or three nucleotides to show that the code was a three-letter code. Nirenberg, Matthaei, and Leder used synthesis of mRNAs to solve the majority of the code charts. Nirenberg and Leder were able to synthesize short three-nucleotide mRNAs to finish solving the code chart in the 1960s.

One Gene—One Enzyme

Once scientists learned how DNA works as a code, they needed to learn the relationships between the genes and the proteins for which they coded. Experiments on the mold *Neurospora* were the first to demonstrate the relationship between genes and enzymes. In the 1940s, George Beadle and Edward Tatum provided evidence that a gene can code for an enzyme. They studied mold spores that were mutated by exposure to X-rays. Examine **Figure 16** to follow along with their experiment.

Normally, *Neurospora* can grow on an artificial medium that provides no amino acids. This type of medium is called minimal medium. Complete medium provides all the amino acids that *Neurospora* needs to function. In Beadle and Tatum's experiment, the spores were exposed to X-rays and grown on a complete medium. To test for a mutated spore, the scientists grew spores on a minimal medium. When a spore was unable to grow on the minimal medium, the mutant was tested to see what amino acid it lacked. When the mold-spore type grew on a minimal medium with a supplement such as arginine, Beadle and Tatum hypothesized that the mutant was missing the enzyme needed to synthesize arginine.

Beadle and Tatum came up with what is known as the "one gene—one enzyme" hypothesis. Today, because we know that polypeptides make up enzymes, **D** their hypothesis has been modified slightly to refer to the fact that one gene codes for one polypeptide.

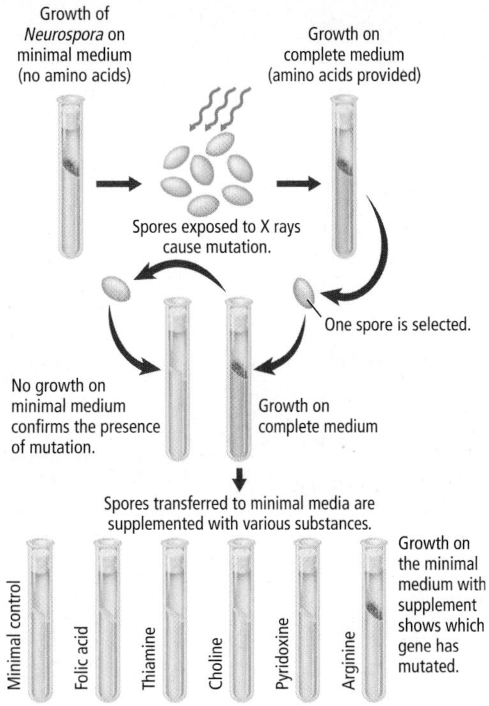

Growth of *Neurospora* on minimal medium (no amino acids)
Growth on complete medium (amino acids provided)
Spores exposed to X rays cause mutation.
One spore is selected.
No growth on minimal medium confirms the presence of mutation.
Growth on complete medium
Spores transferred to minimal media are supplemented with various substances.
Minimal control
Folic acid
Thiamine
Choline
Pyridoxine
Arginine
Growth on the minimal medium with supplement shows which gene has mutated.

■ **Figure 16** The Beadle and Tatum experiment showed that a gene codes for an enzyme. We now know that a gene codes for a polypeptide.

D Develop Concepts

BL OL AL Scaffolding

ASK STUDENTS: *Identify the experimental organism used by Beadle and Tatum.* the mold *Neurospora* ***What was the purpose of growing the mutated mold spores on two different mediums?*** Mutants would grow only on the complete medium. In order to test if a mold spore was a mutant, it had to be shown that it could not grow on the minimal medium. ***Design and draw another set of results for a mold spore that is a niacin mutant.*** Drawings should be similar to Figure 16, but growth would occur only in the niacin tube.

Formative Assessment

Evaluation Write a single template strand sequence of DNA on the board. Have students write the complementary sequence, the mRNA sequence, the transfer RNAs, and the amino acid sequence of the polypeptide synthesized from this code.

Remediation Use interlocking toy building blocks with colors representing bases as follows: Red = A, Green = G, Yellow = C, Black = T, and Blue = U. Build a DNA template strand with the blocks. Have students build a complementary DNA strand, an mRNA strand, and tRNAs. Have students decipher the colors of the blocks to determine which amino acids are being coded.

Section 3 Assessment

Section Summary

- Three major types of RNA are involved in protein synthesis: mRNA, tRNA, and rRNA.
- The synthesis of the mRNA from the template DNA is called transcription.
- Translation is the process through which the mRNA attaches to the ribosome and a protein is assembled.
- In eukaryotes, mRNA contains introns that are excised before leaving the nucleus. A cap and poly-A tail are added to the mRNA.
- One gene codes for one polypeptide.

Understand Main Ideas

1. MAIN Idea **Summarize** the process by which the DNA code is made into a protein.
2. **Describe** the function of each of the following in protein synthesis: rRNA, mRNA, and tRNA.
3. **Differentiate** between codons and anticodons.
4. **Explain** the role of RNA polymerase in mRNA sythesis.
5. **Conclude** why Beadle and Tatum's "one gene, one enzyme" hypothesis has been modified since they presented it in the 1940s.

Think Critically

MATH in Biology

6. If the genetic code used four bases as a code instead of three, how many code units could be encoded?

Section 3 Assessment

1. RNA is synthesized from the template strand of DNA and used to assemble amino acids into proteins.
2. rRNA is a major component of the ribosome, mRNA carries a complementary code of the template strand of DNA to the ribosome for protein synthesis, and tRNA transports amino acids to the ribosome for protein synthesis.
3. Codons are the three-nucleotide code units on DNA or mRNA. Anticodons are the three-nucleotide code units on tRNA that complement the mRNA codon.
4. RNA polymerase initiates mRNA synthesis during transcription.
5. Further study and experimentation have allowed scientists to learn more information and further refine the hypothesis.
6. $4 \times 4 \times 4 \times 4 = 4^4 = 256$

✓ Assessment Online Quiz

Section 4

MAIN Idea

BL OL AL Mutation
ASK STUDENTS: ***What words and images come to mind when you hear the words* mutation *or* mutant?** Students might bring up stories or movies about science-fiction mutants. Allow an open discussion of what they associate with these words. Point out that in Latin the root *mutare* means "change." Lead students to see that certain things can change the DNA in the genotype, which can eventually cause changes in the phenotype of the organism. These changes can have a positive impact, negative impact, or no impact at all.

R Reading Strategy
EL BL OL AL
Directed Reading Have students make three columns on a sheet of paper. At the top of the left column, have them write *What I Know;* at the top of the middle column, *What I Want to Know,* and at the top of the third column *What I've Learned.* Have students fill in the left and middle columns before reading Section 4. After they read the text, have students fill in the right column.

Concepts in Motion
Animation

Section 4

Reading Preview

Essential Questions

- How are bacteria able to regulate their genes by two types of operons?
- How do eukaryotes regulate the transcription of genes?
- What are the various types of mutations?

Review Vocabulary

prokaryote: organism that does not have membrane-bound organelles and DNA that is organized in chromosomes

New Vocabulary

gene regulation
operon
mutation
mutagen

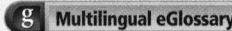

g Multilingual eGlossary

Gene Regulation and Mutation

MAIN Idea **Gene expression is regulated by the cell, and mutations can affect this expression.**

Real-World Reading Link When you type a sentence on a keyboard, it is important that each letter is typed correctly. The sentence "The fat cat ate the rat" is quite different from "The fat cat ate the hat." Though there is a difference of only one letter between the two sentences, the meaning is changed.

R Prokaryote Gene Regulation

How do prokaryotic cells regulate which genes will be transcribed at particular times in the lifetime of an organism? **Gene regulation** is the ability of an organism to control which genes are transcribed in response to the environment. In prokaryotes, an operon often controls the transcription of genes in response to changes in the environment. An **operon** is a section of DNA that contains the genes for the proteins needed for a specific metabolic pathway. The parts of an operon include an operator, promoter, regulatory gene, and the genes coding for proteins. The operator is a segment of DNA that acts as an on/off switch for transcription. A second segment of DNA, called the promoter, is where the RNA polymerase first binds to the DNA. The bacteria *Escherichia coli (E. coli)* respond to tryptophan, which is an amino acid, and lactose, which is a sugar, through two operons.

The *trp* operon In bacteria, tryptophan synthesis occurs in a series of five steps, and each step is catalyzed by a specific enzyme. The five genes coding for these enzymes are clustered together on the bacterial chromosome with a group of DNA that controls whether or not they are transcribed. This cluster of DNA is called the tryptophan *(trp)* operon and is illustrated in **Figure 17.**

Figure 17 The *trp* operon is an example of the gene expression of repressible enzymes.

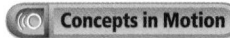

Concepts in Motion
Animation

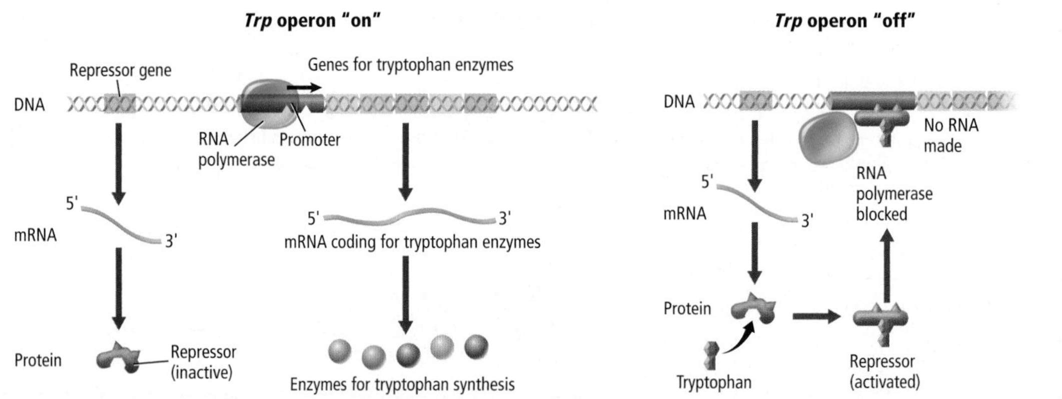

> *"Education is what remains after one has forgotten what one has learned in school."*
> —Albert Einstein

The *trp* operon is referred to as a repressible operon because transcription of the five enzyme genes normally is repressed, or turned off. When tryptophan is present in the cell's environment, the cell has no need to synthesize it and the *trp* repressor gene turns off, or represses, the transcription process by making a repressor protein. Tryptophan in *E. coli* combines with an inactive repressor protein to activate it, and the complex binds to the operator in the promoter sequence. If the repressor is bound to the operator, RNA polymerase cannot bind to it, which prevents the transcription of the enzyme genes. This prohibits the synthesis of tryptophan by the cell.

When tryptophan levels are low, the repressor is not bound to tryptophan and is inactive—it does not bind to the operator. The RNA polymerase is able to bind to the operator, turning on transcription of the five enzyme genes. This transcription enables the synthesis of tryptophan by the cell. Notice the location of the repressor protein in **Figure 17** when the operon is turned both off and on.

Reading Check **Summarize** the effect of tryptophan on the *trp* operon.

The *lac* operon When lactose is present in the cell, *E. coli* makes enzymes that enable it to use lactose as an energy source. The lactose (*lac*) operon, illustrated in **Figure 18,** contains a promoter, an operator, a regulatory gene, and three enzyme genes that control lactose digestion. In the *lac* operon, the regulatory gene makes a repressor protein that binds to the operator in the promoter sequence and prevents the transcription of the enzyme genes.

When a molecule called an inducer is present, the inducer binds to the repressor and inactivates it. In the *lac* operon, the inducer is allolactose, a molecule that is present in food that contains lactose. Thus, when lactose is present, the allolactose binds to the repressor and inactivates it. With the repressor inactivated, RNA polymerase then can bind to the promoter and begin transcription. The *lac* operon is called an inducible operon because transcription is turned on by an inducer.

CAREERS IN BIOLOGY

Microbiologist Scientists who study microbes, primarily prokaryotes, are called microbiologists. They might research to learn about which genes control the production of particular proteins or how a protein affects the life of a cell.

■ **Figure 18** The *lac* operon is an example of the gene expression of inducible enzymes.
Identify *what the repressor is bound to when the lac operon is turned off.*

Concepts in Motion Animation

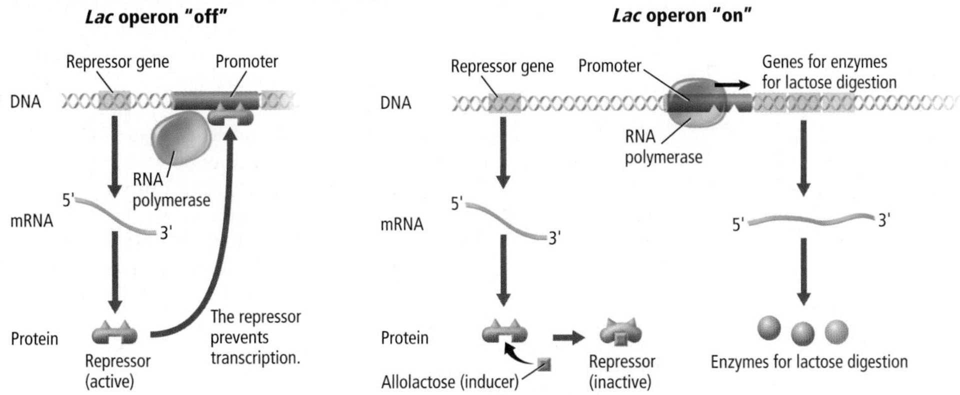

■ **Caption Question Fig. 18** The repressor is bound to the promoter.

Reading Check When tryptophan is present, the operon is off.

S Skill Practice

OL AL Visual Literacy Have students carefully study Figures 17 and 18.

SAY TO STUDENTS: ***Compare the two types of prokaryotic genetic regulation pathways: the* lac *operon and* trp *operon.*** Have students make a table summarizing their comparison between the two types of regulation pathways.

D Develop Concepts

BL OL AL Scaffolding

ASK STUDENTS: ***Which type of prokaryotic regulation pathway,* lac *or* trp *operon, works by preventing the transcription of genes?*** *trp* operon ***Explain the function of the five genes coding for proteins in the* trp *operon.*** These genes code for enzymes involved in the synthesis of tryptophan. ***Predict what will occur when tryptophan is added to the medium in which bacteria are growing.*** The tryptophan will combine with the inactive repressor and activate the repressor, turning off the *trp* operon.

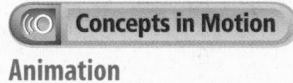

Concepts in Motion Animation

D Develop Concepts

BL OL

Clarify a Misconception

ASK STUDENTS: ***Do muscle cells and nerve cells contain the same genes?*** yes Students do not always understand that every cell in the body has the same DNA in it (exclusive of gametes). Every body cell contains the same genes. DNA regulation is very important in cell specialization. Cells of different types, such as neurons and muscle cells, have different types of genes turned on and turned off.

W Writing Support

BL OL Informal Writing

Inform students that the regulation of the transcription of eukaryotic genes involves much more than turning them on and off. It also involves speeding up or slowing down their transcription.

SAY TO STUDENTS: ***Use the analogy of making a car go faster or slower to write a brief description on the role of activators and repressors.*** Activators can make transcription go faster, just as pushing on the gas pedal of a car makes it go faster. Repressors can slow transcription down in the same way a car can be slowed down by stepping on the brake pedal.

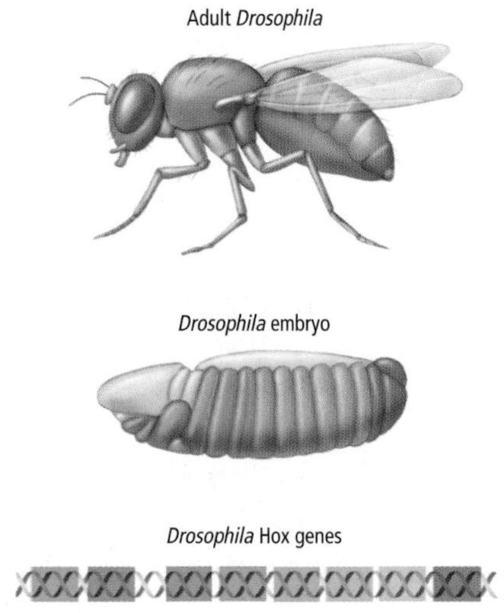

Figure 19 Hox genes are responsible for the general body pattern of most animals. Notice that the order of the genes is the same as the order of the body sections the genes control.

D Eukaryote Gene Regulation

Eukaryotic cells also must control what genes are expressed at different times in the organism's lifetime. In eukaryotic cells, many genes interact with one another, requiring more elements than a single promoter and operator for a set of genes. The organization and structure of eukaryotic cells is more complex than in prokaryotic cells, increasing the complexity of the control system.

Controlling transcription One way that eukaryotes control gene expression is through proteins called transcription factors. Transcription factors ensure that a gene is used at the right time and that proteins are made in the right amounts. There are two main sets of transcription factors. One set of transcription factors forms complexes that guide and stabilize the binding of the RNA polymerase to a promoter. The other set includes regulatory proteins that help control the rate of transcription. For instance, proteins called activators fold DNA so that enhancer sites are close to the complex and increase the rate of gene transcription. Repressor proteins also bind to specific sites on the DNA and prevent the binding of activators.

The complex structure of eukaryotic DNA also regulates transcription. Recall that eukaryotic DNA is wrapped around histones to form nucleosomes. This structure provides some inhibition of transcription, although regulatory proteins and RNA polymerase still can activate specific genes even when they are packaged in the nucleosome. W

Hox genes Gene regulation is crucial during development. Recall that multicellular eukaryotes develop from a single cell called a zygote. The zygote undergoes mitosis, producing all the different kinds of cells needed by the organism. Differentiation is the process through which the cells become specialized in structure and function. One group of genes that controls differentiation has been discovered. These genes are called homeobox (Hox) genes. Hox genes are important for determining the body plan of an organism. They code for transcription factors and are active in zones of the embryo that are in the same order as the genes on the chromosome. For example, the colored regions of the fly and fly embryo in **Figure 19** correspond to the colored genes on the piece of DNA in the figure. These genes, transcribed at specific times, and located in specific places on the genome, control what body part will develop in a given location. One mutation in the Hox genes of fruit flies has yielded flies with legs growing where their antennae should be. Studying these flies has helped scientists understand more about how genes control the body plan of an organism. Similar clusters of Hox genes that control body plans have been found in all animals.

Content Background

Teacher FYI Experiments with Hox genes in *Drosophila* have yielded a wealth of information about how development occurs in animals. The Hox gene clusters are located in the same order on the chromosome as the order of the body sections the genes control. The order of these genes is highly conserved in species, indicating an ancient origin. In fact, most variations between species are in the number of Hox gene clusters and in the number of genes in the clusters. Some evidence suggests that Hox genes are involved in human birth defects.

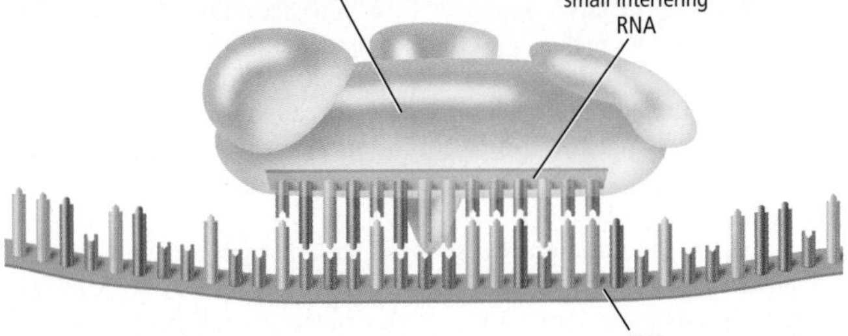

■ **Figure 20** RNA interference can stop the mRNA from translating its message.
Describe ***how the RNA-protein complex prevents the translation of the mRNA.***

RNA interference Another method of eukaryotic gene regulation is RNA interference (RNAi). Small pieces of double-stranded RNA in the cytoplasm of the cell are cut by an enzyme called dicer. The resulting double-stranded segments are called small interfering RNA. They bind to a protein complex that degrades one strand of the RNA. The resulting single-stranded small interfering RNA and protein complex bind to sequence-specific sections of mRNA in the cytoplasm, causing the mRNA in this region to be cut and thus preventing its translation. **Figure 20** shows the single-stranded small interfering RNA and protein complex binding to the mRNA. Research and clinical trials are being conducted to investigate the possibility of using RNAi to treat cancer, diabetes, and other diseases.

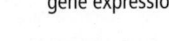

Reading Check **Explain** how RNA interference can regulate eukaryotic gene expression.

Mutations

Do you ever make mistakes when you are typing an assignment? When you type, sometimes you might strike the wrong key. Just as you might make a mistake when typing, cells sometimes make mistakes during replication. However, these mistakes are rare, and the cell has repair mechanisms that can repair some damage. Sometimes a permanent change occurs in a cell's DNA and this is called a **mutation.** Recall that one inheritance pattern that Mendel studied was round and wrinkled pea seeds. It is now known that the wrinkled phenotype is associated with the absence of an enzyme that influences the shape of starch molecules in the seeds. Because the mutation in the gene causes a change in the protein that is made, the enzyme is nonfunctional.

Types of mutations Mutations can range from changes in a single base pair in the coding sequence of DNA to the deletions of large pieces of chromosomes. Point mutations involve a chemical change in just one base pair and can be enough to cause a genetic disorder. A point mutation in which one base is exchanged for another is called a substitution. Most substitutions are missense mutations, where the DNA code is altered so that it codes for the wrong amino acid. Other substitutions, called nonsense mutations, change the codon for an amino acid to a stop codon. Nonsense mutations cause translation to terminate early. Nearly all nonsense mutations lead to proteins that cannot function normally.

Reading Strategy

BL OL Vocabulary Chart Have students make a three-column vocabulary chart. In the first column, have them write the new vocabulary terms for Section 4. In the second column, have them write the definition after reading the text. Then have them come up with a memory clue, such as a sketch or a word association, and have them write down their clue in the third column.
EL COOP LEARN Have students work in pairs.
AL Instead of a chart, have students write a paragraph describing the relationship between the vocabulary terms for this section.

■ **Caption Question Fig. 20** Small interfering RNA binds to a protein complex that degrades one strand of the RNA.

Reading Check It can prevent translation of sections of mRNA.

Differentiated Instruction

Below Level Alternative activities should be used to address the needs of students who are performing below grade level. The vocabulary chart described on this page is a valuable tool to use with students who struggle with reading, allowing them to develop visual clues they can use to recall the meanings of difficult vocabulary terms.

For more tips, see pages 14T–15T.

Content Background

Real-World Connection *Science* magazine called the discovery of RNAi the "Breakthrough of the Year 2002." The use of RNAi as a genetic therapy to silence a specific gene that has gone bad has entered human therapeutic clinical trials. One disease researchers are concentrating their efforts on is macrodegeneration of eyes.

W Writing Support

BL OL AL COOP LEARN

Creative Writing Have students work in pairs to research health issues related to mutations and then construct a poster on the topic. The purpose of the poster might be to educate people about the type of mutation involved, or to warn people about mutagenic agents that could increase the risk of developing a disease. Caution students to be sensitive in the way they approach their topic.

S Skill Practice

EL BL OL AL Visual Literacy

Have students study Table 3. Write various normal and mutant sequences on the board or give them to students as a handout. **ASK STUDENTS:** ***Identify the type of mutation that is demonstrated in each of the sequences.*** Encourage students to use the information in Table 3 to help them.

Review

Personal Tutor

Listen to a teacher explain mutations.

Concepts in Motion

Interactive Table

VOCABULARY

ACADEMIC VOCABULARY

Substitution

the act of replacing one thing with another

The substitution of adenine for guanine in the DNA caused a dysfunctional protein.

Review Personal Tutor

Another type of mutation that can occur involves the gain or loss of a nucleotide in the DNA sequence. Insertions are additions of a nucleotide to the DNA sequence, and the loss of a nucleotide is called a deletion. Both of these mutations change the multiples of three, from the point of the insertion or deletion. These are called frameshift mutations because they change the "frame" of the amino acid sequence. **Table 3** illustrates various types of mutations and their effect on the DNA sequence.

Sometimes mutations are associated with diseases and disorders. One example is alkaptonuria. Patients with this disorder have a mutation in their DNA coding for an enzyme involved in digesting the amino acid phenylalanine. This mutation results in the black-colored homogentisic acid that discolors the urine. Studies have shown that patients with alkaptonuria have a high occurrence of frameshift and missense mutations in a specific region of their DNA. **Table 3** lists some more examples of diseases associated with different types of mutations. W

S

Table 3 Mutations — Concepts in Motion Interactive Table

Mutation Type	Analogy Sentence	Example of Associated Disease
Normal	THE BIG FAT CAT ATE THE WET RAT	
Missense (substitution)	THE BIZ FAT CAT ATE THE WET RAT	Achondroplasia: improper development of cartilage on the ends of the long bones of arms and legs resulting in a form of dwarfism
Nonsense (substitution)	THE BIG RAT	Muscular dystrophy: progressive muscle disorder characterized by the progressive weakening of many muscles in the body
Deletion (causing frameshift)	THB IGF ATC ATA TET HEW ETR AT	Cystic fibrosis: characterized by abnormally thick mucus in the lungs, intestines, and pancreas
Insertion (causing frameshift)	THE BIG ZFA TCA TAT ETH EWE TRA	Crohn's disease: chronic inflammation of the intestinal tract, producing frequent diarrhea, abdominal pain, nausea, fever, and weight loss
Duplication	THE BIG FAT FAT CAT ATE THE WET RAT	Charcot-Marie-Tooth disease (type 1A): damage to peripheral nerves leading to weakness and atrophy of muscles in hands and lower legs
Expanding mutation (tandem repeats) **Generation 1** **Generation 2** **Generation 3**	 THE BIG FAT CAT ATE THE WET RAT THE BIG FAT CAT CAT CAT ATE THE WET RAT THE BIG FAT CAT CAT CAT CAT CAT CAT ATE THE WET RAT	Huntington's disease: a progressive disease in which brain cells waste away, producing uncontrolled movements, emotional disturbances, and mental deterioration

Research Citation

Formative Assessment Educational research indicates that assessment should be timely and ongoing. An evaluation of students' understanding throughout a lesson provides the teacher with valuable information to be used in planning remediation and future instruction. (Bransford, et al., 2000)

Research bibliography on pages 32T–34T

Large portions of DNA can also be involved in a mutation. A piece of an individual chromosome containing one or more genes can be deleted or moved to a different location on the chromosome, or even to a different chromosome. Such rearrangements of the chromosome often have drastic effects on the expression of these genes.

Connection to Health In 1991, a new kind of mutation was discovered that involves an increase in the number of copies of repeated codons, called tandem repeats. The increase in repeated sequences seems to be involved in a number of inherited disorders. The first known example was fragile X syndrome—a syndrome that results in a number of mental and behavioral impairments. Near the end of a normal X chromosome, there is a section of CGG codons that repeat about 30 times. Individuals with fragile X have CGG codons that repeat hundreds of times. The syndrome received its name because the repeated area on the tip of the X chromosomes appears as a fragile piece hanging off the X chromosome, as illustrated in **Figure 21.** Currently, the mechanism by which the repeats expand from generation to generation is not known.

■ **Figure 21** Fragile X syndrome is due to many extra repeated CGG units near the end of the X chromosome, making the lower tip of the X chromosome appear fragile.

Reading Check **Describe** three types of mutations.

Protein folding and stability You might expect that large changes in the DNA code, such as frameshift mutations or changes in position, lead to genetic disorders. However, small changes like substitutions also can lead to genetic disorders. The change of one amino acid for another can change the sequence of amino acids in a protein enough to change both the folding and stability of the protein, as illustrated in **Figure 22.**

An example of a genetic disorder caused by a single point mutation is sickle-cell disease. In the case of sickle-cell disease, the codon for a glutamic acid (GAA) has been changed to a valine (GUA) in the protein. This change in composition changes the structure of hemoglobin and is the cause of this disorder.

■ **Figure 22** A single amino acid substitution can cause the genetic disorder sickle-cell disease.
Recall *what happens to the protein with the substituted amino acid.*

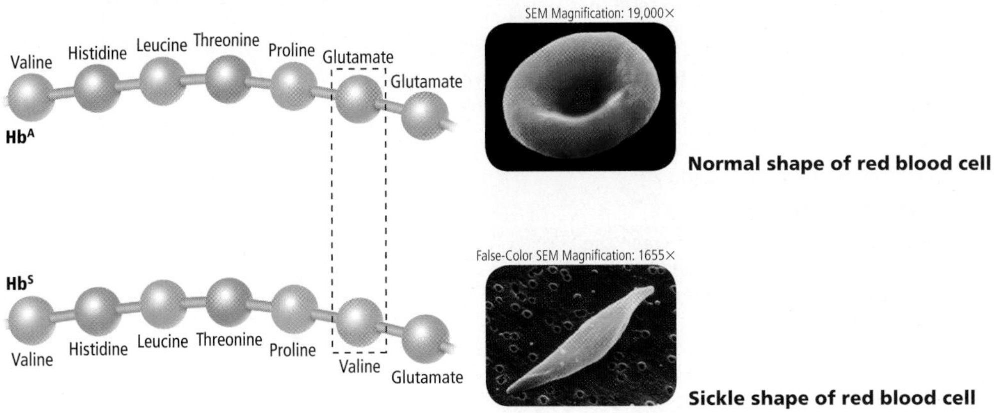

Develop Concepts

AL Activity Use sickle-cell disease and cystic fibrosis as topics for a discussion about how a small change in a gene can cause major effects on the phenotype. Have students research how mutations result in each disorder.

ASK STUDENTS: ***What mutation causes sickle-cell disease?*** a point mutation in the gene that codes for the hemoglobin protein Review the quaternary structure with students: The hemoglobin molecule is made of four polypeptide chains, two identical alpha chains, and two identical beta chains. In the two beta chains, there is a single mutation in the sixth codon, which causes a glutamic acid to be replaced by a valine. These two changes (one in each beta chain) cause a misfolding of hemoglobin under low oxygen and lead to sickle-cell disease. ***What mutation causes cystic fibrosis?*** a change in the gene that codes for a chloride channel The most common cause of this disorder is due to a deletion of three nucleotides of the 508th codon. The loss of the phenylalanine amino acid results in the disorder known as cystic fibrosis.

Reading Check Answers may include any three of the following: point mutation—involving a single base (substitution); insertion—addition of a base to the sequence; deletion—removing a base from a sequence; duplication—repetition of a gene or base; tandem repeats—multiple repetitions of a gene or base.

■ **Caption Question Fig. 22** The protein hemoglobin is defective and causes red blood cells to have a deformed, sickle shape.

C Critical Thinking

BL OL AL Theorize

ASK STUDENTS: ***When you go to a dentist for X-rays, why do they cover you with a lead-filled blanket?*** X-rays are a mutagenic agent. The lead blanket protects your body, especially the reproductive glands (ovaries and testes), from exposure to X-rays, because X-rays cannot pass through lead. The X-ray technician will often leave the room to avoid exposure.

DATA ANALYSIS LAB 2

About the Lab

- The environment you live in contains many potential mutagens. The Ames test can screen many chemicals quickly and inexpensively.
- Also see Maron, Dorothy M. and Bruce N. Ames. 1983. Revised methods for the *Salmonella* mutagenicity test. *Mutation Research* 113: 173-215.

Think Critically

1. The greater the amount of compound in the culture, the greater the reversion rate.
2. A is the strongest mutagen, producing the most revertant colonies.

Hemoglobin is made of four polypeptide chains, which are two sets of two identical chains. The molecule also contains a large carbon-ring structure that binds iron called the heme group. The substituted glutamic acid is located near the start of one set of chains, as shown in **Figure 22.** Glutamic acid is a polar amino acid, but the valine that substitutes for it in sickle-cell disease is nonpolar. Because of the charge difference, the sickle-cell hemoglobin folds differently than normal hemoglobin. The abnormal folding of the protein caused by the mutation results in a change to the sickle shape of the red blood cell. Numerous other diseases involve problems with protein folding, including Alzheimer's disease, cystic fibrosis, diabetes, and cancer.

VOCABULARY

WORD ORIGIN

Mutagen

comes from the Latin word *mutare,* meaning *to change* and from the Greek word *genes,* meaning *born*

Causes of mutation Some mutations, especially point mutations, can occur spontaneously. During replication, DNA polymerase sometimes adds the wrong nucleotides. Because the DNA polymerase has a proofreading function, the wrong nucleotide gets added only for one in one hundred thousand bases; it goes unfixed in less than one in one billion.

Certain chemicals and radiation also can damage DNA. Substances which cause mutations are called **mutagens** (MYEW tuh junz). Many different chemicals have been classified as mutagens. Some of these chemicals affect DNA by changing the chemical structure of the bases. Often these changes cause bases to mispair, or bond, with the wrong base. Other chemical mutagens have chemical structures that resemble nucleotides so closely that they can substitute for them. Once these imposter bases are incorporated into the DNA, it can not replicate properly. This type of chemical has become useful medically, especially in the treatment of HIV—the virus that causes AIDS. Many drugs used to treat HIV and other viral infections mimic various nucleotides. Once the drug is incorporated in the viral DNA, the DNA cannot copy itself properly. C

DATA ANALYSIS LAB 2

Based on Real Data*

Interpret the Graph

How can we know if a compound is a mutagen? The Ames test is used to identify mutagens. The test uses a strain of bacteria that cannot make the amino acid histidine. The bacteria are exposed to a suspected mutagen and grow on a medium without histidine. The bacteria that grow have a mutation called a reversion because they reverted to the natural condition of making histidine. The compounds in the graph were Ames tested.

Think Critically

1. **Describe** the relationship between the amount of the compound and the mutation.
2. **Analyze** which compound is the strongest mutagenic compound.

*Data obtained from: Ames. B.N. 1979. Identifying environmental chemicals causing mutations and cancer. *Science.* 204: 587-593

Data and Observations

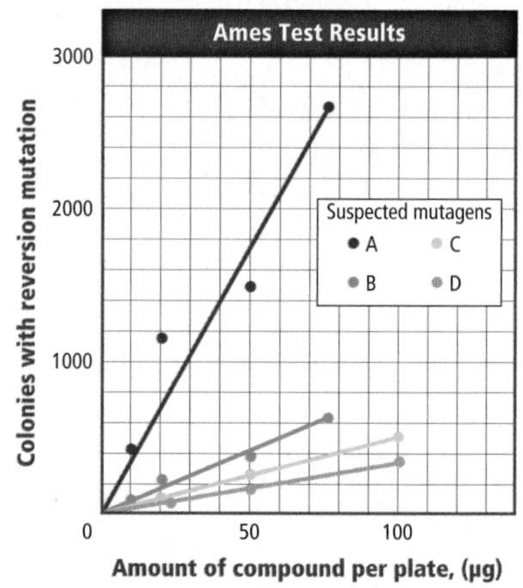

Demonstration

Protein Folding Use both a coiled section and a straight section of telephone cord to demonstrate the shape of a protein. If telephone cords are not available, use straight and coiled shoelaces. Tell students the cord represents the chain of amino acids. Use a coiled telephone cord to demonstrate the helical structure, called an alpha helix, found in sections of a protein. Take the coiled cord and twist it into a ball shape. Some proteins, called globular proteins, consist of this type of structure. Take a section of straight telephone cord, and fold it back and forth on top of itself. Tell students this demonstrates the second most common type of structure of a protein, called a beta sheet. Point out that most proteins have sections of both alpha helixes and beta sheets. Est. time: 10 min

High-energy forms of radiation, such as X-rays and gamma rays, are highly mutagenic. When the radiation reaches the DNA, electrons absorb the energy. The electrons can escape their atom, leaving behind a free radical. Free radicals are charged atoms with unpaired electrons that react violently with other molecules, including DNA. Ultraviolet (UV) radiation from the Sun contains less energy than X-ray radiation and does not cause electrons to be ejected from the atoms. However, UV radiation can cause adjacent thymine bases to bind to each other, disrupting the structure of DNA, as shown in **Figure 23.** DNA with this structure disruption, or kink, are unable to replicate properly unless repaired.

Body-cell v. sex-cell mutation When a mutation in a body cell, also called a somatic cell, escapes the repair mechanism, it becomes part of the genetic sequence in that cell and in future daughter cells. Somatic cell mutations are not passed on to the next generation. In some cases, the mutations do not cause problems for the cell. They could be sequences not used by the adult cell when the mutation occurred, the mutation might have occurred in an exon, or the mutation might not have changed the amino acid for which it was coded. These mutations are called neutral mutations. When the mutation results in the production of an abnormal protein, the cell might not be able to perform its normal function, and cell death might occur. Recall that mutations in body cells that cause the cell cycle to be unregulated can lead to cancer. All of these effects are contained within the cells of the organism as long as only body cells are affected.

When mutations occur in sex cells, also called germ-line cells, the mutations are passed on to the organism's offspring and will be present in every cell of the offspring. In many cases, these mutations do not affect the function of cells in the organism, though they might affect the offspring drastically. When the mutations result in an abnormal protein in the sex cell, the offspring is impacted. However, the offspring is not impacted when an abnormal protein is produced in an isolated body cell. C

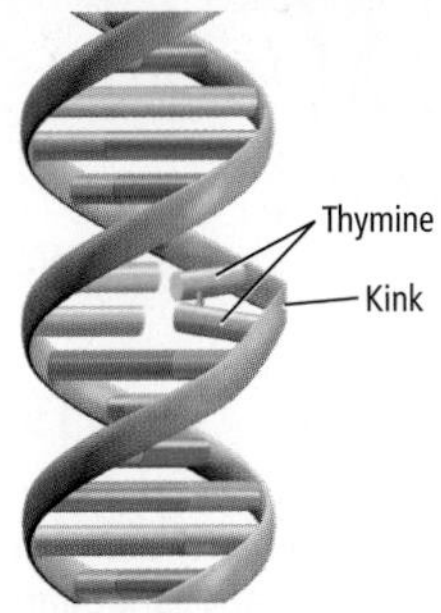

■ **Figure 23** Ultraviolet radiation can cause adjacent thymines to bind to each other instead of to their complementary bases, making the DNA "kink" and preventing replication.

C Critical Thinking

BL OL AL Infer

ASK STUDENTS: ***Why is a mutation in a sex cell considered potentially more harmful than one in a body cell?*** Unlike a mutation in a body cell, a mutation in a sex cell could be passed on to the next generation.

Formative Assessment

Evaluation Prepare a quiz showing a normal section of DNA and a mutant section of DNA. **ASK STUDENTS:** ***Identify the type of mutation that is shown.*** Answers will depend on the quiz material, but students should be able to identify mutations in particular codons.

Remediation Obtain a table similar to Table 3 but without the caption or labels. Distribute copies, and have students identify the types of mutations in the table. Write the correct mutations on the board so that students can compare their answers.

Section 4 Assessment

Section Summary

- Prokaryotic cells regulate their protein synthesis through a set of genes called operons.
- Eukaryotic cells regulate their protein synthesis using various transcription factors, eukaryotic nucleosome structures, and RNA interference.
- Mutations range from point mutations to the deletion or movement of large sections of the chromosome.
- Mutagens, such as chemicals and radiation, can cause mutations.

Understand Main Ideas

1. MAIN Idea **Relate** gene regulation and mutations.
2. **Identify** the two main types of mutagens.
3. **Diagram** how adding lactose to a culture affects the *lac* operon of *E. coli*.
4. **Analyze** how a point mutation can affect the overall protein shape and function, using hemoglobin as an example.
5. **Compare and contrast** prokaryotic and eukaryotic gene regulation.

Think Critically

6. **Explain** why most mutations in eukaryotes are recessive.
7. **Hypothesize** why DNA replication has such accuracy.

WRITING in **Biology**

8. Write an article describing how Hox genes regulate development in animals.

Section 4 Assessment

1. Gene regulation ordinarily ensures accurate replication of DNA, but occasionally a mutation occurs that has a significant effect on the phenotype.
2. radiation and chemicals that change the normal structure of DNA
3. Diagrams should show that milk turns on the production of lactose-digesting enzymes.
4. Point mutation in a hemoglobin gene causes the protein to fold abnormally.
5. In prokaryotes, gene regulation is usually controlled by an operon; regulation in eukaryotic cells involves many regulatory genes.
6. Individuals carry two alleles for each feature. It is unlikely that both will code for mutant proteins, so the normal allele is usually expressed and recessive genes will be passed on.
7. DNA polymerase "proofreads" the replication; repair systems fix the DNA.
8. Articles should indicate that Hox genes control cell differentiation in developing embryos.

Purpose

Students will describe the pros and cons of gene patenting.
C.2, E.2, F.6, G.1

Anticipatory Guide

ASK STUDENTS: ***What is a gene?*** Tell students that a gene is a functional unit that controls inherited trait expression that is passed on from one generation to another generation. ***Where are genes located in the body?*** Tell students that genes are segments of DNA, which are found on chromosomes in the nucleus of every cell in the human body.

Background

Scientists have linked genes called connexin-26 and connexin-30 to hearing loss. Some have proposed that hospitals routinely test newborn infants for these genes if the newborns fail their initial hearing screening, much as babies are now routinely tested for other conditions. But because a company holds patents on the connexin-26 and connexin-30 genes, organizations such as the Association for Molecular Pathology worry that access to a test for the genes will be—and indeed, already has been—limited. "Thus, this particular patent threatens not just individual patient care and access, but public health for the entire population," the AMP wrote in a May 2009 letter to the chair of the Secretary's Advisory Committee on Genetics, Health and Society at the National Institutes of Health (NIH) Office of Biotechnology Activities.

Biology & Society

Who owns genes?

Can a company own parts of the human body? That is an ethical debate that has raged since 1977, when universities and private companies first started seeking patents on genes. To date, about 20 percent of all human genes have been patented. This issue has made headlines since a company patented the BRCA1 and BRCA2 genes, mutations of which have been linked to breast cancer and ovarian cancer.

Agricultural gene patents have also sparked fierce debate. In recent decades, companies have modified the genes in many plants to incorporate them with desirable traits, such as resistance to diseases and pests. Companies have received patents on these modified plant genes.

What is a patent? A patent grants the exclusive right to make a profit from the sale of an invention. Often, people or businesses have invested years and large amounts of money researching and developing an invention. The profits they receive from holding patents help them recoup their investments, as well as provide money for future research.

A patent on nature Opponents argue that patenting genes will hinder free and open scientific research and will harm patients seeking medical care. If companies own patents on genes, they can refuse to allow other scientists to use the genes in their work, possibly preventing important discoveries. The high cost of genetic testing and therapies related to patented genes can deter patients from receiving treatments.

Agricultural implications Agricultural gene patents pose an additional problem for farmers. If winds or animals bring seeds containing patented genes to the fields of a farmer who has not bought the rights to use those seeds, the company who holds the patent can sue the farmer.

Soybeans

Corn

Around the world, the amount of land devoted to the cultivation of genetically modified plants is rising. Soybeans and corn are two crops that are often genetically modified.

In the past, farmers have lost these court cases, even though it is impossible to stop natural forces from transferring seeds.

As companies continue to seek patents on genes, the debate is certain to continue. For now, the patenting of genes is legal. But in the future, ethical and practical considerations might swing the pendulum the other way.

DEBATE in Biology

Research Have students further research the issue of gene patenting. Divide the class into two teams, one for gene patenting and one against it and stage a debate.

DEBATE in Biology

Activity If students do not know how to begin their research on this topic, suggest that they type the keywords "gene patenting" into an online search engine. They also could search the database of the USPTO to find its ruling on gene patenting. (Check this citation: Federal Register: January 5, 2001, Volume 66, Number 4, Page 1092-1099.) Position statements on gene patenting can be found on the Web sites of various organizations, such as the American Medical Association, the Association for Molecular Pathology, and the American College of Medical Genetics.

WebQuest

BIOLAB

FORENSICS: HOW IS DNA EXTRACTED?

Background: DNA tests are important for biologists, doctors, and even detectives. Imagine that you are working in a lab where someone has brought a sample of corn from a crime scene to be analyzed. You decide to test the DNA of the corn to look for genes to identify the type of corn. Before the DNA sequence can be examined, the DNA must be extracted.

Question: *How can DNA be extracted?*

Materials

corn kernels (50 g)
beakers (2)
blender
cheesecloth (4 squares—30 cm on each edge)
rubber band
glass spooling hook
homogenization medium (100–150 mL)
plastic centrifuge tube (30–50 mL)
contact lens cleaning tablet (containing papain)
95% ethanol (12 mL)
distilled water (3 mL)
test tube
container of ice
water bath at 60°C
stirring rod
timer or clock

Safety Precautions

Procedure

1. Read and complete the lab safety form.
2. Carefully weigh out 50 g of corn kernels.
3. Place the corn kernels into a beaker and cover with homogenization medium that has been warmed to 60°C. Place the beaker in a 60°C water bath for 10 min. Gently stir every 45 s.
4. Remove the beaker from the water bath and chill quickly in an ice bath for 5 min.
5. Pour the mixture into a blender and homogenize, or blend, to achieve a consistent texture.
6. Filter the homogenized mixture through four layers of cheesecloth into a clean large beaker on ice.
7. Pour 15 mL of the filtrate into a 30–50 mL plastic centrifuge tube.
8. Dissolve one contact lens cleaning tablet in 3 mL of distilled water in a test tube. Add this to the filtrate tube and mix gently.
9. Hold the filtrate tube at an angle and slowly pour 12 mL of cold 95% ethanol down the side of the tube.
10. Observe the DNA rising into the alcohol layer as a cloudy suspension of white strings. Use a hooked glass rod to spool the DNA, and allow it to dry.
11. **Cleanup and Disposal** Clean your lab area, disposing of chemicals and materials as directed by your teacher. Be sure to wash your hands when you are finished.

Analyze and Conclude

1. **Describe** the appearance of the DNA in suspension and once it has dried.
2. **Explain** why you put the corn kernels into the blender.
3. **Think Critically** Why is it important not to contaminate a sample of DNA that is to be sequenced? How would you know if you had contaminated your sample?

WRITING in Biology

Report Imagine you are the first researcher to extract DNA from corn. Write a report detailing your methods and possible applications of your discovery.

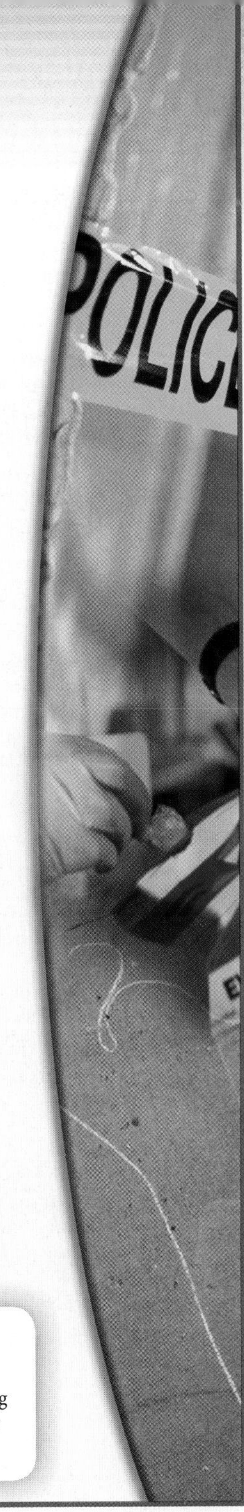

Analyze and Conclude

1. Answers will vary. It looks like white thread in suspension.
2. This physically breaks open the cells and releases their contents.
3. If the sample is contaminated, DNA from another substance might be present.

WRITING in Biology

RUBRIC Use the modifiable rubric found on your eTeacherEdition Online to assess writing assignments.

BIOLAB

Inquiry BioLab

For a lab worksheet, use your eTeacherEdition Online.

RUBRIC A rubric for evaluating BioLabs is found on your eTeacherEdition Online.

Est. Time 50 min

Content Background
Extracting DNA from corn kernels and other plant tissues involves breaking the tissues apart and then breaking down the cell to release DNA from the nucleus. Heating and homogenizing break down tissue and cell walls. Detergents break down the outer cell and the nuclear membranes and release the DNA from the cell. Enzymes are added to degrade proteins and make the DNA molecules easier to spool. Finally, the DNA must be precipitated out of solution, using ethanol.

Alternative Materials
95% isopropyl alcohol can be substituted for ethanol; meat tenderizer can be substituted for the contact lens cleaning tablet.

Safety Precaution Approve lab safety forms before work begins.

Teaching Strategy For homogenizing medium, mix 25 g SDS, 4.4 g NaCl, 2.2 g sodium citrate, and 0.15 g ETDA. Add distilled water to make 500 mL.

Alternative Teaching Demo
If you run out of time, show students the video lab as an alternative to performing it themselves.

Cleanup and Disposal Have students dispose of unused corn and husks and used cheesecloth in the regular trash. Dispose of liquid wastes down the drain to a sanitary sewer.

Chapter 12

Study Guide

ConnectED

Students can use the following to review the chapter.

Review

Vocabulary eGames
Vocabulary eFlashcards
Vocabulary PuzzleMaker

Assessment

Online Quizzes
Online Test Practice
Standardized Test Practice

Use the *ExamView® Assessment Suite* CD-ROM to:

- create multiple versions of tests
- create modified tests with one mouse click
- edit existing questions and add your own questions
- build tests aligned with state standards using built-in state curriculum tags
- change English tests to Spanish with one mouse click
- track students' progress using the Teacher Management System

Chapter 12 Study Guide

THEME FOCUS Scientific Inquiry Many different scientists and studies have contributed to our understanding of molecular genetics, and further studies are changing the way we practice science.

BIG Idea DNA is the genetic material that contains a code for proteins.

Section 1 DNA: The Genetic Material

double helix (p. 330)
nucleosome (p. 332)

MAIN Idea The discovery that DNA is the genetic code involved many experiments.

- Griffith's bacterial experiment and Avery's explanation first indicated that DNA is the genetic material.
- The Hershey-Chase experiment provided evidence that DNA is the genetic material of viruses.
- Chargaff's rule states that in DNA the amount of cytosine equals the amount of guanine and the amount of thymine equals the amount of adenine.
- The work of Watson, Crick, Franklin, and Wilkins provided evidence of the double-helix structure of DNA.

Section 2 Replication of DNA

semiconservative replication (p. 333)
DNA polymerase (p. 334)
Okazaki fragment (p. 334)

MAIN Idea DNA replicates by making a strand that is complementary to each original strand.

- The enzymes DNA helicase, RNA primase, DNA polymerase, and DNA ligase are involved in DNA replication.
- The leading strand is synthesized continuously, but the lagging strand is synthesized discontinously, forming Okazaki fragments.
- Prokaryotic DNA opens at a single origin of replication, whereas eukaryotic DNA has multiple areas of replication.

Section 3 DNA, RNA, and Protein

RNA (p. 336)
messenger RNA (p. 336)
ribosomal RNA (p. 336)
transfer RNA (p. 336)
transcription (p. 337)
RNA polymerase (p. 337)
intron (p. 337)
exon (p. 337)
codon (p. 338)
translation (p. 338)

MAIN Idea DNA codes for RNA, which guides protein synthesis.

- Three major types of RNA are involved in protein synthesis: mRNA, tRNA, and rRNA.
- The synthesis of the mRNA from the template DNA is called transcription.
- Translation is the process through which the mRNA attaches to the ribosome and a protein is assembled.
- In eukaryotes, mRNA contains introns that are excised before leaving the nucleus. A cap and poly-A tail are added to the mRNA.
- One gene codes for one polypeptide.

Section 4 Gene Regulation and Mutation

gene regulation (p. 342)
operon (p. 342)
mutation (p. 345)
mutagen (p. 348)

MAIN Idea Gene expression is regulated by the cell, and mutations can affect this expression.

- Prokaryotic cells regulate their protein synthesis through a set of genes called operons.
- Eukaryotic cells regulate their protein synthesis using various transcription factors, eukaryotic nucleosome structures, and RNA interference.
- Mutations range from point mutations to the deletion or movement of large sections of the chromosome.
- Mutagens, such as chemicals and radiation, can cause mutations.

Review Vocabulary PuzzleMaker

For additional practice with vocabulary, have students access the Vocabulary Puzzlemaker online.

Review Vocabulary eGames

Section 1

Vocabulary Review

Each of the following sentences is false. Make the sentence true by replacing the underlined word with the correct vocabulary term from the Study Guide page.

1. The twisted ladder shape of DNA is called a <u>nucleotide</u>
2. A <u>double helix</u> consists of DNA wrapped around the histone proteins.

Understand Main Ideas

3. What are the basic building blocks of DNA and RNA?
   A. ribose **C.** nucleotides
   B. purines **D.** phosphorus
4. If a section of DNA has 27 percent thymine, how much cytosine will it have?
   A. 23 percent **C.** 46 percent
   B. 27 percent **D** 54 percent
5. Which was a conclusion of Griffith's work with *Streptococcus pneumoniae?*
   A. DNA is the genetic material in viruses.
   B. The structure of DNA is a double helix.
   C. Bacteria exposed to DNA can incorporate the DNA and change phenotype.
   D. The amount of thymine equals the amount of adenine in DNA.

Refer to the figure below to answer questions 6 and 7.

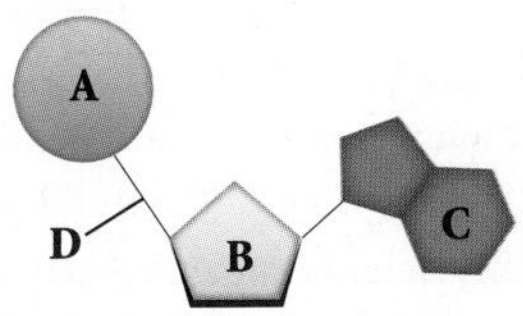

6. What is the entire labeled structure called?
   A. nucleotide **C.** base
   B. RNA **D.** phosphate
7. Which label represents the coding part of DNA?
   A. A **C.** C
   B. B **D.** D

Constructed Response

8. **Short Answer** Explain how DNA forms chromosomes in eukaryotic cells.

Use the figure below to answer question 9.

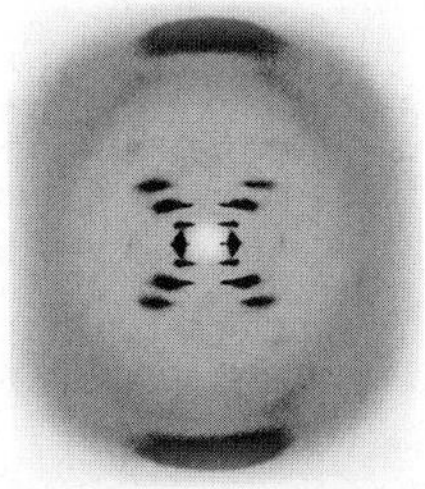

9. **THEME FOCUS Scientific Inquiry** Summarize the experiments and data shown in the photo that led to the discovery of DNA.

Think Critically

10. **Design** How might you use radioactive phosphorus to demonstrate that the transforming compound of bacteria in Griffith's experiment was DNA?
11. **MAIN Idea** How would the results of the Hershey-Chase experiment have been different if protein were the genetic material?

Section 2

Vocabulary Review

Write a sentence defining each of the following vocabulary terms.

12. DNA polymerase
13. semiconservative replication
14. Okazaki fragment

Understand Main Ideas

15. With what does the synthesis of a new strand of DNA begin?
    A. RNA primer
    B. nucleotide unit
    C. messenger RNA
    D. transfer RNA

Chapter 12

Assessment

Section 1

Vocabulary Review

1. double helix
2. nucleosome

Understand Main Ideas

3. C
4. A
5. C
6. A
7. C

Constructed Response

8. DNA coils around histones to form nucleosomes, which coil to form chromatin fibers. The chromatin fibers supercoil to make chromosomes.
9. Franklin took the photo using the X-ray diffraction technique. The circle shows the twisted shape of the rails of the DNA "ladder." The X indicates where the bases cross, forming "rungs" of the twisted ladder.

Think Critically

10. By radioactively labeling the smooth bacteria DNA before they were killed, one could track the radioactive DNA as it was picked up and incorporated by the rough bacterial cells.
11. They would have found that it was radioactive sulfur that was passed from generation to generation in the virus rather than the radioactive phosphorus found in the DNA.

Section 2

Vocabulary Review

12. DNA polymerase is the enzyme that facilitates DNA replication.
13. Semiconservative replication is the method by which DNA makes copies of itself.
14. Okazaki fragments are short strands of new DNA produced during the replication of the lagging strand.

Understand Main Ideas

15. A

Understand Main Ideas

16. B

Constructed Response

17. DNA helicase unzips the DNA, RNA primase adds a short RNA primer, DNA polymerase places the proper complementary nucleotide into place, and DNA ligase links the Okazaki fragments together.

18. Diagram should show the leading strand and the lagging strand and include labels for DNA polymerase, DNA helicase, Okazaki fragments, and DNA ligase.

Think Critically

19. In bacteria, there is one origin of replication, and replication proceeds in both directions. In eukaryotes, there are multiple origins of replication along the DNA strand, so this is a eukaryotic cell.

20. Eukaryotic chromosomes can be composed of up to one million base pairs. DNA replication can proceed at a faster rate with multiple areas of replication.

21. One strand of DNA serves as a template to make the matching strand. The matching strand is made of complementary bases.

Section 3

Vocabulary Review

22. mRNA contains the code from the DNA strand; tRNA has anticodons that correspond to the codons on the mRNA strand.

23. RNA polymerase catalyzes the transcription of mRNA, which contains the codons that are translated into amino acids during translation.

24. Introns are the parts of pre-mRNA that interrupt the code contained in the exons.

Understand Main Ideas

25. C

26. B

27. A

16. Which is true about the elongation of the lagging strand?
- **A.** does not require a template strand
- **B.** produces Okazaki fragments
- **C.** requires the action of RNA ligase
- **D.** proceeds by continually adding nucleotides to the 3' end

Constructed Response

17. Short Answer List the enzymes involved in replication and describe their functions.

18. MAIN Idea Summarize the process of DNA replication in a diagram. Add labels to explain what is happening.

Think Critically

Use the figure below to answer questions 19 and 20.

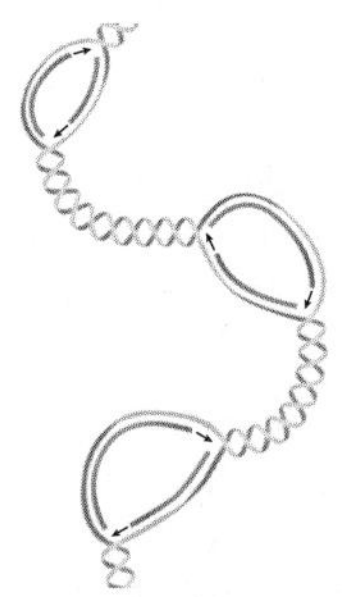

19. Determine Imagine that you are a scientist looking at a cell through a microscope. You see DNA replicating in several areas. Determine what type of cell you are looking at based on the origins of replication.

20. Hypothesize why it is important for the DNA in the figure to have multiple origins of replication.

21. Infer how complementary base pairing is responsible for semiconservative replication.

Section 3

Vocabulary Review

Write a sentence that connects the vocabulary terms in each pair.

22. mRNA — tRNA

23. codon — RNA polymerase

24. intron — exon

Understand Main Ideas

25. Which correctly lists the changes to eukaryotic pre-mRNA to form mRNA?
- **A.** cap added, introns excised, and poly T tail added
- **B.** cap added, exons excised, and poly T tail added
- **C.** cap added, introns excised, and poly A tail added
- **D.** cap added, exons excised, and poly A tail added

Use the figure below to answer questions 26 and 27.

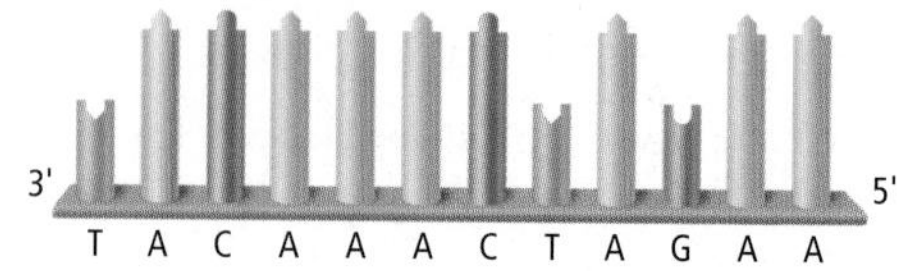

26. What is the mRNA sequence for the template strand DNA sequence in the figure?
- **A.** 5' ATGTTTGATCTT 3'
- **B.** 5' AUGUUUGAUCUU 3'
- **C.** 5' TACAAACTAGAA 3'
- **D.** 5' UACAAACUAGAA 3'

27. What is the sequence for the nontemplate strand of the DNA in the figure?
- **A.** 5' ATGTTTGATCTT 3'
- **B.** 5' AUGUUUGAUCUU 3'
- **C.** 5' TACAAACTAGAA 3'
- **D.** 5' UACAAACUAGAA 3'

Constructed Response

28. Short Answer Compare and contrast transcription and translation. Indicate where they occur in prokaryotic cells and eukaryotic cells.

29. MAIN Idea Describe the experiment that led to the One Gene–One Enzyme hypothesis.

Think Critically

30. Identify the mRNA sequence and orientation if the nontemplate strand has the sequence 5' ATGCCAGTCATC 3'. Use **Figure 14** to determine the amino acid sequence coded by the mRNA.

Constructed Response

28. Transcription involves the opening of the DNA and the synthesis of a complementary mRNA strand to the template strand of the DNA. Translation involves making a protein from the mRNA and occurs in the cytoplasm on a ribosome. In prokaryotes, both translation and transcription take place in the cytoplasm, since they have no nucleus. In eukaryotes, transcription takes place in the nucleus and translation takes place in the cytoplasm. In both, translation takes place on the ribosome.

29. Mold spores were mutated by exposing them to X rays. If the mutated spore could not grow on a minimal medium, it was tested to see what amino acid it lacked.

Think Critically

30. 5' AUGCCAGUCAUC 3'; amino acid sequence: methionine (start), proline, valine, isoleucine

Section 4

Vocabulary Review

Write the vocabulary term from the Study Guide page that describes each of the following processes.

31. regulation of a prokaryotic genome

32. control of the functional units of DNA

33. changes in DNA sequence

Understand Main Ideas

34. Which demonstrates an insertion mutation of the sequence 5' GGGCCCAAA 3'?
- **A.** 5' GGGGCCAAA 3'
- **B.** 5' GGGCCAAA 3'
- **C.** 5' GGGAAACCC 3'
- **D.** 5' GGGCCCAAAAAA 3'

35. Which is true about eukaryotic gene regulation?
- **A.** Eukaryotic gene regulation is exactly like prokaryotic gene regulation.
- **B.** Replication factors guide the binding of eukaryotic RNA polymerase to the promoter.
- **C.** Activator proteins fold DNA to enhancer sites that increase the rate of gene transmission.
- **D.** Repressor proteins bind to activators, preventing them from binding to the DNA.

36. Which is not a type of mutation?
- **A.** base substitutions
- **B.** insertions
- **C.** RNA interference
- **D.** translocation

Constructed Response

37. Short Answer Illustrate the effect of adding tryptophan to a culture of *E. coli.*

38. Short Answer Describe RNA interference.

Think Critically

39. Infer why base substitutions in the third position are least likely to cause a change in the amino acid for which it coded.

40. MAIN Idea Hypothesize how it might be possible for bacteria to respond to environmental stress by increasing the rate of mutations during cell division.

Summative Assessment

41. BIG Idea Explain the central dogma of protein synthesis.

42. WRITING in Biology The discovery of DNA and its structure required many scientists to research, conduct experiments, and publish their findings. Write about a scientific event that required scientists to build on others' findings to produce results.

43. WRITING in Biology The book *Jurassic Park* by Michael Crichton presents the idea of isolating DNA from extinct organisms and "resurrecting" them. If this were possible, should this be done? Defend your opinion in an essay.

DBQ Document-Based Questions

Data obtained from: Watson, J.D. and Crick, F.H.. 1953. Molecular Structure of Nucleic Acids. *Nature* 171: 737-738.

The following excerpts are from Watson and Crick's description of the structure of DNA.

"The novel feature of the structure is the manner in which the two chains are held together by the purine and pyrimidine bases. The planes of the bases are perpendicular to the fibre axis. They are joined together in pairs, a single base from one chain being hydrogen-bonded to a single base from the other chain so that the two lie side by side with identical z-co-ordinates. One of the pair must be a purine and the other a pyrimidine for bonding to occur."

"It has not escaped our notice that the specific pairing we have postulated immediately suggests a possible copying mechanism for the genetic material."

44. Draw a diagram of DNA structure based on the description above.

45. According to the description, how are the bases joined together?

46. What did Watson and Crick see as a possible copying mechanism?

Section 4

Vocabulary

31. operon

32. gene regulation

33. mutation

Understand Main Ideas

34. D

35. C

36. C

Constructed Response

37. Tryptophan acts as a corepressor, binding to the inactive repressor, activating it, and shutting off the enzymes needed to synthesize tryptophan.

38. RNA interference involves small pieces of RNA that bind to mRNA and interfere with its expression.

Think Critically

39. The third position for many amino acids could be any of the DNA codes, and a change in the third position will not change the amino acid for which it coded.

40. Accept any logical hypothesis. Answers might include reduction in the amount of checking enzymes produced. Increased mutations might lead to an adaptation that increases chances of survival under changing environmental conditions.

Summative Assessment

41. The central dogma of protein synthesis is DNA codes for RNA and RNA guides the synthesis of proteins.

42. Answers will vary, but should involve a situation where people used teamwork to determine or answer a common question, problem, or activity.

43. Answers will vary. Students should defend their opinions.

DBQ Document-Based Questions

Watson, J. D. and Crick, F. H. 1953. Molecular structure of nucleic acids. *Nature* 171: 737–738.

44. The diagram should show the side rails of sugar bonded to phosphate. The steps of the ladder are thymine double bonded (hydrogen bonds) to adenine and cytosine triple bonded (hydrogen bonds) to guanine.

45. Cytosine bonds to guanine and thymine bonds to adenine.

46. The hydrogen bonds could break and the parental strands serve as a template for the synthesis of new strands.

Assessment Online Test Practice

Standardized Test Practice

Multiple Choice

1. A 5. D
2. A 6. A
3. C 7. C
4. A 8. C

Short Answer

9. The law of independent assortment states that a random distribution of alleles occurs during gamete formation. Therefore, a dihibrid cross of YyRr would produce a phenotype ratio of 9:3:3:1.

	YR	*Yr*	*yR*	*yr*
YR	*YYRR*	*YYRr*	*YyRR*	*YyRr*
Yr	*YYRr*	*YYrr*	*YyRr*	*Yyrr*
yR	*YyRR*	*YyRr*	*yyRR*	*yyRr*
yr	*YyRr*	*Yyrr*	*yyRr*	*yyrr*

10. Answers can vary, but should show the link between technology and new understandings of DNA. For example: X-ray diffraction was a technique for taking pictures of molecular structures. Franklin used this technique to find that the DNA molecule had a double helix shape.
11. Coat variations that occur only in females are likely caused by dosage compensation. The degree of expression would depend on the number of alleles present in the females. Sex-linked genes do not likely cause the effects, unless the genes are not expressed or are lethal in males.
12. The genotypes homozygous for both traits are *RRYY, RRyy, rrYY,* and *rryy.* The homozygous genotypes are 25% of the total. The easiest way to determine the percent of offspring homozygous for both traits would be to use a Punnett square.
13. Mendel's work showed that there are very regular patterns for inheritance, so it opened up questions about what causes these patterns.
14. The organism would have five chromosomes in its karyotype. Monosomy is the absence of one chromosome from a pair. The organism has a chromosome number of $2n = 6$, or six chromosomes. The loss of one chromosome would give a total of five.

Standardized Test Practice

Cumulative

Multiple Choice

1. Which macromolecule can be formed using the sugars produced by plants during photosynthesis?
   - **A.** cellulose
   - **B.** DNA
   - **C.** lipid
   - **D.** protein

Use the diagram below to answer questions 2 and 3.

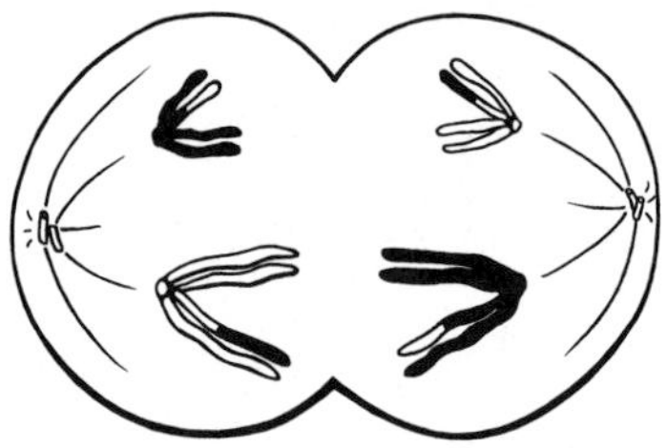

2. Which stage of meiosis is represented in the diagram?
   - **A.** anaphase I
   - **B.** anaphase II
   - **C.** metaphase I
   - **D.** metaphase II

3. Which process can take place during the stage of meiosis that follows the stage in the diagram?
   - **A.** change to diploid
   - **B.** crossing over
   - **C.** cytokinesis
   - **D.** DNA replication

4. What enzyme is responsible for "unzipping" the DNA strand during replication?
   - **A.** DNA helicase
   - **B.** DNA ligase
   - **C.** DNA polymerase
   - **D.** RNA primase

Use the illustration below to answer question 5.

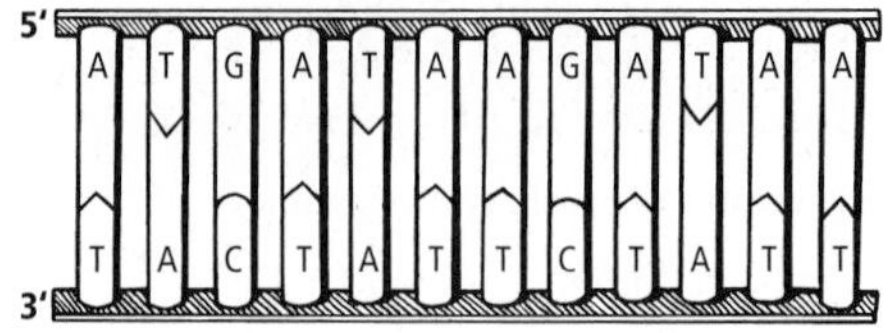

5. Which sequence is possible for mRNA formed from the DNA strand shown in the illustration?
   - **A.** 5'AATAGAATAGTA3'
   - **B.** 5'AAUAGAAUAGUA3'
   - **C.** 5'ATGATAAGATAA3'
   - **D.** 5'AUGAUAAGAUAA3'

6. Which cells would likely undergo apoptosis?
   - **A.** cells between fingers
   - **B.** cells reproducing normally
   - **C.** cells reproducing slowly
   - **D.** cells surrounding the heart

7. Which genotype could be the one of a person whose blood type is A?
   - **A.** I^BI^B
   - **B.** ii
   - **C.** I^Ai
   - **D.** I^AI^B

8. Which sex chromosomes are present in a person with Kleinfelter Syndrome?
   - **A.** OY
   - **B.** XO
   - **C.** XXY
   - **D.** XYY

Short Answer

9. Using the law of independent assortment, describe a dihybrid cross of heterozygous yellow, round-seed pea plants (YyRr). Include a Punnett square and phenotype ratios in your response.

10. Give an example of a technological development, and explain how it contributed to scientists' understanding of the structure of DNA.

11. Which probably causes the coat color variations that occur only in the females of a certain animal? Give a reason to support your conclusion.

12. Suppose you perform a dihybrid cross between two organisms with the genotype RrYy. What percentage of the offspring would be homozygous for both traits? Explain how you determined the answer.

13. Why do you think Mendel's work preceded the search for molecules involved in inheritance?

14. Suppose an organism (with a chromosome number of $2n = 6$) has monosomy of chromosome 3. How many chromosomes are in the organism's karyotype? Explain your answer.

15. Explain why the number of bases in a strand of mRNA can be different from the number in the DNA from which it was synthesized.

16. Explain why a hypothesis must be testable.

Extended Response

Use the figure below to answer question 17.

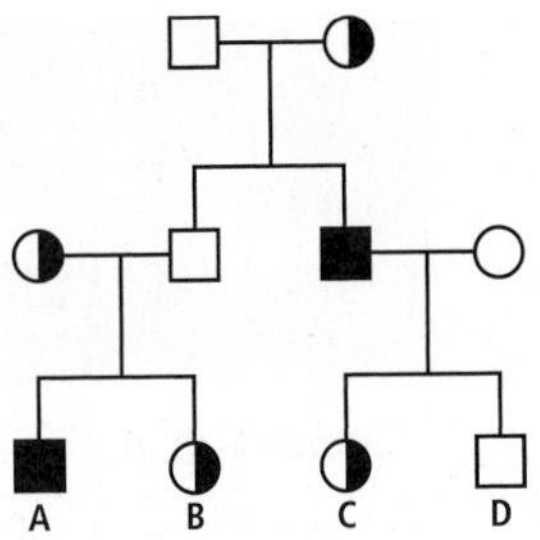

17. Describe the pattern of inheritance of the disease tracked in the pedigree above.

18. Human nerve cells seldom divide after they are formed. Evaluate how this might affect a person with a spinal cord injury.

19. Explain the role that publication of findings had in the discovery of DNA's structure.

Essay Question

For certain kinds of research studies, scientists recruit pairs of twins to be participants or subjects of the research. They might recruit identical or fraternal twins, depending on the focus of the study. Twins can be particularly helpful in studies about genetics and heredity.

Using the information in the paragraph above, answer the following question in essay format.

20. Imagine you are a research scientist. Write a plan for a research study that would require participants to be twins. Explain what you are trying to learn, whether you are looking for identical or fraternal twins, and why it is important to have twins as subjects for your study.

NEED EXTRA HELP?																				
If You Missed Question . . .	1	2	3	4	5	6	7	8	9	10	11	12	13	14	15	16	17	18	19	20
Review Section . . .	8.2	10.1	10.1	12.2	12.3	9.3	11.2	11.3	11.2	12.2	11.2	10.2	12.2	11.3	11.2	12.3	11.1	9.1	12.1	11.2

15. Introns that are not needed for coding of proteins are taken out of the mRNA sequence. Also, a chain of adenine nucleotides might be added to the 3′ end of the chain.

16. A hypothesis is a tentative explanation for a specific research question about a phenomenon. A hypothesis must be testable in order to determine if it is a valid explanation for the phenomenon. If a hypothesis is not testable, it cannot be supported by evidence.

Extended Response

17. This is a sex-linked disease and the gene causing the disease is recessive. It is sex-linked because the disease itself appears much more frequently in males, while females are usually just carriers of the gene for the disease, indicating that they have another gene on their second X-chromosome that is dominant and covers the gene of the disease tracked in the pedigree. The gene causing the disease tracked in the pedigree is recessive because it can occur only in females who receive the gene for this disease from both parents.

18. The damaged nerves in the spinal cord would not be able to repair themselves by dividing and making new nerve cells. This means that a spinal cord injury is usually permanent.

19. Answers can vary, but should describe how the publication of Watson and Crick's ideas about structure, in addition to Franklin's publication about her findings about the shape of DNA, made the double helix public knowledge in the scientific community. This, in turn, made it possible for others to try replicating their findings, or to determine whether the findings agreed with other evidence about DNA's structure.

Essay Question

20. Answers can vary. Students should clearly state the purpose of the study and the reason for having twins involved. For instance, students might propose doing research about a health issue. They could propose doing research on a disease that is caused by both genetic and environmental factors, such as heart disease or diabetes. The study could also pertain to other health issues, such as the development of behavioral characteristics or complex physical characteristics such as height and weight. Identical twins could be useful for the study because they are genetically the same. Differences between identical twins presumably come from environmental factors, because there are no genetic differences between the twins. On the other hand, fraternal twins can be included in a study to show which traits are affected by genetic factors. Fraternal twins are genetically different but can have similar environmental factors in their upbringing. Consequently fraternal twins can also be useful in a twin study.

Chapter 13 Organizer:
Genetics and Biotechnology

LabManager™
Customize any lab with the LabManager™ CD-ROM.

Essential Questions	National Science Standards	Materials and Planning	
		Estimated times include cleanup and disposal, but do not include teacher prep time. For cleanup and disposal guidelines, see page 39T.	Est. Time (min)
Section 1 1. How is selective breeding used to produce organisms with desired traits? 2. What are similarities and differences between inbreeding and hybridization? 3. How does a Punnett square test cross help assess the genotypes of organisms?	UCP.2, UCP.3; A.1, A.2; C.2; G.1, G.3	**Launch Lab,** p. 358: deck of cards	15
		Demonstration, p. 360: chocolate bars, marshmallows, graham crackers	15
		MiniLab 1, p. 361: labeled drawing of a lily flower, fresh lily flower, magnifying lens, cotton swab	45
Section 2 1. What are the different tools and processes used in genetic engineering? 2. How does genetic engineering manipulate recombinant DNA? 3. What are the similarities between selective breeding and genetic engineering? 4. How can genetic engineering and biotechnology be used to improve human life?	UCP.2, UCP.3; A.1, A.2; C.2; E.1, E.2; F.1, F.5, F.6; G.1, G.2	**Demonstration,** p. 365: magnets, sifter, gravel, sand	10
		MiniLab 2, p. 365: straight paper DNA sequence, circular paper DNA sequence, scissors	40
Section 3 1. What are the components of the human genome? 2. How do forensic scientists use DNA fingerprinting? 3. How can information from the human genome be used to treat human diseases?	UCP.2, UCP.3; A.1, A.2; C.2; E.1, E.2; F.1, F.5, F.6; G.1, G.3	**Demonstration,** p. 372: pin, book	5
		BioLab, p. 381: various DNA samples, electrophoresis chamber, power source, micropipette and tips, prepared agarose gels, restriction enzyme, microcentrifuge tubes and rack, sample-loading dye, nontoxic dye, staining and destaining containers, DNA fragments of known size, ruler, ice in a foam container, water bath at 37°C	40

Suggested Time for Each Lesson

Class	Chapter Opener	Section 1	Section 2	Section 3	Assessment
Basic	45 min	90 min	90 min	45 min	45 min
General	25 min	45 min	65 min	45 min	45 min
Honors	5 min	85 min	135 min	45 min	45 min

ConnectED

connectED.mcgraw-hill.com

Access interactive learning opportunities and teaching resources using these icons located throughout your StudentWorks™ Plus Online and eTeacherEdition Online.

Chapter 13 Section Resources	Additional Chapter 13 Resources	Technology
FAST FILE Unit 3 Resources: Launch Lab Worksheet* MiniLab Worksheet* Study Guide (English/Spanish)* Section Quick Check **Reading Essentials 13.1** **Science Notebook 13.1*** **FAST FILE Unit 3 Resources:** MiniLab Worksheet* Study Guide (English/Spanish)* Section Quick Check **Reading Essentials 13.2** **Science Notebook 13.2*** **FAST FILE Unit 3 Resources:** BioLab Worksheet* Study Guide (English/Spanish)* Section Quick Check **Reading Essentials 13.3** **Science Notebook 13.3***	**FAST FILE Unit 3 Resources:** Chapter Diagnostic Test Concept Mapping* Real-World Biology Enrichment Chapter Tests A, B, and C **Transparencies:** Bellringer Transparencies* Biology Concepts Transparencies* **Lab Resources:** Laboratory Manual* Probeware Lab Manual* Forensics Lab Manual* Pre-AP Lab Manual* Open Inquiry in Biology* Guided Inquiry in Biology*	**Teaching Tools:** eTeacherEdition Online Classroom Presentation Toolkit CD-ROM* LabManager™ CD-ROM* Video Lab DVD* Virtual Lab CD-ROM* What's BIOLOGY Got To Do With It? StudentWorks™ Plus Online* **Chapter Assessment Tools:** Classroom Presentation Toolkit CD-ROM* *ExamView® Assessment Suite* CD-ROM **Web-Based Resources:** • StudentWorks™ Plus Online • eTeacherEdition Online • Animations* • The Interactive Time Line* • Interactive Tables* • Online Quizzes • Online Test Practice • Standardized Test Practice • Virtual Labs* • Multilingual eGlossary* • Vocabulary eGames* • Vocabulary eFlashcards • WebQuests • Personal Tutors

While all resources listed are appropriate for English learners, the * indicates resources with a strong visual or hands-on component for EL.

Teaching strategies and activities have been coded for differentiated instruction.

AL Activities for students working above grade level	**OL** Activities for students working on grade level	**BL** Activities for students working below grade level	**EL** Activities for English learners (also ELL)	**COOP LEARN** Activities designed for small cooperative group work

CHAPTER 13

Launch Lab
How does selective breeding work?

Inquiry Launch Lab

For a lab worksheet, use your eTeacherEdition Online.

RUBRIC A rubric for evaluating Launch Labs is found on your eTeacherEdition Online.

Est. Time 15 min

Alternative Materials A set of 52 marbles of four different colors can be used instead of playing cards—13 marbles of each color. Include a paper bag for drawing out pairs of marbles.

Safety Precautions Approve lab safety forms before work begins. Watch out for paper cuts.

Teaching Strategies
- Encourage students to think about why they are laying the cards out in pairs instead of one at a time.
- Have students think about how this simulation would change if they wished to select two desired traits (two suits) instead of one.

Procedure
1. Read and complete the lab safety form.
2. Shuffle a **deck of cards.** Choose one suit to represent the gene you wish to select.
3. Lay the entire deck face up in 26 pairs.
4. Select the pairs that contain at least one card from your chosen suit.
5. Record the number of cards remaining and calculate the percentage of cards not selected from the starting pile.
6. Shuffle the remaining cards and repeat Steps 2-4 until all of your cards are of the suit you selected.

Analysis
1. **Infer** why the cards were laid out in pairs. Cards are laid out in pairs because genes are typically inherited in pairs of alleles, one allele from each parent.
2. **Relate** changes in the percentage of cards discarded after each round to how the percentage of genes might change in a population. As the number of cards not selected decreases, the percentage of the selected gene (suit) increases. With a higher percentage of a particular gene in a population, the chance that an individual will have a copy of that gene increases.

CHAPTER 13
Genetics and Biotechnology

ConnectED

Your one-stop online resource
connectED.mcgraw-hill.com

- Video
- Audio
- Review
- Inquiry
- WebQuest
- Assessment
- Concepts in Motion
- Multilingual eGlossary

Launch Lab
How does selective breeding work?

A deck of cards can represent the genome of a population of organisms. In this lab, you will model selective breeding to create a population of cards with similar suits.

For a lab worksheet, use your StudentWorks™ Plus Online.

Inquiry Launch Lab

FOLDABLES®

Make a three tab book and label it as shown. Use it to organize your notes about DNA tools.

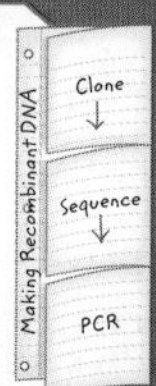

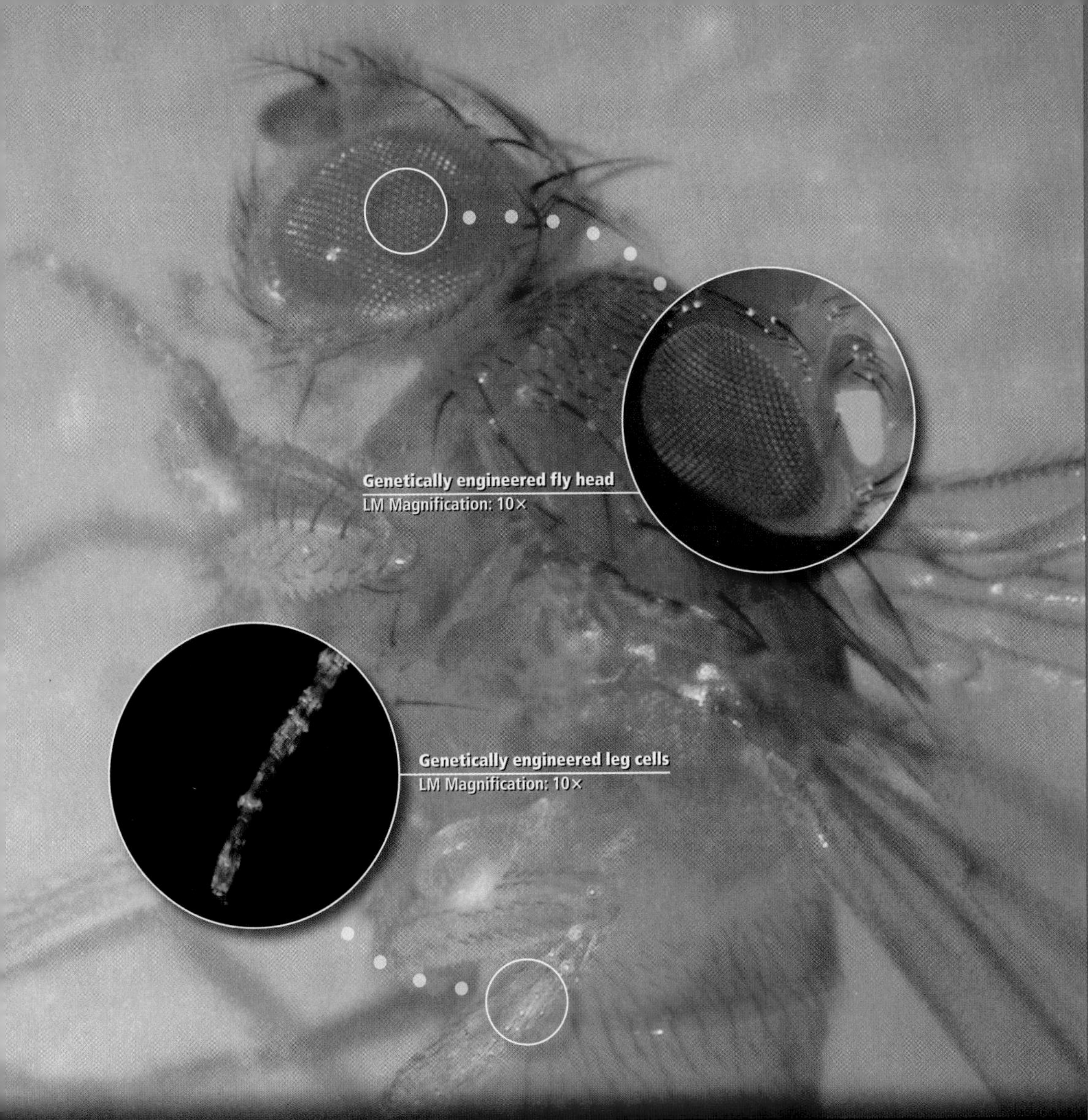

THEME FOCUS Scientific Inquiry
New technology leads to molecular discoveries and better understanding of genetic inheritance.

BIG Idea Genetic technology improves human health and quality of life.

Section 1 • Applied Genetics
Section 2 • DNA Technology
Section 3 • The Human Genome

THEMES

Scientific Inquiry The completion of the Human Genome Project led to many new technologies and discoveries.

Diversity The genetics of each organism is the basis of diversity within species.

Energy Electricity provides the energy needed for gel electrophoresis.

Homeostasis Vectors provide a stable environment in which DNA and genes are inserted into gene therapy patients.

Change Genetic engineering makes potentially beneficial mutations in a controlled way.

Introduce the Chapter

Apply Biology

ASK STUDENTS: ***What provides the genetic information that instructs the cells to grow, divide, and survive?*** DNA Scientists have been studying DNA for decades to try to understand more about how humans and other organisms develop and respond to changes in their environment. The fly in the photo has had the gene for green fluorescent protein (GFP) inserted into its genome. Because of this protein, the fly glows green when exposed to UV light.

ASK STUDENTS: ***What are some potential uses for technology that allow a gene for a protein to be inserted into an organism?*** Answers will vary. Students might suggest new treatments/cures for diseases or tracking cells in experiments.

BIG Idea

Outline Have students outline the chapter by writing the Big Idea for the chapter and the Main Ideas for each section. Have students write new vocabulary terms in the appropriate section. Have students refer to previous chapters for terms that have been introduced earlier in the book. Under each Main Idea, tell students to write down at least three key points that summarize the section. Some students may benefit from receiving an outline that is partially completed. Other students may find it easier to select a few words from each paragraph and write a sentence using each of these words.

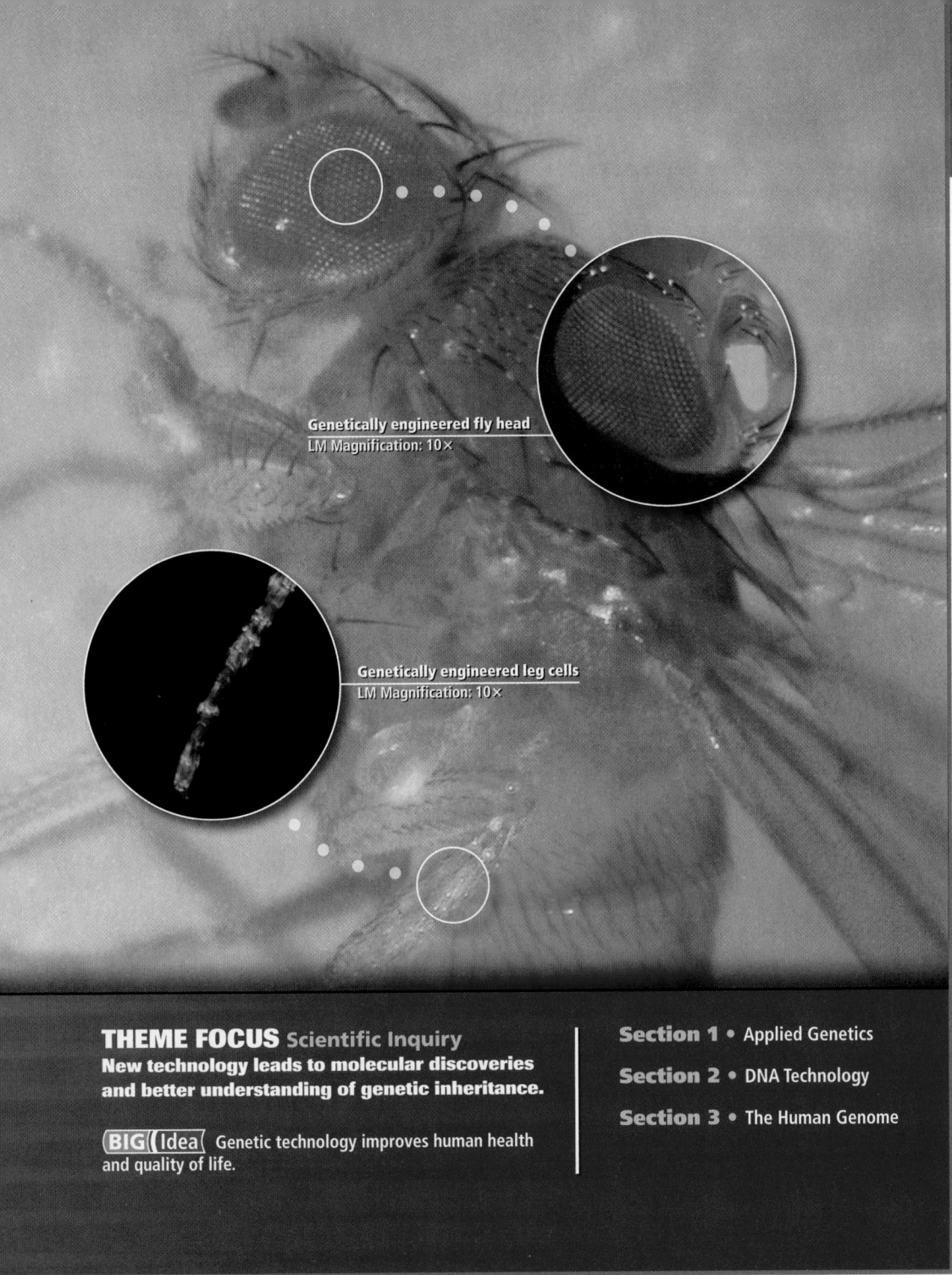

Section 1

MAIN Idea

BL OL AL

Produce Desired Traits Show students tomatoes of different sizes and shapes.

ASK STUDENTS: ***Why are there so many sizes and shapes of tomatoes?*** Different sizes and shapes are suited for different types of food. Remind students that most of the foods we eat are the result of genetic selection.

Reading Strategy

OL AL **Brainstorm** In small groups, have students think about what comes to mind when they read each new vocabulary term. Make a list of the ideas on the board and, after reading the section, compare the list on the board to the definitions in the text.

BL Read vocabulary and definitions aloud to struggling students before they begin the brainstorming exercise.

S Skill Practice

EL BL OL **Visual Literacy**

Point out the differences in the physical features of the dogs in Figure 1.

ASK STUDENTS: ***How do these traits relate to how humans use the dogs?*** Possible answers: strong muscles for pulling heavy loads, large ears that help in hearing.

Develop Concepts

BL OL AL

Activate Prior Knowledge

Review Gregor Mendel's laws of inheritance with students.

ASK STUDENTS: ***What does*** **heterozygous** ***mean?*** Two different alleles are present for a particular trait. ***What does*** **homozygous** ***mean?*** Two alleles for a particular trait are the same.

Section 1

Reading Preview

Essential Questions

- How is selective breeding used to produce organisms with desired traits?
- What are similarities and differences between inbreeding and hybridization?
- How does a Punnett square test cross help assess the genotypes of organisms?

Review Vocabulary

hybrid: organism that is heterozygous for a particular trait

New Vocabulary

selective breeding
inbreeding
test cross

g Multilingual eGlossary

Applied Genetics

MAIN Idea **Selective breeding is used to produce organisms with desired traits.**

Real-World Reading Link Coin collectors separate rare coins from all other coins because the rare ones are more valuable. Just as certain coins are selected for their value, certain plants and animals have been selected and bred to produce organisms with traits that are valuable to humans.

Selective Breeding

You might be familiar with different breeds of dogs, such as Saint Bernards, huskies, and German shepherds. Observe some of the phenotypic traits of these breeds in **Figure 1.** All three have strong, muscular bodies. Saint Bernards have traits such as a keen sense of smell that make them good rescue dogs. Huskies are endurance runners and pull sleds long distances. German shepherds are highly trainable for special services.

Since ancient times, humans have bred animals with certain traits to obtain offspring that have desired traits. As a result, these traits become more common. Breeding for desired traits is not restricted to animals alone. Plants also are bred to produce desired traits, such as larger fruits and shorter growing times. The process by which desired traits of certain plants and animals are selected and passed on to their future generations is called **selective breeding.** Through the processes of hybridization and inbreeding, desired traits can be passed on to future generations.

S

Saint Bernard
Rescue dog

Husky
Sled dog

German shepherd
Service dog

Figure 1 Dogs have traits that make them suited for different tasks: Saint Bernard—keen sense of smell; husky—endurance to run long distances; and German shepherd—high trainability.

Differentiated Instruction

Below Level Teachers can provide additional help on reading assignments to students who are working below level. Provide these students with a copy of the text in which important concepts or words are highlighted to help them identify essential information.

For more tips, see pages 14T–15T.

Demonstration

Analogy Bring chocolate bars, marshmallows, and graham crackers. Make s'mores. Explain how combining desired tastes from food items is analogous to the process by which breeders mate two organisms, each with a desirable trait, to produce offspring with both desired traits. Est. time: 15 min

Hybridization Recall that crossing parent organisms with different forms of a trait to produce offspring with specific traits results in hybrids. Farmers, animal breeders, scientists, and gardeners often use the production of hybrids, also known as hybridization. They select traits that will give hybrid organisms a competitive edge. These hybrid organisms can be bred to be more disease-resistant, to produce more offspring, or to grow faster. For example, plant breeders might choose to cross two different varieties of tomato plants in order to produce a hybrid that has both the disease resistance of one parent and the fast growth rate of the other parent.

Care must be taken to identify organisms with desired traits and successfully cross them to yield the right combination of traits from both parents. A disadvantage of hybridization is that it is time consuming and expensive. For example, it took rice breeders three decades to produce hybrid rice varieties that can produce higher yields than nonhybrid varieties. Because hybrids can be bred to be more nutritious, to have the ability to adapt to a wide range of changes in the environment, and to produce greater numbers of offspring, the advantages of hybridization sometimes outweigh the disadvantages.

D **Inbreeding** Once a breeder observes a desired trait in an organism, a process is needed to ensure that the trait is passed on to future generations. This process, in which two closely related organisms are bred to have the desired traits and to eliminate the undesired ones in future generations, is called **inbreeding.**

Pure breeds are maintained by inbreeding. Clydesdale horses, Angus cattle, and German shepherd dogs are all examples of organisms produced by inbreeding. You might have seen Clydesdale horses at parades and petting zoos. Horse breeders first bred the Clydesdale horse in Scotland hundreds of years ago for use as a farm horse. Because of their strong build, agility, and obedient nature, Clydesdales originally were inbred and used extensively for pulling heavy loads.

A disadvantage of inbreeding is that harmful recessive traits also can be passed on to future generations. Inbreeding increases the chance of homozygous recessive offspring. If both parents carry the recessive allele, the harmful trait likely will not be eliminated.

✓ **Reading Check** **Describe** the disadvantages associated with hybridization and inbreeding.

MiniLab 1

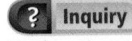

? Inquiry MiniLab

Model Hybridization

How are hybrid lilies produced? In this lab, you will examine techniques used by both professional plant breeders and amateur gardeners to produce the wide variety of lilies you might see growing in landscaped areas.

Procedure

1. Read and complete the lab safety form.
2. Obtain a **labeled drawing of a lily flower** and a **fresh open lily flower.** Examine the flower with a **hand lens** and identify the male anthers and the female pistil.
3. Use a **cotton swab** to gently rub an anther to pick up pollen.
4. Trade flowers with another lab group and, using the cotton swab, gently apply the pollen from your flower to the stigma of the pistil of the new flower.

Analysis

1. **Infer** When breeders hybridize lilies, they transfer pollen to the stigma of an unopened lily flower and then cover the stigma with a foil cap. Why do you think this would be necessary?
2. **Think Critically** A breeder produces a hybrid lily which then is allowed to grow and produce seeds naturally. When these seeds are planted, the new lily plants do not have the same characteristics as the hybrid parent. Hypothesize why this would occur.

? Inquiry Launch Lab

Review Based on what you have read about selective breeding, how would you now answer the analysis questions?

? Inquiry Launch Lab

Assess Content Development

Assess how understanding has developed when students revisit the Launch Lab analysis questions.

✓ **Reading Check** Hybridization can take long amounts of time and is expensive. Inbreeding can allow harmful recessive traits to appear more frequently.

GOING GREEN For the MiniLab, use faded flowers from a florist shop. Another source of free flower specimens is funeral homes after a funeral. Make sure the flowers you use in the MiniLab have obvious stamens and pistils.

D Develop Concepts

BL OL AL

Clarify a Misconception

ASK STUDENTS: ***Do pure breeds have a genetic advantage or disadvantage over mixed breeds?*** Students may have difficulty grasping why pure breeds may be at a disadvantage. Although pure breeds will reliably exhibit a desired trait, a population of pure breeds also lacks genetic diversity.

MiniLab 1

? Inquiry MiniLab

For a lab worksheet, use your eTeacherEdition Online.

✻RUBRIC A rubric for evaluating MiniLabs is found on your eTeacherEdition Online.

Est. Time 45 min

Additional Materials Visit the Internet to download drawings.

Safety Precaution Approve lab safety forms before work begins.

Teaching Strategy Ask members of a local gardening group to share their plant hybridization experiences with the class.

Analysis

1. These precautions ensure that no other pollen will come into contact with the lily, and, therefore, the breeder knows the genetic makeup of the offspring.
2. The hybrid lily is heterozygous and when it self-fertilizes, the resulting combinations will be heterozygous, homozygous dominant, and homozygous recessive. These genotypes will result in some phenotypes that are not like the hybrid lily.

LabManager™

Customize this lab with the LabManager™ CD-ROM.

Critical Thinking

BL OL Predict

ASK STUDENTS: ***Predict the appearances of different species of domesticated animals over generations. Assume they lived in different environments.*** Answers could include: change in the growth and thickness of hair to protect from cold weather or short, thin hair, and an increased number of pores on the body to release heat in a hot environment. Be sure students do not mistake seasonal/geographical changes in animal appearance with genetic changes/adaptations.

Writing Support

OL AL Persuasive Writing

Have students choose one purebred organism and write an essay discussing the advantages and disadvantages of purebred organisms. For example, have students explore the advantages and disadvantages of monoculture crops.

Formative Assessment

Evaluation Have students outline the differences between inbreeding and hybridization. Reinforce that these are types of selective breeding.

Remediation Have students review the section and make a chart to organize the characteristics of inbreeding and hybridization.

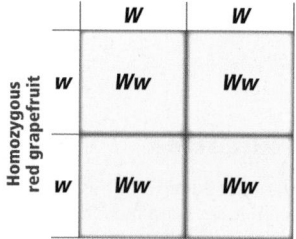

Homozygous white grapefruit

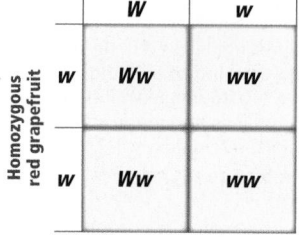

Homozygous red grapefruit	*W*	*W*
w	*Ww*	*Ww*
w	*Ww*	*Ww*

Heterozygous white grapefruit

Homozygous red grapefruit	*W*	*w*
w	*Ww*	*ww*
w	*Ww*	*ww*

■ **Figure 2** The genotype of a white grapefruit tree can be determined by the results of a test cross with a homozygous red grapefruit.

Test Cross

An important thing a breeder has to determine when producing a hybrid is the genotype of the hybrid. Once a breeder observes the desired trait, if the trait is dominant, then the genotype of the organism could be homozygous dominant or heterozygous. The exact genotype is determined by performing a test cross. A **test cross** involves breeding an organism that has the unknown genotype with one that is homozygous recessive for the desired trait. If the parent's genotype is homozygous dominant, all the offspring will have the dominant phenotype; if it is heterozygous, the offspring will show a 1:1 phenotypic ratio.

Performing a test cross Suppose a breeder wants to produce hybrid white grapefruits. In grapefruit trees, white fruit color is the dominant trait, while red is recessive. Therefore, the red grapefruit trees in the orchard must be homozygous recessive (*ww*). The genotype of the hybrid white grapefruit tree obtained by the breeder can be homozygous dominant (*WW*) or heterozygous (*Ww*) for the white color. Therefore, the breeder has to perform a test cross to determine the genotype of the white grapefruit tree. Remember when performing a cross, pollen from the flower of one plant is transferred to the female organ in a flower of another plant.

Results As shown in the top Punnett square in **Figure 2,** if the white grapefruit tree is homozygous dominant (*WW*) and is crossed with a red grapefruit tree (*ww*), then all the offspring will be heterozygous (*Ww*) and white in color. In this case, all of the offspring will have the dominant phenotype. However, as shown in the second Punnett square in **Figure 2,** if the white grapefruit tree is heterozygous (*Ww*), then half the number of offspring will be white and half will be red, and the phenotypic ratio will be 1:1. Review the results in the Punnett squares in **Figure 2.** If the white grapefruit tree is homozygous, all offspring will be heterozygous—white in color. If the tree is heterozygous, half of the test-cross offspring will be white and half will be red.

Section 1 Assessment

Section Summary

- Selective breeding is used to produce organisms with traits that are considered desirable.
- Hybridization produces organisms with desired traits from parent organisms with different traits.
- Inbreeding creates pure breeds.
- A test cross can be used to determine an organism's genotype.

Understand Main Ideas

1. MAIN Idea **Assess** the effect of selective breeding on food crops.
2. **Describe** three traits that might be desired in sheep. How can these traits be passed on to the next generation? Explain.
3. **Compare and contrast** inbreeding and hybridization.
4. **Predict** the phenotype of offspring from a test cross between a seedless orange (*ss*) and an orange with seeds (*Ss*).

Think Critically

5. **Evaluate** Should a cow and a bull that both carry recessive alleles for a mutation that causes decreased milk production be bred? Why or why not?

MATH in Biology

6. A breeder performs a test cross to determine the genotype of a black cat. He crosses the black cat (*BB* or *Bb*) with a white cat (*bb*). If 50 percent of the offspring are black, what is the genotype of the black cat?

Section 1 Assessment

1. Selective breeding can have positive effects on the production of food crops, including increasing production and quality with lower maintenance and fewer unusable crops. However, selective breeding is also expensive and time consuming.
2. Longer, denser hair, faster maturation to adulthood, increased lean mass; traits are passed on through hybridization or inbreeding.
3. Both inbreeding and hybridization are ways to get desired traits for an offspring. Inbreeding involves breeding closely related organisms that share the same desired trait, while hybridization involves breeding parents with different desired traits.
4. Half the oranges would have seeds and half would be seedless.
5. A cow and a bull that are closely related and are both homozygous recessive for an undesirable trait should not be inbred because the "bad" trait will be passed on to all offspring.
6. The genotype of the black cat is *Bb*.

Assessment Online Quiz

Reading Preview

Essential Questions

- What are the different tools and processes used in genetic engineering?
- How does genetic engineering manipulate recombinant DNA?
- What are the similarities between selective breeding and genetic engineering?
- How can genetic engineering and biotechnology be used to improve human life?

Review Vocabulary

DNA: the genetic material of all organisms, composed of two complementary chains of nucleotides wound in a double helix

New Vocabulary

genetic engineering
genome
restriction enzyme
gel electrophoresis
recombinant DNA
plasmid
DNA ligase
transformation
cloning
polymerase chain reaction
transgenic organism

Multilingual eGlossary

DNA Technology

MAIN Idea Researchers use genetic engineering to manipulate DNA.

Real-World Reading Link Have you seen a handmade patchwork quilt? Patchwork quilts are created by combining different pieces of fabric. Scientists use a similar process and combine DNA from different sources to create an organism with unique traits.

Genetic Engineering

By about 1970, researchers had discovered the structure of DNA and had determined the central dogma that information flowed from DNA to RNA and from RNA to proteins. However, scientists did not know much about the function of individual genes. Suppose your friend told you the final score of a high school football game but did not tell you how each player contributed to the game. Your curiosity about the details of the game is similar to the curiosity scientists experienced because they did not know how each gene contributed to a cell's function.

The situation changed when scientists began using **genetic engineering,** technology that involves manipulating the DNA of one organism in order to insert exogenous DNA (the DNA of another organism). For example, researchers have inserted a gene for a bioluminescent protein called green fluorescent protein (GFP) into various organisms. GFP, which is a substance naturally found in jellyfishes that live in the north Pacific Ocean, emits a green light when it is exposed to ultraviolet light. Organisms that have been genetically engineered to synthesize the DNA for GFP, such as the mosquito larvae shown in **Figure 3,** can be easily identified in the presence of ultraviolet light. The GFP DNA is attached to exogenous DNA to verify that the DNA has been inserted into the organism. These genetically engineered organisms are used in various processes, such as studying the expression of a particular gene, investigating cellular processes, studying the development of a certain disease, and selecting traits that might be beneficial to humans. D

Magnification: unavailable

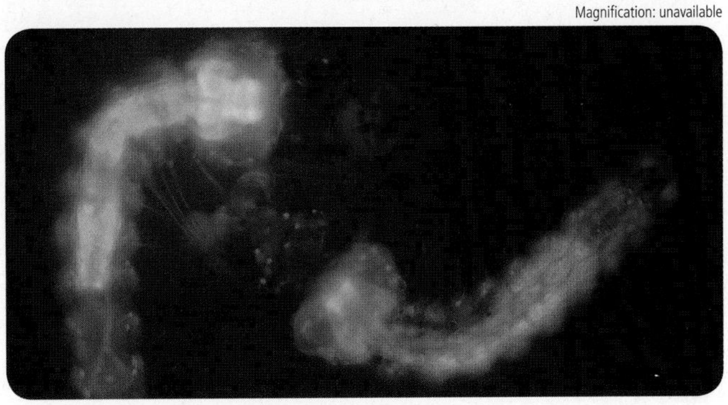

Genetically engineered mosquito larvae

Figure 3 The gene for green fluorescent protein (GFP) was introduced into mosquito larvae so that researchers could verify that exogenous DNA was inserted.
***Predict** how genetic engineering might be used in the future by the medical field.*

Caption Question Fig. 3 Possible answer: Genetic engineering could be used to eliminate genetic disorders.

Section 2

MAIN Idea

BL OL AL

Genetic Engineering

ASK STUDENTS: ***What comes to mind when you hear the term genetic engineering?*** Have one student serve as a scribe and write the answers on the board. If students need prompting, provide them with examples of genetically engineered organisms, such as Dolly the sheep, debates on human cloning, yeast cells that produce human insulin, and disease-resistant corn.

D Develop Concepts

OL Community Connection

Help students think about the impact of genetic engineering on their community.

ASK STUDENTS: ***Who benefits from genetic engineering?*** Possible answers: people who use medicines produced through genetic engineering or people who eat foods grown by farmers who use genetic engineering. ***What risks are associated with genetically engineered products?*** risks include drug-resistant diseases, loss of native organisms

BL Present struggling students with a specific example of using genetically engineered products, such as eating genetically modified corn versus eating selectively bred corn.

AL Have students working above level read ahead to the section about transgenic organisms. Have them think of an organism whose genes could be used to make a transgenic organism with helpful characteristics. Have students prepare an advertising brochure to promote their new hypothetical transgenic organism to a target audience.

Develop Concepts

OL Scaffolding

ASK STUDENTS: ***What is genetic engineering?*** technology that involves manipulating the DNA of one organism in order to insert the DNA of another organism ***How can genetic engineering be used?*** to produce plants and animals with desired traits ***What is an organism's genome?*** the total DNA present in the nucleus of each cell ***How can scientists study specific genes within an organism's genome?*** by using DNA tools to manipulate DNA and isolate genes from the rest of the genome

R Reading Strategy

BL OL AL

Content-Specific Words Ask a student to volunteer to use the term *restriction* in a sentence. (Restriction can mean limitation.) Ask another volunteer to read the boldfaced definition of restriction enzymes. Point out that some words used every day can have different scientific meanings.

AL Have students investigate the logic of the term *restriction enzymes.* They restrict the DNA of invading organisms from entering the host bacterium that produce the enzymes, and they are used to cleave DNA.

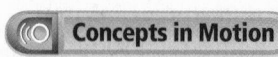

Concepts in Motion

Animation

S Skill Practice

BL OL Visual Literacy Have students use paper cutouts to model cuts made by restriction enzymes, similar to the one shown in Figure 4.

VOCABULARY

ACADEMIC VOCABULARY

Manipulate

to manage or utilize skillfully

Scientists use technology to manipulate genetic information in order to test scientific hypotheses.

DNA Tools

You have learned that selective breeding is used to produce plants and animals with desired traits. Genetic engineering can be used to increase or decrease the expression of specific genes in selected organisms. It has many applications from human health to agriculture.

An organism's **genome** is the total DNA present in the nucleus of each cell. As you will learn in the next section, genomes, such as the human genome, can contain millions and millions of nucleotides. In order to study a specific gene, DNA tools can be used to manipulate DNA and to isolate genes from the rest of the genome.

Restriction enzymes Some types of bacteria contain powerful defenses against viruses. These cells contain proteins called **restriction enzymes** that recognize and bind to specific DNA sequences and cleave the DNA within that sequence. A restriction enzyme, also called an endonuclease (en doh NEW klee ayz), cuts the viral DNA into fragments after it enters the bacteria. Since their discovery in the late 1960s, scientists have identified and isolated hundreds of restriction enzymes. Restriction enzymes are used as powerful tools for isolating specific genes or regions of the genome. When the restriction enzyme cleaves genomic DNA, it creates fragments of different sizes that are unique to every individual.

EcoRI One restriction enzyme that is used widely by scientists is known as *EcoR*I. As illustrated in **Figure 4,** *EcoR*I specifically cuts DNA containing the sequence GAATTC. The ends of the DNA fragments created by *EcoR*I are called sticky ends because they contain single-stranded DNA that is complementary. The ability of some restriction enzymes to create fragments with sticky ends is important because these sticky ends can be joined together with other DNA fragments that have complementary sticky ends.

Reading Check **Generalize** how restriction enzymes are used.

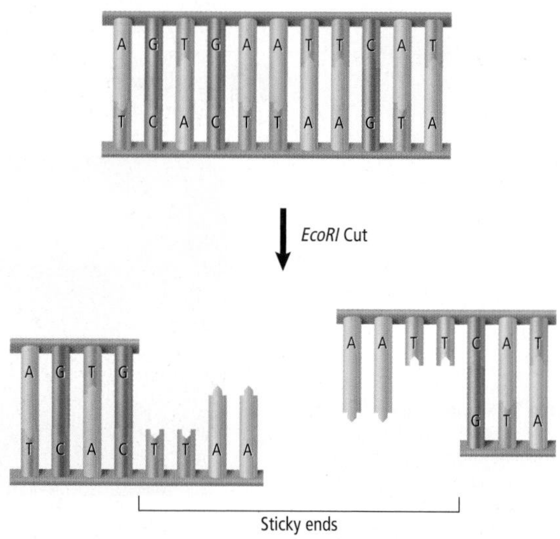

Figure 4 DNA containing the sequence GAATTC can be cut by the restriction enzyme *EcoR*I to produce sticky ends.

Concepts in Motion

Animation

Reading Check Restriction enzymes are used to isolate specific genes or regions of the genome.

Loading the gel Solution containing DNA is dropped into holes at one end of the gel with a pipette.

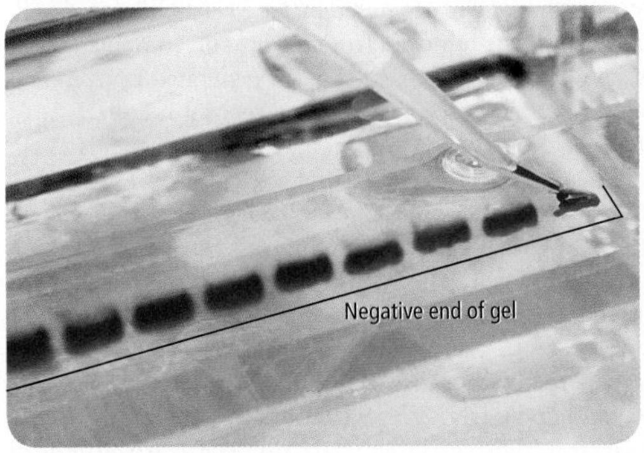

Fragment pattern A staining solution binds to the separated DNA fragments in the gel, making them visible under ultraviolet light.

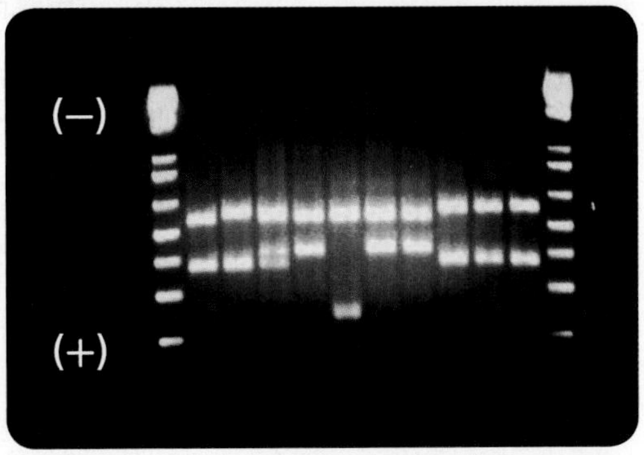

■ **Figure 5** When the loaded gel is placed in an electrophoresis tank and the electric current is turned on, the DNA fragments separate.

However, not all restriction enzymes create sticky ends. Some enzymes produce fragments containing blunt ends—created when the restriction enzyme cuts straight across both strands. Blunt ends do not have regions of single-stranded DNA and can join to any other DNA fragment with blunt ends.

Connection to Physics **Gel electrophoresis** An electric current is used to separate DNA fragments according to the size of the fragments in a process called **gel electrophoresis. Figure 5** shows how the DNA fragments are loaded on the negatively charged end of a gel. When an electric current is applied, the DNA fragments move toward the positive end of the gel. The smaller fragments move farther faster than the larger ones. The unique pattern created based on the size of the DNA fragment can be compared to known DNA fragments for identification. Also, portions of the gel containing each band can be removed for further study.

MiniLab 2

Model Restriction Enzymes

Inquiry MiniLab

How are sticky ends modeled? Use scissors and tape to produce paper DNA fragments with sticky ends and a recombinant DNA plasmid.

Procedure

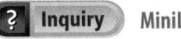

1. Read and complete the lab safety form.
2. Obtain one **straight paper DNA sequence** from your teacher, which will represent genomic DNA, and one **circular paper DNA sequence,** which will represent a plasmid.
3. Find each GAATTC sequence recognized by the restriction enzyme *EcoRI* and cleave the genome and plasmid DNA using **scissors**.
4. Use **tape** to make a recombinant DNA plasmid.

Analysis

1. **Compare** your plasmid to those made by other lab groups. How many different recombinant plasmids could be made using this particular genomic sequence? Explain.
2. **Infer** what enzyme was represented by the scissors. Explain.

Demonstration

Separation Use magnets to illustrate why DNA (being negatively charged) migrates toward the positive end during gel electrophoresis. Use a sifter to separate particles (sand, gravel, etc.) of different sizes, and explain to students that agarose gels contain tiny pores, like the holes in the sifter, that allow molecules of different sizes to be separated. Est. time: 10 min

MiniLab 2

Inquiry MiniLab

For a lab worksheet, use your eTeacherEdition Online.

RUBRIC A rubric for evaluating MiniLabs is found on your eTeacherEdition Online.

Est. Time 20 min

Teaching Strategies

- To make the straight paper DNA sequence, cut a strip of colored paper and write a base pair sequence along the sides. Make the ends “sticky” by using the GAATTC sequence shown in Figure 4.
- To make the circular paper DNA sequence, cut a strip of colored paper (use a different color) and write a base pair sequence along the sides. Include at least one site with the GATTC sequence. Tape the ends of the circular paper DNA sequence to form a circle with the base sequence showing on the outside.
- Use scissors to model a restriction enzyme, and cut the circular paper DNA to form sticky ends. Insert the straight paper DNA, and attach all the pieces together with tape to form the recombinant DNA plasmid.

Analysis

1. Answers will depend on how many places the circular DNA was cut. If the circular DNA had 3 cuts, there could be two plasmids that result.
2. The scissors represented the restriction enzyme EcoRI because they cut the DNA regions containing GAATTC.

LabManager™

Customize this lab with the LabManager™ CD-ROM.

R Reading Strategy

EL BL Directed Reading

Before reading the text under the heading *Recombinant DNA Technology,* have students create a chart with columns titled *What I know now, What I think I'll learn,* and *What I learned.* Have students preview the text and fill out the first two columns. Have students fill out the third column, paying close attention to the new vocabulary terms. After the students read the text, have them fill out the fourth column.

Writing Support

BL OL Technical Writing

Have students prepare a laboratory manual for studying DNA. In the manual students should describe how DNA is studied and provide step-by-step instructions for preparing recombinant DNA.

AL Have students compare and contrast restriction enzymes and DNA ligase. Restriction enzymes cut strands at specific locations, and ligase reforms the bond between nucleotides but is not sequence-specific. Both are found naturally in various organisms and have been utilized in biotechnology applications.

R Recombinant DNA Technology

When DNA fragments have been separated by gel electrophoresis, fragments of a specific size can be removed from the gel and combined with DNA fragments from another source. This newly generated DNA molecule, with DNA from different sources, is called **recombinant DNA.** Recombinant DNA technology has revolutionized the way scientists study DNA because it enables individual genes to be studied.

Large quantities of recombinant DNA molecules are needed in order to study them. A carrier, called a vector, transfers the recombinant DNA into a bacterial cell called the host cell. Plasmids and viruses are commonly used vectors. **Plasmids**—small, circular, double-stranded DNA molecules that occur naturally in bacteria and yeast cells—can be used as vectors because they can be cut with restriction enzymes. If a plasmid and a DNA fragment obtained from another genome have been cleaved by the same restriction enzyme, the ends of each DNA fragment will be complementary and can be combined, as shown in **Figure 6.** An enzyme normally used by cells in DNA repair and replication, called **DNA ligase,** joins the two DNA fragments chemically. Ligase joins DNA fragments that have sticky ends as well as those that have blunt ends.

Examine **Figure 6** again. Notice that the resulting circular DNA molecule contains the plasmid DNA and the DNA fragment isolated from another genome. This recombinant plasmid DNA molecule now can be inserted into a host cell so that large quantities of this type of recombinant DNA can be made.

Reading Check **Relate** restriction enzymes to recombinant DNA.

Figure 6 Recombinant DNA is created by joining together DNA from two different sources.

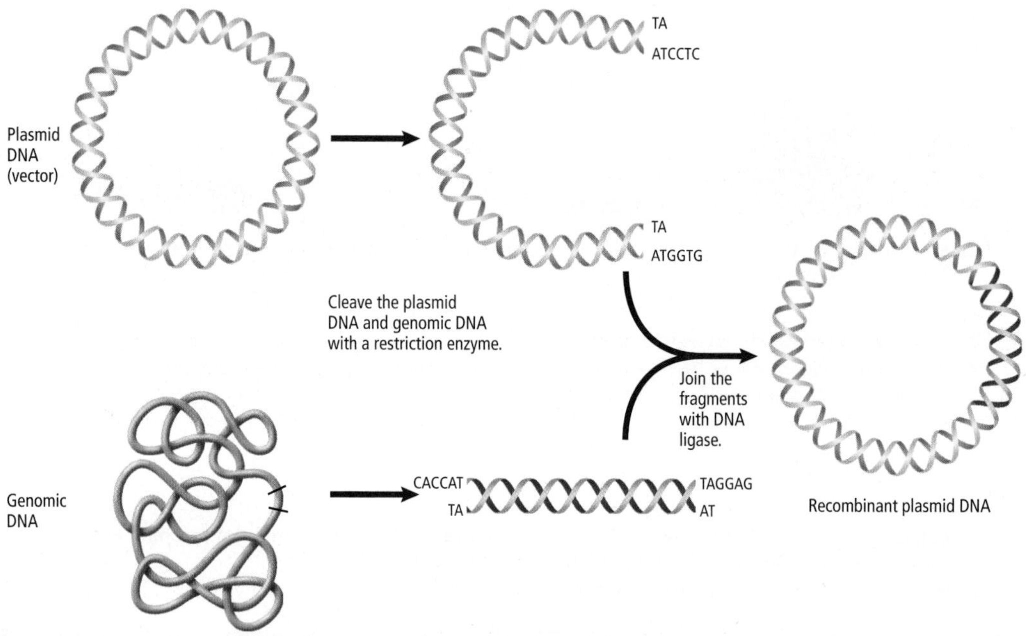

Reading Check Restriction enzymes cut DNA into fragments. Some of these fragments are then combined to make recombinant DNA.

Research Citation

Write Educational research indicates that students benefit when asked to write in a variety of styles. For example, the technical writing assignment described on this page will help students to develop language skills and become engaged with the material.

(Carrasquillo and Rodriguez, 1996)

Research bibliography on pages 32T–34T

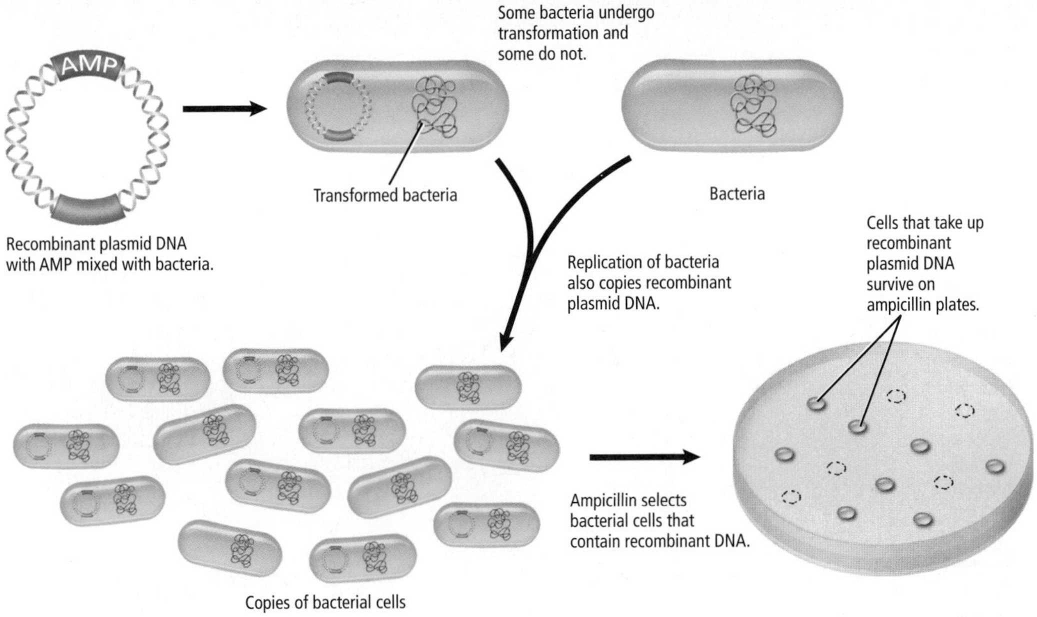

Some bacteria undergo transformation and some do not.
AMP
AMP
Transformed bacteria
Bacteria
Recombinant plasmid DNA with AMP mixed with bacteria.
Replication of bacteria also copies recombinant plasmid DNA.
Cells that take up recombinant plasmid DNA survive on ampicillin plates.
Ampicillin selects bacterial cells that contain recombinant DNA.
Copies of bacterial cells

■ **Figure 7** Clones containing copies of the recombinant DNA can be identified and used for further study when the bacterial cells that do not contain recombinant DNA die.

Gene cloning To make a large quantity of recombinant plasmid DNA, bacterial cells are mixed with recombinant plasmid DNA. Some of the bacterial cells take up the recombinant plasmid DNA through a process called **transformation,** as shown in **Figure 7.** Bacterial cells can be transformed using electric pulsation or heat. Recall that all cells, including bacterial cells, have plasma membranes. A short electric pulse or a brief rise in temperature temporarily creates openings in the plasma membrane of the bacteria. These temporary openings allow small molecules, such as the recombinant plasmid DNA, to enter the bacterial cell. The bacterial cells make copies of the recombinant plasmid DNA during cell replication. Large numbers of identical bacteria, each containing the inserted DNA molecules, can be produced through this process called **cloning.**

Recombinant plasmid DNA contains a gene that codes for resistance to an antibiotic such as ampicillin (AMP). Researchers use this gene to distinguish between bacterial cells that have taken up the recombinant plasmid DNA and those that have not. Notice in **Figure 7** that when the transformed bacterial cells are exposed to the specific antibiotic, only the bacterial cells that have the plasmid survive.

DNA sequencing The sequence of the DNA nucleotides of most organisms is unknown. Knowing the sequence of an organism's DNA or of a cloned DNA fragment provides scientists with valuable information for further study. The sequence of a gene can be used to predict the function of the gene, to compare genes with similar sequences from other organisms, and to identify mutations or errors in the DNA sequence. Because the genomes of most organisms are made up of millions of nucleotides, the DNA molecules used for sequencing reactions first must be cut into smaller fragments using restriction enzymes.

VOCABULARY

SCIENCE USAGE V. COMMON USAGE

Transformation

Science usage: process by which one type of bacterium takes up the DNA from another source

Transformation of bacteria involves the uptake of plasmid DNA.

Common usage: the act of change

The transformation of the room was complete with the addition of new drapes.

FOLDABLES®

✱RUBRIC A rubric for evaluating Foldables is found on your eTeacherEdition Online.

Going Further

SAY TO STUDENTS: ***On the back of your three-tab Foldable, label and record what you recall about transgenic animals, transgenic plants, and transgenic bacteria. Determine the pros and cons of developing transgenic organisms.***

Develop Concepts

Clarify a Misconception

BL OL ASK STUDENTS: ***Where might you find bacteria?*** almost anywhere Students may not realize that bacteria are all around us. Explain to students that bacteria present in the environment usually are not visible to the unaided eye because the populations of these microbes are not concentrated enough to be seen.

AL To help students visualize bacterial colonies, have students prepare several agar plates. Have students swab classroom surfaces and their hands. Then have them apply the swab to the agar plates. Leave one uninoculated plate exposed to classroom air for several hours. Seal the plates with masking tape and incubate them for a few days to determine the extent of growth. Have students identify the bacterial colonies on the plates.

Content Background

Teacher FYI Biotechnology companies sell plasmids that allow researchers to create recombinant DNA molecules with special properties. For example, plasmids can contain genes for fluorescent proteins (green, yellow, red, etc). Plasmids can contain genes for enzymes that allow for activation of a specific function, and they also can contain "tags" that allow the protein translated from the recombinant DNA molecule to be purified.

Reading Strategy

OL AL COOP LEARN

Reading Circles Organize students into groups of five. Assign each student in the group one of the following roles: discussion director, passage master, connector, illustrator, and summarizer. You may wish to model the roles. Have each student perform his or her assigned role as the group members read aloud the passage under the heading *Polymerase chain reaction.* The discussion director will read the section aloud. The passage master will define the vocabulary term *polymerase chain reaction.* The connector will help explain why this process fits into this section. The illustrator will provide an analogy from everyday life for the term *polymerase chain reaction.* The summarizer will restate important concepts in the section.

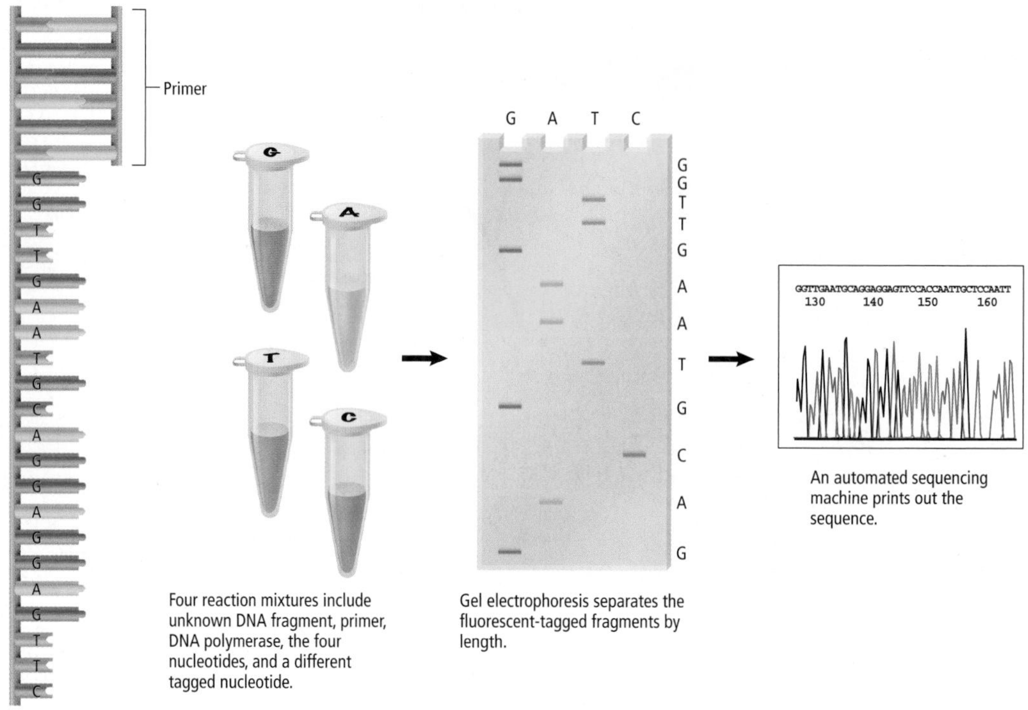

■ **Figure 8** DNA can be sequenced using fluorescent-tagged nucleotides.
Describe *how the sequence of the original DNA template is determined.*

Follow **Figure 8** to understand how DNA is sequenced. Scientists mix an unknown DNA fragment, DNA polymerase, and the four nucleotides—A, C, G, T—in a tube. A small amount of each nucleotide is tagged with a different color of fluorescent dye, which also modifies the structure of the nucleotide. Every time a modified fluorescent-tagged nucleotide is incorporated into the newly synthesized strand, the reaction stops. This produces DNA strands of different lengths. The sequencing reaction is complete when the tagged DNA fragments are separated by gel electrophoresis. The gel is then analyzed in an automated DNA sequencing machine that detects the color of each tagged nucleotide. The sequence of the original DNA template is determined from the order of the tagged fragments.

R

Polymerase chain reaction Once the sequence of a DNA fragment is known, a technique called the **polymerase chain reaction** (PCR) can be used to make millions of copies of a specific region of a DNA fragment. PCR is extremely sensitive and can detect a single DNA molecule in a sample. PCR is useful because this single DNA molecule then can be copied, or amplified, numerous times to be used for DNA analysis. Follow **Figure 9** as you read about the steps of PCR.

Step 1 PCR is performed by placing the DNA fragment to be copied, DNA polymerase, the four DNA nucleotides, and two short single-stranded pieces of DNA called primers in a tube. The primers are complementary to the ends of the DNA fragment that will be copied and used as starting points for DNA synthesis. PCR begins when the tube is heated.

■ **Caption Question Fig. 8** Scientists mix an unknown DNA fragment, DNA polymerase, and the four nucleotides in four tubes. In each tube, a small amount of a different nucleotide is added. These nucleotides are tagged with fluorescent dye that changes the structure of the nucleotide. The reaction stops when the modified nucleotide binds to the strand. This produces strands of different lengths. Gel electrophoresis separates the strands, and a sequencing machine detects the color of the tagged fragments and determines the sequence of the strand.

Inquiry BioLab

The lab at the end of the chapter can be used at this point in the lesson.

Step 2 The heat separates the two strands of the template DNA fragment. When the tube is cooled, the primers can bind to each strand of the template DNA. An automated machine called a thermocycler is used to cycle the tube containing all of the components involved in PCR through various hot and cool temperatures.

Step 3 As shown in **Figure 9,** each primer is made to bind to one strand of the DNA fragment. Once the primers are bound, DNA polymerase incorporates the correct nucleotides between the two primers as in DNA replication. This process of heating, cooling, and nucleotide incorporation is repeated 20 to 40 times, resulting in millions of copies of the original fragment. Because the separation of DNA strands requires heat, the DNA polymerase used in PCR has to be able to withstand high temperatures. This special DNA polymerase was isolated from a thermophilic, or heat-loving, bacterium such as those found living in the hot springs of Yellowstone National Park.

R S Because PCR can detect a single DNA molecule in a sample, it has become one of the most powerful tools used by scientists. PCR is not used only by researchers in laboratories, but also by forensic scientists to identify suspects and victims in crime investigations, and by doctors to detect infectious diseases, such as AIDS.

Reading Check **Describe** the polymerase chain reaction using an analogy.

Figure 9 PCR is a biological version of a copy machine. During each PCR cycle, the reaction mixture is heated to separate the DNA strands and then cooled to allow primers to bind to complementary sequences. The DNA polymerase then adds nucleotides to form new DNA molecules.

Concepts in Motion
Animation

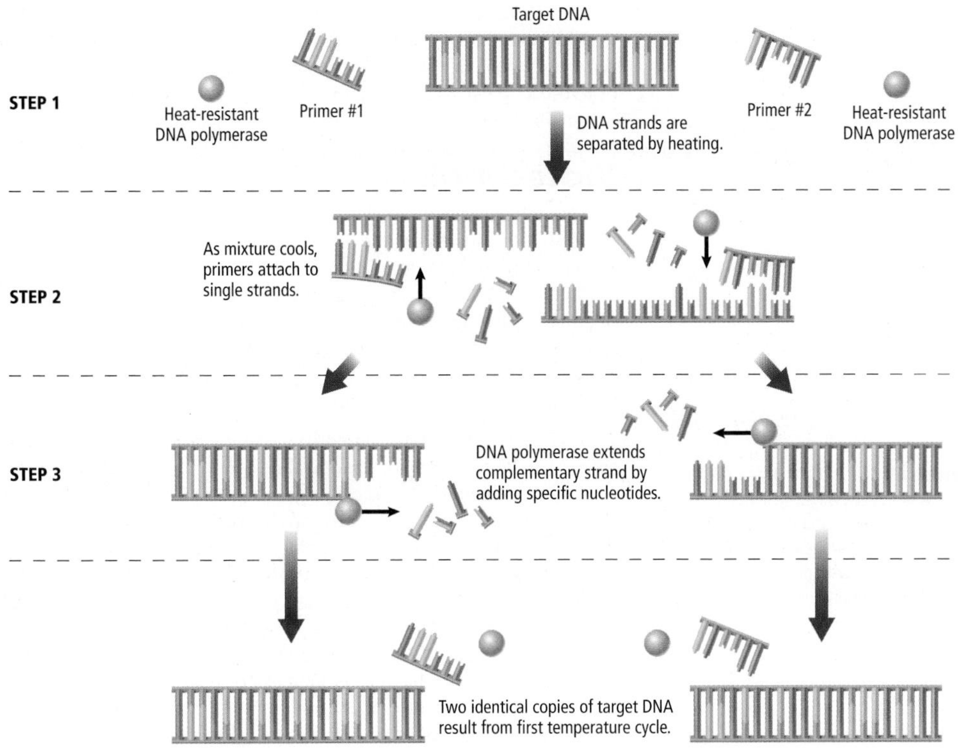

Target DNA
STEP 1
Heat-resistant DNA polymerase
Primer #1
Primer #2
Heat-resistant DNA polymerase
DNA strands are separated by heating.
STEP 2
As mixture cools, primers attach to single strands.
STEP 3
DNA polymerase extends complementary strand by adding specific nucleotides.
Two identical copies of target DNA result from first temperature cycle.

Reading Check Answers will vary. Students' answers might include an analogy of a photocopying machine. Using a single molecule of DNA, the polymerase chain reaction creates multiple copies. Remind students that no analogy is perfect.

R Reading Strategy

EL BL OL Illustrate After reading, have students create an illustration of DNA molecules undergoing the three stages of the polymerase chain reaction. Illustrations should include: separation of the strands of the DNA template, annealing (binding) of a primer to the single-stranded DNA template, extension of the DNA template, and the insertion of the correct nucleotides based on the sequence of the template DNA.

AL Tell students that it is common to perform 30 rounds of PCR in a lab. Ask them to predict the number of fragments that would be produced after performing 30 rounds of PCR. 1.07×10^9

S Skill Practice

OL Make a Graph Have students plot a graph showing the number of new DNA molecules created with every cycle of the polymerase chain reaction. Graphs should have cycles on the x-axis and the number of DNA molecules (starting with 1) on the y-axis. Graphs should show exponential increase in DNA molecules as cycle number increases: 1st cycle = 1 DNA molecule, 2nd cycle = 2, 3rd cycle = 4, 4th cycle = 8, 5th cycle = 16, etc.

BL Have students work in pairs and provide the pairs with labeled graphs.

Concepts in Motion
Animation

Concepts in Motion
Interactive Table

S Skill Practice

BL OL Visual Literacy Have students make flashcards that contain the information from Table 1. Have students quiz each other using the flashcards. Then have students select two flashcards at a time and explain how the two cards are related. For example, using restriction enzymes in DNA polymerase chain reaction is a form of gene cloning.

R Reading Strategy

OL Discussion Groups
After reading the text under the heading *Biotechnology,* have students debate the scientific advantages and scientific disadvantages of genetic engineering. Remind students to focus on the science—not the emotions— associated with the issue.
AL Have students conduct research to support the advantages and disadvantages the class discusses.

D Develop Concepts

OL Community Connection
Have students use the school library resources to research transgenic peanuts and soybeans. Discuss the implications of producing plants that lack certain genes or have extra copies of them.

Table 1 **Genetic Engineering** Concepts in Motion Interactive Table

Tool/Process	Function	Applications
Restriction enzymes Ex: *EcoRI*	Cut DNA strands into fragments	Used to create DNA fragments with sticky ends or blunt ends that can join with other DNA fragments
Gel electrophoresis	Separates DNA fragments by size	Used to study DNA fragments of various sizes
Recombinant DNA technology	Combines a DNA fragment with DNA from another source (exogenous DNA)	Used to create recombinant DNA to be used to study individual genes and genetically engineered organisms, and in the treatment of certain diseases
Gene cloning	Produces large numbers of identical recombinant DNA molecules	Used to create large amounts of recombinant DNA to be used in genetically engineered organisms
DNA sequencing	Identifies the DNA sequence of cloned recombinant DNA molecules for further study	Used to identify errors in the DNA sequence, to predict the function of a particular gene, and to compare to other genes with similar sequences from different organisms
Polymerase chain reaction (PCR)	Makes copies of specific regions of sequenced DNA	Used to copy DNA for any scientific investigation, including forensic analysis and medical testing

S

Genetic engineering uses powerful tools, summarized in **Table 1,** to study and manipulate DNA. Although researchers investigate many different problems, their experimental procedures often include cleavage by a restriction enzyme, isolation of fragments, combination with exogenous DNA, cloning or PCR, and identification of sequences.

Biotechnology

Biotechnology—the use of genetic engineering to find solutions to problems—makes it possible to produce organisms that contain individual genes from another organism. Recall that organisms such as the mosquito larvae shown in **Figure 3** have a gene from another organism. Such organisms, genetically engineered by inserting a gene from another organism, are called **transgenic organisms.** Transgenic animals, plants, and bacteria are used not only for research, but also for medical and agricultural purposes. R

Transgenic animals Currently, scientists produce most transgenic animals in laboratories for biological research. Mice, fruit flies, and the roundworm *Caenorhabditis elegans,* also called *C. elegans,* are widely used in research laboratories around the world to study diseases and develop ways to treat them. Some transgenic organisms, such as transgenic livestock, have been produced to improve the food supply and human health. Transgenic goats have been engineered to secrete a protein called antithrombin III, which is used to prevent human blood from forming clots during surgery. Researchers are working to produce transgenic chickens and turkeys that are resistant to diseases. Several species of fishes also have been genetically engineered to grow faster. In the future, transgenic organisms might be used as a source of organs for organ transplants. D

CAREERS IN BIOLOGY

Geneticist Using many of the DNA tools, a geneticist might research genes, inheritance, and the variations of organisms. Some geneticists are medical doctors who diagnose and treat genetic conditions.

Differentiated Instruction

Above Level The community connection activity on this page will allow gifted students to make valuable connections between their learning and real-world applications. They will benefit from using a variety of resources, and they should be taught the value of using all available resources.

For more tips, see pages 14T–15T.

■ **Figure 10** This researcher is examining cotton plant leaves. The leaf on the left has been genetically engineered to resist insect infestation.

Transgenic plants Many species of plants have been genetically engineered to be more resistant to insect or viral pests. In 2006, about 69.9 million hectares grown by 7 million farmers in 18 countries were planted with transgenic crops. These crops included herbicide- and insecticide-resistant soybeans, corn, cotton, and canola. Scientists now are producing genetically engineered cotton, as shown in **Figure 10,** that resists insect infestation of the bolls. Researchers also are developing peanuts and soybeans that do not cause allergic reactions.

Other crops are being grown commercially and being field-tested. These crops include sweet-potato plants that are resistant to a virus that could kill most of the African harvest, rice plants with increased iron and vitamins that could decrease malnutrition in Asian countries, and a variety of plants able to survive extreme weather conditions. Prospective crops include bananas that produce vaccines for infectious diseases, such as hepatitis B, and plants that produce biodegradable plastics.

Transgenic bacteria Insulin, growth hormones, and substances that dissolve blood clots are made by transgenic bacteria. Transgenic bacteria also slow the formation of ice crystals on crops to protect them from frost damage, clean up oil spills more efficiently, and decompose garbage.

Section 2 Assessment

Section Summary

- Genetic engineering is used to produce organisms that are useful to humans.
- Recombinant DNA technology is used to study individual genes.
- DNA fragments can be separated using gel electrophoresis.
- Clones can be produced by transforming bacteria with recombinant DNA.
- The polymerase chain reaction is used to make copies of small DNA sequences.
- Transgenic organisms are being created to increase the quality of human life.

Understand Main Ideas

1. MAIN Idea **Sequence** how recombinant DNA is made and manipulated.
2. **Explain** why some plasmids contain a gene for resistance to an antibiotic.
3. **Describe** how genetic engineering can improve human health.
4. **Contrast** one major difference between selective breeding and genetic engineering.

Think Critically

5. **Evaluate** Several popular movies and books involve mutated organisms. Are these transgenic organisms a possibility? Why or why not?

WRITING in **Biology**

6. Why would a business synthesize and sell DNA? Who would their customers be? Write a list of possible uses for DNA that is synthesized in a laboratory.

Formative Assessment

Evaluation

ASK STUDENTS: ***How can a gene in a mouse genome be used to create recombinant DNA for use in experiments?*** Isolate DNA from the mouse and digest it into manageable pieces. Use PCR to amplify the gene and ligate it into a plasmid. Transform bacteria with the recombinant DNA to create enough of the DNA to use in experiments. Have students relate all of the steps involved in the creation of recombinant DNA.

Remediation Make four simple paper models of DNA molecules, two with blunt ends and two with sticky ends. The sticky ends should join like pieces of a jigsaw puzzle. Use the models to reinforce that DNA molecules with sticky ends and molecules with blunt ends join differently.

ASK STUDENTS: ***Why do DNA molecules with sticky ends combine differently than molecules with blunt ends?*** Because sticky ends create jigsaw puzzle-like patterns that can only be combined with another molecule in a limited number of ways.

Section 2 Assessment

1. Genomic DNA is broken up using restriction enzymes. Desired DNA fragments are isolated. The fragment is inserted into a plasmid (a vector) using DNA ligase. The plasmid with the desired fragment is inserted into a host cell so that many copies can be made.
2. Plasmids contain antibiotic resistance genes to select which bacteria cells were successfully transformed with the plasmid.
3. by making medicines more widely available or by reducing the need for pesticides
4. Genetic engineering directly inserts DNA from one organism into another, whereas selective breeding influences an organism's genome through breeding.
5. Answers should reference a specific movie and show knowledge of transgenic organisms and the pace at which biotechnology is advancing.
6. A company might synthesize DNA that covers up a defective gene in an individual's genome and sell it to companies and people who use pharmaceuticals. Synthesized DNA might be used in agriculture, pesticides, medicines, or cosmetics, too.

Section 3

MAIN Idea

BL OL AL The Human Genome

ASK STUDENTS: ***What impact does knowing the sequence of the human genome have on human health?*** Answers may include the ability to treat many diseases, such as cancer, once the defective genes are identified. Knowing which genes are implicated in breast cancer or diabetes might lead to an earlier treatment or cure for those diseases. Respect student privacy by avoiding direct questions about personal health situations, including questions about health insurance.

R Reading Strategy

EL BL OL

Active Comprehension Have a student volunteer read aloud the first paragraph under the heading *The Human Genome Project.* **ASK STUDENTS:** ***What more would you like to know about the Human Genome Project?*** List questions that students ask on the board. Tell students to keep these questions in mind when reading the section. After students finish reading, review the questions and determine if they were answered in the text.

S Skill Practice

OL AL Take Notes Have students take notes on key characteristics of the human genome and think about the number of nucleotides and the difference between noncoding and coding regions. Afterward, lead a discussion about coding and noncoding regions, and have students share their thoughts. **BL** Give struggling students guided notes.

Section 3

Reading Preview

Essential Questions

- What are the components of the human genome?
- How do forensic scientists use DNA fingerprinting?
- How can information from the human genome be used to treat human diseases?

Review Vocabulary

codon: the triplet of bases in the DNA or mRNA

New Vocabulary

DNA fingerprinting
bioinformatics
DNA microarray
single nucleotide polymorphism
haplotype
pharmacogenomics
gene therapy
genomics
proteomics

g Multilingual eGlossary

The Human Genome

MAIN Idea Genomes contain all of the information needed for an organism to grow and survive.

Real-World Reading Link When you put together a jigsaw puzzle, you might first find all the border pieces and then fill in the other pieces. Sequencing the human genome can be compared to putting together a jigsaw puzzle. Just as you have to figure out which puzzle pieces fit together, scientists had to determine the sequence of the base pairs along the length of a human chromosome.

R The Human Genome Project

S The Human Genome Project (HGP) was an international project that was completed in 2003. A genome is the complete genetic information in a cell. The goal of the HGP was to determine the sequence of the approximately three billion nucleotides that make up human DNA and to identify all of the human genes. If all the nucleotides in the human genome were the size of the type on this page and fused together in one continuous line, the line would extend from Los Angeles, California, to Panama, as illustrated in **Figure 11.**

Though the HGP is finished, analysis of the data generated from this project will continue for many decades. To complete this huge task, researchers also have studied the genomes of several other organisms, including the fruit fly, the mouse, and *Escherichia coli*—the bacterium present in the human intestines. Studies in nonhuman organisms help to develop the technology required to handle the large amounts of data produced by the Human Genome Project. These technologies help to interpret the function of newly identified human genes.

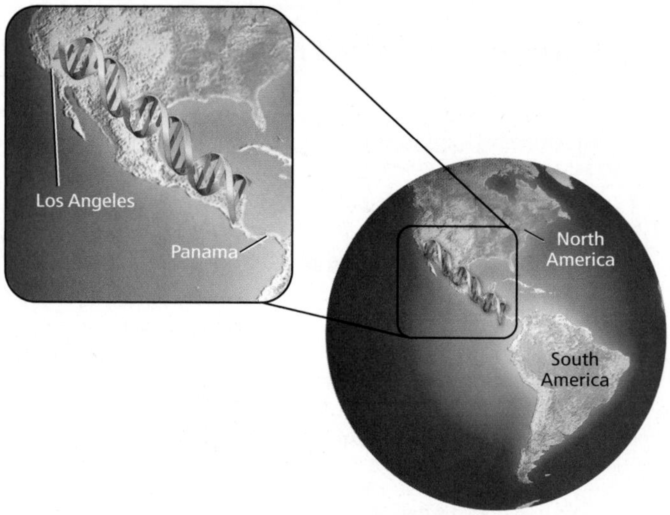

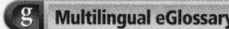

Figure 11 If all the DNA in the human genome were fused together in one continuous line, it would stretch from California to Panama.

Demonstration

Size and Scale To demonstrate the size of the human genome, bring a pin and a book to class. Explain that the human genome is approximately the size of the book, but that a cell is smaller than the tip of the pin. Encourage students to think of ways that all the information can fit into such a small area. Est. time: 5 min

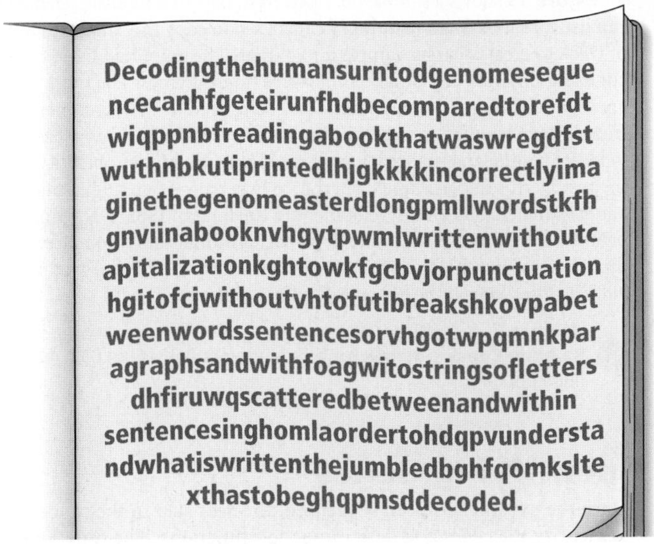
Decodingthehumansurntodgenomeseque
ncecanhfgeteirunfhdbecomparedtorefdt
wiqppnbfreadingabookthatwaswregdfst
wuthnbkutiprintedlhjgkkkkincorrectlyima
ginethegenomeasterdlongpmllwordstkfh
gnviinabooknvhgytpwmlwrittenwithoutc
apitalizationkghtowkfgcbvjorpunctuation
hgitofcjwithoutvhtofutibreakshkovpabet
weenwordssentencesorvhgotwpqmnkpar
agraphsandwithfoagwitostringsofletters
dhfiruwqscatteredbetweenandwithin
sentencesinghomlaordertohdqpvundersta
ndwhatiswrittenthejumbledbghfqomkslte
xthastobeghqpmsddecoded.

■ **Figure 12** The genetic information contained within the human genome has to be decoded in order to uncover important sequences.
Interpret *the text by decoding the jumbled sentences.*

Sequencing the genome Human DNA is organized into 46 chromosomes. In order to determine one continuous human genome sequence, each of the 46 human chromosomes was cleaved. Several different restriction enzymes were used in order to produce fragments with overlapping sequences. These fragments were combined with vectors to create recombinant DNA, cloned to make many copies, and sequenced using automated sequencing machines. Computers analyzed the overlapping regions to generate one continuous sequence.

Decoding the sequence of the human genome can be compared to reading a book that was printed in code. Imagine the genome as words in a book written without capitalization, punctuation, or breaks between words, sentences, or paragraphs. Suppose there are strings of letters scattered between and within sentences. **Figure 12** illustrates how a page from such a book might look. In order to understand what is written, you have to decode the jumbled text. Similarly, scientists had to decode the genetic code in the human genome.

After sequencing the entire human genome, scientists observed that less than two percent of all of the nucleotides in the human genome code for all the proteins in the body. That is, the genome is filled with long stretches of repeated sequences that have no direct function. These regions are called noncoding sequences.

DNA fingerprinting Unlike the protein-coding regions of DNA that are almost identical among individuals, the long stretches of noncoding regions of DNA are unique to each individual. When these regions are cut by restriction enzymes, as described earlier in this chapter, the set of DNA fragments produced is unique to every individual. **DNA fingerprinting** involves separating these DNA fragments using gel electrophoresis in order to observe the distinct banding patterns that are unique to every individual. Forensic scientists use DNA fingerprinting to identify suspects and victims in criminal cases, to determine paternity, and to identify soldiers killed in war.

VOCABULARY
ACADEMIC VOCABULARY
Sequence (SEE kwens)
a continuous series
The sequence of colors formed a beautiful pattern.

W

Inquiry Virtual Lab

CAREERS IN BIOLOGY

Forensic Scientist Genetic engineering is a technology used widely by forensic scientists. They use the various tools and processes, such as DNA fingerprinting, in criminal and archaeological investigations.

Develop Concepts
BL OL

Clarify A Misconception
ASK STUDENTS: ***How are the roles of DNA and RNA different?*** Students might confuse the roles of the two. DNA is a storehouse for genetic information, but that information has to be transmitted by a messenger (RNA).

W Writing Support
OL Creative Writing Have students write a sentence or paragraph that is jumbled and has to be decoded to be understood.
BL Cut up the paragraphs of a short story, and have students put the paragraphs back in order.

Critical Thinking
OL AL Infer Students should know that proteins are made of amino acids and that proteins are translated using messenger RNA as a template. Remind students what a codon is.
ASK STUDENTS: ***How many nucleotides comprise a codon?*** 3 ***What would happen if a nucleotide was skipped when mRNA is transcribed?*** The codons would be different, and this would lead to different amino acids and perhaps a different protein. Remind students about the importance of codons in decoding the genetic information contained in DNA.

■ **Caption Question Fig. 12** Students should find the following text embedded in the figure: *Decoding the human genome can be compared to reading a book that was printed incorrectly. Imagine the genome as words in a book written without capitalization or punctuation, without breaks between words, sentences, or paragraphs, and with strings of letters scattered between and within sentences. In order to understand what is written, the jumbled text has to be decoded.*

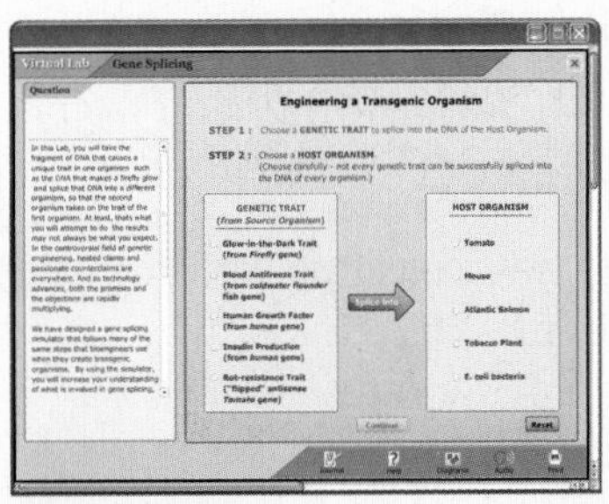

Inquiry Virtual Lab In this lab, students will explore the unique traits carried by fragments of DNA.

W Writing Support

OL Narrative Writing

SAY TO STUDENTS: ***Imagine that a lunch bag was left on the bus and you had to use DNA fingerprinting to identify the owner. The lunch bag had a strand of hair, a fingernail, or an eyelash on it.*** Have students write a narrative describing the process of identifying the owner of the bag. The narrative should include isolating the DNA from the material found on the lunch bag and on a possible owner, then using PCR to make lots of the DNA, using restriction enzymes to break the DNA into fragments, and using gel electrophoresis to observe the distinct banding patterns. DNA from the owner and the material found on the bag should match.

BL Have struggling students make a list of how they would proceed.

AL Have students draw a sample gel showing the possible DNA patterns of the evidence and suspects. Then have students trade gels with other students and see if they can determine the owner of the bag.

R Reading Strategy

OL AL Supplemental Reading

Have students read about how criminals are identified using DNA fingerprinting. Have students find a related article in the library and take notes for discussion in class.

BL Offer struggling students resources that convey these concepts at a lower reading level.

Concepts in Motion

The Interactive Time Line

■ **Figure 13** People can be identified using the genetic information contained in blood, hair, semen, or skin.

Figure 13 shows a sample obtained from hair that forensic scientists can use for DNA fingerprinting. PCR is used to copy this small amount of DNA to create a larger sample for analysis. The amplified DNA then is cut using different combinations of restriction enzymes. The fragments are separated by gel electrophoresis and compared to DNA fragments from known sources, such as victims and suspects in a criminal case, to locate similar fragmentation patterns. There is a high probability that the two DNA samples came from the same person if two fragmentation patterns match. Since its development in England in 1985, DNA fingerprinting has been used not only to convict criminals but also to free innocent people who had been wrongfully imprisoned. **Figure 14** provides a closer look at the history of genetic technology. W R

Reading Check **Summarize** how forensic scientists use DNA fingerprinting.

Identifying Genes

Once the genome has been sequenced, the next step in the process is to identify the genes and determine their functions. The functions of many of the genes in the human genome are still unknown. Researchers use techniques that integrate computer analysis and recombinant DNA technology to determine the function of these genes.

For organisms such as bacteria and yeast, whose genomes do not have large regions of noncoding DNA, researchers have identified genes by scanning the sequence for open reading frames (or ORFs, pronounced "orphs"). ORFs are stretches of DNA containing at least 100 codons that begin with a start codon and end with a stop codon. While these sequences might indicate a gene, they will be tested to determine if these sequences produce functioning proteins.

■ **Figure 14**

Discoveries in Genetics

Many studies in genetics have led to advances in biotechnology.

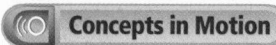

Concepts in Motion

The Interactive Timeline

1959 Down syndrome is the first chromosomal abnormality identified in humans.

1972 Paul Berg creates the first recombinant DNA molecules.

1973 Herbert Boyer, Annie Chang, Stanley Cohen, and Robert Helling discover that recombinant DNA reproduce if inserted into bacteria.

1983 Kary Mullis invents the polymerase chain reaction, for which he will be awarded the Nobel Prize in 1993.

Reading Check By comparing biological evidence with samples taken from a person accused of a crime, forensic scientists can confirm whether a person was present when a crime was committed. This information can be used as evidence in court.

Content Background

Cultural Diversity The DNA used to sequence the human genome was from an individual with genetic mutations in several genes. Explain to students the importance of sequencing the DNA from several individuals to establish the normal or wild-type sequences of genes.

Recall that a codon is a group of three nucleotides that code for an amino acid. Researchers look for the start codon AUG and a stop codon such as UAA, UGA, or UAG. ORF analysis has been used to identify correctly over 90 percent of genes in yeast and bacteria. However, the identification of genes in more complex organisms such as humans requires more sophisticated computer programs called algorithms. These algorithms use information, such as the sequence of the genomes of other organisms, to identify human genes.

Bioinformatics

The completion of the HGP and the sequencing of the genomes of other organisms have resulted in large amounts of data. Not only has this enormous amount of data required careful storage, organization, and indexing of sequence information, but it also has created a new field of study. This field of study, called **bioinformatics,** involves creating and maintaining databases of biological information. The analysis of sequence information involves finding genes in DNA sequences of various organisms and developing methods to predict the structure and function of newly discovered proteins. Scientists also study the evolution of genes by grouping protein sequences into families of related sequences and comparing similar proteins from different organisms.

R DNA Microarrays

Analyzing all the expressed genes from a given organism or a specific cell type can be useful. This analysis can be done using **DNA microarrays,** which are tiny microscope slides or silicon chips that are spotted with DNA fragments. DNA microarrays can contain a few genes, such as the genes that control the cell cycle, or all of the genes of the human genome. Therefore, a large amount of information can be stored in one small slide or chip. DNA microarrays help researchers determine whether the expression of certain genes is caused by genetic factors or environmental factors.

Study Tip

BioJournal As you read about the human genome, list several beneficial uses of this information.

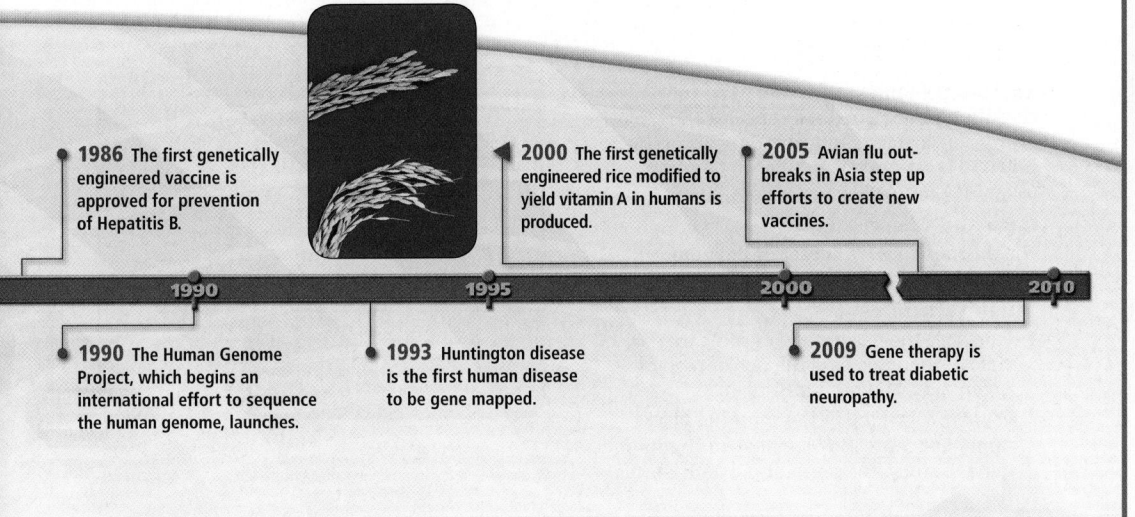

1986 The first genetically engineered vaccine is approved for prevention of Hepatitis B.

2000 The first genetically engineered rice modified to yield vitamin A in humans is produced.

2005 Avian flu outbreaks in Asia step up efforts to create new vaccines.

1990 1995 2000 2010

1990 The Human Genome Project, which begins an international effort to sequence the human genome, launches.

1993 Huntington disease is the first human disease to be gene mapped.

2009 Gene therapy is used to treat diabetic neuropathy.

Develop Concepts

BL OL AL

Integrate Computer Science Reinforce the importance of computers in biology and in analyzing the genomes of humans and other organisms. Discuss new career fields created with the Human Genome Project. Encourage students to research these career fields in the library.

R Reading Strategy

OL AL **Panel Discussion** Have students read the text under the heading *DNA Microarrays* and research how microarrays are performed. Organize a panel of students who will act as scientists willing to explain how DNA microarrays can be used to diagnose cancer and other diseases. BL Have struggling students listen to the panel and ask questions.

Content Background

Teacher FYI The rough draft of the human genome was completed in 2000. However, researchers continue to learn more information about the human genome. For example, early estimates put the number of genes around 100,000. Then scientists began estimating closer to 30,000 genes. In 2004, the estimate was again dropped to 20,000–25,000 genes.

There is still debate about the number of genes and how to determine the exact number. It will be quite a while before the scientific community reaches a consensus on the exact number of genes.

DATA ANALYSIS LAB 1

About the Lab

- Explain to students why a gene could be higher in cancer cells than in normal cells. Since cancers are masses of cells that grow uncontrollably, genes that cause the cells to proliferate could be higher in these cells.
- Cells also grow more when growth-promoting factors are present, so genes that make estrogen could be higher in cancer cells.
- The over-production of estrogen has been linked to breast, ovarian, and endometrial cancers.
- Also see Magee, et al. 2001. Expression profiling reveals hepsin overexpression in prostate cancer. *Cancer Research* 61: 5692–5696.

Think Critically

1. Of the 253 dots, 48 are red (19 percent), 32 are yellow (13 percent), and 173 are green (68 percent).
2. Black spots occur where there was no expression of a particular gene in either the normal or the cancer cell. For example, this could be a gene that is only expressed during embryogenesis.
3. Based on a microarray chip, genes could be selected that had either higher expression in prostate cancer cells or higher expression in normal cells. One of these genes could then be studied as a potential cause of prostate cancer.

Follow the steps involved in doing the DNA microarray experiment shown in **Figure 15.** mRNA from two different populations of cells is isolated and converted into complementary DNA (cDNA) strands using an enzyme called reverse transcriptase. The complementary DNA from each cell population is labeled with a specific fluorescent dye—for example, red for cancer cells and green for normal cells. Both pools of complementary DNA are combined on the microarray slide and incubated.

Figure 15 shows the fluorescent signals that are produced when the microarray slide is analyzed. When the expression of a gene is the same in both the normal and cancer cells, a yellow spot is produced on the chip. If the expression of a gene is higher in cancer cells, then the spot formed is red. However, if the expression is higher in normal cells, then the spot formed is green.

Because one DNA microarray slide can contain thousands of genes, researchers can examine changes in the expression patterns of multiple genes at the same time. Scientists also are using DNA microarrays to identify new genes and to study changes in the expression of proteins under different growth conditions.

The Genome and Genetic Disorders

Although more than 99 percent of all nucleotide base sequences are exactly the same in all people, sometimes there are variations that are linked to human diseases. These variations in the DNA sequence that occur when a single nucleotide in the genome is altered are called **single nucleotide polymorphisms** or SNPs. For a variation to be considered an SNP, it must occur in at least one percent of the population. Many SNPs have no effect on cell function, but scientists hypothesize that SNP maps will help identify many genes associated with many different types of genetic disorders.

DATA ANALYSIS LAB 1

Based on Real Data*

Apply Concepts

How can DNA microarrays be used to classify types of prostate cancer? The gene expression profiles between normal prostate cells and prostate cancer cells can be compared using DNA microarray technology.

Data and Observations

The diagram shows a subset of the data obtained.

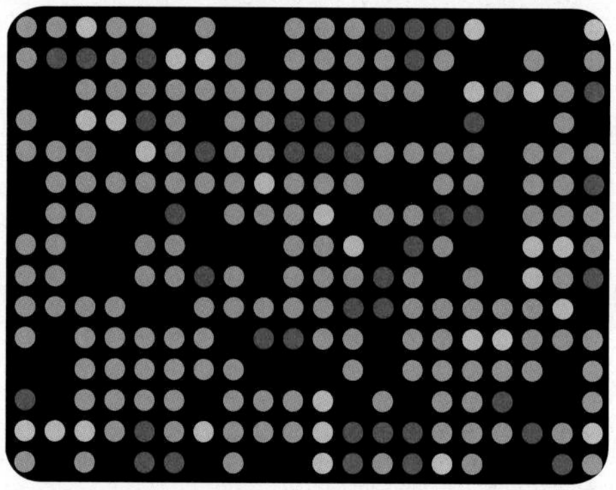

Think Critically

1. **Calculate** the percentage of spots that are yellow. Then calculate the percentage of green spots and red spots.
2. **Explain** why some of the spots are black.
3. **Apply Concepts** How would you choose a gene to study as a cause of prostate cancer?

*Data obtained from: Lapointe, et al. 2004. Gene expression profiling identifies clinically relevant subtypes of prostate cancer. *PNAS* 101: 811–816.

Research Citation

Real-World Applications Educational research indicates that students will retain more information when it resonates with their own personal interests. The Data-Analysis Lab on this page allows students to visualize a challenging real-world problem and connect their learning with real-world situations. (Steen and Forman, 1995)

Research bibliography on pages 32T–34T

Visualizing Microarray Analysis

S **Figure 15**
In this experiment, the expression of thousands of human genes was detected by DNA microarray analysis. Each spot on the microarray chip represents a gene. A red spot indicates the expression of a gene is higher in cancer cells compared to normal cells. A green spot indicates the expression in normal cells is higher. Yellow spots indicate no difference in the expression between cancer cells and normal cells.

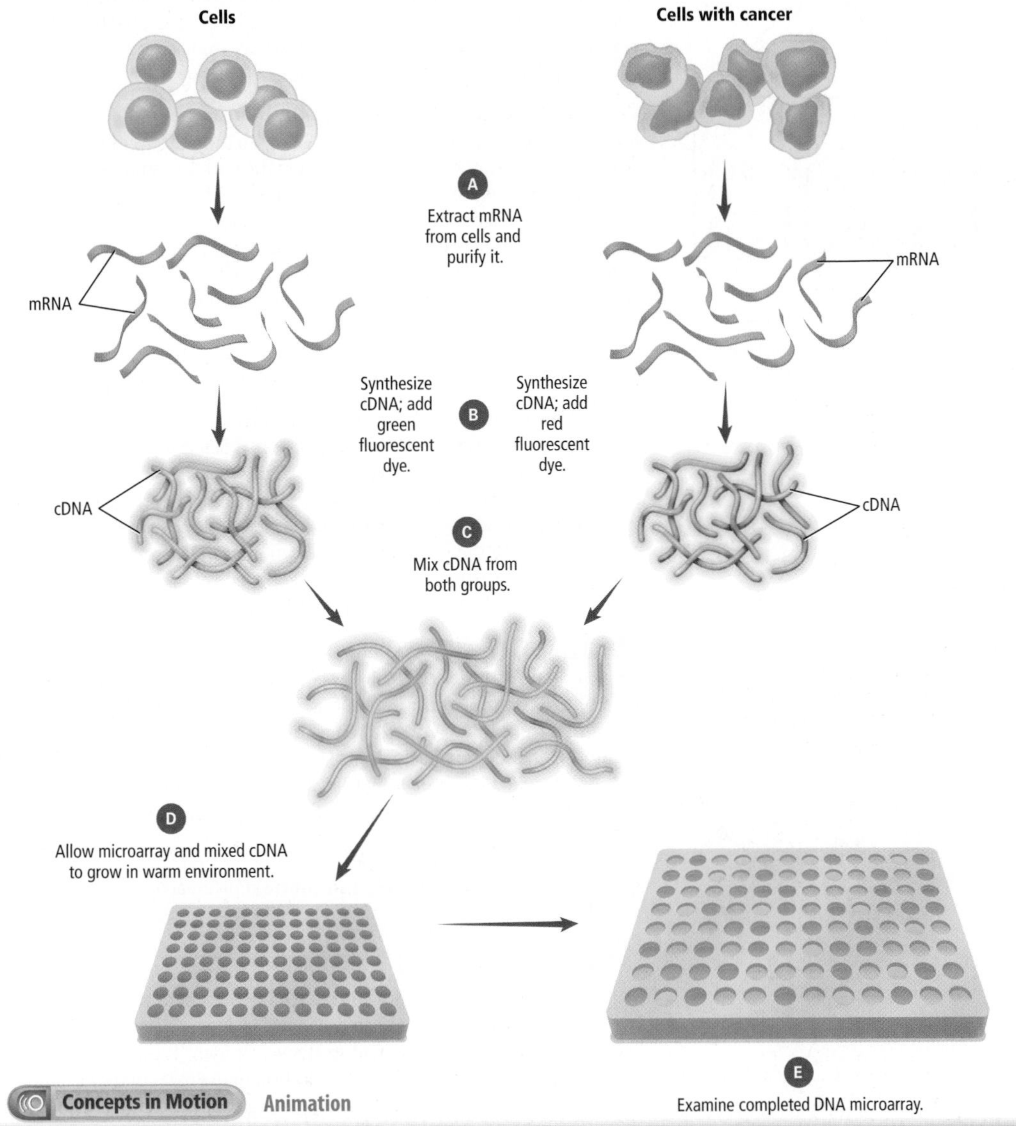

Cells
Cells with cancer
A
Extract mRNA from cells and purify it.
mRNA
mRNA
Synthesize cDNA; add green fluorescent dye.
B
Synthesize cDNA; add red fluorescent dye.
cDNA
cDNA
C
Mix cDNA from both groups.
D
Allow microarray and mixed cDNA to grow in warm environment.
E
Examine completed DNA microarray.

Concepts in Motion **Animation**

> *"The world does not pay for what a person knows. But it pays for what a person does with what he knows."*
>
> –LAURENCE LEE

Differentiated Instruction

Below Level When preparing the assessment for the chapter, consider what modifications might be necessary for students who perform below level. These students might benefit if they are provided with a quiet setting in which to take the test. Dividing the test into small sections might also help students with learning disabilities focus more efficiently.

For more tips, see pages 14T–15T.

Visualizing Microarray Analysis

Purpose

Students will learn about new methods that are used to simultaneously analyze numerous genes. E.2

S Skill Practice

EL OL Concept Map Have students construct a concept map that outlines the applications and steps involved in microarray analysis. Concept maps should include the following steps:

1. Extract mRNA from normal cells and cancer cells.
2. Synthesize cDNA from normal cells and cancer cells and dye each kind with a distinctive color.
3. Mix cDNA from both groups.
4. Allow microarray and mixed cDNA to grow in a warm environment.

BL Help struggling students by having them make image maps instead of concept maps. An image map uses pictures, images, and symbols instead of words.

Skill Practice

OL Visual Literacy Students might not understand that the cells, cDNA fragments, and plates are each drawn in a different scale. **SAY TO STUDENTS:** ***List these items in order of size, from smallest to largest: microarray plate, cancer cell, and cDNA fragment.*** A cDNA fragment is much smaller than a cancer cell, which is much smaller than a microarray plate. Explain to students that the illustration shows these materials out of scale so they can visualize the process.

Concepts in Motion **Animation**

S Skill Practice

OL Visual Literacy Have students look at Figure 16.

ASK STUDENTS: ***What are chromosomes?*** stretches of DNA that contain thousands of genes ***How do haplotypes relate to chromosomes?*** Haplotypes are regions of linked variations in the human genome. Remind students that although the human genome is 3 billion nucleotides long, it is divided into 46 chromosomes. Some of these chromosomes contain many genes clustered in tandem and other chromosomes contain a few genes and large expanses of nucleotides that do not code for proteins.

R Reading Strategy

EL Brainstorm Have students read the new vocabulary on this page. In small groups, have students brainstorm ideas that come to mind when they see and hear each term. Write ideas on the board and refer to these ideas after reading the page. Have students write the ideas in a column and the definitions of each new term in another column for comparison. **BL** Offer struggling students a list of vocabulary words to evaluate. Pronounce each word for the students.

Reading Check Gene therapy is a technique that attempts to correct mutated genes. Pharmacogenomics is the study of how genetic inheritance affects the response to drugs.

S

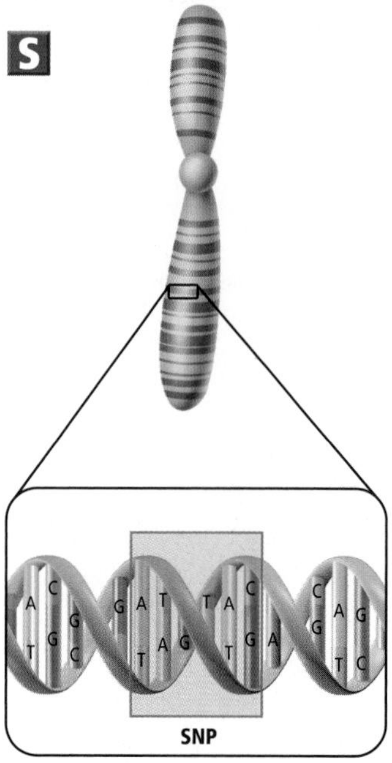

Figure 16 The HapMap project involves grouping all adjacent SNPs that are inherited together into haplotypes.

Figure 17 DNA can be encapsulated in a virus and delivered into a patient to replace a defective gene. Once the virus enters the cells, the genetic information is released into the nucleus and inserted into the genome.

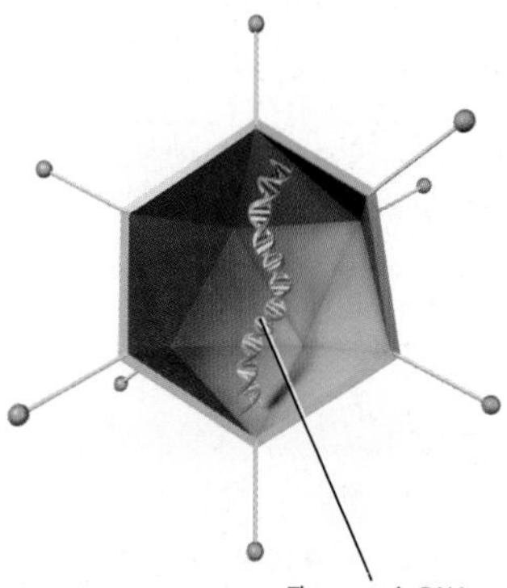

The HapMap project An internationl group of scientists is creating a catalog of common genetic variations that occur in humans. Linked genes are inherited together and similarly, genetic variations located close together also tend to be inherited together. Therefore, regions of linked variations in the human genome, known as **haplotypes,** can be located. The project to create this catalog is called the haplotype map, or HapMap project. Assembling the HapMap involves identifying groups of SNPs in a specific region of DNA. R

Figure 16 shows how the genome is divided into haplotypes. Once completed, the HapMap will describe what these variations are, where they occur in our DNA, and how they are distributed among people within populations and among populations in different parts of the world. This information will help researchers find genes that cause disease and affect an individual's response to drugs.

Pharmacogenomics Sequencing the human genome combines the knowledge of genes, proteins, and SNPs with other areas of science. The study of how genetic inheritance affects the body's response to drugs is called **pharmacogenomics** (far muh koh jeh NAW mihks). The benefits of pharmacogenomics include more accurate dosing of drugs that are safer and more specific. Researchers hope that pharmacogenomics will allow for drugs to be custom-made for individuals based on their genetic makeups. Prescribing drugs based on an individual's genetic makeup will increase safety, speed recovery, and reduce side effects. Perhaps one day when you are sick, your doctor will read your genetic code and prescribe medicine tailor-made for you.

Gene therapy A technique aimed at correcting mutated genes that cause human diseases is called **gene therapy.** Scientists insert a normal gene into a chromosome to replace a dysfunctional gene. In most gene therapy studies, inserting a normal gene into a viral vector, like the one in **Figure 17,** produces recombinant DNA. Target cells in the patient are infected with the virus and the recombinant DNA material is released into the affected cells. Once deposited into cells, the normal gene inserts itself into the genome and begins functioning.

Connection to Health In 1990, the first clinical gene therapy trial at the National Institutes of Health was conducted on a four year old child with severe combined immunodeficiency (SCID). The Food and Drug Administration (FDA) monitors new medical trials, including gene therapy. Gene therapy has seen its share of setbacks, but the possibilities are endless when it comes to new treatments. Recent gene therapy trials include work with diabetes, cancer, retinal disease, Parkinson's disease, and others.

Reading Check **Compare and contrast** pharmacogenomics to gene therapy.

Genomics and Proteomics

Sequencing the human genome began what researchers call "the genomic era." **Genomics** is the study of an organism's genome. Genomics has become one of the most powerful strategies for identifying human genes and interpreting their functions. In addition to the mass of data obtained from sequencing the genomes of multiple organisms, scientists also are investigating the proteins produced by these genes.

Content Background

Teacher FYI Not all of the DNA in a cell is on human chromosomes. Mitochondria have their own DNA. Mitochondrial DNA codes for genes the mitochondria need to function. The mitochondrial DNA is very stable and mutates much less frequently than chromosomal DNA. This stability has helped scientists identify the genetic relationships between groups of people and map migration routes of our early human ancestors.

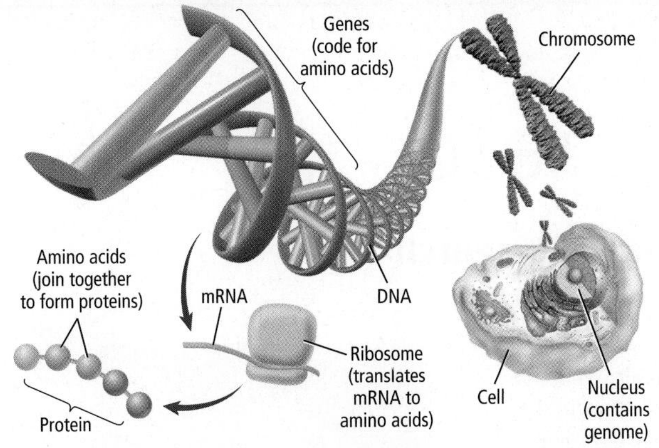

■ **Figure 18** The central dogma is that the information in genes flows from DNA to RNA and RNA to proteins.

Genes are the primary information storage units, whereas proteins are the machines of a cell. Recall that when a gene is expressed, a protein is produced, as illustrated in **Figure 18.** Therefore, an understanding of how proteins function also is important. For instance, if the genome represents the words in a dictionary, the proteome, which represents all the proteins found in a cell, provides the definition of these words and how to use these words in a sentence. The large-scale study and cataloging of the structure and function of proteins in the human body is called **proteomics.** Proteomics allows researchers to look at hundreds or thousands of proteins at the same time. This type of broad analysis will better define both normal and disease states. Scientists anticipate that proteomics will revolutionize the development of new drugs to treat diseases such as Type II diabetes, obesity, and atherosclerosis.

Video
What's BIOLOGY Got To Do With It?

R

Section 3 Assessment

Section Summary

- Researchers who worked on the HGP sequenced all nucleotides in the human genome.
- DNA fingerprinting can be used to identify individuals.
- DNA microarrays allow researchers to study all the genes in the genome simultaneously.
- Gene therapy might be used in the future to correct genetic disorders.
- Genomics is the study of an organism's genome and proteomics is the study of the proteins in the human body.

Understand Main Ideas

1. MAIN Idea **Relate** the human genome to blueprints for a house.
2. **Analyze** the role of DNA fingerprinting in criminal investigations.
3. **Indicate** why the HapMap project is useful in diagnosing human disease.
4. **Explain** the process of gene therapy. What is the ultimate goal of gene therapy?

Think Critically

5. **Hypothesize** Most of the human genome consists of noncoding DNA. Where did all of this noncoding DNA originate?

MATH in Biology

6. If 1.5 percent of the human genome consists of protein-coding sequences, and the entire genome has 3.2×10^9 nucleotides, how many codons are in the human genome? Remember that a codon is three nucleotides in length.

R Reading Strategy

EL OL AL Fix-Up Strategy

Have students choose one or more parts of the text under the heading *Genomics and Proteomics* that they had difficulty understanding. Group students according to their selections, and have them write three questions (with correct answers) pertaining to their chosen part. Share questions with the class, allowing other groups to answer questions.

Formative Assessment

Evaluation Have students examine diagrams of microarray data in this section.
ASK STUDENTS: ***Why are the spots colored differently? What can the different colors represent?*** When the expression of a gene is the same in the normal and cancer cells, the spot is yellow. If the expression is higher in the cancer cells, then the spot is red. If the expression is higher in the normal cells, then the spot is green.

Remediation Students struggling with microarray assay may benefit from drawing flowcharts that show what happens in the assay. Student charts may vary slightly, but all charts should show the steps in sequence and identical assay outcomes: If the expression of a gene is the same in both normal and cancer cells, the spot is yellow. If the expression is higher in the cancer cells, then the spot is red. If the expression is higher in the normal cells, then the spot is green.

Section 3 Assessment

1. Like a blueprint, the human genome contains all of the information required for the construction of an organism.
2. DNA fingerprinting has improved the accuracy of identifying criminals and victims because every person has a unique pattern of DNA fragments that are created when nonprotein–coding DNA is digested.
3. The HapMap project can improve a doctor's ability to diagnose diseases because regions of the genome that contain several mutations would be correlated to different disease states. Thus, the doctor could sequence specific regions of a patient's DNA and determine whether a patient is predisposed to a particular disease.
4. Use of vectors to transmit functioning DNA into patients; goal is new treatments and possible cures for diseases.
5. The human genome contains lots of nonprotein–coding DNA because, over time, humans have integrated DNA from other organisms, such as viruses.
6. 1.6×10^7 codons

Assessment **Online Quiz**

In the Field

Purpose

Students will explore how a scientific discovery in one organism can help scientists investigate other organisms.
E.2

Anticipatory Guide

ASK STUDENTS: ***Have you ever seen a firefly? What form of energy do fireflies use to produce light?*** Chemical energy in the form of ATP Tell students that as they read the feature, they will learn more about how natural luminescence is used in scientific investigations.

Background

Bioluminescence is a property found in both land and marine organisms. In many bioluminescent organisms, such as fireflies, the enzyme luciferase assists in the oxidation of the substrate protein luciferin. Luciferin glows when it is oxidized. Some organisms, such as flashlight fish, live in a symbiotic relationship with bioluminescent bacteria. The bacteria live in pockets near the eyes of the fish. The fish live in environments that receive very little or no sunlight, so the light from the bacteria allow the fish to see.

In the Field

Career: Biomedical Research

Illuminating Medical Research

Have you ever watched fireflies glow on a summer evening? A chemical reaction in firefly cells produces light through a process called bioluminescence. Many marine organisms, like the jellyfish shown in the image, are also bioluminescent. The jellyfish species *Aequorea victoria* has emerged as a hero to biomedical researchers. This jellyfish produces a substance called green fluorescent protein (GFP), which makes parts of its body shine with an emerald green light.

Green fluorescent protein was first observed in bioluminescent jellyfishes.

Shining Light on Cell Functions Found off the west coast of North America, the diminutive *Aequorea victoria* is only five to ten centimeters in diameter. Its cells contain aequorin, a bioluminescent protein that emits a deep blue light. GFP absorbs this light and converts it into a glowing emerald green. In the early 1990s, scientists removed the GFP gene from *Aequorea victoria* and cloned it. Today, biomedical researchers can fuse GFP to other proteins inside cells of living organisms. When illuminated with light of a specific frequency, these marked proteins glow, making it possible to observe their behavior during cell processes.

Biological Marking at Work GFP allows scientists to determine where proteins are located during different stages of a cell's life, and to observe how proteins interact to produce disease. Researchers can attach GFP to a virus and observe the spread of the virus throughout the host.

By injecting tumor cells marked with GFP, scientists can analyze how they develop, spread, and destroy healthy cells over time. Bioluminescent imaging can be used to evaluate the effectiveness of various treatments on these types of tumors. Ultimately, scientists hope to incorporate GFP directly into human tumor cells, then use bioluminescence to identify the mass as a separate cell population within the body. Easily differentiated from healthy cells and tissues, the glowing cancerous cells would be marked for treatment.

WRITING in Biology

Research and Communicate GFP is used to investigate the effectiveness of gene therapy, vaccines, and cancer treatments. Research how GFP is used in cancer studies and share your findings with classmates.

WRITING in Biology

✻RUBRIC Use the modifiable rubric found on your eTeacherEdition Online to assess writing assignments.

Follow-Up Discussion

Have students share their findings with the class. Have the class brainstorm additional uses for GFP. Make a list of the possible new uses for GFP and post the list on the board. Have interested students choose one of these new uses for GFP, and look into the viability of the project. Have students report their findings to the class.

WebQuest

BIOLAB

FORENSICS: HOW CAN GENETIC ENGINEERING BE USED TO SOLVE A CRIME?

Background: **Although all humans are similar genetically, variations do occur in certain segments of DNA. When cut with restriction enzymes, the variety of sizes of these fragments can be used to determine the source of a sample of DNA. In this lab, DNA from suspects will be analyzed.**

Question: *Based on the DNA samples, were any of the suspects at the scene?*

Materials

various DNA samples
electrophoresis chamber
power source
micropipette and tips
prepared agarose gels
restriction enzyme
microcentrifuge tubes and rack
sample-loading dye
nontoxic dye
staining and destaining containers
DNA fragments of known size (control)
ruler
ice in foam container
water bath at 37°C

Safety Precautions

Procedure

1. Read and complete the lab safety form.
2. Read the entire procedure.
3. Label your DNA samples.
4. Design and construct a data table you can use to record your observations when you perform gel electrophoresis of your samples.
5. Your teacher will instruct you how to prepare your samples, set up the gel electrophoresis equipment, load your samples, and run the electrophoresis.
6. Use the gel-staining dye to detect the location of DNA fragments in the gel for each of your samples.
7. Use a ruler to measure (in mm) the distance of each migrated DNA band from the wells. Record this information in your table.
8. **Cleanup and Disposal** Wash and return all reusable materials. Dispose of gels and other reagents in properly labeled containers. Wash your hands thoroughly.

Analyze and Conclude

1. **Interpret Data** Based on your observations, predict which suspect is incriminated by the DNA evidence.
2. **Think Critically** While the amount of DNA needed for electrophoresis is not large, the amount that can be extracted from a few hairs might not be enough. How might forensic scientists solve this problem?
3. **Error Analysis** DNA fingerprints have a very high level of accuracy if they are run correctly. What are some sources of error that could lead to inaccurate results?
4. **Plan Ahead** Suggest ways that you could improve your procedure and methods to avoid the sources of error listed in your answer for question 3. Try out your plans.

WRITING in Biology

Plan a procedure. Find a news article describing the use of DNA fingerprinting in investigations such as a criminal investigation or identifying a bacterium involved in a disease outbreak. Write a mock lab that explains the techniques and steps that might be taken in the situation described by the article.

BIOLAB

? Inquiry BioLab

For a lab worksheet, use your eTeacherEdition Online.

RUBRIC A rubric for evaluating BioLabs is found on your eTeacherEdition Online.

Est. Time 40 min

Content Background
Although all human DNA is estimated to be 99.9% similar, individual variations do occur. If these variations occur in introns, they typically do not have any phenotypic effect but can be used to distinguish between individuals.

Safety Precautions Approve lab safety forms before work begins. Because students will be working with electricity, be absolutely sure they understand how to set up the electrophoresis equipment safely. Follow any other safety precautions recommended by the kit you purchase.

Teaching Strategy Point out to students that this lab only models how forensic scientists carry out DNA fingerprinting. In the real world, more elaborate techniques have to be used when dealing with human DNA because of its complexity.

Alternative Teaching Demo
Instead of running their own gels, students may be given photographs of gels to complete the analysis portion of the lab.

WRITING in Biology

RUBRIC Use the modifiable rubric found on your eTeacherEdition Online to assess writing assignments.

Analyze and Conclude

1. Student answers will vary but should be supported by the evidence.
2. PCR could be used to amplify the sample and make millions of copies of the DNA in question.
3. Samples could be contaminated by DNA from other sources. The temperature for incubating the restriction enzymes with the DNA samples might have been incorrect. If electrophoresis is not run long enough, bands of DNA will not separate properly. If electrophoresis is run too long, all DNA bands will migrate to the bottom of the gel.
4. Answers will vary. Students should include plans to improve DNA collection, handling of samples, or running of samples.

Chapter 13

Study Guide

ConnectED

Students can use the following to review the chapter.

Review

Vocabulary eGames
Vocabulary eFlashcards
Vocabulary PuzzleMaker

Assessment

Online Quizzes
Online Test Practice
Standardized Test Practice

Use the *ExamView® Assessment Suite* CD-ROM to:

- create multiple versions of tests
- create modified tests with one mouse click
- edit existing questions and add your own questions
- build tests aligned with state standards using built-in state curriculum tags
- change English tests to Spanish with one mouse click
- track students' progress using the Teacher Management System

Chapter 13 Study Guide

THEME FOCUS Scientific Inquiry The discovery and development of the PCR technique has led to many applications and uses within the science community and beyond.

BIG Idea Genetic technology improves human health and quality of life.

Section 1 Applied Genetics

selective breeding (p. 360)
inbreeding (p. 361)
test cross (p. 362)

MAIN Idea Selective breeding is used to produce organisms with desired traits.

- Selective breeding is used to produce organisms with traits that are considered desirable.
- Hybridization produces organisms with the desired traits from parent organisms with different traits.
- Inbreeding creates pure breeds.
- A test cross can be used to determine an organism's genotype.

Section 2 DNA Technology

genetic engineering (p. 363)
genome (p. 364)
restriction enzyme (p. 364)
gel electrophoresis (p. 365)
recombinant DNA (p. 366)
plasmid (p. 366)
DNA ligase (p. 366)
transformation (p. 367)
cloning (p. 367)
polymerase chain reaction (p. 368)
transgenic organism (p. 370)

MAIN Idea Researchers use genetic engineering to manipulate DNA.

- Genetic engineering is used to produce organisms that are useful to humans.
- Recombinant DNA technology is used to study individual genes.
- DNA fragments can be separated using gel electrophoresis.
- Clones can be produced by transforming bacteria with recombinant DNA.
- The polymerase chain reaction is used to make copies of small DNA sequences.
- Transgenic organisms are being created to increase the quality of human life.

Section 3 The Human Genome

DNA fingerprinting (p. 373)
bioinformatics (p. 375)
DNA microarray (p. 375)
single nucleotide polymorphism (p. 376)
haplotype (p. 378)
pharmacogenomics (p. 378)
gene therapy (p. 378)
genomics (p. 378)
proteomics (p. 379)

MAIN Idea Genomes contain all of the information needed for an organism to grow and survive.

- Researchers who worked on the HGP sequenced all nucleotides in the human genome.
- DNA fingerprinting can be used to identify individuals.
- DNA microarrays allow researchers to study all the genes in the genome simultaneously.
- Gene therapy might be used in the future to correct genetic disorders.
- Genomics is the study of an organism's genome and proteomics is the study of the proteins in the human body.

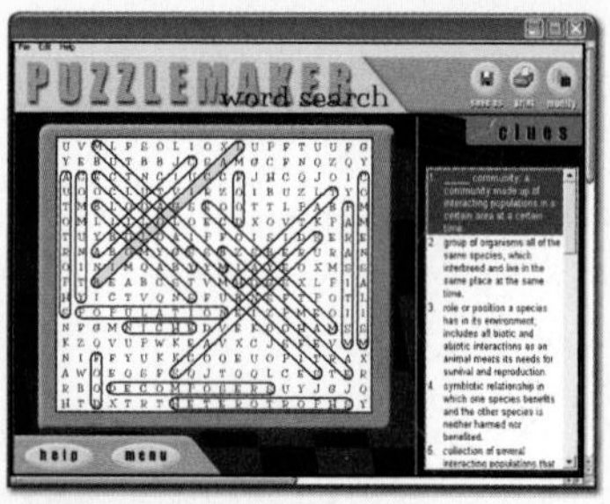

Review **Vocabulary PuzzleMaker**

For additional practice with vocabulary, have students access the Vocabulary PuzzleMaker online.

Review **Vocabulary eGames**

Section 1

Vocabulary Review

Fill in the blanks with the correct term from the Study Guide page.

1. A __________ is used to determine the genotype of a plant or animal.
2. The offspring produced by __________ are homozygous for most traits.

Understand Main Ideas

Use the illustration below to answer questions 3 and 4.

Heterozygous white grapefruit (top); Homozygous red grapefruit (side)

	W	w
w	Ww	ww
w	Ww	ww

3. What is the genotypic ratio of the offspring in the cross above?
   A. 1:2:1
   B. 1:1
   C. All are homozygous recessive.
   D. All are heterozygous.
4. The cross above could be used to determine the genotype of a parent with a dominant phenotype. What is this type of cross called?
   A. a homozygous cross
   B. a heterozygous cross
   C. a test cross
   D. a parental cross

Constructed Response

5. **THEME FOCUS Scientific Inquiry** Predict the phenotype of the parent plants of hybrid tomato plants that grow fast and are resistant to pesticides. Explain.
6. **Short Answer** How do polygenic traits affect selective breeding?
7. **MAIN Idea** Discuss the advantages and disadvantages of selective breeding.

Think Critically

8. **Explain** why purebred animals do not exist in the wild.
9. **Determine** Suppose a phenotype is controlled by more than one gene. Can a test cross be used to determine the genotype? Why or why not?

Section 2

Vocabulary Review

Fill in the blank with the correct vocabulary term from the Study Guide page.

10. Transgenic animals are produced by __________.
11. Biologists use __________ to join two DNA molecules together.
12. During __________, a cell takes in DNA from outside the cell.
13. Small, circular DNA molecules that are found in bacterial cells are called __________.

Understand Main Ideas

Use the illustration below to answer question 14.

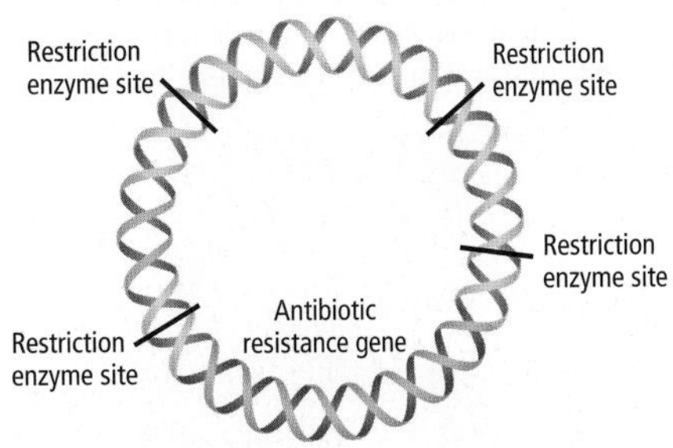

14. What is the role of the molecule above in DNA cloning?
    A. to carry the foreign DNA into the host cell
    B. to identify the source of DNA as foreign
    C. to identify the host cell that has taken up the gene of interest
    D. to make the foreign DNA susceptible to digestion with enzymes

Chapter 13

Assessment

Section 1

Vocabulary Review

1. test cross
2. inbreeding

Understand Main Ideas

3. B
4. C

Constructed Responses

5. A hybrid is an organism that has been bred to show the favorable characteristics of two parents, each of which has one of the favorable characteristics. Therefore, one parent was fast growing and the other parent was resistant to pesticides.
6. Polygenic traits are those that are influenced by multiple pairs of alleles. In selective breeding, organisms with desired traits are bred to pass on those traits. If traits are affected by multiple genes, knowing how the different combinations of genes interact is important to getting the desired traits from your crosses.
7. Some advantages of selective breeding are that plants and animals are created that can grow faster, produce more offspring (or fruit), and withstand attack from bacteria. Some disadvantages of selective breeding are that it is time intensive, expensive, and requires several generations to produce offspring with the desired traits.

Think Critically

8. Purebred animals do not exist in the wild because mating usually occurs between organisms that are distantly related.
9. If all the genes that contribute to a specific trait are known, then a test cross can be used. One organism used in the cross should be homozygous recessive for all genes controlling the specific trait.

Section 2

Vocabulary Review

10. genetic engineering
11. ligase
12. transformation
13. plasmids

Understand Main Ideas

14. A

Assessment Online Test Practice

15. B
16. A

Constructed Response

17. Genetic engineering could decrease the natural selection of genes important for an organism to respond to its environment or result in the creation of organisms with unexpected phenotypes.
18. All of the bacteria colonies would grow, but you would not be able to determine which cells took up the plasmid.
19. The polymerase chain reaction has three main steps: first is heating to high temperatures to separate the strands of the DNA template, second is cooling to a temperature that allows for the primers to bind to the complementary region of the DNA template, third is extension where the DNA polymerase incorporates new deoxy-nucleotides into daughter strands.

Think Critically

20. a. the third lane
b. the first lane
c. the second lane
21. The largest fragment (1633 bp) should be closest to the negative side of the gel, followed by the 1400 bp fragment, the 1108 bp fragment, the 601 bp fragment, and the 257 bp fragment (which should be at the positive end of the gel).
22. a. The original DNA molecule is circular because the *Hind*III digest resulted in only one fragment.
b. Map will show *EcoRI* sites 180 degrees from each other and the *Hind*III site between the *EcoRI* sites, but not 90 degrees from the *EcoRI* sites.

Section 3

Vocabulary Review

23. bioinformatics
24. haplotypes

---

15. Based on the sequences below, which enzyme produces a blunt end? *The cut site is indicated by the *.*

A. *Eag*I	C*GGCC G G CCGG*C
B. *Eco*RV	GAT*ATC CTA*TAG
C. *Nsi*I	A TGCA*T T*ACGT A
D. *Taq*I	T*CG A A GC*T

16. Why is the polymerase chain reaction used?
A. to amplify DNA
B. to cut DNA
C. to ligate DNA
D. to separate DNA

Constructed Response

17. MAIN Idea Predict what effect genetic engineering will have on the evolution of a species.

18. Short Answer Suppose you transform bacteria with a recombinant DNA plasmid and by mistake grow the transformed cells without an antibiotic. What result would you observe? Why?

19. Interpret the Figure Refer to **Figure 9** to make a flowchart diagramming the steps in the PCR.

Think Critically

20. Conclude A recombinant DNA molecule was created by joining a plasmid vector and a DNA fragment. Gel electrophoresis verified that the plasmid and the DNA fragment ligated.

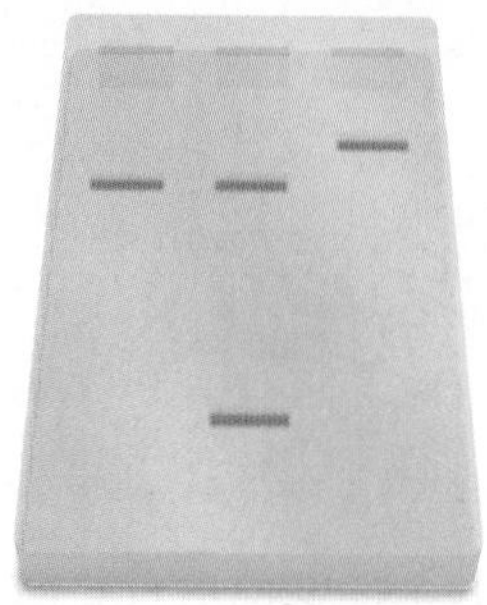

a. Which lane in the gel corresponds to the recombinant DNA?
b. Which lane corresponds to the plasmid?
c. Which lane represents cleaving using a restriction enzyme of the recombinant DNA molecule?

21. Differentiate The plasmid below was cut to produce the five fragments shown in the diagram. The fragments then were separated by gel electrophoresis. Draw a diagram of a gel and the location of each fragment. Label ends as positive or negative.

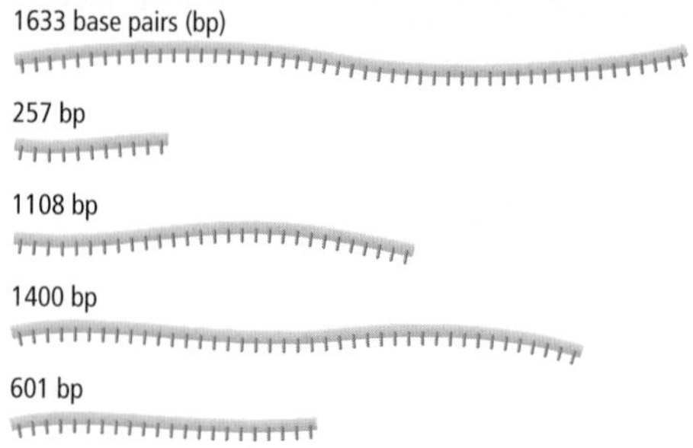

22. Assess A small DNA molecule was cleaved with several different restriction enzymes, and the size of each fragment was determined by gel electrophoresis. The following data were obtained.

DNA Fragmentation Patterns Created by *Eco*RI and *Hind*III

Enzyme	Number of Fragments	Fragment Size (kilobases)
*Eco*RI	2	1.5 kb 1.5 kb
*Hind*III	1	3.0 kb
*Eco*RI + *Hind*III	3	0.8 kb 0.7 kb 1.5 kb

a. Is the original DNA linear or circular?
b. Draw a restriction-site map showing distances consistent with the data.

Section 3

Vocabulary Review

Fill in the blanks with the correct vocabulary term from the Study Guide page.

23. The field of __________ uses computers to index and organize information created by sequencing the human genome.

24. Genetic variations that are located close together are called __________.

Understand Main Ideas

25. Which statement about the human genome is false?
- **A.** The human genome contains approximately 25,000 genes.
- **B.** The human genome contains long stretches of DNA with no known function.
- **C.** The human genome was sequenced by scientists from around the world.
- **D.** The human genome contains nucleotide sequences that all code for proteins.

26. What are variations in specific nucleotides that are linked to human diseases called?
- **A.** proteomes
- **B.** haplotypes
- **C.** single nucleotide polymorphisms
- **D.** genomes

27. For what purpose is DNA fingerprinting used?
- **A.** to sequence DNA from bacteria
- **B.** to separate DNA fragments
- **C.** to identify individuals who have committed crimes
- **D.** to identify single nucleotide polymorphisms

Constructed Response

28. Short Answer Discuss the advantages and disadvantages of using DNA microarrays.

29. Short Answer List three ways patients will benefit from pharmacogenomics.

30. MAIN Idea What impact does sequencing the human genome have on diagnosing and treating diseases?

Think Critically

31. Describe how DNA microarrays and DNA sequencing can be used to identify a defective gene.

32. CAREERS IN BIOLOGY A forensic scientist finds a strand of hair at a crime scene. Draw a flowchart and explain the steps that the forensic scientist has to take to determine the identity of the person to whom the hair belongs.

Summative Assessment

33. BIG Idea Explain the importance of the completion of the human genome project. What are some health discoveries that are a result of this project?

34. WRITING in Biology Write a paragraph discussing the approach you would take to create a transgenic organism and the drawbacks to creating it.

DBQ Document-Based Questions

The data below were obtained during a study on mosquito biting patterns. DNA fingerprints were obtained from individuals A, B, and C who were bitten by mosquitoes. In order to determine which mosquitoes bit each individual, a group of mosquitoes was collected and their DNA fingerprints were obtained. The mosquitoes were numbered 1–8.

Use the data to answer the questions below.

Data obtained from: Michael, et al. 2001. Quantifying mosquito biting patterns on humans by DNA fingerprinting of blood meals. *American Journal of Tropical Medicine and Hygiene* 65(6): 722–728.

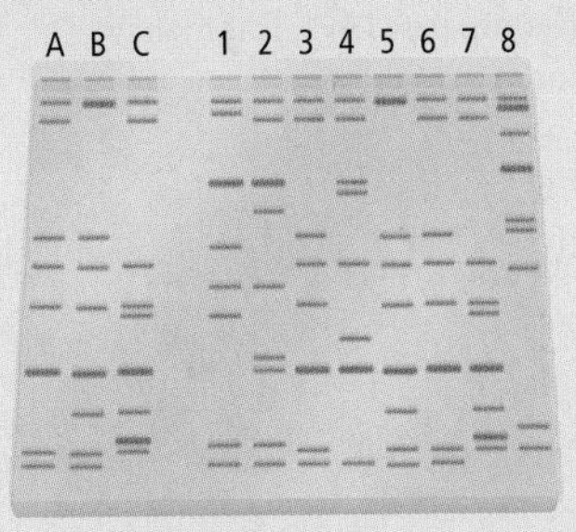

35. Examine the banding patterns and match each individual with the mosquito(es) that bit him or her.

36. What can researchers gain by knowing which mosquito bit which individual?

37. Based on your answer to question 35, what is a disadvantage of using this DNA fingerprinting to identify disease-carrying mosquitoes in the environment?

Understand Main Ideas

25. D

26. C

27. C

Constructed Responses

28. Microarrays can analyze entire genomes all at once, but they are very expensive.

29. Pharmacogenetics will decrease side effects to drugs, allow screening for diseases, and allow doctors to give more accurate doses of drugs.

30. Sequencing the human genome allows scientists to compare the genomic sequences of people from different populations and who have specific diseases to look for mutations or polymorphisms.

Think Critically

31. DNA sequencing can be used to identify defective genes by sequencing the DNA of people with a specific disease and comparing the sequence to people who do not have the disease. Microarrays can be used to compare the expression of genes in people with and people without the disease.

32. Students' flowcharts should show the following: Extraction of the DNA, then PCR to amplify the DNA, then digestion of the amplified DNA using restriction enzymes followed by gel electrophoresis. Fragmentation patterns should be compared to the fragmentation patterns of DNA extracted from known individuals.

WRITING in Biology

RUBRIC Use the modifiable rubric found on your eTeacherEdition Online to assess writing assignments.

34. Answers will vary. Paragraphs should refer to real genes and real processes.

DBQ Document-Based Questions

Michael, et al. 2001. Quantifying mosquito biting patterns on humans by DNA fingerprinting of blood meals. *American Journal of Tropical Medicine and Hygiene 65(6): 722–728.*

35. A was bitten by 3 and 6, B was bitten by 5, and C was bitten by 7.

36. If an individual gets sick, they can know which mosquitoes transmitted the disease.

37. A drawback to this technique is that multiple mosquitoes can bite an individual, making it difficult to identify the mosquito responsible for spreading the pathogen.

Summative Assessment

33. With the completion of the HGP, scientists are able to locate the gene sources for many debilitating diseases. Testing for genetic predisposition to breast cancer, Alzheimer's, and other genetic disorders is possible. New treatments, such as gene therapy, and better medicines have also resulted from this work.

Assessment Online Test Practice

Standardized Test Practice

Multiple Choice

1. D 5. C
2. C 6. B
3. B 7. D
4. C 8. B

Short Answer

9. Answers go from left to right.
   A. Male who inherited the gene for the disease and, therefore, has the disease.
   B. Female who has one gene for the disease, but does not express the disease, she is a carrier.
   C. Female who has one gene for the disease, but does not express the disease, she is a carrier.
   D. Male who did not inherit the gene for the disease, and therefore does not have the disease.
10. Most of the proteins that make up the human body are the same in all people. The genetic differences among humans are very small.
11. Hemophilia is a sex-linked recessive gene carried on the X-chromosome. The father's genotype is X^hY. The mother's genotype is X^hX^H. The probability that they will have a son is 0.5 and the probability that they will have any child with hemophilia is 0.5. The probability that they will have a son with hemophilia is $(0.5 \times 0.5) = 0.25$, or 25 percent.
12. The first major process is transcription, which occurs in the nucleus of cells. During transcription, messenger RNA is synthesized using a sequence of bases on DNA as a template. The second major process is translation, which occurs in the cytoplasm of cells. During translation, a protein is synthesized using the base sequence of messenger RNA as a template. At the end of translation, a complete protein chain has been formed.

Standardized Test Practice

Cumulative

Multiple Choice

1. Which describes the process of cytokinesis?
   A. chromosomes duplicate
   B. spindle disintegrates
   C. nucleus disappears
   D. cytoplasm divides

Use the illustration below to answer questions 2 and 3.

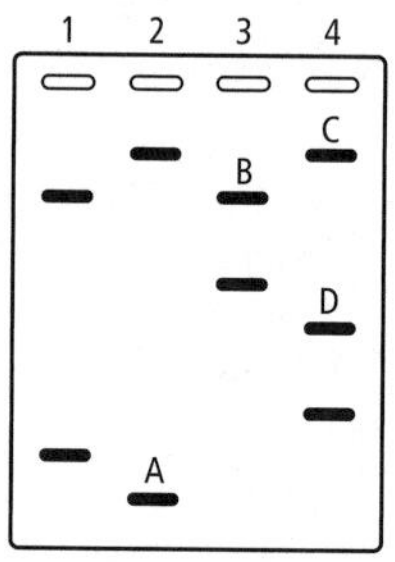

2. The figure above shows bands of DNA that were separated using gel electrophoresis. Which band contains the smallest DNA fragments?
   A. Band A
   B. Band B
   C. Band C
   D. Band D

3. What could the results of this gel electrophoresis show to a scientist?
   A. the amount of noncoding DNA present
   B. the fingerprint of a person's DNA
   C. the number of genes in a piece of DNA
   D. the random patterns of DNA

4. Which process plays a part in genetic recombination?
   A. asexual reproduction
   B. cytokinesis
   C. independent assortment
   D. mitotic division

5. Which correctly lists the following terms in order from smallest to largest: DNA, chromatin, chromosomes, nucleosomes?
   A. chromatin, chromosomes, DNA, nucleosomes
   B. chromosomes, DNA, chromatin, nucleosomes
   C. DNA, nucleosomes, chromatin, chromosomes
   D. nucleosomes, DNA, chromatin, chromosomes

Use the figure below to answer question 6.

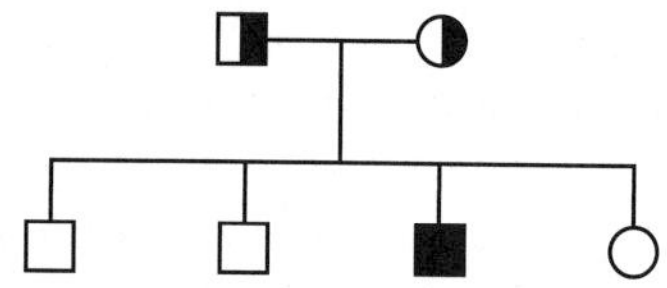

6. In a particular family, one child out of four is born with Tay-Sachs disease. Which pair of symbols represents the parents of these offspring?
   A. 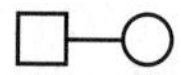
   B. 
   C. 
   D. 

7. Which is a stop codon in mRNA?
   A. AUG
   B. AUU
   C. CAU
   D. UAA

8. In a triploid organism, how many alleles are present for each gene per cell?
   A. 1
   B. 3
   C. 6
   D. 9

Short Answer

Use the figure below to answer question 9.

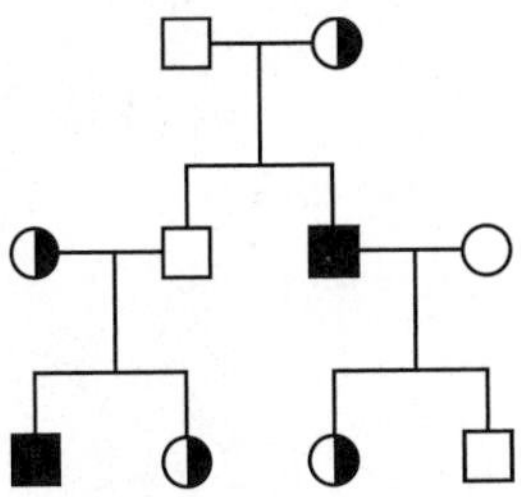

9. The pedigree in the figure tracks a recessive, sex-linked genetic disease. Explain the meaning of the symbols in the last generation.

10. Why are the protein-coding regions of most human genomes identical?

11. If hemophilia is a sex-linked recessive gene, what is the chance that a father with hemophilia and a mother who is a carrier for hemophilia will have a boy with hemophilia? Explain.

12. Compare and contrast the two major processes in protein synthesis.

13. List three genetic disorders; classify them as dominant or recessive; and name the affected organ systems.

14. Why might it take many generations to develop a purebred animal?

15. List the purine bases and the pyrimidine bases in DNA; explain their importance in DNA structure.

Extended Response

16. Give the names of two DNA mutations, and illustrate how each one would change the following DNA sequence.

    CGATTGACGTTTTAGGAT

17. Chemosynthetic autotrophs might have evolved long before the photosynthetic ones that currently are more common on Earth. Propose an explanation for this difference in evolution.

18. Explain how the noncoding sequences in the human genome make it difficult to interpret the DNA code.

19. Even though chloroplasts and mitochondria perform different functions, their structures are similar. Relate the similarity of their structures to their functions.

Essay Question

Suppose a scientist uses gel electrophoresis to separate the DNA extracted from a cell line. After performing the experiment, the scientist observes that several bands are missing and that other bands have traveled to the far end of the gel.

Using the information in the paragraph above, answer the following question in essay format.

20. Using what you know about DNA separation and gel electrophoresis, explain what might have gone wrong with the experiment. Then, describe how to adjust the experimental procedures to test your explanation.

NEED EXTRA HELP?																				
If You Missed Question . . .	1	2	3	4	5	6	7	8	9	10	11	12	13	14	15	16	17	18	19	20
Review Section . . .	9.2	13.2	13.3	10.3	12.1	11.1	12.3	10.3	11.1	13.3	11.3	12.3	11.2	13.1	12.1	12.4	2.2	13.3	7.3	13.2

13. Answers will vary. Possible answers include the following: Cystic fibrosis is a recessive genetic disorder that affects the digestive system and respiratory system. Tay-Sachs disease is recessive and affects the nervous system. Huntington's disease is dominant and affects the nervous system.
14. To produce a pure breed, one must ensure that only alleles coding for the desired form of the trait are present. Because of the allelic frequencies of a population and the fact that some alleles might be masked by the dominant allele, creating a pure breed can take many generations.
15. Purine bases: adenine, guanine; pyrimidine bases: cytosine, thymine. A pyrimidine base to hold the two strands of the DNA chain together. Adenine pairs with thymine; guanine pairs with cytosine.

Extended Response

16. Answers will vary. The chart below shows a possible answer:

Mutation	New sequence
Duplication	CGA**TTG**TTGACGTTTTAGGAT
Insertion (frameshift)	CGA**G**TTGACGTTTTAGGAT

17. Chemosynthesis might have been the only way of making food before there was enough carbon dioxide in the atmosphere for photosynthesis to occur. Also, the environment might have been more conducive to chemosynthesis because certain inorganic gases and chemicals were available in the atmosphere.
18. Noncoding sequences are areas of the code that cannot be read. Anyone who tries to decode the genome has to determine which areas are noncoding and which areas code for proteins.
19. Both chloroplasts and mitochondria are structured to provide a lot of surface area. This is important because the processes taking place—photosynthesis and energy production from sugars—can be maximized with a greater surface area on which the reactions can take place.

Essay Question

20. Answers will vary. One possibility is that the gel electrophoresis process ran for too much time. Because it ran for too long, the separated bands ran off the gel entirely, so it is impossible to observe how they are spaced. The problem could be corrected by running the gel electrophoresis process a second time, for half as much time. That way, all the DNA fragments that form the bands might still be in the gel.

UNIT 4

History of Biological Diversity

Preview the Unit

Have students preview the chapters in this unit and make a concept map or graphic organizer relating the Themes, Big Ideas, and Main Ideas. Students' maps should show a hierarchy between Big Ideas and Main Ideas and the interconnectedness of the Themes.

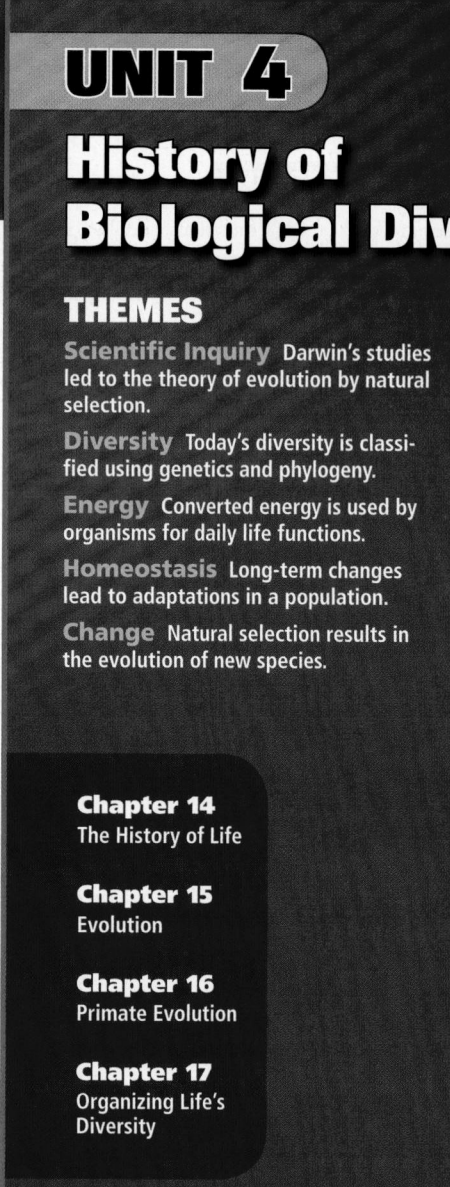

Chapter 14
The History of Life
BIG Idea Fossils provide key evidence for understanding the origin and the history of life on Earth.

Chapter 15
Evolution
BIG Idea The theory of evolution is supported by natural selection and explains the diversity of life.

Chapter 16
Primate Evolution
BIG Idea Evolutionary change in a group of small, tree-living mammals eventually led to a diversity of species that includes modern humans.

Chapter 17
Organizing Life's Diversity
BIG Idea Evolution underlies the classification of life's diversity.

WebQuest
Careers in Biology

UNIT 4

History of Biological Diversity

THEMES

Scientific Inquiry Darwin's studies led to the theory of evolution by natural selection.

Diversity Today's diversity is classified using genetics and phylogeny.

Energy Converted energy is used by organisms for daily life functions.

Homeostasis Long-term changes lead to adaptations in a population.

Change Natural selection results in the evolution of new species.

WebQuest **CAREERS IN BIOLOGY**

Paleontologists study the origins of life on Earth by studying the fossil records. Paleontologists work with other scientists to identify fossils of microscopic organisms, plants, invertebrates, and vertebrates at archaeological sites.

5-Minute UNIT LAUNCH

Visual Literacy—Tables Guide students to the pages in this unit that contain tables, such as Table 1 (p. 422) and Table 2 (p. 471).

ASK STUDENTS: ***What similarities do these tables share? How do they help you to understand the main concepts? Be specific in your responses.*** Student responses will vary, but should explain how the tables can facilitate understanding.

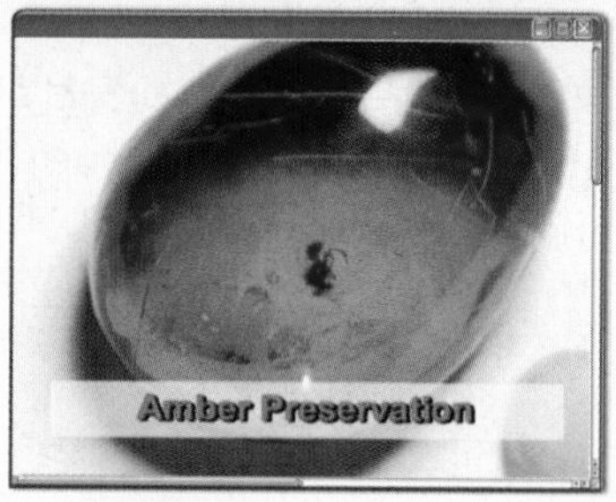

Video

What's BIOLOGY Got To Do With It?
A paleontologist explains how fossils help us understand the past.

Misconceptions

In each section, *Clarify a Misconception* provides you with the information to dispel a common student misconception. A question will help you elicit the misconception, and an explanation will help you correct it.

Below is a preview of misconceptions from each chapter in this unit.

Before studying Chapter 14, students might think that most species are in the fossil record and there are only a few "missing links." Chapter 14 will explain that most organisms were never fossilized because conditions weren't right, but conditions during various spans of time have provided fossils that offer abundant information about past environments (p. 394).

Before studying Chapter 15, students might think that individual organisms evolve. Chapter 15 will explain that populations, not individuals within the populations, evolve (p. 421).

Before studying Chapter 16, students might think that humans evolved from chimpanzees, gorillas, or some other primate that is alive today. Chapter 16 will explain that evolutionary theory suggests that all three species evolved from a common ancestor that is no longer living (p. 463).

Before studying Chapter 17, students might think that most fungi are harmful to humans. Chapter 17 will explain that only about 0.1 percent of known fungi species cause disease in humans (p. 501).

SERVICE LEARNING/COMMUNITY SERVICE

Real-World Experience Arrange for students to volunteer at a local zoo, a wildlife preserve, a natural history museum, or a university geology department, where they can gain additional information about adaptations and evolution. Students will benefit from combining textbook information with their real-world experiences (Zeldin and Tarlov, 1997).

Research bibliography on pages 32T–34T

Chapter 14 Organizer:
The History of Life

LabManager™
Customize any lab with the LabManager™ CD-ROM.

Essential Questions	National Science Standards	Materials and Planning	
		Estimated times include cleanup and disposal, but do not include teacher prep time. For cleanup and disposal guidelines, see page 39T.	Est. Time (min)
Section 1 1. What are the similarities and differences between Earth's early environment and Earth's current environment? 2. What is a typical sequence of events in fossilization? 3. How are the different techniques for dating fossils used? 4 What are the major events on the geologic time scale?	UCP.1–4; A.1, A.2; C.3, C.6; D.3; G.1–3	**Launch Lab,** p. 390: skeletal parts, teeth, diagrams and/or photos of animal skeletons	20
		Activity, p. 393: variety of fossils	10
		Demonstration, p. 394: plaster of Paris, shell or other hard object, modeling clay, cotton swab, petroleum jelly, disposable container such as a shoebox	20
		Demonstration, p. 395: stack of old newspapers or magazines	10
		MiniLab 1, p. 396: container; rocks of various sizes, color, and texture; several soil types; small shells; bones; and fragments	25
		Demonstration, p. 396: alarm clock	5
Section 2 1. What are the differences between spontaneous generation and biogenesis? 2. What might have been the sequence of events that led to cellular life? 3. What is the endosymbiont theory?	UCP.2–5, A.1, A.2; B.2, B.3; C.1, C.3, C.6; D.2; E.1; F.3, F.4; G.1–3	**Demonstration,** p. 406: model or transparency of a cell	15
		BioLab, p. 409: beef broth, Erlenmeyer flasks, ring stands, graduated cylinder, wire gauzes, string, rubber stoppers, bunsen burners, 5-cm plastic tubing, 30-cm plastic tubing	60, 10 per day

Suggested Time for Each Lesson

Class	Chapter Opener	Section 1	Section 2	Assessment
Basic	45 min	90 min	90 min	45 min
General	25 min	55 min	55 min	45 min
Honors	25 min	45 min	90 min	20 min

ConnectED

connectED.mcgraw-hill.com

Access interactive learning opportunities and teaching resources using these icons located throughout your StudentWorks™ Plus Online and eTeacherEdition Online.

Chapter 14 Section Resources	Additional Chapter 14 Resources	Technology
FAST FILE Unit 4 Resources: Launch Lab Worksheet* MiniLab Worksheet* Study Guide (English/Spanish)* Section Quick Check **Reading Essentials 14.1** **Science Notebook 14.1*** **FAST FILE Unit 4 Resources:** BioLab Worksheet* Study Guide (English/Spanish)* Section Quick Check **Reading Essentials 14.2** **Science Notebook 14.2***	**FAST FILE Unit 4 Resources:** Chapter Diagnostic Test Concept Mapping* Real-World Biology Enrichment Chapter Tests A, B, and C **Transparencies:** Bellringer Transparencies* Biology Concepts Transparencies* **Lab Resources:** Laboratory Manual* Probeware Lab Manual* Forensics Lab Manual* Pre-AP Lab Manual* Open Inquiry in Biology* Guided Inquiry in Biology*	**Teaching Tools:** eTeacherEdition Online Classroom Presentation Toolkit CD-ROM* LabManager™ CD-ROM* Video Lab DVD* Virtual Lab CD-ROM* What's BIOLOGY Got To Do With It? StudentWorks™ Plus Online* **Chapter Assessment Tools:** Classroom Presentation Toolkit CD-ROM* *ExamView® Assessment Suite* CD-ROM **Web-Based Resources:** • StudentWorks™ Plus Online • eTeacherEdition Online • Animations* • The Interactive Time Line* • Interactive Tables* • Online Quizzes • Online Test Practice • Standardized Test Practice • Virtual Labs* • Multilingual eGlossary* • Vocabulary eGames* • Vocabulary eFlashcards • WebQuests • Personal Tutors

While all resources listed are appropriate for English learners, the * indicates resources with a strong visual or hands-on component for EL.

Teaching strategies and activities have been coded for differentiated instruction.

AL Activities for students working above grade level	**OL** Activities for students working on grade level	**BL** Activities for students working below grade level	**EL** Activities for English learners (also ELL)	**COOP LEARN** Activities designed for small cooperative group work

CHAPTER 14

Launch Lab
What can skeletal remains reveal?

Inquiry Launch Lab

For a lab worksheet, use your eTeacherEdition Online.

RUBRIC A rubric for evaluating Launch Labs is found on your eTeacherEdition Online.

Est. Time 20 min

Teaching Strategies

- Choose animals whose characteristics should be familiar to students. Provide diagrams and photographs of animal skeletons, as well as bones and teeth if available.
- Provide examples as students develop lists in step 2 of the procedure. Include characteristics such as size, color, movement, food habits, body covering, and social behavior.

Procedure

1. Read and complete the lab safety form.
2. choose an unidentified animal from the list provided by your teacher.
3. Imagine that the animal you selected has been extinct for millions of years. Study **skeletal parts, teeth, diagrams,** and **photos** provided.
4. Based on skeletal remains alone, list the animal's physical and behavioral characteristics.
5. Learn the identity of your animal from your teacher. Now make a new list of characteristics.

CHAPTER 14
The History of Life

ConnectED
Your one-stop online resource
connectED.mcgraw-hill.com

- Video
- Audio
- Review
- Inquiry
- WebQuest
- Assessment
- Concepts in Motion
- Multilingual eGlossary

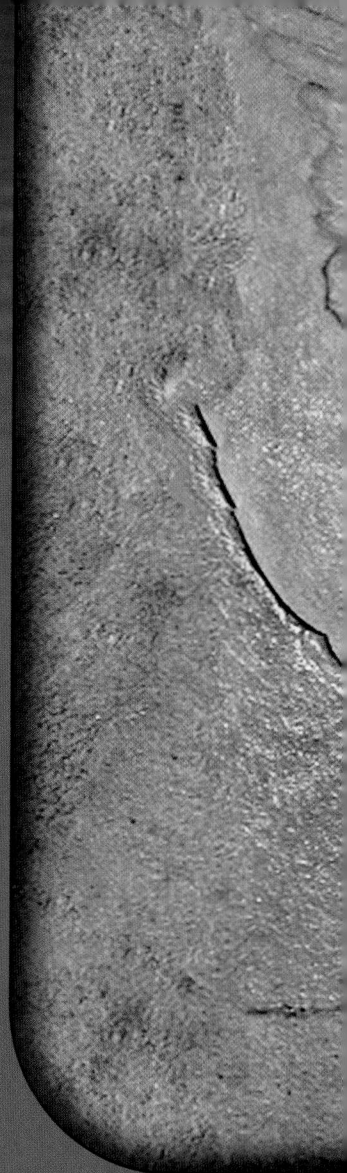

Launch Lab
What can skeletal remains reveal?

Fossils are all that remain of extinct organisms. Paleontologists study fossils to understand how organisms looked and behaved when they lived on Earth. In this lab, you will infer an organism's characteristics based on skeletal remains.

For a lab worksheet, use your StudentWorks™ Plus Online.

Inquiry Launch Lab

FOLDABLES®
Make a folded chart using the titles shown. Use it to organize your notes on the scientists.

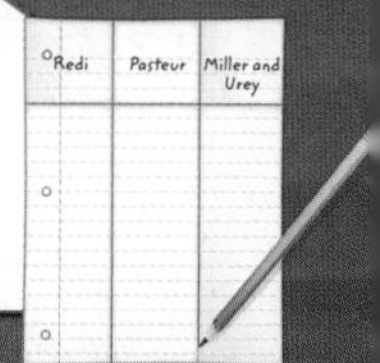

Analysis

1. **Compare** the two lists. Do fossils limit what paleontologists can infer about an extinct organism? Explain. Paleontologists can infer many physical characteristics of an animal based on fossil remains, including size, weight, body structure and posture, movement, and general food source. They can only guess about characteristics such as color, body covering, metabolic processes, offspring, and social behavior based on knowledge of the organism's environment, habitat, or other information.
2. **Conclude** what general characteristics can be inferred about animals based on fossils. Fossils are helpful in identifying physical characteristics related to skeletal features such as length, height, body structure and posture, and method of movement. The shape of a tooth gives clues to an organism's diet.

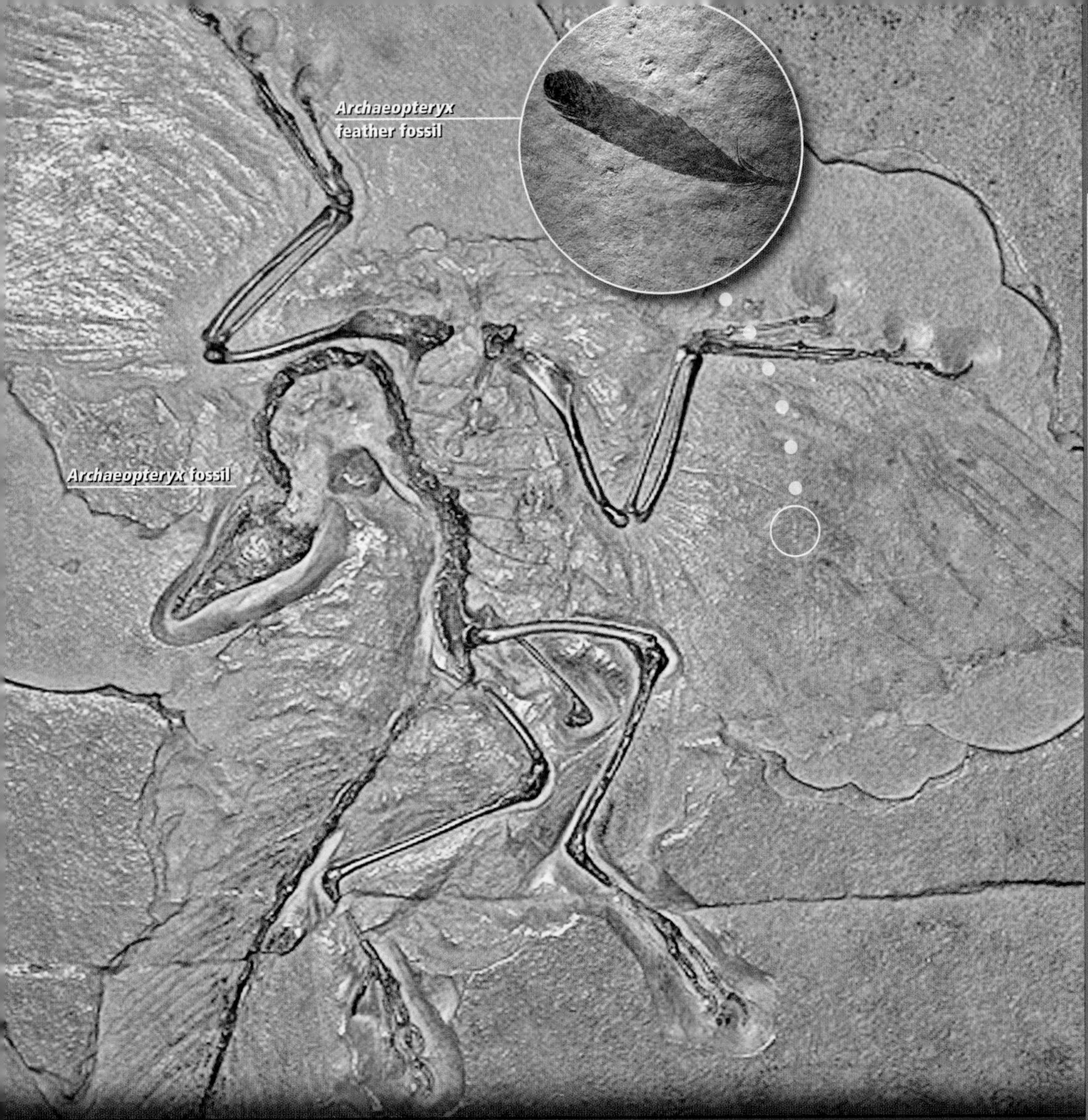

THEME FOCUS Change
Various lines of evidence indicate changes in Earth's environment and life forms over time.

BIG Idea Fossils provide key evidence for understanding the origin and the history of life on Earth.

Section 1 • Fossil Evidence of Change

Section 2 • The Origin of Life

THEMES

Scientific Inquiry Studies using carbon and radioactive dating determine the age of Earth.

Diversity The fossil record shows the diversity of organisms that have lived on Earth.

Energy Energy from lightning is thought to be involved in the origin of life.

Homeostasis Changes in Earth's environment over time led to mass extinctions that maintained homeostasis.

Change Fossil evidence shows how the diversity of organisms has changed over time.

Introduce the Chapter

Fossils

TELL STUDENTS: ***Fossils are the key to understanding past life on Earth. However, not all fossils are as dramatic as the one shown on this page.***

ASK STUDENTS: ***Can you suggest some information that fossils might reveal?*** Answers will vary, but may include that fossils can reveal diet, behavior, anatomy, physiology, or even ecology. In this chapter, students will learn how paleontologists can tell these things about fossils.

BIG Idea

Anticipation Guide Before students begin to read the chapter, direct them to the Big Idea on the Chapter Opener page.

SAY TO STUDENTS: ***The strongest evidence for change during Earth's history, from the earliest life to the present, is found in fossils.*** Call on two students to read the Main Ideas on this page and the Section 2 opener page. Have other students identify how the Main Ideas relate to the themes of scientific inquiry, change, and diversity. Encourage all students to take notes that explain each new major concept they learn in the chapter.

Section 1

MAIN Idea

BL OL AL Evidence of Change **ASK STUDENTS:** ***What is the main evidence available to scientists about life in the past?*** fossils **SAY TO STUDENTS:** ***Without fossils, we would lose much of our understanding about Earth's history. Fossils provide insight into the organisms, the environments, and the geology of life long ago.***

D Develop Concepts

EL BL OL AL Discuss Have students discuss books they might have read or movies they might have seen that describe earlier times in the history of Earth. Show students some pictures from movies that depict prehistoric times. **ASK STUDENTS:** ***How do the events shown in this picture differ from the scientific evidence we have about this period?*** Answers will vary depending on the picture. Use students' answers to start a list on the board of fictional information shown versus depictions that are supported by evidence. ***What is the main mistake usually made in movies about the earliest Earth history?*** Most show living things (often dinosaurs and people) that did not exist at the same time.

S Skill Practice

EL BL OL

Making Comparisons Have students make two columns labeled *Early Earth* and *Earth Today*. As students read this section, have them make comparisons between early and modern land environments and atmospheric composition.

Section 1

Reading Preview

Essential Questions

- What are the similarities and differences between Earth's early environment and Earth's current environment?
- What is a typical sequence of events in fossilization?
- How are the different techniques for dating fossils used?
- What are the major events on the geologic time scale?

Review Vocabulary

extinction: the death of all individuals of a species

New Vocabulary

fossil
paleontologist
relative dating
law of superposition
radiometric dating
half-life
geologic time scale
epoch
period
era
eon
Cambrian explosion
K-T boundary
plate tectonics

Multilingual eGlossary

Fossil Evidence of Change

D MAIN Idea Fossils provide evidence of the change in organisms over time.

Real-World Reading Link Did you know that when you look at the stars at night you are looking into the past? The stars are so far away that the light you see left the stars thousands and sometimes millions of years ago. You also are looking into the past when you look at rocks. The rocks formed thousands or even millions of years ago. Rocks can tell us what Earth was like in the distant past, and sometimes they can tell us what lived during that time.

S Earth's Early History

What were the conditions on Earth as it formed, and how did life arise on a lifeless planet? Because there were no people to witness Earth's earliest history, it might seem that this is an unsolvable mystery. Like any good mystery, however, it left clues behind. Each clue to Earth's history and life's origin is open to investigation by the scientists who study the history of the Earth.

Land environments By studying other planets in the solar system and rocks on Earth, scientists conclude that Earth was a molten body when it formed about 4.6 billion years ago. Gravity pulled the densest elements to the center of the planet. After about 500 million years, a solid crust formed on the surface, much like the crust that forms on the top of lava, shown in **Figure 1.** The surface was rich in lighter elements, such as silicon. From the oldest rocks remaining today, scientists infer that Earth's young surface included a number of volcanic features. In addition, the cooling interior radiated much more heat to the surface than it does today. Meteorites would have caused additional heating as they crashed into Earth's surface. If there had been any life on Earth, it most likely would have been consumed by the intense heat.

Molten lava flow

Figure 1 Lava, molten rock ejected from volcanoes, forms a crust as it cools.
Infer *the importance of the crust to the origin of life on Earth.*

Caption Question Fig. 1 Possible answer: Earth's crust had to have cooled and solidified before life could have existed on Earth because before that time, the heat would have been too intense for organisms to survive.

Differentiated Instruction

Below Level Students who are working below grade level will benefit when they understand the goals of a lesson from the beginning. Explain the learning expectations at the beginning of a lesson to help these students.

For more tips, see pages 14T–15T.

Atmosphere Because of its gravitational field, Earth is a planet that is able to maintain an atmosphere. However, no one can be certain about the exact composition of Earth's early atmosphere. The gases that likely made up the atmosphere are those that were expelled by volcanoes. Volcanic gases today include water vapor (H_2O), carbon dioxide (CO_2), sulfur dioxide (SO_2), carbon monoxide (CO), hydrogen sulfide (H_2S), hydrogen cyanide (HCN), nitrogen (N_2), and hydrogen (H_2). Scientists infer that the same gases would have been present in Earth's early atmosphere. The minerals in the oldest known rocks suggest that the early atmosphere, unlike today's atmosphere, had little or no free oxygen.

D

C

Clues in Rocks

Earth eventually cooled to the point where liquid water formed on its surface, which became the first oceans. It was a short time after this—maybe as little as 500 million years—that life first appeared. The earliest clues about life on Earth date to about 3.5 billion years ago.

The fossil record A **fossil** is any preserved evidence of an organism. Six categories of fossils are shown in **Table 1.** Plants, animals, and even bacteria can form fossils. Although there is a rich diversity of fossils, the fossil record is like a book with many missing pages. Perhaps more than 99 percent of the species that ever have lived are now extinct, but only a tiny percentage of these organisms are preserved as fossils.

Most organisms decompose before they have a chance to become fossilized. Only those organisms that are buried rapidly in sediment are readily preserved. This occurs more frequently with organisms living in water because the sediment in aquatic environments is constantly settling, covering, and preserving the remains of organisms.

VOCABULARY
WORD ORIGIN
Fossil
from the Latin word *fossilis,* meaning *dug up*

Video
What's BIOLOGY Got To Do With It?

Table 1 Categories of Fossil Types

Concepts in Motion Interactive Table

Category	Trace fossil	Molds and casts	Replacement	Petrified or permineralized	Amber	Original material
Example					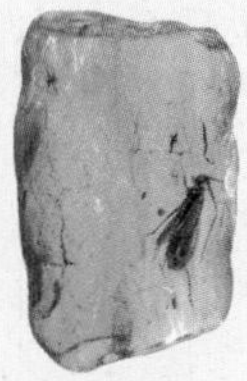	
Formation	A trace fossil is any indirect evidence left by an organism. Footprints, burrows, and fossilized feces are trace fossils.	A mold is an impression of an organism. A cast is a mold filled with sediment.	The original material of an organism is replaced with mineral crystals that can leave detailed replicas of hard or soft parts.	Empty pore spaces are filled in by minerals, such as in petrified wood.	Preserved tree sap traps an entire organism. The sap hardens into amber and preserves the trapped organism.	Mummification or freezing preserves original organisms.

Activity

Fossil Variety Display a variety of fossils one at a time. Whenever possible, try to use fossils that were obtained from the local area. (Local geological societies are a good resource for obtaining fossil samples. Many biological supply houses sell fossil casts. Some fossil dealers donate damaged specimens to schools. Check with local colleges for fossils that may be loaned or donated to the school. Also, check to see if there is a graduate student or professor that may be willing to come to the school to do a demonstration for a day.) Have students examine the fossils and identify the category of each and the way in which the fossil was formed. Est. time: 10 min

C Critical Thinking

BL OL AL Infer

SAY TO STUDENTS: ***If Earth was larger and its density remained the same, there would be a stronger gravitational field and, potentially, a thicker atmosphere. If it was smaller, the opposite would be true.***
ASK STUDENTS: ***What would be the effect on the atmosphere if the density was less, but the size was the same?*** There would be a weaker gravitational field and, therefore, a thinner atmosphere.

D Develop Concepts

OL AL Integrate Chemistry

SAY TO STUDENTS: ***If you have ever smelled rotten eggs or the acrid odor from a match just after it has been struck, you have smelled hydrogen sulfide. Hydrogen sulfide is a gas made by combining sulfur with hydrogen.***
ASK STUDENTS: ***What is the formula for hydrogen sulfide, and how many atoms of each element does it take to make a molecule of hydrogen sulfide?*** H_2S; two hydrogen atoms and one sulfur atom

Skill Practice

EL BL OL

Use Graphic Organizers

Instruct students to make layered graphic organizers by using two pieces of paper that are attached at the top. Have them cut the top piece of paper into six equal horizontal tabs. On the top tab, have students label the category of fossil; on the back of this tab, have them draw an example of the fossil. On the second sheet, have them write a description of how each fossil was formed. They can use Table 1 as a reference.

Concepts in Motion
Interactive Table

D Develop Concepts

BL OL

Clarify a Misconception

Many students harbor the misconception that most species can be found in the fossil record and that there are only a few "missing links" that have yet to be observed. **ASK STUDENTS:** ***Have you ever seen a dead bird around your home or an animal that has been struck and killed by a car?*** Most students will answer that they have. ***Do you think these animals will become fossils?*** No, they were either eaten by carrion feeders or carried off by the sanitation department. Point out that fossilization is a rare occurrence. Most organisms are never fossilized because the conditions are not just right. However, many fossils have formed that provide abundant information about past environments because large spans of time have provided many opportunities for fossilization.

Writing Support

BL OL Informal Writing Have students imagine that they are paleontologists on a dig in Utah. Have them write a letter to a friend explaining their work for a day. Give students the opportunity to share their letters with the class.

S Skill Practice

BL Observe and Infer Have students suggest other analogies for the law of superposition other than stacking newspapers. possible answer: layers of old paint on a house

Figure 2 **(A)** Organisms usually become fossilized after they die and are buried by sediment. **(B)** Sediments build up in layers, eventually encasing the remains in sedimentary rock. **(C)** Minerals replace, or fill in the pore space of, the bones and hard parts of the organism. **(D)** Erosion can expose the fossils.

Study Tip

Background Knowledge Check Based on what you know, predict the meaning of each new vocabulary term before reading the section. As you read, check the actual meaning compared to your prediction.

D

Fossil formation Fossils do not form in igneous (IHG nee us) or metamorphic (meh tuh MOR fihk) rocks. Igneous rocks form when magma from Earth's interior cools. Metamorphic rocks form when rocks are exposed to extreme heat and pressure. Fossils usually do not survive the heat or pressure involved in the formation of either of these kinds of rocks.

Nearly all fossils are formed in sedimentary rock through the process illustrated in **Figure 2.** The organism dies and is buried in sediments. The sediments build up until they cover the organism's remains. In some cases, minerals replace the organic matter or fill the empty pore spaces of the organism. In other cases, the organism decays, leaving behind an impression of its body. The sediments eventually harden into rock.

A **paleontologist** (pay lee ahn TAH luh jist) is a scientist who studies fossils. He or she attempts to read the record of life left in rocks. From fossil evidence, paleontologists infer the diet of an organism and the environment in which it lived. In fact, paleontologists often can create images of extinct communities.

Connection to Earth Science When geologists began to study rock layers, or strata, in different areas, they noticed that layers of the same age tended to have the same kinds of fossils no matter where the rocks were found. The geologists inferred that all strata of the same age contained similar collections of fossils. This led to the establishment of a relative age scale for rocks all over the world.

Dating fossils **Relative dating** is a method used to determine the age of rocks by comparing them with those in other layers. Relative dating is based on the **law of superposition,** illustrated in **Figure 3,** which states that younger layers of rock are deposited on top of older layers. The process is similar to stacking newspapers in a pile as you read them each day. Unless you disturb the newspapers, the oldest ones will be on the bottom. S

Demonstration

Plaster Casts Show students how fossils form by making a plaster cast. Do this by pressing a shell or another hard object into a layer of modeling clay set inside a shoe box or another type of disposable container. Remove the shell and use a cotton swab to gently coat the shell's impression with petroleum jelly. Pour plaster of Paris into the impression. Let the plaster set. Then remove the plaster from the clay and show the "fossil" to students. Point out that the main requirement for fossilization is that the material must be buried quickly. Est. time: 20 min

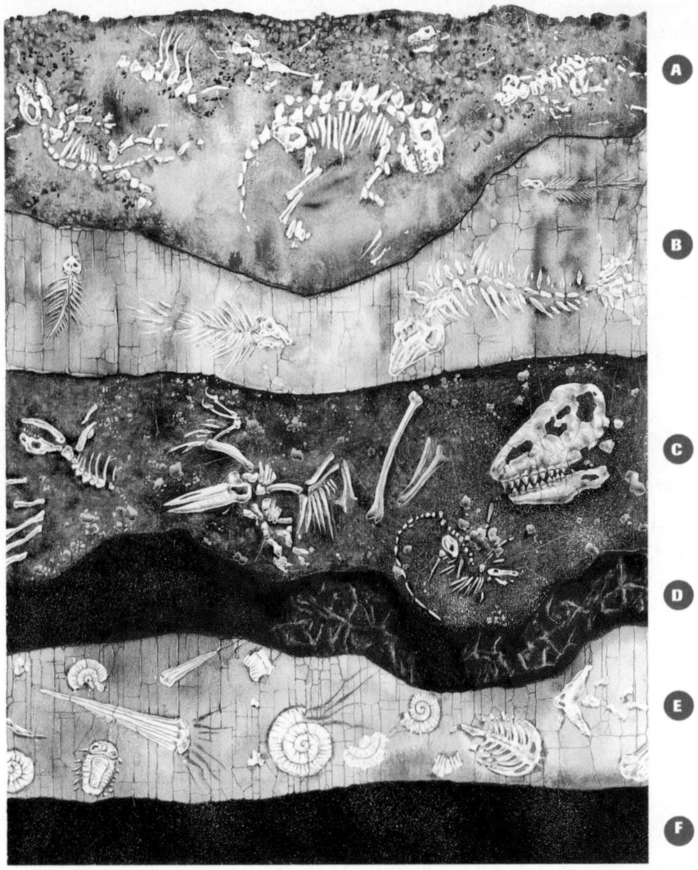

■ **Figure 3** According to the law of superposition, rock layers are deposited with the youngest undisturbed layers on top. **Infer** *which layer shows that an aquatic ecosystem replaced a land ecosystem.*

S

Radiometric dating uses the decay of radioactive isotopes to measure the age of a rock. Recall that an isotope is a form of an element that has the same atomic number but a different mass number. The method requires that the **half-life** of the isotope, which is the amount of time it takes for half of the original isotope to decay, is known. The relative amounts of the radioactive isotope and its decay product must also be known.

One radioactive isotope that is commonly used to determine the age of rocks is Uranium 238. Uranium 238 (U^{238}) decays to Lead 206 (Pb^{206}) with a half life of 4510 million years. When testing a rock sample, scientists calculate the ratio of the parent isotope to the daughter isotope to determine the age of the sample.

Radioactive isotopes that can be used for radiometric dating are found only in igneous or metamorphic rocks, not in sedimentary rocks, so isotopes cannot be used to date rocks that contain fossils. Igneous rocks that are found in layers closely associated with fossil-bearing sedimentary rocks often can be used for assigning relative dates to fossils.

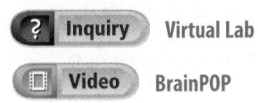

? Inquiry Virtual Lab

Video BrainPOP

S Skill Practice

BL OL Visual Literacy Have students examine the sequence of events shown in Figure 3.
ASK STUDENTS: ***What are some places today where sediment might quickly cover organisms and produce fossils in the future?*** Streambeds, lakes, oceans, sand dunes, and landslides are all likely candidates that students might suggest. ***Are unaltered fossils in ice and amber formed the same way as those in the illustration?*** No, unaltered fossils are trapped in ice or tree sap first. ***Are trace fossils formed the same way?*** No, trace fossils, such as a worm's burrow or a bird's tracks, are only the indirect evidence of the organism.

Develop Concepts

BL OL

Activate Prior Knowledge

ASK STUDENTS: ***Why is it important for paleontologists to understand the basics of chemistry, geology, and physics?*** Student responses will vary, but might include suggestions that although principles from each field provide some of the evidence, none supplies all of it.
AL ASK STUDENTS: ***How is chemistry related to paleontology?*** The chemistry of the rocks may give an indication about what the environment was like. ***How is geology related to paleontology?*** Geology can explain how the fossils got to be where they are. ***How is physics related to paleontology?*** Physics can help to explain the rock's formation or why bones were crushed in a particular way.

Video Brain POP

■ **Caption Question Fig. 3** Layer B

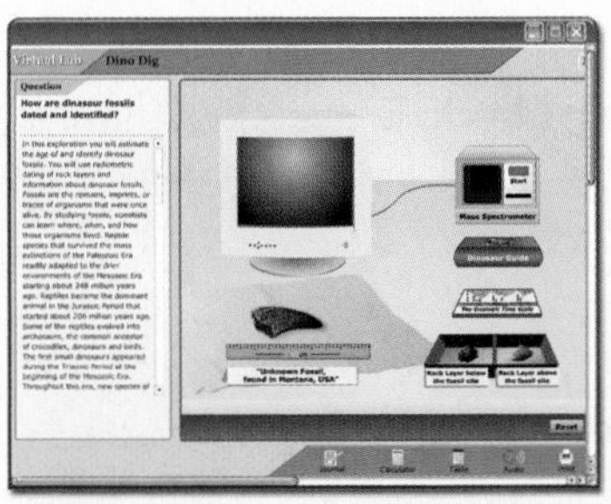

? Inquiry **Virtual Lab** Students will use radiometric dating techniques to determine the age of rock layers and fossil remains.

Demonstration

Relative Dating Use a stack of old newspapers or magazines that are chronologically arranged to illustrate the law of superposition and relative dating. You can also demonstrate how geological processes such as faulting and folding can change the original order by shifting older periodicals to younger parts of the stack.
Est. time: 10 min

MiniLab 1

Inquiry MiniLab

For a lab worksheet, use your eTeacherEdition Online.

RUBRIC A rubric for evaluating MiniLabs is found on your eTeacherEdition Online.

Est. Time 25 min

Additional Materials rocks of varying size, color, and texture; several soil types; small shells, bones, and fragments

Safety Precaution Approve lab safety forms before work begins.

Teaching Strategies

- Prepare containers by adding varying amounts of shell and bone, soil, and rock particles. Add water to the container and shake until sedimentary particles are well mixed. Then let the particles settle.
- Point out that while the materials settled out in the short term based on density, sedimentary rock forms in layers over long periods of time. The oldest material, not the densest, will be found in the deepest layers.

Analysis

1. Answers will vary. The oldest fossils are found in the deepest layers; the youngest fossils are found closest to the surface.
2. Possible answer: If different layers contained the same materials, I would conclude the environment did not change over a long period of time. If some layers didn't overlap, I would look for disturbances in the strata and compare the strata to other sites in the area.

LabManager™

Customize this lab with the LabManager™ CD-ROM.

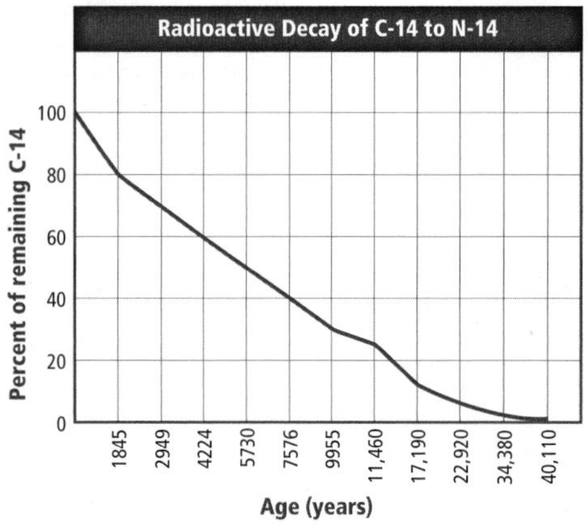

Figure 4 The graph shows how the percent of carbon-14 remaining in a sample indicates age.

Interpret the graph ***What would the age of a bone be if it contained only 10 percent of C-14?***

Materials, such as mummies, bones, and tissues, can be dated directly using carbon-14 (C-14). Given the half-life of carbon-14, shown in **Figure 4,** only materials less than 60,000 years old can be dated accurately with this isotope.

The Geologic Time Scale

Think of geologic time as a ribbon that is 4.6 m long. If each meter represents one billion years, each millimeter represents one million years. Earth was formed at one end of the ribbon, and humans appear at the tip of the opposite end.

The **geologic time scale** is a record of Earth's history. Major geological and biological events in Earth's history can be identified within the geologic time scale. Because geologic time spans more than 4 billion years, subdivisions of time are used to identify how many millions of years ago (mya) an event occurred. The geologic time scale is divided into two segments—Precambrian time and the Phanerozoic eon.

Epochs, which last several million years, are the smallest units of geologic time. **Periods,** which last tens of millions of years, are divisions of geologic time consisting of two or more epochs. An **era,** which lasts hundreds of millions of years, is a unit of geologic time consisting of two or more periods. An **eon** is the longest unit of time in the geologic time scale and can include billions of years. **Figure 5** shows a portion of the geologic time scale that includes the Phanerozoic eon.

Reading Check **Explain** why C-14 would not be useful for dating something from the Precambrian.

MiniLab 1

Inquiry MiniLab

Correlate Rock Layers Using Fossils

How can paleontologists establish relative age? Scientists use fossils from many locations to piece together the sequence of Earth's rock layers. This is the process of correlation.

Procedure

1. Read and complete the lab safety form.
2. Your teacher will assign you to a group and will give your group a **container** with layers of material embedded with fossils.
3. Carefully remove each layer, noting any embedded materials.
4. Make a sketch of the cross section, and label each layer and any materials contained within it.
5. Collect copies of sketches from the other groups and use them to determine the sequence of all the layers the class has studied.

Analysis

1. **Describe** the materials in each cross section. What patterns did you observe?
2. **Explain** how your analysis would be different if different layers contained the same materials. What if some of the layers didn't overlap? Suggest a way to gather additional data that might resolve these issues.

Demonstration

Time Scale Demonstrate the geologic time scale using an alarm clock set to 12:00. Tell students that each of the 12 h increments represents roughly 375 million years of Earth's history. Set the clock to 9:30 to represent the first living cells; 10:56 to represent the end of the Precambrian; and 11:33 to represent the end of the Paleozoic era. Est. time: 5 min

Caption Question Fig. 4 approximately 20,000 y

Reading Check C-14 does not have a long enough half life to date something that old.

Visualizing the Geologic Time Scale

Figure 5
This figure illustrates the Phanerozoic eon of the geologic time scale. The major biologic events during the Phanerozoic eon are described in the figure. All of the times listed are approximate and as in all science fields, continuing research and discoveries might result in future revisions.

Eon	Era	Period	Epoch	MYA	Biological events
Phanerozoic	Cenozoic	Neogene	Holocene		• Humans form civilizations
			Pleistocene	0.01	• Ice ages occur • Modern humans appear
			Pliocene	1.8	• Hominins appear • Flowering plants are dominant
			Miocene	5.3	• Apes appear • Climate is cooler
			Oligocene	23.0	• Monkeys appear • Climate is mild
		Paleogene	Eocene	33.9	• Flowering plants scattered • Most mammal orders exist
			Paleocene	55.8	• Mammals, birds, and insects scatter • Climate is tropical
	Mass extinction K-T Boundary				
	Mesozoic	Cretaceous		65.5	• Flowering plants appear • Dinosaur population peaks
		Jurassic		145.5	• First birds appear • Dinosaurs scatter • Forests are lush
		Mass extinction			
		Triassic		199.6	• Gymnosperms are dominant • Dinosaurs appear • First mammals appear
	Mass extinction				
	Paleozoic	Permian		251.0	• Reptiles scatter • Gymnosperms appear
		Carboniferous		299.0	• Ferns and evergreens make up forests • Amphibians appear • Insects scatter
		Mass extinction			
		Devonian		359.2	• Sharks and bony fishes appear • Tetrapods appear
		Silurian		416.0	• Coral and other invertebrates are dominant • Land plants and insects appear
		Mass extinction			
		Ordovician		443.7	• First vertebrates appear • First plants appear
		Cambrian		488.3	• Cambrian explosion • All body plans arise

Concepts in Motion Animation

"Education is learning what you didn't even know you didn't know."

—Daniel J. Boorstin

Visualizing the Geologic Time Scale

Purpose

Students will assess lengths of geologic eras and periods and identify when biological events occurred. UCP.2, UCP.3, UCP.4, C.3, D.3

Skill Practice

BL OL Sequence Emphasize the sequence of events illustrated by the geologic time scale.

SAY TO STUDENTS: ***The geologic time scale is a model that helps in comprehending biological events. Eras and periods are defined by geological events, such as particular layers in the rocks or when chemicals such as oxygen become present.***

ASK STUDENTS: ***In which era did the Cretaceous period occur?*** Mesozoic ***In which period of the Paleozoic era did vertebrates first appear?*** Ordovician

Skill Practice

EL BL COOP LEARN

Use a Model Give pairs of students a 5-meter roll of paper. Cash register paper works well, as does butcher paper. Have students use a meterstick to copy the eras, periods, and biological events in their proper sequence.

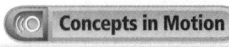

Concepts in Motion
Animation

R Reading Strategy

EL BL OL Anticipation Guide Before they read the summary of events in the various eras of geological history, have students answer "true" or false" to ten statements about the content. After they read, have students validate or revise their answers.

C Critical Thinking

OL AL Hypothesize
ASK STUDENTS: ***Why do you think it took 113 years to add the Ediacaran period to the geologic time scale?*** Possible answer: Scientists found new fossils from that time and so they added the period. Because this period was between 630 and 542 million years ago, little evidence about it was available. It has taken this long for scientists to be confident that they knew enough to justify a new period.

D Develop Concepts

EL BL OL Activity Set up microscopes with samples of *Oscillatoria, Nostoc,* or another cyanobacteria. Have students sketch and label what they see. Explain to students that by the Paleozoic era, the photosynthetic action of organisms similar to the cyanobacteria had increased oxygen levels from nearly zero to near today's level.
AL ASK STUDENTS: ***Infer how these organisms obtain energy.*** with their chlorophyll through photosynthesis ***What is a waste product of photosynthesis?*** oxygen ***How did increasing the atmosphere's oxygen levels affect the development of life on Earth?*** It allowed oxygen-requiring organisms to evolve.

Reading Check photosynthesis or chemoautotrophic processes

Caption Question Fig. 6 These organisms filled the atmosphere with oxygen.

Figure 6 Fossils much like these stromatolites are found in rocks almost 3.5 billion years old.
Explain *the importance of the organisms that left these stromatolites.*

Precambrian The first 4 billion years of Earth's history make up the Precambrian. This is nearly 90 percent of Earth's entire history, stretching from the formation of Earth to the beginning of the Paleozoic era about 542 million years ago. During the Precambrian, Earth formed and life first appeared. Eventually, autotrophic prokaryotes, much like the cyanobacteria that made the stromatolites in **Figure 6,** enriched the atmosphere with oxygen. Eukaryotic cells also emerged, and by the end of the Precambrian, life was flourishing and the first animals had appeared. R

Extensive glaciation marked the second half of the Precambrian. This might have delayed the further evolution of life until the ice receded at the beginning of the Ediacaran (ee dee UH kur uhn) period. The Ediacaran period was added to the time scale in 2004. It was the first new period added to the time scale since 1891 and reflects new knowledge of Earth's history. The Ediacaran period lasted from about 630 million years ago to about 542 million years ago, representing about three quarters of a meter on the time ribbon at the end of the Precambrian. Simple organisms, such as the fossil in **Figure 7,** inhabited Ediacaran marine ecosystems. Food chains probably were short, and were dominated by animals that consumed tiny particles suspended in the water and by animals that ate debris on the bottom of the sea. C

Reading Check **Infer** the process by which early autotrophic prokaryotes produced oxygen.

The Paleozoic era A drastic change in the history of animal life on Earth marked the start of the Paleozoic (pay lee uh ZOH ihk) era. In the space of just a few million years, the ancestors of most major animal groups diversified in what scientists call the **Cambrian explosion.** Not all major groups of organisms evolved rapidly at this time, and paleontologists still do not know when the rapid changes started or ended.

Major changes in ocean life occurred during the Paleozoic. More importantly, it seems the first life on land emerged during this era. Life in the oceans continued to evolve through the Cambrian period. Fish, land plants, and insects appeared during the Ordovician and Silurian periods. Organisms of many kinds, including huge insects, soon flourished in swampy forests that dominated the land, as shown in **Figure 8.** Tetrapods, the first land vertebrates (animals with backbones), emerged in the Devonian period. By the end of the Carboniferous period, the first reptiles were roaming the forests. D

Figure 7 Paleontologists disagree about scarce Ediacaran fossils such as this one. Some paleontologists suggest that they are relatives of today's living invertebrates such as segmented worms, while others think they represent an evolutionary dead end of giant protists or simple metazoans.

Research Citation

Anticipation Guides Educational research indicates that anticipation guides like the one described on this page can help students better understand reading assignments. Asking students to think about the content before they read will activate their background knowledge and precipitate discussion. (Readence, Bean, and Baldwin, 1985)

Research bibliography on pages 32T–34T

Figure 8 During the Carboniferous period, swamp forests covered much of Earth's land surface. Insects dominated the air, and tetrapods flourished in freshwater pools. **Infer** *how the plants of the Paleozoic era were different from those of today.*

A mass extinction ended the Paleozoic era at the end of the Permian period. Recall that a mass extinction is an event in which many species become extinct in a short time. Mass extinctions have occurred every several million years with varying frequencies. Between 60 and 75 percent of the species W alive went extinct in each of these events. During the Permian mass extinction, 90 percent of marine organisms disappeared. Geologists disagree about the cause of the Permian extinction, but most agree that geological forces, including increased volcanic activity, would have disrupted ecosystems or changed the climate.

The Mesozoic era At the beginning of the Triassic period, the ancestors of early mammals were the dominant land animals. Mammals and dinosaurs first appeared late in the Triassic period, and flowering plants evolved from nonflowering plants. Birds evolved from a group of predatory dinosaurs in the middle Jurassic period. For the rest of the Mesozoic, reptiles, such as the dinosaurs illustrated in **Figure 9,** were the dominant organisms on the planet. Then, about 65 million years ago, a meteorite struck Earth.

The primary evidence for this meteorite impact is found in a layer of material between the rocks of the Cretaceous (krih TAY shus) period and the rocks of the Paleogene period, the first period of the Cenozoic era. Paleontologists call this layer the **K-T boundary.** Within this layer, scientists find unusually high levels of an element called iridium. Iridium is rare on Earth, but relatively common in meteorites. Therefore, the presence of iridium on Earth indicates a meteorite impact.

Many scientists think that this impact is related to the mass extinction at the end of the Mesozoic era, which eliminated all dinosaurs, with the exception of their avian and reptilian descendents, many marine invertebrates, and numerous plant species. The meteorite did not wipe out all of these species, but the debris from the impact probably stayed in the atmosphere for months or even years, affecting global climate. Species that could not adjust to the changing climate disappeared.

Reading Check **Recall** the dominant land animals in the Triassic and Jurassic periods.

Figure 9 The dominant organisms during the Mesozoic era were dinosaurs. A mass extinction occurred at the end of the Mesozoic era that eliminated approximately 60 percent of all species living during the Mesozoic era.

W Writing Support

BL OL Summary Writing

Have students write a summary of what the Paleozoic era was like using the following terms: *invertebrates, land plants, swamp, amphibian, armored fish,* and *reptiles.*

Develop Concepts

AL Integrate Math

SAY TO STUDENTS: ***Over 1.5 million species have been named and described. Suppose that a mass extinction was expected to occur in a hundred years.***

ASK STUDENTS: ***If the mass extinction was an "average" one in which 30 percent of the species survived, how many species would there be after the extinctions?*** 1.5 million × 0.30 = 0.45 million, or 450,000 Discuss the likelihood of humans surviving such a mass extinction event. Ask students to consider the organisms on which humans rely. Possible answer: Humans rely mostly on flowering plants for their food. Humans rely on photosynthetic organisms for oxygen. Have students consider what would happen to humans if the organisms on which humans rely became extinct. Ask students how humans might survive without these organisms.

Caption Question Fig. 8 There were no flowering plants.

Reading Check Dinosaurs were the dominant animals during the Mesozoic era.

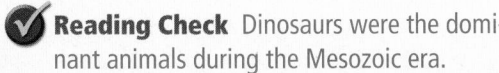

Differentiated Instruction

Above Level When assigning written work, encourage gifted students to monitor their own and other students' progress. Develop rubrics that can be used for self-editing and peer-editing of written work to encourage these students to reflect on and evaluate the quality of their work.

For more tips, see pages 14T–15T.

Concepts in Motion
Animation

Formative Assessment

Evaluation Provide a mixed list of example fossils, categories of fossils, and methods of fossil formation using Table 1. (Example list item: example fossil—a sabertoothed cat from the La Brea Tar Pits; category—original material; method of fossil formation—preservation) Have students rearrange the list so that it provides an accurate match between fossil category, method of fossilization, and example.

Remediation Have students write the categories of fossils on six index cards, the way fossils are formed on six cards, and an example from each category on six cards. Once they have decks of 18 cards, have students shuffle the deck and work in groups of three to place the three appropriate cards together. Alternatively, students can make up their own matching games to play with the cards.

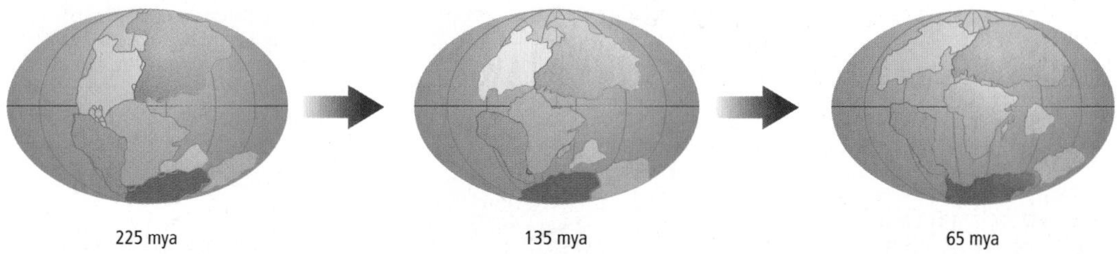

Figure 10 These illustrations show the movement of Earth's major tectonic plates from about 225 million years ago, when all of the continents were joined into one landmass called Pangaea, to 65 million years ago.

Concepts in Motion
Animation

Scientists also think that the course of evolution in the Cenozoic era was shaped by the massive geological changes shown in **Figure 10** that characterized the Mesozoic era. While it might appear to us that continents are immobile, they have been moving since they formed. Alfred Wegener, a German scientist, presented the first evidence for continental drift in the 1920s. Continental drift has since become part of the theory of plate tectonics. **Plate tectonics** describes the movement of several large plates that make up the surface of Earth. These plates, some of which contain continents, move atop a partially molten layer of rock underneath them.

The Cenozoic era The most recent era is the one in which mammals became the dominant land animals. At the beginning of the Cenozoic (sen uh ZOH ihk) era, which means "recent life," most mammals were small and resembled shrews. After the mass extinction at the end of the Mesozoic era, mammals began to diversify into distinct groups, including primates—the group to which you belong. Humans appeared very recently, near the end of the geologic time scale, in the current Neogene period. Humans survived the last ice age, but many species of mammals did not. To get an idea of how recently modern humans have appeared, you need to remove about two threads at the end of your geologic time ribbon. These threads represent the time that humans have existed on Earth.

Section 1 Assessment

Section Summary

- Fossils provide evidence of past life.
- Relative dating and radiometric dating are two methods used to determine the age of fossils.
- The geologic time scale is divided into eras, periods, and epochs.
- Major events in the geological time scale include both biological and geological changes.

Understand Main Ideas

1. MAIN Idea **Discuss** how fossils provide evidence of change from the earliest life-forms to those alive today.
2. **Diagram** a typical sequence of events in fossilization.
3. **Discuss** two ways that radiometric dating can be used to establish the age of a fossil.
4. **Compare** Earth's early land environment with today's land environment.

Think Critically

5. **Infer** what changes you might observe in the fossil record that would indicate the occurrence of a mass extinction.

MATH in Biology

6. Out of the total of Earth's history (approximately 4.6 billion years), modern humans have existed for only 100,000 years. To put this in perspective, calculate the percentage of Earth's history that modern humans have existed.

Section 1 Assessment

1. The record of fossils shows the appearance of different organisms at different geological times. As evidenced by fossils, species have changed from unicellular life-forms to the most complex forms through time.
2. Possible answer: death, followed by rapid burial, followed by additional sedimentation and fossilization, and erosion
3. Unaltered material younger than 60,000 years old can be dated directly using carbon-14. Fossils have to be dated relative to radioisotopes in adjacent igneous or metamorphic rocks.
4. Earth's early land environment was hot and Earth was molten lava. Once a solid crust formed, life could begin. Today's land environments are lush with plant and animal vegetation.
5. Many fossils before the event would be absent after it, and new species would have appeared.
6. 0.002 percent

Assessment Online Quiz

Reading Preview

Essential Questions

- What are the differences between spontaneous generation and biogenesis?
- What might have been the sequence of events that led to cellular life?
- What is the endosymbiont theory?

Review Vocabulary

amino acid: building blocks for proteins

New Vocabulary

spontaneous generation
theory of biogenesis
endosymbiont theory

Multilingual eGlossary

R The Origin of Life

MAIN Idea Evidence indicates that a sequence of chemical events preceded the origin of life on Earth and that life has evolved continuously since that time.

Real-World Reading Link In a recipe, some steps can be out of order, but some steps have to occur earlier than others or the end result will be different from what was intended. In the same way, to arrive at the pattern of life that is seen today, events leading to the emergence of life had to occur in specific ways.

Origins: Early Ideas

Perhaps one of the oldest ideas about the origin of life is spontaneous generation. **Spontaneous generation** is the idea that life arises from nonlife. For example, at one time people thought that mice could be created by placing damp hay and corn in a dark corner, or that mud could give rise to worms, insects, and fish. These ideas might seem humorous to us today, but before much was known about reproduction, it is easy to see how someone might form these conclusions.

One of the first recorded investigations of spontaneous generation came in 1668. Francesco Redi, an Italian scientist, tested the idea that flies arose spontaneously from rotting meat. He hypothesized that flies—not meat—produced other flies. In his experiment, illustrated using present-day equipment in **Figure 11,** Redi observed that maggots, the larvae of flies, appeared only in flasks that were open to flies. Closed flasks had no flies and no maggots. The results of his experiments failed to convince everyone, however. Although people were beginning to use the microscope during Redi's time and knew that organisms invisible to the naked eye could be found almost everywhere, some thought that these tiny organisms must arise spontaneously, even if flies did not.

Figure 11 Francesco Redi showed that flies and maggots did not arise spontaneously from rotting meat.
Infer *the purpose of the covered flask in Redi's experiment.*

Content Background

Teacher FYI The material in this section will be controversial for some students. You might wish to emphasize that no one is certain about life's origins, but that this section will lay out the scientific evidence from various observations, inferences, and experiments. The section includes only scientific hypotheses that can be tested. Also emphasize that ideas about the origins of life are separate from the theory of evolution, which students will study in detail in later chapters.

Section 2

MAIN Idea

BL OL AL Life's Origins

SAY TO STUDENTS: ***People have speculated about life's origins for centuries. However, it has been only for the past sixty years or so that scientists have experimented to understand how life might have begun. Look again at the geologic time scale and consider what you have learned about the diverse environments in which organisms live today.***
ASK STUDENTS: ***What environmental conditions do you think scientists might simulate to investigate the origins of life?*** Answers will vary, but might include an atmosphere with water vapor, carbon monoxide, carbon dioxide, sulfur compounds, hydrogen cyanide, nitrogen and hydrogen gases; little or no oxygen; very warm temperatures; and, aquatic habitats.

R Reading Strategy

EL BL OL COOP LEARN

Preview the Text Before reading, have students examine the section headings, the captions, and the bolded text. Then have them share with a partner one thing they think they will learn in this section. Next, have them ask one question that might be answered in this section. Have each pair write down their two sentences and two questions. After you discuss the section, have the pairs reexamine their sentences and questions to determine if their sentences were correct and if their questions were answered.

Caption Question Fig. 11
A covered flask ensured no flies were in the experimental group.

S Skill Practice

BL OL AL Visual Literacy

Have students use Figure 11 and Figure 12 to compare the scientific methods used by Redi and Pasteur. Call on individual students to identify one of the scientific methods used and where it was used in one or the other experiment. Have other students explain the purpose of using each method described. Sample answer: Both Redi and Pasteur used controlled experiments to test their hypotheses. Each experiment had one variable—the exposure to air.

C Critical Thinking

OL Draw Conclusions

ASK STUDENTS: ***Why was spontaneous generation more difficult to disprove with microbes than with multicellular animals?*** Because microbes are invisible without a microscope, are found in nearly every environment, and often don't reproduce sexually, it seemed more reasonable that they should arise spontaneously.

Writing Support

AL Summary Writing

Have students research the work of John Needham, Lazzaro Spallanzani, and Anton van Leeuwenhoek and write a summary of how their work related to the experiments conducted by Redi and Pasteur.

FOLDABLES®

✱RUBRIC A rubric for evaluating Foldables is found on your eTeacherEdition Online.

Going Further Have students imagine that they live in the 1800s and are presenting a paper that introduces the idea of spontaneous generation. Have them outline their arguments.

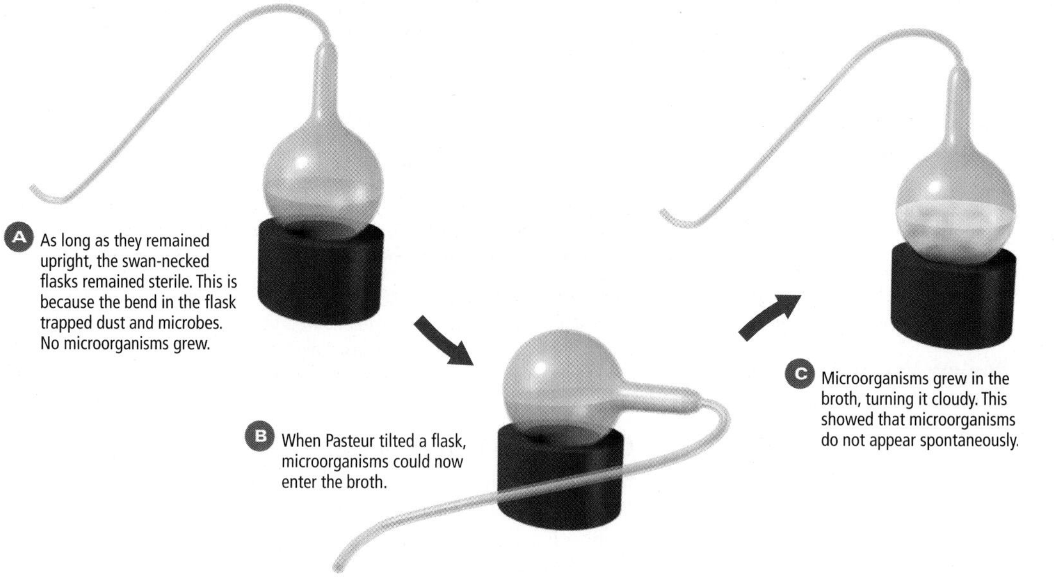

A As long as they remained upright, the swan-necked flasks remained sterile. This is because the bend in the flask trapped dust and microbes. No microorganisms grew.
B When Pasteur tilted a flask, microorganisms could now enter the broth.
C Microorganisms grew in the broth, turning it cloudy. This showed that microorganisms do not appear spontaneously.

■ **Figure 12** Pasteur's experiment showed that sterile broth remained free of microorganisms until exposed to air.

S

FOLDABLES® Incorporate information from this section into your Foldable.

The idea of spontaneous generation was not completely rejected until the mid-1800s. It was replaced by the **theory of biogenesis** (bi oh JEN uh sus), which states that only living organisms can produce other living organisms. Louis Pasteur designed an experiment to show that biogenesis was true even for microorganisms. Pasteur's experiment is illustrated in **Figure 12.** In one flask, only air was allowed to contact a sterile nutrient broth. Nutrient broth supports the growth of microorganisms. In another flask, both air and microorganisms were allowed to contact the broth. No microorganisms grew in the first container. They did, however, grow in the second container. C

Origins: Modern Ideas

If life can arise only from preexisting life, then how did the first life-form appear? Most biologists agree that life originated through a series of chemical events early in Earth's history. During these events, complex organic molecules were generated from simpler ones. Eventually, simple metabolic pathways developed. Such pathways allowed molecules to be synthesized or broken down more efficiently. These pathways might have led to the emergence of life as we know it. How this happened is a topic of ongoing research among scientists today.

Simple organic molecule formation The primordial soup hypothesis was an early hypothesis about the origin of life. Scientists Alexander Oparin and John Haldane suggested this hypothesis in the 1920s. They thought that if Earth's early atmosphere had a mix of certain gases, organic molecules could have been synthesized from simple reactions involving those gases in the early oceans. UV light from the Sun and electric discharge in lightning might have been the primary energy sources. They thought that these organic molecules would have eventually supplied the precursors to life.

Research Citation

Main Ideas Educational research indicates that students should have experience in identifying and discussing the main idea of a lesson. Use the suggestions on the previous page for introducing the Main Idea of the section so that students will understand the larger context of the ideas introduced in this lesson. (National Research Council, 2005)

Research bibliography on pages 32T–34T

Connection to Chemistry In 1953, American scientists Stanley Miller and Harold Urey were the first to show that simple organic molecules could be made from inorganic compounds, as proposed by Oparin and Haldane. Miller and Urey built a glass apparatus, illustrated in **Figure 13,** to simulate the early Earth conditions hypothesized by Oparin. They filled the apparatus with water and the gases that they thought had made up the early atmosphere. The water was boiled and electric discharges were used to simulate lightning as an energy source. Upon examination, the resulting mixture contained a variety of organic compounds including amino acids. Because amino acids are the building blocks of proteins, this discovery supported the primordial soup hypothesis.

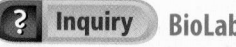

Later, other scientists found that hydrogen cyanide could be formed from even simpler molecules in simulated early Earth environments. Hydrogen cyanide can react with itself to eventually form adenine, one of the nucleotide bases in the genetic code. Many other experiments have since been carried out under conditions that probably reflect the atmosphere of early Earth more accurately. The final reaction products in these experiments were amino acids and sugars as well as nucleotides.

Some scientists suggest that the organic reactions that preceded life's emergence began in the hydrothermal volcanic vents of the deep sea, where sulfur forms the base of a unique food chain. Still others think that meteorites brought the first organic molecules to Earth.

CAREERS IN BIOLOGY

Evolutionary Biochemist Scientists who study chemistry and how it relates to life are biochemists. Evolutionary biochemists specifically study the structure and function of molecules from Earth's early history.

D

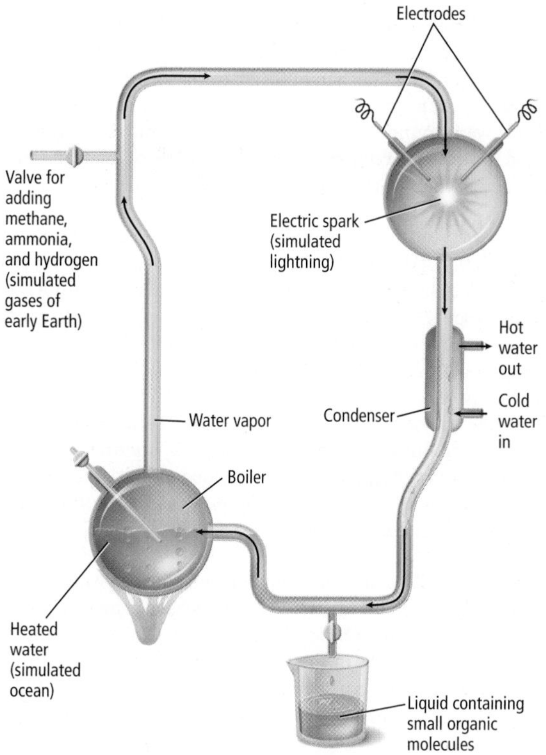

Concepts in Motion
Animation

■ **Figure 13** The Miller-Urey experiment showed for the first time that organic molecules could be produced from gases proposed to have made up the atmosphere of early Earth .

Reading Strategy

EL OL COOP LEARN

Identify Main Ideas Have students read the text under the heading *Origins: Modern Ideas.* Instruct students to list the main ideas from this part of Section 2 on a piece of paper. After students have finished reading, have them discuss their lists in groups and compare their lists with one another. Instruct each group to form a master list of the main ideas of the text. Have students use this list to write a summary of this portion of the section.

D Develop Concepts

OL AL

Discuss Students might be aware of some hypotheses that compete with that of Miller-Urey. Discuss the self-correcting nature of science as a class.

SAY TO STUDENTS: ***There is often disagreement among scientists about how to interpret data and observations. Sometimes one or the other hypothesis is supported, sometimes both are supported, and sometimes both are not supported. The nature of science is self-correcting, and when new information is learned through observations and experiments, it is added to what is already known to improve the accuracy of hypotheses or theories about an event or process.***

Concepts in Motion
Animation

Inquiry BioLab

The lab at the end of the chapter can be used at this point in the lesson.

Content Background

Teacher FYI Steps to chemical synthesis are difficult to trace. As chemical synthesis became more important, different materials must have segregated physically. Cells eventually developed the ability to take in food and expel waste. Recent experiments and computer simulations have studied membranes and how incorporated proteins might permit selective permeability.

D Develop Concepts

OL Activate Prior Knowledge

Have students orally review what they know about amino acids and nucleotides. Emphasize the importance of these two types of organic molecules in protein synthesis and cell replication.

ASK STUDENTS: ***What are proteins formed from?*** amino acids ***Why is protein important to organisms?*** Protein is the principal component of all cells. ***What are nucleotides?*** the base units of DNA and RNA ***What role does DNA play in a cell?*** DNA determines inherited characteristics. ***What role does RNA play in a cell?*** RNA aids in protein synthesis.

Develop Concepts

AL Scaffolding

ASK STUDENTS: ***Who were the two men primarily responsible for proving the theory of biogenesis?*** Redi and Pasteur ***What event did Miller and Urey show that could have happened as a precursor to cells?*** They showed that simple organic molecules could form from a primitive atmosphere. ***Describe the primordial soup hypothesis.*** The primordial soup hypothesis proposes that the simple molecules formed in Earth's early oceans. ***What kind of system do scientists hypothesize must have evolved before the first cells?*** They suggest a replication system based on proteins, RNA, or DNA.

Review

Personal Tutor

Listen to a teacher explain protein formation.

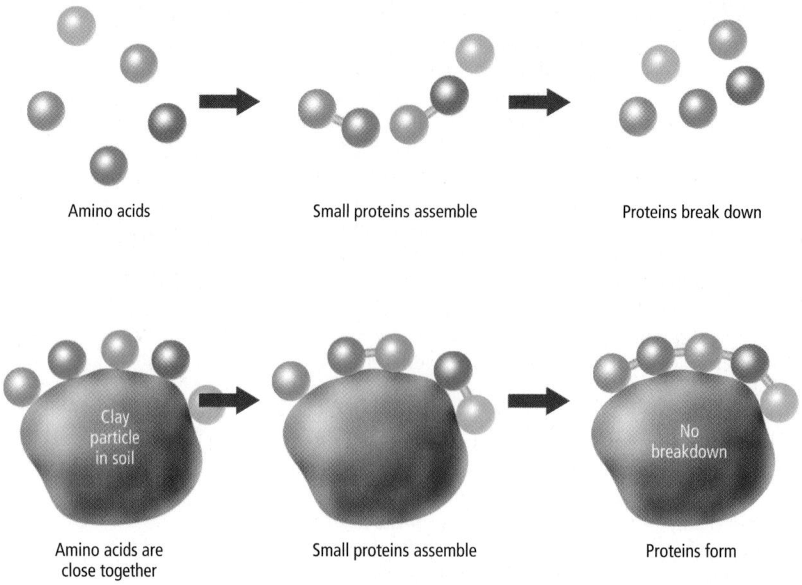

■ **Figure 14** Without clay, amino acids could have formed small, unstable proteins. In the presence of clay, amino acids might have come together in a more stable manner.

Review **Personal Tutor**

Making proteins Wherever the first organic molecules originated, it is clear that the next critical step was the formation of proteins. Amino acids alone are not sufficient for life. Life requires proteins, which are chains of amino acids. In the Miller-Urey experiment, amino acids could bond to one another, but they could separate just as quickly. One possible mechanism for the formation of proteins would be if amino acids were bound to a clay particle, as illustrated in **Figure 14.** Clay would have been a common sediment in early oceans, and it could have provided a framework for protein assembly. D

Genetic code Another requirement for life is a coding system for protein production. All modern life has such a system, based on either RNA or DNA. Because all DNA-based life-forms also contain RNA, and because some RNA sequences appear to have changed very little through time, many biologists consider RNA to have been life's first coding system. Researchers have been able to demonstrate that RNA systems are capable of evolution by natural selection. Some RNAs also can behave like enzymes. These RNA molecules, called ribozymes, could have carried out some early life processes. Other researchers have proposed that clay crystals could have provided an initial template for RNA replication, and that eventually the resulting molecules developed their own replication mechanism.

Molecules to cells Another important step in the evolution of life was the formation of membranes. Researchers have tested ways of enclosing molecules in membranes, allowing early metabolic and replication pathways to develop. In these studies, as in other origin-of-life research, the connection between the various chemical events and the overall path from molecules to cells remains unresolved. However, scientists continue to search for the connection.

VOCABULARY

ACADEMIC VOCABULARY

Mechanism
an instrument or process by which something is done or comes into being
The mechanism for protein synthesis was unknown for a long time.

Content Background

Teacher FYI There is a "proteins first" school that suggests that proteins, being more easily formed than RNA or DNA, were first on the scene. The first proteins were probably much shorter than any that exist in life today, because of the unlikelihood of forming useful long ones out of a "soup" of amino acids.

D

Cellular Evolution

What were the earliest cells like? Scientists don't know because the first life left no fossils. The earliest fossils are 3.5 billion years old. Chemical markings in rocks as old as 3.8 billion years suggest that life was present at that time even though no fossils remain. Scientists recently announced the discovery of what appeared to be fossilized microbes in rock that is 3.5 billion years old. This suggests that cellular activity had become established very early in Earth's history.

The first cells Scientists hypothesize that the first cells were prokaryotes. Recall that prokaryotic cells are much smaller than eukaryotic cells, and they lack a defined nucleus and most other organelles. Many scientists think that modern prokaryotes called archaea (ar KEE uh) are the closest relatives of Earth's first cells. These organisms often live in extreme environments, such as the hot springs of Yellowstone Park or the volcanic vents in the deep sea, such as the one shown in **Figure 15.** These are environments similar to the environment that might have existed on early Earth.

■ **Figure 15** Some archaea live near deep-sea hydrothermal vents. They use energy from inorganic molecules to form the base of the vent food web.
Infer *why some scientists think archaea most resemble the first cells.*

Photosynthesizing prokaryotes Scientists think that oxygen was absent from Earth's earliest atmosphere until about 1.8 billion years ago. Any oxygen that appeared earlier than 1.8 billion years ago likely bonded with free ions of iron as oxygen does today. Evidence that iron oxide was formed by oxygen generated by early life is found in unique sedimentary rock formations, such as those shown in **Figure 16,** that are between about 1.8 billion and 2.5 billion years old. Scientists hypothesize that after 1.8 billion years ago, the early Earth's free iron was saturated with oxygen, and oxygen instead began accumulating in the atmosphere.

Many scientists think that photosynthesizing prokaryotes evolved not long after the archaea—very early in life's history. Fossil evidence of these primitive prokaryotes, called cyanobacteria, has been found in rocks as old as 3.5 billion years. Cyanobacteria eventually produced enough oxygen to support the formation of an ozone layer. Once an ozone shield was established, conditions would be right for the appearance of eukaryotic cells.

D

Reading Check **Create** a list of the steps that led to the formation of the ozone layer in Earth's atmosphere.

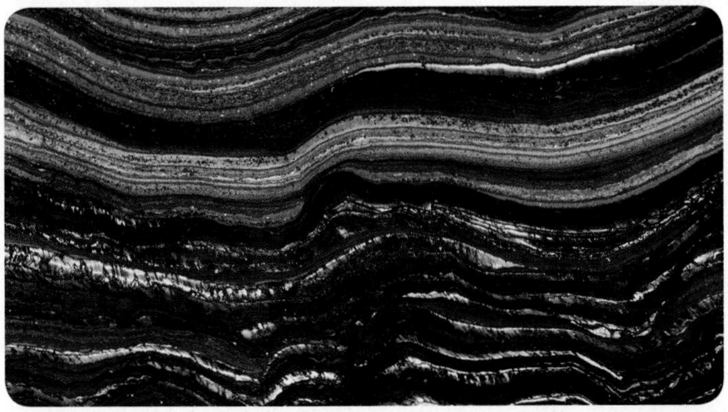

■ **Figure 16** These rock formations, called banded iron formations, or BIFs, are unique sedimentary deposits. These rocks formed as a result of free oxygen production by photosynthetic bacteria billions of years ago. Because this deposit is a result of an organism, BIFs are considered trace fossils.

D Develop Concepts

BL OL

Clarify a Misconception
ASK STUDENTS: ***How do you think the first cells obtained the energy they needed?*** Students might say that the first cells were likely photosynthetic or chemosynthetic. Inform students that this is a controversial topic among biologists. Fossils of early microorganisms appear to be more like heterotrophs than autotrophs. If the "primordial soup" hypothesis is correct, then there might have been organic molecules that could have been used as food for the first heterotrophic cells. Also, modern autotrophs are chemically more complex than the simplest heterotrophs.

D Develop Concepts

BL OL **Discuss** Prompt a discussion by having students brainstorm a list of the similarities between autotrophic and heterotrophic prokaryotes and eukaryotic cell organelles, such as chloroplasts and mitochondria. Write students' suggestions on the board. Make sure students consider such attributes as size, metabolism, DNA content, ribosome size, and others. Use the list to begin a discussion of the endosymbiont theory.

■ **Caption Question Fig. 15** Some archaea live in an environment that might have existed on early Earth.

Reading Check The steps involved in creating the ozone layer include: 1. All of the free iron was saturated with oxygen, 2. oxygen began accumulating in the atmosphere, 3. cyanobacteria began producing enough oxygen to help produce the ozone layer.

Differentiated Instruction

Hearing Impaired Measures should be taken to ensure that students who are hearing impaired can take part in and benefit from class discussion. Always be sure to face students when you speak and encourage other students to do the same so that hearing impaired students can follow the discussion more easily.

For more tips, see pages 14T–15T.

DATA ANALYSIS LAB 1

About the Lab

- You might wish to form study groups to complete this activity. Alternatively, you could alter the questions for students performing below level.
- Also see Nisbet, E.G. and N.H. Sleep. 2001. The habit and nature of early life. *Nature* 409(6823): 1083–1091.

Think Critically

1. The cytoplasm of a eukaryote, the host cell, engulfed an alga containing a plastid and surrounded it in a vacuole (phagocytosis). Over time, the contents of the vacuole changed into another type of plastid.
2. In Figure 17, eukaryotes acquired mitochondria and chloroplasts. Secondary endosymbiosis explains how other plastids formed from eukaryotes that did not contain them originally.

Develop Concepts

AL Discuss Tell students that in addition to the endosymbiont theory, Lynn Margulis and Dorion Sagan suggested that cells acquired other cells and genomes from other organisms. They call this process *symbiogenesis.* According to Margulis and Sagan, symbiogenesis is a major factor in the evolution of life on Earth. They state that long-term genomic mergers result in much greater evolutionary change than DNA mutations and natural selection. Have students discuss whether they agree with this hypothesis. Ask them to support their opinions with facts.

The endosymbiont theory Eukaryotic cells appeared in the fossil record about 1.8 billion years ago, around two billion years after life first formed. Eukaryotic cells have complex internal membranes, which enclose various organelles, including mitochondria and, in plant cells, chloroplasts. Mitochondria metabolize food through cellular respiration, and chloroplasts are the site of photosynthesis. Both mitochondria and chloroplasts are about the size of prokaryotic cells and contain similar prokaryote features. This led some scientists to speculate that prokaryotic cells were involved in the evolution of eukaryotic cells.

In 1966, biologist Lynn Margulis proposed the endosymbiont theory. According to the **endosymbiont theory,** the ancestors of eukaryotic cells lived in association with prokaryotic cells. In some cases, prokaryotes even might have lived inside eukaryotes. Prokaryotes could have entered a host cell as undigested prey, or they could have been internal parasites. Eventually, the relationship between the cells became mutually beneficial, and the prokaryotic symbionts became organelles in eukaryotic cells. This theory explains the origin of chloroplasts and mitochondria, as illustrated in **Figure 17.**

Evidence for the endosymbiont theory When Margulis first proposed the endosymbiont theory, many scientists were hesitant to accept it. There is evidence, however, that at least mitochondria and chloroplasts formed by endosymbiosis. For example, mitochondria and chloroplasts contain their own DNA. It is arranged in a circular pattern, just as it is in prokaryotic cells. Mitochondria and chloroplasts also have ribosomes that more closely resemble those in prokaryotic cells than those in eukaryotic cells. Finally, like prokaryotic cells, mitochondria and chloroplasts reproduce by fission, independent from the rest of the cell.

DATA ANALYSIS LAB 1

Based on Real Data*

Analyze Scientific Illustrations

How did plastids evolve?
Chloroplasts belong to a group of organelles called plastids, which are found in plants and algae. Chloroplasts perform photosynthesis. Other plastids store starch and make substances needed as cellular building blocks or for plant function.

Think Critically

1. **Summarize** the process described in the diagram. Include the definition of phagocytosis in your description.
2. **Compare** secondary endosymbiosis to the endosymbiont theory described in **Figure 17.**

Data and Observations

The illustration shows a way these plastids might have evolved.

Plastid origin

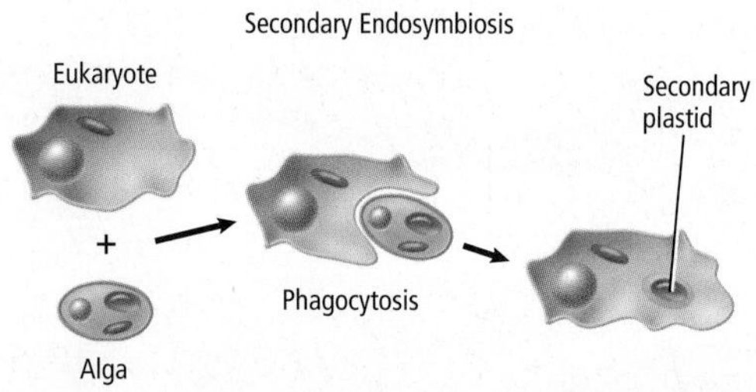

*Data obtained from: Dyall, S.D., et al. 2004. Ancient invasions: from endosymbionts to organelles. *Science* 304: 253–257.

Demonstration

Endosymbiont Theory Use a large model or a transparency of a cell to demonstrate the various organelles that scientists think evolved from prokaryotic cells. For example, note how mitochondria and chloroplasts are the same size as prokaryotes that are alive today. You can also indicate information about the genetic material contained in each of these organelles being more like that of prokaryotes than that in the nucleus.
Est. time: 15 min

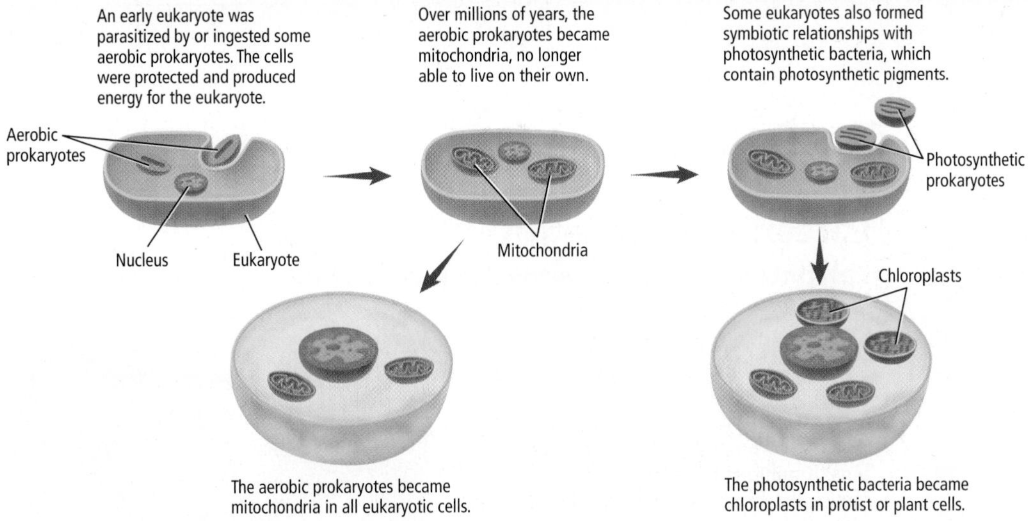

An early eukaryote was parasitized by or ingested some aerobic prokaryotes. The cells were protected and produced energy for the eukaryote.
Over millions of years, the aerobic prokaryotes became mitochondria, no longer able to live on their own.
Some eukaryotes also formed symbiotic relationships with photosynthetic bacteria, which contain photosynthetic pigments.
Aerobic prokaryotes
Nucleus
Eukaryote
Mitochondria
Photosynthetic prokaryotes
Chloroplasts
The aerobic prokaryotes became mitochondria in all eukaryotic cells.
The photosynthetic bacteria became chloroplasts in protist or plant cells.

■ **Figure 17** This illustration shows how Margulis hypothesized that eukaryotic cells and their organelles evolved.

Concepts in Motion
Animation

Though the endosymbiont theory is widely endorsed, it is important to understand that scientists do not know the early steps that led to the emergence of life or to its early evolution. It is unlikely that any traces of the first life will ever be found. What scientists do know is that the conditions on Earth shortly after it took shape allowed the precursors of life to form.

The evolution of life is better understood than how the first life appeared. Fossil, geologic, and biochemical evidence supports many of the proposed steps in life's subsequent evolution. However, future discoveries might alter any or all of these steps. Scientists will continue to evaluate new evidence and test new theories in years to come.

Section 2 Assessment

Section Summary

- Spontaneous generation was disproved in favor of biogenesis.
- The origin of life is hypothesized to be a series of chemical events.
- Organic molecules, such as amino acids, might have been formed from simpler molecules on early Earth.
- The first cells probably were autotrophic and prokaryotic.
- The endosymbiont theory explains how eukaryotic cells might have evolved from prokaryotic cells.

Understand Main Ideas

1. MAIN Idea **Infer** why scientists hypothesize that chemical events preceded the origin of life on Earth.
2. **Compare and contrast** spontaneous generation and biogenesis.
3. **Discuss** why prokaryotic cells probably appeared before eukaryotic cells.
4. **Hypothesize** whether prokaryotic cells might have been symbiotic before the evolution of eukaryotic cells.

Think Critically

5. **Describe** the hypothesized sequence of chemical and biological events that preceded the origin of eukaryotic cells.

WRITING in **Biology**

6. Write a persuasive paragraph that explains why many scientists accept the endosymbiont theory.

Concepts in Motion
Animation

Develop Concepts

OL AL COOP LEARN Debate Have students form teams and organize a debate about the origins of life. Each team should defend one viewpoint and research the scientific evidence that supports it and the weaknesses of the opposing viewpoints. After the debate, have students review all viewpoints presented based on the scientific evidence communicated by the teams. See the Skillbuilder Handbook for debate tips.

Formative Assessment

Evaluation Have students create a board game that explains the possible chemical steps leading to cellular life. After the students have had the opportunity to play their games, give a quick oral quiz to test their understanding of the basic sequence of events.

Remediation Assign study buddies or student mentors for those students who have difficulty understanding the hypothesized sequence of events leading to cellular life. Instruct the mentor to alert you when the other partner understands the material.

Section 2 Assessment

1. Scientists have been unable to test any other alternatives, and chemical methods seem most likely. In addition, scientists have been able to generate necessary biomolecules from hypothesized precursors present on early Earth.
2. Spontaneous generation is the idea that life arises from nonliving materials. Biogenesis states that only living things can produce living things.
3. Prokaryotic cells have simpler structures than eukaryotic cells have.
4. Possible answer: If prokaryotic cells linked symbiotically within early nucleated cells (eukaryotic), then they could have been mutually beneficial to each other and eventually evolved into eukaryotic cells.
5. Simple organic molecules joined to form complex molecules due to reactions fueled by energy sources. Eventually, amino acids and then proteins formed in protocells. RNA probably existed before DNA. Prokaryotic cells were symbiotic to produce eukaryotic cells.
6. Answers should include the fact that mitochondria and chloroplasts are about the same size as prokaryotes and have their own DNA and ribosomes similar to those of prokaryotes.

Assessment **Online Quiz**

In the Field

Purpose

Students will understand that science involves a constant revision of theories based on emerging data and observations. This evolving process ultimately leads to increased understanding of the biological world.
UCP.4, UCP.5, C.3

Anticipatory Guide

ASK STUDENTS: ***How do scientists learn about organisms that lived on Earth millions of years ago?*** Possible answer: Scientists study fossilized remains of organisms. ***Do you think scientists can answer all the questions they might have about a particular organism based on fossilized remains? Why or why not?*** Answers will vary. Point out that paleontologists make inferences about organisms and habitats based on fossils. Due to limitations in the data they can collect, their interpretations do not always agree. For example, based on evidence from the fossil record, scientists have differing opinions about when birds diverged from dinosaurs.

Background

The fossil fields of China's Liaoning Province, where the *C. zoui* fossil was found, are unusual. Organisms in this region were buried in fine-grained sediment resulting from volcanic eruptions. The quick rate of burial resulted in little or no oxygen available in the sediment to promote decay, which increased the state of preservation of the organisms buried here.

In the Field

Career: Paleontologist

Paleontologists Debate the Evolution of Birds

Along lakeshores in northeastern China 130 million years ago, volcanic eruptions sealed the fate of millions of organisms. Ash rains buried dinosaurs, mammals, fish, insects, and amphibians. Entombed for tens of millions of years, their bodies fossilized, sometimes leaving impressions of feathers, fur, and even stomach contents! Today, in the fossil-rich area of the Laioning Province in China, paleontologists are making important discoveries about life in the early Cretaceous period.

Caudipteryx zoui is an important fossil that shows that some dinosaurs had feathers.

A feathered dinosaur Organisms like the fossil specimen *Caudipteryx zoui* in the figure cause excitement in the paleontology community. In the fossil of *C. zoui,* there are clear traces of feathers from head to tail on the roughly one-meter long dinosaur. These feathers were not used for flight, but might have provided more stability for bipedal running.

An early bird A 130 million year old fossil of a new bird species, *Confuciusornis dui,* was discovered in the same general area as *C. zoui. C. dui* appears to have been a well-developed, tree-dwelling bird, not a feathered dinosaur that lived on the ground. *C. dui* and *C. zoui* lived during roughly the same time in history—between 120–150 mya. The coexistence of *C. dui* and *C. zoui* in this region provides an example of ancestral and derived species living together.

Link to the past Paleontologists often interpret fossil evidence to make evolutionary connections between organisms. Paleontologists agree that an evolutionary link exists between birds and dinosaurs. They share many anatomical features, including hollow, thin-walled bones, flexible wrists, clawed hands, and a fused collarbone that forms a wishbone. Paleontologists think that birds came from dinosaurs, but they continue to debate about when the divergence took place. Fossil finds like those in China help to provide evidence and insight into the evolution of birds.

CAREERS IN BIOLOGY

Interview a Paleontologist
Work with a team to create a list of questions you would like to ask a paleontologist. Conduct an interview with a paleontologist at a local college or university. Use the information you gather to write an article which describes what you learned from the conversation.

DEBATE in Biology

RUBRIC Use the modifiable rubric found on your eTeacherEdition Online to assess writing assignments.

Follow-Up Discussion
Have students form small groups and discuss their opinions of the evolution of birds. Instruct students to support their opinions with facts from the feature.

WebQuest

BIOLAB

IS SPONTANEOUS GENERATION POSSIBLE?

Background: **In the mid-1800s, Louis Pasteur conducted an experiment that showed that living organisms come from other living organisms—not from nonliving material. Pasteur's classic experiment, which disproved the notion of spontaneous generation, laid an essential foundation for modern biology by supporting the concept of biogenesis. In this lab, you will carry out an experiment based on Pasteur's work.**

Question: *How can the idea of spontaneous generation be disproved?*

Materials

beef broth
graduated cylinder
Erlenmeyer flask (2)
ring stand (2)
wire gauze (2)
string
rubber stopper (2)
Bunsen burner (2)
5 cm of plastic tubing
30 cm of plastic tubing

Safety Precautions

Procedure

1. Read and complete the lab safety form.
2. Study the description of Louis Pasteur's classic experiment that disproved spontaneous generation.
3. Design and construct a data table to record changes in color, smell, and the presence of sediments.
4. Label the flasks "A" and "B." Flask A will be capped with a stopper holding a 5-cm piece of tubing. Flask B will be capped with a stopper holding a 30-cm piece of tubing.
5. Place 50 mL of beef broth in each flask. Cap each flask with the appropriate stopper.
6. Put each flask on a wire gauze on a ring stand over a Bunsen burner.
7. Bend the tubing on Flask B until it forms a U-shape. The bottom of the U should be near the base of the flask. Tie the end of the tubing to the ring stand to hold the U-shape.
8. Boil the broth in each flask for 30 min.
9. After the equipment and broth cool, move the apparatuses to an area of the lab where they will not be disturbed.
10. Observe the flasks over the next two weeks. Record your observations in your data table.
11. **Cleanup and Disposal** Dispose of beef broth according to your teacher's instructions. Clean and return all equipment to the appropriate location.

Analyze and Conclude

1. **Describe** the experimental procedure you followed. How does it compare to the steps followed by Louis Pasteur?
2. **Compare** your findings to Pasteur's findings.
3. **Describe** why it is important for scientists to verify one another's data.
4. **Think Critically** Explain how Pasteur's findings disprove spontaneous generation.
5. **Error Analysis** If your results did not match Pasteur's results, explain a possible reason for the difference.

WRITING in Biology

Pasteur's experiment resulted in wide acceptance of biogenesis by the scientific community. Write an essay explaining how Pasteur's work contributed to some of the central ideas of biology.

Analyze and Conclude

1. Answers will vary. Students should summarize the procedure. Pasteur's experiment used sterile nutrient broth, while this experiment used beef broth. Our process also involved heating the broth.
2. Microorganisms grew in the broth that was exposed to microorganisms in the environment.
3. Verification supports experimental results. The peer review process checks for faulty procedures and eliminates bias.
4. If organisms could be produced from nonliving material, microorganisms would have grown in both the sterile broth that was exposed to air and in the sterile broth that was sealed completely.
5. Answers will vary. The sterile broth might have been contaminated after boiling.

BIOLAB

Inquiry BioLab

For a lab worksheet, use your eTeacherEdition Online.

RUBRIC A rubric for evaluating BioLabs is found on your eTeacherEdition Online.

Est. Time 60 min, and 10 min per day for two weeks

Content Background Spontaneous generation was a widely accepted idea that nonliving material could give rise to living organisms. Louis Pasteur's classic experiment disproved this notion.

Safety Precautions Approve lab safety forms before work begins. Prior to beginning the lab, reinforce proper lab techniques for heating a liquid to boiling and for handling hot glassware. Be careful not to melt the plastic tubing when heating during the experiment. Glass tubing is another option for the experiment.

Teaching Strategy Make sure students understand the design and findings of Pasteur's original experiment before allowing them to begin the investigation.

Alternative Teaching Demo Students could read about Pasteur's classic experiment, discuss his findings, and then create a diagram that outlines the steps he followed and the conclusions reached.

WRITING in Biology

RUBRIC Use the modifiable rubric found on your eTeacherEdition Online to assess writing assignments.

GOING GREEN If you do not have the materials listed, ask students to design an experiment using materials already in the kitchen and left over food from the school cafeteria.

Chapter 14

Study Guide

ConnectED

Students can use the following to review the chapter.

Review

Vocabulary eGames
Vocabulary eFlashcards
Vocabulary PuzzleMaker

Assessment

Online Quizzes
Online Test Practice
Standardized Test Practice

Use the *ExamView® Assessment Suite* CD-ROM to:

- create multiple versions of tests
- create modified tests with one mouse click
- edit existing questions and add your own questions
- build tests aligned with state standards using built-in state curriculum tags
- change English tests to Spanish with one mouse click
- track students' progress using the Teacher Management System

Chapter 14 Study Guide

THEME FOCUS Change Scientists study the fossil record and perform experiments to learn about the changes that lead to the origin and diversity of life on Earth.

BIG Idea **Fossils provide key evidence for understanding the origin and the history of life on Earth.**

Section 1 Fossil Evidence of Change

fossil (p. 393)
paleontologist (p. 394)
relative dating (p. 394)
law of superposition (p. 394)
radiometric dating (p. 395)
half-life (p. 395)
geologic time scale (p. 396)
epoch (p. 396)
period (p. 396)
era (p. 396)
eon (p. 396)
Cambrian explosion (p. 398)
K-T boundary (p. 399)
plate tectonics (p. 400)

MAIN Idea **Fossils provide evidence of the change in organisms over time.**

- Fossils provide evidence of past life.
- Relative dating and radiometric dating are two methods used to determine the age of fossils.
- The geologic time scale is divided into eras, periods, and epochs.
- Major events in the geologic time scale include both biological and geological changes.

Section 2 The Origin of Life

spontaneous generation (p. 401)
theory of biogenesis (p. 402)
endosymbiont theory (p. 406)

MAIN Idea **Evidence indicates that a sequence of chemical events preceded the origin of life on Earth and that life has evolved continuously since that time.**

- Spontaneous generation was disproved in favor of biogenesis.
- The origin of life is hypothesized to be a series of chemical events.
- Organic molecules, such as amino acids, might have been formed from simpler molecules on early Earth.
- The first cells probably were autotrophic and prokaryotic.
- The endosymbiont theory explains how eukaryotic cells might have evolved from prokaryotic cells.

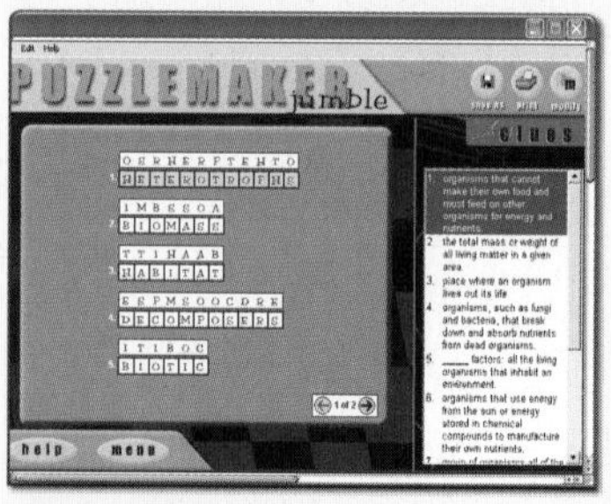

Review **Vocabulary PuzzleMaker**

For additional practice with vocabulary, have students access the Vocabulary PuzzleMaker online.

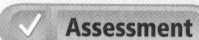

Review **Vocabulary eGames**

Chapter 14 Assessment

Section 1

Vocabulary Review

Choose the vocabulary term from the Study Guide page that best describes each of the following phrases.

1. determining the age of a fossil by radioactive elements

2. the remains or evidence of an organism

3. scientist who studies fossils

Understand Main Ideas

Use the table below to answer questions 4 and 5.

Radioactive Isotope	Product of Decay	Half-Life (Years)
Carbon-14	Nitrogen-14	5730
Chlorine-36	Argon-36	300,000
Beryllium-10	Boron-10	1.52 million
Uranium-235	Lead-207	700 million

4. According to the table above, if one-fourth of the original radioactive carbon is present in a fossil, what is the fossil's age?
A. 2857.5 years old
B. 5730 years old
C. 11,460 years old
D. 17,145 years old

5. Which isotope would be best for measuring the age of a rock layer estimated to be about one million years old?
A. beryllium-10
B. carbon-14
C. chlorine-36
D. uranium-235

6. Which fossil type provides the most anatomical information to paleontologists?
A. trace
B. molds
C. replacement
D. amber

Use the graph below to answer questions 7 and 8.

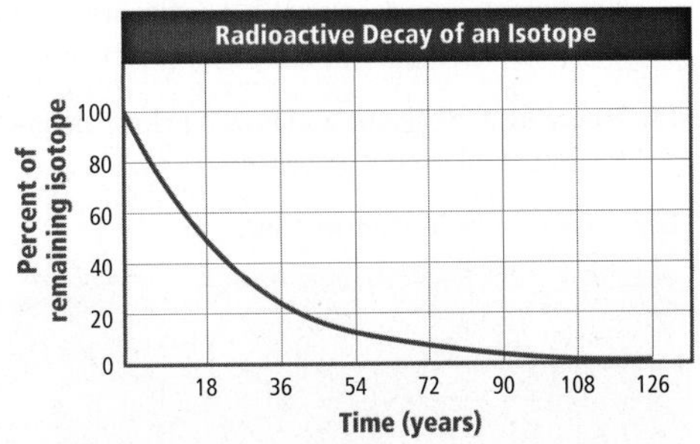

7. Which is the half-life of the radioactive isotope shown in the graph?
A. 18 years **C.** 54 years
B. 36 years **D.** 72 years

8. Assuming that you can only date material that has at least one percent of the radioisotope remaining, which age would be too old to date with this isotope?
A. 35 years **C.** 75 years
B. 50 years **D.** 125 years

9. What era followed the mass extinction at the end of the Permian period?
A. Cambrian
B. Mesozoic
C. Paleozoic
D. Neogene

10. Nearly all fossils occur in what kind of rocks?
A. batholithic
B. igneous
C. metamorphic
D. sedimentary

Constructed Response

11. Short Answer How does the law of superposition help paleontologists?

12. Open Ended Explain the geologic time scale using an analogy other than a ribbon of time.

13. Short Answer Calculate the percentage of Earth's existence occupied by the Cenozoic era (65 million years). Show your work.

Chapter 14

Assessment

Section 1

Vocabulary Review

1. radiometric dating
2. fossil
3. paleontologist

Understand Main Ideas

4. C
5. A
6. D
7. A
8. D
9. B
10. D

Constructed Response

11. It allows them to do relative dating of fossils.

12. Student analogies will vary. One possible analogy could be a clock.

13. $\frac{65{,}000{,}000}{4{,}600{,}000{,}000} \times 100 = 1.4\%$

Think Critically

14. Amber is made from hardened tree sap, so the environment likely would have been a forest.

15. Student responses will vary, but they should explain the kind of information such as environment, diet, etc. that can be gained from the fossil category they choose.

16. The fossil layer could not be older than the Mesozoic era. A scientist should look below this layer to learn about the Permian mass extinction.

Section 2

Vocabulary Review

17. spontaneous generation

18. endosymbiont theory

Understand Main Ideas

19. A
20. B
21. C
22. C
23. C
24. A

Chapter 14 Assessment

Think Critically

14. Infer Imagine that you found a piece of amber in a sedimentary rock layer. What environment likely was present at the time of the fossil's formation?

15. Describe a fossil type and how it helps paleontologists understand an organism's anatomy.

Use the photo below to answer question 16.

16. MAIN Idea If you found the above fossil of a flowering plant in a layer of rock, what would you conclude about the age of the layer? Would you look in layers above or below the layer with the flower to learn about the Permian mass extinction?

Section 2

Vocabulary Review

Replace the underlined words with the correct vocabulary term from the Study Guide page.

17. The belief that organisms originate from nonliving matter was disproven by Redi and Pasteur.

18. The explanation that bacteria might have lived inside prokaryotes and eventually became organelles was proposed by Lynn Margulis.

Understand Main Ideas

19. Pasteur's experiments led to which theory?
A. biogenesis theory
B. endosymbiont theory
C. evolution theory
D. spontaneous generation theory

Use the illustration below to answer questions 20 and 21.

20. The organisms represented in the photo above had which effect on early Earth?
A. produced the first amino acids
B. increased oxygen in the atmosphere
C. became the first mitochondria
D. consumed the first heterotrophs

21. When did the fossils of organisms like those in the photo first appear in the fossil record?
A. 1.0 million years ago
B. 2.0 million years ago
C. 3.5 billion years ago
D. 4.5 billion years ago

22. Clay most likely was involved in which process?
A. producing the first oxygen in the atmosphere
B. forming the first plasma membranes
C. providing a framework for amino acid chains
D. capturing prokaryotes for chloroplast evolution

23. Scientists have fossil evidence for which idea for the origin of life?
A. first amino acids
B. first RNA
C. first cells
D. first autotrophs

24. Banded iron formations are important evidence for which idea in the early evolution of life?
A. photosynthetic autotrophs
B. endosymbiont organelles
C. heterotrophic prokaryotes
D. heterotrophic eukaryotes

Assessment Online Test Practice

Constructed Response

25. **Open Ended** What would you expect the first step to be in the emergence of life from nonliving matter?
26. MAIN Idea Explain the significance of the Miller-Urey experiment for understanding the origin of cells.
27. **Open Ended** Which evidence do you think is most important for the endosymbiont hypothesis? Why?

Think Critically

28. **Sequence** the hypothesized events that led from a lifeless Earth to the presence of eukaryotic cells.
29. **Compare** the contributions of Redi and Pasteur in disproving spontaneous generation.

Use the photo below to answer question 30.

30. THEME FOCUS Change How is the hot spring shown above similar to conditions on early Earth? What kind of organisms can survive in this type of environment?
31. **Infer** How was evolution affected by the increase in oxygen caused by the first photosynthetic organisms?
32. CAREERS IN BIOLOGY How could a biochemist studying DNA sequences provide evidence for the endosymbiont theory?
33. **Analyze** and critique the endosymbiont theory. What are its strengths and weaknesses?

Summative Assessment

34. BIG Idea There are six major fossil types discussed in **Table 1**. Create a hierarchy of the fossil types in **Table 1** based on the amount and type of information obtained from the fossil. Write a paragraph supporting your hierarchy.
35. WRITING in Biology Assume that you are a scientist searching for the cause of a mass extinction. Several causes have been hypothesized. Write a paragraph that explains how you could use dating methods to accept or reject them.
36. WRITING in Biology Explain the importance of a particular fossil being found in both South America and Africa.
37. Make a list of requirements for the existence of life. Put them in the order in which you think that they had to occur in order for life to begin successfully.
38. Explain why paleontologists find radiometric dating important.
39. Based on what you know about laws and theories, could the endosymbiont theory become a law? Explain your answer.

DBQ Document-Based Questions

"Probably all of the organic beings which have ever lived on this Earth have descended from some one primordial form."
Charles Darwin in *The Origin of Species*, 1859.

40. If Darwin was alive today, do you think he would include proteins among "organic beings"? Why or why not?
41. Use the quote above to support why you think Darwin would or would not have supported the endosymbiont theory.
42. Discuss what Darwin might have meant by the phrase, "...descended from some one primordial form."

Constructed Response

25. simple organic molecule formation
26. The Miller-Urey experiment showed that organic molecules could be produced from the gaseous mixture that many scientists thought composed early Earth's atmosphere.
27. Students may choose evidence for either chloroplasts or mitochondria. Accept either if the reason is supported.

Think Critically

28. simple organic molecules; complex organic molecules; protocells; genetic material; prokaryotic cells; symbiosis of prokaryotic cells; eukaryotic cells
29. Redi showed that multicellular organisms do not arise spontaneously. Pasteur showed that microorganisms do not arise spontaneously, either. Both helped support the theory of biogenesis.
30. hot, sulfuric; some archaea
31. The oxygen formed an ozone layer, which shielded Earth from much of the Sun's radiation and paved the way for eukaryote evolution.
32. Possible answer: The biochemist could determine how similar mitochondrial DNA was to prokaryotic DNA.
33. Answers should include the resemblance of mitochondria and chloroplasts to prokaryotic cells and that no traces of early life can prove the theory.

Summative Assessment

34. Paragraphs should include reasoning that show knowledge of the fossil type and the information that those fossils provide.
35. Answers will depend on the hypothesis students discuss.
36. A fossil of a particular species being found on both continents of South America and Africa helps to prove the theory of plate tectonics and continental drift and the landmass of Pangaea.
37. formation of amino acids, creation of genetic material, and generation of protocells
38. Radiometric dating provides a specific date for fossils rather than a relative one.
39. No, it could not. Theories do not become laws, and laws do not become theories.

DBQ Document-Based Questions

Darwin, Charles. 1859. *The Origin of Species*.

40. Darwin probably would have not considered proteins "organic beings" because they are not living cells.
41. Possible answer: Darwin would have supported the theory because it indicates that eukaryotes evolved from more primitive organisms.
42. Darwin meant that all organisms evolved from an ancestral organism.

Assessment Online Test Practice

Standardized Test Practice

Multiple Choice

1. B
2. C
3. C
4. D
5. B
6. A
7. A

Short Answer

8. 3' ACATCTGTGTTAATG 5'
9. When the thymine dimer forms, the adjacent thymine bases will be bound to each other—not to their corresponding base. This forms a kink in the DNA strand, which affects the replication of DNA and potentially disrupts the translation of that region of DNA.
10. In petrified fossils, the open spaces fill with minerals. In replacement fossils, minerals replace the actual material of the organism.
11. Answers may vary, but they should paraphrase the following steps.
    - A. The DNA fragment to be copied is mixed with the four DNA nucleotides. Then it is heated.
    - B. When the mixture heats up, the DNA strands separate; and when it cools, the DNA binds with the primers.
    - C. The DNA polymerase enzyme links the correct nucleotides in sequence to replicate the DNA. This whole process happens many times.
12. Oxygen reacts with some minerals to form oxides. The early rocks found on Earth do not contain oxides, so scientists infer that there was little or no oxygen in the atmosphere.

Standardized Test Practice

Cumulative

Multiple Choice

1. Which is associated with gene regulation in prokaryotic cells?
   - A. DNA pairing
   - B. repressor proteins
   - C. RNA interference
   - D. transcription factor

Use the illustration below to answer questions 2 and 3.

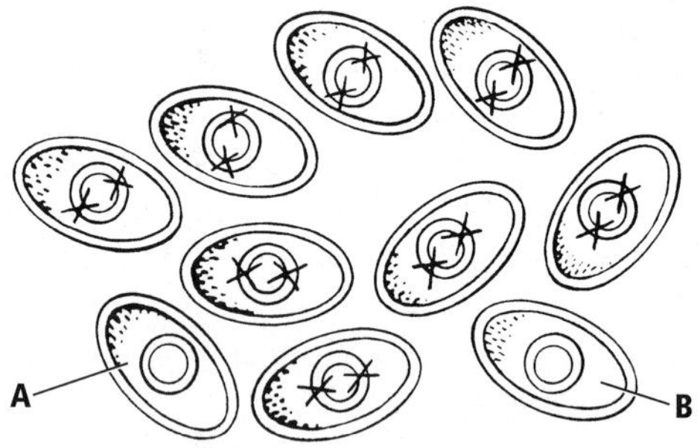

2. The bacterial cells in the figure above were transformed after they were mixed with recombinant DNA—represented by "XX" in the diagram. Which is one possible reason that Cells A and B do not have the new recombinant DNA plasmid?
   - A. Cells A and B are resistant to antibiotics.
   - B. Cells A and B do not have plasma membranes.
   - C. Cells A and B did not take up the DNA fragment.
   - D. Cells A and B initially had different plasmids.

3. In the figure, which step is likely to happen after the transformation of bacterial cells?
   - A. Cells with the new plasmid will die after exposure to an antibiotic.
   - B. Cells with the new plasmid will replicate quicker.
   - C. Cells without the new plasmid will die after exposure to an antibiotic.
   - D. Cells without the new plasmid will replicate more quickly.

4. A piece of DNA has the following sequence: CCCCGAATT. Suppose a mutation causes the following change: CCTCGAATT. Which term describes this mutation?
   - A. chromosomal
   - B. deletion
   - C. duplication
   - D. missense

Use the graph below to answer question 5.

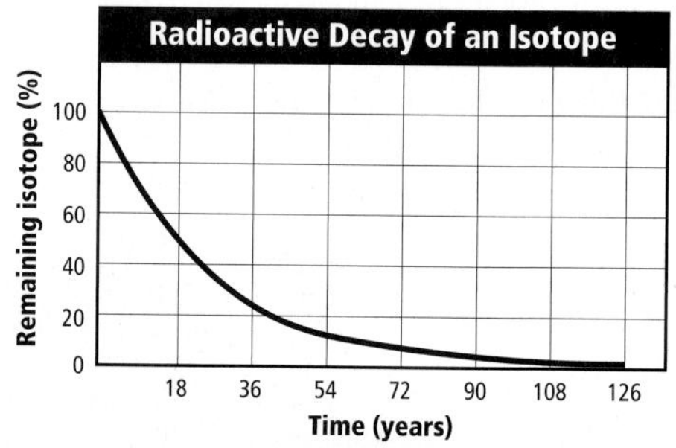

5. How much of the original isotope remains after 10 years?
   - A. 50 percent
   - B. 75 percent
   - C. 10 percent
   - D. 30 percent

6. Which causes DNA fragments to separate during gel electrophoresis?
   - A. charge on the fragments
   - B. DNA extraction of chemicals
   - C. gel medium components
   - D. source of the DNA

7. Where can Barr bodies be found?
   - A. female body cells
   - B. female sex cells
   - C. male body cells
   - D. male sex cells

Short Answer

Use the illustration below to answer questions 8 and 9.

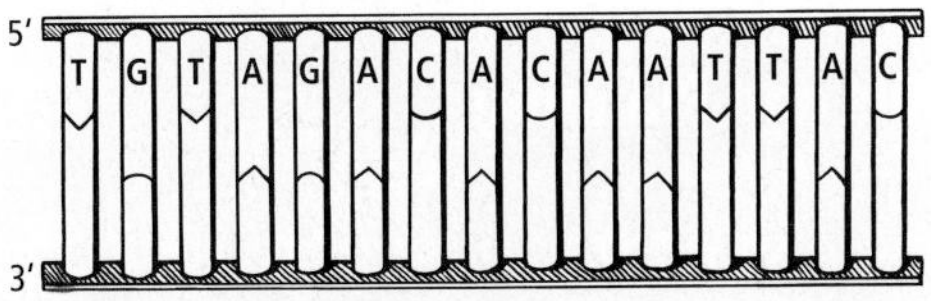

8. The diagram shows a molecule of DNA. What is the complementary DNA strand base code? Be sure to indicate the orientation of the strand.

9. Suppose the adjacent thymine bases in the figure formed a dimer after being exposed to ultraviolet radiation. How would the dimer affect the structure of the DNA molecule?

10. Describe the difference between petrified and replacement fossils.

11. Explain the three steps that take place in a polymerase chain reaction (PCR).

12. Describe why scientists infer that oxygen was absent from the early atmosphere on Earth.

13. Use a chart to show the role that different enzymes play in the replication of DNA. Be sure to put the steps in the correct order.

14. What are restriction enzymes? Assess why they are an important tool for genetic engineering.

15. How does a paleontologist use geologic principles for the relative dating of fossils?

Extended Response

16. How is selective breeding related to genetic engineering?

17. Appraise how your body temperature is related to homeostasis.

Essay Question

Some genes contain instructions for controlling when our cells grow, divide, and die. Certain genes that promote cell division are called oncogenes. Others that slow down cell division, or cause cells to die at the right time, are called tumor suppressor genes. It is known that cancers can be caused by DNA mutations (changes) that "turn on" oncogenes or "turn off" tumor suppressor genes.

The BRCA genes (BRCA1 and BRCA2) are tumor suppressor genes. When they are mutated, they no longer function to suppress abnormal growth and breast cancer is more likely to develop. Certain inherited DNA changes can result in a high risk for the development of breast cancer in people who carry these genes and are responsible for the cancers that run in some families.

Using the information in the paragraph above, answer the following question in essay format.

18. How could oncogenes and tumor suppressor genes play a part in the development of breast cancer? Use what you know about molecular genetics to write an essay explaining how these genes might contribute to the formation of tumors.

NEED EXTRA HELP?																		
If You Missed Question . . .	1	2	3	4	5	6	7	8	9	10	11	12	13	14	15	16	17	18
Review Section . . .	12.4	13.2	13.2	12.4	14.1	13.2	11.2	12.2	12.4	14.1	13.2	14.2	12.3	13.2	14.1	13.2, 12.2	1.1	12.3, 12.4

13. Answers can vary in wording.

Enzyme	Role of the enzyme
Single DNA molecule ready for replication.	
DNA helicase	"unzips" or unwinds the DNA helix
RNA primase	adds a short segment of RNA on the end of each DNA strand
DNA polymerase	acts as a catalyst in adding new DNA nucleotides, starting from the 3' end
DNA ligase	links two DNA nucleotides
Two identical DNA strands formed.	

14. Restriction enzymes are bacterial enzymes that recognize short nucleotide sequences in DNA and cut the DNA molecules at specific points. The enzymes can be used to break up large DNA molecules into shorter pieces. Then DNA fragments from different sources can be reassembled into larger molecules that have recombined sequences of DNA. Restriction enzymes are an important tool in genetic engineering because they allow scientists to make new DNA molecules that can manufacture specific proteins.

15. According to the law of superposition, younger rock layers are laid down on top of older rock layers. By knowing which rock layer a fossil comes from, a paleontologist knows whether the fossil was formed earlier or later than fossils in other layers.

Extended Response

16. In selective breeding, certain desirable traits from animals and plants are passed on to the next generations, affecting the genetic makeup of future generations. Similarly, in genetic engineering, genes for particular traits are inserted into an organism's genetic material, and are passed on to future generations.

17. The systems in the human body must be kept within a certain temperature range to work properly. Keeping the body temperature within its proper range is part of maintaining homeostasis. For example, sweating helps to keep a human body from overheating.

Essay Question

18. Oncogenes cause cells to divide more than normal. Tumor suppressor genes cause cells to stop dividing or even die. These genes control how cells multiply and grow. Genes control the production of certain proteins that might be involved, for example, in signaling a cell to grow, divide, or die. As cells multiply, the gene—particularly an oncogene—would be carried to the daughter cells, and the process would continue. In the case of uncontrolled cell division, this could then lead to the formation of a tumor.

Chapter 15 Organizer:
Evolution

Essential Questions	National Science Standards	Materials and Planning: Estimated times include cleanup and disposal, but do not include teacher prep time. For cleanup and disposal guidelines, see page 39T.	Est. Time (min)
Section 1 1. What evidence convinced Darwin that species could change over time? 2. What are the four principles of natural selection? 3. How can natural selection change a population?	UCP.1, UCP.3, UCP.4, UCP.5; A.1, A.2; C.2, C.3, C.4, C.5; F.4; G.1, G.2, G.3	**Launch Lab,** p. 416: black paper, red paper, scissors	20
		Demonstration, p. 420: pictures of Galápagos finches	10
Section 2 1. How do fossils provide evidence of evolution? 2. How does morphology provide evidence of evolution? 3. How does biochemistry provide evidence of evolution?	UCP.1–5; A.1, A.2; C.2, C.3, C.4, C.5; F.4; G.1, G.2, G.3	**Demonstration,** p. 424: various vertebrate skeletons	15
		Demonstration, p. 425: model or picture of human skeleton	5
		Demonstration, p. 426: various vertebrate embryos	15
		Demonstration, p. 428: pictures of soldiers in camouflage	5
		MiniLab 1, p. 429: specimens of Monarch and viceroy butterflies	15
		Demonstration, p. 429: culture plate of bacteria, filter paper, antibiotic, plate	15
Section 3 1. What are the conditions of the Hardy-Weinberg principle? 2. What patterns can be observed in evolution? 3. What factors influence speciation?	UCP.1–5; A.1, A.2; C.2, C.3, C.4, C.6; F.4; G.1, G.2, G.3	**Demonstration,** p. 438: map of Arizona	5
		BioLab, p. 443: small, medium, and large beads; forceps; short-nosed pliers; tray or pan; stopwatch	50

Suggested Time for Each Lesson

Class	Chapter Opener	Section 1	Section 2	Section 3	Assessment
Basic	45 min	90 min	90 min	90 min	45 min
General	25 min	100 min	55 min	90 min	45 min
Honors	5 min	85 min	135 min	90 min	45 min

ConnectED
connectED.mcgraw-hill.com

Access interactive learning opportunities and teaching resources using these icons located throughout your StudentWorks™ Plus Online and eTeacherEdition Online.

Chapter 15 Section Resources	Additional Chapter 15 Resources	Technology
FAST FILE Unit 4 Resources: Launch Lab Worksheet* Study Guide (English/Spanish)* Section Quick Check **Reading Essentials 15.1** **Science Notebook 15.1*** **FAST FILE Unit 4 Resources:** MiniLab Worksheet* Study Guide (English/Spanish)* Section Quick Check **Reading Essentials 15.2** **Science Notebook 15.2*** **FAST FILE Unit 4 Resources:** Study Guide (English/Spanish)* Section Quick Check **Reading Essentials 15.3** **Science Notebook 15.3***	**FAST FILE Unit 4 Resources:** Chapter Diagnostic Test Concept Mapping* Real-World Biology Enrichment Chapter Tests A, B, and C **Transparencies:** Bellringer Transparencies* Biology Concepts Transparencies* **Lab Resources:** Laboratory Manual* Probeware Lab Manual* Forensics Lab Manual* Pre-AP Lab Manual* Open Inquiry in Biology* Guided Inquiry in Biology*	**Teaching Tools:** eTeacherEdition Online Classroom Presentation Toolkit CD-ROM* LabManager™ CD-ROM* Video Lab DVD* Virtual Lab CD-ROM* What's BIOLOGY Got To Do With It? StudentWorks™ Plus Online* **Chapter Assessment Tools:** Classroom Presentation Toolkit CD-ROM* *ExamView® Assessment Suite* CD-ROM **Web-Based Resources:** • StudentWorks™ Plus Online • eTeacherEdition Online • Animations* • The Interactive Time Line* • Interactive Tables* • Online Quizzes • Online Test Practice • Standardized Test Practice • Virtual Labs* • Multilingual eGlossary* • Vocabulary eGames* • Vocabulary eFlashcards • WebQuests • Personal Tutors

While all resources listed are appropriate for English learners, the * indicates resources with a strong visual or hands-on component for EL.

Teaching strategies and activities have been coded for differentiated instruction.

AL Activities for students working above grade level	**OL** Activities for students working on grade level	**BL** Activities for students working below grade level	**EL** Activities for English learners (also ELL)	**COOP LEARN** Activities designed for small cooperative group work

CHAPTER 15

Launch Lab
How does selection work?

? Inquiry Launch Lab

For a lab worksheet, use your eTeacherEdition Online.

RUBRIC A rubric for evaluating Launch Labs is found on your eTeacherEdition Online.

Est. Time 20 min

Additional Material scissors

Teaching Strategies

- Divide the class into groups of two for this activity.
- As students consider how these populations might change over time, remind them that mating among surviving members of the population will offset deaths that occur as a result of predation and other causes.

Procedure

1. Read and complete the lab safety form.
2. Work in groups of two to cut ten 3-cm-by-3-cm squares out of a piece of **black paper** and a piece of **red paper**.
3. Make two groups of ten squares: one with two red squares and the other with eight red squares.
4. Number the squares in each group, making sure that Square 1 is always red.
5. Place the squares numbered-side-down, then choose a red square from each group and record its number.
6. Repeat Step 5 ten times.

CHAPTER 15
Evolution

ConnectED

Your one-stop online resource
connectED.mcgraw-hill.com

Video
Audio
Review
Inquiry
WebQuest
Assessment
Concepts in Motion
Multilingual eGlossary

Launch Lab
How does selection work?

Predators can cause changes in populations by choosing certain organisms as prey. In this lab, you will look at how prey populations might respond to a predator.

For a lab worksheet, use your StudentWorks™ Plus Online.

? Inquiry Launch Lab

FOLDABLES®

Make a four-door book and label each door with one of the four principal ideas of natural selection. Use it to organize your notes on natural selection.

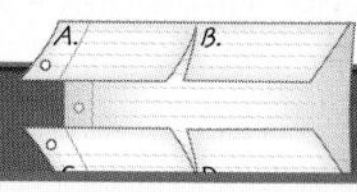

Analysis

1. **Compare** the number of times you chose Square 1 in the group with two red squares versus the group with eight red squares. Answers will vary. Square 1 is less likely to be chosen in the group with eight red squares.
2. **Infer** A predator prefers red squares. In which group is Square 1 less likely to be eaten? Explain. It is less likely Square 1 from the group with eight red squares will be eaten because there are more red squares in that group that the predator can choose from.

THEME FOCUS Scientific Inquiry
The theory of evolution was developed as a result of scientific inquiry.

BIG Idea The theory of evolution is supported by natural selection and explains the diversity of life.

- **Section 1** • Darwin's Theory of Evolution by Natural Selection
- **Section 2** • Evidence of Evolution
- **Section 3** • Shaping Evolutionary Theory

Introduce the Chapter

Coevolution

SAY TO STUDENTS: ***The petals of the orchid in the photo look similar to a female bee. The scent and appearance of the flower draws bees to the flower where they aid in pollination. This is an example of two species that have evolved in relationship to one another. Think of some other examples in which species coevolve.*** Answers will vary. Students might suggest plant/pollinator, parasite/host, or predator/prey combinations.

BIG Idea

Directed Reading Have students create a three-column chart. In the left column, students should write the Big Idea for the chapter and the Main Idea of each section. In the middle column, students should write questions they have about the Big Idea and Main Ideas. As they read, have them answer their questions in the third column.

THEMES

Scientific Inquiry The theory of evolution was developed as a result of scientific inquiry.

Diversity The diversity of life on Earth is explained by natural selection.

Energy Energy is a resource for which organisms compete, according to one principle of natural selection.

Homeostasis Populations may evolve due to a long-term disruption in homeostasis.

Change Environmental change can result in a change in allele frequencies of a population over time.

Section 1

MAIN Idea

BL OL AL Natural Selection
ASK STUDENTS: ***How can you observe how species have changed over time?*** Possible answers: study fossil evidence or compare and contrast similar species that likely descended from a common ancestor.

R Reading Strategy

EL BL OL K-W-L Chart Divide students into groups of three. Have each group fold a piece of paper into three columns. Have students write "Know" above the first column, "Want to Know" above the second column, and "Learned" above the third column. Have groups brainstorm what they already know about evolution and Charles Darwin and record this in the K column. Then have groups write questions about what they want to know in the W column. After reading and discussing Section 1, have groups review what they wrote in the K and W columns. Tell groups to use the L column to correct any misconceptions they had in the K column, answer questions from the W column, and record other information that they learned.

W Writing Support

EL BL OL COOP LEARN
Creative Writing In small groups, have students write an illustrated story based on what they learn about the voyage of HMS *Beagle* from this section. You may extend this assignment by having students conduct additional research.

Reading Check He read *Principles of Geology,* saw marine fossils on mountains, experienced earthquakes, and observed the animals of the Galápagos Islands.

Section 1

Reading Preview

Essential Questions

- What evidence convinced Darwin that species could change over time?
- What are the four principles of natural selection?
- How can natural selection change a population?

Review Vocabulary

selective breeding: the process by which a breeder develops a plant or animal to have certain traits

New Vocabulary

artificial selection
natural selection
evolution

g Multilingual eGlossary

Darwin's Theory of Evolution by Natural Selection

MAIN Idea Charles Darwin developed a theory of evolution based on natural selection.

Real-World Reading Link Today, a jet can travel from London to New York in hours. Imagine how different things were when it took almost five years for Charles Darwin to circle the globe aboard a small, cramped ship.

R Developing the Theory of Evolution

When Charles Darwin, shown in **Figure 1,** boarded the HMS *Beagle* in 1831, the average person thought that the world was about 6000 years old. Almost everyone, including the young Darwin, thought that animals and plants were unchanging. The concept of gradual change over time was still years away.

Darwin on the HMS *Beagle* The primary mission of the *Beagle* was to survey the coast of South America. In 1831, the *Beagle* set sail from England for Maderia and then proceeded to South America, as shown on the map in **Figure 2.** Darwin's role on the ship was as a naturalist and companion to the captain. His job was to collect biological and geological specimens during the ship's travels. Darwin had a degree in theology from Christ's College, Cambridge, although he previously had studied medicine and the sciences.

Over the course of the ship's five-year voyage, Darwin made extensive collections of rocks, fossils, plants, and animals. He also read a copy of Charles Lyell's *Principles of Geology*—a book proposing that Earth was millions of years old. This book influenced his thinking as he observed fossils of marine life at high elevations in the Andes, unearthed giant fossil versions of smaller living mammals, and saw how earthquakes could lift rocks great distances very quickly.

Figure 1 Charles Darwin (1809–1882) posed for this portrait shortly after he returned from his voyage aboard the HMS *Beagle*.

The Galápagos Islands In 1835, the *Beagle* arrived in the Galápagos (guh LAH puh gus) Islands off the coast of South America. Darwin was initially disappointed by the stark barrenness of these volcanic islands. However, as he began to collect mockingbirds, finches, and other animals on the four islands that he visited, he noticed that the different islands seemed to have their own, slightly different varieties of animals. These differences, however, only sparked a mere curiosity. He took little notice of the comment from the colony's vice governor that the island origins of the giant tortoises could be identified solely by the appearance of the tortoises' shells. W

Reading Check Summarize some of the experiences or observations that influenced Darwin during his voyage on the *Beagle.*

Content Background

Teacher FYI Charles Darwin's father, Robert, had a successful medical practice. His mother, Susannah Wedgwood, came from a family of wealthy pottery makers. Charles grew up in luxury in a large house with servants. As a child, Darwin collected minerals, insects, and birds. Even though he was a curious child, he did poorly in school. Charles, at age 16, was sent to live with his older brother to study medicine at Edinburgh University. After two years, he dropped out because he thought the lectures were dull and because he was sickened by the only two operations he witnessed, both performed without the use of anesthetic.

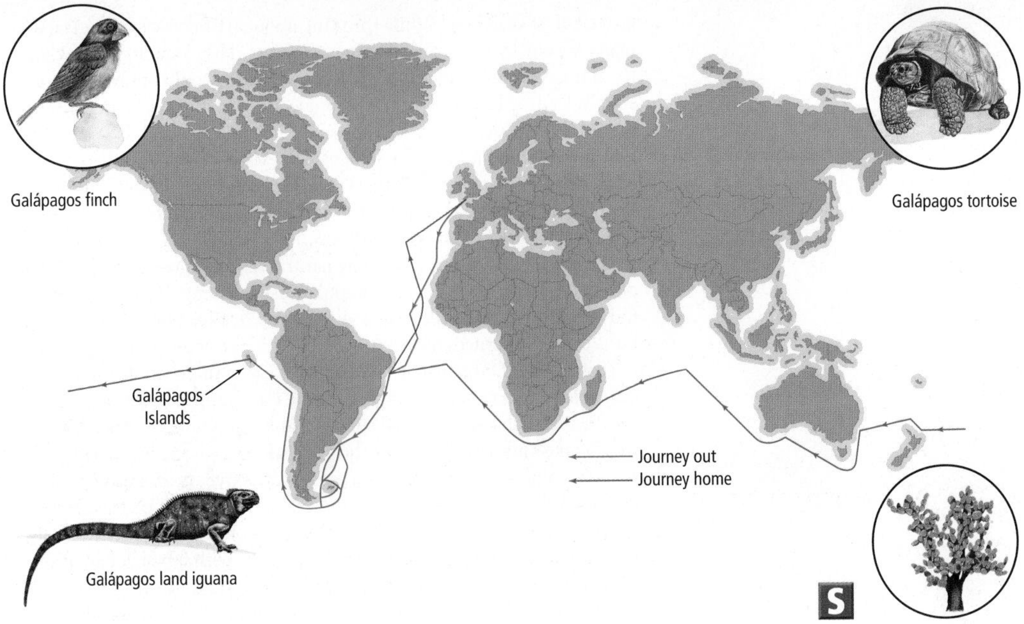

■ **Figure 2** The map shows the route of the *Beagle's* voyage. The species shown are all unique to the Galápagos Islands.
Infer ***How did the first organisms reach the Galápagos Islands?***

A few years after Darwin returned to England, he began reconsidering his observations. He took note of the work of John Gould, an ornithologist who was classifying the birds Darwin brought back from the Galápagos. Gould discovered that the Galápagos finches were separate species and determined that the finches of the Galápagos did not live anywhere else in South America. In fact, almost every specimen that Darwin had collected on the islands was new to European scientists. These new species most closely resembled species from mainland South America, although the Galápagos and the mainland had different environments. Island and mainland species should not have resembled one another so closely unless, as Darwin began to suspect, populations from the mainland changed after reaching the Galápagos.

Darwin continued his studies Darwin hypothesized that new species could appear gradually through small changes in ancestral species, but he could not see how such a process would work. To understand it better, he turned to animal breeders—pigeon breeders in particular.

Different breeds of pigeons have certain distinctive traits that also are present in these breeds' offspring. A breeder can promote these traits by selecting and breeding pigeons that have the most exaggerated expressions of those traits. For example, to produce pigeons with fan-shaped tails, the breeder will breed pigeons with the most fan-shaped tails. The process of directed breeding to produce offspring with desired traits, referred to as selective breeding was called **artificial selection** by Darwin.

Artificial selection also occurs when humans develop new breeds of dogs or new strains of crop plants. Darwin inferred that if humans could change species by artificial selection, then perhaps the same process could work in nature. Further, Darwin thought that, given enough time, perhaps this process could produce new species.

■ **Caption Question Fig. 2** Birds and insects could have flown. Seeds may have drifted on the wind or been brought by birds. Reptiles could have drifted on large rafts of vegetation. Mammals arrived on boats with humans.

Differentiated Instruction

Behavior Disorders When placing students in cooperative learning groups, which is what two activities on this page require, establish clear rules and expectations for behavior.

For more tips, see pages 14T–15T.

S Skill Practice

BL OL Visual Literacy Have students observe the route of the HMS *Beagle* on Figure 2.

ASK STUDENTS: ***Describe the location of the Galápagos Islands.*** The islands are west of South America. Explain that Darwin spent much time along the coast of South America because Captain Fitzroy wanted to make a good map.

Reading Strategy

EL BL OL COOP LEARN

Make Connections Have students work in pairs to read the section. Instruct students to make a list of observations Darwin made in the Galápagos. When reading through the principles of natural selection, have the students identify which observations from the Galápagos support which principles.

ASK STUDENTS: ***How did what Darwin saw and experienced influence his theories?*** Students' responses should demonstrate critical thinking and accurate understanding that Darwin saw a variation in species on different islands, which suggested that change had occurred.

C Critical Thinking

BL OL AL COOP LEARN

Design an Experiment Have students work in pairs.

SAY TO STUDENTS: ***A particular tropical fish has a rather drab body, but the males have a few colored spots on their sides and tails. Design an experiment to determine if artificial selection can be used to develop a more brightly colored variety.*** Student experiments will vary, but all should use selection from a population to choose the brightest colored males or those with the most colored spots to breed with females produced by such males. Experiments should also indicate that several rounds of selection are needed to develop the new variety.

Natural selection While thinking about artificial selection, Darwin read an essay by economist Thomas Malthus. The essay suggested that the human population, if unchecked, eventually would outgrow its food supply, leading to a competitive struggle for existence. Darwin realized that Malthus's ideas could be applied to the natural world. He reasoned that some competitors in the struggle for existence would be better equipped for survival than others. Those less equipped would die. This is the process of **natural selection.** Here, finally, was the framework for a new theory about the origin of species.

Darwin's theory of evolution by natural selection has four basic principles that explain how traits of a population can change over time. First, individuals in a population show differences, or variations. Second, variations can be inherited, meaning that they are passed down from parent to offspring. Third, organisms have more offspring than can survive on available resources. The average cardinal, for example, lays nine eggs each summer. If each baby cardinal survived and reproduced just once, it would take only seven years for the first pair to have produced one million birds. Finally, variations that increase reproductive success will have a greater chance of being passed on than those that do not increase reproductive success. If having a fantail helps a pigeon reproduce successfully, future generations would include more pigeons with fan-shaped tails.

FOLDABLES® Incorporate information from this section into your Foldable.

Given enough time, natural selection could modify a population enough to produce a new species. Natural selection is now considered the mechanism by which evolution takes place. **Figure 3** shows how natural selection might modify a population of sunflowers.

Reading Check **Explain** the four principles of natural selection.

DATA ANALYSIS LAB 1

Based on Real Data*

Interpret the Data

How did artificial selection change corn? Plant breeders have made many changes to crops. In one of the longest experiments ever conducted, scientists selected maize (corn) for oil content in kernels.

Data and Observations

Look at the graph and compare the selection in the different plant lines.

Line IHO was selected for high oil content, and line ILO was selected for low oil content. The direction of selection was reversed in lines RHO (started from IHO) and RLO (started from ILO) at generation 48. In line SHO (derived from RHO), selection was switched back to high oil content at generation 55.

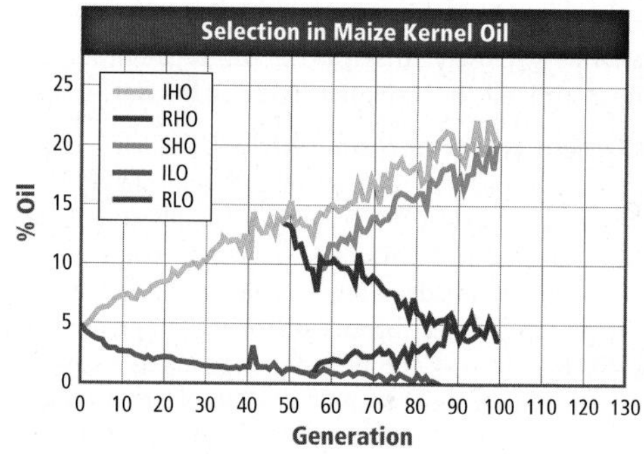

Think Critically

1. **Measure** What were the highest and lowest percentages of oil seen in the experiment?
2. **Predict** If the trend continues for line RHO, approximately how many generations will it take until the oil content reaches zero percent?

*Data obtained from: Hill, W. G. 2005. A century of corn selection. *Science* 307: 683-684.

FOLDABLES®

RUBRIC A rubric for evaluating Foldables is found on your eTeacherEdition Online.

Going Further Have students select one type of natural selection to research: stabilizing selection, directional selection, or disruptive selection. Instruct students to prepare and present an oral report that explains how this type of natural selection might eventually lead to the evolution of a new species, or speciation.

Students should begin by summarizing the type of natural selection they are researching, explaining how this type of natural selection could eventually lead to a new species, and outlining a specific example of speciation that illustrates their point.

DATA ANALYSIS LAB 1

About the Lab

- Point out that the lines represent averages for the population and not individual plants.
- Also see Laurie, Chasalow, et al. 2004. The genetic architecture of response to long-term artificial selection for oil concentration in the maize kernel. *Genetics* 168(4): 2141-2155.

Think Critically

1. highest – 22 percent; lowest – 0 percent
2. between 110 and 120 generations

Reading Check First, individuals in a population have variations. Second, variations can be inherited from parents by offspring. Third, organisms produce more offspring than can survive on the food supply. Fourth, variations that increase reproductive success will be more likely to be passed on to the next generation.

Demonstration

BL OL AL Darwin's Finches Bring pictures of several different species of Galápagos finches to class. Have students examine the beaks of the finches. Point to a species with a short, thick beak.

ASK STUDENTS: ***What type of food do you think this bird most likely eats?*** seeds—the short, thick beak acts like a nutcracker to break the seeds up Then show a species with a thin, pointed beak. ***What type of food do you think this bird most likely eats?*** insects—the thin, pointed beak acts like tweezers to pick insects out of bark Use the pictures of the finches to start a discussion about how natural selection could result in the different beak shapes seen in the Galápagos finches.

Est time: 10 min

Visualizing Natural Selection

Figure 3
Natural selection is the mechanism by which, if given enough time, a population—in this case, a population of sunflowers—could be modified to produce a new species. There are four principles of natural selection that explain how this can occur: variation, heritability, overproduction, and reproductive advantage.

Variation Individuals in a population differ from one another. For example, some sunflowers are taller than others.

Heritability Variations are inherited from parents. Tall sunflowers produce tall sunflowers, and short sunflowers produce short sunflowers.

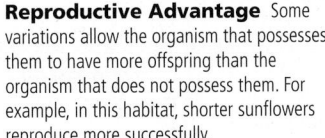

Overproduction Populations produce more offspring than can survive. Each sunflower has hundreds of seeds, most of which will not germinate.

Reproductive Advantage Some variations allow the organism that possesses them to have more offspring than the organism that does not possess them. For example, in this habitat, shorter sunflowers reproduce more successfully.

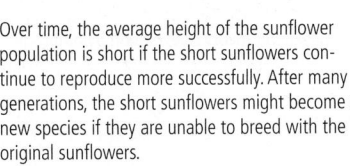

Over time, the average height of the sunflower population is short if the short sunflowers continue to reproduce more successfully. After many generations, the short sunflowers might become a new species if they are unable to breed with the original sunflowers.

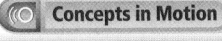

Concepts in Motion Animation

Visualizing Natural Selection

Purpose
Students will visualize the four principal ideas of natural selection.
UCP.2, UCP.4, C.3

Develop Concepts
EL BL OL Discuss Lead students in a discussion of each of the four principles of natural selection using the information about tortoises to reinforce the concept. Provide students with visual examples of natural selection, such as the changing coloration of peppered moths, so that students can generalize the process with other organisms.
AL Have students come up with their own examples.

Develop Concepts
BL OL Clarify a Misconception
ASK STUDENTS: ***Is an individual organism able to evolve over the course of its life?*** no Students might think that individual organisms evolve, but this is not correct. Explain that individuals in the population either have or do not have a particular heritable variation, and that they do not evolve them during their lifetimes. Point out that populations, not individuals within the populations, evolve.

Concepts in Motion
Animation

Activity

BL OL AL Natural Selection Tell students about a fictional crevice lizard that lives in cracks in rocks. Freezing and thawing have widened these cracks, and lizards that are now in large crevices are more easily captured and eaten. Have students use the principles of natural selection to predict how future generations of the crevice lizard population will change over time. As generations pass, larger lizards will be selected. If the cracks continue to widen, then the average size of crevice lizards in the population will most likely continue to increase as well. Est. time: 20 min

Concepts in Motion Interactive Table

D Develop Concepts

BL OL COOP LEARN

Travelogue Have groups of students research the Galápagos Islands and produce a travel brochure about the islands' finch species. The travel brochure should include information about finches from the four major Galápagos finch genera: *Geospiza* (the ground finches), *Camarhynchus* (the tree finches), *Certhidea* (the warbler finch), and *Pinaroloxias* (the Cocos finch).

Formative Assessment

Evaluation

ASK STUDENTS: ***What are the four principles of natural selection?*** See p. 420. ***Why is understanding natural selection key to understanding evolution?*** Natural selection is one mechanism by which evolution occurs.

Remediation Have students create a diagram with four sections that shows how a fictional population of spotted insects might evolve to be a striped population over time. Have them label each section of the diagram with one of the principles of natural selection.

Table 1 Basic Principles of Natural Selection — Concepts in Motion Interactive Table

Principle	Example
Individuals in a population show variations among others of the same species.	The students in a classroom all look different.
Variations are inherited.	You look similar to your parents.
Animals have more young than can survive on the available resources.	The average cardinal lays nine eggs per summer. If each cardinal lived only one year and all offspring survived, in seven years there would be a million cardinals.
Variations that increase reproductive success will be more common in the next generation.	If having a fan-shaped tail increases the reproductive success of pigeons, then more pigeons in the next generation will have fan-shaped tails.

The Origin of Species

Darwin had likely formulated his theory of evolution by natural selection by about 1840. Soon after, he began writing a multivolume book compiled of evidence for evolution and explaining how natural selection might provide a mechanism for the origin of species. **Table 1** summarizes the principles of natural selection described in Darwin's work. He continued to compile evidence in support of his theory for many years. For example, he spent eight years studying relationships among barnacles.

In 1858, Alfred Russel Wallace, another English naturalist, proposed a theory that was almost identical to Darwin's theory. Both men's ideas were presented to the Linnean Society of London. One year later, Darwin published *On the Origin of Species by Means of Natural Selection*—a condensed version of the book he had started many years before.

In his book, Darwin used the term *evolution* only on the last page. Today, biologists use the term **evolution** to define cumulative changes in groups of organisms through time. Natural selection is not synonymous with evolution; it is a mechanism by which evolution occurs. D

VOCABULARY
WORD ORIGIN
Evolve
comes from the Latin word *evolvere*, meaning *unroll* or *unfold*

Section 1 Assessment

Section Summary

- Darwin drew from his observations on the HMS *Beagle* and later studies to develop his theory of evolution by natural selection.
- Natural selection is based on ideas of variation, inheritance, excess reproduction, and advantages of certain traits in certain environments.
- Darwin reasoned that the process of natural selection eventually could result in the appearance of new species.

Understand Main Ideas

1. MAIN Idea **Describe** the evidence Charles Darwin gathered that led to his theory of evolution.
2. **Explain** how the idea of artificial selection contributed to Darwin's ideas on natural selection.
3. **Identify** the four principles of natural selection and provide examples not used in this section.
4. **Discuss** Wallace's contribution to the theory of evolution by natural selection.

Think Critically

5. **Infer** the consequences for evolution if species did not vary.

WRITING in Biology

6. Write a short story about what it might have been like to visit the Galápagos Islands with Darwin.

Section 1 Assessment

1. Darwin gathered fossils in South America, specimens in the Galápagos and other locations, and made observations all along the route.
2. Darwin observed that individuals are variable, and the variations are heritable. He also realized that selection could lead to changes in a species over time.
3. Possible answer: organisms produce more young than can survive (e.g., spiders lay hundreds of eggs); individuals in populations have variation (e.g., each horse in a herd is unique); variations can be inherited (e.g., child resembles parents); variations increasing reproductive success will be more common in next generation (e.g., colorful plumes more common in next generation of birds if they make birds more successful at finding mates.)
4. Wallace came to the same conclusions as Darwin.
5. Evolution would not occur if species did not have variations.
6. Answers will vary but should show an understanding of what Darwin saw on the Galápagos Islands.

Assessment Online Quiz

Reading Preview

Essential Questions

- How do fossils provide evidence of evolution?
- How does morphology provide evidence of evolution?
- How does biochemistry provide evidence of evolution?

Review Vocabulary

fossil: remains of an organism or its activities

New Vocabulary

derived trait
ancestral trait
homologous structure
vestigial structure
analogous structure
embryo
biogeography
fitness
camouflage
mimicry

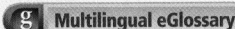

Multilingual eGlossary

R Evidence of Evolution

MAIN Idea Multiple lines of evidence support the theory of evolution.

Real-World Reading Link The evidence for evolution is like a set of building blocks. Just as you cannot build something with only one building block, one piece of evidence does not make a theory. The evidence for evolution is more convincing when it is supported by many pieces of evidence, just as a structure is more sturdy when it is built with many blocks.

Support for Evolution

Darwin's book *On the Origin of Species* demonstrated how evolution might happen. The book also provided evidence that evolution has occurred on our planet. The concepts of natural selection and evolution are different, though related. Darwin's theory of evolution by natural selection is part of the larger theory of evolution. Recall that a theory provides an explanation for a natural phenomenon based on observations. Theories explain available data and suggest further areas for experimentation. The theory of evolution states that all organisms on Earth have descended from a common ancestor.

The fossil record Fossils provide a record of species that lived long ago, and they supply some of the most significant evidence of evolutionary change. This record can show how ancient species are similar to current species, as illustrated in **Figure 4.** Fossils also show that some species, such as the horseshoe crab, have remained unchanged for millions of years. The fossil record is an important source of information for determining the ancestry of organisms and patterns of evolution.

S **Figure 4** The giant armadillo-like glyptodont, *Glyptodon*, is an extinct animal that Darwin thought must have been related to living armadillos.
Observe *What features of the 2000-kg glyptodont are similar to those of the 4-kg armadillo?*

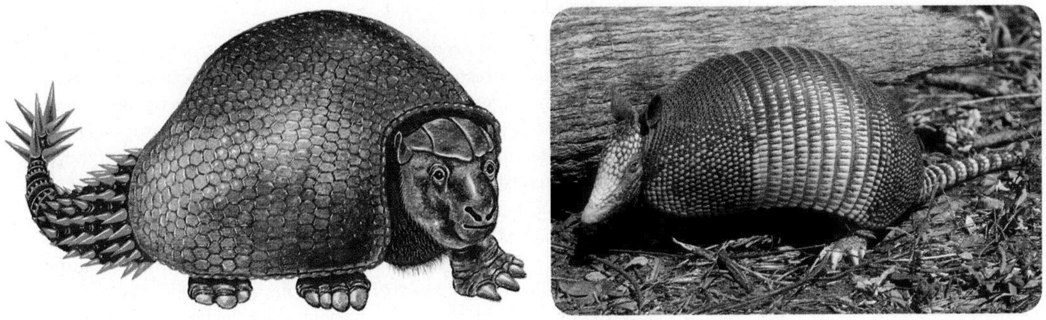

Glyptodont

Armadillo

Research Citation

Vocabulary Educational research indicates that students should be provided with explicit strategies to use in understanding new vocabulary. The reading strategy described on the next page helps students learn content-specific terms by introducing them to strategies for deciphering unfamiliar words.
(Baumann and Kameenui, 1991)

Research bibliography on pages 32T–34T

Caption Question Fig. 4 The glyptodont and armadillo are both shaped similarly and both had armored body coverings.

Section 2

MAIN Idea

BL OL AL

Evidence of Evolution
ASK STUDENTS: ***What evidence supports the theory of evolution by natural selection?*** Student responses will vary, but may include ideas that relate to observations of variations in populations, fossils, and traits that allow populations to thrive in particular environments. Since the time of Darwin, his theory has been constantly tested.

R Reading Strategy

EL BL OL **Directed Reading**
Have students examine the headings, figures, table, captions, and bolded words in Section 2. Ask students to brainstorm a list of questions that might be answered by the text. Provide examples such as: ***What are derived traits? How is a California kingsnake different from a western coral snake?*** Record students' questions on the board. Then have students read the section. Afterward, ask students to answer the questions on the board.

S Skill Practice

EL AL **Visual Literacy** Refer students to Figure 4. Have students make two lists, one of ancestral traits that the armadillo shares with the glyptodont, and another of derived traits that have evolved since glyptodonts. Possible answer: ancestral traits—body armor, four limbs, tail; derived traits—elongated nose, linear "joints" in body armor, smaller body Have students use their lists to discuss whether the shared ancestral traits offer evidence of evolution.

■ **Figure 5** This artist's rendering of *Archaeopteryx* shows that it shares many features with modern birds while retaining ancestral dinosaur features.

W

Connection to Earth Science Although Darwin recognized the limitations of the fossil record, he predicted the existence of fossils intermediate in form between species. Today, scientists studying evolutionary relationships have found hundreds of thousands of transitional fossils that contain features shared by different species. For example, certain dinosaur fossils show feathers of modern birds and teeth and bony tails of reptiles. **Figure 5** shows an artist's rendering of *Archaeopteryx,* one of the first birds. *Archaeopteryx* fossils provide evidence of characteristics that classify it as a bird, and also show that the bird retained several distinct dinosaur features. R

Researchers consider two major classes of traits when studying transitional fossils: derived traits and ancestral traits. **Derived traits** are newly evolved features, such as feathers, that do not appear in the fossils of common ancestors. **Ancestral traits,** on the other hand, are more primitive features, such as teeth and tails, that do appear in ancestral forms. Transitional fossils provide detailed patterns of evolutionary change for the ancestors of many modern animals, including mollusks, horses, whales, and humans.

VOCABULARY
WORD ORIGIN
Homologous
comes from the Greek words *homos,* meaning *same,* and *logos,* meaning *relation* or *reasoning*

Comparative anatomy Why do the vertebrate forelimbs shown in **Figure 6** have different functions but appear to be constructed of similar bones in similar ways? Evolutionary theory suggests that the answer lies in shared ancestry.

Homologous structures Anatomically similar structures inherited from a common ancestor are called **homologous structures.** Evolution predicts that an organism's body parts are more likely to be modifications of ancestral body parts than they are to be entirely new features. The limbs illustrated in **Figure 6** move animals in different ways, yet they share similar construction. Bird wings and reptile limbs are another example. Although birds use their wings to fly and reptiles use their limbs to walk, bird wings and reptile forelimbs are similar in shape and construction, which indicates that they were inherited from a common ancestor. While homologous structures alone are not evidence of evolution, they are an example for which evolution is the best available explanation for the biological data.

W Writing Support

AL Presentation Writing

Have students research the hoatzin, a primitive bird from the rain forests of South America, and prepare a slideshow presentation comparing its features with those of *Archaeopteryx* illustrated in Figure 5. Students' presentations should include the following information: The hoatzin is living, and *Archaeopteryx* is extinct; both species have claws on their wings; both have long necks; the hoatzin is a weak flyer, as most likely was *Archaeopteryx.* After presentations are given, have students discuss whether the hoatzin most likely evolved from a bird similar to *Archaeopteryx.*

R Reading Strategy

BL OL

Content-Specific Words Point out that some familiar words have specific meanings in a science context.

ASK STUDENTS: ***How could you use the word* intermediate *in a sentence?*** Answers will vary. ***Use the word* form *in a sentence.*** Answers will vary, depending on the definition chosen. Explain that the term *form* in paleontology is often used to mean a fossil representing a species.

ASK STUDENTS: ***What is meant by* intermediate *as used in the text under the heading* Connection to Earth Science?** There are fossils that have some, but not all, of the features of species that came before and after them.

Demonstration

Comparative Anatomy In addition to the illustrations in Figure 6, you can use the wings of a bird and the arms or hands of a mammal to demonstrate homology in both organisms. You might be able to obtain skeletons of various animals from biological supply houses to show homology in other body structures. If possible, compare specimens from each of the vertebrate classes. In addition to showing homology in animals, bring in two different plant species and show students homologous structures. For example, point out that cactus spines and leaves of trees are all homologous structures. Est time: 15 min

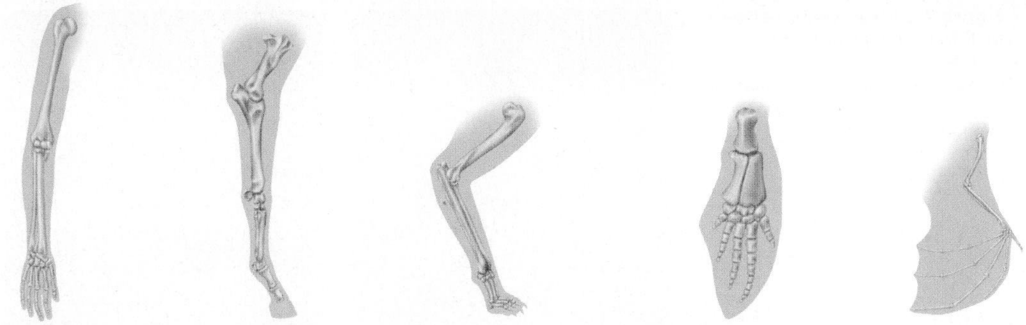

■ **Figure 6** The forelimbs of vertebrates illustrate homologous structures. Each limb is adapted for different uses, but they all have similar bones.
Infer *which of the forelimbs shown would most likely resemble a whale's pectoral fin.*

C

R **Vestigial structures** In some cases, a functioning structure in one species is smaller or less functional in a closely related species. For example, most birds have wings developed for flight. Kiwis, however, have very small wings that cannot be used for flying. The kiwi wing is a kind of homologous structure called a vestigial structure. **Vestigial structures** are structures that are the reduced forms of functional structures in other organisms. **Table 2** illustrates some vestigial structures in different species. Evolutionary theory predicts that features of ancestors that no longer have a function for that species will become smaller over time until they are lost.

D

Table 2 **Vestigial Structures** — Concepts in Motion Interactive Table

Trait	Example	Description
Snake pelvis	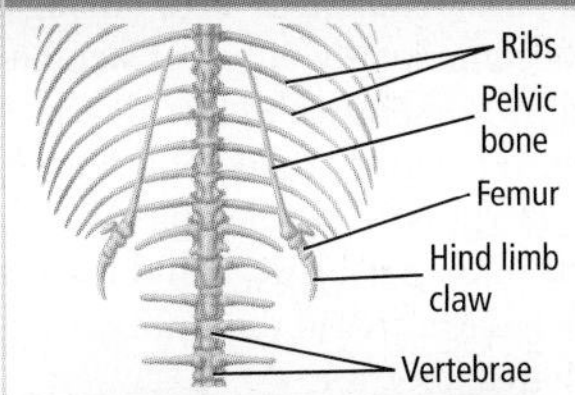	The pelvis is the attachment point for legs and is therefore nonfunctional in an animal without legs.
Kiwi wings		The wings of kiwis are too small to be of any use in flight.
Human appendix	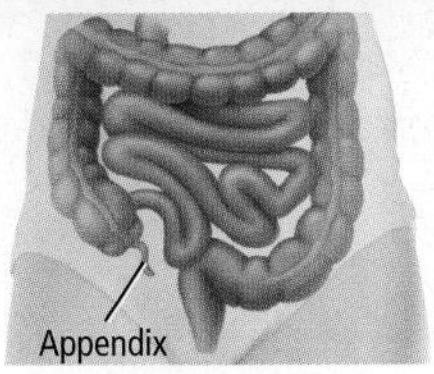	This is a 5- to 15-cm-long structure that is important for digestion in many mammals, but is of limited use in humans and some apes.

Demonstration

Vestigial Structures Show students a model or picture of a human skeleton. Point out the coccyx bones at the end of the sacrum.
ASK STUDENTS: ***What do you think is the function of this group of bones?*** Answers will vary. Point out that the bones do not attach to any major muscle group or protect any portion of the spinal cord. In addition, no body movements are produced along the coccyges' joints.
If humans had several more coccyges, how might our bodies be different? More coccyges would form a tail on the human body. Explain to students that the coccyx bones are in fact vestigial structures. Some humans are born with more coccyx bones than others. Babies with extra coccyges look like they have a small tail. Usually, surgeons remove the coccyx tail shortly after birth. Est. time: 5 min

C Critical Thinking

BL OL Draw Conclusions

The limbs illustrated in Figure 6 all show bones of the forelimbs.
ASK STUDENTS: ***Why are all mammals' forelimbs homologous?*** All mammals are descended from a common ancestor that had forelimbs.

R Reading Strategy

BL OL AL COOP LEARN

Brainstorm Have students read this page, paying particular attention to the definition of the term *vestigial structure.* In small groups, have students brainstorm a list of other structures that might be vestigial in some animals. Answers will vary. For example, some legless lizards have reduced leg bones, whales have remnants of hindlimb bones, and blind cave fish have eye sockets with no eyes.

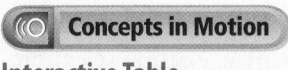

Concepts in Motion
Interactive Table

D Develop Concepts

BL OL

Clarify a Misconception

ASK STUDENTS: ***Are all vestigial structures completely useless?*** no Although some students may think all vestigial structures are no longer used by the organism, the definition of a vestigial structure is one that has a reduced or rudimentary function in the adult—it need not be completely useless.

■ **Caption Question Fig. 6**
porpoise's forelimb

S Skill Practice

BL OL AL

Compare and Contrast

ASK STUDENTS: ***What similarities and differences exist between homologous structures and analogous structures?*** Both are morphological adaptations. Homologous structures involve common ancestry, but analogous structures evolved independently. ***Give examples of each that are not mentioned in the text.*** Possible answer: homologous structure—five-digit foot shared by most reptiles and mammals; analogous structure—fish fin and whale fin

Develop Concepts

BL OL AL

Clarify a Misconception

ASK STUDENTS: ***Are organisms able to consciously direct the course of their own evolution?*** No. Students may think that natural selection satisfies an individual's desire to evolve. Natural selection is directed by environmental circumstances, not by an individual's or population's need or desire for some future requirement.

S Skill Practice

OL **Visual Literacy** Have students examine Figure 8.

SAY TO STUDENTS: ***Identify which embryo is a mammal and which embryo is a bird.*** left image: chick; right image: rat (However, students will not be able to differentiate from the photos alone.) Explain that these photos illustrate comparative embryology.

Reading Check Vestigial structures have the same evolutionary origins as fully functional features in related species, hence they are homologous.

Caption Question Fig. 7 Because they are constructed very differently but serve the same purpose.

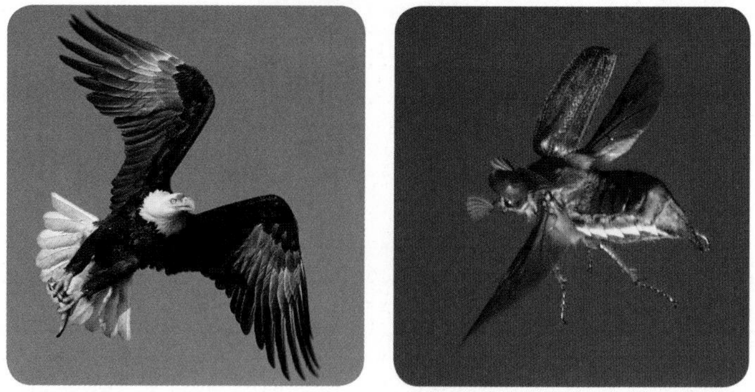

Bald eagle — May beetle

Figure 7 Eagles and beetles use their wings to fly, but their wing structures are different.

Explain *how scientists know that the wings of eagles and beetles are analogous structures.*

Not all anatomically similar features are evidence of common ancestry. **Analogous structures** can be used for the same purpose and can be superficially similar in construction but are not inherited from a common ancestor. As shown in **Figure 7**, the wings of an eagle and the wings of a beetle have the same function. They both enable the organism to fly. However, the wings are constructed in different ways and from different materials. While analogous structures do not indicate close evolutionary relationships, they do show that functionally similar features can evolve independently in similar environments. S

Reading Check **Explain** why vestigial structures are considered examples of homologous structures.

Comparative embryology Vertebrate embryos provide more glimpses into evolutionary relationships. An **embryo** is an early, prebirth stage of an organism's development. Scientists have found that vertebrate embryos exhibit homologous structures during certain phases of development but become totally different structures in the adult forms. The embryos shown in **Figure 8,** like all vertebrate embryos, have a tail and paired structures called pharyngeal pouches. In fish, the pouches develop into gills. In reptiles, birds, and mammals, these structures become parts of the ears, jaws, and throats. Although the adult forms differ, the shared features in the embryos suggest that vertebrates evolved from a shared ancestor.

S

Figure 8 Embryos reveal evolutionary history. Bird and mammal embryos share several developmental features.

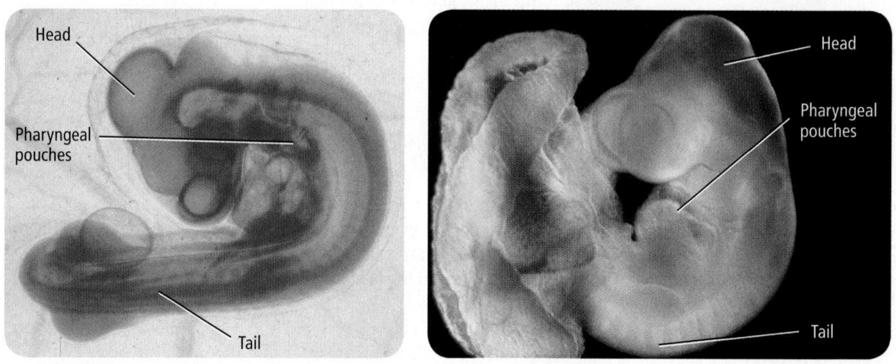

Bird embryo — Mammal embryo

Demonstration

EL BL OL AL **Comparative Embryology** Tell students that, in 1828, German naturalist Ernst von Baer was the first to suggest that the more closely related two species were, the more similar their stages of development. Show students embryos from various vertebrate species (these can be obtained from biological supply houses). Without telling students the embryos' species, have students examine the embryos and try to determine which embryos come from the most closely related species. After students have made their determinations, reveal the species names and have students check whether their determinations were correct. Est. time: 15 min

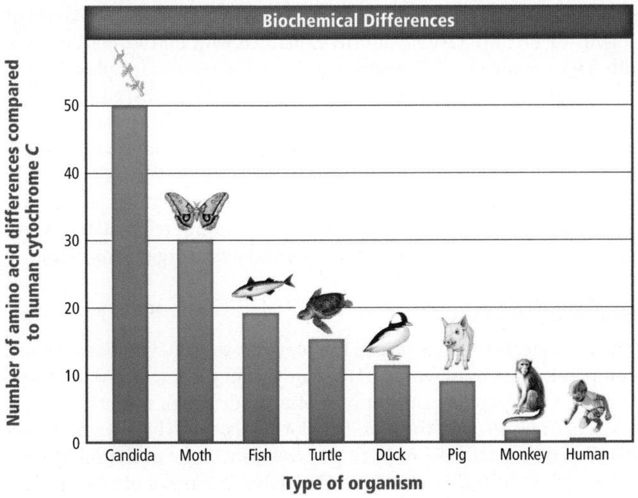

Figure 9 This illustration compares amino acid sequences of cytochrome *c* in humans and other organisms.
Infer ***Would the cytochrome c of a reptile or a bird be expected to have more amino acid differences when compared with that of a human? Explain.***

S

Comparative biochemistry Scientific data also show that common ancestry can be seen in the complex metabolic molecules that many different organisms share. Cytochrome *c* is an enzyme that is essential for respiration and is highly conserved in animals. This means that despite slight variations in its amino acid sequence, the molecule has changed very little over time.

Evolutionary theory predicts that molecules in species with a recent common ancestor should share certain ancient amino acid sequences. The more closely related the species are, the greater the number of sequences that will be shared. This predicted pattern is what scientists find to be true in cytochrome *c*. For example, as illustrated in **Figure 9,** the cytochrome *c* in the pig and in the monkey share more amino acid sequences with humans than the cytochrome *c* in the duck shares with humans.

Connection to Chemistry Scientists have found similar biochemical patterns in other proteins, as well as in DNA and RNA. DNA and RNA form the molecular basis of heredity in all living organisms. The fact that many organisms have the same complex molecules suggests that these molecules evolved early in the history of life and were passed on through the life-forms that have lived on Earth. Comparisons of the similarities in these molecules across species reflect evolutionary patterns seen in comparative anatomy and in the fossil record. Organisms with closely related morphological features have more closely related molecular features.

Geographic distribution The distribution of plants and animals that Darwin saw during his South American travels first suggested evolution to Darwin. He observed that animals on the South American mainland were more similar to other South American animals than they were to animals living in similar environments in Europe. The South American mara, for example, inhabited a niche that was occupied by the English rabbit. You can compare a mara and an English rabbit in **Figure 10.** Darwin realized that the mara was more similar to D other South American species than it was to the English rabbit because it shared a closer ancestor with the South American animals.

S

Figure 10 The mara *(Dolichotis patagonum)* exists in a niche similar to that of the English rabbit *(Oryctolagus cuniculus).*

Mara

English rabbit

S Skill Practice

BL OL Visual Literacy Have students summarize the information presented in the table. Tell students that monkeys have DNA that is more than 98 percent similar to humans. Have students examine Figure 9.
ASK STUDENTS: ***How many significant cytochrome c differences would you predict monkeys to have from humans?*** one or two

S Skill Practice

BL OL Visual Literacy Have students examine Figure 10.
ASK STUDENTS: ***In what ways does the mara resemble the rabbit?*** The ears and back legs are elongated, and the shape of their head is similar.

D Develop Concepts

AL Integrate Geography
Have students research the geographic distribution of euphorbia and cacti. Have students report on the environments where each plant is found and the adaptations of each plant.
ASK STUDENTS: ***How is the relationship between the euphorbia and cacti similar to that of the rabbit and mara?*** Both have evolved similar adaptations to similar environments, but they are not closely related species of plants.

Differentiated Instruction

Below Level Assist students who perform below level by providing them with samples of finished products. When students have a model of what is expected of them, they will better understand how to meet those expectations.

For more tips, see pages 14T–15T.

Caption Question Fig. 9 A reptile would have more differences because it is more distantly related to a human.

GOING GREEN Many hand washing soaps have antimicrobial chemicals in them. According to the principles of natural selection, what might happen to bacteria continually exposed to these chemicals? Ask students what would be a "green" and better alternative to antimicrobial handsoap. Use a green alternative to antimicrobial hand soap in your classroom and lab.

R Reading Strategy

BL OL Build Vocabulary

Explain that the term *biogeography* is derived from the Greek words *bios,* meaning *life; ge,* meaning *earth;* and *graphein,* meaning *write.* Biogeography deals with questions about the distribution of plants and animals. The patterns of species distribution can usually be explained through a combination of historical factors, the area and isolation of landmasses, and abiotic conditions.

Reading Strategy

EL BL OL Frayer Model Have students develop a Frayer Model for the terms *fitness, camouflage,* and *mimicry.*

SAY TO STUDENTS: ***Make a square on a piece of paper for each word. In the upper left quadrant of a square, have students write the definition of the term. In the upper right quadrant, list characteristics of the term. In the lower left quadrant, report examples. Finally, in the lower right quadrant, report non-examples.***

Develop Concepts

BL OL AL Scaffolding

ASK STUDENTS: ***How do fossils indicate evolution?*** Fossils are a direct record of previous evolutionary patterns. ***Why are physiological adaptations important in studying natural selection?*** Some physiological adaptations have evolved by natural selection within a few years. ***How do homologous and analogous structures differ?*** Homologous structures involve common ancestry. Analogous structures, although similar in function, do not involve common ancestry. ***How does embryology offer evidence for evolution?*** Embryos show homologous structures during development that are evidence of evolution.

Patterns of migration were critical to Darwin when he was developing his theory. Migration patterns explained why, for example, islands often have more plant diversity than animal diversity: the plants are more able to migrate from the closest mainland as seeds, either by wind or on the backs of birds. Since Darwin's time, scientists have confirmed and expanded Darwin's study of the distribution of plants and animals around the world in a field of study now called **biogeography.** Evolution is intimately linked with climate and geological forces, especially plate tectonics, which helps explain many ancestral relationships and geographic distributions seen in fossils and living organisms today. R

Adaptation

The five categories discussed in the previous section—the fossil record, comparative anatomy, comparative embryology, comparative biochemistry, and geographic distribution—offer evidence for evolution. Darwin drew on all of these except biochemistry—which was not well developed in his time—to develop his own theory of evolution by natural selection. At the heart of his theory lies the concept of adaptation.

Types of adaptation An adaptation is a trait shaped by natural selection that increases an organism's reproductive success. One way to determine how effectively a trait contributes to reproductive success is to measure fitness. **Fitness** is a measure of the relative contribution that an individual trait makes to the next generation. It often is measured as the number of reproductively viable offspring that an organism produces in the next generation.

The better an organism is adapted to its environment, the greater its chances of survival and reproductive success. This concept explains the variations Darwin observed in the finches' beaks on the Galápagos Islands. Because the environments differed on each island, different beak characteristics were selected for.

VOCABULARY

SCIENCE USAGE V. COMMON USAGE

Adaptation

Science usage: a trait shaped by natural selection to increase the survival or reproductive success of an organism

The prehensile tail of monkeys is an adaptation for life in trees.

Common usage: adjustment or change

The movie script is an adaptation of the original play.

Camouflage Some species have evolved morphological adaptations that allow them to blend in with their environments. This is called **camouflage** (KA muh flahj). Camouflage allows organisms to become almost invisible to predators, as shown in **Figure 11.** As a result, more of the camouflaged individuals survive and reproduce.

Figure 11 It would be easy for a predator to overlook a leafy sea dragon, *Phycodurus eques,* in a sea grass habitat because of the animal's effective camouflage.

Demonstration

BL OL Camouflage Tell students that the military uses the principles of camouflage when designing their uniforms. Show students pictures of soldiers in desert and forest camouflage gear. Point out that the camouflage has two basic elements: color and pattern. Explain that the colors are meant to match the colors in the surrounding environment. The patterns are visually disruptive in order to mask the outline of the soldier's body.

ASK STUDENTS: ***How does a soldier's camouflage compare with an animal's camouflage?*** A soldier's camouflage is not a natural adaptation, as is an animal's. However, both types of camouflage work to hide a body within a certain environment. Est. time: 5 min

California kingsnake

Western coral snake

■ **Figure 12** Predators avoid the harmless California kingsnake because it has color patterns similar to those of the poisonous western coral snake.

Mimicry Another type of morphological adaptation is mimicry. In **mimicry,** one species evolves to resemble another species. You might expect that mimicry would make it difficult for individuals in one species to find and breed with other members of their species, thus decreasing reproductive success. However, mimicry often increases an organism's fitness. Mimicry can occur in a harmless species that has evolved to resemble a harmful species, such as the example shown in **Figure 12.** Sometimes mimicry benefits two harmful species. In both cases, the mimics are protected because predators can't always tell the mimic from the animal that it is mimicking, so they learn to avoid them both.

✓ **Reading Check** **Compare** mimicry and camouflage.

Antimicrobial resistance Species of bacteria that originally were killed by penicillin and other antibiotics have developed drug resistance. For almost every antibiotic, at least one species of resistant bacteria exists. One unintended consequence of the continued development of antibiotics is that some diseases, which were once thought to be contained, such as tuberculosis, have re-emerged in more harmful forms.

MiniLab 1

Investigate Mimicry

? Inquiry MiniLab

Why do some species mimic the features of other species? Mimicry is the process of natural selection that shapes one species of organism to look similar to another species. Natural selection has shaped the nontoxic viceroy butterfly to look like the toxic monarch butterfly. Investigate the mimicry displayed during this lab.

Procedure

1. Read and complete the lab safety form.
2. Create a data table for recording your observations and measurements of the **monarch** and **viceroy butterflies.**
3. Observe the physical characteristics of both butterfly species and record your observations in your data table.

Analysis

1. **Compare and contrast** the physical characteristics of the two butterfly species.
2. **Hypothesize** why the viceroy butterflies have bright colors that are highly visible.

MiniLab 1

? Inquiry MiniLab

For a lab worksheet, use your eTeacherEdition Online.

RUBRIC A rubric for evaluating MiniLabs is found on your eTeacherEdition Online.

Est. Time 15 min

Alternative Materials preserved specimens of other organisms displaying mimicry

Safety Precaution Approve lab safety forms before work begins.

Teaching Strategy Divide students into small groups and provide each group with a pair of preserved specimens.

Analysis

1. The monarch butterfly is dark orange with black veins and a row of white spots on the edge of its wings. The viceroy has the same color pattern except for a black horizontal strip across the bottom of its wings.
2. Answers may vary, but the bright colors serve as warnings to advertise the toxicity to predators.

LabManager™

Customize this lab with the LabManager™ CD-ROM.

Demonstration

Antibiotic Resistance Tell students that antibiotic resistance is a type of physiological adaptation. Obtain a culture plate of bacteria. Place four 1-cm pieces of filter paper that have been dipped in an antibiotic on the plate. After a few days, show students the various widths of bands where bacteria have been killed. Also point out the disks with no band where the bacteria have become resistant to the antibiotic. If culture plates are not available, use photos of plates with clear zones of inhibition. Explain the growing threat of antibiotic resistance as bacteria develop adaptations to resist drugs used to cure disease. Est. time: 15 min

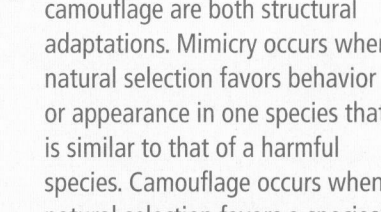

✓ **Reading Check** Mimicry and camouflage are both structural adaptations. Mimicry occurs when natural selection favors behavior or appearance in one species that is similar to that of a harmful species. Camouflage occurs when natural selection favors a species' resemblance to an object in the environment such as a twig or leaf.

Formative Assessment

Evaluation

ASK STUDENTS: ***How do mimicry and camouflage increase the fitness of a species?*** These morphological adaptations increase the chances that individuals in the population will produce more offspring than those without the adaptation. ***How would an albino of a species that is normally green and lives among leaves be less fit?*** The albino variant would stand out among the leaves and be more likely to be eaten before it could reproduce.

Remediation Help students understand that morphological adaptations increase fitness by having them make a chart listing two variations for each of five traits for an animal. Students should place a checkmark by each adaptation that would increase fitness. Examples for a cheetah might be a long and short tail, with a checkmark by the long variant because it helps the animal maintain balance while running.

Figure 13 Spaces between arches set in a square to support a dome are called spandrels and are often decorative. Some features in organisms might be like spandrels, a consequence of another adaptation.

Consequences of adaptations Not all features of an organism are necessarily adaptive. Some features might be consequences of other evolved characteristics. Biologists Stephen Jay Gould and Richard Lewontin made this point in 1979 in a paper claiming that biologists tended to overemphasize the importance of adaptations in evolution.

Spandrel example To illustrate this concept, they used an example from architecture. Building a set of four arches in a square to support a dome means that spaces called spandrels will appear between the arches, as illustrated in **Figure 13.** Because spandrels are often decorative, one might think that spandrels exist for decoration. In reality, they are an unavoidable consequence of arch construction. Gould and Lewontin argued that some features in organisms are like spandrels because even though they are prominent, they do not increase reproductive success. Instead, they likely arose as an unavoidable consequence of prior evolutionary change.

Human example A biological example of a spandrel is the helplessness of human babies. Humans give birth at a much earlier developmental stage than other primates do. This causes them to need increased care early in their lives. Many scientists think that the helplessness of human babies is a consequence of the evolution of big brains and upright posture. To walk upright, humans need narrow pelvises, which means that babies' heads must be small enough to fit through the pelvic opening at birth. In contrast, scientists previously thought that the helplessness of human infants provided an adaptive advantage, such as increased attention from parents and more learning.

Section 2 Assessment

Section Summary

- Fossils provide strong direct evidence to support evolution.
- Homologous and vestigial structures indicate shared ancestry.
- Examples of embryological and biochemical traits provide insight into the evolution of species.
- Biogeography can explain why certain species live in certain locations.
- Natural selection gives rise to features that increase reproductive success.

Understand Main Ideas

1. MAIN Idea **Describe** how fossils provide evidence of evolution.
2. **Explain** what natural selection predicts about mimicry, camouflage, homologous structures, and vestigial structures.
3. **Indicate** how biochemistry provides evidence of evolution.
4. **Compare** the morphological evidence and the biochemical evidence supporting evolution.

Think Critically

5. **Hypothesize** Evidence suggests that the bones in bird wings share a number of features with the bones of dinosaur arms. Based on this evidence, what hypothesis could you make about the evolutionary relationship between birds and dinosaurs?
6. **Apply** Research has shown that if a prescribed dose of an antibiotic is not taken completely, some bacteria might not be killed and the disease might return. How does natural selection explain this phenomenon?

Section 2 Assessment

1. Fossils reveal similarities between extinct and living species and include some forms that have features linking major groups.
2. They indicate a shared ancestry, and individuals with those features have higher fitness compared to individuals without them.
3. Complex biochemicals found in diverse species probably did not evolve independently. Therefore, they indicate common ancestry.
4. Morphological evidence centers around the anatomy of a species, and biochemical evidence centers around the biomolecular chemistry of the species.
5. Birds and dinosaurs shared a common ancestor.
6. By not taking the complete dose, variations that made some of the bacteria resistant to the drug have an increased chance of being passed on to the next generation. The following generation would have a greater percentage of resistant bacteria.

Assessment Online Quiz

Section 3

Reading Preview

Essential Questions

- What are the conditions of the Hardy-Weinberg principle?
- What patterns can be observed in evolution?
- What factors influence speciation?

Review Vocabulary

allele: alternate forms of a character trait that can be inherited

New Vocabulary

Hardy-Weinberg principle
genetic drift
founder effect
bottleneck
stabilizing selection
directional selection
disruptive selection
sexual selection
prezygotic isolating mechanism
postzygotic isolating mechanism
allopatric speciation
sympatric speciation
adaptive radiation
gradualism
punctuated equilibrium

g Multilingual eGlossary

R Shaping Evolutionary Theory

MAIN Idea The theory of evolution continues to be refined as scientists learn new information.

Real-World Reading Link The longer you operate a complicated piece of electronics, the better you understand how it works. The device does not change, but you become more familiar with its functions. Scientists have been studying evolution for almost 150 years, yet they are still learning new ways in which evolution leads to changes in species.

Mechanisms of Evolution

Natural selection remains a central theme in evolution. It explains how organisms adapt to their environments and how variations can give rise to adaptations within species. Scientists now know that natural selection is not the only mechanism of evolution. Studies in population genetics and molecular biology led to the development of evolutionary theory. At the center is the understanding that evolution occurs at the population level, with genes as the raw material.

Population genetics At the turn of the twentieth century, genes had not been discovered. However, the allele was understood to be one form of an inherited character trait, such as eye color, that gets passed down from parent to offspring. Scientists did not understand why dominant alleles would not simply overpower recessive alleles in a population.

In 1908, English mathematician Godfrey Hardy and German physician Wilhelm Weinberg independently came up with the same solution to this problem. They showed mathematically that evolution will not occur in a population unless allelic frequencies are acted upon by forces that cause change. In the absence of these forces, the allelic frequency remains the same and evolution doesn't occur. According to this idea, which is now known as the **Hardy-Weinberg principle,** when allelic frequencies remain constant, a population is in genetic equilibrium. This concept is illustrated in **Figure 14.**

Figure 14 According to the Hardy-Weinberg principle, even though the number of owls doubled, the ratio of gray to red owls remained the same.

Section 3

MAIN Idea

BL OL AL

Shaping Evolutionary Theory

ASK STUDENTS: ***Other than natural selection, how else might species change over time?*** Possible answers: selective breeding, isolation of mating groups, genetic mutation, etc.

SAY TO STUDENTS: ***Evolution can be the result of many different environmental and genetic circumstances. In this section, you will learn about the five principle mechanisms of evolution: natural selection, gene flow, genetic drift, mutation, and nonrandom mating.***

R Reading Strategy

EL BL OL Vocabulary Chart

Have students create a three-column chart. In column one, they will write each new vocabulary term as they encounter it in Section 3. Students should write the definition of the term in the middle column. Finally, in the third column, students should create a memory clue in the form of a sketch or word association. For example, students might draw a *Y*-shaped arrow to illustrate the term *divergent evolution.*

Research Citation

Integrate Mathematics Educational research indicates that activities like the one described on the next page can help students learn to communicate mathematically. While writing their explanations of the Hardy-Weinberg principle, students will learn to communicate in ways that demonstrate their understanding. (Lampert and Cobb, 2003)

Research bibliography on pages 32T–34T

D Develop Concepts

OL Integrate Math

SAY TO STUDENTS: ***In a population of dogs, an allele for short ears (E) is dominant, while the allele for long ears (e) is recessive. For every 100 dogs in the population, 16 have long ears. Use the Hardy-Weinberg equation to calculate the frequencies of the E allele (frequency = p) and the e allele (frequency = q).*** Since q^2 is the frequency of the ee genotype, and $q^2 = 0.16$ (16 ÷ 100), then $q = 0.4$ and $p = 0.6$.

AL Have students research the mathematical background for the Hardy-Weinberg Principle and write a short paper using the formula to show that they understand the mathematical ramifications.

S Skill Practice

BL OL AL Visual Literacy

Have students study Table 3. Then explore what might cause some of the "violations" that lead to the consequences of the Hardy-Weinberg principle.

ASK STUDENTS: ***What could cause a population to shrink in size?*** Possible answers: a rapid environmental change, an increase in the population size of a local predatory species, or the spread of an infectious disease. ***What might cause an organism to emigrate from an area?*** Possible answer: An organism might go searching for a better food source, might be carried away by a storm, might not be able to find a willing mate in the area.

Concepts in Motion

Interactive Table

Reading Check A population will be in equilibrium when the distribution of genotypes remains constant over time.

CAREERS IN BIOLOGY

Biometrician Almost all scientific research papers include some statistics. Many researchers consult biometricians—people who specialize in statistics related to biology—to help design studies and analyze study results.

Connection to Math To illustrate the Hardy-Weinberg principle, consider a population of 100 humans. Forty people are homozygous dominant for earlobe attachment *(EE)*. Another 40 people are heterozygous *(Ee)*. Twenty people are homozygous recessive *(ee)*. In the 40 homozygous dominant people, there are 80 *E* alleles (2 *E* alleles × 40); and in the 20 homozygous recessive people, there are 40 *e* alleles (2 *e* alleles × 20). The heterozygous people have 40 *E* alleles and 40 *e* alleles. Summing the alleles, we have 120 *E* alleles and 80 *e* alleles for a total of 200 alleles. The *E* allele frequency is 120/200, or 0.6. The *e* allele frequency is 80/200, or 0.4.

The Hardy-Weinberg principle states that the allele frequencies in populations should be constant. This often is expressed as $p + q = 1$. For our example, p can represent the *E* allele frequency and q can represent the *e* allele frequency.

Squaring both sides of the equation yields the new equation $p^2 + 2pq + q^2 = 1$. This equation allows us to determine the equilibrium frequency of each genotype in the population: homozygous dominant (p^2), heterozygous (2pq), and homozygous recessive (q^2). From the above example, $p = 0.6$, and $q = 0.4$, so $(0.6)(0.6) + 2(0.6)(0.4) + (0.4)(0.4) = 1$. In the example population, the equilibrium frequency for homozygous dominant will be 0.36, the equilibrium frequency of heterozygous will be 0.48, and the equilibrium frequency of homozygous recessive will be 0.16. Note that the sum of these frequencies equals one. D

Reading Check **Determine** when a population is in equilibrium.

Conditions According to the Hardy-Weinberg principle, a population in genetic equilibrium must meet five conditions: there must be no genetic drift, no gene flow, no mutation, mating must be random, and there must be no natural selection. Populations in nature might meet some of these requirements, but hardly any population meets all five conditions for long periods of time. If a population is not in genetic equilibrium, at least one of the five conditions has been violated. These five conditions, listed in **Table 3,** are known mechanisms of evolutionary change.

S

Table 3 **The Hardy-Weinberg Principle** — Concepts in Motion Interactive Table

Condition	Violation	Consequence
The population is very large.	Many populations are small.	Chance events can lead to changes in population traits.
There is no immigration or emigration.	Organisms move in and out of the population.	The population can lose or gain traits with movement of organisms.
Mating is random.	Mating is not random.	New traits do not pass as quickly to the rest of the population.
Mutations do not occur.	Mutations occur.	New variations appear in the population with each new generation.
Natural selection does not occur.	Natural selection occurs.	Traits in a population change from one generation to the next.

Content Background

Teacher FYI The Hardy-Weinberg principle only holds true for populations that are in genetic equilibrium and populations in which relatives are not likely to mate with one another. The human population is one such population. Because of this, the Hardy-Weinberg equation can be used to predict the frequency of alleles in humans. For example, there are three alleles that determine blood type in humans: *A*, *B*, and *O*. If the frequency for the *A* allele in a population is 0.258 and the frequency for the *O* allele is 0.673, then the frequency for the *B* allele will be 0.069 $(1 - 0.258 - 0.673 = 0.069)$. That means that the percentage of people who have type B blood is about 9.8 percent. $[(0.069)^2 + 2(0.069)(0.673) = 0.097635]$

Genetic drift Any change in the allelic frequencies in a population that results from chance is called **genetic drift.** Recall that for simple traits, only one of a parent's two alleles passes to the offspring, and that this allele is selected randomly through independent assortment. In large populations, enough alleles "drift" to ensure that the allelic frequency of the entire population remains relatively constant from one generation to the next. In smaller populations, however, the effects of **C** genetic drift become more pronounced, and the chance of losing an allele becomes greater.

Founder effect The founder effect is an extreme example of genetic drift. The **founder effect** can occur when a small sample of a population settles in a location separated from the rest of the population. Because this sample is a random subset of the original population, the sample population carries a random subset of the population's genes. Alleles that were uncommon in the original population might be common in the new population, and the offspring in the new population will carry those alleles. Such an event can result in large genetic variations in the separated populations.

The founder effect is evident in the Amish and Mennonite communities in the United States, in which the people rarely marry outside their own communities. The Old Order Amish have a high frequency **W** of six-finger dwarfism. All affected individuals can trace their ancestry back to one of the founders of the Order.

Bottleneck Another extreme example of genetic drift is a **bottleneck,** which occurs when a population declines to a very low number and then rebounds. The gene pool of the rebound population often is genetically similar to that of the population at its lowest level, that is, it has reduced diversity. Researchers think that cheetahs in Africa experienced a bottleneck 10,000 years ago, and then another one about 100 years ago. Throughout their current range, shown in **Figure 15,** cheetahs are so genetically similar that they appear inbred. Inbreeding decreases fertility, and might be a factor in the potential extinction of this endangered species.

Reading Check **Explain** how genetic drift affects populations.

Study Tip

Concept Map Make a concept map, placing the term *evolution* in the top oval. The second row of ovals should contain the following terms: *genetic drift, gene flow, nonrandom mating, mutation,* and *natural selection.* As you read the chapter, fill in definitions and write examples that illustrate each term.

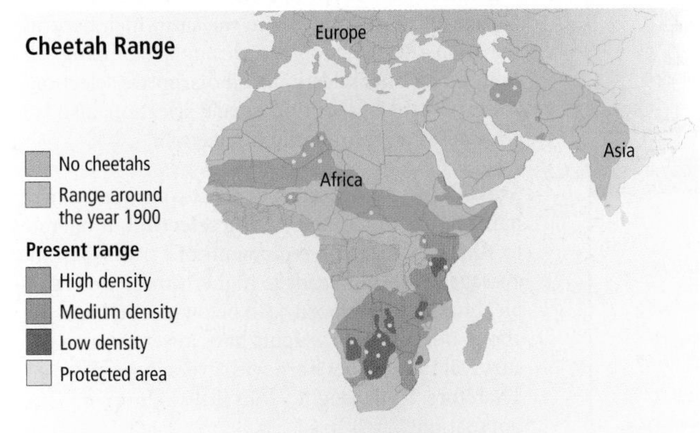

S

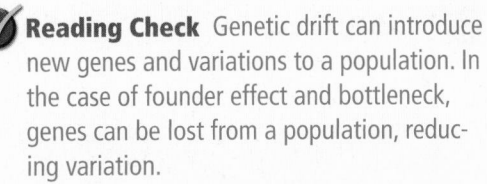

■ **Figure 15** The map shows the present range of cheetahs in Africa. It is believed that cheetahs had a much larger population until a bottleneck occurred.
Apply Concepts ***What effect has the bottleneck had on the reproductive rate of cheetahs?***

C Critical Thinking

AL Infer

ASK STUDENTS: ***Why does genetic drift have its greatest effects in small, isolated populations?*** The gene pool is small in isolated populations. Therefore, the effects of a small change may be magnified as the population expands.

W Writing Support

BL OL Summary Writing

Have students write a paragraph that explains why the founder effect can have a great effect on a small population's gene pool. Students' answers should indicate that the founder effect results when a group of individuals with a different allele frequency than the original population becomes isolated from the original population

S Skill Practice

BL OL AL Visual Literacy

Have students examine Figure 15. **SAY TO STUDENTS:** ***Scientists hypothesize that a viral disease may have killed much of the population, causing the bottleneck.*** **ASK STUDENTS:** ***What factors in Africa today may be preventing the cheetah from recovering in much of its previous range?*** Human activity is probably the largest factor that limits the present cheetah population's range. Decreased birthrate and survival due to inbreeding may also be a contributing factor.

■ **Caption Question Fig. 15** The reproductive rate has declined, and the species appears to be extremely inbred.

Reading Check Genetic drift can introduce new genes and variations to a population. In the case of founder effect and bottleneck, genes can be lost from a population, reducing variation.

S Skill Practice

BL OL AL COOP LEARN

Visual Literacy Have pairs of students compare and contrast each of the three graphs in Figure 16. Call on volunteers to describe the effects of each type of illustrated selection. Stabilizing selection decreases genetic diversity. Directional selection increases the frequency of a previously rare allele. Disruptive selection increases the frequency of two or more previously rare alleles. Provide students with additional examples of each selection mechanism. For example, pesticide resistance in insects and artificial selection in animal and plant breeds are all directional selection. Human birth weights show stabilizing selection, and Northern water snakes show disruptive selection.

D Develop Concepts

BL OL AL

Clarify a Misconception

ASK STUDENTS: ***Does evolution occur by chance alone?*** No. Many students will think that evolution means that life changed "by chance." Random (chance) mutations are the underlying source of genetic variation. However, natural selection, the process by which some variants survive and reproduce differentially, is not random.

R Reading Strategy

BL OL **Activate Background Vocabulary** Point out that four of the vocabulary terms in this section include the term *selection.* Review the definition of selection. Then have students use their background knowledge to infer the meanings of the four vocabulary terms. Stabilizing selection, for example, tends to move the extremes of a population toward the mean, or average, for a characteristic.

S

Review Personal Tutor

Figure 16 Natural selection can alter allele frequencies of a population in three ways. The bell-shaped curve shown as a dotted line in each graph indicates the trait's original variation in a population. The solid line indicates the outcome of each type of selection pressure.

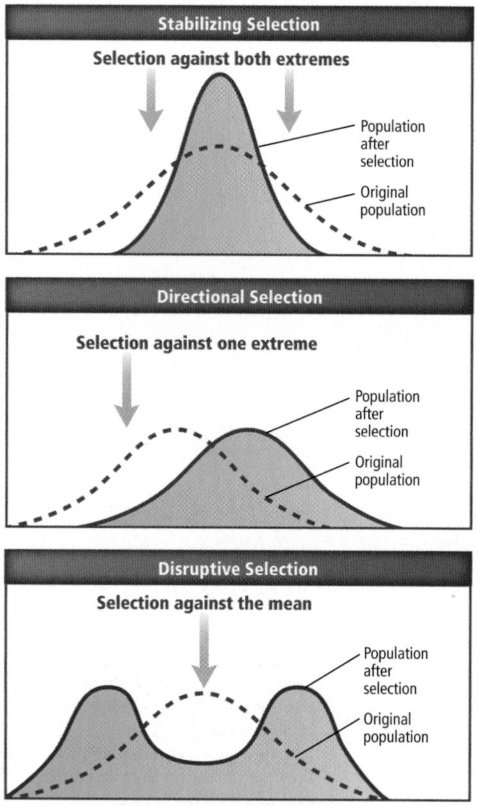

Gene flow A population in genetic equilibrium experiences no gene flow. It is a closed system, with no new genes entering the population and no genes leaving the population. In reality, few populations are isolated. The random movement of individuals between populations, or migration, increases genetic variation within a population and reduces differences between populations.

Nonrandom mating Rarely is mating completely random in a population. Usually, organisms mate with individuals in close proximity. This promotes inbreeding and could lead to a change in allelic proportions favoring individuals that are homozygous for particular traits.

Mutation Recall that a mutation is a random change in genetic material. The cumulative effect of mutations in a population might cause a change in allelic frequencies and thus violate genetic equilibrium. Although many mutations cause harm or are lethal, occasionally a mutation provides an advantage to an organism. This mutation will then be selected for and become more common in subsequent generations. In this way, mutations provide the raw material upon which natural selection works.

Reading Check **Summarize** how mutation violates the Hardy-Weinberg principle.

Natural selection The Hardy-Weinberg principle requires that all individuals in a population be equally adapted to their environment and thus contribute equally to the next generation. As you have learned, this rarely happens. Natural selection acts to select the individuals that are best adapted for survival and reproduction. Natural selection acts on an organism's phenotype and changes allelic frequencies. **Figure 16** shows three main ways in which natural selection alters phenotypes: through stabilizing selection, directional selection, and disruptive selection. A fourth type of selection, sexual selection, also is considered a type of natural selection. D

Stabilizing selection The most common form of natural selection is **stabilizing selection.** It operates to eliminate extreme expressions of a trait when the average expression leads to higher fitness. For example, human babies born with below-normal and above-normal birth weights have lower chances of survival than babies born with average weights. Therefore, birth weight varies little in human populations. R

Reading Check Mutation violates the Hardy-Weinberg principle because it introduces new variation, which changes allele frequencies.

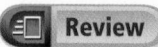

"There is a brilliant child locked inside every student."

—Marva Collins

Review **Personal Tutor**

Listen to a teacher explain types of selection.

Directional selection If an extreme version of a trait makes an organism more fit, **directional selection** might occur. This form of selection increases the expression of the extreme versions of a trait in a population. One example is the evolution of moths in industrial England. The peppered moth has two color forms, or morphs, as shown in **Figure 17.** Until the mid-1850s, nearly all peppered moths in England had light-colored bodies and wings. Beginning around 1850, however, dark moths began appearing. By the early 1900s, nearly all peppered moths were dark. Why? Industrial pollution favored the dark-colored moths at the expense of the light-colored moths. The darker the moth, the more it matched the sooty background of its tree habitat, and the harder it was for predators to see. Thus, more dark moths survived, adding more genes for dark color to the population. This conclusion was reinforced in the mid-1900s, when the passage of air pollution laws led to the resurgence of light-colored moths. This phenomenon is called industrial melanism.

Directional selection also can be seen in Galápagos finches. For three decades in the latter part of the twentieth century, Peter and Rosemary Grant studied populations of these finches. The Grants found that during drought years, food supplies dwindled and the birds had to eat the hard seeds that they normally ignored. Birds with the largest beaks were more successful in cracking the tough seed coatings than were birds with smaller beaks. As a result, over the duration of the drought, birds with larger beaks came to dominate the population. In rainy years, however, the directional trend was reversed, and the population's average beak size decreased.

■ **Figure 17** The peppered moth exists in two forms: light-colored and dark-colored.
Infer ***how natural selection might have caused a change in the frequencies of the two forms.***

W

W Writing Support

AL Formal Writing Have students research the British ecologist H. B. D. Kettlewell's experiments on directional selection in peppered moths and write an article that analyzes the strengths and weaknesses of his experimental methods.

DATA ANALYSIS LAB 2

About the Lab

- Also see Cook. 2000. Changing views on melanic moths. *Biol J Linn Soc* 69: 431–441.

Think Critically

1. about 50 percent
2. Virginia might have maintained a low amount of air pollution throughout the study period.

DATA ANALYSIS LAB 2

Based on Real Data*

Interpret the Graph

How does pollution affect melanism in moths? The changing frequencies of light-colored and dark-colored moths have been studied for decades in the United States. The percentage of the melanic, or dark, form of the moth was low prior to the Industrial Revolution. It increased until it made up nearly the entire population in the early 1900s. After antipollution laws were passed, the percentage of melanic moths declined, as shown in the graph.

Think Critically

1. **Interpret** the percent decrease in Pennsylvania melanic moth population.
2. **Hypothesize** why the percentage of melanic moths might have remained at a relatively low level in Virginia.

Data and Observations

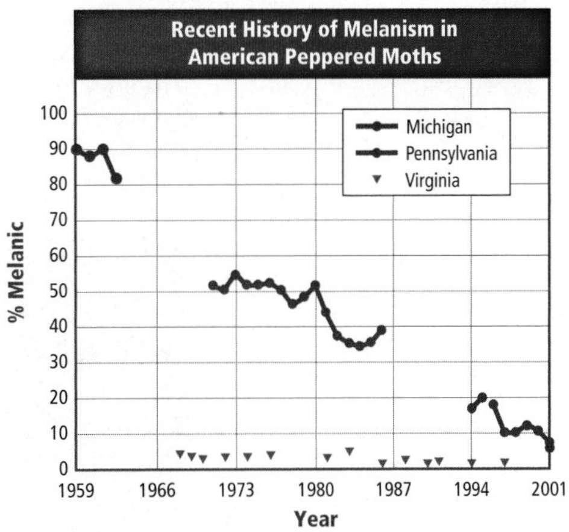

*Data obtained from: Grant, B. S. and L. L. Wiseman. 2002. Recent history of melanism in American peppered moths. *Journal of Heredity* 93: 86-90.

Differentiated Instruction

Below Level Students performing below grade level might need additional time to complete their work. Provide these students with extended time on tests, projects, and other assignments to accommodate their needs.

For more tips, see pages 14T–15T.

■ **Caption Question Fig. 17** Predators might have differentially removed those moths that stood out from their background.

Inquiry Launch Lab

Assess Content Development
Assess how understanding has developed when students revisit the Launch Lab analysis questions.

Critical Thinking

OL AL Analyze

ASK STUDENTS: ***Considering what you know about the Hardy-Weinberg principle, why do you think most scientists suggest speciation occurs at a low rate in large populations?*** One of the tenets of Hardy-Weinberg is that a very large population does not evolve. Point out that this is because the number of mutations would be so small that a variation would be quickly diluted or eliminated from the gene pool. In small populations, this is not true. As variations build up in a small population, speciation can occur. ***Why is it almost impossible for alleles to be bred out of a large population?*** The Hardy-Weinberg principle states that the frequencies of alleles in a population do not change unless evolutionary forces act on the population, and evolutionary forces do not usually act on large populations.

Inquiry BioLab

The lab at the end of the chapter can be used at this point in the lesson.

Figure 18 Northern water snakes have two different color patterns, depending on their habitats. Intermediate color patterns would make them more visible to predators.

Disruptive selection Another type of natural selection, **disruptive selection,** is a process that splits a population into two groups. It tends to remove individuals with average traits but retain individuals expressing extreme traits at both ends of a continuum. Northern water snakes, illustrated in **Figure 18,** are an example. Snakes living on the mainland shores inhabit grasslands and have mottled brown skin. Snakes inhabiting rocky island shores have gray skin. Each is adapted to its particular environment. A snake with intermediate coloring would be disadvantaged because it would be more visible to predators.

Inquiry Launch Lab

Review Based on what you have learned about adaptation, how would you now answer the analysis questions?

Sexual selection Another type of natural selection, in which change in frequency of a trait is based on the ability to attract a mate is called **sexual selection.** This type of selection often operates in populations in which males and females differ significantly in appearance. Usually in these populations, males are the largest and most colorful of the group. The bigger the tail of a male peacock, as shown in **Figure 19,** the more attractive the bird is to females. Males also evolve threatening characteristics that intimidate other males; this is common in species, such as elk and deer, where the male keeps a harem of females.

Darwin wondered why some qualities of sexual attractiveness appeared to be the opposite of qualities that might enhance survival. For example, the peacock's tail, while attracting females, is large and cumbersome, and it might make the peacock a more likely target for predators. Although some modern scientists think that sexual selection is not a form of natural selection, others think that sexual selection follows the same general principle: brighter colors and bigger bodies enhance reproductive success, whatever the chances are for long-term survival.

Figure 19 Peacocks that have the largest tails tend to attract more peahens. The frequency of this trait increases because of sexual selection.

Content Background

Real-World Connection All forms of selection, including natural selection, disruptive selection, and sexual selection, work on phenotypes rather than genotypes. Because of this, undesirable or destructive alleles can survive indefinitely in a population. For example, the allele for cystic fibrosis is common among Caucasians because it is often not the phenotype of the carrier.

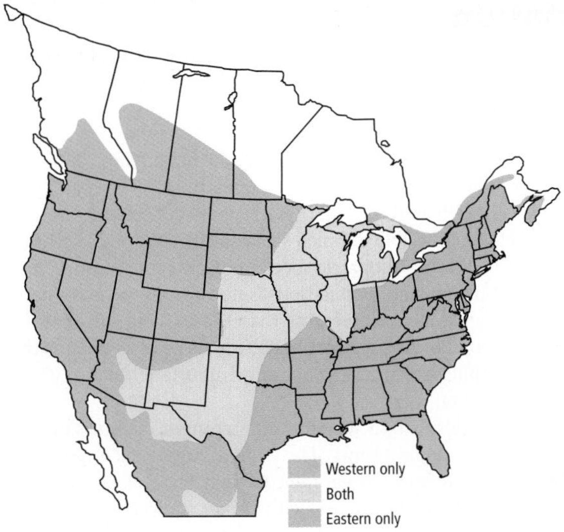

■ **Figure 20** The map shows the overlapping ranges of the Eastern meadowlark and Western meadowlark. While the two are similar in appearance, their songs separate them behaviorally.
Infer ***how different songs prevent the meadowlarks from breeding.***

S

R Reproductive Isolation

Mechanisms of evolution—genetic drift, gene flow, nonrandom mating, mutation, and natural selection—violate the Hardy-Weinberg principle. To what extent each mechanism contributes to the origin of new species is a major topic of debate in evolutionary science today. Most scientists define speciation as the process whereby some members of a sexually reproducing population change so much that they can no longer produce fertile offspring with members of the original population. Two types of reproductive isolating mechanisms prevent gene flow among populations. **Prezygotic isolating mechanisms** operate before fertilization occurs. **Postzygotic isolating mechanisms** operate after fertilization has occurred to ensure that the resulting hybrid remains infertile.

Prezygotic isolation Prezygotic isolating mechanisms prevent reproduction by making fertilization unlikely. These mechanisms prevent genotypes from entering a population's gene pool through geographic, ecological, behavioral, or other differences. For example, the Eastern meadowlark and the Western meadowlark, pictured in **Figure 20,** have overlapping ranges and are similar in appearance. These two species, however, use different mating songs and do not interbreed. Time is another factor in maintaining a reproductive barrier. Closely related species of fireflies mate at different times of night, just as different species of trout live in the same stream but breed at different times of the year.

Postzygotic isolation When fertilization has occurred but a hybrid offspring cannot develop or reproduce, postzygotic isolation has occurred. Postzygotic isolating mechanisms prevent offspring survival or reproduction. A lion and a tiger are considered separate C species because even though they can mate, the offspring—a liger, shown in **Figure 21**—is sterile.

? Inquiry Virtual Lab

■ **Figure 21** The offspring of a male lion and a female tiger is a liger. Ligers are sterile.

R Reading Strategy

BL OL Activate Background Vocabulary Write the terms *prezygotic isolation* and *postzygotic isolation* on the board. Review the definition of *isolation, pre-,* and *post-*. Then have students use their background knowledge to infer the meanings of the two terms and write responses on the board. Prezygotic isolation occurs before fertilization. Postzygotic isolation occurs afterward.

S Skill Practice

BL OL Visual Literacy Have students examine Figure 20. **ASK STUDENTS:** ***The distribution of how many meadowlark species are shown on the map?*** two ***Why do the two meadowlark species not attempt to mate with one another?*** They have different mating songs and times.

OL AL ASK STUDENTS: ***Do you think Eastern meadowlarks and Western meadowlarks always had such large overlapping territories? Explain your answer.*** No; most likely two populations of a single meadowlark species became geographically isolated for a while, which caused allopatric speciation. By the time the populations' territories overlapped again, the populations had evolved into two different species.

C Critical Thinking

AL Evaluate
ASK STUDENTS: ***Why are behaviors such as courting songs and displays in birds extremely important as an isolating mechanism in populations?*** Different courtship behavior can prevent the mating between two closely related species that could otherwise breed and produce viable offspring.

■ **Caption Question Fig. 20** Possible answer: the meadowlarks respond more to songs when searching for mates than to visual recognition.

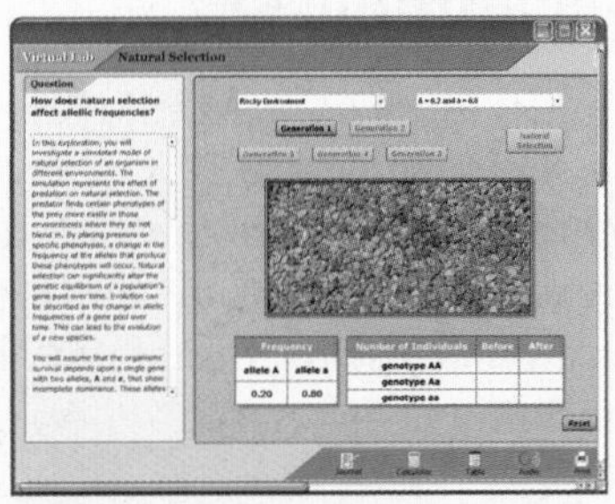

? **Inquiry Virtual Lab** Students will investigate a model of natural selection of an organism in different environments.

Critical Thinking

BL OL AL **Analyze**

SAY TO STUDENTS: ***Suppose some members of a tree frog population begin mating a month earlier than the other members of the same population. What type of isolation will occur?*** reproductive isolation ***What type of speciation does reproductive isolation cause?*** sympatric speciation

Develop Concepts

EL BL OL AL COOP LEARN

Activity Have groups of three or four students prepare a poster about one of the isolating mechanisms discussed in this section. Once groups have completed their posters, they should give a short oral presentation. Posters should demonstrate how the isolating mechanism separates a population.

Speciation

For speciation to occur, a population must diverge and then be reproductively isolated. Biologists usually recognize two types of speciation: allopatric and sympatric.

Allopatric speciation In **allopatric speciation,** a physical barrier divides one population into two or more populations. The separate populations eventually will contain organisms that, if enough time has passed, will no longer be able to breed successfully with one another. Most scientists think that allopatric speciation is the most common form of speciation. Small subpopulations isolated from the main population have a better chance of diverging than those living within it. This was the conclusion of biologist Ernst Mayr, who argued as early as the 1940s that geographic isolation was not only important but also was required for speciation.

VOCABULARY

ACADEMIC VOCABULARY

Isolation
the condition of being separated from others
After infection, a patient is kept in isolation from other patients to prevent the infection from spreading.

Geographic barriers can include mountain ranges, channels between islands, wide rivers, and lava flows. The Grand Canyon, pictured in **Figure 22,** is an example of a geographic barrier. The Kaibab squirrel is found on the canyon's north rim, while the Abert squirrel lives on the south rim. Scientists think that the two types of squirrels diverged from an ancestral species and today are reproductively isolated by the width of the canyon. While these animals officially belong to the same species, they demonstrate distinct differences and, in time, they might diverge enough to be classified as separate species.

Sympatric speciation In **sympatric speciation,** a species evolves into a new species without a physical barrier. The ancestor species and the new species live side-by-side during the speciation process. Evidence of sympatric evolution can be seen in several insect species, including apple maggot flies, which appear to be diverging based on the type of fruit they eat. Scientists think that sympatric speciation happens fairly frequently in plants, especially through polyploidy. Recall that polyploidy is a mutation that increases a plant's chromosome number. As a result, the plant is no longer able to interbreed with the main population.

■ **Figure 22** The Grand Canyon is a geographic barrier separating the Abert and Kaibab squirrels.

Demonstration

Geographic Isolation Ask students to compare and contrast the two species of squirrels shown in Figure 22. Obtain a state map of Arizona, and point out the North Rim and the South Rim of the Grand Canyon. Then explain that the Abert's squirrel is widespread in pine forests in New Mexico, Arizona, Colorado, and Utah. The Kaibab squirrel, a very close relative of the Abert's squirrel, is found only on the North Rim. Est time: 5 min

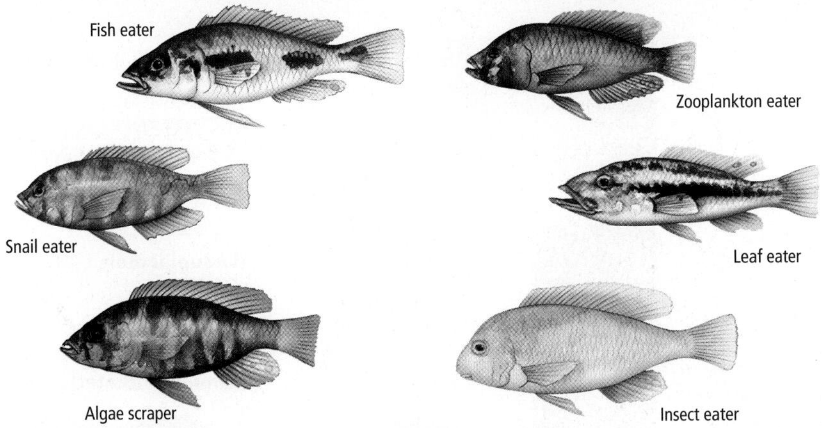

■ **Figure 23** More than 300 species of cichlid fishes once lived in Lake Victoria. Their adaptive radiation is remarkable because it is thought to have occurred in less than 14,000 years.

Patterns of Evolution

Many details of the speciation process remain unresolved. Relative to the human life span, speciation is a long process, and first-hand accounts of speciation are expected to be rare. However, evidence of speciation is visible in patterns of evolution.

Adaptive radiation More than 300 species of cichlid fish, six of which are illustrated in **Figure 23,** once lived in Africa's Lake Victoria. Data show that these species diverged from a single ancestor within the last 14,000 years. This is a dramatic example of a type of speciation called **adaptive radiation.** Adaptive radiation, also called divergent evolution, can occur in a relatively short time when one species gives rise to many species in response to the creation of a new habitat or another ecological opportunity. Likely, a combination of factors caused the explosive radiation of the cichlids, including the appearance of a unique double jaw, which allowed these fish to exploit various food sources. Adaptive radiation often follows large-scale extinctions. Adaptive radiation of mammals at the beginning of the Cenozoic era following the extinction of dinosaurs likely produced the diversity of mammals visible today.

Coevolution Many species evolve in close relationship with other species. The relationship might be so close that the evolution of one species affects the evolution of other species. This is called coevolution. Mutualism is one form of coevolution. Mutualism occurs when two species benefit each other. For example, comet orchids and the moths that pollinate them have coevolved an intimate dependency: the foot-long flowers of this plant perfectly match the foot-long tongue of the moth, shown in **Figure 24.**

In another form of coevolution, one species can evolve a parasitic dependency on another species. This type of relationship is often called a coevolutionary arms race. The classic example is a plant and an insect pathogen that is dependent on the plant for food. The plant population evolves a chemical defense against the insect population. The insects, in turn, evolve the biochemistry to resist the defense. The plant then steps up the race by evolving new defenses, the insect escalates its response, and the race goes on. Complex coevolutionary relationships like these might reflect thousands of years of evolutionary interaction.

■ **Figure 24** By coevolving, this moth and the comet orchid it pollinates exist in a mutualistic relationship.

Content Background

Teacher FYI Cichlid species around the world exhibit an extraordinary amount of diversification because they are capable of rapid genetic change. In addition, many cichlids can change the shape of their teeth and skulls in response to a change in diet. For instance, the Victorian snail-crusher *(Astatoreochromis alluaudi)* was introduced to several African lakes to help control the snail populations. But these cichlids began to feed on insects instead of snails. Thus, they stopped growing the large teeth and strong muscles needed for crushing snail shells. The Victorian snail-crusher and other cichlids are able to adapt to an incredibly wide range of environmental conditions.

W Writing Support

AL Formal Writing Have students research adaptive radiation in a particular group of organisms and write an abstract. You might suggest orchids, cichlids, Darwin's finches, Hawaiian honeycreepers, and mammals as appropriate groups to research. Give students the following pointers on abstract writing:

- The abstract should be brief (no more than 200 words).
- In the abstract, explain why people should be interested in the subject.
- Describe research that has been done on the subject.
- Briefly explain the results and conclusion of the research.

C Critical Thinking

BL OL AL Infer Show students a picture of a hummingbird feeding out of a long-necked flower. Point out the shape of the flower and the hummingbird's beak.
ASK STUDENTS: ***What is this an example of?*** coevolution ***Why would it benefit the flower to coevolve with the hummingbird?*** The hummingbird can efficiently disperse the flower's pollen to other plants of the same species. ***Why would it benefit the hummingbird to coevolve with the flower?*** The hummingbird's adaptations allow it to reach the nectar deep within the flower. ***Does coevolution always form relationships that benefit both species involved? Explain your answer.*** No, species in prey-predator relationships coevolve in order to more readily escape or capture one another.

Concepts in Motion

Interactive Table

S Skill Practice

EL BL OL Visual Literacy

Have students examine Table 4. Then ask students to make their own charts showing convergent evolution. Tell students not to use any animals pictured in Table 4. Instruct students to illustrate their charts. Example animal pairs: whale and shark; bat and flying bird; duck and platypus

D Develop Concepts

OL AL

Clarify a Misconception

ASK STUDENTS: ***If the theory of gradualism is true, does that necessarily mean then that the theory of punctuated equilibrium is false?*** no Many students might think this is the case. However, both hypotheses may account for patterns in the fossil record depending on the species in question.

S

Table 4 Convergent Evolution

Concepts in Motion Interactive Table

Niche	Placental Mammals	Australian Marsupials
Burrower	 **Mole**	 **Marsupial mole**
Anteater	 **Lesser anteater**	 **Numbat (anteater)**
Mouse	 **Mouse**	 **Marsupial mouse**
Glider	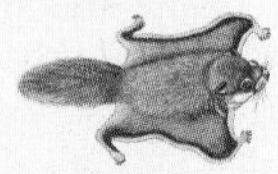 **Flying squirrel**	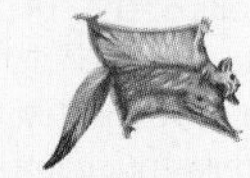 **Flying phalanger**
Wolf	 **Wolf**	 **Tasmanian wolf**

Convergent evolution Sometimes unrelated species evolve similar traits even though they live in different parts of the world. This is called convergent evolution. Convergent evolution occurs in environments that are geographically far apart but have similar ecology and climate. The mara and rabbit discussed in Section 2 provide an example of convergent evolution. The mara and the rabbit are unrelated, but because they inhabit similar niches, they have evolved similarities in morphology, physiology, and behavior. **Table 4** shows examples of convergent evolution between Australian marsupials and the placental mammals on other continents.

Rate of speciation Evolution is a dynamic process. In some cases, as in a coevolutionary arms race, traits might change rapidly. In other cases, traits might remain unchanged for millions of years. Most scientists think that evolution proceeds in small, gradual steps. This is a theory called **gradualism.** A great deal of evidence favors this theory. However, the fossil record contains instances of abrupt transitions. For example, certain species of fossil snails looked the same for millions of years, and then the shell shape changed dramatically in only a few thousand years. The theory of **punctuated equilibrium** attempts to explain such abrupt transitions in the fossil record. According to this theory, rapid spurts of genetic change cause species to diverge quickly; these periods punctuate much longer periods when the species exhibit little change. D

Differentiated Instruction

Visually Impaired When presenting visual information as described on this page, provide additional support for students who are visually impaired. Describe the visuals and summarize conclusions that should be drawn from the information presented.

For more tips, see pages 14T–15T.

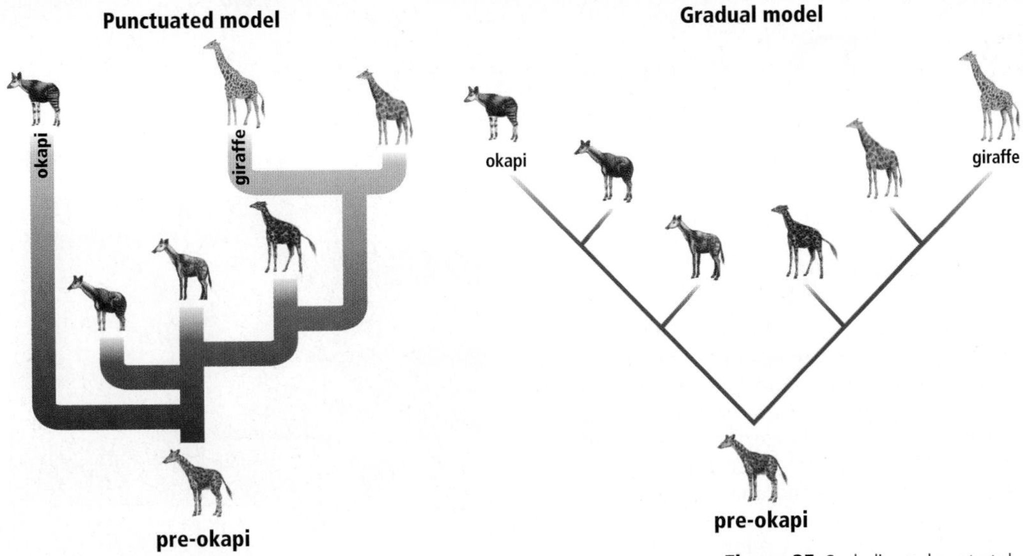

■ **Figure 25** Gradualism and punctuated equilibrium are two competing models describing the tempo of evolution.

Concepts in Motion
Animation

The two theories for the tempo of evolution are illustrated in **Figure 25.** The tempo of evolution is an active area of research in evolutionary theory today. Does most evolution occur gradually or in short bursts? Fossils can show only morphological structures. Changes in internal anatomy and function go unnoticed. How, then, does one examine the past for evidence?

The question of the tempo of evolution is an excellent illustration of how science works. Solving this puzzle requires insights from a variety of disciplines using a variety of methods. Like many areas of scientific endeavor, evolution offers a complex collection of evidence, and it does not yield easily to simple analysis.

Section 3 Assessment

Section Summary

- The Hardy-Weinberg principle describes the conditions within which evolution does not occur.
- Speciation often begins in small, isolated populations.
- Selection can operate by favoring average or extreme traits.
- Punctuated equilibrium and gradualism are two models that explain the tempo of evolution.

Understand Main Ideas

1. MAIN Idea **Describe** one new mechanism of evolution that scientists learned after Darwin's book was published.
2. **Identify** three of the conditions of the Hardy-Weinberg principle.
3. **Discuss** factors that can lead to speciation.
4. **Indicate** which pattern of evolution is shown by the many species of finches on the Galápagos Islands.

Think Critically

5. **Design an Experiment** Biologists discovered two populations of frogs separated by the Amazon River. What experiment could be designed to test whether the two populations are one species or two?

MATH in Biology

6. What type of mathematical results would you expect from the experiment you designed above if the two populations diverged only recently?

Concepts in Motion
Animation

Formative Assessment

Evaluation On the board, draw graphs similar to those in Figure 16, but do not include the labels. Choose a student to tell where one label should be placed on one of the graphs. Continue asking students at random for labels. Then choose three students to tell the types of selection depicted. Choose three other students to define the type of selection. Finally, have three more students give an example of each kind of selection.

Remediation
If students have difficulty with the task above, provide them with labeled drawings and refer them to the text under the headings *Natural selection, Stabilizing selection, Disruptive selection,* and *Sexual selection.* After providing time for review, ask them a few questions about the graphs, such as, "What does the dotted line indicate?" The dotted line shows the trait's original variation within the population.

Section 3 Assessment

1. Genetics, genetic drift, punctuated equilibrium, or other reasonable answers.
2. Answers should include three of the following: large populations, random mating, no immigration or emigration, no mutation, no natural selection.
3. Answers should involve an isolating mechanism.
4. Adaptive radiation or divergent evolution.
5. Student responses will vary, but should include a control and some type of mating plan. Perhaps males from one side will be mated with females from the other side of the river.
6. Two separate, but recently diverged, species would be expected to have low reproduction rates, but not zero. In addition students may indicate that most or all of the hybrid offspring are sterile, or that the number of chromosomal differences would be small.

Assessment Online Quiz

BioDiscoveries

Purpose

Students will learn about the biodiversity of Madagascar, including the large number of endemic species. They will also learn about the unusual traits of the giant leaf-tailed gecko and the pygmy mouse lemur.

C.6, F.3, F.4

Anticipatory Guide

ASK STUDENTS: ***What is biodiversity?*** Tell students that biodiversity is the number of different species living in a specific area. ***Why is biodiversity important?*** Biodiversity increases the stability of an ecosystem and contributes to the health of the biosphere. It provides direct and indirect value to humans.

Background

The baobab tree, also known as the bottle tree, is important to the people of Madagascar. There are eight known species of this tree, and six are found on Madagascar. These trees have extremely thick trunks where they store water collected during the rainy season. (They also store water in their branches.) Lemurs pollinate the largest of the baobab trees, Grandidier's baobab (*Adansonia grandidieri*), while bats pollinate other species of the tree. The people of Madagascar often tap the trunks of baobab trees in order to obtain water. They also eat the tree's seeds.

BioDiscoveries

Madagascar: Island of Biodiversity

Move over, Galapagos Islands—another island is emerging as a prime example of biodiversity. Thousands of species of rare plants and animals live on Madagascar, including lemurs, frogs, geckos, chameleons, butterflies, and orchids. Scientists estimate that 80 percent of Madagascar's plants and animals are endemic, that is, they do not live anywhere else in the world. A scientific study published in 2009 reported that up to 221 new species of frogs had been found on Madagascar, which nearly doubles the number of amphibians found on the island so far.

The gaint leaf-tailed gecko (above) and the pygmy mouse lemur (right) are both species that live only on Madagascar.

Giant leaf-tailed gecko One of the reptile species is the giant leaf-tailed gecko (*Uroplatus fimbriatus*). As the name indicates, the tails of these nocturnal geckos are shaped like leaves, which helps camouflage them from predators. If a predator grabs a gecko's tail, it breaks off so the gecko can escape. The tail will grow back, but it might have a different appearance. These geckos' colorings also help them blend with their rainforest home, as they have some ability to change color to better blend with the trees.

Giant leaf-tailed geckos have other fascinating characteristics. They do not have eyelids, so they use their tongues to lick their eyeballs clean. Their toes are equipped with tiny bristles that allow them to run up smooth, vertical surfaces. And when these geckos are startled, they lift their heads and tails, open their mouths, and bark or scream.

Pygmy mouse lemur Lemurs are a group of primates that are endemic to Madagascar. There are 88 species of lemurs on the island, and the smallest is the pygmy mouse lemur (*Microcebus myoxinus*), the tiniest primate in the world.

The pygmy mouse lemur is just 6 centimeters long with a 13 centimeter tail. It weighs only 30 grams. These nocturnal animals live mainly in trees and eat insects and fruit. The pygmy mouse lemur has large ears that it uses to listen for predators.

New species are discovered on Madagascar every year. As larger numbers of scientists turn their attention to this island, its status as one of the most important areas of biodiversity on the planet is likely to grow.

PUBLIC SPEAKING AND SOCIAL NETWORKING

Scavenger Hunt Your teacher will divide your class into several groups, giving each group a list of five species that are endemic to Madagascar. With your group, research the species. Present your findings to the class.

Public Speaking

Assist your students as they research species endemic to Madagascar. Help them choose credible print and online sources. If the needed equipment is available, encourage students to create electronic presentations that can be shown to the class. This will make it easier to display photographs of the endemic species.

BIOLAB

CAN SCIENTISTS MODEL NATURAL SELECTION?

Background: Natural selection is the mechanism that Darwin proposed to explain evolution. Through natural selection, traits that allow individuals to have the most offspring in a given environment tend to increase in the population over time.

Question: *How can natural selection be modeled in a laboratory setting?*

Materials

small, medium, and large beads
forceps
short-nosed pliers
tray or pan
stopwatch

Safety Precautions

Procedure

1. Read and complete the lab safety form.
2. Divide into groups of three. One student will use forceps to represent one adult member of a predator population, one will use pliers to represent another adult member of the predator population, and the third will keep time and score.
3. Mix prey items (beads) on a tray or pan.
4. In 20 seconds, try to pick up all possible beads using forceps or pliers.
5. After 20 seconds, assign three points for each large bead, two points for each medium bead, and one point for each small bead.
6. Add up the points and use the following rules: survival requires 18 points, and the ability to produce a new offspring requires an additional 10 points.
7. Determine the number of survivors and the number of offspring.
8. Repeat the procedure 10 times and combine your data with the other groups.

Analyze and Conclude

1. **Calculate** Combining all of the trials of all of the groups, determine the percentage of forceps and pliers that survived.
2. **Evaluate** Using data from the entire class, determine the total number of offspring produced by the forceps adult and the plier adult.
3. **Summarize** The original population was divided evenly between the forceps adult and the plier adult. If all of the adults left, what would be the new population ratio? Use the results from the entire class.
4. **Infer** Given the survival and reproduction data, predict what will happen to the two organisms in the study. Which adult—the forceps or the pliers—is better adapted to produce more offspring?
5. **Conclude** Using the principles of natural selection, how is this population changing?

APPLY YOUR SKILL

Make Inferences Given the results of the experiment, how will the prey populations (beads) change as the predator population changes? Explain your inference.

BIOLAB

Inquiry BioLab

For a lab worksheet, use your eTeacherEdition Online.

RUBRIC A rubric for evaluating BioLabs is found on your eTeacherEdition Online.

Est. Time: 50 min

Content Background
A population is made up of all the members of a species that live in an area. While individuals in a population share similar traits, variation among these traits exists. Populations interact to form communities. Among the species in any given community, tremendous variation can exist in features including body size, shape, and structure. Some variations can affect an organism's chances of surviving and reproducing in an environment.

Alternative Materials Different types of seeds or beans could be used in place of the beads to complete this activity.

Safety Precautions Approve lab safety forms before work begins. Remind students to handle tweezers and pliers carefully.

Teaching Strategy Have a chart prepared that is accessible to each group for compiling class data. The chart may be electronic or drawn on a chalk or white board, and should be visible to the entire class for use in analysis and discussion.

Alternative Teaching Demo This exercise could be completed by having the teacher lead data collection from a single set of four trials for both tweezers and pliers. Data could be analyzed through whole-class discussion.

Apply Your Skill The prey population that is selected most often by the predators will decline. The population of prey that is selected least will increase.

Analyze and Conclude

1. To calculate the percentage, students should divide the number of tweezers/pliers that survived by the total number of tweezers/pliers in the community. Answers will vary based on class data.
2. To determine the number of offspring produced in the community, students should calculate the number of offspring produced by the tweezers/pliers in each group, and then add the group numbers.
3. To calculate the ratio, students should write (the number of offspring tweezers): (the number of offspring pliers). Answers will vary based on class data.
4. Answers will vary based on class data. If the survival percentage is low, the population will not persist. If relatively few offspring are produced, the population will likely decline over generations.
5. The population that produces the most offspring will be most likely to grow over time. Body structure variations that make it easier to obtain food are likely to be passed to offspring by surviving individuals.

Chapter 15

Study Guide

ConnectED

Students can use the following to review the chapter.

Review

Vocabulary eGames
Vocabulary eFlashcards
Vocabulary PuzzleMaker

Assessment

Online Quizzes
Online Test Practice
Standardized Test Practice

Use the *ExamView®* *Assessment Suite* CD-ROM to:

- create multiple versions of tests
- create modified tests with one mouse click
- edit existing questions and add your own questions
- build tests aligned with state standards using built-in state curriculum tags
- change English tests to Spanish with one mouse click
- track students' progress using the Teacher Management System

Chapter 15 Study Guide

THEME FOCUS Scientific Inquiry Extensive collections of rocks, fossils, plants, and animals, as well as the study of selective breeding contributed to the development of the theory of evolution.

BIG Idea The theory of evolution is supported by natural selection and explains the diversity of life.

Section 1 Darwin's Theory of Evolution by Natural Selection

artificial selection (p. 419)
natural selection (p. 420)
evolution (p. 422)

MAIN Idea **Charles Darwin developed a theory of evolution based on natural selection.**

- Darwin drew from his observations on the HMS *Beagle* and later studies to develop his theory of evolution by natural selection.
- Natural selection is based on ideas of excess reproduction, variation, inheritance, and advantages of certain traits in certain environments.
- Darwin reasoned that the process of natural selection eventually could result in the appearance of new species.

Section 2 Evidence of Evolution

derived trait (p. 424)
ancestral trait (p. 424)
homologous structure (p. 424)
vestigial structure (p. 425)
analogous structure (p. 426)
embryo (p. 426)
biogeography (p. 428)
fitness (p. 428)
camouflage (p. 428)
mimicry (p. 429)

MAIN Idea **Multiple lines of evidence support the theory of evolution.**

- Fossils provide strong direct evidence to support evolution.
- Homologous and vestigial structures indicate shared ancestry.
- Examples of embryological and biochemical traits provide insight into the evolution of species.
- Biogeography can explain why certain species live in certain locations.
- Natural selection gives rise to features that increase reproductive success.

Section 3 Shaping Evolutionary Theory

Hardy-Weinberg principle (p. 431)
genetic drift (p. 433)
founder effect (p. 433)
bottleneck (p. 433)
stabilizing selection (p. 434)
directional selection (p. 435)
disruptive selection (p. 436)
sexual selection (p. 436)
prezygotic isolating mechanism (p. 437)
postzygotic isolating mechanism (p. 437)
allopatric speciation (p. 438)
sympatric speciation (p. 438)
adaptive radiation (p. 439)
gradualism (p. 440)
punctuated equilibrium (p. 440)

MAIN Idea **The theory of evolution continues to be refined as scientists learn new information.**

- The Hardy-Weinberg principle describes the conditions within which evolution does not occur.
- Speciation often begins in small, isolated populations.
- Selection can operate by favoring average or extreme traits.
- Punctuated equilibrium and gradualism are two models that explain the tempo of evolution.

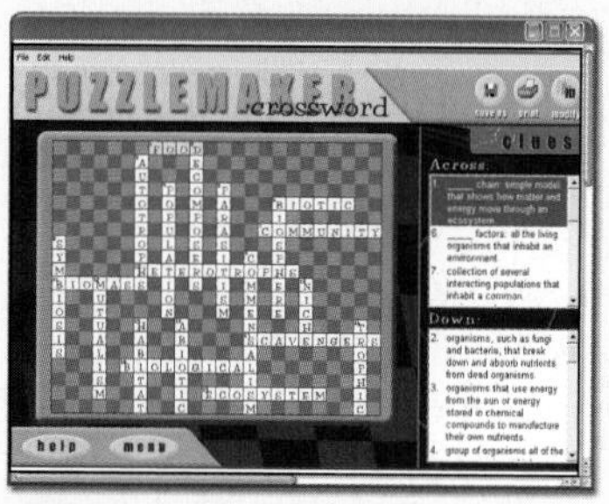

Review **Vocabulary PuzzleMaker**

For additional practice with vocabulary, have students access the Vocabulary PuzzleMaker online.

Review **Vocabulary eGames**

Chapter 15 Assessment

Section 1

Vocabulary Review

Replace the underlined portions of the sentences below with words from the Study Guide to make each sentence correct.

1. Natural selection is a mechanism for species change over time.
2. Selective breeding was used to produce purebred Chihuahuas and cocker spaniels.
3. Differential survival by members of a population with favorable adaptations is a mechanism for a theory developed by Charles Darwin.

Understand Main Ideas

4. Which best describes the prevailing view about the age of Earth and evolution before Darwin's voyage on the HMS *Beagle?*
   A. Earth and life are recent and have remained unchanged.
   B. Species evolved rapidly during the first six thousand to a few hundred thousand years.
   C. Earth is billions of years old, but species have not evolved.
   D. Species have evolved on Earth for billions of years.

Use the photo below to answer question 5.

5. Which statement about the tortoise above would be part of an explanation for tortoise evolution based on natural selection?
   A. All tortoises look like the above tortoise.
   B. Tortoises with domed shells have more young than tortoises with flat shells.
   C. All the tortoises born on the island survive.
   D. The tortoise shell looks nothing like the shell of either parent.

Constructed Response

6. MAIN Idea Summarize Darwin's theory of evolution by using an example.
7. **Short Answer** How is artificial selection similar to natural selection?

Think Critically

8. **Sequence** Sequence events leading to evolution by natural selection.
9. **Recognize Cause and Effect** What is the likely evolutionary effect on a species of an increase in global temperatures over time?

Section 2

Vocabulary Review

The sentences below include terms that have been used incorrectly. Make the sentences true by replacing the italicized word with a vocabulary term from the Study Guide page.

10. Anatomical parts that have a reduced function in an organism are *analogous structures.*
11. *Biogeography* is a measure of the relative contribution an individual trait makes to the next generation.
12. *Camouflage* occurs when two or more species evolve adaptations to resemble each other.

Understand Main Ideas

Use the photos below to answer question 13.

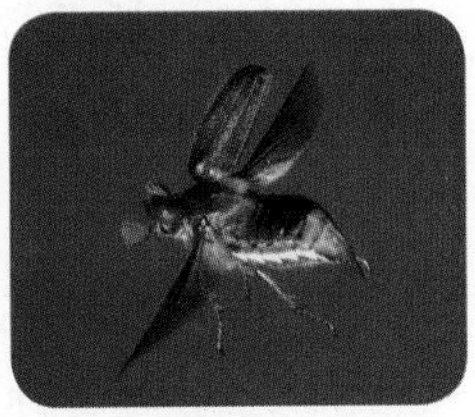

13. These organisms have similar features that are considered what kind of structures?
   A. vestigial
   B. homologous
   C. analogous
   D. comparative

Chapter 15

Assessment

Section 1

Vocabulary Review

1. evolution
2. artificial selection
3. natural selection

Understand Main Ideas

4. A
5. B

Constructed Response

6. Student examples will vary. Each population has individuals with variations. Individuals with the most beneficial variations are more successful at survival and reproduction. Their variations eventually become the majority in the population.
7. Both are examples of evolution. However, artificial selection is directed by humans selecting the variations. Natural selection is directed when the environment selects the variations to be passed on to the next generation.

Think Critically

8. 1. Populations produce individuals with inheritable variations.
   2. Populations produce more offspring than can survive.
   3. Individuals with desirable variations for a particular environment survive and reproduce at a greater rate.
   4. Desirable variations increase in the population over time.
9. Some species will likely respond by evolving adaptations to the increasing temperatures over time. Others may migrate to remain in the same climatic conditions. Others may become extinct if they cannot adapt.

Section 2

Vocabulary Review

10. vestigial structures
11. fitness
12. mimicry

Understand Main Ideas

13. C

Understand Main Ideas
14. B
15. A
16. D
17. D

Constructed Response
18. Cytochrome *c* is an enzyme found in the metabolic systems of many different and seemingly unrelated species. Because this molecule is complex, it probably did not evolve separately in each of these species. The similarities in structure indicate common ancestry, and the amount of difference in sequence is an index of divergence since the last shared ancestor.
19. The conclusion is that the insects have evolved to develop a resistance to previously effective pesticides.
20. Fossils occur in many locations. Some of these fossils show transitional links between major groups. Other fossils show similarities between extinct species and those alive today.

Think Critically
21. Student responses will vary. The experiment should have a control. It should involve artificial selection for some color pattern that should be stated by the student. For instance, the student may select for a vertical pattern to camouflage against vertical weeds in the background.
22. adaptive radiation or divergent evolution

Use the photo below to answer question 14.

14. The photo of the bird above shows what kind of morphological adaptation?
A. vestigial organ
B. camouflage
C. mimicry
D. analogous structure

15. Which is not an example of a morphological adaptation?
A. Cytochrome *c* is similar in monkeys and humans.
B. Butterflies evolve similar color patterns.
C. A harmless species of snake resembles a harmful species.
D. Young birds have adaptations for blending into the environment.

16. Industrial melanism could be considered a special case of which of the following?
A. embryological adaptation
B. mimicry
C. physiological adaptation
D. structural adaptation

17. Which sets of structures are homologous?
A. a butterfly's wing and a bat's wing
B. a moth's eyes and a cow's eyes
C. a beetle's leg and a horse's leg
D. a whale's pectoral fin and a bird's wing

Constructed Response

18. Short Answer Describe how cytochrome *c* provides evidence of evolution.

19. Short Answer What can be concluded from the fact that many insects are resistant to certain pesticides?

20. MAIN Idea Why are fossils considered to provide the strongest evidence supporting evolution?

Think Critically

21. THEME FOCUS Scientific Inquiry How could you design an experiment to show that a species of small fish has the ability to evolve a camouflage color pattern?

22. CAREERS IN BIOLOGY An evolutionary biologist is studying several species of closely related lizards found on Cuba and surrounding islands. Each species occupies a somewhat different niche, but in some ways they all look similar to the green anole lizard found in Florida. Suggest the pattern of lizard evolution.

Section 3

Vocabulary Review

Choose the vocabulary term from the Study Guide page that best matches each of the following descriptions.

23. one species evolves over millions of years to become two different but closely related species

24. a species evolves into a new species without a physical barrier

25. the random changes in gene frequency found in small populations

Understand Main Ideas

Use the figure below to answer question 26.

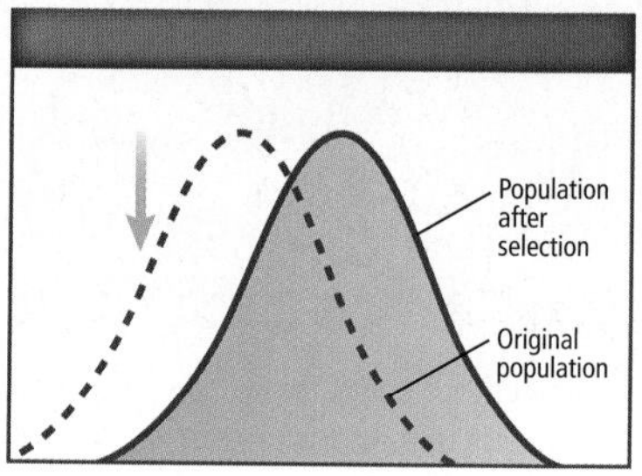

26. The graph above best represents which kind of selection?
A. directional
B. disruptive
C. sexual
D. stabilizing

Section 3
Vocabulary Review
23. gradualism
24. sympatric speciation
25. genetic drift

Understand Main Ideas
26. A
27. C

Constructed Response
28. Many populations are small, mating is not random, animals migrate, and mutations occur.
29. The clams with the strongest muscles will survive and produce more offspring, and if the strength is heritable, the offspring will have stronger muscles. If stronger muscles are larger, over time this leads to a population with larger muscles.

Assessment Online Test Practice

Use the photo below to answer question 27.

27. The plant in the above illustration looks like a cactus but is classified in a completely separate group of plants. This would be an example of which mechanism?
   A. adaptive radiation
   B disruptive selection
   C. convergent evolution
   D. punctuated equilibrium

Constructed Response

28. **Open Ended** Discuss why the Hardy-Weinberg principle is often violated in real populations.

29. **Open Ended** Sea stars eat clams by pulling apart the two halves of a clam's shell. Discuss how this could result in directional selection of clam muscle size.

30. **Short Answer** Compare and contrast genetic drift and natural selection as mechanisms of evolution.

Think Critically

31. **Make and Use Graphs** Draw a graph that would illustrate a population that has a wide variation of color from light to dark brown. Then draw on the same graph what that population would look like after several years of stabilizing selection. Label your graph.

32. MAIN Idea What would you conclude about the evolutionary process that produces two unrelated species that share similar niches on different continents?

Summative Assessment

33. BIG Idea Imagine that there has been a major climate shift. Most of Earth is covered in ice, and the equatorial regions are temperate. Describe how plant and animal distribution might change over time through natural selection. Also, describe new available niches that could develop and the types of organisms that may fill them.

34. *WRITING in* **Biology** Imagine that you are Charles Darwin and write a letter to your father detailing your observations aboard the Beagle.

35. *WRITING in* **Biology** Write a paragraph that explains why a genetic bottleneck can be an important evolutionary factor for a species.

36. Choose three lines of evidence that support evolution. Give an example of each.

DBQ Document-Based Questions

Darwin,Charles. 1859. *On the Origin of Species by Means of Natural Selection, or the Preservation of Favoured Races in the Struggle for Life.*

Naturalists continually refer to external conditions, such as climate, food, etc., as the only possible cause of variation. In one very limited sense, as we shall hereafter see, this may be true; but it is preposterous to attribute to mere external conditions, the structure, for instance, of the woodpecker, with its feet, tail, beak, and tongue, so admirably adapted to catch insects under the bark of trees.

37. In Darwin's time, most naturalists considered only external conditions as causes of variation. What nonexternal mechanism did Darwin propose as a cause of variation?

38. How would modern scientists explain the nonexternal mechanisms that Darwin proposed?

39. Consider Darwin's example of the woodpecker. Explain the role that natural selection has producing a bird species with a woodpeckerlike beak.

30. Genetic drift is a random consequence of small population size. Natural selection is determined by environmental conditions and is therefore definitely not random.

Think Critically

31. Students should draw a graph with a wide "bell-shaped" curve at the beginning of the experiment. At the end, a population should be superimposed that has a narrower "bell-shaped" curve with its mean around the medium brown. The *Y*-axis should be labeled population size or numbers and the *X*-axis should be labeled with light to brown color at the extremes.
32. The process is probably convergent evolution.

Summative Assessment

33. Answers will vary, but should show an understanding that organisms can not choose to adapt to new environments. Organisms with favorable characteristics will survive to reproduce, and therefore pass on their genes. Answers should also describe new niches, and the characteristics that organisms would need to fill them.

34. Letters will vary, but should talk about life aboard the ship, finding various fossils that resemble living forms, or various species on the Galapagos Islands.

35. Student responses will vary, but may include the cheetah or other populations that have experienced a genetic bottleneck. The paragraph should explain that all the individuals may be nearly genetically identical after such an event

36. Evidence includes the fossil record, comparative embryology, comparative biochemistry, vestigial structures, and homologous structures.

DBQ Document-Based Questions

Darwin,Charles. 1859. *On the Origin of Species by Means of Natural Selection, or the Preservation of Favoured Races in the Struggle for Life.*

37. Darwin based his theory on the existence of individual variations that are inherited and exist in all organisms.
38. The genes—their mutations and modes of action—are today understood to be the source of variations that Darwin proposed.
39. Some members of a population of tree-living birds might have been born with longer beaks than other members. More of the birds with long beaks survived than those with shorter beaks because they were better adapted for finding food under tree bark. Over time, the population included mostly birds with long beaks.

Standardized Test Practice

Multiple Choice

1. C
2. B
3. D
4. D
5. D
6. A
7. D
8. A

Short Answer

9. There are at least three possibilities: no amino acids form, different amino acids form, and the same amino acids form. It will depend on the chemicals used.
10. UV radiation in sunlight or radioactive decay
11. Scientists could isolate, from a microorganism, the DNA that codes for the desired protein. The DNA could be attached to a plasmid that would be inserted into the cells of a particular kind of bacteria. The protein would be produced by the bacterial cells and collected for use.
12. Answers might vary. Positive: plants with greater nutritional value can be grown; crops with resistance to certain diseases or insects can be developed. Negative: the expenses needed to make transgenic plants may make agriculture more expensive; the new transgenic crops may develop unexpected genetic problems because of the new genes.
13. Excess reproduction explains how there are always more offspring in a given generation of organisms than the available resources can sustain. Therefore, there must be some process (natural selection) by which some survive and others (those that are less fit) do not.
14. A primitive cell would benefit from the presence of mitochondria because the mitochondria produce excess energy the cell could use.

Standardized Test Practice

Cumulative

Multiple Choice

1. Which experimental setup did Francesco Redi use to test the idea of spontaneous generation?
   - **A.** a flask filled with all the chemicals present on early Earth
   - **B.** mice sealed in jars with lit candles and jars with unlit candles
   - **C.** rotten meat in covered jars and uncovered jars
   - **D.** special flasks that were filled with broth

Use the illustration below of tortoises on two different islands to answer questions 2 and 3.

Large Island

Small Island

2. The above illustrates which principle of natural selection?
   - **A.** inheritance
   - **B.** variation
   - **C.** differential reproduction
   - **D.** overproduction of offspring

3. Tortoises that have shells with higher openings can eat taller plants. Others can only reach vegetation close to the ground. Judging from the differences in the tortoises' shells, what kind of vegetation would you expect to find on the large and small islands?
   - **A.** Both islands have a dense ground cover of low-growing plants.
   - **B.** Both islands have similar plants, but vegetation is more spread out on the large island.
   - **C.** On the large island, the land is mostly dry, and only tall trees grow.
   - **D.** The small island is less grassy, and plants grow with their leaves farther above ground.

4. A dinosaur footprint in rocks would be which kind of fossil?
   - **A.** cast fossil
   - **B.** petrified fossil
   - **C.** replacement fossil
   - **D.** trace fossil

5. Which concept is essential for the process of DNA fingerprinting?
   - **A.** location of genes for related traits on different chromosomes
   - **B.** organization of human DNA into 46 chromosomes
   - **C.** provision by DNA of the codes for proteins in the body
   - **D.** uniqueness of each person's pattern of noncoding DNA

6. Chargaff's rules led to the understanding of which aspect of DNA structure?
   - **A.** base pairing
   - **B.** helix formation
   - **C.** alternation of deoxyribose and phosphate
   - **D.** placement of 3' and 5' carbons

Use the Punnett square below to answer question 7.

	B	?
b		
b		

7. A test cross, shown in the Punnett square above, is used to determine the genotype of an animal that is expressing a dominant gene (B) for a particular characteristic. If the animal is homozygous for the dominant trait, which percentage of its offspring will have the dominant gene?
   - **A.** 25%
   - **B.** 50%
   - **C.** 75%
   - **D.** 100%

8. What prevents the two strands of DNA from immediately coming back together after they unzip?
   - **A.** addition of binding proteins
   - **B.** connection of Okazaki fragments
   - **C.** parting of leading and lagging strands
   - **D.** use of multiple areas of replication

Short Answer

Use the diagram of Miller and Urey's experiment below to answer questions 9 and 10.

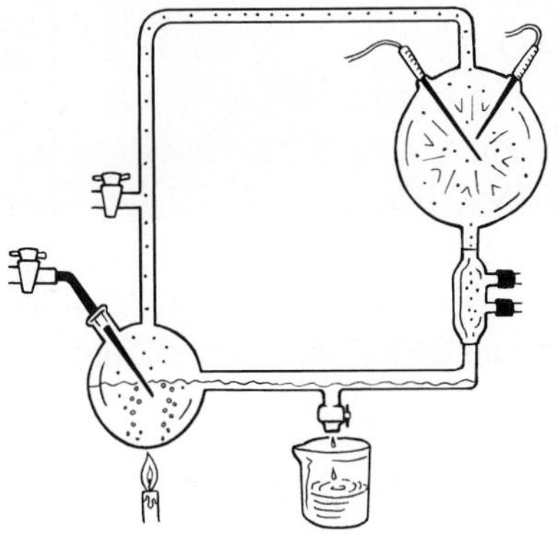

9. What are the possible consequences of a different mix of gases in the apparatus?

10. Some scientists think that lightning might not have been present on Earth in the past. What other energy sources might have caused these reactions?

11. Describe briefly how scientists could use a particular kind of bacteria to synthesize a specific protein.

12. Predict two positive outcomes and two negative outcomes of using transgenic plants for agricultural purposes.

13. Explain the connection between excess reproduction and the concept of natural selection as formulated by Darwin.

14. How would a primitive cell benefit from a symbiotic relationship with a mitochondrion?

Extended Response

Use the diagram below to answer questions 15 and 16.

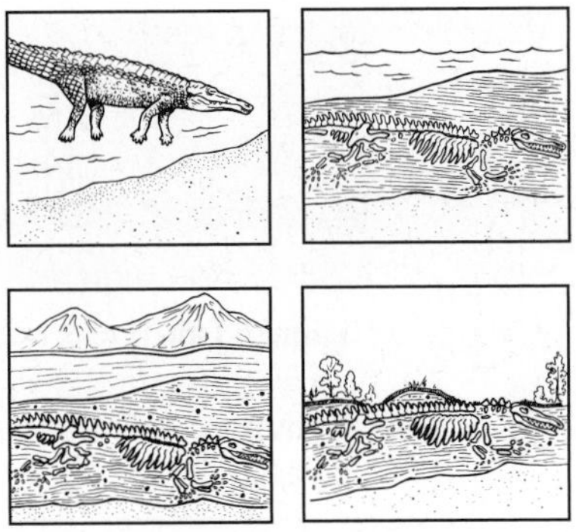

15. Describe the process illustrated in the figure.

16. Explain why a fossil is more likely to form in a wet environment than in a dry environment.

Essay Question

Scientists think that archaea living today are similar to ancient archaea. Many archaea today are found in places such as hot springs, deep-ocean hydrothermal vents, polar ice, and other extreme environments. The organisms living in these environments might be similar to organisms that existed in the distant past.

Using the information in the paragraph above, answer the following question in essay format.

17. Scientists also study organisms in extreme environments to help identify where life might exist on other planets. Why would understanding the origins of life on Earth help with discovering life on other planets?

NEED EXTRA HELP?																	
If You Missed Question . . .	1	2	3	4	5	6	7	8	9	10	11	12	13	14	15	16	17
Review Section . . .	14.2	15.1, 15.3	15.1	14.1	12.1	13.1	10.2	12.2	14.2	14.2	13.2	13.2	15.1	14.2	14.1	14.1	14.2

Extended Response

15. The figure is illustrating fossil formation. Usually, when a fossil forms, an animal dies and is covered with sediment. As the sediment builds up in layers, the remains eventually are encased in rock. Minerals replace the pore space of the bones and hard parts of the organism. Over time, erosion can cause the fossil to be exposed.

16. The remains of plants and animals must be buried quickly before they decay. In a wet environment, the remains are more likely to be covered with sediments faster than in a dry environment.

Essay Question

17. Other planets may have conditions similar to some of the extreme environments found on Earth. If scientists understand the archaea that live in these extreme environments, they may have a better chance to discover and understand organisms on other planets.

Chapter 16 Organizer:
Primate Evolution

LabManager™
Customize any lab with the LabManager™ CD-ROM.

Essential Questions	National Science Standards	Materials and Planning: Estimated times include cleanup and disposal, but do not include teacher prep time. For cleanup and disposal guidelines, see page 39T.	Est. Time (min)
Section 1 1. What are the characteristics of primates? 2. What are the similarities and differences between major primate groups? 3. How can the evolution of primates be traced?	UCP.1–5; A.1, A.2; C.3, C.4, C.6; G.1, G.2, G.3	**Launch Lab,** p. 450: textbook	15
		Activity, p. 452: brick, hammer, variety of nuts (such as Brazil nuts, walnuts, pecans)	10
		Demonstration, p. 453: models or pictures of brains of humans and other animals	10
		Activity, p. 455: globe or wall map of the world, flags or pins	10
		Demonstration, p. 457: nature video of a monkey using a prehensile tail	10
Section 2 1. What are the features of hominoids and hominins? 2. How can hominoid evolution be traced from *Proconsul* to *Homo?* 3. What are the similarities between the various australopithecine species?	UCP.2–5; A.1, A.2; C.3, C.6; E.1, E.2; G.1, G.2, G.3	**Demonstration,** p. 461: graph showing the ratio of brain size relative to body size for several mammals	10
		Demonstration, p. 463: human skull, ruler or pointer	5
		MiniLab 1, p. 464: masking tape, pen or pencil, paper, shoelaces, closed door, stopwatch	15
Section 3 1. How can the species in the genus *Homo* be described? 2. What is the Out-of-Africa hypothesis? 3. What are the similarities and differences between Neanderthals and modern humans?	UCP.2–5; A.1, A.2; C.3, C.6; E.1, E.2; G.1, G.2, G.3	**Demonstration,** p. 467: pictures of sharp, stone tools used by *H. habilis*	10
		MiniLab 2, p. 468: copies of a world map with longitude and latitude markings	25
		Demonstration, p. 472: photos of early decorative artifacts and cave paintings	10
		BioLab, p. 475: envelope with paper bones and clues, paper, pencil, ruler	40

Suggested Time for Each Lesson

Class	Chapter Opener	Section 1	Section 2	Section 3	Assessment
Basic	45 min	90 min	90 min	90 min	45 min
General	25 min	55 min	55 min	45 min	45 min
Honors	—	—	20 min	15 min	10 min

ConnectED

connectED.mcgraw-hill.com

Access interactive learning opportunities and teaching resources using these icons located throughout your StudentWorks™ Plus Online and eTeacherEdition Online.

Chapter 16 Section Resources	Additional Chapter 16 Resources	Technology
FAST FILE Unit 4 Resources: Launch Lab Worksheet* Study Guide (English/Spanish)* Section Quick Check **Reading Essentials 16.1** **Science Notebook 16.1*** **FAST FILE Unit 4 Resources:** MiniLab Worksheet* Study Guide (English/Spanish)* Section Quick Check **Reading Essentials 16.2** **Science Notebook 16.2*** **FAST FILE Unit 4 Resources:** MiniLab Worksheet* BioLab Worksheet* Study Guide (English/Spanish)* Section Quick Check **Reading Essentials 16.3** **Science Notebook 16.3***	**FAST FILE Unit 4 Resources:** Chapter Diagnostic Test Concept Mapping* Real-World Biology Enrichment Chapter Tests A, B, and C **Transparencies:** Bellringer Transparencies* Biology Concepts Transparencies* **Lab Resources:** Laboratory Manual* Probeware Lab Manual* Forensics Lab Manual* Pre-AP Lab Manual* Open Inquiry in Biology* Guided Inquiry in Biology*	**Teaching Tools:** eTeacherEdition Online Classroom Presentation Toolkit CD-ROM* LabManager™ CD-ROM* Video Lab DVD* Virtual Lab CD-ROM* What's BIOLOGY Got To Do With It? StudentWorks™ Plus Online* **Chapter Assessment Tools:** Classroom Presentation Toolkit CD-ROM* *ExamView® Assessment Suite* CD-ROM **Web-Based Resources:** • StudentWorks™ Plus Online • eTeacherEdition Online • Animations* • The Interactive Time Line* • Interactive Tables* • Online Quizzes • Online Test Practice • Standardized Test Practice • Virtual Labs* • Multilingual eGlossary* • Vocabulary eGames* • Vocabulary eFlashcards • WebQuests • Personal Tutors

While all resources listed are appropriate for English learners, the * indicates resources with a strong visual or hands-on component for EL.

Teaching strategies and activities have been coded for differentiated instruction.

AL Activities for students working above grade level	**OL** Activities for students working on grade level	**BL** Activities for students working below grade level	**EL** Activities for English learners (also ELL)	**COOP LEARN** Activities designed for small cooperative group work

CHAPTER 16

Launch Lab
What are the characteristics of primates?

Inquiry Launch Lab

For a lab worksheet, use your eTeacherEdition Online.

RUBRIC A rubric for evaluating Launch Labs is found on your eTeacherEdition Online.

Est. Time 15 min

Safety Precaution Approve lab safety forms before work begins.

Teaching Strategy Students can work individually or in pairs.

Procedure

1. Read and complete the lab safety form.
2. Scan through the pictures of primates in Section 1 of this chapter. Do not read the text.
3. Explain what physical features you see in primates that appear in humans.
4. Create a data table in which to record your observations.

Analysis

1. **Compare** the human and ape characteristics in your table. Which features are similar? Similarities include forward-facing eyes, dexterous and long fingers, nimble limbs, upright posture, well-defined face area, small ears; differences include hairiness, length of arms and legs, and snout/nose structure.
2. **Contrast** How are primates different from the cats and dogs and other mammals around you? Accept all reasonable responses; students might say that primates are more intelligent, or that they have opposable digits.

CHAPTER 16

Primate Evolution

ConnectED
Your one-stop online resource
connectED.mcgraw-hill.com

- Video
- Audio
- Review
- Inquiry
- WebQuest
- Assessment
- Concepts in Motion
- Multilingual eGlossary

Launch Lab
What are the characteristics of primates?

If you've been to the zoo or seen pictures of African wildlife, you have probably observed monkeys, chimpanzees, and gorillas. Maybe you've even seen pictures of lemurs. What makes these animals primates? What makes you a primate? In this lab, you will investigate the features that you share with these other primates.

For a lab worksheet, use your StudentWorks™ Plus Online.

Inquiry Launch Lab

FOLDABLES®

Make a three-tab book with the labels shown. Use it to organize your notes on monkeys.

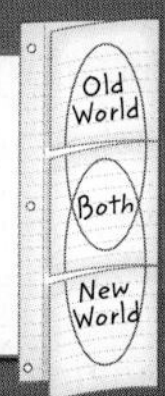

THEME FOCUS Change
The changes that separated hominins from hominoids took place over 20–25 million years.

BIG Idea Evolutionary change in a group of small, tree-living mammals eventually led to a diversity of species that includes modern humans.

Section 1 • Primates

Section 2 • Hominoids to Hominins

Section 3 • Human Ancestry

THEMES

Scientific Inquiry Scientists are sequencing the genomes of different primates to better understand their relationship to humans.

Diversity Primates are a large, diverse group of more than 200 living species.

Energy All primates obtain energy by ingesting other organisms.

Homeostasis Primates have adaptations that enable them to maintain homeostasis.

Change Natural selection has resulted in changes in primates over long periods of time.

Introduce the Chapter

Primates Up Close

SAY TO STUDENTS: ***Howler monkeys like the one in the photo live in rain forests of Central and South America. Like other organisms, they have adaptations that make them well suited to their environment. How might the adaptations called out in the photos help howler monkeys live?*** Answers will vary. Students might respond that binocular vision helps them look for food, or that a prehensile tail makes them adapted for life in trees. Accept all reasonable responses. ***What are some other adaptations of howler monkeys?*** Answers will vary. As students make suggestions, write them on the board. When students are finished, point out that all primates, including humans, share certain characteristics. Circle the adaptations on the list that humans share.

BIG Idea

Monitor Comprehension Ask students to monitor themselves as they read the chapter. Tell them they should slow down when they encounter new or difficult concepts, new vocabulary, or text that contains large amounts of information. Give a brief oral quiz after they've finished reading. If they do not understand the Big Idea or a Main Idea, have them reread, review, or continue reading to clarify what is unclear.

Section 1

MAIN Idea

BL OL AL Primate Ancestry
SAY TO STUDENTS: *All primates have a common ancestor.*
ASK STUDENTS: *What is the basis for this statement?* Answers should include the fossil record as well as anatomical and behavioral similarities. Use student answers to begin a discussion of this section.

D Develop Concepts
OL AL Brainstorm
ASK STUDENTS: *What makes humans different from all other species?* Possible answer: the human brain and its abilities to perform highly sophisticated cognitive tasks. Students might suggest several characteristics, such as verbal communication and binocular vision, but most characteristics students suggest will not be unique to humans. When students offer such answers, give examples of other species that share the characteristics. Try to use characteristics of primates that are discussed in this section.

Caption Question Fig. 1 An opposable digit is useful for grasping tree limbs and for maintaining balance in the trees.

Section 1

Reading Preview

Essential Questions
- What are the characteristics of primates?
- What are the similarities and differences between major primate groups?
- How can the evolution of primates be traced?

Review Vocabulary
extinction: the disappearance of a species when the last of its members dies

New Vocabulary
opposable first digit
binocular vision
diurnal
nocturnal
arboreal
anthropoid
prehensile tail
hominin

Multilingual eGlossary

Figure 1 This squirrel monkey is using its opposable digits to hold its dinner—a lantern fly.
Infer *other ways that a primate might use an opposable digit.*

Primates

MAIN Idea **Primates share several behavioral and biological characteristics, which indicates that they evolved from a common ancestor.**

Real-World Reading Link You can often tell that your aunts, uncles, or cousins are related to you. Perhaps they have the same color hair or similar features, or they are as tall as you are. Just as you can tell that you are related to your biological family, characteristics of primates show that they are also a related family.

D Characteristics of Primates

Humans, apes, monkeys, and lemurs belong to a group of mammals called primates. Though primates are highly diverse, they share some general features. Some primates have a high level of manual dexterity, which is the ability to manipulate or grasp objects with their hands. They usually also have keen eyesight and long, highly movable arms. Compared to other animals, they have large brains. The primates with the largest brains, which includes humans, have the capacity to reason.

Manual dexterity Primates are distinguished by their flexible hands and feet. All primates typically have five digits on each hand and foot; as you know, humans have fingers and toes. Most have flat nails and sensitive areas on the ends of their digits. The first digits on most primates' hands are opposable, and the first digit on many primates' feet are opposable. An **opposable first digit,** either a thumb or a great toe, is set apart from the other digits. This digit can be brought across the palm or foot so that it touches or nearly touches the other digits. This action allows the primate to grasp an object in a powerful grip. Some primates also have lengthened first digits that provide added dexterity. **Figure 1** shows a monkey using its opposable thumbs to grasp its food.

Senses Though there are exceptions, primates rely more on vision and less on their sense of smell than other mammals do. Their eyes, protected by bony eye sockets, are on the front of their face. This creates overlapping fields of vision, often called **binocular vision.** Forward-looking eyes allow for a greater field of depth perception and enable primates to judge relative distance and movement of an object.

Most primates are **diurnal** (di YUR nul), which means they are active during the day. Because these primates are active in daylight, most also have color vision. Primates that are **nocturnal** (nahk TUR nul) are active at night. They see only in black and white. An increased sense of vision is generally accompanied by a decreased sense of smell. Nocturnal primates' snouts are smaller and their faces tend to be flattened, which increases the degree of binocular vision. Their teeth are reduced in size and usually are unspecialized, meaning that they are suitable for many different types of diets.

Activity

BL OL AL Opposable Thumbs Bring in a brick, a hammer, and a few nuts, such as Brazil nuts, walnuts, and pecans. Have a student try to crack the nuts without the use of his or her thumb. Have a second student do the same thing using the thumb. Ask students why an opposable thumb is useful for primates. (Check if students have nut allergies before asking them to participate.) Est. time: 10 min

Differentiated Instruction

Visually Impaired When conducting the Launch Lab discussion described on the previous page, be sure that students can participate. Speak clearly and keep noise levels down in the classroom. Students with impaired vision will rely more on information that is presented verbally rather than visually.

For more tips, see pages 14T–15T.

Locomotion Another characteristic of primates is their flexible bodies. Primates have limber shoulders and hips and primarily rely on hind limbs for locomotion. Most primates live in trees and have developed an extraordinary ability to move easily from branch to branch. When on the ground, all primates except humans walk on all four limbs. Many primates can walk upright for short distances, and many have a more upright posture compared to four-legged animals.

D **Complex brains and behaviors** Primates tend to have large brains in relation to their body size. Their brains have fewer areas devoted to smell and more areas devoted to vision. They also tend to have larger areas devoted to memory and the coordination of arm and leg movement. Along with larger brains, many primates have problem-solving abilities and well-developed social behaviors, such as grooming and communicating. Most diurnal primates spend a great deal of time socializing by spending time grooming each other. In addition, many primates have complex ways of communicating to each other, which include a wide range of facial expressions.

Reproductive rate Most primates have fewer offspring than other animals. Usually, primates give birth to one offspring at a time. Compared to other mammals, pregnancy is long, and newborns are dependent on their mothers for an extended period of time. For many primates, this time period allows for the increased learning of complex social interactions. A low reproductive rate, the loss of tropical habitats, and human predation has threatened some primate populations. Many are endangered. **Figure 2** illustrates the tropical areas of the world, such as Africa and Southeast Asia, where primates live.

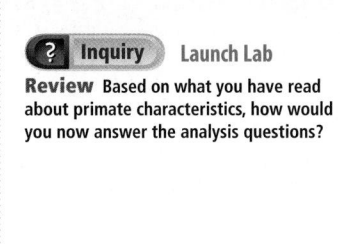

? Inquiry Launch Lab

Review Based on what you have read about primate characteristics, how would you now answer the analysis questions?

S

■ **Figure 2** Nonhuman primates live in a broad area spanning most of the world's tropical regions. Use this map as you read about the different primates.

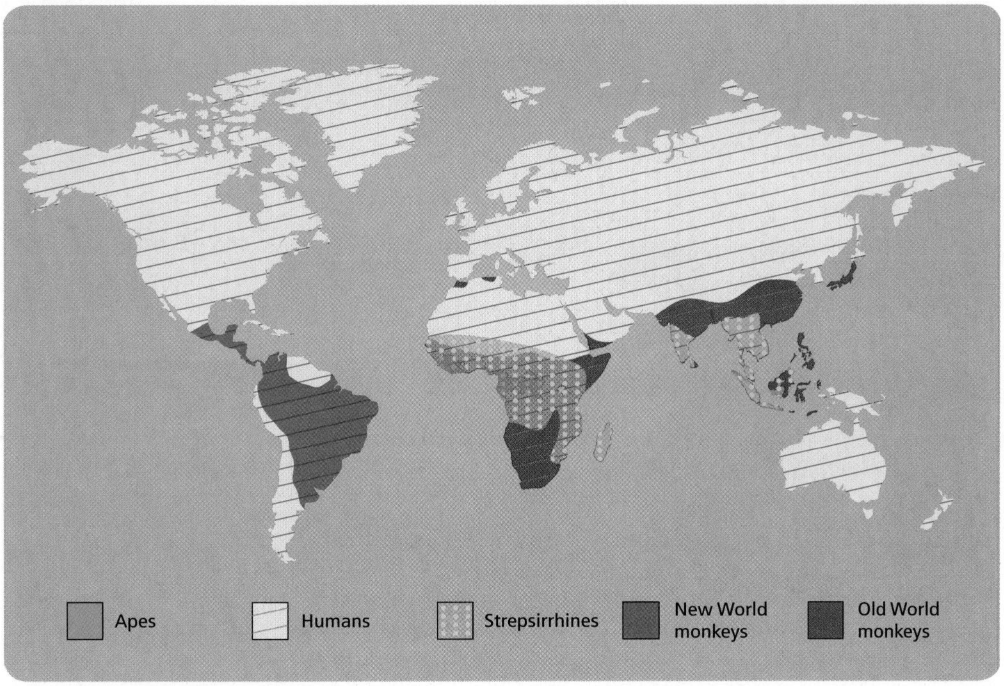

Demonstration

Complex Brains Use models or illustrations to show differences in the brains of humans in comparison with other animals. If you use models, be sure to allow each student to examine the models individually.
Est. time: 10 min

? Inquiry Launch Lab

Assess Content Development
Assess how understanding has developed when students revisit the Launch Lab analysis questions.

D Develop Concepts

EL BL OL AL Use Models Use a model brain (or a preserved brain if one is available) to demonstrate the major parts, such as the medulla, cerebellum, and cerebrum. As you name each part, write the name of the part on the board or on an overhead transparency and describe its role. Review by asking students to point to the part that performs each role as you say the role.

S Skill Practice

OL AL Compare and Contrast
ASK STUDENTS: ***Why do primates need to learn social behaviors?*** Most primates live in groups.
SAY TO STUDENTS: ***List some of the social behaviors that might take young primates some time to learn.*** learning roles of dominance within the group and complex behaviors such as those associated with eating and mating ***How do these behaviors compare with those that humans learn?*** In many ways, the behaviors are similar, but might be less complex than those in human society.

Develop Concepts

BL OL Integrate Geography
ASK STUDENTS: ***Why do all of the primate species appear to live in a broad band in the tropics?*** Scientists think that the primates first evolved in tropical rain forests and most still live in tropical areas. Humans are the major exception.

Visualizing Primates

Purpose
Students will compare and contrast examples of six primate groups.
UCP.4, UCP.5, C.3

Critical Thinking
OL AL Imagine
SAY TO STUDENTS: ***Imagine that a new species of primates has just been discovered living on the island of Madagascar. What adaptations might members of this species have? For what would these adaptations be useful?***
Answers should include primate characteristics such as opposable thumbs (useful for grasping food and bringing it to the mouth) and long tails (useful for balancing while jumping from branch to branch).

Writing Support
BL OL AL Technical Writing
Have students choose one group of primates to research. After they complete their research, have students write a one- or two-paragraph physical description of the group.

Concepts in Motion
Animation

Visualizing Primates

Figure 3
Primates are members of a highly diverse order of mammals. Most primates share common features such as binocular vision and opposable digits.

A The strepsirrhines are relatively small, have large eyes, and are nocturnal. They resemble the earliest primates.
B New World monkeys are characterized by relatively long tails. Many have prehensile tails.
C Old World monkeys resemble New World monkeys but lack prehensile tails. Some have reduced tails.
D Asian apes are long-armed and inhabit tropical rain forests. Apes lack tails.
E African apes live in family groups or small bands and display complex social behavior.
F Humans, *Homo sapiens,* are the only living species in the hominin group. Hominins are unique because they possess the ability to walk for long distances on two legs.

Concepts in Motion **Animation**

Activity
BL OL AL Observe Primates If possible, take a field trip to observe primates in a local zoo. Have students take notes on the behavior they observe in each different species of primate.
Est. time: 2 h

Primate Groups

Primates are a large, diverse group of more than 200 living species. Examine **Figure 3** as you read about this diverse group. Most primates are **arboreal** (ar BOHR ee uhl), or tree-dwelling. Arboreal primates live in the world's tropical and subtropical forests. Primates that live on the ground are considered terrestrial primates.

Primates are classified into two subgroups based on characteristics of their noses, eyes, and teeth. The most basic subgroup is the strepsirrhines (STREP sihr ines) (also called "wet-nosed primates"), such as the lemur. The second subgroup consists of the haplorhines (HAP lohr ines), also called "dry-nosed primates." The haplorhines include the **anthropoids** (AN thruh poydz), a group of large-brained, diurnal monkeys and hominoids.

Reading Check **Differentiate** between strepsirrhines and haplorhines.

Strepsirrhines

Strepsirrhines can be identified by their large eyes and ears. However, they are the only primates that rely predominantly on smell for hunting and social interaction. Some members of this primate group can be found in tropical Africa and Asia. Most are found in Madagascar and nearby islands. As Madagascar drifted away from the African mainland, these animals evolved which left them reproductively isolated. This isolation resulted in their diversification. **Table 1** lists characteristics of some strepsirrhine groups.

Vocabulary
Word Origin
Lemur
comes from Latin, meaning *spirit of the night*

R C

Table 1 Characteristics of Strepsirrhines Concepts in Motion Interactive Table

Group	Lemurs	Aye-Ayes	Lorises	Galagos
Example				
Active Period	Large—diurnal Small—nocturnal	Nocturnal	Nocturnal	Mostly nocturnal
Range	Madagascar	Madagascar	Africa and Southeast Asia	Africa
Characteristics	• Vertical leaper • Uses long bushy tail for balance • Herbivores and omnivores	• Taps bark, listens, fishes out grubs with long third finger	• Small and slow climber, solitary • Lack tails • Some have toxic secretions	• Small and fast leaper • No opposable digit • Long tail

Reading Check Strepsirrhines are wet-nosed and more primitive.

R Reading Strategy

OL Predict

ASK STUDENTS: ***As the human population increases on the island of Madagascar, what do you think will happen to populations of lemurs?*** In recent years, several lemur species have become endangered as a result of hunting and encroachment by humans. As the human population grows, this trend is likely to continue.

Skill Practice

EL BL OL

Make an Illustrated Table

Have students make a five-column table. Tell them to list the groups of primates in the first column. Have them use the other columns to list the distinguishing characteristics, examples, areas where they live, and draw a sketch or paste a magazine photo of a group member.

C Critical Thinking

AL Evaluate

ASK STUDENTS: ***What might have led to the evolution of an aye-aye's dependence on echolocation to find food?*** Echolocation is an adaptation for survival that allows the aye-aye to find food in the darkness. Aye-ayes might have become nocturnal to avoid diurnal predators.

Concepts in Motion
Interactive Table

Content Background

Teacher FYI All modern primates, except humans, have an opposable great toe (known as the "big toe") that is widely separated from the other digits. This feature enables these primates to grab branches with their feet as well as with their hands.

Activity

OL AL Primate Biogeography As you discuss the primate groups, place flags or pins on a globe or wall map of the world to indicate where members of each group are found. Have students discuss geographical relationships of the groups with reference to their similarities and differences. Est. time: 10 min

D Develop Concepts

OL AL

Activate Prior Knowledge

ASK STUDENTS: ***What do you think the new evidence is that suggests the tarsier is more closely related to monkeys than to lemurs?*** Students might suggest that the evidence comes from a comparison of morphological features. Inform students that the new evidence comes from DNA studies. Point out that DNA comparisons reveal that tarsiers and monkeys share a more recent common ancestor than either does with lemurs and other strepsirrhines.

R Reading Strategy

OL Morphological Word Analysis Tell students to look up the roots of the word *prehensile.* *Pre-* comes from the Latin word meaning "before" and *hendere* means "to grasp or seize." Have students repeat this exercise for the terms *primate* and *anthropoid.* The term *primate* comes from the Latin word *primus,* meaning "first," and anthropoid comes from the Greek word *anthrop,* meaning "man," and suffix *-oid,* meaning "resembling."

FOLDABLES®

RUBRIC A rubric for evaluating Foldables is found on your eTeacherEdition Online.

Going Further On the back of their Foldables, have each student draw another Venn diagram and use it to review what he or she has learned about the similarities and differences between the two groups of primates—strepsirrhines and haplorhines.

■ **Figure 4** Lemurs vary in their size and color. Some lemurs, like this sifaka, spend time on the ground.

FOLDABLES®
Incorporate information from this section into your Foldable.

■ **Figure 5** This spider monkey uses its prehensile tail as a fifth limb.

Most small lemurs are nocturnal and solitary. Only a few large species, such as the sifaka shown in **Figure 4,** are diurnal and social. The indri is unique because it does not have a tail, unlike most lemurs that use their bushy tails for balance as they jump from branch to branch. Lorises are similar to lemurs but are found primarily in India and Southeast Asia. Galagos (ga LAY gohs), also called bushbabies, are found only in Africa.

Haplorhines

The second group of primates is a much larger group. The haplorhines include tarsiers, monkeys, and apes. The apes, in turn, include gibbons, orangutans, gorillas, chimpanzees, and humans.

The tarsier is found only in Borneo and the Philippines. It is a small, nocturnal creature with large eyes. It has the ability to rotate its head 180 degrees like an owl. It lives in trees, where it climbs and leaps among the branches. The tarsier shares characteristics with both lemurs and monkeys. Scientists once classified it with the lemurs, but new evidence suggests that it is more closely related to anthropoids, which makes it part of the haplorhine group. D

Anthropoids are generally larger than strepsirrhines, and they have large brains relative to their body size. They are more likely to be diurnal, with eyes adapted to daylight and sometimes to color. Anthropoids also have more complex social interactions. They tend to live longer than lemurs and other strepsirrhines. The anthropoids are split into the New World monkeys and the Old World monkeys. "New World" refers to the Americas; "Old World" refers to Africa, Asia, and Europe. New World monkeys are the only monkeys that live in the Americas.

New World monkeys The New World monkeys are a group of about 60 species of arboreal monkeys that inhabit the tropical forests of Mexico, Central America, and South America. New World monkeys include the marmosets and tamarins. These are among the smallest and most unique primates. Neither species has fingernails or opposable digits.

The New World monkeys also include the squirrel monkeys, spider monkeys, and capuchin monkeys. Some of these monkeys have opposable digits, and most are diurnal and live together in social bands. Most are also distinguished by their prehensile (pree HEN sul) tails. A **prehensile tail** functions like a fifth limb. It can grasp tree branches or other objects and support a monkey's weight, as shown in **Figure 5.** R

Old World monkeys Old World monkeys live in a wide variety of habitats throughout Asia and Africa, from snow-covered mountains in Japan to arid grasslands in Africa. Some Old World monkeys live in Gibraltar, which is located at the southern tip of Spain. There are about 80 species in this group, including macaques and baboons in one subgroup, and colobus and proboscis monkeys in another. Old World monkeys are similar to New World monkeys in many ways. They are diurnal and live in social groups. However, their noses tend to be narrower and their bodies are usually larger. They also spend more time on the ground. None have prehensile tails, and some have no tails. Most Old World monkeys have opposable digits.

GOING GREEN Ask students to bring in cereal, cracker, or other clean empty food boxes that they have saved. Use the boxes for storing Foldables for grading or student use. Cut the front of the box on a diagonal to make a window for easy sorting.

W **Apes** Only a handful of ape species exist today. Apes generally have larger brains in proportion to their body size than monkeys. They also have longer arms than legs, barrel-shaped chests, no tails, and flexible wrists. They are often highly social and have complex vocalizations. They are classified into two subcategories: the lesser apes, which include the gibbons and siamangs, and the great apes, which include orangutans, gorillas, chimpanzees, and humans.

Lesser apes The Asian gibbons and their close relatives, the larger siamangs, are the arboreal gymnasts of the ape family. Though they have the ability to walk on either two or four legs like all great apes, they generally move from branch to branch using a hand-over-hand swinging motion called brachiation. This motion, as shown in **Figure 6,** enables an adult gibbon to move almost 3 m in one swing.

Great apes Orangutans are the largest arboreal primates and the only great ape species that lives exclusively in Asia. Orangutans are large enough that the males are often more comfortable on the ground, though they are not efficient walkers. Female orangutans give birth once every eight years and nurse their young for up to six years. A male orangutan, with prominent cheek pads, and a female orangutan with her offspring are shown in **Figure 7.**

The gorillas are the largest of the primates. Like all great apes, they are predominantly terrestrial animals. They walk on all four limbs, supporting themselves by their front knuckles. Also, like other great apes, they use sticks as simple tools in the wild, and some living in captivity have been taught to recognize written characters and numbers. D

Figure 6 Lesser apes, such as this gibbon, move through trees primarily by brachiation—a hand-over-hand swinging motion.

S

Figure 7 Male orangutans are much larger and more solitary than females. The females spend most of their time raising their offspring.

Demonstration

Prehensile Tail Show an excerpt from a nature video that illustrates the function of a prehensile tail in New World monkeys. Est. time: 10 min

Content Background

Teacher FYI Mountain gorillas are an endangered species, numbering about 500 in the world. They are found only in the mountain jungles of Zaire, Rwanda, and Uganda. Lowland gorillas are slightly larger and more numerous than mountain gorillas. They live in tropical forests from southern Nigeria to the Congo River.

W Writing Support

BL OL Summary Writing

Have students research an Old World monkey and write a report summarizing its physical and behavioral traits. Ask them to include at least one unusual feature of the primate they select. An example is the male mandrill baboon, whose face bears a blue muzzle and bright red stripe. This colorful feature is an adaptation for mating because it attracts females.

D Develop Concepts

BL OL AL

Clarify a Misconception

Some students might have the misconception that gorillas and chimpanzees are more closely related to each other than to humans.

ASK STUDENTS: ***Of gorillas, chimpanzees, and humans, which two primate groups are the most closely related?*** Answers will vary. Inform students that, based on DNA comparisons, chimpanzees are more closely related to humans than to any other primate species, including gorillas.

S Skill Practice

BL OL Compare and Contrast

Have students use the photos in Figures 6 and 7 to determine differences between the gibbon and the orangutan, which are both Asian apes. The gibbon spends more time in trees and appears to be more primitive than the orangutan.

D Develop Concepts

BL OL

Clarify a Misconception
Students often think that hominins, including humans, existed at the same time as the dinosaurs. **SAY TO STUDENTS:** ***Sometimes dinosaurs and humans or other hominins appear together in stories or movies. Why are these always fictional accounts?*** The dinosaurs were extinct before the evolution of hominins. Point out that the dinosaurs became extinct approximately 65 million years ago, long before hominins evolved.

S Skill Practice

BL OL AL COOP LEARN

Visual Literacy Have students work in pairs to write a summary of the diverging pattern of primate evolution as illustrated in Fig. 9. **SAY TO STUDENTS:** ***Begin your summary with this sentence: "The common ancestor of all primate groups lived about 35 million years ago." End your summary with this sentence: "Because the split between humans and chimpanzees occurred relatively recently, their genes have not had much time to acquire many genetic differences."***

Caption Question Fig. 8
strepsirrhines

Figure 8 The bonobo is slightly smaller than the chimpanzee. Like the chimpanzee, it is structurally and behaviorally similar to humans.

Chimpanzees and their close relatives, the bonobos, are also knucklewalkers. They have well-developed communication systems, such as body positions and gestures, and social behavior, and they live in a wide variety of habitats. They are more like humans in their physical structure and behavior than any other primates are. The bonobo, shown in **Figure 8,** is slightly smaller than the chimpanzee. It was once called the "pygmy chimpanzee," but it now is considered a separate species.

Humans are included in the great ape family. They are then classified in a separate subcategory of hominids called hominins. **Hominins** are humanlike primates that appear to be more closely related to present-day humans than they are to present-day chimpanzees and bonobos. Though many species of hominins have existed on Earth, only one species—the group to which you belong—survives today. The diagram in **Figure 9** illustrates evolutionary relationships among primates. D

Primate Evolution

Most primates today are arboreal. Prehensile tails, long limbs, binocular vision, brachiation, and opposable digits are traits that help them take full advantage of their forest environments.

Arboreal adaptation Some scientists suggest that primates evolved from ground-dwelling animals that searched for food in the top branches of forest shrubbery. They then evolved into additional food-gathering niches in trees. For example, the flexible hand with its opposable digits evolved not to grasp tree branches but to catch insects. Other scientists suggest that the rise of flowering plants provided new niche opportunities, and that arboreal adaptations allowed primates to take advantage of the fruits and flowers of trees.

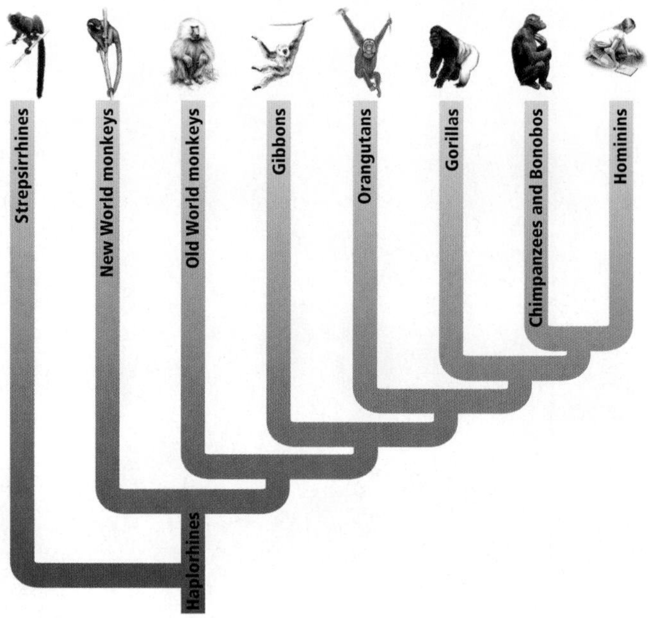

S

Figure 9 This branching diagram illustrates the diverging pattern of primate evolution.
Interpret *Which primate was the earliest to diverge?*

Content Background

Real-World Connection Bonobos, numbering fewer than 20,000 today, face extinction as a result of human activities. Natives onced lived in harmony with the bonobos. However, warfare forced the natives deeper into the forest where they cut down the trees in which bonobos lived. In addition to destroying the bonobo habitat, the natives, who were hard-pressed to find food, started to eat bushmeat. *Bushmeat* is a term that refers to wildlife species that are used for meat though not traditionally considered game animals.

D **Primate ancestors** Genetic data suggest that the first primates probably lived about 85 mya, when dinosaurs still roamed Earth. However, the earliest primate fossils do not appear in the fossil record until the beginning of the Eocene epoch, about 60 mya. One of the earliest fossil primates, called *Altiatlasius* (al tee aht lah SEE us), was a small, nocturnal animal that ate insects and fruits using its hands and feet for grasping. It might have resembled the tiny tree shrew in **Figure 10,** but it had some features similar to those of lemurs today. Learn more about the early evolution of primates in **Data Analysis Lab 1.**

Diverging primates Lemurlike primates were widespread by about 50 mya, and many species existed on all continents except Australia and Antarctica. Sometime around 50 mya, and possibly earlier, the anthropoids diverged from the tarsiers; this might have occurred in Asia, where the tarsiers are found today. The earliest anthropoids leaped less and walked more than the strepsirrhines and tarsiers, but they were still tiny and their brains were still small. By the end of the Eocene, 30–35 mya, the anthropoids had diverged and spread widely.

Displacement Many early strepsirrhines appear to have become extinct by the end of the Eocene. This might have been caused by a change in climate. Many major geological events took place at the end of the Eocene and temperatures became cooler. Or, it could have been caused by the divergence of the anthropoids. The anthropoids of this time generally were larger and had bigger brains than the strepsirrhines did. Thus, the anthropoids might have outcompeted some of the strepsirrhines for resources. This idea is supported by the observation that today, the nocturnal strepsirrhines do not interact with the diurnal anthropoids when the habitats of these two groups overlap.

Figure 10 The earliest primate ancestor might have looked like this tree shrew.

DATA ANALYSIS LAB 1

Based on Real Data*

Interpret Scientific Illustrations

When did early primate lineages diverge?

The fossil record for primate evolution is sparse. In the simplified primate evolutionary tree at right, the green diagram shows the present divergence according to known fossils. The red diagram shows the time line with presumed fossils filling the gaps. Use the diagrams to answer the following questions.

Think Critically

1. **Summarize** why lemurs, lorises, and bushbabies are considered descendants of the earliest primates.
2. **Extrapolate** how far back the divergence of the lemurs might have occurred.
3. **Infer** whether tarsiers are more closely related to apes or to lemurs.

Data and Observations

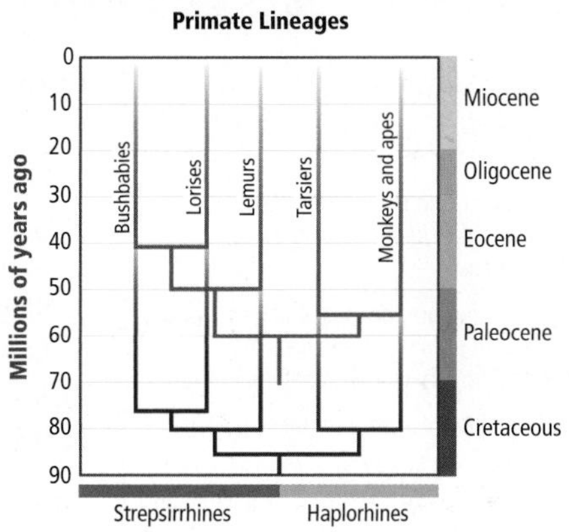

*Data obtained from: Martin, Robert D. 2003. Paleontology: combing the primate record. *Nature* 422: 388–391.

Research Citation

Prior Knowledge Educational research indicates that students will retain more information that is presented to them when they can make connections to prior knowledge or experiences they have had outside the classroom. By referring to what students have previously learned in Chapter 14, as suggested in the *About the Lab* text, you can help them make these connections. (Stanic and Kilpatrick, 1989)

Research bibliography on pages 32T–34T

D Develop Concepts

OL Discuss Have a student read the paragraph under the heading *Primate ancestors.*

ASK STUDENTS: ***What primate characteristics would be present in the fossils of early primates that would indicate that the animals lived in trees?*** The fossils might show opposable digits for climbing and grasping and a prehensile tail.

DATA ANALYSIS LAB 1

About the Lab

- The purpose of the lab is to show the present understanding of primate divergence in relation to current hypotheses that are based on the incomplete fossil record.
- Students might encounter problems understanding the superimposed diagrams. Point out that the red one is based on what is known and the green one is based on what is expected to be found at a later date.
- Point out that the K-T boundary represents the end of the Cretaceous period and the beginning of the Tertiary period 65 million years ago.
- Also see Murphy, et al. 2001. Resolution of the early placental mammal radiation using bayesian phylogenetics. *Science* 294: 2348–2351.

Think Critically

1. The bushbabies, lorises, and lemurs were first to diverge from the ancestral primates.
2. 80 million years, according to the shadow diagram
3. apes

Formative Assessment

Evaluation

ASK STUDENTS: ***What are the characteristics shared by all primates?*** mobile limb structure, opposable first digit, binocular vision, color vision, well-developed brain, reduced reproductive rate ***Why is binocular vision a useful adaptation for primates?*** It allows good depth perception and three-dimensional vision, which are useful for moving through trees and catching moving prey.

Remediation If students are unable to recall primate characteristics, have them use their textbooks to make a list of the characteristics in their journals. For each characteristic, have students define new terms and give an example of the characteristic in a primate other than humans.

Monkeys The end of the Eocene also saw the appearance of the monkeys. Early monkeys had larger brains than their anthropoid ancestors did, and their eyes were more forward-looking. Their snouts were less pointed and they relied less on smell. Scientists hypothesize that the New World monkeys diverged from the line that gave rise to the Old World monkeys sometime between 35 and 25 mya in Africa. While the Old World monkeys continued to evolve in Africa, the New World monkeys developed distinct characteristics in South America. By this time, Africa and South America had separated into two continents. How, then, did the New World monkeys arrive in South America?

Journey to South America Many scientists hypothesize that the New World monkeys evolved from an isolated group of ancestral anthropoids that somehow drifted to South America from Africa, perhaps on rafts of vegetation and soil, much like how the ancestors of lemurs might have drifted to Madagascar from the African mainland. Some scientists suggest that the New World monkeys might have diverged from the anthropoid lineage and made their journey millions of years earlier, when sea levels were lower and the continents were closer.

VOCABULARY

ACADEMIC VOCABULARY

Diverge
to become different in character or form
Their ideas diverged so much that they could not come to an agreement.

Aegyptopithecus In Africa and Asia, anthropoids continued to evolve. Many anthropoid fossils have been found at a site in present-day Egypt called the Fayum Basin. Now a desert, the Fayum was predominantly tropical when dozens of anthropoid species lived there 36–31 mya. The largest among them was *Aegyptopithecus* (ee gypt oh PIH thuh kus), often called the dawn ape. Some scientists hypothesize that this arboreal animal, which was about the size of a domestic cat, was ancestral to the apes. It might have been part of the anthropoid line that split from the Old World monkeys and might have given rise to orangutans, gorillas, chimpanzees, and humans.

Section 1 Assessment

Section Summary

- All primates share certain anatomical and behavioral characteristics.
- Primates include lemurs, New World monkeys, Old World monkeys, apes, and humans.
- Strepsirrhines are the most primitive living lineages of primates to evolve. They diverged from haplorhines before 55 mya.
- Anthropoids diverged from tarsiers by 50 mya.
- New World monkeys are the only nonhuman primates in the Americas.

Understand Main Ideas

1. MAIN Idea **List** four characteristics that are representative of most primates that lead paleoanthropologists to conclude that primates share a common ancestry.
2. **Describe** how the characteristics of primates make them well-adapted for an arboreal lifestyle.
3. **Diagram** the evolutionary relationships of primates.
4. **Compare and contrast** major primate groups.

Think Critically

5. **Hypothesize** how the breakup of Pangaea might have contributed to the evolutionary history of primates.

MATH in Biology

6. Assume that life on Earth began 3.5 billion years ago. To the nearest percent, how much of this time have anthropoids been living?

Section 1 Assessment

1. possible answers: manual dexterity, binocular vision, mobile arms, relatively large brains
2. Mobile limbs and grasping hands are useful for moving through tree branches. Binocular vision helps gauge the distance to the next branch. Producing only one or two offspring makes it easier to move around.
3. The first primate may have appeared about 85 mya. From a common ancestor, the New World monkeys diverged from the Old World monkeys and the rest of the anthropoid lineage about 30 to 35 mya.
4. Answers will vary, but should include a description of the strepsirrhines and the haplorhines, including the anthropoids.
5. Isolation allowed New World monkeys to evolve independently of other primate groups.
6. 50 million/3.5 billion × 100 = 1.43 percent

Assessment Online Quiz

Reading Preview

Essential Questions

- What are the features of hominoids and hominins?
- How can hominoid evolution be traced from *Proconsul* to *Homo*?
- What are the similarities between the various australopithecine species?

Review Vocabulary

savanna: a flat grassland of tropical or subtropical regions

New Vocabulary

hominoid
bipedal
australopithecine

g Multilingual eGlossary

R Hominoids to Hominins

MAIN Idea Hominins, a subgroup of the hominoids, likely evolved in response to climate changes of the Miocene epoch.

Real-World Reading Link Have you ever tried to put together a puzzle that is missing some of its pieces? Human evolution is like that puzzle. Scientists who try to understand how humans evolved are slowed by the holes in the fossil record. Recent advances in genetics and molecular biology have helped, but the puzzle that is human evolution remains only partially assembled.

Hominoids

Hominoids (HAH mih noydz) include all nonmonkey anthropoids—the living and extinct gibbons, orangutans, chimpanzees, gorillas, and humans. The fossil transition from early anthropoid to ape is not clear; very few fossils from the late Oligocene epoch exist. The earliest hominoid fossils appear in the fossil record only about 25 mya, at the beginning of the Miocene epoch. These hominoids retained some ancestral primate features. For example, most had bodies adapted for brachiation. There is evidence that they had relatively large brains and had shoulders and hips that moved freely, and some might even have had the ability to stand on two legs.

Connection to Chemistry Scientists use fossils to help them determine when ancestral hominoids diverged into the hominoids that exist today. However, because the fossil record for hominoids is so sparse, scientists also turn to biochemical data to help them with this task. By comparing the DNA of living hominoid species, researchers conclude that gibbons likely diverged first from an ancestral anthropoid, followed by orangutans, gorillas, chimpanzees and bonobos, and finally, humans. **Figure 11** shows the potential divergence of these species. Chimpanzees and bonobos are the closest living relatives to humans. All three share at least 96 percent of their DNA sequences.

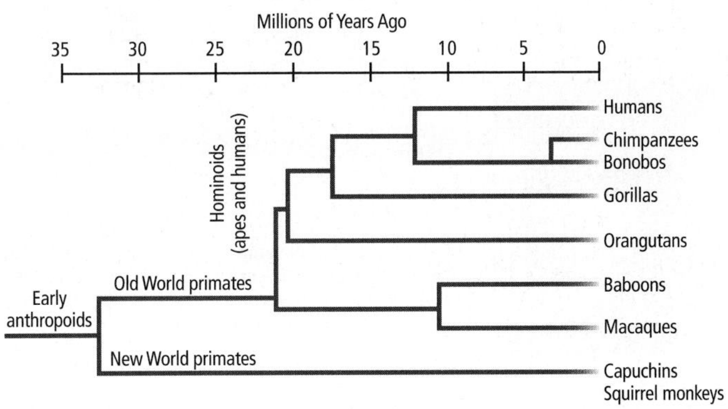

S

Figure 11 Orangutans, gorillas, bonobos, and chimpanzees all diverged from an ancestral anthropoid.

Section 2

MAIN Idea BL OL AL

Hominoids to Hominins

SAY TO STUDENTS: Hominoid *is a term that includes the Asian apes, African apes, and hominins. Hominins, which include modern humans, evolved after the apes.*

ASK STUDENTS: ***What characteristics evolved in hominoids that made them different from other primates and led to the evolution of hominins?*** Possible answers include greater manual dexterity, increased brain size, and bipedal locomotion.

R Reading Strategy EL BL OL

Assessment Preview Before students read Section 2, have them read the section assessment questions.

SAY TO STUDENTS: ***As you read this section, keep the section assessment questions in mind to help you identify the most important information.***

S Skill Practice BL OL AL **Visual Literacy**

Direct students' attention to Figure 11.

ASK STUDENTS: ***Which hominoid shares the lowest percentage of its DNA sequences with humans? Explain.*** Because orangutans diverged first, some 20 million years ago, they should have the most genetic differences from humans.

Demonstration

OL AL Hominoid Characteristics

On the board, list and illustrate hominoid characteristics. If possible, find and reproduce a graph that shows the ratio of brain size relative to body size for several mammalian groups. Est. time: 10 min

Differentiated Instruction

English Learners When assigning the Reading Strategy activity described on this page, pair students who share the same first language. These students can discuss the section assessment question in their first language, allowing them to understand some of the concepts before reading the section.

For more tips, see pages 14T–15T.

D Develop Concepts

Integrate Geography Africa first became connected to Eurasia around 18 million years ago, causing major geological upheavals by pushing up some of the world's youngest mountain ranges, including the Pyrenees and the Alps, as well as the mountains and rift valleys of East Africa. During the Kisingiri volcano eruption, whole populations of *Proconsul* were killed.

Writing Support

BL OL AL COOP LEARN

Technical Writing Have students work in small groups to research additional information about a fossil hominoid from Europe or Asia. Ask them to write a summary describing the hominoid and present it to the class.

W Writing Support

OL **Journal Writing** Have students study Figure 13.

ASK STUDENTS: ***How do you think our knowledge of human origins has changed over the past 150 years? Write your ideas in your journal.*** Read the journal entries and share a few with the whole group, or ask volunteers to read their entries aloud.

Concepts in Motion

The Interactive Timeline

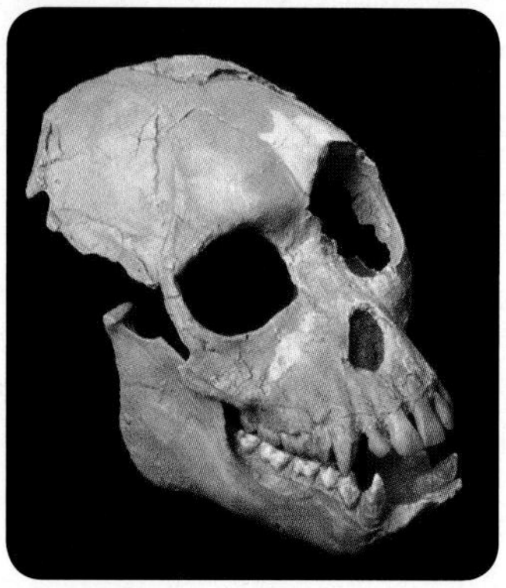

■ **Figure 12** *Proconsul* was an early, small-brained hominoid that might have been a human ancestor.

Hominoid characteristics Hominoids are the largest of the primates, and they have the largest brain size in relation to their body size. They tend to have broad pelvises, long fingers, no tail, and flexible arm and shoulder joints. They also have semi-upright or upright posture, and, except for hominins, their arms are longer than their legs. Their teeth are less specialized than those of other animals, and their molars have a distinctive pattern that scientists use to distinguish hominoid fossils from other primate fossils.

Hominoid biogeography During the Miocene epoch (24–5 mya), the world's climate became warmer and drier. As a result, tropical rain forests in Africa began to shrink. Many new animals, including new hominoids, evolved as they adapted to the changing environments. Between about 23 and 14 mya, perhaps as many as 100 hominoid species existed. Early hominoids were more diverse than the modern apes, and they migrated from Africa to Europe and Asia.

Proconsul The best-known hominoid fossils, and some of the oldest, are those from the genus *Proconsul*. **Figure 12** shows a fossil skull of one *Proconsul* species discovered by Mary Leakey in Kenya in 1948. This *Proconsul* species generally had the smallest brains of the hominoids. Most had freely moving arms and legs, and while they lived predominantly in trees, some might have had the ability to walk upright. Some scientists think that this *Proconsul* species is a human ancestor, but others suggest that one of the European hominoids—whose fossils are in some ways more humanlike than *Proconsul*—might have returned to Africa at the end of the Miocene and given rise to the human line. D

Hominins

The lineage that most likely led to humans split off from the other African apes sometime between 8 and 5 mya. The hominins include humans and all their extinct relatives. These extinct relatives are more closely related to humans than to chimpanzees. The time line in **Figure 13** highlights some important hominin discoveries.

W

■ **Figure 13**
Hominin Evolution
Discoveries have shaped our understanding of how *Homo sapiens* evolved from hominoids.

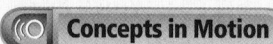

Concepts in Motion
The Interactive Timeline

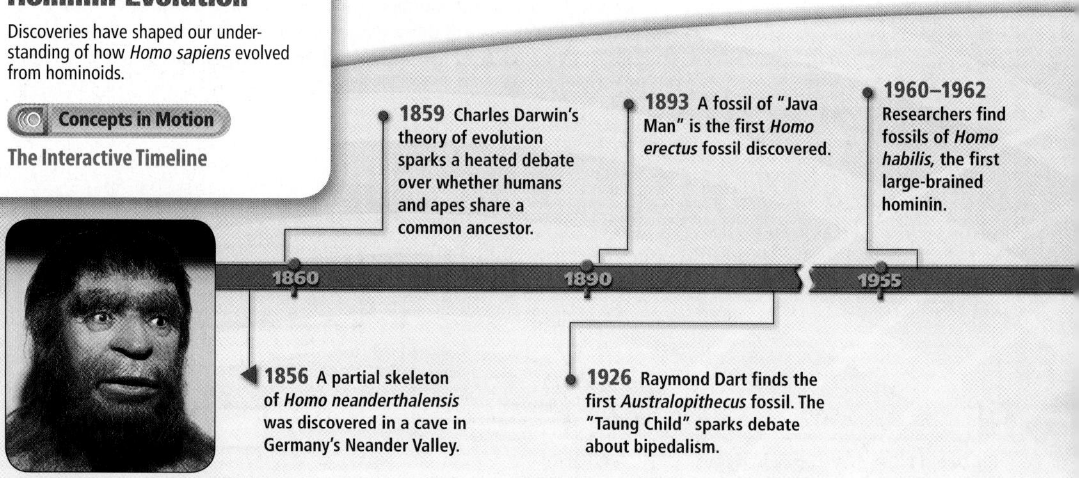

1859 Charles Darwin's theory of evolution sparks a heated debate over whether humans and apes share a common ancestor.
1893 A fossil of "Java Man" is the first Homo erectus fossil discovered.
1960–1962 Researchers find fossils of Homo habilis, the first large-brained hominin.
1860
1890
1955
1856 A partial skeleton of Homo neanderthalensis was discovered in a cave in Germany's Neander Valley.
1926 Raymond Dart finds the first Australopithecus fossil. The "Taung Child" sparks debate about bipedalism.

Content Background

Teacher FYI The *Proconsul* skull Mary Leakey unearthed would be the first of many discoveries she would make in Africa. In 1959, she discovered a hominid skull, which she reconstructed from hundreds of fragments. Now classified as *Australopithecus boisei,* this skull revealed the great antiquity of hominids in Africa. Previously, scientists had thought that humans evolved only a few hundred thousand years ago. *Australopithecus bosei* was dated to 1.75 million years ago, radically changing the time line of human evolution.

Chimpanzee	Hominin
Skull attaches posteriorly	Skull attaches inferiorly
Spine slightly curved	S-shaped spine
Arms longer than legs and used for walking	Arms shorter than legs and not used for walking
Long, narrow pelvis	Bowl-shaped pelvis
Femur angled outward	Femur angled inward

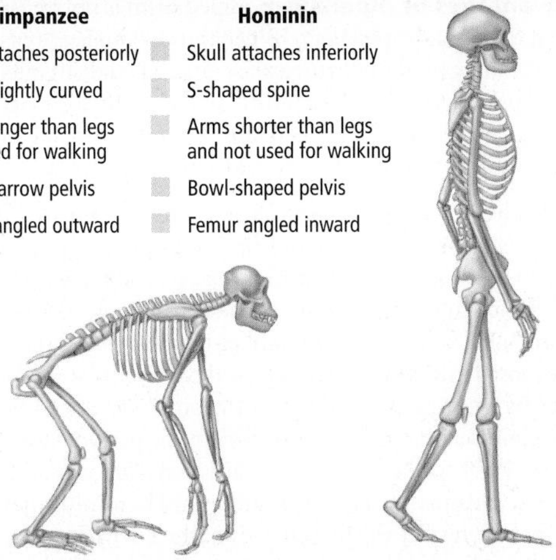

■ **Figure 14** A comparison between chimpanzee and hominin skeletons illustrates evolutionary changes leading to bipedalism.
Observe and Infer ***What differences in the lengths of the arms and the legs do you detect?***

S

D **Hominin characteristics** Hominins have bigger brains than other hominoids, with more complexity in parts of the brain where high-level thought occurs. The hominin face is thinner and flatter than those of other hominoids. Hominin teeth are also smaller. With lengthened thumbs and more flexible wrists, hominins have high manual dexterity. Hominins are also **bipedal,** which means that they can walk upright on two legs.

Examine **Figure 14,** which illustrates anatomical differences in a quadruped and a biped. When becoming bipedal, hominins developed a fully upright stance, shortened arms, restructured pelvic bones and foot bones, and a change in the position of the head on the spinal cord. In quadrupedal animals, or those that walk on all four limbs, the foramen magnum—the hole in the skull where the spine extends from the brain—is located at the back of the skull. In hominins, it is positioned at the base of the skull. S

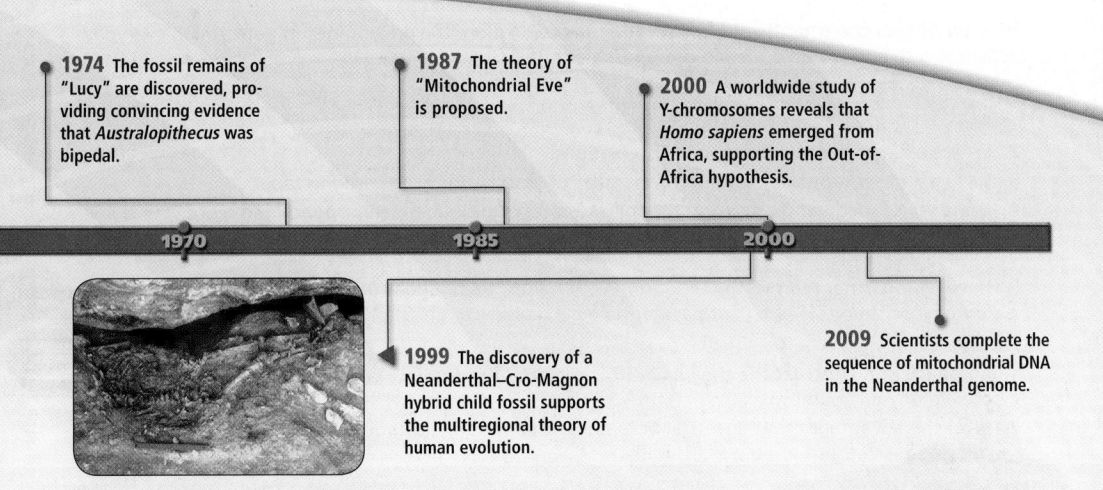

1974 The fossil remains of "Lucy" are discovered, providing convincing evidence that *Australopithecus* was bipedal.

1987 The theory of "Mitochondrial Eve" is proposed.

2000 A worldwide study of Y-chromosomes reveals that *Homo sapiens* emerged from Africa, supporting the Out-of-Africa hypothesis.

1970 1985 2000

1999 The discovery of a Neanderthal–Cro-Magnon hybrid child fossil supports the multiregional theory of human evolution.

2009 Scientists complete the sequence of mitochondrial DNA in the Neanderthal genome.

Demonstration

BL OL AL Bipedalism Show the class a human skull and point out the foramen magnum. Use a ruler or pointer to show how the location of the foramen magnum at the base of the skull indicates that the individual stood upright and was bipedal. Then place the ruler or pointer at the back of the skull to demonstrate how the location of the foramen magnum indicates that the individual would have been quadrapedal. Est. time: 5 min

S Skill Practice

BL OL

Recognize Cause and Effect

After students have studied Figure 14, have them explain the effect of evolving an S-shaped spine.
An S-shaped spine allows an upright stance not afforded by a straight spine, such as those seen in the chimpanzee and gorilla.

D Develop Concepts

BL OL AL

Clarify a Misconception

Some students might think that modern humans evolved from apes.
ASK STUDENTS: ***Does the theory of evolution imply that humans evolved from apes?*** Apes and humans share a common ancestor. Humans did not evolve from modern apes; rather, modern humans and modern apes evolved from a common ancestor that had some ape characteristics and some human characteristics.

S Skill Practice

BL OL Sketch

SAY TO STUDENTS: ***Based on your reading, make a sketch of your conception of a hominin. Below your sketch, write a description of the hominin you drew.***

■ **Caption Question Fig. 14** The arms of the hominin are shorter in relation to its legs than those of the chimpanzee.

D Develop Concepts

EL BL OL AL COOP LEARN

Think-Pair-Share Have students read the information on this page and think about what it means in terms of the evolution of hominins. Tell them to quietly share what they have learned with a partner, determine whether they agree, and discuss their conclusions.

MiniLab 1

? Inquiry MiniLab

For a lab worksheet, use your eTeacherEdition Online.

RUBRIC A rubric for evaluating MiniLabs is found on your eTeacherEdition Online.

Est. Time 15 min

Alternative Materials a watch with second hand

Safety Precaution Approve lab safety forms before work begins.

Teaching Strategies
- Have students work in pairs.
- Encourage students with taped hands to find creative ways to complete the tasks.

Analysis
1. More time and effort is needed to complete each task when the thumb is taped to the hand.
2. An opposable thumb makes tasks much easier and require less time to complete.

LabManager™

Customize this lab with the LabManager™ CD-ROM.

Reading Check Advantages: easier travel; see farther; use of hands. Disadvantages: bigger target for predators; requires more energy.

D **Disadvantages of bipedalism** Bipedalism is not necessarily more efficient than quadrupedalism. Bipedal individuals are easier for predators to see, they might not run as fast, and bipedalism puts greater strain on the hips and back. Also, standing upright defies gravity and therefore requires more energy. Why, then, did hominins become bipedal when their ancestors were so well adapted to life in the trees?

Advantages of bipedalism There is no single answer to the question of why bipedalism developed. Bipedalism could have been selected for because it uses less energy than walking on all fours over long distances. Also, standing upright could have made it easier to see food sources. Walking upright for long distances might also have reduced the total area of the body exposed to sunlight and increased the area exposed to cooling winds.

One hypothesis explaining bipedalism is based on the idea that the African landscape was changing during the period when hominins evolved. Many scientists suggest that bipedalism was an adaptation to the new environment. The most successful hominins may have been those that evolved at the boundaries of the environments. Bipedalism would have allowed them to carry objects while walking through the forest, and to see above tall grasses to find food and avoid predators.

Another hypothesis, based on fossils of *Ardipithecus ramidus*, suggests that bipedalism evolved due to social structure. Fossils indicate that a social structure existed in which males cooperated with females to raise offspring. Males may have traveled through the forest to find food for their offspring. Bipedalism would have allowed *Ar. ramidus* to keep hands free while traveling with food or other objects.

Reading Check **Summarize** the advantages and disadvantages of bipedalism.

MiniLab 1

Observe the Functions of an Opposable Thumb

? Inquiry MiniLab

How do opposable thumbs aid in everyday tasks? Explore the advantages of performing everyday activities with and without the aid of opposable thumbs.

Procedure
1. Read and complete the lab safety form.
2. Create a data table to record your observations.
3. Have a partner tape your thumbs to the sides of your hands with **masking tape.**
4. Using your taped hands, perform the following tasks: pick up a **pen or pencil** and write your name on a **piece of paper,** tie your **shoelaces,** and open a **closed door.** Have your partner use a **stopwatch** to time each task.
5. Have your partner remove the tape from your hands, then repeat the activities in Step 4 with the use of your thumbs. Have your partner time each task.

Analysis:
1. **Compare and contrast** the time and effort required to complete each task with and without the aid of your thumbs.
2. **Infer** the advantages that ancestral primates with opposable thumbs would have had over competitors without opposable thumbs.

Content Background

Teacher FYI Bipedalism resulted in a change in body proportions. Gorillas walk on all fours; therefore, all four limbs support their body mass. As a result, a gorilla's upper limbs account for about 15 percent of its body mass, while its lower limbs account for about 18 percent of its body mass. In contrast, the lower limbs in humans, who walk upright, account for about 35 percent of their body mass, while the upper limbs account for only about 8 percent of their body mass.

Hominin fossils Bipedalism evolved before many other hominin traits, and it is often used to identify hominin fossils. The earliest fossils of species that show some degree of bipedalism are 6–7 million years old. Evidence of true bipedalism has been suggested by the fossilized remains of *Ar. ramidus* and the australopithecines (aw stray loh PIH thuh seens).

Australopithecines lived in the east-central and southern parts of Africa between 4.2 and 1 mya. They were small—the males were only about 1.5 m tall—and they had apelike brains and jaws. However, their teeth and limb joints were humanlike.

The Taung child Anthropologist Raymond Dart (1893–1988) identified the first australopithecine fossil, the "Taung child," in Africa in 1926. He called the species *Australopithecus africanus,* meaning "southern ape from Africa." *A. africanus* likely lived between 3.3 and 2.3 mya. The placement of the foramen magnum in the skull of the Taung child, shown in **Figure 15,** convinced Dart that *A. africanus* was bipedal. Not everyone agreed, because *A. africanus* had a small brain. Some scientists thought that larger brains evolved before bipedalism. The question continued to be debated for many years, even after the discovery of other African australopithecine fossils such as *A. bosei* and *A. robustus,* which indicated bipedalism and small brains.

Lucy In 1974 in Kenya, anthropologist Donald Johanson discovered an australopithecine skeleton that helped resolve the debate. Lucy is one of the most complete australopithecine fossils ever found. She was a member of the species *A. afarensis,* which lived between 4 and 2.9 mya.

Lucy was about the size of a chimpanzee. She had the typical australopithecine skull and small brain, and her arms were still somewhat long in proportion to her legs. She also had finger bones that were more curved than those of modern humans, which indicates that she was capable of arboreal activity. However, her hip and knee joints were W humanlike. It was clear that she walked upright. A few years later, Mary Leakey uncovered further evidence that australopithecines were bipedal C when she discovered fossilized australopithecine footprints. Lucy's skeleton and the footprints of her relatives are illustrated in **Figure 16.**

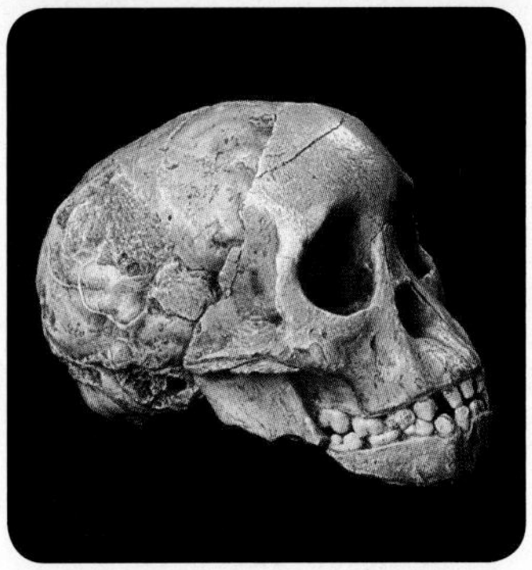

■ **Figure 15** The Taung child skull convinced Raymond Dart that *A. africanus* walked upright.

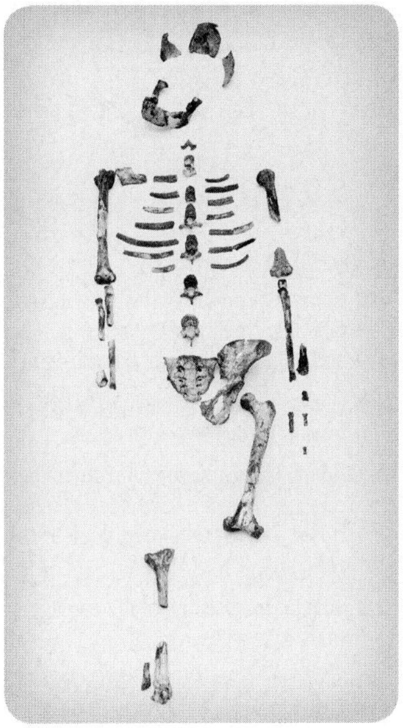

■ **Figure 16** Fossilized footprints indicate that Lucy was bipedal. Though incomplete, this skeleton of Lucy indicates that *A. afarensis* had a small brain but also had the ability to walk upright.
Infer *what bones scientists would examine to determine if Lucy walked upright.*

W Writing Support

AL Persuasive Writing Anthropologists known as lumpers focus on common characteristics in different fossils and attribute differences to diversity within the group. In contrast, anthropologists known as splitters focus on the differences and are more likely to assign a fossil to a different species based on these differences. Johanson, who classified Lucy as a separate species, is a splitter. Have students research Lucy and write a position that either supports or rejects Johanson's classification as a separate species.

C Critical Thinking

OL AL Hypothesize
SAY TO STUDENTS: ***Lucy walked upright about 3.2 mya, but hominins did not begin to walk long distances until about 2 mya. Suggest a reason that it took more than 1 million years before hominins began to walk upright for long distances.*** Possible answers: environmental conditions did not favor long walks, the hominin muscular and skeletal systems did not yet permit long treks.

Develop Concepts

OL AL Scaffolding
ASK STUDENTS: ***Into which group of primates are the monkeys and apes placed?*** anthropoids ***How do hominins differ from anthropoids?*** larger frontal lobes, flatter faces, smaller teeth, and increased manual dexterity ***Which was probably the first group of hominins?*** australopithecines ***Contrast the brain cases of anthropoids and hominins.*** hominins: foramen magnum in the bottom of the skull; anthropoids: foramen magnum in the back of the skull ***Infer what this meant for hominins.*** Hominins walked bipedally.

■ **Caption Question Fig. 16** pelvis, femurs, skull (foramen magnum)

Content Background

Teacher FYI Lucy was so named because a popular Beatles song that contained the name was playing in the camp where the anthropologists were first examining the fossil. The well-preserved fossilized footprints in Figure 16 are known as the Laetoli footprints and extend about 25 meters along the ground. The footprints were made possible by a volcanic eruption that spewed a layer of fine ash on the ground. Apparently, a light rain followed, turning the ash into a cementlike substance. Two hominins left their footprints in the ash, which was covered up by another volcanic eruption. Anthropologists uncovered the footprints in 1976.

? Inquiry BioLab

The lab at the end of the chapter can be used at this point in the lesson.

D Develop Concepts

AL Active Research Have students further research the classification of *Australopithecus* and *Paranthropus* species. When they have completed their research, have them present their findings to the class in the form of possible cladograms.

Formative Assessment

Evaluation To evaluate the third objective for this section, ask students to write a paragraph that compares *A. afarensis* and *A. africanus.* Both are bipedal australopithecines, but *A. afarensis* was more apelike and likely spent some time in trees. It had a shorter stature and smaller brain. *A. africanus* evolved about 3.3 to 2.3 mya.

Remediation Have students review the section and then create a table comparing *A. afarensis* and *A. africanus.*

VOCABULARY

WORD ORIGIN

Australopithecine
from the Latin word *australis,* meaning *southern,* and the Greek word *pithekos,* meaning *ape.*

Mosaic pattern Like other hominin fossils, Lucy and her relatives show a patchwork of human and apelike traits. In this way, they follow a mosaic pattern of evolution. Mosaic evolution occurs when different body parts or behaviors evolve at different rates. For example, hominins developed the ability to walk upright nearly two million years before they developed modern flat faces and larger brains.

Hominin evolution Within the last 30 years, scientists have discovered many more early hominin fossils. Some defy characterization and have led to new genus designations. Scientists have estimated that *Kenyanthropus platyops* (ken yan THROH pus • PLAT ee ops), for example, lived between 3.5 and 3.2 mya. Some scientists think that *K. platyops,* which means "flat-faced man," represents a completely new hominin genus.

Paranthropus There is also confusion about where *A. bosei* and *A. robustus* fit in the classification of hominins. Traditionally, these two species have been classified as robust forms of australopithecines, distinguished from the smaller, more slender forms by their size and muscular jaws. Today, many scientists prefer to put these primates in a separate genus called *Paranthropus.* Paranthropoids, which thrived between 2 and 1.2 mya, were an offshoot of the human line that lived alongside human ancestors but were not directly related. D

Overlapping hominins However they are classified, these robust hominins appear to have lived alongside some of the slender australopithecines. They might have overlapped, for example, with *A. garhi,* an African australopithecine that was discovered in 1999. The illustration of the evolution of hominins is more like a bush than a tree. Many species lived successfully for years, often overlapping with earlier species and then—for unknown reasons—became extinct. By 1 mya, all australopithecines had disappeared from the fossil record. The only hominin fossils found after that time belong to the genus *Homo.*

Section 2 Assessment

Section Summary

- Hominoids are all of the apes, including gibbons, orangutans, gorillas, chimpanzees, and humans and their extinct relatives.
- Several species of hominins appear in the fossil record.
- Hominins include humans, australopithecines, and other extinct species more closely related to humans than to chimpanzees.
- Bipedalism was one of the earliest hominin traits to evolve.

Understand Main Ideas

1. MAIN Idea **Summarize** how the climate of the Miocene epoch impacted the evolution of hominins.
2. **Describe** characteristics unique to hominoids.
3. **Describe** characteristics unique to hominins.
4. **Outline** hominoid evolution from *Proconsul* to *Homo.*
5. **Compare** australopithecine species.

Think Critically

6. **Discuss** Do you think hominins would have evolved if the climate had not changed during the Miocene epoch? Why?
7. **Classify** If you found a primate skeleton with arms shorter than legs, in what general category would you place it?

Section 2 Assessment

1. Grasses evolved on the savanna as forests were reduced. The new environment led to a radiation of hominins.
2. large body sizes, largest absolute and relative brain sizes among the primates, unique molar teeth, lack tails
3. bipedalism, larger brains, position of foramen magnum
4. Student answers might vary, but should indicate that *Proconsul* is one of the oldest hominoid fossils and is thought to be a human ancestor. Hominins including the various genera and species in the "hominin bush" are represented by several important fossils including the Taung child and Lucy. Students should include the genera *Paranthropus* and *Homo* in their answers.
5. *A. afarensis* was a small australopithecine that had a relatively small brain, but was bipedal. *A. africanus* was a later bipedal species that had a bigger brain.
6. Most students will indicate that hominoids would not have evolved if there had not been adaptation to the new environment.
7. hominin

Assessment Online Quiz

Reading Preview

Essential Questions

- How can the species in the genus *Homo* be described?
- What is the Out-of-Africa hypothesis?
- What are the similarities and differences between Neanderthals and modern humans?

Review Vocabulary

mitochondrion: an organelle found in eukaryotic cells containing genetic material and responsible for cellular energy

New Vocabulary

Homo
Neanderthal
Cro-Magnon

g Multilingual eGlossary

Human Ancestry

MAIN Idea **Tracing the evolution of the genus *Homo* is important for understanding the ancestry of humans, the only living species of *Homo*.**

Real-World Reading Link Have you ever heard anyone use the term "cave man" in an insulting way? Unfortunately, this term is used sometimes to indicate brutish behavior. However, the people who lived in caves 40,000 years ago were very much like modern humans. Their art was beautiful, and their tools were sophisticated.

R The Genus *Homo*

The African environment became considerably cooler between 3 and 2.5 mya. Forests became smaller in size, and the range of grasslands was extended. The genus ***Homo,*** which includes living and extinct humans, first appeared during these years. Although the fossil record is lacking fossils, many scientists infer that they evolved from an ancestor of the australopithecines.

Homo species had bigger brains, lighter skeletons, flatter faces, and smaller teeth than their australopithecine ancestors. They are also the first species known to control fire and to modify stones for tool use. As they evolved, they developed language and culture.

***Homo habilis* used stone tools** The earliest known species that is generally accepted as a member of the genus *Homo* is *Homo habilis,* called "handy man" because of its association with primitive stone tools. This species lived in Africa between about 2.4 and 1.4 mya. **Figure 17** shows a scientific illustrator's idea of what *H. habilis* might have looked like.

H. habilis possessed a brain averaging 650 cm^3, about 20 percent larger than that of the australopithecines. It also had other *Homo* species traits, including a smaller brow, reduced jaw, flatter face, and more humanlike teeth. Like australopithecines, it was small, long-armed, and seems to have retained the ability to climb trees. Other *Homo* species might have coexisted with *H. habilis,* among them a species called *Homo rudolfensis.* Because few fossils of *H. rudolfensis* have been found, its exact relationship to the rest of the *Homo* line is uncertain.

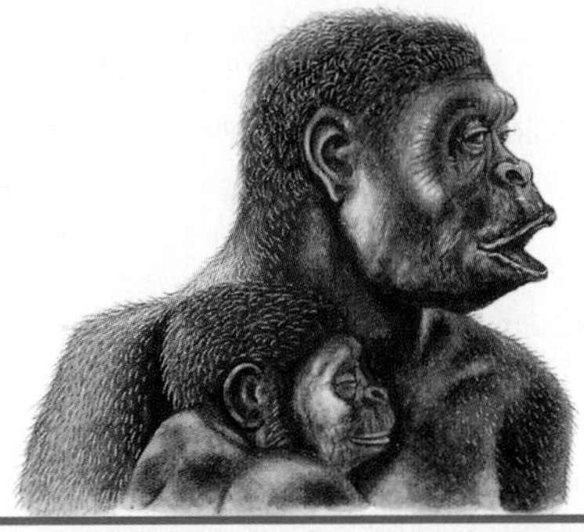

Figure 17 Scientific illustrators use fossils and their knowledge of anatomy to create drawings of what *H. habilis* might have looked like.

Section 3

MAIN Idea

BL OL AL The Genus *Homo*
ASK STUDENTS: ***What is the scientific name for humans?*** *Homo sapiens* Inform students that the genus to which humans belong has a single living species, but anthropologists have found evidence of several other extinct species that they classify in the genus. Point out that new fossils are being found in Africa, Asia, and Europe that extend and refine scientific understanding on an almost-weekly basis.

R Reading Strategy

EL BL OL Take Notes Tell students that this section contains information, including important dates, about several species that belong to the genus *Homo.* Have them take notes as they read by putting information into three columns labeled *Species, Dates,* and *Description.*

Develop Concepts

EL BL OL AL COOP LEARN

Time Line Have students work in pairs to create time lines for the information presented in this section. Time lines should include approximate beginning and ending dates for each species. Students may also make sketches and notes above and below their time lines.

Demonstration

BL OL AL Tool Users Show students photographs of the sharp stone tools that have been found with *H. habilis* fossils and describe how these tools were used. For example, sharp tools may have been used to cut meat from the bones of animals for food. Est. time: 10 min

Differentiated Instruction

Below Level The way in which you assess students at the conclusion of the chapter may need to be modified to accommodate students who perform below level. Allow these students to give their answers orally or dictate to a scribe if they struggle with putting their answers into writing.

For more tips, see pages 14T–15T.

S Skill Practice

OL AL Discuss

SAY TO STUDENTS: ***Scientists use models and drawings like the ones shown in Figure 18 to infer what extinct hominins looked like. How might reconstructions and artists' renditions vary?*** Answers will vary. Explain to students that careful research and data collection is done to make sure reconstructions are realistic. However, differences in the interpretation of the data might exist.

MiniLab 2

Inquiry MiniLab

For a lab worksheet, use your eTeacherEdition Online.

RUBRIC A rubric for evaluating MiniLabs is found on your eTeacherEdition Online.

Est. Time 25 min

Additional Materials copies of small world maps with numerical longitude and latitude axes

Safety Precaution Approve lab safety forms before work begins.

Teaching Strategy Discuss with students why hominin fossils are difficult to find. For instance, consider the sheer number of potential sites around the world.

Analysis

1. after 2 million years ago; Eurasia
2. *H. erectus* and *H. neanderthalensis*; *H. sapiens* and *H. neanderthalensis*. Overlapping suggests that the species co-existed.

LabManager™

Customize this lab with the LabManager™ CD-ROM.

■ **Figure 18** Models of nonliving species can be created from fossil remains. *H. ergaster* appeared in the fossil record about 1.8–1.3 mya.

Homo ergaster **migrated** Within about 500,000 years of the appearance of *H. habilis,* another *Homo* species, *Homo ergaster,* emerged with an even larger brain. *H. ergaster,* illustrated in **Figure 18,** appeared only briefly in the fossil record, from about 1.8 to 1.3 mya. *H. ergaster* was taller and lighter than *H. habilis,* and had longer legs and shorter arms. Its brain averaged 1000 cm^3, and it had a rounded skull, reduced teeth, and what many scientists think was the first human nose (with the nostrils facing downward). S

Tools Carefully made hand axes and other tools associated with *H. ergaster* fossils suggest to some scientists that *H. ergaster* was a hunter, but others think that *H. ergaster* was primarily a scavenger and used the tools to scrape the meat off scavenged bones.

MiniLab 2

Explore Hominin Migration

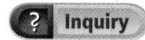

Inquiry MiniLab

Where did early hominins live? Scientists carefully record the locations where fossils are found. The latitude and longitude coordinates represent the known geographic points of each *Homo* species' range.

Procedure

1. Read and complete the lab safety form.
2. Plot the following fossil sites on the map that your teacher gives you. Use a different color for each species. When you are finished, lightly shade in the approximate boundaries.
   H. habilis (2.4–1.4 million years ago): 37°E: 4°S, 36°E: 3°N, 36°E: 7°N, 43°E: 8°N
   H. erectus (2 million–400,000 years ago): 112°E: 38°N, 13°E: 47°N, 7°W: 34°N, 112°E: 8°S
   H. neanderthalensis (300,000–200,000 years ago): 8°E: 53°N, 66°E: 39°N, 5°W: 37°N, 36°E: 33°N
   H. sapiens (195,000 years ago–present): 70°E: 62°N, 24°E: 30°S, 138°E: 34°S, 112°E: 38°N, 99°W: 19°N, 102°W: 32°N

Analysis

1. **Hypothesize** when was the earliest that hominins could have migrated out of Africa. Where did they go? Use the map you made for reference.
2. **Determine** what sets of fossils overlapped in geographic ranges. What does this suggest?

Content Background

Teacher FYI *H. ergaster* represents a major change in the relative sizes of the sexes. Before *H. ergaster* appeared, the male of the species weighed significantly more than the female. For example, a male gorilla weighs about twice as much as a female, and an *A. afarensis* male was 1.5 times heavier than a female. However, such a marked difference in body weight between males and females became significantly reduced with the evolution of *H. ergaster.* Today, an average human male is only about 1.2 times heavier than an average human female.

■ **Figure 19** *H. erectus* might have lived in caves, made tools, and used fire.
Explain *some of the advantages* **H. erectus** *would have over* **H. ergaster.**

Migration Both scavenging and hunting are associated with a migratory lifestyle, and *H. ergaster* appears to have been the first African *Homo* species to migrate in large numbers to Asia and possibly Europe, perhaps following the trail of migrating animals. The later Eurasian forms of *H. ergaster* are called *Homo erectus.* Because *H. ergaster* shares features with modern humans, scientists hypothesize that *H. ergaster* is an ancestor of modern humans.

***Homo erectus* used fire** *H. erectus,* illustrated in **Figure 19,** lived between 1.8 million and 400,000 years ago and appears to have evolved from *H. ergaster* as it migrated out of Africa. While some scientists consider *H. ergaster* and *H. erectus* a single species, *H. erectus* appears to have evolved traits that the early African *H. ergaster* species did not have. Members of this species seem to have been more versatile than their predecessors, and they adapted successfully to a variety of environments. *H. erectus* includes "Java Man," discovered in Indonesia in the 1890s, and "Peking Man," discovered in China in the 1920s.

In general, *H. erectus* was larger than *H. habilis* and had a bigger brain. It also had teeth that were more humanlike. Brain capacity ranged from about 900 cm^3 in early specimens to about 1100 cm^3 in later ones. It was as tall as *H. sapiens,* but it had a longer skull, lower forehead, and thicker facial bones than either *H. ergaster* or *H. sapiens.* It also had a more prominent S browridge. Evidence indicates that *H. erectus* made sophisticated tools, used fire, and sometimes lived in caves.

***Homo floresiensis*—"The Hobbit"** In 2003 a curious set of fossils were discovered on the Indonesian island of Flores. These fossils, which are about 18,000 years old, are heavily debated in the scientific community. Some scientists think they might represent a species called *Homo floresiensis* (flor eh see EN sus). Others think that the fossils belong to early human dwarfs and do not warrant classification as a D separate species. *H. floresiensis,* nicknamed "The Hobbit," was only about 1 m tall when fully grown. While it had brain and body proportions like all the australopithecines, primitive stone tools were found with its fossils. In 2007 a study showed that *H. floresiensis* had apelike wrist bones—further support for its status as a separate species. You can compare *H. floresiensis* and *H. sapiens* skulls in **Figure 20.**

Reading Check What are the evolutionary relationships among *H. habilis, H. ergaster,* and *H. erectus?*

S

■ **Figure 20** Scientists are debating whether *H. floresiensis* is a new species. The *H. floresiensis* skull on the left is smaller than the human skull on the right.
Infer *what this skull comparison might predict about the evolutionary relationship between* **H. floresiensis** *and* **H. sapiens.**

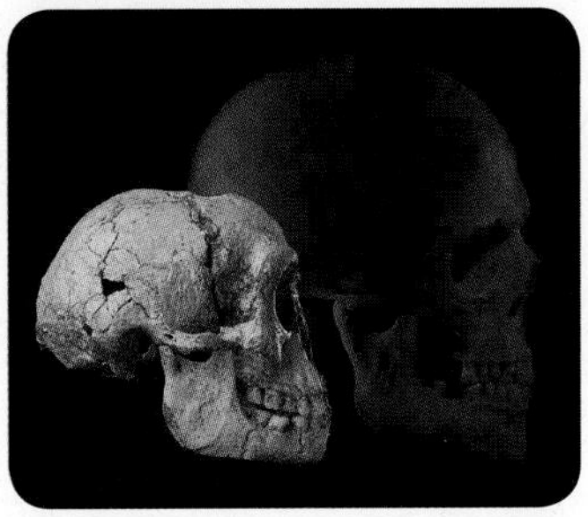

S Skill Practice

BL Use Math Skills

ASK STUDENTS: ***If* Homo erectus *diverged from* Homo ergaster *1.8 mya and died out possibly about 400,000 years ago, about how long did the species exist?*** 1,400,000 years

D Develop Concepts

OL AL Integrate Geography

ASK STUDENTS: ***Which continent was home to* H. floresiensis?** Asia, which includes Flores Island of Indonesia

S Skill Practice

BL OL AL Visual Literacy

Point out to students the size difference in the *Homo floresiensis* skull and the *Homo sapiens* skull in Figure 20.

TELL STUDENTS: ***Because* H. floresiensis *appears to have been so small, scientists and the media referred to the fossil as "the hobbit" when it was discovered.***

■ **Caption Question Fig. 19** Possible answer: The bigger brain of *H. erectus* allowed more complex thoughts.

Reading Check All are members of the genus *Homo. H. habilis* was the first member of the genus. *H. ergaster* and *H. erectus* are both thought to have evolved from *H. habilis.* Some scientists consider *H. ergaster* and *H. erectus* to be part of the same species.

■ **Caption Question Fig. 20** Because the species was on a remote island, *H. floresiensis* probably did not come into contact with modern humans.

Research Citation

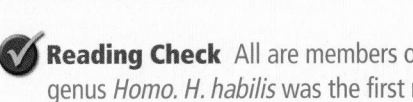

Skill Practice Educational research indicates that students will be more likely to master a skill if ample opportunities for practice are provided. The Skill Practice described on this page will help students to master math skills and will also illustrate a valuable connection between math and science. (Anderson, 1995)

Research bibliography on pages 32T–34T

D Develop Concepts

BL OL

Clarify a Misconception

SAY TO STUDENTS: ***Describe a typical Neanderthal.*** Students might think that Neanderthals were brutish, subhuman animals. Inform students that Neanderthals were thick-boned with large browridges and prominent noses. Their brains were larger than those of modern humans. Neanderthals probably used spoken language, possessed social skills, and were not the brutes often portrayed in movies.

Critical Thinking

AL **Infer**

SAY TO STUDENTS: ***Paleontologists are often finding older fossils of hominins. Suggest a reason for this.*** According to the law of superposition, younger fossils should be found first. Paleontologists are finding older fossils in rock strata that are lower, and therefore older than those previously examined.

W Writing Support

BL COOP LEARN

Technical Writing Have students work in pairs to create a three-column brochure about Neanderthals. The brochure should include information about physical features, places in which Neanderthals lived, and their daily lives.

Reading Check *H. heidelbergensis* is thought to be the link between *H. ergaster* and *H. sapiens.*

***Homo heidelbergensis*—traits** The transition from *H. ergaster* to modern humans appears to have occurred gradually. Numerous transitional fossils have been found that display a mixture of *H. ergaster* and *H. sapiens* traits. These fossils are often categorized as *Homo heidelbergensis,* but some scientists put them in the category *Homo sapiens.* These humans generally had larger brains and thinner bones than *H. ergaster* did, but they still had browridges and receding chins.

Reading Check **Relate** *H. heidelbergensis* to *H. sapiens.*

***Homo neanderthalensis* built shelter** A distinct human species called *Homo neanderthalensis,* or the **Neanderthals,** evolved exclusively in Europe and Asia about 200,000 years ago, likely from *H. erectus* or a *Homo* intermediary. Neanderthals were shorter but had more muscle mass than most modern humans do. Their brains were sometimes even larger than the brains of modern humans, though the brains might have been organized in different ways. Neanderthals had thick skulls, bony browridges, and large noses. They also had a heavily muscled, robust stature, as illustrated in **Figure 21.** Evidence of heavy musculature appears in the extremely large muscle attachments and the bowing of the long bones.

Neanderthals lived near the end of the Pleistocene ice age, a time of bitter cold. Their skeletons reflect lives of hardship; bone fractures and arthritis seem to have been common. There is evidence that they used fire and constructed complex shelters. They hunted and skinned animals, and it is possible that they had basic language. There is also some evidence that they cared for their sick and buried their dead.

Are Neanderthals our ancestors? In some areas of their range, particularly in the Middle East and southern Europe, Neanderthals and modern humans overlapped for as long as 10,000 years. Some scientists suggest that the two species interbred. However, some studies suggest that Neanderthals were a distinct species that likely did not contribute to the modern human gene pool. As new information is discovered, scientists continue to debate the interactions between Neanderthals and modern humans. Neanderthals became extinct about 30,000 years ago.

Figure 21 *H. neanderthalensis* had much thicker bones than modern humans and a pronounced browridge. Neanderthals were hunters who used fire and tools.

Content Background

Teacher FYI Neanderthal fossils were first discovered in 1856 in the Neander Valley in Germany. Neanderthals lived throughout Europe and also in Asia and the Middle East.

Emergence of Modern Humans

The species that displaced the Neanderthals, *Homo sapiens*, is characterized by a more slender appearance than all other *Homo* species. They have thinner skeletons, rounder skulls, and smaller faces with prominent chins. Their brain capacity averages 1350 cm^3. *H. sapiens* first appeared in the fossil record, in what is now Ethiopia, about 195,000 years ago. These early *H. sapiens* made chipped hand axes and other sophisticated stone tools. They appear to have had the ability to use a range of resources and environments, and at some point they began migrating out of Africa. **Table 2** compares modern humans with other *Homo* species.

Table 2 **Characteristics of the *Homo* species** Concepts in Motion Interactive Table

Species	Skull	Time in fossil record	Characteristics
Homo habilis	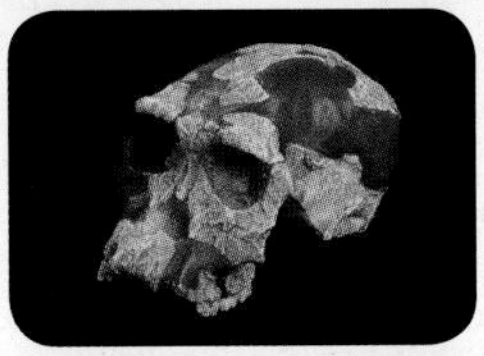	2.4–1.4 million years ago	• Average brain had a capacity of 650 cm^3 • Used tools
Homo ergaster	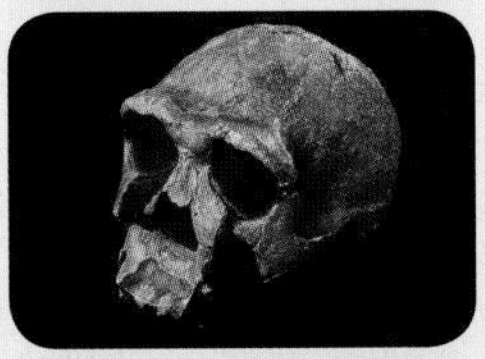	1.8–1.2 million years ago	• Average brain had a capacity of 1000 cm^3 • Had thinner skull bones • Had humanlike nose
Homo erectus		1.8 million–400,000 years ago	• Average brain had a capacity of 1000 cm^3 • Had thinner skull bones • Used fire
Homo neanderthalensis	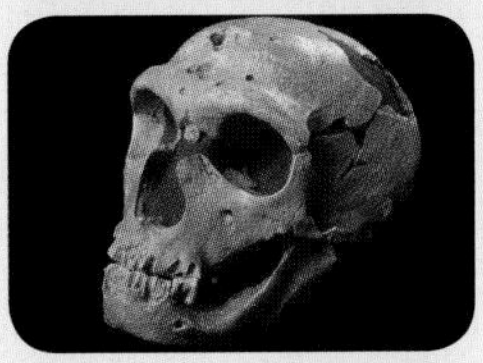	300,000–200,000 years ago	• Average brain had a capacity of 1500 cm^3 • Buried their dead • Possibly had a language
Homo sapiens		195,000 years ago to present	• Average brain has a capacity of 1350 cm^3 • Does not have browridge • Has a small chin • Has language and culture

Develop Concepts

OL AL Scaffolding

ASK STUDENTS: ***What is the genus to which all hominins belong?*** *Homo* ***Why was* H. habilis *given its scientific name?*** Evidence indicates that *H. habilis* made and used tools, and the scientific name means "handy man." ***What evidence do we have that* H. erectus *may not have become extinct 400,000 years ago, but their descendants might have survived until about 12,000 years ago?*** *H. erectus* lived in Java 50,000 years ago, and recent evidence found on the island of Flores indicates that it might have lived there even longer. ***What are some differences between Neanderthals and modern humans?*** Neanderthals seem to be a separate species with different DNA than modern humans. However, they did use fire, hunt animals, and bury their dead. Some evidence suggests there was spoken language.

Concepts in Motion

Interactive Table

"The whole purpose of education is to turn mirrors into windows."

—Sydney J. Harris

S Skill Practice

BL OL Visual Literacy Have students look at Figure 22 and determine which hominin species coexisted. Point out that only one hominin species currently exists.

D Develop Concepts

OL AL

Activate Prior Knowledge

Inform students that the Y chromosome does not usually undergo genetic recombination.

ASK STUDENTS: ***Why is the Y chromosome useful in tracing the human family tree?*** Genes on the Y chromosome are usually passed unchanged in males from one generation to the next. Any changes arising from mutations are easy to identify and track. Inform students that scientists have examined the patterns of gene variations in the Y chromosomes of more than 1000 European males. Nearly 80 percent shared a single pattern, suggesting that modern Europeans have a common ancestor.

Develop Concepts

AL Activate Prior Knowledge

ASK STUDENTS: ***Hypothesize what role mitochondrial DNA plays in mitochondria.*** This DNA codes for proteins that are involved in the stages of cellular respiration that occur within the mitochondria.

Reading Check The evidence consists of studies of mitochondrial DNA and Y chromosomes in contemporary humans.

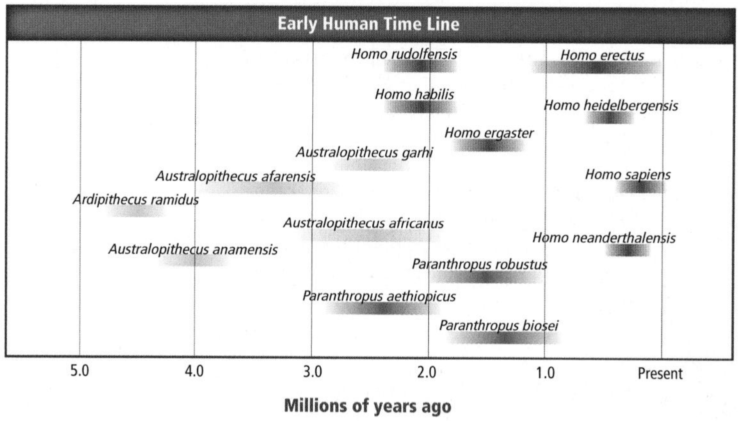

Figure 22 The period of existence of several early hominins overlapped until about 30,000 years ago.

S

Out-of-Africa hypothesis The world's population 200,000 years ago looked significantly different from how it does today. It was inhabited by a morphologically diverse genus of hominins, including primitive humans, Neanderthals, and modern humans, as illustrated in **Figure 22.** By 30,000 years ago, however, only modern humans remained. Some scientists propose that these modern humans evolved from several dispersed populations of early *Homo* species at the same time in different areas of the world. According to this multiregional evolution model, modern races of humans arose in isolated populations by convergent evolution.

Most scientists explain the global dominance of modern humans with the African Replacement model or, more commonly, the Out-of-Africa hypothesis. According to this hypothesis, which was first proposed by Christopher Stringer and Peter Andrews of the British Museum of Natural History in 1988, modern humans evolved only once, in Africa, and then migrated to all parts of the world, eventually displacing other hominins.

"Mitochondrial Eve" The Out-of-Africa hypothesis was supported by mitochondrial DNA analysis of contemporary humans in the early 1990s. Mitochondrial DNA changes very little over time, and humans living today have nearly identical mitochondrial DNA. Researchers Allan Wilson and Rebecca Cann of the University of California, Berkeley, reasoned that the population with the most variation should be the population that has had the longest time to accumulate diversity. This was exactly what they found in the mitochondrial DNA of Africans. Because mitochondrial DNA is inherited only from the mother, this analysis suggested that *H. sapiens* emerged in Africa about 200,000 years ago from a hypothetical "Mitochondrial Eve."

Later, work by other scientists studying DNA sequences in the male Y chromosome yielded similar results. While some scientists think that a single movement of only a few hundred modern humans ultimately gave rise to the world's current population, others think the process occurred in phases, with some interbreeding among the species that humans displaced. D

Study Tip

Discussion Group Discuss with your classmates what you've learned about human evolution. What characteristics of early hominins have surprised you or your classmates?

Reading Check **Describe** evidence in support of the Out-of-Africa hypothesis.

Demonstration

The Advent of Culture Archaeologists look mainly at a society's art and burial practices to find clues about its culture. *Homo sapiens* first started producing art around 40,000 years ago. Show students pictures of the decorative artifacts and cave drawings, similar to those in Figure 23, that first appeared around this period. Inform them where these were discovered and include any other pertinent information.
Est. time: 10 min

■ **Figure 23** Cro-Magnons were known for their sophisticated cave paintings, tools, and weapons. The painting on the left was found in Lascaux Cave in France.

The beginning of culture The first evidence of complex human culture appeared in Europe only about 40,000 years ago, shortly before the Neanderthals disappeared. Unlike the Neanderthals, early modern humans expressed themselves symbolically and artistically in decorative artifacts and cave drawings, as illustrated in **Figure 23.** They developed sophisticated tools and weapons, including spears and bows and arrows. They were the first to fish, the first to tailor clothing, and the first to domesticate animals. These and many other cultural expressions marked the appearance of fully modern humans, the subspecies *Homo sapiens.* Some people call them **Cro-Magnons.** They represent the beginning of historic hunter-gatherer societies.

Connection to History Humans continued their migration throughout Europe and Asia. They probably reached Australia by boat and traveled to North America via a land bridge from Asia. From North America, they spread to South America. They adapted to new challenges along the way, leaving behind a trail of artifacts that we study today.

C

Section 3 Assessment

Section Summary

- The genus *Homo* is thought to have evolved from genus *Australopithecus.*
- Of the many species that have existed in the hominin group, only one species survives today.
- The first member of the genus *Homo* was *H. habilis.*
- The Out-of-Africa hypothesis suggests that humans evolved in Africa and migrated to Europe and Asia.
- *H. neanderthalensis* became extinct about 30,000 years ago, and *H. sapiens* moved into those areas inhabited by *H. neanderthalensis* at about the same time.

Understand Main Ideas

1. MAIN Idea **Hypothesize** why only one genus and species remains in the hominin group.
2. **Describe** how *H. habilis* might have lived.
3. **Apply** what you have learned about the Out-of-Africa hypothesis to what you know about the arrival of *H. sapiens* in North America.
4. **Compare and contrast** *H. neanderthalensis* and *H. sapiens.*

Think Critically

5. **Classify** how you would classify a fossil that was found in France and dated at about 150,000 years old if the skull had a thick browridge, but in most other ways appeared human.

WRITING in **Biology**

6. **Hypothesize** the importance of language to the early modern humans and how it might have contributed to their success.

C Critical Thinking

OL AL Infer

SAY TO STUDENTS: ***The Neanderthals disappeared from Europe after the Cro-Magnons arrived. What do you think contributed to the disappearance of Neanderthals?*** Responses will vary. Students might infer that the Cro-Magnons fought with Neanderthals and won, or they might say that Cro-Magnons had more efficient survival skills.

Formative Assessment

Evaluation To determine whether students have met the second objective of the section, ask a series of questions about the Out-of-Africa hypothesis that can be answered with "True" or "False." Sample questions: The Out-of-Africa hypothesis suggests that humans evolved multiple times in many different places. false Ancient human migration patterns support the Out-of-Africa hypothesis. true

Remediation Have students work in pairs to find the information in the text that provides the answers to the questions they missed. Then have students individually write a description in their own words describing the Out-of-Africa hypothesis.

Section 3 Assessment

1. *H. sapiens* might have outcompeted some of the other contemporary species of the genus.
2. Members of *H. habilis* were small and primitive-faced, similar to australopithecines. They constructed tools. They were small and had long arms, which might have helped them climb trees.
3. Once humans migrated from Africa to Asia, they might have followed game across the Bering land bridge into North America.
4. *H. neanderthalensis* appeared fully human but had a large brow-ridge and a stronger and shorter frame than *H. sapiens.* The brain of *H. neanderthalensis* was sometimes larger than that of *H. sapiens.*
5. *H. neanderthalensis*
6. Language is important to communication. It allows people to pass down knowledge to their offspring and to share ideas with each other. Language also provides a sense of identity and leads to the preservation of knowledge in written form.

BioDiscoveries

Purpose

Students will learn that scientists exchange many ideas and hypotheses while doing research on a topic. They will also learn about a possible new species of human called *Homo floresiensis.*
UCP.2, UCP.4, A.2, C.3, G.2

Anticipatory Guide

ASK STUDENTS: ***What is the scientific name for modern humans?*** Homo sapiens ***What is a species?*** A species is a group of organisms that can interbreed and produce fertile offspring.

Background

Scientists think that the organisms evolved on the island of Flores via a process called *insular dwarfing.* Insular dwarfing occurs when animals, usually mammals, are confined to a small environment such as an island. In a place where there are not many resources, a large body that needs many Calories is not an asset, so the animals decline in size over time.

Some scientists have said that the tiny creatures' brains are too small to support the dwarfing hypothesis. They argue that the brains of the "hobbits" are not on a scale with the rest of its body. But a recent study showed that in cases of dwarfing on islands, over time, the brain can shrink more than the body. In order to function, brain cells need more Calories than other body cells. Organisms with fewer brain cells need less food, and that is an advantage in a place where resources are limited.

A New Species... or Something Else?

In 2003, scientists found a partial skeleton and fragments of six or more other skeletons in a cave on the island of Flores, Indonesia. The "hobbits," as the scientists dubbed them, were humanlike beings a little over three feet tall, with heads the size of grapefruits and chimpanzee-sized brains. Tests revealed that the partial skeleton and fragments ranged between 13,000 and 95,000 years old.

These little creatures are the cause of a big disagreement within the scientific community. Since their discovery, some scientists have claimed the "hobbits" are *Homo sapiens*, or modern humans, with a medical condition that caused their diminutive stature. Others insist that they are a new species, *Homo floresiensis.* Scientists on each side are using scientific methods to uncover the truth. Their different interpretations of the data are part of the collaborative scientific process.

Diseased modern humans? Scientists who doubt the "new species hypothesis" proposed several hypotheses to explain the tiny creatures' sizes and other characteristics. Some suggested that the "hobbits" were pygmies who suffered from microcephaly, a rare, sometimes genetic neurological disorder that results in a smaller-than-normal head. Other scientists have hypothesized that the miniature humans had hypothyroidism.

A new species? Most scientists who support the hypothesis that the "hobbits" are the new species *Homo floresiensis* think that they evolved from members of *Homo erectus*, a precursor to modern humans. Some, however, think that the "hobbits" evolved from an even earlier species of human called *Homo habilis.* Once on the island of Flores, scientists think that the organisms evolved to be dwarflike.

Scientists search for fossils at a cave site called Liang Bau on the island of Flores.

Structural differences Both groups of scientists are using the structural data provided by the bone fragments. These include the skull, wrist, foot, and shoulders. As more bone fragments are discovered and studied, more pieces are added to the puzzle.

WRITING in Biology

Peer Review Research the controversial fossils found on Flores. Write an article as though you are one of the researchers. Include your hypothesis, evidence, and conclusions. Submit your article to your classmates for peer review.

WRITING in Biology

RUBRIC Use the modifiable rubric found on your eTeacherEdition Online to assess writing assignments.

Activity

Help students with their research by suggesting possible sources. Scientific journals such as *Nature* and *National Geographic* are good places to start. Typing the words *Homo floresiensis* into a search engine will give students a wealth of research possibilities. Review with students the ways in which they can determine whether online sources are credible and reliable.

WebQuest

BIOLAB

WHAT CAN YOU LEARN ABOUT BIPEDALISM FROM COMPARING BONES?

Background: Humans and chimpanzees have the same number of bones in the same places, but humans walk upright and chimpanzees do not. Can you identify the skeletal features that enable humans to walk upright on two legs? Assume that you are a paleontologist and have been given chimpanzee and human bones to identify and assemble. Then, you receive a third set. How is the mystery skeleton related to the human and chimpanzee skeletons?

Question: *What unique skeletal features did humans evolve to become bipedal?*

Materials

envelopes containing paper bones and clues (2)
paper, pencil, and ruler

Safety Precautions

Procedure

1. Read and complete the lab safety form.
2. Make a data table to help you compare the following characteristics of each of the three fossil sets you will examine: skull, rib cage, pelvis, arms, legs, and feet.
3. Make sure your teacher approves your table.
4. Open envelope #1.
5. Using the clues in your envelope, identify the bones, determine to which species they belong, and write down at least one distinguishing characteristic of each on your data table.
6. Open envelope #2.
7. Using the new set of clues, classify each new bone as chimpanzee, human, similar to both, similar to chimpanzee, or similar to human. Record the data in your table.

Analyze and Conclude

1. **List** features that a scientist might use to determine if a fossil organism was bipedal.
2. **Think Critically** Based on your knowledge, do you think the mystery fossil is bipedal? Why?
3. **Conclude** What organism do you think your mystery bones represent?
4. **Compare** your table with those of other students in the class. Did you arrive at the same conclusions? If not, discuss the differences.
5. **Experiment** Chimpanzees cannot completely straighten—or lock—their knees as humans can and must use more muscles when standing upright. Try standing for 10 s with your knees locked and for 10 s with your knees bent. Describe how your legs feel at the end.
6. **Reason,** from your mystery fossil bones, what it means to say that humans evolved in a mixed, or mosaic, pattern.

WRITING in Biology

Research and discuss why bipedalism is often thought of as an evolutionary compromise. List skeletal injuries that humans suffer as a result of walking upright.

Analyze and Conclude

1. its legs, pelvis, position of foramen magnum, and feet
2. Based on the legs, pelvis, and feet, it is a biped.
3. This fossil represents *Australopithecus afarensis,* Lucy in particular.
4. Students may differ in their interpretations, as scientists often do.
5. This experiment gives students an understanding of why chimpanzees don't stand for long in an upright position.
6. Humans have evolved to have a mixture of some of the traits that different primates have.

BIOLAB

Inquiry BioLab

For a lab worksheet, use your eTeacherEdition Online.

RUBRIC A rubric for evaluating BioLabs is found on your eTeacherEdition Online.

Est. Time 40 min

Safety Precaution Approve lab safety forms before work begins.

Content Background Bipedalism was likely the first hominin trait to appear in our ancestors. It preceded the development of a large brain and other hominin traits. Scientists often use bipedalism as a diagnostic to label a fossil as hominin, and the search for the oldest bipedal hominin is thus a search for humans' oldest ancestor.

Teaching Strategies

- This exercise could be performed individually or in pairs. Compilation of the data table could be a group activity. "Clues" could be read aloud to the class as a group instead of included in the separate envelopes.
- Encourage class discussion about the differences between chimpanzees and humans; discuss the DNA evidence v. observational evidence.

Alternative Teaching Demo Show students pictures of bones from humans, chimpanzees, and Lucy. As a class, have students try to identify which bones belong to which species. Then have students answer the Analyze and Conclude questions.

WRITING in Biology

RUBRIC Use the modifiable rubric found on your eTeacherEdition Online to assess writing assignments.

Chapter 16

Study Guide

ConnectED

Students can use the following to review the chapter.

Review

Vocabulary eGames
Vocabulary eFlashcards
Vocabulary PuzzleMaker

Assessment

Online Quizzes
Online Test Practice
Standardized Test Practice

Use the *ExamView®* *Assessment Suite* CD-ROM to:

- create multiple versions of tests
- create modified tests with one mouse click
- edit existing questions and add your own questions
- build tests aligned with state standards using built-in state curriculum tags
- change English tests to Spanish with one mouse click
- track students' progress using the Teacher Management System

Chapter 16 Study Guide

THEME FOCUS Change The changes that separated hominins from hominoids, such as larger brains and bipedalism, took place over 20–25 million years ago.

BIG Idea **Evolutionary change in a group of small, tree-living mammals eventually led to a diversity of species that includes modern humans.**

Section 1 Primates

opposable first digit (p. 452)
binocular vision (p. 452)
diurnal (p. 452)
nocturnal (p. 452)
arboreal (p. 455)
anthropoid (p. 455)
prehensile tail (p. 456)
hominin (p. 458)

MAIN Idea **Primates share several behavioral and biological characteristics, which indicates that they evolved from a common ancestor.**

- All primates share certain anatomical and behavioral characteristics.
- Primates include lemurs, New World monkeys, Old World monkeys, apes, and humans.
- Strepsirrhines are the most primitive living lineages of primates to evolve. They diverged from haplorhines before 55 mya.
- Anthropoids diverged from tarsiers by 50 mya.
- New World monkeys are the only nonhuman primates in the Americas.

Section 2 Hominoids to Hominins

hominoid (p. 461)
bipedal (p. 463)
australopithecine (p. 465)

MAIN Idea **Hominins, a subgroup of the hominoids, likely evolved in response to climate changes of the Miocene epoch.**

- Hominoids are all of the apes, including gibbons, orangutans, gorillas, chimpanzees, and humans and their extinct relatives.
- Several species of hominins appear in the fossil record.
- Hominins include humans, australopithecines, and other extinct species more closely related to humans than to chimpanzees.
- Bipedalism was one of the earliest hominin traits to evolve.

Section 3 Human Ancestry

Homo (p. 467)
Neanderthal (p. 470)
Cro-Magnon (p. 473)

MAIN Idea **Tracing the evolution of the genus *Homo* is important for understanding the ancestry of humans, the only living species of *Homo*.**

- The genus *Homo* is thought to have evolved from the genus *Australopithecus*.
- Of the many species that have existed in the hominin group, only one species survives today.
- The first member of the genus *Homo* was *H. habilis*.
- The Out-of-Africa hypothesis suggests that humans evolved in Africa and migrated to Europe and Asia.
- *H. neanderthalensis* went extinct about 30,000 years ago and *H. sapiens* moved into those areas inhabited by *H. neanderthalensis* about the same time.

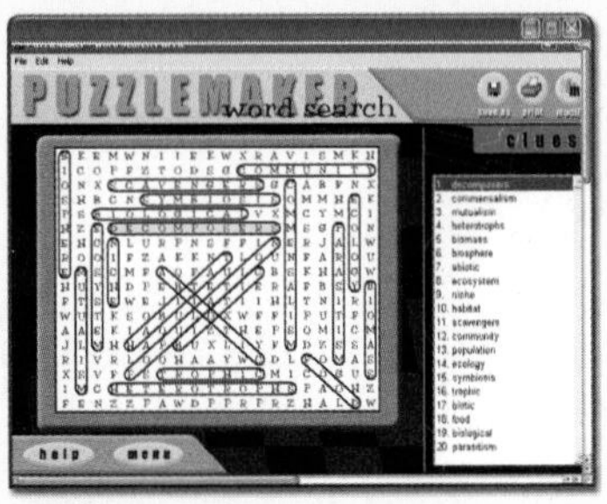

Review **Vocabulary PuzzleMaker**

For additional practice with vocabulary, have students access the Vocabulary PuzzleMaker online.

Review Vocabulary eGames

Section 1

Vocabulary Review

Replace each underlined word or phrase with the correct vocabulary term from the Study Guide page.

1. A fifth limb might be used by a primate to grip a limb while engaged in reaching for and eating food.
2. Primates that are active at night are "wet-nosed" primates.
3. Depth perception evolved as the faces of primates became flattened.

Understand Main Ideas

Use the figure below to answer question 4.

4. Which is the term for the movement demonstrated by this gibbon?
   A. brachiation
   B. knuckle-walking
   C. quadruped movement
   D. upright locomotion
5. Which group was the first to evolve?
   A. African apes
   B. hominins
   C. New World monkeys
   D. Old World monkeys
6. Which adaptation results in a better gripping ability?
   A. complex brain
   B. flexible forelimbs
   C. opposable digits
   D. prehensile tail
7. The first primates most resembled which animal?
   A. gibbon
   B. gorilla
   C. tamarin
   D. lemur

Constructed Response

8. **Open Ended** Describe the usefulness of binocular and color vision.
9. **Short Answer** Which groups of primates make up the anthropoids?

Think Critically

10. **Hypothesize** Why do you think primate fossils have not been found on Antarctica?
11. MAIN Idea Suppose that while on a trip to Brazil, you found a fossil of a primate that closely resembles a squirrel monkey. Into which group of anthropoids would the specimen be placed?

Section 2

Vocabulary Review

Define the following vocabulary terms in complete sentences.

12. australopithecine
13. bipedal
14. hominoid

Understand Main Ideas

15. Which hominin species made the fossilized footprints shown in **Figure 16**?
    A. *A. afarensis*
    B. *A. africanus*
    C. *Paranthropus*
    D. *Proconsul*
16. Which hominoid might be ancestral to apes and humans?
    A. *A. afarensis*
    B. *A. africanus*
    C. *Paranthropus*
    D. *Proconsul*

Assessment

Section 1

Vocabulary Review

1. prehensile tail
2. nocturnal
3. Binocular vision

Understand Main Ideas

4. A
5. C
6. C
7. D

Constructed Response

8. Binocular vision allows depth perception, and color vision provides greater visual acuity. Both are important adaptations for a lifestyle lived in trees.
9. New World monkeys, Old World monkeys, Asian apes, African apes, and hominins

Think Critically

10. Antarctica may have drifted away from the other continents before the evolution of the first primates.
11. New World monkeys

Section 2

Vocabulary Review

12. Australopithecines were small, apelike hominins that lived in Africa between 4.2 and 1 mya.
13. Bipedal is walking upright.
14. Hominoids are all nonmonkey anthropoids.

Understand Main Ideas

15. A
16. D

17. C
18. C

Constructed Response

19. *Paranthropus* might have evolved from an ancestral australopithecine and might not be a direct human ancestor.
20. The foramen magnum is located at the base of the skull in primates that are bipedal. It is located in back of the skull of primates and other vertebrates that are not bipedal.

Think Critically

21. Bipedalism might have been an adaptation to the new savanna environment.
22. Biochemical evidence, such as mitochondrial DNA, is useful in making time lines for divergence because this DNA does not undergo recombination.

Section 3

Vocabulary Review

23. *Homo*
24. Neanderthals
25. *Homo sapiens*

Understand Main Ideas

26. C
27. A
28. A
29. B
30. B

17. Which is the correct sequence of fossils as evidenced by the fossil record?
A. *A. africanus, A. afarensis, Paranthropus, Proconsul*
B. *Proconsul, A. afarensis, A. africanus, Paranthropus*
C. *Proconsul, Paranthropus, A. afarensis, A. africanus*
D. *Paranthropus, Proconsul, A. africanus, A. afarensis*

18. *A. afarensis* was bipedal but exhibited apelike traits. What type of evolutionary pattern might account for this?
A. convergence
B. mosaic
C. divergence
D. coevolution

Constructed Response

19. Open Ended Discuss the debate regarding the classification of *Paranthropus*.

Use the figure below to answer question 20.

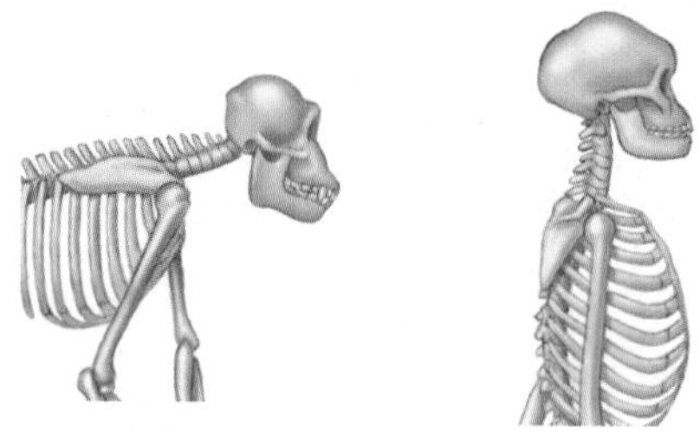

20. Short Answer Describe the relevance of the foramen magnum's location to bipedalism.

Think Critically

21. MAIN Idea Explain how climate change might have contributed to the evolution of bipedalism.

22. THEME FOCUS Change Why is biochemical evidence important in helping scientists learn about the divergence of primate groups?

Section 3

Vocabulary Review

Each of the following sentences is false. Make each sentence true by replacing the underlined word with a vocabulary term from the Study Guide page.

23. The genus *Australopithecus* is thought to be ancestral to the genus *Proconsul*.

24. Cro-Magnons were adapted to cold climates. They eventually were replaced by modern humans.

25. *H. neanderthalensis* is the scientific name for modern humans.

Understand Main Ideas

Use the figure below to answer question 26.

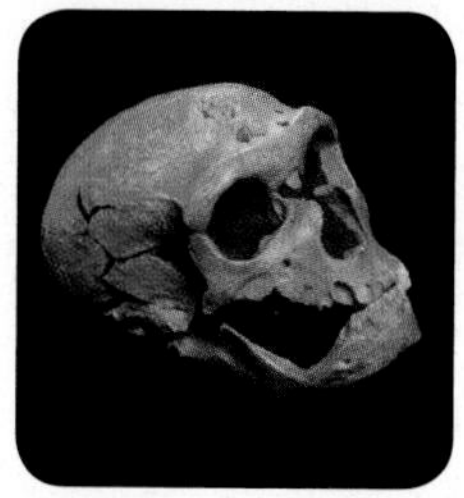

26. The large brain and thickened browridges illustrated by the skull above are characteristic of which species?
A. Cro-Magnons
B. modern *H. sapiens*
C. Neanderthals
D. *Proconsul*

27. The first undisputed member of the hominin group was which of the following?
A. *A. africanus*
B. *H. antecessor*
C. *H. ergaster*
D. *H. habilis*

28. Which hominin was likely the first to migrate long distances?
A. *H. ergaster*
B. *H. antecessor*
C. *H. neanderthalensis*
D. *H. sapiens*

29. Which hominin likely first used fire, lived in caves, and made tools?
A. *H. ergaster*
B. *H. erectus*
C. *H. neanderthalensis*
D. *H. sapiens*

30. *H. heidelbergensis* is generally considered part of which group?
A. Neanderthals
B. *H. sapiens*
C. Cro-Magnons
D. australopithecines

Use the figure below to answer questions 31 and 32.

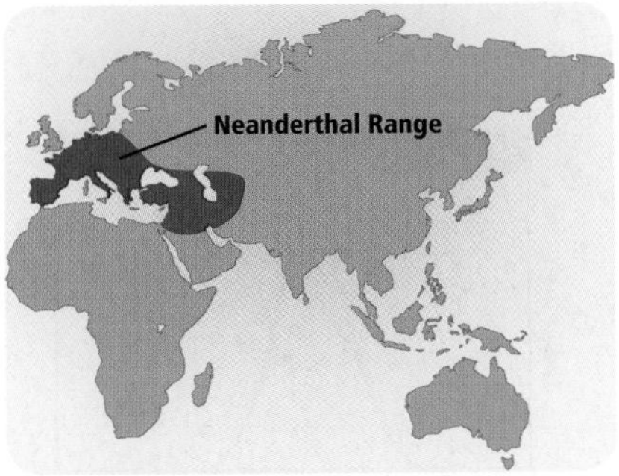

31. The map above represents the geographic range of which species?
A. *Homo erectus*
B. *Homo sapiens*
C. *Homo neanderthalensis*
D. *Homo heidelbergensis*

32. During what time did the species represented on the map live?
A. 300,000–200,000 years ago
B. 100,000–12,000 years ago
C. 2.4–1.4 million years ago
D. 1.8–1.2 million years ago

Constructed Response

33. MAIN Idea Describe the importance of *H. habilis* in human evolution.

34. Short Answer Describe the importance of fire to the migration of early *Homo* species.

35. Open Ended From what you have learned about the evolution of primates, do you think *Homo sapiens,* our species, will continue to evolve? Why?

Think Critically

36. Apply Concepts Explain why mitochondrial DNA instead of nuclear DNA is used to study the evolution of modern humans.

37. Predict If modern humans had not arrived in Europe, do you think Neanderthals would have persisted?

38. Hypothesize How might *H. floresiensis* have coexisted with modern humans?

Summative Assessment

39. BIG Idea Identify three characteristics that modern humans share with other primates, and three that separate them from other primates. Infer why the three that separate humans from other primates are important.

40. WRITING in Biology Write a paragraph to describe what you imagine a day in the life of *A. afarensis* to have been like.

DBQ Document-Based Questions

Scientists generally consider walking, but not running, to be a key trait in the evolution of humans. Like apes, humans are poor sprinters when compared to quadruped animals such as horses and dogs. Unlike apes, but like some quadrupeds, humans are capable of endurance running (ER), running long distances over extended time periods. The graph below compares speed during ER to length of an organism's stride (two steps for a human).

Data obtained from: Bramble, D. and Lieberman, D. 2004. Endurance running and the evolution of *Homo*. *Nature* 432: 345–352.

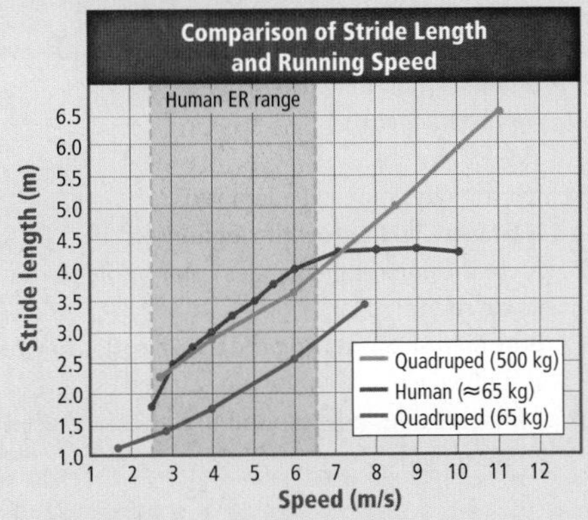

41. During ER, is the stride length of a human more like that of a 65-kg quadruped or a 500-kg quadruped?

42. Is a human more efficient at endurance running than a similar-sized quadruped, such as a cheetah or a leopard? Explain.

31. C
32. A

Constructed Response

33. *H. habilis* was the earliest member of the genus. Several traits, including a larger brain size and smaller teeth, evolved first in this group.
34. The use of fire allowed early humans to extend their range into the cold northern climates. Without fire, they could not have survived the harsh winters of temperate environments.
35. Humans will continue to change, but this might or might not involve changes in gene frequencies.

Think Critically

36. Unlike nuclear DNA, mitochondrial DNA does not vary much over time. Therefore, the changes that occur in mitochondrial DNA can be more easily charted in studies of evolutionary relationships.
37. Answers will vary. Students might suggest that the Neanderthals would not have become extinct without the invasion of modern humans.
38. *H. floresiensis,* because of its small size, might have remained hidden in the rain forest after modern humans arrived on Flores.

Summative Assessment

39. Answers will vary. Possible similarities: opposable digits, long gestation period, reliance on vision. Differences: more complex brain, language and culture, more slender build. Importance: higher level thought processes, increased communication, and quicker and more agile movement.

40. Answers will vary, but encourage imagination.

WRITING in Biology

RUBRIC Use the modifiable rubric found on your eTeacherEdition Online to assess writing assignments.

DBQ Document-Based Questions

Bramble, D. and Lieberman, D. 2004. Endurance running and the evolution of *Homo*. *Nature* 432: 345–352.

41. 500-kg quadruped
42. Yes. Humans have longer legs, so their strides are longer.

Assessment Online Test Practice

Standardized Test Practice

Multiple Choice

1. A
2. B
3. D
4. D
5. A
6. D
7. A

Short Answer

8. The black guinea pig has a genotype of either BB or Bb. If you cross it with a white guinea pig (bb), you can observe whether any of the offspring are white. If any offspring are white, the parent with black fur had a genotype of Bb.

	B	B
b	Bb	Bb
b	Bb	Bb

	B	b
b	Bb	bb
b	Bb	bb

9. The adaptation is mimicry. The feather color pattern of the second bird mimics the pattern of the first bird. The color pattern of the first bird is a selective advantage that warns potential predators not to prey on birds with this color pattern. Presumably potential predators learn not to eat birds with this color pattern because they are poisonous. The similar color pattern of the second bird is a selective advantage also. It misleads potential predators into not preying on birds with this color pattern.
10. According to the multiregional hypothesis, humans evolved in different regions around the world from different populations. The Out-of-Africa hypothesis says that modern humans are descended from a population in Africa. Some members of this population migrated to different places around the world.

Standardized Test Practice

Cumulative

Multiple Choice

1. A scientific understanding of which natural process helped Darwin formulate the concept of natural selection?
   A. artificial selection
   B. continental drift
   C. group selection
   D. plant genetics

Use the diagram below to answer question 2.

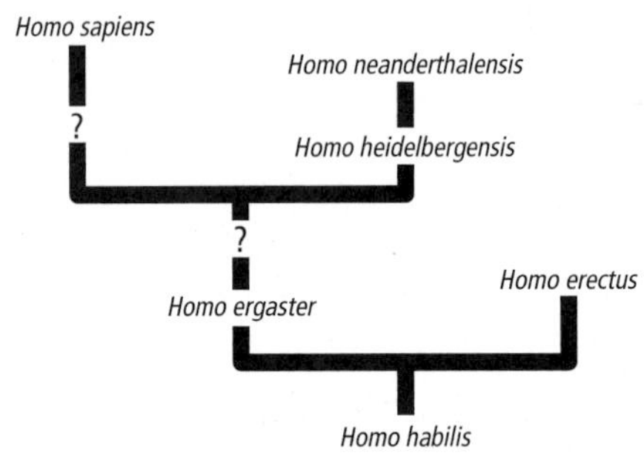

2. According to the diagram of the evolution of genus *Homo*, which is an ancestor of *Homo sapiens*?
   A. *Homo erectus*
   B. *Homo ergaster*
   C. *Homo neanderthalensis*
   D. *Homo rudolfensis*

3. Which is a physiological adaptation?
   A. A beaver's teeth grow throughout its life.
   B. A chameleon's skin changes color to blend in with its surroundings.
   C. A human sleeps during the day in order to work at night.
   D. An insect does not respond to a chemical used as an insecticide.

4. Which process can include the use of selective breeding?
   A. curing a tree of a disease
   B. finding the gene that makes a type of tree susceptible to disease
   C. mapping the genome of a fungus that causes disease in trees
   D. producing trees that resist certain diseases

Use the illustration below to answer question 5.

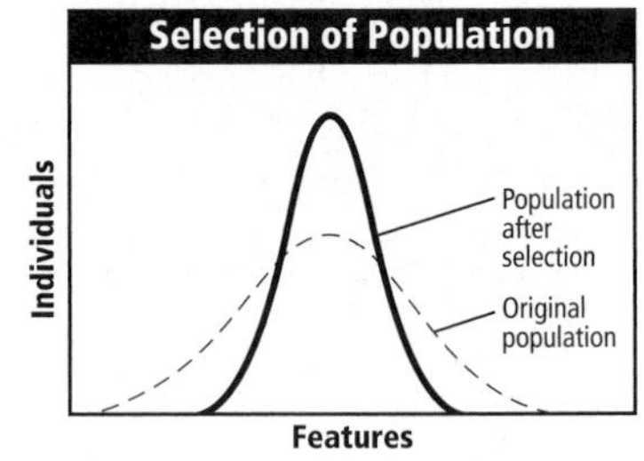

5. Which description fits the graph above?
   A. Average-sized features are selected for in population X.
   B. Larger features are selected for in population X.
   C. Smaller features are selected for in population X.
   D. Average-sized features are selected against in population X.

6. Which sequence correctly traces the order of hominin evolution?
   A. *Australopithecus afarensis* → *Australopithecus africanus* → *Proconsul* → *Homo*
   B. *Australopithecus africanus* → *Australopithecus afarensis* → *Proconsul* → *Homo*
   C. *Homo* → *Australopithecus africanus* → *Australopithecus afarensis* → *Proconsul*
   D. *Proconsul* → *Australopithecus afarensis* → *Australopithecus africanus* → *Homo*

7. Which of the following is NOT a reason why scientists support the endosymbiont theory?
   A. Mitochondria and chloroplasts are found living outside eukaryotic cells.
   B. Mitochondria and chloroplasts reproduce by fission.
   C. The size and structure of mitochondria and chloroplasts is similar to prokaryotic cells.
   D. The genetic material in mitochondria and chloroplasts is circular.

Short Answer

8. The gene that controls the fur color of guinea pigs codes for either dominant black fur (B) or recessive white fur (b). Suppose you want to find the genotype of a black guinea pig. Explain how you would do a test cross. Then use one or both Punnett squares below to show possible test-cross results.

9. A species of bird has a chemical in its tissue that is poisonous to many potential predators. Suppose you find another bird with a coloring pattern similar to the feathers of the first bird. What is this adaptation? Explain its importance.

10. Contrast the multiregional hypothesis and the Out-of-Africa hypothesis for human evolution.

11. Malathion is a pesticide used to control mosquitoes. Suppose a population of mosquitoes develops an ability to survive malathion spraying. How does this phenomenon fit with the ideas of variation and heritability in natural selection?

Use the figure below to answer question 12.

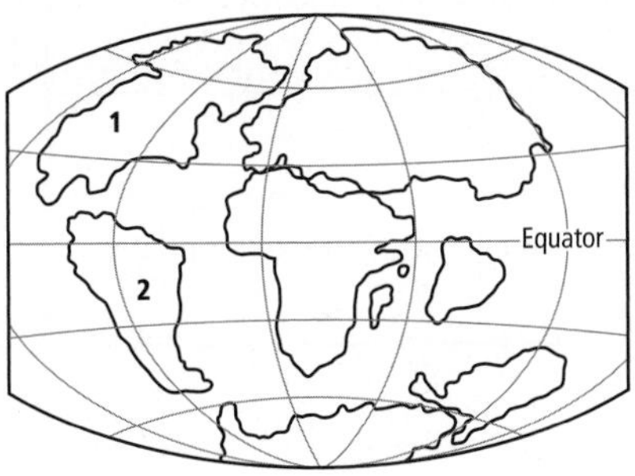

12. Discuss how land species and environments might change if the two numbered continents in the figure collided.

Extended Response

13. Suppose you are explaining human evolution to someone who is unfamiliar with the topic. Hypothesize why *Homo sapiens* is the only surviving member of the human family.

14. Some aggressive bacterial infections are treated with combinations of antibiotics. How would such a treatment affect drug resistance?

Essay Question

"If evolution almost always occurs by rapid speciation in small, peripheral isolates, then what should the fossil record look like? We are not likely to detect the event of speciation itself. It happens too fast, in too small a group, isolated too far from the ancestral range. Only after its successful origin will we first meet the new species as a fossil—when it reinvades the ancestral range and becomes a large central population in its own right. During its recorded history in the fossil record, we should expect no major change."

Gould, Stephen Jay. "Ladders, Bushes, and Human Evolution," *Natural History* 85 (April 1976): 30–31.

Using the information in the paragraph above, answer the following question in essay format.

15. Gould's research in evolution was devoted, in part, to explaining his theory of punctuated equilibrium. In an essay, explain why the fossil record is incomplete.

NEED EXTRA HELP?

If You Missed Question . . .	1	2	3	4	5	6	7	8	9	10	11	12	13	14	15
Review Section . . .	15.1	16.3	15.2	13.1	15.3	16.2	14.2	13.1	15.3	16.3	15.1	14.1	16.3	15.2	15.3

11. The allele for malathion resistance had to be in the population. This is a natural variation in the population and it is heritable. Because of natural selection, this allele becomes more abundant in the population because it contributes to the fitness of the mosquitoes for survival.

12. The joining of the continents will create a land passage between two formerly isolated continents. Land species that have not encountered each other previously will meet. Some land species will expand into new territories and might interbreed with closely related species from the other continent. Some land species might become extinct.

Extended Response

13. There were several other human-like species living at different times, and these species were living in different regions of Earth. *Homo sapiens* might have driven the other species out of existence or might have been more fit to survive. Modern humans ended up spreading or migrating from Africa to different parts of the world.

14. Because the bacteria causing the infection are probably not resistant to all antibiotics, using multiple antibiotics at once could ensure that the infection is stopped without creating a situation where new strains of drug-resistant bacteria are naturally selected.

Essay

15. The fossil record reveals the remains of some of the organisms that lived in the past. Fossilized organisms are useful because they can be compared with organisms living in the present, or with other organisms from the fossil record. Fossil remains can allow scientists to see subtle changes in organisms that happened at certain times during evolutionary history. The problem with the fossil record is that it does not include all organisms that existed. To be preserved as a fossil an organism must have died under particular conditions. Unusual organisms that could be a link between different species are typically not found in the fossil record.

Chapter 17 Organizer:
Organizing Life's Diversity

Essential Questions	National Science Standards	Materials and Planning: Estimated times include cleanup and disposal, but do not include teacher prep time. For cleanup and disposal guidelines, see page 39T.	Est. Time (min)
Section 1 1. What are the similarities and differences between Aristotle's and Linnaeus's methods of classification? 2. Using binomial nomenclature, how are scientific names written? 3. What are the categories used in biological classification?	UCP.1, UCP.2, UCP.4; A.2; C.3, C.5; G.1, G.2, G.3	**Launch Lab,** p. 482: photo of desert organisms, pencil, paper, textbook	20–25
		Demonstration, p. 484: several common plants and animals (or photos of them)	10
		Activity, p. 487: ten different buttons	10
		MiniLab 1, p. 488: one shoe from each student	25
		Demonstration, p. 488: a live example or photograph of an organism from each of the six kingdoms	10
Section 2 1. What are the similarities and differences between species concepts? 2. What are the methods used to reveal phylogeny? 3. How is a cladogram constructed?	UCP.1, UCP.2, UCP.4, UCP.5; A.1, A.2; C.3; E.1, E.2; G.1, G.2, G.3	**Demonstration,** p. 490: two different goldfish in a goldfish bowl or photographs of two different goldfish	5
		Activity, p. 491: textbook	20
		Demonstration, p. 493: broccoli, cabbage, cauliflower, and kale (or photos of each)	10
		Demonstration, p. 495: wall clock, watch	5
		Demonstration, p. 497: tree limb with leaves and branches	5
Section 3 1. What are the major characteristics of the three domains? 2. What are the differences among the six kingdoms? 3. How are organisms classified at the kingdom level?	UCP.1, UCP.2, UCP.4, UCP.5; A.1, A.2; C.1, C.3, C.6; G.1, G.2, G.3	**MiniLab 2,** p. 500: prepared slides of bacteria or photomicrographs of bacteria, compound light microscope	25
		Demonstration, p. 501: living or preserved specimens or photos of several types of fungi	5
		Demonstration, p. 502: examples or photos of plants such as mosses and liverworts, ferns, conifers and their cones, and flowering plants	15
		BioLab, p. 505: paper, pencil, examples of cladograms, photographs of various organisms, books describing characteristics of organisms	90

Suggested Time for Each Lesson

Class	Chapter Opener	Section 1	Section 2	Section 3	Assessment
Basic	45 min	135 min	90 min	90 min	45 min
General	25 min	90 min	65 min	90 min	45 min
Honors	—	10 min	15 min	45 min	20 min

ConnectED

connectED.mcgraw-hill.com

Access interactive learning opportunities and teaching resources using these icons located throughout your StudentWorks™ Plus Online and eTeacherEdition Online.

Chapter 17 Section Resources	Additional Chapter 17 Resources	Technology
FAST FILE Unit 4 Resources: Launch Lab Worksheet* MiniLab Worksheet* Study Guide (English/Spanish)* Section Quick Check **Reading Essentials 17.1** **Science Notebook 17.1*** **FAST FILE Unit 4 Resources:** Study Guide (English/Spanish)* Section Quick Check **Reading Essentials 17.2** **Science Notebook 17.2*** **FAST FILE Unit 4 Resources:** MiniLab Worksheet* BioLab Worksheet* Study Guide (English/Spanish)* Section Quick Check **Reading Essentials 17.3** **Science Notebook 17.3***	**FAST FILE Unit 4 Resources:** Chapter Diagnostic Test Concept Mapping* Real-World Biology Enrichment Chapter Tests A, B, and C **Transparencies:** Bellringer Transparencies* Biology Concepts Transparencies* **Lab Resources:** Laboratory Manual* Probeware Lab Manual* Forensics Lab Manual* Pre-AP Lab Manual* Open Inquiry in Biology* Guided Inquiry in Biology*	**Teaching Tools:** eTeacherEdition Online Classroom Presentation Toolkit CD-ROM* LabManager™ CD-ROM* Video Lab DVD* Virtual Lab CD-ROM* What's BIOLOGY Got To Do With It? StudentWorks™ Plus Online* **Chapter Assessment Tools:** Classroom Presentation Toolkit CD-ROM* *ExamView® Assessment Suite* CD-ROM **Web-Based Resources:** • StudentWorks™ Plus Online • eTeacherEdition Online • Animations* • The Interactive Time Line* • Interactive Tables* • Online Quizzes • Online Test Practice • Standardized Test Practice • Virtual Labs* • Multilingual eGlossary* • Vocabulary eGames* • Vocabulary eFlashcards • WebQuests • Personal Tutors

While all resources listed are appropriate for English learners, the * indicates resources with a strong visual or hands-on component for EL.

Teaching strategies and activities have been coded for differentiated instruction.

AL Activities for students working above grade level	**OL** Activities for students working on grade level	**BL** Activities for students working below grade level	**EL** Activities for English learners (also ELL)	**COOP LEARN** Activities designed for small cooperative group work

CHAPTER 17

Launch Lab
How can desert organisms be grouped?

Inquiry Launch Lab

For a lab worksheet, use your eTeacherEdition Online.

RUBRIC A rubric for evaluating Launch Labs is found on your eTeacherEdition Online.

Est. Time 20–25 min

Additional Materials photo of a desert, such as the photo on this page

Teaching Strategies

- Help students understand that a classification system for living things provides a framework for biologists to study the characteristics, similarities, differences, and relationships between organisms.
- Reinforce the concept that while organisms can be grouped in a variety of ways, some strategies are more effective and provide more useful information than others.

Procedure

1. Read and complete the lab safety form.
2. List the desert organisms in the **photo**.
3. Identify physical characteristics, behaviors, or other factors that vary among the organisms in your list. Choose one factor you can use to sort them into groups.
4. Sort the list based on the factor you selected.
5. Brainstorm a list of desert organisms not shown in the photo. Add each to the appropriate group.

CHAPTER 17

Organizing Life's Diversity

ConnectED

Your one-stop online resource
connectED.mcgraw-hill.com

- Video
- Audio
- Review
- Inquiry
- WebQuest
- Assessment
- Concepts in Motion
- Multilingual eGlossary

Launch Lab

How can desert organisms be grouped?

You might think of a desert as a place without much biodiversity, but a wide variety of species have adaptations for desert life. Some adaptations are useful for grouping these organisms. In this lab, you will develop a system for grouping desert organisms.

For a lab worksheet, use your StudentWorks™ Plus Online.

Inquiry Launch Lab

FOLDABLES®

Make a layered look book Foldable. Label it as shown. Use it to organize your notes about the six kingdoms.

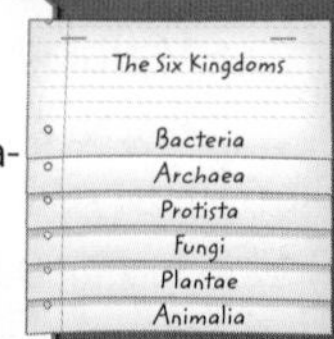

Analysis

1. **Compare and contrast** your grouping strategy with those developed by other students. Students should find both similarities and differences in their grouping strategies.
2. **Determine** What modifications would make your system more useful? Answers will vary, but any modification that eliminates a possible confusion as to why organisms were placed in the same group would be useful.

Differentiated Instruction

Behavior Disorders Prior to labs and other group activities, establish clear rules and expectations for class conduct. Look for and praise positive behaviors. Clear expectations coupled with positive reinforcement will increase the likelihood of compliance from students with behavior disorders.

For more tips, see page 14T–15T.

THEME FOCUS Diversity
Scientists have always searched for ways to classify the biodiversity observed on Earth.

BIG Idea Evolution underlies the classification of life's diversity.

Section 1 • The History of Classification

Section 2 • Modern Classification

Section 3 • Domains and Kingdoms

Introduce the Chapter

Organizing Life's Diversity

ASK STUDENTS: ***What can you tell about the diversity of desert organisms from the photographs on this page?*** Student responses will vary, but may include that there appears to be few organisms that live in the desert. Point out that although a desert might not seem like a suitable environment for life, desert ecosystems are home to many organisms, including various plants, lichens, insects, reptiles, and other organisms.

BIG Idea

Assess Prior Knowledge

Have students brainstorm what they know about classification. **ASK STUDENTS:** ***How is classification used every day?*** Students might name different types of music, clothing styles, and so on. ***Do you know the scientific names of any species?*** They might know that humans are *Homo sapiens.* Tell students to make an outline of each section and write questions about anything they do not understand.

Sample outline:
I. History of Classification
  A. Early Systems
  B. Taxonomic Categories
  C. Systematic Applications

GOING GREEN For the Launch Lab, collect samples of local organisms. For example, if you live near the sea, you might have a variety of mollusks' shells and other animal parts washed on shore. Do not choose ones that are protected by law.

THEMES

Scientific Inquiry Continuing scientific research led to the development of the modern classification system.

Diversity Organisms are classified using genetics and phylogeny.

Energy Some organisms are classified based upon how they obtain and use energy.

Homeostasis The use of Latin as the naming convention for organisms provided stability to the scientific world.

Change The classification system is constantly evolving with each new species that is discovered.

Section 1

MAIN Idea

BL OL AL **Organizing Life**

ASK STUDENTS: ***Why do scientists organize or classify living things?*** Grouping living things based on their similarities makes it easier to study organisms, locate information, and identify relationships. It also aids in communicating with other scientists.

ASK STUDENTS: ***What other systems of classification do you see in daily life?*** Answers will vary, but may include systems used in automobile dealerships, department stores, supermarkets, hardware stores, and schools.

R Reading Strategy

EL BL OL **Assessment Preview**

Before students read Section 1, have them read the section assessment questions on page 489.

SAY TO STUDENTS: ***Read the section with these questions in mind to help you identify the most important information.***

Concepts in Motion

Interactive Table

D Develop Concepts

Community Connection

If possible, take students to a local nature trail or a botanical garden. Identify plants and animals as Aristotle might have done, as shown in Table 1. Point out similarities and differences between the organisms observed.

EL BL OL Have students recreate Table 1 with only the headings. As they identify plants and animals, have them record them in the correct place on the table.

Section 1

Reading Preview

Essential Questions

- What are the similarities and differences between Aristotle's and Linnaeus's methods of classification?
- Using binomial nomenclature, how are scientific names written?
- What are the categories used in biological classification?

Review Vocabulary

morphology: the structure and form of an organism or one of its parts

New Vocabulary

classification
taxonomy
binomial nomenclature
taxon
genus
family
order
class
phylum
division
kingdom
domain

Multilingual eGlossary

The History of Classification

MAIN Idea **Biologists use a system of classification to organize information about the diversity of living things.**

Real-World Reading Link Think about how frustrating it would be if you went into a music store and all the CDs were in one big pile. You might need to go through all of them to find the one you want. Just as stores group CDs according to type of music and artist, biologists group living things by their characteristics and evolutionary relationships.

R Early Systems of Classification

Has anyone ever told you to get organized? You are probably expected to keep your room in order. Your teachers might have asked you to organize your notes or homework. Keeping items or information in order makes them easier to find and understand. Biologists find it easier to communicate and retain information about organisms when the organisms are organized into groups. One of the principal tools for this is biological classification. **Classification** is the grouping of objects or organisms based on a set of criteria.

Aristotle's system More than two thousand years ago, the Greek philosopher Aristotle (384–322 B.C.) developed the first widely accepted system of biological classification. Aristotle classified organisms as either animals or plants. Animals were classified according to the presence or absence of "red blood." Aristotle's "bloodless" and "red-blooded" animals nearly match the modern distinction of invertebrates and vertebrates. Animals were further grouped according to their habitats and morphology. Plants were classified by average size and structure as trees, shrubs, or herbs. **Table 1** shows how Aristotle might have divided some of his groups.

D

Table 1 Aristotle's Classification System

Concepts in Motion — Interactive Table

Plants		
Herbs	**Shrubs**	**Trees**
Violets Rosemary Onions	Blackberry bush Honeysuckle Flannelbush	Apple Oak Maple
Animals with red blood		
Land	**Water**	**Air**
Wolf Cat Bear	Dolphin Eel Sea bass	Owl Bat Crow

Demonstration

BL OL **Aristotle's System** Display several common plants and animals (or photos of them) and call on students at random to identify how Aristotle might have classified them.

AL Have students explain why Aristotle would have classified them the way he did. Est. time: 10 min

Aristotle's system was useful for organizing, but it had many limitations. Aristotle's system was based on his view that species are distinct, separate, and unchanging. The idea that species are unchanging was common until Darwin presented his theory of evolution. Because of his understanding of species, Aristotle's classification did not account for evolutionary relationships. Additionally, many organisms do not fit easily into Aristotle's system, such as birds that do not fly or frogs that live both on land and in water. Nevertheless, many centuries passed before Aristotle's system was replaced by a new system that was better suited to the increased knowledge of the natural world.

Linnaeus's system In the eighteenth century, Swedish naturalist Carolus Linnaeus (1707–1778) broadened Aristotle's classification method and formalized it into a scientific system. Like Aristotle, he based his system on observational studies of the morphology and the behavior of organisms. For example, he organized birds into three major groups depending on their behavior and habitat. The birds in **Figure 1** illustrate these categories. The eagle is classified as a bird of prey, the heron as a wading bird, and the cedar waxwing is grouped with the perching birds.

Linnaeus's system of classification was the first formal system of taxonomic organization. **Taxonomy** (tak SAH nuh mee) is a discipline of biology primarily concerned with identifying, naming, and classifying species based on natural relationships. Taxonomy is part of the larger branch of biology called systematics. Systematics is the study of biological diversity with an emphasis on evolutionary history.

Binomial nomenclature Linnaeus's method of naming organisms, called binomial nomenclature, set his system apart from Aristotle's system and remains valid today. **Binomial nomenclature** (bi NOH mee ul • NOH mun klay chur) gives each species a scientific name that has two parts. The first part is the genus (JEE nus) name, and the second part is the specific epithet (EP uh thet), or specific name, that identifies the species. Latin is the basis for binomial nomenclature because Latin is an unchanging language, and, historically, it has been the language of science and education.

■ **Figure 1** Linnaeus would have classified these birds based on their morphological and behavioral differences.
Infer *in which group Linnaeus might have placed a robin.*

American bald eagle
Bird of prey

Great blue heron
Wading bird

Cedar waxwing
Perching bird

Content Background

Teacher FYI Linnaeus based his classification solely on observable characteristics. Classification systems currently reflect evolutionary relationships as well. Cladistics is a method of classifying organisms based on inferred common ancestry, as shown in the branching of an evolutionary family tree. A diagram of such a family tree is called a cladogram, which students will learn about in Section 2.

■ **Caption Question Fig. 1** perching bird

W Writing Support

BL OL Journal Writing Have students imagine they are Linnaeus (who classified plants and animals based on behavior and structural similarities) and write a journal entry using his system to classify everything they see in one day.

D Develop Concepts

BL OL AL Integrate History Carolus Linnaeus was born Carl Linnaeus. Carolus is the Latinized form of his first name. His full name sounds like two Latin words, just like the two Latin names he used to classify organisms. Linnaeus used his system to classify more than 11,000 plants and animals.

R Reading Strategy

EL BL OL Build Vocabulary Explain the term *binomial nomenclature* by pointing out the common prefix *bi-* and the two word parts that mean "name": *-nomial* and *nomen-*.

ASK STUDENTS: ***What are some other words you know of that use the prefix bi-?*** bicycle, biennial, biweekly, bimonthly, bilingual, etc. ***Using the word*** **two,** ***what do each of these words mean?*** Answers will depend on the words chosen.

S Skill Practice

BL OL Visual Literacy Have students examine the photos in Figure 1.

ASK STUDENTS: ***What morphological differences do you notice among the birds?*** Answers should include differences in beak structure and foot structure. Morphological differences among the birds in Figure 1 helped Linnaeus classify them.

S Skill Practice

BL OL AL Visual Literacy

ASK STUDENTS: ***By what common name do you know the bird in Figure 2?*** The answer is *cardinal,* but students might say "red bird." ***What plants or animals have more than one common name?*** Responses will vary, but examples might include raccoon—masked bandit; parakeet—budgie; and caribou—reindeer.

AL Using the above examples or others students give, have students discuss why many plants and animals have more than one common name.

Reading Strategy

AL Differentiate Point out that the text under the heading *Early Systems of Classification* contains these terms: *classification, taxonomy,* and *binomial nomenclature.* Have students reread the text and then explain differences in meaning among the three terms. Classification is a process of assigning an organism to a particular group. Taxonomy is a scientific discipline that deals with classification. Binomial nomenclature is a two-part name given to species.

W Writing Support

BL OL AL Journal Writing

Have students imagine that they have discovered a new organism. Tell them to describe it and give it a scientific name using binomial nomenclature. Have them explain the basis of the name.

Reading Check Latin is an unchanging language that has historicallly been the language of scientists.

Caption Question Fig. 2 possible answers: rabbit, sunfish, sparrow

Figure 2 *Cardinalis cardinalis* is a bird with many common names and is seen throughout much of the United States. It is the state bird of Illinois, Indiana, Kentucky, North Carolina, and Ohio.
Identify *some other animals that have multiple common names.*

S

VOCABULARY
WORD ORIGIN
Binomial nomenclature
comes from the Latin words *bi,* meaning *two; nomen,* meaning *name;* and *calatus,* meaning *list.*

W

Biologists use scientific names for species because common names vary in useage. Many times the bird shown in **Figure 2** is called a redbird, sometimes it is called a cardinal, and other times it is called a Northern cardinal. In 1758, Linnaeus gave this bird its scientific name, *Cardinalis cardinalis.* The use of scientific names avoids the confusion that can be created with common names. Binomial nomenclature also is useful because common names can be misleading. If you were doing a scientific study on fish, you would not include starfish in your studies. Starfish are not fish. In the same way, great horned owls do not have horns and sea cucumbers are not plants.

When writing a scientific name, scientists follow these rules.

- The first letter of the genus name is always capitalized, but the rest of the genus name and all letters of the specific epithet are lowercase.
- If a scientific name is written in a printed book or magazine, it should be italicized.
- When a scientific name is written by hand, both parts of the name should be underlined.
- After the scientific name has been written once completely, the genus name often will be abbreviated to the first letter in later appear-ances. For example, the scientific name of *Cardinalis cardinalis* can be written *C. cardinalis.*

Reading Check **Explain** why Latin is the basis for many scientific names.

Modern classification systems The study of evolution in the 1800s added a new dimension to Linnaeus's classification system. Many scientists at that time, including Charles Darwin, Jean-Baptiste Lamarck, and Ernst Haeckel, began to classify organisms not only on the basis of morphological and behavioral characteristics. They also included inferred evolutionary relationships in their classification systems. Today, while modern classification systems remain rooted in the Linnaeus tradition, they have been modified to reflect new knowledge about evolutionary ancestry.

Content Background

Real-World Connection The Northern cardinal (*Cardinalis cardinalis*) is one of the most easily recognized birds in North America. It is the only crested bird with a conical beak, except in small areas of the southwestern United States where the pyrrhuloxia (*Cardinalis sinuatus*), a close relative of the Northern cardinal, also lives. The conical beak is well adapted for crushing seeds. The song and calls of the two birds are often indistinguishable.

Taxonomic Categories

Think about how things are grouped in your favorite video store. How are the DVDs arranged on the shelves? They might be arranged according to genre—action, drama, or comedy—and then by title and year. Although taxonomists group organisms instead of DVDs, they also subdivide groups based on more specific criteria. The taxonomic categories used by scientists are part of a nested-hierarchical system—each category is contained within another, and they are arranged from broadest to most specific.

R **Species and genus** A named group of organisms is called a **taxon** (plural, taxa). Taxa range from having broad diagnostic characteristics to having specific characteristics. The broader the characteristics, the more species the taxon contains. One way to think of taxa is to imagine nesting boxes—one fitting inside the other. You have already learned about two taxa used by Linnaeus—genus and species. Today, a **genus** (plural, genera) is defined as a group of species that are closely related and share a common ancestor.

Note the similarities and differences among the three species of bears in **Figure 3.** The scientific names of the American black bear *(Ursus americanus)* and Asiatic black bear *(Ursus thibetanus)* indicate that they belong to the same genus, *Ursus.* All species in the genus *Ursus* have massive skulls and similar tooth structures. Sloth bears *(Melursus ursinus),* despite their similarity to members of the genus *Ursus,* usually are classified in a different genus, *Melursus,* because they are smaller, have a different skull shape and size, and have two fewer incisor teeth than bears of the genus *Ursus.*

D **Family** All bears, both living and extinct species, belong to the same family, Ursidae. A **family** is the next higher taxon, consisting of similar, related genera. In addition to the three species shown in **Figure 3,** the Ursidae family contains six other species: brown bears, polar bears, giant pandas, Sun bears, and Andean bears. All members of the bear family share certain characteristics. For example, they all walk flatfooted and have forearms that can rotate to grasp prey closely.

CAREERS IN BIOLOGY

Wildlife Biologist A scientist who studies organisms in the wild is called a wildlife biologist. Wildlife biologists might study populations of bears or work to educate the public about nature.

■ **Figure 3** All species in the genus *Ursus* have large body size and massive skulls. Sloth bears are classified in the genus *Melursus.*

Ursus americanus
American black bear

Ursus thibetanus
Asiatic black bear

Melursus ursinus
Sloth bear

R Reading Strategy

EL OL COOP LEARN

Draw Conclusions Put students in pairs and have them read the text below the heading *Species and genus.* Then have students ask each other the following questions: ***What name is given to groups of related organisms?*** taxon, singular; taxa, plural ***What do the following two organisms have in common—*****Canis lupus** ***(the wolf) and*** **Anarrhichas lupus** ***(the wolf fish)?*** Although these two organisms are very different animals, they have the same species name. ***Can you identify an organism from just the species name?*** No; as this example demonstrates, you need both the genus and species names.

Critical Thinking

AL **Analyze** Have students choose four different mammals and research the full taxonomic classification of each mammal. Have them determine which mammals are the most and least closely related.

D Develop Concepts

OL AL

Clarify a Misconception

ASK STUDENTS: ***Is the green anole a chameleon?*** no The green anole is a lizard in the family Polychrotidae. A chameleon belongs to a different family, Chamaeleonidae. Students often confuse organisms from different species, genera, and families. Such confusion is often based on similar morphology and not evolutionary relationships.

Activity

BL OL AL **Physical Differences** Show students ten different buttons. Ask students to use similarities and differences in the buttons to develop a classification system. For example, students might place large buttons in one group and small buttons in a second group. Another possibility is grouping the buttons according to the number of holes they have. Students should recognize that there is more than one way to classify objects, including living things. Est. time: 10 min

Develop Concepts

BL OL Reinforcement Show students a seashell guide that contains a dichotomous key. If possible, use the key to classify a variety of seashells that you show the class.

MiniLab 1

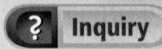

? Inquiry MiniLab

For a lab worksheet, use your eTeacherEdition Online.

✱RUBRIC A rubric for evaluating MiniLabs is found on your eTeacherEdition Online.

Est. Time 25 min

Alternative Materials This activity can be completed using a mixture of different seed types.

Safety Precaution Approve lab safety forms before work begins.

Teaching Strategy Tell students that scientists do not group organisms based on their use, but rather on characters such as structural and genetic similarities. For example, it would not be valid to classify shoes based on function, such as athletic shoes and non-athletic shoes.

Analysis

1. Answers will depend on how groups were developed.
2. Characteristics of the unknown organisms must be compared to those of each group.
3. A classification system can be more effective if it has groups subdivided based on specific criteria.

LabManager™

Customize this lab with the LabManager™ CD-ROM.

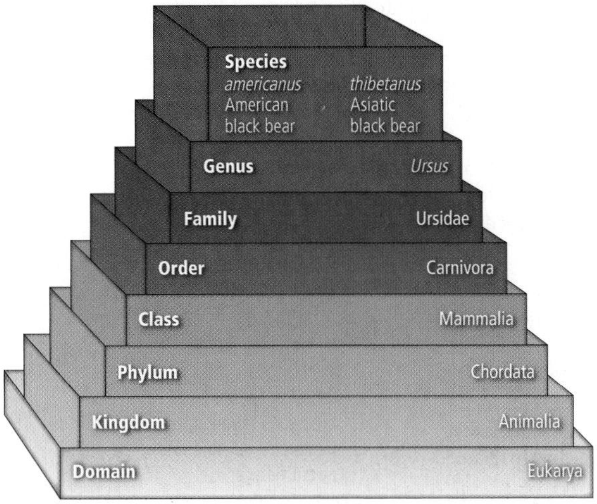

■ **Figure 4** Taxonomic categories are contained within one another like nesting boxes. Notice that the American black bear and Asiatic black bear are different species; however, their classification is the same for all other categories.

Figure 4 shows how the taxa are organized into a hierarchical system. The figure also shows the complete classification from domain to species for the American black bear and the Asiatic black bear. Notice that the only difference in the classification of the two different bears is in the species category.

Higher taxa An **order** contains related families. A **class** contains related orders. The bears in **Figure 3** belong to the order Carnivora and class Mammalia. A **phylum** (FI lum) (plural, phyla) or **division** contains related classes. The term *division* is used instead of *phylum* for the classification of bacteria and plants. Sometimes scientists break the commonly used taxa into subcategories, such as subspecies, subfamilies, infraorders, and subphyla.

The taxon composed of related phyla or divisions is a **kingdom**. Bears are classified in phylum Chordata, Kingdom Animalia, and Domain Eukarya. The **domain** is the broadest of all the taxa and contains one or more kingdoms. The basic characteristics of the three domains and six kingdoms are described later in this chapter.

MiniLab 1

? Inquiry MiniLab

Develop a Dichotomous Key

How can you classify items? Scientists group organisms based on their characteristics. These groups are the basis for classification tools called dichotomous keys. A dichotomous key consists of a series of choices that lead the user to the correct identification of an organism. In this lab, you will develop a dichotomous key as you group familiar objects.

Procedure

1. Read and complete the lab safety form.
2. Remove one **shoe** and make a shoe pile with other shoes from your group.
3. Write a question in your dichotomous key regarding whether the shoe has a characteristic of your choice. Divide the shoes into two groups based on that distinguishing characteristic.
4. Write another question for a different characteristic in your dichotomous key. Divide one of the subgroups into two smaller groups based on this distinguishing characteristic.
5. Continue dividing shoes into subgroups and adding questions to your key until there is only one shoe in each group. Make a branching diagram to identify each shoe with a distinctive name.
6. Use your diagram to classify your teacher's shoe.

Analysis

1. **Relate** taxa to the other groups you used to classify shoes. Which group relates to kingdom, phyla, and so on?
2. **Explain** how you were able to classify your teacher's shoe in Step 6.
3. **Critique** how your classification system could be modified to be more effective.

Demonstration

BL OL Kingdoms Hold up an example of each of the six kingdoms as you introduce the concept to students. Suggestions include any live plant or animal, a mushroom purchased from a store or fungus growing on bread, and a culture plate containing bacterial cultures. If you cannot find a member of Kingdom Archaea, use a photograph instead. As you show the example from each kingdom, call on a student to identify the organism and its kingdom. Est. time: 10 min

■ **Figure 5** This systematist is studying a cactus to determine if it is a new species.

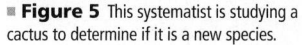

D Systematics Applications

Scientists who study classification provide detailed guides that help people identify organisms. Many times a field guide will contain a dichotomous (di KAHT uh mus) key, which is a key based on a series of choices between alternate characteristics. You can find out whether a plant or animal is poisonous by using a dichotomous key to identify it.

CAREERS IN BIOLOGY Systematists, like the one shown in **Figure 5** also work to identify new species and relationships among known species. They incorporate information from taxonomy, paleontology, molecular biology, and comparative anatomy in their studies. While the discovery of new species is exciting and important, learning a new connection between species also impacts science and society. For example, if a biologist knows that a certain plant such as the Madagascar periwinkle, *Catharanthus roseus,* produces a chemical that can be used to treat cancer, he or she knows that it is possible related plants also might produce the same or similar chemicals.

Section 1 Assessment

Section Summary

- Aristotle developed the first widely accepted biological classification system.
- Linnaeus used morphology and behavior to classify plants and animals.
- Binomial nomenclature uses the Latin genus and species to give an organism a scientific name.
- Organisms are classified according to a nested hierarchical system.

Understand Main Ideas

1. MAIN Idea **Explain** why a biological classification system is important.
2. **Summarize** the rules for using binomial nomenclature.
3. **Compare and contrast** how modern classification systems differ from those used by Aristotle and Linnaeus.
4. **Classify** a giant panda, *Ailuropoda melanoleuca,* completely from domain to species level by referring to **Figure 4.**

Think Critically

WRITING in **Biology**

5. Write a short story describing an application of biological classification.
6. **Consider** where you would expect to see more biodiversity: among members of a phyla or among members of a class. Why?
7. **Differentiate** between taxonomy and systematics.

D Develop Concepts

OL Use Analogies Inform students that all classification systems are hierarchical in that they rank organisms from larger to smaller groups. This process is similar to one used by a post office to sort mail according to zip-code, street, and house number.

ASK STUDENTS: ***Which post-office category is analogous to the species level?*** house number

Develop Concepts

BL OL AL Research Have students use the school library to research the common and scientific names of their state animal, bird, and flower.

Formative Assessment

Evaluation Have students describe an example of how the lack of a classification system might affect their daily lives. An example might be a library that does not classify books according to subject. Finding a particular book would be much more difficult.

Remediation Draw a stair-step pattern on the board with eight steps. Label each step with one of the taxonomic categories. Begin with domain on the bottom, going up to species at the top. As you discuss various categories, point to the one being discussed.

Section 1 Assessment

1. It organizes living things, making it easier to study them and see relationships among organisms.
2. Answers should reflect the bulleted list on page 486.
3. Aristotle's system was based on arbitrary characteristics that were often confusing. Linnaeus based his system on observable characteristics, including morphology and behavior. Modern classification includes evolutionary relationships.
4. Eukarya, Animalia, Chordata, Mammalia, Carnivora, Ursidae, *Ailuropoda, Ailuropoda melanoleuca*
5. Stories should describe an application of biological classification.
6. More biological diversity exists among the members of a phylum because it is more inclusive, containing more organisms. The only exception is a phyla that contains only one species.
7. Taxonomy is the scientific discipline dealing with species classification, and systematics is the study of past and present biological diversity with an emphasis on evolutionary history.

✓ Assessment **Online Quiz**

Section 2

Reading Preview

Essential Questions

- What are the similarities and differences between species concepts?
- What are the methods used to reveal phylogeny?
- How is a cladogram constructed?

Review Vocabulary

evolution: the historical development of a group of organisms

New Vocabulary

phylogeny
character
molecular clock
cladistics
cladogram

Multilingual eGlossary

Modern Classification

MAIN Idea Classification systems have changed over time as information has increased.

Real-World Reading Link Did you ever try a new way of organizing your school notes? Just as you sometimes make changes in the way you do something based on a new idea or new information, scientists adjust systems and theories in science when new information becomes available.

R Determining Species

It is not always easy to define a species. Organisms that are different species by one definition might be the same species by a different definition. As knowledge increases, definitions change. The concept of a species today is much different than it was 100 years ago.

Typological species concept Aristotle and Linnaeus thought of each species as a distinctly different group of organisms based on physical similarities. This definition of species is called the typological species concept. It is based on the idea that species are unchanging, distinct, and natural types, as defined earlier by Aristotle. The type specimen was an individual of the species that best displayed the characteristics of that species. When another specimen was found that varied significantly from the type specimen, it was classified as a different species. For example, in **Figure 6** the color patterns on the butterflies' wings are all slightly different. At one time, they might have been classified as three different species because of these differences, but now they are classified as the same species.

Because we now know that species change over time, and because we know that members of some species exhibit tremendous variation, the typological species concept has been replaced. However, some of its traditions, such as reference to type specimens, remain.

Figure 6 Although these tropical butterflies vary in their color patterns, they are classified as different varieties of the same species, *Heliconius erato.*
Describe *why early taxonomists might have classified them as separate species.*

Section 2

MAIN Idea

BL OL AL

New Classification Models
Since Aristotle and Linnaeus, increasing information has led to changes in classification systems.
ASK STUDENTS: ***What kinds of useful information for classification do you think we know about today that early scientists didn't know?*** Student responses will vary but can include information about DNA, cell types, cell organelles, and evolution.

R Reading Strategy

EL BL OL AL COOP LEARN

Brainstorm Have students read the text under the heading *Determining Species.* Organize students into groups of three or four and have them brainstorm ideas that come to mind when they see the word *species.* Record ideas from each group on the board.
ASK STUDENTS: ***Why is it not always correct to classify using the typological species concept?*** Physical similarities do not always reflect a close evolutionary relationship between organisms.
AL Have students give examples that illustrate this. Student responses will vary but should include two groups of animals that share some physical traits but are not closely related. Bats and birds is one example.

Caption Question Fig. 6 Early taxonomists classified them as separate species because of the differences in their patterns.

Demonstration

Species Differences To illustrate variations in species, show two different goldfish *(Carassius auratus)* in a goldfish bowl. You could also use photographs. Use one common goldfish and one fancy goldfish, such as one with goggle eyes, calico or black coloration, or double fins. Est. time: 5 min

D **Biological species concept** Theodosius Dobzhansky and Ernst Mayr, two evolutionary biologists, redefined the term species in the 1930s and 1940s. They defined a species as a group of organisms that is able to interbreed and produce fertile offspring in a natural setting. This is called the biological species concept, and it is the definition for species used throughout this textbook. Though the butterflies in **Figure 6** have variable color patterns, they can interbreed to produce fertile offspring and therefore are classified as the same species.

There are limitations to the biological species concept. For example, wolves and dogs, as well as many plant species, are known to interbreed and produce fertile offspring even though they are classified as different species. The biological species concept also does not account for extinct species or species that reproduce asexually. However, because the biological species concept works in most everyday experiences of classification, it is used often.

Phylogenetic species concept In the 1940s, the evolutionary species concept was proposed as a companion to the biological species concept. The evolutionary species concept defines species in terms of populations and ancestry. According to this concept, two or more groups that evolve independently from an ancestral population are classified as different species. More recently, this concept has developed into the phylogenetic species concept. **Phylogeny** (fi LAH juh nee) is the evolutionary history of a species. The phylogenetic species concept defines a species as a cluster of organisms that is distinct from other clusters and shows evidence of a pattern of ancestry and descent. When a phylogenetic species branches, it becomes two different phylogenetic species. For example, recall that when organisms become isolated—geographically or otherwise—they often evolve different adaptations. Eventually, they might become different enough to be classified as a new species.

This definition of a species solves some of the problems of earlier concepts because it applies to extinct species and species that reproduce **R** asexually. It also incorporates molecular data. **Table 2** summarizes the three main species concepts.

Study Tip

Note Discussions While you read, use self-adhesive notes to mark passages that you do not understand. In addition, mark passages you do understand and can explain to others with your own explanations, examples, and ideas. Then, discuss them with your classmates.

? Inquiry Launch Lab

Review Based on what you have read about classification systems, how would you now answer the analysis questions?

Table 2 Species Concepts — Concepts in Motion Interactive Table

Species Concept	Description	Limitation	Benefit
Typological species concept	Classification is determined by the comparison of physical characteristics with a type specimen.	Alleles produce a wide variety of features within a species.	Descriptions of type specimens provide detailed records of the physical characteristics of many organisms.
Biological species concept	Classification is determined by similar characteristics and the ability to interbreed and produce fertile offspring.	Some organisms, such as wolves and dogs that are different species, interbreed occasionally. It does not account for extinct species.	The working definition applies in most cases, so it is still used frequently.
Phylogenetic species concept	Classification is determined by evolutionary history.	Evolutionary histories are not known for all species.	Accounts for extinct species and considers molecular data.

Activity

Phylogenetic Species Have students review the pages on which *Homo ergaster, H. heidelbergensis,* and *H. sapiens* are illustrated or discussed. Point these out to students as you discuss the phylogenetic species concept and note that this was the first way to speak about species in terms of their evolutionary history. Est. time: 20 min

? Inquiry Launch Lab

Assess Content Development
Assess how understanding has developed when students revisit the Launch Lab analysis questions.

D Develop Concepts

BL OL AL

Clarify a Misconception

Most students will be able to recognize that Chihuahuas, poodles, and Labrador retrievers are all dogs, but might not understand the basis for the grouping, and might even think that the different breeds are different species. Remind students that all dogs are classified as *Canis familiaris.*

ASK STUDENTS: ***What is the basis for grouping retrievers and Chihuahuas as members of the same species?*** Student responses will vary, but some students might indicate that all dogs can exchange genes. Although a mating between a Chihuahua and a Labrador retriever is not easy because of their size differences, gametes from the two breeds can fuse to form a fertilized egg. The resulting offspring will be able to reproduce with another dog (unlike the offspring of two similar, but separate, species such as a donkey and a horse).

Concepts in Motion
Interactive Table

R Reading Strategy

OL Dialogue with Text

Review the classification taxon of species with students. Encourage students to describe the differences between each of the three species concepts. Have them compare their descriptions to those in Table 2.

W Writing Support

OL AL Summary Writing

Have students write a summary of some of the morphological characters that could be used to classify different groups of dinosaurs. **BL** Instead of a summary, have students make a list of morphological characters.

C Critical Thinking

BL OL AL Evaluate

ASK STUDENTS: ***Why might some taxonomists say that fossils are not all that remain of dinosaurs?*** As close relatives of the theropod dinosaurs, modern birds are likely to have DNA similar to their evolutionary ancestors.

S Skill Practice

BL OL Visual Literacy

ASK STUDENTS: ***How do the oviraptor and sparrow in Figure 7 seem different from each other? How do they seem similar?*** Answers will vary, but some students might say that, unlike the sparrow, the oviraptor has grasping hands and a uniquely shaped skull; both have feathers and have a similar build.

AL ***What evidence is there that these species are related?*** See above answers. ***Do their differences suggest that they are not related?*** Answers will vary, but should be based on observations of characteristics.

VOCABULARY

SCIENCE USAGE V. COMMON USAGE

Character

Science usage: a feature that varies among species

Organisms are compared based on similar characters

Common usage: imaginary person in a work of fiction—a play, novel, or film

The queen was my favorite character in the book.

Characters

To classify a species, scientists often construct patterns of descent, or phylogenies, by using **characters**—inherited features that vary among species. Characters can be morphological or biochemical. Shared morphological characters suggest that species are related closely and evolved from a recent common ancestor. For example, because hawks and eagles share many morphological characters that they do not share with other bird species, such as keen eyesight, hooked beaks, and taloned feet, they should share a more recent common ancestor with each other than with other bird groups.

Morphological characters When comparing morphological characters, it is important to remember that analogous characters do not indicate a close evolutionary relationship. Remember that analogous structures are those that have the same function but different underlying construction. Homologous characters, however, might perform different functions but show an anatomical similarity inherited from a common ancestor. W

Birds and dinosaurs Consider the oviraptor and the sparrow shown in **Figure 7.** At first you might think that dinosaurs and birds do not have much in common and do not share a close evolutionary relationship. A closer look at dinosaur fossils shows that they share many features with birds. Some fossil dinosaur bones, like those of the large, carnivorous theropod dinosaurs, show that their bones had large hollow spaces. Birds have bones with hollow spaces. In this respect, they are more like birds than most living reptiles, such as alligators, lizards, and turtles, which have dense bones. Also, theropods have hip, leg, wrist, and shoulder structures that are more similar to birds than to other reptiles. C Recently, scientists have discovered some fossil dinosaur bones that suggest some theropods had feathers. W The evidence provided by these morphological characters indicates that theropod dinosaurs are related more closely to modern birds than they are to other reptiles.

Reading Check **Explain** how morphological characters have influenced the classification of dinosaurs and birds.

S

Figure 7 This artist's conception of *Oviraptor philoceratops* might not appear to be related to the sparrow *Zonotrichia leucophrys*, but these animals share many characteristics that indicate a shared evolutionary history.
***Deduce** which similarities might prompt you to think that these species are more closely related than was commonly thought.*

Oviraptor philoceratops

Zonotrichia leucophrys

W Writing Support

BL OL AL Technical Writing

Have students write a description of a common species, such as a dog or a cat, without providing the name. Have them trade papers and try to identify the species from the description.

"To teach is to learn twice."
—JOSEPH JOUBERT

Reading Check Morphological similarities, such as bones with hollow spaces, show that birds are more closely related to dinosaurs than to other reptiles.

Caption Question **Fig. 7** Structures of their bones and even the possibility of feathers reveal their close relationship.

■ **Figure 8** The representation of chromosome-banding patterns for these homologous chromosomes illustrates the evidence of a close evolutionary relationship among the chimpanzee, gorilla, and orangutan.

D **Biochemical characters** Scientists use biochemical characters, such as amino acids and nucleotides, to help them determine evolutionary relationships among species. Chromosome structure and number is also a powerful clue for determining species similarities. For example, members of the mustard family (Cruciferae)—including broccoli, cauliflower, and kale—all look different in the garden, but these plants have almost identical chromosome structures. This is strong evidence that they share a recent common ancestor. Likewise, the similar appearance of chromosomes among chimpanzees, gorillas, and orangutans suggests a shared ancestry. **Figure 8** shows the similar appearance of a chromosome-banding pattern in these three primates.

DNA and RNA analyses are powerful tools for reconstructing phylogenies. Remember that DNA and RNA are made up of four nucleotides. The nucleotide sequences in DNA define the genes that direct RNA to make proteins. The greater the number of shared DNA sequences between species, the greater the number of shared genes—and the greater the evidence that the species share a recent common ancestor.

Scientists use a variety of techniques to compare DNA sequences when assessing evolutionary relationships. They can sequence and compare whole genomes of different organisms. They can compare genome maps made by using restriction enzymes. They also use a technique called DNA-DNA hybridization, during which single strands of DNA from different species are melted together. The success of the hybridization depends on the similarity of the sequences—complementary sequences will bind to each other, while dissimilar sequences will not bind. Comparing the DNA sequences of different species is an objective, quantitative way to measure evolutionary relationships. C

VOCABULARY

ACADEMIC VOCABULARY

Corresponding
being similar or equivalent in character, quantity, origin, structure, or function
The corresponding sequences matched perfectly.

D Develop Concepts

BL OL

Activate Prior Knowledge
Have students review the relationship between DNA and chromosomes. Remind them that DNA is the molecule of heredity, and chromosomes are structures that contain DNA.

Develop Concepts

BL OL AL COOP LEARN

Activity Provide groups of three or four students with a table listing the different sequences of cytochrome *c* in a variety of organisms. Explain that cytochrome *c* is a protein found in all aerobic organisms. This protein's amino acid sequence has been used to determine the degree of relatedness between species. Have each group identify evolutionary relationships among these organisms. When students are finished, emphasize that this process is similar to what taxonomists do to classify organisms based on biological characteristics.

C Critical Thinking

OL AL **Infer**

ASK STUDENTS: ***Do you think morphological characters or genetic characters are more accurate to use when classifying organisms? Explain.*** Genetic characters might be more accurate to use because an organism's phenotype does not completely reveal its genotype. The best is to use a combination of different characters.

Demonstration

Chromosomal Characters Hold up broccoli, cabbage, cauliflower, and kale (or photos) and inform students that those vegetables have almost identical chromosome structures because they were all bred using artificial selection beginning with the same species. Students may be surprised to find out that the common species is mustard, *Brassica rapa*. Est. time: 10 min

S Skill Practice

BL OL Visual Literacy

ASK STUDENTS: ***Looking at Figure 9, what physical similarities can you see between the individuals of the different elephant populations?*** body size, ears

DATA ANALYSIS LAB 1

About the Lab

- Point out that a large difference in DNA sequences is a good indicator of species separation. If a 50 percent difference is enough to separate organisms into two different genera, a 25 percent difference would usually be considered more than enough to separate two groups into species.
- Also see Barriel et al. 1999. Molecular phylogeny of Elephantidae. Extreme divergence of the extant forest African elephant. *Royal Academy of Sciences, Series III* 322(6): 447–454.

Think Critically

1. DNA sequences
2. Finding genetic differences almost half as large as those between two genera indicates that the elephants are two different species.
3. morphological, biochemical, and behavioral character differences
4. The forest-dwelling species of African elephant *Loxodonta cyclotis* would be in danger. *Loxodonta africanas* may become the only species in the African elephant genus.

African elephant (savanna) **African elephant (forest)** **Asiatic elephant**

Figure 9 The two populations of African elephants have been classified as the same species; however, DNA analysis shows that they might be separate species. The Asiatic elephant belongs to a separate genus.

S

A species example The classification of elephants is one example of how molecular data has changed traditional taxonomic organization. **Figure 9** shows pictures of elephants that live in the world today. Taxonomists have classified the Asiatic elephant *(Elephas maximus)* as one species and the African elephant *(Loxodonta africana)* as another for over 100 years. However, they have classified the two types of African elephant as the same species, even though the two populations look different. The forest-dwelling elephants are much smaller and have longer tusks and smaller ears than the savanna-dwelling elephants. Even so, scientists thought that the elephants interbred freely at the margins of their ranges. Recent DNA studies, however, show that the African elephants diverged from a common ancestor about 2.5 million years ago. Scientists have proposed renaming the forest-dwelling elephant *Loxodonta cyclotis*. Use **Data Analysis Lab 1** to explore molecular evidence for renaming the forest-dwelling elephant.

DATA ANALYSIS LAB 1

Based on Real Data*

Draw a Conclusion

Are African elephants a separate species? Efforts to count and protect elephant populations in Africa were based on the assumption that all African elephants belong to the same species. Evidence from a project originally designed to trace ivory samples changed that assumption.

A group of scientists studied the DNA variation among 195 African elephants from 21 populations in 11 of the 37 nations in which African elephants range and from seven Asian elephants. They used biopsy darts to obtain plugs of skin from the African elephants. The researchers focused on a total of 1732 nucleotides from four nuclear genes that are not subject to natural selection. The following paragraph shows the results of the samples.

*Data obtained from: Roca, A.L., et al. 2001. Genetic evidence for two species of elephants in Africa. *Science* 293(5534): 1473-1477.

Data and Observations

"Phylogenetic distinctions between African forest elephant and savannah elephant population corresponded to 58% of the difference in the same genes between elephant genera Loxodonta (African) and Elephas (Asian)."

Think Critically

1. **Describe** the type of evidence used in the study.
2. **Explain** the evidence that there are two species of elephants in Africa.
3. **Propose** other kinds of data that could be used to support three different scientific names for elephants.
4. **Infer** Currently, *Loxodonta africana* is protected from being hunted. How might reclassification affect the conservation of forest elephants?

Differentiated Instruction

Visually Impaired When discussing information presented in the figures from the book, be sure to describe the information so that students can participate in the discussion and understand important concepts.

For more tips, see page 14T–15T.

R **Molecular clocks** You know that mutations occur randomly in DNA. As time passes, mutations accumulate, or build up, in the chromosomes. Some of these mutations do not affect the way cells function, and they are passed down from parent to offspring. Systematists can use these mutations to help them determine the degree of relationship among species. A **molecular clock** is a model that is used to compare DNA sequences from two different species to estimate how long the species have been evolving since they diverged from a common ancestor. **Figure 10** illustrates how a molecular clock works.

Scientists use molecular clocks to compare the DNA sequences or amino acid sequences of genes that are shared by different species. The differences between the genes indicate the presence of mutations. The more mutations that have accumulated, the more time that has passed since divergence. When the molecular clock technique was first introduced in the 1960s, scientists thought the rate of mutation within specific genes was constant. Hence, they used the clock as an analogy. However, scientists now know that the speed by which mutations occur is not always the same in a single gene or amino acid sequence.

The rate of mutation is affected by many factors, including the type of mutation, where it is in the genome, the type of protein that the mutation affects, and the population in which the mutation occurs. In a single organism, different genes might mutate, or "tick," at different speeds. This inconsistency makes molecular clocks difficult to read. Researchers try to compare genes that accumulate mutations at a relatively constant rate in a wide range of organisms. One such gene is the gene for cytochrome *c* oxidase, which is found in the mitochondrial DNA of most organisms.

Despite their limitations, molecular clocks can be valuable tools for determining a relative time of divergence of a species. They are especially useful when used in conjunction with other data, such as the fossil record.

S

Reading Check **Explain** what the molecular clock model uses to compare DNA.

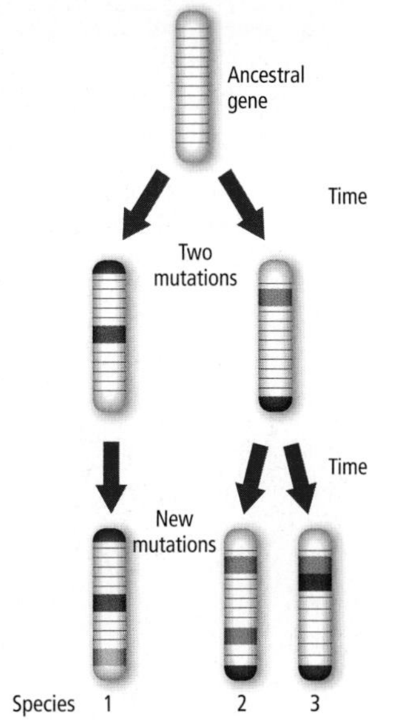

■ **Figure 10** This molecular clock diagram shows how mutations might accumulate over time.
Infer *why a clock is not a good analogy for this process.*

Phylogenetic Reconstruction

The most common systems of classification today are based on a method of analysis called cladistics. **Cladistics** (kla DIHS tiks) is a method that classifies organisms according to the order that they diverged from a common ancestor.

Character types Scientists consider two main types of characters when doing cladistic analyses. An ancestral character is found within the entire line of descent of a group of organisms. Derived characters are present in members of one group of the line but not in the common ancestor. For example, when considering the relationship between birds and mammals, a backbone is an ancestral character because both birds and mammals have a backbone and so did their shared ancestor. However, birds have feathers and mammals have hair. Therefore, having hair is a derived character for mammals because only mammals have an ancestor with hair. Likewise, having feathers is a derived character for birds.

VOCABULARY
WORD ORIGIN
Cladistics
comes from the Greek word *klados,* meaning *sprout* or *branch*

R Reading Strategy
BL OL COOP LEARN

Preview the Text Have students study Figure 10 before they read the text under the heading *Molecular clocks.* After students have read the information, call on one student to summarize why a clock is an appropriate analogy. Have another student describe why molecular clocks are useful for studies of phylogeny.

S Skill Practice
BL OL

Recognize Cause and Effect
ASK STUDENTS: ***What effects are possible from mutations?*** If the mutation occurs in a noncoding part of a DNA sequence, there should be no observable effect. However, if the mutation occurs in a DNA sequence that codes for a product, there can be beneficial effects, negative effects, or no effect at all. No effect occurs if the mutation is in a single base that results in the same amino acid being inserted into a protein.

Inquiry BioLab

The lab at the end of the chapter can be used at this point in the lesson.

Demonstration

Use an Analogy Display a wall clock and a watch as analogies for molecular clocks. Point out that time clocks are predictable in their behavior, while molecular clocks are unpredictable because mutations are random events. Est. time: 5 min

■ **Caption Question Fig. 10** Mutations, unlike time measured by clocks, often occur at varying rates.

Reading Check The molecular clock looks for dissimilar genes, representing a mutation that occurred.

S Skill Practice

BL OL AL COOP LEARN

Compare and Contrast Have students work in pairs to compare and contrast the molecular clock and cladogram models pictured in Figure 10 and Figure 11.

ASK STUDENTS: ***What similarities do you notice between the two models?*** Both models use a proposed phylogeny and similarities and differences between species in their classification schemes. ***What differences do you notice?*** The molecular clock model uses mutations to determine phylogenetic distance, and the cladogram model uses derived characters that can be genetic, chromosomal, structural, or physiological features to differentiate between organisms.

R Reading Strategy

EL BL OL AL **Illustrate** After they read this page, have students create a cladogram of everyday objects. You might suggest that the cladogram be for entertainment devices, such as a musical instrument, a book, a radio, a television, and a video game. Students might use characters such as whether the device can be made by hand and whether it uses electricity. Have students place the items in the order that they were developed.

Concepts in Motion

Animation

Review

Personal Tutor

CAREERS IN BIOLOGY

Evolutionary Geneticist An evolutionary geneticist uses genetic analysis to establish evolutionary relationships. Often, they work at colleges and universities where they teach and perform research.

Cladograms Sytematists use shared derived characters to make a cladogram. A **cladogram** (KLAD uh gram) is a branching diagram that represents the proposed phylogeny or evolutionary history of a species or group. A cladogram is a model similar to a pedigree. Just as a pedigree's branches show direct ancestry, a cladogram's branches indicate phylogeny. The groups used in cladograms are called clades. A clade is one branch of the cladogram.

Constructing a cladogram **Figure 11** is a simplified cladogram for some major plant groups. This cladogram was constructed in the following way. First, two species were identified, conifers and ferns, to compare with the lily species. Then, another species was identified that is ancestral to conifers and ferns. This species is called the outgroup. The outgroup is the species or group of species on a cladogram that has more ancestral characters with respect to the other organisms being compared. In the diagram below, the outgroup is moss. Mosses are more distantly related to ferns, conifers, and lilies.

The cladogram is constructed by sequencing the order in which derived characters evolved with respect to the outgroup. The closeness of clades in the cladogram indicate the number of characters shared. The group that is closest to the lily shares the most derived characters with lilies and thus shares a more recent common ancestor with lilies than with the groups farther away. The nodes where the branches originate represent a common ancestor. This common ancestor generally is not a known organism, species, or fossil. Scientists hypothesize its characters based on the traits of its descendants.

The primary assumption The primary assumption that systematists make when constructing cladograms is that the greater the number of derived characters shared by groups, the more recently the groups share a common ancestor. Thus, as shown in **Figure 11,** lilies and conifers have three derived characters in common and are presumed to share a more recent common ancestor than lilies and ferns, which share only two characters.

A cladogram also is called a phylogenetic tree. Detailed phylogenetic trees show relationships among many species and groups of organisms. **Figure 12** illustrates a phylogenetic tree that shows the relationships among the domains and kingdoms of the most commonly used classification system today. R

S

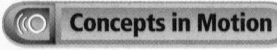

Concepts in Motion

Animation

Review

Personal Tutor

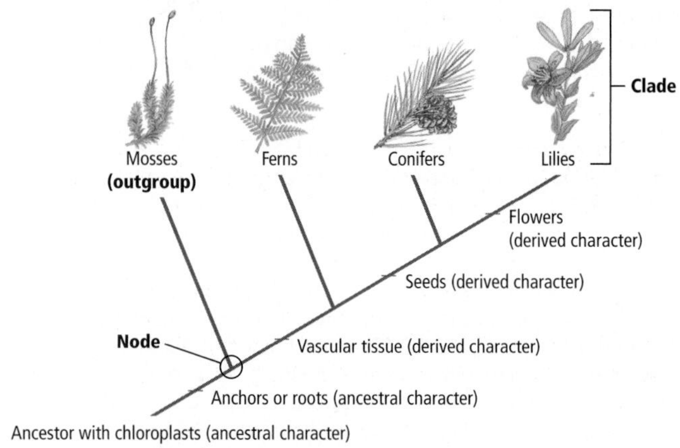

Figure 11 This cladogram uses the derived characters of plant taxa to model its phylogeny. Groups that are closer to the lily on the cladogram share a more recent common ancestor.
***Identify** which clades have chloroplasts but do not produce seeds.*

Caption Question Fig. 11 mosses and ferns

Research Citation

Compare and Contrast Educational research shows that identifying similarities and differences, like the Skill Practice activity on this page, is an effective instructional strategy that helps students classify and understand relationships among things or ideas. (Flick, 1992)

Research bibliography on pages 32T–34T

Visualizing the Tree of Life

Figure 12
This phylogenetic tree shows the main branches in the "tree of life." Notice the three domains and the four kingdoms of Domain Eukarya. All of the branches are connected at the trunk, which is labeled *Common Ancestor.*

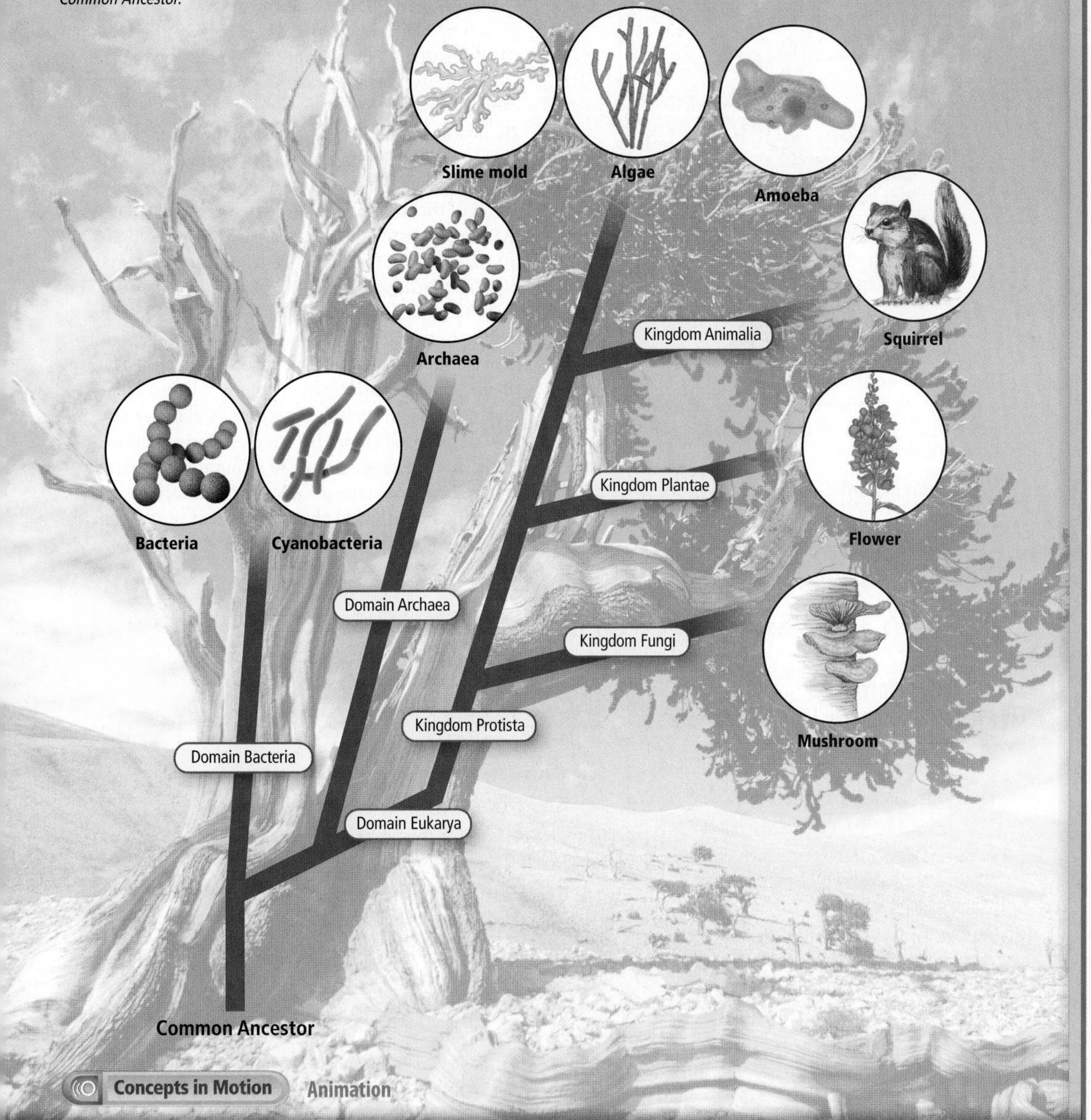

Demonstration

BL OL Tree of Life Bring in an actual tree's limb to use as an analogy for the illustration on this page. As you discuss the illustration, point to parts of the limb. Tell students that the leaves at the tips of the branches represent species. The leaves that are farther from the trunk represent species that are more different from their evolutionary ancestor than leaves closer to the trunk. Est. time: 5 min

Visualizing the Tree of Life

Purpose

Students will visualize classification based on a phylogenetic tree. UCP.2, UCP.4, C.3

Skill Practice

BL OL AL Visual Literacy Use this figure to clarify some phylogenetic relationships.

ASK STUDENTS: ***Which domain was ancestral to Domain Eukarya?*** Domain Archaea ***According to the diagram, which group is the most recent ancestor to plants, animals, and fungi?*** Kingdom Protista

Critical Thinking

BL OL Predict

ASK STUDENTS: ***Imagine that this model was constructed as a three-dimensional tree. Predict what would represent the tree's trunk.*** The trunk would be the line between the common ancestor and the first branch into Domain Bacteria and Domain Archaea.

Concepts in Motion
Animation

Concepts in Motion
Animation

Formative Assessment

Evaluation Have students refer to Table 2 as you ask a series of questions about the species concept to determine if they understand the benefits and limitations with each one. For example, inform students that a horse and a donkey share morphological characters, and they can mate. However, the mules they produce are sterile.
ASK STUDENTS: ***Do a horse and a donkey belong to the same species? What species concept are you using to support your answer?*** If they are using a biological species concept, the animals belong to different species.

Remediation Construct a deck of 12 index cards. On each card, write the information in each of the twelve cells of Table 2. Shuffle the deck and give it to a student. Have the student place the cards so that they reconstruct Table 2 without referring to the textbook.

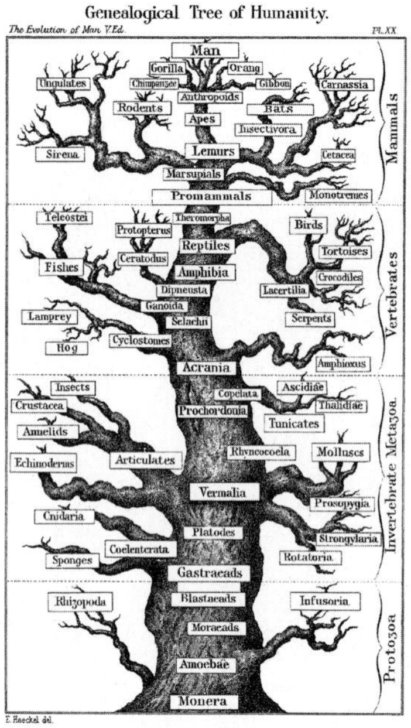

■ **Figure 13** This illustration, made by Ernst Haeckel in the nineteenth century, was one of the first graphic depictions of evolutionary relationships.

Concepts in Motion
Animation

Connection to History **The tree of life** In his book *On the Origin of Species*, Charles Darwin used the analogy of a tree to suggest that all of the species developed from one or a few species. He imagined the tree's trunk to represent ancestral groups and each of the branches to have similar species. From each branch, smaller and smaller branches grew. Finally, at the tips of the twigs of these branches were the leaves, consisting of individual living species. This concept was developed further, and the term *tree of life* was coined by German biologist Ernst Haeckel (1834–1919). **Figure 13** shows Haeckel's Genealogical Tree of Humanity. Haeckel was the first to represent phylogenies in the form of a tree, and while his phylogenies are no longer completely accurate, they represent the first step in the reconstruction of phylogenies.

The tree of life diagram in **Figure 13** is a representation of the diversity of living organisms. A tree of life that incorporates all known organisms is almost unimaginably large. Scientists have discovered and described nearly 1.75 million species, and they estimate that millions more remain unclassified. Assembling a comprehensive tree of life requires a convergence of data from phylogenetic and molecular analysis. It also requires collaboration among many scientists representing many disciplines, from molecular biology to Earth science to computer science. Many scientists think that the construction of a comprehensive tree of life, though an enormous task, is an important goal. Knowing how all organisms are related would benefit industry, agriculture, medicine, and conservation.

Section 2 Assessment

Section Summary

- The definition of species has changed over time.
- Phylogeny is the inferred evolutionary history of a species, evidence for which comes from a variety of studies.
- A molecular clock uses comparisons of DNA sequences to estimate phylogeny and rate of evolutionary change.
- Cladistic analysis models evolutionary relationships based on sequencing derived characters.

Understand Main Ideas

1. **MAIN Idea** **Describe** how the changing species concept has affected classification systems.
2. **Summarize** the different concepts of a species.
3. **Describe** some methods used to determine phylogeny.
4. **Organize** the following derived characters on a cladogram in order of ascending complexity: multicellular, hair, backbone, unicellular, and four appendages.

Think Critically

MATH in Biology

5. **Describe** the mathematical challenges of counting the "ticks" of a molecular clock.
6. **Evaluate** the analogy of a tree for the organization of species based on phylogeny.
7. **Indicate** the hypothetical evolutionary relationship between two species if their DNA sequences share a 98 percent similarity.

Section 2 Assessment

1. Many species have been reclassified as a result of application of the biological and phylogenetic species concepts.
2. typological: based on physical characteristics; biological: based on the ability to interbreed and produce fertile offspring; phylogenetic: based on evolutionary history
3. comparison of morphological, biochemical, chromosomal, and behavioral characteristics
4. unicellular, multicellular, backbone, four appendages, hair
5. Different genes mutate at different speeds.
6. Possible answer: A tree is a suitable analogy because its trunk represents the common ancestor, and its branches can be used to show the evolutionary history leading to modern organisms.
7. They share a recent common ancestor.

Assessment **Online Quiz**

Reading Preview

Essential Questions

- What are the major characteristics of the three domains?
- What are the differences among the six kingdoms?
- How are organisms classified at the kingdom level?

Review Vocabulary

eukaryote: an organism composed of one or more cells containing a nucleus and membrane-bound organelles

New Vocabulary

archaea
protist
fungus

R

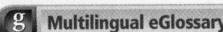

Multilingual eGlossary

Inquiry Virtual Lab

S

Domains and Kingdoms

MAIN Idea The most widely used biological classification system has six kingdoms within three domains.

Real-World Reading Link What have you learned about the size of a kingdom as compared to a city, a village, or an individual home in your history classes? How does this knowledge help you understand the classification system?

Grouping Species

The broadest category in the classification system used by most biologists is the domain. There are three domains: Bacteria, Archaea, and Eukarya. Within these domains are six kingdoms: Bacteria, Archaea, Protists, Fungi, Plantae, and Animalia. Organisms are classified into domains according to cell type and structure, and into kingdoms according to cell type, structure, and nutrition.

This three-domain, six-kingdom classification system has been in use for less than three decades. It was modified from a system that did not have domains but had five kingdoms after scientists discovered an entirely new kind of organism in the 1970s. These new organisms are unicellular prokaryotes that scientists named archaea (ar KEE uh). Subsequent biochemical studies found that archaea are significantly different from the only other prokaryotes then known—the bacteria—and, in 1990, they were renamed and a new classification scheme was proposed to accommodate them. Archaea are now members of their own domain.

Domain Bacteria

Connection to Chemistry Bacteria, members of Domain and Kingdom Bacteria, are prokaryotes whose cell walls contain peptidoglycan (pep tih doh GLY kan). Peptidoglycan is a polymer that contains two kinds of sugars that alternate in the chain. The amino acids of one sugar are linked to the amino acids in other chains, creating a netlike structure that is simple and porous, yet strong. Two examples of bacteria are shown in **Figure 14.**

Figure 14 Bacteria vary in their habitats and their methods of obtaining nourishment. The bacteria *Mycobacterium tuberculosis* that cause tuberculosis are heterotrophs. Cyanobacteria, such as *Anabaena,* are autotrophs.

Color-Enhanced SEM Magnification: 15,000×

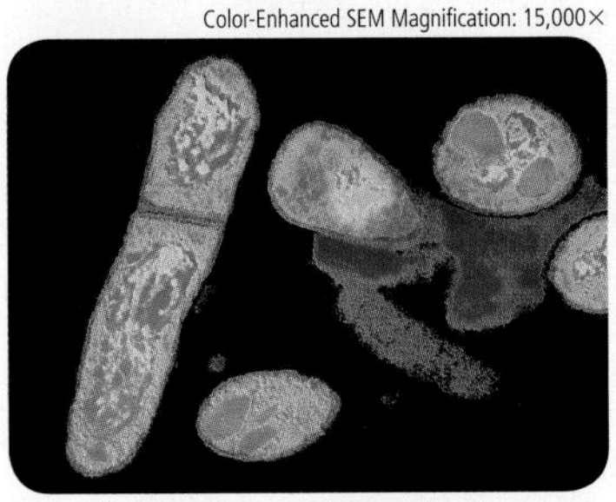

Mycobacterium tuberculosis

LM Magnification: 450×

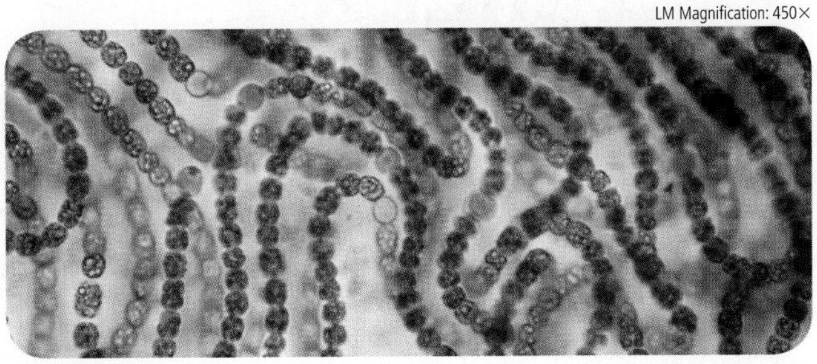

Anabaena

Section 3

MAIN Idea

BL OL AL

Domains and Kingdoms

ASK STUDENTS: ***From what you learned in Section 1 of this chapter, name the two broadest taxa.*** domain and kingdom ***In this section, you will learn how to classify any organism into these two groups. Which kingdoms can you already name?*** Most students will already know Kingdom Animalia and Kingdom Plantae, but fewer will be able to identify the other four kingdom names—Fungi, Protista, Archaea, and Bacteria.

AL Have students give specific examples of organisms from each of the six kingdoms.

R Reading Strategy

EL BL OL **Frayer Model** Have students develop a Frayer model for this section's new vocabulary. Have them draw a square on their paper for each vocabulary term and divide each square into four quadrants. In the upper-left quadrant, have students write the definition of the term; in the upper-right quadrant, list characteristics of the term; in the lower-left quadrant, record examples; and in the lower right quadrant, record nonexamples.

S Skill Practice

BL OL AL **Visual Literacy**

Have students examine Figure 14. **ASK STUDENTS:** ***Why was the bacterium shown in the left photo given its species name?*** The species name *tuberculosis* is based on the fact that the bacterium causes this disease. Explain to students that *Anabaena* is the name of a genus of cyanobacteria and does not refer to a specific species of cyanobacteria.

Content Background

Teacher FYI The taxonomic rank of domain, proposed by Carl Woese in 1990, resulted from research showing that the ribosomal RNA nucleotide sequences of organisms fell into three different groups. Woese proposed that three domains be established, each recognizing the difference in the ribosomal RNAs of organisms.

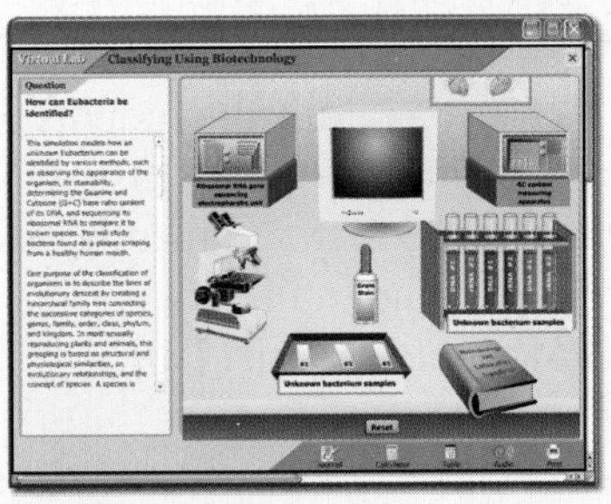

Inquiry Virtual Lab This lab models how an unknown bacterium can be identified by various methods.

C Critical Thinking

BL OL AL Classify

ASK STUDENTS: ***Into which domain and kingdom would you classify a prokaryote that uses sulfuric acid for its energy source?*** Archaea, Kingdom and Domain are synonymous for this group of organisms. ***Into which domain and kingdom would you classify a prokaryote that is a photoautotroph?*** Bacteria, Kingdom and Domain are synonymous for this group.

MiniLab 2

? Inquiry MiniLab

For a lab worksheet, use your eTeacherEdition Online.

RUBRIC A rubric for evaluating MiniLabs is found on your eTeacherEdition Online.

Est. Time 25 min

Alternative Materials This activity could be completed using photomicrographs of bacteria.

Safety Precaution Approve lab safety forms before work begins.

Teaching Strategy Students could perform this lab in pairs.

Analysis

1. Most bacteria have one of three basic shapes: rod-shaped (bacilli), sphere-shaped (cocci), and spiral-shaped (spirilla).
2. Answers will depend on cell types used. Some bacteria grow in long chains, while others form clumps.
3. The data can be used to develop a classification system based on morphological features such as shape.

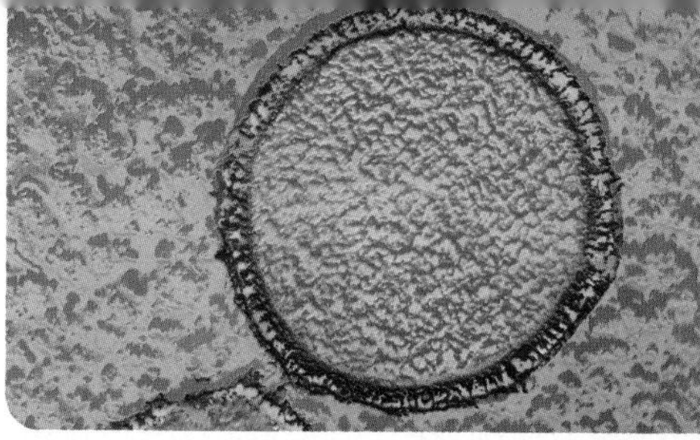

■ **Figure 15** This electron microscope image of *Staphylothermus marinus* shows the cell wall (green) and cell contents (pink). *S. marinus* is an extremophile found in deep ocean thermal vents.

Bacteria are a diverse group that can survive in many different environments. Some are aerobic organisms that need oxygen to survive, while others are anaerobic organisms that die in the presence of oxygen. Some bacteria are autotrophic and produce their own food, but most are heterotrophic and get their nutrition from other organisms. Bacteria are more abundant than any other organism. There are probably more bacteria in your body than there are people in the world. You can view some different types of bacteria in **MiniLab 2.**

VOCABULARY

WORD ORIGIN

Archaea
comes from the Greek word *archaios,* meaning *ancient* or *primitive.*

Domain Archaea

Archaea (ar KEE uh), the species classified in Domain Archaea, are thought to be more ancient than bacteria and yet more closely related to eukaryote ancestors. Their cell walls do not contain peptidoglycan, and they have some of the same proteins that eukaryotes do. They are diverse in shape and nutrition requirements. Some are autotrophic, but most are heterotrophic. Archaea are called extremophiles because they can live in extreme environments. They have been found in boiling hot springs, salty lakes, thermal vents on the oceans' floors, and in the mud of marshes where there is no oxygen. The archaea *Staphylothermus marinus,* shown in **Figure 15,** is found in deep ocean thermal vents and can live in water temperatures up to 98°C. C

MiniLab 2

Compare Bacteria

? Inquiry MiniLab

How do the physical characteristics of various types of bacteria compare? Investigate the different features of bacteria by viewing prepared bacteria slides under the microscope.

Procedure

1. Read and complete the lab safety form.
2. Observe the prepared **slides of bacteria** with a **compound light microscope.**
3. Create a data table to compare the shapes and features of the bacteria you observe.
4. Compare and contrast the bacteria from the prepared slides. Record your observations and comparisons in your data table.

Analysis

1. **Compare and contrast** the shapes of the individual bacteria cells that you observed.
2. **Describe** whether any of your bacteria samples formed colonies. What does a colony look like?
3. **Design** a classification system for the bacteria that you observed based on the collected data.

Content Background

Teacher FYI Inform students that the proteins used in forensic DNA testing were first obtained from archaea living in the hot springs of Yellowstone National Park.

Differentiated Instruction

English Learners Students with limited English proficiency might not understand the procedure instructions for the MiniLab on this page. To ensure their comprehension, ask English learners to repeat the instructions to you and clarify if necessary.

For more tips, see pages 14T–15T.

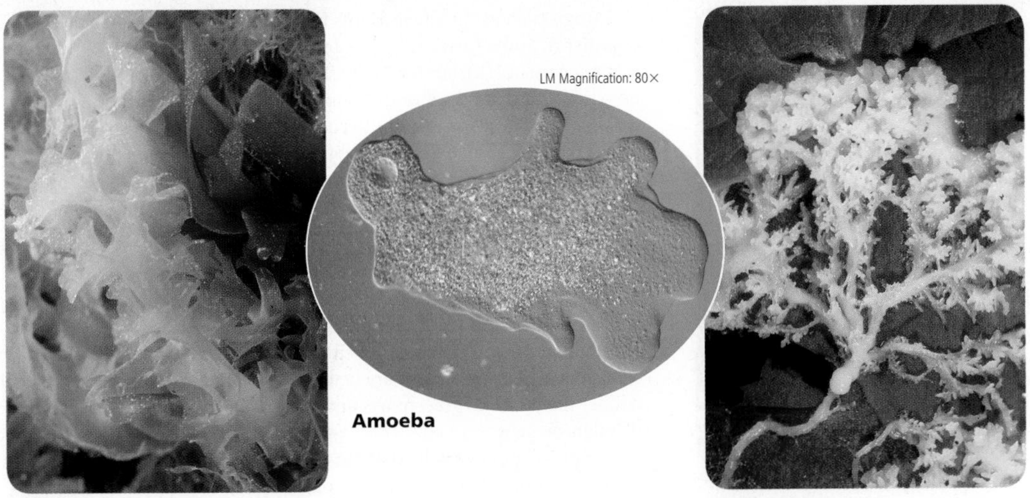

Kelp

Amoeba

Slime mold

Figure 16 These protists look different, but they all are eukaryotes, live in moist environments, and do not have organs.
Infer *which of these protists are plantlike, animal-like, or funguslike.*

Domain Eukarya

Cells with a membrane-bound nucleus and other membrane-bound organelles are called eukaryotic cells. All organisms with these cells are called eukaryotes and are classified in Domain Eukarya. Domain Eukarya contains Kingdom Protista, Kingdom Fungi, Kingdom Plantae, and Kingdom Animalia.

Kingdom Protista The wide variety of species shown in **Figure 16** belong to Kingdom Protista. Members of Kingdom Protista are called protists. **Protists** are eukaryotic organisms that can be unicellular, colonial, or multicellular. Unlike plants or animals, protists do not have organs. Though protists are not necessarily similar to each other, they do not fit in any other kingdoms. They are classified into three broad groups.

The plantlike protists are called algae. All algae, such as kelp, are autotrophs that perform photosynthesis. Animal-like protists are called protozoans. Protozoans, such as amoebas, are heterotrophs. Funguslike protists include slime molds and mildews, and they comprise the third group of protists. Euglenoids (yoo GLEE noyds) are a type of protist that has both plantlike and animal-like characteristics. They usually are grouped with the plantlike protists because they have chloroplasts and can perform photosynthesis.

D **Kingdom Fungi** A **fungus** is a unicellular or multicellular eukaryote that absorbs nutrients from organic materials in its environment. Members of Kingdom Fungi are heterotrophic, lack motility—the ability to move—and have cell walls. Their cell walls contain a substance called chitin (KI tun)—a rigid polymer that provides structural support. A fungus consists of a mass of threadlike filaments called hyphae (HI fee). Hyphae are threadlike filaments that are responsible for the fungus's growth, feeding, and reproduction. Fungi fossils exist that are over 400 million years old, and there are more than 70,000 known species.

Video BrainPOP

FOLDABLES®
Incorporate information from this section into your Foldable.

D Develop Concepts

BL OL

Clarify a Misconception
ASK STUDENTS: ***Are most fungi, especially mushrooms, pathogenic or infectious?*** no Tell students that only about 100 of the more than 100,000 known species of fungi cause disease in humans.

Although most fungi do not cause disease in humans, only people who are mushroom experts should harvest or eat wild mushrooms.

Some fungi can be pathogenic without being ingested. One example is *Candida albicans*—the cause of thrush, yeast infections, and sometimes dangerous blood infections. *C. albicans* is part of the natural flora present on human skin and in human saliva, intestines, and the vaginal tract. If growth of this fungi becomes unchecked, it can cause an infection.

FOLDABLES®

RUBRIC A rubric for evaluating Foldables is found on your eTeacherEdition Online.

Going Further On the back of their Foldables, have students explain why a knowledge of classification would be important to a zookeeper, a landscape architect, or a paleontologist.

Video BrainPOP

Demonstration

Fungi Diversity Demonstrate the diversity of Kingdom Fungi with living examples, preserved specimens, or photos. You can buy several types of mushrooms from grocery stores, or you can pick them from their natural habitat. Collect lichens and bracket fungi, if possible. Be aware, however, that some students might have fungus allergies. Est. time: 5 min

Caption Question Fig. 16 The kelp is plantlike, the amoeba is animal-like, and the slime mold is funguslike.

Concepts in Motion

Interactive Table

S Skill Practice

BL OL AL Visual Literacy

ASK STUDENTS: ***By looking at Table 3, how can you explain that at one time all the species in the Kingdoms Bacteria and Fungi and some species in Protista were grouped in the Kingdom Plantae?*** There were only two kingdoms—plants and animals. Because fungi, bacteria, and algae have cell walls, they were included with the plants.

D Develop Concepts

BL OL AL Scaffolding

ASK STUDENTS: ***Which domain contains the most kingdoms?*** Domain Eukarya ***List the four kingdoms in Domain Eukarya.*** Protista, Fungi, Plantae, Animalia ***Differentiate between Kingdom Protista and Kingdom Fungi.*** Responses will vary, but students should indicate that members of Kingdom Fungi have eukaryotic cells with chitin in the cell walls, and that members of the Kingdom Protista have eukaryotic cells with cellulose in some. ***Classify an organism that is multicellular, has cell walls, is photosynthetic, and has well-developed tissues and organs.*** Kingdom Plantae

Reading Check Plants are multicellular, have cell walls made of cellulose, and have cells that are organized into tissues.

■ **Figure 17** Fungi come in a variety of sizes, from microscopic yeasts to multicellular forms, such as the mushrooms shown here.

Fungi, such as the mushrooms in **Figure 17,** are heterotrophic organisms. Some fungi are parasites—organisms that grow and feed on other organisms. Other fungi are saprobes—organisms that get their nourishment from dead or decaying organic matter. Unlike heterotrophs that digest their food internally, fungi secrete digestive enzymes into their food source and then absorb digested materials directly into their cells. Fungi that live in a mutualistic relationship with algae are called lichens. Lichens get their food from the algae that live among their hyphae.

Kingdom Plantae There are more than 250,000 species of plants in Kingdom Plantae (PLAN tuh). These organisms form the base of all terrestrial habitats. All plants are multicellular and have cell walls composed of cellulose. Most plants contain chloroplasts, where photosynthesis is carried out, but a few plants are heterotrophic. For example, the parasitic dodder plant has no green parts and extracts its food from host plants through suckers.

All plants possess cells that are organized into tissues, and many plants also possess organs such as roots, stems, and leaves. Like the fungi, plants lack motility. However, some plants do have reproductive cells that have flagella, which propel them through water. The characteristics of plants and members of the other five kingdoms are summarized in **Table 3.** D

Reading Check **Describe** three characteristics of plants.

S

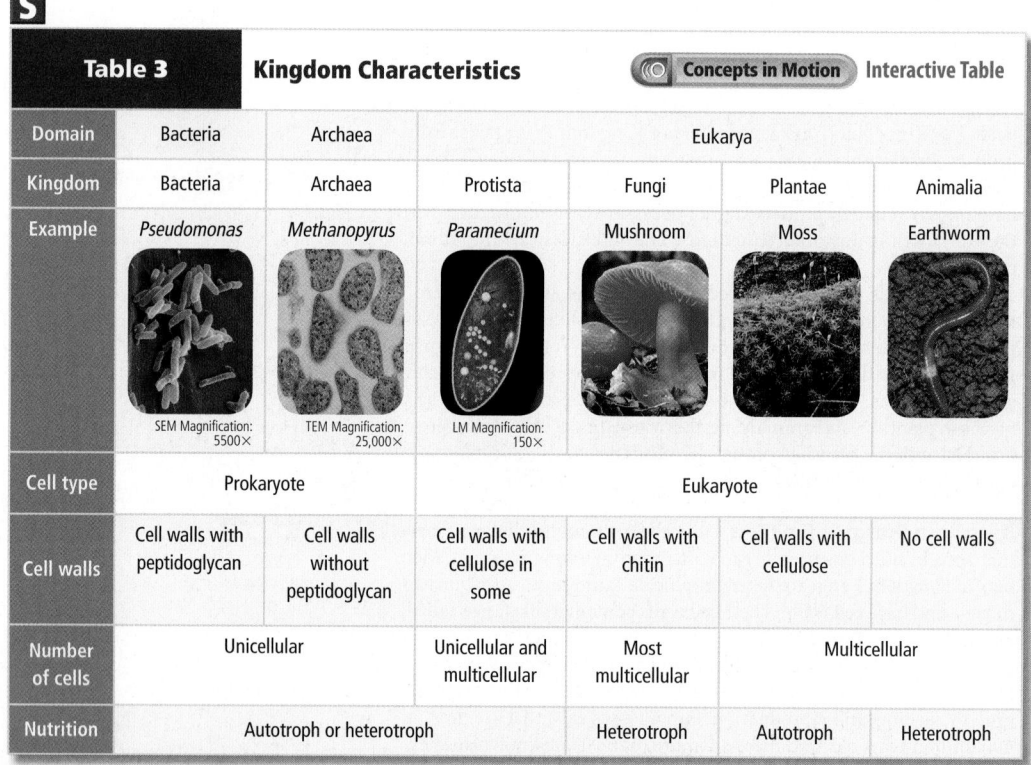

Table 3 Kingdom Characteristics Concepts in Motion Interactive Table

Domain	Bacteria	Archaea	Eukarya			
Kingdom	Bacteria	Archaea	Protista	Fungi	Plantae	Animalia
Example	*Pseudomonas* 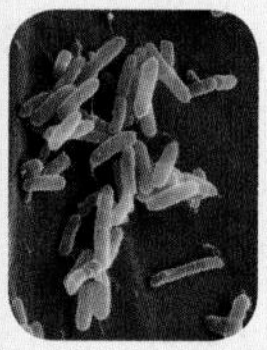 SEM Magnification: 5500×	*Methanopyrus* 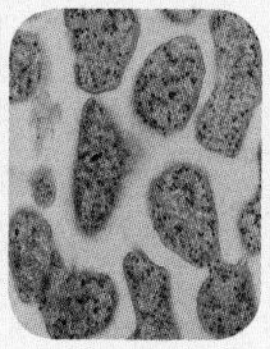 TEM Magnification: 25,000×	*Paramecium* 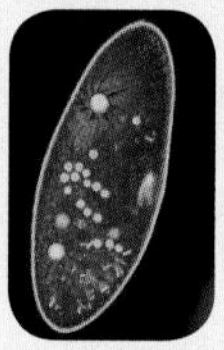 LM Magnification: 150×	Mushroom 	Moss 	Earthworm 
Cell type	Prokaryote		Eukaryote			
Cell walls	Cell walls with peptidoglycan	Cell walls without peptidoglycan	Cell walls with cellulose in some	Cell walls with chitin	Cell walls with cellulose	No cell walls
Number of cells	Unicellular		Unicellular and multicellular	Most multicellular	Multicellular	
Nutrition	Autotroph or heterotroph			Heterotroph	Autotroph	Heterotroph

Demonstration

BL OL AL Plant Diversity Show students a variety of plants as you discuss their classification. If possible show mosses and liverworts, ferns, conifers or their cones, and flowering plants. Relate the specimens to Aristotle's system of classifying herbs, shrubs, and trees. Est. time: 15 min

Research Citation

Question Educational research indicates that teachers should use a variety of questioning strategies to improve student comprehension of material. The scaffolding strategy on this page will actively engage students in the text and guide them to a deeper level of understanding. (Jorgensen, 1998)

Research bibliography on pages 32T–34T

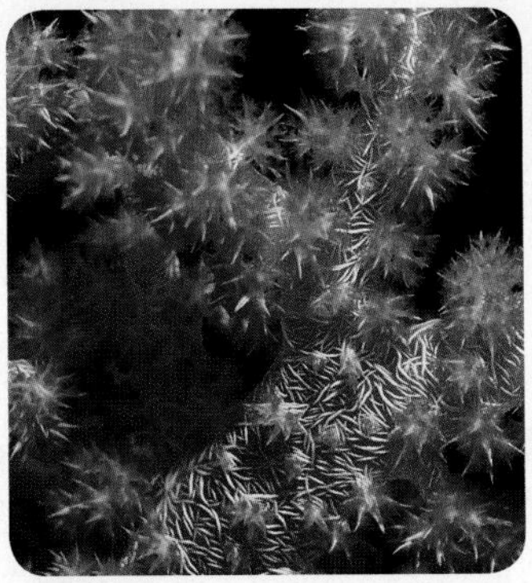

Coral

Fish

Rabbit

■ **Figure 18** Members of Kingdom Animalia can look very different from each other, even though they are in the same kingdom.

Kingdom Animalia Members of Kingdom Animalia are commonly called animals. More than one million animal species have been identified. All animals are heterotrophic, multicellular eukaryotes. Animal cells do not have cell walls. All animal cells are organized into tissues, and most tissues are organized into organs, such as skin, a stomach, and a brain. Animal organs often are organized into complex organ systems, like digestive, circulatory, or nervous systems. Animals range in size from a few millimeters to many meters. They live in the water, on land, and in the air. **Figure 18** shows some of the variety of organisms classified in Kingdom Animalia. Most animals are motile, although some, such as coral, lack motility as adults.

Viruses—an exception Have you ever experienced a cold or the flu? If so, you have had a close encounter with a virus. A virus is a nucleic acid surrounded by a protein coat. Viruses do not possess cells, nor are they cells, and are not considered to be living. Because they are nonliving, they usually are not placed in the biological classification system.

Section 3 Assessment

Section Summary

- Domains Bacteria and Archaea contain prokaryotes.
- Organisms are classified at the kingdom level based on cell type, structures, and nutrition.
- Domain Eukarya contains four kingdoms of eukaryotes.
- Because viruses are not living, they are not included in the biological classification system.

Understand Main Ideas

1. MAIN Idea **State** the three domains and the kingdoms in each.
2. **Compare and contrast** characteristics of the three domains.
3. **Explain** the difference between Kingdom Protista and Kingdom Fungi.
4. **Classify** to the kingdom level an organism that has organ systems, lacks cell walls, and ingests food.

Think Critically

5. **Summarize** the reasons why systematists separated Domain Bacteria from Domain Archaea.

WRITING in **Biology**

6. Write an essay for or against including viruses in the biological classification system.

Develop Concepts

BL COOP LEARN **Kinesthetic**

Have students create a skit about classifying an organism. Have students refer to Table 3 on the previous page for ideas for organisms to classify. Have each student in the skit play the role of an organism and go through the process of being classified.

Formative Assessment

Evaluation Show students pictures of organisms and provide other descriptive information, if necessary, such as whether the organism is unicellular and if the cells contain organelles. Have students identify the domain and kingdom to which each organism belongs.

Remediation Show students the pictures of the organisms. Review characteristics of the organism and lead a class discussion of the reasons why each organism is classified into a particular domain and kingdom.

Section 3 Assessment

1. Domain Bacteria is synonymous with Kingdom Bacteria. Domain Archaea is synonymous with Kingdom Archaea. Domain Eukarya contains Kingdoms Protista, Fungi, Plantae, and Animalia.
2. Refer to Table 3.
3. Answers will vary. Cell walls of some protists contain cellulose. Cell walls of fungi are often composed of chitin.
4. Kingdom Animalia
5. Biochemical studies showed that archaea and bacteria were as different from each other as they are from eukaryotes.
6. Answers will vary. In their arguments against the inclusion of viruses, students might point out that they are not composed of cells and are not even considered living. In their arguments in favor of the inclusion, students can point to the fact that they have genetic material, which is characteristic of other life.

WRITING in **Biology**

RUBRIC Use the modifiable rubric found on your eTeacherEdition Online to assess writing assignments.

Assessment Online Quiz

CUTTING-EDGE BIOLOGY

Purpose
Students will understand real-world applications of biology. E.2

Anticipatory Guide
ASK STUDENTS: ***What is a UPC code?*** Almost every product worldwide has a UPC bar code, which is a unique UPC number.
ASK STUDENTS: ***Can you think of a way that UPC codes could be used in biology?*** Assigning bar codes to species could be used in biology for species identification. Tell students that as they read the feature, they will learn how bioinformatics can create a database of DNA barcodes to help us organize information about the almost two million species that we know about.

Background
Over the last few decades, advances in science—specifically molecular biology and genomic technologies—have led to an abundance of information. Computers are used not only to store all this data, but also to generate a database that organizes, indexes, and analyzes the data. A biological database allows for easy access to this information. Bioinformatics is a field of science that combines biology with computer and information sciences. The ultimate goal is to create a global network for sharing information. New insights into the molecular basis of life—such as DNA bar coding—allow scientists to advance their knowledge of evolutionary biology.

CUTTING-EDGE BIOLOGY

DNA BAR CODES

Most people would find it odd if their friend collected vials containing muscles from 940 different species of fish—but then again most people have not undertaken a project as ambitious as this one.

DNA UPC Paul Herbert, a geneticist at the University of Guelph in Ontario, Canada, is trying to gather cell samples from all of the world's organisms. With small pieces of tissue no larger than the head of a pin, Herbert and his international colleagues are working to assign DNA bar codes to every living species.

Herbert has shown that the segment of mitochondrial DNA, called cytochrome *c* oxidase I, or COI, can be used as a diagnostic tool to tell animal species apart. The COI gene is simple to isolate and allows for identification of an animal. A different gene would need to be used for plants. Just like UPC codes, the DNA segment sequence could be stored in a master database that would allow for easy access to the material. A hand scanner, when supplied with a small piece of tissue, such as a scale, a hair, or a feather, could identify the species almost instantly.

Potential benefits This technology has several potential benefits. A doctor might use it to pinpoint disease-causing organisms quickly to prevent epidemics or to determine what antivenom to give a snakebite victim. Health inspectors could scan foods for plant and animal contaminants. People who are curious about their surroundings could learn what lives around them. Farmers would be able to identify pests and use species-specific methods for their removal.

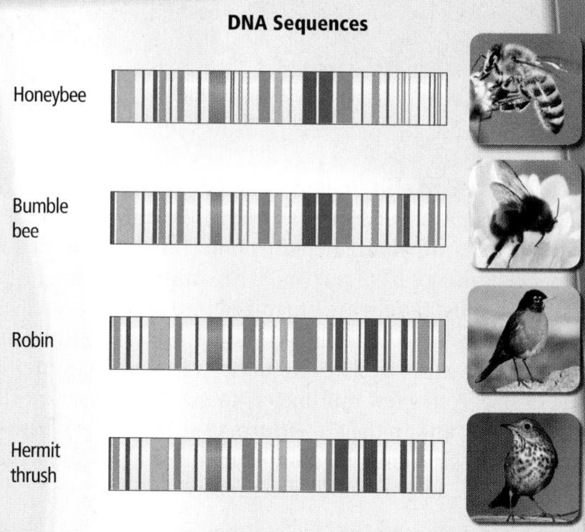

This representation of DNA barcodes shows that more closely related species would have more similar barcodes.

A new way to classify Using bioinformatics—a field of science in which biology, computer science, and information technology merge—to create a database of DNA barcodes allows taxonomists to classify more organisms quickly.

Currently, taxonomists have identified approximately 1.75 million species. Scientists estimate that anywhere between 10 and 100 million species exist. Historically, species have been classified using morphology, genetics, phylogeny, habitat, and behavior. While the bar codes would not replace classic taxonomic methods, they could supplement them by giving scientists another tool to use.

E-COMMUNICATION
Fact Finder Think of at least three questions you have about DNA bar coding. Research to find answers to your questions. Then, share your questions and answers with your class by e-mailing them to your teacher.

Follow-Up Activity
Organize students into groups of five. For each group, have a set of 15 cards prepared as follows: pictures of three bird species, three mammal species, three plant species, three bacterial species, and three fish species. Some should be easily differentiated; some should be more difficult. On each species card, include a UPC code (from a grocery item) and short description of the animal. Glue an identical UPC code for each species to cardboard, and write the scientific name of the animal. Hand each group a set of cards and have them classify each animal traditionally using the Linnaean method. Provide classification standards to help them do so (i.e., Mammals have mammary glands). Then have them match the animal using the bar codes. Have them explain which method they thought was the easiest. Then have them identify which method was the most accurate. Est. time: 15 min

WebQuest

BIOLAB

HOW CAN ORGANISMS BE GROUPED ON A CLADOGRAM?

Background: **When a cladogram is made, derived characters are used to divide the organisms into groups called clades. In this exercise, you will use simulated data to learn how to make a simple cladogram and then make your own cladogram.**

Question: *How can you use organisms' characteristics to construct a cladogram?*

Materials
paper and pencil
examples of cladograms
photographs of various organisms
books describing characteristics of organisms

Procedure
1. Read and complete the lab safety form.
2. Examine the data table provided.
3. Compare the shared derived characteristics of the sample organisms. Assume that all the characteristics of your outgroup are ancestral. To make the data easier to compare, note that a "0" has been assigned to each ancestral character and a "1" to all derived characters.
4. Use the information to develop a cladogram that best shows the relationships of the organisms.
5. Make sure your teacher approves your cladogram before you proceed.
6. Choose four organisms from one of the domains you have studied that you believe are closely related.
7. Develop a table of derived characteristics of these organisms similar to the table you used in Step 2. Use your table to develop a cladogram that groups the organisms based on their shared derived characters.

Data Table for Cladistic Analysis

Organisms	Characters			
	1	2	3	4
A	b(1)	a(0)	a(0)	b(1)
B	b(1)	b(1)	b(1)	a(0)
C	b(1)	a(0)	b(1)	a(0)

Data obtained from: Lipscomb, D. 1998. Basics of cladistic analysis. George Washington University. http://www.gwu.edu/~clade/faculty/lipscomb/Cladistics.pdf

Analyze and Conclude
1. **Think Critically** How did you determine which were the ancestral and which were the derived characters of the organisms you examined?
2. **Explain** how you determined which characteristics to use to separate the clades.
3. **Explain** which organism is the outgroup on your cladogram. Why?
4. **Critique** Trade data tables with another lab group. Use their data to draw a cladogram. Compare the two cladograms and explain any differences.
5. **Error Analysis** What type of error would mistaking analogous structures as homologous introduce into a cladogram? Examine your second cladogram and determine if you have made this error.

APPLY YOUR SKILL
Construct Molecular data, such as the amino acid sequences of shared proteins, can be used to make cladograms. Research cytochrome *c*, a protein important in aerobic respiration, and decide how it could be used to construct a cladogram.

Analyze and Conclude
1. Answers should indicate that the ancestral characters were those shared by all the organisms in the group they chose. The derived characters are those shared only by some of the organisms or by only one of the organisms.
2. Students should indicate they used derived characteristics to separate the clades, and that shared derived characteristics indicate a more common recent ancestor.
3. The outgroup chosen for each cladogram will vary, but students should indicate that they understand that the outgroup represents an organism with ancestral characters of the clade.
4. Students critiques will vary. Some groups may draw cladograms that are identical, but other groups may differ. They will likely find that although the cladograms may look different, the same organisms were placed into clades together in each.
5. If an analogous structure is thought to be homologous, two organisms will be assumed to be more closely related than they actually are.

BIOLAB

? Inquiry BioLab

For a lab worksheet, use your eTeacherEdition Online.

✱RUBRIC A rubric for evaluating BioLabs is found on your eTeacherEdition Online.

Est. Time 90 min

Content Background Drawing cladograms is not an intuitive task and not one students will easily master. Many different methods are used to construct cladograms. In this lab, the information from one character at a time is considered. This method is called the Hennig Argumentation. (Lipscomb, D. 1998. Basics of cladistic analysis. George Washington University. http://www.gwu.edu/~clade/faculty/lipscomb/Cladistics.pdf)

Safety Precaution Approve lab safety forms before work begins.

Teaching Strategies
- Look at the sample cladogram and go over it as as a group first to prepare students to work on their own.
- You might wish to find previously constructed cladograms of several different groups of organisms. Have these groups of organisms available for groups to choose to work with. Have students compare their cladograms to the previously constructed ones.

Alternative Teaching Demo Project an image and work with the simulated data as a group. Pick a group of related organisms ahead of time and then assign one organism to each lab group. Have the group develop a list of characteristics of the organism, then brainstorm as a class to develop the table of derived characters. Have each group draw a cladogram based on this table.

Chapter 17 Study Guide

![ConnectED]

Students can use the following to review the chapter.

Review

Vocabulary eGames
Vocabulary eFlashcards
Vocabulary PuzzleMaker

Assessment

Online Quizzes
Online Test Practice
Standardized Test Practice

Use the *ExamView® Assessment Suite* CD-ROM to:

- create multiple versions of tests
- create modified tests with one mouse click
- edit existing questions and add your own questions
- build tests aligned with state standards using built-in state curriculum tags
- change English tests to Spanish with one mouse click
- track students' progress using the Teacher Management System

Chapter 17 Study Guide

THEME FOCUS Diversity Earth's diverse organisms are classified and organized into a hierarchy of domains and kingdoms using phylogeny and genetics.

BIG Idea Evolution underlies the classification of life's diversity.

Section 1 The History of Classification

classification (p. 484)
taxonomy (p. 485)
binomial nomenclature (p. 485)
taxon (p. 487)
genus (p. 487)
family (p. 487)
order (p. 488)
class (p. 488)
phylum (p. 488)
division (p. 488)
kingdom (p. 488)
domain (p. 488)

MAIN Idea Biologists use a system of classification to organize information about the diversity of living things.

- Aristotle developed the first widely accepted biological classification system.
- Linnaeus used morphology and behavior to classify plants and animals.
- Binomial nomenclature uses the Latin genus and species to give an organism a scientific name.
- Organisms are classified according to a nested hierarchical system.

Section 2 Modern Classification

phylogeny (p. 491)
character (p. 492)
molecular clock (p. 495)
cladistics (p. 495)
cladogram (p. 496)

MAIN Idea Classification systems have changed over time as information has increased.

- The definition of species has changed over time.
- Phylogeny is the inferred evolutionary history of a species, evidence for which comes from a variety of studies.
- A molecular clock uses comparisons of DNA sequences to estimate phylogeny and rate of evolutionary change.
- Cladistic analysis models evolutionary relationships based on sequencing derived characters.

Section 3 Domains and Kingdoms

archaea (p. 500)
protist (p. 501)
fungus (p. 501)

MAIN Idea The most widely used biological classification system has six kingdoms within three domains.

- Domains Bacteria and Archaea contain prokaryotes.
- Organisms are classified at the kingdom level based on cell type, structures, and nutrition.
- Domain Eukarya contains four kingdoms of eukaryotes.
- Because viruses are not living, they are not included in the biological classification system.

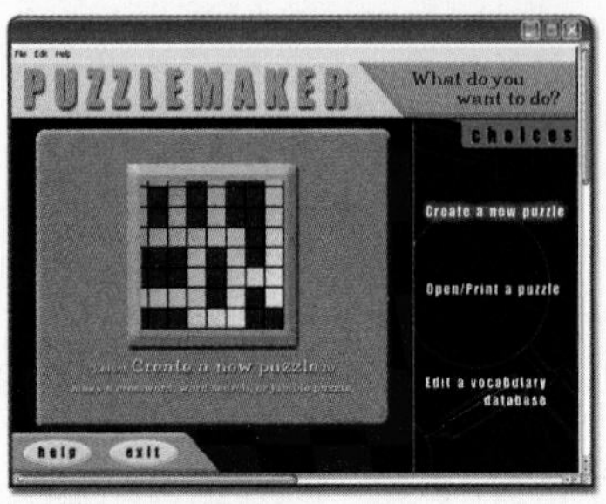

Review **Vocabulary PuzzleMaker**

For additional practice with vocabulary, have students access the Vocabulary PuzzleMaker online.

Review **Vocabulary eGames**

Section 1

Vocabulary Review

Match each definition with the correct term from the Study Guide page.

1. system of naming species using two words
2. taxon of closely related species that share a recent common ancestor
3. branch of biology that groups and names species based on studies of their different characteristics

Understand Main Ideas

4. On what did Linnaeus base his classification?
   A. derived characters
   B. binomial nomenclature
   C. morphology and habitat
   D. evolutionary relationship

Use the table to answer questions 5 and 6.

Classification of Selected Mammals

Kingdom	Animalia	Animalia	Animalia	Animalia
Phylum	Chordata	Chordata	Chordata	Chordata
Class	Mammalia	Mammalia	Mammalia	Mammalia
Order	Cetacea	Carnivora	Carnivora	Carnivora
Family	Mysticeti	Felidae	Canidae	Canidae
Genus	*Balenopora*	*Felis*	*Canis*	*Canis*
Species	*B. physalis*	*F. catus*	*C. latrans*	*C. lupus*
Common name	Blue whale	Domestic cat	Coyote	Wolf

5. Which animal is the most distant relative to the others?
   A. wolf
   B. coyote
   C. domestic cat
   D. blue whale

6. At which level does the domestic cat diverge from the coyote?
   A. family **C.** order
   B. class **D.** genus

Constructed Response

7. **THEME FOCUS Diversity** Explain the rules and uses of binomial nomenclature.
8. **Short Answer** Why is seahorse not a good scientific name?

Think Critically

9. **MAIN Idea** How does the system of classification relate to the diversity of species?

Section 2

Vocabulary Review

Differentiate between the following pairs.

10. phylogeny, character
11. cladogram, molecular clock

Understand Main Ideas

Use the figure below to answer questions 12 and 13.

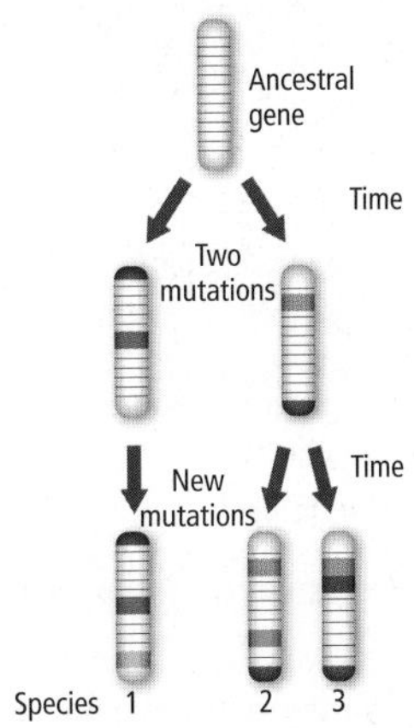

12. What does this figure represent?
   A. pedigree **C.** molecular clock
   B. cladogram **D.** phylogenetic tree

13. What do the colored bands in the figure represent?
   A. mutations **C.** ancestral characters
   B. derived characters **D.** genomes

Chapter 17 Assessment

Section 1

Vocabulary Review

1. binomial nomenclature
2. genus
3. taxonomy

Understand Main Ideas

4. C
5. D
6. A

Constructed Response

7. Each organism is given two Latin names. The first identifies the genus; the second name indicates the species name.
8. A seahorse is a common name that implies a relationship exists between this organism and a horse.

Think Critically

9. Creating categories and organizing them into a classification system makes it easier for scientists to study organisms and identify relationships among organisms.

Section 2

Vocabulary Review

10. Phylogeny is the evolutionary history of a species. A character is an inherited feature that varies among the members of a species.
11. A cladogram is a branching diagram that represents the evolution of a species or other taxon. A molecular clock is a model that uses comparisons of DNA sequences to estimate how long species have been evolving independently.

Understand Main Ideas

12. C
13. A

Assessment Online Test Practice

14. B
15. B
16. B
17. D

Constructed Response

18. If the scientists use different characters, the cladograms will be different.
19. First, the characters to be used in the cladogram must be identified. Next, these characters are arranged in a linear fashion in the order in which they evolved as compared to an ancestral outgroup. Finally, a line is drawn to connect each organism or group to the line of characters, producing a branch.
20. The more similar the biochemical characters of two organisms, the closer the evolutionary relationship is between them.

Think Critically

21. The typological species concept is based on a comparison of physical characteristics. The phylogenetic species concept is determined by evolutionary history.
22. Molecular clocks should be used with genes that mutate at a relatively consistent rate. In cases where mutations are less consistent, molecular clocks can be used in conjunction with other data (fossil record) to establish evolutionary relationships.
23. Morphological characters, such as feathers and bone structures, are used as evidence of shared ancestry.

Section 3

Vocabulary Review

24. protist
25. Archaea
26. fungi

Understand Main Ideas

27. D
28. B

14. Which species concept defines a species as a group of organisms that are able to reproduce successfully in the wild?
    - **A.** typological species concept
    - **B.** biological species concept
    - **C.** evolutionary species concept
    - **D.** phylogenetic species concept

Use the figure below to answer questions 15 and 16.

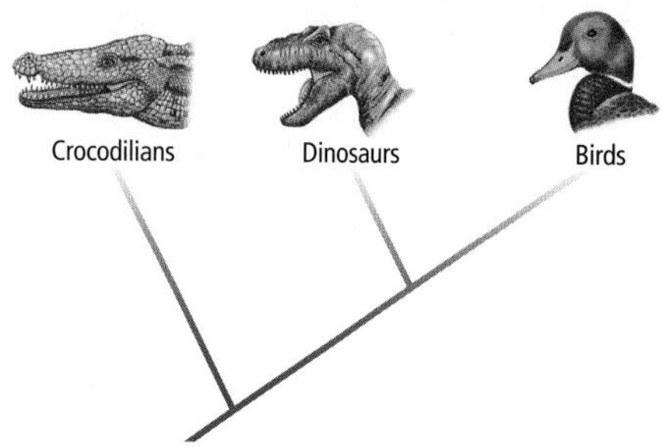

15. According to the figure, which organism diverged last?
    - **A.** alligators
    - **B.** birds
    - **C.** crocodiles
    - **D.** dinosaurs

16. Which is represented by the figure?
    - **A.** pedigree
    - **B.** cladogram
    - **C.** molecular clock
    - **D.** character

17. Which does not affect the rate of mutation in a molecular clock?
    - **A.** type of mutation
    - **B.** location of gene in genome
    - **C.** the protein affected
    - **D.** the time of divergence

Constructed Response

18. **Open Ended** Two scientists produce two different cladograms for the same groups of organisms. Explain how the differences are possible.

19. **Short Answer** Describe how to make a cladogram. Include the types of characters that are used and the judgments you must make about the characters.

20. **Short Answer** Summarize how biochemical characters can be used to determine phylogeny.

Think Critically

21. MAIN Idea Differentiate between the typological species concept and the phylogenetic species concept.

22. **Decide** How should molecular clocks be used if not all mutations occur at the same rate? Should they be considered reliable evidence of phylogeny? Explain your answer.

Use the figure below to answer question 23.

23. **Evaluate** evidence that suggests that the two organisms in the figure are closely related.

Section 3

Vocabulary Review

Replace the italicized words with the correct vocabulary terms from the Study Guide page.

24. Algae are a type of *archaea.*

25. *Bacteria* are called extremophiles because they grow in extreme environments.

26. Some types of *protists* are used to make food products like bread and cheese.

Understand Main Ideas

27. Which taxon contains one or more kingdoms?
    - **A.** genus
    - **B.** phylum
    - **C.** family
    - **D.** domain

28. In which kingdom would prokaryotes found living in acid runoff likely be classified?
    - **A.** Bacteria
    - **B.** Archaea
    - **C.** Fungi
    - **D.** Protista

Use the photograph below to answer question 29.

29. In which kingdom would this organism, which has chloroplasts, cell walls, but no organs, be classified?
    A. Plantae **C.** Protista
    B. Animalia **D.** Fungi

30. Which substance would most likely be in the cell walls of an organism with chloroplasts and tissues?
    A. peptidoglycan **C.** hyphae
    B. chitin **D.** cellulose

Constructed Response

31. MAIN Idea Indicate the relationship between domains and kingdoms.

32. **Short Answer** Predict in which domain a taxonomist would place a newly discovered photosynthetic organism that has cells without membrane-bound organelles and no peptidoglycan.

33. **Open Ended** Write an argument for or against including Bacteria and Archaea in the same domain. How would this affect the phylogenetic tree of life?

Think Critically

34. **Analyze** Using the model in **Figure 12,** decide which three of the kingdoms in Domain Eukarya evolved from the fourth.

35. **CAREERS IN BIOLOGY** A biologist studied two groups of frogs in the laboratory. The groups looked identical and produced fertile offspring when interbred. However, in nature, they do not interbreed because their reproductive calls are different and their territories do not overlap. Use your knowledge of species concepts and speciation to decide why they should or should not be placed in the same species.

Summative Assessment

36. BIG Idea Life on Earth was organized by Aristotle into three categories. Why has the classification system become so complex since Aristotle's time?

37. Draw a cladogram or phylogenetic tree that displays the order of evolution of the six kingdoms. Explain the reasoning for your interpretation.

38. WRITING in Biology Suppose you found a cricket near your home. After a biologist from a local university studies your find, you learn that the cricket is a new species. Write a paragraph to explain how the biologist might have determined that the cricket is a new species.

DBQ Document-Based Questions

Data obtained from: Blaxter, M. 2001. Sum of the arthropod parts. *Science* 413:121-122.

Scientists continue to debate about evolutionary relationships among organisms. Groups of arthropods were thought to be related in the way shown on the left, but new molecular evidence suggests that the grouping on the right is more accurate.

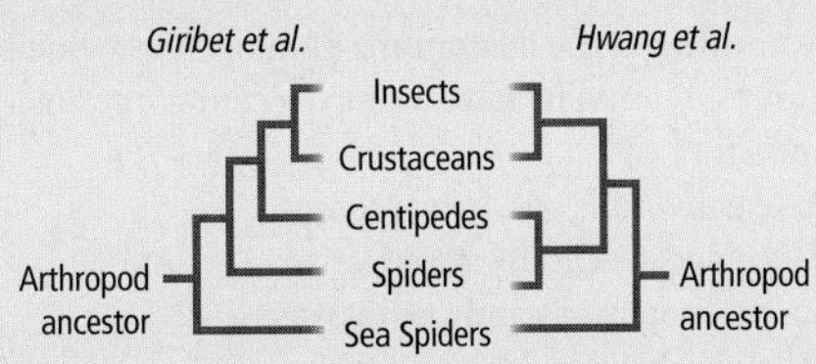

39. Compare and contrast the two cladograms. How did the molecular evidence change the relationship between centipedes and spiders?

40. To which group are crustaceans most closely related?

41. Which group in the cladogram appears to be the most ancestral?

29. C
30. D

Constructed Response

31. Domains are a category higher than, and containing, one or more kingdoms. There are greater fundamental differences between domains than between kingdoms.
32. Archaea
33. An argument for placing them in the same domain can be made by pointing out that they have more characteristics in common (unicellular prokaryotes that can be either heterotrophic or autotrophic) than not in common (cell wall composition). An argument against this can be made by pointing out that members of the Domain Archae live in extreme environments and therefore are unique. Placing them in the same or different domains does not affect the phylogenetic tree of life, as prokaryotes remain the most ancient of life forms.

Think Critically

34. Fungi, plants, and animals evolved from a recent common ancestor of protists.
35. They should not be placed in the same species because they do not interbreed to produce fertile offspring in nature. The biological species concept requires that fertile offspring are produced.

Summative Assessment

36. Many more species have been discovered since Aristotle's time. The discovery of DNA and genetic material has also led to a much more complicated classification system.
37. Students might sequence the order of evolution from Kingdom Bacteria organisms to unicellular protists, which have organized membrane bound nuclei, to Kingdom Archaea organisms, which can live in harsh environments and have no cell nucleus.

WRITING in Biology

38. The cricket may have had different structures, or, more likely, its sequences of DNA or RNA were observed to be very different from other similar species.

DBQ Document-Based Questions

Blaxter, M. 2001. Sum of the arthropod parts. *Science* 413: 121–122.

39. They have a recent common ancestor.
40. insects
41. sea spiders

Assessment Online Test Practice

Standardized Test Practice

Multiple Choice

1. A 5. D
2. D 6. A
3. C 7. A
4. D 8. A

Short Answer

9. Answers may vary. Accept logical answers.
   Binocular vision: Helps with depth perception; useful when climbing trees
   Rods and cones in retinas of the eyes: Allows for color vision; useful during the day for finding food
   Opposable thumb: Allows hand to grasp better; useful for climbing
10. Molecular clocks can show mutation-related changes in DNA, so they can track changes that might not show up in the morphological characters of organisms. Additionally, if calibrated, they provide possible timelines, which morphological characters usually do not.
11. Homologous structures might be similar-looking; they developed from the same evolutionary ancestor. Analogous structures developed from different evolutionary ancestors, even though their structures might appear to be similar.
12. Answers can vary. One advantage is that bipedalism frees the arms to engage in activities such as food getting, defense, and building rather than walking. Another advantage is that bipedalism allows an apelike animal to see farther when it is walking upright than when it is walking on four limbs.
13. Aristotle classified organisms based on similarities of appearance and behavior. A fundamental difference between plants and animals is that plants do not move and animals do. That difference was probably the basis of his classification system. Because microscopes had not been invented, people were not aware of microscopic organisms.
14. "Lucy" is the nickname of a skeleton of *Australopithecus afarensis.* The skeleton is relatively complete and is approximately 3 million years old. The skeleton is evidence that a group of hominids had bipedal posture before large brain sizes developed.

Standardized Test Practice

Cumulative

Multiple Choice

1. Which data shows that Neanderthals are not the ancestors of modern humans?
A. differences in Neanderthal and human DNA
B. evidence from Neanderthal burial grounds
C. muscular build of Neanderthals, as compared to humans
D. patterns of Neanderthal extinction

Use the illustration below to answer questions 2 and 3.

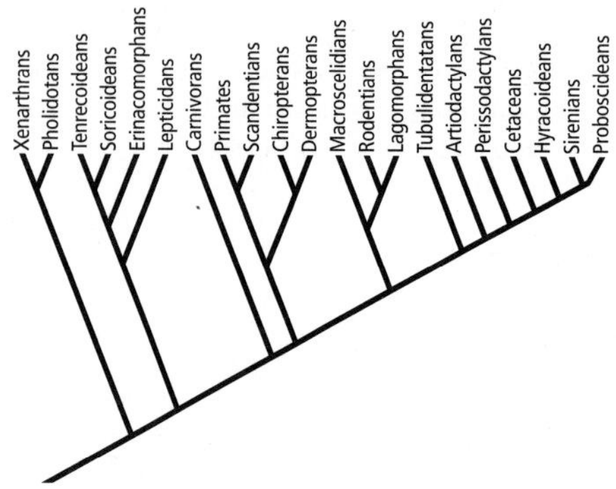

2. According to the cladogram of mammals, which two groups of animals have a more recent common ancestor?
A. carnivorans and chiropterans
B. cetaceans and hyracoideans
C. dermopterans and carnivorans
D. rodentians and lagomorphans

3. Which mammal is most closely related to bats (chiropterans)?
A. carnivorans
B. xenarthrans
C. primates
D. rodentians

4. Which radioactive isotope would be used to determine the specific age of a Paleozoic rock formation?
A. Beryllium-10 (1.5 million years)
B. Carbon-14 (5715 years)
C. Thorium-232 (14 billion years)
D. Uranium-235 (704 million years)

5. According to the Hardy-Weinberg principle, which situation would disrupt genetic equilibrium?
A. A large population of deer inhabits a forest region.
B. A particular population of flies mates randomly.
C. A population of flowering plants always has the same group of natural predators.
D. A small population of birds colonizes a new island.

Use the diagram below to answer question 6.

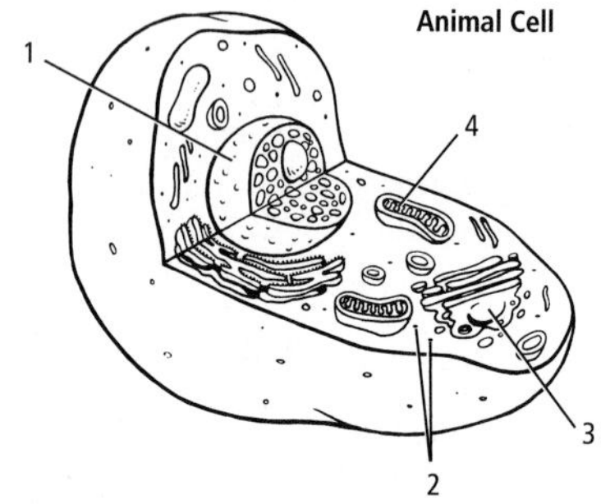

6. Which labeled structure contains the cell's genetic information?
A. 1
B. 2
C. 3
D. 4

7. Which structure is a vestigial structure?
A. human appendix
B. deer horns
C. multiple cow stomachs
D. snake tail

8. According to the endosymbiont theory, which part of the eukaryotic cell evolved from a prokaryotic cell?
A. chloroplast
B. golgi apparatus
C. nucleus
D. ribosome

Short Answer

9. List three primate adaptations found in humans, and explain how each one relates to a tree-dwelling habitat.

10. Assess how molecular clocks are useful in investigating phylogeny in ways that morphological characteristics are not.

11. In terms of their evolution, how are homologous structures and analogous structures different?

12. Assess the advantage of bipedalism.

13. Infer why Aristotle only used two kingdoms to classify living things.

14. Assess the significance of the discovery of the Lucy fossil.

15. Contrast one of the characteristics of living things with the characteristics of nonliving things such as rocks.

Use the figure below to answer question 16.

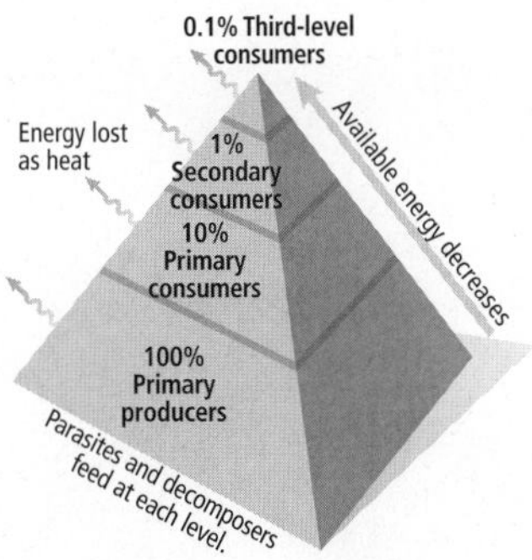

16. How much energy from one trophic level is available to organisms at the next higher trophic level?

Extended Response

17. How could a mutagen cause a change in the protein for which a DNA strand is coding? Trace the effect of a specific mutation through the process of protein synthesis.

18. Assess the value of the binomial system of naming organisms.

19. Name two animals that you would expect to have similar chromosomal characters. Design an experiment to test whether they are similar.

Essay Question

Scientists often use multiple types and sources of data in order to determine when different groups of organisms evolved. Taken together, the data can help construct an evolutionary history.

Using the information in the paragraph above, answer the following question in essay format.

20. What kind of evidence could help scientists determine whether bacteria or archaea evolved earlier on Earth? Write an essay that justifies what specific kinds of data would need to be collected to make this judgment.

NEED EXTRA HELP?																				
If You Missed Question . . .	1	2	3	4	5	6	7	8	9	10	11	12	13	14	15	16	17	18	19	20
Review Section . . .	16.3	17.2	17.2	14.1	15.3	16.2	15.2	14.2	16.1	7.2	15.2	16.2	17.1	16.2	1.1	2.2	12.3	17.1	17.2	17.2, 17.3

15. Answers may vary. Characteristics of living things include (1) has one or more cells, (2) displays organization, (3) reproduces, (4) grows and develops, (5) responds to the environment, (6) maintains homeostasis, (7) uses energy, and (8) adapts over time. A rock does not have any of these characteristics, except that it displays organization because it consists of minerals with defined chemical structural compostion.

16. About 10 percent of the energy from one trophic level is available to organisms at the next higher trophic level.

Extended Response

17. Answers can vary, but should show the pathway from a mutagen, to a mutation, to a change in the amino acid sequence, to a difference in the protein synthesized. Students should give a specific example of where the mutation could happen. For example, an added thymine nucleotide at the beginning of the sequence would cause a frameshift mutation, and the first amino acid formed in the protein would be different. This protein would not work as it is supposed to, and this could cause disease or some malfunction in the body.

18. The binomial system has value because the language used for naming, Latin, never changes. Also, scientists around the world can understand the name. Moreover, common names for organisms are often confusing. Other answers are possible.

19. Answers can vary. Two animals should be relatively closely related, like bats and rodents, or two kinds of worms. A scientist could test for similar chromosomal characters by looking at the DNA sequences in the two organisms and judging how different they really are on a genetic level.

Essay Question

20. Scientists could look at the DNA to determine similarities and differences between them. Generally the organisms with the less complex DNA and structures are thought to have originated earlier.

UNIT 5

Bacteria, Viruses, Protists, and Fungi

Preview the Unit

Have students preview the chapters in this unit and make a concept map or graphic organizer relating the Themes, Big Ideas, and Main Ideas. Students' maps should show a hierarchy between Big Ideas and Main Ideas and the interconnectedness of the Themes.

Chapter 18
Bacteria and Viruses
BIG Idea Bacteria are microscopic organisms, and viruses are nonliving microscopic agents that invade cells.

Chapter 19
Protists
BIG Idea Protists are a diverse group of unicellular and multicellular organisms that do not necessarily share the same evolutionary history.

Chapter 20
Fungi
BIG Idea Kingdom Fungi is made up of four phyla based on unique structures, methods of nutrition, and methods of reproduction.

UNIT 5

Bacteria, Viruses, Protists, and Fungi

THEMES

Scientific Inquiry The development of microscopes and new techniques allowed scientists to study archaea, bacteria, viruses, protists, and fungi.

Diversity The different ways of classifying archaea, bacteria, fungi, and protists highlight the incredible diversity of these organisms.

Energy While all archaea, bacteria, protists, and fungi use the energy stored in organic compounds, only some of them are capable of producing high-energy compounds.

Homeostasis Organisms utilize a variety of methods, such as contractile vacuoles, to maintain homeostasis.

Change By closely examining the similarities and differences among organisms, scientists are able to infer possible phylogenetic relationships.

WebQest **CAREERS IN BIOLOGY**

Microbiologists study the growth and characteristics of microscopic organisms, including bacteria, viruses, protists, and fungi. Environmental microbiologists, like the one shown here, focus their research on biological and chemical pollutants in the environment.

5-Minute UNIT LAUNCH

Activate Prior Knowledge Create three columns on the board and label them *Prokaryotes, Protists,* and *Fungi.* Have students brainstorm what they already know about these different groups of organisms and write their answers in the appropriate columns. Ask students to write the lists in their notebooks and circle one characteristic in each column that they want to learn more about. Encourage students to look for this information as they read the unit.

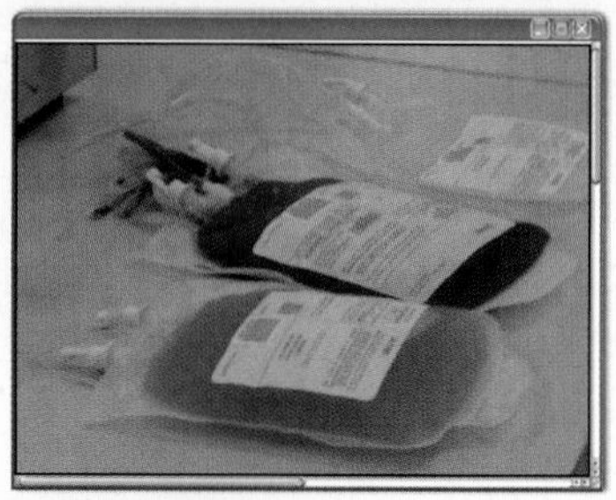

Video

What's BIOLOGY Got To Do With It?
This video discusses blood supply testing to prevent disease transmission.

Misconceptions

In each section, *Clarify a Misconception* provides you with the information to dispel a common student misconception. A question will help you elicit the misconception, and an explanation will help you correct it.

Below is a preview of misconceptions from each chapter in this unit.

Before studying Chapter 18, students might think all bacteria are harmful to humans. Chapter 18 will explain that most bacteria are harmless and even beneficial to humans (p. 522).

Before studying Chapter 19, students might think that all protists are unicellular organisms. Chapter 19 will explain that many protists, such as the red and brown algae, are large, multicellular organisms (p. 543).

Before studying Chapter 20, students might think that ringworm is caused by a worm under the skin. Chapter 20 will explain that ringworm is a fungus that causes a mark on the skin resembling the shape of a worm (p. 591).

SERVICE LEARNING/COMMUNITY SERVICE

Science Tutors Students can prepare kits to help elementary teachers present information about prokaryotes, protists, and fungi to their classes. Kits can include pictures, vocabulary flashcards, and activities to help students learn. Students should assist elementary teachers when they present the material to their classes. Teaching younger students will strengthen the students' own science learning (Eyler and Giles, 1999).

Research bibliography on pages 32T–34T

Chapter 18 Organizer:
Bacteria and Viruses

LabManager™
Customize any lab with the LabManager™ CD-ROM.

Essential Questions	National Science Standards	Materials and Planning Estimated times include cleanup and disposal, but do not include teacher prep time. For cleanup and disposal guidelines, see page 39T.	Est. Time (min)
Section 1 1. What are the differences between archaea and bacteria and their subcategories? 2. What are the survival methods of bacteria at both the individual and population levels? 3. How are bacteria beneficial to humans?	UCP.1, UCP.2, UCP.3; A.1, A.2; C.3, C.4, C.5, C.6; F.1, F.5; G.1, G.3	**Launch Lab,** p. 514: compound light microscope, slides of animal and bacterial cells, photographs of animal and bacterial cells	15
		MiniLab 1, p. 519: four slides of bacteria, microscope, photographs of bacteria	20
		Demonstration, p. 519: banana peel, small glass jar, plastic sandwich bag, rubber band, toy cow	5
		Demonstration, p. 520: package of uncooked meat, sterile cotton swabs, four petri dishes filled with agar	10 per day
		Demonstration, p. 522: two cucumbers	5
		Demonstration, p. 523: carton of pasteurized milk, petri dish filled with agar	10
Section 2 1. What is the general structure of a virus? 2. What are similarities and differences in the lytic cycle, the lysogenic cycle, and retroviral replication? 3. What is the relationship between a prion's structure, replication, and action and its ability to cause disease?	UCP.1, UCP.2, UCP.3; A.1, A.2; C.4; F.1, F.5, F.6; G.1, G.2, G.3	**Demonstration,** p. 525: spray bottle of water, food coloring	10
		Activity, p. 527: pot of cooked white rice or cinnamon or glitter	10
		Design Your Own BioLab, p. 533: bacteria cultures, sterile nutrient agar, petri dishes, antibiotic disks, control disks, forceps, Bunsen burner, marking pen, long-handle cotton swabs, 70% ethanol, thermometer, container, disinfectant, autoclave disposal bag	75

Suggested Time for Each Lesson

Class	Chapter Opener	Section 1	Section 2	Assessment
Basic	45 min	45 min	45 min	45 min
General	25 min	55 min	55 min	45 min
Honors	10 min	15 min	135 min	65 min

ConnectED

connectED.mcgraw-hill.com

Access interactive learning opportunities and teaching resources using these icons located throughout your StudentWorks™ Plus Online and eTeacherEdition Online.

Chapter 18 Section Resources	Additional Chapter 18 Resources	Technology
FAST FILE Unit 5 Resources: Launch Lab Worksheet* MiniLab Worksheet* Study Guide (English/Spanish)* Section Quick Check **Reading Essentials 18.1** **Science Notebook 18.1*** **FAST FILE Unit 5 Resources:** BioLab Worksheet* Study Guide (English/Spanish)* Section Quick Check **Reading Essentials 18.2** **Science Notebook 18.2***	**FAST FILE Unit 5 Resources:** Chapter Diagnostic Test Concept Mapping* Real-World Biology Enrichment Chapter Tests A, B, and C **Transparencies:** Bellringer Transparencies* Biology Concepts Transparencies* **Lab Resources:** Laboratory Manual* Probeware Lab Manual* Forensics Lab Manual* Pre-AP Lab Manual* Open Inquiry in Biology* Guided Inquiry in Biology*	**Teaching Tools:** eTeacherEdition Online Classroom Presentation Toolkit CD-ROM* LabManager™ CD-ROM* Video Lab DVD* Virtual Lab CD-ROM* What's BIOLOGY Got To Do With It? StudentWorks™ Plus Online* **Chapter Assessment Tools:** Classroom Presentation Toolkit CD-ROM* *ExamView® Assessment Suite* CD-ROM **Web-Based Resources:** • StudentWorks™ Plus Online • eTeacherEdition Online • Animations* • The Interactive Time Line* • Interactive Tables* • Online Quizzes • Online Test Practice • Standardized Test Practice • Virtual Labs* • Multilingual eGlossary* • Vocabulary eGames* • Vocabulary eFlashcards • WebQuests • Personal Tutors

While all resources listed are appropriate for English learners, the * indicates resources with a strong visual or hands-on component for EL.

Teaching strategies and activities have been coded for differentiated instruction.

AL Activities for students working above grade level	**OL** Activities for students working on grade level	**BL** Activities for students working below grade level	**EL** Activities for English learners (also ELL)	**COOP LEARN** Activities designed for small cooperative group work

CHAPTER 18

Launch Lab
What are the differences between animal cells and bacterial cells?

Inquiry Launch Lab

For a lab worksheet, use your eTeacherEdition Online.

RUBRIC A rubric for evaluating Launch Labs is found on your eTeacherEdition Online.

Est. Time 15 min

Alternative Materials photographs of animal cells and bacterial cells, such as Figure 1 and Figure 4, and computer slides of animal cells and bacterial cells.

Safety Precaution Approve lab safety forms before work begins.

Teaching Strategies
- Let students know that viruses are too small to be observed with classroom microscopes.
- It may be helpful to have a class discussion on what defines life. Review the characteristics of life they have studied so far.

Procedure
1. Read and complete the lab safety form.
2. Use a **compound light microscope** to observe the slides of **animal and bacterial cells**.
3. Complete a data table listing the similarities and differences between the two types of cells.

CHAPTER 18
Bacteria and Viruses

ConnectED

Your one-stop online resource
connectED.mcgraw-hill.com

- Video
- Audio
- Review
- Inquiry
- WebQuest
- Assessment
- Concepts in Motion
- Multilingual eGlossary

Launch Lab
What are the differences between animal cells and bacterial cells?

You are already familiar with animal cells. How do animal cells compare to the cells of bacteria? Bacteria are the most common organisms in your environment. In fact, billions of bacteria live on and in your body. Many species of bacteria can cause diseases. What makes bacteria different from your own cells?

For a lab worksheet, use your StudentWorks™ Plus Online.

Inquiry Launch Lab

FOLDABLES®

Make a two-tab book using the labels shown. Use it to organize your notes on viral infections.

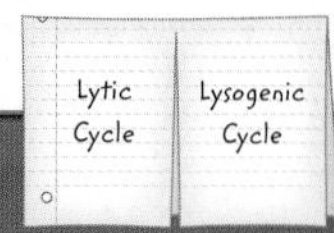

Analysis
1. **Describe** the different cells that you observed. What did you notice about each? Students should observe that the animal cell has characteristics of a eukaryotic cell, whereas the bacterial cell contains characteristics found in a prokaryotic cell.
2. **Infer** whether they are living things. What leads you to these conclusions? Yes, animal and bacterial cells are living things because they can live independently.

THEME FOCUS Diversity
Prokaryotes are the most abundant organisms on Earth.

BIG Idea Bacteria are microscopic organisms, and viruses are nonliving microscopic agents that invade cells.

Section 1 • Bacteria

Section 2 • Viruses and Prions

THEMES

Scientific Inquiry Scientists continue to develop vaccines and antibiotics to treat illnesses.

Diversity Disease-causing bacteria and viruses result in a wide variety of symptoms.

Energy Prokaryotes can be photoautotrophs, heterotrophs, or chemoautotrophs.

Homeostasis Some bacteria can form endospores when homeostasis is severely disrupted.

Change The genetic material in viruses can change quickly due to mutations during replication.

Introduce the Chapter

Magnifying Microbes

ASK STUDENTS: ***Why are different types of microscopes used to view the different objects shown in these pictures?*** Bacteria and viruses are too small to be seen with the naked eye. Some types of microscopes are more powerful than others.

Typical classroom microscopes have a maximum magnification of around 400× to 450×. Even magnified 400 times, bacteria will appear very small. Viruses are so small that they cannot be seen with these microscopes. Powerful electron microscopes are needed to view viruses. Some electron microscopes can magnify objects 200,000×.

BIG Idea

Two-Column Chart Have students draw a line lengthwise down the center of a piece of paper. Tell them to label the left column *prokaryotes* and the right column *viruses.* As students read the chapter, have them list characteristics of both groups, making side-by-side comparisons when possible. Example: Prokaryotes can be viewed with a light microscope; viruses can be viewed only with an electron microscope. Prokaryotes require a source of energy; viruses do not need energy. Prokaryotes can reproduce on their own; viruses need a host cell for reproduction.

Section 1

MAIN Idea

BL OL AL

Prokaryote Diversity

ASK STUDENTS: ***Are there different types of prokaryotes? Do you know of any examples? Are all bacteria basically alike? Explain the similarities and differences.*** Students might know that bacteria are tiny, microscopic structures, but students probably will not have much more background. To introduce them to the great amount of diversity among prokaryotic cells, project Figure 1 (available on page 516 in your eTeacherEdition Online) on a screen.

S Skill Practice

BL OL Concept Map

SAY TO STUDENTS: ***Write the word* prokaryote *in the center of a piece of paper. Write examples of prokaryotes in a bicycle-wheel fashion around the word* prokaryote *as you read the text under the heading* Diversity of Prokaryotes.** Students' examples should include archaea, bacteria, cyanobacteria, thermoacidophiles, halophiles, and methanogens. Other important terms include autotrophs, heterotrophs, and saprotrophs.

EL Have students create a chart with two rows labeled *Bacteria* and *Archaea* and two columns labeled *Where they are found* and *Cell walls.* Have students fill in the chart as they read.

Section 1

Reading Preview

Essential Questions

- What are the differences between archaea and bacteria and their subcategories?
- What are the survival methods of bacteria at both the individual and population levels?
- How are bacteria beneficial to humans?

Review Vocabulary

prokaryotic cell: cell that does not contain any membrane-bound organelles

New Vocabulary

bacteria
nucleoid
capsule
pilus
binary fission
conjugation
endospore

g Multilingual eGlossary

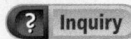

? Inquiry Video Lab

Bacteria

MAIN Idea Prokaryotes are diverse organisms that live in nearly all environments.

Real-World Reading Link What do yogurt, cheese, and strep throat have in common? You might wonder what food and disease have in common, but they each are the result of microscopic organisms called bacteria.

S

Diversity of Prokaryotes

Many scientists think that the first organisms on Earth were microscopic, unicellular organisms called prokaryotes. Today, prokaryotes are the most numerous organisms on Earth. They are found everywhere from the depths of the oceans to the highest mountaintops. Some prokaryotes are the only organisms able to survive in hostile environments, such as the water in hot sulfur springs or the Great Salt Lake. The word *prokaryote* is a Greek word that means *before a nucleus.*

All prokaryotes were once classified into one group—Kingdom Monera—based on their lack of a nucleus and membrane-bound organelles. However, modern research has shown that great differences exist among prokaryotes. They are now divided into two domains—Domain Bacteria and Domain Archaea. **Bacteria** (sometimes called eubacteria) are prokaryotic organisms that belong to Domain Bacteria. Bacteria live in nearly every environment on Earth and are important in the human body, industry, and food production. Archaea (previously called archaeabacteria) live in extreme environments and are sometimes called extremophiles. Archaea have been found to have some similarities with eukaryotic cells, such as cytoplasm proteins and histones. **Figure 1** shows representatives of these two domains.

Figure 1 Archaea are similar to the first life-forms on Earth. The middle photo shows cells of bacteria. The right photo shows cyanobacteria.

Color-Enhanced SEM Magnification: unavailable | Color-Enhanced SEM Magnification: 23,000× | Color-Enhanced SEM Magnification: 260×

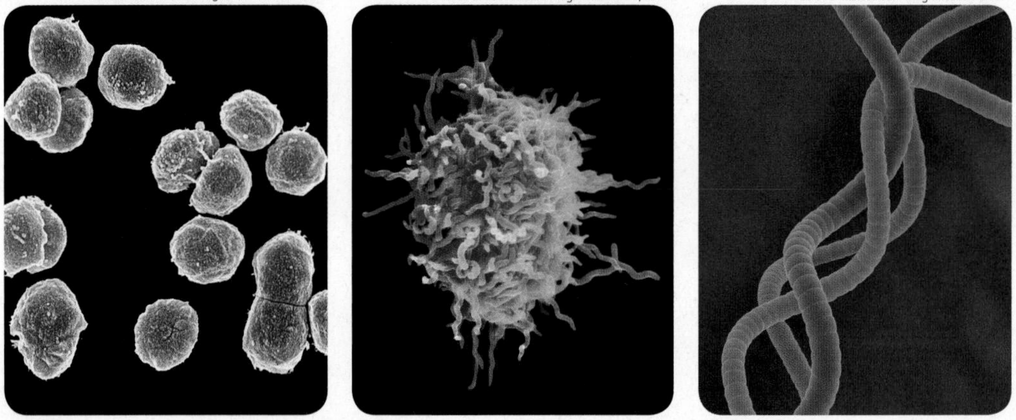

Archaea | **Bacteria** | **Cyanobacteria**

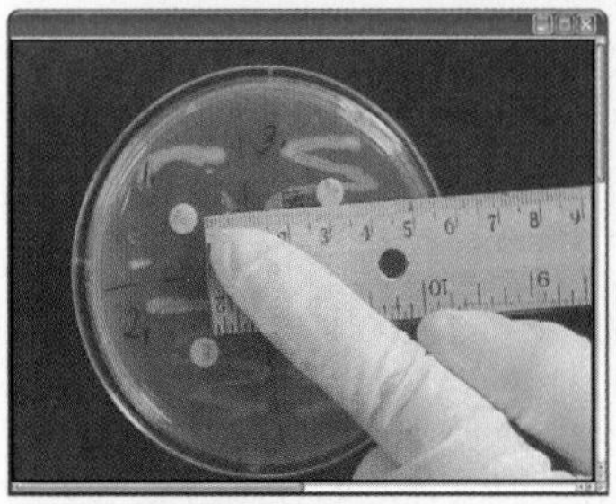

? Inquiry **Video Lab** Students will study the effectiveness of various types of antibiotics on bacteria.

Differentiated Instruction

English Learners Give students an overview of the lesson using a graphic organizer such as the concept map described on this page.

For more tips, see pages 14T–15T.

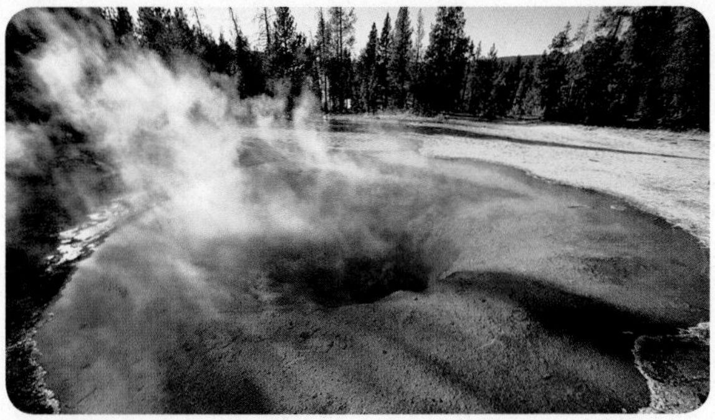

Hot springs

Great Salt Lake

Bacteria Bacteria are the most-studied organisms and are found almost everywhere except in extreme environments, where mostly archaea are found. Bacteria have strong cell walls that contain peptidoglycan. Some bacteria have a second cell wall, a property that can be used to classify them. Additionally, some bacteria, such as the cyanobacteria in **Figure 1,** are photosynthetic.

Archaea In extreme environments that are hostile to most other forms of life, archaea predominate. Some archaea called thermoacidophiles (thur muh uh SIH duh filz) live in hot, acidic environments, including sulfur hot springs, shown in **Figure 2,** thermal vents on the ocean floor, and around volcanoes. These archaea thrive in temperatures above 80°C and pH levels of 1–2. Some of these archaea cannot survive temperatures as low as 55°C. Many are strict anaerobes, which means that they die in the presence of oxygen.

Other archaea called halophiles (HA luh filz) live in very salty environments. The salt concentration in your cells is 0.9 percent, oceans average 3.5 percent salt, and the salt concentrations in the Great Salt Lake, shown in **Figure 2,** and the Dead Sea can be greater than 15 percent. Halophiles have several adaptions that allow them to live in salty environments. Halophiles usually are aerobic, and some carry out a unique form of photosynthesis using a protein instead of the pigment chlorophyll.

The methanogens (meh THAHN oh jenz) are the third group of archaea. These organisms are obligate anaerobes, which means they cannot live in the presence of oxygen. They use carbon dioxide during respiration and give off methane as a waste product. Methanogens are found in sewage treatment plants, swamps, bogs, and near volcanic vents. Methanogens even thrive in the gastrointestinal tract of humans and other animals and are responsible for the gases that are released from the lower digestive tract.

Differences between bacteria and archaea Bacteria and archaea have many differences that have led them to be classified in different domains. Recall that there are three domains. Based on their classification, we understand that bacteria and archaea are as different from each other as they are from eukaryotic cells. Some differences include: bacterial cell walls contain peptidoglycan but archaea do not; different lipids in their plasma membranes; and different ribosomal proteins and RNA. The ribosomal proteins in archaea are similar to those of eukaryotic cells.

■ **Figure 2** Some members of Domain Archaea can live in hostile environments, such as the sulfur hot springs in Yellowstone National Park and the Great Salt Lake in Utah.
Identify *in what other hostile places you might find archaea.*

Video BrainPOP

VOCABULARY
WORD ORIGIN
Halophile
halo- from the Greek word *hals,* meaning *salt*
-phile from the Greek word *phileo,* meaning *like.*

Video BrainPOP

■ **Caption Question Fig. 2** Archaea can also be found in thermal vents in the ocean floor and around volcanoes.

C Critical Thinking

OL Assess For years, cyanobacteria were called blue-green algae. **ASK STUDENTS:** ***Why do you think these organisms were once grouped with the other types of algae?*** Superficially, there is a close resemblance to other algae. Cyanobacteria are aquatic, as are most other algae. Cyanobacteria also carry on photosynthesis. Many types of cyanobacteria have similar light and nutrient requirements to other algae. ***Why do you think they are now grouped with bacteria?*** Scientists discovered that cyanobacteria lack a nucleus and other internal membrane systems.

S Skill Practice

BL OL Visual Literacy Have students examine Figure 2. **ASK STUDENTS:** ***What do environments where archaea live have in common?*** They are at the extremes of habitability (very hot, very salty, etc); conditions such as these would have existed more widely during Earth's early history.

W Writing Support

BL OL AL Summary Writing Have students read about the differences between bacteria and archaea. **SAY TO STUDENTS:** ***Write a paragraph that explains these differences in more detail.*** Bacteria have peptidoglycan; archaea do not. Peptidoglycan provides strength for the cell wall and also gives shape to the bacteria. Ribosomal proteins are different in bacteria and archaea. Ribosomes consist of RNA and proteins. Archaea genes have introns, while bacterial genes lack introns. Introns are noncoding nucleic acid sequences. Archaea are the only organisms known to survive in extreme environments. These environments include hot springs, thermal vents, areas with a high salt concentration, and highly acidic environments.

? Inquiry Launch Lab

Assess Content Development
Assess how understanding has developed when students revisit the Launch Lab analysis questions.

Critical Thinking

AL Hypothesize

ASK STUDENTS: ***What would happen to one of your cells if it were placed in a very salty environment or in a hypertonic solution?*** Water would leave the cell via osmosis. ***How do you think halophiles can survive in environments with high salt concentrations?*** Halophiles conserve inert solutes in their cytoplasm, which minimizes water loss.

S Skill Practice

OL Visual Literacy Have students examine Figure 3.

SAY TO STUDENTS: ***Create flashcards for the following structures: plasmid, pilus, capsule, flagellum, chromosome, plasma membrane, and cell wall. On the back of each card, draw an image and write a description of each structure. Indicate which structures are also found in eukaryotic cells.*** plasma membrane, cell wall, sometimes a flagellum, and chromosome

D Develop Concepts

BL OL AL Discuss

ASK STUDENTS: ***What are the functions of pili?*** Pili are structures used for attachment, and are involved with sexual reproduction of some bacteria. ***What role do pili play in sexual reproduction?*** They allow two cells to attach and exchange genetic information.

Figure 3 Prokaryotic cells have structures that are necessary for carrying out life processes.
Compare and contrast ***how a bacterial cell differs structurally from a eukaryotic cell.***

S

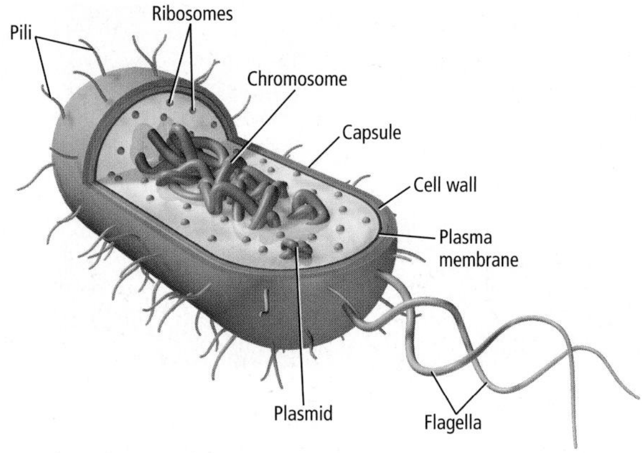

Prokaryote Structure

Prokaryotes are microscopic, unicellular organisms. They have some characteristics of all cells, such as DNA and ribosomes, but they lack a nuclear membrane and other membrane-bound organelles, such as mitochondria and chloroplasts. Although a prokaryotic cell is very small and doesn't have membrane-bound organelles, it has all it needs to carry out life functions. Examine **Figure 3** as you read about the structure of prokaryotic cells.

Chromosomes The chromosomes in prokaryotes are arranged differently from the chromosomes found in eukaryotic cells. Their genes are found on a large, circular chromosome in an area of the cell called the **nucleoid.** Many prokaryotes also have at least one smaller piece of DNA, called a *plasmid,* which also has a circular arrangement.

Capsule Some prokaryotes secrete a layer of polysaccharides around the cell wall, forming a **capsule,** illustrated in **Figure 3.** The capsule has several important functions, including preventing the cell from drying out and helping the cell attach to surfaces in its environment. The capsule also helps prevent bacteria from being engulfed by white blood cells and shelters the cells from the effects of antibiotics.

Pili Structures called pili are found on the outer surface of some bacteria. **Pili** (singular, pilus) are submicroscopic, hairlike structures that are made of protein. Pili help bacterial cells attach to surfaces. Pili also can serve as a bridge between cells. Copies of plasmids can be sent across the bridge, thus providing some prokaryotes with new genetic characteristics. This is one way of transferring the resistance to antibiotics. **D**

Size Even when using a typical light microscope, prokaryotes are small when magnified 400 times. Prokaryotes are typically only 1 to 10 micrometers long and 0.7 to 1.5 micrometers wide. Study **Figure 4,** which shows a bacterial cell and a human cell. Notice the relative size of bacterial cells found adjacent to a cheek cell.

Recall that small cells have a larger, more favorable surface area-to-volume ratio than large cells. Because prokaryotes are so small, nutrients and other substances the cells need can diffuse to all parts of the cell easily.

? Inquiry Launch Lab

Review **Based on what you've read about bacterial cells, how would you now answer the analysis questions?**

Figure 4 A size comparison shows how a human cheek cell is much larger than bacteria found in a human mouth.

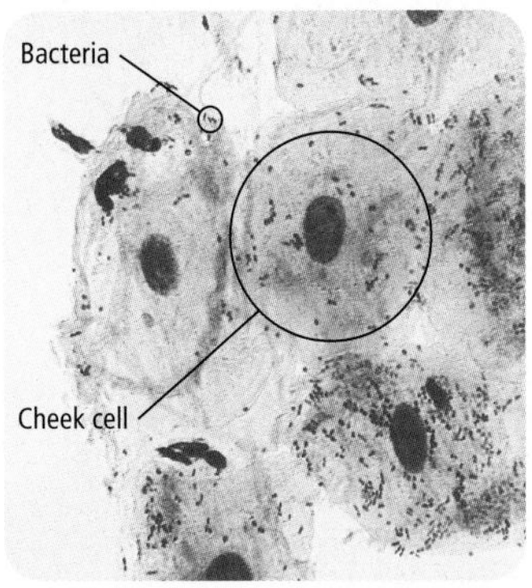

Stained LM Magnification: 400×

Caption Question **Fig. 3** A bacterial cell lacks membrane-enclosed organelles such as mitochondria and chloroplasts. Bacteria also lack a nuclear membrane. Bacteria may have a capsule, pili, and at least one plasmid.

Research Citation

K-W-L Chart Educational research indicates the value of having students complete K-W-L charts like the one described on page 521. Students must make connections between new concepts and previous learning and extend their thinking by asking themselves what new information they would like to learn. (Ogle, 1986)

Research bibliography on pages 32T–34T

Prokaryote Characteristics

As with other types of organisms, prokaryotes now can be identified using molecular techniques. By comparing DNA, evolutionary relationships can be determined. Historically, scientists identified prokaryotes using criteria such as shape, cell wall, and movement.

Shape There are three general shapes of prokaryotes, as shown in **Figure 5.** Spherical or round prokaryotes are called cocci (KAHK ki) (singular, coccus), rod-shaped prokaryotes are called bacilli (buh SIH li) (singular, bacillus), and spiral-shaped prokaryotes, or spirilli (spi RIH li) (singular, spirillium), are called spirochetes (SPI ruh keets).

Cell walls Scientists also classify bacteria according to the composition of their cell walls. All bacterial cells have peptidoglycan in their cell walls. Peptidoglycan is made of disaccharides and peptide fragments. Biologists add dyes to the bacteria to identify the two major types of bacteria—those with and those without an outer layer of lipid—in a technique called Gram's stain.

Bacteria with a large amount of peptidoglycan appear dark purple once they are stained and are called Gram-positive. Bacteria with the lipid layer have less peptidoglycan and appear light pink after staining. These bacteria are called Gram-negative. Because some antibiotics work by attacking the cell wall of bacteria, physicians need to know the type of cell wall that is present in the bacteria that they suspect is causing illness to prescribe the proper antibiotic.

Movement Although some prokaryotes are stationary, others use flagella for movement. Prokaryotic flagella are made of filaments, unlike the flagella of eukaryotes, which are made of microtubules. Flagella help prokaryotes move toward light, higher oxygen concentration, or chemicals such as sugar or amino acids that they need to survive. Other prokaryotes move by gliding over a layer of secreted slime.

Color-Enhanced SEM Magnification: 6500×

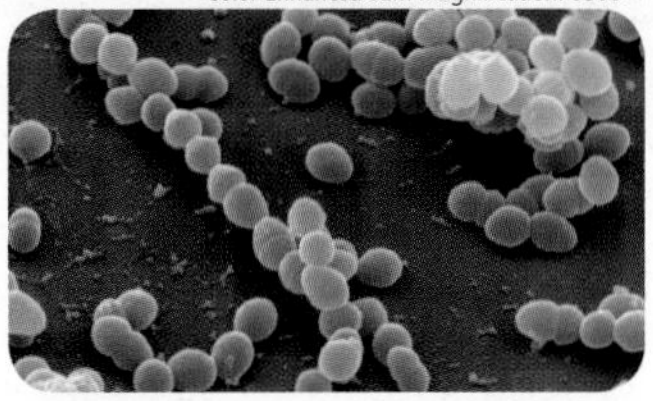

Cocci

Color-Enhanced SEM Magnification: 50,000×

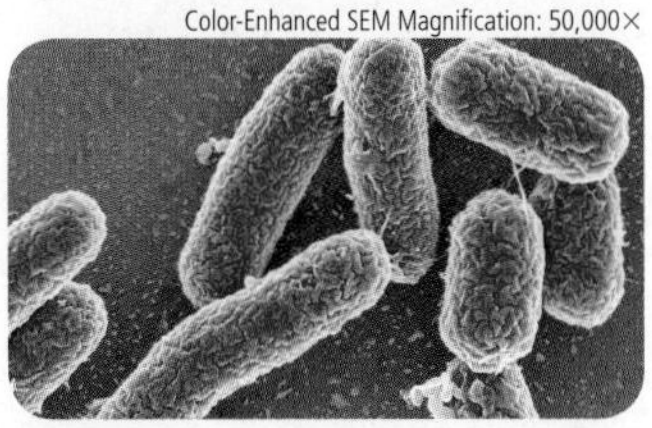

Bacilli

Color-Enhanced SEM Magnification: 2000×

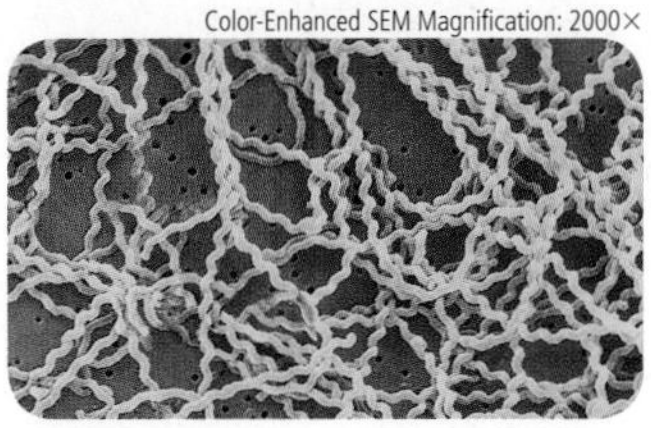

Spirochetes

■ **Figure 5** There are three shapes of prokaryotes: cocci, bacilli, and spirochetes.

MiniLab 1

Classify Bacteria

Inquiry MiniLab

What types of characteristics are used to divide bacteria into groups? Bacteria can be stained to show the differences in peptidoglycan (PG) in their cell walls. Based on this difference in their cell walls, bacteria are divided into two main groups.

Procedure

1. Read and complete the lab safety form.
2. Choose four different **slides of bacteria** that have been stained to show cell wall differences. The slides will be labeled with the names of the bacteria and marked either thick PG layer or thin PG layer.
3. Use the oil immersion lens of your **microscope** to observe the four slides.
4. Record all of your observations, including those about the cell color, in a data table.

Analysis

1. **Interpret Data** Based on your observations, make a hypothesis about how to differentiate between the two groups of bacteria.
2. **Describe** two different cell shapes that you observed on the slides.

MiniLab 1

Inquiry MiniLab

For a lab worksheet, use your eTeacherEdition Online.

✻RUBRIC A rubric for evaluating MiniLabs is found on your eTeacherEdition Online.

Est. Time 20 min

Alternative Materials photographs of bacteria, such as Figures 1 and 5

Safety Precaution Approve lab safety forms before work begins.

Teaching Strategies

- Consider purchasing a sample slide set that has slides showing a variety of visible bacteria. You can obtain these from a biological supply company.
- Cyanobacteria such as *Nostoc, Anabaena, Oscillatoria,* and *Gloeocapsa* are easily viewed under high-power magnification (400×).
- Remind students that many of the slides are stained and do not represent the true color of the bacteria.

Analysis

1. Answers will vary. Sample hypothesis: Bacteria may be differentiated by differences in their structure or shape.
2. Answers will vary. Students might describe cocci as round, bacilli as oblong, and spirochetes as spiral-shaped.

Demonstration

BL OL AL Production of Methane Place a banana peel in a small glass jar without a lid. Attach a plastic sandwich bag to the top of the jar with a rubber band. This seal must be airtight. Place the jar in a warm spot where it can be observed for approximately one week. Beside the jar, place a toy cow. At the end of the week, the plastic bag will expand.

ASK STUDENTS: ***What is causing the bag to expand?*** The bag is being filled with methane and other gases that are being released by anaerobic bacteria. Tell students that the cow standing next to the jar simulates digestion. The bacteria present in their digestive tracts cause cattle to produce a large amount of methane. Est. time: 5 min

D Develop Concepts

EL OL AL Integrate Math

SAY TO STUDENTS: ***Imagine that one day you left a part of your chicken salad sandwich on the kitchen counter around noon. Assume that the sandwich was infected at that time with a bacterium (single-bacteria cell). Assuming your kitchen provided ideal conditions for bacteria growth, how many bacteria cells would there be in your sandwich at 3 P.M. that day?*** If the bacteria population doubles every 20 min, there would be 512 cells at 3 P.M.

BL OL Extension

Have students prepare a line graph based on the scenario presented above. Tell them to be sure to include proper labels. The *x*-axis will represent time (min) and the *y*-axis will represent the number of bacteria cells. This will be an exponential growth curve, the line will be shaped roughly like the letter "J." Have students performing below level share data to complete the graph.

W Writing Support

OL AL Formal Writing

SAY TO STUDENTS: ***Write a short newspaper or magazine article on the risks of leaving food sitting out or not treating an open wound in relation to the replication of a disease-causing bacteria.*** Major points of the article should include the rapid reproduction of bacteria and preventative measures to check bacterial growth. These include the proper cooking and refrigeration of food or the use of antiseptics.

Caption Question Fig. 6
conjugation

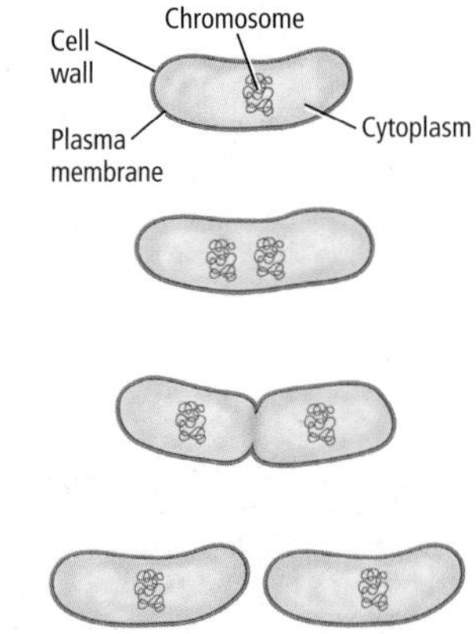

Binary fission

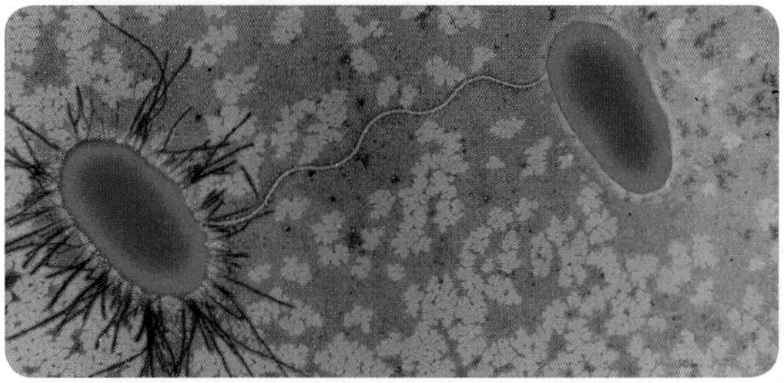

Conjugation

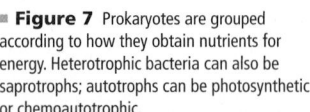

Figure 6 Binary fission is an asexual form of reproduction used by some prokaryotes. Conjugation is a method of exchanging genetic material used by some prokaryotes.
Analyze ***Which means of reproducing shown here exchanges genetic information?***

Reproduction of Prokaryotes

Most prokaryotes reproduce by an asexual process called binary fission, illustrated in **Figure 6. Binary fission** is the division of a cell into two genetically identical cells. In this process, the prokaryotic chromosome replicates, and the original chromosome and the new copy separate. As this occurs, the cell gets larger by elongating. A new piece of plasma membrane and cell wall forms and separates the cell into two identical cells. Under ideal environmental conditions, this can occur quickly—as often as every 20 minutes. If conditions are just right, one bacterium could become one billion bacteria through binary fission in just ten hours. D

Some prokaryotes exhibit a form of reproduction called **conjugation,** in which two prokaryotes attach to each other and exchange genetic information. As shown in **Figure 6,** the pilus is important for the attachment of the two cells so that there can be a transfer of genetic material from one cell to the other. In this way, new gene combinations are created and diversity of prokaryote populations is increased. W

Metabolism of Prokaryotes

Anaerobic prokaryotes do not use oxygen for growth or metabolism. Obligate anaerobes cannot live or grow in the presence of oxygen. They obtain energy through fermentation. Facultative anaerobes can grow either in the presence of oxygen or without it. Obligate aerobes require oxygen to grow. Besides being classified by how they use oxygen, prokaryotes can also be classified by how they obtain energy for cellular respiration or fermentation, as shown in **Figure 7.**

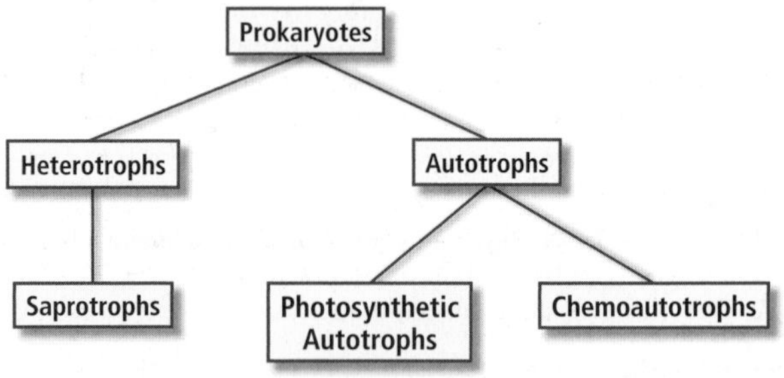

Figure 7 Prokaryotes are grouped according to how they obtain nutrients for energy. Heterotrophic bacteria can also be saprotrophs; autotrophs can be photosynthetic or chemoautotrophic.

Demonstration

BL OL Bacteria and Food Obtain a package of uncooked meat. Four days before performing this demonstration, set out a small amount of meat at room temperature. Keep the remaining meat in a refrigerator. Set out another sample of meat every day until there are four samples. Roll a sterile cotton swab over a sample of meat and then roll it over the surface of a petri dish filled with nutrient agar. Keep petri dishes sealed in case of pathogen growth. Repeat this procedure for the other three samples, using a fresh swab for each sample. Observe the plates 48 h later. The longer the meat was left sitting out, the more bacteria growth should be present. Point out that bacterial growth is natural, and not always a sign of contamination. (Be certain to wear safety gloves and wash hands after handling the meat.) Est. time: 10 min per day

Heterotrophs Some prokaryotes are heterotrophs; they cannot synthesize their own food and must take in nutrients. Many heterotrophic bacteria are saprotrophs, or saprobes. They obtain their energy by decomposing organic molecules associated with dead organisms or organic waste.

Photoautotrophs Some bacteria are photosynthetic autotrophs (AW tuh trohfs); they carry out photosynthesis in a manner similar to plants. These bacteria must live in areas where there is light, such as shallow ponds and streams, to synthesize organic molecules to use as food.

Scientists once thought that these organisms were eukaryotes and called them blue-green algae. Later, it was discovered that they were prokaryotes and they were renamed cyanobacteria. These bacteria, like plants, are ecologically important because they are at the base of some food chains and release oxygen into the environment. Cyanobacteria are thought to have been the first group of organisms to release oxygen into Earth's early atmosphere, approximately three billion years ago.

Chemoautotrophs A second type of bacteria are autotrophs that do not require light for energy. These organisms are called chemoautotrophs. They break down and release inorganic compounds that contain nitrogen or sulfur, such as ammonia and hydrogen sulfide, in a process called chemosynthesis. Some chemoautotrophs are important ecologically because they keep nitrogen and other inorganic compounds cycling through ecosystems.

Study Tip

Summarization Write a summary paragraph that addresses the diversity of prokaryotes, how they reproduce, and the importance of prokaryotes.

D Survival of Bacteria

How can bacteria survive if their environment becomes unfavorable? They have several mechanisms that help them survive such environmental challenges as a lack of water, an extreme temperature change, and a lack of nutrients.

Endospores When environmental conditions are harsh, some types of bacteria produce a structure called an **endospore.** The bacteria that cause anthrax, botulism, and tetanus are examples of endospore producers. An endospore can be thought of as a dormant cell. Endospores are resistant to harsh environments and might be able to survive extreme heat, extreme cold, dehydration, and large amounts of ultraviolet radiation. Any of these conditions would kill a typical bacterial cell.

As illustrated in **Figure 8,** when a bacterium is exposed to harsh environments, a spore coat surrounds a copy of the bacterial cell's chromosome and a small part of the cytoplasm. The bacterium itself might die, but the endospore remains. When environmental conditions become favorable again, the endospore grows, or germinates, into a new bacterial cell. Endospores are able to survive for long periods of time. Because a bacterial cell usually produces only one endospore, this is considered a survival mechanism rather than a type of reproduction.

Figure 8 Endospores can survive extreme environmental conditions.

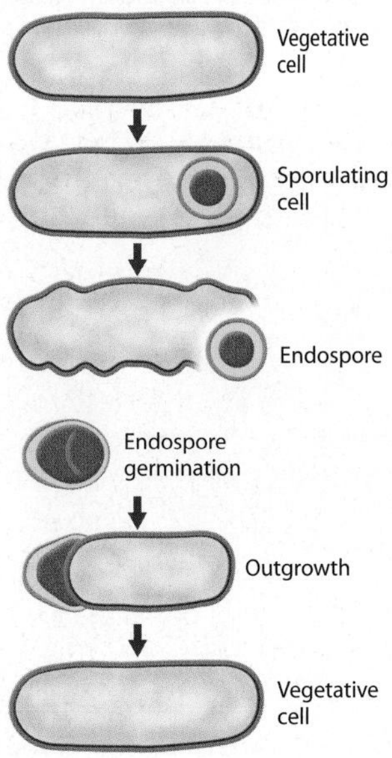

Writing Support

OL Creative Writing

SAY TO STUDENTS: ***Write a story in the first person about an endospore-forming bacterium.***

Example: One day, I was lying around on a dead leaf when a young child began to use a magnifying lens to concentrate the Sun's rays in order to burn a hole in the leaf. It started to get very hot, and I knew I was going to die. Fortunately, I had already formed an endospore. I perished, but my endospore survived. Hopefully, someday the conditions will be right for the endospore to germinate into a "new me."

BL Have students create a comic strip about an endospore-forming bacterium.

D Develop Concepts

EL BL OL K-W-L Chart Have students make three columns on a sheet of paper. From left to right, the columns should be titled *What I* **K***now, What I* **W***ant to Know,* and *What I've* **L***earned.* Have students fill in the left and middle columns before reading the text below the head *Survival of Bacteria.* After they read, have students complete the third column. Lead a discussion about what they learned, asking them to share any misconceptions they had before the reading.

Content Background

Teacher FYI The toxin produced by the bacteria *Clostridium botulinum* is the most powerful toxin known to humans. The bacteria are anaerobic spore-formers found in the soil and other places. Improperly home-canned vegetables provide the anaerobic environment necessary for the bacteria to produce the toxin that causes this disease. The toxin released by the bacteria can cause respiratory paralysis leading to death. Boiling a food source for at least 10 min should destroy the toxin.

C Critical Thinking

AL Consider Mutations can be beneficial to a population of organisms because they provide genetic variability in a population. **ASK STUDENTS:** ***How might mutations in bacteria be harmful to humans?*** Mutations could cause more resistant strains of bacteria to evolve. Mutations can (and sometimes do) make current antibiotics or vaccinations ineffective.

D Develop Concepts

BL OL

Clarify a Misconception

ASK STUDENTS: ***Do most types of bacteria cause disease?*** Students may confuse beneficial bacteria and disease-causing bacteria. Most bacteria do not cause human disease, but are benign or actually beneficial. Some bacteria cause disease in other animals or plants.

R Reading Strategy

EL BL OL AL COOP LEARN

Discussion Triads Divide the class into three groups. Assign each group one of the subcategories of *Ecology of Bacteria* (*Nutrient cycling and nitrogen fixation, Normal flora,* and *Foods and medicines*).

SAY TO STUDENTS: ***Reread text under your assigned heading and explain these benefits in your own words.*** Answers will vary.

Writing Support

BL OL Creative Writing Have students prepare a classified ad describing a type of bacteria. Example: Unicellular organism that lacks a nucleus is looking for a job as a decomposer. I am microscopic, have a circular chromosome and a plasmid. My species does not cause disease.

CAREERS IN BIOLOGY

Food Scientist Food scientists help protect the flavor, color, texture, nutritional quality, and safety of our food. They test for amounts of nutrients and the presence of harmful organisms such as bacteria.

Mutations If the environment changes and bacteria are not well adapted to the new conditions, extinction of the bacteria is a possibility. Because bacteria reproduce quickly and their population grows rapidly, genetic mutations can help bacteria survive in changing environments. Mutations, which are changes or random errors in a DNA sequence, lead to new forms of genes, new gene combinations, new characteristics, and genetic diversity. If the environment happens to change, some bacteria in a population might have the right combination of genes to allow them to survive and reproduce. From the human point of view, this can lead to problems, such as antibiotic-resistant bacteria, which may cause disease and are hard to treat. C

D Ecology of Bacteria

When many people think of bacteria, they immediately think of germs or disease. Most bacteria do not cause disease, and many are beneficial. In fact, it has been said that humans owe their lives to bacteria because they help fertilize fields, recycle nutrients, protect the body, and produce foods and medicines.

R **Nutrient cycling and nitrogen fixation** Recall that nutrients are cycled in an ecosystem. Some organisms get their energy from the cells and tissues of dead organisms and are called decomposers or detrivores. Saprobes are decomposers, returning vital nutrients to the environment. Without nutrient recycling, all raw materials necessary for life would be used up. Without nitrogen fixation, far more fertilizer would be needed for growing plants.

Connection to Chemistry All forms of life require nitrogen. Nitrogen is a key component of amino acids, the building blocks of proteins. Nitrogen also is needed to make DNA and RNA. Most of Earth's nitrogen is found in the atmosphere in the form of nitrogen gas (N_2). Certain types of bacteria can use nitrogen gas directly. These bacteria have enzymes that can convert nitrogen gas into nitrogen compounds by a process called nitrogen fixation. Some of these bacteria live in soil.

■ **Figure 9** Nitrogen-fixing bacteria on a plant root nodule are able to remove nitrogen from the air and convert it into a form the plant can use.

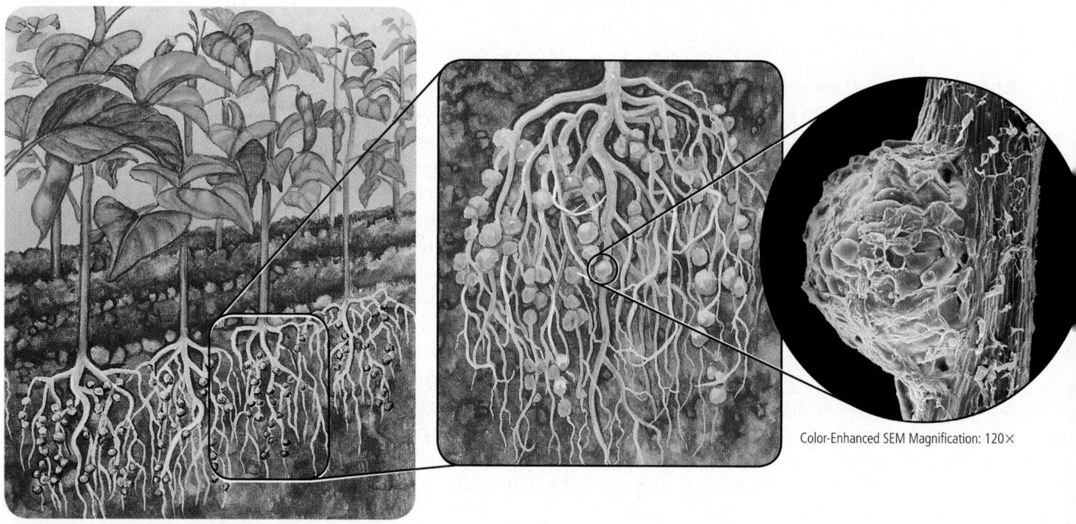

Demonstration

BL OL AL Decomposers Before discussing the text about bacteria, slice a few thin sections of a cucumber. Then, slice a few thin sections of a new, fresh cucumber the morning you begin discussing the benefits of bacteria.

ASK STUDENTS: ***Why do the two cucumbers look different?*** Responses might include that the older cucumber is drying out or rotting. ***What is happening to the molecules in the cucumber?*** Bacteria are decomposing the cucumbers and returning substances to the environment. Est. time: 5 min

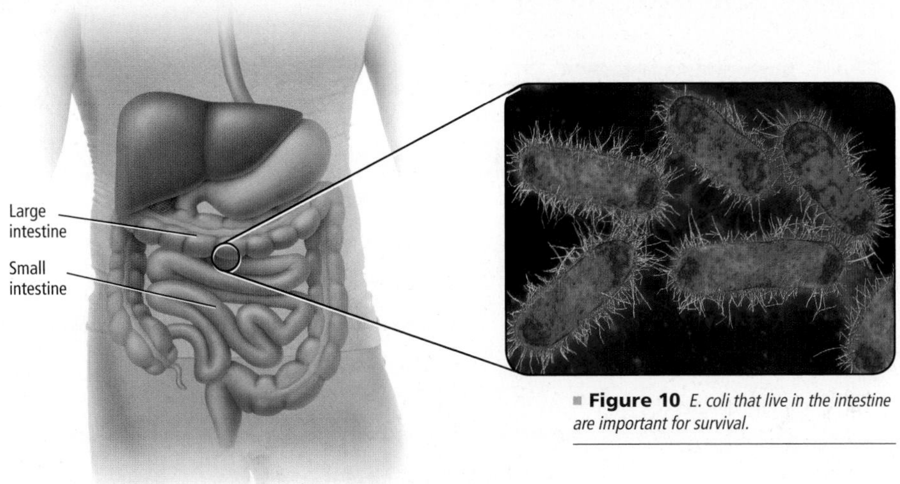

■ **Figure 10** *E. coli that live in the intestine are important for survival.*

Some nitrogen-fixing bacteria live in a symbiotic relationship in the root nodules of plants such as soybeans, clover, and alfalfa. The bacteria use the nitrogen in the atmosphere to produce forms of nitrogen the plant can use. The plants then are able to take up ammonia (NH_3) and other forms of nitrogen from the soil. These plants are at the base of a food chain, and the nitrogen is passed along to organisms that eat them. **Figure 9** shows where nitrogen-fixing bacteria live on root nodules.

Normal flora Your body is covered with bacteria inside and out. Most of the bacteria that live in or on you are harmless. These are called normal flora. Normal flora are of great importance to the body. By living and replicating on the body, they compete with harmful bacteria and prevent them from taking hold and causing disease.

A certain type of bacterium called *Escherichia coli (E. coli)* lives inside your intestines and is illustrated in **Figure 10.** Some *E. coli* strains can cause food poisoning. The type that lives in the digestive tracts of humans and other mammals is harmless and important for survival. The *E. coli* that live in humans make vitamin K, which humans absorb and use in blood clotting. In this symbiotic relationship, *E. coli* are provided with a warm place and food with which to live. In return, the bacteria provide the body with an essential nutrient.

S **Foods and medicines** Think about what you have eaten in the last few days. Have you had pizza? How about a cheeseburger? Cheese, yogurt, buttermilk, and pickles, as well as other foods, are made with the aid of bacteria.

Bacteria are even used in the production of chocolate. Although bacteria are not found in the chocolate products you eat, bacteria are used to break down the covering of cocoa beans during the production of cocoa. Bacteria also are responsible for the commercial production of vitamins, such as vitamin B_{12} and riboflavin.

Bacteria are important in the fields of medicine and research. Although some bacteria cause disease, others are useful in fighting disease. Streptomycin, bacitracin, tetracycline, and vancomycin are commonly prescribed antibiotics that were originally made by bacteria.

Reading Check **Describe** ways that bacteria are beneficial.

S Skill Practice

BL OL Research Have students research one aspect of the use of bacteria in food production. Have students present an oral report or make a poster if appropriate. Example of major points to be included: *Lactobacillus bulgaricus* and *Streptococcus thermophilus* are two types of bacteria used to make yogurt. These ferment lactose and produce lactic acid. Lactic acid makes the yogurt more acidic and causes the proteins found in milk to thicken. The acidic conditions help prevent the growth of pathogenic bacteria in the yogurt.

AL Have students discuss the metabolic by-products of the bacteria that are useful in food production.

Develop Concepts

BL OL AL Integrate History Present background information on the discovery of penicillin by Sir Alexander Fleming.

ASK STUDENTS: ***What effect did this discovery have on humans?*** Penicillin has saved countless lives over the years and also led to the discovery and development of other antibiotics. ***Even if you personally have never been administered penicillin, how has the drug indirectly affected your life?*** Some students might know someone whose life was saved by penicillin.

Inquiry BioLab

The lab at the end of the chapter can be used at this point in the lesson.

Reading Check Bacteria aid in food production and in the development of medicines. Also, beneficial bacteria prevent harmful bacteria from taking hold and causing disease in humans.

Demonstration

BL OL AL Pasteurization Obtain a carton of pasteurized milk. Remove 1 mL of milk and squirt it onto petri dish containing nutrient agar. Let the petri dish sit at room temperature for at least 48 h. The agar will show a large amount of bacterial growth. **ASK STUDENTS:** ***What does the term* pasteurization *mean?*** The partial sterilization of foods such as milk to make them safe to ingest. Inform students that the purpose of this demonstration is to illustrate that pasteurization does not completely sterilize the food, but reduces the amount of bacteria so illness should not occur. In some cases, beneficial bacteria are added to dairy products after pasteurization. Est. time: 10 min

Concepts in Motion
Interactive Table

D Develop Concepts

OL AL COOP LEARN

Medicine's Most Wanted
In pairs, have students research a type of pathogenic bacteria and make a "Wanted Poster" on their assigned bacteria. The poster should include the name of the organism, a mug shot (drawing or photo), where the organism could be found, how it gets into the body, how it causes harm, any demographic group that is especially susceptible, and how it can be eliminated.

Formative Assessment

Evaluation
ASK STUDENTS: ***How do endospores ensure the survival of a population of bacteria?*** Endospores are highly resistant to harsh environments. Even if the bacteria cells die, the endospores can survive to germinate when conditions become favorable.

Remediation Students should review Figure 8 and copy it onto the left side of a piece of paper. For each of the six steps in the figure, have students write a sentence describing what has occurred.

Table 1 **Human Bacterial Diseases** Concepts in Motion Interactive Table

Category	Disease
Sexually transmitted diseases	Syphilis, gonorrhea, chlamydia
Respiratory diseases	Strep throat, pneumonia, whooping cough, tuberculosis, anthrax
Skin diseases	Acne, boils, infections of wounds or burns
Digestive tract diseases	Gastroenteritis, many types of food poisoning, cholera
Nervous system diseases	Botulism, tetanus, bacterial meningitis
Other diseases	Lyme disease, typhoid fever

Disease-causing bacteria Only a small percentage of bacteria cause disease. Some of the diseases caused by bacteria are listed in **Table 1.** The small percentage of bacteria that cause disease do so in two ways. Some bacteria multiply quickly at the site of infection before the body's defense systems can destroy them. In cases of serious infections, bacteria then might spread to other parts of the body.

Other bacteria secrete a toxin or other substance that might cause harm. The bacteria that cause botulism secrete a toxin that paralyzes cells in the nervous system. Bacteria that cause cavities in teeth use sugar in the mouth for energy, and in turn secrete acids that erode the teeth.

Bacteria also can cause disease in plants, and most plants can become infected. Such infections can destroy entire crops and have long-ranging consequences on local ecosystems. For example, citrus canker, a bacterial disease that kills orange trees, has severely impacted the Florida citrus crop and prompted eradication programs. **D**

Section 1 Assessment

Section Summary

- Many scientists think that prokaryotes were the first organisms on Earth.
- Prokaryotes belong to two domains.
- Most prokaryotes are beneficial.
- Prokaryotes have a variety of survival mechanisms.
- Some bacteria cause disease.

Understand Main Ideas

1. MAIN Idea **Diagram** a bacterium.
2. **Discuss** possible rationales that taxonomists might have used when deciding to group prokaryotes into two distinct domains instead of in one group.
3. **Explain** survival mechanisms of bacteria at both the individual and population levels.
4. **List** three examples of how bacteria are beneficial to humans.

Think Critically

5. **Analyze** why it is more difficult for biologists to understand the diversity in prokaryotes as compared to plants or animals.

MATH in Biology

6. Imagine that today at 1 P.M., a single *Salmonella* bacterial cell landed on potato salad sitting on your kitchen counter. Assuming your kitchen provides an optimal environment for bacterial growth, how many bacterial cells will be present at 3 P.M. today?

Section 1 Assessment

1. Diagrams should include representations of the cell wall, chromosome, pili, and capsule.
2. The two groups have different biochemical and genetic components and they live in different environments.
3. Individually, bacteria form endospores that are resistant to harsh environments. Random genetic mutations allow bacteria as a population to adapt to new conditions
4. Bacteria recycle nutrients in an ecosystem. *E. coli* produces vitamin K. Some bacteria are used to make antibiotics or other medicines.
5. The diversity in prokaryotes exists on the cellular level and is not visible to the naked eye.
6. 64

Assessment Online Quiz

Section 2

Reading Preview

Essential Questions

- What is the general structure of a virus?
- What are similarities and differences in the lytic cycle, the lysogenic cycle, and retroviral replication?
- What is the relationship between a prion's structure, replication, and action and its ability to cause disease?

Review Vocabulary

protein: large, complex polymer composed of carbon, hydrogen, oxygen, nitrogen, and sometimes sulfur

New Vocabulary

virus
capsid
lytic cycle
lysogenic cycle
retrovirus
prion

g Multilingual eGlossary

R Viruses and Prions

MAIN Idea **Viruses and prions are smaller and less complex than bacteria; they invade cells and can alter cellular functions.**

Real-World Reading Link "It's Cold and Flu Season," "1918 Spanish Flu Epidemic Kills Millions," "New Cases of SARS Reported," "Number of H1N1 Cases Increases"—headlines tell many stories about diseases that spread worldwide. What do colds, severe acute respiratory syndrome (SARS), and types of flu have in common? They all are caused by viruses.

Viruses

Although some viruses are not harmful, other viruses are known to infect and harm all types of living organisms. A **virus** is a nonliving strand of genetic material within a protein coat. Most biologists don't consider viruses to be living because they do not exhibit all of the characteristics of life. Viruses have no organelles to take in nutrients or use energy, they cannot make proteins, they cannot move, and they cannot replicate on their own. In humans, some diseases, such as those listed in **Table 2,** are caused by viruses. Just as there are some bacteria that cause sexually transmitted disease, some viruses can cause sexually transmitted diseases—such as genital herpes and AIDS. These viruses can be spread through sexual contact. Diseases caused by these viruses have no cure or vaccine to prevent them.

Virus size Viruses are some of the smallest disease-causing structures that are known. They are so small that powerful electron microscopes are needed to study them. Most viruses range in size from 5 to 300 nanometers (a nanometer is one billionth of a meter). It would take about 10,000 cold viruses to span the period at the end of this sentence.

Table 2 Human Viral Diseases — Concepts in Motion Interactive Table

Category	Disease
Sexually transmitted diseases	AIDS (HIV), genital herpes
Childhood diseases	Measles, mumps, chicken pox
Respiratory diseases	Common cold, influenza
Skin diseases	Warts, shingles
Digestive tract diseases	Gastroenteritis
Nervous system diseases	Polio, viral meningitis, rabies
Other diseases	Smallpox, hepatitis

Demonstration

BL OL AL Transmission of Viruses While students are busy, turn your back to the class and pretend to sneeze. Using a spray bottle, spray the board with water. Inform the students that although you used water for this demonstration, this simulates the microscopic spread of body secretions when one sneezes. Tell the students each droplet of water contains multiple viral particles in it. Discuss with students the importance of sneezing or coughing into the crook of the arm instead of the hands. Food coloring can be added if you are spraying the water onto a light-colored surface.
Est. time: 10 min

Section 2

MAIN Idea

BL OL AL Viruses and Prions
ASK STUDENTS: ***Are viruses and prions considered cells?*** Viruses and prions are much less structurally complex than cells. Student responses will vary for viruses; they probably have not heard of prions. Project Figure 11, or 14, examples of a virus; and Figure 4, a bacteria cell, on a screen (the pages with these images are available on the eTeacherEdition Online). Point out to students the complexity of a bacteria cell compared to a virus.

R Reading Strategy

EL BL OL SQ3R Before reading, have students first **S**urvey Section 2, focusing on headings. Next, have students write **Q**uestions about key points made in this section. Then, have students **R**ead the section and make notes related to the questions. Finally, have students **R**ecite vocabulary and **R**eview for meaning.

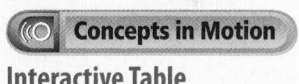

Concepts in Motion
Interactive Table

GOING GREEN Local hospitals and medical clinics may be willing to donate their out-of-date gloves and non-pathogenic bacterial cultures for classroom use. Using these materials that would otherwise be thrown out saves resources.

S Skill Practice

EL BL OL Visual Literacy

Have students work in small groups to design and make a model of viruses based on Figure 11. Have a variety of materials available; some suggested items are modeling clay, yarn, plastic straws, pipe cleaners, cardboard tubing, marshmallows, and small pieces of candy. All models should include nucleic acids and a capsid.

D Develop Concepts

BL OL AL

Activate Prior Knowledge

ASK STUDENTS: ***Based on the cell theory, should viruses be considered living?*** No; the third part of the cell theory states that all living things are made of cells. Viruses are not cellular.

Develop Concepts

BL OL AL Reporter for a Day

Assign students to find a current article about viruses in a newspaper or news magazine. Students should be prepared to verbally summarize the article to the class. Students can also be divided into groups for this activity.

Reading Check Sketches should show nucleic acids, DNA, or RNA in their core, and an outer protein coat.

■ **Figure 11** Viruses have several different types of arrangements, but all viruses have at least two parts: an outer capsid portion made of proteins, and genetic material.

S

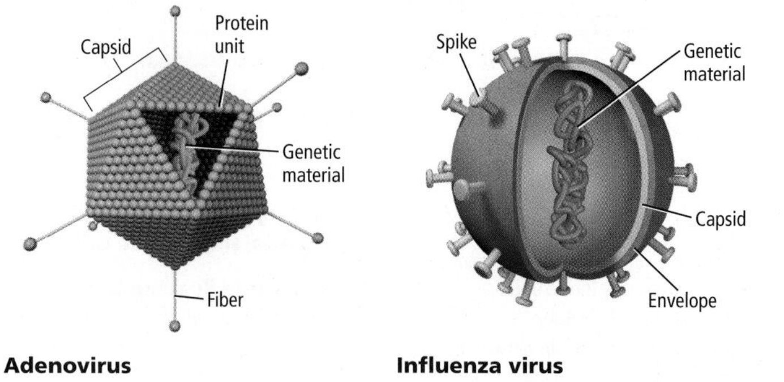

CAREERS IN BIOLOGY

Virologist Virologists study the natural history of viruses and the diseases they cause. Most virologists spend many hours in the laboratory conducting experiments.

Virus origin Although the origin of viruses is not known, scientists have several theories about how viruses evolved. One theory, now considered to be most likely, is that viruses came from parts of cells. Scientists have found that the genetic material of viruses is similar to cellular genes. These genes somehow developed the ability to exist outside of the cell. **D**

Virus structure **Figure 11** shows the structures of adenovirus, influenza virus, bacteriophage, and tobacco mosaic virus. Adenovirus infection causes the common cold, and influenza virus is responsible for causing the flu. A virus that infects bacteria is called a bacteriophage (bak TIHR ee uh fayj). Tobacco mosaic virus causes disease in tobacco leaves. The outer layer of all viruses is made of proteins and is called a **capsid.** Inside the capsid is the genetic material, which could be DNA or RNA, but never both. Viruses generally are classified by the type of nucleic acid they contain.

Reading Check **Sketch** the general structure of a virus.

■ **Figure 12**

The History of Smallpox

Though it has been eradicated, smallpox has been an important and deadly disease throughout history.

Concepts in Motion

The Interactive Timeline

1157 B.C. Smallpox kills Egyptian Pharaoh Ramses V. Two centuries earlier, Egyptian prisoners caused the first known smallpox epidemic when they were captured by the Hittites in Syria.

243 B.C. A terrible epidemic ravages China. Invading Huns bring smallpox to China, where the disease is called "Hun-pox."

0 — 1000 — 1500

1017 A hermit in China introduces mild cases of smallpox into humans to build immunity (variolation).

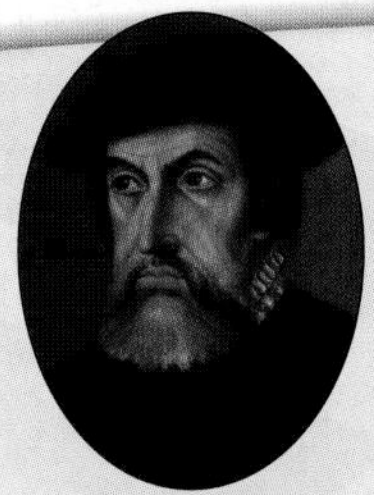

1519 Hernando Cortes and his crew spread smallpox to Mexico, which decimates the Aztec population.

Differentiated Instruction

Below Level Students benefit when instruction incorporates a variety of modalities. Provide students with opportunities to say, hear, write, read or act out important concepts.

For more tips, see pages 14T–15T.

Research Citation

Reading Strategies Educational research indicates that teachers should provide strategies for students that will increase their reading comprehension. Strategies like the SQ3R discussed on the previous page help students acquire self-questioning skills and retain information they have read. (McTeague, 1996)

Research bibliography on pages 32T–34T

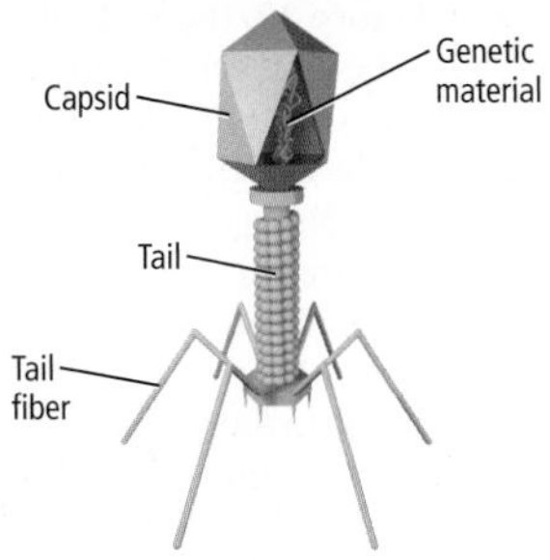

Bacteriophage

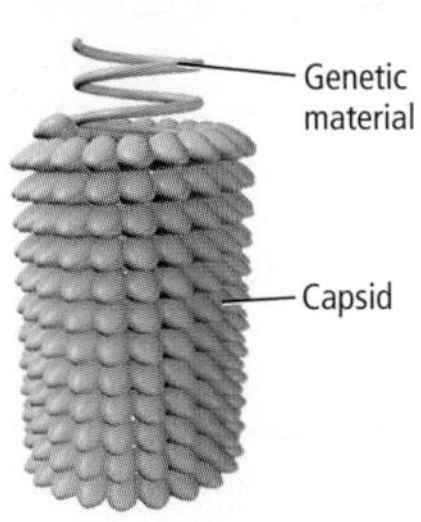

Tobacco mosaic virus

Connection to History The virus that causes smallpox is a DNA virus. Outbreaks of smallpox have occurred in the human population for thousands of years. A successful program of worldwide vaccination eliminated the disease, and routine vaccination was stopped. For a closer look at the history of the discovery of the virus that causes smallpox and smallpox vaccination, examine **Figure 12.**

W Viral Infection

To replicate, a virus must enter a host cell. The virus attaches to the host cell using specific receptors on the plasma membrane of the host. Different types of organisms have receptors for different types of viruses, which explains why many viruses cannot be transmitted between different species.

Once the virus successfully attaches to a host cell, the genetic material of the virus enters the cytoplasm of the host. In some cases, the entire virus enters the cell and the capsid is broken down quickly, exposing the genetic material. The virus then uses the host cell to replicate by either the lytic cycle or the lysogenic cycle.

VOCABULARY

ACADEMIC VOCABULARY

Widespread
widely diffused or prevalent
Finding a cure for HIV is of widespread interest in the world.

C

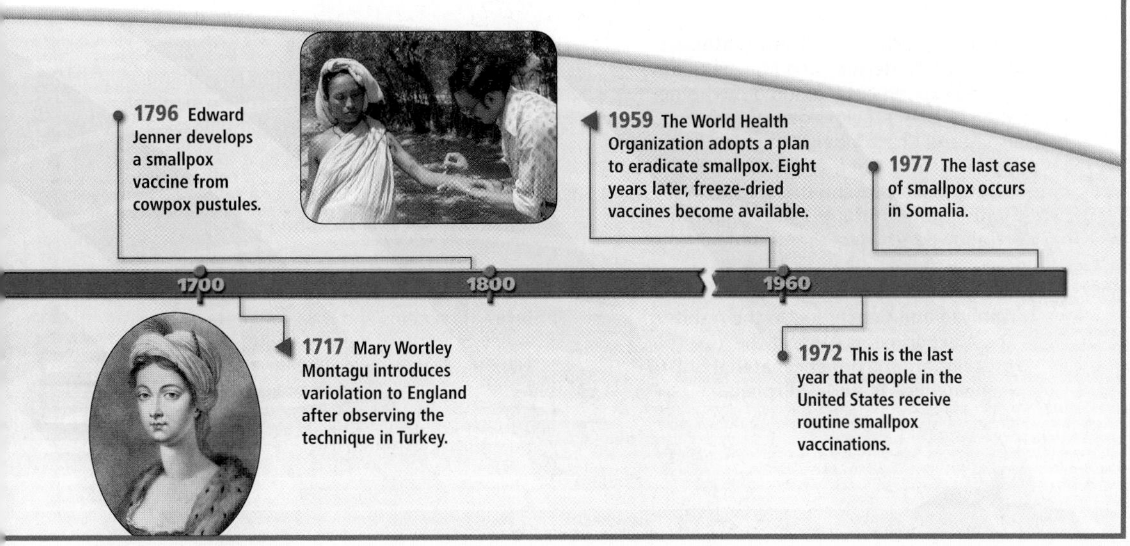

1796 Edward Jenner develops a smallpox vaccine from cowpox pustules.
1959 The World Health Organization adopts a plan to eradicate smallpox. Eight years later, freeze-dried vaccines become available.
1977 The last case of smallpox occurs in Somalia.
1700
1800
1960
1717 Mary Wortley Montagu introduces variolation to England after observing the technique in Turkey.
1972 This is the last year that people in the United States receive routine smallpox vaccinations.

W Writing Support

OL Creative Writing When a virus infects a host cell, the host cell replicates the virus. The analogy can be made that the cell becomes a virus factory.

SAY TO STUDENTS: ***Write a short story using this analogy.*** Students could indicate that the viral nucleic acids are like a blueprint or that the organelles in the cytoplasm are like an assembly line.

C Critical Thinking

BL OL AL Consider In 1979, the World Health Organization declared that smallpox had been eradicated. However, the United States and Russian governments are still keeping cultures of the virus. Have students research why the viruses are being kept and debate if these cultures should be kept or destroyed. Proponents of destroying these cultures argue that the virus could cause a great deal of harm if the virus were to get into the environment, especially since widespread vaccination programs are not currently being used. Others argue that these cultures are valuable for scientific research in case the virus or a similar virus was to emerge.

Concepts in Motion

The Interactive Timeline

Activity

OL Transmission of Pathogens Prepare a pot of cooked white rice and allow the rice to cool. Each grain of rice represents a pathogen (a disease-causing organism). Put your hand in the rice, which should be sticky, then shake hands with a student. Instruct that student to shake hands with two other students. Those students should shake hands with two more students. Touching different objects, such as a pencil, drinking glass, or doorknob and showing students the residue can modify this activity. Cinnamon or glitter can be used instead of rice for this activity. Once the activity is completed, have students wash their hands. Explain how this action helps to reduce the spread of pathogens. Est. time: 10 min

FOLDABLES®

RUBRIC A rubric for evaluating Foldables is found on your eTeacherEdition Online.

Going Further On separate index cards, have students explain the similarities and differences between the lytic and lysogenic cycles.

DATA ANALYSIS LAB 1

About the Lab

- The Hershey-Chase experiments are classic studies. Their findings led to future studies by Rosalind Franklin, James Watson, and Francis Crick. These landmark studies led to the discovery that DNA is the heredity material of living organisms.
- Also see Holton, C.S., et al. 1959. *Plant pathology: problems and progress, 1908–1958.* University of Wisconsin Press. Watson, J. D., and F. H. C. Crick. 1953. A structure for deoxyribose nucleic acid. *Nature* 171: 737–738.

Think Critically

1. The results support the idea that DNA is the genetic material. Most of the viral DNA entered the host, while most of the protein remained outside the cell. The radioactive DNA was replicated in the cell.
2. If both proteins and DNA had entered the cell, this would have not provided a possible explanation to the question. However, it would have been useful information in designing future experiments, as are most data.

Lytic cycle In the **lytic cycle,** illustrated in **Figure 13,** the host cell makes many copies of the viral RNA or DNA. The viral genes instruct the host cell to make more viral protein capsids and enzymes needed for viral replication. The protein coat forms around the nucleic acid of new viruses. These new viruses leave the cell by exocytosis or by causing the cell to burst, or lyse, releasing new viruses that are free to infect other cells. Viruses that replicate by the lytic cycle often produce active infections. Active infections usually are immediate, meaning that symptoms of the illness caused by the virus start to appear one to four days after exposure. The common cold and influenza are two examples of widespread viral diseases that are active infections.

FOLDABLES® Incorporate information from this section into your Foldable.

Lysogenic cycle In some cases, the viral DNA might enter the nucleus of the host cell. In the **lysogenic cycle,** also illustrated in **Figure 13,** the viral DNA inserts, or integrates, into a chromosome in a host cell. Once integrated, the infected cell will have the viral genes permanently. The viral genes might remain dormant for months or years. Then, at some future time, the viral genes might be activated by many different factors. Activation results in the lytic cycle. The viral genes instruct the host cell to manufacture more viruses. The new viruses will leave the cell by exocytosis or by causing the cell to lyse.

Many disease-causing viruses have lysogenic cycles. Herpes simplex I is an example of a virus that causes a latent infection. This virus is transmitted orally, and a symptom of this infection is cold sores. When the viral DNA enters the nucleus, it is inactive. It is thought that during times of stress, whether physical, emotional, or environmental, the herpes genes become activated and the production of viruses occurs.

DATA ANALYSIS LAB 1

Based on Real Data*

Model Viral Infection

Is protein or DNA the genetic material? In 1952, Alfred Hershey and Martha Chase designed experiments to find out whether protein or DNA provides genetic information. Hershey and Chase labeled the DNA of bacteriophages—viruses that infect bacteria—with a phosphorus isotope and the protein in the capsid with a sulfur isotope. The bacteriophages were allowed to infect the bacteria E. coli.

Data and Observations

- At least 80 percent of the sulfur-containing proteins stayed on the surface of the host cell.
- Most of the viral DNA entered the host cell upon infection.
- After replication inside the host cell, 30 percent or more of the copies of the virus contained radioactive phosphorus.

Think Critically

1. **Analyze and Conclude** Do the results of these experiments support the idea that proteins are the genetic material or DNA is the genetic material? Explain.
2. **Infer** If proteins and DNA had entered the cell, would these data be useful to answer Hershey and Chase's question?

*Data obtained from: Hershey, A.D. and Chase, M. 1952. Independent functions of viral protein and nucleic acid in growth of bacteriophage. *Journal of General Physiology* 36: 39–56.

"The most important part of teaching is to teach what it is to know."

—Simone Weil

Visualizing Viral Replication

Figure 13
In the lytic cycle, the entire replication process occurs in the cytoplasm. The viruses' genetic material enters the cell, and the cell replicates the viral RNA or DNA. The viral genes instruct the host cell to manufacture capsids and assemble new viral particles. The new viruses then leave the cells.

In the lysogenic cycle, the viral DNA inserts into a chromosome of the host cell. Many times, the genes are not activated until later. Then the viral DNA instructs the host cell to make more viruses.

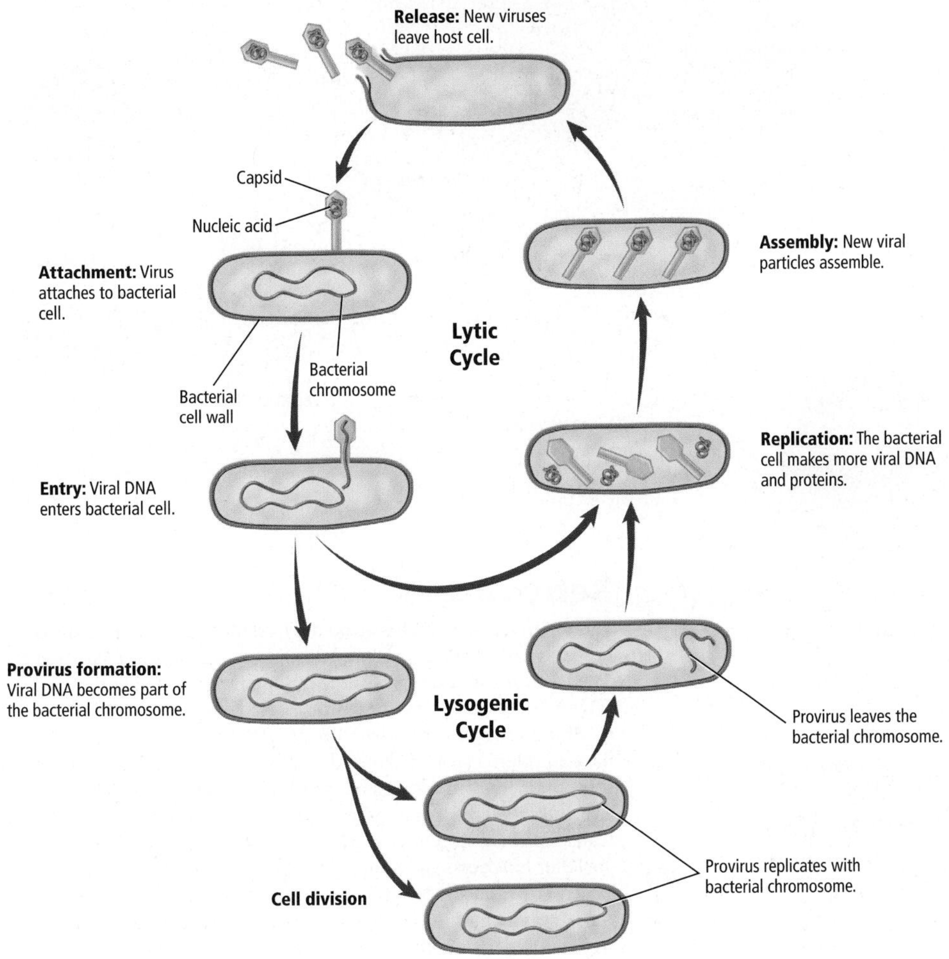

Release: New viruses leave host cell.
Capsid
Nucleic acid
Attachment: Virus attaches to bacterial cell.
Bacterial cell wall
Bacterial chromosome
Lytic Cycle
Assembly: New viral particles assemble.
Replication: The bacterial cell makes more viral DNA and proteins.
Entry: Viral DNA enters bacterial cell.
Provirus formation: Viral DNA becomes part of the bacterial chromosome.
Lysogenic Cycle
Provirus leaves the bacterial chromosome.
Provirus replicates with bacterial chromosome.
Cell division

Concepts in Motion Animation

Research Citation

Problem Solving Educational research indicates that solving challenging problems can help students learn new skills and concepts. Data Analysis labs like the one on the previous page allow students to develop conceptual understanding while thinking about the problem presented in the lab. **(Grouws and Cebutla, 2000)**

Research bibliography on pages 32T–34T

Visualizing Viral Replication

Purpose

Students will understand the current hypothesis on the replication of viruses.
C.4

S Skill Practice

EL BL OL AL Visual Literacy

Have students examine Figure 13. Provide pipe cleaners or twist ties, paper clips, and beads, and have students model the lytic cycle of viral replication as shown in the diagram.

Concepts in Motion
Animation

D Develop Concepts
BL OL AL

Clarify a Misconception

ASK STUDENTS: ***Can a person get HIV from a mosquito bite? Can you get HIV from sharing a glass? Can someone get HIV if he or she is sneezed or coughed on by a person who is HIV positive?*** Answers will vary. Current research indicates that none of these situations transmits HIV. If a mosquito bites an individual who has HIV, the virus is digested by the mosquito. HIV is transmitted only through the exchange of bodily fluids. Saliva and tears could have small numbers of HIV particles, but blood, semen, and vaginal secretions are the only bodily fluids with enough HIV particles for the disease to be transmitted.

W Writing Support
BL OL AL **Informal Writing**

SAY TO STUDENTS: ***Write a note in your own words explaining the replication of HIV to a friend who does not understand it.*** Students should show an understanding of the concept of reverse transcription.

Develop Concepts
BL OL AL

Clarify a Misconception

ASK STUDENTS: ***Are antibiotics effective against viruses?*** Antibiotics are effective only against bacteria; they have no effect against viruses.

Concepts in Motion

Animation

■ **Caption Question Fig. 14**

Reverse transcriptase allows DNA to be formed from an RNA template.

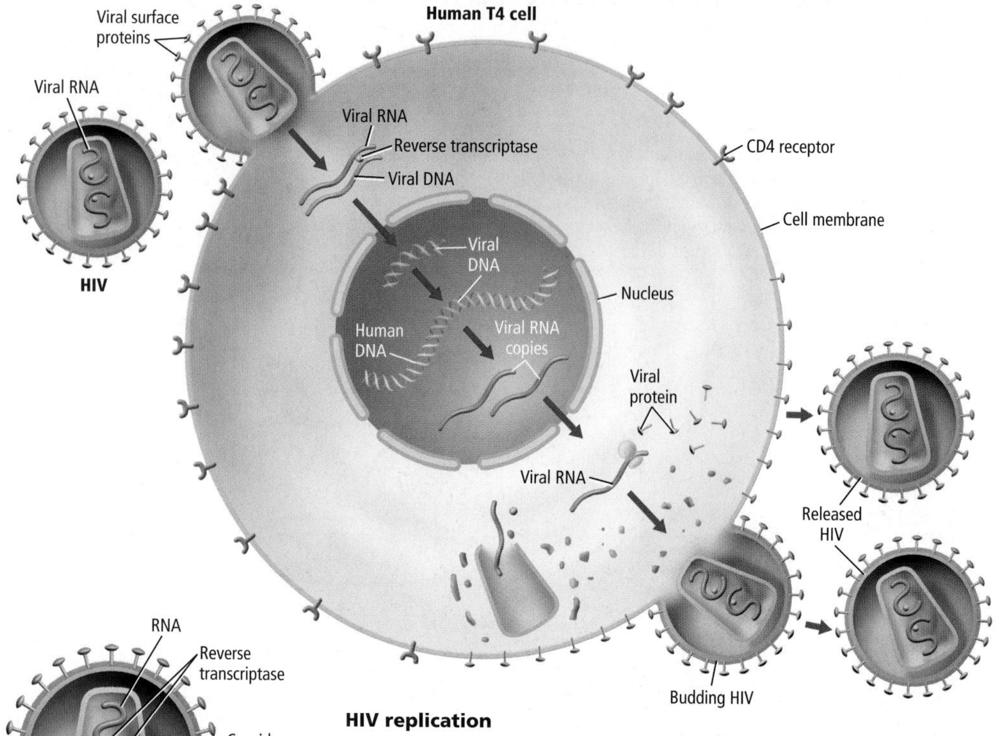

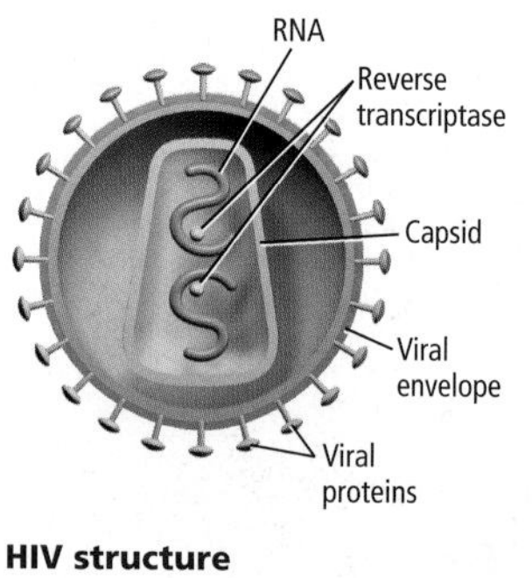

■ **Figure 14** The genetic material and replication cycle of a retrovirus, such as HIV, is different from that of DNA viruses.
Infer ***what is unique about the function of reverse transcriptase.***

Concepts in Motion

Animation D

Retroviruses

Some viruses have RNA instead of DNA for their genetic material. This type of virus is called a **retrovirus** and has a complex replication cycle. The best-known retrovirus is the human immunodeficiency virus (HIV). Some cancer-causing viruses also belong to this group.

Figure 14 shows the structure of HIV. Like all viruses, retroviruses have a protein capsid. Surrounding the capsid is a lipid envelope, which was obtained from the plasma membrane of a host cell. RNA and an enzyme called reverse transcriptase are in the core of the virus. Reverse transcriptase is the enzyme that transcribes DNA from the viral RNA.

Refer to **Figure 14** as you learn about the replication cycle of HIV. When HIV attaches to a cell, the virus moves into the cytoplasm of the host cell and the viral RNA is released. Reverse transcriptase synthesizes DNA using the viral RNA as a template. Then, the DNA moves into the nucleus of the host cell and integrates into a chromosome. The viral DNA might lie inactive for a period of years before it is activated. Once it is activated, RNA is transcribed from the viral DNA, and the host cell manufactures and assembles new HIV particles. W

Content Background

Teacher FYI Many HIV patients are treated with a drug regimen known as a "triple cocktail." Two of the drugs interfere with the transcription (reverse) of DNA from RNA. The other drug is a protease inhibitor, which interferes with the assembly of new viral particles. Together, these are effective in slowing down the progression of HIV in an individual.

Prions

A protein that can cause infection or disease is called a proteinaceous (pro te NAY shuhs) infectious particle, or a **prion** (PREE ahn). Although diseases now believed to be caused by prions have been studied for decades, they were not well understood until 1982, when Stanley B. Prusiner first identified that the infectious particle was a protein.

Prions normally exist in cells, although their function is not well understood. Normal prions are shaped like a coil. Mutations in the genes that code for these proteins occur, causing the proteins to be misfolded. Mutated prions are shaped like a piece of paper folded many times. Mutated prions are associated with diseases known as transmissible spongiform encephalopathies (SPUN gee form • in SEH fuh la pah thees) (TSE). Examples of diseases caused by prions include mad cow disease in cattle, Creutzfeldt-Jakob disease (CJD) in humans, scrapie (SKRAY pee) in sheep, and chronic wasting disease in deer and elk.

Prion infection **Figure 15** shows a normal brain compared with a brain infected with prions. What scientists find fascinating about these misfolded proteins is that these prions can cause normal proteins to mutate. These prions infect nerve cells in the brain, causing them to burst. This results in spaces in the brain, hence the description of spongiform (spongelike) encephalopathy (brain disease).

In the mid-1980s, a new variant of CJD, or nvCJD, was discovered in England. Scientists do not fully agree on the origin of nvCJD, but a leading hypothesis is that the prions are transmitted from cattle. Abnormal prions can be found in the brains and spinal cords of cattle. The hypothesis is that if the spinal cord is cut in the butchering process, the prions might contaminate the beef and then be transmitted to humans that eat the beef. Although this mode of transmission is not agreed upon, the United States government has strict regulations concerning the importation of cattle and beef from other countries.

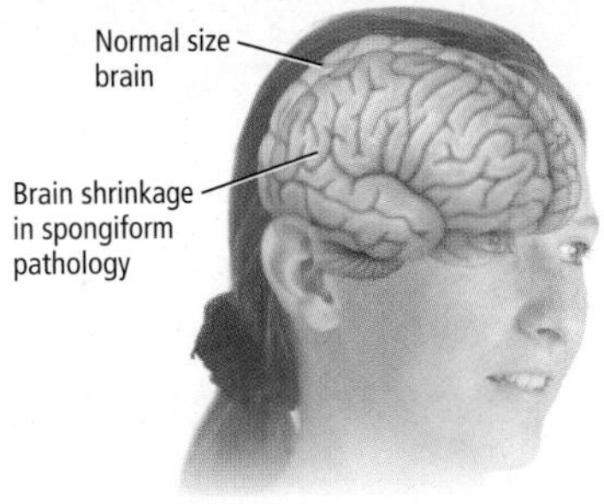

■ **Figure 15** A normal brain compared with the brain of a patient with Creutzfeldt-Jakob disease is pictured here.

D

Section 2 Assessment

Section Summary

- Viruses have a nucleic acid core and a protein-containing coat.
- Viruses are classified by their genetic material.
- Viruses have three different patterns of replication.
- Many viruses cause disease.
- Proteins called prions also might cause disease.

Understand Main Ideas

1. MAIN Idea **Describe** how viruses and prions can alter cell functions.
2. **Compare and contrast** similarities and differences in the replication of a herpes simplex virus with a human immunodeficiency virus.
3. **Draw** a diagram of a virus and label the parts.
4. **Sequence** the steps in the process of how prions might be transmitted from cattle to humans.

Think Critically

5. **Propose** ideas for the development of drugs that could stop viral replication cycles.

WRITING in Biology

6. Write a paragraph explaining why it is difficult to make drugs or vaccines that effectively fight against HIV, given the fact that each time reverse transcriptase works, it makes a slight miscopy.

D Develop Concepts

BL OL AL Scaffolding

ASK STUDENTS: ***What is a prion?*** a misfolded protein ***How do prions replicate?*** When a misfolded protein comes into contact with a normal protein, it causes it to misfold also. Both misfolded proteins will come into contact with normal proteins and cause them to become misfolded too. ***Propose a strategy that would slow the spread of prions.*** Ideas could include targeting an enzyme involved with protein replication, or marking a prion as something foreign for the immune system to destroy.

Formative Assessment

Evaluation

SAY TO STUDENTS: ***Using herpes simplex I as an example, describe the replication of a virus, including viral latency.*** Herpes simplex I replicates using a lysogenic-cycle. First, a virus attaches to a host cell and the viral DNA enters the cytoplasm and the nucleus. The viral DNA attaches to a chromosome in the host cell. The viral DNA remains inactive, but later is activated and codes for the formation of new viral particles. New viruses are assembled in the cytoplasm of the host cell and then released.

Remediation Have students review Figure 13. Use a diagram similar to Figure 13 and remove any labels and captions. Have students label and describe in writing the events associated with each step of the diagram.

Section 2 Assessment

1. Viruses cause an infected cell to make more viruses; prions cause proteins inside cells to mutate and change shape and function incorrectly.
2. Herpes viruses have DNA; HIV has RNA. HIV contains reverse transcriptase. Similarity: genetic material from both enters the host cell nucleus.
3. Students should provide a diagram similar to 11.
4. possible answers: cattle-butchering process releases prions into the meat—humans consume infected meat—prions travel to the brain
5. prevent a virus from attaching to host cells; disrupt the viral replication process; prevent the final assembly of new viral particles
6. Paragraphs should indicate that each time HIV replicates, a slightly different type of the virus forms, so drugs or vaccines might be ineffective.

WRITING in Biology

RUBRIC Use the modifiable rubric found on your eTeacherEdition Online to assess writing assignments.

BioDiscoveries

Purpose

Students will understand that viruses can jump from other animals to humans.
F.1, C.1

Anticipatory Guide

ASK STUDENTS: ***What is a virus?*** Tell students that a virus is a nonliving strand of genetic material that cannot replicate on its own. Viruses have a nucleic acid core and a protein coat, and they can invade cells and alter cellular function. ***What do you know about "swine flu"?*** Students might have misconceptions about the illness. Emphasize that the virus that infects humans, novel influenza A H1N1, is not the same virus or group of viruses that sickens pigs and is called "swine flu."

Background

Two proteins, called hemagglutinin (H) and neuraminidase (N), are found on the surface of every influenza virus. They are two of the eight genes that each virus carries. These proteins allow influenza viruses to infect cells. Sometimes, viruses mix or trade proteins. This type of sudden, major change in the influenza A virus is called antigenic shift. It forms new influenza A subtypes with new combinations of H and N proteins. Most people do not have immunity against new viruses formed by antigenic shift, which is why novel influenza A H1N1 can spread so rapidly.

BioDiscoveries

Exploring Inter-species Virus Transmission

While you were sniffling through yet another winter cold, did you ever wonder where the virus originated? Some viruses circulate only among humans, but other viruses can jump from animals to humans. Sometimes, both animals and humans can be infected with the same type of virus, while other viruses must change genetically in order to move from animals to humans.

H1N1 In the spring of 2009, a virus that was initially dubbed "swine flu" began to sweep across the globe. Since then, scientists have discovered that the virus, now called novel influenza A H1N1, passed from pigs to humans early that year. The new virus is what scientists call a quadruple reassortant virus because it contains two swine flu genes, an avian (bird) flu gene, and a human flu gene.

HIV Probably the most notorious virus to make the animal-to-human jump is HIV (human immunodeficiency virus), the virus that leads to AIDS (acquired immunodeficiency syndrome). HIV attacks the human immune system by destroying white blood cells. Scientists have discovered that in the late 1800s, the main strain of the virus, HIV-1 group M, jumped from a subspecies of chimpanzees to humans in Cameroon, a country in West Central Africa. Scientists hypothesize that the virus first infected people who were killing chimpanzees to sell for meat. The blood from the slaughtered primates got into scratches and bites on the human hunters, effectively transmitting HIV-1.

Ebola virus The often fatal disease called Ebola hemorrhagic fever (Ebola HF) is caused by the Ebola virus. Humans, as well as chimpanzees, gorillas, and monkeys, can be infected by subtypes of the virus.

Scientists have traced HIV and Ebola back to chimpanzees.

Scientists are not yet sure of the origins of the Ebola virus, but they think it is carried by a species of animal native to Africa and the Philippines and is spread to humans when they come into contact with infected animals. The Ebola virus has never infected anyone in the United States.

Monitoring public health In response to the spread of H1N1, scientists and public health specialists have called for greater monitoring of the health of swine populations around the world. In the future, viruses that pass from animals to humans might spur the same kinds of actions in order to lessen the possibility of epidemics.

CAREERS IN BIOLOGY

Interview an epidemiologist Write down several questions that you have about these types of viruses. Also, write down several questions about what is involved in a career in epidemiology. If possible, ask a scientist your questions.

CAREERS IN BIOLOGY

Activity Prepare students for the epidemiologist's visit by having them research the career and the viruses discussed in this feature. Tell them that reliable, credible online sources include the Centers for Disease Control and Prevention (CDC), the National Institutes of Health (NIH), and the World Health Organization (WHO). While students are doing their research, encourage them to formulate questions about the career and about the viruses. If an epidemiologist cannot visit your school, arrange for a conference call or a video conference, if possible.

WebQuest

BIOLAB

Design Your Own

HOW CAN THE MOST EFFECTIVE ANTIBIOTICS BE DETERMINED?

Background: **A patient is suffering from a serious bacterial infection. As the doctor, you must choose from several new antibiotics to treat the infection.**

Question: *How can the effectiveness of antibiotics be tested?*

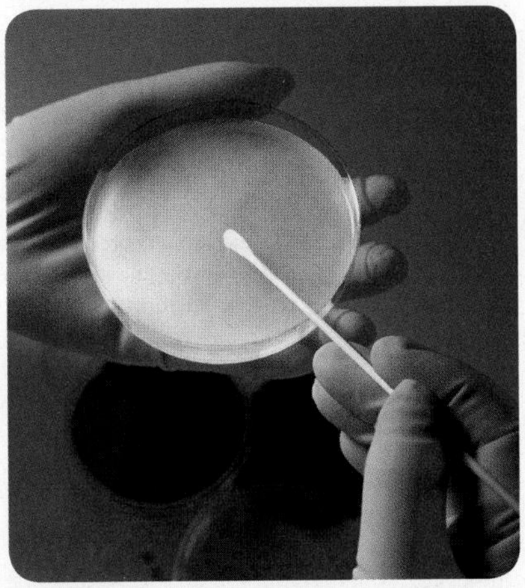

Materials

bacteria cultures
sterile nutrient agar
petri dishes
antibiotic disks
control disks
forceps
Bunsen burner
marking pen
long-handled cotton swabs
70% ethanol
thermometer
container
disinfectant
autoclave disposal bag

Safety Precautions

WARNING: ***Clean your work area with disinfectant after you finish.***

Plan and Perform the Experiment

1. Read and complete the lab safety form.
2. Design an experiment to test the effectiveness of different antibiotics. Identify the controls and variables in your experiment.
3. Create a data table for recording your observations and measurements.
4. Make sure your teacher approves your plan before you proceed.
5. Conduct your experiment.
6. **Cleanup and Disposal** Dispose of all materials according to your teacher's instructions. Disinfect your area.

Analyze and Conclude

1. **Compare and contrast** What are the effects of the different antibiotics for the bacteria species that you tested?
2. **Hypothesize** Why would a doctor instruct you to take all of your prescribed antibiotics for a bacterial infection even if you start feeling better before the pills run out?
3. **Explain** What were the limitations of your experimental design?
4. **Error Analysis** Compare and contrast the observations and measurements collected by your group with the data from the experiments designed by other groups. Identify possible sources of error in your experimental data.

COMMUNITY INVOLVEMENT

Create a Poster Misuse of antibiotic prescriptions and use of antibacterial household items are contributing to antibiotic-resistant bacteria. Research the causes of bacterial resistance to drugs and the steps that people in your community can take to help solve this problem. Create a poster display to educate the people in your community about this issue.

Analyze and Conclude

1. Results will depend on the antibiotic disks and bacterial cultures used. Most of the antibiotic disks should show inhibition zones. Untreated control disks should have no inhibition zones.
2. Not completing the treatment can allow the bacteria that have survived to rebound and make a person ill again, and surviving bacteria can develop resistance to the antibiotic.
3. Answers will vary; an antibiotic might work in an agar culture but not in humans.
4. Answers will vary. Sources of error include using expired antibiotic disks, contaminating antibiotic disks, contaminating bacterial cultures due to unsterile procedures, and misidentifying antibiotic disks.

BIOLAB

Design Your Own

? Inquiry **BioLab**

For a lab worksheet, use your eTeacherEdition Online.

RUBRIC A rubric for evaluating BioLabs is found on your eTeacherEdition Online.

Est. Time 75 min

Content Background All antibiotics work by altering the metabolism of microorganisms to prevent them from growing and reproducing. The disk technique used in this lab has students observe and measure the zone of inhibition created by an antibiotic, which is a clear area around an antibiotic disk where bacteria cannot grow.

Teaching Strategies

- Have students sterilize the forceps with the flame of a Bunsen burner (then cool) before using them to place the antibiotic disks onto the agar plates.
- Have students make their observations 24 and 48 h after placing the disks in the cultures and measure, the zone of inhibition.

Alternative Teaching Demo Prepare the plate cultures within two hours of use. Have students brainstorm an experiment for testing the effectiveness of the antibiotics; create a data table for observations and measurements; mark off the antibiotic quadrants in the petri dishes and place the antibiotic disks in the quadrants.

Cleanup and Disposal Have students clean work areas with disinfectant. Dispose of the bacterial culture tubes and agar tubes in the autoclave disposal bag.

Chapter 18

Study Guide

ConnectED

Students can use the following to review the chapter.

Review

Vocabulary eGames
Vocabulary eFlashcards
Vocabulary PuzzleMaker

Assessment

Online Quizzes
Online Test Practice
Standardized Test Practice

Use the *ExamView® Assessment Suite* CD-ROM to:

- create multiple versions of tests
- create modified tests with one mouse click
- edit existing questions and add your own questions
- build tests aligned with state standards using built-in state curriculum tags
- change English tests to Spanish with one mouse click
- track students' progress using the Teacher Management System

Chapter 18 Study Guide

THEME FOCUS Diversity Prokaryotes are the most abundant organisms on Earth, and cover nearly every surface.

BIG Idea **Bacteria are microscopic organisms, and viruses are nonliving microscopic agents that invade cells.**

Section 1 Bacteria

bacteria (p. 516)
nucleoid (p. 518)
capsule (p. 518)
pilus (p. 518)
binary fission (p. 520)
conjugation (p. 520)
endospore (p. 521)

MAIN Idea **Prokaryotes are diverse organisms that live in nearly all environments.**

- Many scientists think that prokaryotes were the first organisms on Earth.
- Prokaryotes belong to two domains.
- Most prokaryotes are beneficial.
- Prokaryotes have a variety of survival mechanisms.
- Some bacteria cause disease.

Color-Enhanced SEM Magnification: 50,000×

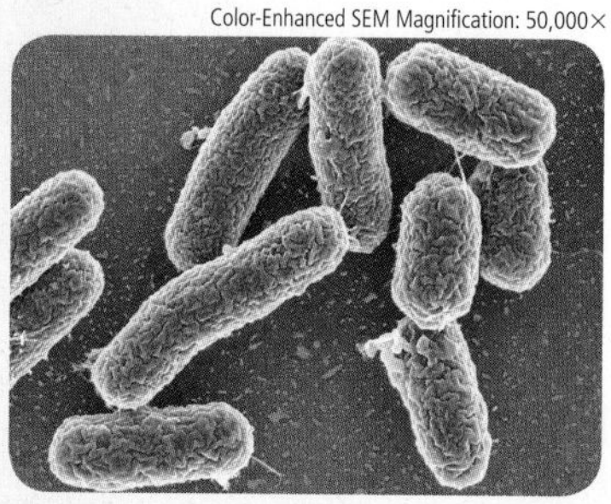

Section 2 Viruses and Prions

virus (p. 525)
capsid (p. 526)
lytic cycle (p. 528)
lysogenic cycle (p. 528)
retrovirus (p. 530)
prion (p. 531)

MAIN Idea **Viruses and prions are smaller and less complex than bacteria; they invade cells and can alter cellular functions.**

- Viruses have a nucleic acid core and a protein-containing coat.
- Viruses are classified by their genetic material.
- Viruses have three different patterns of replication.
- Many viruses cause disease.
- Proteins called prions also might cause disease.

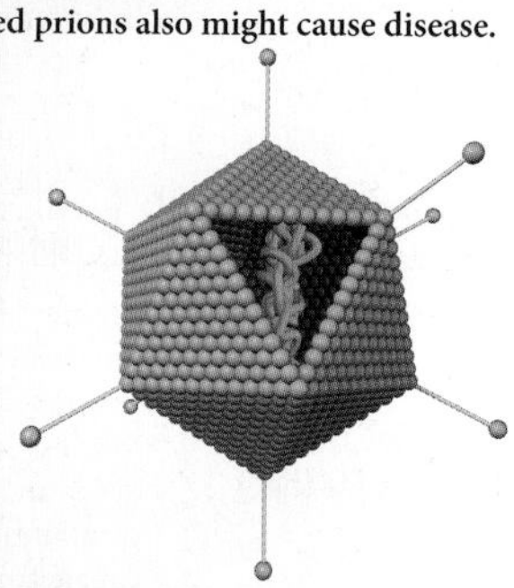

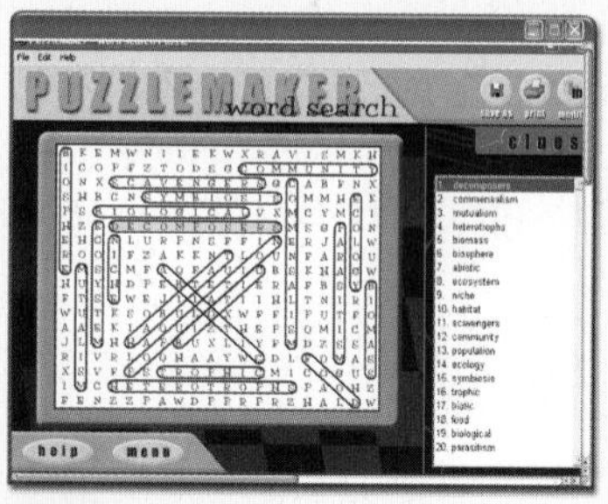

Review **Vocabulary PuzzleMaker**

For additional practice with vocabulary, have students access the Vocabulary PuzzleMaker online.

Review **Vocabulary eGames**

Section 1

Vocabulary Review

For each set of terms below, choose the one that does not belong and explain why it does not belong.

1. capsule, pilus, endospore
2. binary fission, nitrogen fixation, conjugation
3. endospore, nucleoid, nitrogen fixation

Understand Main Ideas

4. Which organism is not included in Domain Archaea?
   A. cyanobacteria
   B. methanogens
   C. halophiles
   D. thermoacidophiles

5. Why is an electron microscope useful when studying bacteria?
   A. Electrons can penetrate through the capsules surrounding bacteria.
   B. Bacteria are tiny.
   C. Bacteria move quickly; the electrons stun the bacteria.
   D. Bacteria organelles are small and tightly packed together.

Use the figure below to answer questions 6 and 7.

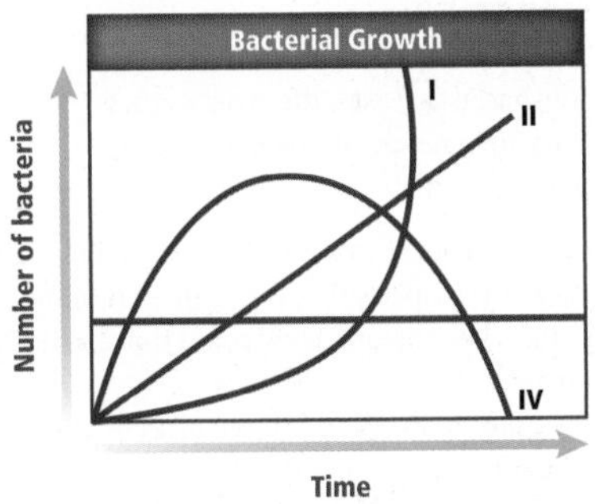

6. Which line on the graph best indicates the growth rate of a population of bacteria living in ideal conditions?
   A. line I **C.** line III
   B. line II **D.** line IV

7. Which line on the graph best indicates the growth rate of a population of bacteria exposed to an effective antibiotic?
   A. line I **C.** line III
   B. line II **D.** line IV

8. You have just been named a contestant on a reality show. Your first challenge is to swallow microbes. Which would be the most dangerous to swallow?
   A. thermoacidophiles
   B. halophiles
   C. *Escherichia coli*
   D. a bacteriophage

Use the photos below to answer question 9.

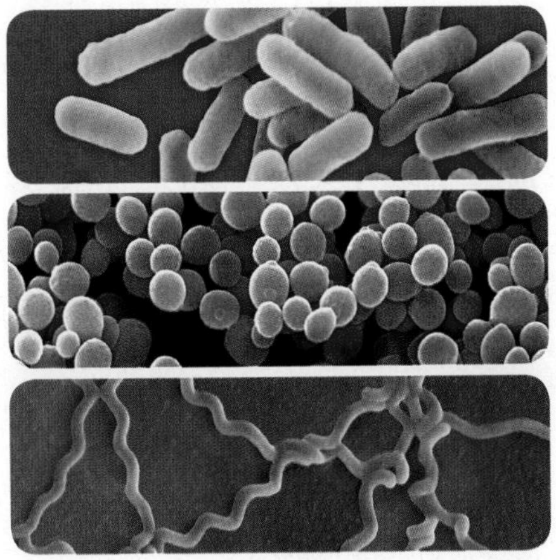

9. Which is the correct identification for the bacteria shown above?
   A. I—cocci, II—bacilli, III—spirochetes
   B. I—bacilli, II—cocci, III—spirochetes
   C. I—spirochetes, II—cocci, III—bacilli
   D. I—bacilli, II—spirochetes, III—cocci

10. What is the likely cause of tooth decay?
    A. a lysogenic virus infecting the living cells of the tooth
    B. bacteria feeding on the sugar in the mouth and producing acid
    C. an excess of vitamin K production by bacteria in the mouth
    D. nitrogen-fixing bacteria releasing ammonia that is eroding the tooth enamel

Chapter 18

Assessment

Section 1

Vocabulary Review

1. Possible answers: Pilus does not belong, as it is a projection on the outer surface of some bacteria; capsule and endospore involve the whole bacterium (capsule covers the outside of the cell wall; endospore is a dormant complete cell). Endospore does not belong; it is a dormant and complete cell, while capsule and pilus refer to prokaryotic structure.
2. Nitrogen fixation does not belong, as binary fission and conjugation are methods of reproduction.
3. Nitrogen fixation does not belong, as it is a metabolic process in an active cell, rather than a physical structure.

Understand Main Ideas

4. A
5. B
6. A
7. C
8. C
9. B
10. B

Constructed Response

11. Possible answer: Bacteria are decomposers in ecosystems, breaking down detritus and returning nutrients to the environment.

12. Some bacteria form endospores that are resistant to environmental extremes. Their rapid reproduction and resistance to certain types of antibiotics also make them difficult to destroy.

13. Primary arguments are based upon the fossil record that indicates the existence of tiny cells dating back 3.5 billion years. Also, certain bacteria can survive in conditions thought to be present on early Earth.

Think Critically

14. There may not be any free oxygen in the environment, limiting the type of organisms that could survive.

15. If the nitrogen cycle were broken, nitrogen would be limited for use in the amino acids of living organisms.

16. Answers will vary, and may include that prokaryotes have a large, circular chromosome, a plasmid, a capsule, are usually round, rod-shaped, or spiral-shaped, have peptidoglycan in their cell walls, survive on a wide variety of nutrients, and live almost everywhere on Earth.

Section 2

Vocabulary Review

17. Both are viral replication processes.

18. Both can cause disease.

19. A prion is a protein; a capsid is made of proteins.

20. A retrovirus is a type of virus. Both contain protein and both are smaller than bacteria.

Constructed Response

11. Open Ended Make an argument for or against the following statement: Living organisms on Earth owe their lives to bacteria.

12. THEME FOCUS **Diversity** Describe characteristics of bacteria (both at the individual and population level) that make them tough to destroy.

13. Open Ended What types of arguments do you think biologists use when they say that prokaryotes were the first organisms on Earth?

Think Critically

14. Speculate what life on Earth might be like if cyanobacteria had never evolved.

15. Predict any ecological consequences that would result if all types of nitrogen-fixing bacteria suddenly became extinct.

16. MAIN Idea Describe some of the diverse characteristics of prokaryotes.

Section 2

Vocabulary Review

Use what you know about the vocabulary terms on the Study Guide page to describe what the terms in each pair below have in common.

17. lytic cycle, lysogenic cycle

18. prion, virus

19. capsid, prion

20. virus, retrovirus

Understand Main Ideas

21. Viruses contain which substances?
- **A.** genetic material and a capsid
- **B.** a nucleus, genetic material, and a capsid
- **C.** a nucleus, genetic material, a capsid, and ribosomes
- **D.** a nucleus, genetic material, a capsid, ribosomes, and a plasma membrane

Use the figure below to answer questions 22 and 23.

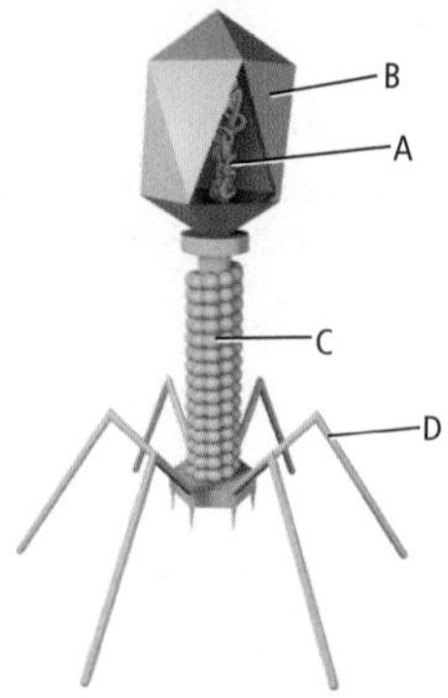

22. Which labeled structure represents the genetic material of a virus?
- **A.** A
- **B.** B
- **C.** C
- **D.** D

23. Which structure represents the capsid of a virus?
- **A.** A
- **B.** B
- **C.** C
- **D.** D

24. HIV is a retrovirus. What does this mean?
- **A.** Viral RNA is used to make DNA.
- **B.** Viral DNA is used to make RNA.
- **C.** Protein is made directly from viral RNA.
- **D.** Protein is made directly from viral DNA.

25. Which statement about prions is true?
- **A.** Prions are renegade pieces of RNA that infect cells.
- **B.** Prions are infectious proteins.
- **C.** Prion-based diseases affect only cows.
- **D.** Prions are a newly discovered type of genetic material.

26. Imagine that a patient in a hospital has died mysteriously. A doctor suspects that the cause of death is Creutzfeldt-Jacob disease. How could this diagnosis be confirmed?
- **A.** by examining the blood to see if there is a high viral count
- **B.** by asking the patient's family and friends if the patient consumed a lot of meat
- **C.** by examining the brain to see if there are a lot of spaces in the tissue
- **D.** by examining nerve cells to see if they have been affected by a bacterial neurotoxin

Understand Main Ideas

21. A
22. A
23. B
24. A
25. B
26. C
27. A

Constructed Response

28. Viruses lack many features of living organisms. In addition, the cell theory states that all living things are made of cells; viruses are acellular.

29. Students might think that quarantining the infected individuals will quarantine the virus. Students might think that it is unfair to isolate infected individuals. Students might also make the connection that a quarantine does not mean the virus has been isolated; it may continue to spread.

Assessment Online Test Practice

Use the figure below to answer question 27.

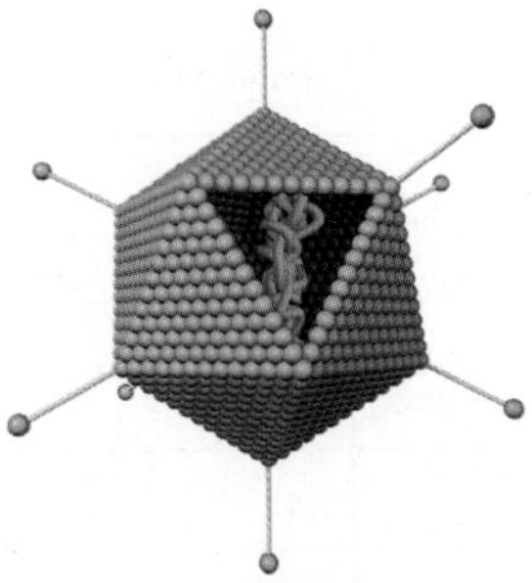

27. Which organisms does this virus infect?
 A. humans
 B. bacteria
 C. plants
 D. fungi

Constructed Response

28. **Open Ended** Make an argument for or against the following statement: Viruses are living organisms.

29. **Open Ended** Should people with highly contagious, potentially deadly viruses be quarantined? Defend your response.

30. MAIN Idea Make an argument for or against the following statement: Prions are just viruses that lack a capsid.

Think Critically

31. **Infer** why it is more difficult to make an antiviral drug that fights a virus that replicates through the lysogenic cycle than it is to make one that fights a virus that replicates through the lytic cycle.

32. **Evaluate** why it is easier to make drugs that fight bacteria than drugs that fight viruses, even though viruses are structurally less complex than bacteria.

33. **Hypothesize** and develop a technique to slow down or stop a viral replication cycle.

34. **Develop** a list of careers that are associated with bacteria, viruses, and prions.

Summative Assessment

35. BIG Idea You have learned that bacteria are microscopic organisms, and viruses are nonliving agents that invade cells. Compare and contrast bacteria and viruses beyond the previous statement.

36. WRITING in Biology Prepare a newspaper article that clearly explains the differences between treatment and prevention for bacterial infections versus viral infections.

37. WRITING in Biology Compose a sentence that explains each step in the sequence of events in the replication of HIV.

DBQ Document-Based Questions

U.S. Data: Centers for Disease Control http://www.cdc.gov/flu/avian/pdf/avianflufacts.pdf.
Global Data: Scotland Government http://www.scotland.gov.uk/library5/health/pfle-00.asp

There were three worldwide influenza epidemics during the twentieth century. The number of deaths is presented in the table below.

	Spanish Flu	Asian Flu	Hong Kong Flu
Years	1918–1919	1957–1958	1968–1969
U.S. deaths	500,000	70,000	34,000
Global deaths	20–40 million	1 million	1–4 million

38. Which epidemic was the most deadly?

39. Why were deaths from the Hong Kong flu not as high in the United States compared to the Asian flu but were higher worldwide?

40. Hypothesize why a flu epidemic eventually stops instead of eliminating all human life.

41. Research statistics about a current strain of the flu. Copy the table and add a column about the flu that you researched. Is the current strain considered an "epidemic"? Site data to support your answer.

30. Prions are infectious proteins; a virus without a capsid would be just a piece of genetic material.

Think Critically

31. Viral nucleic acid enters the nucleus of the host cell in the lysogenic cycle; once this happens, drugs that affect DNA replication could have an adverse effect on the host cell. This is not a concern with viruses that replicate using the lytic cycle.
32. Viruses are dependent on host cells for replication. Using a drug that interferes with viral replication may also interfere with the metabolism of a host.
33. Answer will vary, but the techniques should attack at least one phase in the viral replication process (e.g., attachment).
34. microbiologist, doctor, food scientist, virologist, cell biologist

Summative Assessment

35. Answers will vary. Bacteria and viruses are both responsible for diseases, but some types of both are not harmful. Bacteria are cells, and have cell walls; viruses do not. Both bacteria and viruses have genetic material.
36. Major differences should include antibiotics can be used to treat bacterial infections, but not viral infections. Vaccinations are used to prevent viral infections.
37. The HIV particle attaches to a host cell. Viral RNA enters the cytoplasm of the host cell. Reverse transcriptase forms DNA along the RNA template. Viral DNA enters the nucleus of the host cell. The viral DNA directs the replication of new viral particles. The new viruses leave the cell via exocytosis.

DBQ Document-Based Questions

U.S. Data: Center for Disease Control http://www.cdc.gov/flu/avian/pdf/avianflufacts.pdf.

Global Data: Scotland Government http://www.scotland.gov.uk/library5/health/pfle-00.asp

38. Spanish flu
39. Better medical treatments were available in the United States than in many parts of the world.
40. The genetic variation in the human population ensures that some individuals will have a combination of traits that allow them to fight off the virus and survive.
41. Answers will vary depending on the strain of flu researched. Direct students to the World Health Organization and Center for Disease Control if they have difficulty finding the data.

Assessment Online Test Practice

Standardized Test Practice

Multiple Choice

1. D 5. B 9. B
2. C 6. C
3. B 7. B
4. A 8. B

Short Answer

10. Evidence that the two kinds of mosquitoes can interbreed and produce fertile offspring in natural settings would support the idea that the two types of mosquitoes are one species.
11. The basic shapes are rodlike (bacilli), spheres (cocci), and spiral (spirilla, spirochetes). The bacilli can occur singly, in pairs, or in chains. The cocci can occur singly, in clusters, or as twisted chains. The spiral bacteria may be short and rigid or longer and more flexible.
12. The typological species concept is based on the idea that species are distinct and unchanging. Organisms were considered different species based on how they varied from the type specimen. The phylogenetic species concept is based on the idea that organisms change. The phylogenetic species concept defines species based on their evolutionary history and relationships.
13. Being bipedal, hominids were able to move about over greater distances, even in grasslands where there were fewer trees. The adaptation helped primates to transition from being tree-dwelling to land-dwelling.
14. Alternation of generations is the key characteristic.
15. Ancestral character: vascular tissue; Derived character: carpels

Standardized Test Practice

Cumulative

Multiple Choice

1. Which primate is an Asian ape?
A. baboon
B. gorilla
C. lemur
D. orangutan

Use the chart below to answer questions 2 and 3.

Common Name	Scientific Name
Grey wolf	*Canis lupus*
Red wolf	*Canis rufus*
African hunting dog	*Lycaon pictus*
Pampas fox	*Pseudalopex gymnocercus*

2. Which animal is related most closely to the Sechura fox *Pseudalopex sechurae*?
A. African hunting dog
B. grey wolf
C. pampas fox
D. red wolf

3. Which kind of difference is a valid reason to classify the red wolf and pampas fox in separate genera?
A. different prey
B. differences in key DNA sequences
C. different structures of skulls
D. different ages of evolutionary origin

4. Which describes the role of an endospore in bacteria?
A. a dormant state of bacteria that can survive in unfavorable conditions
B. a form of sexual reproduction in bacteria during which genetic information is exchanged
C. a protective covering that bacteria secrete to protect themselves against harsh environments
D. a tiny hairlike structure made of proteins that attaches the bacteria to a surface

5. Which information constitutes a scientific hypothesis?
A. defined data
B. proven explanation
C. published conclusion
D. reasonable guess

Use the table below to answer questions 6 and 7.

Identifying Bacteria			
Bacterial Strain	**Gram Staining**	**Morphology**	**Related Disease**
Bacillus cereus	Gram-positive	Rods; arranged in chains	Meningitis
Escherichia coli	Gram-negative	Cocci	Traveler's diarrhea
Pseudomonas aeruginosa	Gram-negative	Rodlike; occur in pairs or short chains	Pneumonia
Serratia mercescens	Gram-negative	Rodlike	Pneumonia

6. Which kind of bacteria stains gram-negative and appears rodlike in short chains?
A. *Bacillus cereus*
B. *Escherichia coli*
C. *Pseudomonas aeruginosa*
D. *Serratia marcescens*

7. Which related disease would be associated with a bacterium that is gram-negative and in paired rods?
A. meningitis
B. pneumonia
C. cystic fibrosis
D. traveler's diarrhea

8. Which taxon gives you the most general information about an organism?
A. class
B. domain
C. family
D. phylum

9. A population of rodents on an island makes up a distinct species that is similar to a species found on the mainland. Which process caused this speciation?
A. behavioral isolation
B. geographic isolation
C. reproductive isolation
D. temporal isolation

Short Answer

10. Suppose that two mosquitoes are classified as different species using the typological species concept. What data could scientists use, under the biological species concept, to show that they are the same species?

11. Compare the basic shapes of bacteria.

12. Contrast the typological species concept and the phylogenetic species concept.

13. Hypothesize how the evolution of bipedalism made it possible for hominoids to survive better in the drier African environment of the Miocene epoch.

Use the illustration below to answer questions 14 and 15.

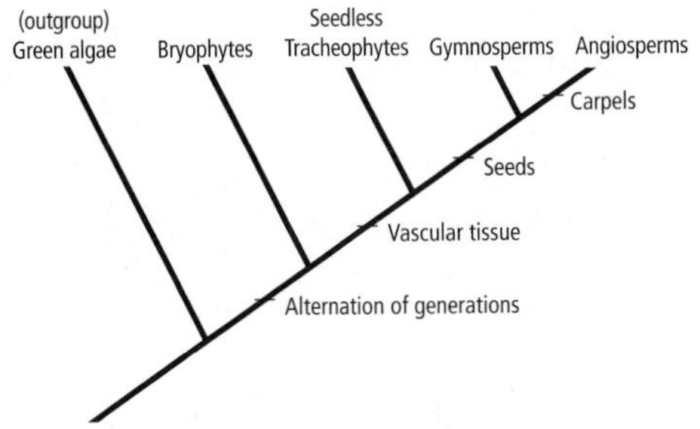

14. According to the plant cladogram, what characteristic separates plants from earlier organisms?

15. Specify an example of an ancestral character and a derived character among angiosperms.

Extended Response

16. Certain bacteria fix nitrogen in the root nodules of a bean plant. Assess how the location of those bacteria in nodules is beneficial to the bacteria and the plants.

17. Give one justification for why a farmer might plant beans in the fields when not growing other crops.

18. Compare and contrast Domain Bacteria and Domain Archaea.

19. Justify why a doctor would not prescribe an antibiotic to treat the flu.

Essay Question

Although scientists have made many discoveries to piece together the steps in human and primate evolution, there are still areas of disagreement and gaps in the evidence. For instance, not all scientists agree about the naming of different species in the genus *Homo*, or about the ways to depict the human evolutionary tree.

Using the information in the paragraph above, answer the following question in essay format.

20. Write an essay that describes an area of debate in human evolution that interests you. What are some aspects of the debate or disagreement that you would want to find out more about? What kind of research would you be able to do if you were going to investigate this debate further?

NEED EXTRA HELP?																				
If You Missed Question . . .	1	2	3	4	5	6	7	8	9	10	11	12	13	14	15	16	17	18	19	20
Review Section . . .	16.1	17.1	17.1	18.1	1.2	18.1	18.1	17.1	15.3	17.2	18.1	17.1	16.2	17.2	17.2	18.1	18.1	17.3	18.2	16.2, 16.3

Extended Response

16. Answers can vary. Bacteria live in the nodules on the roots of the bean plant where they are protected from harmful changes in the soil environment. The bacteria fix nitrogen from the air and convert it into a form that can be used by the plant.

17. Answers can vary. Beans have bacteria in their roots that fix nitrogen. This process adds extra nitrogen to the soil in a form that can be used by crops that are grown in the soil afterwards.

18. Compare: Both are Prokaryotes with a cell wall. Contrast: Domain Bacteria: Cell walls contain peptidoglycans. Organisms are found in most environments. Domain Archaea: Cell walls do not contain peptidoglycans. Many organisms are found in extreme environments.

19. Antibiotics are not effective against viruses because viruses do not have any of the cellular processes that antibiotics affect.

Essay

20. One possible area of debate that could be explored is the lineage of hominid species and the number of different species that existed. This area could be explored through discovery and analysis of more fossils, particularly fossils that show clear evidence the hominid species are completely different, or are related.

Chapter 19 Organizer:
Protists

LabManager™
Customize any lab with the LabManager™ CD-ROM.

Essential Questions	National Science Standards	Materials and Planning: Estimated times include cleanup and disposal, but do not include teacher prep time. For cleanup and disposal guidelines, see page 39T.	Est. Time (min)
Section 1 1. How are protists classified? 2. How might some protisits with mitochondria have evolved? 3. How might some protists with chloroplasts have evolved? 4. Why might the organization of Kingdom Protista change?	UCP.2, UCP.4, UCP.5; A.1, A.2; C.1, C.3, C.4, C.5; E.1; F.4; G.1	**Launch Lab,** p. 540: different types of protists, compound microscope	10–15
		Demonstration, p. 542: pictures of protists or living protists	10
		Demonstration, p. 543: 65-m piece of string	5
Section 2 1. What are the characteristics of protozoans? 2. What are the structures and organelles of protozoans? 3. What are the life cycles of protozoans?	UCP.2, UCP.4; A.1, A.2; C.1, C.4, C.5, C.6; F.4; G.1, G.2	**Demonstration,** p. 548: two blank transparencies, marking pen, scissors	10
		Demonstration, p. 550: sock, bag of dried peas or beans	15
Section 3 1. What are the characteristics of the different phyla of algae? 2. What is the role of secondary photosynthetic pigments that are characteristic of some algae? 3. How do diatoms differ from most other types of algae?	UCP.2, A.1, A.2; C.1, C.4, C.6; F.4, F.5; G.1, G.2	**Demonstration,** p. 553: pictures of various types of algae	10
		Demonstration, p. 554: slides or pictures of diatoms	10
		MiniLab 1, p. 558: samples of one type of green algae	20, 15 per day
Section 4 1. What are the characteristics of cellular and acellular slime molds? 2. How are the life cycles of cellular and acellular slime molds similar? 3. How do water molds obtain their nutrition?	UCP.2, UCP.4; A.1, A.2; C.1, C.4; E.1, E.2; F.3, F.4, F.5; G.1, G.2	**Demonstration,** p. 561: specimens of funguslike protists	20
		MiniLab 2, p. 564: slides of different specimens of slime molds, microscope	15–20
		BioLab, p. 567: cultures of live protozoa, compound microscope, glass slides and coverslips, materials to produce stimuli	45

Suggested Time for Each Lesson

Class	Chapter Opener	Section 1	Section 2	Section 3	Section 4	Assessment
Basic	45 min	90 min	45 min	45 min	45 min	45 min
General	25 min	45 min	55 min	45 min	55 min	45 min
Honors	5 min	40 min	90 min	45 min	30 min	25 min

ConnectED

connectED.mcgraw-hill.com

Access interactive learning opportunities and teaching resources using these icons located throughout your StudentWorks™ Plus Online and eTeacherEdition Online.

Chapter 19 Section Resources

FAST FILE Unit 5 Resources:
Launch Lab Worksheet*
Study Guide (English/Spanish)*
Section Quick Check

Reading Essentials 19.1
Science Notebook 19.1*

FAST FILE Unit 5 Resources:
Study Guide (English/Spanish)*
Section Quick Check

Reading Essentials 19.2
Science Notebook 19.2*

FAST FILE Unit 5 Resources:
MiniLab Worksheet*
Study Guide (English/Spanish)*
Section Quick Check

Reading Essentials 19.3
Science Notebook 19.3*

FAST FILE Unit 5 Resources:
MiniLab Worksheet*
BioLab Worksheet*
Study Guide (English/Spanish)*
Section Quick Check

Reading Essentials 19.4
Science Notebook 19.4*

Additional Chapter 19 Resources

FAST FILE Unit 5 Resources:
Chapter Diagnostic Test
Concept Mapping*
Real-World Biology
Enrichment
Chapter Tests A, B, and C

Transparencies:
Bellringer Transparencies*
Biology Concepts Transparencies*

Lab Resources:
Laboratory Manual*
Probeware Lab Manual*
Forensics Lab Manual*
Pre-AP Lab Manual*
Open Inquiry in Biology*
Guided Inquiry in Biology*

Technology

Teaching Tools:
eTeacherEdition Online
Classroom Presentation Toolkit CD-ROM*
LabManager™ CD-ROM*
Video Lab DVD*
Virtual Lab CD-ROM*
What's BIOLOGY Got To Do With It?
StudentWorks™ Plus Online*

Chapter Assessment Tools:
Classroom Presentation Toolkit CD-ROM*
ExamView® Assessment Suite CD-ROM

Web-Based Resources:
- StudentWorks™ Plus Online
- eTeacherEdition Online
- Animations*
- The Interactive Time Line*
- Interactive Tables*
- Online Quizzes
- Online Test Practice
- Standardized Test Practice
- Virtual Labs*
- Multilingual eGlossary*
- Vocabulary eGames*
- Vocabulary eFlashcards
- WebQuests
- Personal Tutors

While all resources listed are appropriate for English learners, the * indicates resources with a strong visual or hands-on component for EL.

Teaching strategies and activities have been coded for differentiated instruction.

AL Activities for students working above grade level	**OL** Activities for students working on grade level	**BL** Activities for students working below grade level	**EL** Activities for English learners (also ELL)	**COOP LEARN** Activities designed for small cooperative group work

CHAPTER 19

Launch Lab
What is a protist?

Inquiry Launch Lab

For a lab worksheet, use your eTeacherEdition Online.

RUBRIC A rubric for evaluating Launch Labs is found on your eTeacherEdition Online.

Est. Time 10–15 min

Alternative Materials photos or digital images of protists, such as many of the figures in this chapter

Teaching Strategies

- Each station should be labeled with the type of environment where the protist represented there is found.
- Have each student or team prepare a data table prior to beginning observations.

Procedure

1. Read and complete the lab safety form.
2. Construct a data table to record your observations.
3. Observe **different types of protists** with a **microscope,** noting their similarities and differences. Record your observations, notes, and illustrations in your data table.

Analysis

1. **Organize** the protists with similar characteristics into groups using the data that you collected. Accept all reasonable answers. Brainstorm and develop a class list of characteristics for each category of protist.
2. **Infer** which of your groups are animal-like, plantlike, or fungus-like. Students should be able to infer that animal-like protists have structures that enable them to move and capture food, and plantlike protists have structures that enable them to make food.

Cleanup and Disposal

Chemical preservatives are considered a low-level toxic material. Preserved specimens should be returned to their original container and stored in a secure location. Any living specimen should be disposed of according to the instructions that came with the cultures. Never release any purchased living creature into the wild, regardless of size.

CHAPTER 19

Protists

ConnectED

Your one-stop online resource
connectED.mcgraw-hill.com

- Video
- Audio
- Review
- Inquiry
- WebQuest
- Assessment
- Concepts in Motion
- Multilingual eGlossary

Launch Lab
What is a protist?

Kingdom Protista is similar to a drawer or closet in which you keep odds and ends that do not seem to fit in any other place. Kingdom Protista is composed of three groups of organisms that do not fit in any other kingdom. In this lab, you will observe the three groups of protists.

For a lab worksheet, use your StudentWorks™ Plus Online.

Inquiry Launch Lab

FOLDABLES®

Make a three-tab book as shown. Use it to organize your notes on the three groups of protists.

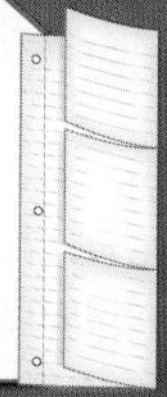

GOING GREEN To avoid the disposal of plastic jars and packing materials from protists purchased from a supplier, collect local pond water for protist observation.

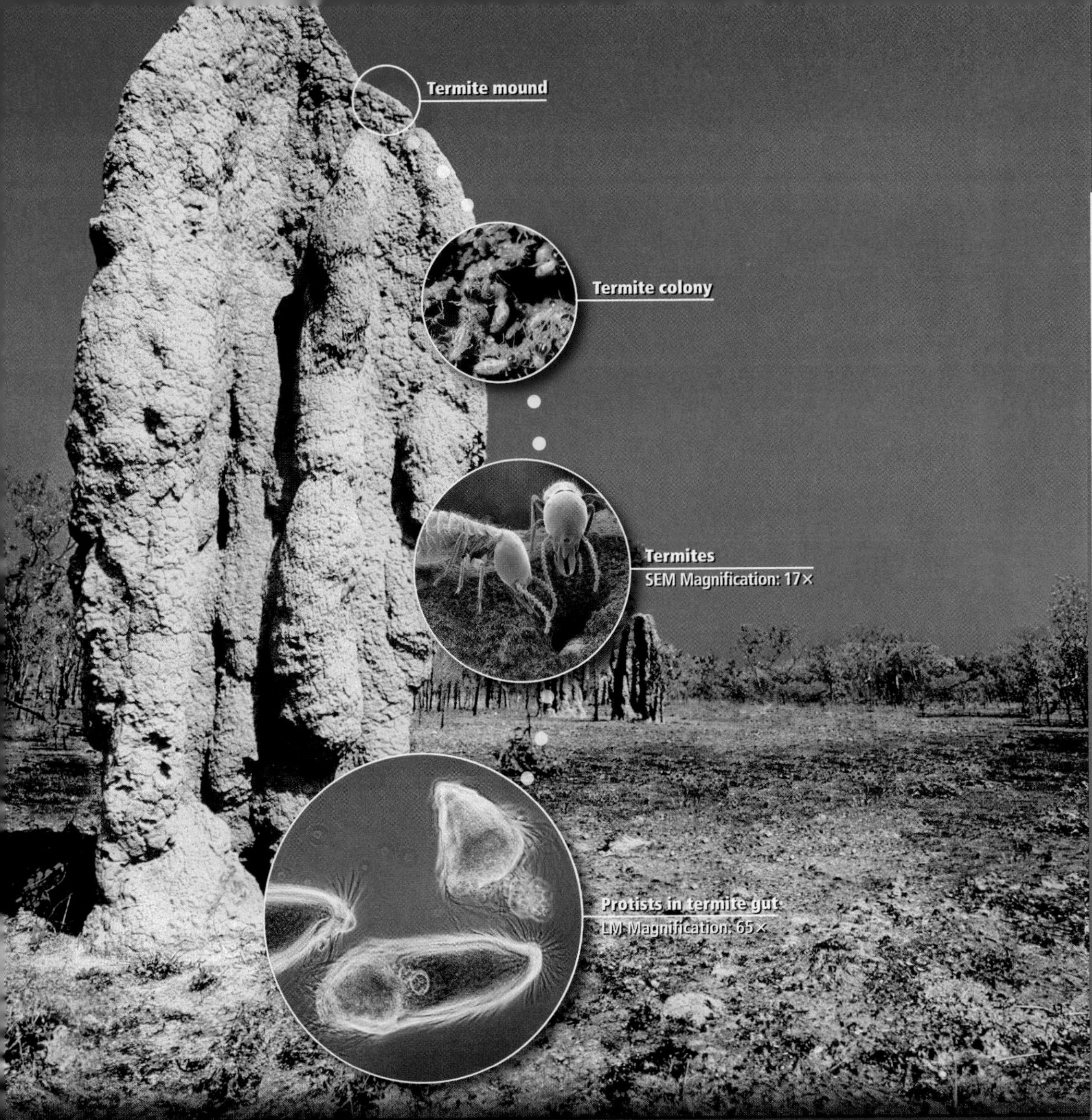

THEME FOCUS Homeostasis
Some protists have a specific organelle that helps maintain homeostasis.

BIG Idea Protists are a diverse group of unicellular and multicellular organisms that do not necessarily share the same evolutionary history.

Section 1 • Introduction to Protists

Section 2 • Protozoans—Animal-like Protists

Section 3 • Algae—Plantlike Protists

Section 4 • Funguslike Protists

Introduce the Chapter

Tiny Protists

ASK STUDENTS: ***What are some of the similarities and differences among the protists pictured here?*** Possible answers: similarities—they are all microscopic; they live all around us; they might have flagella or cilia for movement; differences—they are different shapes and sizes

SAY TO STUDENTS: ***These organisms are members of Kingdom Protista and they represent different types of protists.***

BIG Idea

Outline Have students outline the chapter by writing the Big Idea for the chapter and Main Ideas for each section. As students read the chapter they can take notes for each section.

sample outline:

Chapter 19 Big Idea: Protists are a diverse group of unicellular and multicellular organisms that do not necessarily share the same evolutionary history.

I. Section 1 Main Idea: Protists are a diverse group of organisms that are subdivided based on their methods of obtaining nutrition.
   A. Diversity of Protists
      1. Classifying Protists
      2. Habitats

THEMES

Scientific Inquiry Scientists are still deciphering the evolutionary relationships between protists and other kingdoms.

Diversity Kingdom Protista is composed of diverse unicellular and multicellular organisms.

Energy Some protists obtain energy by ingesting food, by photosynthesis, or by decomposing organic material.

Homeostasis Some protists have a contractile vacuole which expels excess water to maintain homeostasis.

Change Some protists are able to change shape in response to chemical stimuli.

Section 1

MAIN Idea

BL OL AL

The Diversity of Protists

SAY TO STUDENTS: *Scientists use many different methods to classify, or group, organisms.*

ASK STUDENTS: *What are some characteristics scientists might use to divide protists into different groups?* Possible answers: nutrition, habitat, structure, and evolutionary relationships

SAY TO STUDENTS: *Protists are organisms that do not fit in the other kingdoms. They form a diverse group of organisms with a wide range of characteristics. In this text, protists are classified by their method of obtaining nutrition. This is just one method of classifying this group of organisms. As biologists learn more information about the evolutionary history of these organisms, the classification of these organisms most likely will change.*

D Develop Concepts

BL OL AL **Analogy** Collect a variety of objects that are similar in only one way. For example, metal stapler, binder clips, metal pen, scissors, etc.

ASK STUDENTS: *What is one characteristic that these objects all share?* Sample answer: The objects are made of metal.

SAY TO STUDENTS: *Sometimes objects that appear very different are grouped together based on one similar characteristic. Similarly, protists are often characterized by their method of obtaining nutrition.*

Video Brain POP

Caption Question Fig. 1
Sample answer: This protist is a parasite, so it might consume blood or other tissue found in the host organism.

Section 1

Reading Preview

Essential Questions

- How are protists classified?
- How might some protists with mitochondria have evolved?
- How might some protists with chloroplasts have evolved?
- Why might the organization of Kingdom Protista change?

Review Vocabulary

heterotroph: organism that cannot make its own food and must get its energy and nutrients from other organisms

New Vocabulary

protozoan
microsporidium

g Multilingual eGlossary

Video BrainPOP

Introduction to Protists

MAIN Idea Protists form a diverse group of organisms that are subdivided based on their method of obtaining nutrition.

Real-World Reading Link Hurricanes, such as Katrina in 2005, bring winds and water surges that leave destruction and devastation. Contaminated flood waters, damaged sewage systems, and crowded shelters provide breeding grounds for infectious bacteria, viruses, and microorganisms called protists.

Protists

Protists are classified more easily by what they are not than by what they are. Protists are not animals, plants, or fungi because they do not have all of the characteristics necessary to place them in any of these kingdoms. Kingdom Protista was created to include this diverse group of more than 200,000 organisms.

All protists share one important trait: they are eukaryotes. Recall that eukaryotic cells contain membrane-bound organelles. Like all eukaryotes, the DNA of protists is found within the membrane-bound nucleus. Although protists have a cellular structure similar to other eukaryotes, there are remarkable differences in their reproductive methods. Some reproduce asexually by mitosis, while others exchange genetic material during meiosis.

D **Classifying protists** Because they are such a diverse group of organisms, some scientists classify protists by their method of obtaining nutrition. Protists are divided into three groups using this method: animal-like protists, plantlike protists, and funguslike protists. The **protozoan** (proh tuh ZOH un) (plural, protozoa or protozoans), shown in **Figure 1,** is an example of an animal-like protist because it is a heterotroph—it ingests food. Additional examples of protists and a summary of characteristics are shown in **Table 1.**

Color-Enhanced SEM Magnification: 1000×

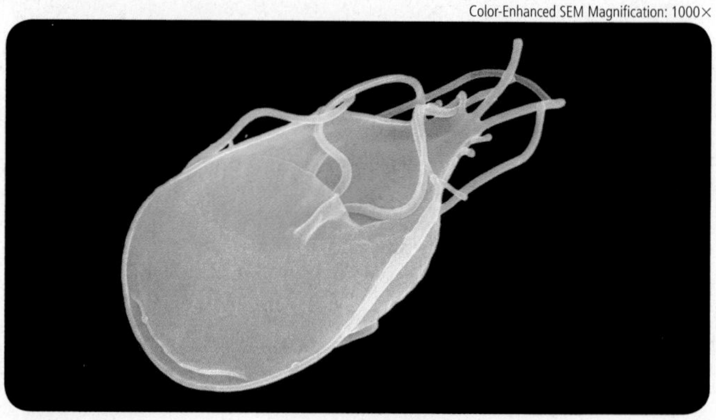

Giardia lamblia

Figure 1 This animal-like protist is a parasite that might be found in the intestinal tract of a person who has consumed contaminated water.
Infer *how this protist obtains its nutrients.*

Demonstration

Protists Collect images or use living protists from a biological supply company or collected from pond water or hay infusions. Use a variety of protists from each of the three groups. Display the images for the class by group (animal-like, plantlike, and funguslike) or view them in microscopes. Point out the characteristics of each group. Explain to students that one unifying characteristic of all protists is that they do not belong to the animal, plant, fungi, bacteria or archaea kingdom. Est. time: 10 min

R **Animal-like protists** An amoeba is an example of a unicellular, animal-like protist or protozoan. Protozoans are heterotrophs and usually ingest bacteria, algae, or other protozoans. The amoeba shown in **Table 1** is in the process of capturing and ingesting another unicellular protozoan—a paramecium.

Plantlike protists A giant kelp, shown in **Table 1,** is an example of a plantlike protist that makes its own food through photosynthesis. Plantlike protists are commonly referred to as algae (AL jee) (singular, alga). Some algae are microscopic. The unicellular algae *Micromonas* are about 10^{-6} m in diameter. Other forms of algae are multicellular and are quite large. Giant kelp, *Macrocystis pyrifera,* can grow up to 65 m long.

Funguslike protists The water mold in **Table 1** is an example of a funguslike protist that is absorbing nutrients from a dead salamander. Funguslike protists are similar to fungi because they absorb their nutrients from other organisms. These organisms are not classified as fungi because funguslike protists contain centrioles—small, cylindrical organelles that are involved in mitosis and usually are not found in the cells of fungi. Fungus and funguslike protists also differ in the composition of their cell walls. D

Reading Check **Compare and contrast** the three groups of protists.

VOCABULARY
WORD ORIGIN
Protist
comes from the Greek word *protistos,* meaning *the very first*

FOLDABLES®
Incorporate information from this section into your Foldable.

Table 1 The Protists — Concepts in Motion Interactive Table

	Animal-like protists (Protozoans)	Plantlike protists (Algae)	Funguslike protists
Group	Ciliates, amoebas, apicomplexans, and zooflagellates	Euglenoids, diatoms, dinoflagellates, green algae, red algae, brown algae, yellow-green algae, and golden-brown algae	Slime molds, water molds, and downy mildews
Example	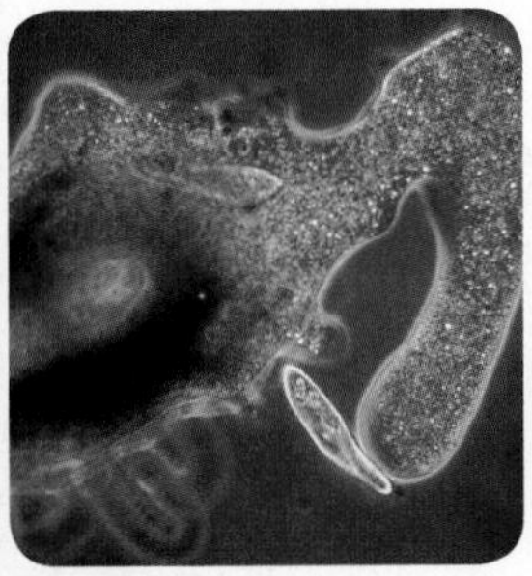 **Amoeba**	 **Giant kelp**	 **Water mold**
Distinguishing Characteristics	• Considered animal-like because they consume other organisms for food • Some are parasites.	• Considered plantlike because they make their own food through photosynthesis • Some consume other organisms or are parasites when light is unavailable for photosynthesis.	• Considered funguslike because they feed on decaying organic matter and absorb nutrients through their cell walls • Some slime molds consume other organisms and a few slime molds are parasites.

Reading Check Animal-like protists are unicellular heterotrophs. Plantlike protists make their own food. Funguslike protists cannot make their own food. They absorb nutrition from other organisms.

Demonstration

Scale Show students a roll of string 65-m long and tell them that it represents how long giant kelp can grow. Remind students that although many members of the protist kingdom are unicellular or even microscopic, there are some very large members. Est. time: 5 min

R Reading Strategy

BL COOP LEARN

Active Comprehension
Have students read this page aloud with a partner.
ASK STUDENTS: ***What else would you like to know about protists?*** Have a student write the responses on the board. Have students keep these ideas in mind as they read the section.

FOLDABLES®

RUBRIC A rubric for evaluating Foldables is found on your eTeacherEdition Online.
Going Further On the back of your Foldable, draw a concept map illustrating the animal-like characteristics of each group studied. Concept maps should include the following: animal-like protists are heterotrophs that usually can move on their own, some plantlike protists are heterotrophic, and funguslike protists are heterotrophs that feed on decaying organic matter. .

D Develop Concepts

BL OL AL

Clarify a Misconception
ASK STUDENTS: ***Are all protists unicellular organisms?*** No. Many students may think that this is the case.
TELL STUDENTS: ***Although most protists are unicellular organisms, some protists, such as the red and brown algae, are large, multicellular organisms.***

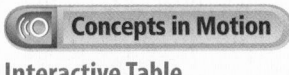

Concepts in Motion
Interactive Table

Develop Concepts

EL BL Vocabulary Have students list the important terms after reading and discussing the section. Write each term on an index card. Tape the cards on students' backs (one card per student). Have students with cards walk around the class so that everyone can see the words. Then have the class give each student clues about the term taped on his or her back. Students then can try to guess the term on their back.

W Writing Support

BL OL AL Writing Summary Have students summarize the different habitats where protists often are found. damp or aquatic habitats, including the inside of other organisms and in the hair of other organisms

C Critical Thinking

BL OL AL Hypothesize
ASK STUDENTS: ***Why is the sloth's hair a suitable habitat for algae?*** The hair provides a warm, moist environment. When the sloth is in the uppermost branches of the tree, the algae receive light for photosynthesis.

DATA ANALYSIS LAB 1

About the Lab

- *Ginkgo biloba* is a vascular seed plant.
- It is yet to be determined whether this relationship is mutualistic or not.
- Also see Lewis, et al. 2004. *Biological Bulletin* 207: 87–92.

Thinking Critically

1. The diameter is approximately 3×10^{-6} m.
2. The algae cells are within the plant cells.

■ **Figure 2** The protists, green algae, live in the fur of this tree sloth, forming a symbiotic relationship.
Infer ***What type of symbiotic relationship do these organisms have?***

Inquiry Launch Lab
Review Based on what you've read about protists, how would you now answer the analysis questions?

Habitats Protists typically are found in damp or aquatic environments such as decaying leaves, damp soil, ponds, streams, and oceans. Protists also live in symbiotic relationships. **Microsporidia** (MI kroh spo rih dee uh) (singular, microsporidium) are microscopic protozoans that cause disease in insects. Some species of microsporidia can be used as insecticides. New technology might allow these microsporidia to be used to control insects that destroy crops.

One beneficial protist lives in the hair of a sloth, shown in **Figure 2.** A sloth is a large, slow-moving mammal that lives in the uppermost branches of trees in tropical rain forests. The sloth spends most of its life hanging upside down. Green algae help the brown sloth blend into the leaves on the tree, providing camouflage for the sloth. C W

DATA ANALYSIS LAB 1

Based on Real Data*

Interpret Scientific Illustrations

What is the relationship between green alga and *Ginkgo biloba* cells? In 2002, scientists in France reported the first confirmed symbiotic relationship between plantlike protists called green algae and a land plant's cells. The figure at the right represents an alga inside a cell from the *Ginkgo biloba* tree.

Think Critically

1. **Examine** the figure and estimate the size of the algal cell.
2. **Explain** why the term endophytic (en duh FIT ihk) is appropriate to describe these algae. The prefix *endo* means "within" and the suffix *-phyte* means "plant."

Data and Observations

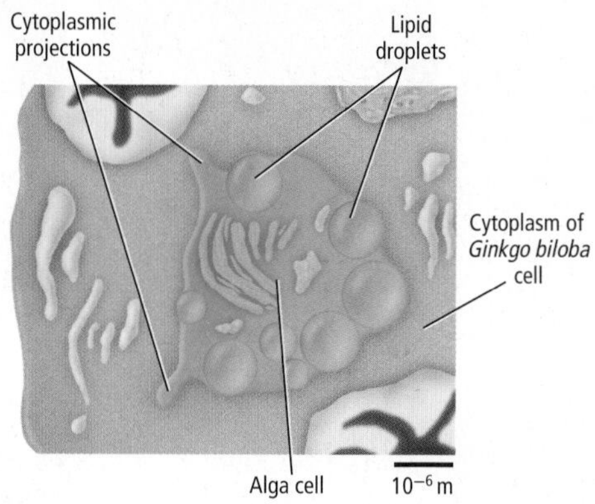

*Data obtained from: Tremoullaux-Guiller, et al. 2002. Discovery of an endophytic alga in *Ginkgo biloba. American Journal of Botany* 89(5): 727–733.

■ **Caption Question Fig. 2** The type of symbiotic relationship they display is mutualism.

Inquiry Launch Lab
Assess Content Development
Assess how understanding has developed when students revisit the Launch Lab analysis questions.

Differentiated Instruction

Below Level Students who perform below level may need additional support to benefit from lectures. Make lectures as interactive as possible and tape lectures for students to use as a reference.

For more tips, see pages 14T–15T.

Origin of Protists

Recall the theory of endosymbiosis, which was proposed by Lynn Margulis. This theory suggests that eukaryotes, including protists, formed when a large prokaryote engulfed a smaller prokaryote. The two organisms lived symbiotically. Eventually, the organisms evolved into a single, more highly developed organism. Some scientists think that the mitochondria and chloroplasts found in some eukaryotes, including protists, were once individual organisms. Protists might have been the first eukaryotes to appear billions of years ago.

Grouping protists by how they obtain nutrition is a convenient method of classifying them. However, this method does not consider an organism's evolutionary history. Scientists are still trying to sort out the evolutionary relationships between protists and the other kingdoms. As scientists learn more information, the organization of Kingdom Protista most likely will change.

The diagram in **Figure 3** shows the current understanding of the evolutionary history of protists based on the theory of endosymbiosis. Notice in the diagram that all of the protists have a common ancestral eukaryotic cell. Examine the diagram and find where mitochondria entered into the evolutionary process. Mitochondria became part of protist cells early in the evolutionary process. Now, locate where chloroplasts entered cells. Follow the path of the arrow and you can see that algae are the only protists with chloroplasts and that undergo photosynthesis.

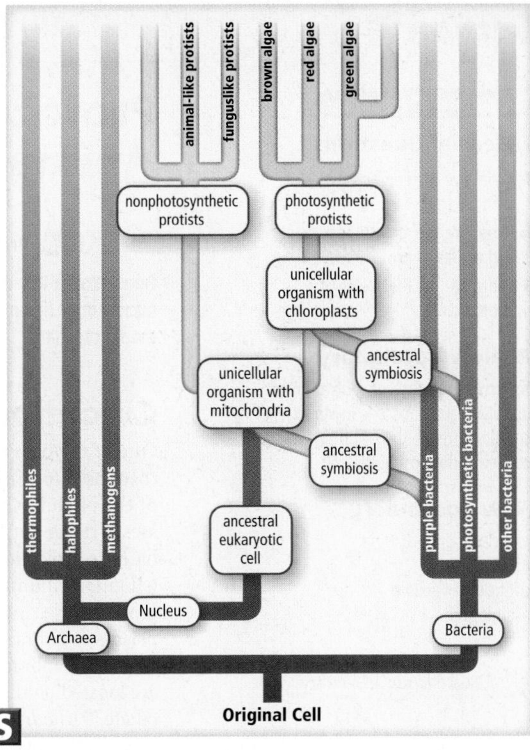

S

■ **Figure 3** This diagram shows how the theory of endosymbiosis explains the evolution of the protist kingdom.

Section 1 Assessment

Section Summary

- Protists include unicellular and multicellular eukaryotes.
- Protists are classified by their methods of obtaining food.
- The first protists might have formed through endosymbiosis.
- Protists might have been the first eukaryotic cells with chloroplasts and mitochondria, evolving billions of years ago.

Understand Main Ideas

1. MAIN Idea **Explain** why some scientists use nutrition to classify organisms in Kingdom Protista.
2. **Sketch** a diagram that illustrates how the first protists might have formed from prokaryotes.
3. **Explain** why scientists have classified protists in one kingdom when they are such a diverse group.

Think Critically

4. **Apply Concepts** What if you discovered a new protist? What characteristics would help you decide the group in which it belongs?
5. **Compare and contrast** using nutrition methods and evolutionary relationships to classify protists.

S Skill Practice

BL OL AL Visual Literacy Have students examine Figure 3 and infer which groups of protists are most closely related. animal-like and funguslike protists or brown algae, red algae, and green algae; These groups diverged from their respective common ancestors at roughly the same time.

Formative Assessment

Evaluation

ASK STUDENTS: ***What are the three kinds of protists, and how does each kind of protist obtain nutrition?*** Animal-like protists get their food by ingesting other organisms. Plantlike protists make their own food through photosynthesis, though some also consume other organisms. Funguslike protists feed on decaying matter and absorb nutrients though the cell walls.

Remediation Have students make flashcards to help them identify the three different kinds of protists. On the front of each card, students can draw pictures of one kind of protist. On the back of each card students can write how each kind of protist obtains nutrition. Students can use the cards alone or in pairs.

Inquiry BioLab

The lab at the end of the chapter can be used at this point in the lesson.

Section 1 Assessment

1. This is a simple way to classify such a diverse group of organisms.
2. Check students' drawings against Figure 3.
3. This kingdom is necessary for the classification of all organisms that don't fit into the other kingdom categories.
4. method of obtaining nutrition; presence of chloroplasts or mitochondria
5. Classifying protists by how they obtain nutrition is a convenient and easy method, but is not the best method because it does not consider evolutionary history. Thus, organisms that share the same mode of nutrition might or might not be as closely related as two protists that do not have the same way of obtaining food.

Assessment Online Quiz

Section 2

MAIN Idea

BL OL AL

Heterotrophic Protists

ASK STUDENTS: ***What does heterotrophic mean?*** describes an organism that is unable to make its own food and must get it from other organisms

SAY TO STUDENTS: ***All the protists we are going to read about in this section get their food from other organisms, so they are heterotrophic.***

Develop Concepts

EL BL OL **Use Models** Have students make a model of a ciliate. They can use thread, string, or yarn for the cilia and construction paper for the cell body. Alternatively, they could use a sock to model the cell or use the fluid-filled balls with small rubbery extensions available for purchase at toy or discount stores.

D Develop Concepts

AL **Integrate Math**

ASK STUDENTS: ***Approximately how many ciliates could be found in 1 cm² of mud?***

$$\frac{20{,}000{,}000 \text{ ciliates}}{1 \text{ m}^2} \times \frac{1 \text{ m}^2}{10{,}000 \text{ cm}^2}$$

$$= 2000 \text{ ciliates/cm}^2$$

Section 2

Reading Preview

Essential Questions

- What are the characteristics of protozoans?
- What are the structures and organelles of protozoans?
- What are the life cycles of protozoans?

Review Vocabulary

hypotonic: the concentration of dissolved substances is lower in the solution outside the cell than the concentration inside the cell

New Vocabulary

pellicle
trichocyst
contractile vacuole
pseudopod
test

g Multilingual eGlossary

Protozoans—Animal-like Protists

MAIN Idea **Protozoans are animal-like, heterotrophic protists.**

Real-World Reading Link Have you ever looked at pond water under a microscope? If you saw tiny organisms darting around, then you most likely have seen protozoans.

Ciliophora

One of the characteristics that biologists use to further classify protozoans into different phyla is their method of movement. Members of the phylum Ciliophora (sih lee AH fuh ruh), also known as ciliates (SIH lee ayts), are animal-like protists that have numerous short, hairlike projections. Recall that some unicellular organisms use cilia (singular, cilium) to propel themselves through water and to move food particles into the cell. Some ciliates have cilia covering their entire plasma membrane, while others have groups of cilia covering parts of their membrane, as shown in **Figure 4.** Note that the *Stentor's* cilia are located on the anterior end; they help propel food into the cell. The ciliate *Trichodina pediculus* has two visible sets of cilia. The outer ring is used for movement, and the inner ring is used for feeding.

There are more than 7000 species of ciliates. They are abundant in most aquatic environments—ocean waters, lakes, and rivers. They also are found in mud, and it is estimated that as many as 20 million ciliates can inhabit one square meter in some mud flats. D

■ **Figure 4** *Stentor* and *Trichodina pediculus* are protozoans that have cilia.

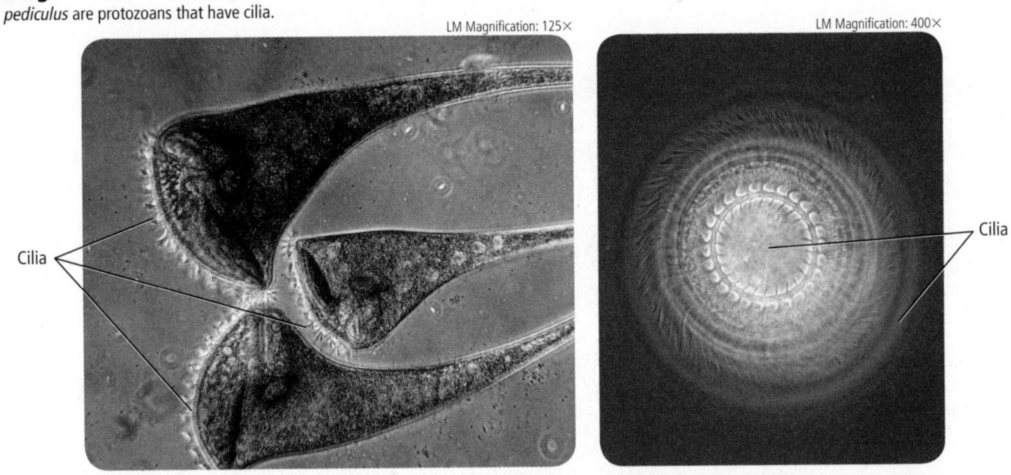

***Stentor*—use cilia for feeding**

***Trichodina pediculus*—use cilia for feeding and movement**

Differentiated Instruction

Behavior Disorders When working with students who have behavior disorders, limit the opportunity for problems by scheduling activities to minimize downtime. Students will be more likely to exhibit positive behaviors if they are busy and engaged with the lesson.

For more tips, see pages 14T–15T.

"Education is hanging around until you've caught on."

–Robert Frost

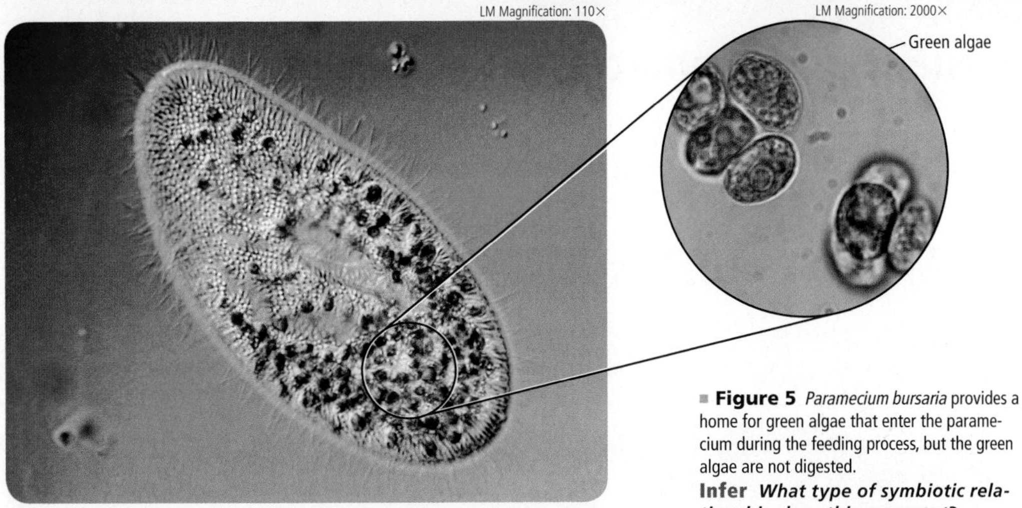

Paramecium bursaria

■ **Figure 5** *Paramecium bursaria* provides a home for green algae that enter the paramecium during the feeding process, but the green algae are not digested.
Infer ***What type of symbiotic relationship does this represent?***

R **Paramecia** Some of the most commonly studied ciliates are found in the genus *Paramecium* (per uh MEE see um) (plural, paramecia). The paramecium in **Figure 5** lives symbiotically with green algae. The green algae undergo photosynthesis, providing nutrients to the paramecium.

A paramecium is a unicellular protozoan. It is enclosed by a layer of membrane called a **pellicle.** Directly beneath the pellicle is a layer of cytoplasm called ectoplasm. Embedded in the ectoplasm are the **trichocysts** (TRIH kuh sihsts), which are elongated, cylindrical bodies that can discharge a spinelike structure. The function of trichocysts is not completely understood, but they might be used for defense, as a reaction to injury, as an anchoring device, or to capture prey.

Cilia The cilia on the paramecium in **Figure 5** are used for movement and feeding. Cilia completely cover the organism—including the oral groove. Locate the oral groove on the paramecium in **Figure 6.** The cilia covering the wall of the oral groove are used to guide food, primarily bacteria, into the gullet. Once the food reaches the end of the gullet, it is enclosed in a food vacuole. Enzymes within the food vacuole break down the food into nutrients that can diffuse into the cytoplasm of the paramecium. Waste products from the paramecium are excreted through the anal pore.

Contractile vacuoles Because freshwater paramecia live in a hypotonic environment, water constantly enters the cell by osmosis. Recall that a hypotonic solution is one in which the concentration of dissolved substances is lower in the solution outside the cell than the concentration inside the cell. The **contractile vacuoles,** shown in **Figure 6,** collect the excess water from the cytoplasm and expel it from the cell. The expelled water might contain waste products, which is another way that paramecia can excrete waste. Paramecia often have two or three contractile vacuoles that help to maintain homeostasis in the cell.

Reading Check **Explain** why the contractile vacuoles are necessary in hypotonic environments to maintain homeostasis.

CAREERS IN BIOLOGY

Microbiologist A microbiologist studies organisms that usually are seen only with a microscope. One area of study in which a microbiologist can specialize is the study of protists. Microbiologists can work as researchers, teachers, and in other fields.

VOCABULARY

SCIENCE USAGE V. COMMON USAGE

Expel

Science usage: to force out
Contractile vacuoles expel water from cells.

Common usage: to force to leave
The principal will expel students for breaking school rules.

Develop Concepts

BL OL

Clarify a Misconception

ASK STUDENTS: ***Which best describes the shape of a paramecium: a plate or an egg?*** an egg
Students might think paramecia and other protists are flat organisms, but they are actually three-dimensional. This misconception can be clarified by showing students a film or electron micrographs of protozoans.

R Reading Strategy

EL OL AL **Brainstorm** Have students read the new vocabulary words found on this page: pellicle, trichocyst, and contractile vacuole. In small groups, have students brainstorm ideas that come to mind when they see each word. Record all ideas for all to view. Then have students add to their list as they read the text.
BL Read the words to students in a large group before students perform the activity. Use chart paper, transparencies, or the board to record responses.

■ **Caption Question** **Fig. 5** The type of symbiotic relationship is mutualism.

Reading Check The contractile vacuoles collect and expel water from the paramecium, which helps maintain homeostasis.

Differentiated Instruction

Above Level Students who perform above grade level should be encouraged to extend their thinking. Emphasize conceptual thinking with gifted students by asking additional how/why/what-if questions.

For more tips, see pages 14T–15T.

Visualizing Paramecia

Purpose
Students will understand the structure of paramecia and the process of conjugation.
C.2

S Skill Practice
EL BL Visual Literacy Have students sketch the diagrams in Figure 6 in their notebooks. Provide each student with a blank transparency and have students label their diagrams by overlaying the transparency and writing the labels on it. Students can use this transparency as a study tool to help them learn the structure of paramecia and the process of conjugation.

Writing Strategy
AL Informal Writing Have students write a paragraph explaining why conjugation is easily confused with reproduction. Have students explain why it is not a form of reproduction. Ask them to assess the value of conjugation to the species. Because new individuals are not produced, conjugation is not reproduction. The value of conjugation is that it increases the genetic diversity of the species.

Concepts in Motion
Animation

Visualizing Paramecia

Figure 6
S Paramecia are unicellular organisms with membrane-bound organelles. They undergo a process called conjugation in which a pair of paramecia will exchange genetic information, as shown in the diagram at the bottom of the page. This is not considered sexual reproduction because new individuals are not formed.

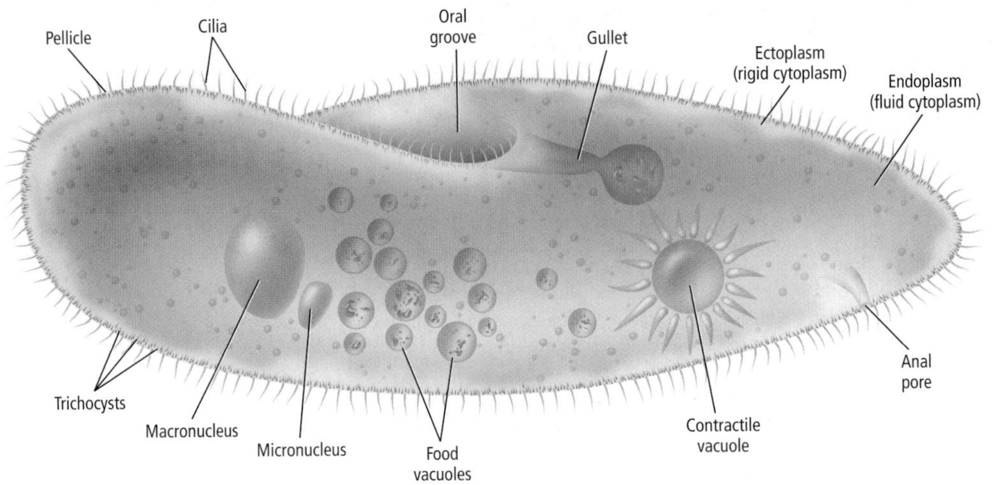

Conjugation

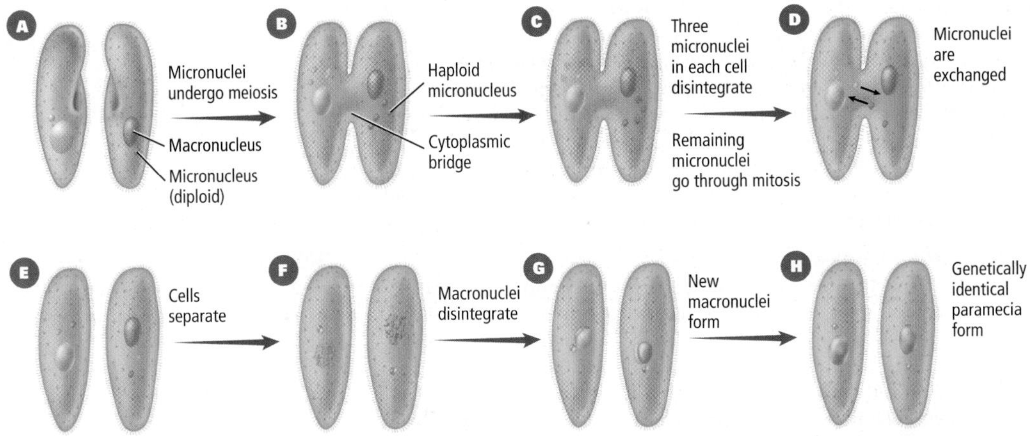

Concepts in Motion Animation

Demonstration
Conjugation Draw the outline of paramecia on two blank transparencies. Color and cut several small circles out of another transparency—these will represent the micronuclei. Use a different color for each paramecia. Overlay one paramecium sheet on the other and draw the cytoplasmic bridge. Demonstrate the meiotic division of the micronuclei by manipulating the circles within one of the paramecia. Three of the micronuclei disintegrate—represent this by removing them. The remaining micronucleus divides. Repeat with the second paramecium. Show the exchanged micronuclei traveling through the cytoplasmic bridge—one of each color—and fusing with the remaining micronuclei in each cell. Manipulate the circles to indicate that the micronuclei multiply in each cell, and show how some of them fuse to form a macronucleus. Est. time: 10 min

Reproduction in ciliates All known ciliates have two kinds of nuclei: the macronucleus and a smaller micronucleus. A cell might contain more than one of each of these nuclei. Both nuclei contain the genetic information for the cell. The macronuclei contain multiple copies of the cell's genome, which controls the everyday functions of the cell, such as feeding, waste elimination, and maintaining water balance within the cell. The micronucleus is used for reproduction.

Ciliates reproduce asexually by binary fission. During this process, the macronucleus elongates and splits rather than undergoing mitotic division. Most ciliates maintain genetic variation by undergoing conjugation—a sexual process in which genetic information is exchanged. Conjugation is considered a sexual process, but it is not considered sexual reproduction because new organisms are not formed.

The process of conjugation for *Paramecium caudatum* is typical of most ciliates and is illustrated in **Figure 6.** During conjugation, two paramecia form a cytoplasmic bridge and their diploid micronuclei undergo meiosis. After three of the newly formed haploid micronuclei dissolve, the remaining micronucleus undergoes mitosis. One micronucleus from each connected cell is exchanged, and the two paramecia separate. The macronucleus disintegrates in each paramecium, and the micronuclei combine and form a new, diploid macronucleus. Each cell now contains a macronucleus, micronuclei, and a new combination of genetic information.

Reading Check **Explain** the purpose of the cytoplasmic bridge, shown in **Figure 6,** during conjugation.

VOCABULARY
SCIENCE USAGE V. COMMON USAGE
Conjugation
Science usage: an exchange of genetic information without reproduction
Genetic variation is increased in paramecia through a process called conjugation.

Common usage: in grammar, an arrangement of the correct form of a verb
Victoria is practicing the conjugation of Spanish verbs.

D

C

DATA ANALYSIS LAB 2

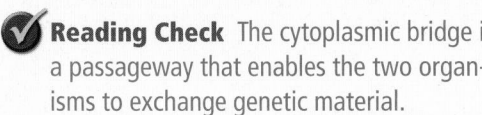

Based on Real Data*

Recognize Cause and Effect

How does solution concentration affect the contractile vacuole? The contractile vacuole moves water from inside a paramecium back into its freshwater environment. Researchers have studied the effects of solution concentrations on paramecia.

Data and Observations

Paramecia were allowed to adapt to various solutions for 12 h. Then, they were placed into hypertonic and hypotonic solutions. The graphs show the change in rate of water flow out of the contractile vacuole over time.

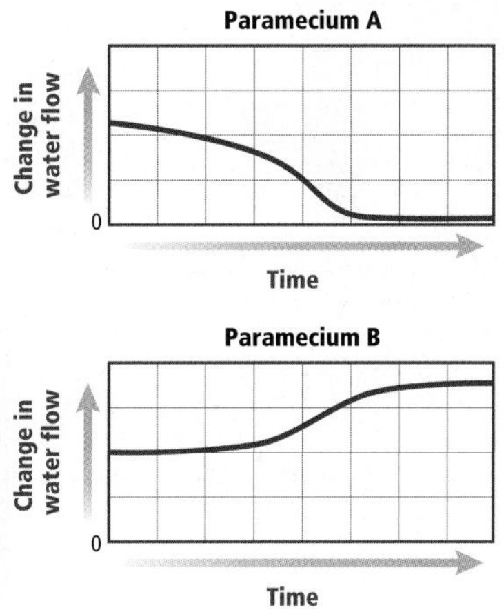

Think Critically

1. **Analyze** What do the downward and upward slopes in the graphs indicate about the contractile vacuole?
2. **Infer** which paramecium was placed into a hypertonic solution. Explain.

*Data obtained from: Stock, et al. 2001. How external osmolarity affects the activity of the contractile vacuole complex, the cytosolic osmolarity and the water permeability of the plasma membrane in *Paramecium Multimicronucleatum. The Journal of Experimental Biology* 204: 291–304.

Reading Check The cytoplasmic bridge is a passageway that enables the two organisms to exchange genetic material.

D Develop Concepts

EL BL OL COOP LEARN

Activity Have students form pairs and write the steps of conjugation on a piece of paper. Have students cut the paper so that each step is on its own piece. Have the student pairs shuffle the papers and trade their steps with another pair. Then have them work in pairs to put the steps in the correct order.

C Critical Thinking

AL **Infer** Have students explain why contractile vacuoles are often missing in marine and parasitic amoebas. Marine environments are generally hypertonic so the cells would be losing water, and the environment in a host would likely be isotonic.

DATA ANALYSIS LAB 2

About the Lab

- The contractile vacuole helps maintain osmotic balance in the paramecium.
- When the paramecium is placed in a hypotonic solution, the contractile vacuole collects water rapidly.
- The contractile vacuole consists of collecting ducts, a central reservoir, and a tube that connects to a pore in the plasma membrane.
- Also see Iwamoto et al. 2005. *The Journal of Experimental Biology* 208 (Pt 3): 523–37

Think Critically

1. The downward slope indicates that the contractile vacuole is filling with water. The upward slope indicates that the contractile vacuole is being emptied.
2. Paramecium A; The slope of the graph indicates that its contractile vacuole is emptying.

C Critical Thinking

BL OL AL Evaluate Have students evaluate the role of diffusion in maintaining homeostasis in an amoeba. Diffusion eliminates wastes and brings in necessary materials. Oxygen diffuses into the cell. In addition, in some amoebas, water diffuses into the contractile vacuole and is expelled from the cell. All of these are necessary for the cell's survival.

Develop Concepts

EL BL OL Use Models Have students construct a model of an amoeba. Challenge them to design a model that illustrates movement or food capture using pseudopods. Students could use a sock or pillowcase with their hand inside to mimic a pseudopod. They might also use fluid-filled balls available at toy or discount stores.

C Critical Thinking

BL OL

Compare and Contrast Have students compare and contrast amoebas with tests and amoebas without tests. Both have pseudopods, but amoebas with tests have hard coverings.

W Writing Support

AL Technical Writing Have students write a paragraph about what would happen if an amoeba had tests but could not form pseudopods. The amoeba would not be able to extend cytoplasm through openings in the test to trap food.

BL Have students develop a comic strip or flipbook about an amoeba.

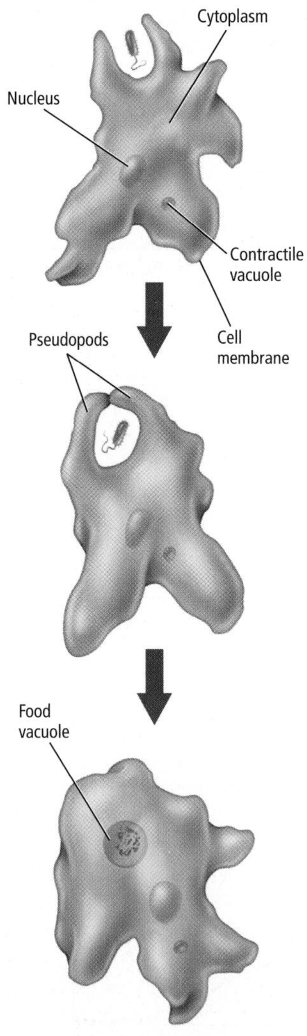

■ **Figure 7** Chemical stimuli from smaller organisms can cause the amoeba to form pseudopods from their cell membrane.

Sarcodina

Members of the phylum Sarcodina (sar kuh DI nuh), also called sarcodines (SAR kuh dinez), are animal-like protists that use pseudopods for feeding and locomotion. A **pseudopod** (SEW duh pahd) is a temporary extension of cytoplasm and is shown in **Figure 7.** These extensions surround and envelop a smaller organism, forming a food vacuole. Digestive enzymes are secreted and break down the captured organism.

Some of the most commonly studied sarcodines are found in the genus *Amoeba.* Most amoebas are found in saltwater, although some freshwater species live in streams, in the muddy bottoms of ponds, and in damp patches of moss and leaves. Some amoebas are parasites that live inside an animal host.

Amoeba structure The structure of an amoeba is simple, as shown in **Figure 7.** Amoebas are enveloped in an outer cell membrane and an inner thickened cytoplasm called ectoplasm. Inside the ectoplasm, the cytoplasm contains a nucleus, food vacuoles, and occasionally a contractile vacuole. Notice that an amoeba does not have an anal pore like the paramecium. Waste products and undigested food particles are excreted by diffusion through the cell membrane into the surrounding water. The oxygen needed for cellular processes also diffuses into the cell from the surrounding water.

Foraminiferans (fuh rah muh NIH fur unz) and radiolarians (ray dee oh LER ee unz) are types of amoebas that have tests. A **test** is a hard, porous covering similar to a shell, which surrounds the cell membrane. Most of these amoebas live in marine environments, although there are some freshwater species.

Connection to Earth Science Foraminiferans have tests made of calcium carbonate ($CaCO_3$), grains of sand, and other particles cemented together. Geologists use the fossilized remains of foraminiferans to determine the age of some rocks and sediments, and to identify possible sites for oil drilling. Radiolarians, another type of amoeba with tests, shown in **Figure 8,** have tests made mostly of silica (SiO_2).

Amoeba reproduction Amoebas reproduce by asexual reproduction during which a parent cell divides into two identical offspring. During harsh environmental conditions, some amoebas become cysts that help them survive until environmental conditions improve and survival is more likely.

■ **Figure 8** Radiolarians have tests made of silica. Foraminiferans and radiolarians extend their pseudopods through openings in their tests.

Demonstration

BL OL Amoeboid Movement Use a sock filled with dried peas or beans to demonstrate amoeboid movement. Show students how the amoeba moves forward by pushing its cytoplasm (peas) forward. The empty sock also can be used to show the pseudopods reaching out and surrounding food. Also view amoebas under a microscope.

ASK STUDENTS: ***How would you suggest improving the model so it is a more accurate representation of the amoeba's movement?*** Answers will vary, but students might suggest that the sock needs smaller projections to be pseudopods. Est. time: 15 min

Apicomplexa

Animal-like protists that belong to the phylum Apicomplexa (ay puh KOM pleks uh) are also known as sporozoans (spo ruh ZOH unz). They are called sporozoans because they produce spores at some point in their life cycle. Spores are reproductive cells that form without fertilization. Sporozoans lack contractile vacuoles and methods for locomotion. Respiration and excretion occur by diffusion through the plasma membrane.

C

All sporozoans are parasitic. Recall that parasites get their nutritional requirements from a host organism. Sporozoans infect vertebrates and invertebrates by living as internal parasites. Organelles at one end of the organism are specialized for penetrating host cells and tissues, allowing them to get their nutrients from their host.

The life cycle of sporozoans has both sexual and asexual stages. Often two or more hosts are required for an organism to complete a life cycle. The life cycle of *Plasmodium,* which causes malaria, is shown in **Figure 9.**

Sporozoans cause a variety of illnesses in humans, some of which are fatal. The sporozoans responsible for the greatest number of human deaths are found in the genus *Plasmodium.* These parasites cause malaria in humans and are transmitted to humans by female *Anopheles* mosquitoes. Malaria causes fever, chills, and other flulike symptoms. Its greatest impact is in tropical and subtropical regions where factors such as high temperature, humidity, and rainfall favor the growth of mosquitoes and sporozoans, and preventative measures are too costly.

VOCABULARY
WORD ORIGIN
Apicomplexa
apicalis from Latin; meaning *uppermost point or tip*
complexus from Latin; meaning *comprised of multiple objects*

■ **Figure 9** Malaria is caused by the sporozoan *Plasmodium*, which is transmitted by mosquitoes.
Describe ***the asexual state of this sporozoan.***

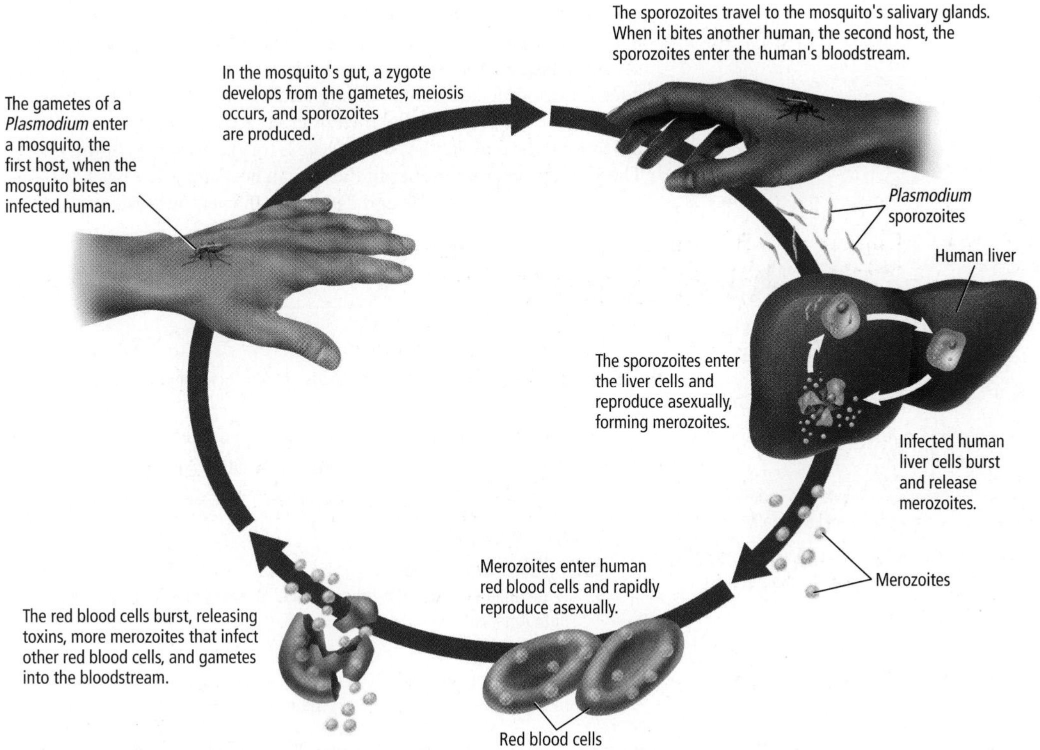
The sporozoites travel to the mosquito's salivary glands. When it bites another human, the second host, the sporozoites enter the human's bloodstream.
In the mosquito's gut, a zygote develops from the gametes, meiosis occurs, and sporozoites are produced.
The gametes of a Plasmodium enter a mosquito, the first host, when the mosquito bites an infected human.
Plasmodium sporozoites
Human liver
The sporozoites enter the liver cells and reproduce asexually, forming merozoites.
Infected human liver cells burst and release merozoites.
Merozoites
Merozoites enter human red blood cells and rapidly reproduce asexually.
The red blood cells burst, releasing toxins, more merozoites that infect other red blood cells, and gametes into the bloodstream.
Red blood cells

Content Background

Teacher FYI The tsunami of 2004 killed more than 165,000 people. As horrific as that disaster was, members of the World Health Organization pointed out that about the same number of lives are lost each month worldwide due to malaria. Initially, there was concern that the tsunami would lead to an outbreak of malaria due to the poor living conditions of the refugees and the pools of brackish water, which are breeding grounds for mosquitoes. However, there was little increase in malaria cases.

Reading Strategy

OL AL Supplemental Reading
Have students research human diseases caused by sporozoans and prepare a short oral presentation. Students should include the name of the organism, the disease it causes, the symptoms, and the available treatment.
BL Provide resources that are easier to read for struggling students, such as *Fighting Infectious Diseases,* a book by Robert Snedden.

Develop Concepts

BL Integrate Social Studies
Provide students with a map of the world and have them indicate where malaria is a critical health concern. Students should find that malaria is common in tropical and subtropical regions throughout the world.

C Critical Thinking

AL Evaluate
ASK STUDENTS: ***Why don't apicomplexans have contractile vacuoles or mechanisms for locomotion?*** Apicomplexans are parasitic, so they live in a host. The host environment is isotonic, so there is no need for contractile vacuoles. The need for motility is somewhat reduced for parasites because they are contained within their host.

Develop Concepts

OL AL
Integrate Social Studies
Have students research the impact that diseases caused by apicomplexans or zooflagellates have on developing countries. Students can work in small groups to prepare a poster or other visual aids for their presentation.

■ **Caption Question Fig. 9** The asexual stage begins when the sporozoites enter the liver cells and reproduce asexually, forming merozoites. Those merozoites infect red blood cells and reproduce asexually there.

R Reading Strategy

EL OL Directed Reading Have students make two columns on a piece of paper. Tell them to label one column *American sleeping sickness* and the other column *African sleeping sickness.* As students read about the diseases, have them fill in the columns with information about the diseases. Information should include the organism that causes the disease, which organism spreads the disease, and the symptoms of the disease.

BL Have struggling students work in pairs.

AL Have students refer to the text as these diseases are discussed during the lecture.

Formative Assessment

Evaluation

ASK STUDENTS: ***What characteristic do all groups of animal-like protists share?*** They are all heterotrophs. ***What characteristic is different among the groups?*** Each group of animal-like protists moves using organs distinctive to that group.

Remediation Have students create a table with four columns: *Ciliophora, Sarcodina, Sporozoan,* and *Zooflagellates*. Have students label rows in the table with the following: *Nutrition, Reproduction,* and *Locomotion*. Have students use the information in this section to fill in the table.

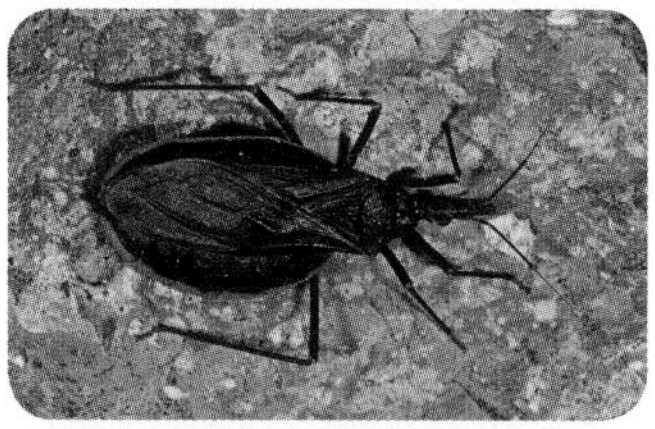

Reduviid bug

Tsetse fly

■ **Figure 10** The insects that carry protozoans from person to person are controlled by insecticides.

Zoomastigina

Protozoans in the phylum Zoomastigina (zoh oh mast tuh JI nuh) are called zooflagellates. Zooflagellates (zoh oh FLA juh layts) are animal-like protozoans that use flagella for movement. Flagella are long whip-like projections that protrude from the cell and are used for movement. Some zooflagellates are free living, but many are parasites.

At least three species of zooflagellates from the genus *Trypanosoma* (TRY pan uh zohm uh) cause infectious diseases in humans that often are fatal because of limited treatment options. One species found in Central and South America causes Chagas' disease, sometimes called American sleeping sickness. The second species causes East African sleeping sickness. The third species causes West African sleeping sickness.

American sleeping sickness The zooflagellates that cause Chagas' disease are similar to the sporozoans that cause malaria in that they have two hosts in their life cycles and insects spread the diseases through the human population. The reduviid bug (rih DEW vee id) bug, shown in **Figure 10,** serves as one host for the protist in Central and South America. The parasitic zooflagellates reproduce in the gut of this insect. The reduviid bug gets its nutrients by sucking blood from a human host. During the feeding process, the zooflagellates pass out of the reduviid body through its feces. The zooflagellates enter the human body through the wound site or mucus membranes. Once the zooflagellate enters the body, it multiplies in the bloodstream and can damage the heart, liver, and spleen.

African sleeping sickness The life cycles of the zooflagellates that cause both African sleeping sicknesses are similar to the one that causes American sleeping sickness. The insect host is the tsetse (SEET see) fly, shown in **Figure 10.** The blood-sucking tsetse fly becomes infected when it feeds on an infected human or other mammal. The zooflagellate reproduces in the gut of the fly and then migrates to its salivary glands. When the fly bites the human, the zooflagellate is transferred to the human host. The zooflagellates reproduce in the human host and cause fever, inflammation of the lymph nodes, and damage to the nervous system. R

Section 2 Assessment

Section Summary

- Protozoans are unicellular protists that feed on other organisms to obtain nutrients.
- Protozoans live in a variety of aquatic environments.
- Protozoans reproduce in a variety of ways, including sexually and asexually.
- Protozoans have specialized methods for movement, feeding, and maintaining homeostasis.

Understand Main Ideas

1. MAIN Idea Compare the methods of feeding, locomotion, and reproduction of three groups of protozoa.
2. **Explain** the function of three organelles found in protozoans.
3. **Diagram** and explain the life cycle of a member of the genus *Plasmodium.*
4. **Explain** why paramecium conjugation is not considered sexual reproduction.

Think Critically

WRITING in Biology

5. Create an informational brochure about zooflagellates for people living in South America.

MATH in Biology

6. There are approximately 50,000 species of protozoa, of which about 7000 are ciliates. What percentage of protozoans are ciliates?

Section 2 Assessment

1. All protozoans obtain their nutrition by consuming other organisms. sarcodina—locomotion, use pseudopods; reproduction—asexual; sporozoan—locomotion, moved by host; reproduction—asexual and sexual stages and produce spores; zooflagellates—locomotion, use flagella; reproduction requires host organisms
2. Student explanations should include how the organelles help maintain homeostasis.
3. Check students' diagrams against Figure 9.
4. New organisms are not formed.
5. Student brochures should include information about how *Trypanosoma* can cause sleeping sickness.

WRITING in Biology

✱RUBRIC Use the modifiable rubric found on your eTeacherEdition Online to assess writing assignments.

6. 14 percent

Reading Preview

Essential Questions

- What are the characteristics of the different phyla of algae?
- What is the role of secondary photosynthetic pigments that are characteristic of some algae?
- How do diatoms differ from most other types of algae?

Review Vocabulary

chloroplasts: chlorophyll-containing organelles found in the cells of green plants and some protists that capture light energy and convert it to chemical energy

New Vocabulary

bioluminescent
colony
alternation of generations

Multilingual eGlossary

Algae—Plantlike Protists

MAIN Idea **Algae are plantlike, autotrophic protists that are the producers for aquatic ecosystems.**

Real-World Reading Link Have you ever looked at a group of people and wondered what they had in common? You might discover that they like the same type of music or they like the same type of sports. Most plantlike protists have something in common—they make their own food.

Characteristics of Algae

The group of protists called algae (singular, alga) is considered plantlike because the members contain photosynthetic pigments. Recall that photosynthetic pigments enable organisms to produce their own food using energy from the Sun in a process called photosynthesis. Algae differ from plants because they do not have roots, leaves, or other structures typical of plants.

The light-absorbing pigments of algae are found in chloroplasts. In many algae, the primary pigment is chlorophyll, which is the same pigment that gives plants their characteristic green color. Many algae also have secondary pigments that allow them to absorb light energy in deep water. As water depth increases, much of the sunlight's energy is absorbed by the water. These secondary pigments allow algae to absorb light energy from wavelengths that are not absorbed by water. Because these secondary pigments reflect light at different wavelengths, algae are found in a variety of colors, as shown in **Figure 11.**

Reading Check **Explain** the function of chloroplasts and photosynthetic pigments in algae.

LM Magnification: 160×

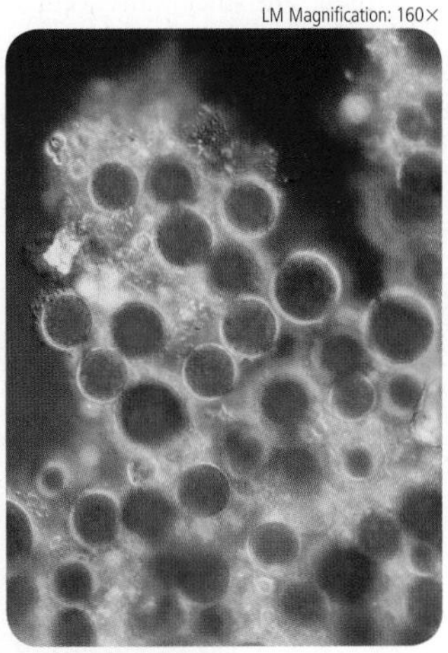

Red algae

LM Magnification: 250×

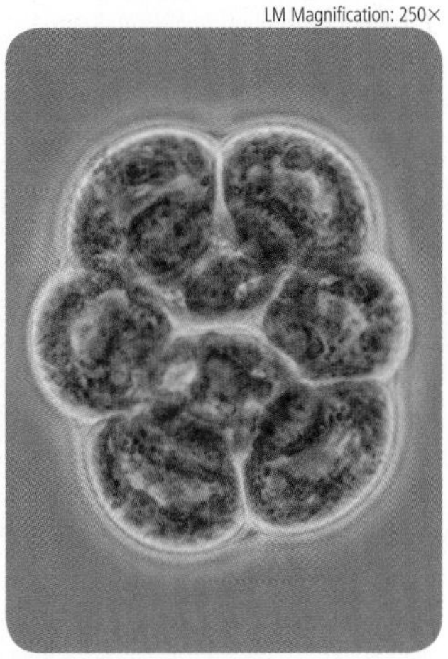

Green algae

Figure 11 Algae vary in color because they contain different pigments.

Demonstration

OL Classify Algae Collect pictures of numerous types of algae, including at least one type of algae from each group discussed in this section, or collect or order actual algae. **ASK STUDENTS:** ***How would you group or classify these algae?*** Answers will vary, but some students may suggest using color or structure—unicellular versus multicellular. Explain that scientists have used both methods. Est. time: 10 min

Section 3

MAIN Idea

BL OL AL

Plant Characteristics Brainstorm with students to come up with a list of plant characteristics. The list might include roots, leaves, and photosynthetic pigments. Write them on the board and have students copy them. As they read, students should underline the characteristics that also apply to algae (photosynthetic pigments).

Skill Practice

EL BL Make a Table Have students skim the section to determine the different types of algae they are going to be reading about. diatoms, dinoflagellates, euglenoids, chrysophytes, brown algae, green algae, and red algae Have students construct a table with the different algae as column headings. As they read the section they can fill in characteristics for each type of algae.

Develop Concepts

AL Clarify a Misconception
ASK STUDENTS: ***What do you think of when you hear the word seaweed?*** Some students might say plants found along the seashore. This is partly true. Seaweeds are found in the sea, but they are actually protists. They are the multicellular species of algae that live in the world's oceans. Species include kelp, sea lettuce, and bladder wracks. Seaweeds dominate the rocky intertidal and subtidal areas of most oceans and provide food and shelter for other marine organisms.

Reading Check Photosynthetic pigments in chloroplasts enable algae to conduct photosynthesis.

C Critical Thinking

BL OL AL Evaluate

ASK STUDENTS: ***Is the oil found in diatoms a beneficial or harmful characteristic for the diatom?*** Both; It is beneficial because it provides buoyancy, allowing diatoms to absorb sunlight for photosynthesis. It is harmful because it makes them an attractive food source.

D Develop Concepts

AL Scaffolding

ASK STUDENTS: ***How do diatoms reproduce?*** asexually and sexually ***Describe the process of asexual reproduction in diatoms.*** The two halves separate and each half produces a new half that can fit inside the old one. ***What problem does this eventually create?*** the diatoms get smaller and smaller ***When do diatoms undergo sexual reproduction?*** When diatoms reach a certain minimum size, they produce gametes that fuse, forming a zygote that develops into a full-size diatom.

W Writing Support

OL Summary Writing Have students summarize diatom reproduction in their own words. Sample answer: Diatoms separate into halves, and make a new half that can fit inside the old half. This process makes smaller and smaller diatoms. When diatoms reach a certain minimum size, sexual reproduction begins. Gametes are made and fuse into zygotes. The zygotes become full-sized diatoms.

EL In pairs, have students list 5–10 important steps in diatom reproduction. Then, have the students orally describe each step in a sentence. Have one student in each pair be the recorder, and write down the sentences. When students are finished, students will have a summary paragraph.

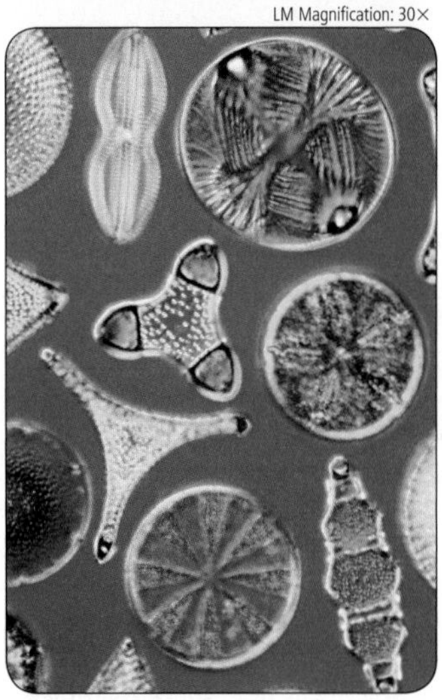

■ **Figure 12** The various species of diatoms have different shapes and sizes.

C

Diversity of Algae

Algae have more differences than only their colors. For example, many algae exist as single cells, whereas others are huge multicellular organisms reaching 65 m in length. Some unicellular algae are referred to as phytoplankton—meaning "plant plankton." Phytoplankton are vital in aquatic ecosystems because they provide the base of the food web in these environments. As a by-product of photosynthesis, they also produce much of the oxygen found in Earth's atmosphere.

The great diversity of algae makes them a challenge to classify. Algologists usually use three criteria to classify algae: the type of chlorophyll and secondary pigments, the method of food storage, and the composition of the cell wall.

Diatoms The unicellular algae shown in **Figure 12** are members of the phylum Bacillariophyta (BAH sih LAYR ee oh FI tuh). These intricately shaped organisms are called diatoms. Look at **Figure 13** and notice that the diatom consists of two unequal halves—one fits neatly inside the other, forming a small box with a lid.

Connection to Physics Diatoms are photosynthetic autotrophs. They produce food by photosynthesis using chlorophyll and secondary pigments called carotenoids, which give diatoms their golden-yellow color. Diatoms store their food as oil instead of as carbohydrates. The oil not only makes diatoms a nutritious food source for many marine animals, but it also provides buoyancy. Oil is less dense than water, so diatoms float closer to the surface of the water, where they can absorb energy from the Sun for photosynthesis.

Diatoms reproduce both sexually and asexually, as illustrated in **Figure 14.** Asexual reproduction occurs when the two separated halves each create a new half that can fit inside the old one. This process produces increasingly smaller diatoms. When a diatom is about one-quarter of its original size, sexual reproduction is triggered and gametes are produced. The gametes fuse to form a zygote that develops into a full-sized diatom. The reproduction cycle then repeats. D

The hard silica walls of the diatom last long after the diatom has died. The silica walls accumulate on the ocean floor to form sediment known as diatomaceous earth. This sediment is collected and used as an abrasive and a filtering agent. The gritty texture of many tooth polishes and metal polishes is due to the presence of diatom shells. W

CAREERS IN BIOLOGY

Algologist A biologist who specializes in the study of algae is an algologist. Algologists might work at fish hatcheries or conduct marine research.

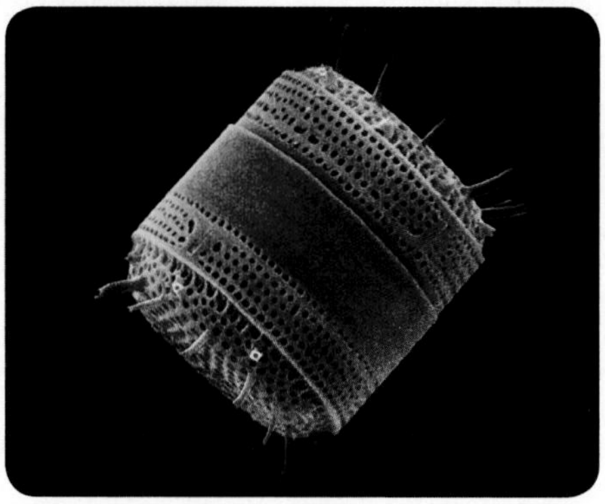

■ **Figure 13** Diatoms are found in both marine and freshwater environments. A unique feature of the diatom is its cell wall made of silica.

Demonstration

Diatom Diversity Most biological supply companies sell slides that show the different shapes of diatoms. If you don't have slides, old supply catalogs, the Internet, and the *Glencoe Biology* Classroom Presentation Toolkit provide images of the incredible diversity and beauty of this group. Est. time: 10 min

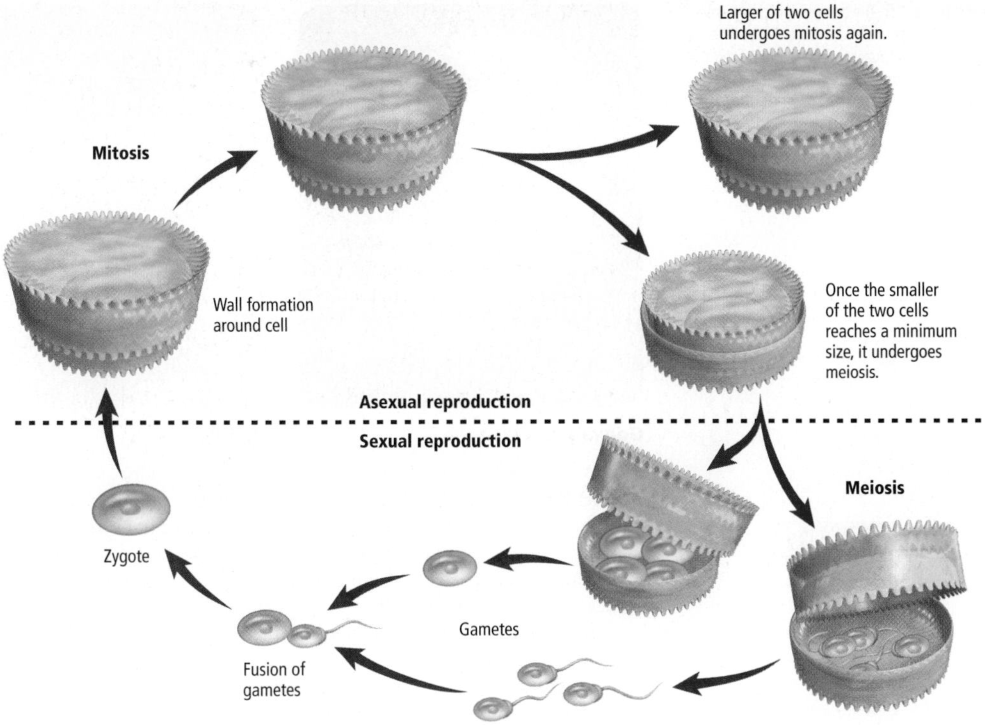

■ **Figure 14** Diatoms reproduce asexually for several generations before undergoing sexual reproduction.

Dinoflagellates Plantlike protists that are members of the phylum Pyrrophyta (puh RAH fuh tuh) are called dinoflagellates (di nuh FLA juh layts). Most members of the phylum are unicellular and have two flagella at right angles to one another. As these flagella beat, a spinning motion is created, so dinoflagellates spin as they move through the water. Some members in this group have cell walls made of thick cellulose plates that resemble helmets or suits of armor. Other members of this group are **bioluminescent,** which means that they emit light. Although there are a few freshwater dinoflagellates, most are found in saltwater. Like diatoms, photosynthetic dinoflagellates are a major component of phytoplankton.

Dinoflagellates vary in how they get their nutritional requirements. Some dinoflagellates are photosynthetic autotrophs, and other species are heterotrophs. The heterotrophic dinoflagellates can be carnivorous, **S** parasitic, or mutualistic. Mutualistic dinoflagellates have relationships with organisms such as jellyfishes, mollusks, and corals.

Algal blooms When food is plentiful and environmental conditions are favorable, dinoflagellates reproduce in great numbers. These population explosions are called algal blooms. Algal blooms can be harmful when they deplete the nutrients in the water. When the food supply diminishes, the dinoflagellates die in large numbers. As the dead algae decompose, the oxygen supply in the water is depleted, suffocating fish and other marine organisms. Additional fish suffocate when their gills become clogged with the dinoflagellates.

VOCABULARY
WORD ORIGIN
Pyrrophyta
pyro– prefix; from Greek; meaning *fire*
–phyton from Greek word *phyton,* meaning *plant*

Writing Support

AL Creative Writing Have students write a poem or short story about how the two flagella of dinoflagellates work together. Answers should indicate that the flagella are at right angles to each other. As the flagella beat, they spin. The spinning motion moves the organism.

S Skill Practice

OL Compare and Contrast
Have students compare and contrast the photosynthetic and heterotrophic dinoflagellates. Heterotrophic dinoflagellates can be carnivorous, parasitic, or mutualistic. Photosynthetic dinoflagellates produce their own food by photosynthesis.

Reading Strategy

BL OL COOP LEARN

Supplemental Reading
Organize students into five groups. Assign the groups the following types of dinoflagellates: marine photosynthetic, freshwater photosynthetic, mutualistic, carnivorous, and parasitic. Have the groups research the following characteristics for the type of dinoflagellate they have been assigned: Where can they be found? How do they get their nutrition? How do they reproduce? What effect do these dinoflagellates have on people? Have students share their findings in a short oral presentation to the class.

Differentiated Instruction

English Learners When placing students in groups for the supplemental reading activity described on this page, consider grouping strategies that will help the English learners. Set up groups of students with different levels of English language proficiencies so students with limited English language proficiency can be assisted by English speakers.

For more tips, see pages 14T–15T.

W Writing Support

AL Persuasive Writing Have students propose another possible method to monitor red tide blooms. Answers will vary, but should demonstrate student understanding that red tides are caused by high concentrations of dinoflagellates. The methods proposed by students should involve a means of detecting the bloom and communicating this information to scientists.

Reading Strategy

AL Supplemental Reading Provide copies of newspaper articles about red tides or have students research the topic. Have students discuss the economic impact these red tide blooms might have on the affected communities.

S Skill Practice

EL OL Visual Literacy Write a description of a typical euglenoid on the board before students read this page. Then have students read the text and draw and label a euglenoid. When they are finished, have them compare their pictures to Figure 16. Ask students how they would classify euglenoids.

■ **Figure 15** The microscopic organism *Gonyaulax catanella* is one species of dinoflagellate that causes red tides. During red tides, many marine organisms die and shellfish can be too toxic for humans to eat.

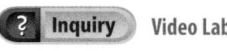

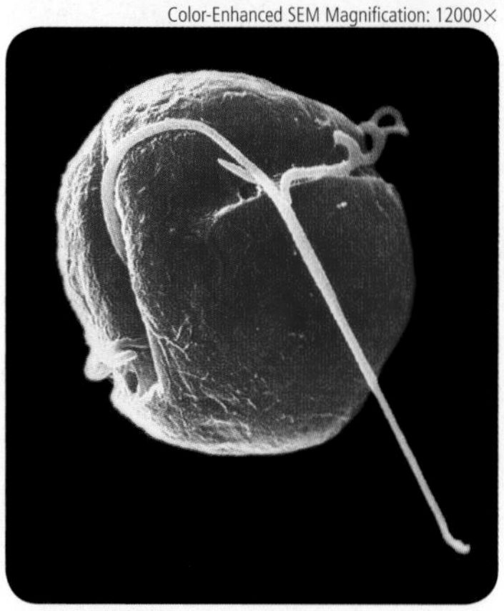

Gonyaulax catanella

Red tide

Inquiry Video Lab

Red tides Some dinoflagellates have red photosynthetic pigments, and when they bloom, the ocean is tinged red, as shown in **Figure 15.** These blooms are called red tides. Red tides can be a serious threat to humans because some species of dinoflagellates produce a potentially lethal nerve toxin. The toxins affect people primarily when people eat shellfish. Shellfish that feed by filtering particles ingest the toxic dinoflagellates from the water. The toxins become concentrated in tissues of the shellfish. People and other organisms can become seriously ill or die from consuming these toxic shellfish.

Red tides must be closely monitored. One method scientists use to track red tides is reviewing satellite images. However, floating robots are being developed that can constantly measure the concentration of red tide algae. If the concentration becomes too high, scientists can issue a warning to stop shellfish harvesting. W

■ **Figure 16** *Euglena gracilis* are unicellular, plantlike algae that have characteristics of both plants and animals.

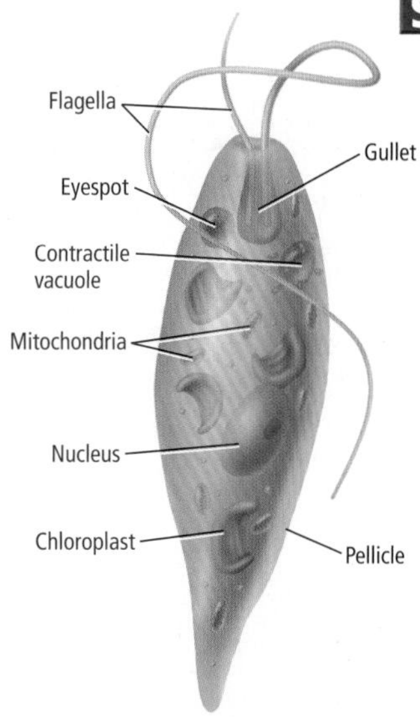

S

Euglenoids Members of the phylum Euglenophyta are unicellular, plantlike protists called euglenoids (yoo GLEE noydz). Most euglenoids are found in shallow freshwater, although some live in saltwater. Euglenoids are challenging to classify because they have characteristics of both plants and animals. Most euglenoids contain chloroplasts and photosynthesize, which is characteristic of plants, yet they lack a cell wall. Euglenoids also can be heterotrophs. When light is not available for photosynthesis, some can absorb dissolved nutrients from their environments. Others can ingest other organisms such as smaller euglenoids, which is a characteristic of animals. There even are a few species of euglenoids that are animal parasites.

The structure of a typical euglenoid is shown in **Figure 16.** Notice that instead of a cell wall, a flexible, tough outer membrane, called a pellicle, surrounds the cell membrane, which is similar to a paramecium's structure. The pellicle allows euglenoids to crawl through mud when the water level is too low to swim. Note the flagella that are used to propel the euglenoid toward food or light. The eyespot is a light-sensitive receptor that helps orient the euglenoid toward light for photosynthesis. The contractile vacuole serves the same purpose in the euglenoid as it does in a paramecium. It expels excess water from the cell to maintain homeostasis inside the cell.

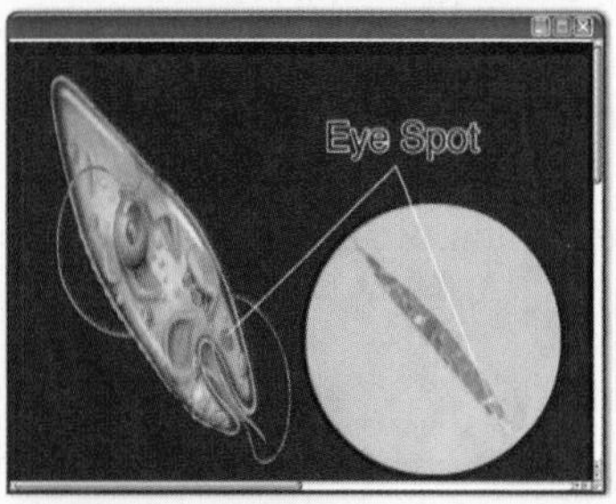

Inquiry **Video Lab** Students will observe and compare how *Paramecia* and *Euglena* respond to light.

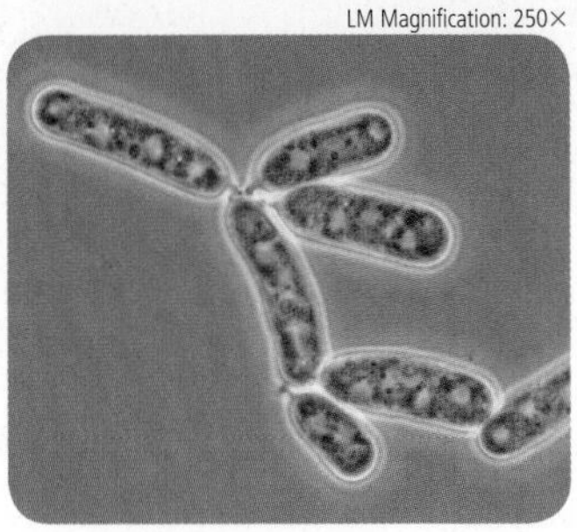

Yellow-green algae

Golden-brown algae

■ **Figure 17** Chrysophytes, like yellow-green and golden-brown algae, have carotenoids—secondary pigments used in photosynthesis.

Chrysophytes Yellow-green algae and golden-brown algae are in phylum Chrysophyta (KRIS oh fyt uh) and are called chrysophytes (KRIS oh fytz). Like diatoms, these algae have yellow and brown carotenoids that give them their golden brown color. The algae in **Figure 17** are two examples of organisms from this phylum. Most members of this phylum are unicellular, but some species form D colonies. A **colony** is a group of cells that join together to form a close association. The cells of chrysophytes usually contain two flagella attached at one end of the cell. All chrysophytes are photosynthetic, but some species also can absorb dissolved organic compounds through their cell walls or ingest food particles and prokaryotes. They reproduce both asexually and sexually, although sexual reproduction is rare. Chrysophytes are components of both freshwater and marine plankton.

Reading Check **Identify** the substance that gives chrysophytes their golden-brown color.

Study Tip

Shared Reading Read two paragraphs aloud to a classmate. Have your partner summarize the key ideas. Then switch roles.

Brown algae Brown algae are members of phylum Phaeophyta (FAY oh FI tuh) and are some of the largest multicellular plantlike algae. These algae get their brown color from a secondary carotenoid pigment called fucoxanthin (fyew ko ZAN thun). Most of the 1500 species of brown algae live along rocky coasts in cool areas of the world. Look back at **Table 1** to see kelp, an example of a brown alga. The body of a kelp is called the thallus, as shown in **Figure 18.** The blades are the flattened portions, the stipe is the stalklike part, the holdfast is the rootlike structure, and the bladder is the bulging portion of the alga. The bladder is filled with air and keeps the alga floating near the surface of the water where light is available for photosynthesis.

■ **Figure 18** Underwater kelp forests provide a habitat for many marine organisms, as well as provide algin, which is an additive used in many products.
Explain ***What is the function of the bladder in kelp?***

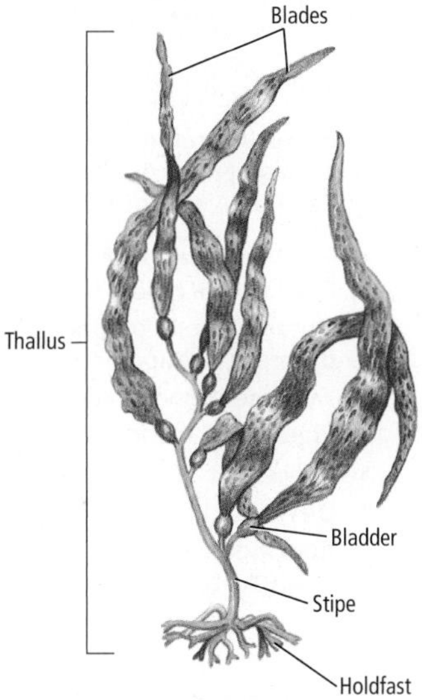

Green algae The diverse group of algae from phylum Chlorophyta (kloh RAH fy tuh) contains more than 7000 species. Green algae have several characteristics in common with plants. Green algae and plants both contain chlorophyll as a primary photosynthetic pigment, which gives both groups a green color. Both green algae and plant cells have cell walls, and both groups store their food as carbohydrates. These shared characteristics lead some scientists to think that there is an evolutionary link between these two kingdoms.

Most species of green algae are found in freshwater, but about ten percent are marine species. Green algae also are found on damp ground, tree trunks, and in snow. Green algae even are found in the fur of some animals, such as the sloth shown in **Figure 2.**

D Develop Concepts

BL OL

Integrate Social Studies

ASK STUDENTS: ***Have you ever heard the term*** **colony** ***used before to describe a group of organisms living together?*** One possible answer is that human settlers often lived in colonies. ***Do you think the early colonists and the colonial algae have anything in common?*** Answers will vary, but students might suggest that there is "safety in numbers."

AL **ASK STUDENTS:** ***What are some of the benefits of human settlers living in a colony?*** The colonists helped each other by working together to grow food, build shelters, etc. ***How might*** **Volvox** ***share benefits?*** The *Volvox* colony provides protection and shelter for the young daughter cells within the sphere.

Reading Check The substances are yellow and brown carotenoids.

■ **Caption Question Fig. 18** The bladder helps the kelp float. When the kelp is higher in the water, it is exposed to more sunlight than when it is lower in the water. The kelp needs sunlight for photosynthesis.

Content Background

Real-World Connection The alginates from the cell walls of brown algae are used in a wide range of commercial applications including thickening agents and colloid stabilizers in foods, textiles, cosmetics, pharmaceuticals, and paper products. Algin is found in foods such as desserts, milkshake mixes, dairy products, and canned foods.

S Skill Practice

EL BL OL AL Visual Literacy Have students examine the three algae in Figure 19.

ASK STUDENTS: ***Do you notice anything similar in the three algae?*** green color; made of cells ***What is different?*** number and arrangement of cells

MiniLab 1

? Inquiry MiniLab

For a lab worksheet, use your eTeacherEdition Online.

RUBRIC A rubric for evaluating MiniLabs is found on your eTeacherEdition Online.

Est. Time 20 min (15 min every other day for a week)

Safety Precaution Approve lab safety forms before work begins.

Teaching Strategy Students can brainstorm and collaborate to form hypotheses and design the investigation.

Analysis

1. Sample answer: the presence of oxygen bubbles indicates that photosynthesis is occurring
2. Answers will vary. Algae contain chlorophyll and undergo photosynthesis. Algae require light to photosynthesize. If they are placed in a dark location, they will die.
3. Sample answer: chloroplasts

LabManager™

Customize this lab with the LabManager™ CD-ROM.

S

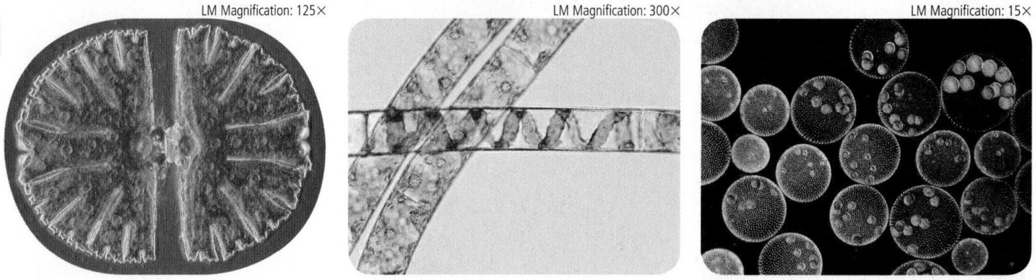

Desmids ***Spirogyra*** ***Volvox***

■ **Figure 19** *Desmids* are unicellular green algae that have elaborate cell walls. The green alga *Spirogyra* is named for its spiraling chloroplasts. Many cells that make up the *Volvox* colony have daughter colonies within the larger colony.

There are a variety of growth patterns exhibited by green algae. The unicellular algae *Desmids*, shown in **Figure 19,** are characterized by their symmetrically divided cells. Notice how the cells have two identical sides that are connected by a bridge. Another growth pattern is found in *Spirogyra*, shown in **Figure 19.** *Spirogyra* is a multicellular green alga characterized by its long, thin filaments. The name *Spirogyra* comes from the spiral pattern of the chloroplasts. *Volvox,* shown in **Figure 19,** is an example of an alga that has a colonial growth pattern.

The single cells of the *Volvox* colony are held together by a gelatinlike secretion called cytoplasmic strands. Each cell has flagella that beat in unison to move the colony. *Volvox* colonies might include hundreds or even thousands of cells that form a hollow ball. Smaller colonies, called daughter colonies, form balls inside the larger colony. When the daughter cells have matured, they digest the parental cell and become free-swimming.

Reading Check **Identify** three growth patterns of green algae.

MiniLab 1

Investigate Photosynthesis in Algae

? Inquiry MiniLab

How much sunlight do green algae need to undergo photosynthesis? Algae contain photosynthetic pigments that allow them to produce food by using energy from the Sun. Observe green algae to determine whether the amount of light affects photosynthesis.

Procedure:

1. Read and complete the lab safety form.
2. Obtain samples of **green algae** from your teacher. Place the sample of each type of algae in different locations in the classroom. Be sure that one location is completely dark.
3. Hypothesize what will happen to the algae in each location.
4. Check each specimen every other day for a week. Record your observations.

Analysis

1. **Describe** the evidence that you used to determine whether photosynthesis was occurring.
2. **Conclude** whether your hypothesis was supported. Explain.
3. **Identify** which organelles you would expect to see if you looked at each type of alga under a microscope.

Reading Check divided cells, spiral filaments, and colonial or hollow ball

Coralline

■ **Figure 20** The red photosynthetic pigments allow the red algae to live in deep water and still use sunlight to photosynthesize.
Explain ***how the red photosynthetic pigments make this possible.***

Red Algae Most red algae in phylum Rhodophyta (roh dah FI duh) are multicellular. Look at **Figure 20** to see how red algae got their name. These organisms contain red photosynthetic pigments called phycobilins that give them a red color. These pigments enable the red algae to absorb green, violet, and blue light that can penetrate water to a depth of 100 m or more. This allows red algae to live and photosynthesize in deeper water than other algae.

D Some red algae also contribute to the formation of coral reefs. The cell walls of the red alga *Coralline* contain calcium carbonate. The calcium carbonate binds together the bodies of other organisms called stony coral to form coral reefs.

VOCABULARY
ACADEMIC VOCABULARY
Supplement
something that completes or makes an addition
Vitamins are taken to supplement one's diet.

Uses for Algae

Algae are used as a source of food for animals and people worldwide. In coastal areas of North America and Europe, algae are fed to farm animals as a food supplement. Algae are found in many dishes and processed foods, as described in **Table 2.** Algae are nutritious because of their high protein content and because they contain minerals, trace elements, and vitamins. Some of the substances found in algae also are used to stabilize or improve the texture of processed foods, without adding fat to those products. D

Table 2 **Some Uses for Algae** Concepts in Motion Interactive Table

Type of Algae	Uses
Red algae	A species of red alga, *Porphyra,* is called nori, which is dried, pressed into sheets, and used in soups, sauces, sushi, and condiments. Some species of red algae provide agar and carrageenan, which are used in the preparation of scientific gels and cultures. Agar also is used in pie fillings and to preserve canned meat and fish. Carrageenan is used to thicken and stabilize puddings, syrups, and shampoos.
Brown algae	Brown algae are used to stabilize products, such as syrups, ice creams, and paints. The genus *Laminaria* is harvested and eaten with meat or fish and in soups.
Green algae	Species from the genera *Monostroma* and *Ulva,* also called sea lettuce, are eaten in salads, soups, relishes, and in meat or fish dishes.
Diatoms	Diatoms are used as a filtering material for processes such as the production of beverages, chemicals, industrial oils, cooking oils, sugars, water supplies, and the separation of wastes. They are also used as abrasives.

D Develop Concepts

BL Integrate Chemistry The walls of some red algae contain calcium carbonate. This calcium carbonate is one of the materials that combine with corals to form coral reefs.

ASK STUDENTS: ***What elements do you think are in calcium carbonate?*** calcium, carbon, and oxygen Tell students that the molecular formula for calcium carbonate is $CaCO_3$.

ASK STUDENTS: ***How many atoms are in the calcium carbonate molecule?*** five

D Develop Concepts

EL BL OL AL Activity Have students collect product labels listing agar, carrageenan, and algin. Have students share their labels using a bulletin board displayed in class.

Concepts in Motion
Interactive Table

■ **Caption Question Fig. 20** Red pigment absorbs blue light waves. Blue light waves travel deeper into the water than other light waves.

Content Background

Cultural Diversity Nori is a Japanese seaweed paper. It is made from various types of red algae. It is used for sushi, rice balls, and as a decorative topping for some dishes. Nori can be purchased at Asian groceries or in the Japanese foods section of the local grocery.

Develop Concepts

BL OL AL

Clarify a Misconception

ASK STUDENTS: ***How might the terms* sporophyte *and* gametophyte *be misleading?*** Phyte means plant, and sporophytes and gametophytes are not always plants.

Review

Personal Tutor

Listen to a teacher explain algae life cycles.

Formative Assessment

Evaluation ASK STUDENTS: ***Why are algae difficult to classify?*** Algae live in diverse environments, have diverse life cycles, and vary greatly in their nutritional requirements. ***What are some of the diverse characteristics of algae?*** Algae can be unicellular, colonial, or multicellular. They are found in a variety of colors.

Remediation Students struggling with the characteristics of algae might benefit from outlining this section. Students can begin with the title *Diversity of Algae.* Below that, they can list the smaller headings: *Diatoms, Dinoflagellates, Euglenoids, Chrysophytes, Brown Algae, Green Algae,* and *Red Algae.* Have students answer the following questions for each: *Is it unicellular or multicellular? Does it form colonies? Where is it found? Does it move? How does it get its nutrition?*

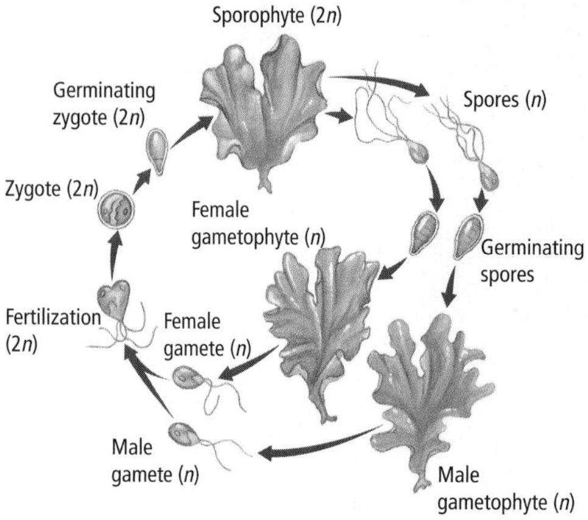

Figure 21 The life cycle of many algae, including the sea lettuce *Ulva* shown here, includes an alternation between a diploid and haploid generation. Alternation of generations is also found in members of both the plant and fungi kingdoms.

Review Personal Tutor

Life Cycles of Algae

Algae can alternate between spore-producing forms and gamete-producing forms. They can reproduce sexually as well as asexually. Green algae also reproduce asexually through fragmentation, a process in which a multicellular individual breaks into separate pieces and each grows into an individual organism.

Alternation of generations The life cycles of many algae exhibit a pattern called alternation of generations, illustrated in **Figure 21** for the sea lettuce *Ulva.* **Alternation of generations** is a life cycle of algae that takes two generations to complete a life cycle, one that reproduces sexually and one that reproduces asexually. Organisms alternate between a diploid *(2n)* form and a haploid *(n)* form, each of which is considered a generation.

Haploid and diploid generations The haploid form of the organism is called the gametophyte generation because it produces gametes. This generation begins with spores and ends with male and female gametes. Gametes from two different organisms combine to form a zygote with two complete sets of chromosomes. The diploid form begins with fertilization and ends when the sporophyte creates spores. The zygote develops into the sporophyte *(2n).* In the sporophyte, some cells divide by meiosis and become haploid spores *(n).* Spores are reproductive cells that develop into gametophytes. The new gametophytes continue the cycle, as shown in **Figure 21.**

Section 3 Assessment

Section Summary

- Algae are autotrophic protists.
- Algae are important producers of oxygen and food for aquatic ecosystems.
- Euglenoids, diatoms, and dinoflagellates are unicellular algae.
- Red, brown, and green algae have multicellular forms.
- The life cycles of algae include an alternation of generations.

Understand Main Ideas

1. MAIN Idea **Explain** why algae are considered the primary producers for aquatic and marine ecosystems.
2. **Describe** the major characteristics of three phyla of algae.
3. **Explain** why you would expect to find more evidence of diatoms than green algae in a sample of ocean floor sediment.
4. **Apply** what you know about photosynthesis to explain why most algae live at or near the surface of the water.

Think Critically

5. **Design an experiment** to determine the optimum color of light to grow green algae.
6. **Summarize** the role of secondary photosynthetic pigments in algae.

WRITING in Biology

7. Write a brief public service announcement explaining the dangers of eating shellfish during a red tide.

Section 3 Assessment

1. because they photosynthesize their own food
2. diatoms—photosynthesize, silica cell wall; dinoflagellates—photosynthesize, some are heterotrophic, have two flagella, and some are bioluminescent; euglenoids—photosynthesize and some are heterotrophic, have an eyespot, and have flagella; chrysophytes—photosynthesize, and some are heterotrophic, and some form colonies
3. Green algae decompose, but the silica cell walls of diatoms do not.
4. to receive sunlight for photosynthesis
5. Experiments should include materials needed, procedure, and defined variables.
6. Secondary pigments allow algae to photosynthesize in deep water.
7. Students' announcements should include information about the toxins present in a red tide.

WRITING in Biology

RUBRIC Use the modifiable rubric found on your eTeacherEdition Online to assess writing assignments.

Assessment Online Quiz

Reading Preview

Essential Questions

- What are the characteristics of cellular and acellular slime molds?
- How are the life cycles of cellular and acellular slime molds similar?
- How do water molds obtain their nutrition?

Review Vocabulary

cellulose: a glucose polymer that forms the cell walls of plants and some funguslike protists

New Vocabulary

plasmodium
acrasin

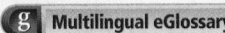

g Multilingual eGlossary

Funguslike Protists

MAIN Idea Funguslike protists obtain their nutrition by absorbing nutrients from dead or decaying organisms.

Real-World Reading Link Have you ever heard the saying, "Don't judge a book by its cover"? The same could be said of funguslike protists. At first glance, they look like fungi. But when they are examined more closely, many traits are revealed that are not true of fungi.

Slime Molds

As you can imagine, funguslike protists are protists that have some characteristics of fungi. Fungi and slime molds use spores to reproduce. Like fungi, slime molds feed on decaying organic matter and absorb nutrients through their cell walls. However, fungi and slime mold differ in the composition of their cell walls. Fungi cell walls are composed of a substance called chitin (KI tun). Chitin is a complex carbohydrate that is found in the cell walls of fungi, and in the external skeletons of insects, crabs, and centipedes. The cell walls of funguslike protists do not contain chitin, as a true fungus does. The cell walls of these protists contain cellulose or celluloselike compounds.

D Slime molds are found in a variety of colors, ranging from yellows and oranges to blue, black, and red, as shown in **Figure 22.** They usually are found in damp, shady places where decaying organic matter is located, such as on a pile of decaying leaves or on rotting logs. Slime molds are divided into two groups: acellular slime molds and cellular slime molds.

Reading Check Compare and contrast fungi and slime molds.

■ **Figure 22** Slime molds have a variety of colors and shapes, but they all have funguslike characteristics.
***Infer** Where might these slime molds be obtaining their nutrition?*

Myxamoebae slime mold

Red raspberry slime mold

Section 4

MAIN Idea

BL OL AL Funguslike Protists
ASK STUDENTS: ***What are some characteristics of fungi?*** Accept all reasonable responses. Students might say that fungi grow in damp areas and are decomposers. Explain that the organisms in this section once were grouped with fungi because some of their characteristics were similar to fungi. However, they are now classified as protists.

D Develop Concepts

BL OL AL

Integrate Earth Science

Slime molds are vital to maintaining the health of soil in many places, including the rain forests in Guatemala. The soil in those forests is rich in slime molds that quickly decompose organic matter on the rain forest floor. However, when whole forests are cut down, sunlight dries the forest floor. The slime molds dry up and become inactive or die.
ASK STUDENTS: ***What problem might occur when the decomposers in soil no longer break down organic matter?*** The nutrients are no longer recycled and made available to other organisms; undecomposed material would accumulate.

■ **Caption Question Fig. 22**
They might be getting nutrition from a decaying leaf and a decaying log.

Reading Check Fungi and funguslike protists absorb their nutrients from decaying organisms through their cell walls. They differ in the composition of their cell walls. Funguslike protists do not contain chitin in their cell walls.

Demonstration

Funguslike Protists Bring in examples of funguslike protists from your yard, logs, bark chips, or the floor of forests. You can visit local florists, garden shops, or nurseries and ask for samples of funguslike protists. In class, have students sort the materials and determine whether they are true funguslike protists or whether they belong in other phyla.
ASK STUDENTS: ***How did you determine to which phyla each protist belonged? Is there anyone who disagrees? Why?*** Est. time: 20 min

Develop Concepts

EL BL OL Use Models Have students use modeling clay to make three-dimensional models of the different stages of the acellular slime mold life cycle.

S Skill Practice

EL BL OL Visual Literacy Have students make cards illustrating each stage of the life cycle of acellular slime molds, as shown in Figure 23. Each card should contain enough information to identify the stage it represents. On the other side of the card, have students write a sentence identifying the stage. After the cards are made, shuffle them, and ask students to take turns putting the cards in sequence.

BL Organize students into groups. Have each student write a description of a step in the slime mold life cycle. A recorder in each group can assemble the sentences into a paragraph.

AL Have students make the cards for homework. Have students exchange cards and put them in sequence.

W Writing Support

OL Summary Writing Have students take notes as they read about acellular slime molds. Then have them use their notes to write a summary of the life cycle. If students have made clay models in the preceding activity, have one student read their summary of the slime mold's life cycle out loud while another student manipulates the models.

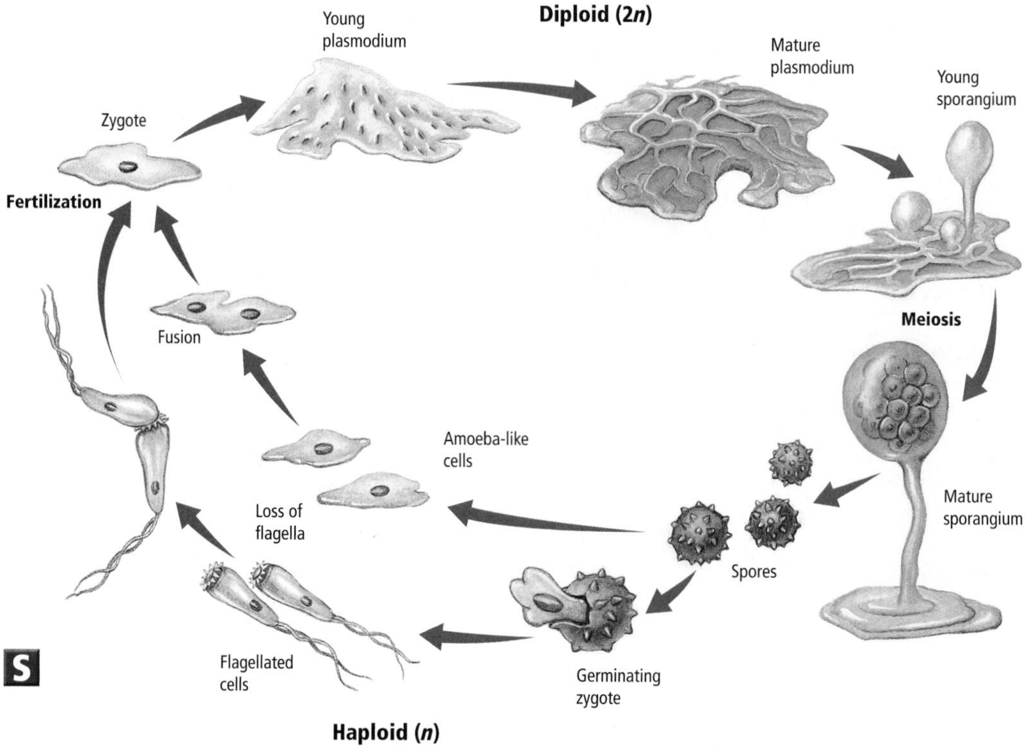

S

■ **Figure 23** Acellular slime mold goes through haploid and diploid phases during its life cycle.

Acellular slime molds Funguslike protists called acellular slime molds are found in the phylum Myxomycota (mihk soh mi COH tuh). They are acellular because they go through a phase in their life cycle in which the nucleus divides but no internal cell walls form, resulting in a mass of cytoplasm with multiple nuclei. W

Follow the life cycle of a typical acellular slime mold, shown in **Figure 23.** Acellular slime molds begin life as spores, usually when conditions are harsh—such as during a drought. In the presence of water, the spore produces a small mass of cytoplasm, or an amoeboid cell, or a cell with a flagella. The cell is propelled by the flagella until it comes in contact with a favorable surface. Then, the flagella permanently retract and the cell produces pseudopods that allow it to move like an amoeba. Both the flagellated cell and the amoeba-like cell are gametes and are haploid *(n)*.

When two gametes unite, the next phase of the life cycle begins. The fertilized cells undergo repeated divisions of the nuclei, forming a plasmodium. A **plasmodium** (plaz MOH dee um) is a mobile mass of cytoplasm that contains many diploid nuclei but no separate cells. This is the feeding stage of the organism. It creeps over the surface of decaying leaves or wood like an amoeba and can grow as large as 30 cm in diameter. When food or moisture becomes limited, the slime mold develops spore-producing structures. Spores are produced through meiosis and dispersed by the wind. Once the spores are in the presence of water, the cycle repeats.

VOCABULARY

ACADEMIC VOCABULARY

Phase
a particular state in a regular cycle of changes
The phases of the Moon are based on the positions of Earth, the Sun, and the Moon.

Research Citation

Models Educational research indicates that models are valuable tools for helping students understand difficult concepts. The activity described on this page asks students to create models of the stages of a life cycle, providing them with concrete examples of abstract information. (Hitt and Townsend, 2004)

Research bibliography on pages 32T–34T

Content Background

Teacher FYI Because slime molds produce few hard structures, except for spores, they have left almost no fossil record. In addition, slime molds tend to live in damp environments which are not conducive to preservation of organic material. The few slime mold fossils that have been found were embedded in amber.

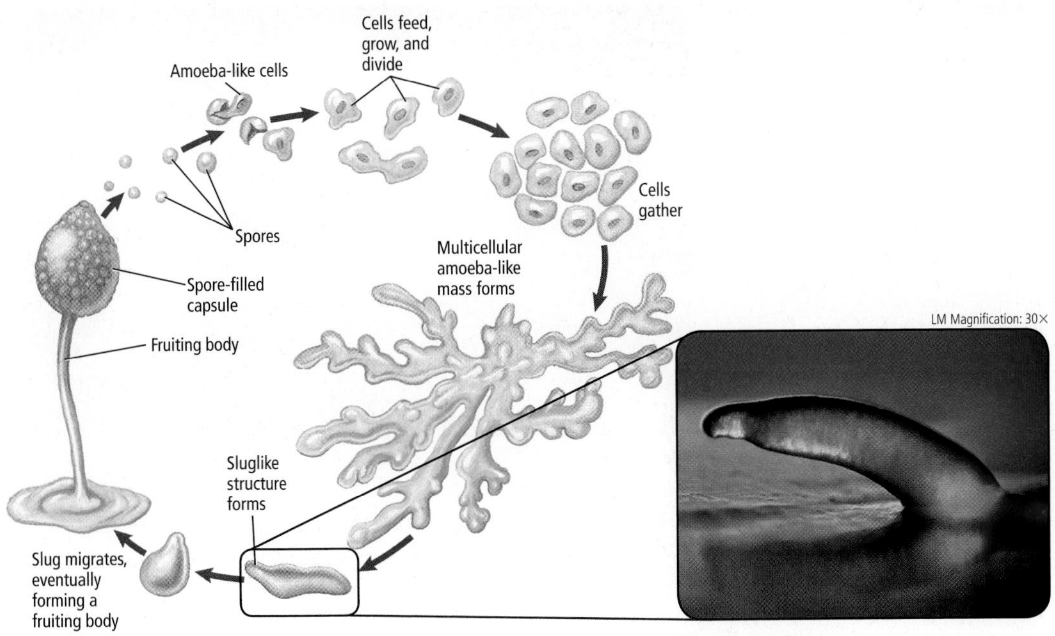

■ **Figure 24** Cellular slime molds reproduce both sexually and asexually. Amoeba-like cells congregate during asexual reproduction, shown above, to form a sluglike colony, which functions like a single organism.
Explain *why the sluglike stage is considered a colony.*

Cellular slime molds Cellular slime molds are found in the phylum Acrasiomycota (uh kray see oh my COH tuh). These funguslike protists creep over rich, moist soil and engulf bacteria. Unlike acellular slime molds, they spend most of their life cycle as single amoeba-like cells and have no flagella.

The life cycle of cellular slime molds is shown in **Figure 24.** When food is plentiful, the single amoeba-like cells reproduce rapidly by sexual reproduction. During sexual reproduction, two haploid amoebas unite and form a zygote. The zygote develops into a giant cell and undergoes meiosis followed by several divisions by mitosis. Eventually, the giant cell ruptures, releasing new haploid amoebas.

When food is scarce, the single amoeba-like cells reproduce asexually. The starving amoeba-like cells give off a chemical called **acrasin** (uh KRA sun). The amoeba-like cells begin to congregate in response to the chemical signal, forming a sluglike colony that begins to function like a single organism. The colony migrates for a while, eventually forming a fruiting body, like the one shown in **Figure 25.** The fruiting body produces spores. Once the spores are fully developed, they are released. The spores germinate, forming amoeba-like cells, and the cycle repeats.

Reading Check **Infer** why the stages in the life cycle of cellular slime molds contribute to their long-term survival.

■ **Figure 25** Cellular slime molds produce fruiting bodies that contain spores during part of their life cycle.

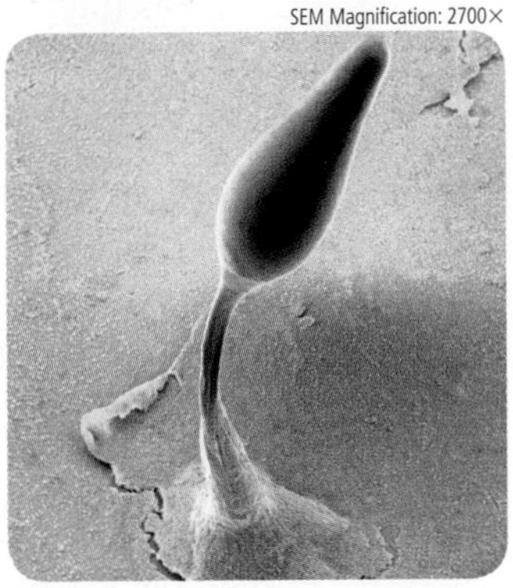

R Reading Strategy

BL Build Vocabulary
ASK STUDENTS: ***What is the structural difference between acellular and cellular slime molds?*** Cellular slime molds tend to be single cells, and acellular slime molds are masses of protoplasm—not separate cells.
What do you think the prefix a- means? not or no; acellular means *not cellular*

D Develop Concepts

BL OL Activity Have students construct a Venn diagram in their notebooks showing the similarities and differences between acellular and cellular slime molds. The Venn diagram should include differences in structure and reproduction. Both are funguslike protists.

Reading Check When conditions are difficult, the slime mold can form spores. When conditions are better, the slime mold can reproduce.

■ **Caption Question Fig. 24**
The sluglike stage is considered a colony because it is a cluster of individual organisms functioning as a single organism.

Research Citation

Reading Strategies Educational research indicates that teachers should provide students with strategies to help them gain meaning from reading assignments. By using the strategy described on this page, students will learn to categorize information and create points of comparison to organize their thinking. (Horowitz, 1985)

Research bibliography on pages 32T–34T

Develop Concepts

BL OL AL

Clarify a Misconception

ASK STUDENTS: ***What do you think of when you hear the names* water mold *and* downy mildew?** Answers will vary, but students might say that they are types of fungi. Students will learn that although we tend to think of fungi and molds as related organisms, that is not necessarily the case. Tell students that it can be confusing because there are powdery mildews that are in the fungus kingdom (ascomycetes), yet downy mildews (oomycetes) are in the protist kingdom.

MiniLab 2

Inquiry MiniLab

For a lab worksheet, use your eTeacherEdition Online.

RUBRIC A rubric for evaluating MiniLabs is found on your eTeacherEdition Online.

Est. Time 15–20 min

Safety Precaution Approve lab safety forms before work begins.

Teaching Strategy Students should read the analysis questions before they begin the lab.

Analysis

1. Answers will depend on the type of slime mold the students received. Acellular slime molds may contain thousands of nuclei floating freely in the cytoplasm. The cellular slime molds contain individual cells.
2. Student answers should discuss similarities in structure.
3. Student classifications should be scientifically supported.

LabManager™

Customize this lab with the LabManager™ CD-ROM.

■ **Figure 26** This water mold is absorbing nutrients found in this dead insect.
Explain *the funguslike characteristics of water molds.*

LM Magnification: 10×

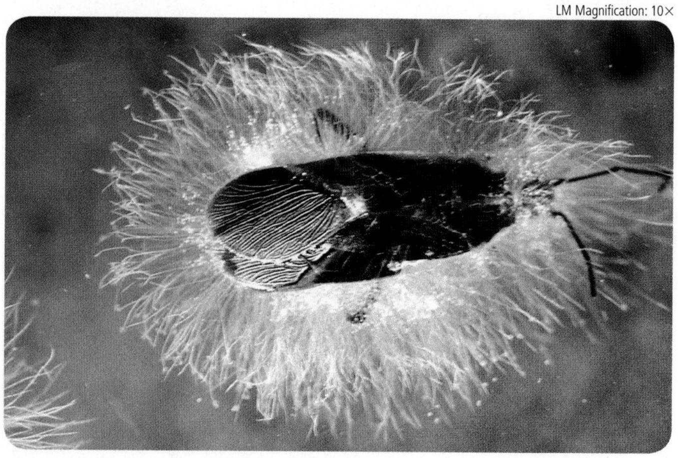

Water mold

Water Molds and Downy Mildew

There are more than 500 species of water molds and downy mildews in the phylum Oomycota (oo oh my COH tuh). Most members of this group of funguslike protists live in water or damp places. Some absorb their nutrients from the surrounding water or soil, while others obtain their nutrients from other organisms, as shown in **Figure 26.**

Originally, water molds were considered fungi because of their method of obtaining nutrients. Like fungi, water molds envelop their food sources with a mass of threads; they break down the tissue and absorb the nutrients through their cell walls. Although this is characteristic of fungi, water molds differ from fungi in the composition of their cell walls and their production of flagellated reproductive cells. Recall that the cell walls of funguslike protists are composed of cellulose and celluloselike compounds.

Reading Check **Compare and contrast** water molds and fungi.

MiniLab 2

Investigate Slime Molds

Inquiry MiniLab

What is a slime mold? In a kingdom of interesting creatures, slime molds perhaps are the most interesting. Observe different types of slime molds and observe the unusual nature of their bodies.

Procedure

1. Read and complete the lab safety form.
2. Obtain **slides of different specimens of slime molds.** Examine the slides under a **microscope.**
3. Create a data table to record your information. Sketch and describe each specimen.

Analysis

1. **Compare and contrast** the specimens.
2. **Identify** specimens that have similar characteristics. Explain why the specimens are similar.
3. **Think Critically** How would you classify each specimen that you examined? Explain.

Reading Check Both obtain their nutrition in similar ways, but they differ in the composition of their cell walls. Water molds also produce flagellated reproductive cells.

■ **Caption Question** **Fig. 26** They surround a decaying organism with a mass of threads and absorb nutrients from the decaying organisms through their cell walls.

Infected potato

Healthy potato

■ **Figure 27** Compare the infected potato on the left with the normal one on the right. *Phytophthora infestans* will destroy the harvested potato in a matter of weeks.

Connection to History One member of phylum Oomycota has had a far-reaching impact. The downy mildew *Phytophthora infestans* (FI toh fah thor uh • in FEST unz) infects potato plants and destroys potatoes, as shown in **Figure 27.** This organism devastated the potato crop of Ireland in the 19th century. Because the potato was the country's primary food source, about one million people died of starvation or famine-related diseases in Ireland. Ironically, during this time, many other agricultural products were produced in Ireland. The Irish farmers could not afford to purchase the agricultural products, so the products were exported to Britain. The British government did provide some assistance to the farmers, but it was too little to prevent the widespread famine. During this time, a large number of people emigrated from Ireland to the United States to escape the terrible famine.

C

Section 4 Assessment

Section Summary

- The cell walls of funguslike protists do not contain chitin.
- Slime molds, water molds, and downy mildew grow in aquatic or damp places.
- Acellular slime molds form a plasmodium that contains many nuclei but no separate cells.
- Cellular slime molds form colonies of cells to reproduce.
- Water molds envelop their food source with a mass of threads.

Understand Main Ideas

1. **MAIN Idea** **Explain** how funguslike protists obtain their nutrition.
2. **Compare** characteristics of cellular and acellular slime molds.
3. **Describe** how amoeba-like cells move.
4. **Outline** the life cycles of cellular and acellular slime molds.
5. **Classify** an organism that has cell walls made of cellulose and absorbs its nutrients from dead organisms.

Think Critically

6. **Design an experiment** to determine the moisture requirements of an acellular slime mold.
7. **Recommend** a procedure that a garden-shop owner should follow to prevent slime molds from growing on his or her wooden benches.

WRITING in Biology

8. Write a short newspaper article about the Irish Potato Famine.

Writing Support

BL OL Summary Writing

Have students research other plant diseases caused by downy mildews and write a summary of their findings.

C Critical Thinking

AL Analyze

ASK STUDENTS: ***Why do you think most treatments for downy mildews are called "fungicides"?*** The classification of downy mildews in Kingdom Protista is relatively recent. The name is a holdover from the past. Although a downy mildew is not a fungus, it was thought to be a fungus for so long, that the treatments for it are still often called fungicides. ***Are true "fungicides" effective against downy mildews? Why, why not?*** No; they are not true fungi.

Formative Assessment

Evaluation

ASK STUDENTS: ***What are the different types of funguslike protists?*** cellular and acellular slime molds, water molds, and downy mildews

Remediation Have students review the types of organisms by reading aloud the headings in Section 4. After they read each heading, have students list characteristics of each group on the board. Then have students copy the lists into their notebooks.

Section 4 Assessment

1. Funguslike protists absorb nutrients from other organisms.
2. Acellular slime molds go through a phase in which the nucleus divides but cell walls do not form. Cellular slime molds spend most of life as single amoeba-like cells.
3. Amoeba-like cells can move by means of pseudopods. Amoeba-like cells can also congregate in response to a chemical signal, forming a single colony.
4. Answers may vary in format, but should include the information summarized in Figures 23 and 24.
5. The organism is a funguslike protist.
6. Designs should show an understanding of scientific process and characteristics of acellular slime molds.
7. Possible answer: Apply a preservative to the wood to prevent decay.
8. Check students' articles. Students should present a balanced account of the famine.

In the Field

Purpose
Students will understand how knowledge of the structure and shell-building capabilities of diatoms can be applied to engineering materials and devices on the atomic level.
F.6

Anticipatory Guide
ASK STUDENTS: ***Have you heard the term* nanotechnology*? What do you think it means?*** Nanotechnology is a branch of science and engineering devoted to the design and production of extremely small materials and devices built from individual atoms and molecules. Remind students that the prefix *nano-* is the metric number 10^{-9}, or one billionth (1/1,000,000,000).
SAY TO STUDENTS: ***Diatoms use materials in their environment to build more complex structures than nanotechnologists currently can build. Scientists are using their knowledge of diatoms to create materials and system components that are smaller than the width of a human hair.***

Background
Diatoms are found in all aquatic and moist environments on Earth. While scientists are not sure exactly how many species of diatoms there are, they number at least in the thousands. Each species has a unique shell design, and organisms of each species create precise, intricate shells. Nanotechnologists think they can apply their knowledge of how diatoms create shells to produce nanoscale structures quickly, inexpensively, at room temperature and pressure, and without using toxic chemicals.

In the Field

Career: Nanotechnologist

Diatoms: Living Silicon Chips

Diatoms have recently gained the attention of nanotechnologists—scientists who engineer devices on the atomic level. Diatoms build intricate shells with incredible precision and regularity. Nanotechnologists think these organisms could be used to build useful structures from silicon on the atomic level.

Nature's nanotechnologists Humans still have a lot to learn from diatoms about constructing materials on the nanoscale. Currently, nanotechnologists etch features onto silicon and other materials to produce components. The process is costly, time-consuming, and generates chemical waste.

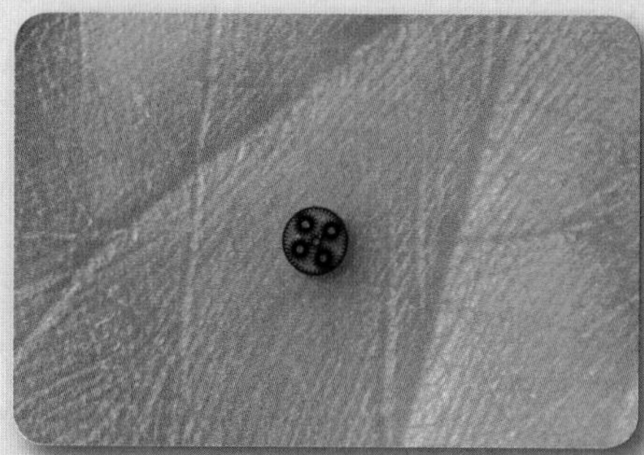

Silicon dioxide shell in a hand

Living silicon chips Diatoms have been described as living silicon chips because they construct their shells atom by atom. Silicon derived from seawater is processed into intricate microstructures to form a rigid silica shell, such as the one shown in the photo. Each diatom species forms a unique and potentially useful shell structure.

Color-Enhanced SEM Magnification: 390×

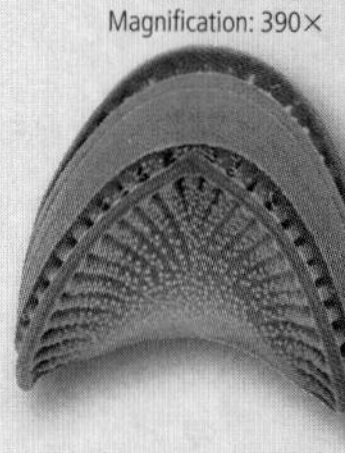

Color-Enhanced SEM Magnification: 390×

Diatoms

To create nanomaterials from diatoms, scientists prepare feeding solutions containing silicon and other elements that they wish to test. The diatoms take these elements in and use them to build shells. When diatoms replace silicon atoms in their shell with elements like magnesium or titanium, a structurally intact unit with a desired shape and chemical makeup is produced. Scientists are working to use diatom shell patterns, many of which cannot currently be duplicated by nanotechnologists, as templates to build components with desired specifications.

Future applications Diatoms might prove to be an important tool in the evolving science of nanotechnology with potential applications in biomedicine, telecommunications, and energy storage and production.

WRITING in Biology

Newspaper Article The worldwide need for nanotechnology workers could reach two million by the year 2015. Write a want ad for a specific career in nanotechnology.

WRITING in Biology

RUBRIC Use the modifiable rubric found on your eTeacherEdition Online to assess writing assignments.

Follow-Up Discussion
Have students form small groups and discuss their research of the field of nanotechnology. Instruct each group should poll its members to find how they feel about pursuing a career in nanotechnology. Lead the class in a discussion about the variety of careers available in the field. Have students create a list of current nanotechnology careers. The list might include materials engineering, biochemistry, and bioengineering.

WebQuest

BIOLAB

Design Your Own

INVESTIGATE: HOW DO PROTOZOANS BEHAVE?

Background: Animals respond and react to the world around them. One such type of reaction is known as *taxis,* in which an animal orients itself toward (positive) or away (negative) from a stimulus. Some of the things to which animals respond are light (phototaxis), temperature (thermotaxis), chemicals (chemotaxis), and gravity (gravitaxis).

Question: *How do simple, unicellular, animal-like protozoans respond to stimuli?*

Materials

cultures of live protozoans
compound microscope
glass slides and coverslips
materials needed to produce stimuli

Safety Precautions

WARNING: ***Use care when handling slides. Dispose of any broken glass in a container provided by your teacher.***

LM Magnification: 390×

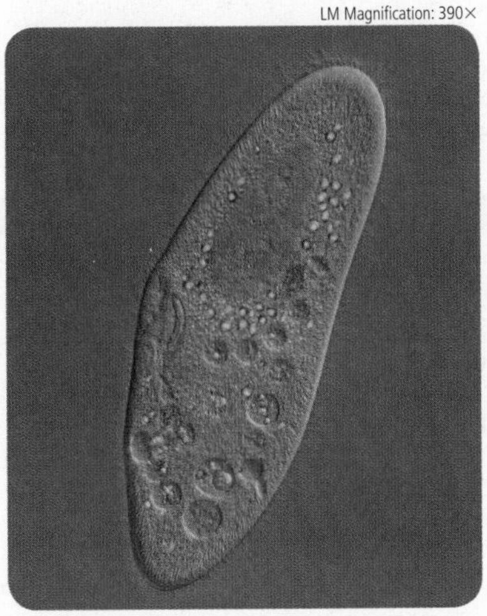

Plan and Perform the Experiment

1. Read and complete the lab safety form.
2. Design an experiment to answer the question to the left. Reword the original question to include the taxis you plan to investigate.
3. Make sure your teacher approves your plan before you proceed.
4. Collect the materials and supplies needed and begin conducting your experiment.
5. Dispose of your protozoan cultures as instructed by your teacher.

Analyze and Conclude

1. **Observe and Infer** Some protozoans often are described as animal-like. What animal-like characteristics did you observe?
2. **State the Problem** What stimuli were you trying to test with your experimental design?
3. **Hypothesize** What was your hypothesis for the question to be solved?
4. **Summarize** What data did you collect during the experiment?
5. **Analyze and Conclude** Did your data support your hypothesis? What is your conclusion?
6. **Error Analysis** Compare your data and conclusions with those of other students in your class. Explain the differences in the data.

WRITING in Biology

Report In this lab, you tested the response of an organism to a stimuli. Write a short report critiquing your methods. Include ways in which you can improve your techniques.

Analyze and Conclude

1. Protozoans are not photosynthetic; they must take in food; they have a cell membrane.
2. Sample answer: Do Protozoans Respond to Light?
3. Students should restate their initial hypothesis.
4. Check students' data.
5. Accept conclusions that are supported by data.
6. Accept all reasonable responses.

WRITING in Biology

RUBRIC Use the modifiable rubric found on your eTeacherEdition Online to assess writing assignments.

Student critiques should be honest and realistic. Remind students that every scientist learns from mistakes and unexpected results.

BIOLAB

Design Your Own

Inquiry BioLab

For a lab worksheet, use your eTeacherEdition Online.

RUBRIC A rubric for evaluating BioLabs is found on your eTeacherEdition Online.

Est. Time 45 min

Content Background Protozoans display an amazing array of behaviors, considering that most types are microscopic. In this lab, students will experimentally investigate some of these behaviors, known collectively as *taxes.*

Safety Precautions Approve lab safety forms before work begins. As students plan their experiments and as you approve them, be aware of any special safety situations their experiments may present.

Teaching Strategies

- Students could work individually or in small groups in this lab.
- With student-planned experiments, it is not possible to anticipate exactly what materials and supplies may be required. However, students will need cultures of live protozoans. The ciliate *Paramecium* works well as an experimental subject in most situations.

Alternative Teaching Demo
As a class, have students select one specific taxis to investigate and then brainstorm and plan an experiment to investigate that taxis. Set up the experiment and have students observe the results. If you have the proper equipment, project the results for all students to see.

Chapter 19

Study Guide

ConnectED

Students can use the following to review the chapter.

Review

Vocabulary eGames
Vocabulary eFlashcards
Vocabulary PuzzleMaker

Assessment

Online Quizzes
Online Test Practice
Standardized Test Practice

Use the *ExamView® Assessment Suite* CD-ROM to:

- create multiple versions of tests
- create modified tests with one mouse click
- edit existing questions and add your own questions
- build tests aligned with state standards using built-in state curriculum tags
- change English tests to Spanish with one mouse click
- track students' progress using the Teacher Management System

Chapter 19 Study Guide

THEME FOCUS Homeostasis Some protists, such as paramecia and euglenoids, have a contractile vacuole that expels excess water from the cell to maintain homeostasis inside the cell.

BIG Idea **Protists are a diverse group of unicellular and multicellular organisms that do not necessarily share the same evolutionary history.**

Section 1 Introduction to Protists

protozoan (p. 542)
microsporidium (p. 544)

MAIN Idea **Protists form a diverse group of organisms that are subdivided based on their method of obtaining nutrition.**

- Protists include unicellular and multicellular eukaryotes.
- Protists are classified by their methods of obtaining food.
- The first protists might have formed through endosymbiosis.
- Protists might have been the first eukaryotic cells with chloroplasts and mitochondria, evolving billions of years ago.

Section 2 Protozoans—Animal-like Protists

pellicle (p. 547)
trichocyst (p. 547)
contractile vacuole (p. 547)
pseudopod (p. 550)
test (p. 550)

MAIN Idea **Protozoans are animal-like, heterotrophic protists.**

- Protozoans are unicellular protists that feed on other organisms to obtain nutrients.
- Protozoans live in a variety of aquatic environments.
- Protozoans reproduce in a variety of ways, including sexually and asexually.
- Protozoans have specialized methods for movement, feeding, and maintaining homeostasis.

Section 3 Algae—Plantlike Protists

bioluminescent (p. 555)
colony (p. 557)
alternation of generations (p. 560)

MAIN Idea **Algae are plantlike, autotrophic protists that are the producers for aquatic ecosystems.**

- Algae are autotrophic protists.
- Algae are important producers of oxygen and food for aquatic ecosystems.
- Euglenoids, diatoms, and dinoflagellates are unicellular algae.
- Red, brown, and green algae have multicellular forms.
- The life cycles of algae include an alternation of generations.

Section 4 Funguslike Protists

plasmodium (p. 562)
acrasin (p. 563)

MAIN Idea **Funguslike protists obtain their nutrition by absorbing nutrients from dead or decaying organisms.**

- The cell walls of funguslike protists do not contain chitin.
- Slime molds, water molds, and downy mildew grow in aquatic or damp places.
- Acellular slime molds form a plasmodium that contains many nuclei but no separate cells.
- Cellular slime molds form colonies of cells to reproduce.
- Water molds envelop their food source with a mass of threads.

Review **Vocabulary PuzzleMaker**

For additional practice with vocabulary, have students access the Vocabulary PuzzleMaker online.

Review **Vocabulary eGames**

Section 1

Vocabulary Review

Answer the following questions with complete sentences.

1. What is another name for animal-like protists?
2. What are microscopic protozoans that are found in the guts of insects?

Understand Main Ideas

3. Which process is most likely the way in which the first protists formed?
   A. aerobic respiration **C.** endosymbiosis
   B. decomposition **D.** photosynthesis
4. MAIN Idea Which method below is used to divide protists into three groups?
   A. method of getting food
   B. method of movement
   C. type of reproduction
   D. type of respiration
5. Which is least likely to be a suitable environment for protists?
   A. decaying leaves **C.** damp soil
   B. the ocean **D.** dry sand

Use the photo below to answer questions 6 and 7.

LM Magnification: 125×

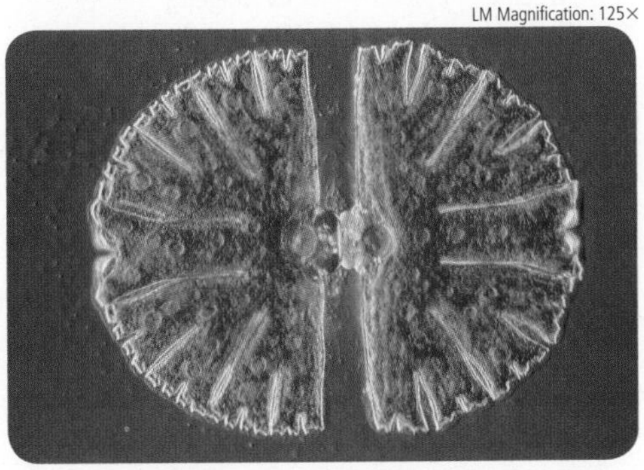

6. To which group does the protist belong?
   A. algae **C.** funguslike
   B. animal-like **D.** protozoans
7. Which term best describes this protist?
   A. acellular **C.** multicellular
   B. eukaryotic **D.** prokaryotic

Constructed Response

8. **Open Ended** Describe three locations near your home or school where you could find protists.
9. **Short Answer** Explain the differences between animal-like protists, plantlike protists, and funguslike protists.

Think Critically

10. **Predict** changes in protist populations if an area had an above-average amount of rainfall.

Section 2

Vocabulary Review

Define each structure. Provide an example of an organism where each structure could be found.

11. pseudopod
12. contractile vacuole
13. test

Understand Main Ideas

Use the diagram below to answer question 14.

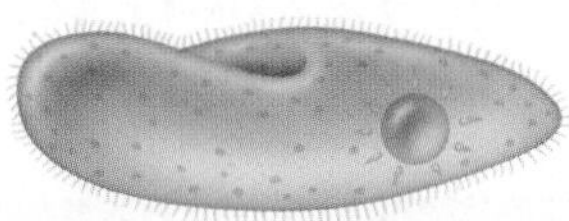

14. Which structure does this organism use for movement?
    A. cilia
    B. contractile vacuole
    C. flagella
    D. pseudopodia
15. **THEME FOCUS Homeostasis** What does the paramecium's contractile vacuole help regulate inside the cell?
    A. amount of food **C.** movement
    B. amount of water **D.** reproduction
16. Which are most likely to form fossils?
    A. apicomplexans **C.** foraminifera
    B. flagellates **D.** paramecia

Assessment Online Test Practice

Chapter 19 Assessment

Section 1

Vocabulary Review

1. protozoans
2. microsporidia

Understand Main Ideas

3. C
4. A
5. D
6. A
7. B

Constructed Response

8. Answers will vary, but should include locations that provide for the needs of protists, such as damp or aquatic places.
9. They differ in the way they obtain nutrition. Animal-like protists are heterotrophic and ingest bacteria, algae, or other protozoans. Plantlike protists are photosynthetic, and make their own food. Funguslike protists absorb nutrients through their cell walls.

Think Critically

10. There would be an increase in the number of protists because they thrive in damp, moist environments.

Section 2

Vocabulary Review

11. a temporary extension of cytoplasm; sarcodines
12. an organelle that collects water and expels it from the cell; ciliates
13. a hard, porous covering similar to a shell, which surrounds the plasma membrane; radiolarians

Understand Main Ideas

14. A
15. B
16. C

Constructed Response

17. The termites would not be able to digest the wood because the flagellates help it break down the cellulose.
18. Two paramecia come together and form a cytoplasmic bridge. They then exchange micronuclei and separate.

Think Critically

19. Sample answer: Controlling mosquito populations with pesticides, and eliminating standing water where mosquitoes might breed.
20. Answers will vary. Students should consider the fact that protozoans live in aquatic environments.

Section 3

Vocabulary Review

21. alternation of generations
22. colony
23. bioluminescent

Understand Main Ideas

24. B
25. D
26. B
27. C
28. B

Constructed Response

29. These organisms have hard shell-like structures that would be more likely to form fossils than the softer material of other algae.
30. Repeated asexual reproduction gradually reduces the size of the diatoms. Sexual reproduction restores it.
31. Sporophytes produce spores that grow into the gametophytes. The gametophytes then produce gametes that grow into sporophytes.

Think Critically

32. Freshwater algae tend to be unicellular and saltwater algae are both unicellular and multicellular.

Constructed Response

17. MAIN Idea Explain why termites might die if their symbiotic flagellates died.

18. **Short Answer** Describe the process of conjugation in paramecia.

Think Critically

19. **Apply Concepts** Recommend several options that villagers might consider to slow down the spread of malaria.

20. **Research Information** Research other diseases that are caused by protozoans. Use a map and plot locations where the diseases occur.

Section 3

Vocabulary Review

Match each definition below with the correct vocabulary term from the Study Guide page.

21. a life cycle of algae that requires two generations
22. a group of cells living together in close association
23. gives off light

Understand Main Ideas

Use the photo below to answer question 24.

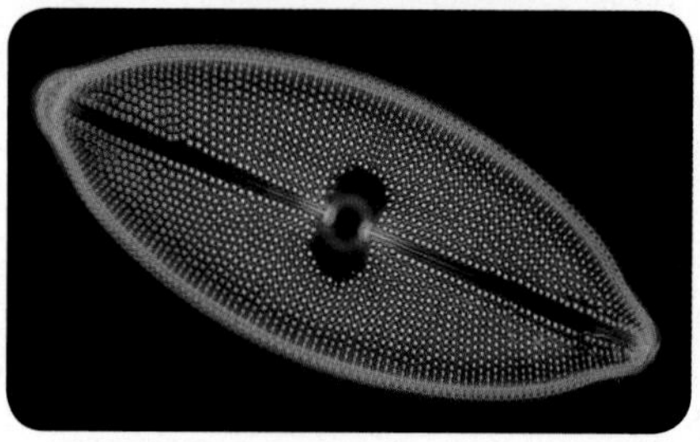

24. Where does this organism store its excess food?
    A. cellulose **C.** protein
    B. oil **D.** carbohydrate

25. Which are used in the human food supply?
    A. dinoflagellates **C.** protozoans
    B. euglenoids **D.** red algae

26. Which organism has silica walls?
    A. brown alga **C.** dinoflagellate
    B. diatom **D.** euglenoid

Use the illustration below to answer questions 27 and 28.

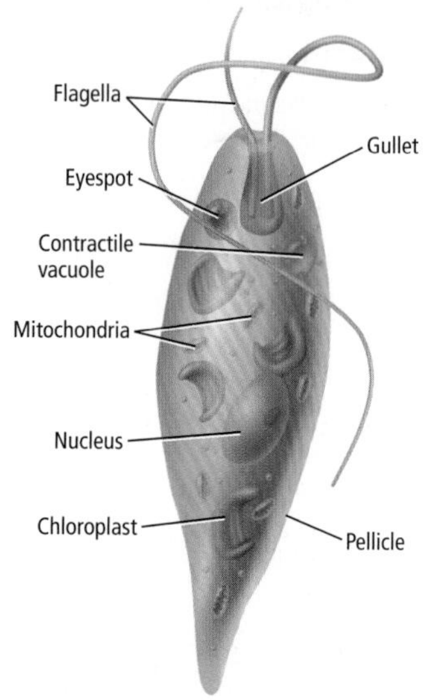

27. Which structures are used by the organism above for movement?
    A. cilia **C.** flagella
    B. contractile vacuoles **D.** pseudopods

28. Which structure is used to sense light?
    A. chloroplast **C.** nucleus
    B. eyespot **D.** pellicle

Constructed Response

29. **Open Ended** Why are there more fossils of diatoms, foraminiferans, and radiolarians than of other algae?

30. **Short Answer** Explain why diatoms must sometimes reproduce sexually.

31. **Short Answer** Explain the relationship between the sporophyte and gametophyte in alternation of generations.

Think Critically

32. **Analyze** the difference between freshwater algae and marine algae.

33. MAIN Idea Explain the effects of a marine parasite that kills all phytoplankton.

Section 4

Vocabulary Review

Replace the underlined words with the correct vocabulary term from the Study Guide page.

34. A motile organism that consists of many diploid nuclei but no separate cells is a protoplasm.

35. Starving amoeboid cells give off a chemical called arsenic.

Understand Main Ideas

36. Acellular slime molds have many nuclei, but which structure do they lack?
A. chromosomes
B. spores
C. separate cells
D. cilia

37. Which is present in the life cycle of water molds in a flagellated form?
A. nuclei
B. plasmodia
C. pseudopods
D. reproductive cells

Constructed Response

38. MAIN Idea Compare and contrast a water mold and a cellular slime mold.

39. **Open Ended** Describe some environmental conditions that might lead to the production of spores by an acellular slime mold.

Think Critically

40. **Analyze and Conclude** During the multinucleated plasmodial stage, could acellular slime molds be classified as multicellular organisms? Explain your reasoning.

Summative Assessment

41. BIG Idea If you were a taxonomist given the task of organizing protists into groups, would you use the same method described in this book? Explain your answer.

42. Choose one protist and imagine a new organelle or structure that is going to develop. How will this new condition affect the protist? Will this change increase or decrease the chance of survival?

43. Is it possible to describe the typical protist? Hypothesize why the organisms in Kingdom Protista are more diverse than the organisms in any of the other kingdoms.

44. WRITING in Biology Write a descriptive essay describing the types of environments where you would expect to find protists. Be sure to include details about biotic and abiotic factors in the environments.

DBQ Document-Based Questions

The text below describes a new detection method for finding microscopic organisms in water sources.

The protozoans *Giardia lamblia* and *Cryptosporidium parvom* are major causes of waterborne intestinal diseases throughout the world. A very sensitive detection method was developed using the DNA amplification procedure—polymerase chain reaction. This procedure can detect the presence of incredibly small amounts of these pathogens—as little as a single cell in two liters of water.

Data obtained from: Guy, et al. 2003. Real-time PCR for quantification of *Giarida* and *Cryptosporidium* in environmental water samples and sewage. *Applications of Environmental Biology* 2003 69(9): 5178-5185.

45. Explain how this detection method might be used by municipal water departments.

46. Analyze the significance of this research for global human health concerns, especially in remote regions of the world.

47. Predict how this detection method might be used to monitor the level of organisms that cause red tides.

33. Answers will vary. Eventually the rest of the ocean life would die because phytoplankton are the base of the food chain.

Section 4

Vocabulary Review

34. plasmodium
35. acrasin

Understand Main Ideas

36. C
37. D

Constructed Response

38. Possible answer: Water molds have threadlike masses that break down tissue and allow them to absorb nutrients through their cell walls. Cellular slime molds spend most of their life cycle as single amoeba-like cells that absorb nutrients through their cell walls.
39. Possible answer: drought or extreme hot or cold temperatures

Think Critically

40. No, because the plasmodium is composed of only one cell.

Summative Assessment

41. Answers will vary, but student methods should reflect an understanding of how protists are organized ecologically, as well as an awareness of the fact that protists might be organized in a phylogenetic way.

WRITING in Biology

RUBRIC Use the modifiable rubric found on your eTeacherEdition Online to assess writing assignments.

42. Students' selection of organelles should be based in science and supported by logical arguments.

43. Kingdom Protista includes all unicellular organisms that have a nucleus, which is a group of more than 200,000 known species. It is impossible to describe the "typical" protist.

44. Answers will vary. Descriptions should include information about biotic factors, such as plant life, and abiotic factors, such as moisture content and temperature. Protists usually are found in moist or aquatic environments.

DBQ Document-Based Questions

Guy, et al. 2003. Real-time PCR for quantification of *Giardia* and *Cryptosporidium* in environmental water samples and sewage. *Applied and Environmental Biology* 2003 69(9): 5178-5185.

45. A municipal water supply department can use this method to test for pathogens in the water supply.

46. This procedure can be used to test water supplies worldwide, including in developing countries, in order to prevent diseases.

47. This procedure could be used to test for the presence of dinoflagellates that cause red tides and would lead to an early alert system.

Assessment Online Test Practice

Standardized Test Practice

Multiple Choice

1. B 5. D
2. D 6. B
3. A 7. B
4. C 8. D

Short Answer

9. Parts are (1) flagella, (2) pili, (3) plasma membrane, (4) DNA or RNA, (5) cell wall, and (6) capsule. The flagella cause movement. Pili help attach cells to surfaces. The plasma membrane separates the contents of the cell from its surroundings. DNA or RNA is the genetic material. The cell wall is a protective structure that defines the shape of the cell. The capsule is a sticky protective coat.
10. Answers can vary. For example, a typical bacterium is surrounded by a thick protective wall that keeps it from getting crushed easily and allows it to resist changes in temperature and pressure.
11. You should wear safety goggles to protect your eyes, gloves for burn protection, and clothing protection to avoid stains and possible contact with hot liquids.
12. One possible answer is that fungi are heterotrophs and plants are autotrophs. Another answer is that fungi have chitin in cell walls and plants have cellulose. Other answers are possible.

Extended Response

13. Answers will vary. Answers might include interrupting the replication of HIV, breaking down the reverse transcriptase, or preventing the binding of HIV to white blood cells.

Standardized Test Practice

Cumulative

Multiple Choice

1. Which environment would likely have chemosynthetic autotrophic eubacteria?
   A. coral reef
   B. deep-ocean volcanic vent
   C. lake in the mountains
   D. soil near a spring

Use the diagram below to answer questions 2 and 3.

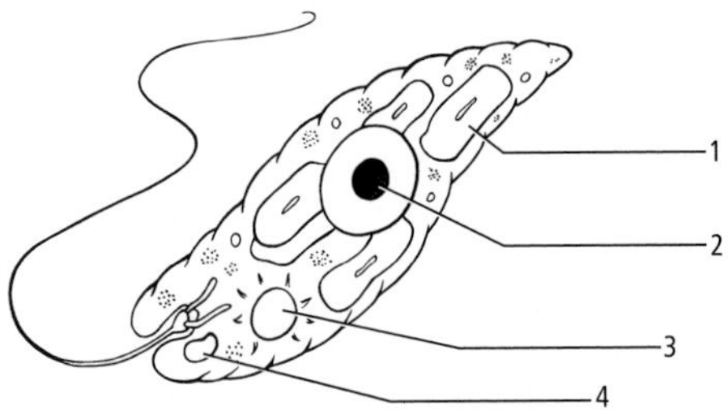

2. Which number represents the eyespot of the *Euglena?*
   A. 1
   B. 2
   C. 3
   D. 4

3. Which number represents an organelle that captures energy for the cell from sunlight?
   A. 1
   B. 2
   C. 3
   D. 4

4. Which do the two bats *Craseonycteris thonglongyai* and *Noctilio leporinus* have in common?
   A. division
   B. genus
   C. phylum
   D. species

5. Suppose you are investigating bone characteristics of two birds to determine how closely they are related in terms of phylogeny. Which type of evidence are you using?
   A. biochemical characters
   B. cellular characters
   C. chromosomal characters
   D. morphological characters

Use the diagram below to answer question 6.

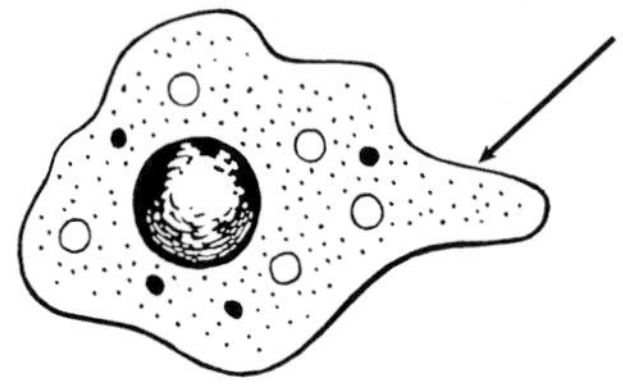

6. Members of the phylum Sarcodina use this structure for locomotion and which other activity?
   A. conjugation
   B. feeding
   C. protection
   D. reproduction

7. How do prions harm their host?
   A. by activating synthesis of viral RNA
   B. by causing normal proteins to mutate
   C. by deactivating part of the host's DNA
   D. by disrupting the way cells reproduce

8. Which could be a derived, rather than ancestral, character in one group of vertebrates?
   A. nervous system
   B. organized systems of tissues
   C. role of ATP in mitochondria
   D. wings used for flight

Short Answer

Use the diagram below to answer questions 9 and 10.

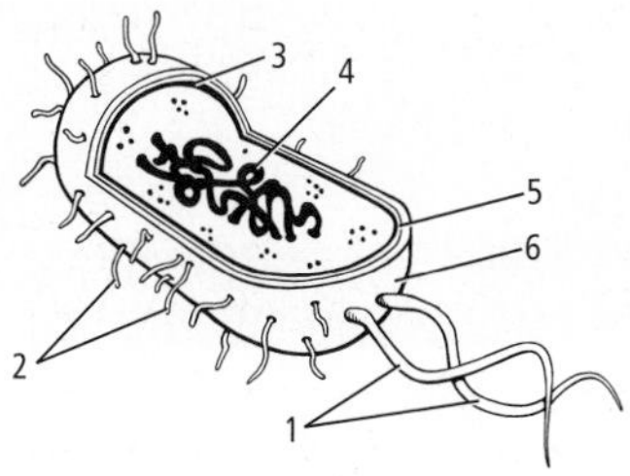

9. Name the parts of this bacterium and classify each part according to its function.

10. From the diagram, deduce how the structure of a typical bacterium enables it to survive in a harsh environment that frequently changes.

11. Imagine that you have been asked to do an experiment in which you boil different leaves and flower petals in different solutions to extract the pigments. State what safety equipment would be appropriate for your experiments and give reasoning for your choices.

12. Organisms in Kingdom Fungi and Kingdom Plantae used to be classified in the same kingdom. State a reason why they are now classified in different kingdoms.

13. Write a hypothesis about how the life cycle of a retrovirus, such as HIV, might be disrupted to slow or stop the reproduction of the virus.

Extended Response

Use the illustration below to answer question 14.

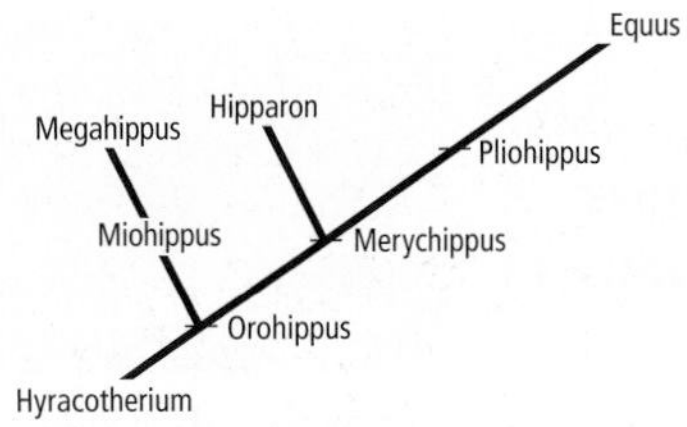

14. The figure above shows the evolution of horses, including the modern-day horse, *Equus.* Does this diagram support the idea of gradualism or of punctuated equilibrium? Explain your answer.

Essay Question

One challenge that people face is the presence of antibiotic-resistant bacteria. Antibiotics are used to treat many diseases. Generally, they improve the quality of life of people. However, the widespread use and misuse of antibiotics has created antibiotic-resistant bacteria. This means that some diseases caused by bacteria no longer can be cured with the same antibiotics. Doctors must use new and stronger antibiotics to cure the diseases. This gives bacteria an opportunity to develop a resistance to the new antibiotics. Unfortunately, antibiotic resistance in bacteria is spreading faster than new antibiotics are being developed.

Using the information in the paragraph above, answer the following question in essay format.

15. Evaluate how the characteristics of bacteria contribute to the rapid development of antibiotic-resistant bacteria.

NEED EXTRA HELP?															
If You Missed Question . . .	1	2	3	4	5	6	7	8	9	10	11	12	13	14	15
Review Section . . .	18.1	19.3	19.3	17.1	17.2	19.2	18.2	17.2	18.1	18.1	1.3	17.3	18.2	15.3	18.1

14. This diagram shows punctuated equilibrium. Different species of horses evolved at different times over millions of years. This was probably due to demands of the climate and environment. During the intervals between the appearance of new species, few evolutionary changes occurred.

Essay Question

15. Students should discuss how the rapid rate of reproduction, the exchanges of genetic material during sexual reproduction, and mutations contribute to bacteria quickly developing resistance to antibiotics.

Chapter 20 Organizer:
Fungi

LabManager™
Customize any lab with the LabManager™ CD-ROM.

Essential Questions	National Science Standards	Materials and Planning: Estimated times include cleanup and disposal, but do not include teacher prep time. For cleanup and disposal guidelines, see page 39T.	Est. Time (min)
Section 1 1. What are the major characteristics of organisms in Kingdom Fungi? 2. How do fungi obtain nutrients and how does that include their role as decomposers? 3. What are the three types of asexual reproduction in fungi?	UCP.1, UCP.2, UCP.5; A.1, A.2; C.1, C.4, C.5, C.6;	**Launch Lab,** p. 574: various samples of fungi	20
		Demonstration, p. 576: fungi specimens or photos of fungi	10
		Demonstration, p. 577: 2-L soda bottles (2), clear tape, needle, organic matter, soil	5 per week
		Demonstration, p. 578: dry yeast, clear dish, sugar, water, incubator	15
		MiniLab 1, p. 580: 250-mL Erlenmeyer flasks, water, sugar, dry yeast, glass rod	30
		Demonstration, p. 580: white mushroom, white paper, hair spray	5
Section 2 1. What are the four major phyla of fungi? 2. What are the distinguishing traits of each fungus phylum? 3. What are the reproductive strategies of each fungus phylum?	UCP.1–5; A.1, A.2; C.1, C.3, C.4, C.5, C.6; G.1, G.2, G.3	**Demonstration,** p. 582: illustrations of various fungi such as those in Beatrix Potter books	10
		Activity, p. 583: bread, spray bottle, water, petri dishes, magnifying lenses or microscopes	15
		MiniLab 2, p. 583: bread, spray bottle, water, self-sealing bag, salt, ruler	55
Section 3 1. What are the characteristics of lichens? 2. What are the characteristics of mycorrhizal relationships? 3. What are some beneficial and harmful effects that fungi can have on humans?	UCP.1–5; A.1, A.2; C.3, C.4, C.5, C.6; F.1, F.4, F.5; G.1, G.2, G.3	**Demonstration,** p. 590: petri dish, filter paper, ampicillin solution, plate of *E. coli*	15
		Activity, p. 590: fungal hyphae, spray bottle, water, NaCl solution, microscope	10
		Develop Concepts, p. 588: lichen sample, magnifying lens or microscope	10
		Design Your Own BioLab, p. 593: mold, plain powdered gelatin, bread, sugar, cotton swab, aluminum foil or plastic wrap, small cup, thermometer, graduated cylinder, spray bottle	110

Suggested Time for Each Lesson

Class	Chapter Opener	Section 1	Section 2	Section 3	Assessment
Basic	45 min	45 min	45 min	45 min	45 min
General	25 min	45 min	45 min	65 min	45 min
Honors	5 min	20 min	20 min	25 min	20 min

ConnectED

connectED.mcgraw-hill.com

Access interactive learning opportunities and teaching resources using these icons located throughout your StudentWorks™ Plus Online and eTeacherEdition Online.

Chapter 20 Section Resources	Additional Chapter 20 Resources	Technology
FAST FILE Unit 5 Resources: Launch Lab Worksheet* MiniLab Worksheet* Study Guide (English/Spanish)* Section Quick Check **Reading Essentials 20.1** **Science Notebook 20.1*** **FAST FILE Unit 5 Resources:** MiniLab Worksheet* Study Guide (English/Spanish)* Section Quick Check **Reading Essentials 20.2** **Science Notebook 20.2*** **FAST FILE Unit 5 Resources:** BioLab Worksheet* Study Guide (English/Spanish)* Section Quick Check **Reading Essentials 20.3** **Science Notebook 20.3***	**FAST FILE Unit 5 Resources:** Chapter Diagnostic Test Concept Mapping* Real-World Biology Enrichment Chapter Tests A, B, and C **Transparencies:** Bellringer Transparencies* Biology Concepts Transparencies* **Lab Resources:** Laboratory Manual* Probeware Lab Manual* Forensics Lab Manual* Pre-AP Lab Manual* Open Inquiry in Biology* Guided Inquiry in Biology*	**Teaching Tools:** eTeacherEdition Online Classroom Presentation Toolkit CD-ROM* LabManager™ CD-ROM* Video Lab DVD* Virtual Lab CD-ROM* What's BIOLOGY Got To Do With It? StudentWorks™ Plus Online* **Chapter Assessment Tools:** Classroom Presentation Toolkit CD-ROM* *ExamView® Assessment Suite* CD-ROM **Web-Based Resources:** • StudentWorks™ Plus Online • eTeacherEdition Online • Animations* • The Interactive Time Line* • Interactive Tables* • Online Quizzes • Online Test Practice • Standardized Test Practice • Virtual Labs* • Multilingual eGlossary* • Vocabulary eGames* • Vocabulary eFlashcards • WebQuests • Personal Tutors

While all resources listed are appropriate for English learners, the * indicates resources with a strong visual or hands-on component for EL.

Teaching strategies and activities have been coded for differentiated instruction.

AL Activities for students working above grade level	**OL** Activities for students working on grade level	**BL** Activities for students working below grade level	**EL** Activities for English learners (also ELL)	**COOP LEARN** Activities designed for small cooperative group work

CHAPTER 20

Launch Lab
What differences exist among fungi?

Inquiry Launch Lab

For a lab worksheet, use your eTeacherEdition Online.

RUBRIC A rubric for evaluating Launch Labs is found on your eTeacherEdition Online.

Est. Time 20 min

Safety Precautions Approve lab safety forms before work begins. Alert students not to inhale spores or particles from any of the samples. Find out if any students have mold allergies and allow those students to observe photos instead of samples.

Teaching Strategies

- Grocery stores typically carry several varieties of mushrooms. Samples can be found in moist, wooded areas or on decaying vegetation. Rotting produce or cheese can also yield interesting specimens.
- Students will recognize obvious physical differences among fungi. They might need help, however, in analyzing similarities among the samples they examine.

CHAPTER 20
Fungi

ConnectED

Your one-stop online resource
connectED.mcgraw-hill.com

- Video
- Audio
- Review
- Inquiry
- WebQuest
- Assessment
- Concepts in Motion
- Multilingual eGlossary

Launch Lab
What differences exist among fungi?

Fungi display enormous diversity. The organisms in this kingdom vary in size from a single cell to a fungus found in the Malheur National Forest that is 5.6 km wide! In this lab, you will observe some of the differences among fungi.

For a lab worksheet, use your StudentWorks™ Plus Online.

Inquiry Launch Lab

FOLDABLES®

Make a trifold book using the titles shown. Use it to organize your notes on fungi.

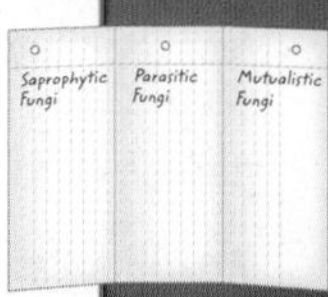

Procedure

1. Read and complete the lab safety form.
2. Create a data table to record your observations of the **fungi samples** provided by your teacher.
3. Study each fungus carefully. Wash your hands thoroughly after handling fungus.
4. Describe each fungus sample as completely as you can. Include properties like color, shape, size, and growth medium.
5. Dispose of fungi and clean your work station according to your teacher's instructions.

Analysis

1. **Contrast** What physical characteristics varied most among your samples? Fungi probably varied in size, color, odor, physical structure, and nutrient source.
2. **Compare** any similarities you observed or can infer among the fungi you examined. Possible answer: Most fungi seem to produce a powdery substance (spores) and be made of filaments.

THEME FOCUS Energy
Fungi obtain energy in three ways.

BIG Idea The Kingdom Fungi is made up of four phyla based on unique structures, methods of nutrition, and methods of reproduction.

Section 1 • Introduction to Fungi
Section 2 • Diversity of Fungi
Section 3 • Ecology of Fungi

Introduce the Chapter

Types of Fungi

ASK STUDENTS: ***What do you think of when you hear the term fungus?*** possible answer: mushrooms Although mushrooms are indeed fungi, there are many other types of fungi and *Pilobolus* is one interesting example.

BIG Idea

Collect Provide students with natural history, outdoor, or cooking magazines. Instruct them to collect pictures of fungi growing in different habitats such as on food, on logs, in soil, and as part of lichens. Have the students look closely at the pictures. **ASK STUDENTS:** ***How are the fungi in these areas different from one another?*** Answers will vary depending on pictures. ***What are some characteristics these fungi might share?*** They are all decomposers, they have chitin in their cell walls, and they are composed of cells. Students will learn about many different common characteristics of fungi as well as the characteristics that make them such a diverse group.

THEMES

Scientific Inquiry The discovery of *Penicillium notatum* as a source of penicillin resulted in new medicines.

Diversity Fungi are diverse and vary based on physical characteristics, method of nutrition, and method of reproduction.

Energy Fungi obtain energy by decomposing organic material and absorbing the nutrients.

Homeostasis Mycorrhizae increase a plant's ability to absorb water and nutrients, contributing to the homeostasis of plant cells.

Change Some fungi change in appearance and chromosome number throughout their life cycles.

Section 1

MAIN Idea

BL OL AL

Fungi Characteristics

ASK STUDENTS: ***How have you encountered fungi?*** Possible answers: mold on bread, athlete's foot or ringworm, food such as truffles or mushrooms ***What do you think are some common characteristics of fungi?*** Write students' answers on the board. Possible answers: heterotrophic, some are parasitic, often reproduce using spores, multicellular, etc.

R Reading Strategy

BL OL Anticipation Guide

Before students read the text, have them copy the list of fungi characteristics they generated during the Main Idea discussion. As they read the section, have them circle the characteristics that are common to all fungi. Encourage students to consider if any of the listed characteristics not found in the text might be valid characteristics.

Reading Strategy

EL BL Build Vocabulary Have students record this section's new vocabulary terms on a sheet of paper. As they work through the section, have them place each new term under one or more of the following categories: *structure, nutrition,* or *reproduction.* Structure: chitin, hypha, mycelium, fruiting body, septum, haustorium; nutrition: septum, haustorium; reproduction: fruiting body, spore, sporangium

Section 1

Reading Preview

Essential Questions

- What are the major characteristics of organisms in Kingdom Fungi?
- How do fungi obtain nutrients and how does that include their role as decomposers?
- What are the three types of asexual reproduction in fungi?

Review Vocabulary

decomposer: an organism that feeds on and breaks down dead organisms, recycling nutrients back into food webs

New Vocabulary

chitin
hypha
mycelium
fruiting body
septum
haustorium
spore
sporangium

g Multilingual eGlossary

Introduction to Fungi

R MAIN Idea Fungi are unicellular or multicellular eukaryotic heterotrophs that are decomposers.

Real-World Reading Link When you listen to the radio, how is it that you can always identify your favorite group? Maybe it is by the common characteristics of the band, such as their instruments or the lead singer's voice. Organisms in the same kingdom also share common, identifying characteristics.

Characteristics of Fungi

Some of the largest and oldest organisms on Earth belong to Kingdom Fungi. When you see the word *fungi* (FUN ji) (singular, fungus), you might envision the mushrooms found in grocery stores or ones that grow in your backyard. In eastern Oregon, there is a honey mushroom that is so big that it is called the "Humongous Fungus." The honey mushroom, similar to the one shown in **Figure 1,** is estimated to be at least 2400 years old. All fungi are eukaryotic heterotrophs. More than 100,000 species of fungi have been identified.

Multicellular fungi Most members of Kingdom Fungi, such as the honey mushroom, are multicellular. At first glance, you might think that these multicellular fungi look like plants. Although they do not contain chloroplasts, at one time fungi were classified as plants because they appeared to have some characteristics similar to plants. However, after careful study, scientists decided that fungi are different enough to be placed in their own kingdom.

Unicellular fungi Yeasts are unicellular fungi. They are found throughout the world in soils, on plant surfaces, and even in the human body. While there are hundreds of different kinds of yeasts, the most familiar yeasts are used commercially to produce breads, beer, and wine. The yeast *Candida albicans,* shown in **Figure 1,** can cause a yeast infection in humans.

Figure 1 Most fungi are multicellular, such as this honey mushroom growing on a tree. Some fungi are unicellular, such as this yeast colony called *Candida albicans.*

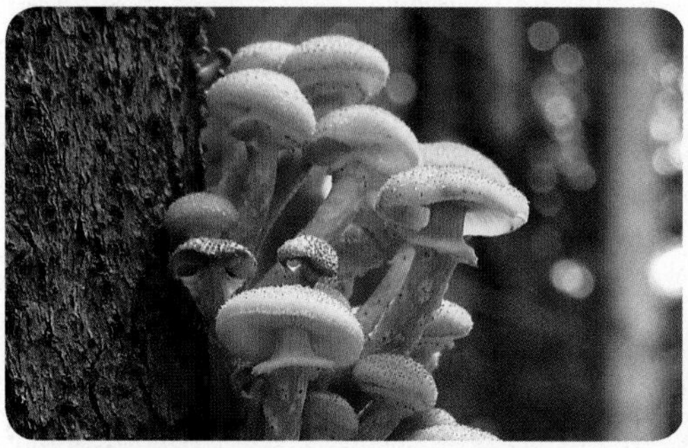

Honey mushroom

Color-Enhanced SEM Magnification: 1250×

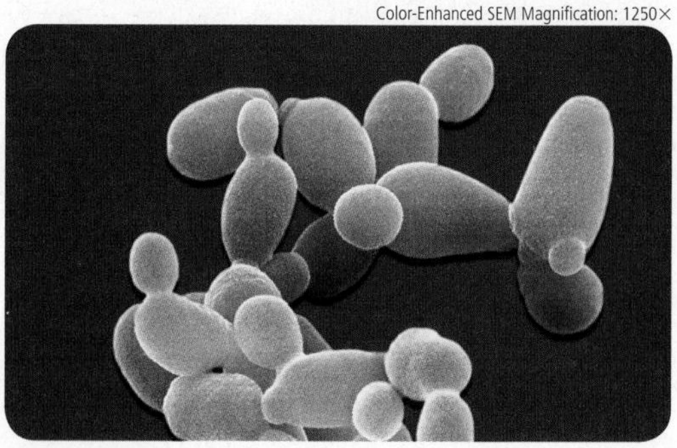

Colony of *Candida albicans*

Demonstration

OL AL Fungi Show students fungi specimens, such as yeast, mushrooms, bread mold, mold on fruit, or show them a collection of pictures of different fungi. If any students are allergic to molds, show photographs of molds instead of actual specimens.
ASK STUDENTS: ***How do fungi obtain nutrients?*** If some of the samples are green or greenish blue, some students might predict that the organisms are autotrophic. The students learned in Chapters 2 and 17 that fungi are heterotrophic decomposers. Est time: 10 min

D Major Features in Fungi

Some features that distinguish fungi from plants include their cell walls, their hyphae, and their cross walls.

Cell walls One significant difference between plants and fungi is the composition of their cell walls. Plants have cell walls composed of cellulose, while fungi have cell walls composed of chitin. **Chitin** (KI tun) is a strong, flexible polysaccharide that is found in the cell walls of all fungi and in the exoskeletons of insects and crustaceans. Recall that polysaccharides are carbohydrate polymers that are composed of many simple sugar subunits. Chitin is one of the most abundant organic compounds on Earth.

Hyphae The physical structure of fungi also differs from plants. Look at the magnified image of the fungus in **Figure 2** and notice that it is composed of long chains of cells. Without a microscope, they appear to be threadlike filaments. These filaments are the basic structural units that make up the body of a multicellular fungus and are called **hyphae** (HI fee) (singular, hypha). Hyphae grow at their tips and branch repeatedly to form a netlike mass called a **mycelium** (mi SEE lee um) (plural, mycelia). While the mycelium is visible in some fungi, it is packed so tightly in mushrooms that it is almost impossible to distinguish the individual hyphae. The fungus that you see above ground, illustrated in **Figure 2,** is a reproductive structure called the **fruiting body.** The hyphae form all parts of the mushroom, including the fruiting body above ground and the mycelium below ground. The extensive hyphae of fungi give them an advantage in obtaining nutrients by providing a large surface area for nutrient absorption.

Reading Check **Describe** the structural unit of a mushroom.

Connection to History Fungal hyphae are found in the works of many medieval painters. Victorian illustrators often linked fairies and toadstools (another name for mushrooms). Today, the colorful spotted cap of a *Fly Agaric* mushroom often is associated with a gnome or sprite in children's stories.

VOCABULARY
WORD ORIGIN
Hypha
comes from the Greek word *hyphos*, meaning *web*

■ **Figure 2**
Left: The visible body and underground structure of a multicellular fungus are made up of long chains of cells called hyphae.
Right: A multicellular fungus consists of an above-ground fruiting body and a below-ground mycelium.
Infer *What are the advantages of a fungus having a filamentous body?*

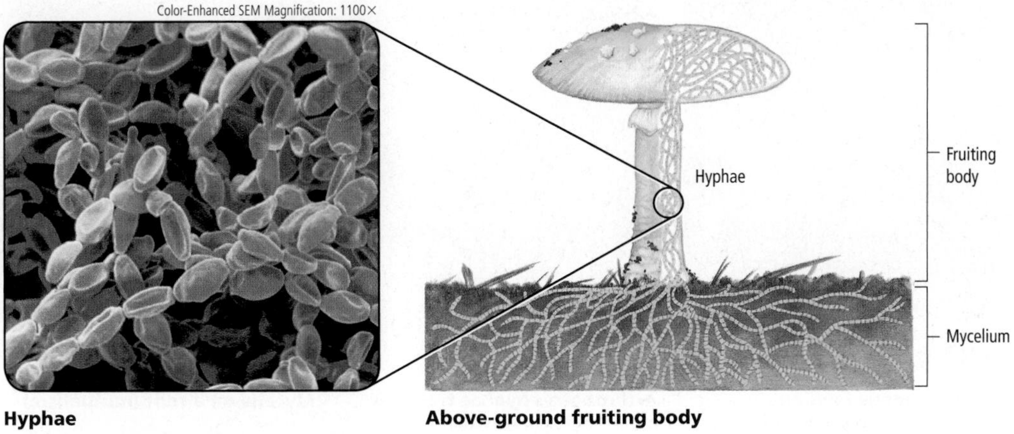

D Develop Concepts

OL AL

Clarify a Misconception

ASK STUDENTS: ***Is a fungus a type of plant?*** No; Fungi are not plants, but some students might say yes. Ask the following question of students who say yes: ***What characteristics of fungi make you think they are plants?*** Answers will vary but could include that they grow outdoors and need sunlight. Tell students that fungi do not need sunlight to get their food. Only lichens need sunlight because of the cyanobacteria that live in the fungi. Ask the following question of students who say no: ***What characteristics of fungi make you think they are not plants?*** Answers will vary but could include that fungi body structures are unlike those of plants. Write student answers on the board and have a discussion with students about which of their ideas are misconceptions.

Develop Concepts

OL AL

Activate Prior Knowledge

ASK STUDENTS: ***What is a polymer?*** large molecule composed of repeating subunits ***What are some common carbohydrate polymers found in living things?*** starch, cellulose, and other large carbohydrates

■ **Caption Question** **Fig. 2** The extensive hyphae of fungi, which form long filaments, give fungi an advantage in obtaining nutrients by providing a large surface area for nutrient absorption.

Reading Check A mushroom is composed of tightly packed hyphae.

Demonstration

Compost Column Cut off the tops of two 2-L soda bottles. Cut off the bottom of one bottle. Use clear tape to attach the bottomless bottle to the other bottle. The bottles should now be joined to form a tall column. Poke several small holes into the sides of the column with a needle. Fill the column with leaves and other organic matter. (Do not include dairy products, meats, or other items high in protein.) Add about 5 cm of soil on top and keep well moistened. Do not store in direct sunlight. Have students observe the changes that occur each week. Est. time: 5 min per week

C Critical Thinking

AL Infer

ASK STUDENTS: ***Why does the rapid movement of materials through the pores in cross-walls or through the aseptate hyphae result in the hyphae growing so rapidly?*** Cells need a constant supply of raw materials and energy to grow. The rapid movement of materials through the hyphae provides a constant supply of needed materials for cell growth.

S Skill Practice

OL Visual Literacy Have students make three-dimensional models of septate and aseptate hyphae using Figure 3 as a guide. Provide straws, plastic tubing, or waxed yarn for students to use.

S Skill Practice

BL Compare and Contrast

Have students compare and contrast the methods of obtaining nutrients used by humans and fungi. Humans ingest their food and then digest it. Fungi digest and then ingest. Both use enzymes to break down organic material.

FOLDABLES®

✻RUBRIC A rubric for evaluating Foldables is found on your eTeacherEdition Online.

Going Further On the back of their Foldable, have students research and describe one example of each of the three types of fungi they wrote on the front tabs.

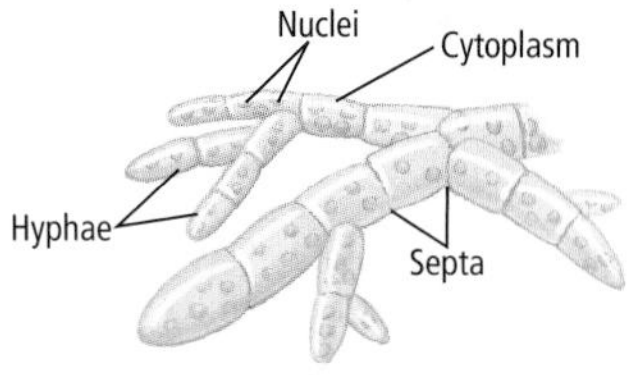

Septate Hyphae

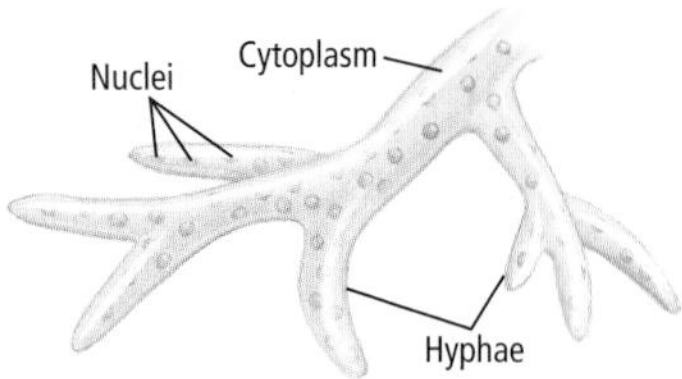

Aseptate Hyphae

■ **Figure 3**
Top: Some fungi have hyphae that are divided by cross walls called septa.
Bottom: Other fungi do not have hyphae with septa.

S

Cross walls In many fungi, hyphae are divided into cells by cross walls called **septa** (singular, septum), as shown in **Figure 3.** The septa have large pores that allow nutrients, cytoplasm, organelles, and, in some cases, nuclei to flow between cells.

Some fungi are aseptate, meaning that they have no septa. The cytoplasm, containing hundreds or thousands of nuclei, flows freely through the hyphae. This condition is a result of repeated mitosis without cytokinesis. Nutrients and other materials flow very quickly through aseptate hyphae. C

Nutrition in Fungi

Unlike humans, who ingest their food and then digest it, fungi digest their food before they ingest it. Many fungi produce enzymes that break down organic material, allowing the nutrients to be absorbed through their thin cell walls. All fungi are heterotrophs, but there are three types of fungi that differ in how they obtain their nutrients.

Saprophytic fungi A saprobe is an organism that feeds on dead organisms or organic wastes. Saprophytic fungi, such as the bracket fungus shown in **Figure 4,** are decomposers and recycle nutrients from dead organisms back into food webs. The fungus in **Figure 5** also is a saprobe.

Parasitic fungi Parasitic fungi absorb nutrients from the living cells of another organism, called a host. Many parasitic fungi produce specialized hyphae called **haustoria** (haws TOH ree ah), which grow into the host's tissues and absorb their nutrients. *Arthrobotrys* is a group of parasitic soil fungi that trap prey with rings of hyphae.

Mutualistic fungi Some fungi live in a mutualistic relationship with another organism, such as a plant or an alga. The mycelia of a particular fungus cover the root of a soybean plant. The fungus receives sugar from the host plant. The mycelia increase water uptake and mineral absorption for the host plant. S

■ **Figure 4** Fungi can obtain food in one of three different ways: through decomposition, through parasitism, and through mutualism.

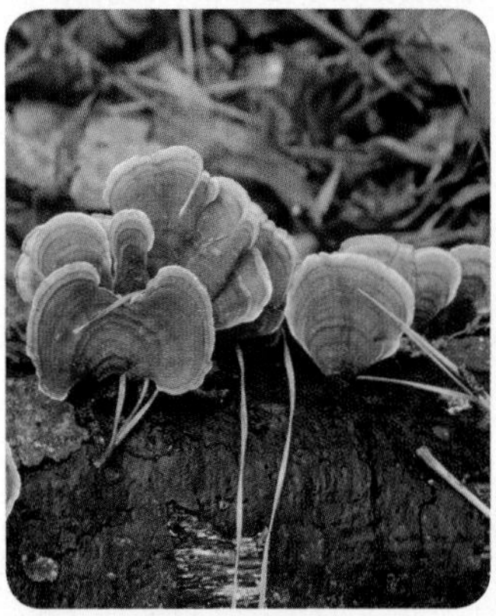

Bracket fungus feeding on a log (decomposition)

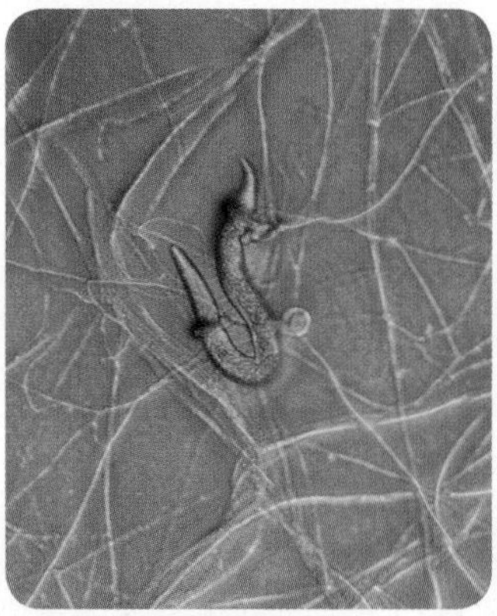

***Arthrobotrys* hyphae trapping a nematode (parasitism)**

Color-Enhanced SEM Magnification: 150×

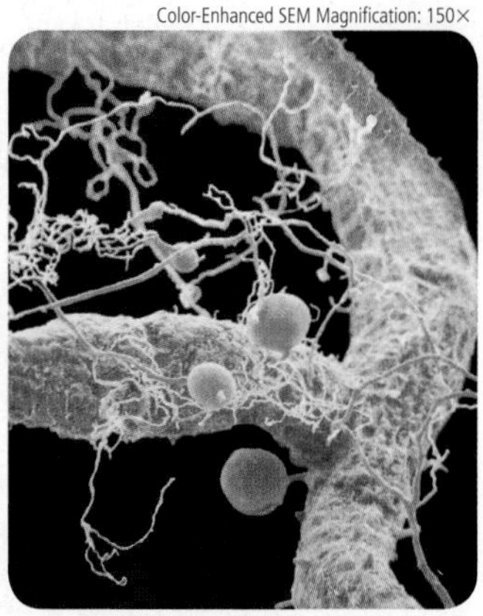

Mycelia on a root (mutualism)

Demonstration

BL OL AL Yeast Show students some dry yeast in a clear dish.
ASK STUDENTS: ***Is it alive?*** Answers will vary. Mix the yeast with sugar and water and incubate in a warm place (around 25°C). Add 5–10 g of yeast and 10 g of sugar to 200 mL of water. ***What do you think will happen?*** Answers will vary, but some students might suggest that it will start to bubble or grow. After 20–30 min, the mixture will start to bubble. ***What is happening?*** The yeast is metabolizing the sugar and releasing carbon dioxide. ***What will most likely happen when the sugar runs out?*** The yeast will stop metabolizing the sugar, no more carbon dioxide will be produced, the yeast will die, carbon dioxide will diffuse out of the mixture, and then the mixture will collapse. Est time: 15 min

Visualizing a Fairy Ring

Figure 5

Fungi produce spores in reproductive structures called *fruiting bodies*. A fruiting body is made up of hyphae that grow outward by extending their lengths, growing into new areas where a fresh supply of nutrients can be found in the soil. This creates a ring of mushrooms called a fairy ring.

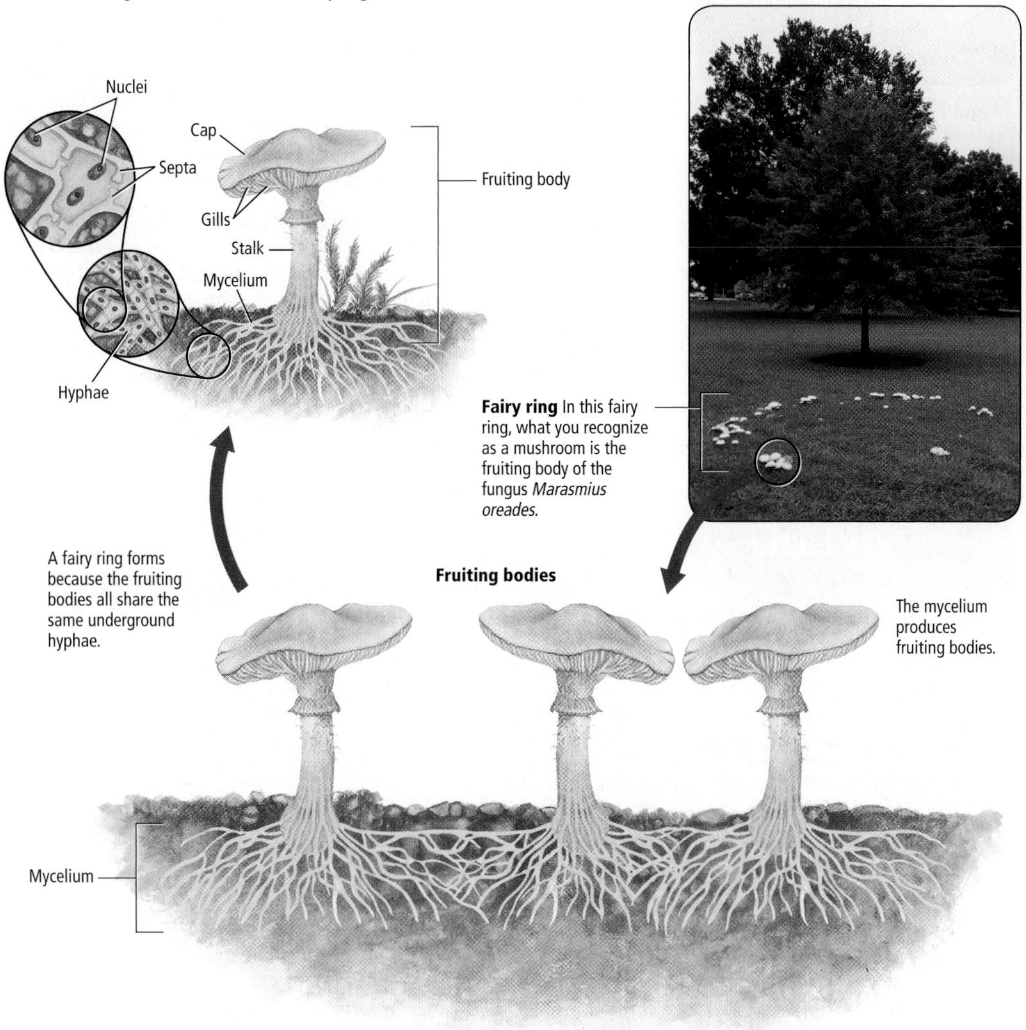

Nuclei
Cap
Septa
Gills
Stalk
Mycelium
Hyphae
Fruiting body
Fairy ring In this fairy ring, what you recognize as a mushroom is the fruiting body of the fungus *Marasmius oreades*.
A fairy ring forms because the fruiting bodies all share the same underground hyphae.
Fruiting bodies
The mycelium produces fruiting bodies.
Mycelium

Concepts in Motion Animation

Visualizing a Fairy Ring

Purpose

Students will visualize the internal structure of a common fungus and understand its life cycle. UCP.5, C.5

Reading Strategy

OL COOP LEARN

Supplemental Reading Divide the class into three groups. Have one group research *Marasmius oreades,* have the second group research other fungi that form similar structures, and have the last group research myths about fairy rings. Each group should work together to prepare a short presentation to the class.

Develop Concepts

BL OL **Integrate Health** Warn students that not all mushrooms are edible. In fact, many of them are poisonous. Caution students that they should never eat mushrooms unless they have been purchased from a reliable source or collected by a trained mycologist. AL Have students research mushrooms indigenous to the local area. Ask students to prepare a list of characteristics and photos, including which are edible or poisonous.

Concepts in Motion Animation

Content Background

Teacher FYI Arthrobotrys fungi commonly are found in soil and decaying plant material. The fungus captures nematodes with several different devices, but the most common are constricting rings and sticky networks of hyphal loops. When the nematode happens to enter one of the rings in search of bacteria and other food particles, the ring constricts. This constriction is caused by the swelling of the cells of the ring and can be so forceful it can almost cut the nematode in half. The sticky loops have a gluelike substance that holds the nematode. Once the nematodes are trapped, the hyphae grows into the worm and digests it. Soon after digesting a nematode, the fungus reproduces by forming clusters of asexual spores called conidia.

S Skill Practice

BL OL AL Make a Table Have students make a table with two columns—one for asexual reproduction and one for sexual reproduction. As they read about fungi reproduction, have them fill in a description of the different strategies for asexual and sexual reproduction.

Caption Question Fig. 6 asexual, budding

MiniLab 1

Inquiry MiniLab

For a lab worksheet, use your eTeacherEdition Online.

RUBRIC A rubric for evaluating MiniLabs is found on your eTeacherEdition Online.

Est. Time 30 min

Safety Precaution Approve lab safety forms before work begins.

Teaching Strategy Students will observe the production of foam at the top of the flasks containing sugar. Explain that the foam contains yeast cells that produce gases as they consume sugar and multiply. The greater the foam, the greater the yeast activity and the more yeast present.

Cleanup and Disposal Designate an area for the collection and disposal of yeast.

Analysis

1. The greater the availability of sugar, the greater the yeast reproduction.
2. Yeast can obtain energy through anaerobic respiration, so though growth may slow, the yeast would not die until the sugar ran out.

LabManager™
Customize this lab with the LabManager™ CD-ROM.

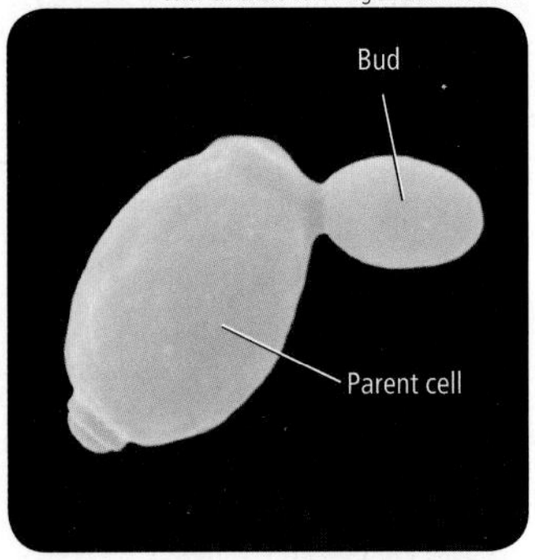

Figure 6 Notice how the plasma membrane is begining to separate the bud from the parent cell.
Identify *what type of reproduction is shown.*

Inquiry Video Lab

S Reproduction in Fungi

Fungi are classified by their structure and patterns of reproduction. Some fungi can reproduce only asexually through mitosis. Asexual reproduction in fungi also includes fragmentation, budding, and spore production. Many fungi can reproduce both asexually and sexually. Sexually reproducing fungi produce spores by the process of meiosis.

Budding Unicellular yeast cells reproduce asexually by budding. As shown in **Figure 6,** the new cell develops while attached to the parent cell. The plasma membrane pinches off to partially separate the new individual from the parent cell.

Fragmentation Fragmentation is a form of asexual reproduction that occurs when the mycelium of a fungus is physically broken apart, or fragmented. This can occur in a number of different ways. One example is by an animal digging in the soil where a fungus is growing. If the fragments of mycelia land in a location with suitable growing conditions, the hyphae will grow into new mycelia.

Spore production Most fungi are able to reproduce sexually and asexually by producing spores. A **spore** is a haploid reproductive cell with a hard outer coat. Spores develop into a new organism without the fusion of gametes. When one of these microscopic spores lands in suitable conditions, it generates haploid hyphae. These hyphae can fuse with the hyphae of other compatible fungi to become diploid. The diploid hyphae can then produce fruiting bodies that will produce zygotes. The zygotes go through meiosis to produce haploid spores, and the cycle repeats.

MiniLab 1

Inquiry MiniLab

Examine Yeast Growth

What is the relationship between yeast reproduction and the availability of food? Yeasts are unicellular fungi. These organisms feed on sugars, producing carbon dioxide and ethyl alcohol in the process. Yeasts reproduce asexually and multiply quickly under optimal growth conditions.

Procedure

1. Read and complete the lab safety form.
2. Label four **250-mL Erlenmeyer flasks** 1–4.
3. Create a data table to record your results.
4. Add **100 mL warm water** to each flask, and do not cover the flasks.
5. Add 0.0 g, 0.5 g, 1.0 g, or 1.5 g of **table sugar** to each one of the flasks.
6. Add one packet of **dry yeast** to each flask. Stir the contents of the flasks with a **glass rod** until the contents are thoroughly mixed.
7. Observe and record the changes in the flasks every five minutes for 20 minutes.
8. Clean up your work station according to your teacher's instructions.

Analysis

1. **Conclude** What is the relationship between yeast reproduction and the availability of sugar?
2. **Analyze** How might your results have changed if the flasks had been covered during your experiment?

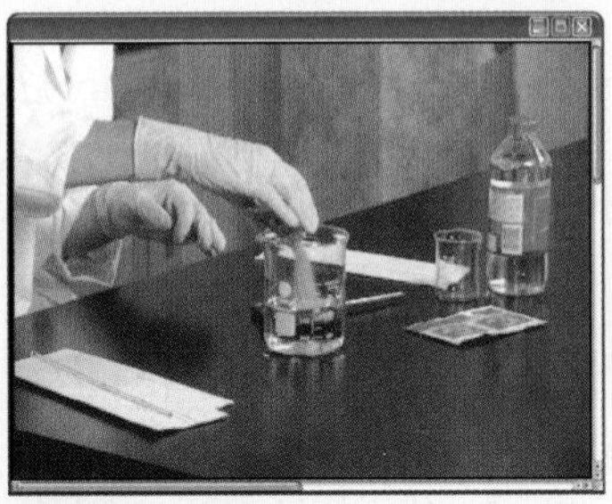

Inquiry Video Lab In this lab, students will view how temperature affects yeast metabolism.

Demonstration

Spore Print Make a spore print by cutting the cap off of a white mushroom. Leave it gill side down on a piece of white paper for several days. The spores released by the gills will create a pattern. Spray the print with hair spray. Label the structures that you can see. Est. time: 5 min

Adaptations for survival Most fungi, like the puffball fungi shown in **Figure 7,** produce trillions of spores. Producing such large quantities of spores is an adaptation for survival. This adaptation ensures that at least a small percentage of the spores will land in suitable locations and begin to grow, producing the next generation.

Additional adaptations for survival include the physical traits of the spores. They are so small and lightweight that wind and even the smallest animals, such as insects, can disperse them. A spore also is protected by its cell wall. This wall often is tough and waterproof, which allows the spore to survive extremes of temperature and moisture.

Examine **Figure 7** again to see the cloud of spores being released. When spores are dispersed by wind, the spores can travel hundreds of miles across land and water. In fact, fungal spores can be found almost everywhere.

Figure 7 Puffball fungi can produce trillions of spores. The slight touch of an animal brushing against the fungus or a falling raindrop can trigger the release of spores.

Sporophores The fruiting body of a spore-forming fungus is called a sporophore (SPOH ruh for) and is characteristic of that species of fungus. The classification of a fungus is based primarily on the type of sporophore that it produces. For example, in some primitive fungi, such as black bread mold, specialized hyphae called sporangiophores (spuh RAN jee uh forz) have a spore-containing structure called a sporangium (plural, sporangia) on each of their tips. A **sporangium** is a sac or case in which spores are produced. The sporangia provide protection for the spores, preventing them from drying out prematurely.

In Section 2, you will learn that some fungi have common names such as sac fungi and club fungi. These names are descriptive for the type of sporophores that these fungi produce. Section 2 also contains information about the life cycles and the types of spores and sporophores produced by members of each of the major phyla of fungi.

Section 1 Assessment

Section Summary

- Fungi produce hyphae that form a netlike mass called a mycelium.
- There are three different methods by which fungi obtain food.
- Fungi can reproduce asexually by budding, fragmentation, or producing spores.
- Most fungi can reproduce sexually, also by producing spores.

Understand Main Ideas

1. MAIN Idea **Name** three major characteristics of Kingdom Fungi.
2. **Diagram** the difference between septate and aseptate hyphae.
3. **State** how fungi feeding differs from animal feeding.
4. **Contrast** the methods that parasitic, saprophytic, and mutualistic fungi use to obtain food.
5. **Explain** three methods of asexual reproduction in fungi.

Think Critically

6. **Predict** how a slice of bread that is left out on a table for a few weeks can become covered with bread mold. From where does the mold come?

WRITING in **Biology**

7. Fungi can be used as a biocontrol to control common insect pests. Research and write an article for a gardening magazine about the value of fungi in your garden. Include several examples of fungi used in gardens.

Writing Support

OL Creative Writing Have students write a short story or poem about the trials and tribulations of a fungal spore looking for a good spot to start a new life. Stories and poems will vary. Make sure students' accounts are scientifically accurate.

Formative Assessment

Evaluation

ASK STUDENTS: ***How do fungi get their nutrients?*** Fungi produce digestive enzymes that break down organic material and absorb the nutrients. Fungi can obtain their nutrients from three sources—dead organisms, parasitic relationships, and mutualistic relationships.

Remediation Divide students into groups of three and have them read and discuss the paragraph about nutrients. Encourage each member of the group to explain aloud one source of nutrients.

Section 1 Assessment

1. Fungi are unicellular or multicellular, are heterotrophs, have bodies composed of hyphae, and have cell walls composed of chitin.
2. Diagrams should resemble Figure 3.
3. Fungi digest their food before ingesting it; animals usually ingest then digest.
4. Parasitic fungi absorb nutrients from the host organism. Saprophytic fungi feed on wastes or dead organic matter. Mutualistic fungi live in a symbiotic relationship with another organism such as cyanobacteria or algae.
5. budding–a new parent cell develops while attached to the parent cell; fragmentation–mycelium is fragmented and dispersed, the fragments grow into new mycelia; spore production–reproductive haploid cells produce spores which can be spread
6. Possible answer: Mold spores in the air can land on the bread. The spores will grow into mycelia, which will absorb nutrients from the bread.
7. Articles will vary. Articles should point out that several types of fungi could potentially be used as insecticides, and some are commercially available in sprays and powders.

Assessment Online Quiz

Section 2

MAIN Idea

BL OL AL Diversity
ASK STUDENTS: ***How many different ways could garden flowers be organized into groups?*** Students might suggest organizing based on some of the following characteristics: color, height, bloom time, number of petals, or flower size. Inform students that just as they see diversity among flowers, diversity is also true of the fungi kingdom. Each fungus species exhibits many different characteristics.

Reading Strategy

BL Build Vocabulary Point out to students that the first two vocabulary terms (stolon and rhizoid) are types of hyphae. The rest of the new vocabulary terms refer to reproductive structures.

C Critical Thinking

OL Evaluate Have students evaluate the phylogenetic tree in Figure 8 and determine which fungi are most closely related to Ascomycota. Basidiomycota fungi
AL ASK STUDENTS: ***What might have caused the different fungal groups to diversify?*** Possible answers: climatic changes in certain regions, reproductive isolation, establishment of niches, genetic variation, or genetic mutation

GOING GREEN For MiniLab 2, ask students to bring from home two clear discarded jars with lids. Have them cut slices of bread to fit the jars, then follow the lab procedure. Emphasize that using glass jars instead of plastic bags reduces landfill waste.

Section 2

Reading Preview

Essential Questions

- What are the four major phyla of fungi?
- What are the distinguishing traits of each fungus phylum?
- What are the reproductive strategies of each fungus phylum?

Review Vocabulary

flagellated: having projections that propel organisms with a whiplike motion

New Vocabulary

stolon
rhizoid
gametangium
conidiophore
ascocarp
ascus
ascospore
basidiocarp
basidium
basidiospore

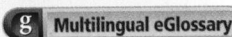

g Multilingual eGlossary

C

Diversity of Fungi

MAIN Idea Fungi exhibit a broad range of diversity and are classified into four major phyla.

Real-World Reading Link Think of the many sizes, shapes, and colors of insects that you might have seen. While they are all insects, they are very diverse. Within Kingdom Fungi, there is also much diversity in structures and life cycles.

Classification of Fungi

Biologists use fungal structure and methods of reproduction to divide fungi into four major phyla—Chytridiomycota, Zygomycota, Ascomycota, and Basidiomycota. The cladogram shown in **Figure 8** shows the evolutionary relationships among the phyla of fungi as they currently are understood.

Fungi are likely to have colonized land with plants more than 450 million years ago, possibly as a result of mutualistic associations with plants. Yet, molecular evidence supports the view that fungi are more closely related to animals than to plants. Evidence suggests that fungi and animals diverged from a common protist ancestor.

Chytrids

The fungi in the phylum Chytridiomycota (ki TRIHD ee oh mi koh tuh) often are referred to as chytrids (KI trihdz). Some chytrids are saprophytes, whereas others parasitize protists, plants, and animals. Most chytrids are aquatic, and they are unique among fungi because they produce flagellated spores. For this reason, scientists originally grouped chytrids with protists.

Chytrids, like the one in **Figure 8,** have been reclassified as new information about them has become available. Recent molecular evidence suggests that chytrids are related more closely to fungi than to protists because of similar protein and DNA sequences. Another characteristic that indicates a close relationship with fungi is chitin-containing cell walls. There is evidence that chytrids were perhaps the first fungi and are the evolutionary link between funguslike protists and fungi.

■ **Figure 8** **Left:** This phylogenetic tree shows the evolutionary relationships of the phyla of fungi. **Right:** This chytrid is more similar to fungi than to protists.

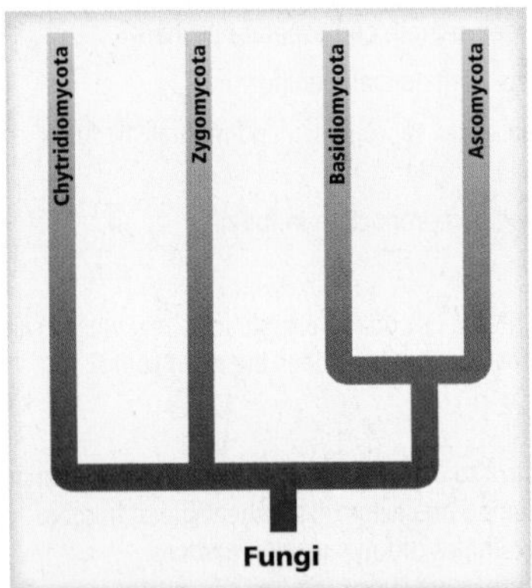

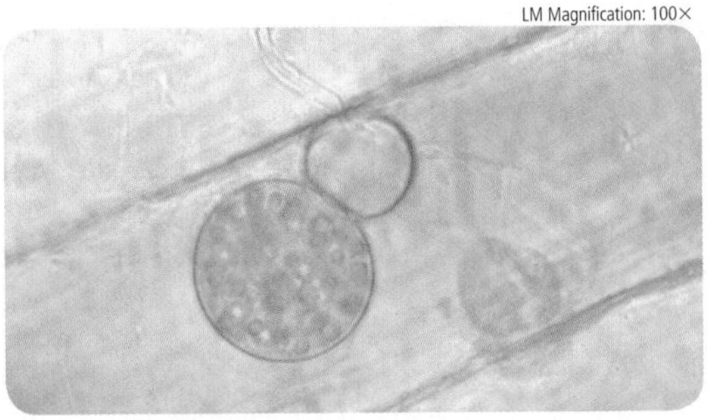

Chytrid

Demonstration

OL Illustrations Find examples of art that contain pictures of various fungi. Beatrix Potter is one children's book author that used many mushrooms in her illustrations. **ASK STUDENTS:** ***Are the drawings scientifically accurate?*** Answers will depend on the illustrations. Students should use their knowledge of fungi structure to answer this question. Est. time: 10 min

Common Molds

The most familiar member of the phylum Zygomycota (zi goh mi KOH tuh) is a common mold that grows on bread and other foods called *Rhizopus stolonifer.* Common molds are mostly terrestrial, and some live in mutualistic relationships with plants. Molds form a type of hyphae called **stolons** (STOH lunz) that spread across the surface of food. Another type of hyphae, called **rhizoids** (RIH zoydz), penetrates the food and absorbs nutrients, as shown in **Figure 9.** Other functions of rhizoids include anchoring the mycelium and producing digestive enzymes. Zygomycetes also can be found on decaying plant and animal material.

Life cycle Zygomycetes reproduce both asexually and sexually, as illustrated in **Figure 9.** Asexual reproduction occurs when sporangia form at the tips of upright hyphae called sporangiophores. Within each sporangium are thousands of haploid spores that can be spread by wind or other air movements. When released, spores will produce new hyphae if they land in a favorable environment.

If conditions in the environment are no longer favorable to sustain life, zygomycetes can reproduce sexually. There are no defined male and female fungi, but rather plus (+) and minus (–) mating strains. Haploid hyphae from two compatible mating strains—one plus and one minus—fuse. Each hypha produces a **gametangium** (ga muh TAN jee um) (plural, gametangia), which is a reproductive structure that contains a haploid nucleus. As shown in **Figure 9,** the two haploid nuclei from each gametangium fuse to form a diploid zygote. The zygote develops a thick wall and becomes a dormant zygospore (ZI guh spor), sometimes called a zygosporangium.

MiniLab 2

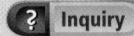

Inquiry MiniLab

Investigate Mold Growth

How does salt affect mold growth? Chemical preservatives, including salt (sodium chloride), often are used to influence mold growth on a variety of foods.

Procedure

1. Read and complete the lab safety form.
2. Obtain two slices of **bread.** Touch one object in the room with both sides of both slices.
3. Using a **spray bottle** filled with **water,** lightly moisten both sides of both slices of bread evenly.
4. Place one bread slice in a **self-sealing bag.** Seal the bag and label it with your name, date, and the object that touched the bread.
5. Sprinkle **salt** on both sides of the second slice of bread. Place the slice in another bag and seal it. Label this bag as you did the first, but note that salt was added.
6. Create a table to record your observations.
7. Record observations daily for ten days. Your table should include descriptions, as well as measurements of any mold that has formed.

Analysis

1. **Identify** Which slice grew more mold?
2. **Conclude** Did the salt affect mold growth?
3. **Analyze** Why did the salt affect the mold?

■ **Figure 9** *Rhizopus stolonifer,* a common bread mold, is an example of a zygomycete that undergoes both asexual and sexual reproduction.

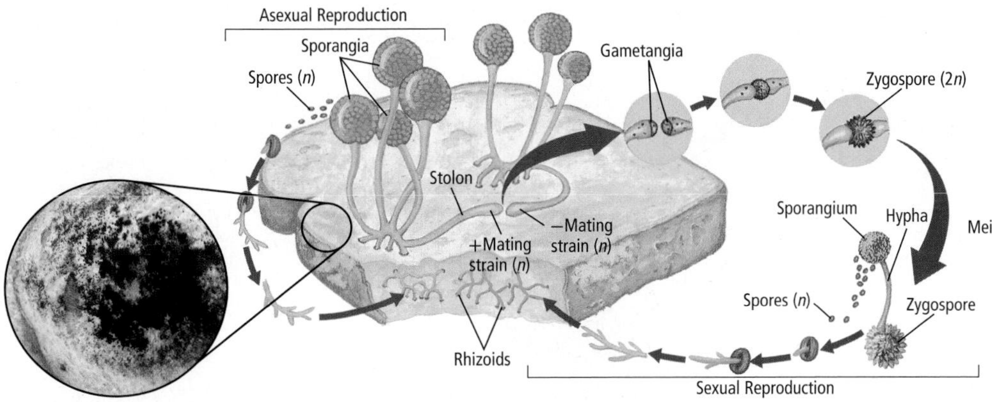

Develop Concepts

BL OL AL Scaffolding

ASK STUDENTS: ***What is the difference between the types of hyphae?*** Stolons grow across the surface; rhizoids grow into the food. ***What other type(s) of hyphae might this fungus produce?*** reproductive hyphae ***Assess the success of the zygomycetes' reproductive strategies.*** Asexual reproduction produces thousands of spores; sexual reproduction produces spores with genetic diversity.

MiniLab 2

Inquiry MiniLab

For a lab worksheet, use your eTeacherEdition Online.

RUBRIC A rubric for evaluating MiniLabs is found on your eTeacherEdition Online.

Est. Time 55 min

Additional Material Students should use a ruler to measure changes in diameter.

Safety Precautions Approve lab safety forms before work begins. Tell students not to open their bags after sealing.

Teaching Strategies

- Purchase outdated bread about a week before starting the lab.

Cleanup and Disposal Wipe all work stations with a mild bleach solution. Sealed plastic bags can be thrown into the trash can.

Analysis

1. the slice without the added salt
2. Yes, it slowed mold growth.
3. Student answers will vary but should include discussion of osmotic pressure or salt concentration.

Activity

OL Rhizopus Structure Have students examine the structure of *Rhizopus* on bread. Prepare the bread by misting it with water and leaving it in an airtight container for two weeks. On the day of the activity, take small chunks of the bread and put them in closed petri dishes. Students can use magnifying lenses or dissecting microscopes to study the structures.

SAY TO STUDENTS: ***Describe what you see.*** Students should identify hyphae and the dark gametangia. Have them make labeled drawings of their observations. Est. time: 15 min

Writing Support

OL AL Creative Writing

Tell students that among the many varieties of sac fungi, two are considered to be gourmet delicacies: morels and truffles. Have students write a newspaper article titled "Fungi as Food" that features morels and/or truffles. Tell students to include information about the habitats of these fungi and the ways they are gathered and prepared for food.

Develop Concepts

OL AL

Clarify a Misconception

ASK STUDENTS: ***What temperatures are most conducive to fungal reproduction?*** Students might think all fungi grow best in warm temperatures (70–90°F). While this is true of many species, there are fungi that are capable of growing in high temperatures (130–150°F) or even below freezing. ***Do all fungi require a great deal of moisture in order to grow and reproduce?*** Most fungi do require a great deal of moisture, but there are also species of fungi that can grow on dried grains and fruits. These types of fungi, such as the sac fungi *Claviceps purpurea* that infects cereal grasses, are a serious health hazard.

CAREERS IN BIOLOGY

Mycologist A mycologist studies various aspects about fungi such as their biochemistry, genetics, evolution, classification, and economic uses.

The zygospore can remain dormant for months until environmental conditions improve. Then, the zygospore germinates and undergoes meiosis to produce hyphae with a sporangium. Each haploid spore formed in the new sporangium can grow into a new mycelium. This process of sexual reproduction provides greater genetic diversity that helps ensure the survival of the species by allowing zygomycetes to survive in changing environments.

Sac Fungi

There are more than 60,000 species of sac fungi found in the phylum Ascomycota (AS koh mi koh tuh). It contains more species than any other phylum of fungi. Species found in this phylum are referred to as ascomycetes or sac fungi. Although the most well-known ascomycetes—yeasts—are unicellular and microscopic, most members of this group are multicellular.

Life Cycle Sac fungi can reproduce both sexually and asexually. During asexual reproduction, spores are formed at the tips of the hyphae. These spore-producing hyphae are called **conidiophores** (koh NIH dee uh forz), and the spores they generate are called conidia. Instead of forming inside sporangia, conidia form externally at the tips of the conidiophore. These spores are dispersed easily by wind, water, and animals.

■ **Figure 10** The fungus *Aspergillus* releases spores from the tips of a conidiophore during asexual reproduction.

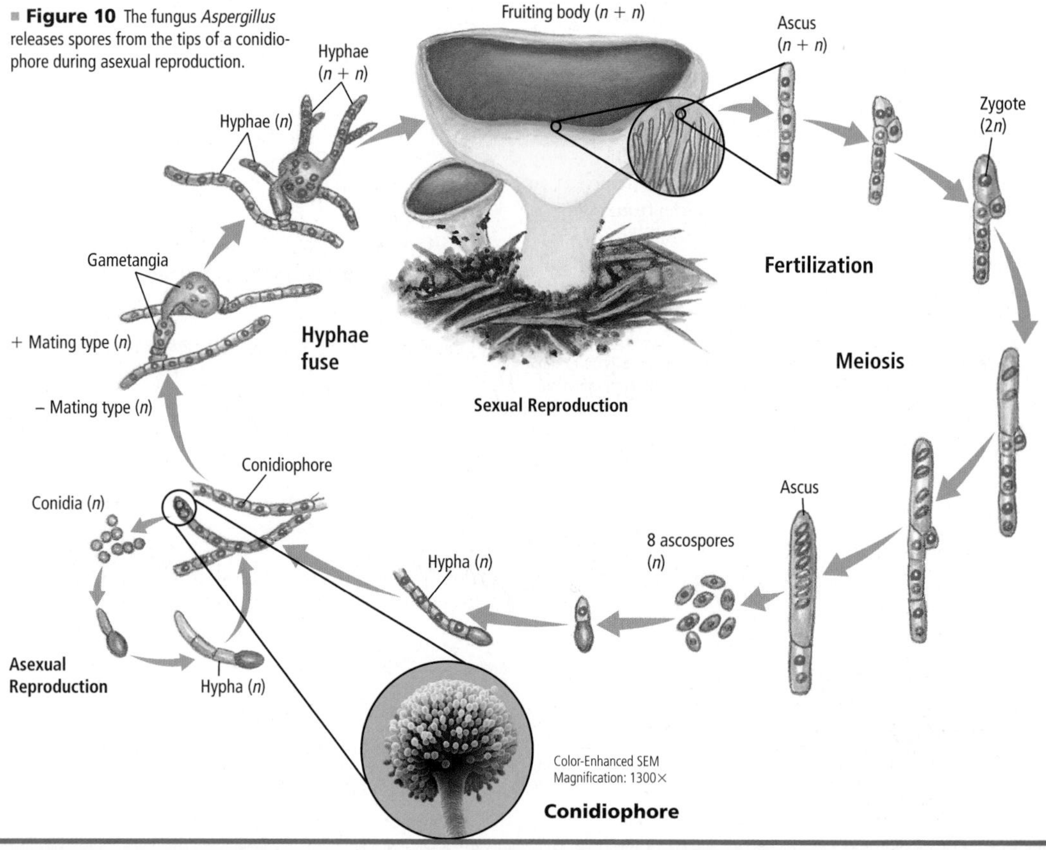

Research Citation

Inquiry Educational research indicates that question-driven instruction promotes student motivation and learning. Ask students to come up with a question they want to answer. An I-Chart is an inquiry chart that can be used to support content-area inquiry and research. (Hoffman, 1992)

Research bibliography on pages 32T–34T

Differentiated Instruction

Physically Disabled When teaching students with physical disabilities, it is important that you understand their limitations while also fostering independence. Offer praise related to the students' abilities.

For more tips, see pages 14T–15T.

Ascomycete sexual reproduction is a complicated process, illustrated in **Figure 10.** It takes place when hyphae from opposite mating types fuse and one nucleus from each type pairs off in separate cells. The hyphae that continue to grow are septate. Each cell contains two haploid nuclei—one from each mating type. Eventually, the hyphae will develop a specialized reproductive structure called an **ascocarp.** Within the ascocarp, the haploid nuclei fuse to form a zygote. The zygote divides by meiosis, producing four haploid nuclei. These nuclei then divide by mitosis, forming a total of eight haploid nuclei. The nuclei develop into spores in the **ascus,** a saclike structure. Spores produced by an ascus are called **ascospores.** Just like other spores, when growing conditions are W favorable, each ascospore can develop into a haploid mycelium.

Club Fungi

Table 1 compares the characteristics of the fungi in phylum Basidiomycota with the fungi in other phyla. Among the 25,000 members of the Basidiomycota (buh SIH dee oh mi koh tuh) phylum are the mushrooms, perhaps the most commonly recognized type of fungus.

Study Tip

Tables Write a short paragraph using the table below to compare the number of phyla and the approximate number of species in each phylum. Predict how these numbers will compare to the numbers for plants and animals.

S **Table 1** **Fungi Phyla** Concepts in Motion Interactive Table

Phylum (Common Name)	Example	Number of Species	Characteristics
Chytridiomycota (chytrids)	Magnification: unavailable 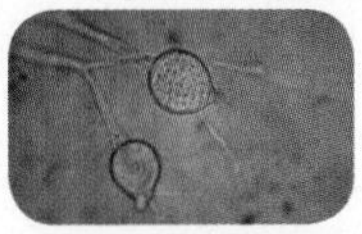	1300+	• Unicellular • Most are aquatic • Some are saprophytic, while others are parasitic • Produce flagellated spores
Zygomycota (common molds)	LM Magnification: 4× 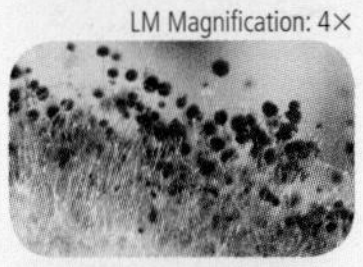	800	• Multicellular • Most are terrestrial • Many form mutualistic relationships with plants • Reproduce sexually and asexually
Ascomycota (sac fungi)	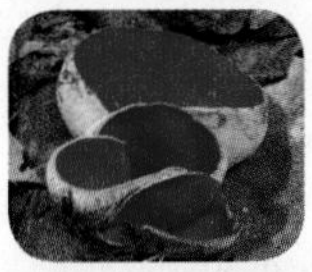	60,000+	• Most are multicellular, but some are unicellular • Variety of habitats • Saprophytic, parasitic, or mutualistic • Reproduce sexually and asexually
Basidiomycota (club fungi)	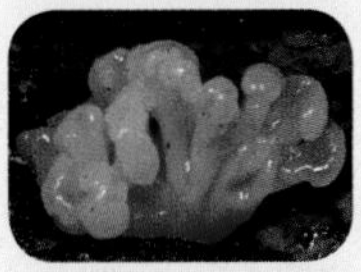	25,000	• Most are multicellular • Most are terrestrial • Saprophytic, parasitic, or mutualistic • Rarely reproduce asexually
Deuteromycota (imperfect fungi)		25,000	• No sexual stage observed • Very diverse group • Might not be considered a true phylum

Content Background

Teacher FYI Ascomycetes are a well-known group of fungi. Members range from the well-known yeast to the producer of penicillin (*Penicillium chrysogenum*), the edible morel, and *Neurospora crassa* (red bread mold)—famous as the one-gene-one-enzyme organism. The infamous ascomycetes include *Aspergillus flavus,* which produces aflatoxin—the most potent known natural carcinogen. Although currently we place the members of Deuteromycota in a separate phylum, scientists have found that the nucleic acid sequences of deuteromycetes and ascomycetes suggest that they are closely related.

W Writing Support

BL OL Technical Writing

Have students list the steps of Ascomycetes' sexual reproduction. 1. hyphae of opposite mating types fuse 2. one nucleus from each type pair off in separate cells 3. septate hyphae continue to grow with two haploid nuclei 4. hyphae form an ascocarp 5. haploid nuclei fuse to form zygote 6. zygote divides meiotically—produces four haploid nuclei 7. nuclei divide mitotically 8. nuclei develop into spores in ascospores

Concepts in Motion

Interactive Table

S Skill Practice

EL BL OL Visual Literacy

Have students recreate columns 1, 2, and 4 of Table 1 on a separate sheet of paper. Ask students to place each of the following questions into the correct row of their copied tables:

- What type of fungi are mushrooms? club fungi
- Which phylum has the most species of fungi? sac fungi
- Which fungus grows on bread and other types of food? common molds
- Which type of fungus is yeast? chytrids
- Which fungus decomposes wood? club fungi

Skill Practice

OL Use Math Skills

ASK STUDENTS: ***What percentage of the total fungi species does each phylum contain?*** Chytridiomycota 2 percent, Zygomycota <1 percent, Ascomycota 54 percent, Basidiomycota 22 percent, and Deuteromycota 22 percent

Develop Concepts

AL

Activate Prior Knowledge

ASK STUDENTS: ***What is the tough polymer in wood?*** cellulose ***What are the subunits of this polymer?*** glucose ***How do you think fungi are able to break down cellulose?*** with specific enzymes found in fungi of phylum Basidiomycota

Formative Assessment

Evaluation

ASK STUDENTS: ***What are the distinguishing traits of the fungi phyla?*** They have different structures and means of reproduction. Chytridiomycota—aquatic, flagellated sperm; Zygomycota—terrestrial, reproduce sexually and asexually; Ascomycota—multicellular and unicellular, reproduce sexually and asexually; Basidiomycota—terrestrial, saprophytic, parasitic, rarely reproduce asexually; Deuteromycota—no sexual reproduction known

Remediation Have students make flash cards with the name of the phylum on one side and the characteristics on the other. Have them work in pairs to quiz each other.

■ **Figure 11** This club fungus, called bird's nest fungus or *Crucibulum vulgare,* has basidiocarps that resemble eggs in a bird's nest.

Species found in phylum Basidiomycota also are called basidiomycetes (buh SIH dee ah mi see teez) or club fungi. They can be saprophytic, parasitic, or mutualistic. The saprophytic basidiomycetes are major decomposers of wood. They produce enzymes that can break down complex polymers found in wood, such as lignin.

Life Cycle Basidiomycetes rarely produce asexual spores. They spend most of their life cycle as dikaryotic mycelia, meaning that each cell has two nuclei. The mycelium periodically will reproduce sexually by forming **basidiocarps** (buh SIH dee oh karpz), or fruiting bodies, as shown in **Figure 11.** The mushrooms that you see growing in the woods or that you add to your salad are basidiocarps.

Basidiocarps can grow quickly, sometimes appearing full-grown in a few hours or overnight, with rapid growth resulting from cell enlargement rather than cell division. The underside of the cap is composed of **basidia** (singular, basidium), club-shaped hyphae that produce spores. Within the basidia, the two nuclei fuse to form a diploid nucleus. This nucleus divides meiotically into four haploid nuclei that will develop into **basidiospores,** the haploid spores released by basidia during reproduction. The basidiospores can be dispersed by wind, water, or animals. It is estimated that some mushrooms will produce as many as a billion basidiospores.

Other Fungi

Organisms in phylum Deuteromycota share only one unique trait—sexual reproduction in these fungi never has been observed. Because these fungi appear to lack a sexual stage, they are referred to as imperfect fungi. Scientists currently use modern genetic techniques, such as DNA and protein comparisons, to reassign some of these fungi into one of the other four phyla.

Section 2 Assessment

Section Summary

- There are four major phyla of fungi.
- Zygomycetes reproduce sexually by forming zygospores.
- Ascomycetes produce ascospores within a saclike structure called an ascus during sexual reproduction.
- Basidiomycetes produce basidiospores during sexual reproduction.
- Sexual reproduction in the phylum Deuteromycota has never been observed.

Understand Main Ideas

1. MAIN Idea **Identify** two characteristics of each of the four major phyla of fungi.
2. **Explain** why fungi produce so many spores.
3. **Diagram** the life cycle of ascomycetes.
4. **Describe** What are imperfect fungi?
5. **Compare** sexual reproduction in ascomycetes and basidiomycetes.

Think Critically

6. **Predict** what might happen to an ecosystem if a virus destroyed all of the basidiomycetes. What effect would that have on the recycling of nutrients in a forest?

WRITING in Biology

7. Write a news story detailing how a scientist reclassified a species of imperfect fungi once sexual reproduction was identified.

Section 2 Assessment

1. Possible answer: Chytridiomycota—aquatic, flagellated sperm; Zygomycota—terrestrial, reproduce sexually and asexually; Ascomycota—most multicellular, reproduce sexually and asexually; Basidiomycota—terrestrial, saprophytic
2. The chance that a spore will land in a hospitable environment and grow is very small.
3. Diagrams should resemble Figure 10.
4. They exhibit no sexual stage.
5. Possible answer: Ascomycetes use condiophores to produce asexual spores; basidiomycetes use basidia to produce sexual spores.
6. Answers will vary. Organic matter would not decompose and would build up in forests. Growth would be inhibited because nutrients would not recycle. Structure and composition of the forest would change.
7. DNA analysis could be used. The species would most likely belong to the phyla Ascomycota.

Assessment Online Quiz

Reading Preview

Essential Questions

- What are the characteristics of lichens?
- What are the characteristics of mycorrhizal relationships?
- What are some beneficial and harmful effects that fungi can have on humans?

Review Vocabulary

bioremediation: the use of organisms to detoxify a polluted area

New Vocabulary

lichen
bioindicator
mycorrhiza

g Multilingual eGlossary

Ecology of Fungi

MAIN Idea Lichens and mycorrhizae demonstrate important symbiotic relationships between fungi and other organisms.

Real-World Reading Link You might think that the only time you encounter fungi is when you order mushrooms on pizza or when you take a nature walk. You might be surprised to know that some antibiotics are derived from fungi, and that athlete's foot is caused by fungi.

Fungi and Photosynthesizers

D Lichens and mycorrhizae are two examples of mutualistic relationships between fungi and other organisms. Recall that mutualism is a type of symbiosis in which both organisms benefit from the relationship.

Lichens A symbiotic relationship between a fungus and an alga or a photosynthetic partner is called a **lichen** (LI ken). The fungus usually is an ascomycete, but lichens also may contain basidiomycetes. The photosynthetic partner is either a green alga or cyanobacterium, which provides food for both organisms. The fungus provides a dense web of hyphae in which the alga or cyanobacterium can grow. Examine **Figure 12** to see the structure of a lichen. Notice that fungal tissues account for most of the mass of a lichen.

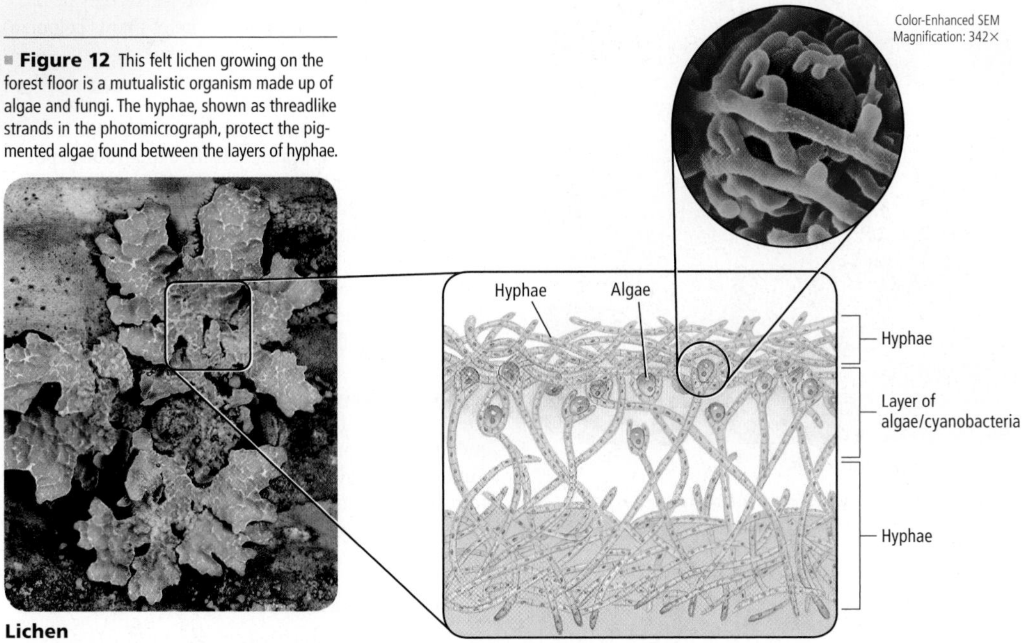

■ **Figure 12** This felt lichen growing on the forest floor is a mutualistic organism made up of algae and fungi. The hyphae, shown as threadlike strands in the photomicrograph, protect the pigmented algae found between the layers of hyphae.

Section 3

MAIN Idea

BL OL AL Ecology of Fungi

ASK STUDENTS: ***Can you imagine what our neighborhood would look like if there were no fungi?*** Possible answer: The neighborhood would be covered in trash. Remind students that fungi serve an important role in our environment as decomposers. Our ecosystems would be filled with organic trash if it were not for fungi.

ASK STUDENTS: ***What other important roles do you think fungi have in our environment?*** Students could suggest that fungi have beneficial and harmful roles. Have students speculate about what some of these roles might be, and suggest that they read the section to see how accurate their speculations were.

EL As students read, have them make a list of beneficial and harmful roles of fungi.

D Develop Concepts

BL OL

Clarify a Misconception

ASK STUDENTS: ***Are all fungi harmful?*** no Some students believe that all fungi are harmful since they may be most familiar with the fungi that grow on food. Students will learn that fungi are used in the preparation of many foods, such as bread, and drugs such as penicillin. Fungi also serve a vital role in the decomposition of dead organisms and waste products.

"Too often we give children answers to remember rather than problems to solve."

—Roger Lewin

Research Citation

Writing Educational research indicates that writing can be used as a learning tool to promote language development. For English learners, integrate language and content as much as possible. (Swain, 1996)

Research bibliography on pages 32T–34T

Develop Concepts

BL OL AL Activity Have students examine lichen using a hand lens or dissecting microscope. Lichen often can be found growing on trees or on stones. Students may be surprised to find out that they cannot actually see the separate fungi and alga partners within the lichen.

ASK STUDENTS: ***What evidence do you see that suggests that there is a photosynthetic partner present?*** Most lichens have a green or bluish green cast. (Lichens with yellow or orange casts contain carotenoid, a light-absorbing pigment that absorbs different wavelengths of light than chlorophyll does.)

Reading Strategy

OL Build Vocabulary

ASK STUDENTS: ***What does it mean when someone says "the feeling is mutual"?*** It means that both people feel the same way. ***What are mutualistic relationships?*** relationships where both organisms benefit

AL Have students give a quick oral review of mutualism. Have them include an example of mutualism in their review.

Writing Support

AL COOP LEARN

Creative Writing Using reality TV shows as a guide, have students work in groups to create a contest to see which lichens can survive various environmental conditions and pollutants. Ask the groups to write a script for their contests. Tell students that while their scripts may be humorous, they must also be scientifically accurate.

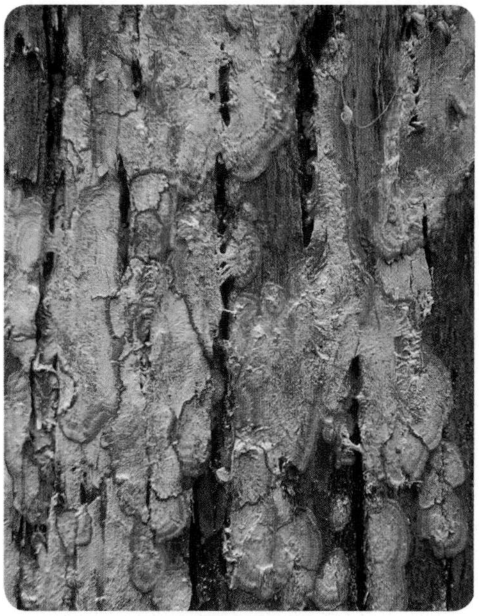

Red blanket lichen on cypress bark

Lepraria on basalt rock

■ **Figure 13** Lichens grow in harsh enviroments, such as the surfaces of trees or bare rocks, where fungi, algae, and cyanobacteria would not grow alone.

Explain *why lichens often are pioneer species.*

Diversity of lichens There are over 25,000 species of lichens. To see two of the different forms, examine **Figure 13.** Because they need only light, air, and minerals to grow, lichens are found in some of the harshest environments. Lichens absorb needed minerals from rainwater or from dust in the air. The fungus traps rainwater, but it also can absorb moisture from the air. Some fungi produce toxic compounds that keep animals, including insects, from eating the lichen. Fungi also inhibit moss and bacterial growth.

Although a few types of lichens can be found in deserts or the tropics, the majority of these organisms grow in temperate or arctic areas. They form the primary ground cover on the tundra, providing food for grazing animals. Caribou utilize an enzyme called lichenase (LI kun ayz) to help them digest the lichen.

Lichens also survive severe drought. They dry out, stop photosynthesis, and become brittle. Pieces can break off, blow away, and reestablish in another location—a form of asexual reproduction. When water is available again, the lichens rapidly absorb large quantities of the water and begin photosynthesis again.

Recall that a pioneer species is a species that can grow with little soil or on rocks. Lichens often are the pioneer species in an area of newly cleared soil or rock following natural disasters, such as fire or volcanic activity. Acids produced by the fungal portion of the lichen help penetrate and break down rocks to help form soil. As lichens become established, they help trap soil and fix nitrogen, which helps plants colonize the new soil.

Lichens as bioindicators Because they absorb much of their water and minerals from the air and rain, lichens are especially sensitive to airborne pollutants. When air pollution levels rise in an area, lichens often will die. In addition, lichens typically do not grow in or near cities where air pollution is high. They usually are found in rural areas where there is little or no air pollution. Lichens absorb pollutants that are dissolved in rain and dew. Because of their sensitivity to pollution, lichens are important bioindicators.

A **bioindicator** is a living organism that is sensitive to changes in environmental conditions and is one of the first organisms to respond to changing conditions. The levels of air pollutants in an area can be correlated to the changes in lichen growth. As the level of pollution decreases, the populations of lichens increase.

Reading Check **Explain** why lichens are bioindicators.

Differentiated Instruction

Behavior Disorders In your interactions with students who have behavior disorders, it is important to communicate acceptance regardless of the student's behavior.

For more tips, see pages 14T–15T.

■ **Caption Question Fig. 13** Lichens can grow with little or no soil.

Reading Check Lichens absorb pollutants, such as radioactive particles, from the air.

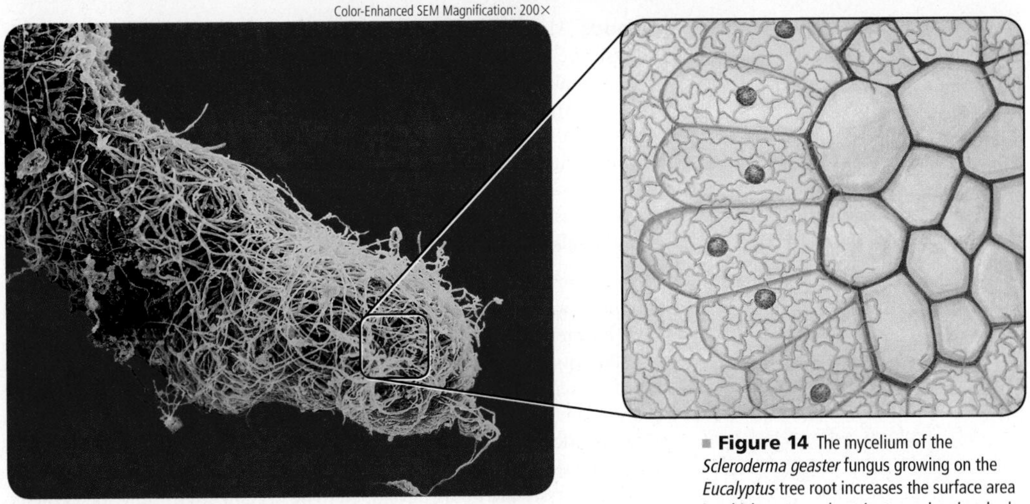

■ **Figure 14** The mycelium of the *Scleroderma geaster* fungus growing on the *Eucalyptus* tree root increases the surface area in which water and nutrients can be absorbed by the root.
Explain ***How does the fungus benefit from this relationship?***

Mycorrhizae Another mutalistic relationship involving a fungus is a **mycorrhiza** (my kuh RHY zuh) (plural, mycorrhizae)—a symbiotic relationship between a specialized fungus and plant roots. Plants with mycorrhizae are healthier and more vigorous than similar plants that lack mycorrhizae. Other plant species, such as orchids, cannot survive without mutualistic partners. Orchid seeds will not germinate unless they are infected by a fungal partner or provided with the fungal carbohydrate trehalose.

Figure 14 shows a mycorrhizal relationship between a *Schleroderma geaster* fungus and a *Eucalyptus* tree. The fungus absorbs and concentrates various minerals for the plant. The hyphae of the fungus also increase the plant's root surface area for water and mineral absorption. In return, the fungus receives carbohydrates and amino acids from the plant.

Between 80 and 90 percent of plants, including primitive plants, have mycorrhizae. Mycorrhizae are extremely important in natural habitats and for agricultural crops. Crops associated with mycorrhizae include corn, carrots, potatoes, tomatoes, and strawberries.

Fungi and Humans

For the most part, fungi have a positive effect on the lives of humans. Their most important role is as decomposers, assisting with the recycling of nutrients found in dead organisms. Decomposing organic matter makes nutrients available for other organisms and prevents dead organisms and their wastes from littering the surface of Earth.

Beneficial fungi Fungi have many medical uses. The ascomycete *Penicillium notatum* can be used as a source of penicillin. This antibiotic has saved countless lives. Chemical compounds found in the fungus *Claviceps purpurea* are used to reduce high blood pressure, to control excessive bleeding, to treat migraine headaches, and to promote contractions during childbirth. The Norwegian deuteromycete *Tolypocladium inflatum* is the source for cyclosporine. Cyclosporine is an immune suppressant drug given to organ transplant patients to keep their bodies from rejecting new organs.

VOCABULARY
ACADEMIC VOCABULARY
Cooperate
to work or act together toward a common end or purpose
Organisms that cooperate with members of their own or different species might be more successful than those organisms that do not cooperate.

S Skill Practice
BL OL
Compare and Contrast Have students compare and contrast the mutualistic relationships of lichens and mycorrhizae. Both involve fungi; lichen is often a result of a mutualistic relationship between fungi and algae, while mycorrhizae are a result of a mutualistic relationship between fungi and plants.

C Critical Thinking
OL AL Infer Tell students that stone-washed denim is produced by culturing the fungus *Trichodema reesii.* The enzymes released by the fungus partially digest the cotton fabric.
ASK STUDENTS: ***Although the production of these enzymes makes them useful to us, how does the fungus benefit?*** The enzymes are cellulose-degrading enzymes, which help the fungus digest the cell walls of plants. Cotton is a plant product that contains cellulose.

Writing Support
OL Informal Writing
SAY TO STUDENTS: ***Prepare a dinner menu that lists recipes containing fungi. Include illustrations in your menu.*** Answers might include yeast breads, blue cheese dressing, stuffed mushrooms, or pizza with mushrooms.

■ **Caption Question Fig. 14**
The fungus can absorb carbohydrates and amino acids from the plant.

Content Background

Teacher FYI Mycorrhizal fungi might explain the ability for some species of non-photosynthetic plants to survive. Researchers have found that Indian pipes, colorless and heterotrophic anthophytes (flowering plants), must obtain all their nutrients from mycorrhizal fungi. When radioactive carbon in the form of carbon dioxide gas was administered to a pine tree, the radioactivity was detected in the tissues of Indian pipes that were a considerable distance away from the pine. Scientists infer that mycorrhizal fungi provide the transport for nutrients.

DATA ANALYSIS LAB 1

About the Lab

- There is a *Fusarium* that infects tomatoes as well as other vegetable crops. *Fusarium* "wilts" are a common problem for farmers.
- Also see Reid, T.C. and M.K. Hausbeck. 1999. Control of *Fusarium* root rot of asparagus with different forms of chloride salt. *Phytopathology* 89: S65.

Think Critically

1. 13.9 percent increase in spear number; 22.9 percent increase in spear mass
2. Spear number and spear mass increase.
3. Possible answer: Either it kills the fungi or makes the plant more resistant. For testing hypotheses, accept all reasonable answers.

Develop Concepts

BL OL AL

Clarify a Misconception

ASK STUDENTS: *What causes ringworm?* Students might think it is caused by a worm under the skin. It actually is brought about by a fungus that causes a reddish mark on the skin resembling the shape of a worm. This would be a good opportunity to remind students that common names often are misleading, which is why scientists prefer the scientific names that are the same no matter where you live or what language you speak.

CAREERS IN BIOLOGY

Food Technologist A food technologist can choose from a range of jobs, including the development of new food products and setting standards for producing, packaging, and marketing food technologies. They also might test products for nutritional and microbiological quality.

Foods Many of the foods we eat are made from fungi or fungal products. The most obvious are the many different mushrooms that we eat. Yeast makes bread rise by releasing carbon dioxide gas during fermentation. Another product of fermentation is the alcohol found in beer and wine. Truffles are fungi and are one of the most expensive food items. Many other fungi are enjoyed similarly as delicacies. The flavors of some cheeses, such as Brie, Camembert, and Roquefort, are the result of fungi. The citrus flavor found in sodas is created by the fungus *Aspergillus*. This fungus also is used to make soy sauce.

Bioremediation Fungi also can be used for cleaning the environment of pollutants that are threatening some ecosystems. The fungi are mixed with water or soil, where they decompose organic materials in the pollutants. During this process, called bioremediation, the pollutants are broken down into harmless substances. The rate at which microorganisms, such as fungi and bacteria, remove environmental pollutants can be increased if additional nutrients are added to the water or soil. Bioremediation is a relatively new scientific field, and new discoveries and processes are being developed to be used in environmental clean-up projects.

Connection to Chemistry Researchers are using white-rot fungi to break down top priority pollutants, such as dyes and polycyclic aromatic hydrocarbons (PAHs). PAHs are carcinogenic (cancer-causing) molecules. Researchers also are taking advantage of the fact that these fungi contain enzymes that degrade lignin, a molecule found in wood fiber that hardens and strengthens the cell walls of plants, enabling wood to be recycled. These enzymes also can attach to structurally similar chemicals, including many human-made pollutants.

DATA ANALYSIS LAB 1

Based on Real Data*

Interpret the Data

Does the addition of salt to soil affect asparagus production? *Fusarium oxysporum* is a disease-causing organism of many crops, including asparagus. The fungus penetrates the roots and spreads up through the plant, often reducing the flow of water to the stem and leaves. Infected plants produce fewer and smaller spears than healthy plants do. The fungus stays in the soil year after year.

Data and Observations

Salt (sodium chloride) treatment is a common method for suppressing disease in plants. The table shows data collected after an asparagus field was treated with a dusting of salt.

Asparagus Production		
	Spear number	Spear mass
Before treatment with salt	78.2	1843.2
After treatment with salt	89.1	2266.1

Think Critically

1. **Calculate** the percentage change in spear number and spear mass.
2. **Interpret** how the salt treatment affects the asparagus crop.
3. **Hypothesize** why salt might have this effect on the plants. How would you test your hypothesis?

*Data obtained from: Elmer, W.H. 2002. Influence of formononetin and NaCl on mycorrhizal colonization and fusarium crown and root rot of asparagus. *Plant Disease* 86(12): 1318-1324.

Demonstration

BL OL AL **Fungi as Antibiotics** Demonstrate the antibiotic nature of some fungi by inoculating a petri dish with *E. coli* or another bacterium. (Bacteria can be obtained from a biological supply house.) In front of the class, dip a 1-cm piece of filter paper into an ampicillin solution and then place it in the dish. Have students check the dish after 48 h. Est. time: 15 min

Activity

OL AL **Shrink Cells** Have students examine fungal hyphae under a dissecting microscope as they mist the hyphae with a 15% NaCl solution. Repeat the activity with distilled water. Have students draw the changes they see and explain what caused them. The cell became hypotonic, then hypertonic. Tie content to the Data Analysis Lab. Est. time: 10 min

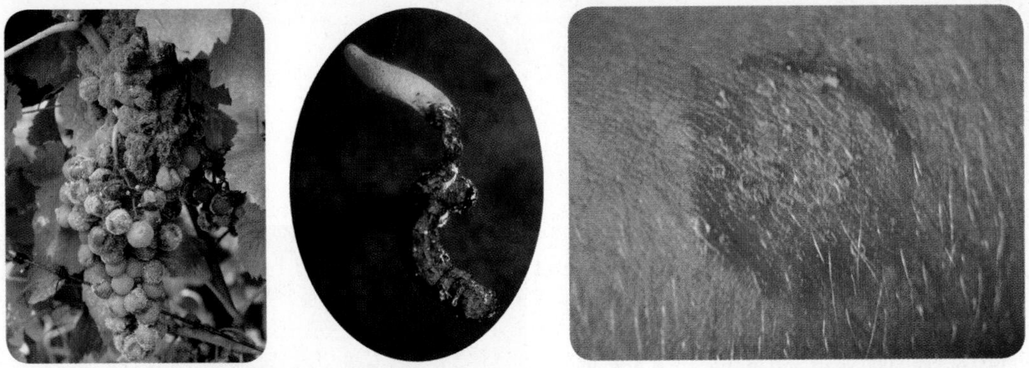

■ **Figure 15** Parasitic fungi can be harmful to humans as well as to other organisms.
Left: Grapes are infected by a fungus that causes noble rot.
Middle: Scarlet caterpillar fungus can kill caterpillars.
Right: Ringworm is caused by a fungus.

Harmful fungi Some fungi can be harmful to other organisms. For example, American elm trees are killed by the fungus *Ceratocystis ulmi* and American chestnut trees are killed by the fungus *Endothia parasitica.* The fungi quickly spread from tree to tree, and they have killed many trees in North America. Agricultural crops are also damaged by fungi. The fungal parasite *Leptoterochila medicaginis* causes leaf blotch in alfalfa plants and can diminish crop production by as much as 80 percent. The ripe grapes shown in **Figure 15** have been infected with the parasitic fungus *Botrytis cinerea,* causing what is known as noble rot. The fungus attacks the grapes and causes an increase in their sugar content, making most of them unusable. However, certain wines are produced from such grapes in France.

Fungi can also parasitize humans and other animals. The parasitic fungus *Cordyceps militaris* can infect the larvae and pupae of butterflies and moths, as shown in **Figure 15.** Athlete's foot, ringworm, yeast infections, and oral thrush are infections in humans that are caused by fungi. **Figure 15** shows skin infected with ringworm, which can be caused by several species of fungi.

R

R Reading Strategy

OL AL Supplemental Reading

Have students choose one harmful fungus mentioned in the text or have them pick one of their own. Students should read additional material about the fungus and report what they have learned to the class.

Formative Assessment

Evaluation

ASK STUDENTS: ***Name two types of mutualistic relationships involving fungi.*** lichen and mycorrhizae

Remediation Ask students to reread the text under the headings *Lichens* and *Mycorrhizae.* Summarize the characteristics on the board. Lichens are a symbiotic association between a fungus and algae or another photosynthetic partner. Mycorrhiza is a relationship between a fungus and plant roots.

Section 3 Assessment

Section Summary

- Lichens are examples of mutualistic relationships between a fungus and an alga or a cyanobacterium.
- Mycorrhizae help plants obtain water and minerals by increasing the surface area of their roots.
- Compounds obtained from fungi are used for a variety of medicines.
- Many foods eaten by people are made from fungi.
- Fungi can have adverse effects on humans and plants.

Understand Main Ideas

1. MAIN Idea **Identify** the characteristics of the mutualistic relationship between fungi and algae.
2. **Explain** why lichens are important for the environment.
3. **Apply** what you know about enzymes to design a lichenase enzyme for lichen-eating animals.
4. **Construct** a table to show the beneficial and harmful effects of fungi on humans.

Think Critically

5. **Infer** the effect on world food production if a fungicide was discovered that destroys all of the fungi in agricultural settings.

MATH in Biology

6. Lichens grow an average of one centimeter per year. How long would it take for a lichen to grow the width of your hand?

Section 3 Assessment

1. The fungus provides protection and the alga provides food.
2. Lichens help trap soil and fix nitrogen.
3. Answers will vary but should include that enzymes break down substances into smaller molecules. Lichenase would break down lichens into more easily digestible material.
4. Answers will vary, but may include some of the following:

	Beneficial	Harmful
Agriculture	Growth stimulus	Fungal diseases
Medicine	Penicillin	Fungal infections, poisons
Food	Mushrooms, brewing	Molds in storage

5. Answers will vary, but students should consider both positive and negative effects of fungi.
6. Answers will vary between 6 to 12 years depending on the width of students' hands.

Biology & Society

Purpose

Students will learn how fungi can be used to fight diseases.
UPC.5, C.5

Anticipatory Guide

ASK STUDENTS: ***How many of you have taken penicillin for an infection?*** Remind students that penicillin is a fungus and is one of the most widely used fungi that are part of the pharmaceutical industry in the world. ***How many of you have relatives taking cholesterol medicine?*** Answers will vary. Tell students that some cholesterol medicines are derived from fungi. ***How many of you know of someone that has had an organ transplant?*** Answers will vary. Explain that some of the drugs used to aid the transplant, such as immunosuppressive drugs, are derived from fungi.

Background

The Iceman was found with the eggs of the parasitic whipworm *Trichuris trichiur* in his colon. The presence of these eggs would have caused diarrhea. By carrying the birch fungus, the Iceman would have found relief from the diarrhea by ingesting some of the fungus that would have purged the body of the eggs.

Biology & Society

Fungi Superheroes

The Iceman, whose mummified corpse was discovered in 1991, provided a picture of what life was like 5000 years ago in the Stone Age. In his belt were two walnut-sized lumps of birch fungus (known as the chaga mushroom). This fungus can both cause diarrhea and serve as an antibiotic. The chaga mushroom helped alleviate the effects of the parasites that were living in the Iceman's colon by helping his body eliminate the parasite's eggs.

A folk hero The chaga mushroom has been used as a traditional folk remedy in Eastern European countries since the sixteenth century and has been mentioned in Chinese texts dating back 4600 years. Chaga mushrooms have been used as a treatment for tuberculosis, various cancers, and intestinal ailments, usually crushed up and ingested as an herbal tea.

Chaga mushroom Chaga is a parasitic fungus that grows from the trunks of birch trees. In Russia, chaga is known as the "birch-killer" because it leads to the tree's death within five to seven years. It is estimated that as few as 1 in 15,000 birch trees have chaga. Chaga which grow on birch trees in Siberia are particularly prized among herbalists. Their high concentration of beneficial compounds is attributed to their ability to persist in the relatively harsh environment.

Making better cancer drugs Current scientific research is backing up the claims that folk medicine has maintained for generations. Chaga transforms the compound "betulin" found in the bark of the birch tree into a form which can be ingested. Betulin has been shown to exhibit anti-malarial, anti-inflammatory, and anti-HIV activity, in addition to being toxic toward some tumor cells. In 1998, a study showed that betulin, in the form of betulinic acid, triggered apoptosis (programmed cell death) when injected into tumor cells.

The chaga mushroom is a parasitic fungus that feeds off birch, alder, and beech trees.

Chaga mushrooms contain high levels of antioxidants, known to inhibit the cell-damaging effects of free radicals (highly reactive, unpaired electrons). A 2005 study revealed that extracts from the mushroom protected DNA in human lymphocytes against oxidative damage. In addition, active polysaccharides present in the mushroom have been found to stimulate the immune system.

Scientists estimate that more than one million species of fungi exist and many are unidentified. The National Cancer Institute is collecting 1000 fungi samples yearly from the tropical rain forests to see if the fungi might contain disease-fighting compounds. In the meantime, researchers continue to study existing herbal remedies in order to reinforce or dispel the claims made of these natural curatives.

MAKE A BOARD GAME

Work with a Team Create a board game depicting the development of a cancer treatment based on the discovery of a fungus found living on a plant in the rain forest. Conduct additional research regarding drug development, drugs developed from fungi, and drug treatment in cancer research.

Follow-Up Discussion

After the students create the board games, provide them with the opportunity to play the games. Then, hold a discussion for students to provide information about some of the obstacles and triumphs experienced during the game and to provide feedback to the creators of the game.

WebQuest

BIOLAB

Design Your Own

HOW DO ENVIRONMENTAL FACTORS AFFECT MOLD GROWTH?

Molds can grow under a wide range of conditions. Consider the differences in your kitchen alone. Molds can grow in a cool refrigerator or in a dark bread box on the counter. They grow on foods that contain varying amounts of sugar, protein, and moisture.

Question: *How does a specific environmental factor change the rate of mold growth?*

Materials

Choose materials that would be appropriate for this lab. Possible materials include:

mold from a food source
plain powdered gelatin (containing protein only)
bread
sugar
prepared gelatin in a small cup
cotton swab
aluminum foil or plastic wrap
small cup
thermometer
graduated cylinder
spray bottle

Safety Precautions

WARNING: ***Never eat food used in the lab.***

Plan and Perform the Experiment

1. Read and complete the lab safety form.
2. Make a list of environmental factors that might affect mold growth. Based on this list, develop a question to investigate.
3. Design an experiment that will help you answer this question. Remember, only one environmental factor should vary in your experimental conditions.
4. Write your hypothesis and design a data table.
5. Make sure your teacher has approved your experiment before you proceed.
6. Use cotton swabs to transfer mold from the food source to your trial cups.
7. Record observations for 5–7 days.
8. **Cleanup and Disposal** Place trial cups in the area designated by your teacher. Clean and return all equipment used in the lab. Wash your hands thoroughly.

Analyze and Conclude

1. **Identify** What is the independent variable and dependent variable in your experiment? Explain how the independent variable was changed.
2. **Compare** Describe differences that you noticed among trial samples.
3. **Describe** What steps did you take to limit variables in this experiment? Make a list of constants.
4. **Interpret the Data** How did the environmental factor that you changed affect the rate of mold growth?
5. **Conclude** Was your hypothesis supported? Explain.
6. **Error Analysis** Is it possible that more than one variable was introduced in your experiment? How would you change your experimental plans?

WRITING in Biology

Communicate Share your results with other groups. Develop a class list of environmental factors tested and results obtained. Based on these results, create a list of environmental factors that lead to optimal growth of the mold utilized in this experiment.

Analyze and Conclude

1. Answers will vary. The independent variable is based on the environmental factor the student chooses to investigate. The dependent variable is the rate of mold growth over time.
2. Answers will vary. Students may report differences in mold growth.
3. Answers will vary, but should include a list of conditions the student held the same for each trial.
4. Answers will vary. Environmental factors may have increased or decreased mold growth.
5. Answers will vary based on the students' hypotheses, but should include supporting data.
6. Possible answer: When the cotton swab is used to introduce the mold from the food source to the gelatin, nutrients from the food source are also introduced. To decrease the amount transferred, only a limited amount of food should be introduced to the mold.

BIOLAB

Design Your Own

Inquiry BioLab

For a lab worksheet, use your eTeacherEdition Online.

RUBRIC A rubric for evaluating BioLabs is found on your eTeacherEdition Online.

Est. Time 110 min

Content Background

A variety of environmental factors affect mold growth, including water availability, temperature, light, and nutrient type and concentration.

Alternative Materials

This activity could be completed using bread rather than gelatin. Once a moist chamber is prepared, the mold will be sealed inside, limiting exposure for students with allergies.

Safety Precautions

Approve lab safety forms before work begins. Some students may have mold allergies. Limit exposure by having these students wear face masks and gloves.

Teaching Strategies

- Carefully review experimental designs. Students should focus on a single environmental factor.
- Students might need direction in measuring and describing mold growth. Ideas include estimating the diameter at its widest point, estimating the circumference using a piece of string, or tracking changes using a digital camera.

Alternative Teaching Demo

This activity could be set up as a demonstration. Students could view changes in mold growth over a 5–7 day period.

WRITING in Biology

RUBRIC Use the modifiable rubric found on your eTeacherEdition Online to assess writing assignments.

Chapter 20

Study Guide

ConnectED

Students can use the following to review the chapter.

Review

Vocabulary eGames
Vocabulary eFlashcards
Vocabulary PuzzleMaker

Assessment

Online Quizzes
Online Test Practice
Standardized Test Practice

Use the *ExamView®* *Assessment Suite* CD-ROM to:

- create multiple versions of tests
- create modified tests with one mouse click
- edit existing questions and add your own questions
- build tests aligned with state standards using built-in state curriculum tags
- change English tests to Spanish with one mouse click
- track students' progress using the Teacher Management System

Chapter 20 Study Guide

THEME FOCUS Energy A fungus obtains energy in one of three ways: decomposition, parasitism, or mutualism.

BIG Idea **Kingdom fungi is made up of four phyla based on unique structures, methods of nutrition, and methods of reproduction.**

Section 1 Introduction to Fungi

chitin (p. 577)
hypha (p. 577)
mycelium (p. 577)
fruiting body (p. 577)
septum (p. 578)
haustorium (p. 578)
spore (p. 580)
sporangium (p. 581)

MAIN Idea **Fungi are unicelluar or multicellular eukaryotic heterotrophs that are decomposers.**

- Fungi produce hyphae that form a netlike mass called a mycelium.
- There are three different methods by which fungi obtain food.
- Fungi can reproduce asexually by budding, fragmentation, or producing spores.
- Most fungi can reproduce sexually, also by producing spores.

Section 2 Diversity of Fungi

stolon (p. 583)
rhizoid (p. 583)
gametangium (p. 583)
conidiophore (p. 584)
ascocarp (p. 585)
ascus (p. 585)
ascospore (p. 585)
basidiocarp (p. 586)
basidium (p. 586)
basidiospore (p. 586)

MAIN Idea **Fungi exhibit a broad range of diversity and are classified into four major phyla.**

- There are four major phyla of fungi.
- Zygomycetes reproduce sexually by forming zygospores.
- Ascomycetes produce ascospores within a saclike structure called an ascus during sexual reproduction.
- Basidiomycetes produce basidiospores during sexual reproduction.
- Sexual reproduction in the phylum Deuteromycota has never been observed.

Section 3 Ecology of Fungi

lichen (p. 587)
bioindicator (p. 588)
mycorrhiza (p. 589)

MAIN Idea **Lichens and mycorrhizae demonstrate important symbiotic relationships between fungi and other organisms.**

- Lichens are examples of mutualistic relationships between a fungus and an alga or a cyanobacterium.
- Mycorrhizae help plants obtain water and minerals by increasing the surface area of their roots.
- Compounds obtained from fungi are used for a variety of medicines.
- Many foods eaten by people are made from fungi.
- Fungi can have adverse effects on humans and plants.

Review **Vocabulary PuzzleMaker**

For additional practice with vocabulary, have students access the Vocabulary PuzzleMaker online.

Review **Vocabulary eGames**

Section 1

Vocabulary Review

Each of the following sentences is false. Make each sentence true by replacing the italicized word with a vocabulary term found on the Study Guide page.

1. *Hyphae* is/are the cross walls between fungal cells.

2. *Chitin* is/are the threadlike filaments found in certain fungi.

3. A tough, flexible polysaccharide is called *septa.*

Understand Main Ideas

4. MAIN Idea Which does not describe a method by which fungi obtain food?
A. parasitism **C.** photosynthesis
B. decomposition **D.** mutualism

5. Which structure of fungi is different from plants?
A. composition of cytoplasm
B. composition of cell walls
C. exoskeletons
D. cellulose

Use the image to answer question 6.

Color-Enhanced SEM Magnification: 1100×

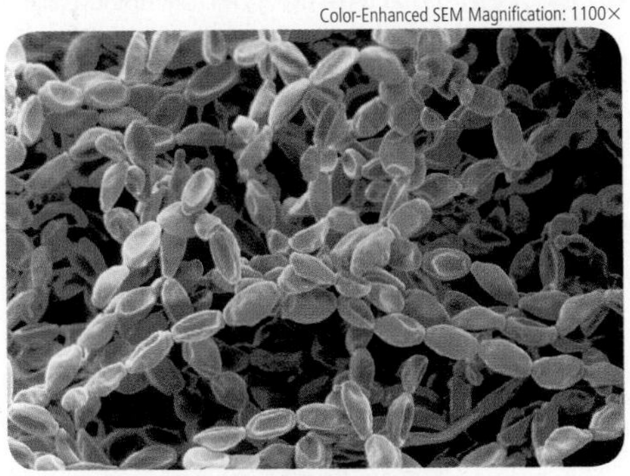

6. What is the structure shown above?
A. hyphae **C.** chitin
B. septae **D.** spores

7. Which can be used for asexual and sexual reproduction?
A. gametes **C.** fragmentation
B. budding **D.** spores

Use the diagram to answer question 8.

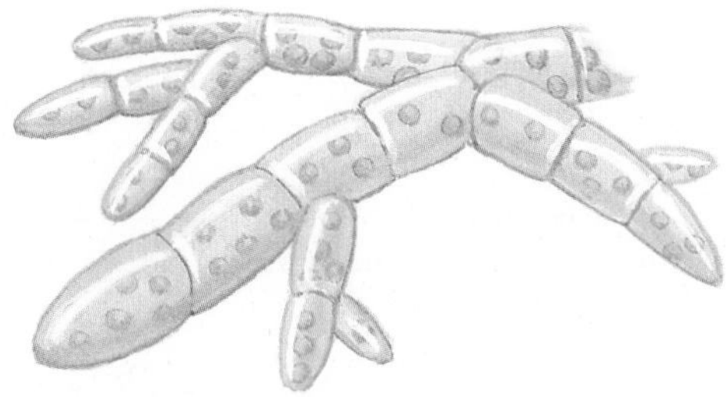

8. What is the structure shown above?
A. mycelium
B. spore
C. septate hyphae
D. aseptate hyphae

Constructed Response

9. THEME FOCUS Energy Distinguish between parasitic fungi and saprophytic fungi.

10. Short Answer Distinguish between hyphae and mycelia.

11. Open Ended Hypothesize the best method of reducing the number of mold spores in your classroom. How would you test your hypothesis?

Think Critically

12. Infer how the structure of the aseptate hyphae allows for more rapid growth.

13. Assess the ability of fungi to disperse their spores.

Section 2

Vocabulary Review

Explain the differences between the vocabulary terms in the following sets.

14. stolon, rhizoid

15. ascospore, ascus

16. basidiocarp, basidia

Chapter 20 Assessment

Section 1

Vocabulary Review

1. septa
2. hyphae
3. chitin

Understand Main Ideas

4. C
5. B
6. A
7. D
8. C

Constructed Response

9. Saprophytes are decomposers and parasites feed off their hosts.
10. Hyphae make up the mycelium; they are the building blocks.
11. Answers will vary but might include use filters, use air conditioning, create a dry environment, or build a new school. Accept all reasonable proposals for testing the hypothesis.

Think Critically

12. The nutrients in hyphae circulate rapidly. Growth energy goes into increasing length rather than diameter.
13. Fungi rely on the environment to spread spores—wind, water, animals, etc. are involved. Increased appeal to animals such as odor, color, or taste might help. Structural changes allowing easier transport by wind and water would also be factors.

Section 2

Vocabulary Review

14. Stolons develop along the food surface; rhizoids penetrate to form anchors and absorb nutrients.
15. Ascospores are borne by the ascus.
16. Both are fruiting bodies. Basidiocarp refers to the fruiting body grown from the mycelium. Basidia are club-shaped hyphae that produce spores.

Assessment Online Test Practice

Understand Main Ideas
17. D
18. B
19. B
20. B
21. B

Constructed Response
22. Answers will vary. Students will most likely describe reproduction in a zygomycete, ascomycete, or deuteromycete.
23. Graphic organizers will vary depending on the species the students researched.
24. Answers will vary but should include chitin-containing cell walls, absorption of nutrients from the environment, and molecular evidence.

Think Critically
25. See student experimental design. Scientific methods should be applied.
26. Student should collect data and calculate percentage.

Section 3

Vocabulary Review
27. lichen
28. mycorrhiza
29. bioindicator

Understand Main Ideas
30. C

Understand Main Ideas

17. Which fungi have flagellated spores?
A. basidiomycetes
B. zygomycetes
C. ascomycetes
D. chytridiomycetes

18. What is the function of stolons?
A. to penetrate the food
B. to spread across the surface of food
C. to digest the food
D. to reproduce

19. Which is a unicellular fungi?
A. bread mold
B. yeast
C. mushroom
D. Bird's Nest fungus

Use the diagram to answer question 20.

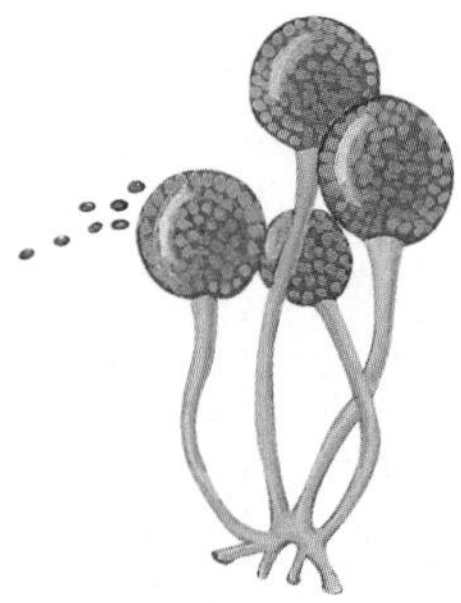

20. Within which structure do the fungi in the diagram form their spores?
A. ascocarp
B. sporangium
C. ascus
D. ascophore

21. What word best describes the structure you identified in question 20?
A. bud
B. haploid
C. diploid
D. fragmented

Constructed Response

22. Short Answer Choose one type of fungus that reproduces asexually and describe the process.

23. Open Ended Research the different size spores produced by basidiomycetes and prepare a graphic organizer for the class.

24. MAIN Idea Compose an argument to defend the placement of chytrids in Kingdom Fungi instead of Kingdom Protista.

Think Critically

25. Design an experiment to determine if homemade bread is more or less likely to grow fungus than commercially produced bread.

26. Collect and interpret data on how many of your classmates have mold allergies. Calculate the percentage of allergic classmates.

Section 3

Vocabulary Review

Use what you know about the vocabulary terms found on the Study Guide page to answer the following questions.

27. What term describes a symbiotic relationship between a fungus and an alga?

28. MAIN Idea What term describes a symbiotic relationship between a fungus and a plant root?

29. What is the name of a living organism that is sensitive to environmental pollutants?

Understand Main Ideas

Use the image to answer question 30.

30. In an area recovering from a forest fire, what is this lichen's main function?
A. absorbing water
B. bioindicator
C. pioneer species
D. keeping insects away

Assessment Online Test Practice

31. Why are lichens important bioindicators?
   A. They are susceptible to drought.
   B. They are unicellular.
   C. They are mutualistic.
   D. They are susceptible to air pollutants.

Use the image below to answer question 32.

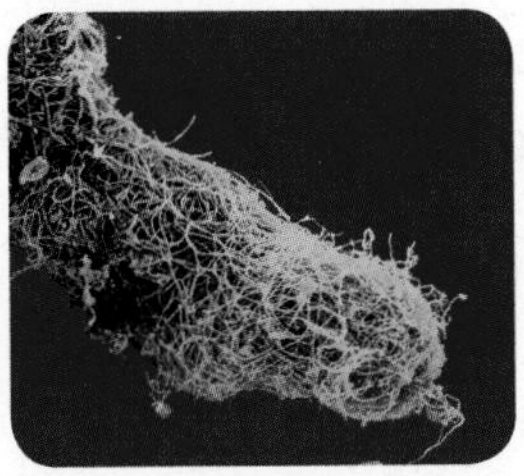

32. How is this mycorrhiza benefiting the plant?
   A. increases the surface area for gathering light
   B. decreases the need for water
   C. increases the surface area of the roots
   D. decreases the temperature

Constructed Response

33. **Short Answer** In what ways are fungi beneficial to humans?

34. **Short Answer** Evaluate the role of lichens in arctic environments.

Think Critically

35. **Predict** how the availability of the antibiotic penicillin during World War II impacted the soldiers.

36. **Design an experiment** that will allow you to test the antibiotic effects of two or three common fungi.

37. **CAREERS IN BIOLOGY** Write a want ad for a mycologist in a research labratory.

38. **Design** an organism that cultivates its own food production using fungi. How might the fungi benefit from this relationship?

39. **Hypothesize** why mycorrhizae might have been important for the colonization of land by plants. What kind of evidence would you look for to support your hypothesis?

Summative Assessment

40. **BIG Idea** Imagine that you are a scientist that has discovered a new species of fungi. Describe its physical characteristics, method of obtaining nutrition, and method of reproduction. How would you classify this new species of fungi?

41. **WRITING in Biology** Imagine yourself as a fungal spore landing near your home or school. Evaluate your chances of survival.

DBQ Document-Based Questions

Data obtained from: http://sbr.ipmpipe.org/cgi-bin/sbr/public.cgi

This map shows where Asian soybean rust Phakopsora pachyrhizi *is found in the United States. It is a recent arrival from Brazil and other parts of South America. Its presence in each state was officially diagnosed by the USDA. Soybean rust is a disease caused by the fungus* Phakopsora pachyrhizi, *which recently has become a problem for soybean farmers in the United States. Losses from this infection can amount to 80 percent of the crop.*

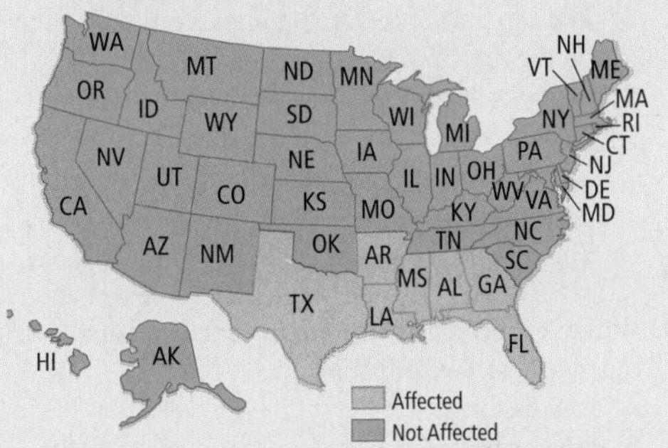

42. Evaluate the map and speculate about the factors affecting the distribution of soybean rust in the U.S.

43. Apply what you know about fungi to recommend a course of action to eradicate this fungus.

44. Estimate the impact of this fungus on the future of soybean production in the U.S.

31. D
32. C

Constructed Response

33. Fungi are used directly for food and in the cultivation and manufacturing of food. They help rid the environment of dead animals and organic materials.
34. Lichens are the major source of ground cover. They also provide nutrition for grazing animals.

Think Critically

35. Thousands of lives were saved because penicillin cured infections in wounded soldiers. The discovery of penicillin's usefulness as a medicine coincided with an event that had major impact on our world.
36. Experimental design should include creating an appropriate culture for testing and structure for eliminating the impact of environment on the experiment.
37. Ads will vary depending on the area in which the students request the mycologist be specialized.
38. Designs will vary. Students might design organisms that protect the fungi they eat.
39. Possible answer: Mycorrhizae might have been able to break down nutrients so that they could be absorbed by plant roots. To prove this idea, you could look for evidence that plants become malnourished when mycorrhizae are not present.

Summative Assessment

40. Possible answer: physical characteristics: multicellular, club-shaped hyphae, and fruiting body; method of obtaining nutrition: parasitism; method of reproduction: spore production; classification: Basidiomycota.

41. Answers will vary. Students should describe the possible locations they might land and how the locations would be conducive or detrimental to their growth.

WRITING in Biology

RUBRIC Use the modifiable rubric found on your eTeacherEdition Online to assess writing assignments.

DBQ Document-Based Questions

Stokstad, E. 2004. Plant pathologists gear up for battle with dread fungus. *Science* 306: 1672–1673.

42. Possible answer: The soybean rust might be distributed by wind or animals.
43. Possible answer: Use beneficial fungi to kill the harmful fungi.
44. Possible answer: The fungus will cause soybean crop production to fall.

Assessment Online Test Practice

Standardized Test Practice

Multiple Choice

1. A 5. D
2. C 6. D
3. B 7. B
4. D 8. C

Short Answer

9. Possible answers include the following.
Amoeba have pseudopods, a temporary extension of the cytoplasm that allows the amoeba to pull itself.
Paramecium have cilia, short hairlike structures that allow it to move.
Trypanosoma have flagella, single, long, whiplike structure that propels the organism.
10. Classification would depend on observations of its structures, feeding habit, and form of locomotion. For example, single-celled organisms are classified as prokaryotes or eukaryotes. Suppose the organism was eukaryotic and heterotrophic. It could be classified as an animal-like protozoan. If the organism lacked cilia or flagella, it could be an amoeba. An amoeba has the ability to move around on a surface, such as mud.
11. Accept all logical answers. One possible answer is that technology cannot stop people from fighting with one another. Technology can affect some aspects of human behavior but cannot change the underlying motives of people.
12. Answers might vary. Protists are classified together because they are not animals, plants, or fungi. Feeding habits are the main characteristics used to classify the three main groups of protists. Animal-like protists are heterotrophic. Plantlike protists are autotrophic. Funguslike protists absorb nutrients from other organisms.

Standardized Test Practice

Cumulative

Multiple Choice

1. Which are autotrophic protists commonly referred to as?
   A. algae
   B. protozoans
   C. slime molds
   D. water molds

Use the diagram below to answer questions 2 and 3.

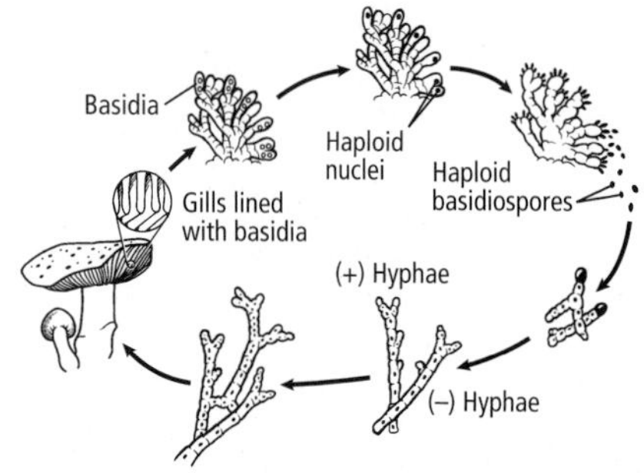

2. What part of this life cycle can be used to explain why many mushrooms grow quickly?
   A. The cap pulls in organic matter from the soil to fill the mushroom.
   B. The gills in the cap rapidly divide to form the mushroom.
   C. The hyphae grow and extend rapidly to form the mushroom.
   D. The basidia grow and lengthen the mushroom.

3. Which occurrence pictured in the diagram allows the mating types to fuse?
   A. basidia form
   B. hyphae unite
   C. mushroom forms
   D. spores release

4. A certain tree-dwelling primate has a prehensile tail and nails on its digits. To which group of primates would you expect this animal to belong?
   A. Asian apes
   B. New World monkeys
   C. Old World monkeys
   D. prosimians

5. Which occurs during the lytic cycle of a viral infection?
   A. The host cell becomes a factory that continually makes more copies of the virus.
   B. The host cell undergoes cell division that makes more copies of the virus.
   C. The virus incorporates its nucleic acid into the DNA of the host cell and lies dormant.
   D. The virus takes over the cell, makes copies of itself, and usually kills the host cell.

Use the figure below to answer question 6.

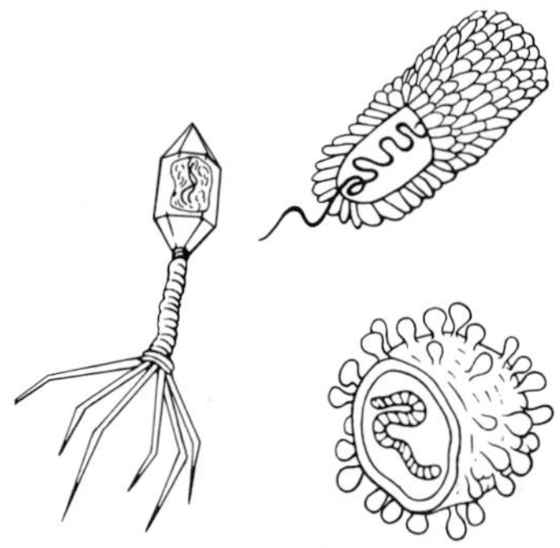

6. On what property do scientists base their classification of viruses?
   A. capsid proteins
   B. chromosome number
   C. host resistance
   D. type of genetic material

7. Which characteristic distinguishes australopithecines from earlier hominoids?
   A. binocular vision
   B. bipedalism
   C. fingernails
   D. opposable thumbs

8. Which is a characteristic of an acellular slime mold?
   A. cytoplasm with many cells
   B. locomotion by means of cilia
   C. plasmodium with many nuclei
   D. reproduction by fragmentation

Short Answer

Use the diagram below to answer question 9.

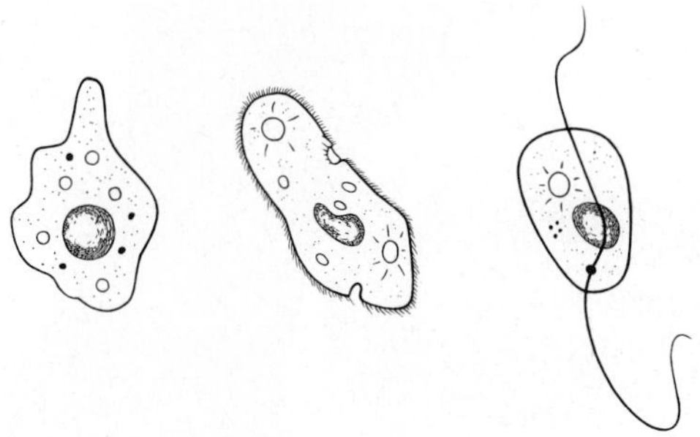

9. Identify the structure used for locomotion in each of these organisms. Briefly describe how each structure functions.

10. Imagine that you found a unicellular organism living in the mud at the bottom of a pond. Write a plan to determine how you would classify it.

11. Some people think that technology can solve all human problems. Name and critique an example of a problem that technology might not be able to solve.

12. What characteristics are used to classify protists into three groups? Explain your answer.

13. Describe how sexual reproduction begins in ascomycetes and assess its significance.

14. Give examples of three ways that fungi are important for human foods.

Extended Response

15. Create a flowchart to show how isolation of a small population can lead to speciation.

16. Assess the value of mycorrhizae for plants.

17. Evaluate how viruses benefit from their small size and simple composition.

18. Imagine that you've noticed that mushrooms grow in one corner of a field every time it rains. Give a reason why picking the mushrooms immediately following a rainshower will not stop them from growing back.

Essay Question

Light is needed for photosynthesis to take place. Algae depend on the energy from light to carry out photosynthesis. The main photosynthetic pigment of green algae is chlorophyll. Sunlight is composed of all of the different wavelengths of visible light, but only blue light and red light are absorbed by chlorophyll. Other algae contain larger amounts of other pigments, such as carotenoids. Carotenoids absorb energy from green light. Because algae live in water, this becomes important because water absorbs the different colors of light at different rates.

Using the information in the paragraph above, answer the following question in essay format.

19. Red light does not penetrate into water. Algae in water must be able to use light energy that is available under water. Write an essay about why carotenoids are better than chlorophyll for algae living well below the surface of water.

NEED EXTRA HELP?																			
If You Missed Question . . .	1	2	3	4	5	6	7	8	9	10	11	12	13	14	15	16	17	18	19
Review Section . . .	19.3	20.2	20.2	16.1	18.2	18.2	16.2	19.4	19.2	19.2	18.1	1.2	20.2	20.3	15.3	20.2	18.2	20.2	19.3

13. Sexual reproduction begins when two hyphae from opposite mating types fuse and one nucleus from each type pair off in separate cells. The significance of sexual reproduction is that it allows for the recombination of genetic material in Ascomycetes.

14. Answers will vary. Examples might include baking (yeast making bread rise), edible mushrooms (truffles), and providing flavoring for foods (flavor in colas).

Extended Response

15. Wording for the answers can vary.

Isolation of a small part of the population occurs.
↓
Alleles in the gene pool that increase fitness are naturally selected.
↓
Allele frequency in the population is gradually changed.
↓
Populations develop such differences that they cannot interbreed.
↓
A new species has formed.

16. Mycorrhizae are symbiotic relationships between the roots of plants and certain fungi. The fungi help plants to absorb water and minerals. The fungi receive carbohydrates and amino acids from the plants. Plants that have mycorrhizal relationships appear more healthy and vigorous. Some plants cannot survive without mycorrhizal fungi.

17. Because viruses are small, they can get to host cells very easily and they are easily spread between hosts. In the host cell viruses can quickly assemble their comparatively simple parts in large numbers.

18. The mycelium of the fungus extends through a large area of the soil. The mushrooms appear as reproductive structures of the fungus. Picking the mushrooms destroys the reproductive structures above ground, but does not destroy the mycelium that is growing in the ground. When conditions are right, more mushrooms will grow back from the mycelium.

Essay Question

19. Algae living well below the surface have little or no red light available for photosynthesis. Carotenoids do not absorb red light. They can absorb other wavelengths of light in ranges that are available. This gives the certain algae the ability to live much deeper in the water and still obtain energy. Because the different algae do well at different levels, competition for resources, such as sunlight and dissolved minerals in the water, is reduced and all the different algae can thrive.

UNIT 6

Plants

Preview the Unit

Have students preview the chapters in this unit and make a concept map or graphic organizer relating the Themes, Big Ideas, and Main Ideas. Students' maps should show a hierarchy between Big Ideas and Main Ideas and the interconnectedness of the Themes.

Chapter 21
Introduction to Plants
BIG Idea Plants have changed over time and are now a diverse group of organisms.

Chapter 22
Plant Structure and Function
BIG Idea The diverse nature of plants is due to the variety of their structures.

Chapter 23
Reproduction in Plants
BIG Idea The life cycles of plants include various methods of reproduction.

WebQuest
Careers in Biology

UNIT 6
Plants

THEMES

Scientific Inquiry The study of adaptations in plants has contributed to the understanding of evolutionary changes.

Diversity The 300,000 types of plants found on Earth have different types of leaves, stems, and roots, and they fill different niches.

Energy Using the process of photosynthesis, plants convert the Sun's energy to chemical energy.

Homeostasis A combination of structures and processes maintains homeostasis in plants.

Change Changes in the plant kingdom can be inferred by comparing primitive plants to the more structurally advanced plants.

WebQuest **CAREERS IN BIOLOGY**

Botanists are scientists who study plants. Botanists might specialize in many disciplines from bryology (the study of mosses and simple plants) to dendrology (the study of trees and woody plants). This giant sequoia researcher is a dendrologist.

5-Minute UNIT LAUNCH

Connect to Students' Lives Organize the class into small groups. Have each group brainstorm a list of all the things we get from plants. Provide each group with poster board or space on the board to list their ideas. Have students divide the list into categories such as food, shelter, fuel, etc.

Video

What's BIOLOGY Got To Do With It?
This video discusses enviromental friendliness and corn products.

Misconceptions

In each section, *Clarify a Misconception* provides you with the information to dispel a common student misconception. A question will help you elicit the misconception, and an explanation will help you correct it.

Below is a preview of misconceptions from each chapter in this unit.

Before studying Chapter 21, students might think that they can determine which direction is north by finding where moss grows on trees. Chapter 21 will explain that, contrary to common belief, moss does not only grow on the north side of trees, but tends to grow where there is shade and moisture (p. 612).

Before studying Chapter 22, students might think that all plant cells are green. Chapter 22 will explain that some plant cells do not contain chloroplasts and are therefore not green. It is the chlorophyll contained in the chloroplasts that appears green (p. 633).

Before studying Chapter 23, students might think that all plants are pollinated by bees or other insects. Chapter 23 will explain that although this is true for most flower pollination, it is not true of most major food crops. These are either wind pollinated, self-pollinated, or propagated using vegetative reproduction (p. 671).

SERVICE LEARNING/COMMUNITY SERVICE

Teach Others Sample text Have students design and create a "Plant Walk" on the school grounds or a nearby park. Students should identify and label the plants so other students can use the "Walk" to help them learn about different local plants. Students also can create identification keys or guides to help others learn more about the plants. Research has shown that students are more committed to projects when they have a voice in the development and implementation of those projects (Zeldin and Tarlov, 1997).

Research bibliography on pages 32T–34T

Chapter 21 Organizer: Introduction to Plants

LabManager™
Customize any lab with the LabManager™ CD-ROM.

Essential Questions	National Science Standards	Materials and Planning Estimated times include cleanup and disposal, but do not include teacher prep time. For cleanup and disposal guidelines, see page 39T.	Est. Time (min)
Section 1 **1.** How do the characteristics of plants and green algae compare? **2.** What are the adaptations of plants to land environments? **3.** What is the importance of vascular tissue to plant life on land? **4.** What is alternation of generations of plants? **5.** What are the divisions of the plant kingdom?	UCP1–5; A.1, A.2; C.3, C.4, C.5; E.1, E.2; F.1, F.3, F.4, F.6; G.1, G.2, G.3	**Launch Lab,** p. 602: plant specimens	20
		MiniLab 1, p. 605: leaves from a deciduous tree, lettuce leaves, conifer needles, triple-beam balance, plastic plate	20
		Demonstration, p. 605: sponge, waxed paper	5
		Activity, p. 608: samples of four plant groups, such as moss, ferns, seeds, pine cone, grass blade, flowers on stems, deciduous tree leaf	15
Section 2 **1.** What are the structures of nonvascular plants? **2.** What are the similarities and differences between the nonvascular plant divisions?	UCP.1, UCP.2, UCP.5; A.1, A.2; C.3, C.4; D.2; F.3, F.4; G.1, G.2	**Demonstration,** p. 611: sphagnum moss, water	15
Section 3 **1.** What are the characteristics of seedless vascular plants? **2.** What are the similarities and differences between the characteristics of club mosses and ferns?	UCP.1–5; A.1, A.2; C.3, C.4, C.5, C.6; F.3; G.1, G.2, G.3	**Demonstration,** p. 615: samples of the horsetail Equisetum	15
Section 4 **1.** What are the similarities and differences among the seed plants? **2.** What are the divisions of gymnosperms? **3.** What are the life spans of angiosperms?	UCP.1–5, A.1, A.2; C.3, C.4, C.5, C.6; E.1, E.2; F.1, F.2, F.3, F.4, F.5, F.6; G.1, G.2, G.3	**Demonstration,** p. 617: seeds with dispersal mechanisms, such as dandelions, milkweed, burrs, maple samara, acorn, and fruit with seeds inside	15
		MiniLab 2, p. 620: SI ruler, magnifying lens, variety of conifer leaf samples	25
		BioLab, p. 623: local field guide, metric ruler, magnifying lens	90

Suggested Time for Each Lesson

Class	Chapter Opener	Section 1	Section 2	Section 3	Section 4	Assessment
Basic	45 min	90 min	45 min	45 min	45 min	45 min
General	25 min	90 min	55 min	55 min	45 min	45 min
Honors	5 min	20 min	45 min	45 min	45 min	20 min

ConnectED

connectED.mcgraw-hill.com

Access interactive learning opportunities and teaching resources using these icons located throughout your StudentWorks™ Plus Online and eTeacherEdition Online.

Chapter 21 Section Resources

FAST FILE Unit 6 Resources:
Launch Lab Worksheet*
MiniLab Worksheet*
Study Guide (English/Spanish)*
Section Quick Check

Reading Essentials 21.1
Science Notebook 21.1*

FAST FILE Unit 6 Resources:
Study Guide (English/Spanish)*
Section Quick Check

Reading Essentials 21.2
Science Notebook 21.2*

FAST FILE Unit 6 Resources:
Study Guide (English/Spanish)*
Section Quick Check

Reading Essentials 21.3
Science Notebook 21.3*

FAST FILE Unit 6 Resources:
MiniLab Worksheet*
BioLab Worksheet*
Study Guide (English/Spanish)*
Section Quick Check

Reading Essentials 21.4
Science Notebook 21.4*

Additional Chapter 21 Resources

FAST FILE Unit 6 Resources:
Chapter Diagnostic Test
Concept Mapping*
Real-World Biology
Enrichment
Chapter Tests A, B, and C

Transparencies:
Bellringer Transparencies*
Biology Concepts Transparencies*

Lab Resources:
Laboratory Manual*
Probeware Lab Manual*
Forensics Lab Manual*
Pre-AP Lab Manual*
Open Inquiry in Biology*
Guided Inquiry in Biology*

Technology

Teaching Tools:
eTeacherEdition Online
Classroom Presentation Toolkit CD-ROM*
LabManager™ CD-ROM*
Video Lab DVD*
Virtual Lab CD-ROM*
What's BIOLOGY Got To Do With It?
StudentWorks™ Plus Online*

Chapter Assessment Tools:
Classroom Presentation Toolkit CD-ROM*
ExamView® Assessment Suite CD-ROM

Web-Based Resources:
- StudentWorks™ Plus Online
- eTeacherEdition Online
- Animations*
- The Interactive Time Line*
- Interactive Tables*
- Online Quizzes
- Online Test Practice
- Standardized Test Practice
- Virtual Labs*
- Multilingual eGlossary*
- Vocabulary eGames*
- Vocabulary eFlashcards
- WebQuests
- Personal Tutors

While all resources listed are appropriate for English learners, the * indicates resources with a strong visual or hands-on component for EL.

Teaching strategies and activities have been coded for differentiated instruction.

AL Activities for students working above grade level	**OL** Activities for students working on grade level	**BL** Activities for students working below grade level	**EL** Activities for English learners (also ELL)	**COOP LEARN** Activities designed for small cooperative group work

CHAPTER 21

Launch Lab
What characteristics differ among plants?

Inquiry Launch Lab

For a lab worksheet, use your eTeacherEdition Online.

RUBRIC A rubric for evaluating Launch Labs is found on your eTeacherEdition Online

Est. Time 20 min

Alternative Materials Photos of a variety of plants can be used.

Teaching Strategies

- Give students specific examples of characteristics to look for during the activity. Examples include leaf size, shape, color, and grouping; presence or absence of flowers, fruit, and seeds; thickness of stem, stalk, or trunk; shrublike or treelike appearance; presence of vines.
- Remind students that they are looking for characteristics of these plants that make them similar to or different from each other.

Procedure

1. Read and complete the lab safety form.
2. Label five **plant specimens** using the letters *A*, *B*, *C*, *D*, and *E*.
3. Study each plant carefully. Wash your hands thoroughly after handling plant material.
4. Based on your observations, list characteristics that describe the differences and similarities among these plants.
5. Rank your list of characteristics based on what you consider the most and least important.

CHAPTER 21

Introduction to Plants

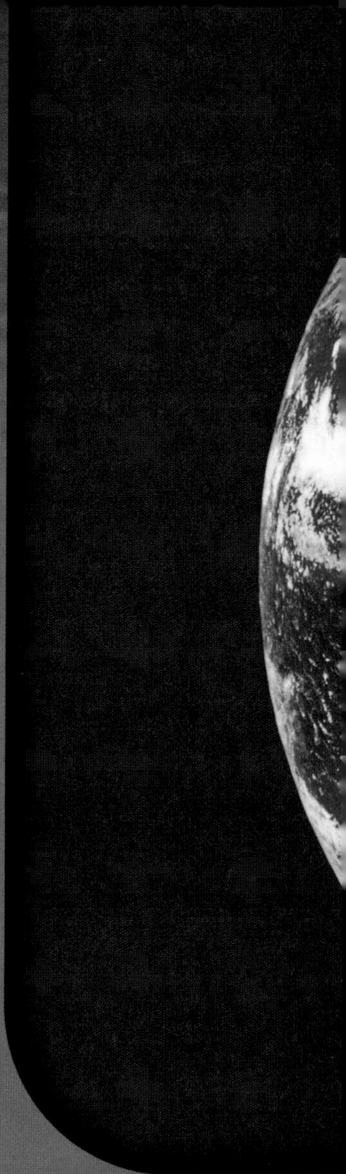

ConnectED

Your one-stop online resource
connectED.mcgraw-hill.com

- Video
- Audio
- Review
- Inquiry
- WebQuest
- Assessment
- Concepts in Motion
- Multilingual eGlossary

Launch Lab
What characteristics differ among plants?

Scientists use specific characteristics to group plants within the plant kingdom. In this lab, you will examine some of the characteristics of plants.

For a lab worksheet, use your StudentWorks™ Plus Online.

Inquiry Launch Lab

FOLDABLES®

Make a layered-look book using the labels shown. Use it to organize your notes on plant adaptations.

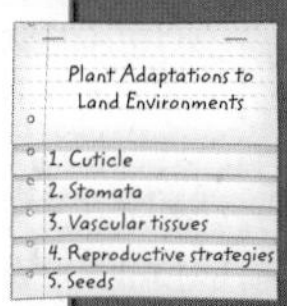

Analysis

1. **Compare** your list to your classmates' lists. Answers will vary depending upon students' lists.
2. **Describe** the diversity among the plants that you studied. Answers will vary based on plants chosen for the study, but students should recognize that there is diversity within the plant kingdom.
3. **List** plant characteristics that you could not observe that might be useful in organizing these plants into groups.

Students should recognize that the presence and absence of leaves, flowers, pollen, fruit, and seeds may vary seasonally. They might suggest that classifying according to molecular/genetic characteristics might be helpful.

THEME FOCUS Diversity
The 300,000 types of plants found all over Earth fill different niches.

BIG Idea Plants have changed over time and are now a diverse group of organisms.

THEMES

Scientific Inquiry The study of adaptations in plants has contributed to the understanding of evolution.

Diversity The niches that were available for plants to fill resulted in a large diversity of plants.

Energy Plants convert light energy to chemical energy via photosynthesis.

Homeostasis Structural adaptations allowed plants to colonize land and maintain homeostasis.

Change Plants have changed over time due to environmental changes on Earth.

Introduce the Chapter

Plants Have students look at the chapter opener photo on this page.

ASK STUDENTS: ***How would you describe the plants in the three photos?*** Answers will vary, but students might list evergreen trees, cacti, and lily pads in their responses. Record student responses. Then, as students read the chapter, have them replace the common terms in their descriptions with accurate scientific terms (*conifer* for evergreen tree, *agave plants* for cacti, and *water lilies* for lily pads).

BIG Idea

Use visuals A few days before you begin this chapter, ask students to collect pictures of as many different land plants as possible. Remind students that there are different groups of land plants, such as mosses, grasses, and trees. On the day you begin this chapter, display the pictures.

ASK STUDENTS: ***Where do you think each kind of plant in the pictures grows?*** Answers will vary depending on photos but may include cacti that grow in dry deserts, firs that grow in mountain forests, and wildflowers that grow on sunny grasslands. Have students find and read the main ideas of this chapter and then consider what adaptations allow each type of plant to grow in a particular land environment.

Section 1

MAIN Idea

BL OL Plant Evolution Show students two pictures, one of a desert and one of a swamp. **ASK STUDENTS:** ***Do you think the same types of plants grow in these two areas?*** no ***Why not?*** Students might suggest that different climates or amounts of water could affect the types of plants that grow in an area. Explain that different plants do grow in different environments and that as the environments on Earth changed, plant evolution occurred.

AL Have students propose some ways that plants in deserts or swamps are adapted to their environments. Desert plants have a covering to keep from drying out. Swamp plants have large leaf areas that are adaptations to limited sunlight.

W Writing Support

EL OL Technical Writing Have students skim through the chapter and list all plant divisions on lined paper, leaving several lines between each. As students read the chapter, have them add descriptions for the different plant divisions.

BL Give students a graphic organizer with the plant divisions listed and point out pages where they will find descriptions.

S Skill Practice

EL AL Visual Literacy To help students visualize the fossil record, have students copy the evolutionary tree in Figure 1 and, after researching, add dates for the events shown.

Section 1

Reading Preview

Essential Questions

- How do the characteristics of plants and green algae compare?
- What are the adaptations of plants to land environments?
- What is the importance of vascular tissue to plant life on land?
- What is alternation of generations of plants?
- What are the divisions of the plant kingdom?

Review Vocabulary

limiting factor: any abiotic or biotic factor that restricts the existence, numbers, reproduction, or distribution of organisms

New Vocabulary

stomata
vascular tissue
vascular plant
nonvascular plant
seed

g Multilingual eGlossary

Plant Evolution and Adaptations

MAIN Idea **Adaptations to environmental changes on Earth contributed to the evolution of plants.**

Real-World Reading Link Perhaps you have seen a photo of your ancestors and noticed that some of your living relatives resemble people in the photo. In a similar way, scientists who study evolution notice common characteristics among ancient groups of organisms and present-day groups.

W Plant Evolution

Plants are vital to our survival. The oxygen we breathe, the food we eat, and many of the things that make our lives comfortable, such as clothing, furniture, and our homes, come from or are parts of plants. If you were asked to describe a plant, would you describe a tree, a garden flower, or a houseplant? Biologists describe plants as multicellular eukaryotes with tissues and organs that have specialized structures and functions. For example, most plants have photosynthetic tissues, and organs that anchor them in soil or to an object or another plant. However, does this description apply to ancient plants?

Connection to Earth Science Recall that Earth is about 4.6 billion years old. Can you imagine ancient Earth without land plants? That was the case until about 400 million years ago, when primitive land plants appeared. However, fossil evidence from about 500 million years ago indicates that the shallow waters of ancient Earth were filled with a variety of organisms—archaea, bacteria, algae and other protists, and animals, such as sponges, corals, and worms.

There is strong evidence, including biochemical and fossil evidence, that multicellular land plants and present-day green algae share a common ancestor, as diagrammed in the evolutionary tree in **Figure 1.** This common ancestor might have been able to survive periods of drought. Through natural selection, drought-resistant adaptations in that ancestor, such as protected embryos and other survival characteristics, might have passed to future generations. When scientists compare present-day plants and present-day green algae, they find the following common characteristics:

- cell walls composed of cellulose
- cell division that includes the formation of a cell plate
- the same type of chlorophyll used in photosynthesis
- similar genes for ribosomal RNA
- food stored as starch
- the same types of enzymes in cellular vesicles

S

■ **Figure 1** This evolutionary tree shows the relationship of ancient freshwater green algae to present-day plants.

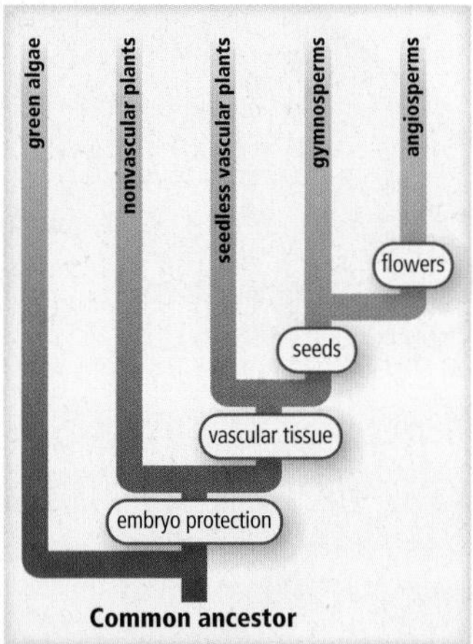

Content Background

Teacher FYI Dr. Richard McCourt, from the Academy of Natural Sciences, reported in 2001 that his research indicated that land plants most likely invaded from freshwater instead of salt water, as was commonly believed. He used gene sequencing to compare the DNA of ancient land and freshwater algae and found that the closest relative of land plants is a type of algae called stoneworts, which often have lime encrusted along their filaments.

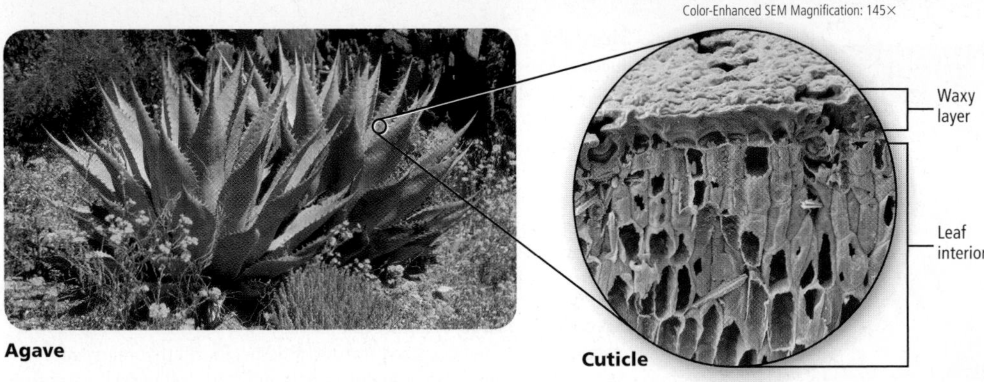

■ **Figure 2** The cuticle is produced by the outer layer of cells. Plants in dry environments often have a thick waxy layer over the cuticle.
***Infer** what advantage this waxy layer provides to plants in dry environments.*

Plant Adaptations to Land Environments

While living on land might seem advantageous for many organisms, there are challenges for land organisms that aquatic organisms do not face. Over time, plants that inhabited land developed adaptations that helped them survive limited water resources as well as other environmental factors.

C **Cuticle** Have you ever noticed that some plant leaves appear shinier than others, or that some leaves have a grayish appearance, such as those of the agave in **Figure 2?** An adaptation found on most aboveground plant parts is a fatty coating called the cuticle on the outer surface of their cells. Wax can also be a component of the cuticle, giving it a grayish appearance. Fats and waxes are lipids and are insoluble in water. Because of this, the cuticle helps prevent the evaporation of water from plant tissues and can also act as a barrier to invading microorganisms.

VOCABULARY
WORD ORIGIN
Cuticle
from the Latin diminutive word *cuticula,* meaning *skin*

MiniLab 1

Compare Plant Cuticles

? Inquiry MiniLab

Does the cuticle vary among different types of plants? Plant leaves are covered with a cuticle that reduces water loss. The thickness of cuticle material varies among plants.

Procedure

1. Read and complete the lab safety form.
2. Observe the **plant leaves** provided by your teacher. Write a description of each leaf type.
3. Pile each type of leaf on separate but identical **plastic plates.** Measure the mass and then adjust the number of leaves on each plate until they are of equal mass. Record the masses.
4. The next day, examine each plate of leaves. Record your observations.
5. Measure the mass of each plate of leaves and record the data.

Analysis

1. **Interpret Data** Which leaves appeared to have lost more water? Do the data support your observations?
2. **Infer** which leaves might have a thicker cuticle.

Demonstration

Cuticle Ten minutes before class, completely wrap a damp sponge in waxed paper to allow water vapor to accumulate on the inside. Show students the wrapped sponge. Point out that this is the same way that the cuticle on leaves and stems prevents water evaporation from the plant. Est. time: 5 min

■ **Caption Question Fig. 2** prevents excess water loss

C Critical Thinking

EL BL Infer Show students a fresh leaf that has been sprayed with water.
ASK STUDENTS: ***Why is the water beading up on the leaf?*** because of the cuticle ***How does the cuticle help a plant conserve water?*** The cuticle prevents water loss from the plant.

MiniLab 1

? Inquiry Mini Lab

For a lab worksheet, use your eTeacherEdition Online.

RUBRIC A rubric for evaluating MiniLabs is found on your eTeacherEdition Online.

Est. Time 20 min

Additional Materials leaves from a deciduous tree; thin lettuce leaves; conifer needles; triple-beam balance

Safety Precautions Approve lab safety forms before work begins.

Teaching Strategy Students should understand the basic function of the plant cuticle prior to beginning this exercise.

Cleanup and Disposal Designate an area for students to place plant material, then dispose of it properly. Have students wash hands thoroughly after handling plant material.

Analysis

1. lettuce leaves; yes, the data should support this observation.
2. Students should infer that the leaves that lost the least amount of water had thicker cuticles.

LabManager™
Customize this lab with the LabManager™ CD-ROM.

D Develop Concepts

BL OL AL

Clarify a Misconception
Students often assume that stomata are only on the lower surfaces of leaves.

ASK STUDENTS: ***Where are stomata found?*** leaves ***Is that the only part of a plant where we find stomata?*** No, they are also found in green stems. Show students pictures of plants with soft green stems. ***How do these cells get carbon dioxide for photosynthesis?*** through stomata Show students a picture of a water-lily leaf such as the one on page 603. ***Where do you think the stomata are located on this leaf?*** upper side To exchange gases with air, stomata must be on an upper surface, because the bottom surface is under water.

R Reading Strategy

BL OL COOP LEARN

Frayer Model To use the Frayer model for the new vocabulary terms *vascular tissue* and *vascular plants,* have pairs of students fold a paper into four sections. In the upper-left quadrant, have them write *vascular tissue* and *vascular plants* with definitions. In the upper-right quadrant, have them list characteristics of the terms, and have them list examples of plants in the lower-left quadrant. In the last quadrant, have them list nonexamples (nonvascular plants).

FOLDABLES

RUBRIC A rubric for evaluating Foldables is found on your eTeacherEdition Online.

Going Further

SAY TO STUDENTS: ***Give examples of what would happen to land plants if each of the adaptations had not taken place. For example, what would happen to a leaf without a cuticle in a dry climate?*** It would dry out.

SEM Magnification: 1000×

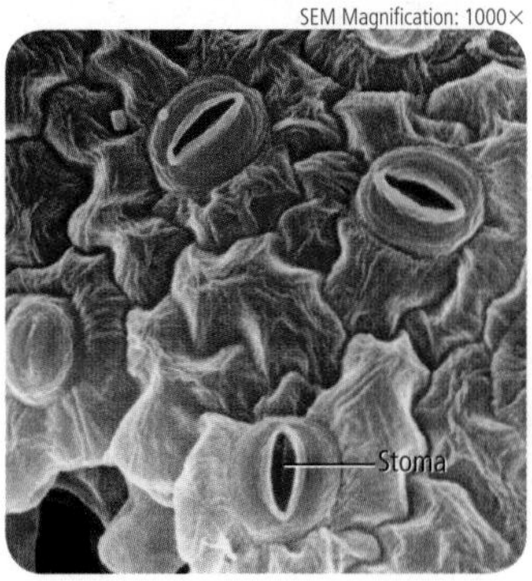

■ **Figure 3** Stomata are common on the lower surfaces of most plants' leaves.

FOLDABLES Incorporate information from this section into your Foldable.

Inquiry Virtual Lab

Stomata Like algae, most plants carry on photosynthesis, which produces glucose and oxygen from carbon dioxide and water. The exchange of gases between plant tissues and the environment is necessary for photosynthesis to occur. If the cuticle reduces water loss, it also might prevent the exchange of gases between a plant and its environment. **Stomata** (singular, stoma) are openings in the outer cell layer of leaves and some stems, as shown in **Figure 3.** They are adaptations that enable the exchange of gases even with the presence of a cuticle on a plant. Although photosynthesis can occur in some green stems, plant leaves usually are the sites of photosynthesis and are where most stomata are found. D

Vascular tissues Another plant adaptation to land environments is **vascular tissue**—specialized transport tissue. Recall that many substances slowly move into and out of cells and from cell to cell by osmosis or diffusion. However, vascular tissue enables faster movement of substances than by osmosis and diffusion, and over greater distances. Plants with vascular tissue are called **vascular plants,** like those in **Figure 4.** In some plants, substances slowly move from cell to cell by osmosis and diffusion. These are **nonvascular plants** and lack specialized transport tissues. R

Vascular tissues also provide structure and support. The presence of thickened cell walls in some vascular tissue provides additional support. Therefore, vascular plants can grow larger than nonvascular plants can.

Reproductive strategies A spore is a haploid cell capable of producing an organism. Some land plants reproduce by spores that have waterproof protective coverings. However, the gametophytes of those land plants must have a film of water covering them for sperm to swim to eggs. Water is a limiting factor in the environments of these plants. Seed plants have adaptations that enable a sperm to reach an egg without the presence of water.

Reading Check **Explain** why vascular plants can grow larger than nonvascular plants.

■ **Figure 4** Vascular plants have many shapes and sizes.
Identify *the plants that you recognize.*

■ **Caption Question Fig. 4** Answers may include: pumpkins, grass, ivy, and flowers. Do not expect students to give specific names for the plants pictured.

Reading Check Thickened cell walls in some vascular tissue provides support and structure.

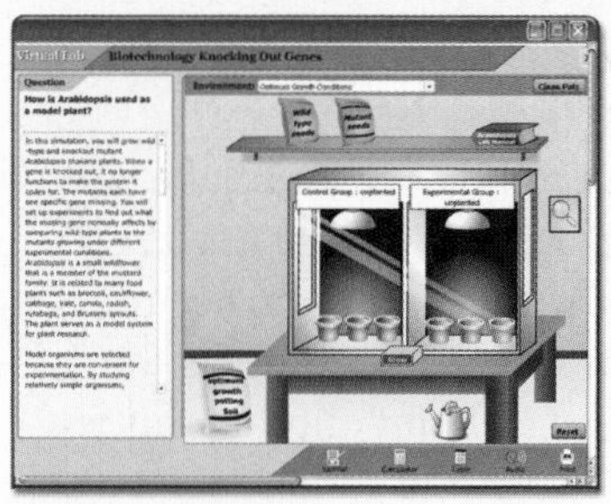

Inquiry Virtual Lab Students will compare a wild-type plant to a mutant plant growing under different experimental conditions.

Seeds The evolution of the seed was another important adaptation that helped ensure the success of some vascular plants. A **seed,** as shown in **Figure 5,** is a plant structure that contains an embryo, contains nutrients for the embryo, and is covered with a protective coat. These features enable seeds to survive harsh environmental conditions and then sprout when favorable conditions exist. Seeds also can have different structural adaptations that help scatter them. You will read more about these structural adaptations of seeds in Section 4 of this chapter.

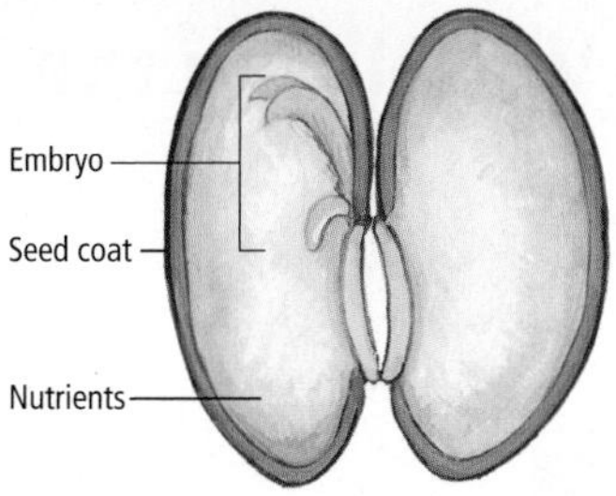

■ **Figure 5** The seed coat protects the embryo—the new sporophyte generation.

Alternation of Generations

Recall that the life cycles of some organisms include an alternation of generations—a haploid gametophyte generation and a diploid sporophyte generation. The gametophyte generation produces gametes—sperm and eggs. Some plants produce sperm and eggs on separate gametophytes, while others produce them on one gametophyte. When a sperm fertilizes an egg, a diploid zygote forms that can undergo countless mitotic cell divisions to form a multicellular sporophyte. The sporophyte generation produces spores that can grow to form the next gametophyte generation.

Depending on the type of plant, one generation is dominant over the other. The dominant generation is usually larger and accounts for more time in the plant's life cycle. Most of the plants you see—houseplants, grasses, garden plants, and trees—are the diploid sporophyte generation for those plants. During plant evolution, the trend was from dominant gametophytes to dominant sporophytes that contain vascular tissue. In land plants, the gametophyte generation of vascular plants is microscopic, as shown in **Figure 6,** but is larger in nonvascular plants and can be observed without a magnifying device. You will see more examples of gametophytes and sporophytes later in this chapter.

VOCABULARY
ACADEMIC VOCABULARY
Dominant (DAH muh nunt)
most immediately noticeable
Oaks are the dominant trees in some forests.

D

Reading Check **Identify** the generation of a plant's life cycle that produces sperm and eggs.

■ **Figure 6** The sporophyte of a maple tree—the roots, trunk, and branches—is larger than the tiny male gametophyte found in its pollen. The maple sporophyte also lives longer than the pollen.

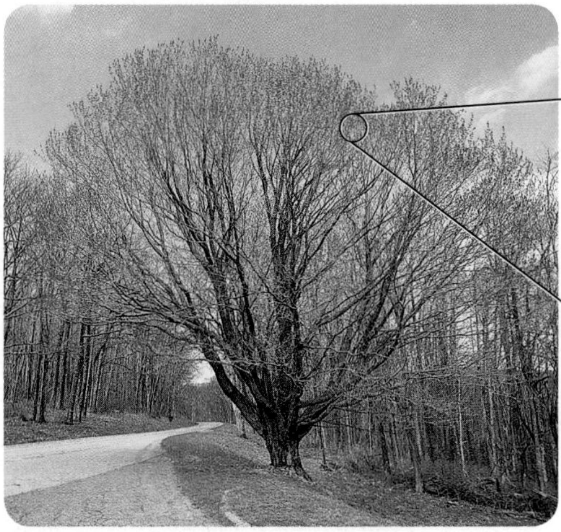

Sporophyte generation—maple tree

Color-Enhanced SEM Magnification: 155×

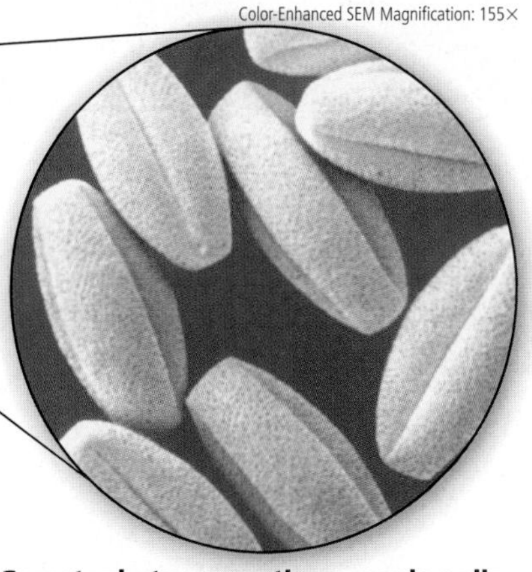

Gametophyte generation—maple pollen

D Develop Concepts

OL Scaffolding

SAY TO STUDENTS: ***Define* diploid *and* haploid.** Most cells are diploid, meaning they contain two sets of chromosomes ($2n$). Sex cells, or gametes, are haploid, meaning they contain one set of chromosomes (n). ***Classify the gametophyte and sporophyte generations as being diploid or haploid.*** Sporophyte is diploid; gametophyte is haploid. ***Distinguish between the sporophyte and gametophyte based on what they produce.*** A sporophyte produces spores; a gametophyte produces gametes—sperm and egg. ***Summarize the process of alternation of generations.*** The sporophyte generation ($2n$) produces spores that can grow to form the next gametophyte generation. The gametophyte generation (n) produces gametes—the egg and sperm. The egg and sperm fuse to form the zygote that is the first cell of the next sporophyte generation. Be sure students understand that the sporophyte generation, which is diploid, is so named because it produces the spores, which are haploid.

Develop Concepts

OL AL Activity Have each student draw a diagram of alternation of generations but substitute blanks for some stages. They can then exchange diagrams with their classmates and fill in the blanks.

Reading Check The gametophyte generation produces sperm and eggs.

Differentiated Instruction

English Learners Provide English learners with many opportunities to discuss the material being studied prior to assignments. These students will benefit from both small groups and class discussions.

For more tips, see pages 14T–15T.

Visualizing the Plant Kingdom

Purpose

Students will understand which distinguishing characteristics are used to divide plants into nonvascular, seedless vascular, and seed plants.
C.3, C.6

S Skill Practice

EL OL COOP LEARN

Visual Literacy Have students work in pairs to study and then select one of the three plant groups shown. At home, have them construct a model to illustrate one of that group's major distinguishing characteristics. For example, a vascular plant model might contain a pipe or straw to represent the vascular tissue. A model of nonvascular plant tissue could be cut out of a sponge to show that it absorbs water directly from its environment. A seed plant might be represented by an object inside a box or envelope.
AL Have students make models showing two or more characteristics, write a paragraph explaining their model, and present it to the class.

Concepts in Motion
Animation

Visualizing the Plant Kingdom

Figure 7
One way to classify the divisions of the plant kingdom is as either nonvascular or vascular plants. In addition, vascular plants can be classified as nonseed or seed plants.

S

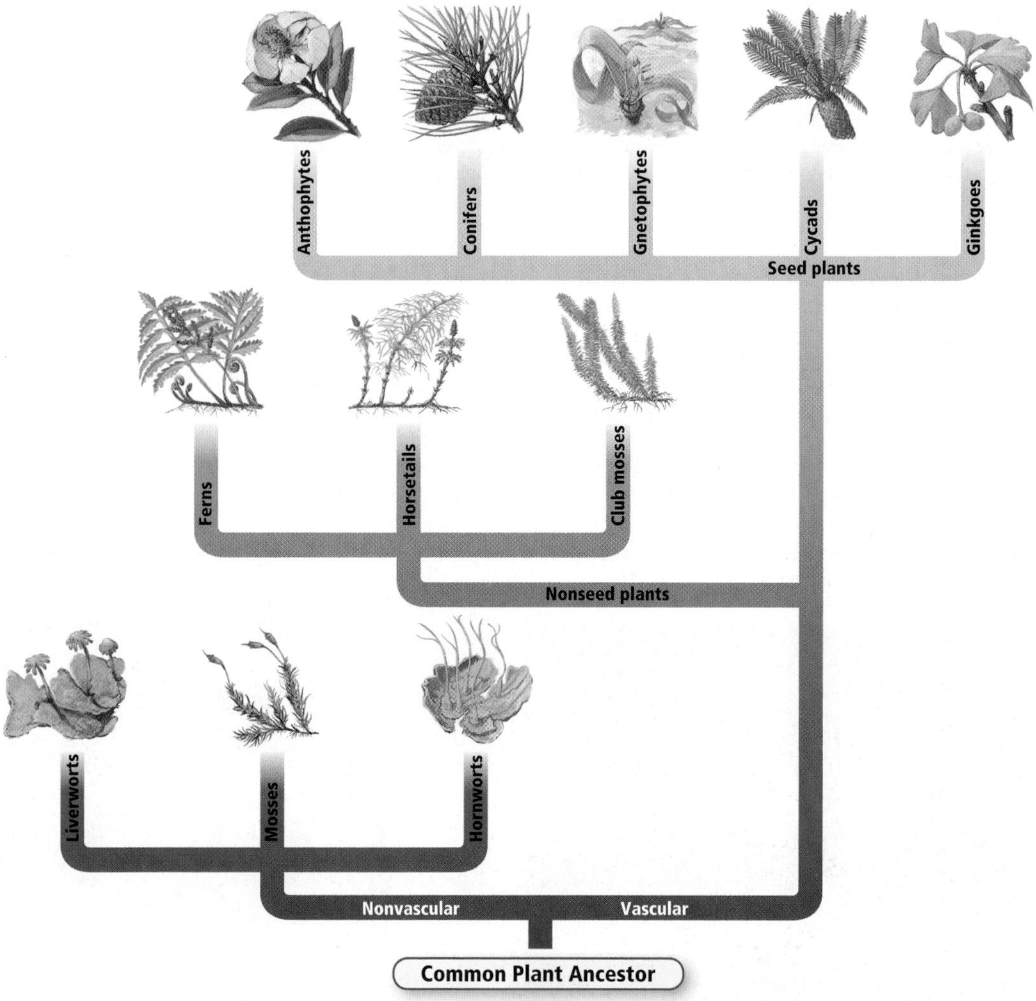

Concepts in Motion Animation

Demonstration

EL BL **Classify** Bring examples of the four different groups of plants to class. Examples might include mosses, flowers on stems, ferns, and seed plants, represented by a maple leaf, pine cone, or grass blade. Show the specimens to students.
ASK STUDENTS: ***To which group does each of these specimens belong?*** Have them classify the plants based on the characteristics. Est. time: 15 min

Plant Classification

Over time, plant adaptations resulted in a diversity of plant characteristics. Botanists use these characteristics to classify all plants of Kingdom Plantae into divisions. Recall that other kingdoms, except for bacteria, are divided into phyla, not divisions. When referring to members of a division, it is common practice to drop the *–a* from the division name and add *–es*. For example, members of Division Bryophyta are called bryophytes (BRI uh fites).

The plant divisions can be placed in two groups—the nonvascular plants and the vascular plants, eleven of which are illustrated in **Figure 7.** As you learned in this section, nonvascular plants lack specialized transport tissues. They include the following:

- bryophytes—mosses;
- anthocerophytes (an tho SAIR uh fites)—hornworts;
- hepaticophytes (hih PA tih koh fites)—liverworts.

You also learned that vascular plants have specialized transport tissues. Vascular plants are divided into two smaller groups—plants that do not produce seeds and plants that produce seeds. Two seedless vascular plants discussed later in this chapter include the following:

- lycophytes (LI kuh fites)—club mosses;
- pterophytes (TER uh fites)—ferns and horsetails.

Also discussed are the following five seed-producing vascular plants:

- cycadophytes (si KAH duh fites)—cycads or sago palms;
- gnetophytes (NEE tuh fites)—joint firs;
- ginkgophytes (GIHN koh fites)—ginkgoes;
- coniferophytes (kuh NIHF uh ruh fites)—pines and similar plants;
- D anthophytes (AN thuh fites)—flowering plants.

CAREERS IN BIOLOGY

Botanist Individuals who study plant life are botanists. They study the interactions of plants and the environment, and the structures and functions of plants. They might identify new plant species. A botanist can teach, conduct research, or work at a botanical garden, plant nursery, or greenhouse, or for a governmental agency.

Inquiry Launch Lab

Review Based on what you've read about plant characteristics, how would you now answer the analysis questions?

Section 1 Assessment

Section Summary

- Plants are multicellular organisms, and most are photosynthetic.
- Evidence indicates that ancient, unicellular, freshwater green algae were the ancestors of present-day plants.
- Present-day plants and green algae have many common characteristics.
- Over time, plants developed several adaptations for living on land.
- Plants alternate between a sporophyte and a gametophyte generation.

Understand Main Ideas

1. MAIN Idea **Identify** adaptations that make it possible for plants to survive on land.
2. **Explain** why scientists hypothesize that green algae and plants share a common ancestor.
3. **Name** the plant divisions. Which ones are seedless vascular plants?
4. **Differentiate** between a gametophyte and a sporophyte.

Think Critically

5. **Apply** what you know about lipids to explain why the cuticle helps prevent water loss in plants.
6. **Assess** the importance of a plant's vascular tissue to its ability to live on land.

WRITING in **Biology**

7. Find a poem about any plant and then analyze its scientific accuracy.

Inquiry Launch Lab

Assess Content Development
Assess how understanding has developed when students revisit the Launch Lab analysis questions.

D Develop Concepts

BL OL AL COOP LEARN

Activity Place students in groups of two or three. Assign each group one of the twelve plant divisions. Have students collect pictures of plants in their assigned division and write descriptions of each plant. Use the pictures to create a class bulletin board.

Formative Assessment

Evaluation

ASK STUDENTS: ***What are some plant adaptations to life on land?*** cuticle; stomata; broad flat leaves; vascular tissue; seed production ***How is the cuticle a beneficial adaptation for some plants?*** It reduces water loss through leaves; prevents evaporation from plant tissues; also acts as a barrier to invading microorganisms.

Remediation Organize students into small groups and assign each group one adaptation. Have them discuss and evaluate the adaptations. Write a list of adaptations and challenges to life on land on the board. Have students match the adaptation to the challenge(s).

Section 1 Assessment

1. cuticle, roots, vascular tissue, seed production
2. Plants and green algae share many traits, such as cellulose cell walls, type of chlorophyll, and storing food as starch.
3. Bryophyta, Anthocerophyta, Hepaticophyta, Lycophyta, Pterophyta, Cyadophyta, Gnetophyta, Ginkophyta, Coniferophyta; Lycophyta, and Pterophyta are seedless vascular plants.
4. Gametophytes (n) produce gametes and sporophytes ($2n$) produce spores.
5. Answers will vary, but students should indicate that lipids are hydrophobic and therefore repel water.
6. Vascular tissue provides an efficient means of transporting water and nutrients so plants do not have to rely on osmosis and diffusion.
7. *WRITING in* **Biology**
   RUBRIC Use the modifiable rubric found on your eTeacherEdition Online to assess writing assignments.

Assessment Online Quiz

Section 2

MAIN Idea

BL OL AL Nonvascular Plants Collect a variety of objects that can transport water, such as a straw, a piece of hose, plastic plumbing pipe, etc. Show these objects to the students.
ASK STUDENTS: ***What are these objects used for?*** to transport water Remind students that nonvascular plants have to rely on other methods of transport, such as osmosis and diffusion, because they lack vascular tissue.

R Reading Strategy

OL COOP LEARN

Discussion Triad Divide the class into three groups and assign each group one of the plant divisions from this section. Have students read the text and make a list of their division's characteristics to present to the class.
EL Have students read the text and complete the chart:

Division	Where Found	Characteristics
Bryophyta		
Anthocerophyta		
Hepaticophyta		

Writing Support

BL OL Creative Writing Have students write a poem, cinquain, limerick, or haiku about hornworts or liverworts.

S Skill Practice

BL OL COOP LEARN

Visual Literacy Tell students to study Figure 8. Have them work in pairs to draw a diagram showing how water and minerals move from soil into moss.

Section 2

Reading Preview

Essential Questions

- What are the structures of nonvascular plants?
- What are the similarities and differences among the nonvascular plant divisions?

Review Vocabulary

symbiosis: a relationship in which two organisms live together in a close association

New Vocabulary

thallose

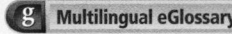

g Multilingual eGlossary

Nonvascular Plants

MAIN Idea Nonvascular plants are small and usually grow in damp environments.

Real-World Reading Link Have you ever used a garden hose to water a lawn or wash a car? Why didn't you carry water from the faucet in a bucket? As you probably realize, using a garden hose to transport water is more efficient than using a bucket. You learned in the previous section that nonvascular plants lack structures that can move water and other substances. However, because of their small size, moving substances by diffusion and osmosis is sufficient for them.

R Diversity of Nonvascular Plants

As shown in the evolutionary tree in **Figure 8,** nonvascular plants make up one of the four major groups of plants that evolved along with green algae from a common ancestor. In general, nonvascular plants usually are small, which enables most materials to move within them easily. These plants often are found growing in damp, shady areas—environments that provide the water needed by nonvascular plants for nutrient transport and reproduction.

Division Bryophyta The most familiar bryophytes are the mosses. You might have seen these small, nonvascular plants growing on a damp log or along a stream. Although they do not have true leaves, mosses have structures that are similar to leaves. Their photosynthetic, leaflike structures usually consist of a layer of cells that is only one cell thick.

Mosses produce rootlike, multicellular rhizoids that anchor them to soil or another surface, as shown in **Figure 8.** Water and dissolved minerals can diffuse into a moss's rhizoids. Although mosses have some tissue that transports water and food, these plants do not have true vascular tissues. Water and other substances move throughout moss by osmosis and diffusion.

S

Figure 8 Embryo protection is a characteristic of nonvascular and vascular plants. The dense carpet of moss—a nonvascular plant—consists of hundreds of moss plants, each with leafy stems and rhizoids.

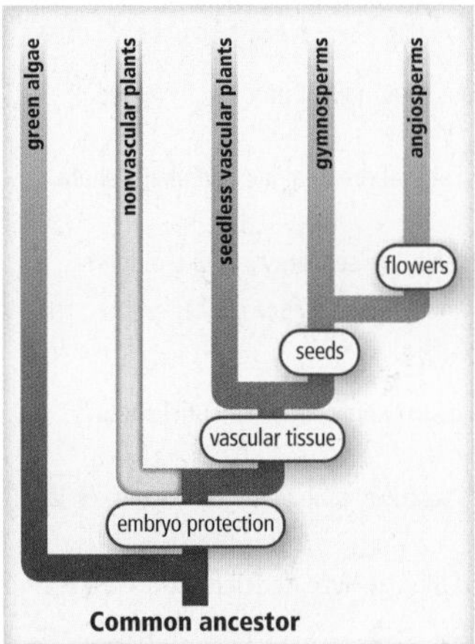

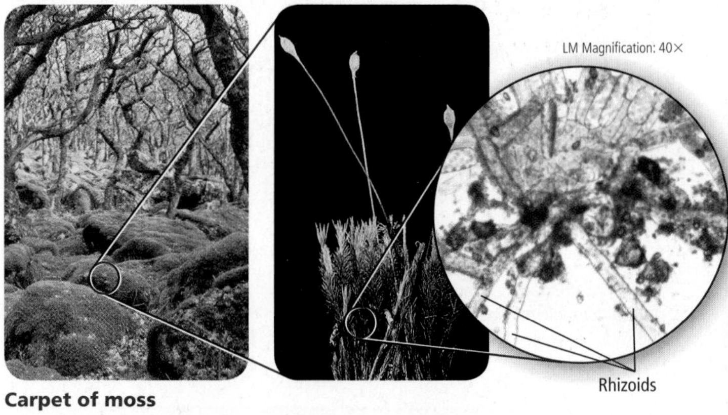

Carpet of moss

Differentiated Instruction

Gifted When assigning students to groups, assign students of varying ability levels to each group. This will promote cooperative learning and encourage teamwork.

For more tips, see pages 14T–15T.

Mosses exhibit variety in structure and growth. Some mosses have stems that grow upright, and others have trailing, vinelike stems. Other mosses form extensive mats that help slow erosion on rocky slopes. Over time, *Sphagnum* (a type of moss) and other plant matter accumulate, decay, and form deep deposits called peat. Peat can be cut into blocks and burned as a fuel. Gardeners and florists often add peat moss to soil to help it retain moisture.

Scientists estimate that as much as one percent of Earth's surface might be covered by bryophytes. Many mosses, like those in **Figure 8,** grow in temperate regions and freeze and thaw without damage. Others can survive an extreme loss of water and then resume growth when moisture returns.

C

Reading Check **Explain** how peat is formed.

Division Anthocerophyta The smallest division of nonvascular plants is division Anthocerophyta. Anthocerophytes are called hornworts because of their hornlike sporophytes, as shown in **Figure 9.** Water and nutrients move in hornworts by osmosis and diffusion. About 100 hornwort species have been identified.

An identifying feature of these plants is the presence of one large chloroplast in each cell of the gametophyte and sporophyte. This feature can be observed under a microscope. However, the hornwort sporophyte produces much of the food used by its sporophyte and gametophyte generations.

While examining hornwort tissue under a microscope, besides the large chloroplast in each cell, you also might observe that the spaces around cells are filled with mucilage, or slime, rather than air. Cyanobacteria in the genus *Nostoc* often grow in this slime. The cyanobacteria and hornwort exhibit mutualism.

DATA ANALYSIS LAB 1

Based on Real Data*

Form a Hypothesis

How does *Nostoc* benefit a hornwort? Cyanobacteria, usually species of *Nostoc,* form mutualistic relationships with a few liverworts and the majority of hornworts.

Data and Observations

Nostoc colonies appear as dark spots within gametophyte tissue, as shown in the photo.

Think Critically

1. **Hypothesize** about the benefit(s) the cyanobacteria receive from the hornwort.
2. **Design** an experiment to test your hypothesis.

*Data obtained from: Costa, J-L., et al. 2001. Genetic diversity of *Nostoc* symbionts endophytically associated with two bryophyte species. *Appl. Envir. Microbiol.* 67: 4393–4396.

■ **Figure 9** The hornlike sporophyte of a hornwort is anchored to the gametophyte.

C Critical Thinking

AL Analyze

ASK STUDENTS: ***Imagine you are working for a landscaper. How would you discourage the growth of mosses under some large shade trees?*** Students might suggest cutting off some lower branches to allow more light to dry out the area or planting shade-tolerant ground cover.

DATA ANALYSIS LAB 1

About the Lab

- There are two forms of the cyanobacterium *Nostoc*—long filamentous, immobile, nitrogen-fixing heterocysts and short-filament, mobile, infective, hormogonia.
- The hornwort has a symbiotic relationship with *Nostoc.*
- When a hornwort needs nitrogen, it releases a chemical called hormogonium-inducing factor, which attracts hormogonia from nearby *Nostoc* to infect the hornwort's slime cavities. The hornwort produces hormogonium-repressing factor to stop further production of hormogonia.
- A different hornwort chemical stimulates the production of nitrogen-fixing heterocysts.
- Also see Crane, P., P. Herendeen, and E. M. Friis. 2004. Fossils and plant phylogeny. *American Journal of Botany* 91:1683–1699.

Think Critically

1. The cyanobacteria receives carbon and possibly protection from the plant.
2. Answers should include a procedure that would grow cyanobacteria with and without the hornwort.

Demonstration

EL BL Hold Water Show students 20 g of slightly moist sphagnum moss. Have student volunteers slowly add water until the sphagnum or peat is saturated.

ASK STUDENTS: ***Why is this characteristic important to the survival of the sphagnum?*** It helps retain water so the moss does not dry out.

Est. time: 15 min

Reading Check Over time *sphagnum* moss and other plant matter accumulate and decay to form deep deposits of peat.

Develop Concepts

BL OL

Clarify a Misconception

ASK STUDENTS: ***If you were lost in the woods, is there a plant that would help you determine which way was north or south?*** Students might answer that they could determine north by finding where the moss grows on trees. Contrary to common belief, moss does not grow only on the north side of trees. In the northern hemisphere, the south side of trees does tend to be warmer and drier because the Sun shines more directly on it. Because most mosses require cool, damp habitats, they do tend to grow mostly on the north side of trees. However, in damp environments such as bogs and swamps or locations where there is a great deal of shade, moss can grow on all sides of the trees.

Formative Assessment

Evaluation

ASK STUDENTS: ***Distinguish between a thallose and a leafy liverwort.*** A thallose liverwort has fleshy, lobed structures, and a leafy liverwort has three rows of thin, leaf-like structures.

Remediation Instruct students to reread the paragraph under the heading *Division Bryophyta.* Then have students write a description of a location in their neighborhood where mosses could grow.

Thallose liverwort

Leafy liverwort

■ **Figure 10** A thallose liverwort's shape resembles lobes of a liver. Leafy liverworts have leaflike structures but not true leaves.

VOCABULARY

SCIENCE USAGE V. COMMON USAGE

Fleshy

Science usage: having a juicy or pulpy texture

Peaches and plums are fleshy fruits.

Common usage: relating to, consisting of, or resembling flesh

The piece of beef was fleshy, not bony.

Division Hepaticophyta Because of their appearance and use as a medicine to treat liver ailments during medieval times, hepaticophytes are referred to as liverworts. This division of nonvascular plants contains more than 6000 species. They are found in a variety of habitats ranging from the tropics to the arctic. Liverworts tend to grow close to the ground and in areas where moisture is plentiful, such as in damp soil, near water, or on damp, decaying logs. A few species can even survive in relatively dry areas. Like other nonvascular plants, water, nutrients, and other substances are transported throughout liverworts by osmosis and diffusion.

Liverworts are classified as either **thallose** (THAL lohs) or leafy. Both are shown in **Figure 10.** A thallose liverwort has a body that resembles a fleshy, lobed structure. Leafy liverworts have stems with flat, thin leaflike structures arranged in three rows—a row on each side of the stem and a row of smaller leaves on the undersurface. Liverworts have unicellular rhizoids, unlike mosses, which have multicellular rhizoids.

DNA analysis has shown that liverworts lack DNA sequences that most other land plants contain. This suggests that liverworts are the most primitive of land plants.

Section 2 Assessment

Section Summary

- Distribution of nonvascular plants is limited by the plants' ability to transport water and other substances.
- Mosses are small plants that can grow in different environments.
- Like other nonvascular plants, hornworts rely on osmosis and diffusion to transport substances.
- The two types of liverworts are classified as thallose and leafy.

Understand Main Ideas

1. MAIN Idea **Summarize** the characteristics of mosses.
2. **Identify** environmental changes that might have influenced the evolution of nonvascular plant structures.
3. **Distinguish** between a liverwort and a hornwort.
4. **Generalize** the economic value of bryophytes.

Think Critically

5. **Apply** what you know about osmosis and diffusion to suggest why nonvascular plants usually are small.
6. **Predict** the changes that would occur at the cellular level when a moss dries out.
7. **Compare and contrast** the habitats of mosses, hornworts, and liverworts.

Section 2 Assessment

1. Mosses are nonvascular, multicellular plants. Gametophytes are photosynthetic, but the sporophytes usually are not. Gametophytes grow from spores. Moisture is required for reproduction.
2. temperature, amount of water, amount of light
3. Hornworts have hornlike sporophytes. Liverworts can be leafy or thallose and have unicellular rhizoids.
4. forms peat used as fuel; peat moss is used to retain soil moisture
5. Osmosis and diffusion move water and materials short distances or from cell to cell. Because mosses rely on these processes to move water and nutrients, it is more efficient to be small and maintain a low ratio of surface area to volume.
6. Answers will vary, but students might suggest that the large vacuole might shrink or the cell might plasmolyze.
7. All generally grow in damp, shady areas. Mosses grow in temperate habitats, can survive dry conditions; liverworts grow from arctic to tropical environments.

Assessment Online Quiz

Section 3

Reading Preview

Essential Questions

- What are the characteristics of seedless vascular plants?
- What are the similarities and differences between the characteristics of club mosses and ferns?

Review Vocabulary

spore: a reproductive haploid cell with a hard outer coat that can develop into a new organism without the fusion of gametes

New Vocabulary

strobilus
epiphyte
rhizome
sporangium
sorus

g Multilingual eGlossary

Seedless Vascular Plants

MAIN Idea **Because they have vascular tissues, seedless vascular plants generally are larger and better adapted to drier environments than nonvascular plants.**

Real-World Reading Link Whether it is to brush your teeth, to get a drink of water, or to wash something, when you turn on a faucet, water flows out. The plumbing in your home carries water to and from different places. The vascular tissue in plants can be thought of as a plant's plumbing because it carries water and dissolved substances throughout the plant.

R Diversity of Seedless Vascular Plants

Club mosses, also known as spike mosses, and the fern group make up the seedless vascular plant group. Keep in mind that although the common name for a club moss identifies it as a moss, it is not like the mosses described in the previous section. As indicated in **Figure 11,** this plant group is one of the three plant groups with vascular tissues. Seedless vascular plants exhibit a great diversity of form and size.

Regardless of their size, an adaptation seen in some seedless vascular plant sporophytes is the strobilus (STROH bih lus) (plural, strobili). A **strobilus** is a compact cluster of spore-bearing structures. The tiny spores produced in the strobilus often are carried by the wind. If a spore lands in a favorable environment, it can grow to form a gametophyte.

Division Lycophyta Present-day lycophytes or club mosses are descendants of the oldest group of vascular plants. Fossil evidence suggests that ancient lycophytes were tree-sized plants—some as tall as 30 m. They formed a large part of the vegetation of Paleozoic forests. After this vegetation died, its remains changed over time and eventually became part of the coal that humans mine for fuel.

Unlike true mosses, the sporophyte generation of lycophytes is dominant. They resemble moss gametophytes, and their reproductive structures that produce spores are club-shaped or spike-shaped, as shown in **Figure 11.**

Figure 11 Seedless vascular plants, such as the club moss called wolf's claw, produce spores in strobili instead of seeds.

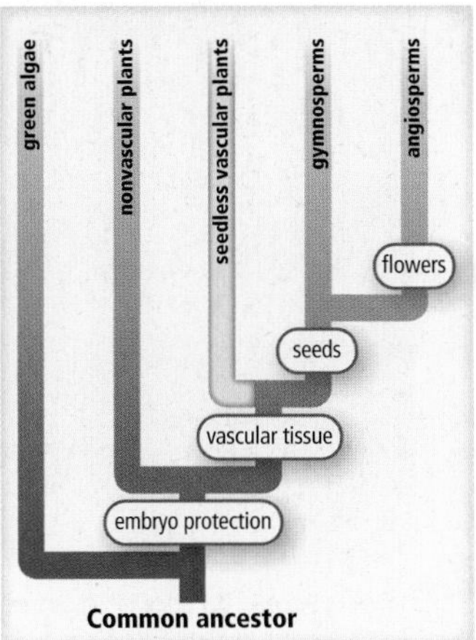

Lycopodium sp.—wolf's claw

Section 3

MAIN Idea

BL OL AL

Seedless Vascular Plants

ASK STUDENTS: ***Why do you think seedless vascular plants are usually larger than nonvascular plants?*** Vascular tissue can transport water and food for longer distances throughout the plant. ***What do you predict might be some differences in the habitats of nonvascular versus vascular plants?*** Vascular plants could exist in sunnier and drier habitats. ***How could this affect their size?*** Plants exposed to more sunlight might photosynthesize more, resulting in more growth.

Skill Practice

EL BL OL **Visual Literacy**

Have students sketch each type of plant, using the illustrations in this section as guides. As they read the section, have them write characteristics under their pictures.

R Reading Strategy

EL BL **Assessment Preview**

Before reading the section, have students read the section assessment questions. Suggest that students keep these questions in mind as they read the text.

Research Citation

Writing Activities Educational research indicates that writing is a tool that can benefit students in any subject area. Writing activities like the one on the next page help students develop their language skills and deepen their understanding of concepts.

(Carrasquillo and Rodriguez, 1996)

Research bibliography on pages 32T–34T

Develop Concepts

OL Clarify a Misconception

ASK STUDENTS: ***In what division of the plant kingdom do you think you would find spike moss, club moss, or Spanish moss?*** Bryophyta Use this opportunity to remind students that common names can often be misleading. The original common names for these plants come from the fact that they are small, low-growing plants that resemble mosses and grow in similar habitats. Although their common names suggest a close relationship to the nonvascular mosses, they are vascular plants.

Writing Support

OL AL Summary Writing

Have students research how, over time, plants became coal. Have them write a summary of the steps in the coal-forming process.

***Selaginella* sp.**

■ **Figure 12** This club moss belongs to the genus *Selaginella.*

Lycophytes have roots, stems, and small, scaly, leaflike structures. Another name for some lycophytes is ground pines because they resemble miniature pine trees. Their stems are either branched or unbranched and either grow upright or creep along the soil's surface. Roots grow from the base of a stem. Extending down the middle of each scaly leaflike structure is a vein of vascular tissue.

Most of the club mosses belong to two genera—*Lycopodium* and *Selaginella*—like the examples shown in **Figure 11** and **Figure 12.** Many tropical lycophyte species are epiphytes. An **epiphyte** is a plant that lives anchored to an object or another plant. When anchored in treetops, they create another habitat for insects and other small animals in the forest canopy.

Reading Check **Identify** the contribution of ancient lycophytes to present-day economies.

Division Pterophyta This plant division includes ferns and horsetails. The horsetails once were in their own plant division. However, recent biochemical studies reveal that they are closely related to ferns and should be grouped with them.

Connection to Earth Science During the Carboniferous period, about 300–359 million years ago, ferns were the most abundant land plants. Vast forests of treelike ferns existed, and some of them produced seedlike structures. Today, ferns grow in many different environments. Although ferns are most common in moist environments, they can survive dry conditions. When water is scarce, the life processes of some ferns slow so much that the ferns appear to be lifeless. When water becomes available, the ferns resume growth. Examples of ferns growing in diverse habitats are shown in **Figure 13.**

■ **Figure 13** Ferns are a diverse group of plants that occupy a variety of habitats.

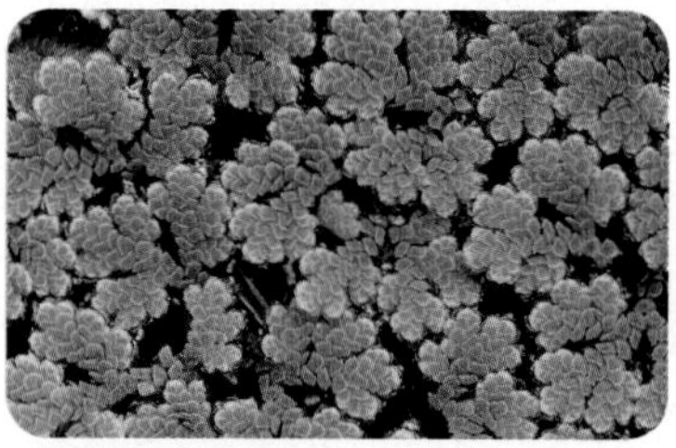

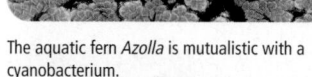

The aquatic fern *Azolla* is mutualistic with a cyanobacterium.

Hawaii is the only U.S. state to which tree ferns are native in tropical forests.

The staghorn fern grows as an epiphyte.

Dryopteris grows best in shady, dry environments.

Reading Check Over time, they became part of the coal mined today.

Differentiated Instruction

Hearing Impaired When hearing-impaired students are in the classroom, arrange seating in a circle when discussing important concepts. This will allow students to see each person's face.

For more tips, see pages 14T–15T.

LM Magnification: 20×

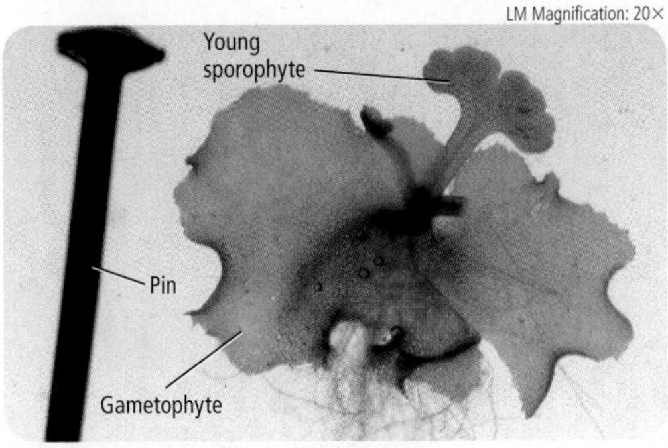

Fern gametophyte and sporophyte

Mature fern sporophyte

■ **Figure 14** Fern gametophytes and sporophytes differ greatly in size and appearance. A mature fern sporophyte is many times larger than the gametophyte.

It is unlikely that you have seen a fern gametophyte like the one in **Figure 14.** This tiny, thin structure is smaller than a pin. It grows from a spore and has male and female reproductive structures. Following fertilization, the sporophyte grows from and is briefly dependent on the gametophyte. One adaptation of some ferns that live in dry areas is that they can produce sporophytes without fertilization. Eventually, the sporophyte produces roots and a thick underground stem called a **rhizome.** The rhizome is a food-storage organ. The aboveground structures of some ferns die at the end of a growing season. The breakdown of the rhizome's stored food releases energy when growth resumes.

C

The familiar parts of a fern are its photosynthetic leafy structures, or fronds, shown in **Figure 14.** The frond is part of the sporophyte generation of ferns. Fronds have branched vascular tissue and vary greatly in size.

DATA ANALYSIS LAB 2

Based on Real Data*

Analyze Models

When did the diversity of modern ferns evolve? Researchers analyzed fossil evidence and DNA sequence data of ferns. They found that ferns have shown greater diversity in more recent evolutionary history. They concluded that the diversity of modern ferns evolved after angiosperms dominated terrestrial ecosystems.

Data and Observations

Observe the two models showing the evolution of the diversity of organisms.

Think Critically

1. **Select** the model that best fits the researchers' conclusion described above.
2. **Infer** Angiosperms are flowering plants. How might angiosperms have influenced fern diversity?

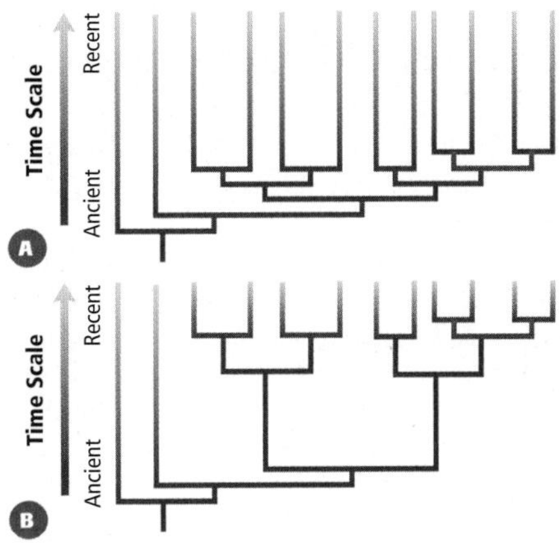

*Data obtained from: Eriksson, Torsten. 2004. Evolutionary biology: Ferns reawakened. *Nature* 428: 480–481.

C Critical Thinking

BL OL Infer

ASK STUDENTS: ***Why would rhizomes help ferns survive in a dry climate?*** The rhizome is an underground food-storage organ that can be produced by sporophytes without fertilization. The ferns above ground may die, but the rhizome's stored food is available to provide energy when the fern's growth resumes.

DATA ANALYSIS LAB 2

About the Lab

- Ferns are a diverse, highly evolved group of plants.
- There are more than 12,000 species of ferns.
- Also see Renzaglia, K. S. and K. C. Vaughn. 2000. *The biology of bryophytes.* Cambridge: Cambridge University Press.
- Also see D. B. Bryant, ed. 1994. *The molecular biology of cyanobacteria.* Boston: Kluwer Academic Publishers.

Think Critically

1. B
2. Angiosperms provided more diverse conditions, such as more shade, which encouraged fern diversity.

Demonstration

AL Silicon Obtain samples of the horsetail Equisetum. If samples are not available, show photos or digital images. Pass the samples to students and have them examine the stems.

TELL STUDENTS: ***This plant stem has a unique characteristic. The cell walls of its epidermal cells contain silicon.*** Have students share ideas about what purpose this might serve. Answers might include that silicon makes the stem sturdier in water-logged areas and could prevent excess water loss during dry spells or protect against herbivores.

Est. time: 15 min

D Develop Concepts

EL BL Activity Have students draw a fern and label the fronds, rhizome, and sori. Collect all drawings and create a fern forest display on the bulletin board.

Formative Assessment

Evaluation

ASK STUDENTS: ***What kinds of adaptations enable ferns to live in a wide variety of habitats?*** Answers will vary but might include tree ferns—specialized support tissue; staghorn fern—structures for attaching to the tree; *Dryopteris*—mechanism for surviving dry conditions; and *Azolla*—specialized tissue for buoyancy.

Remediation Have students examine the different ferns in Figure 13. Tell them to make three columns on a sheet of paper. Have them write the name of each type of fern in Figure 13 in the first column, its habitat in the second column, and its unique adaptation in the third column. Allow them to use their books.

Bird's nest fern

Horsetails

■ **Figure 15** The sori of the bird's nest fern contain spores and form lines on the underside of a frond. Some horsetails produce two different sporophyte stalks—vegetative and reproductive.

Fern spores form in a structure called a **sporangium** (plural, sporangia), and clusters of sporangia form a **sorus** (plural, sori). Sori usually are located on the undersides of fronds, as shown in **Figure 15.**

Figure 15 also shows the typical structure of horsetails—ribbed, hollow stems with circles of scalelike leaves. Like lycophytes, horsetails produce spores in strobili at the tips of reproductive stems. When they are released into a favorable environment, horsetail spores can develop into gametophytes.

D

Another common name for horsetails is scouring rushes. In colonial days, they often were used to scrub pots and pans. Horsetails contain a scratchy substance called silica. You can feel it when you rub your finger along a horsetail stem.

Present-day horsetail species are much smaller than their ancient ancestors. Most horsetails grow in wet areas, such as marshes, swamps, and stream banks. Some species grow in the drier soil of fields and roadsides only because their roots grow into underlying, water-saturated soil.

Section 3 Assessment

Section Summary

- Seedless vascular plants have specialized transport tissues and reproduce by spores.
- The sporophyte is the dominant generation in vascular plants.
- Lycophytes and pterophytes are seedless vascular plants.

Understand Main Ideas

1. MAIN Idea **Create** a table that lists the characteristics of seedless vascular plant groups.
2. **Compare** the sporophyte and gametophyte generations of vascular and nonvascular plants.
3. **Infer** the advantages of the fern sporophyte's initial dependency upon the gametophyte.

Think Critically

4. **Design** an experiment that would test the ability of fern gametophytes to grow on different soils.
5. **Evaluate** the advantage of branching vascular tissue in fern fronds.
6. **Construct** a Venn diagram showing characteristics of club mosses and ferns.

Section 3 Assessment

1. Student tables should include that these are eukaryotic, multicellular organisms with vascular tissues; gametophytes grow from spores; presence of strobili.
2. nonvascular plants—dominant gametophyte and small sporophyte dependent on gametophyte; vascular plants—dominant sporophyte, small gametophyte, sporophyte independent of gametophyte
3. The small sporophyte gets nutrition from the gametophyte until it is large enough to produce its own food.
4. Answers will vary. Students should provide a plan involving growing ferns in different soils.
5. The advantage of branching vascular tissue is that water and nutrients are transported throughout the frond.
6. Accept all reasonable diagrams. Diagrams should reflect that both are vascular plants; sporophyte dominant in both; and both have stroboli-bearing members.

Reading Preview

Essential Questions

- What are the similarities and differences among the seed plants?
- What are the divisions of gymnosperms?
- What are the life spans of angiosperms?

Review Vocabulary

adaptation: inherited characteristic that results from response to an environmental factor

New Vocabulary

cotyledon
cone
annual
biennial
perennial

g Multilingual eGlossary

Vascular Seed Plants

MAIN Idea Vascular seed plants are the most widely distributed plants on Earth.

Real-World Reading Link You put a letter in an envelope to mail it so that the envelope will protect your letter. In a similar way, a new plant is protected within the seed until environmental conditions are favorable for growth.

Diversity of Seed Plants

Vascular seed plants produce seeds. Each seed usually contains a tiny sporophyte surrounded by protective tissue. Seeds have one or more **cotyledons** (kah tuh LEE dunz)—structures that either store food or help absorb food for the tiny sporophyte. Plants whose seeds are part of fruits are called angiosperms. Those plants whose seeds are not part of fruits are called gymnosperms. The word *gymnosperm* comes from two Greek words that together mean *naked seed.*

Seed plants have a variety of adaptations for the dispersal or scattering of their seeds throughout their environments, like those shown in **Figure 16.** Dispersal is important because it limits competition between the new plant and its parent and other offspring.

The sporophyte is dominant in seed plants and produces spores. These spores divide by meiosis to form male gametophytes (pollen grains) and female gametophytes. Each female gametophyte consists of one or more eggs surrounded by protective tissues. Both gametophytes are dependent on the sporophyte generation for their survival.

Figure 16 Examine these structural adaptations for seed dispersal.

The cocklebur has hooks that can attach to an animal's fur or a human's clothing.

The dry fruit of a witch hazel plant can eject its two seeds more than 12 m from the plant.

These pine seeds have winglike structures that enable them to move with the wind.

The coconut, with its seed inside, can float great distances on ocean currents.

Parachute-like structures help disperse milkweed seeds.

Section 4

MAIN Idea

BL OL AL Seed Plants Have students name as many different types of plants as they can. Write the types on the board. Encourage them to think of houseplants, trees, vegetables, and plants they have already read about in this chapter. Create a list of 30-40 plants.

ASK STUDENTS: ***Which of these plants produce seeds?*** As they name the seed-producing plants, put a circle around the name. ***Which type of plant in the list is most common?*** plants that produce seeds Point out that this is true in nature; seed plants are the most abundant type of plant. If students ask about seedless grapes and watermelons, explain that these fruits come from seed plants that are specially bred to eliminate the seeds. Tell students that they will learn many characteristics of seed plants in this section.

Develop Concepts

BL Activity Have students write down the following words: *pollen grain, cotyledon,* and *cone.* As they read, have them write each term's definition and draw a picture of the structure.

EL Give English learners three index cards. Have them write one word or term on each card: *pollen grain, cotyledon, cone.* As they read the section, have them write the definition and draw a picture of the structure on the other side of the card.

Skill Practice

EL OL Visual Literacy Have students draw the five kinds of seeds, using the illustrations in this section as guides. Have them describe the dispersal mechanism of each seed and tell how this helps the plant reproduce.

Demonstration

Seed Dispersal Collect and display examples of seeds with various dispersal mechanisms. Some possibilities are dandelion, milkweed, burrs, maple samara, acorn, and fruit with seeds inside.

ASK STUDENTS: ***How do you think these seeds are dispersed?*** Answers will vary depending on examples.

Est. time: 15 min

W Writing Support

OL AL Technical Writing Have students research toxicity of cycads, such as *Zamia*. They can also research the types of symptoms exhibited by people or pets who have been poisoned due to ingesting cycad tissue. Many victims appear to have nerve damage or neurological problems.

Skill Practice

EL BL Make a Table Have students create a table with five columns—each with the name of one of the seed-plant divisions. Instruct students to write the characteristics of each division in the appropriate column as they read text under the headings *Division Cycadophyta, Division Gnetophyta, Division Ginkgophyta, Division Coniferophyta,* and *Division Anthophyta.*

Inquiry BioLab

The lab at the end of the chapter can be used at this point in the lesson.

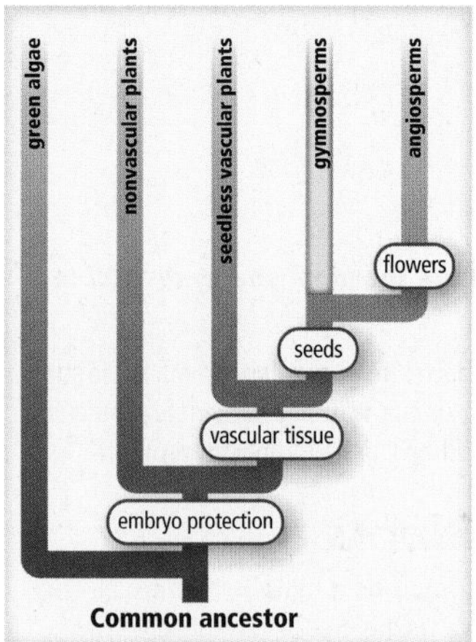

Figure 17 The evolutionary tree above shows that the development of cones was an earlier evolutionary adaptation than flowers.

Earlier in this chapter, you read that water must be present for a sperm to reach an egg in both nonvascular plants and seedless vascular plants. Most seed plants do not require a film of water for this process. This is an important difference between seed plants and other plants. This adaptation enables seed plants to thrive in different environments, including areas where water is scarce.

Division Cycadophyta As shown in the evolutionary tree in **Figure 17,** plants with cones—the gymnosperms—evolved before plants with flowers—the angiosperms. A **cone** is a structure that contains the male or female reproductive structures of cycads and other gymnosperm plants. A male cone produces clouds of pollen grains that produce male gametophytes. Female cones contain female gametophytes. Cycad cones can be as long as 1 m and weigh as much as 35 kg. Male and female cones grow on separate cycad plants.

Because cycads have large divided leaves and some grow more than 18 m tall, people often think that cycads are related to palm trees. However, cycads have structural differences and different reproductive strategies than do palms. While cycads might resemble woody trees, they actually have soft stems or trunks consisting mostly of storage tissue.

The natural habitats of cycads are the tropics or subtropics. There is only one species native to the United States. Its native habitat is southern Florida. Cycads grew in abundance 200 million years ago, but today there are only about 11 genera and 250 species. W

Reading Check **Compare** a cone with a strobilus.

Division Gnetophyta Plants in division Gnetophyta can live as long as 1500–2000 years. There are just three genera of gnetophytes, and each exhibits unusual structural adaptations to its environment.

The genus *Ephedra* is the only gnetophyte genus that grows in the United States. The genus *Gnetum* includes about 30 species of tropical trees and climbing vines. The remaining genus, *Welwitschia,* has only one species—a bizarre-looking plant shown in **Figure 18**—found exclusively in the deserts of southwestern Africa. It has a large storage root and two continuously growing leaves that eventually can exceed 6 m in length. *Welwitschia* takes in available moisture from fog, dew, or rain through its two leaves.

CAREERS IN BIOLOGY

Wood Scientist An individual who is involved in one or more aspects of converting wood to wood products is a wood scientist. A wood scientist can conduct research or work in manufacturing as a product or process developer, quality or production controller, engineer, or manager.

Figure 18 *Welwitschia* leaves are blown about by the wind. This causes them to split many times and makes the two leaves appear as many leaves.

Research Citation

Lesson Format Educational research indicates that effective teachers follow a format for their lessons that includes establishing a purpose, an anticipatory activity, opportunity for practice, and assessment. This format provides consistency for students and valuable information for teachers on their students' progress. (Hunter, 1994)

Research bibliography on pages 32T–34T

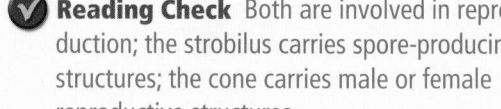

Reading Check Both are involved in reproduction; the strobilus carries spore-producing structures; the cone carries male or female reproductive structures.

Division Ginkgophyta Only one living species, *Ginkgo biloba*, represents division Ginkgophyta. Early in the 19th century, fossil remains of *Ginkgo biloba* were discovered in the state of Washington. The ginkgo disappeared from North America during the last ice age. However, it survived in China, where it was grown for its seeds—a food delicacy eaten only at weddings and during holidays.

This distinctive tree has small, fan-shaped leaves. Like cycads, male and female reproductive systems are on separate plants. The male tree produces pollen grains in strobiluslike cones growing from the bases of leaf clusters, as shown in **Figure 19.** The female tree produces cones, also shown in **Figure 19,** which, when fertilized, develop foul-smelling, fleshy seed coats. Because they tolerate smog and pollution, ginkgoes are popular with gardeners and urban landscapers. However, male trees usually are favored because they do not produce
C foul-smelling fleshy cones.

Male reproductive structures

Female reproductive structures

■ **Figure 19** Both male and female ginkgo reproductive structures grow from the bases of leaf clusters, but on separate trees.
Predict ***how pollen travels to the female reproductive structure.***

Division Coniferophyta Conifers range in size from low-growing shrubs that are several centimeters tall to towering trees over 50 m in height. Pines, firs, cypresses, and redwoods are examples of conifers. Conifers are the most economically important gymnosperms. They are sources of lumber, paper pulp, and the resins used to make turpentine, rosin, and other products.

Reproductive structures of most conifers develop in cones. Most conifers have male and female cones on different branches of the same tree or shrub. The small male cones produce pollen. Larger female cones remain on the plants until the seeds have matured. The characteristics of female cones, such as those shown in **Figure 20,** can be used to identify conifers.

Conifers, like all plants, exhibit adaptations to their environments. What connection can you make between the facts that most conifers have drooping branches and that many conifers grow in snowy climates? Another adaptation is a waxlike coating called cutin that covers conifers' needlelike or scalelike leaves and reduces water loss.

■ **Figure 20** Female cones of conifers can be described as woody, berrylike, or fleshy.

Douglas fir—woody cones **Juniper—berrylike cones** **Pacific yew—fleshy cones**

C Critical Thinking

OL Analyze Ripe ginkgo fruits produce an obnoxious odor if they are crushed and as they decay. **ASK STUDENTS:** ***How has this affected the type of trees gardeners and landscapers have planted?*** There are male and female gingko trees. Because only the female trees produce fruit, landscapers and gardeners prefer to plant the male tree.

Reading Strategy

BL OL AL COOP LEARN

Supplemental Reading Organize students into groups of two or three. Have students choose one of the following topics and find supplemental reading material in the library: fossils in amber, commercial uses of conifers, variations in conifer cones. Have students take notes, collect pictures, and create posters that can be displayed in the classroom.

Writing Support

AL Creative Writing Have students select a seed type (such as jack pine, dandelion, mulberry, or horse chestnut) that displays a requirement for effective dispersal. Have students write a biography of a hypothetical seed's journey from maturation, release, and dispersal to new growth.

In-Text Question Drooping branches are an adaptation to the amount of snowfall.

■ **Caption Question Fig. 19** carried by wind

Differentiated Instruction

Below Level When organizing students into groups for a discussion, pair students who are working below level with students who will be able to act as peer tutors. These partners can help clarify any concepts the students do not understand.

For more tips, see pages 14T–15T.

D Develop Concepts

BL OL

Clarify a Misconception

ASK STUDENTS: *Can trees also be flowering plants?* yes Many students do not realize that trees such as apple, cherry, maple, and oak are flowering plants. Collect pictures of flowers from various trees and have students examine them. Remind students that acorns, maple samaras, and hickory nuts are also fruits produced from the flowers of trees. Point out that conifers are not flowering plants and cones are not fruit.

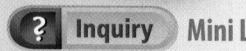

MiniLab 2

Inquiry Mini Lab

For a lab worksheet, use your eTeacherEdition Online.

RUBRIC A rubric for evaluating MiniLabs is found on your eTeacherEdition Online.

Est. Time 25 min

Additional Materials metric ruler, magnifying lens, branches from a variety of coniferous trees

Safety Precaution Approve lab safety forms before work begins.

Teaching Strategy Students might need help in identifying which characteristics to compare.

Cleanup and Disposal Designate an area for students to place used plant material.

Analysis

1. Grouping system should be based on conifer leaf characteristics.
2. Possible answer: Classification system is very detailed and includes all leaf characteristics.

LabManager™

Customize this lab with the LabManager™ CD-ROM.

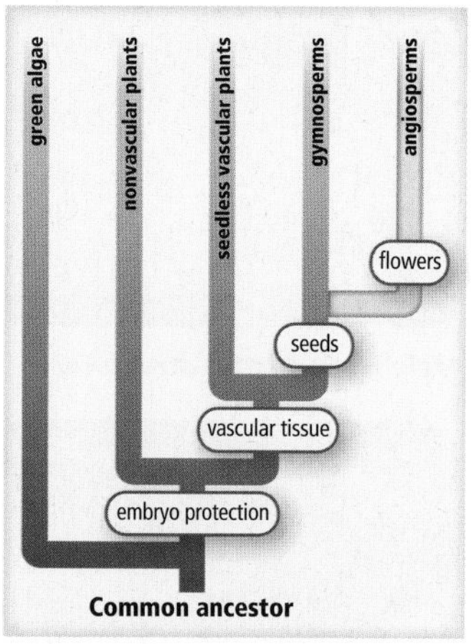

Figure 21 The flowering plants were the most recently evolved of the plant kingdom.

Inquiry Video Lab

Video BrainPOP

When you hear the word *evergreen,* do you think of a pine or another conifer? Most plants in northern temperate regions called evergreens are conifers. However, in subtropical and tropical regions, other plants, such as palms, also are evergreen. Botanists define an evergreen plant as one with some green leaves throughout the year. This adaptation enables it to undergo photosynthesis whenever conditions are favorable. A plant that loses its leaves at the end of the growing season or when moisture is scarce is called deciduous. Some conifers are deciduous, such as larches and bald cypresses. Whether deciduous or evergreen, you can identify a conifer species by its leaves, as demonstrated in **MiniLab 2.**

Reading Check **Explain** why some trees are called evergreens.

Division Anthophyta Flowering plants, also known as anthophytes or angiosperms, are the most widely distributed plants because of adaptations that enable them to grow in terrestrial and aquatic environments. Anthophytes first appeared in the fossil record about 130 million years ago after the appearance of gymnosperms, as shown in **Figure 21.** Today, flowering plants make up more than 75 percent of the plant kingdom.

Traditionally, botanists classified anthophytes as monocots or dicots. The names refer to the number of seed leaves, called cotyledons: a monocot has one seed leaf, and a dicot has two seed leaves. However, botanists now classify dicots as eudicots, based on the structure of their pollen.

Life spans A few weeks or years describe the life spans of anthophytes. An **annual** plant completes its life span—sprouts from a seed, grows, produces new seeds, and dies—in one growing season or less. This group includes many garden plants and most weeds. D

MiniLab 2

Investigate Conifer Leaves

Inquiry MiniLab

What similarities and differences exist among conifer leaves? Some conifer trees are among the tallest and oldest organisms on Earth. Most conifers have needlelike leaves that differ in a variety of ways. Leaf characteristics are important in conifer identification.

Procedure

1. Read and complete the lab safety form.
2. Obtain one of each of the **conifer samples** your teacher has identified. Label each sample by name.
3. Design a data table to record your observations.
4. Compare and contrast the leaves. Make a list of characteristics that you determine are important for describing each sample. Record these characteristics for each conifer sample.
5. Develop a system for grouping the conifer samples. Be prepared to justify your system.
6. Wash your hands thoroughly after handling plant samples.

Analysis

1. **Explain** the reasoning for your classification system.
2. **Compare** your classification system to those created by other students. Explain why your system is an efficient way to classify the conifer samples that you studied.

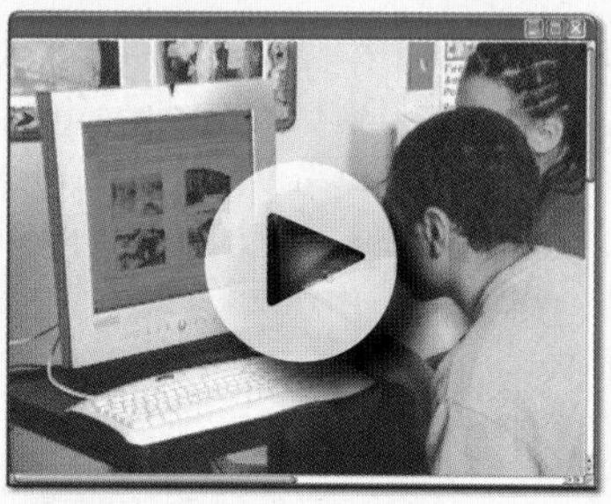

Inquiry **Video Lab** This video lab shows students researching five tree species suitable to plant in their community.

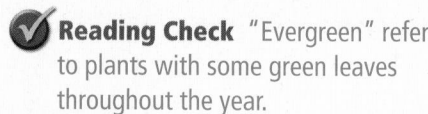

Reading Check "Evergreen" refers to plants with some green leaves throughout the year.

Video BrainPOP

First-year growth

Second-year growth

■ **Figure 22** An evening primrose (a biennial) produces leaves, an underground stem, and roots the first growing season. It flowers in the second year of growth.

A **biennial** plant's life spans two years. During the first year, it produces leaves and a strong root system. Refer to **Figure 22.** Some biennials, such as carrots, beets, and turnips, develop fleshy storage roots that are harvested after the first growing season. If the biennial is not harvested, the aboveground tissues die. However, roots and other underground parts remain alive for biennials that are adapted to their environments. In the second year, stems, leaves, flowers, and seeds grow. The plant's life ends the second year.

Perennial plants can live for several years and usually produce flowers and seeds yearly. Some perennials respond to harsh conditions by dropping leaves, while others completely die back so that only their roots remain alive. They resume growth when favorable growing conditions return. Fruit and shade trees, shrubs, irises, peonies, roses, and many types of berries are perennial plants.

The life spans of all plants are determined genetically and reflect adaptations for surviving harsh conditions. However, all plant life spans are affected by environmental conditions.

D

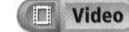

Video

What's Biology Got to Do With It?

Section 4 Assessment

Section Summary

- Vascular seed plants produce seeds containing the sporophyte generation.
- Vascular seed plants exhibit numerous adaptations for living in varied environments.
- There are five divisions of vascular seed plants. Each division has distinct characteristics.
- Flowering plants are annuals, biennials, or perennials.

Understand Main Ideas

1. MAIN Idea **Describe** the advantages of a plant that produces seeds.
2. **Compare and contrast** a gymnosperm and an angiosperm.
3. **Distinguish** between male and female cones of gymnosperms.
4. **Identify** the divisions of gymnosperms.
5. **Differentiate** between a monocot and a eudicot.
6. **Compare and contrast** the three types of anthophyte life spans.

Think Critically

7. **Consider** A Christmas tree farmer saw an advertisement that read, "Bald cypresses—the way to quick profits. Plant these fast-growing trees and harvest them in just five years." Would these trees be profitable for the farmer? Explain.

MATH in Biology

8. The smallest flowering plant is 1 mm tall and the largest conifer can be 90 m tall. How many times taller is the largest conifer than the smallest flowering plant?

D Develop Concepts

AL

Activate Prior Knowledge

Point out that the terms *annual, biennial,* and *perennial* are often used to describe things other than plants.

ASK STUDENTS: ***What are some other examples of what these terms describe?*** annual events, biennial events, a perennial favorite

Have students read about annual, biennial, and perennial plants. Relate the use of these terms in describing plants to their use when talking about the frequency of events.

GOING GREEN To save paper, ask your local newspaper company if they have damaged or short rolls of newsprint that they could give you for classroom use. Students could cut the paper as needed to fit into binders, folders, or for projects.

Formative Assessment

Evaluation Have students summarize the characteristics of anthophytes by writing a paragraph about them.

Remediation Have students obtain pictures of seeds and/or flowers and organize them into annuals, biennials, and perennials.

Section 4 Assessment

1. Seeds provide nutrition and protection for the delicate embryo.
2. Both produce seeds; seeds of angiosperms are part of fruit; seeds of gymnosperms are not.
3. Male cones are papery structures that disintegrate soon after pollen is released. Female cones can be berrylike, fleshy, or woody, and eventually contain seeds.
4. Cycadophyta, Gnetophyta, Ginkgophyta, Coniferophyta.
5. Monocot seeds have one cotyledon; eudicot and dicot seeds have two cotyledons.
6. Annuals complete their life spans in one year or less. Biennials complete their life spans in their second year of growth. Perennials' life spans vary from a few years to centuries.
7. No. Bald cypress trees are deciduous and shed their leaves every year.
8. The largest conifer is 90,000 times larger than the smallest flowering plant.

Assessment Online Quiz

In the Field

Purpose

Students will understand real-world applications of biology. A.2, C.6, E.2, F.6, G.1

Anticipatory Guide

ASK STUDENTS: ***What are the characteristics of pollen?*** Particles are very small, can appear as a fine dust, and can be carried by the wind. ***Do you think pollen of all plant species are the same?*** Pollen differs in diameter, mass, shape, method of transport, and chemical composition.

Background

- Forensic palynology, dating from the 1950s, is part of the larger field of forensic science, the use of scientific methods to solve crimes. This field includes forensic dentistry, forensic pathology, and forensic ballistics.
- Not all pollen types are equally useful to forensic investigators. Pollen from aquatic angiosperms oxidizes quickly when removed from water. Even though lightweight pollen is produced in large amounts, its effectiveness as evidence is reduced because it disperses over large areas.
- Forensic palynologists typically gain the most information from pollen that can be preserved for long periods and pollen that falls quickly to the ground, limiting its dispersal area.

MATH in Biology

April 14—juniper and maple;
May 12—oak;
June 2—mulberry

In the Field

Career: Forensic Palynology

The Proof Is in the Pollen

Forensic palynology (pah luh NAW luh gee), a relatively new science, uses pollen and spore evidence in legal cases to help police solve crimes. A jogger was attacked, dragged to a nearby wooded area, and murdered. The police questioned a key suspect who admitted that he was in the area, but he claimed that he did not see the jogger. He also said that he never had been in the wooded area where the body was found. Was he telling the truth?

Incriminating evidence Soil from the crime scene contained large amounts of pine pollen and fern spores. A survey revealed that no other nearby locations contained both pine trees and ferns. When police searched the suspect's apartment, they found a sweater and pants that they believed he was wearing during the attack. When a forensic palynologist examined the clothes, she found the same pine pollen and fern spores that were at the crime scene. The suspect eventually was tried and convicted of the murder.

Palynologists at a crime scene Detectives collect many types of evidence from a crime scene, including fingerprints. Can palynologists collect fingerprints? In a way, yes. Each seed-plant species produces unique pollen grains. They can be thought of as a species' "fingerprint" and can be used for identification. Also, dirt and dust often contain large amounts of pollen and spores. Fibers in woven fabrics can act as filters and trap pollen and spores. Blown by the wind, pollen can become trapped between strands of hair.

Pollen Count at Crime Scene

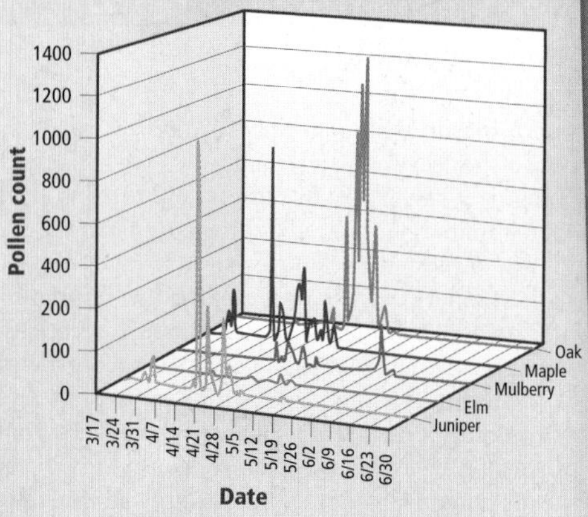

This graph shows the pollen count at a crime scene. It indicates which pollen types were most abundant at a given date.

Forensic palynology A pollen study can help investigators narrow the list of suspects, making this a valuable investigative tool. Because it requires extensive background knowledge and training in collecting and preserving samples without contamination, forensic palynology is a specialized science.

MATH in Biology

Interpret the Graph Examine the graph of tree-pollen counts. What types of pollen might you expect to find if the crime occurred on April 14, May 12, or June 2? Conduct research to find out more about the types of pollen found in your community.

Activity

Have students research to discover what types of pollen are common in your area.

ASK STUDENTS: ***During what months of the year do pollen counts peak in your area?*** Answers will vary based on location. ***Is there anything that happens to humans that indicates changing pollen counts?*** Some students and adults suffer from seasonal allergies.

WebQuest

BIOLAB

FIELD INVESTIGATION: HOW CAN YOU IDENTIFY AND CLASSIFY TREES?

Background: Botanists and others interested in plants often use field guides and dichotomous keys to identify plants. In this BioLab, you will use a field guide to identify trees in a given area. Then, you will create your own dichotomous key to identify the trees in your area.

Question: *What characteristics can be used to identify trees and to create a dichotomous key for them?*

Materials
field guide of trees (for your area)
metric ruler
magnifying lens

Safety Precautions
WARNING: ***Stay within the area of study and be alert for plants, insects, or other organisms that might pose a hazard.***

Procedure
1. Read and complete the lab safety form.
2. Study the field guide provided by your teacher to determine how it is organized.
3. Based on your examination of the field guide and what you learned about plant characteristics in this chapter, make a list of characteristics that will help you identify the trees in your area.
4. Create a data table based on the list you made in Step 3.
5. Use a field guide to identify a tree in the area designated by your teacher. Confirm your identification with your teacher.
6. Record in your data table the characteristics of your identified tree.
7. Repeat Steps 5 and 6 until you have identified all trees required for this lab.
8. Review your data table. Choose the characteristics most helpful in identifying trees. These characteristics will form the basis of your dichotomous key.
9. Determine in what rank the characteristics should appear in the dichotomous key. Create a written description for each characteristic.
10. Create your dichotomous key. The traits described at each step of a dichotomous key usually are pairs of contrasting characteristics. For example, the first step might compare needlelike or scalelike leaves to broad leaves.

Analyze and Conclude
1. **Interpret Data** Based on the data you collected, describe plant diversity in the area you studied.
2. **Critique** Exchange your dichotomous key with a classmate's dichotomous key. Use the key to identify trees in the study area. Give your classmate suggestions to improve his or her key.
3. **Predict** How effective would your dichotomous key be for someone trying to identify trees in the study area? Explain.
4. **Error Analysis** What changes could you make to improve the effectiveness of your dichotomous key?

SHARE YOUR DATA
Compare and Contrast Share your data with the rest of the class and compare it to the data your classmates collected. What plants are common to all of the posted dichotomous keys?

Analyze and Conclude
1. Answers will vary based on the study area chosen. Students should recognize that tree diversity can be relatively high, even within a small area.
2. Characteristics used in tree identification should be included in the dichotomous key. Characteristics will most likely be related to leaf type and placement, bark, flowers, fruit, and tree size.
3. Answers will vary based on the dichotomous key developed.
4. Answers will vary but might include choosing a different defining characteristic for Step 1 of the key, and narrowing or widening the scope of one or more characteristics identified at specific steps.

BIOLAB

? Inquiry BioLab

For a lab worksheet, use your eTeacherEdition Online.

RUBRIC A rubric for evaluating BioLabs is found on your eTeacherEdition Online.

Est. Time 90 min

Content Background Field guides and dichotomous keys can be used to identify trees. Characteristics used in identification include habitat, tree height and diameter, and properties related to leaves, bark, twigs, flowers, and fruit.

Safety Precautions Approve lab safety forms before work begins. Visit the field-study site prior to the lab to determine potential dangers. Establish physical boundaries within which students must remain during the activity. Address the needs of students with known plant allergies.

Teaching Strategies
- Choose a field-study site that includes as much tree diversity as possible.
- Mark the trees you would like students to identify. Label these as *Tree A, Tree B,* etc.
- Provide students with a sample dichotomous key to use as reference as they create their own keys.

Alternative Teaching Demo Students could use an existing dichotomous key to identify trees in the study area.

Chapter 21 Study Guide

Study Guide

ConnectED

Students can use the following to review the chapter.

Review

Vocabulary eGames
Vocabulary eFlashcards
Vocabulary PuzzleMaker

Assessment

Online Quizzes
Online Test Practice
Standardized Test Practice

Use the *ExamView® Assessment Suite* CD-ROM to:

- create multiple versions of tests
- create modified tests with one mouse click
- edit existing questions and add your own questions
- build tests aligned with state standards using built-in state curriculum tags
- change English tests to Spanish with one mouse click
- track students' progress using the Teacher Management System

THEME FOCUS Diversity The 300,000 types of plants found all over Earth have different types of tissues and reproductive methods that allow them to fill different niches.

BIG Idea Plants have changed over time and are now a diverse group of organisms.

Section 1 Plant Evolution and Adaptations

stomata (p. 606)
vascular tissue (p. 606)
vascular plant (p. 606)
nonvascular plant (p. 606)
seed (p. 607)

MAIN Idea Adaptations to environmental changes on Earth contributed to the evolution of plants.

- Plants are multicellular organisms, and most are photosynthetic.
- Evidence indicates that ancient, unicellular, freshwater green algae were the ancestors of present-day plants.
- Present-day plants and green algae have many common characteristics.
- Over time, plants developed several adaptations for living on land.
- Plants alternate between a sporophyte and a gametophyte generation.

Section 2 Nonvascular Plants

thallose (p. 612)

MAIN Idea Nonvascular plants are small and usually grow in damp environments.

- Distribution of nonvascular plants is limited by the plants' ability to transport water and other substances.
- Mosses are small plants that can grow in different environments.
- Like other nonvascular plants, hornworts rely on osmosis and diffusion to transport substances.
- The two types of liverworts are classified as thallose and leafy.

Section 3 Seedless Vascular Plants

strobilus (p. 613)
epiphyte (p. 614)
rhizome (p. 615)
sporangium (p. 616)
sorus (p. 616)

MAIN Idea Because they have vascular tissues, seedless vascular plants generally are larger and better adapted to drier environments than nonvascular plants.

- Seedless vascular plants have specialized transport tissues and reproduce by spores.
- The sporophyte is the dominant generation in vascular plants.
- Lycophytes and pterophytes are seedless vascular plants.

Section 4 Vascular Seed Plants

cotyledon (p. 617)
cone (p. 618)
annual (p. 620)
biennial (p. 621)
perennial (p. 621)

MAIN Idea Vascular seed plants are the most widely distributed plants on Earth.

- Vascular seed plants produce seeds containing the sporophyte generation.
- Vascular seed plants exhibit numerous adaptations for living in varied environments.
- There are five divisions of vascular seed plants. Each division has distinct characteristics.
- Flowering plants are annuals, biennials, or perennials.

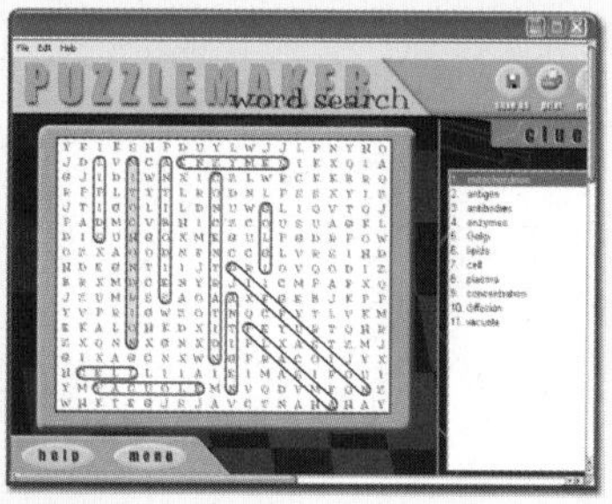

Review Vocabulary PuzzleMaker

For additional practice with vocabulary, have students access the Vocabulary PuzzleMaker online.

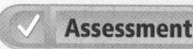

Review Vocabulary eGames

Section 1

Vocabulary Review

For questions 1–3, match each phrase with a vocabulary term from the Study Guide page.

1. plant structure that contains the embryo

2. transport tissue

3. enable exchange of gases

Understand Main Ideas

4. Approximately when did primitive land plants appear?
A. 30 mya
B. 400 mya
C. 500 mya
D. 2000 mya

5. Which is not a trait shared by freshwater green algae and plants?
A. cellulose cell walls
B. chlorophyll
C. food stored as starch
D. contain vascular tissue

6. Which is likely to ensure the survival of the embryo?

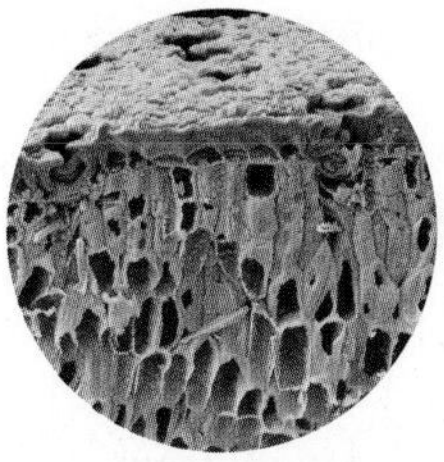
A.

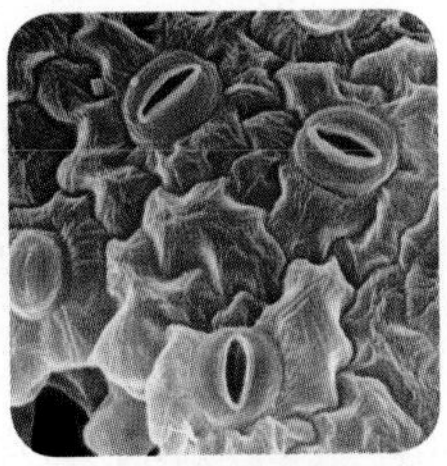
C.

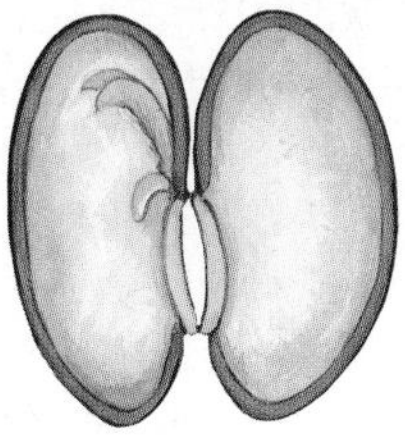
B.

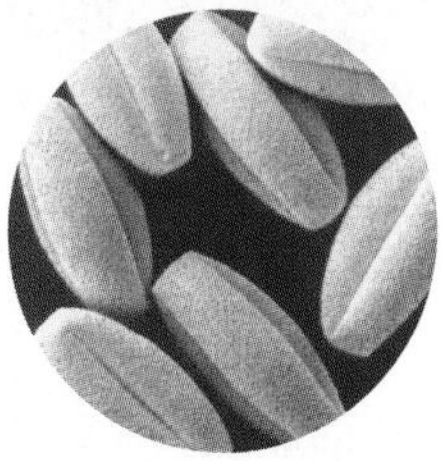
D.

7. Which was a major obstacle for plants to live on land?
A. obtaining enough light
B. obtaining enough soil
C. obtaining enough water
D. obtaining enough oxygen

Constructed Response

8. Short Answer Describe the adaptations that you would expect to find in an aquatic plant.

9. MAIN Idea Of the adaptations discussed in Section 1, which one do you predict would be most important to a plant living in the desert?

Think Critically

10. Organize the adaptations to life on land from the most important to the least important. Defend your decisions.

Section 2

Vocabulary Review

Write a sentence using the following vocabulary term correctly.

11. thallose

Understand Main Ideas

Use the photo below to answer question 12.

12. Which word does not describe the plant shown above?
A. multicellular
B. nonvascular
C. seedless
D. thallose

Chapter 21

Assessment

Section 1

Vocabulary Review
1. seed
2. vascular tissue
3. stomata

Understand Main Ideas
4. B
5. D
6. B
7. C

Constructed Response
8. Answers will vary but should include some mechanism for floating near the water's surface to get light and roots to anchor in the substrate.
9. Answers will vary, but should include some adaptation that reduces water loss.

Think Critically
10. Answers will vary, but students should identify adaptations for obtaining and conserving water as most important because obtaining water is the major obstacle for land plants.

Section 2

Vocabulary Review
11. Sentences will vary, but should reflect that thallose describes a fleshy lobed structure rather than a leafy structure.

Understand Main Ideas
12. D

13. D

Constructed Response
14. The sporophyte gains support and nutrition from the gametophyte.
15. Descriptions will vary but should include a moist environment.

Think Critically
16. Answers will vary, but should include a variety of local plants from many divisions.

Section 3

Vocabulary Review
17. strobilus
18. rhizome
19. epiphyte

Understand Main Ideas
20. A
21. A
22. D
23. D

Constructed Response
24. Ferns have a dominant sporophyte generation, are vascular, and produce spores.
25. Pterophyta—ferns and horsetails; dominant sporophyte generation; has a rhizome; fronds have branched vascular tissue Lycophyta—club mosses; dominant sporophyte generation; have roots, stems, and small, scaly, leaflike structures

Think Critically
26. Spores may easily drop down from the sori to the soil.

Section 4

Vocabulary Review
27. cotyledon
28. perennial
29. cone

---

13. Which is a characteristic of mosses?
    - **A.** vascular tissue
    - **B.** flowers
    - **C.** seeds
    - **D.** rhizoids

Constructed Response

14. **Short Answer** Refer to **Figure 9** and analyze the need for a nonvascular sporophyte to remain dependent on the gametophyte generation.

15. MAIN Idea Describe a habitat in your community that would support nonvascular plants.

Think Critically

16. **Research** nonvascular plants online and make a list of those that grow in your state.

Section 3

Vocabulary Review

For questions 17–19, match each definition with a vocabulary term from the Study Guide page.

17. spore-bearing structures that form a compact cluster
18. thick, underground stem
19. plant that lives anchored to another plant or object

Understand Main Ideas

Use the concept map below to answer question 20.

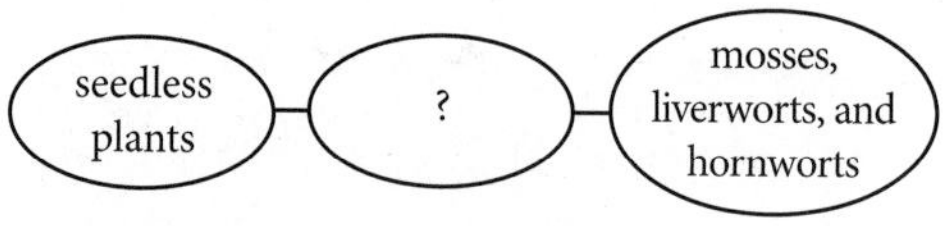

20. Which term correctly completes the concept map shown above?
    - **A.** nonvascular
    - **B.** flowering
    - **C.** vascular
    - **D.** seed-producing

21. What structure contains clusters of sporangia?
    - **A.** sorus
    - **B.** frond
    - **C.** stem
    - **D.** blade

22. Which is not part of the fern sporophyte generation?
    - **A.** rhizome
    - **B.** sorus
    - **C.** frond
    - **D.** rhizoid

23. Which photo shows sori?

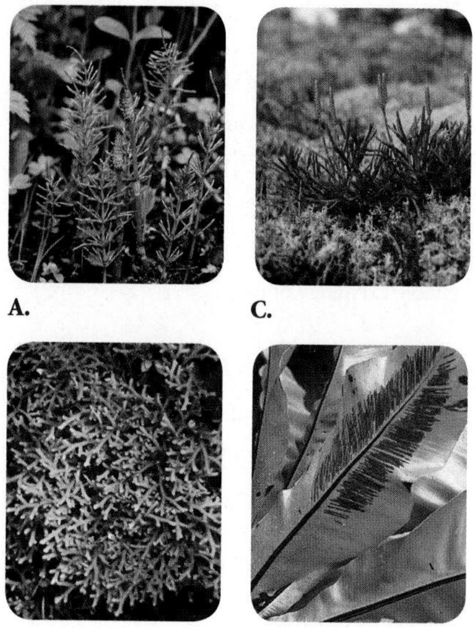

A. C. B. D.

Constructed Response

24. **Short Answer** Summarize the characteristics of ferns.

25. MAIN Idea Differentiate between division Pterophyta and division Lycophyta.

Think Critically

26. **Infer** the advantage of fern sori being on the undersurfaces of fronds rather than on the upper surfaces.

Section 4

Vocabulary Review

For questions 27–29, replace each underlined word with the correct vocabulary term from the Study Guide page.

27. A root of a seed provide nutrients when it sprouts.
28. A plant that lives for several growing seasons is a rhizome.
29. A flower contains the male or female reproduction structures of gymnosperms.

Assessment Online Test Practice

Understand Main Ideas

30. Which plant division has plants with needlelike or scaly leaves?
A. Gnetophyta C. Coniferophyta
B. Anthophyta D. Cycadophyta

Use the photo below to answer question 31.

31. Which plant division has plants that produce female reproductive structures like those shown above?
A. Coniferophyta C. Gnetophyta
B. Anthophyta D. Ginkgophyta

32. Which describes the importance of seed dispersal?
A. ensures more favorable environments for growth
B. creates greater biodiversity
C. limits competition with parent plants and other offspring
D. provides greater resources

Constructed Response

33. Open Ended What might be the adaptive advantage of having a gametophyte dependent on a sporophyte?

34. **THEME FOCUS Diversity** Make a list of the traits that you would use to differentiate between coniferophytes and anthophytes.

Think Critically

35. Compare and contrast cones and strobili.

36. MAIN Idea Infer why there are more conifers than flowering plants in colder environments such as those in northern Canada and Alaska.

Summative Assessment

37. BIG Idea Pick three adaptations described in this chapter and explain why plants needed them to populate land successfully. Then identify one plant division that has each adaptation.

38. WRITING in Biology Imagine that you are one of the first plants that survived living on land. What stories could you tell your grandchildren about the difficulties you faced?

39. Explain the meaning of alternation of generations as it applies to plants.

40. Distinguish between vascular and nonvascular plants.

DBQ Document-Based Questions

Data obtained from: Qiu, Yin-Long, et al. 1998. The gain of three mitochondrial introns identifies liverworts as the earliest land plants. *Nature* 394: 671.

Here we survey 352 diverse land plants and find that three mitochondrial Group II introns are present . . . in mosses, hornworts and all major lineages of vascular plants, but are entirely absent from liverworts, green algae and all other eukaryotes. These results indicate that liverworts are the earliest land plants, with the three introns having been acquired in a common ancestor of all other land plants, and have important implications concerning early plant evolution.

41. Evaluate the research above by making a cladogram.

42. Explain how this research led scientists to suggest that liverworts are the ancestors of all other plants.

43. Apply what you know about polymerase chain reactions to predict how the scientists determined which plants contained these introns.

44. Imagine that a fellow classmate is having trouble understanding the document above. Summarize the main points of the document in your own words, making an effort to clarify any concepts that may be confusing.

Understand Main Ideas

30. C
31. D
32. C

Constructed Response

33. The sporophyte can protect the gametophyte and provide nutrition.

34. Answers will vary, but should include differences between flowers and fruits and cones, and leaf forms.

Think Critically

35. Both are part of the reproductive cycle, but cones produce seeds and strobili produce spores.

36. Conifers are more prevalent in cold, snowy areas than flowering plants because adaptations of conifers—specialized leaves and tree form—enable them to thrive in these conditions. Conifer leaves are needlelike or scalelike with a thick cuticle and sunken stoma for conserving water. Their tree form with the sloping branches is an adaptation to the snow.

Summative Assessment

37. Answers will vary. Possible answer: Cuticle—reduces water lost to evaporation; Pterophyta. Vascular tissue—faster transportation of water and nutrients; Gnetophyta. Seeds—embryo is protected from harsh environmental conditions; Coniferophyta.

38. Check stories for accuracy of content. Stories should also include the need to take up water.

WRITING in Biology

RUBRIC Use the modifiable rubric found on your eTeacher-Edition Online to assess writing assignments.

39. All plants have alternation of generations. They alternate between a $2n$ sporophyte that produces spores and a n gametophyte that produces gametes.

40. Vascular plants contain tubelike cells that can transport water and nutrients great distances, while nonvascular plants rely on diffusion and osmosis for transportation of water and nutrients.

DBQ Document-Based Questions

Data obtained from: Qui, Yin-Long, et al. 1998. The gain of three mitochondrial introns identifies liverworts as the earliest land plants. *Nature* 394: 671.

41. Cladograms should show that liverworts are more ancestral than mosses, hornworts, and vascular plants.

42. Since these introns are absent from liverworts and green algae but found in all other land plants, it suggests that liverworts are most closely related to algae and could be the link between algae and plants.

43. Answers will vary, but students should mention that if the sequence of the introns is known, the polymerase chain reaction can be used to locate the introns in the genome of plants.

44. Answers should restate the information in the document more simply.

Assessment Online Test Practice

Standardized Test Practice

Multiple Choice

1. A
2. C
3. D
4. B
5. B
6. D
7. C
8. C

Short Answer

9. The sporophyte generation is smaller in nonvascular plants than in seedless vascular plants.
10. Answers can vary. Amoebas have an outer plasma membrane and thickened layer of cytoplasm called ectoplasm. As in other organisms, the plasma membrane controls the movement of substances into and out of the cell. The ectoplasm might make possible the movement of the pseudopodia. One possible benefit of having two stiff layers is that they allow for specialization of functions.
11. The wings of bats and the arms of monkeys are homologous structures. Homologous structures are similar structures in different species that share a common ancestor. All mammals, including bats and monkeys, are presumed to share a common ancestor. Homologous structures are considered useful characteristics in classifying organisms because they show similarities among related species.
12. The hyphae spread out over a large area. The hyphae produce and release enzymes that help break down organic matter in the surroundings. Then the hyphae absorb nutrients for the fungus. The fungus can affect its environment by breaking down organic materials wherever the hyphae grow.
13. Layer 2 is the location of photosynthetic organisms, either green algae or cyanobacteria, which provide food for the lichen.

Standardized Test Practice

Cumulative

Multiple Choice

1. Which substance do yeasts produce that causes bread to rise?
A. carbon dioxide
B. ethanol
C. oxygen
D. simple sugars

2. Which must a virus have to attack a host cell?
A. a DNA or RNA sequence that is recognized by the ribosomes of the host cell
B. the enzymes to burst the host cell so that the host cell can be used as raw materials
C. a particular shape that matches the proteins on the surface of the host cell
D. the proper enzyme to puncture the membrane of the host cell

3. Which group of protists is characterized by parasitic behavior?
A. chrysophytes
B. dinoflagellates
C. sarcodines
D. sporozoans

Use the following illustration to answer question 4.

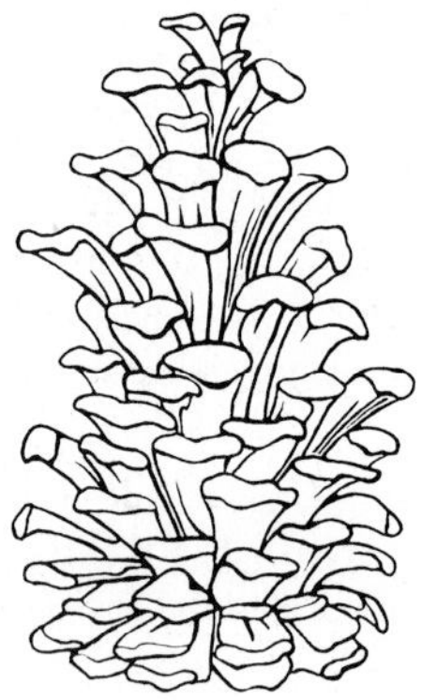

4. In which division of seed plants would you expect to find the structure in the above illustration?
A. Anthophyta
B. Coniferophyta
C. Cycadophyta
D. Ginkgophyta

5. Suppose a cell from the frond of a fern contains 24 chromosomes. How many chromosomes would you expect to find in the spores?
A. 6
B. 12
C. 24
D. 48

Use the diagram below to answer questions 6 and 7.

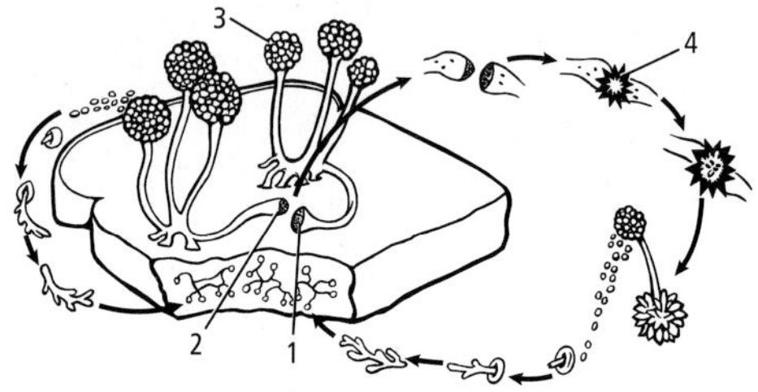

6. Which phylum of fungi has these kinds of reproductive structures?
A. Ascomycota
B. Basidiomycota
C. Deuteromycota
D. Zygomycota

7. Which of these structures is involved in asexual reproduction?
A. 1
B. 2
C. 3
D. 4

8. Why is conjugation important for protists?
A. It expands the habitat.
B. It improves locomotion speed.
C. It increases genetic variation.
D. It restores injured parts.

Short Answer

9. Compare the sporophyte generation in nonvascular plants to the sporophyte generation in seedless vascular plants.

10. Describe the cell membrane and ectoplasm of an amoeba and suggest why it is beneficial for the amoeba to have both structures.

11. What is the relationship between bat wings and monkey arms? Explain the importance of this relationship for the classification of organisms.

12. Describe how a multicellular fungus obtains nutrients from its environment and assess how that affects its role in the environment.

Use the diagram of the lichen below to answer questions 13 and 14.

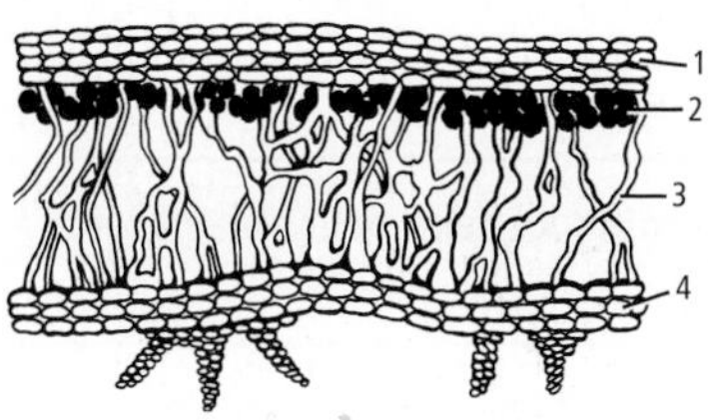

13. Identify and evaluate the importance of the layer of the lichen where photosynthesis takes place.

14. Analyze how the photosynthesizer and fungus benefit from being part of a lichen.

15. Evaluate how spore production gives fungi an advantage in an ecosystem.

Extended Response

Use the diagram below to answer question 16.

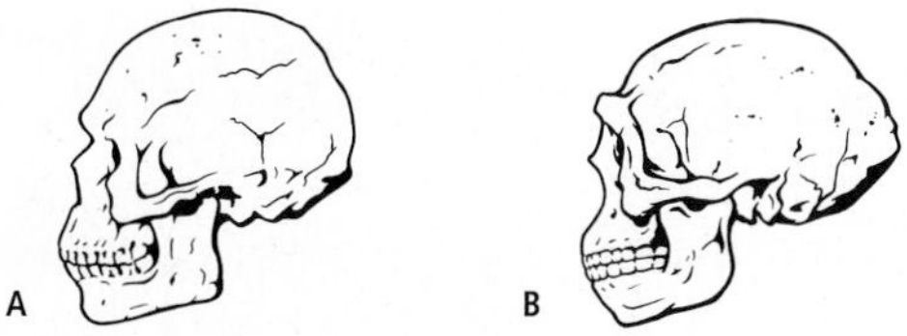

16. Look at the two skulls in the diagram. Infer which one you think is more closely related to *Homo sapiens.* Explain your inference.

17. Compare and contrast reproduction in paramecia and amoebas.

Essay Question

During the 1840s, the potato was an extremely popular crop plant in Ireland. Many people in rural Ireland were completely dependent on potatoes for food. From 1845 to 1847, the potato blight—a funguslike disease—wiped out potato crops. The blight produces spores on the leaves of the potato plant. The spores can be transmitted by water or wind. They are carried into the soil by water, where they infect the potato tubers, and they can survive through winter on the potatoes left buried in the fields. Close to one million people died from starvation and nearly as many left Ireland for America and other countries.

Using the information in the paragraph above, answer the following question in essay format.

18. Write an essay that indicates why potato blight spread so quickly through Ireland and how the spread of the fungus might have been slowed by different farming practices.

NEED EXTRA HELP?																		
If You Missed Question . . .	1	2	3	4	5	6	7	8	9	10	11	12	13	14	15	16	17	18
Review Section . . .	20.1	18.2	19.1	21.4	21.3	20.2	20.3	19.2	21.3	19.2	15.2	20.1	20.3	20.3	20.2	16.3	19.2	20.1

14. The fungus provides a large surface area to trap water. It also breaks down the surface, providing mineral nutrients for the fungus and the photosynthesizer. The photosynthesizer makes food for itself and the fungus.

15. Answers may vary. Spores are small and easily carried by the wind. Spores provide fungi with an opportunity to quickly spread over a large area and into favorable habitats for growth. This gives fungi an adaptive advantage in reproduction.

Extended Response

16. Skull A is from a closer relative of *Homo sapiens.* Students can name any of the following traits: thinner, less elongated skull/cranial bones, smaller jaw, and no obvious depression in the brow ridge.

17. Answers can vary. Both paramecia and amoebas reproduce asexually via binary fission, during which a parent cell divides into two identical offspring. Paramecia will also attach to each other to exchange genetic material during the process of conjugation.

Essay Question

18. Potatoes were the main food source and they were grown everywhere. The potato blight produced many spores that were easily transported from potato field to potato field because the fields were close together. The potato blight might have been slowed if farmers had rotated crops, burned infected plants, or planted fields with a variety of crops so that the potato plants were not so close together.

Chapter 22 Organizer:
Plant Structure and Function

LabManager™
Customize any lab with the LabManager™ CD-ROM.

Section Objectives	National Science Standards	Materials and Planning: Estimated times include cleanup and disposal, but do not include teacher prep time. For cleanup and disposal guidelines, see page 39T.	Est. Time (min)
Section 1 1. What are the major types of plant cells? 2. What are the major types of plant tissues? 3. What are the differences among the functions of plant cells and tissues?	UCP.1, UCP.2, UCP.5; A.1, A.2; C.1, C.4, C.5; F.3	**Launch Lab,** p. 630: potted plants, magnifying lens	20
		Demonstration, p. 633: spring toy, cardboard, balloon	5
		MiniLab 1, p. 634: slice of potato, cross section of celery stalk, slide, iodine, coverslip, microscope, water, dye, paper towel, pear tissue, pencil eraser	45
		Demonstration, p. 634: plants with meristems (houseplant and carrot), cross section of wood, piece of grass or hay	5
		Demonstration, p. 636: jigsaw puzzle, waxed paper	5
		Demonstration, p. 637: radish-seed roots with root hairs, petri dish, paper towel, self-sealing plastic bag	5
Section 2 1. How are the structures of roots, stems, and leaves related to their functions? 2. How do the structures and functions of roots, stems, and leaves compare?	UCP.1, UCP.2, UCP.5; A.1, A.2; C.1, C.4, C.5, C.6	**Demonstration,** p. 640: pictures or samples of different roots, including edible ones like beets, carrots, and radishes	5
		Demonstration, p. 643: white carnations; water; red, blue, and green food coloring; four containers; a knife or scissors to cut stems	5 per day
Section 3 1. What are the major types of plant hormones? 2. How do hormones affect the growth of plants? 3. How are the different types of plant responses alike?	UCP.1, UCP.2, UCP.5; A.1, A.2; B.3; C.1, C.4, C.5, C.6; E.2; G.1, G.2, G.3	**Demonstration,** p. 649: ripe banana, three green bananas, two paper bags	10 per day
		MiniLab 2, p. 650: Venus flytrap, small paintbrush	15
		Design Your Own BioLab, p. 653: gibberellic acid in varying concentrations, poster board, dishwashing liquid, potted dwarf pea-plant seedlings, spray bottles, cotton swabs, light source, large plastic bags, plant fertilizer, distilled water, metric rulers, graph paper	45 per day

Suggested Time for Each Lesson

Class	Chapter Opener	Section 1	Section 2	Section 3	Assessment
Basic	45 min	45 min	45 min	45 min	45 min
General	25 min	45 min	45 min	65 min	45 min
Honors	—	45 min	70 min	45 min	20 min

ConnectED

connectED.mcgraw-hill.com

Access interactive learning opportunities and teaching resources using these icons located throughout your StudentWorks™ Plus Online and eTeacherEdition Online.

Chapter 22 Section Resources	Additional Chapter 22 Resources	Technology
FAST FILE Unit 6 Resources: Launch Lab Worksheet* MiniLab Worksheet* Study Guide (English/Spanish)* Section Quick Check **Reading Essentials 22.1** **Science Notebook 22.1*** **FAST FILE Unit 6 Resources:** Study Guide (English/Spanish)* Section Quick Check **Reading Essentials 22.2** **Science Notebook 22.2*** **FAST FILE Unit 6 Resources:** MiniLab Worksheet* BioLab Worksheet* Study Guide (English/Spanish)* Section Quick Check **Reading Essentials 22.3** **Science Notebook 22.3***	**FAST FILE Unit 6 Resources:** Chapter Diagnostic Test Concept Mapping* Real-World Biology Enrichment Chapter Tests A, B, and C **Transparencies:** Bellringer Transparencies* Biology Concepts Transparencies* **Lab Resources:** Laboratory Manual* Probeware Lab Manual* Forensics Lab Manual* Pre-AP Lab Manual* Open Inquiry in Biology* Guided Inquiry in Biology*	**Teaching Tools:** eTeacherEdition Online Classroom Presentation Toolkit CD-ROM* LabManager™ CD-ROM* Video Lab DVD* Virtual Lab CD-ROM* What's BIOLOGY Got To Do With It? StudentWorks™ Plus Online* **Chapter Assessment Tools:** Classroom Presentation Toolkit CD-ROM* *ExamView® Assessment Suite* CD-ROM **Web-Based Resources:** • StudentWorks™ Plus Online • eTeacherEdition Online • Animations* • The Interactive Time Line* • Interactive Tables* • Online Quizzes • Online Test Practice • Standardized Test Practice • Virtual Labs* • Multilingual eGlossary* • Vocabulary eGames* • Vocabulary eFlashcards • WebQuests • Personal Tutors

While all resources listed are appropriate for English learners, the * indicates resources with a strong visual or hands-on component for EL.

Teaching strategies and activities have been coded for differentiated instruction.

AL Activities for students working above grade level	**OL** Activities for students working on grade level	**BL** Activities for students working below grade level	**EL** Activities for English learners (also ELL)	**COOP LEARN** Activities designed for small cooperative group work

CHAPTER 22

Plant Structure and Function

ConnectED

Your one-stop online resource
connectED.mcgraw-hill.com

- Video
- Audio
- Review
- Inquiry
- WebQuest
- Assessment
- Concepts in Motion
- Multilingual eGlossary

Launch Lab
What structures do plants have?

Most plants have structures that absorb light and others that take in water and nutrients. In this lab, you will examine a plant and observe and describe structures that help the plant survive.

For a lab worksheet, use your StudentWorks™ Plus Online.

Inquiry Launch Lab

FOLDABLES®

Make a folded book with the names of layers of a leaf. Use it to organize your notes on the structure and function of a leaf.

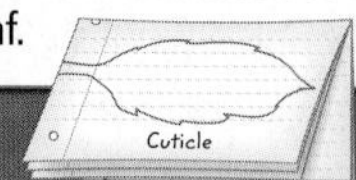

Launch Lab
What structures do plants have?

Inquiry Launch Lab

For a lab worksheet, use your eTeacherEdition Online.

RUBRIC A rubric for evaluating Launch Labs is found on your eTeacherEdition Online.

Est. Time 20 min

Alternative Materials Students could also collect plants and examine them. Or, they could use color photographs or dried pressed plant specimens for observation.

Teaching Strategies

- As students are looking at their plants, encourage them to look closely for specialized parts. Some examples are hairs on leaves, thorns, and thick leaves.
- If students are to collect plants, caution them not to collect plants from parks or private property.

Procedure

1. Read and complete the lab safety form.
2. Carefully examine a **potted plant** provided by your teacher. Use a **magnifying lens** to get a closer look. Make a list of each type of structure you observe.
3. Gently remove the plant from the pot and observe the plant structures in the soil. Do not break up the soil. Record your observations and place the plant back into the pot.
4. Sketch your plant and label each part.

Analysis

1. **Compare** your list with those of other students. What structures were common to all plants? Most lists should include leaves, roots, and stems.
2. **Infer** how each structure might be related to a function of the plant. Students' answers should demonstrate logical connections. For example, leaves have a broad surface area to maximize exposure to sunlight.
3. **Predict** the type of structural adaptations of plants living in dry environments. Answers may include: thick leaves for storage, waterproof covering on leaves, large roots for water storage. Accept all reasonable responses.

Cleanup and Disposal Have students dispose of all plant material in the regular trash and wash their hands when they are finished examining the plants.

THEME FOCUS Homeostasis
Plant cells and tissues work together to maintain structure and balance.

BIG Idea The diverse nature of plants is due to the variety of their structures.

Section 1 • Plant Cells and Tissues

Section 2 • Roots, Stems, and Leaves

Section 3 • Plant Hormones and Responses

Introduce the Chapter

Plants

ASK STUDENTS: ***What benefits do we get from plants?*** Discuss the fact that many people tend to take plants for granted, not realizing what an important role they play in our lives. Have students look at the chapter opener photo and brainstorm about the different functions of the plants in the picture. possible answers: producing oxygen, taking up carbon dioxide, producing food, beautification Point out that the many different roles that plants play in our ecosystem are due to their diverse structures.

BIG Idea

Create a Schematic Drawing

Have students read the Big Idea and the Main Ideas for this chapter. Have students draw a stylized tree with the Big Idea forming the trunk and the Main Ideas branching off from the trunk. Tell them to explain how the Main Ideas are related to the Big Idea. The Big Idea is about the diversity of plant structures and functions, and the Main Ideas help us understand the different levels of structure in plants and how these structures affect their function.

THEMES

Scientific Inquiry Studying plant structures contributes to understanding the evolution of plants.

Diversity Different stems and root systems allow plants to live in diverse habitats.

Energy Roots, stems, and leaves work together to supply needed energy to different parts of the plant.

Homeostasis The epidermis maintains homeostasis by providing a protective layer.

Change Plant structures have modified and changed in response to changing habitats.

Section 1

MAIN Idea

BL OL AL Plant Cells

ASK STUDENTS: ***What are the smallest units that make up your body?*** cells Like all living organisms, plants are composed of cells. In this section, students will learn about the different types of plant cells and tissues.

R Reading Strategy

EL BL OL AL Brainstorm

ASK STUDENTS: ***How do you think green plants make food?*** Green plants make food through photosynthesis in their cells. Write students' responses on the board. **SAY TO STUDENTS:** ***In this section, we will read about leaves—where most photosynthesis occurs. Keep this information about photosynthesis in mind as you read about the structure in which it occurs.***

W Writing Support

OL Summary Writing

Have students write a summary of what they know about plants before they start reading this section. After they have finished reading the section, have them review what they wrote and correct any misconceptions they had.

AL Have students verbally review what they know about plants.

BL Help students make a list of what they know.

D Develop Concepts

BL OL AL

Activate Prior Knowledge

ASK STUDENTS: ***What are some identifying characteristics of typical plant cells?*** chloroplast, cell wall, central vacuole Point out that parenchyma cells are representative of a typical plant cell.

Section 1

Reading Preview

Essential Questions

- What are the major types of plant cells?
- What are the major types of plant tissues?
- What are the differences among the functions of plant cells and tissues?

Review Vocabulary

vacuole: membrane-bound vessicle used for storage or transport

New Vocabulary

parenchyma cell
collenchyma cell
sclerenchyma cell
meristem
vascular cambium
cork cambium
epidermis
guard cell
xylem
vessel element
tracheid
phloem
sieve tube member
companion cell
ground tissue

g Multilingual eGlossary

R Plant Cells and Tissues

W **MAIN Idea** **Different types of plant cells make up plant tissues.**

Real-World Reading Link Buildings are made of a variety of materials. Different materials are used for stairways, plumbing, doors, and the electrical system because each of these has a different function. Similarly, different plant structures have cells and tissues that function efficiently for specific tasks.

D Plant Cells

You can identify a typical plant cell, like the one in **Figure 1,** by the presence of a cell wall and large central vacuole. Also, plant cells can have chloroplasts. However, there are many different types of plant cells—each with one or more adaptations that enable it to carry out a specific function. Three types of plant cells form most plant tissues. Together they provide storage and food production, strength, flexibility, and support.

Parenchyma cells Most flexible, thin-walled cells found throughout a plant are **parenchyma** (puh RENG kuh muh) **cells.** They are the basis for many plant structures and are capable of a wide range of functions, including storage, photosynthesis, gas exchange, and protection. These cells are spherical in shape and their cell walls flatten when they are packed tightly together, as shown in **Table 1.** An important trait of parenchyma cells is that they can undergo cell division when mature. When a plant is damaged, parenchyma cells divide to help repair it.

Depending on their function, parenchyma cells can have special features. Some parenchyma cells have many chloroplasts, also shown in **Table 1.** These cells often are found in leaves and green stems and can carry on photosynthesis, producing glucose. Some parenchyma cells, such as those found in roots and fruits, have large central vacuoles that can store substances such as starch, water, or oils.

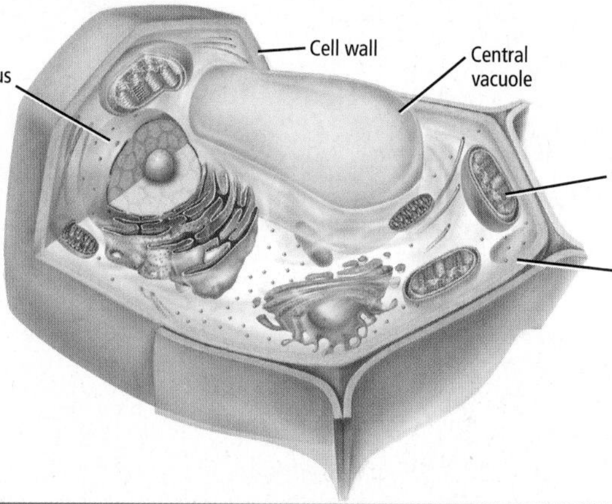

Figure 1 Features unique to a plant cell include a cell wall and a large central vacuole. Plant cells also can contain chloroplasts where photosynthesis occurs.
***Infer** why chloroplasts are not part of all plant cells.*

Content Background

Teacher FYI Students are often fascinated by the many diverse uses of plants and plant products. Although most people are familiar with the common edible plants, many wild plants are also edible. Plants can also be used as pesticides and as poisons. The list of plants that are being used or tested for medicinal uses grows daily. Plants can be used to dye fabric or to provide pigment for paint.

Caption Question Fig. 1 Not all plant cells are exposed to sunlight. For example, plant cells in the roots are not exposed to sunlight and therefore do not undergo photosynthesis. Cells that do not undergo photosynthesis do not need chloroplasts.

S

Table 1 Plant Cells and Functions

Concepts in Motion Interactive Table

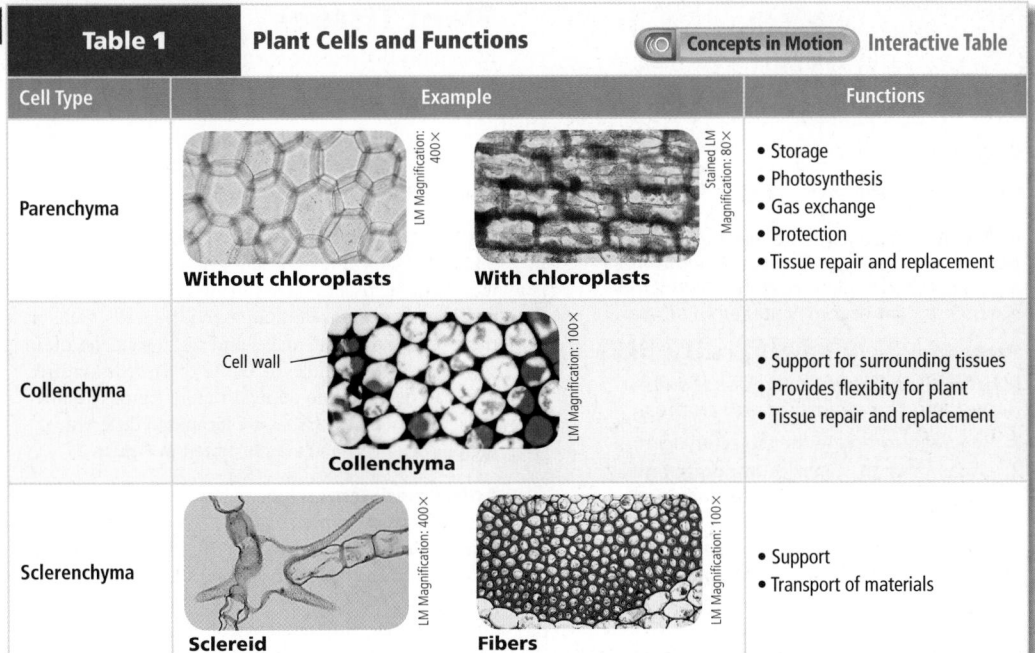

Cell Type	Example	Functions
Parenchyma	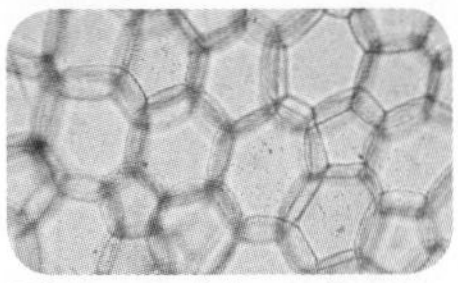 LM Magnification: 400× **Without chloroplasts** 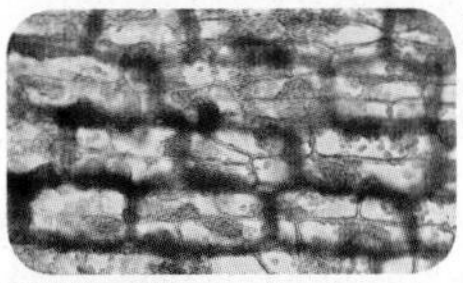 Stained LM Magnification: 80× **With chloroplasts**	• Storage • Photosynthesis • Gas exchange • Protection • Tissue repair and replacement
Collenchyma	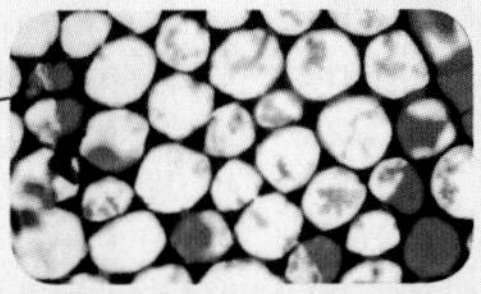 LM Magnification: 100× **Collenchyma**	• Support for surrounding tissues • Provides flexibity for plant • Tissue repair and replacement
Sclerenchyma	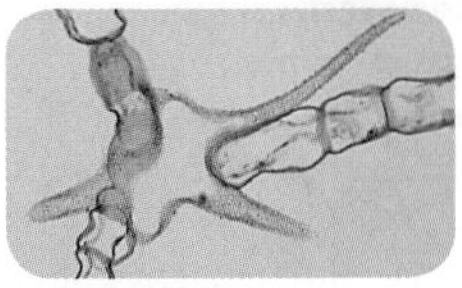 LM Magnification: 400× **Sclereid** 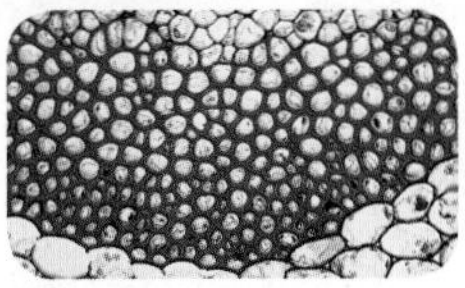 LM Magnification: 100× **Fibers**	• Support • Transport of materials

D **Collenchyma cells** If you have eaten celery, you might be familiar with collenchyma (coh LENG kuh muh) cells. These cells make up those long strings that you can pull from a celery stalk. **Collenchyma cells** are plant cells that often are elongated and occur in long strands or cylinders that provide support for the surrounding cells. As shown in **Table 1,** collenchyma cells can have unevenly thickened cell walls. As a collenchyma cell grows, the thinner portions of its cell wall can expand. Because of this growth pattern, collenchyma cells are flexible and can stretch, which enables plants to bend without breaking. Like parenchyma cells, collenchyma cells retain the ability to undergo cell division when mature.

R **Sclerenchyma cells** Unlike parenchyma and collenchyma cells, **sclerenchyma** (skle RENG kuh muh) **cells** are plant cells that lack cytoplasm and other living components when they mature, but their thick, rigid cell walls remain. These cells provide support for a plant, and some are used for transporting materials within the plant. Sclerenchyma cells make up most of the wood we use for shelter, fuel, and paper products.

There are two types of sclerenchyma cells, sclereids and fibers, as shown in **Table 1.** You might have eaten sclereids—they create the gritty texture of pears. Sclereids are also called stone cells and can be distributed randomly throughout a plant. They are shorter than fibers and are somewhat irregularly shaped. The toughness of seed coats and nut shells results from the presence of sclereids. Sclereids also function in transport. A fiber cell is needle-shaped, has a thick cell wall, and has a small interior space. When stacked end-to-end, fibers form a tough, elastic tissue. Humans have used these fibers for making ropes, linen, canvas, and other textiles for centuries, as shown in **Figure 2.**

■ **Figure 2** Fiber cells in plants have been used to make textiles such as these ancient Egyptian sandals.

Demonstration

Plant Cell Walls Use a spring toy to help students visualize how plant cells with cell walls grow. Explain that cellulose is laid down in bands (called microfibrils) in a circular pattern that resembles the bands of the spring. As the cell grows, it can elongate in only one direction—the same way a spring can expand. The model can be taken further by firmly attaching cardboard to the ends of the spring. A balloon inserted inside the spring and inflated will illustrate the expansion of the cell wall as the cell grows. Est. time: 5 min

Concepts in Motion

Interactive Table

S Skill Practice

EL BL COOP LEARN

Visual Literacy Divide students into groups of three. Have each group examine Table 1 to help them visualize the three types of plant cells. Then have them construct models of the three cell types using the illustrations as a guide. Have each group present its model to the class and explain how it mimics the structure of the cells. Provide paper, pipe cleaners, cotton balls, cardboard, polystyrene peanuts, green markers, and straws.

D Develop Concepts

BL OL AL

Clarify a Misconception

ASK STUDENTS: ***What color are plant cells?*** Students may think that all plant cells are green. ***Are all plant cells green?*** no ***Why not?*** Point out that not all plant cells have chloroplasts. Cells that make up roots and the interior portion of stems are not exposed to light. Therefore, they do not contain chloroplasts. It is the chlorophyll contained in the chloroplasts that appears green to us.

R Reading Strategy

EL BL **Clarify the Text** Have students examine the pronunciation guide for each of the following terms: *parenchyma, collenchyma,* and *sclerenchyma.* Help them pronounce these terms. Remind students that it is easier to remember words and spell them correctly when they can pronounce them.

MiniLab 1

Inquiry MiniLab

For a lab worksheet, use your eTeacherEdition Online.

RUBRIC A rubric for evaluating MiniLabs is found on your eTeacherEdition Online.

Est. Time 45 min

Safety Precaution Approve lab safety forms before work begins.

Alternative Materials Color micrographs of various cell types, such as those in Table 1, could be used if microscopes are not available.

Teaching Strategies

- Make sure the sections of the plants are thin enough for students to view individual cells. Using a single edge razor to slice off a section can help.
- Suggest that students look at each slide prior to staining so they can see how the stain helps in observing the cells.

Analysis

1. Students will observe parenchyma cells on the potato slide, collenchyma cells on the celery slide, and sclerenchyma cells on the pear slide.
2. The cell types were different because the cells were from different plant structures that have different functions. The potato's primary function is carbohydrate storage, so it is composed of mostly parenchyma cells. The celery stalk's main function is support, so it contains many collenchyma cells. The pear is a fruit that surrounds a seed and contains many sclerenchyma cells that cause the gritty texture of the fruit.

LabManager™

Customize this lab with the LabManager™ CD-ROM.

MiniLab 1

Inquiry MiniLab

Observe Plant Cells

How can a microscope be used to distinguish plant cell types? Investigate the three different types of plant cells by making and observing slides of some common plant parts.

Procedure

WARNING: ***Iodine is poisonous if swallowed and can stain skin and clothes.***

1. Read and complete the lab safety form.
2. Obtain a small, thin **slice of potato** and a thin **cross section of a celery stalk** from your teacher.
3. Place the potato slice on a **slide,** add a drop of **iodine,** and cover with a **coverslip.** Use a **microscope** to observe the potato slice. Record your observations.
4. Place the celery slice on a slide, add a drop of **water,** and cover with a coverslip.
5. Put a drop of **dye** at one end of the coverslip, and then touch a **paper towel** to the other end to draw the dye under the coverslip. Use a microscope to observe the celery slice. Record your observations.
6. Obtain a small amount of **pear tissue,** place it on a slide, and add a coverslip.
7. Using a **pencil eraser,** press gently but firmly on the coverslip until the pear tissue is a thin even layer. Use a microscope to observe the pear tissue. Record your observations.

Analysis

1. **Identify** the type of specialized plant cell observed on each slide.
2. **Infer** why there are different cell types in a potato, a celery stalk, and pear tissue.

Plant Tissues

Remember that a tissue is a group of cells that work together to perform a function. Depending on its function, a plant tissue can be composed of one or many types of cells. There are four different tissue types found in plants—meristematic (mer uh stem AH tihk), dermal, vascular, and ground.

Meristematic tissue Throughout their lives, plants can continue to produce new cells in their meristematic tissues. Meristematic tissues make up **meristems**, regions of rapidly dividing cells. Cells in meristems have large nuclei and small vacuoles or, in some cases, no vacuoles at all. As these cells mature, they can develop into many different kinds of plant cells. Meristematic tissues are located in different regions of a plant and are illustrated in **Figure 3.**

Apical meristems Meristematic tissues at the tips of roots and stems, which produce cells that result in an increase in length, are apical (AY pih kul) meristems, as shown in **Figure 3.** This growth is called primary growth. Because plants are usually stationary, stems and roots enter different environments or different areas of the same environments.

Intercalary meristems Another type of meristem, called intercalary (in TUR kuh LAYR ee) meristem, is related to a summer job you might have had—mowing grass. This meristem is found in one or more locations along the stems of many monocots. Intercalary meristem produces new cells that result in an increase in stem or leaf length. If grasses only had apical meristems, they would stop growing after the first mowing. They continue to grow because they have more than one type of meristematic tissue.

Lateral meristems Increases in root and stem diameters result from secondary growth produced by two types of lateral meristems. Only nonflowering seed plants, eudicots, and a few monocots have secondary growth.

The **vascular cambium,** also shown in **Figure 3,** is a thin cylinder of meristematic tissue that can run the entire length of roots and stems. It produces new transport cells in some roots and stems.

In some plants, another lateral meristem, the **cork cambium,** produces cells that develop tough cell walls. These cells form a protective outside layer on stems and roots. Cork tissues make up the outer bark on a woody plant like an oak tree. Recall that cells of cork tissue are what Robert Hooke observed when he looked through his microscope.

Demonstration

Meristems Collect samples of plants that have different meristems. For example, a houseplant and carrot will have an apical meristem. A cross section of wood can be used for vascular cambium and cork cambium. A piece of grass or hay can be used for intercalary meristem. Show these samples to students and ask them to point out the location of the meristems. Est. time: 5 min

Differentiated Instruction

Below Level When beginning the chapter, assist students performing below grade level by providing them with a note outline or a copy of your notes. This will ensure that students know what information is important and will help them perform at the same pace as their peers.

For more tips, see pages 14T–15T.

Visualizing Meristematic Tissues

Figure 3
Most plant growth results from the production of cells by meristematic tissues. Stems and roots increase in length mostly due to the production of cells by apical meristems. A plant's vascular cambium produces cells that increase root and stem diameters.

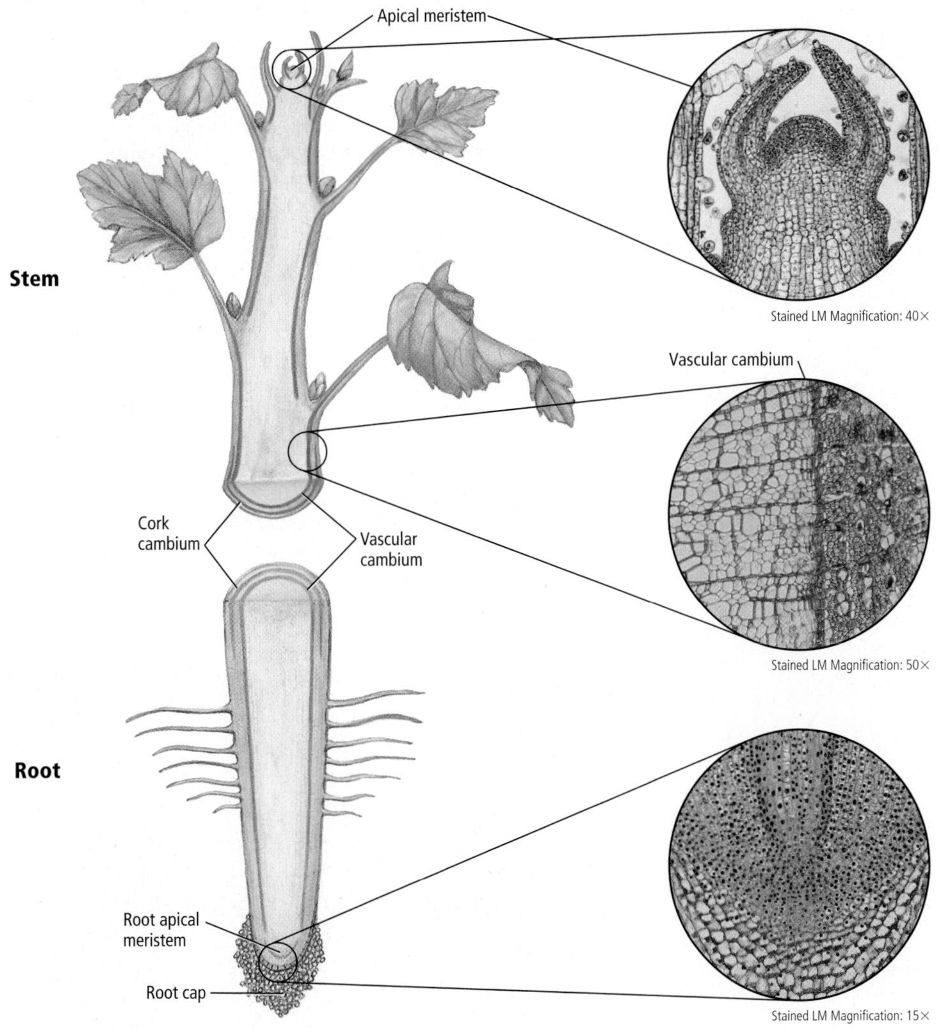

Concepts in Motion Animation

Visualizing Meristematic Tissues

Purpose

Students will learn about the meristem tissue in plants.
C.1

S Skill Practice

EL BL OL AL Visual Literacy
Have students sketch a plant using the diagram shown on this page as a model. Have them label the locations of the meristems. Next to each label, have students indicate what growth is produced by each meristem.

D Develop Concepts

BL OL AL

Integrate Agriculture

ASK STUDENTS: ***What do you think would happen to this plant if the apical meristem were removed?*** Students may suggest that the plant would die, stop growing or grow another meristem. Point out that people often cut off the top of a stem so the lower part of the plant will get bushier. Show students pictures of plants that have just been pruned and the same plants after they have had time to branch out and fill in.

Concepts in Motion
Animation

Research Citation

Skill Practice Educational research indicates that lessons should provide an ample amount of practice so students can master skills. The activity on this page requires that students sketch and label the parts of a plant, providing them with practice necessary to correctly identify plant structures.
(Tafton, 1983)

Research bibliography on pages 32T–34T

C Critical Thinking

BL OL AL Infer

ASK STUDENTS: ***How does the cuticle help reduce water loss?*** The cuticle seals the plant tissue to prevent water from evaporating. ***How might the cuticle of a desert plant be different from the cuticle of a rainforest plant?*** The desert plant will have a thicker cuticle to conserve water.

Develop Concepts

BL OL AL Scaffolding

ASK STUDENTS: ***Why does a plant need water?*** to carry nutrients in the plant and for life processes, such as photosynthesis ***What happens to the water after it travels up the stem and to the leaves of a plant?*** Some water is used in photosynthesis, and some exits the plant through the stomata. ***When might it be beneficial for a plant to have closed stomata?*** It is beneficial when water supplies are low. ***How could the stomata be structured so that it is open only when water is plentiful and closed when water is scarce?*** The two guard cells that make up a stomata are like a set of curved water balloons, one on each side. When water is plentiful, water pressure in the cells is high, and the cells curve outward, creating a hole. When water is scarce and the cells are empty, the cells collapse and the hole disappears.

■ Caption Question Fig. 5

The trichomes are a way to keep predators from eating the plant. The root hairs increase the surface area allowing the plant to absorb more water and nutrients.

■ **Figure 4** The surface of a leaf is composed of tightly-packed epidermal cells that help protect the plant and prevent water loss. Stomata open and close to allow gases in and out.

Stained LM Magnification: 10×

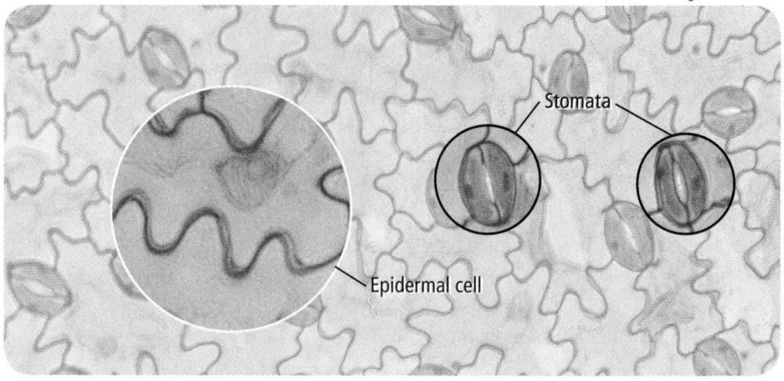

Dermal tissue—the epidermis The layer of cells that makes up the outer covering on a plant is dermal tissue, also called the **epidermis.** Cells of the epidermis resemble pieces of a jigsaw puzzle with interlocking ridges and dips, as shown in **Figure 4.** Most epidermal cells can secrete a fatty substance that forms the cuticle. You might recall that the cuticle helps reduce water loss from plants by slowing evaporation. The cuticle also can help prevent bacteria and other disease-causing organisms from entering a plant. C

VOCABULARY

WORD ORIGIN

Trichome
from the Greek word *trickhma,* meaning *growth of hair*

Stomata Plants can have several adaptations of their epidermis. Recall that the epidermis of most leaves and some green stems have stomata—small openings through which carbon dioxide, water, oxygen, and other gases pass. The two cells that form a stoma are **guard cells.** Changes in the shapes of guard cells result in the opening and closing of stomata, as shown in **Figure 4.**

Trichomes Some epidermal cells on leaves and stems produce hairlike projections called trichomes (TRI kohmz), shown in **Figure 5.** Trichomes can give leaves a fuzzy appearance and can help protect the plant from insect and animal predators. Some trichomes even release toxic substances when touched. Trichomes help keep some plants cool by reflecting light.

Color-Enhanced SEM Magnification: 240×

Magnification: unavailable

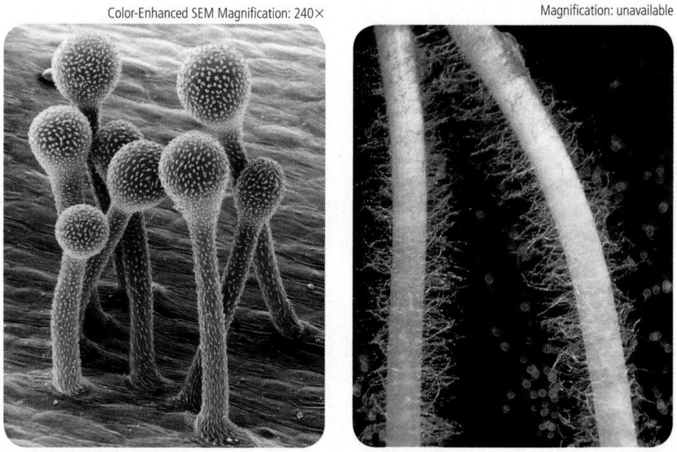

Trichomes on a leaf

Root hairs

■ **Figure 5** Epidermal adaptations help plants survive. The tiny glands at the tip of a trichome can contain toxic substances. Root hairs increase the root's surface area.
Explain *how both of these adaptations are considered survival mechanisms.*

Demonstration

BL OL AL Plant Epidermis Have students examine the pieces of an assembled jigsaw puzzle.

ASK STUDENTS: ***What holds these pieces together?*** The shapes are interlocking. ***If this assembled puzzle were a plant's epidermis what would be on top of it?*** the cuticle

Take a piece of waxed paper and lay it over the puzzle as a model of the plant's epidermis. Explain that scientists often use models to help them understand the structure or function of a biological structure or process. Est. time: 5 min

Root hairs Some roots have root hairs—fragile extensions of root epidermal cells. Root hairs, as shown in **Figure 5,** increase a root's surface area and enable the root to take in a greater volume of materials than it can without root hairs.

Vascular tissues In a plant, the transportation of water, food, and dissolved substances is the main function of two types of vascular tissue—xylem and phloem.

Xylem Water that contains dissolved minerals enters a plant through its roots. The water with dissolved minerals is transported throughout a plant within a system of xylem that flows continuously from the roots to the leaves. **Xylem** (ZI lum) is the water-carrying vascular tissue composed of specialized cells called vessel elements and tracheids (tray KEY ihdz). When mature, each vessel element and tracheid consists of just its cell wall. This lack of cytoplasm at maturity allows water to flow freely through these cells.

Vessel elements are tubular cells that are stacked end-to-end, forming strands of xylem called vessels. Vessel elements are open at each end with barlike strips across the openings. In some plants, mature vessel elements lose their end walls. This enables the free movement of water and dissolved substances from one vessel element to another.

Tracheids are long, cylindrical cells with pitted ends. The cells are found end-to-end and form a tubelike strand. Unlike some mature vessel elements, mature tracheids have end walls. For this reason, tracheids are less efficient than vessel elements at transporting materials. Compare the structure of tracheids to vessel elements in **Figure 6.**

In gymnosperms or nonflowering seed plants, xylem is composed almost entirely of tracheids. However, in flowering seed plants, xylem consists of tracheids and vessels. Because vessels are more efficient at transporting water and materials, scientists propose that this might explain why flowering plants inhabit many different environments.

Reading Check **Explain** the function of vessel elements and tracheids.

CAREERS IN BIOLOGY

Turf Scientist Parks, golf courses, and sports stadiums require the skills of a turf scientist to help maintain the grasses that grow there. He or she has an educational background that includes science, managerial, and business courses.

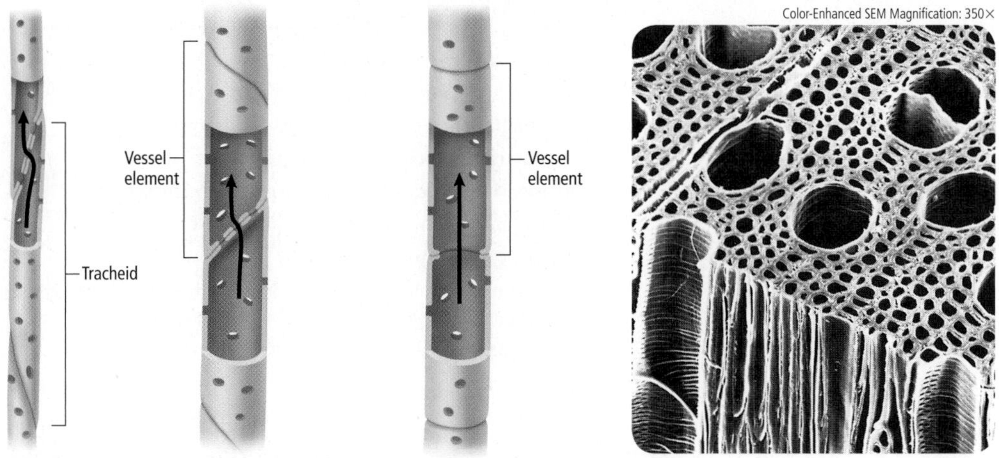

■ **Figure 6** Tracheids and vessel elements are the conducting cells of the xylem.

Demonstration

Root Hairs Show students root hairs on germinating radish-seed roots. Four days prior to the demonstration, put radish seeds in a Petri dish on a damp paper towel and slide the dish into a self-sealing plastic bag. Keep the dish out of direct sunlight. *Brassica rapa* seeds can be used and germinate in 24 h.

ASK STUDENTS: ***What is the benefit of having so many root hairs?*** provides increased surface area for absorption of water and nutrients Est. time: 5 min

D Develop Concepts

BL OL COOP LEARN Research Have students work in pairs and choose one epidermal cell modification to research. Have each pair prepare a poster and a brief presentation for the class. Display posters in the classroom.

AL ASK STUDENTS: ***What are some epidermal cell modifications? Why have these modifications developed?*** Trichomes, guard cells, root hairs, and cuticles are all epidermal modifications. Some of these protect the plant and all help it survive.

W Writing Support

BL Technical Writing Have students read the paragraph about xylem cells. When they are finished, instruct students to write a list of the characteristics of xylem cells in their notebooks. Have students recite their lists, and record their responses on the board. Repeat this for each type of cell.

Develop Concepts

EL AL Activity Purchase tomatoes that still have the stem attached. Cut the stem into short segments. Pass out the segments and a magnifying lens. Have students observe the trichomes and sketch them in their notebooks.

ASK STUDENTS: ***What is the function of these structures?*** to ward off predators Ask students to list potential predators. Possible answers: caterpillars, slugs, deer, and rabbits ***Can you think of any other plants that have similar structures?*** Answers will vary, but may include cucumbers, squash, and cacti.

Reading Check These tissues are involved in the transport of food, water, and other dissolved materials away from the root.

S Skill Practice

OL AL Compare and Contrast

ASK STUDENTS: ***What cells make up the xylem and phloem?*** Vessel elements, tracheids, and sieve-tube members are all tubular-shaped cells. With the exception of vessel elements in some plants, these cells all have ends with some type of perforation. In some cases, the vessel elements lose their end walls. The xylem cells are dead at functional maturity, while the phloem cells still have cytoplasm

BL Write the comparison on the board to provide a visual reference.

Reading Strategy

BL Context-Specific Words

Explain that the term *sink* is used to describe regions where carbohydrates are stored because all the carbohydrates "flow" to this region like water down a sink.

Formative Assessment

Evaluation Have students view parenchyma, sclerenchyma, and collenchyma cells under a microscope and identify the type of cell. **ASK STUDENTS:** ***How were you able to identify the cells?*** differences in cell walls, presence of cytoplasm

Remediation Show students pictures of the different cell types and ask them to point out differences. Review and reinforce by having students describe the cells.

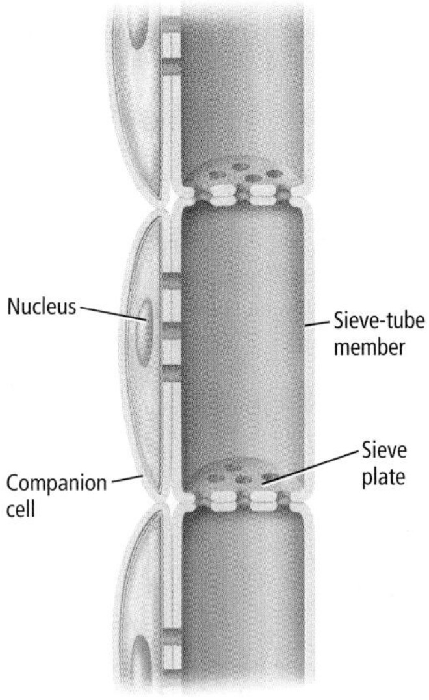

■ **Figure 7** Notice the openings in the sieve plates between the sieve-tube members.

Phloem The main food-carrying tissue is **phloem** (FLOH em). It transports dissolved sugars and other organic compounds throughout a plant. Recall that xylem only transports materials away from the roots. Phloem, however, transports substances from the leaves and stems to the roots and from the roots to the leaves and stems. Although not used for transport, there are sclereids and fibers associated with the phloem. These sturdy sclerenchyma cells provide support for the plant.

Phloem consists of two types of cells, sieve tube members and companion cells, as shown in **Figure 7.** Each **sieve tube member** contains cytoplasm but lacks a nucleus and ribosomes when it is mature. Next to sieve tube members are **companion cells,** each with a nucleus. Scientists hypothesize that this nucleus functions for both the companion cell and the mature sieve tube member. In flowering plants, structures called sieve plates are at the end of the sieve tube members. The sieve plates have large pores through which dissolved substances can flow.

Some of the glucose produced in leaves and other photosynthetic tissue is metabolized by the plant. However, some is converted to other carbohydrates and transported and stored in regions of the plant called sinks. Examples of sinks are the parenchyma storage cells in the root cortex, which are described in the next section of this chapter. The transport in phloem of dissolved carbohydrates from sources to sinks and other dissolved substances is called translocation. S

Ground tissue The category for plant tissues that are not meristematic tissues, dermal tissues, or vascular tissues is ground tissue. **Ground tissues** consist of parenchyma, collenchyma, and sclerenchyma cells and have diverse functions, including photosynthesis, storage, and support. Most of a plant consists of ground tissue. The ground tissue of leaves and green stems contains cells with numerous chloroplasts that produce glucose for the plant. In some stems, roots, and seeds, cells of ground tissue have large vacuoles that store sugars, starch, oils, or other substances. Ground tissues also provide support when they grow between other types of tissue.

Section 1 Assessment

Section Summary

- There are three types of plant cells.
- The structure of a plant cell is related to its function.
- There are several different types of plant tissues—meristematic, dermal, vascular, and ground tissues.
- Xylem and phloem are vascular tissues.

Understand Main Ideas

1. MAIN Idea **Describe** the different types of plant cells in plant tissues.
2. **Compare and contrast** the types of plant cells.
3. **Describe** a root hair and explain its function.
4. **Identify** the location and function of vascular cambium.
5. **Compare** the two types of specialized xylem cells.

Think Critically

6. **Create** a table, using information in this section, that summarizes the structures and functions of the different plant tissues.
7. **Evaluate** the advantage of vessel elements without end walls.

WRITING in Biology

8. Compose a limerick about a type of plant tissue.

Section 1 Assessment

1. Meristematic tissue includes apical cells, intercalary cells, and lateral cells. Dermal cells include epidermal cells and cover the outside of a plant. Guard cells make stomata. Vascular tissue includes xylem, which is made of two kinds of cells—tracheids and vessel elements. Phloem is made of sieve-tube member cells and companion cells. Ground tissue includes all kinds of cells.
2. parenchyma cells: thin-walled, retain ability for mitosis at maturity; collenchyma cells: uneven, thickened cell walls, retain ability for mitosis at maturity; sclerenchyma cells: very thick walls, lack living components at maturity
3. root hair—extension of root epidermal cell that increases surface area
4. vascular cambium—produces new transport cells in roots and stems
5. tracheids—long tubular cells with pitted ends; vessel elements—tubular cells stacked end-to-end
6. Tables should identify each tissue type in an organized manner.
7. free movement of water and dissolved free substances
8. Limericks should be scientifically accurate.

Assessment Online Quiz

Section 2

Reading Preview

Essential Questions

- How are the structures of roots, stems, and leaves related to their functions?
- How do the structures and functions of roots, stems, and leaves compare?

Review Vocabulary

apical meristem: tissue at the tips of roots and stems that produces cells, which results in an increase in length

New Vocabulary

root cap
cortex
endodermis
pericycle
petiole
palisade mesophyll
spongy mesophyll
transpiration

g Multilingual eGlossary

Roots, Stems, and Leaves

MAIN Idea The structures of plants are related to their functions.

Real-World Reading Link Using a fork to eat a lettuce salad usually is more effective than using a spoon. However, if you were eating tomato soup, a spoon would be more useful than a fork. These are examples of the common expression "the right tool for the right job." The same applies in nature. The variety of plant structures relates to the diversity of plant functions.

Roots

If you ever have eaten a carrot, a radish, or a sweet potato, then you have eaten part of a plant root. The root usually is the first structure to grow out of the seed when it sprouts. For most plants, roots take in water and dissolved minerals that are transported to the rest of the plant. If you have tried to pull a weed, you experienced another function of roots; they anchor a plant in soil or to some other plant or object. Roots also support a plant against the effects of gravity, extreme wind, and moving water.

In some plants, the root system is so vast that it makes up more than half of the plant's mass. The roots of most plants grow 0.5 to 5 m down into the soil. However, some plants, such as the mesquite (mes KEET) that grows in the dry southwestern part of the United States, have roots that grow downward as deep as 50 m toward available water. Other plants, such as some cacti, have many, relatively shallow branching roots that grow out from the stem in all directions as far as 15 m. Both root types are adaptations to limited water resources.

Root structure and growth The tip of a root is covered by the **root cap,** as shown in **Figure 8.** It consists of parenchyma cells that help protect root tissues as the root grows. The cells of the root cap produce a slimy substance that, together with the outside layer of cells, form a lubricant that reduces friction as the root grows through the soil, a crack in a sidewalk, or some other material. Cells of the root cap that are rubbed off as the root grows are replaced by new cells produced in the root's apical meristem. Recall from Section 1 that the root's apical meristem also produces cells that increase the root's length. These cells develop into the numerous types of root tissues that perform different functions. C

You also learned in Section 1 that an epidermal layer covers the root. Some root epidermal cells produce root hairs that absorb water and dissolved minerals. The layer below this epidermal layer is the **cortex.** It is composed of ground tissues made of parenchyma cells that are involved in transport and storage of plant substances. The cortex is between the epidermis and the vascular tissues of the root. To reach vascular tissues, all water and nutrients that are taken in by the epidermal cells must move through the cortex.

Reading Check **List** three functions of roots.

Figure 8 The root cap covers the root tip and loses cells as the root grows through soil.

Color-Enhanced SEM Magnification: 220×

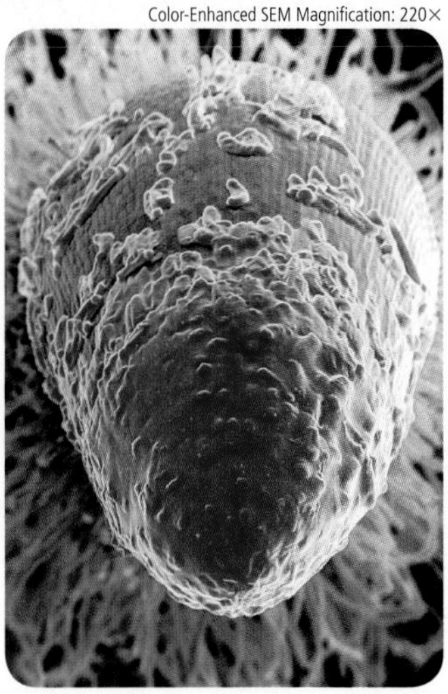

Section 2

MAIN Idea

BL OL AL

Plant Structure and Function

ASK STUDENTS: ***How do the functions of your feet and hands relate to their structure?*** Answers will vary but may include: fingers and thumb allow for grasping and manipulating objects, relatively flat sole and short toes make feet easier to walk on two legs. Point out that plants, like humans, have structures that are for specific functions. ***What plant structures are you familiar with that have a specific function?*** Students will probably be familiar with many structures, such as tree trunks and leaves.

C Critical Thinking

AL Infer

ASK STUDENTS: ***Why does a plant need a root cap?*** The root cap protects the apical meristem that produces new cells so the root can grow. Also, the production of mucus by the root cap reduces the friction as the root moves through the soil.

Reading Check Roots take in water and nutrients, anchor the plant in soil, and store substances.

Differentiated Instruction

Above Level Students who perform above level should be challenged to extend their thinking beyond simple recall of facts. Use critical thinking questions like the one on this page to help students further develop abstract thinking abilities.

For more tips, see pages 14T–15T.

S Skill Practice

EL BL OL AL Visual Literacy

Have students read about root structure and examine Figure 9. Point out that this illustration is of a root cross section. A longitudinal section would be cut from top to bottom of the root. Have students draw a longitudinal section of the root shown in Figure 9.

Concepts in Motion

Animation

Reading Strategy

EL BL

Monitor Comprehension

Emphasize how many new vocabulary terms there are in this section. Remind students to make sure they understand the meaning of the new vocabulary terms when they encounter them in the text. Suggest that if they are unsure of the meaning of a term they reread that portion of the text and use context clues to help them figure out the meaning. Then have students write the meanings in their own words.

Caption Question Fig. 9

Water passes though the root hair in the epidermis, to the cortex, to the endodermis with the Casparian strip, to the pericycle, and into the xylem.

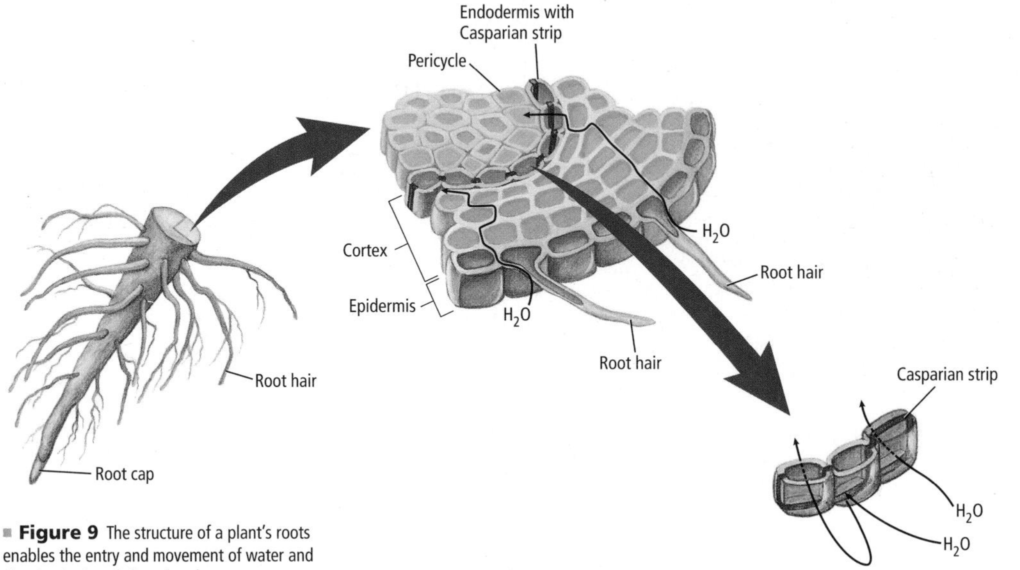

Figure 9 The structure of a plant's roots enables the entry and movement of water and dissolved minerals into the plant.
Sequence ***the tissues through which water passes as it moves from a root hair to xylem tissue of a root.***

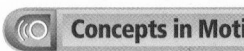

Concepts in Motion

Animation

S

At the inner boundary of the cortex is a layer of cells called the **endodermis,** as illustrated in **Figure 9.** Encircling each cell of the endodermis as part of the cell wall is a waterproof strip called a Casparian strip. Its location is similar to that of mortar that surrounds bricks in a wall. The Casparian strip creates a barrier that forces water and dissolved minerals to pass through endodermal cells rather than around them. Therefore, the plasma membranes of endodermal cells regulate the material that enters the vascular tissues.

The layer of cells directly next to the endodermis toward the center of the root is called the **pericycle.** It is the tissue that produces lateral roots. In most eudicots, and some monocots, a vascular cambium develops from part of the pericycle. Recall that the vascular cambium produces vascular tissues that contribute to an increase in the root's diameter. The vascular tissues, xylem and phloem, are in the center of a root. Monocots and eudicots can be distinguished by the pattern of the xylem and phloem in their roots, as shown in **Figure 10.**

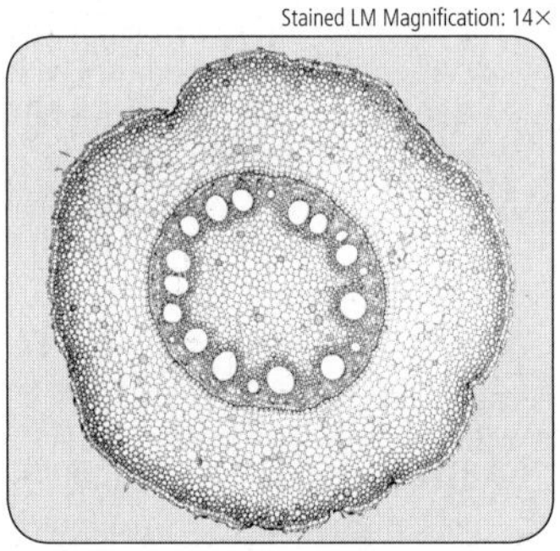

Monocot

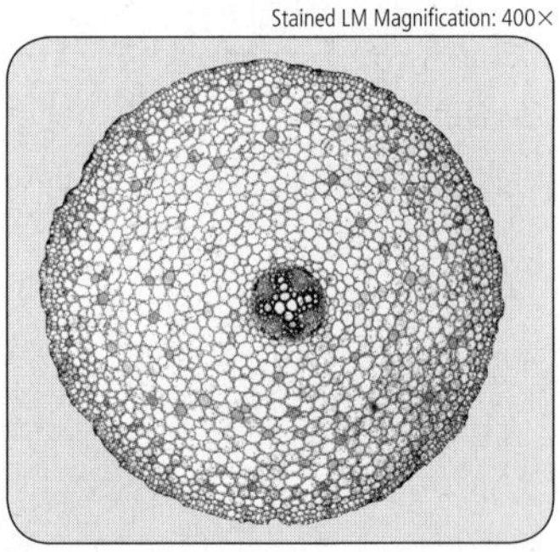

Eudicot

Figure 10 In monocots, strands of xylem and phloem cells alternate, usually surrounding a central core of cells called pith. The xylem in eudicot roots is in the center and forms an X shape. Phloem cells are between the arms of the X.

Demonstration

BL OL Roots Collect pictures or samples of different roots. Be sure to include some of the edible roots, such as beets, carrots, and radishes.

ASK STUDENTS: ***Name some of the different types of cells you could find in these roots.*** parenchyma, collenchyma, and sclerenchyma ***Name some of the different tissues and where in the root they would be found.*** meristematic: near the tip; vascular: in the center; epidermis: covering; ground: between vascular and epidermis Est. time: 5 min

Types of roots The two major types of root systems are taproots and fibrous roots. A taproot system consists of a thick root with few smaller, lateral-branching roots. Some plants, such as radishes, beets, and carrots, as shown in **Table 2,** store food in the parenchyma cells of a taproot. Other taproots, like those of poison ivy plants, grow deep into the soil toward available water.

Fibrous root systems, also shown in **Table 2,** have numerous branching roots that are about the same size and grow from a central point, similar to the way that the spokes of a bicycle wheel are arranged. Plants also can store food in fibrous roots systems. For example, sweet potatoes develop on fibrous roots.

Other root types, also shown in **Table 2,** are adapted to diverse environments. In arid regions, some plants produce huge water-storage roots. Cypress, mangrove, and some other trees that live in water develop modified roots that help supply oxygen to the roots called pneumatophores (new MA toh forz). Adventitious (ad vehn TIH shus) roots form where roots normally do not grow and can have different functions. For example, some tropical trees have adventitious roots that help support their branches. As these roots develop, they resemble trunks.

? Inquiry Launch Lab

Review Based on what you've read about plant structures, how would you now answer the analysis questions?

D

Table 2 Root Systems and Adaptations Concepts in Motion Interactive Table

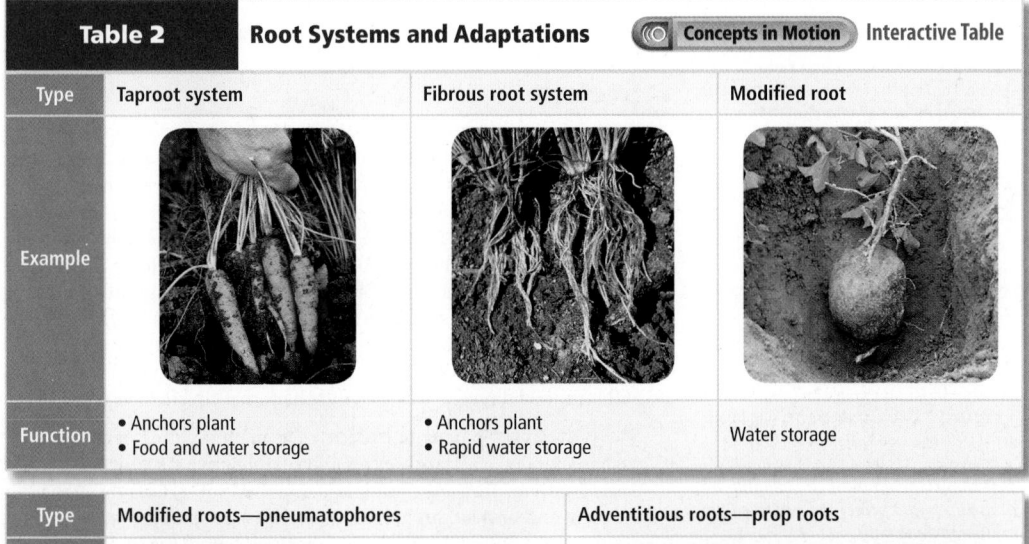

Type	Taproot system	Fibrous root system	Modified root
Example			
Function	• Anchors plant • Food and water storage	• Anchors plant • Rapid water storage	Water storage

Type	Modified roots—pneumatophores	Adventitious roots—prop roots
Example		
Function	Supplied oxygen to submerged roots	Support plant stems

? Inquiry Launch Lab

Assess Content Development
Assess how understanding has developed when students revisit the Launch Lab analysis questions.

Concepts in Motion

Interactive Table

Reading Strategy

OL COOP LEARN

Supplemental Reading

Organize students into five groups and assign each group one of the following terms: *taproot, fibrous root, prop root, pneumatophores,* and *water storage roots.* Have each group research their type of root and present a poster illustrating features of that root type to the class. Instruct students to include the following on their posters: type of root, function, and examples of different plants that have that root type.

BL Make sure research materials are at an appropriate level for students working below grade level.

D Develop Concepts

EL BL OL AL

Clarify a Misconception

ASK STUDENTS: ***Do all plant roots grow into the soil?*** no Many students may assume that the roots of all plants anchor plants in soil. This is not the case. Plants such as Spanish moss, an epiphyte, grow in trees and produces aerial roots that never touch the soil. Show students pictures to illustrate the concept. Contact greenhouses to borrow epiphytes for class.

Differentiated Instruction

Hearing Impaired When placing students in groups for the cooperative learning activity, prepare peers to work with hearing impaired students so that they can fully participate in the group. Remind students to look directly at students with hearing impairments when they are speaking so that they can clearly see their lips and facial expressions.

For more tips, see pages 14T–15T.

Research Citation

Research Educational research indicates the importance of requiring students to perform research like that suggested in the cooperative learning activity on this page. Researching a topic requires that students develop meaningful questions and provide a connection to real-world situations. (Hoffman, 1992)

Research bibliography on pages 32T–34T

S Skill Practice

BL OL Compare and Contrast

ASK STUDENTS: ***What are the similarities and differences between the monocot stem and the eudicot stem?*** Both stems have xylem and phloem and parenchyma cells. The eudicot vascular bundles are arranged in concentric rings, while the vascular bundles of the monocots are scattered throughout the stem.

C Critical Thinking

BL OL AL Judge

ASK STUDENTS: ***What is the value of the bark as a protective tissue?*** Some bark can protect stems from physical damage such as that caused by fire or a scrape. It can also prevent infestation by insects or damage by animals. ***Summarize the importance of the tissues that are being protected.*** Vascular tissue is critical for the transport of water and nutrients and for support. Ground tissue is used for storage of nutrients.

D Develop Concepts

OL AL Integrate History

ASK STUDENTS: ***What can we learn about a region's history by examining the annual growth rings of a tree?*** Answers will vary, but might include learning how old the tree is, or information about periods of drought or other climate issues. The width of a ring corresponds to the characteristics of the growing season. When sunlight and rain are plentiful, the growth rings are wide. During periods of drought, the rings are narrow.

■ Caption Question Fig. 12

During periods of drought, the rings will be narrower than they are when water is abundant.

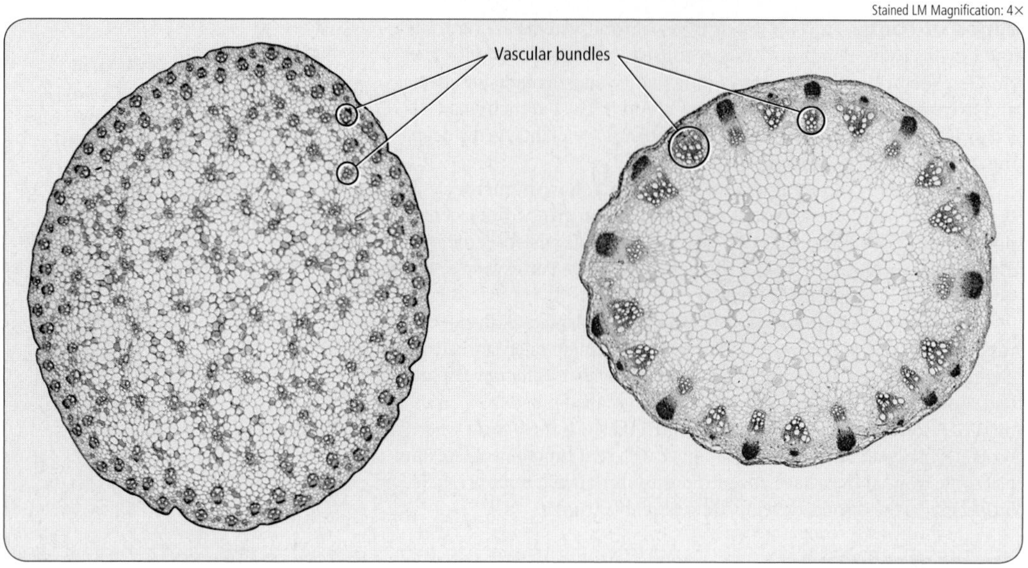

■ **Figure 11** The xylem and phloem of stems are grouped together in vascular bundles. The vascular bundles in a monocot stem are scattered. Eudicot stems have one ring or concentric rings of vascular bundles.

S

■ **Figure 12** An annual growth ring forms in the stem of a woody plant when growth resumes after a period of little or no growth. **Infer** ***how the amount of available moisture might affect the width of an annual growth ring.***

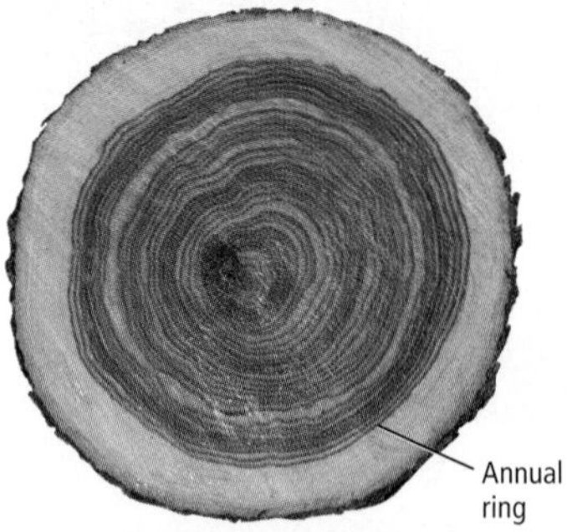

Stems

While you might know that asparagus spears are stems, you might be surprised to learn that there are many types of plant stems. Some stems, like asparagus, are soft, flexible, and green due to the presence of chloroplasts, and therefore can perform photosynthesis. These stems are called herbaceous (hur BAY shus) and most annual plants have this type of stem. Palms and bamboos have rigid, fibrous stems. Trees, shrubs, and many perennials have sturdy, woody stems that do not carry on photosynthesis. Some older plants have stems that are covered with bark. This tough, corky tissue can protect the stem from physical damage and insect invasion. Some trees even have survived a forest fire with minimal damage because of the bark that covers their trunks. C

Stem structure and function The main function of a plant's stem is support of a plant's leaves and reproductive structures. Vascular tissues in stems transport water and dissolved substances throughout the plant and provide support. These tissues are arranged in bundles, or groups, that are surrounded by parenchyma cells. As is true for roots, the pattern of these tissues can be used to distinguish between monocots and eudicots, as shown in **Figure 11.**

Growth of a stem Cells produced by the apical meristem result in an increase in the length of the stem. As the plant grows taller, an increase in stem diameter provides additional support. In annual plants, an increase in stem diameter mostly is due to an increase in cell size. The increase in stem diameter in plants, such as perennial eudicots and conifers, is due to the production of cells by the vascular cambium. The production of xylem and phloem throughout the year can produce annual growth rings. The age of a tree can be estimated by counting the annual growth rings at the base of its trunk, like those of the white oak shown in **Figure 12.** D

Content Background

Teacher FYI The pneumatophores that are produced by mangroves are composed of spongy tissue that rises above the surface of the water. The pneumatophores help plants exchange gases such as O_2 and CO_2 with the environment and the subsurface roots to which they are attached. The mechanism that causes trees to produce pneumatophores is not known.

D **Types of stems** All stems have adaptations that help plants survive. In some plants, these adaptations enable stems to store excess food, and in other plants, they help withstand drought, cold, or heat. While you easily might identify stems of tomatoes and oaks, other plants have stems that do not resemble typical stems.

For example, a white potato is a type of stem called a tuber, which is a swollen, underground stem with buds from which new potato plants can grow. The stem of an onion, a tulip, or a tiger lily is part of a bulb. A bulb is a shortened, compressed stem surrounded by fleshy leaves. Irises and some ferns have rhizomes, which are underground horizontal stems. Some rhizomes store food. Runners, or stolons, are horizontal stems that grow along the soil's surface in nature, like those of strawberry plants and some grasses. Crocuses and gladiolas are examples of plants that form corms. A corm is composed almost entirely of stem tissue with some scaly leaves at its top. Examples of some of these stem types are shown in **Table 3.**

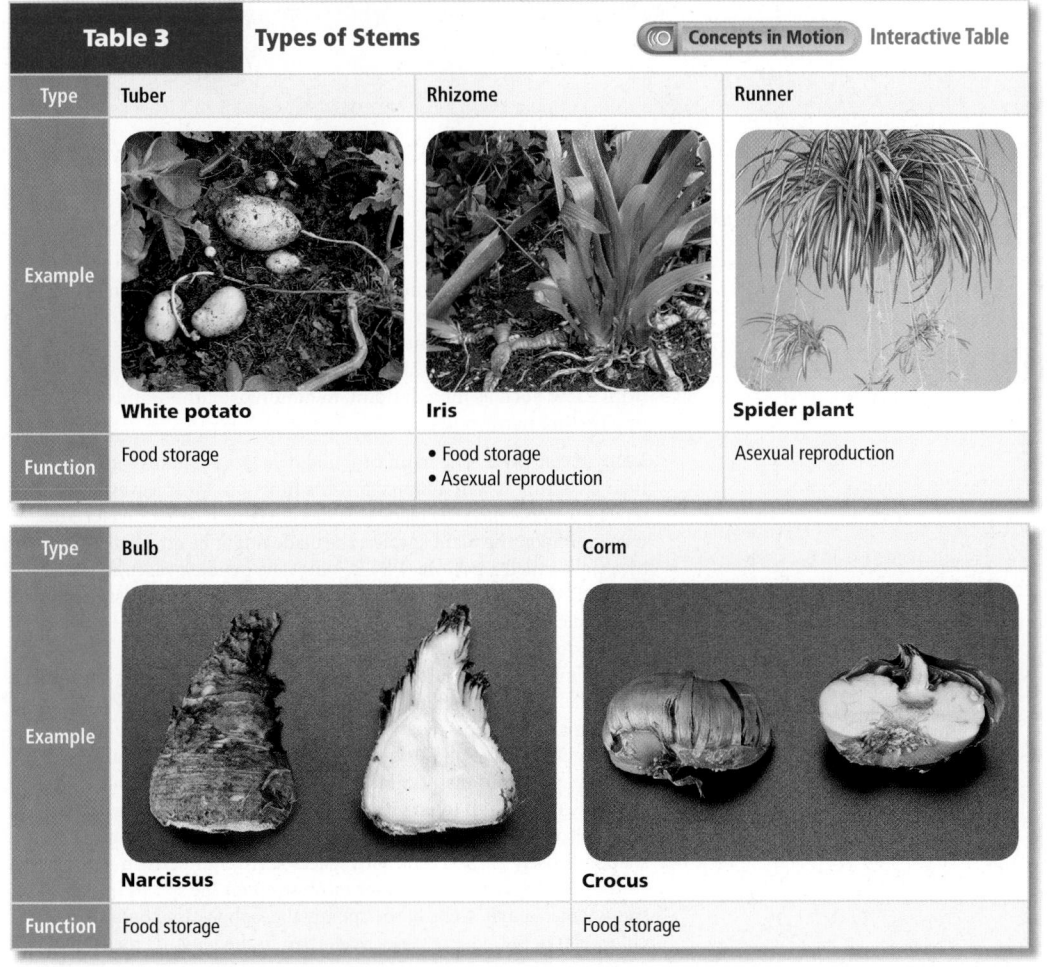

Table 3 **Types of Stems** Concepts in Motion Interactive Table

Type	Tuber	Rhizome	Runner
Example	 **White potato**	 **Iris**	 **Spider plant**
Function	Food storage	• Food storage • Asexual reproduction	Asexual reproduction

Type	Bulb	Corm
Example	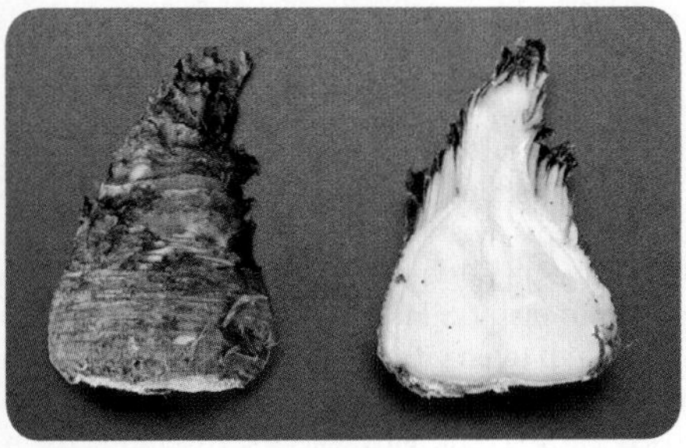 **Narcissus**	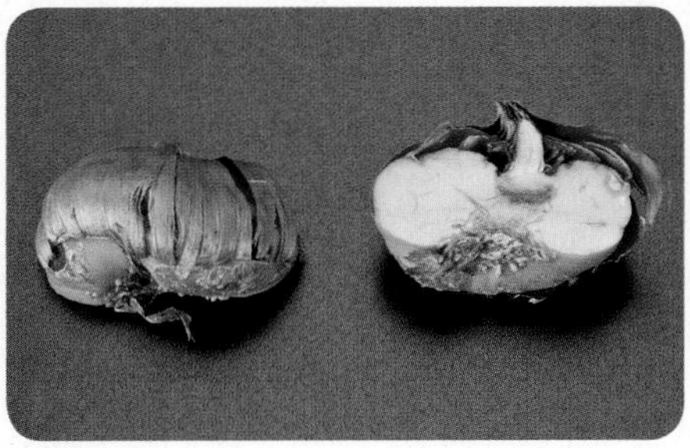 **Crocus**
Function	Food storage	Food storage

D Develop Concepts

EL BL OL AL

Clarify a Misconception

Show students a stalk of celery. **ASK STUDENTS:** ***What part of the plant is this?*** Most students will think that it is a stem. Point out that the term *stalk* is actually short for *leafstalk,* and the stalk of celery is actually part of a leaf. The leafstalk is also referred to as a petiole. Cut several cross sections of the stalk and let students examine them.

ASK STUDENTS: ***Do you see any evidence that this is not a stem?*** Answers will vary. Pass out cross sections of an asparagus stem or any other herbaceous stem and ask students to compare them to the celery stalk.

ASK STUDENTS: ***How do their shapes differ?*** A stalk is crescent shaped, and a stem is round.

Develop Concepts

EL BL OL **Activity** Have students collect pictures of different types of stems and post them on the bulletin board. Use index cards to make the following labels: *tuber bulb, rhizome, runners/stolons,* and *corms.* Ask student volunteers to attach labels to the pictures. Gardening catalogs are a good source of pictures.

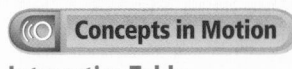

Concepts in Motion
Interactive Table

Demonstration

BL OL AL **Transport** Purchase or ask florists to donate three white carnations. Prepare three solutions of water and food coloring: red, blue, and green. Cut off the bottom of the flower stem to expose fresh tissue. Put one flower in the green solution. Split the bottom of one stem longitudinally about 20 cm up the stem. Carefully put one side of the stem in the blue food coloring and the other side in the red. Leave one carnation in plain water.

ASK STUDENTS: ***What do you think will happen to the stem and the flower?*** Colored solutions will move up the stem. The following day, show students the stem and flower and have students evaluate their hypotheses. Est. time: 5 min each day

D Develop Concepts

EL BL Activity Have students collect leaf specimens and dry them by putting them between sheets of blank newsprint. Stack books or catalogues on the newsprint to flatten the specimens. Have students glue the dried leaves to poster board. Provide plant identification books so students can identify their leaves in the field. Caution students not to collect specimens from parks or private property and warn them of the potential hazards of poisonous plants. To see photos of poison ivy and poison oak, refer to page 1109.

C Critical Thinking

AL Assess

ASK STUDENTS: ***How does the internal structure of a leaf enable photosynthesis to take place?*** The arrangement of palisade cells allows for the maximum number of cells to be exposed to sunlight. The spongy mesophyll has air spaces that allow for exchange of gases with the environment. ***Can you propose a better arrangement for the palisade cells?*** Answers will vary, but students may suggest that if the cells were horizontal rather than vertical, they might get more sunlight.

Caption Question Fig. 13

The cuticle needs to be transparent so light can reach the chloroplasts and the plant can make food.

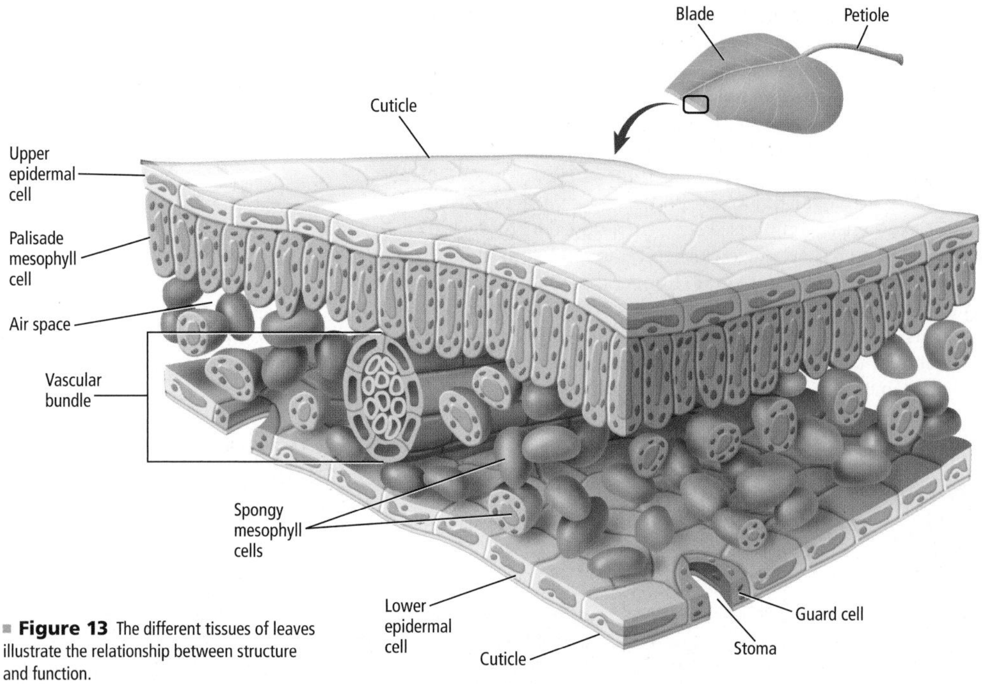

Figure 13 The different tissues of leaves illustrate the relationship between structure and function.
Infer *why having a transparent cuticle is important to a plant.*

Leaves

D There are many shapes and colors of leaves, and their arrangements on plants are different for different species. Also, the sizes of leaves can range from as large as 2 m in diameter to less than 1 mm in length. In a growing season, the number of leaves that a plant can produce varies from a few, such as for a daffodil, to hundreds of thousands produced by a mature hardwood tree.

Leaf structure The main function of leaves is photosynthesis, and their structure is well-adapted for this function. Most leaves have a flattened portion called the blade that has a relatively large surface area. Depending on the plant species, the blade might be attached to the stem by a stalk called a **petiole** (PET ee ohl). The petiole's vascular tissue connects the stem's vascular tissues to the leaf's vascular tissue or veins. Plants such as grasses lack petioles, and their leaf blades are attached directly to the stem.

The internal structure of most leaves is well-adapted for photosynthesis. **Figure 13** shows tightly packed cells directly below a leaf's upper epidermis. This location has the maximum exposure to light, and therefore, most photosynthesis takes place in these column-shaped cells. They contain many chloroplasts and make up the tissue called the **palisade mesophyll** (mehz uh fihl), or palisade layer. Below the palisade mesophyll is the **spongy mesophyll,** consisting of irregularly-shaped, loosely packed cells with spaces surrounding them. Oxygen, carbon dioxide, and water vapor move through the spaces in the spongy mesophyll. Cells of the spongy mesophyll also contain chloroplasts, but have fewer per cell than in the palisade mesophyll. C

VOCABULARY
WORD ORIGIN
Mesophyll
meso- comes from the Greek word *mesos,* meaning *middle*
-phyll comes from the Greek word *phyllon,* meaning *leaf*

Research Citation

Critical Thinking Educational research indicates that students learn best by extending their thinking beyond simple recall of facts. The discussion of the Critical Thinking question on this page provides an opportunity for students to reflect on the text in a meaningful way. (Lambert and Cobb, 2003)

Research bibliography on pages 32T–34T

Differentiated Instruction

Below Level When assessing the leaf collection activity described on this page, consider the work of students performing below grade level according to individual goals. It might be necessary to change the percentage of work required for a passing grade based on individual abilities.

For more tips, see pages 14T–15T.

Gas exchange and transpiration The epidermis covers a leaf. Except for submerged leaves of aquatic plants, the epidermis contains stomata. There usually are more stomata on the underside of leaves than on the upper side. Recall that two guard cells border a stoma. When more water diffuses into the guard cells than out of them, their shapes change in such a way that the stoma opens. Conversely, when more water diffuses out of the guard cells than into them, their shapes change in such a way that the stoma closes. You have learned that carbon dioxide is used in photosynthesis and that oxygen gas is a by-product of photosynthesis. The diffusion of these and other gases into and out of a plant also occurs through stomata.

In most plants, water travels from the roots up through the stems and into the leaves, replacing the water used in photosynthesis and lost from the plant by evaporation. Water evaporates from the inside of a leaf to the outside through stomata in a process called **transpiration** that helps pull the water column upward.

C **Characteristics of leaves** Can you identify a maple tree by looking at its leaves? Some people can use differences in the size, shape, color, and texture of leaves to help them identify types of plants. Some leaves are simple, which means the leaf blade is not divided into smaller parts. Compound leaves have leaf blades that are divided into two or more smaller parts called leaflets, as shown in **Figure 14.**

The arrangement of leaves on the stem, also shown in **Figure 14,** can also be used to distinguish between types of plants. If two leaves are directly opposite of each other on a stem, the growth arrangement is called opposite. An alternate growth arrangement is when the positions of leaves alternate on opposite sides of the stem. A third arrangement, called whorled, is when three or more leaves are evenly spaced around a stem at the same position.

The arrangement of veins in a leaf, or the venation pattern, can also be used to identify leaves. Monocots usually have parallel venation and eudicots usually have branched or netlike venation.

FOLDABLES®
Incorporate information from this section into your Foldable.

? Inquiry Virtual Lab

S

■ **Figure 14** Each species of seed plants has leaves with a unique set of characteristics, some of which are shown here.

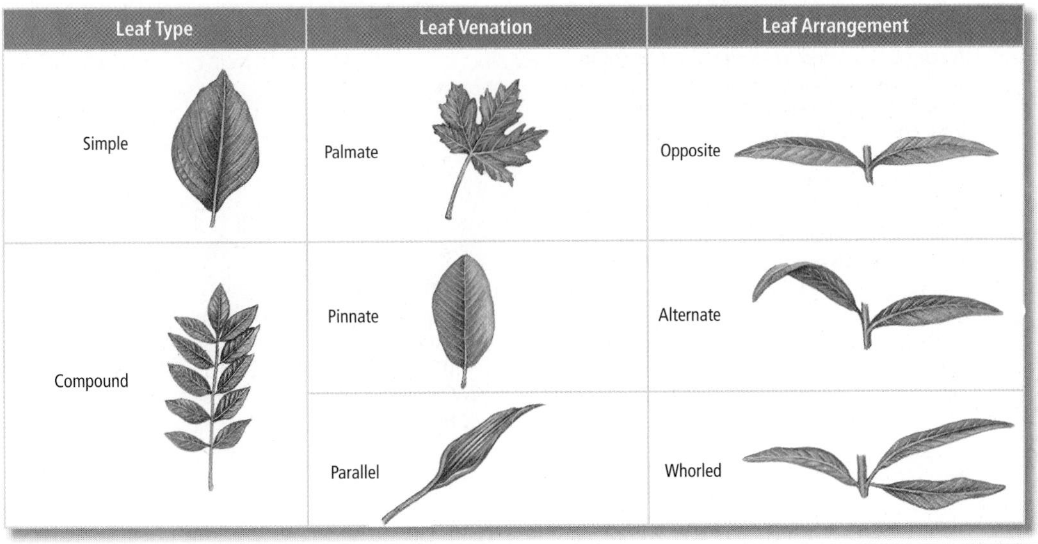

Leaf Type
Leaf Venation
Leaf Arrangement
Simple
Palmate
Opposite
Compound
Pinnate
Alternate
Parallel
Whorled

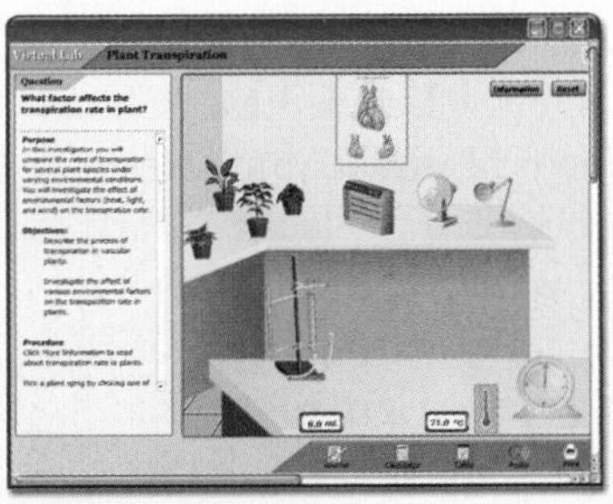

? Inquiry **Virtual Lab** Students will compare the effects of environment on transpiration rates of various plants.

FOLDABLES®

✻RUBRIC A rubric for evaluating Foldables is found on your eTeacherEdition Online.

Going Further Have students sketch the cells of upper and lower epidermises on the back of the appropriate tabs of their Foldables. Sketches should show that there are more stomata on the lower epidermis than on the upper epidermis.

C Critical Thinking

BL OL AL Infer

ASK STUDENTS: ***Why are there generally more stomata on the underside of a leaf than on the upper side?*** Stomata on the upper side of leaves are more exposed to direct sunlight. This exposure increases the rate of evaporation.

S Skill Practice

BL OL AL Visual Literacy

Have students read about monocot and eudicot leaves. Ask students to examine Figure 14 and identify the leaves as monocot or eudicot. The leaves with parallel veins are from a monocot plant. The rest are from dicot plants.

Develop Concepts

EL AL Activity Have students put fresh leaves in plastic sandwich bags and seal them tightly.

ASK STUDENTS: ***What do you think will happen over the next 20 minutes?*** Answers will vary, but students may suggest that the leaves will wilt. After 20 min, have students observe the leaves.

ASK STUDENTS: ***What do you observe in the bags?*** water condensation ***Where did the condensation on the inside of the bag come from?*** transpiration ***How could we increase the amount of condensation?*** Put the bags in the sunlight.

DATA ANALYSIS LAB 1

About the Lab

- *Pieris rapae* caterpillars prefer the leaves of crucifers (plants in the mustard family). They are attracted by the glucosinolates.
- The butterfly lays its egg after "tasting" the leaves with receptors on its feet.
- *P. rapae* caterpillars are agricultural pests.
- Also see Renwick et al. 2001. Dual chemical barriers protect a plant against different larval stages of an insect. *Journal of Chemical Ecology* 27: 1575.

Think Critically

1. The caterpillars prefer the mustard plants to the control plants.
2. In the control samples, the caterpillars had the same response to both the intact leaves and the cut leaves. The caterpillars responded about the same to both intact and cut leaves of Mustard 1. The caterpillars exhibited a slight preference for the cut leaves of Mustard 2. The caterpillars exhibited a large preference for the cut leaves of Mustard 3.
3. Answers will vary. Students might suggest that something about the plants' taste or nutritional value caused them to be favored over the others.

W Writing Support

BL OL AL Summary Writing Have students research cactus spines and write a short summary of their findings. Tell students to include information on the following topics: the difference between spines and thorns, how spines form, and the function of spines.

Figure 15 Cactus spines grow in clusters from small, raised areas on the stem called areoles. The leaves of a jade plant are water-storage organs.

Cactus

Jade plant

VOCABULARY

SCIENCE USAGE V. COMMON USAGE

Spine

Science usage: thin, pointed modified leaf of a cactus or other succulent

The cactus's spines pierced the animal's flesh.

Common usage: the backbone of an animal

The motorcyclist's spine was injured as a result of the accident.

Leaf modifications Although the primary function of leaves is photosynthesis, there are many chemical and structural leaf modifications related to other functions. Many succulents, like the cacti in **Figure 15,** have modified leaves called spines. In addition to reducing water loss, the spines help protect cacti from being eaten by animals. Other succulents have leaves used as water storage sites. The leaves swell with water when water is available, and when water is scarce, these reserves can help ensure the long-term survival of plants. W

DATA ANALYSIS LAB 1

Based on Real Data*

Form a Hypothesis

Do *Pieris* caterpillars prefer certain plants? A scientist wanted to learn what type of input—smell, taste, or touch—helps *Pieris* caterpillars choose food. She used four Petri dishes each of intact leaves and cut leaves. Each set of leaves consisted of a nonmustard family plant (the control) and three different mustard family plants. A caterpillar was added to each dish, and its behavior was observed and recorded.

Data and Observations

The table shows the results of the experiment. *T* represents the caterpillar touched the plant but did not bite it. *A* represents the caterpillar took a bite but then abandoned the leaf. *C* represents that the caterpillar chose the leaf and ate it for a time.

Plants offered	Intact leaves			Cut leaves		
	T	A	C	T	A	C
Control	8	0	0	8	0	0
Mustard 1	14	16	14	17	18	13
Mustard 2	16	18	19	22	24	25
Mustard 3	8	10	9	15	19	23

Think Critically

1. **Examine** the data. What trend do you observe about caterpillars choosing mustard-family plants and control plants?
2. **Compare** the data from intact and cut leaves.
3. **Hypothesize** an explanation for the caterpillars' choice of leaves.

*Data obtained from: Chew, F. S. 1980. Foodplant preferences of *Pieris* caterpillars. *Oecologia* 46: 347–353.

Content Background

Teacher FYI Water may travel as far as 100 m from the roots to the leaves. Research indicates that transpiration is the driving force in this movement of water. Some trees can lose as much as 200 L/h due to transpiration. The spaces between the leaf cells are filled with a mixture of gases—water vapor, CO_2, and O_2. The water vapor diffuses from the moist inside of the leaf to the drier air outside the leaf. This creates a negative pressure on the surfaces of the cells that pulls water from inside the xylem to the interior spaces of the leaf. As this water diffuses out through the stomata, more water is pulled from the xylem to replace it.

Poinsettias

Pitcher plant

■ **Figure 16** Leaf modifications relate to different functions. In poinsettias, bracts change colors and attract pollinators. The inside of the pitcher plant's modified leaf has hairs that grow downward. This prevents a trapped animal from crawling out.

In plants like poinsettias, leaves called bracts at the tips of stems change from green to another color in response to the number of hours of darkness in their environments. These plants usually have tiny flowers at the center of the colored leaves, shown in **Figure 16.** The leaves look like flower petals and attract pollinators.

The leaves of the sundew plant produce a sticky substance that traps insects. The pitcher plant, also shown in **Figure 16,** has cylinderlike modified leaves that fill with water and can trap and drown insects and small animals. Both of these adaptations enable the plants to get nutrients, especially nitrogen, from the insects they capture.

You might be familiar with poison ivy or poison oak that can cause severe skin irritation for some people. These are examples of leaves that contain toxic chemicals that deter organisms from touching them. Some leaves have modifications that deter herbivores from eating them. For example, the epidermis of tomato and squash leaves and stems have tiny hairs with glands at their tips called "trichomes." The glands contain substances that repel insects and other herbivores.

When you read about stems, you learned that bulbs were shortened stems with leaves. A bulb's leaves are modified food storage structures. They provide the dormant bulb with necessary energy resources when favorable growth conditions exist. R

R Reading Strategy

BL OL AL Make Connections Have students read the text under the heading *Leaf modifications* on the previous page. Then ask students if they have ever seen any of these and to share what they know with the class. Have students choose one modification and write a brief summary of how the modification is important to the survival of the species.

BL Discuss this as a class.

Formative Assessment

Evaluation

ASK STUDENTS: ***What are the functions of roots, stems, and leaves?*** Roots anchor the plant, absorb water, and store materials; stems support the plant, transport materials, and hold the leaves and flowers; leaves are the primary site of photosynthesis.

Remediation Have students make a three-column table with the headings *roots, stems,* and *leaves.* Have them reread the section and fill in the function of each part under the appropriate headings. Flash cards can also work for this exercise. Each card contains a structure on one side and a function on the other. Have students form teams to quiz each other.

Section 2 Assessment

Section Summary

- Roots anchor plants and absorb water and nutrients.
- Stems support the plant and hold the leaves.
- Leaves are the sites of photosynthesis and transpiration.
- There are many different modifications of roots, stems, and leaves.
- Modifications help plants survive in different environments.

Understand Main Ideas

1. MAIN Idea **Summarize** the functions of the root cap, cortex, and endodermis.
2. **Compare** a leaf's palisade mesophyll to its spongy mesophyll.
3. **Describe** two leaf modifications and their functions.
4. **Draw** and label the arrangement of vascular tissue in a monocot stem and root and in a eudicot stem and root.

Think Critically

5. **Evaluate** why the role of stomata in a plant is important.
6. MATH in Biology A forest produces approximately 970 kg of oxygen for every metric ton of wood produced. If the average person breathes about 165 kg of oxygen per year, how many people does this forest support?

Section 2 Assessment

1. rootcap—parenchyma cells that protect and lubricate the root; cortex—parenchyma cells involved in storage and transport in the root; endodermis—waterproof strip called "Casparian strip" forces water and dissolved minerals through endodermal cells
2. The palisade mesophyll is a layer of tightly packed cells in the leaf where most photosynthesis takes place. Spongy mesophyll is made of loosely packed cells. The spaces between the cells allow water and gases to move through the leaf.
3. Spines are a leaf modification that protect leaves from being eaten. The leaves of succulent plants are adapted for water storage.
4. Student drawings should include the information found in Figures 10 and 11.
5. Stomata are important because they allow the movement of oxygen into the plant and carbon dioxide and water vapor out of the plant.
6. about 6 people (for one year)

Section 3

MAIN Idea

BL OL AL Role of Hormones Many students may have seen plants bending to the light. **ASK STUDENTS:** ***Can you explain how that happens?*** Answers will vary. Students probably do not know the mechanism involved. In this section, students will learn about plant hormones and responses.

R Reading Strategy

BL OL COOP LEARN

Question a Partner Have students read the text under the heading *Auxin.* Then ask pairs of students to take turns asking each other the following questions: What effect does the hormone have on plant cells? What effect does the hormone have on the plant as a whole? Repeat this activity for each hormone.

EL Help students complete a three-column chart listing plant hormones in the first column and answering the two questions in the second and third columns.

Writing Support

BL OL AL Persuasive Writing Have students write an argument for or against the use of plant hormones in food production. Instruct them to include evidence to support their argument.

Skill Practice

BL Visual Literacy Have students examine Figures 17–19 to locate the source of plant hormones. Have them indicate where auxins, gibberellins, and ethylene are produced in the plants. Ask them to describe the effect these hormones have on plants.

Section 3

Reading Preview

Essential Questions

- What are the major types of plant hormones?
- How do hormones affect the growth of plants?
- How are the different types of plant responses alike?

Review Vocabulary

active transport: the movement of materials across the plasma membrane against a concentration gradient

New Vocabulary

auxin
gibberellins
ethylene
cytokinin
nastic response
tropism

Multilingual eGlossary

Plant Hormones and Responses

MAIN Idea **Hormones can affect a plant's responses to its environment.**

Real-World Reading Link As you might have learned in health class or another science course, various responses of your body are controlled by hormones. When you eat, hormones signal cells of your digestive system to release digestive enzymes. Although plants don't have digestive systems with enzymes, hormones do control many aspects of their growth and development.

Plant Hormones

Hormones are organic compounds that are made in one part of an organism, and then are transported to another part where they have an effect. It takes only a tiny amount of a hormone to cause a change in an organism. Were you surprised to read that plants produce hormones? Plant hormones can affect cell division, growth, or differentiation. Research results indicate that plant hormones work by chemically binding to the plasma membrane at specific sites called receptor proteins. These receptors can affect the expression of a gene, the activity of enzymes, or the permeability of the plasma membrane in the same way hormones affect responses in the human body.

Auxin One of the first plant hormones to be identified was **auxin.** **R** There are different kinds of auxins, but indoleacetic (IHN doh luh see tihk) acid (IAA) is the most widely studied. IAA is produced in apical meristems, buds, young leaves, and other rapidly growing tissues. It moves throughout a plant from one parenchyma cell to the next by a type of active transport. The rate of this movement has been measured at 1 cm per hour. Some auxins also move in the phloem. Also, an auxin moves in only one direction—away from where it was produced.

Connection to Chemistry Auxin usually stimulates the lengthening, or elongation, of cells. Research indicates that in young cells this is an indirect process. Auxin promotes a flow of hydrogen ions through proton pumps from the cytoplasm into the cell wall. This creates a more acidic environment, which weakens the connections between the cellulose fibers in the cell wall. It also activates certain enzymes that help to break down the cell wall. Due to the loss of hydrogen ions in the cytoplasm, water enters the cell, as shown in **Figure 17.** The combination of weakened cell walls and increased internal pressure results in cell elongation.

The effect of auxin in a plant varies greatly depending on its concentration and location. For example, in some plants the concentration of auxin that promotes stem growth can inhibit root growth. Low concentrations of auxin usually stimulate cell elongation. However, at higher concentrations, auxin can have the reverse effect. The presence of other hormones can modify the effects of an auxin.

Figure 17 Auxin promotes the flow of hydrogen ions into the cell wall, which weakens it. Water enters the cell and it lengthens.

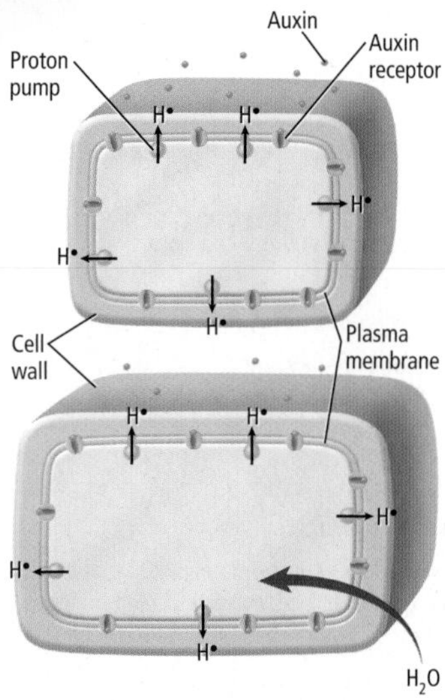

Content Background

Teacher FYI Auxin is transported away from the shoot root or tip via polar auxin transport. When the auxin diffuses into the cell wall (acidic environment) it picks up a H^+, making the auxin neutral. The small, neutral auxin can pass across the plasma membrane. Inside the cell, the auxin loses the H^+. The auxin becomes trapped inside the cell since the membrane is less permeable to ions. The H^+ is pumped out of the cell by ATP-driven proton pumps. The auxin diffuses to the opposite end of the cell, and specific carrier proteins transport the negatively charged auxin across the membrane, using the membrane potential that has been built up by the proton pumps.

The presence of auxin also creates a phenomenon called apical dominance, which is when plant growth is mostly upward with few or no side branches. The auxin produced by an apical meristem inhibits the growth of side or lateral branches. Removing a plant's apical meristem, however, decreases the amount of auxin present. This promotes the growth of side branches. **Figure 18** shows the difference this makes.

Auxins affect fruit formation and inhibit the dropping of fruit. Research results show that the production of auxin slows as cells mature. At the end of the growing season, the decreased amount of auxin in some trees and shrubs causes ripened fruits to fall to the ground and leaves to fall before winter.

Reading Check **Compare and contrast** how different concentrations of auxin can affect a plant.

Gibberellins The group of plant hormones called **gibberellins** causes cell elongation, stimulates cell division, and affects seed growth. Gibberellins are transported in vascular tissue. Dwarf plants often lack either the genes for gibberellins production or the genes for gibberellins protein receptors. When treated with gibberellins, plants that lack the genes for gibberellins but have gibberellins receptors grow taller. Applying gibberellins to a plant can cause an increase in height.

Ethylene The only known gaseous hormone is **ethylene,** a simple compound composed of two carbon and four hydrogen atoms. Ethylene is found in plant tissues such as ripening fruits, dying leaves, and flowers. Since ethylene is a gas, it can diffuse through the spaces between cells. It also is transported within the phloem.

Although ethylene can affect other parts of plants, it primarily affects the ripening of fruits. Ethylene causes cell walls of unripe fruit to weaken and complex carbohydrates to break down into simple sugars. The results of ethylene exposure are fruits that are softer and sweeter than unripe fruits.

Because ripe fruits and vegetables are bruised easily during shipping, growers often pick and ship unripe fruits and vegetables. Once they reach their destinations, a treatment with ethylene speeds up the ripening process. The effects of ethylene are shown below in **Figure 19.**

Figure 18
Top: Auxin inhibits the growth of side or lateral branches.
Bottom: Removing the apical meristem decreases the amount of auxin and the side branches grow.

Video BrainPOP

Figure 19 If the tomato on the left was treated with ethylene, it could be expected to look like the tomato on the right.

Develop Concepts

BL OL

Clarify a Misconception

ASK STUDENTS: ***Have you ever seen a fruit that does not have seeds?*** Answers will vary. Explain that in some cases seedless fruit can be caused by hormone treatment. It can also be an inherited trait. Although spraying some plants with gibberellins will produce fruit without seeds, not all seedless fruits are produced in this manner. Some fruits, like seedless grapes, are genetically seedless.

Inquiry BioLab

The lab at the end of the chapter can be used at this point in the lesson.

GOING GREEN Rather than buying packages of multiple kinds of graph paper, use online resources that allow you to print graph paper for free. Then you can print only as many sheets as you need on recycled paper.

Reading Check High levels of auxin stimulate lengthening or elongation of cells. Auxins affect fruit formation and inhibit the dropping of fruit. Low levels of auxin can cause fruit to fall from the plant.

Video BrainPOP

Demonstration

BL OL AL **Fruit Ripening** Close a ripe banana in a bag with a green banana. Put two unripe bananas in another bag. Be sure the three green bananas are equally unripe. **ASK STUDENTS:** ***What do you think will happen?*** The ripe banana will speed up the ripening of the green banana. Leave the bags at room temperature for two days. Review students' predictions and open the bags. Remind students that the ripe banana is giving off ethylene, which is causing the second banana to ripen more quickly.
Est. time: 10 min per day

MiniLab 2

Inquiry MiniLab

For a lab worksheet, use your eTeacherEdition Online.

RUBRIC A rubric for evaluating MiniLabs is found on your eTeacherEdition Online.

Est. Time 15 min

Alternative Materials Students could also experiment with leaf folding by experimenting with the sensitive plant *Mimosa pudica.* A video of a Venus flytrap's closing could also be used.

Safety Precaution Approve lab safety forms before work begins.

Teaching Strategies

- Make sure that students treat plants gently and do not damage the leaves.
- Warn students to be careful and move slowly when touching trigger hairs so that they only touch the hairs they intend to touch.

Cleanup and Disposal Have students return the plants to where they will be kept and return paintbrushes to storage area.

Analysis

1. Two different hairs must be stimulated to cause the trap to shut. The trap will reopen in about 12 h.
2. Students might realize that a living insect will continue to move. This movement will stimulate more trigger hairs, causing the trap to close more tightly.

LabManager™

Customize this lab with the LabManager™ CD-ROM.

Review Personal Tutor

Listen to a teacher explain tropisms

CAREERS IN BIOLOGY

Plant Physiologist The chemistry of plants, including how plant hormones work, is one of many topics studied by plant physiologists. Many plant physiologists teach and conduct research at universities.

Review Personal Tutor

Cytokinins Growth-inducing **cytokinins** (si tuh KI nihnz) are produced in rapidly dividing cells. They travel to other parts of the plant within xylem. Cytokinins promote cell division by stimulating the production of the proteins needed for mitosis and cytokinesis. Because cytokinins increase the rate of growth, they are often added to the growth media used for plant tissue culture—a laboratory technique for growing plants from pieces of plant tissues. The presence of other hormones, especially auxins, influences the effects of cytokinins. For example, IAA alone stimulates cell elongation, but combined with a cytokinin, it promotes rapid cell division and results in rapid growth.

Reading Check **Describe** two ways hormones can affect plants.

Plant Responses

Have you ever wondered why the leaves of a houseplant grow toward a window, or how a vine can climb a pole? These and other events—roots growing down, stems growing upward, trees dropping their leaves, and leaves of some plants trapping an insect—are due to responses of plants to their environment.

Nastic responses A plant response that causes movement that is not dependent on the direction of the stimulus is a **nastic response.** It is not a growth response, is reversible, and can be repeated. An example of a nastic response is the opening of leaves during the day and the closing of leaves at night to conserve heat, or the movement of *Mimosa pudica* leaflets when they are touched. Nastic movements are caused by a change in water pressure in the leaf cells. Once the stimulus ends, the leaves return to their original positions.

MiniLab 2

Investigate a Plant Response

Inquiry MiniLab

What stimulus causes a Venus flytrap to shut its leaves? A Venus flytrap has specialized leaves that trap and digest insects. In this lab, you will learn what type of stimulus is necessary to trigger the trapping response.

Procedure

1. Read and complete the lab safety form.
2. Examine a **Venus flytrap plant** with open leaves.
3. Using a **small paintbrush,** carefully touch one of the trigger hairs on the inner surface of a leaf.
4. Wait 60 seconds. Now use your paintbrush and touch two different trigger hairs. Alternatively, touch one trigger hair and then touch it again in about ten seconds.
5. After you have stimulated the leaves to snap shut, whenever possible, observe your plant to determine how long it takes the trap to open again.

Analysis

1. **Identify** the type of stimulus necessary to trigger the plant leaf to shut. How long did it take the leaf to reopen?
2. **Think Critically** If you drop a dead insect onto a leaf, the leaf might close. However, it will not close tightly and will reopen later without digesting the insect. Based on this lab, hypothesize how the plant might distinguish between a living insect and a dead one.

Differentiated Instruction

Visually Impaired Students who are visually impaired may struggle with the lab activities in this chapter, which require visual observations of plants. Assist these students by verbally describing the specimens they will be viewing.

For more tips, see pages 14T–15T.

“It is the supreme art of the teacher to awaken joy in creative expression and knowledge.”

—Albert Einstein

Reading Check Hormones can affect plants by causing them to grow. Hormones can also cause fruit to ripen.

Another example of a nastic response is the closing of a Venus flytrap's leaves. Recent research shows that this results from a movement of water within each half of the leaf trap. The movement results in uneven expansion until the leaf's curved shape suddenly changes and snaps the trap shut.

Tropic responses What do you notice about the plants in **Table 4?** These are examples of tropic responses, or tropisms. A **tropism** (TROH pih zum) is a plant's growth response to an external stimulus. If resulting plant growth is toward the stimulus, it is called a positive tropism. If the resulting plant growth is away from the stimulus, it is called a negative tropism. There are several different types of tropisms, including phototropism, gravitropism, and thigmotropism.

Phototropism is a plant growth response to light caused by an unequal distribution of auxin. There is less auxin on the side of the plant toward the light source and more auxin on the side away from the light source. Because auxin can cause cell elongation, the cells on the side away from the light elongate, making that side of the stem longer. This results in the stem curving toward the direction of the light.

Gravitropism is a plant growth response to gravity. Roots generally show a positive gravitropism. The downward growth of roots into soil helps to anchor the plant and brings roots in contact with water and minerals. However, a stem exhibits a negative gravitropism when it grows upward, away from gravity. This growth positions leaves for maximum exposure to light.

Another tropism found in some plants is thigmotropism. This is a growth response to mechanical stimuli, such as contact with an object, another organism, or even wind. Thigmotropism is evident in vining plants that twist around a nearby structure such as a fence or tree. **D**

Concepts in Motion Interactive Table

Table 4 Plant Tropisms

Tropism	Stimulus/ Response	Example
Phototropism	Light • Growth toward light source	
Gravitropism	Gravity • Positive: downward growth • Negative: upward growth	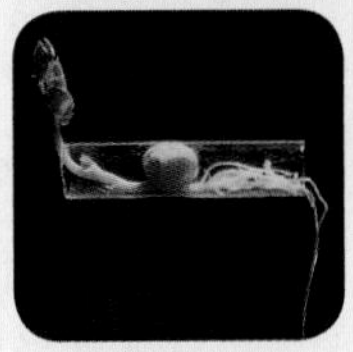
Thigmotropism	Mechanical • Growth toward point of contact	

Concepts in Motion

Interactive Table

D Develop Concepts

BL OL AL Scaffolding

SAY TO STUDENTS: ***List three types of tropisms.*** phototropism, gravitropism, and thigmotropism ***Contrast negative and positive gravitropism.*** Positive gravitropism is growth toward gravity, and negative gravitropism is growth away from gravity. ***Assess the importance of both gravitropisms to the growth and survival of a seed.*** An underground seed would have to rely on gravitropism for directional cues. The root needs to grow down into the soil. The shoot needs to grow toward the light, which would enable the plant to photosynthesize.

Formative Assessment

Evaluation

Have students construct a table listing four different plant hormones and their effects on plant growth. auxin—cell elongation; gibberellins—cell division; cytokinins—cell division; and ethylene—fruit ripening

Remediation Organize the class into small groups and have them discuss the different hormones and their effects on plants. Suggest to students that they write a poem or rap song to help them remember the hormones.

Section 3 Assessment

Section Summary

- Plant hormones are produced in very small amounts.
- There are four main types of plant hormones.
- Hormones can affect cell division, growth, and differentiation.
- Nastic responses are not dependent on the direction of the stimulus.
- Tropisms are responses to stimuli from a specific direction.

Understand Main Ideas

1. MAIN Idea **Identify** plant hormones and classify them according to the effects that they have on a plant.
2. **Describe** three tropisms.
3. **Compare and contrast** tropisms and nastic responses.

Think Critically

4. **Construct** a model to show how auxin can move from one cell to another.
5. **Critique** the scientific basis of the saying, "One rotten apple spoils the whole barrel."

Section 3 Assessment

1. Plant hormones are those chemicals that cause changes in plants. Gibberellins and cytokinins cause cell division. Auxins and cytokinins cause cell elongation. Gibberellins cause seed germination. Ethylene causes fruit to ripen.
2. Phototropism is a plant growth response to light. Gravitropism is a plant growth response to gravity. Thigmotropism is a plant growth response to touch.
3. Tropisms are growth responses in plants that depend on the direction of the stimulus. A nastic response is a response in a plant that does not depend on the direction of the stimulus.
4. Students' models should show the auxin moving quickly and only in the direction away from where it is produced.
5. Sample answer: The saying has some merit. One apple that is rotting because it is over-ripe could be producing enough ethylene to cause the apples around it to become overripe. Those overripe apples could cause other apples to rot as well. The cascading effect of the production of ethylene gas could eventually affect all the apples in the barrel.

Assessment Online Quiz

Purpose

Students will understand that plants respond to gravity and light. Students will also understand that microgravity might pose challenges to growing food crops in space.
A.2, G.1

Anticipatory Guide

ASK STUDENTS: ***What is a tropism?*** Tell students that a tropism is a plant's growth response to an external stimulus. Gravitropism is a plant's growth response to gravity. Phototropism is a plant's growth response to light, and thigmotropism is a plant's growth response to touch or contact.

Background

- Phototropism is caused by an unequal distribution of a plant hormone called auxin, which stimulates the elongation of cells. Auxin moves into the side of the plant stem that is away from the light source, which makes the cells on that side of the stem elongate and bend the stem toward the light source.
- Both positive and negative gravitropism are also caused by the unequal distribution of auxin. However, the hormone works differently in roots than it does in shoots, causing roots to bend in the direction of gravity and shoots to bend away from the direction of gravity.

BioDiscoveries

To Boldly Grow Where No Plant Has Grown Before

Astronauts must take all of the food that they need for their trips when they leave Earth, and many of their meals are dehydrated or freeze-dried to preserve them. But what if astronauts could grow crops on space missions?

Growing plants in space The National Aeronautics and Space Administration (NASA) hopes that astronauts will be able to grow much of their food in space. This will reduce the amount of food that is carried into orbit. To reach this goal, astronauts have been experimenting with plants on space shuttles and on the International Space Station (ISS).

These plants were grown as part of an experiment on the ISS. The roots of plants grown in microgravity grow in many directions.

Tropisms and the effects of microgravity A plant's growth response to gravity is called gravitropism. On Earth, the shoots of a plant grow away from the direction of gravity (negative gravitropism), while the roots of a plant grow toward the direction of gravity (positive gravitropism). On Earth, plants grow toward a light source, usually the Sun. This response is called phototropism.

When astronauts and their plants are in space, they experience microgravity—a condition in which there is little or no measureable effect of gravity. The roots of plants in microgravity do not display gravitropism. They grow in many different directions within the planting medium that is covered to keep its particles from floating away. The shoots of plants in microgravity do display phototropism.

Problems growing plants in space Scientists have determined that a plant's lack of gravitropism in microgravity does not inhibit its growth. However, microgravity does make it difficult to distribute water and oxygen throughout the planting medium and around the shoots of plants. These conditions adversely affect plants when they are producing seeds. Scientists are developing ways to address these problems. For instance, porous tubes buried in the soil can distribute water through capillary action.

Plant growth experiments have continued on recent ISS missions. One 2009 experiment documented the germinatison of tree seeds in a microgravity environment. NASA scientists have not yet reached the goal of astronauts growing their own food, but continuing plant research is bringing them closer.

DESIGN AN EXPERIMENT

Effects of Gravity Using two plants of the same species and the same size, design a container that will allow one of the plants to grow upside down. The other plant will be the control. Provide the same amount of water and light to both plants. Observe the plants everyday and record your observations. After a month has passed, discuss your observations with your classmates.

Design an Experiment

Activity

As students record their observations, encourage them to include the following: What are the constants and the control? What is the variable? What are the roots of the plants doing? What are the shoots of the plants doing? Is one of the plants bigger than the other? Does one have more flowers or fruit than the other? Do the flowers or fruit seem better formed in one of the plants? If time permits, you might want to run the experiment again, using a different species of plant or a different kind of container.

WebQuest

BIOLAB

Design Your Own

HOW DO DWARF PLANTS RESPOND TO GIBBERELLINS?

Background: **Some dwarf plants lack a gene for gibberellin production and some lack gibberellin receptors. In this lab, you will design an experiment to determine if you can change the growth pattern of dwarf pea-plant seedlings by applying gibberellic acid (a form of gibberellins) to them.**

Question: *Can you use gibberellins to change the growth of dwarf pea plants?*

Materials

gibberellic acid in varying concentrations
sheets of poster board or cardboard
dishwashing liquid (wetting agent)
potted dwarf pea-plant seedlings
spray bottles
cotton swabs
light source
large plastic bags
plant fertilizer
distilled water
metric rulers
graph paper
Choose materials that would be appropriate for this lab.

Safety Precautions

Plan and Perform the Experiment

1. Read and complete the lab safety form.
2. Form a hypothesis that explains how gibberellins will affect the growth of dwarf pea plants.
3. Design an experiment to test your hypothesis. Be sure that your experiment has a control group.
4. Make a list of factors that must be constant for your experimental and control groups. Be sure to test only one variable.
5. Determine a way to apply gibberellins to the plants and decide how often you will apply it.
6. Design and construct a data table to record data from your experiment.
7. Make sure your teacher approves your plan before you proceed.
8. Collect the supplies you need and set up your experimental and control plants.
9. Complete the approved experiment.
10. Record measurements and observations of the plants in your data table.
11. Graph the data from your experimental and control groups.
12. **Cleanup and Disposal** Return unused gibberellic acid to your teacher for disposal. Empty spray bottles and thoroughly rinse. Dispose of used cotton swabs in the trash. Dispose of plants as directed by your teacher.

Analyze and Conclude

1. **Analyze** your graph and determine the effect of gibberellic acid on the dwarf pea plants.
2. **Hypothesize** Based on your results, explain why the pea plants are dwarfs.
3. **Think Critically** Why might a genetic change, such as one that causes a plant not to produce gibberellins, be a problem for plants in a natural environment?
4. **Error Analysis** What might have occurred in your experimental setup that could have caused your data to be inaccurate? How would you change your procedure?

SHARE YOUR DATA

Peer Review Compare and contrast your graph to those of other students in your class. What accounts for the differences?

BIOLAB

Design Your Own

? Inquiry BioLab

For a lab worksheet, use your eTeacherEdition Online.

RUBRIC A rubric for evaluating BioLabs is found on your eTeacherEdition Online.

Est. Time 45–90 min per day

Content Background Gibberellins are hormones that cause plants to grow taller and longer, stimulate seed germination, and promote flowering in some plants. The horticulture industry now uses gibberellins commercially in seed germination, stimulation of flowering, and increasing the size of plants.

Alternative Materials Many seeds, including: beans, corn, marigolds, snapdragons, and zinnias, are available as dwarf varieties. The Wisconsin Fast Plant™ *(Brassica rapa)* is also available in a dwarf form.

Safety Precautions Approve lab safety forms before work begins. Have students wear gloves and safety goggles and wash their hands after every application of the hormone.

Teaching Strategies

- Supply the gibberellic acid solutions in the following concentrations: 0.1 mg/L, 1.0 mg/L, 10 mg/L, 100 mg/L. This chemical is restricted by the DEA, but at the time of publication it is available from Science Kit and large biological supply houses.
- Seeds of dwarf plants are also available from lab supply companies. Alternatively, you can find dwarf pea seeds at garden centers.

Analyze and Conclude

1. Gibberellic acid causes plants to grow taller if the plants have gibberellins receptors.
2. The plants do not produce enough gibberellic acid.
3. Sample answer: The plants might not be able to grow tall enough to compete with other plants for sunlight.
4. Student answers may include the following: errors in measurement of the concentration of the gibberellin solutions; drift of spray; mistakes in measurement of height; the sample size was not large enough; and variables of light, watering, temperature, etc. were not well controlled. If the plants did not respond to the gibberellin solutions, they might have a mutation that affects the plant's gibberellin receptors. Students should design an experiment to test this hypothesis if the plants do not respond.

Alternative Teaching Demo
Lead the class through a new hypothesis and data collection related to this concept.

Chapter 22

Study Guide

ConnectED

Students can use the following to review the chapter.

Review

Vocabulary eGames
Vocabulary eFlashcards
Vocabulary PuzzleMaker

Assessment

Online Quizzes
Online Test Practice
Standardized Test Practice

Use the *ExamView® Assessment Suite* CD-ROM to:

- create multiple versions of tests
- create modified tests with one mouse click
- edit existing questions and add your own questions
- build tests aligned with state standards using built-in state curriculum tags
- change English tests to Spanish with one mouse click
- track students' progress using the Teacher Management System

Chapter 22 Study Guide

THEME FOCUS Homeostasis Guard cells, phloem, and xylem are some of the structures that maintain homeostasis by transporting and moving water, oxygen, and other gases throughout the plant.

BIG Idea The diverse nature of plants is due to the variety of their structures.

Section 1 Plant Cells and Tissues

parenchyma cell (p. 632)
collenchyma cell (p. 633)
sclerenchyma cell (p. 633)
meristem (p. 634)
vascular cambium (p. 634)
cork cambium (p. 634)
epidermis (p. 636)
guard cell (p. 636)
xylem (p. 637)
vessel element (p. 637)
tracheid (p. 637)
phloem (p. 638)
sieve tube member (p. 638)
companion cell (p. 638)
ground tissue (p. 638)

MAIN Idea Different types of plant cells make up plant tissues.

- There are three types of plant cells.
- The structure of a plant cell is related to its function.
- There are several different types of plant tissues—meristematic, dermal, vascular, and ground tissues.
- Xylem and phloem are vascular tissues.

Section 2 Roots, Stems, and Leaves

root cap (p. 639)
cortex (p. 639)
endodermis (p. 640)
pericycle (p. 640)
petiole (p. 644)
palisade mesophyll (p. 644)
spongy mesophyll (p. 644)
transpiration (p. 645)

MAIN Idea The structures of plants are related to their functions.

- Roots anchor plants and absorb water and nutrients.
- Stems support the plant and hold the leaves.
- Leaves are the sites of photosynthesis and transpiration.
- There are many different modifications of roots, stems, and leaves.
- Modifications help plants survive in different environments.

Section 3 Plant Hormones and Responses

auxin (p. 648)
gibberellins (p. 649)
ethylene (p. 649)
cytokinin (p. 650)
nastic response (p. 650)
tropism (p. 651)

MAIN Idea Hormones can affect a plant's responses to its environment.

- Plant hormones are produced in very small amounts.
- There are four main types of plant hormones.
- Hormones can affect cell division, growth, and differentiation.
- Nastic responses are not dependent on the direction of the stimulus.
- Tropisms are responses to stimuli from a specific direction.

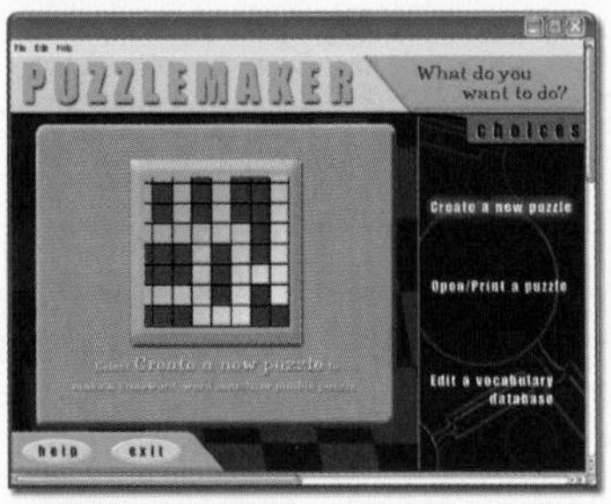

Review **Vocabulary PuzzleMaker**

For additional practice with vocabulary, have students access the Vocabulary PuzzleMaker online.

Review **Vocabulary eGames**

Chapter 22 Assessment

Section 1

Vocabulary Review

Distinguish between the words in each pair.

1. sclerenchyma, collenchyma
2. xylem, phloem
3. epidermis, guard cell

Understand Main Ideas

4. Which is the vascular tissue that transports water and dissolved minerals from roots to leaves?
   A. epidermis **C.** xylem
   B. parenchyma **D.** phloem
5. Which is the region of actively dividing cells at the tip of the stem?
   A. apical meristem **C.** dermal tissue
   B. vascular tissue **D.** lateral meristem

Use the photos below to answer questions 6 and 7.

6. Which image shows a trichome?

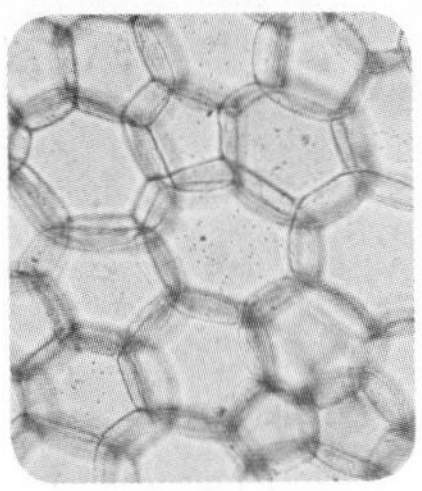

A.

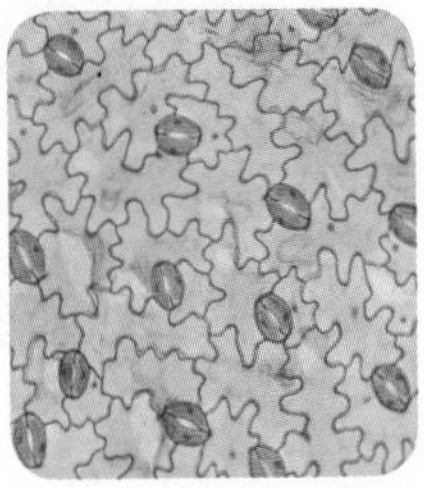

C.

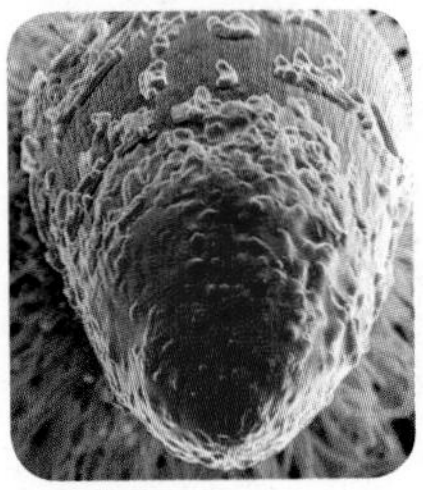

B.

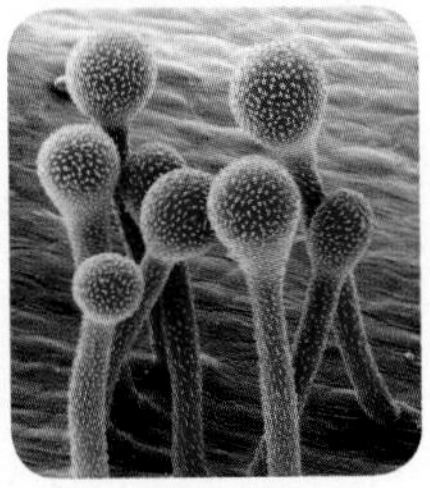

D.

7. Which image shows parenchyma cells?
   A. A **C.** C
   B. B **D.** D
8. Which is one of the differences between nonflowering seed plants and flowering seed plants?
   A. presence of stomata in the roots
   B. amount of sugar stored in the roots
   C. presence of tracheids and vessels
   D. structure of parenchyma cells

Constructed Response

Use the image below to answer question 9.

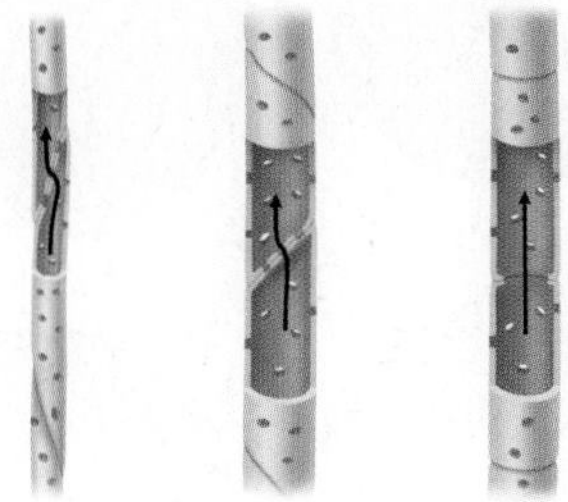

9. **Short Answer** Explain one advantage of these vessels.
10. **Short Answer** Compare and contrast root hairs and trichomes.
11. **THEME FOCUS Homeostasis** How do guard cells and stomata help maintain homeostasis in plant leaves?

Think Critically

12. **MAIN Idea** Construct a graphic organizer that lists each of the four different types of tissue, the function of each, and the types of cells it contains.
13. **Compare** the dermal tissue of plants to your skin. Contrast specific characteristics that make both the dermal tissue and your skin more efficient.

Section 2

Vocabulary Review

Correctly use each set of words in a sentence.

14. endodermis, pericycle
15. petiole, transpiration
16. spongy mesophyll, palisade mesophyll

Chapter 22

Assessment

Section 1

Vocabulary Review

1. Sclerenchyma cells have very thick cell walls and are dead at maturity; collenchyma cells have unevenly thickened cell walls and are alive at maturity.
2. Xylem carries water and dissolved minerals up the stem to the leaves, and phloem transports materials such as sugars and amino acids up and down the plant.
3. The epidermis covers the leaf. The guard cells form stomata in the epidermis.

Understand Main Ideas

4. C
5. A
6. D
7. A
8. C

Constructed Response

9. Tracheids and vessels like those in the figure enable the transport of materials throughout a plant.
10. Root hairs and trichomes are both adaptations of epidermal cells, but root hairs are on roots, and trichomes are on leaves.
11. Guard cells and stomata control the amount of water and gases that are in the leaves by controlling how much of each substance is allowed to pass through.

Think Critically

12. Graphic organizers should contain the following information: There are three kinds of cells in meristematic tissue: apical, intercalary, and lateral. Meristematic tissue is made of rapidly dividing cells found in roots, leaves, and stems. There are four kinds of dermal cells. Epidermal cells cover the outside of the plant. Guard cells make stomata. Trichomes are hairlike projections on leaves. Root hairs are fragile extensions on root epidermal cells. There are two types of vascular tissue: xylem and phloem. Xylem is made of two kinds of cells—tracheids, which are long tubular cells with pitted ends, and vessel elements, which are tubular cells stacked end-to-end. Phloem is made of two kinds of cells: sieve-tube members, which lack nuclei, and companion cells, which have nuclei. Ground tissue is made of all kinds of cells that are not in the above categories. These cells have diverse functions and make up most of a plant.
13. Sample answer: Dermal tissue is like human skin because both tissues protect the organism. However, dermal tissue in plants is unlike human skin, because human skin does not contain chloroplasts, or stomata. Dermal tissue is more efficient for plants because plants need the dermal tissue to make food. Human skin is more efficient for a human body because it is flexible and provides a cooling mechanism that helps the body maintain homeostasis.

Understand Main Ideas

17. Which fill(s) the space between spongy mesophyll cells?
  A. chlorophyll **C.** cells
  B. gases **D.** vascular tissue

18. Which image shows a eudicot stem?

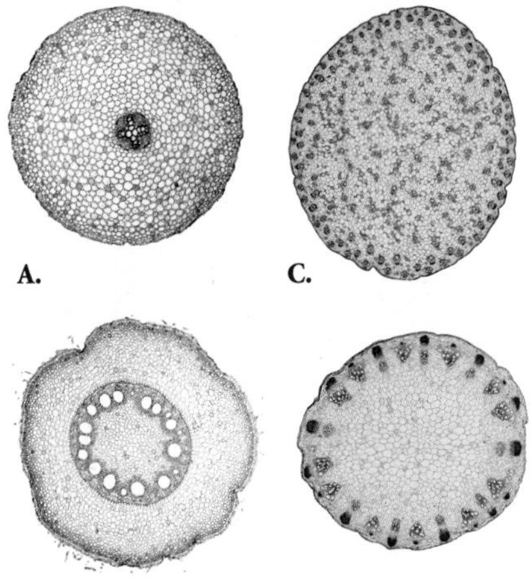

A. **C.**
B. **D.**

19. Which image above shows one ring of vascular bundles?
  A. A **C.** C
  B. B **D.** D

20. Which plant structure is not part of a root?
  A. endodermis **C.** pericycle
  B. root cap **D.** stomata

21. Which control(s) the movement of water vapor through the stomata?
  A. bark
  B. pericycle
  C. guard cells
  D. vascular tissues

Constructed Response

22. **Open Ended** List some environmental factors that might affect transpiration.

23. **Short Answer** Describe the control of materials as they are transported from soil to a root's vascular tissue.

Think Critically

24. MAIN Idea Evaluate some leaf modifications in terms of their functions.

25. **Summarize** the reasons why eudicot stems can have a greater increase in diameter than most monocot stems.

Section 3

Vocabulary Review

Explain the difference between the terms in each pair below. Then explain how they are related.

26. hormone, auxin

27. ethylene, gibberellins

28. tropic response, nastic response

Understand Main Ideas

Use these photos to answer questions 29 and 30.

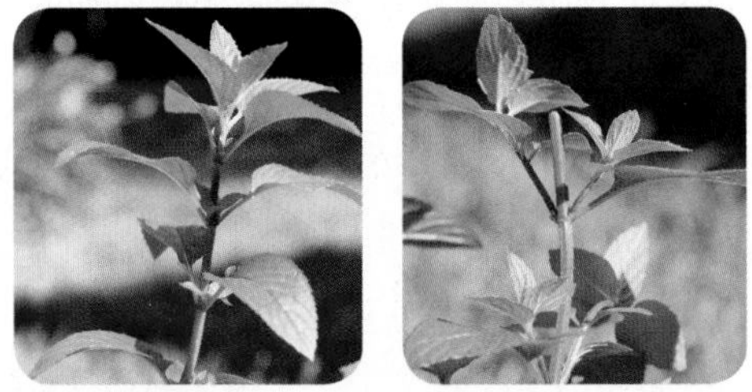

29. What plant condition do these photos show?
  A. apical dominance **C.** leaf drop
  B. dwarfism **D.** nastic movements

30. Which hormone controls this plant condition?
  A. auxin **C.** ethylene
  B. gibberellin **D.** cytokinin

31. Which describes a positive phototropism?
  A. The plant grows away from the light.
  B. The plant grows toward the light.
  C. The plant grows toward gravity.
  D. The plant grows away from gravity.

32. Which is involved in the transport of gibberellins throughout the plant?
  A. cork cambium **C.** vascular tissue
  B. guard cells **D.** apical meristem

Section 2

Vocabulary Review

14. The pericycle is the layer of cells inside the endodermis that produces new lateral roots.
15. Transpiration helps pull water up through the plant to the leaf, which is attached to the stem by a petiole.
16. Spongy mesophyll cells are irregular cells with air spaces around them, but palisade mesophyll cells are columnlike cells that are tightly packed together.

Understand Main Ideas

17. B
18. D
19. D
20. D
21. C

Constructed Response

22. Answers will vary, but should include temperature, drought, and wind.
23. The Casparian strip of the endodermal cells creates a waterproof barrier between the cortex of the root and the vascular tissue. The only way material can get into the vascular tissue is to pass through the cells of the endodermis. This includes passing through the semi-permeable membrane.

Think Critically

24. Answers will vary, but students should state the modification and relate it to its specific function.
25. Because eudicot stems have a vascular cambium that produces lateral growth, the eudicot stems can increase their girth.

Section 3

Vocabulary Review

26. Hormones are chemicals that are produced in one part of the plant that have an effect on another part of the plant. Auxin is one type of hormone.
27. Ethylene is a gas that affects fruit ripening. Gibberellin is a liquid that affects cell division and seed germination. Both are hormones.

Use the images below to answer question 33.

33. Which stem shown above is exhibiting negative gravitropism?
A. A
B. B
C. C
D. D

Constructed Response

34. Open Ended Discuss the pros and cons of the transport of auxin from one parenchyma cell to another instead of in the vascular tissue.

35. MAIN Idea Refer to **Figure 17** and explain how auxin can cause cell elongation.

36. Short Answer Explain why tropic responses are permanent while nastic responses are reversible.

Think Critically

37. Design an experiment to determine if bean plants show apical dominance.

38. Evaluate the following statement: "Seeds soaked in gibberellins will germinate faster than seeds not soaked in gibberellins."

39. CAREERS IN BIOLOGY Farmers must evaluate the use of plant hormones to increase crop production. Do you think it is a good idea? Compare it to the use of growth hormones that are used to increase the milk production of cows.

Summative Assessment

40. BIG Idea Explain how the structure of plants creates diversity and give specific examples to support your answer.

41. WRITING in Biology Imagine you are a beetle and you come upon a Venus flytrap. Write about why you would avoid this plant.

42. WRITING in Biology What if you could develop a new plant hormone? What would you have it do? How would it work and what would you name it?

DBQ Document-Based Questions

A team of biologists studied the effect of temperature and carbon dioxide on ponderosa pines. The graph below represents the amounts of tracheids with various diameters grown at different temperatures.

Use the graph to answer questions 43–45.

Data obtained from: Maherali, H., and DeLucia, E. H. 2000. Interactive effects of elevated CO_2 and temperature on water transport in ponderosa pine. *Amer. Journal of Botany* 87: 243-249.

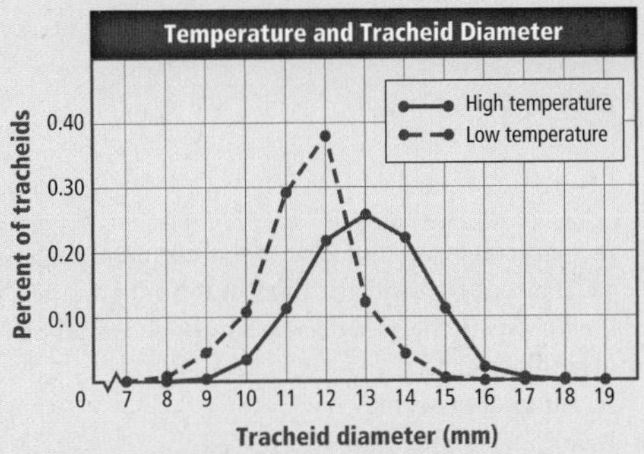

43. What percent of tracheids are 12 mm in diameter for each group measured?

44. How does the temperature affect the diameter of developing tracheid cells?

45. How does the relationship between temperature and diameter relate to the tracheid function?

28. Tropic responses depend on the direction of a stimulus—nastic responses do not.

Understand Main Ideas

29. A
30. A
31. B
32. C
33. C

Constructed Response

34. Sample answer: Moving from one cell to another through active transport ensures the effects of the hormone will be localized. If the hormone were transported through the vascular system, the effects would be felt throughout the plant.

35. As shown in the figure, auxin causes a decrease in pH. The acid loosens the cell walls and the cells can stretch, or elongate.

36. Tropic responses are usually due to changes in cell structure, while nastic responses are often due to changes in water pressure.

Think Critically

37. Answers will vary, but should include a control that is not treated.

38. Answers will vary, but students should consider that gibberellins do hasten seed germination.

39. Answers will vary, but students should acknowledge that farmers, scientists, and consumers should consider the effects of using hormones on plants. Comparisons with the milk industry should be logical and reasonable.

Summative Assessment

40. Structures of plants are designed for a particular function. Each cell, tissue, and structure has a specific purpose and therefore a specific design. For example the root system of water lilies and a saguaro cactus vary tremendously and have different structures.

41. Answers will vary, but should include reference to nastic responses.

42. The hormones students write about should be based on scientific principals.

DBQ Document-Based Questions

Maherali, H., and DeLucia, E. H. 2000. Interactive effects of elevated CO_2 and temperature on water transport in ponderosa pine. *Amer. Journal of Botany* 87: 243-249.

43. High temperature group, 0.22 percent
Low temperature group, 0.38 percent

44. Warmer temperatures increase the diameter of the tracheids.

45. Sample answer: Warmer temperatures cause an increase in the diameter of the tracheids. Tracheids with a larger diameter can transport more material than tracheids with a narrower diameter.

Standardized Test Practice

Multiple Choice

1. C **5.** D
2. A **6.** A
3. A **7.** C
4. B **8.** C

Short Answer

9. Answers can vary, as long as they describe a characteristic of one division that is not in the other division.
  A. club-shaped reproductive structures
  B. branched vascular tissue

10. Answers may vary. Septate hyphae have crosswalls called septa that have large pores. The large pores allow cytoplasm, nutrients, organelles, and sometimes nuclei to move between cells. Aseptate hyphae do not have any crosswalls so all the cytoplasm and organelles flow freely. The cytoplasm can move more easily in aseptate than septate hyphae.

11. Answers may vary. One hypothesis is that adaptations to store excess food enable plants to survive times when conditions are not right for producing food. These conditions might include drought or cold weather. Accept logical answers.

12. Answers may vary. Possible answers include the following.

Annuals	Biennials	Perennials
Grow from seed; live and flower during only one year	Grow from seed; flower during second year	Grow from seed; flower each year; only the above-ground parts die during cold months

13. Xylem transports water and dissolved nutrients from the roots to all parts of the plant. Phloem transports dissolved sugars and other compounds throughout the plant.

Standardized Test Practice

Cumulative

Multiple Choice

1. The Miller-Urey experiment tested which hypothesis?
A. Margulis's endosymbiont theory
B. Miller's amino acid origin
C. Oparin's primordial soup idea
D. Pasteur's biogenesis theory

Use the diagram below to answer question 2.

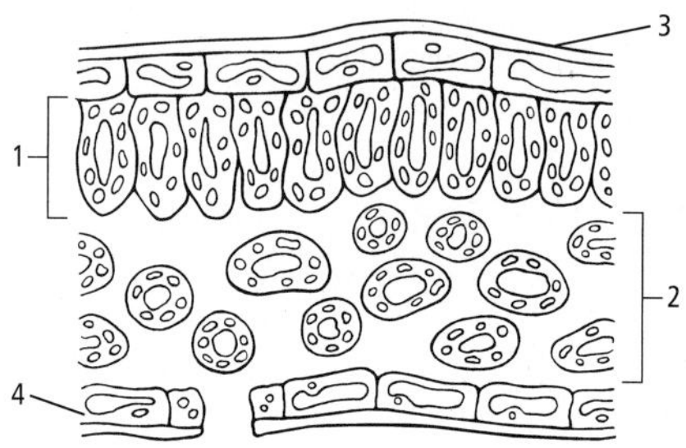

2. Which leaf structure is the site where the most photosynthesis takes place?
A. 1
B. 2
C. 3
D. 4

3. Lichens can be an indicator of environmental quality. If a coal-fired electric plant was built and then the lichens in the area decreased, which would be the most likely cause?
A. air quality decreased
B. annual temperatures decreased
C. humidity patterns changed
D. rainfall patterns changed

4. Which is one method of asexual reproduction that can occur in fungi?
A. conjugation
B. fragmentation
C. segmentation
D. transformation

5. Which development in plants contributed most to the evolution of large trees?
A. alternation of generations
B. flowers
C. seeds
D. vascular tissue

6. Which describes how funguslike protists obtain food?
A. They absorb nutrients from decaying organisms.
B. They obtain nutrients by feeding on unicellular organisms.
C. They have a symbiotic relationship with an animal host, obtaining nutrients from it.
D. They produce sugars as a nutrient source by using energy from sunlight.

7. Which is the function of a plant's root cap?
A. generate new cells for root growth
B. help the root tissues absorb water
C. protect root tissue as the root grows
D. provide support for the root tissues

Use the diagram below to answer question 8.

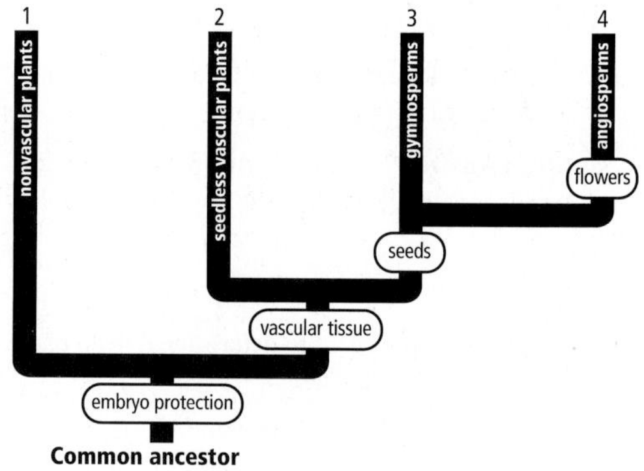

8. Which number represents where you would expect to find cycadophytes on this evolutionary tree?
A. 1
B. 2
C. 3
D. 4

Short Answer

Use the illustration below to answer question 9.

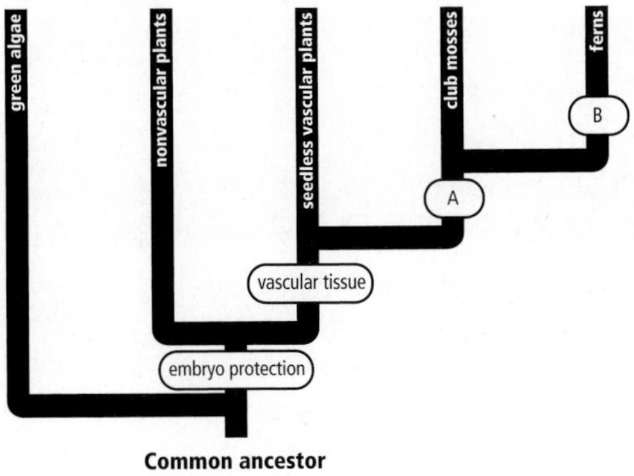

9. Look at the evolutionary tree in the diagram above. What word or phrase would best describe branching points A and B in the diagram?

10. Compare and contrast septate and aseptate hyphae.

11. Write a hypothesis about the benefit of the stem adaptations that allow some plants to store excess food.

12. Use a chart to organize information about how annuals, biennials, and perennials are similar and different.

13. Name and describe the function of the two types of vascular tissue found in plants.

14. What are three characteristics of ancient algae that enabled them to survive and can be found in all plants today?

15. Describe the function of the vascular tissue in a leaf.

Extended Response

Use the illustration below to answer question 16.

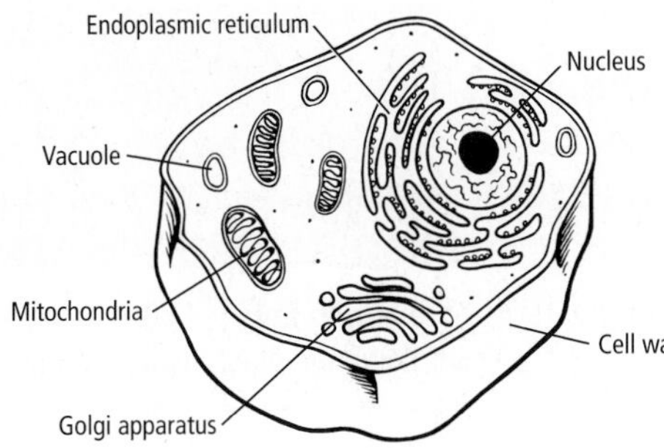

16. Based on the characteristics of the cell above, how would you classify the organism from which it was taken? Justify your method for classifying the organism.

17. Evaluate why the structure of the thylakoid in a chloroplast is well suited for its function.

Essay Question

Imagine that you are planning to turn an area of land near your school into a small garden. You can order seeds to plant, or you can transplant small plants to the site. Your main goal is to have some plants growing in your garden every season of the year.

Using the information in the paragraph above, answer the following question in essay format.

18. Based on what you know about plants and the climate where your school is located, what type of plants would be best to grow? Describe your plan in a well-organized essay, and be sure to explain how the different types of plants you plan to use will meet the criteria for the garden.

NEED EXTRA HELP?

If You Missed Question . . .	1	2	3	4	5	6	7	8	9	10	11	12	13	14	15	16	17	18
Review Section . . .	14.2	22.2	20.3	20.1	21.1, 21.3	19.4	22.2	21.1	21.2	20.1	22.2	21.4	22.1	21.1	22.2	17.3	8.2	21.2, 21.4

14. Answers may vary. Possible answers include the following:
A. autotrophs that produce their own food
B. cell walls that maintain structure
C. food stored as starch

15. The vascular tissue in the leaf has xylem and phloem to move water and mineral nutrients into the leaf and sugar out of the leaf.

Extended Response

16. This could be a fungus. The cell has a cell wall and vacuoles, but it is lacking chloroplasts. It could be a plant cell from a root or inside a stem. Since it is a eukaryotic cell, it cannot be a bacterium or archaea. It also cannot be an animal cell because it has a cell wall.

17. The thylakoid is a folded structure, which gives it a large surface area. All along the membrane of the thylakoid, electron transport is occurring to produce ATP molecules. The folded structure makes it possible for more electron transfer reactions to happen at once, maximizing the use of light energy coming into the leaf.

Essay Question

18. Answers should reflect the kinds of plants that can grow in a region, as well as the times of year when they will actually grow. In tropical or subtropical areas, many plants grow all year, so this is a way to keep the garden growing throughout the year. In temperate regions, there should be a mix of perennial and annual plants. Also, there should be some non-deciduous plants that would remain green throughout the year, in addition to flowering plants that only bloom at certain times.

Chapter 23 Organizer:
Reproduction in Plants

LabManager™
Customize any lab with the LabManager™ CD-ROM.

Essential Questions	National Science Standards	Materials and Planning Estimated times include cleanup and disposal, but do not include teacher prep time. For cleanup and disposal guidelines, see page 39T.	Est. Time (min)
Section 1 1. What are advantages of vegetative reproduction? 2. What are the stages of alternation of generations? 3. What are the similarities among the reproduction of mosses, ferns, and conifers?	UCP.1, UCP.2, UCP.5; A.1, A.2; C.1, C.4, C.5, C.6	**Launch Lab,** p. 660: a moss, fern, male and female conifer cones, and flowering plant, examining tray, magnifying lens, tweezers, metric ruler	20
		Demonstration, p. 662: potatoes with roots growing from eyes	10
		Demonstration, p. 663: materials to make a display of alternation of generations, color-coded markers, pictures of sporophytes and gametophytes	10 per day
		MiniLab 1, p. 666: cones from different conifers, tree identification guidebook	25
Section 2 1. What are the parts of a flower and what are their functions? 2. What are complete, incomplete, perfect, and imperfect flowers? 3. What is the difference between monocot and eudicot flowers? 4. What is photoperiodism?	UCP.1, UCP.2, UCP.5; A.1, A.2; C.1, C.5; G.1, G.2	**Demonstration,** p. 671: pictures of flowers that have different pollination mechanisms	10
		MiniLab 2, p. 672: a variety of flowers	15
Section 3 1. How can the life cycle of a flowering plant be described? 2. What is the process of fertilization and seed formation in flowering plants? 3. What are the different methods of seed dispersal? 4. How do seeds germinate?	UCP.1, UCP.2, UCP.5; C.1, C.4, C.5, C.6; E.1, E.2; F.3; G.1, G.2, G.3	**Demonstration,** p. 677: variety of fruits, knife	20
		Design Your Own BioLab, p. 681: monocot flowers, eudicot flowers, colored pencils	45

Suggested Time for Each Lesson

Class	Chapter Opener	Section 1	Section 2	Section 3	Assessment
Basic	45 min	45 min	45 min	45 min	45 min
General	25 min	55 min	55 min	45 min	45 min
Honors	—	45 min	45 min	45 min	45 min

ConnectED

connectED.mcgraw-hill.com

Access interactive learning opportunities and teaching resources using these icons located throughout your StudentWorks™ Plus Online and eTeacherEdition Online.

Chapter 23 Section Resources	Additional Chapter 23 Resources	Technology
FAST FILE Unit 6 Resources: Launch Lab Worksheet* MiniLab Worksheet* Study Guide (English/Spanish)* Section Quick Check **Reading Essentials 23.1** **Science Notebook 23.1*** **FAST FILE Unit 6 Resources:** MiniLab Worksheet* Study Guide (English/Spanish)* Section Quick Check **Reading Essentials 23.2** **Science Notebook 23.2*** **FAST FILE Unit 6 Resources:** BioLab Worksheet* Study Guide (English/Spanish)* Section Quick Check **Reading Essentials 23.3** **Science Notebook 23.3***	**FAST FILE Unit 6 Resources:** Chapter Diagnostic Test Concept Mapping* Real-World Biology Enrichment Chapter Tests A, B, and C **Transparencies:** Bellringer Transparencies* Biology Concepts Transparencies* **Lab Resources:** Laboratory Manual* Probeware Lab Manual* Forensics Lab Manual* Pre-AP Lab Manual* Open Inquiry in Biology* Guided Inquiry in Biology*	**Teaching Tools:** eTeacherEdition Online Classroom Presentation Toolkit CD-ROM* LabManager™ CD-ROM* Video Lab DVD* Virtual Lab CD-ROM* What's BIOLOGY Got To Do With It? StudentWorks™ Plus Online* **Chapter Assessment Tools:** Classroom Presentation Toolkit CD-ROM* *ExamView® Assessment Suite* CD-ROM **Web-Based Resources:** • StudentWorks™ Plus Online • eTeacherEdition Online • Animations* • The Interactive Time Line* • Interactive Tables* • Online Quizzes • Online Test Practice • Standardized Test Practice • Virtual Labs* • Multilingual eGlossary* • Vocabulary eGames* • Vocabulary eFlashcards • WebQuests • Personal Tutors

While all resources listed are appropriate for English learners, the * indicates resources with a strong visual or hands-on component for EL.

Teaching strategies and activities have been coded for differentiated instruction.

AL Activities for students working above grade level	**OL** Activities for students working on grade level	**BL** Activities for students working below grade level	**EL** Activities for English learners (also ELL)	**COOP LEARN** Activities designed for small cooperative group work

CHAPTER 23

CHAPTER 23

Reproduction in Plants

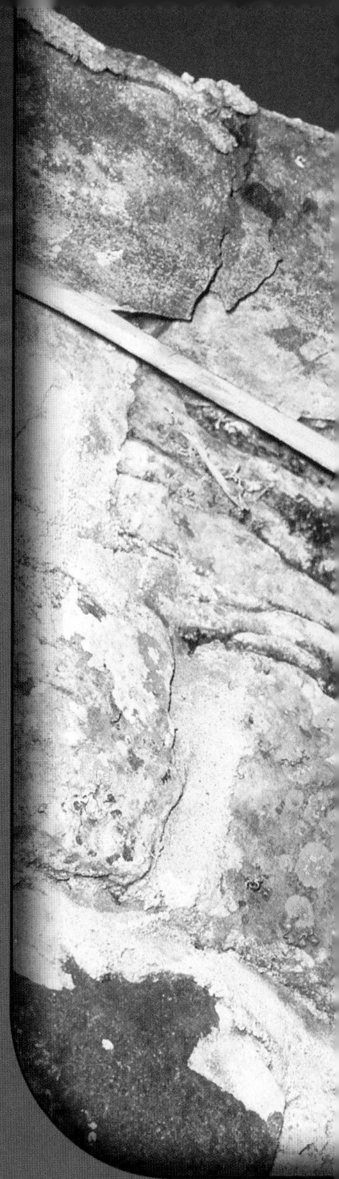

ConnectED

Your one-stop online resource
connectED.mcgraw-hill.com

- Video
- Audio
- Review
- Inquiry
- WebQuest
- Assessment
- Concepts in Motion
- Multilingual eGlossary

Launch Lab

What are plant reproductive structures?

Have you ever noticed that sometimes flowers seem to appear suddenly on trees, shrubs, and other plants in the spring? Have you picked up a cone while walking under pine trees and wondered why these trees have cones? Like many organisms, plants have reproductive structures and reproduce sexually. Mosses, ferns, conifers, and flowering plants have unique reproductive structures. Investigate these structures during this lab.

For a lab worksheet, use your StudentWorks™ Plus Online.

? Inquiry Launch Lab

FOLDABLES®

Make a four-door book and label it with stages of the sporophyte and gametophyte generations. Use it to organize your notes on alternation of generations.

Launch Lab

What are plant reproductive structures?

? Inquiry Launch Lab

For a lab worksheet, use your eTeacherEdition Online.

RUBRIC A rubric for evaluating Launch Labs is found on your eTeacherEdition Online.

Est. Time 20 min

Additional Materials flower, male and female conifer cones, examining tray, magnifying glass, tweezers, metric ruler

Safety Precautions Approve lab safety forms before work begins. Have students wash their hands thoroughly after handling plants or other biological agents.

Teaching Strategies

- Consider having students examine plant reproductive structures outside if the four major groups of plants grow near your school.
- Small fern plants that display the entire life cycle of ferns can be purchased from biological supply companies.
- You will need to guide students toward the identification of the moss antheridia and archegonia and the prothallus and spore producing structures of the fern plants. Review the basic flower structures with students.

Procedure

1. Read and complete the lab safety form.
2. Create a data table to record your observations and measurements of the plant reproductive structures your teacher gives you.
3. Observe the reproductive structures of a moss, fern, conifer, and flowering plant. Record your observations in your data table.

Analysis

1. **Identify** the similarities and differences in the reproductive structures of the plants. All the plants reproduce sexually by producing sperm and egg cells. Other answers will depend on what the student observes.
2. **Describe** how flowering plants might use flowers to reproduce based on what you already know about plants. Answers will vary, but pollen-containing sperm nuclei land on the top of the female flower structure (stigma) and fertilize egg cells in the bottom portion of the female structure (ovule).

THEME FOCUS Change
The reproduction methods of plants have evolved and become more complex.

BIG Idea The life cycles of plants include various methods of reproduction.

Introduce the Chapter

Plant Reproduction

ASK STUDENTS: ***Can you identify the plant in this photo?*** a fern ***How do you think this plant reproduces?*** Answers will vary. Ferns reproduce by creating spores that are spread and grow into gametophytes. Upon fertilization, gametophytes grow into new sporophytes. Students may already know that many plants reproduce sexually. Explain that in this chapter, students will learn about the reproductive strategies of plants, including mosses, ferns, conifers, and flowering plants.

BIG Idea

Compare Collect pictures or samples of moss sporophytes, fern fronds with spores, pine cones, and flowers. (You can use the samples you will use for this chapter's Launch Lab.) Show the samples to students.
ASK STUDENTS: ***What do these specimens all have in common?*** Answers will vary. Emphasize that although the specimens have many differences, they are all reproductive structures.
SAY TO STUDENTS: ***In this chapter, you will learn about alternation of generations in different plants and how plants reproduce.***

THEMES

Scientific Inquiry The study of reproductive methods in plants has led to an understanding of plant evolution.

Diversity Environmental differences have resulted in multiple methods of reproduction within plant species.

Energy Plants require energy obtained through photosynthesis to reproduce.

Homeostasis The alternation of generations provides stability and structure in plant species reproduction.

Change Specialized reproductive methods show evidence of change from early primitive plants.

Section 1

MAIN Idea

BL OL AL

Common Characteristics

ASK STUDENTS: ***Why do pine trees produce cones?*** Answers will vary. After students give their suggestions, explain that pine cones are part of the reproductive cycle or alternation of generations of a conifer. Mosses, ferns, and conifers all go through alternation of generations.

R Reading Strategy

EL BL OL

Assessment Preview Have students read the section assessment questions. Tell students that these questions will help them identify some of the important concepts in Section 1.

D Develop Concepts

BL OL COOP LEARN **Activity**

Have student groups make a bulletin board or hallway display that illustrates the types of plants that can be propagated through vegetative reproduction and the advantages and disadvantages of this method of propagation.

AL Have students propagate a plant, such as an African violet, using vegetative reproduction. Tell students to photograph the steps they take and include the photos in their group's display.

■ **Caption Question Fig. 1** The new liverworts will have a genetic makeup that is identical to the parent liverwort.

Section 1

Reading Preview

Essential Questions

- What are advantages of vegetative reproduction?
- What are the stages of alternation of generations?
- What are the similarities among the reproduction of mosses, ferns, and conifers?

Review Vocabulary

flagellated: having one or more flagellum that propel a cell by whiplike motion

New Vocabulary

vegetative reproduction
chemotaxis
protonema
prothallus
heterosporous
megaspore
microspore
micropyle

g Multilingual eGlossary

Introduction to Plant Reproduction

R **MAIN Idea** **Like all plants, the life cycles of mosses, ferns, and conifers include alternation of generations.**

Real-World Reading Link Have you ever seen photos of your friends when they were younger? Were you able to recognize most of them? Some plants differ greatly in appearances throughout their life stages. Recognizing the same plant throughout the different life stages is not as easy as recognizing your friends from their old photos.

D Vegetative Reproduction

Recall that reproduction without the joining of an egg and a sperm is called asexual reproduction. **Vegetative reproduction** is a form of asexual reproduction in which new plants grow from parts of an existing plant. The new plants are clones of the original plant because their genetic makeups are identical to the original plant.

There are several advantages of vegetative reproduction. It usually is a faster way to grow plants than from a spore or a seed. Remember that an organism produced sexually will have a combination of features from its parents. However, plants produced vegetatively are more uniform than those that result from sexual reproduction. Also, some fruits do not produce seeds, and vegetative reproduction is the only way to reproduce them.

Naturally occurring vegetative reproduction There are many examples of natural vegetative reproduction. When conditions are dry, some mosses dry out, become brittle, and are easily broken and scattered by animals or wind. When conditions improve and water is available, some of these fragments can resume growth. Liverworts reproduce asexually by producing small, cuplike structures on the gametophyte thallus, as shown in **Figure 1.** Strawberry plants produce horizontal stems called stolons. A new strawberry plant can grow at the end of a stolon, and if the stolon is cut, the plant can continue to grow.

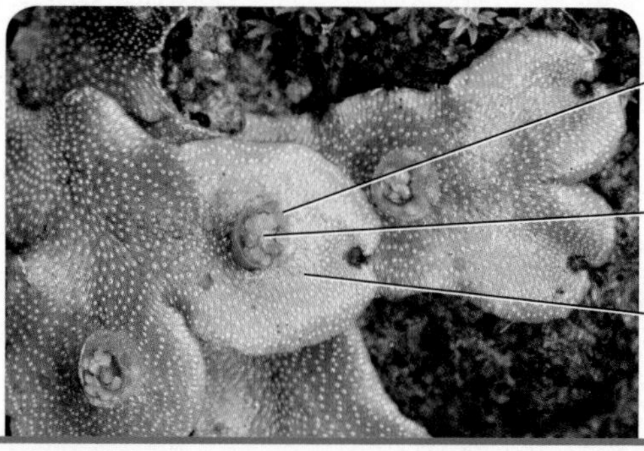

■ **Figure 1** Gemmae (JE mee) cups or splash cups contain small pieces of liverwort tissue. If knocked from or splashed out of the cup, they can grow into plants.
Infer *the genetic makeup of the new liverworts.*

Demonstration

OL AL **Vegetative Reproduction** Show students some potatoes that have started to grow roots from their eyes.

SAY TO STUDENTS: ***Potatoes themselves are not roots. They are modified stems. Potato farmers cut the potatoes into segments, each containing an eye, and plant them. If conditions are suitable, each eye produces a new plant.***

ASK STUDENTS: ***How do these plants compare genetically?*** They are identical, or are clones. Est. time: 10 min

Directed vegetative reproduction Farmers, horticulturists, and scientists have been using vegetative reproduction for years. Leaves, roots, or stems, when cut from certain plants, can grow and become new plants if kept under proper environmental conditions. For example, white potatoes can be cut into sections. As long as each section contains an eye or bud and is planted in a favorable environment, a new plant can grow from the section and produce new potatoes. Some plants can be grown from a few cells of plant tissue using a technique called tissue culture. The plant tissue is grown on nutrient agar in sterile conditions, C as shown in **Figure 2.** Eventually, hundreds of identical plants can be produced.

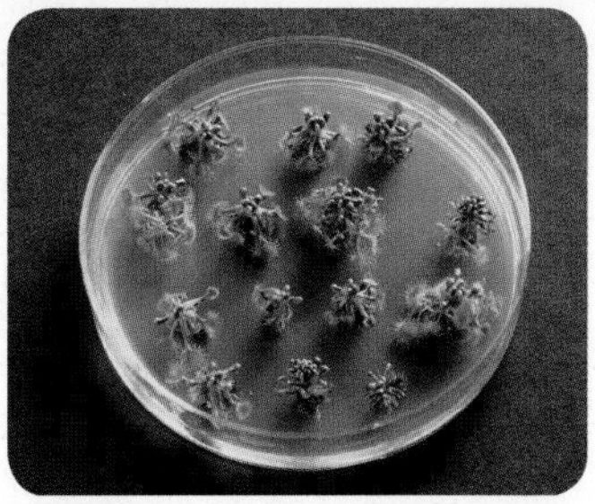

■ **Figure 2** These cactus clones were produced using tissue culture techniques.

Alternation of Generations

The life cycle of a plant includes an alternation of generations that has a diploid ($2n$) sporophyte stage, and a haploid (n) gametophyte stage. As shown in **Figure 3,** the sporophyte stage produces haploid spores that divide by mitosis and cell division and form the gametophyte generation. Depending on the plant species, the size of a gametophyte can be tiny or a larger structure. In the plant kingdom, there is an evolutionary trend for smaller gametophytes as plants become more complex.

The gametophyte stage produces gametes—eggs and sperm. One distinguishing characteristic among plants is how a sperm gets to an egg. Sperm of nonvascular plants and some of the vascular plants must have at least a film of water to reach an egg. Sperm of flowering plants do not need water for the sperm to reach the egg.

Fertilization of an egg by a sperm forms a zygote that is the first cell of the sporophyte stage. As plants evolved and became more complex, sporophytes became larger. In addition to the size of the sporophyte, another distinguishing feature among plants is the growth pattern of the sporophyte. Flowering plants and other vascular plants have sporophytes that live completely independent of the gametophyte. Most nonvascular plants have sporophytes that depend on the gametophyte for support D and food.

CAREERS IN BIOLOGY

Tissue-Culture Technician
Working with plant tissue while maintaining sterile conditions is one of many tasks performed by a technician in a tissue-culture lab. Besides knowledge of plants, a tissue-culture technician needs excellent eye-hand coordination, good concentration skills, and the ability to keep accurate records.

■ **Figure 3** The form of the sporophyte (blue) and gametophyte (yellow) is different for different plant species.

Concepts in Motion Animation

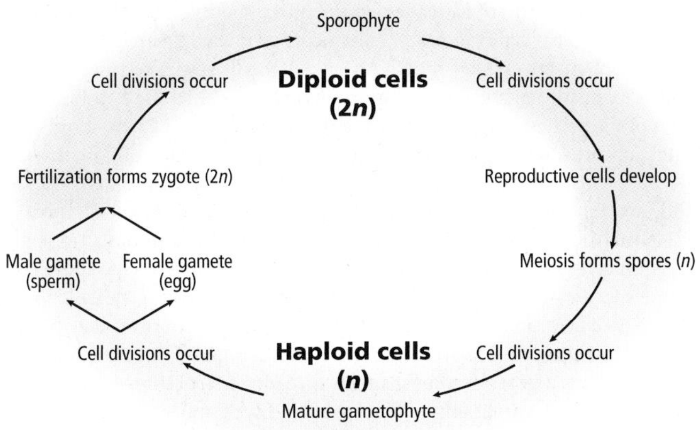

S

C Critical Thinking

AL Infer

ASK STUDENTS: ***Why is it faster to grow plants using vegetative reproduction than to grow them from a spore or seed?*** Vegetative reproduction starts with more cells/tissue than a spore or seed. Also, some seeds have to go through a dormancy period before they will germinate.

D Develop Concepts

BL OL AL

Activate Prior Knowledge

ASK STUDENTS: ***What other organisms also have an alternation of generations?*** fungi, algae, and other plants Remind students that they have learned about alternation of generations in algae, fungi, and other plants in previous chapters. Review the chromosome number of a sporophyte ($2n$) and a gametophyte n with students.

S Skill Practice

BL OL Take Notes Point out that all of the life cycle figures in this section are color-coded to help students identify the gametophyte generation (yellow) and the sporophyte generation (blue). Suggest that students use this same color coding by underlining or highlighting in that color as they take notes about the alternation of generations in mosses, conifers, and anthophytes.

Concepts in Motion

Animation

Demonstration

Alternation of Generations Make a display of the basic steps of alternation of generations using the same color coding as in the text. Review this life cycle with students as they begin this section. As the class begins learning about the life cycle of each type of plant (moss, fern, and conifer), point out the stages on your display. If possible, add pictures of appropriate sporophytes and gametophytes as students study each type of plant. Est. time: 10 min per day

R **Reading Strategy**
BL OL AL Activate Background Vocabulary
ASK STUDENTS: ***What is the difference between antheridia and archegonia?*** Antheridia produce sperm; archegonia produce egg(s). ***Where are the antheridia and archegonia found?*** on gametophytes ***What is the chromosome number of gametophytes?*** *n*

Concepts in Motion
Animation

Develop Concepts
EL BL OL Follow-Up Activity
Have students add appropriate moss sporophyte and gametophyte pictures from magazines to the *Alternation of Generations* display you made earlier in this section. **ASK STUDENTS:** ***Which generation is photosynthetic?*** gametophyte

Reading Strategy
BL OL AL
Supplemental Reading
Have students research the use of mosses by Native Americans as a dressing for wounds and as absorptive material for diapers.

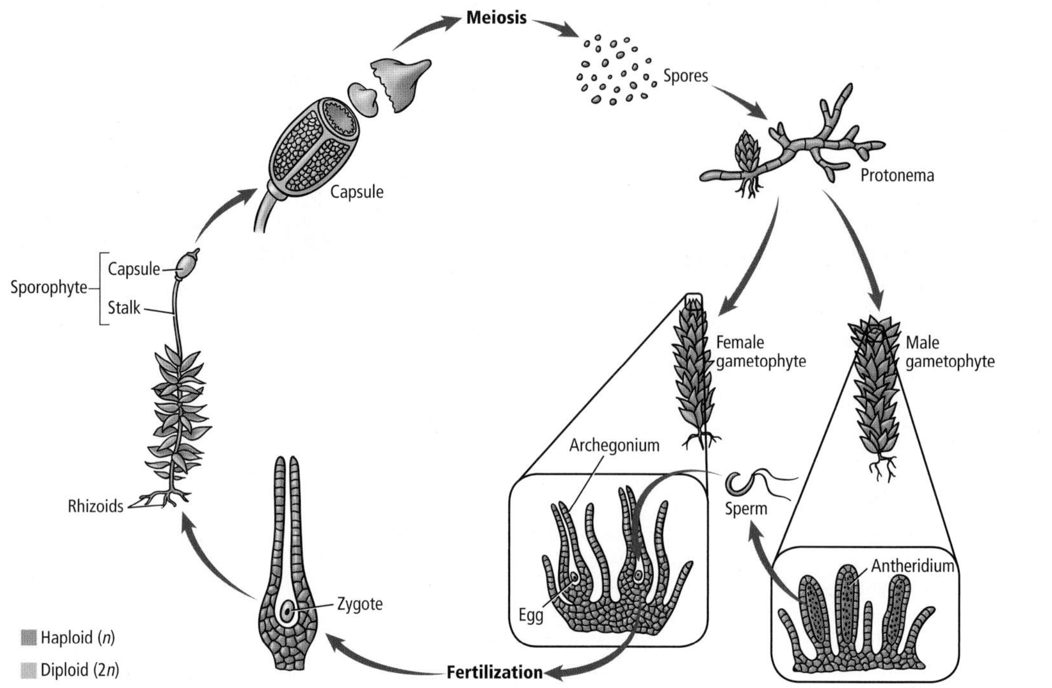

Concepts in Motion
Animation

■ **Figure 4** Spores produced by a moss sporophyte grow into moss gametophyte plants. Following fertilization, the sporophyte develops while attached to the gametophyte and eventually will release spores, continuing the cycle.

VOCABULARY
WORD ORIGIN
Chemotaxis
chemo– comes from the late Greek word *chemeia,* meaning *alchemy*
–taxis comes from the Greek word *taxis,* meaning *responsive movement*

Moss Reproduction and Life Cycle

The reproduction and life cycle of mosses, as shown in **Figure 4,** exhibits alternation of generations and is typical of most nonvascular plants. The dominant stage is the gametophyte stage that you might see growing in damp shady places or on rocks along a stream. Gametophytes produce archegonia and antheridia. These structures can be on the same moss plant or, as is often the case, on separate plants. Depending on the moss species, an archegonium produces one or more eggs. The tissues of the archegonium surround the egg or eggs with a protective layer.

Antheridia produce flagellated sperm that need water to get to the archegonia. If a film of water covers the moss, sperm can move toward archegonia. This is a response to chemicals produced by archegonia and is called **chemotaxis** (kee moh TAK sus). When a sperm fertilizes an egg, it forms the first cell of the sporophyte stage called the zygote. Tissues of the archegonium protect the new sporophyte. The new sporophyte absorbs nutrients from the archegonium as it grows and matures. Because most mature moss sporophytes cannot undergo photosynthesis, they are dependent upon their gametophytes for nutrition and support. **R**

A mature sporophyte consists of a stalk with a capsule at its tip. Certain cells within the capsule undergo meiosis and produce spores. Some species produce up to 50 million spores per capsule. When conditions are favorable, the capsule opens, releasing the spores. If a spore lands in a suitable place, mitotic cell divisions begin. The resulting growth forms a **protonema**—a small, threadlike structure—that can develop into the gametophyte plant, and the cycle repeats.

Content Background

Teacher FYI Chemotaxis helps ensure the fertilization of the egg by attracting the sperm. Drops of rain cause the antheridia to release the sperm. The rain also causes the cap cell of the archegonia to burst. The chemicals that attract the sperm are produced by the neck and canal cells of the archegonium. The sperm swim through a film of rainwater to reach the archegonium and the egg. Chemotaxis is also important in attracting bacteria, fungi, and cyanobacteria to roots to form symbiotic relationships.

Fern Reproduction and Life Cycle

When you visit a forest or a plant conservatory, you might see the lacy fronds of ferns. Fronds are part of a fern's sporophyte stage. If you look closely at a frond, you might find spore-producing structures called sori on it. Each sorus consists of sporangia. Certain cells in a sporangium undergo meiosis and the resulting spores are the beginning of the new gametophyte generation.

If a fern spore lands on damp, rich soil, it can grow and form a tiny heart-shaped gametophyte called a **prothallus** (pro THA lus) (plural, prothalli), as shown in **Figure 5.** Cells of the prothallus contain chloroplasts; therefore, photosynthesis can occur. Most prothalli develop both antheridia and archegonia. Antheridia produce flagellated sperm that need water to move to archegonia. Each archegonium contains one egg. If fertilization occurs, the resulting zygote is the first cell of the sporophyte generation. Chemical reactions between sperm and eggs of the same prothallus can prevent fertilization.

The zygote undergoes mitotic cell divisions and forms a photosynthetic, multicellular sporophyte. Initially, the sporophyte grows on the prothallus and receives support and nutrition. Later, the prothallus disintegrates and the sporophyte develops fronds and a rhizome—a thick underground stem that pro-
S duces roots and supports the photosynthetic fronds.

Conifer Reproduction and Life Cycle

Have you ever seen the surface of a car or a pond covered with fine yellow dust? It's possible that this dust came from one or several plants called conifers. The tree or shrub that you might recognize as a pine or other conifer is that plant's sporophyte generation. Conifers, like a few lycophytes and pterophytes, are **heterosporous** (he tuh roh SPOR us). They
D produce two types of spores that develop into male or female gametophytes.

Female cones Each female cone is composed of many scales. At the base of each scale are two ovules. Within each ovule, meiosis of a cell in the megasporangium produces four **megaspores.** Three of these megaspores disintegrate. The remaining megaspore undergoes mitotic cell divisions and becomes the female gametophyte. When fully developed, the female gametophyte consists of hundreds of cells and contains two to six archegonia. Each archegonium eventually contains an egg.

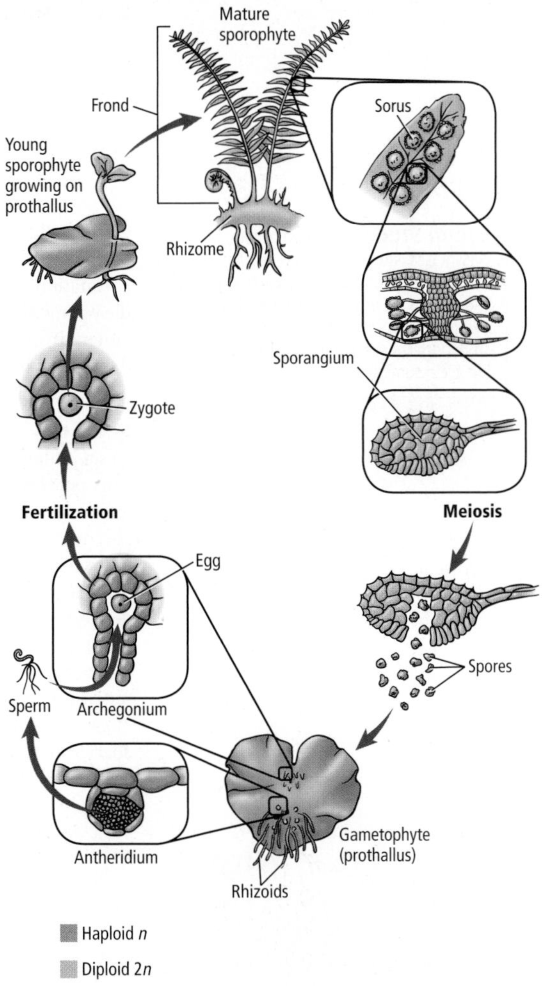

■ **Figure 5** In fern reproduction there usually is a substantial size difference between the sporophyte and gametophyte stages.

S Skill Practice
EL BL OL AL

Observe and Predict Have students use a microscope or a magnifying lens to examine a fern frond with sori- or spore-producing structures. Have students predict the number of spores.

D Develop Concepts
BL OL AL

Activate Prior Knowledge
Remind students that the prefix *hetero-* means "different." Remind students that *heterozygous* means "the presence of two different alleles." *Heterosporous* means the plant produces two different types of spores—microspores and megaspores. Many of the simpler plants, such as mosses and liverworts, are homosporous.

Develop Concepts
EL BL OL **Follow-Up Activity**
Add pictures of conifer sporophytes and gametophytes to your *Alternation of Generations* display.

Develop Concepts
AL **Clarify a Misconception**
ASK STUDENTS: ***Do all plants have cotyledons?*** No, only seed-bearing plants have cotyledons. Due to the names *monocot* and *eudicot,* students may think that anthophytes are the only plants that have cotyledons. These names do refer to the number of cotyledons found in monocots and eudicots. However, conifers and other plants, such as cycads and ginkgos, also have cotyledons.

Content Background

Real-World Connection Your students may have eaten pesto or know what it is. One of the common ingredients in pesto is pine nuts. Pine nuts are not true nuts, but are the seed of different species of pine trees, most commonly *Pinus pinea.* They are harvested and eaten throughout the world. Historically, pine nuts were a staple in the diet of certain Native American tribes. The Paiute and Shoshone harvested pine nuts in the fall and stored them over the winter in stone-lined pits. In their song and dance ceremonies, these groups continue to recognize the importance of pine nuts to their heritage.

Writing Support

BL OL Writing Have students examine prepared microscope slides of male and female pine cones. Have students write a paragraph comparing and contrasting the two cones.

MiniLab 1

Inquiry MiniLab

For a lab worksheet, use your eTeacherEdition Online.

RUBRIC A rubric for evaluating MiniLabs is found on your eTeacherEdition Online.

Est. Time 25 min

Safety Precaution Approve lab safety forms before work begins.

Teaching Strategies

- This lab can be completed during class with cones collected beforehand by you or the students.
- Encourage students to observe the position of the cones while still on the tree as one way to identify conifer species.

Cleanup and Disposal

Properly dispose of the cones. Never release organisms into an environment from which they were not collected.

Analysis

1. Cones vary in size, shape, color, position on the tree branch, type and shape of scales, and how close the scales fit together.
2. Answers will depend on specimen. Accept scientifically sound arguments.

Reading Check Moss gametophytes are generally a couple of centimeters in length, whereas conifer gametophytes are microscopic.

Male cones The pollen-producing cone, commonly called the male cone, consists of small reproductive scales that have hundreds of sporangia. Certain cells in these sporangia undergo meiosis and form **microspores.** A pollen grain, the male gametophyte, consists of four cells and develops from a microspore. Pollen grains are transported on air currents.

W

Reading Check **Compare** the sizes of a moss gametophyte and a pine gametophyte.

Study Tip

Group Study With two other classmates, study the life cycles of mosses, ferns, and conifers. Each of you should choose one of these life cycles and prepare a summary of it. When you study together, teach each other your life cycle summaries.

Pollination When a pollen grain from one species of seed plants lands on the female reproductive structure of a plant of the same species, pollination occurs. If a conifer pollen grain lands near the **micropyle,** or the opening of the ovule, it can be trapped in a sticky substance called a pollen drop. As the pollen drop slowly evaporates or is absorbed into the ovule, the pollen grain is pulled closer to the micropyle. Over the next year, the pollen grain will continue to develop.

Seed development Following pollination, the pollen grain generates a pollen tube. It grows through the micropyle, and into the ovule. This process can take a year or longer. One of the four cells in the pollen grain undergoes mitosis, forming two nonflagellated sperm. The sperm travel in the pollen tube to an egg, as shown in **Figure 6.** Fertilization occurs when an egg and a sperm join to form the zygote. The remaining sperm and the pollen tube disintegrate. The zygote is dependent on the female gametophyte for nutrition as it undergoes mitotic cell divisions that result in the formation of an embryo with one or more cotyledons. These undergo photosynthesis and provide nutrition for the embryo when the seed sprouts.

As the embryo develops, the outside layer of the ovule forms a seed coat. Seed development can take as long as three years. When seeds mature, the female cone opens and releases them.

MiniLab 1

Compare Conifer Cones

Inquiry MiniLab

How do cones from the different conifers compare? Have you ever noticed the many different types of cones that fall from conifers? Investigate the types of cones during this lab.

Procedure [safety icons]

1. Read and complete the lab safety form.
2. Create a data table for recording your observations, measurements, and comparisons of cones.
3. Obtain **cones** from your teacher.
4. Observe the physical characteristics of your cones and record your observations and measurements in your data table. Do not damage the cones in any way.
5. Identify the conifer species of your cones by using a **tree identification guidebook.** Record this data.
6. Return the cones to your teacher.

Analysis

1. **Compare and contrast** the cones.
2. **Determine** whether there were any seeds present. Describe how seeds form in conifers.

Content Background

Teacher FYI The structure of male cones does not show much variability across species. The only variation tends to be the scale arrangement. On the other hand, the structure of female cones can vary considerably from species to species. The shape of a female cone is adapted to aid fertilization by sperm from the same conifer species. In some cases, the cone structure is crucial in species identification. Female cones tend to be found on upper branches of the tree. Scientists infer that this position helps prevent self-pollination because it is unlikely that pollen would be blown upward within a plant.

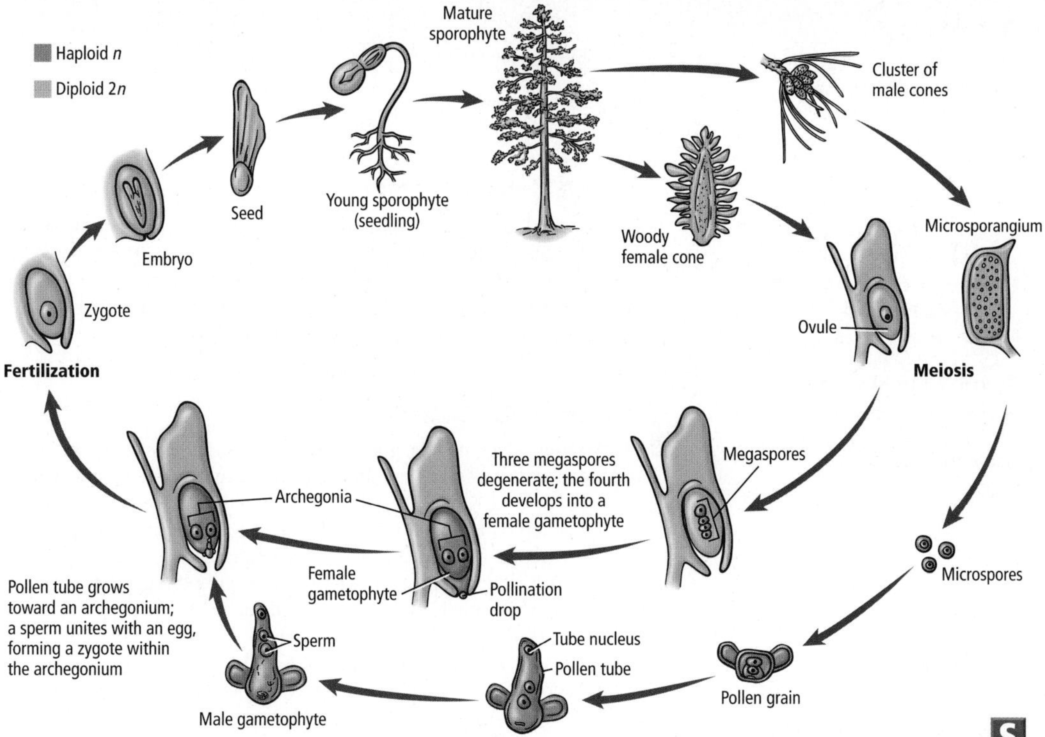

■ **Figure 6** The sporophyte generation is dominant in the life of a conifer.

Concepts in Motion
Animation

Reproduction in conifers is diverse. The time for a conifer life cycle varies from species to species. Not all conifers produce cones. For example, yews produce ovules covered by fleshy tissue. Juniper seed cones look like berries. Regardless of differences, conifer reproduction ensures the survival of this plant division.

Section 1 Assessment

Section Summary

- Vegetative reproduction produces new plants without sexual reproduction.
- The life cycles of plants involve the alternation of generations.
- The moss sporophyte depends on the gametophyte.
- A fern sporophyte can live independently of the gametophyte.
- Conifer gametophytes develop within sporophyte tissues.

Understand Main Ideas

1. MAIN Idea **Describe** the stages of alternation of generations.
2. **Identify** advantages of vegetative reproduction.
3. **Explain** how the fern sporophyte is dependent upon the gametophyte.
4. **Compare and contrast** the life cycles of mosses and conifers.

Think Critically

5. **Determine** how the distribution of conifers might be affected if water was needed for reproduction.

MATH in Biology

6. Calculate the number of spores that could be released in three square meters if the density of moss plants is 100 plants per square meter and the average number of spores released per plant is 10,000.

S Skill Practice

EL BL OL **Visual Literacy**

Have students examine Figure 6. **ASK STUDENTS:** ***How are male and female pine cones different from each other?*** Possible answer: Female cone produces megaspores and eventually eggs; male cone produces microspores and eventually pollen grains.

Concepts in Motion
Animation

Formative Assessment

Evaluation

ASK STUDENTS: ***Which generation is dependent and which is independent in moss and conifer life cycles?*** The moss gametophyte is the dominant generation upon which the sporophyte is dependent. In conifers, the sporophyte is the dominant generation and lives independent of the gametophyte.

Remediation Have students review the moss and conifer life cycles by studying Figures 4 and 6. **ASK STUDENTS:** ***Where does a moss sporophyte grow?*** on the gametophyte ***Where does the sporophyte get its nutrients?*** from the gametophyte ***Does the conifer sporophyte depend on the gametophyte for support, water, or nutrients?*** no

Section 1 Assessment

1. sporophyte $2n$; gametophyte n
2. Vegetative reproduction is a faster reproduction method than sexual reproduction, and only one parent plant is needed for vegetative reproduction to occur.
3. The sporophyte initially develops attached to the gametophyte, depending upon it for food and support.
4. Both life cycles include sporophytes and gametophytes. However, the sporophyte generation is dominant in the conifer life cycle, whereas the gametophyte is dominant in the moss life cycle.
5. Answers will vary but should include that the distribution would be limited to wetter environments or climates.
6. 3,000,000

Assessment Online Quiz

Section 2

MAIN Idea

BL OL AL Flowers

ASK STUDENTS: ***How many flowers can you name?*** Students will most likely be able to name a large number of different flowers. If students do not do so, mention more obscure flowers, such as grass flowers.

TELL STUDENTS: ***We are all familiar with flowers because we see them in nature, in floral arrangements, and on our houseplants. In this section, we are going to learn the important role of flowers in the anthophyte life cycle.***

R Reading Strategy

EL BL OL Brainstorm Write the vocabulary terms on the board in two groups—the first four should be in one group and the rest in the other group. Tell students that all the terms in each group are related to each other and have them hypothesize about their meaning. Write students' ideas on the board and have them check their ideas when they read about the term in the text. The first group of terms refers to the organs of a flower. The second group refers to the flowering response of a plant.

S Skill Practice

EL BL OL Make a Table Have students create a four-column table with the following headings: *Sepals, Petals, Stamens,* and *Pistil.* As they read the text under the heading *Flower Organs,* have them write the function of each organ in the appropriate column.

Concepts in Motion

Animation

Section 2

Reading Preview

Essential Questions

- What are the parts of a flower and what are their functions?
- What are complete, incomplete, perfect, and imperfect flowers?
- What is the difference between monocot and eudicot flowers?
- What is photoperiodism?

Review Vocabulary

nocturnal: active only at night

R New Vocabulary

sepal
petal
stamen
pistil
photoperiodism
short-day plant
long-day plant
intermediate-day plant
day-neutral plant

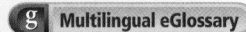

Multilingual eGlossary

Flowers

MAIN Idea Flowers are the reproductive structures of anthophytes.

Real-World Reading Link Have you ever worn a corsage or boutonniere to a dance? Perhaps you have given a flower to someone to let him or her know that he or she is special to you. You probably can think of many other instances when flowers were important to you. However, from a scientific viewpoint, the most important role of flowers is in anthophyte sexual reproduction.

Flower Organs

S Vivid orange, deep purple, ghostly white, fragrant, rancid, spectacular, and inconspicuous—these all are terms that can be used to describe flowers. The colors, shapes, and sizes of flowers are determined by each species' genetic makeup. It is important to remember that flowers can vary in structure and form from species to species.

Flowers have several organs. Some organs provide support or protection, while others can be involved directly in reproduction. In general, flowers have four organs—sepals, petals, stamens, and one or more pistils, illustrated in **Figure 7. Sepals** protect the flower bud and can look like small leaves or even resemble the flower's petals. **Petals** usually are colorful structures that can both attract pollinators and provide them with a landing platform. Sepals and petals, if present, are attached to a flower stalk, called a peduncle.

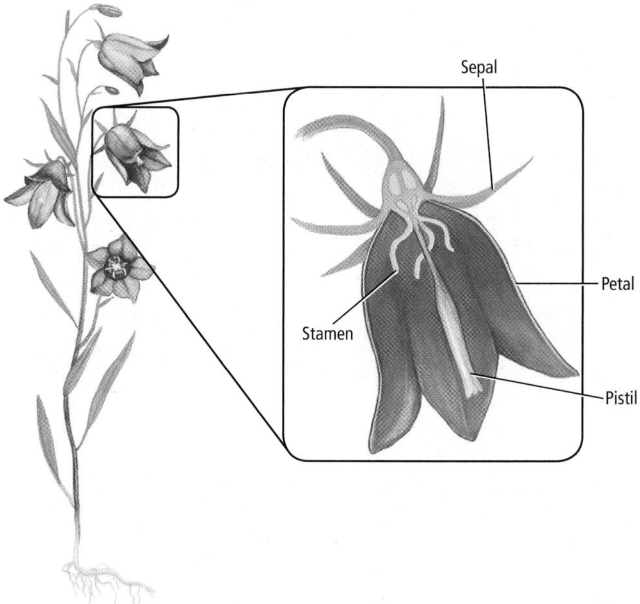

Figure 7 The typical flower has four organs—sepals, petals, stamens, and one or more pistils.

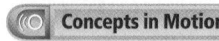

Concepts in Motion

Animation

Research Citation

Reading Strategies Educational research indicates that integrating reading activities like the brainstorming strategy described on this page can help students understand difficult concepts. Reading can help students make connections and develop a broader view of the material, and teachers should provide students with a set of strategies to help them make the reading more meaningful. (Siegal, et al., 1997)

Research bibliography on pages 32T–34T

Most flowers have several **stamens**—the male reproductive organs. A stamen is composed of two parts—the filament and the anther. The filament, or stalk, supports the anther. Inside the anther are cells that undergo meiosis and then mitotic cell divisions, forming pollen grains. Two sperm eventually form inside each pollen grain.

The female reproductive organ of a flower is the **pistil.** In the center of a flower is one or more pistils. A pistil usually has three parts—the stigma, the style, and the ovary. The stigma is the tip of the pistil and is where pollination occurs. The style is the part that connects the stigma to the ovary that contains one or more ovules. A female gametophyte develops in each ovule, and an egg forms inside each female gametophyte.

C

D Flower Adaptations

The flower organs described in the previous paragraphs are typical of most flowers. However, many flowers can have modifications to one or more organs. Scientists categorize flowers using these modifications.

Structural differences Flowers that have sepals, petals, stamens, and one or more pistils are called complete flowers. If a flower is missing one or more of these organs, it is an incomplete flower. For example, wild ginger flowers are called incomplete because they have no petals. Other descriptive terms relating to flower organs are perfect and imperfect. Flowers that have both stamens and pistils are called perfect flowers. Some plants, such as cucumbers and squash, have imperfect flowers. An imperfect flower has either functional stamens or pistils, not both. The stamen-containing, or male, flowers release pollen grains. Following fertilization, a fruit forms from the pistil-containing, or female, flowers.

The number of each flower organ varies from species to species. However, the number of flower organs distinguishes eudicots from monocots. When the petal number for a flower is a multiple of four or five, the plant usually is a eudicot. The number of other organs—the sepals, pistils, and stamens—is often the same multiple of four or five. For example, the members of the mustard family of plants have flowers with four sepals and four petals, as shown in **Figure 8.** Monocots generally have flower organs in multiples of three. The daylily, also shown in **Figure 8,** has three sepals and three petals and six stamens.

VOCABULARY
SCIENCE USAGE V. COMMON USAGE

Stigma

Science usage: the tip of a flower's pistil where pollination occurs
The stigma of an iris's pistil has three parts.

Common usage: a mark of shame or discredit
A criminal record often is a stigma for an individual trying to reenter society.

■ **Figure 8** Some plants can be identified as either a monocot or a eudicot by their flowers.

This plant is related to those whose seeds are used to make canola oil.

At a glance, this daylily's petals and sepals are indistinguishable.

Content Background

Cultural Diversity On the Hawaiian islands, flowers are used in the traditional lei, a necklace presented from one person to another to mark an important event. Different flowers mean different things when presented at various occasions. Double red carnation leis are for graduates or politicians. A lei can signify "welcome," "goodbye," "congratulations," and many other things. In weddings, a *pikake* (jasmine) lei is for the bride, and a *maile* (made of shiny leaves) lei is for the groom.

C Critical Thinking

BL OL AL Assess

ASK STUDENTS: ***What are the nonreproductive flower organs?*** sepals and petals ***What is the importance of the nonreproductive flower organs?*** The sepals can protect the immature flower bud, and petals (and sometimes sepals) can attract pollinators, and provide a landing platform.

D Develop Concepts

BL OL AL

Activate Prior Knowledge

ASK STUDENTS: ***What are some differences between monocots and eudicots?*** pattern of veins in leaves—parallel (monocots) and branched (eudicots); scattered vascular bundles in stem (monocots) and concentric circles of vascular bundles (eudicots); scattered vascular bundles in roots (monocots) and star-shaped xylem tissue in roots (eudicots)

SAY TO STUDENTS: ***These are the distinguishing characteristics of plants. Now we are reading about the differences in their flowers.***

Skill Practice

EL BL OL AL Classify Have students collect pictures of perfect, imperfect, complete, and incomplete flowers. Post pictures on the board. Have students examine the illustrations in the chapter to determine what types of flowers are shown. Have students write brief explanations about how they classified the flowers.

? Inquiry BioLab

The lab at the end of the chapter can be used at this point in the lesson.

Visualizing Pollination

Purpose

Students will recognize the organs of a flower and understand their function.
UCP.5, C.5

Develop Concepts

EL BL OL AL Activity Have students dissect a flower such as a lily or a tulip. As they remove organs from the flower, have them tape the organs to an index card and label each organ. Challenge the students to recreate the floral design as a two-dimensional figure on paper. Have students count the number of sepals, petals, stamens, and pistils and determine if their flower is a monocot or eudicot. Depending on the flower, students may be able to make a longitudinal cut through the ovary to examine the ovules. If this is possible, have students draw the internal structure and label the ovary wall and ovules. Local florists can likely provide spent flowers for this activity.

Skill Practice

BL OL Visual Literacy Have students read the text about pollination mechanisms out loud. Then direct students' attention to Figure 9 and have them discuss which flower(s) fit the description and why.

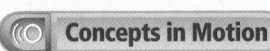

Concepts in Motion
Animation

Visualizing Pollination

Figure 9
Flowers have several adaptations that ensure pollination. Pollen might be carried by the wind or by animals. While feeding, an animal can become covered with pollen and can transfer the pollen to the next flower it visits.

Wind disperses lightweight oak pollen that can cause allergic reactions for many people. Tassels hang down and can wave in the wind.
Hummingbirds are attracted to red flowers. The hummingbird's long beak reaches nectar at the base of this flower. Some yellow and orange pigments reflect light in ranges invisible to the human eye. Even so, the markings are highly visible to bees and other insects.
As night falls, heavy scents and pale colors make it easier for moths to locate certain flowers.
The carrion flower has a rancid odor that attracts fly and beetle pollinators.
Nectar producing flowers often attract insect pollinators as they seek food.

Concepts in Motion Animation

Content Background

Teacher FYI Plants that bear imperfect flowers on separate plants are called dioecious. This term comes from the Greek language and means "two houses"—in this case, "two plants." These plants can be referred to as male or female plants. Some examples of this are asparagus and holly. Monoecious (meaning "of one house") plants have both male and female flowers on one plant. An example of this is squash. The plant produces male flowers early in the season followed by female flowers later in the season.

D **Pollination mechanisms** Different anthophyte species have flowers of distinctive sizes, shapes, colors, and petal arrangements. Many of these adaptations relate to pollination. Some of these adaptations are shown in **Figure 9.**

Self pollination and cross pollination Connection to History Recall that Mendel knew that pea flowers tend to self-pollinate, but also can be cross-pollinated. Self-pollinating flowers can pollinate themselves or another flower on the same plant. Cross-pollinated flowers receive pollen from another plant. Some flowers must be cross-pollinated. This is one reason that pollinators play important roles in anthophyte reproduction. Pollinators provide a way to transfer pollen for flowers that must be cross-pollinated. Pollinators also ensure that reproduction can occur for imperfect flowers, like squash blossoms, as shown in **Figure 10.**

Animal pollination As shown in **Figure 9,** many animal-pollinated flowers are brightly colored, have strong scents, or produce a sweet liquid called nectar. When insects and other small animals move from flower to flower searching for nectar, they can carry pollen from one flower to another flower. Other insects collect pollen for food. The bright colors and sweet scents of peonies, roses, and lilacs attract insects such as bees, butterflies, beetles, and wasps. White or pale yellow flowers are more visible at dusk and at night, and attract nocturnal animals, such as moths and bats. Bird-pollinated flowers often give off little or no aroma. A bird generally has a poor sense of smell, so it usually locates flowers by sight.

Wind pollination Flowers that generally lack showy or fragrant floral parts, also shown in **Figure 9,** usually are wind-pollinated. They produce huge amounts of lightweight pollen. This helps to ensure that some pollen grains will land on the stigma of a flower of the same species. Also, the stamens of wind-pollinated flowers often hang below the petals, exposing them to the wind. The stigma of a wind-pollinated flower is often large, which helps to ensure that a pollen grain might land on it. Wind-pollinated plants include most trees and grasses.

Reading Check **Compare and contrast** pollination mechanisms.

CAREERS IN BIOLOGY

Plant Breeder Knowledge of flower structures, pollination mechanisms, and genetics are essential for a plant breeder. A plant breeder conducts selective breeding by choosing plants with desirable traits, breeding them together, and then recording results.

■ **Figure 10** Honeybees or other insects must transfer pollen from the male squash flower to the female squash flower for the fruit—a squash—to form.
Determine ***whether squash flowers are perfect or imperfect. Explain.***

Content Background

Teacher FYI The flower of one genus of orchid has a petal that resembles a female wasp. Male wasps spread pollen from flower to flower as they visit different flowers trying to mate with the "female." Another flower, the *Rafflesia*, gives off the odor of rotting meat to attract fly pollinators.

Demonstration

AL **Pollination** Collect pictures of flowers that have different pollination mechanisms and have students infer what would be the most likely method of pollination. Est. time: 10 min

D Develop Concepts

BL **OL**

Clarify a Misconception

ASK STUDENTS: ***How do most food crops get pollinated?*** Students are likely to answer that crops are pollinated by animals. Although animal pollination accounts for about 90% of known flower pollination, this is not the case for three major food crops. Wheat, corn, and rice are all wind pollinated. Other crops, such as potatoes, are propagated using vegetative reproduction. Peanuts and beans are self-pollinated.

Writing Support

OL **Creative Writing** Have students write a cinquain or short poem about flowers. Encourage them to include accurate biological facts.

Develop Concepts

EL **BL** **OL** **AL** **COOP LEARN**

Use Models Divide the class into groups and assign each group a type of pollination mechanism (animal-, wind-, or self-pollination). Have each group build a model of a flower that exhibits their pollination mechanism using various craft supplies. Models should be no larger than 0.5 m^3. Flower models can be set up around the room and students can move from model to model to examine the structures. Groups can present their model to the class and explain the function of the structural design.

■ **Caption Question Fig. 10** Squash flowers are imperfect because they either have functional stamens or functional pistils—not both.

Inquiry Launch Lab

Assess Content Development
Assess how understanding has developed when students revisit the Launch Lab analysis questions.

MiniLab 2

Inquiry MiniLab

For a lab worksheet, use your eTeacherEdition Online.

✱RUBRIC A rubric for evaluating MiniLabs is found on your eTeacherEdition Online.

Est. Time 15 min

Safety Precautions Approve lab safety forms before work begins. Pollen stains. Have students wear aprons or lab coats during the lab.

Teaching Strategy Sometimes florists remove certain flower parts to prevent the pollen from staining clothes or to make the cut flower last longer. Have students determine if this was the case with any of their specimens.

Cleanup and Disposal Properly dispose of flower parts. Never place invasive flower species into the natural environment.

Analysis

1. Answers will vary. Students should notice different positioning and numbers of flower organs.
2. Different colors will attract different types of pollinators.
3. Answer will vary, but the size and shape of flowers and their structures are designed to accommodate the size and behaviors of the pollinators that frequent them.

LabManager™
Customize this lab with the LabManager™ CD-ROM.

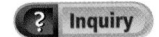

Inquiry Launch Lab

Review Based on what you have read about plant reproduction, how would you now answer the analysis questions?

Photoperiodism After noticing that certain plants only flowered at certain times of the year, plant biologists conducted experiments to explain this observation. The research initially focused on the number of hours of daylight to which the plants were exposed. However, researchers discovered that the critical factor that influenced flowering was the number of hours of uninterrupted darkness, not the number of hours of daylight. This flowering response is known as **photoperiodism** (foh toh PIHR ee uh dih zum). Scientists also learned that the beginning of flower development for each plant species was a response to a range in the number of hours of darkness. This range of hours is called the plant's critical period.

Botanists classify flowering plants into one of four different groups—short-day plants, long-day plants, intermediate-day plants, or day-neutral plants. This classification is based on the critical period. The names reflect the researchers' original focus, which is the number of hours of daylight. It is important to remember that a more accurate term for a short-day plant, for example, would be a long-night plant. As you read the descriptions of these plants, refer to **Figure 11.**

Short-day photoperiodism A **short-day plant** flowers when exposed daily to a number of hours of darkness that is greater than its critical period. For example, a short-day plant could flower when exposed to 16 hours of darkness. Short-day plants flower during the winter, spring, or fall, when the number of hours of darkness is greater than the number of hours of light. Some short-day plants you might recognize are pansies, poinsettias, tulips, and chrysanthemums.

Long-day photoperiodism A **long-day plant** flowers when the number of hours of darkness is less than its critical period. These plants flower during the summer. Examples of long-day plants are lettuce, asters, coneflowers, spinach, and potatoes.

MiniLab 2

Inquiry MiniLab

Compare Flower Structures

How do the structures of flowers vary? Just a quick browse through a flower garden or florist's shop reveals that there is great diversity among flowers. Investigate how flowers differ from species to species.

Procedure

1. Read and complete the lab safety form.
2. Create a data table to record your observations and measurements.
3. Obtain the **flowers** for this lab from your teacher.
4. Observe the differences in structure, color, size, and odor of the flowers. Do not damage the flowers in any way.
5. Make a sketch of each flower and record other observations in your data table.
6. Return the flowers to your teacher.

Analysis

1. **Compare and contrast** the flower structures you observed.
2. **Infer** why the flower petals that you observed were different colors.
3. **Propose** an explanation for the different sizes and shapes of flower structures.

GOING GREEN Tell students that they should use both sides of the paper whether they are handwriting or printing on a computer. If students have old paper from their classes, allow them to use it for assignments as long as an "X" has been marked through the side that is no longer useful.

Differentiated Instruction

Physically Disabled Before performing the MiniLab described on this page, plan ahead for students with physical disabilities. Prepare these students by discussing the activity in advance, including any modifications that may be necessary to enable them to participate.

For more tips, see pages 14T–15T.

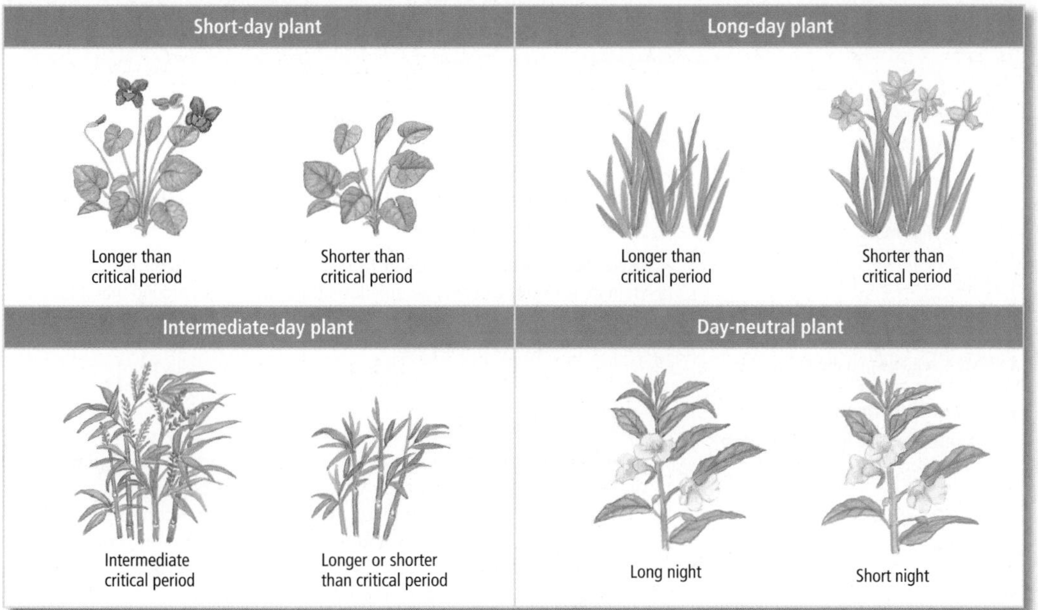

Figure 11 A plant's critical period determines when the plant will flower.

Intermediate-day photoperiodism Many plants that are native to tropical regions are **intermediate-day plants.** This means that they will flower as long as the number of hours of darkness is neither too great nor too few. Sugarcane and some grasses are examples of intermediate-day plants.

Day-neutral photoperiodism Some plants will flower regardless of the number of hours of darkness as long as they receive enough light for photosynthesis that supports growth. A plant that flowers over a range in the number of hours of darkness is a **day-neutral plant.** Buckwheat, corn, cotton, tomatoes, and roses are examples of day-neutral plants.

C W

Section 2 Assessment

Section Summary

- A typical flower has sepals, petals, stamens, and one or more pistils.
- Flowers can be perfect or imperfect, and complete or incomplete.
- Some flower modifications distinguish monocots from eudicots.
- Modifications make flowers more attractive to pollinators.
- Photoperiodism can influence when a plant flowers.

Understand Main Ideas

1. MAIN Idea **Compare and contrast** the function of each of the four organs of a typical flower.
2. **Describe** traits of a typical monocot flower and a typical eudicot flower.
3. **Compare and contrast** complete and incomplete flowers.
4. **Predict** which type of photoperiodism should produce blooms in the spring.

Think Critically

5. **Design** a plan to develop flowers on long-day plants during the winter.
6. **Assess** the importance of pollinators for imperfect flowers.

WRITING in **Biology**

7. Write a description, from the point of view of a pollinator, of a visit to a flower.

C Critical Thinking

AL Evaluate

ASK STUDENTS: ***What is the importance of photoperiodism to commercial growers?*** In order to sell flowers and food crops, growers have to either choose appropriate plants for the natural light conditions or provide artificial lighting/darkness to ensure that flowering occurs at the right time.

W Writing Support

BL OL Summary Writing

After students read about photoperiodism and the four types of plants, have them summarize the appropriate light/dark condition for each type. Students might want to illustrate their work with drawings or pictures of appropriate flowers.

Formative Assessment

Evaluation

ASK STUDENTS: ***What are the four organs of a flower?*** sepal, petal, pistil, stamen ***Describe their functions.*** Sepals protect the flower bud, petals attract pollinators, the pistil produces the female gametophyte, and the stamens produce the male gametophyte.

Remediation Have students work in pairs to review Figure 7. Have them read aloud to each other about each organ of a flower and quiz each other about the functions of each.

Section 2 Assessment

1. Sepals often protect the flower bud, petals can attract pollinators and provide a landing platform, stamens produce pollen, and pistils contain the one or more ovules where the egg is produced.
2. Monocots generally have petals in multiples of threes, and dicots or eudicots generally have petals in multiples of fours or fives.
3. Complete flowers have all four floral organs. Incomplete flowers are missing one or more organs.
4. short-day photoperiodism
5. Possible answer: You could increase the amount of light the plants are exposed to by using artificial light.
6. Imperfect flowers are missing one or more organs so they are not able to self-pollinate. Without pollinators, imperfect flowers would become extinct. The flowers would fail to produce seeds.
7. Answers will vary, but students should correctly describe the anatomy of a flower.

Section 3

MAIN Idea

BL OL AL Seeds and Fruits

ASK STUDENTS: ***What seed or fruit have you eaten lately?*** apples, cashews, bananas, almonds

SAY TO STUDENTS: ***Much of the food we eat is plant material, and seeds and fruits make up a large portion of this food. Flour is used to make breads and pastries, and pasta is made by grinding up the fruits of various grains.***

R Reading Strategy

EL BL OL Active Reading Have students write the section objectives in their notebooks. As they read the section, have them mark the location of this information with self-adhesive notes.

S Skill Practice

EL AL Visual Literacy Have students examine Figure 12 to help them understand how the egg is produced in the anthophyte life cycle. Have students compare this figure to Figures 4 and 6. Draw a Venn diagram on the board to show similarities and differences in egg formation among mosses, conifers, and anthophytes. Have students fill in the diagram. Sample answer:

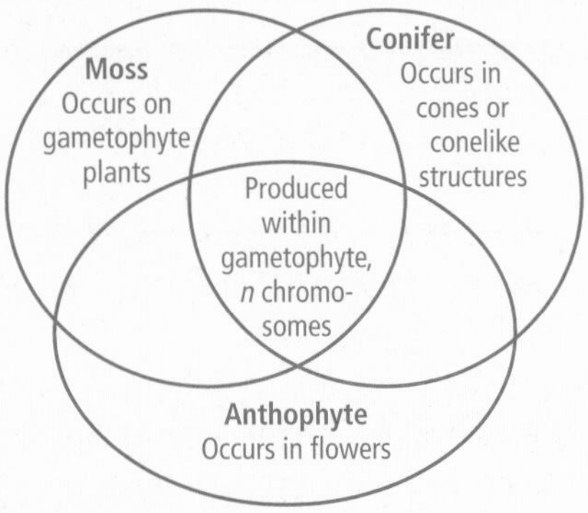

Caption Question Fig. 12 The egg would have half the number of chromosomes that the megaspore had.

Section 3

R Reading Preview

Essential Questions

- How can the life cycle of a flowering plant be described?
- What is the process of fertilization and seed formation in flowering plants?
- What are the different methods of seed dispersal?
- What is seed germination?

Review Vocabulary

cytoskeleton: the long, thin protein fibers that form a cell's framework

New Vocabulary

polar nuclei
endosperm
seed coat
germination
radicle
hypocotyl
dormancy

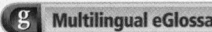

g Multilingual eGlossary

Flowering Plants

MAIN Idea In anthophytes, seeds and fruits can develop from flowers after fertilization.

Real-World Reading Link In 1893, the U.S. Supreme Court ruled that a tomato is legally a vegetable and not a fruit. The justices argued that a tomato is not a fruit because it is not sweet. As you read this section, decide whether this ruling is scientifically accurate.

Life Cycle

Anthophytes are the most diverse and widespread group of plants. They are unique because they have flowers. Anthophytes have distinctive life cycles and, like all plants, exhibit an alternation of generations. Like conifers, the sporophyte generation of anthophytes is dominant and supports the gametophyte generation. However, there are many variations of the anthophyte reproductive process.

Gametophyte development In anthophytes, the development of male and female gametophytes begins in an undeveloped flower. Anthophytes are heterosporous—pistils produce megaspores, and stamens produce microspores. A specialized cell in the ovule of a pistil's ovary undergoes meiosis, producing four megaspores. Usually, three of these megaspores disintegrate and disappear. The nucleus of the functional megaspore undergoes mitosis. Mitotic division continues and the megaspore grows until there is one large cell with eight nuclei. As shown in **Figure 12,** two nuclei migrate toward the center and membranes form around the other six nuclei. The result is three nuclei at each end of the cell and two nuclei in the center called **polar nuclei.** One of the three nuclei at the end closest to the micropyle becomes the egg. The cell that contains the egg and seven nuclei is the female gametophyte.

The development of the female gametophyte and the male gametophyte might or might not occur at the same time. Within the anther, specialized cells undergo meiosis and produce microspores. As shown in **Figure 13,** the nucleus in each microspore undergoes mitosis that forms two nuclei called the tube nucleus and the generative nucleus. A thick, protective cell wall forms around a microspore. At this point, the microspore is an immature male gametophyte, or pollen grain.

S

Figure 12 The megaspore results from meiosis, and the egg results from mitosis. This plant has 12 chromosomes.
***Infer** the chromosome number of the egg.*

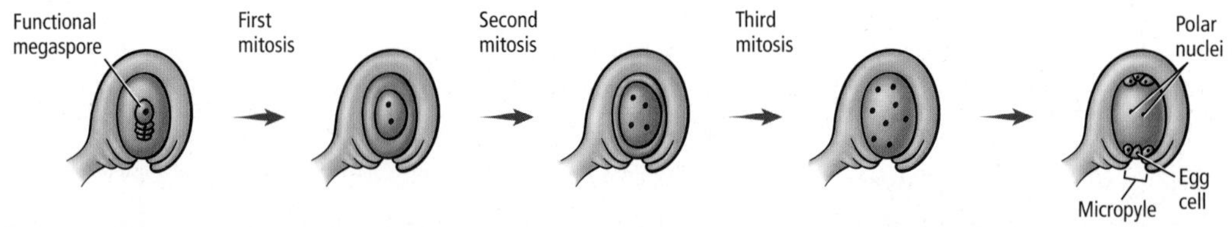

Content Background

Teacher FYI The unifying trait of anthophytes is the production of flowers. There is amazing diversity among the 250,000+ members of this division. One interesting group is the nonphotosynthetic anthophytes. There are about 3000 species of flowering plants that lack chlorophyll. Some of the more common ones are Indian pipes and snow flowers. These plants get their nutrients from photosynthetic plants via mycorrhizal fungi. Many of these plants were originally classified as fungi. However, the presence of flowers has been the deciding factor in reclassifying them as anthophytes.

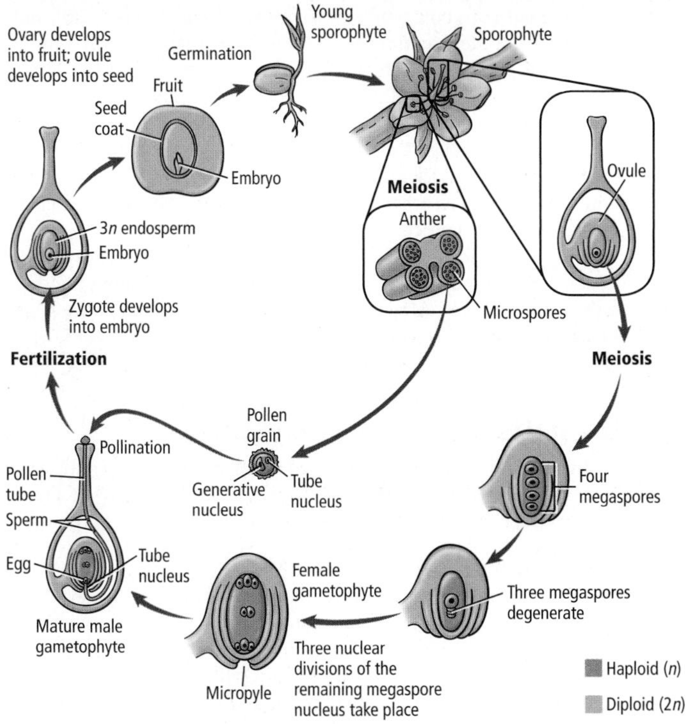

■ **Figure 13** The life cycle of a flowering plant, like a peach, includes gametophyte and sporophyte generations. The male and female gametophytes are surrounded by sporophyte tissue.

S

Scientists can identify the family or genus of a pollen grain by the distinctive outer layer of its cell wall called the exine. This characteristic is useful to paleontologists and forensic investigators. Paleontologists can trace the agricultural history of certain regions using pollen fossils. For over 50 years, forensic scientists have used pollen evidence to help determine where and when some crimes were committed.

Pollination and fertilization Earlier in this chapter, you learned that various flower adaptations help to ensure the successful transfer of pollen from the anther to the stigma of the pistil. Once pollination occurs, the pollen grain can form a pollen tube, which is an extension of the pollen grain. Usually, the pollen tube grows down through the style to the ovary and the two nuclei travel in the pollen tube toward the ovule.

Connection to Chemistry The pollen grain's exine can contain compounds that react with compounds of the pistil's stigma. These reactions can stimulate or inhibit the growth of the pollen tube. For example, in some poppies, when an incompatible pollen grain lands on the stigma, a chemical reaction disrupts the formation of the pollen grain's cytoskeleton. This inhibits the pollen tube's growth. Different mechanisms prevent the incompatible pollen from producing a functional pollen tube. **C**

When a compatible pollen grain lands on a stigma, the pollen grain absorbs substances from the stigma and a pollen tube starts to form, also shown in **Figure 13.** The tube nucleus directs the growth of the pollen tube. However, recent research suggests that the growth of the pollen tube toward the ovule is a chemotaxic response. In some plants, it has been found that calcium affects the direction of the pollen tube's growth.

FOLDABLES®
Incorporate information from this section into your Foldable.

Video BrainPOP

VOCABULARY
ACADEMIC VOCABULARY
Compatible
capable of functioning together
Because agricultural corn's pollen is compatible with sweet corn's pollen, the two crops must be planted some distance apart to prevent contamination of the sweet corn.

S Skill Practice

BL OL Visual Literacy Have students use Figure 13 to help them draw a cartoon depicting an incompatible pollen grain trying to grow into the surface of the stigma of a flower. Instruct students to make their cartoons biologically accurate.

FOLDABLES®

RUBRIC A rubric for evaluating Foldables is found on your eTeacherEdition Online.

Going Further On the back of their Foldables, have students explain why the sporophyte generation lasts longer and is so important to the life cycle of a flowering plant. The sporophyte generation lasts longer because it supports the gametophyte generation. Sporophytes also need time to develop from a zygote into a mature plant. Without the sporophyte, the plant could not produce the haploid spores necessary for survival of the species.

C Critical Thinking

AL Consider

ASK STUDENTS: ***What is the importance of the stigma's incompatibility response?*** The growth of nonspecific pollen tubes could interfere with the growth of the appropriate pollen tubes.

Develop Concepts

EL BL OL AL Activity Have students make a wet mount slide of pollen grains from a lily or *Alstroemeria.* Have them examine the slides under a microscope and look for the structural modifications of the exine. Have students draw and label the pollen grains.

Video BrainPOP

Content Background

Integrate Medicine Many people suffer from allergic reactions to pollen. This is often called hay fever or seasonal allergies. It is actually caused by an allergic immune response—a release of histamines by cells. The allergic immune response starts when antibodies of pollen proteins, which are attached to the mast cells in the nasal passages, encounter pollen proteins. The antibodies' mast cells release histamine and an allergic response occurs. It is estimated that 20–30 percent of the population of developed countries are susceptible to pollen allergies.

C Critical Thinking

AL Assess

ASK STUDENTS: ***What is the value of double fertilization?*** Double fertilization produces a new individual with genetic variation and produces the nutritive tissue—the endosperm. Since the endosperm is also the result of nuclei from two individuals, there is genetic variation among endosperm tissues.

Concepts in Motion

Animation

Review

Personal Tutor

Listen to a teacher describe eudicots and monocots.

Develop Concepts

BL OL Scaffolding

SAY TO STUDENTS: ***Describe the development of a plant embryo.*** The embryo is formed from the 2*n* zygote by cell division. ***Differentiate the endosperm from the embryo.*** The endosperm is 3*n* tissue that provides nourishment for the embryo. ***Evaluate the formation of the seed coat.*** The seed coat is a protective tissue. ***Compare the formation of the seed coat with the formation of the fruit.*** The seed coat is formed from the outside layers of the ovule, and the fruit usually forms from the ovary wall.

Develop Concepts

EL AL

Demonstrate Germination

Place a drop of 10% sucrose solution on a slide and touch a mature anther to the drop to transfer some pollen. After 20–30 minutes, students should be able to view germinating pollen tubes with a microscope. (This demonstration works well with Brassica plants.)

Caption Question Fig. 15 the cotyledon in eudicots and the endosperm in monocots

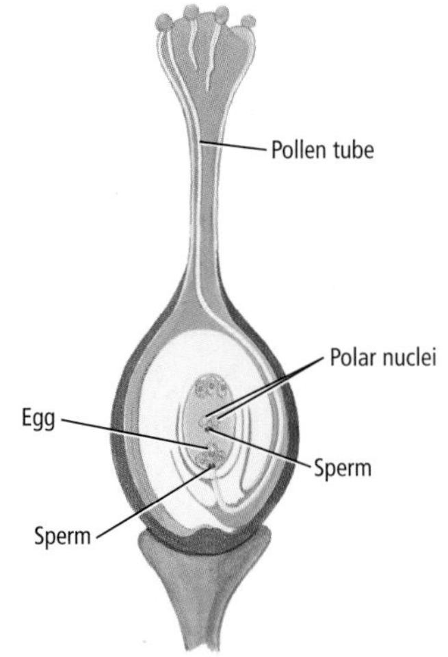

Figure 14 Double fertilization results in the formation of diploid and triploid tissues.

Concepts in Motion

Animation

The length of a pollen tube depends on the length of the pistil, and can vary from a few centimeters or less to more than 50 cm in some corn plants. As the pollen tube grows, the generative nucleus undergoes mitosis, forming two nonflagellated sperm nuclei. The pollen grain is now a mature male gametophyte. When the pollen tube reaches the ovule, it grows through the micropyle and releases the two sperm nuclei. One sperm nucleus fuses with the egg, forming the zygote—the new sporophyte. The other sperm nucleus and the two polar nuclei in the center of the ovule fuse, forming a triploid or 3*n* cell.

Because two fertilizations occur in an anthophyte egg, this is called double fertilization, shown in **Figure 14.** Double ferilization occurs only in anthophytes. After fertilization, the ovule and the ovary begin to develop into the seed and fruit, respectively.

Results of Reproduction

Fertilization is only the beginning of a long process that finally ends with the formation of a seed. In anthophytes, a seed is part of a fruit that develops from the ovary and sometimes other flower organs.

Seed and fruit development The sporophyte begins as a zygote, or a 2*n* cell. Numerous cell divisions produce a cluster of cells that eventually develops into an elongated embryo with one cotyledon in monocots or two cotyledons in eudicots. The 3*n* cell formed as a result of double fertilization undergoes cell divisions. A tissue called the **endosperm** (EN duh spurm) forms as a result of these divisions and provides nourishment for the embryo. Initially, these cell divisions occur rapidly without cell wall formation. As the endosperm matures, cell walls form. In some monocots, the endosperm is the major component of the seed and makes up most of the seed's mass. For example, the coconut palm is a monocot. The liquid inside a fresh coconut is liquid endosperm—cells without cell walls. In eudicots, the cotyledons absorb most of the endosperm tissue as the seed matures. Therefore, the cotyledons of eudicot seeds provide much of the nourishment for the embryo. Examples of eudicot and monocot seeds are shown in **Figure 15.**

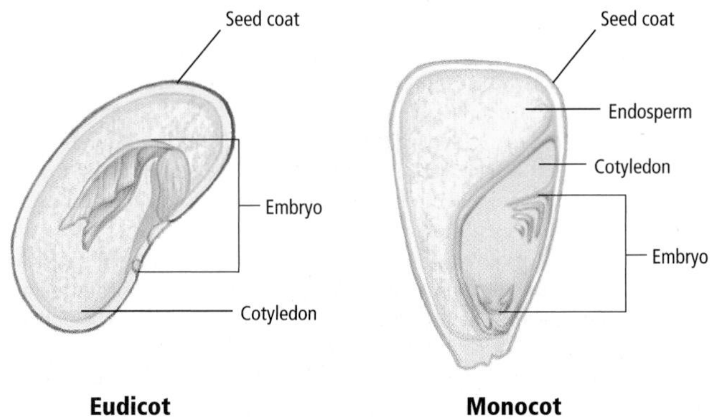

Review Personal Tutor

Figure 15 Seeds of monocots differ from those of eudicots.

***Identify** the embryo's food source in each seed.*

Research Citation

Ample Examples Educational research indicates that students should be provided with concrete examples of concepts that they are learning in order to better understand the material. The activity described on the previous page allows students to do hands-on work with a pollen grain, providing them with an example of its structure. (Trafton, 1983)

Research bibliography on pages 32T–34T

Differentiated Instruction

Hearing Impaired When using the scaffolding activity described on this page, make sure that hearing impaired students are able to participate. Seat these students in the front of the classroom so they are able to see your lips and facial expressions, which will allow them to follow and participate in the discussion.

For more tips, see pags 14T–15T.

As the endosperm matures, the outside layers of the ovule harden and form a protective tissue called the **seed coat.** You might notice the seed coats of beans or peas when you eat them. The seed coat is the thin, outer covering that often comes off or loosens as seeds are cooked.

Have you ever eaten a tomato or cucumber and noticed the number of seeds inside? Depending on the plant, the ovary can contain one ovule or hundreds. As the ovule develops into a seed, changes occur in the ovary that lead to the formation of a fruit.

Fruits form primarily from the ovary wall. In some cases, the fruit consists of the ovary wall and other flower organs. For example, the seeds of the apple are within the core that develops from the ovary. The juicy tissue that we eat develops from other flower parts.

Besides the apple, other fruits, such as peaches and oranges, are fleshy, while some are dry and hard, such as walnuts and grains. Study **Table 1** to learn about types of fruit.

D

Reading Check **Compare and contrast** the formation of a seed and a fruit.

Table 1 **Types of Fruit** Concepts in Motion Interactive Table

Fruit Type	Example of Flower and Fruit	Description
Simple fleshy fruits	  **Peach**	Simple fleshy fruits can contain one or more seeds. Apples, peaches, grapes, oranges, tomatoes, and pumpkins are simple fleshy fruits.
Aggregate fruits	  **Raspberry**	Aggregate fruits form from flowers with multiple female organs that fuse as the fruits ripen. Strawberries, raspberries, and blackberries are examples of aggregate fruits.
Multiple fruits	  **Pineapple**	Multiple fruits form from many flowers that fuse as the fruits ripen. Figs, pineapples, mulberries, and osage oranges are examples of multiple fruits.
Dry fruits	 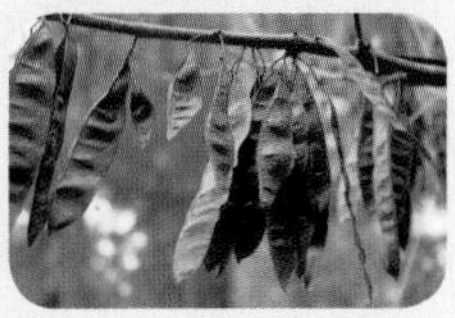 **Redbud**	When mature, these fruits are dry. Examples of dry fruits include pods, nuts, and grains.

D Develop Concepts

BL OL

Clarify a Misconception

ASK STUDENTS: ***What do you think of when I say juniper berry or pine nut?*** Answers will vary, but students may suggest that these are both fruits. Although these terms are commonly used (pine nuts are frequently used in cooking), they are not biologically accurate. Only anthophytes produce fruits, and nuts and berries are types of fruits. Pine nuts, which are actually seeds, and juniper berries, which are fleshy cones, are produced by conifers. Conifers do not develop fruits. This might be an opportunity to discuss the importance of scientific vocabulary. Although it may often seem cumbersome to students, using the correct vocabulary does help prevent confusion.

Concepts in Motion

Interactive Table

Writing Support

OL COOP LEARN

Creative Writing Have students work in groups of 3 to 4. Assign each group a type of nut to research. Instruct students to prepare an advertising campaign in which they inform consumers about their nut, its economic importance, and where it is grown. Have students present their advertisements to the class.

Reading Check Seeds and fruits are both part of anthophyte reproduction. Seeds develop in the ovule and contain the embryo. Fruits are produced from the ovary and may contain one or several seeds.

Demonstration

OL AL **Fruit Identification and Structure** Purchase a variety of fruits, including at least one of each kind described in Table 1. Try to obtain fruits that are traditionally thought of as vegetables so that students can visualize the botanical meaning of the term *fruit.* Cut the fruits in half so students can see the internal structure. Point out differences in location and number of seeds. Then have students identify the type of fruit each specimen represents, and list the identifying characteristics.

ASK STUDENTS: ***Where would you find the embryo?*** inside the seed ***What part of the flower formed the fruit?*** Fruit usually forms from the ovary wall. Est. time: 20 min

D Develop Concepts

BL OL AL Activity Have students design an experiment to investigate the effect of various environmental conditions on the germination of radish seeds. Possible variables could include temperature, salt, or light. Seeds can be grown in petri dishes on damp paper towels. Make sure the towels stay moist.

DATA ANALYSIS LAB 1

About the Lab

- Garlic mustard is a highly invasive plant that is very difficult to eradicate. Seeds can germinate even after being in the soil for several years.
- Garlic mustard originated in Europe and was introduced in the United States for herbal and medicinal purposes.
- Garlic mustard effectively outcompetes native species and has been shown to negatively affect several species of butterflies whose caterpillars feed on the leaves.
- Also see Huang, Renwick, and Chew. 1994/1995. Oviposition stimulants and deterrents control acceptance of *Alliaria rapae* and *P. napi oleracea*. *Chemoecology* 5/6: 79–87.

Think Critically

1. It decreases the percentage of seeds that germinate.
2. Designs will vary but should include a control. Students could grow various seeds in the presence of alfalfa and then grow them without alfalfa.

Seed dispersal In addition to providing some protection for seeds, fruits also help disperse seeds. Dispersal of seeds away from the parent plant increases the survival rate of offspring. For example, when many plants are growing in one area, there is competition for light, water, and soil nutrients. Seeds sprouting next to parent plants and with other offspring compete for these resources.

Fruits that are attractive to animals can be transported great distances away from the parent plant. Animals that gather and bury or store fruits usually do not recover all of them, so the seeds might sprout. Some of the animals, such as deer, bears, and birds, consume fruits. The seeds pass through their digestive tracts undamaged and then are deposited on the ground along with the animals' wastes. Some seeds have structural modifications that enable them to be transported by water, animals, or wind.

Seed germination When the embryo in a seed starts to grow, the process is called **germination.** There are a number of factors that affect germination, including the presence of either water or oxygen (or both), temperature, and those described in **Data Analysis Lab 1.** Most seeds have an optimum temperature for germination. For example, some seeds can germinate when soil is cool, but others need warmer soils.

Germination begins when a seed absorbs water, either as a liquid or gas. As cells take in water, the seed swells; this can break the seed coat. Water also transports materials to the growing regions of the seed.

D Within the seed, digestive enzymes help start the breakdown of stored food. This broken-down food and oxygen are the raw materials for cellular respiration, which results in the release of energy for growth.

DATA ANALYSIS LAB 1

Based on Real Data*

Recognize Cause and Effect

What is allelopathy? In nature, some plants produce chemicals that affect nearby plants. This is called allelopathy (uh LEEL luh pa thee). Some scientists studied the connection between allelopathy and the spread of nonnative plants, such as garlic mustard *Alliaria petiolata*. They investigated the effect of garlic mustard on the seed germination of native plants *Geum urbanum* and *Geum laciniatum*.

Think Critically

1. **Describe** the effect of garlic mustard on seed germination.
2. **Design an experiment** Alfalfa is known to allelopathically inhibit germination of some seeds. Use alfalfa sprouts to investigate their effect on seeds of your choice.

Data and Observations

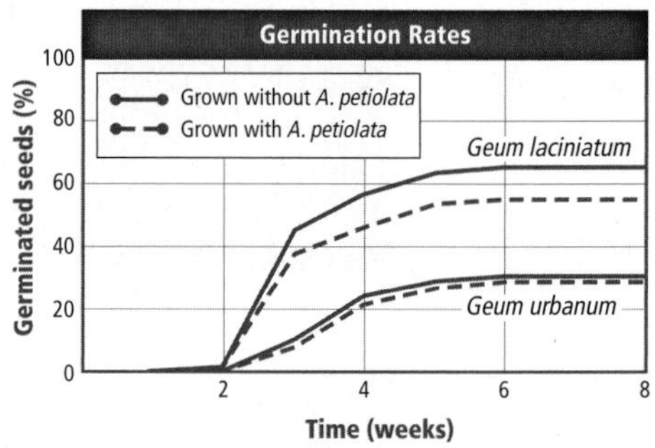

*Data obtained from: Prati, D. and O Bossdorf. 2004. Allelopathic inhibition of germination by *Alliaria petiolata* (Brassicaceae). *Amer. Journal of Bot.* 91(2): 285–288.

Content Background

Teacher FYI Invasive plants are introduced species that lack natural enemies. They thrive beyond their normal range in these areas. These plants tend to be very adaptable and aggressive and have a high reproductive rate. Invasive plants can be damaging to the natural ecosystems by crowding out the native plant species and the animal species that depend on the native species for food and shelter. Invasive plants are a problem throughout the United States, invading both terrestrial and aquatic environments. A Web search [key words: invasive plants] will help you identify problem plants in your area.

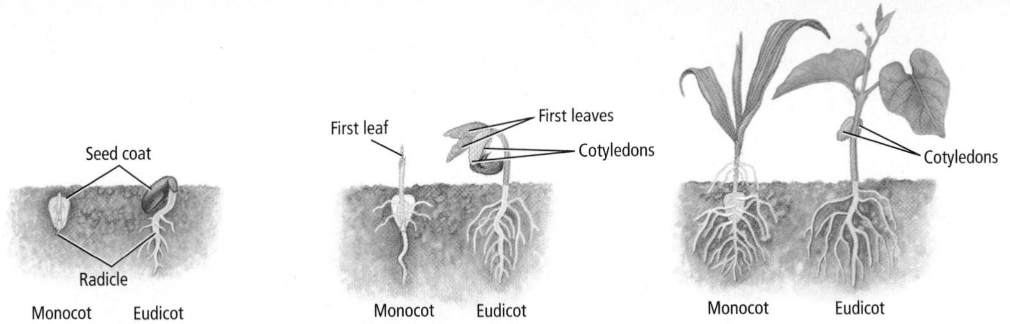

■ **Figure 16** Seed germination differs in monocots and eudicots.

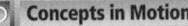

Concepts in Motion
Animation

The first part of the embryo to appear outside the seed is a structure called the **radicle** that starts absorbing water and nutrients from its environment. The radicle, as shown in **Figure 16,** will develop into the plant's root. The **hypocotyl** is the region of the stem nearest the seed and, in many plants, it is the first part of the seedling to appear above the soil. In some eudicots, as the hypocotyl grows, it pulls the cotyledons and the embryonic leaves out of the soil. Photosynthesis begins as soon as the seedling's cells that contain chloroplasts are above ground and exposed to light. In monocots, seedling growth is slightly different because the cotyledon usually stays in the ground when the stem emerges from the soil.

Some seeds can survive harsh environmental conditions, such as drought and cold. Other seeds germinate soon after dispersal and still others can germinate after long periods. Some maple seeds must germinate within two weeks after dispersal or they will not germinate at all. Most seeds produced at the end of a growing season enter **dormancy,** a period of little or no growth. Dormancy is an adaptation that increases the survival rate of seeds exposed to harsh conditions. The length of dormancy varies from species to species.

Section 3 Assessment

Section Summary

- The life cycle of anthophytes includes alternation of generations.
- The development of gametophytes occurs in the flower.
- Double fertilization is unique to anthophytes.
- Seeds provide nutrition and protection for the embryonic sporophyte.
- Fruits help protect and disperse seeds.
- Environmental conditions affect seed germination.

Understand Main Ideas

1. MAIN Idea **Diagram** the steps of the flowering-plant life cycle.
2. **Summarize** the development of the male gametophyte.
3. **Illustrate** the internal structure of a eudicot seed.
4. **Discuss** the importance of double fertilization.
5. **Construct** a graphic organizer that shows the different ways in which seeds can be dispersed.

Think Critically

6. **Evaluate** the mechanism that prevents incompatible pollen from producing a pollen tube.
7. **Compare and contrast** the germination of monocot and eudicot seeds.

MATH in Biology

8. As many as three million seeds can form inside an orchid pod. What is the percentage of germination, if all three million seeds are planted and 1,860,000 germinate?

Concepts in Motion
Animation

Formative Assessment

Evaluation

SAY TO STUDENTS: ***Summarize the life cycle of an anthophyte.*** Gametophytes develop in immature flower; the flower is pollinated and fertilized; seeds and fruit develop; seeds are dispersed, germinate, and grow into a young plant. ***What is double fertilization?*** the fertilization of the egg and the polar nuclei by two different sperm ***Why is this an important step in reproduction?*** It produces a new individual (zygote) and nutritive tissue for that developing individual.

Remediation Have students read the text under the heading *Pollination and fertilization.* Review the process by listing the steps on the board.

ASK STUDENTS: ***How is a 2n zygote formed from an n egg?*** The egg is fertilized by an *n* sperm ***How is a 3n endosperm formed?*** by fertilizing a 2*n* polar nuclei with an *n* sperm ***What is the advantage of the endosperm?*** provides nutrition for the developing embryo

Section 3 Assessment

1. Diagrams should resemble Figure 13.
2. Haploid microspores are produced by meiosis in the anther, the nucleus divides mitotically, the resulting two nuclei become generative nucleus and tube nucleus, and a thick protective covering develops around the pollen grain.
3. Illustrations should resemble the eudicot seed in Figure 15.
4. Double fertilization provides genetic recombination of DNA when the egg and sperm unite. The polar nuclei are fertilized and the resulting tissue provides nutrients to the developing embryo.
5. Graphic organizers will vary but should include dispersion by animals, wind, or water.
6. Answers will vary, but students might suggest that the chemical reactions are effective in preventing the formation of a pollen tube with incompatible pollen grains.
7. Refer to Figure 16 to check answers.
8. 62 percent

Assessment **Online Quiz**

Purpose

Students will defend a position for or against the continuation of interspecies genetic plant modification.
UPC.5, C.2

Anticipatory Guide

ASK STUDENTS: ***If you could purchase a square tomato, would you?*** Answers will vary. ***What advantages would there be if tomatoes were square?*** Students may respond that buying a square tomato would be advantageous in terms of shipping costs, packaging, and storing. ***Would you be concerned about planting genetically engineered square tomatoes in your garden next to a field of wild tomatoes?*** Possible answer: Planting a genetically engineered crop of tomatoes could possibly lead to cross pollination with the wild tomatoes in the field next to the garden.
SAY TO STUDENTS: ***Think about these questions as you read this feature.***

Background

The first major product of genetic modification appeared in 1982 with the production of recombinant human insulin. The first food product came in 1990 with the use of an enzyme in cheese production. Genetic modification in plants is performed in three primary steps: (1) the identification and isolation of nucleotides that will direct the production of a protein; (2) the transfer of a gene into an organism; and (3) gene transfer occurs in a single cell and results in cloning.

Biology & Society

Genetically Modified Plants

Did you have cornflakes, orange juice, or wheat toast for breakfast? If they were purchased from a large grocery store, then there is a good chance you ate genetically modified foods. People have been altering the genetics of plants for centuries through selective breeding. Only recently have scientists modified the genetic makeup of plants through genetic engineering.

What are genetically modified plants? Before genetic engineering, there was selective breeding. For example, if a fungus infected a corn crop, then a farmer would collect seeds from those plants with little or no signs of infection. If the farmer continued to select seeds from fungus-free plants, fungus-resistant corn could be developed over time.

In recent years, scientists have performed intraspecies gene transfers to alter plants. Genes for resistance to insects or disease are transferred from one variety of plant into another variety of the same species. Generally, plants that result from intraspecies gene transfer are considered safe to eat. In 1994, the first genetically modified food became available to the public. It was a tomato that would not soften prematurely.

Other genetically modified plants include corn, soybeans, cotton, wheat, rice, grapples, a cross between an apple and a grape, and pluots, a cross between a plum and an apricot. These products are available in your local grocery stores.

What are the benefits and risks? There are both benefits and risks to creating and using genetically modified plants. Some of the benefits include improved nutritional quality, better crop yields, longer shelf lives, and resistance to herbicides, viruses, and fungi.

These genetically modified minneolas will be harvested and sold in grocery stores around the country. Minneolas are a cross between a mandarin orange and a grapefruit.

One negative aspect of genetically modified crops involves determining the risks and the probability that the modified plants could easily cross-pollinate with wild varieties of plants. Another potentially negative aspect is a controversial modification called the terminator gene. The terminator gene causes plants to produce seeds that cannot germinate. This way, farmers must buy seeds each growing season. Plants with this gene are not currently being sold, but there is no law prohibiting it.

While genetically modified plants provide many benefits, there are also political, social, and economic concerns that impact how we grow our food. Careful consideration of all areas of this issue is important.

DEBATE in Biology

Debate Should interspecies genetic modification of plants continue without any controls? Conduct additional research and prepare arguments that support your side and refute the other side.

DEBATE in Biology

Use Evidence Tell students that to hold an effective debate, they should split into several groups and research the different "sides" of the argument. These sides will debate each other, taking care to focus on facts and evidence and not resorting to emotionalism or personal attacks. After the debate, have the groups prepare letters to the editor stating their viewpoint regarding the continued use of interspecies genetically modified plants. Have students peer edit the letters and submit them to the school newspaper. See the Skillbuilder Handbook for debate tips.

WebQuest

BIOLAB

Design Your Own

HOW DO MONOCOT AND EUDICOT FLOWERS COMPARE?

Background: Flowers are the reproductive structures of flowering plants, and there is great diversity in flower form. Botanists classify flowering plants into two groups—monocots and eudicots—based on the structure of their seeds. However, their flower structures also differ. Explore the differences between these two groups of plants by completing this lab.

Question: *What are the structural differences between monocot and eudicot flowers?*

Materials

monocot flowers
eudicot flowers
colored pencils
Choose other materials that would be appropriate for this lab.

Safety Precautions

WARNING: *Use dissecting tools with extreme caution.*

Plan and Perform the Experiment

1. Read and complete the lab safety form.
2. Choose several features of monocot and eudicot flowers to observe and compare.
3. Create a data table to record your observations of flowers—monocots and eudicots. Include sketches of each flower type.
4. Make sure your teacher approves your plan before you proceed.
5. Make observations as you planned.
6. Label and color-code the female and male reproductive structures and other flower parts of one of your monocot flower sketches.
7. Repeat Step 6 using one of the eudicot flower sketches.
8. **Cleanup and Disposal** Properly dispose of the flower parts. Clean all equipment as instructed by your teacher and return everything to its proper storage location.

Analyze and Conclude

1. **Compare and contrast** the characteristics of monocot and eudicot flowers.
2. **Conclude** Which of the flowers that you examined were monocots? Eudicots?
3. **Error Analysis** Compare your data with the data collected by your classmates. Explain any differences.

APPLY YOUR SKILL

Field Investigation Visit a local florist, greenhouse, or plant conservatory on your own or with a friend. Make a list of monocot and eudicot plants, based on their flower structures, that you observe at the location. Ask permission before touching any plants.

Analyze and Conclude

1. Monocots usually have flower petals in multiples of 3 or 6, parallel veins in leaves, vascular bundles scattered throughout their stems, and fibrous (bushy) roots. Eudicots usually have flower petals in multiples of 4 or 5, netted veins in leaves, vascular bundles on the perimeter of their stems, and thick taproots.
2. Answers will vary, but should include specimens used in the lab.
3. Answers will vary, specimens may not have been perfect examples; pieces and parts may have broken off.

BIOLAB

Design Your Own

Inquiry BioLab

For a lab worksheet, use your eTeacherEdition Online.

RUBRIC A rubric for evaluating BioLabs is found on your eTeacherEdition Online.

Est. Time 45 min

Content Background
In this lab, students will divide flowering plants into two basic groups—monocots and eudicots.

Alternative Materials scalpel, razor blade, dissecting probe, magnifying lens, metric ruler, microscope, and microscope slide and coverslip

Safety Precautions Approve lab safety forms before work begins. Caution students to use scalpels or other sharp instruments with care and to wash their hands thoroughly after handling the flowers and plant parts.

Teaching Strategies
- Local florists can likely provide old flowers for this activity.
- Students can also cut up anthers with a razor blade and compare the number of pollen grains under a microscope.

Alternative Teaching Demo
As a class, students can identify common features for monocots and eudicots. You can dissect the flower stem for students to observe the differences in vascular bundles between the two types of flowers, and all of the class's data can be presented in a data table, slideshow presentation, or in a drawing on the board.

Cleanup and Disposal
Properly dispose of all flower parts. Never place invasive flower species into the local environment.

Chapter 23

Study Guide

ConnectED

Students can use the following to review the chapter.

Review

Vocabulary eGames
Vocabulary eFlashcards
Vocabulary PuzzleMaker

Assessment

Online Quizzes
Online Test Practice
Standardized Test Practice

Use the *ExamView® Assessment Suite* CD-ROM to:

- create multiple versions of tests
- create modified tests with one mouse click
- edit existing questions and add your own questions
- build tests aligned with state standards using built-in state curriculum tags
- change English tests to Spanish with one mouse click
- track students' progress using the Teacher Management System

Chapter 23 Study Guide

THEME FOCUS Change Plants' reproductive methods have changed over time, enabling plants to live in a variety of environmental conditions. Seeds are an adaptation for reproducing without water.

BIG Idea The life cycles of plants include various methods of reproduction.

Section 1 Introduction to Plant Reproduction

vegetative reproduction (p. 662)
chemotaxis (p. 664)
protonema (p. 664)
prothallus (p. 665)
heterosporous (p. 665)
megaspore (p. 665)
microspore (p. 666)
micropyle (p. 666)

MAIN Idea Like all plants, the life cycles of mosses, ferns, and conifers include alternation of generations.

- Vegetative reproduction produces new plants without sexual reproduction.
- The life cycles of plants involve the alternation of generations.
- A fern sporophyte can live independently of the gametophyte.
- Conifer gametophytes develop within sporophyte tissues.

Section 2 Flowers

sepal (p. 668)
petal (p. 668)
stamen (p. 669)
pistil (p. 669)
photoperiodism (p. 672)
short-day plant (p. 672)
long-day plant (p. 672)
intermediate-day plant (p. 673)
day-neutral plant (p. 673)

MAIN Idea Flowers are the reproductive structures of anthophytes.

- A typical flower has sepals, petals, stamens, and one or more pistils.
- Flowers can be perfect or imperfect, and complete or incomplete.
- Some flower modifications distinguish monocots from eudicots.
- Modifications make flowers more attractive to pollinators.
- Photoperiodism can influence when a plant flowers.

Section 3 Flowering Plants

polar nuclei (p. 674)
endosperm (p. 676)
seed coat (p. 677)
germination (p. 678)
radicle (p. 679)
hypocotyl (p. 679)
dormancy (p. 679)

MAIN Idea In anthophytes, seeds and fruits can develop from flowers after fertilization.

- The life cycle of anthophytes includes alternation of generations.
- The development of gametophytes occurs in the flower.
- Double fertilization is unique to anthophytes.
- Seeds provide nutrition and protection for the embryonic sporophyte.
- Fruits help protect and disperse seeds.
- Environmental conditions affect seed germination.

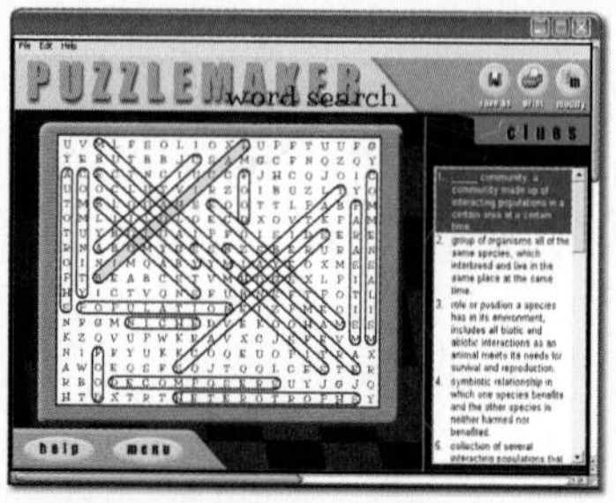

Review **Vocabulary PuzzleMaker**

For additional practice with vocabulary, have students access the Vocabulary PuzzleMaker online.

Review **Vocabulary eGames**

Section 1

Vocabulary Review

The sentences below are incorrect. Make each sentence correct by replacing the italicized word with a vocabulary term on the Study Guide page.

1. The *megaspore* of a conifer develops into the pollen grain.
2. A *protonema* is the gametophyte of a fern.
3. *Chemotaxis* is the growth of a new plant from a piece of the old plant.

Understand Main Ideas

4. Which is a fern prothallus?

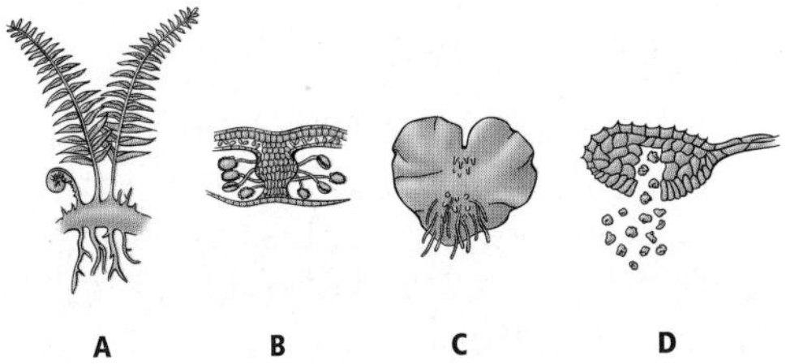

5. Which phrase accurately compares a fern sporophyte to the fern gametophyte?
   A. smaller than
   B. larger than
   C. always independent of
   D. always dependent on
6. From which structure does a conifer female gametophyte develop?
   A. prothallus
   B. fertilized egg
   C. microspore
   D. megaspore
7. Which is not an advantage of vegetative reproduction?
   A. uniform plant features
   B. genetically identical plants
   C. faster reproduction
   D. greater genetic variation

Constructed Response

8. MAIN Idea Create a flowchart showing the reproductive cycle of moss.
9. **Short Answer** What are some advantages and disadvantages of the moss sporophyte growing on the gametophyte?

Use the image below to answer question 10.

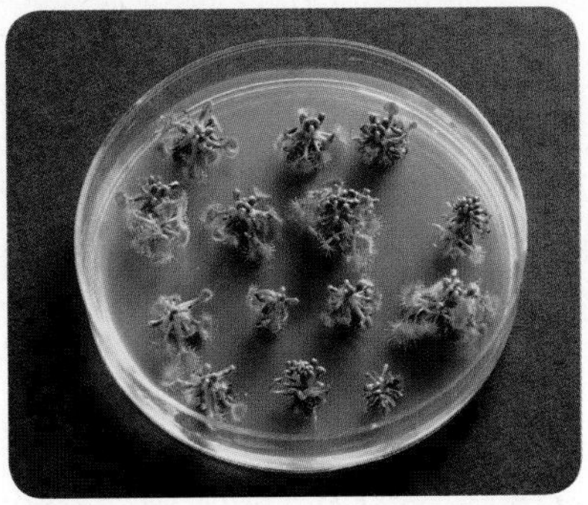

10. **Short Answer** Explain the genetic relationship among the offspring shown above.

Think Critically

11. **Discuss** the advantages or disadvantages of heterosporous plants.
12. THEME FOCUS Change Suggest a possible mechanism for the development of independent sporophyte generations as seen in conifers.

Section 2

Vocabulary Review

Distinguish between the vocabulary terms in each set.

13. pistil, stamen
14. long-day plant, short-day plant
15. petal, sepal

Understand Main Ideas

16. Which flower organ produces pollen?
   A. stamen
   B. pistil
   C. petal
   D. sepal

Chapter 23

Assessment

Section 1

Vocabulary Review

1. microspore
2. prothallus
3. vegetative reproduction

Understand Main Ideas

4. C
5. B
6. D
7. D

Constructed Response

8. Refer to Figure 4 for the steps that should be included in students' flow charts.
9. The advantages are that the sporophyte gains nutrition and support from the gametophyte. One disadvantage could be that the sporophyte is limited in size by the amount of nutrients provided by the gametophyte.
10. The offspring shown are clones; they are genetically identical.

Think Critically

11. Answers will vary. Advantages might include greater genetic variation. Disadvantages might include slower reproduction.
12. Answers will vary, but might include a mechanism by which the zygote is released from the archegonia.

Section 2

Vocabulary Review

13. The pistil contains the ovule(s) that produces the egg(s), and the stamen produces the pollen grain.
14. Long-day plants bloom when the nights are short, and short-day plants bloom when the nights are long.
15. Petals are often brightly colored and are used as an attractant for pollinators. Sepals are usually smaller, green, and can protect the young flower bud.

Understand Main Ideas

16. A

Assessment Online Test Practice

17. What dark/light conditions produce flowers in a short-day plant?
A. hours of darkness are greater than the hours of light
B. hours of darkness are less than hours of light
C. hours of darkness are equal to hours of light
D. hours of darkness and light are not factors

Use the image below to answer question 18.

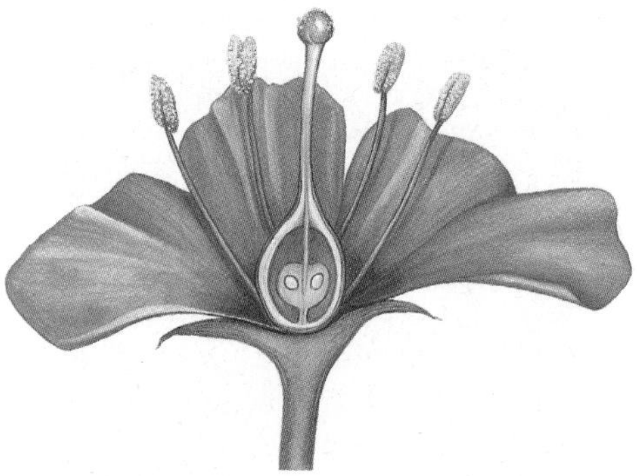

18. Which terms describe the flower above?
A. perfect, complete
B. perfect, incomplete
C. imperfect, incomplete
D. imperfect, complete

19. Which best describes pollen production in wind-pollinated flowers?
A. small amounts of pollen
B. larger pollen grains
C. large amounts of pollen
D. large quantities of nectar

20. Which terms could describe a monocot flower?
A. four sepals, four petals
B. five sepals, ten petals
C. twelve sepals, twelve petals
D. four sepals, eight petals

Constructed Response

21. **Short Answer** Explain why *short-day* and *long-day* are not the best descriptive terms for these types of flowering plants.

22. **Open Ended** Suggest a flower modification that would make water necessary for pollination. Justify your suggestion.

23. MAIN Idea Explain how modifications in flower structure make pollination more successful.

Think Critically

24. **Design** an experiment to test the ability of butterflies to distinguish between a real flower and an artificial flower.

25. **Assess** the benefits of photoperiodism.

Section 3

Vocabulary Review

Explain the relationship between the vocabulary terms in each pair below.

26. dormancy, germination
27. hypocotyl, radicle
28. polar nuclei, endosperm

Understand Main Ideas

29. Which is not part of a seed?
A. cotyledon
B. embryo
C. endosperm
D. pollen

30. Which describes the embryo of an anthophyte?
A. diploid
B. haploid
C. monoploid
D. triploid

31. From what structure does a pollen grain develop?
A. egg
B. embryo
C. endosperm
D. microspore

Use the image below to answer question 32.

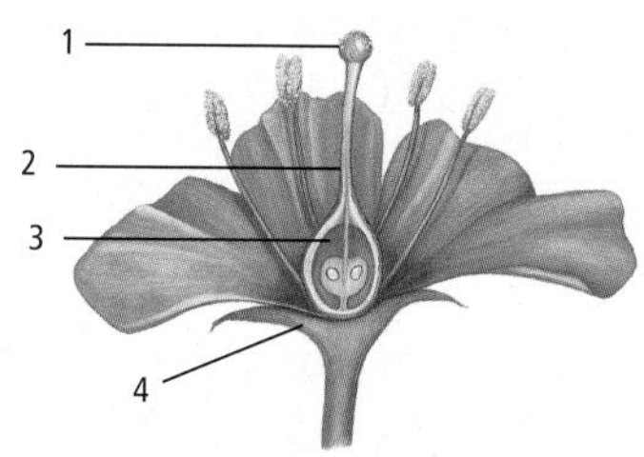

32. From which structure is a fruit usually formed?
A. 1
B. 2
C. 3
D. 4

17. A
18. A
19. C
20. C

Constructed Response

21. The hours of dark are actually the determining factor, not the hours of light.
22. Answers will vary, but students could suggest a mechanism that required water to transport the pollen, such as floating pollen.
23. Answers will vary, but students might talk about various mechanisms that make it more likely that a pollinator will be attracted to the flower or transfer pollen from one flower to another.

Think Critically

24. Answers will vary but should include a control. Students might suggest setting out a real flower and a similar fake flower and counting the number of butterflies that visit each one.
25. Photoperiodism helps ensure that flowers and, therefore, seeds are produced at the optimal time of the year for that specific plant.

Section 3

Vocabulary Review

26. In some plants, dormancy is the period of inactivity before a seed germinates. Germination breaks dormancy.
27. The radicle is the first structure that appears outside the seed when it germinates and becomes a root. The hypocotyl is the first part of the developing plant that emerges above the soil.
28. The polar nuclei consist of two nuclei, but the endosperm is the tissue that develops after the polar nuclei is fertilized. It is 3*n*.

Understand Main Ideas

29. D
30. A
31. D
32. C

33. What is the inactive period of a seed?
   A. alternation of generations
   B. dormancy
   C. fertilization
   D. photoperiodism

Constructed Response

34. **MAIN Idea** Describe the process of the fertilizing of a flowering plant.

35. **Short Answer** Explain why fruit and/or seed dispersal is so important.

36. **Open Ended** Hypothesize why an anthophyte's female gametophyte produces so many nuclei when only two are involved in fertilization.

37. **Open Ended** When a seed germinates, as shown in **Figure 16,** the radicle usually is the first structure to break through the seed coat. Why is this beneficial for the embryo?

Think Critically

Use the graph below to answer questions 38–39.

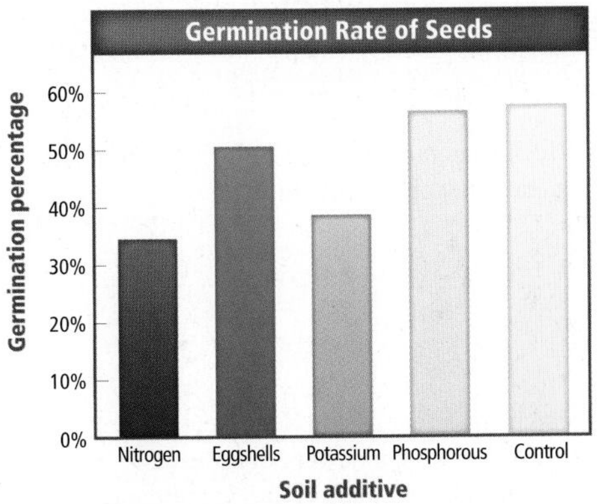

38. **Compare** the effects of each soil additive on the rate of germination to the control's rate of germination.

39. **Design** an experiment to test the effect on the rate of germination for various amounts of a soil additive. Choose one of the soil additives listed in the graph above.

Summative Assessment

40. **BIG Idea** Life cycles, whether in plants or animals, include reproduction. Results of reproduction in plants are seeds and fruits. What else do the various methods of plant reproduction have in common?

41. ***WRITING in* Biology** Write a short story about the life of a pollen grain.

DBQ Document-Based Questions

Data obtained from: Lang, A. et al. 1977. Promotion and inhibition of flower formation in a day-neutral plant in grafts with a short-day plant and a long-day plant. *Proc. Natl. Acad. Sci.* 74 (6): 2412-2416.

The day-neutral plant flowered sooner when it was grafted to the short-day plant that was exposed to its critical period. The flowering of another day-neutral plant also was accelerated when it was grafted to a long-day plant that was exposed to its critical period.

42. Examine the drawings above. Form a hypothesis about why the grafted day-neutral plants flowered before the day-neutral plant that was not grafted.

43. Predict what might happen if a long-day plant was grafted to a short-day plant and they were exposed to the critical period of the short-day plant.

44. Design an experiment to determine the "longest day" under which a long-day plant flowers.

33. B

Constructed Response

34. Seeds and fruits are produced from flowers that have been fertilized.
35. Fruit and/or seed dispersal helps ensure that the new generation is not competing with its parents for light, space, and water.
36. Answers will vary. Students may speculate that the other nuclei provide some nourishment as they are broken down or that the ovule has some mechanism for "choosing" the healthiest or most robust nuclei.
37. The radicle is able to absorb water and nutrients from the environment.

Think Critically

38. The control's germination rate was the greatest with seeds planted in phosphorous-enriched soil following closely behind. None of the soil additives increased the rate of germination.
39. Experiments should include a control and should test the effects of incremental amounts of the soil additive on germination rates.

Summative Assessment

40. Alternation of generations, seed/spore production, all require energy from the Sun, some type of pollination

WRITING in Biology

RUBRIC Use the modifiable rubric found on your eTeacher-Edition Online to assess writing assignments.

41. Answers will vary, but the story should include scientifically accurate information.

DBQ Document-Based Questions

Lang, A. et al. 1977. Promotion and inhibition of flower formation in a day-neutral plant in grafts with a short-day plant and a long-day plant. *Proc. Natl. Acad. Sci.* 74 (6): 2412-2416.

42. Answers will vary, but students may hypothesize that there is some chemical that is transported from the other plants to the day-neutral plant.
43. Answers will vary, but students may predict that a chemical (or hormone) might be transported from the plant receiving the correct day length to the other plant, stimulating flowering.
44. Answers will vary but should include exposure to series of day lengths that become gradually longer.

Standardized Test Practice

Multiple Choice

1. C
2. B
3. D
4. D
5. D
6. B
7. C
8. D

Short Answer

9. Answers may vary. The mold on the bread can produce spores that are quickly spread to other bread. The mold might also spread when hyphae from one piece of contaminated bread touches another piece of bread.
10. Answers may vary. Possible answers include the following: they are usually just a few cells thick; they are small and grow close to the ground, or whatever surface they are growing on; they are generally found in moist, shady environments.
11. The prothallus is the haploid gametophyte so its chromosome number is 7.
12. Because nonvascular plants have thin rhizoids and leaflike structures, water and minerals can move easily into the plants from the soil or from the environment.
13. Parenchyma cells function in storage, photosynthesis, gas exchange, protection, tissue repair, and replacement. Collenchyma cells function as support for surrounding tissues. Sclerenchyma cells function in transporting materials and support.
14. New World monkeys and other anthropoids have a common ancestor, but the New World monkeys evolved separately because the continents separated and they were then geographically isolated from other primates.
15. The climate of Montana is much colder than the climate of Florida. The seeds probably need cold temperatures to germinate.

Standardized Test Practice

Cumulative

Multiple Choice

1. Which vascular tissue is composed of living tubular cells that carry sugars from the leaves to other parts of the plant?
   A. cambium
   B. parenchyma
   C. phloem
   D. xylem

Use the diagram below to answer question 2.

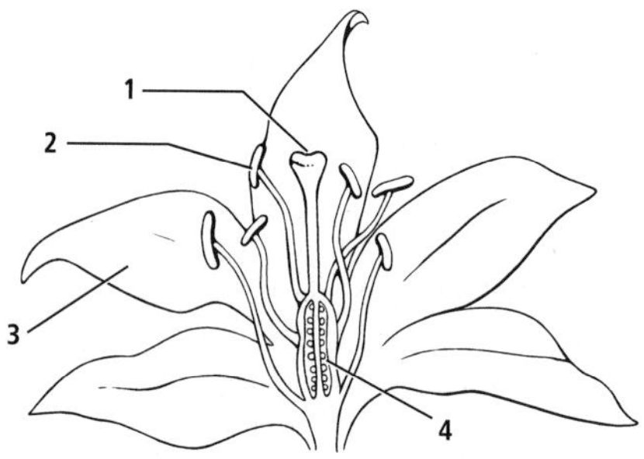

2. Which labeled structure is part of a flower's male reproductive organ?
   A. 1
   B. 2
   C. 3
   D. 4

3. Which statement provides evidence that anthophytes evolved after other seed plants?
   A. About 75 percent of all plants are anthophytes.
   B. Anthophytes do not require water to facilitate the fertilization of an egg.
   C. Prehistoric tree-like ferns were the main coal-forming plants.
   D. The seeds of anthophytes are more advanced than those of other seed plants.

4. Which precedes the haploid generation in seedless vascular plants?
   A. epiphytes
   B. gametophytes
   C. rhizomes
   D. spores

5. Which is the primary pollinator for conifers?
   A. birds
   B. insects
   C. water
   D. wind

Use the diagram below to answer question 6.

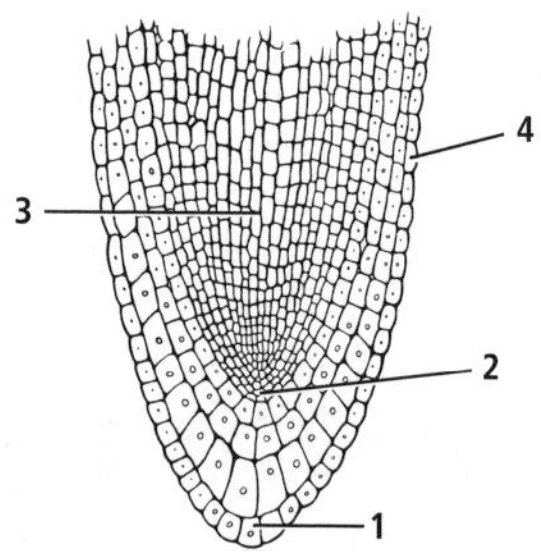

6. Which structure produces cells that result in an increase in length of the root?
   A. 1
   B. 2
   C. 3
   D. 4

7. Which statement is true of an aseptate fungus?
   A. Cell walls are made of cellulose.
   B. Cell walls are made of thin membranes.
   C. Hyphae are not divided by cross walls.
   D. Hyphae are not present except during reproduction.

8. A tuber is an adaptation of which structure?
   A. cell
   B. leaf
   C. root
   D. stem

Short Answer

Use the diagram below to answer question 9.

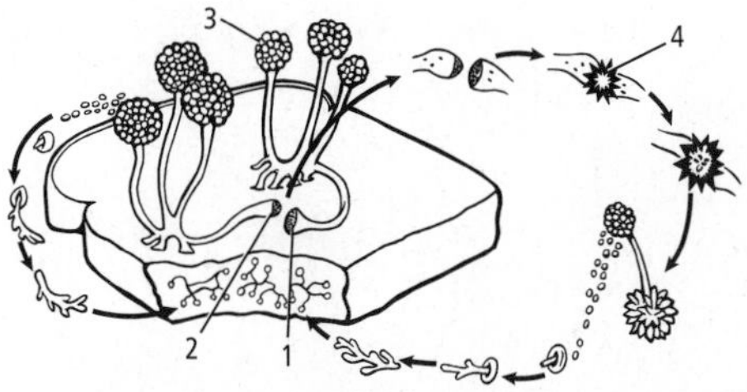

9. Describe two ways that bread mold could spread in a kitchen.

10. List two characteristics of nonvascular plants that compensate for their lack of transport tissues.

11. A certain type of fern has a chromosome number of 14. What would be the chromosome number of the prothallus? Explain why.

12. Explain the benefit to nonvascular plants of having very thin rhizoids and leaflike structures.

13. Name and describe the three types of plant cells and their functions.

14. Interpret how the actions of plate tectonics affected the evolution of primates.

15. Imagine that a friend who lives in Montana gives you some seeds from a plant. You plant the seeds in Florida but they do not grow. Predict why the seeds do not germinate in Florida.

Extended Response

16. Infer how collenchyma cells support surrounding plant tissues.

17. Critique the idea that roots in the ground do not need oxygen to survive.

18. A forest near a city provides drainage for rainfall runoff. A group of citizens is protesting new housing developments in the forest because they believe flooding and property destruction will result. Analyze the value of biodiversity that describes their concern.

19. Suppose that a couple wants to have children and neither the man nor the woman has cystic fibrosis. However, some distant family members have cystic fibrosis. Could their child have the disease? Write an explanation summarizing the risk for this couple.

Essay Question

Water is important for functions in plants. For example, it is one of the reactants in the chemical reactions of photosynthesis. Water enters a plant by diffusion. Most of the water that enters a plant diffuses into roots. Therefore, water must be in a higher concentration in the soil than in the roots. After water enters the roots, it moves through vascular tissue to tissues that contain chloroplasts. The water also diffuses into the plants' cells, making them rigid.

Using the information in the paragraph above, answer the following question in essay format.

20. When more water leaves a plant than enters it, the plant begins to wilt. Explain the role of guard cells in regulating the amount of water in a plant.

NEED EXTRA HELP?

If You Missed Question . . .	1	2	3	4	5	6	7	8	9	10	11	12	13	14	15	16	17	18	19	20
Review Section . . .	22.1	23.2	21.4	21.3	23.1	22.1	20.1	22.2	20.3	21.2	23.1	21.2	22.1	16.1	23.3	22.1	22.2	5.1	11.1	22.2

Extended Response

16. Collenchyma cells have unevenly thickened cell walls.

17. Answers may vary. One possible answer is mangrove trees living in water have special root adaptations that help supply oxygen to the roots. Another answer is that many plants will die if they are kept too long in soaked soil.

18. The citizens are likely concerned about the direct economic effect of biodiversity. Replacing some or all of the forest with housing will reduce the biodiversity of the area. It is likely that the housing development will reduce the drainage area for storm runoff. Consequently there could be flooding that would cause damage to property. The concerns of the citizens seem valid.

19. The child could have cystic fibrosis only if both parents are carriers and if they both give that gene to their child. The couple should understand that a family member with cystic fibrosis does not mean that either of them is a carrier. Even if one of them is a carrier, the child still could not have cystic fibrosis unless the other member of the couple is also a carrier and the child inherited both alleles.

Essay Question

20. When there is not enough water in the leaves, more water diffuses out of the guard cells than into the guard cells. This causes the guard cells to change their shape and close the stomata. Closing the stomata in the leaves reduces the amount of water vapor lost.

UNIT 7

Invertebrates

Preview the Unit

Have students preview the chapters in this unit and make a concept map or graphic organizer relating the Themes, Big Ideas, and Main Ideas. Students' maps should show a hierarchy between Big Ideas and Main Ideas and the interconnectedness of the Themes.

Chapter 24
Introduction to Animals
BIG Idea Animal phylogeny is determined in part by animal body plans and adaptations.

Chapter 25
Worms and Mollusks
BIG Idea Worms and mollusks have evolved to have a variety of adaptations for living as parasites or for living in water or soil.

Chapter 26
Arthropods
BIG Idea Arthropods have evolved to have a variety of adaptations for successful diversity, population, and persistence.

Chapter 27
Echinoderms and Invertebrate Chordates
BIG Idea Echinoderms and invertebrate chordates have features that connect them to the chordates that evolved after them.

WebQuest
Careers in Biology

UNIT 7 Invertebrates

THEMES

Scientific Inquiry Biologists continue to study invertebrates with observations and technology.

Diversity Special adaptations enable invertebrates to live in a wide variety of ecosystems.

Energy Food supplies the energy needed to carry out life functions.

Homeostasis Excretory cells and organs maintain homeostasis in invertebrates.

Change Natural selection over a period of time results in newly evolved species of invertebrates.

WebQuest **CAREERS IN BIOLOGY**

Entomologists are scientists who study insects and their behavioral patterns. Entomologists who conduct research, such as this field entomologist is doing, contribute to a better understanding of the ecosystem's function as a whole.

5-Minute UNIT LAUNCH

Brainstorm

SAY TO STUDENTS: ***Turn to a student near you and brainstorm a list of animals without backbones, called invertebrates, that live in your area. Beside each animal, indicate how you think it is adapted to their habitat.*** Some will know that insects are invertebrates and might describe how their wings are adapted to flight. Other invertebrates students might know about are earthworms and mollusks.

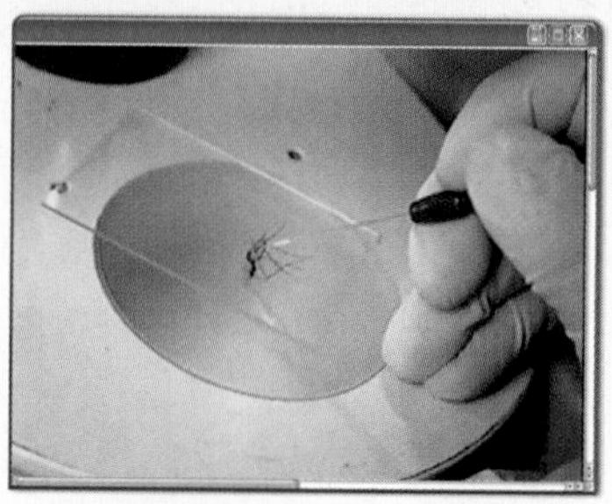

Video
What's BIOLOGY Got To Do With It?
An epidemiologist explains how some illnesses are linked to insects.

Misconceptions

In each section, *Clarify a Misconception* provides you with the information to dispel a common student misconception. A question will help you elicit the misconception, and an explanation will help you correct it.

Below is a preview of misconceptions from each chapter in this unit.

Before studying Chapter 24, students might think that all tissues are solid sheets or blocks of cells. Chapter 24 will explain that blood and nerves are also tissue (p. 698).

Before studying Chapter 25, students might think that, because of their shape, insect larvae are worms. Chapter 25 will explain that insect larvae are not worms but belong to another group of animals called arthropods (p. 727).

Before studying Chapter 26, students might think that all spiders build webs. Chapter 26 will explain that some spiders do not build webs, but hunt for prey instead (p. 772).

Before studying Chapter 27, students might think that the bodies of echinoderms are not any more complex than those of worms and mollusks. Chapter 27 will explain that echinoderms are more complex than either of these two and are closely related to vertebrates (p. 796).

SERVICE LEARNING/COMMUNITY SERVICE

Poster In groups, students can prepare a poster for display in a local community center, town hall, or library. They should gain permission and find out size limitations. The poster should educate people about how to protect an endangered local invertebrate such as a mollusk, or teach citizens how to avoid a local parasitic worm or how to avoid contracting a disease, such as West Nile Virus, that is transmitted by mosquitoes. Drawing pictures is a powerful way for students to learn concepts (**Marzano, Pickering, & Pollack, 2001**).

Research bibliography on pages 32T–34T

Chapter 24 Organizer:
Introduction to Animals

LabManager™

Customize any lab with the LabManager™ CD-ROM.

Essential Questions	National Science Standards	Materials and Planning	
		Estimated times include cleanup and disposal, but do not include teacher prep time. For cleanup and disposal guidelines, see page 39T.	Est. Time (min)
Section 1 1. How do adaptations enable animals to live in different habitats? 2. How is structure and function related in animals? 3. What are the stages of embryonic development in animals?	UCP.1–5; A.1, A.2; C.1, C.3, C.4, C.5, C.6; E.2; F.3, F.6; G.1, G.2	**Launch Lab,** p. 690: two small organisms, preserved specimens of fan coral and red algae, magnifying lens or stereomicroscope	15
		Demonstration, p. 692: transparency of fictitious family tree; projector	10
		MiniLab 1, p. 693: hydras, brine shrimp; petri dish, magnifying lens or stereomicroscope	60
		Demonstration, p. 694: microscopes, various types of tissues, such as bone marrow, muscle, blood, and epidermis	10
Section 2 1. How are animal body plans related to phylogeny? 2. How are body cavities related to animal phylogeny? 3. What are the two types of coelomate development?	UCP.1–5; A.1, A.2; C.1, C.3, C.5, C.6; E.1, E.2; F.1; G.1, G.2	**Demonstration,** p. 700: household items such as a bowl and a screwdriver	5
		MiniLab 2, p. 702: slides of earthworm and hydra cross sections, microscope, labeled diagrams of the cross sections	30
Section 3 1. What are the characteristics of sponges and cnidarians? 2. How are sponges and cnidarians alike and different? 3. What is the ecological importance of sponges and cnidarians?	UCP.1–5; A.1, A.2; C.1, C.3, C.4, C.5, C.6; F.4, F.5	**Demonstration,** p. 710: photos of jellyfishes, corals, sea anemones	10
		Demonstration, p. 712: preserved samples of a hydroid colony, a jellyfish, a sea anemone, and a piece of coral	15
		Demonstration, p. 713: dried endoskeletons of sea urchin and sea star, model of shark skeleton and vertebrate skeleton	10
		Design Your Own BioLab, p. 717: wading boots, tweezers, aquarium, petri dishes, stereomicroscopes	90

Suggested Time for Each Lesson

Class	Chapter Opener	Section 1	Section 2	Section 3	Assessment
Basic	45 min	45 min	45 min	45 min	45 min
General	25 min	45 min	65 min	45 min	45 min
Honors	10 min	35 min	45 min	70 min	20 min

ConnectED

connectED.mcgraw-hill.com

Access interactive learning opportunities and teaching resources using these icons located throughout your StudentWorks™ Plus Online and eTeacherEdition Online.

Chapter 24 Section Resources

FAST FILE Unit 7 Resources:
Launch Lab Worksheet*
MiniLab Worksheet*
Study Guide (English/Spanish)*
Section Quick Check

Reading Essentials 24.1
Science Notebook 24.1*

FAST FILE Unit 7 Resources:
MiniLab Worksheet*
Study Guide (English/Spanish)*
Section Quick Check

Reading Essentials 24.2
Science Notebook 24.2*

FAST FILE Unit 7 Resources:
BioLab Worksheet*
Study Guide (English/Spanish)*
Section Quick Check

Reading Essentials 24.3
Science Notebook 24.3*

Additional Chapter 24 Resources

FAST FILE Unit 7 Resources:
Chapter Diagnostic Test
Concept Mapping*
Real-World Biology
Enrichment
Chapter Tests A, B, and C

Transparencies:
Bellringer Transparencies*
Biology Concepts Transparencies*

Lab Resources:
Laboratory Manual*
Probeware Lab Manual*
Forensics Lab Manual*
Pre-AP Lab Manual*
Open Inquiry in Biology*
Guided Inquiry in Biology*

Technology

Teaching Tools:
eTeacherEdition Online
Classroom Presentation Toolkit CD-ROM*
LabManager™ CD-ROM*
Video Lab DVD*
Virtual Lab CD-ROM*
What's BIOLOGY Got To Do With It?
StudentWorks™ Plus Online*

Chapter Assessment Tools:
Classroom Presentation Toolkit CD-ROM*
ExamView® Assessment Suite CD-ROM

Web-Based Resources:

- StudentWorks™ Plus Online
- eTeacherEdition Online
- Animations*
- The Interactive Time Line*
- Interactive Tables*
- Online Quizzes
- Online Test Practice
- Standardized Test Practice
- Virtual Labs*
- Multilingual eGlossary*
- Vocabulary eGames*
- Vocabulary eFlashcards
- WebQuests
- Personal Tutors

While all resources listed are appropriate for English learners, the * indicates resources with a strong visual or hands-on component for EL.

Teaching strategies and activities have been coded for differentiated instruction.

AL Activities for students working above grade level	**OL** Activities for students working on grade level	**BL** Activities for students working below grade level	**EL** Activities for English learners (also ELL)	**COOP LEARN** Activities designed for small cooperative group work

CHAPTER 24

Launch Lab
What is an animal?

? Inquiry Launch Lab

For a lab worksheet, use your eTeacherEdition Online.

RUBRIC A rubric for evaluating Launch Labs is found on your eTeacherEdition Online.

Est. Time 15 min

Additional Materials
preserved specimens of fan coral and red algae

Alternative Materials Color photographs of fan coral and red algae may also be used.

Teaching Strategies
- Students are not expected to know which one is the animal. Live examples of these organisms would have given them better clues.
- Use videos of the living organisms to help students understand the differences between the two organisms.

Procedure
1. Read and complete the lab safety form.
2. Observe the **two organisms** you are given.
3. Compare and contrast the organisms using a **hand lens** or **stereomicroscope** if available.
4. Describe any specialized structures that you observe.
5. Based on your observations, predict how the form of each organism might be an adaptation to its habitat.

CHAPTER 24

Introduction to Animals

ConnectED
Your one-stop online resource
connectED.mcgraw-hill.com

Video
Audio
Review
Inquiry
WebQuest
Assessment
Concepts in Motion
Multilingual eGlossary

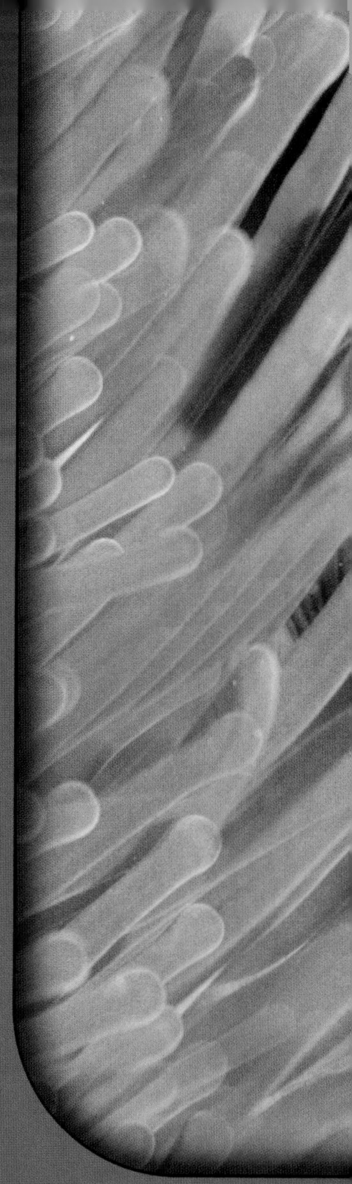

Launch Lab
What is an animal?

Although animals share some characteristics with all other living organisms, they also have unique characteristics. In this lab, you will compare and contrast two organisms and determine which one is an animal.

For a lab worksheet, use your StudentWorks™ Plus Online.
? Inquiry Launch Lab

FOLDABLES®
Make a layered-look book using the titles shown. Use it to organize your notes on body plans.

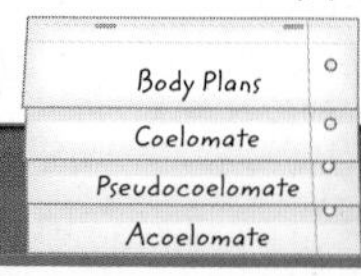

Analysis
1. **Identify** any structures that might be specific to animals. Answers will depend on the chosen organisms, but may include cells with cell membranes and no cell walls, mouth, gut, and organs of movement such as legs.
2. **Predict** which one of these organisms is more likely to be an animal. Explain your prediction based on your observations. Answers will vary, but predicting which is the animal should refer to characteristics of multicellular, eukaryotic heterotrophs.

Differentiated Instruction

English Learners When English learners are in the classroom, use a variety of question types throughout the lesson. Use questions that will not require the students with limited English to rely on speech to demonstrate their understanding.

For more tips, see pages 14T–15T.

THEME FOCUS Diversity
Animals have a wide variety of characteristics, including body plans and adaptations.

BIG Idea Animal phylogeny is determined in part by animal body plans and adaptations.

Section 1 • Animal Characteristics
Section 2 • Animal Body Plans
Section 3 • Sponges and Cnidarians

THEMES

Scientific Inquiry Biologists study the similarities and difference between animal phyla.

Diversity Symbiotic, defensive, and other physical adaptations are a source of diversity among animals.

Energy Animals are heterotrophic and depend on other organisms as a source of food.

Homeostasis Animal body plans function to maintain homeostasis within each type of organism.

Change Body plans, symmetry, and body cavities have evolved over time to become specialized for each species.

Introduce the Chapter

Adaptations of Animals

ASK STUDENTS: ***In what way are scales of fishes an adaptation to aquatic life?*** Scales protect the insides of the fish while allowing the fish to swim easily and quickly through water. ***In what way might the nematocysts of sea anemones, such as those shown in the photo, ensure its survival?*** Sea anemones are protected from predators and can sting and subdue prey animals they use as food.

BIG Idea

What is an animal? Show the class pictures from magazines, posters, and biological supply catalogues of a variety of organisms, including protozoa, algae, and animals with simple and complex body plans. Be sure to include nonmammals as well as mammals.
ASK STUDENTS: ***Which of these organisms are classified as animals? How can you tell if they are animals?*** Sample answer: Animals are multicellular and they must eat other organisms for nutrients.

Section 1

MAIN Idea

BL OL AL Animal Features
Alternately hold up a live animal, such as a mouse or a snake in a clear container, and a potted plant. **ASK STUDENTS:** ***In what ways do animals differ from plants?*** feeding—animals are heterotrophic and must feed on other organisms to get nutrients, plants are autotrophic; movement—most animals can move around during some life stage, most plants stay in one place; cell structure—plant cells have cell walls, animal cells do not

EL Have English learners answer yes/no questions and choice questions such as, *Do most animals move from place to place?*

D Develop Concepts

EL BL OL COOP LEARN

Clarify a Misconception

Students do not always recognize that simple invertebrates are animals. Have each student make a list of five different animals. In groups of four, have them examine the lists and identify those that are not examples of terrestrial animals. Select an invertebrate that was not on any list, such as a jellyfish or a leech, and write the name on the board. Have students turn to specific pages in the animal chapters that show a variety of animals.
ASK STUDENTS: ***Can this organism make its own food?*** no ***What kind of organisms cannot make their own food and feed on other organisms?*** heterotrophs
Remind students that animals are heterotrophs. ***Is this example an animal?*** yes

AL Give students five invertebrates that do not look like typical animals. Have them brainstorm what these organisms eat and how they obtain food.

Section 1

Reading Preview

Essential Questions
- How do adaptations enable animals to live in different habitats?
- How is structure and function related in animals?
- What are the stages of embryonic development in animals?

Review Vocabulary
protist: diverse group of unicellular or multicellular eukaryotes that lack complex organ systems and live in moist environments

New Vocabulary
invertebrate
exoskeleton
endoskeleton
vertebrate
hermaphrodite
zygote
internal fertilization
external fertilization
blastula
gastrula
endoderm
ectoderm
mesoderm

Multilingual eGlossary

Animal Characteristics

MAIN Idea Animals are multicellular, eukaryotic heterotrophs that have evolved to live in many different habitats.

Real-World Reading Link When you think of animals, you might think of creatures that are furry and fuzzy. However, animals can have other outer coverings, such as feathers on birds and scales on fishes. Some animals even might be mistaken for plants.

General Animal Features

Recall that biologists have created an evolutionary tree to organize the great diversity of living things. The ancestral animals at the beginning of the evolutionary tree are eukaryotic and multicellular—they are made up of many cells. The tiger in **Figure 1** and all other present-day animals might have evolved from choanoflagellates (KOH uh noh FLA juh layts), which are protists that formed colonies in the sea 570 million years ago. Choanoflagellates, such as the ones shown in **Figure 1,** might have been the earliest true animals. As animals evolved from this multicellular ancestor, they developed adaptations in structure that enabled them to function in numerous habitats. These features mark the branching points of the evolutionary tree and are discussed in the next section. In this section, you will learn about the characteristics that all animals have in common.

Feeding and Digestion

Animals are heterotrophic, so they must feed on other organisms to obtain nutrients. A sea star obtains its food from a clam it has pried open, and a butterfly feeds on nectar from a flower. The structure or form of an animal's mouth parts determines how its mouth functions. You can investigate how some animals obtain food by performing **MiniLab 1.** After obtaining their food, animals must digest it. Some animals, such as sponges, digest their food inside specific cells. Others, such as earthworms and humans, digest their food in internal body cavities or organs. **D**

Figure 1 Present-day animals, such as this Bengal tiger, might have evolved from choanoflagellates such as this colony of *Zoothamnium.*

Bengal tiger

LM Magnification: 50×

Colony of *Zoothamnium*

Demonstration

Family Tree Make a transparency of a fictitious family tree and project it on a screen. Explain that all the people depicted are related to each other.
ASK STUDENTS: ***Where are the family's original parents?*** at the bottom of the tree ***Which people are brothers and sisters?*** Brothers and sisters are directly above their parents. ***Which people are the youngest?*** the people at the top ***Which are the oldest?*** the people at the bottom ***How is this family tree like the classification of animals?*** Animals on their "tree" are grouped based on the adaptations they developed during the course of evolution.
Be sure students understand that an animal's family tree is not divided by generations like a human family tree. Est. time: 10 min

Support

Just as animals digest their food in different ways, they support their bodies in different ways. Between 95 and 99 percent of animal species are **invertebrates**—animals without backbones. The bodies of many invertebrates are covered with **exoskeletons,** which are hard or tough outer coverings that provide a framework of support. Exoskeletons also protect soft body tissues, prevent water loss, and provide protection from predators. As the animal grows, like the cicada in **Figure 2,** it must shed the old exoskeleton and make a new one. This process is called molting.

Some invertebrates, such as sea urchins and sea stars, have internal skeletons called **endoskeletons.** If an animal has an endoskeleton and a backbone, it is called a **vertebrate.** An endoskeleton grows with the animal, like the squirrel in **Figure 2.** The material making up the endoskeleton varies. Sea urchins and sea stars have endoskeletons made of calcium carbonate, sharks have endoskeletons made of cartilage, and fishes, amphibians, reptiles, birds, and mammals have endoskeletons made of bone. An endoskeleton protects internal organs, provides support for the body, and can provide an internal brace for muscles to pull against.

Reading Check **Distinguish** between vertebrates and invertebrates.

Habitats

D Animal bodies have a variety of adaptations, such as those for feeding, digestion, and support. These body variations enable animals to live in numerous habitats. Vertebrates and invertebrates live in oceans, in freshwater, and on land. They can be found in deserts, grasslands, rain forests, polar regions, and all other land biomes and aquatic ecosystems.

Cicada

Squirrel

■ **Figure 2** A cicada must shed its old exoskeleton (outlined in white) in order to grow.
A squirrel has an endoskeleton that grows as the squirrel grows.
***Infer** how an exoskeleton might be a disadvantage for animals.*

MiniLab 1

Investigate Feeding in Animals

? Inquiry MiniLab

How do animals obtain food? Small aquatic animals called hydras consume brine shrimp as their food source.

Procedure

1. Read and complete the lab safety form.
2. Obtain several **hydras** in a **plastic Petri dish** containing **water.**
3. Add several **brine shrimp** to the dish. Using a **hand lens or stereomicroscope,** observe the activity of the hydras.
4. Record your observations.

Analysis

1. **Draw Conclusions** Based on your observations, how do the hydras react to the food?
2. **Infer** What factors in their environment might influence how the hydras find food?

Reading Check Vertebrates are animals that have endoskeletons and backbones. Invertebrates do not have backbones.

■ **Caption Question Fig. 2** An exoskeleton is rigid and can restrict how large an animal can grow. An inverteberate must shed its exoskeleton in order to grow a new one.

D Develop Concepts

EL BL OL

Activate Prior Knowledge
Have students read the text under the heading *Habitats* and then create the following chart:

	Aquatic	Land
Vertebrates		
Invertebrates		

SAY TO STUDENTS: ***Make a list of animals that fit into these four categories.*** The squares should contain examples of aquatic vertebrates, land vertebrates, aquatic invertebrates, and land invertebrates.

MiniLab 1

? Inquiry MiniLab

For a lab worksheet, use your eTeacherEdition Online.

RUBRIC A rubric for evaluating MiniLabs is found on your eTeacherEdition Online.

Est. Time 60 min

Safety Precaution Approve lab safety forms before work begins.

Teaching Strategy Make sure the hydras have not been fed recently so they will be more likely to eat the brine shrimp.

Cleanup and Disposal Return animals to appropriate containers.

Analysis

1. Hydras use tentacles to capture and paralyze shrimp.
2. In a watery environment, the hydras must capture food as it moves past.

LabManager™
Customize this lab with the LabManager™ CD-ROM.

W Writing Support

AL Technical Writing Have students research and write detailed descriptions of a particular kind of tissue, and describe recent research and discoveries about this tissue. Students may select from muscle, blood, bone, nerve, or epidermal tissue.

S Skill Practice

BL OL AL COOP LEARN

Visual Literacy Have students study the time line in Figure 3, making note of the advances in systems of classification since the 1500s. In groups of two or three, have students select one classification scheme and prepare a "picture map" showing how effective they think it was on its own and how it advanced the scientific classification of animals. When creating a picture map, have students use pictures and symbols rather than words or phrases. Have each group share its picture map with the class.

Inquiry BioLab

The lab at the end of the chapter can be used at this point in the lesson.

CAREERS IN BIOLOGY

Systematist Using observation, inference, and the latest technology, a systematist classifies new species based on evolutionary relationships.

Animal Cell Structure

No matter where an animal lives or what adaptations it has, its cells do not have cell walls. Recall that plants also are multicellular organisms, but their cells have cell walls. The cells of all animals, except sponges, are organized into structural and functional units called tissues. A tissue is a group of cells that is specialized to perform a specific function. For example, nerve tissue is involved in the transmission of nerve impulses throughout the body and muscle tissue enables the body to move. W

Connection to History Beginning with Aristotle in the fourth century B.C. and continuing into the nineteenth century, living organisms were classified into two kingdoms—Animalia (animals) and Plantae (plants). In 1866, Ernst Haeckel, a German scientist, proposed adding a third kingdom called Protista. The organisms in this kingdom are mainly unicellular eukaryotes. Some protists have cell walls, while others do not, making them neither plant nor animal. During the 1960s, as more was learned about cell structure, bacteria and fungi were placed into their own kingdoms. **Figure 3** illustrates how the classification of living things continues to develop.

Movement

The evolution of nerve and muscle tissues enables animals to move in ways that are more complex and faster than organisms in other kingdoms. This is one notable characteristic of the animal kingdom. A gecko running across a ceiling, a mosquito buzzing around your ear, and a school of minnows swimming against the current are all exhibiting movements unique to animals. Some animals are stationary as adults, yet most have a body form that can move during some stage of development.

S

■ **Figure 3**

History of Classification

The process of scientifically classifying organisms began in 350 B.C. when Aristotle, a Greek philosopher, placed organisms into two large groups—plant and animal. Advances in scientific knowledge and technology helped develop the classification system we use today.

Concepts in Motion The Interactive Timeline

1500 — 1600 — 1700 — 1800

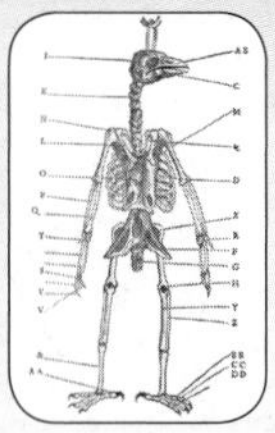

1555 The book *L'Histoire de la Nature des Oyseaux* (Natural History of Birds) uses body form and structures to classify species.

1682 Naturalist John Ray establishes the use of species as the basic unit of classification.

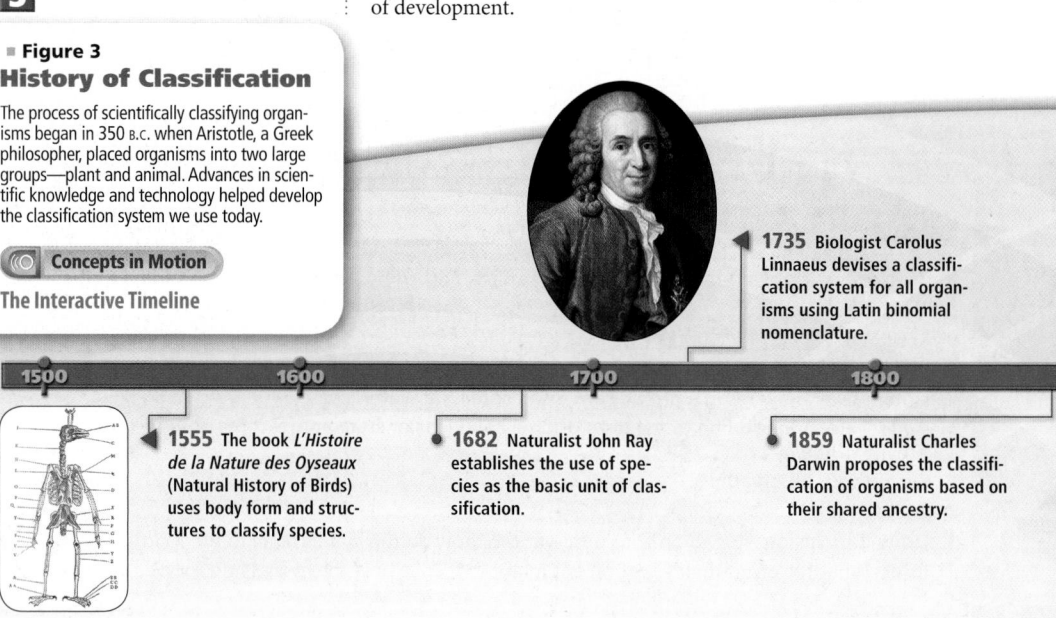

1735 Biologist Carolus Linnaeus devises a classification system for all organisms using Latin binomial nomenclature.

1859 Naturalist Charles Darwin proposes the classification of organisms based on their shared ancestry.

Demonstration

Tissues Set up four microscope stations with prepared slides of various types of tissues, such as bone marrow, muscle, blood, and epidermis. Have groups of students move from one station to the next to observe the various tissues. Because blood cells are difficult to see under classroom microscopes, be sure blood cells are observable on the prepared blood cell slides.

ASK STUDENTS: ***In what way are all the tissues alike?*** They are made of cells. Point out that the different types of cells are different in appearance, but all are cells.

Est. time: 10 min

Reproduction

Most animals reproduce sexually, although some species can reproduce asexually. Most commonly in sexual reproduction, male animals produce sperm and female animals produce eggs. Some animals, such as earthworms, are **hermaphrodites** (hur MAF ruh dites), which produce both eggs and sperm in the same animal body. In general, hermaphrodites produce eggs and sperm at different times, so another individual of the same species still is needed for sexual reproduction.

Fertilization occurs when the sperm penetrates the egg to form a fertilized egg cell called the **zygote** (ZI goht). Fertilization can be internal or external. **Internal fertilization** occurs when the sperm and egg combine inside the animal's body. For example, male turtles fertilize the eggs of the female internally. **External fertilization** occurs when egg and sperm combine outside the animal's body. This process requires an aquatic environment for the sperm to swim to the egg. In many fishes, the female lays eggs in the water and the male sheds sperm over the eggs, as shown in **Figure 4.**

Recall that asexual reproduction means that a single parent produces offspring that are genetically identical to itself. Although few animal species reproduce asexually, when they do, they use one or more methods to do so. Some of the common methods of asexual reproduction follow.

- budding—an offspring develops as a growth on the body of the parent
- fragmentation—the parent breaks into pieces and each piece can develop into an adult animal
- regeneration—a new organism can regenerate, or regrow, from the lost body part if the part contains enough genetic information
- parthenogenesis (par thuh noh JE nuh sus)—a female animal produces eggs that develop without being fertilized

Reading Check **Infer** the advantages and disadvantages of asexual reproduction in animals.

Figure 4 Fertilization is external in some fishes. In the photo, strands of sperm are being shed over eggs laid in the water.
Infer *why animals lay a large number of eggs when fertilization is external.*

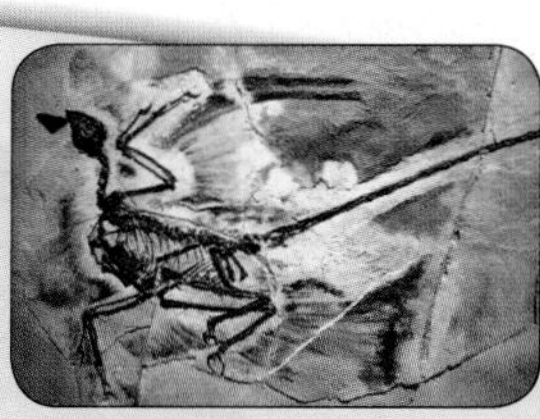

1891 Marine zoologist Mary Jane Rathbun begins establishing the basic taxonomic information on crustaceans.

1900

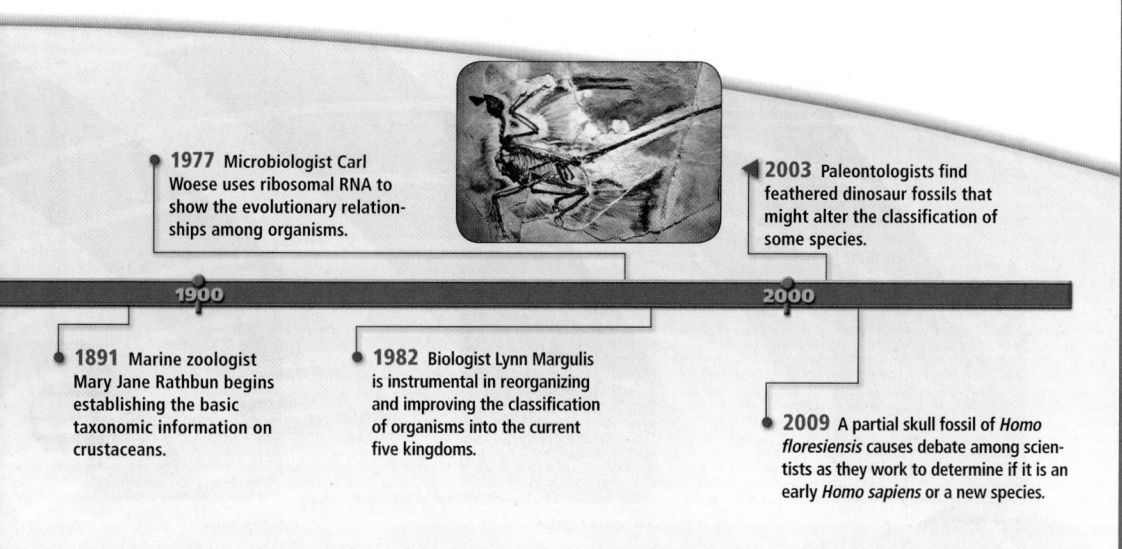

1977 Microbiologist Carl Woese uses ribosomal RNA to show the evolutionary relationships among organisms.

1982 Biologist Lynn Margulis is instrumental in reorganizing and improving the classification of organisms into the current five kingdoms.

2000

2003 Paleontologists find feathered dinosaur fossils that might alter the classification of some species.

2009 A partial skull fossil of *Homo floresiensis* causes debate among scientists as they work to determine if it is an early *Homo sapiens* or a new species.

R Reading Strategy

EL BL Preview the Text Have students list the new vocabulary words found on this page.
SAY TO STUDENTS: *Write down what you think are the meanings of the words or terms. Do not look in the glossary. After reading the text under the heading* **Reproduction,** *check your list. Correct your definitions according to what you have read.*

Writing Support

BL Summary Writing
Have students write a summary paragraph that describes the main characteristics of animals. They should write their summaries with wide margins for adding examples of these features in the margin.

Concepts in Motion
The Interactive Timeline

Caption Question Fig. 4 Many of the eggs laid externally do not survive, so it is necessary to provide many offspring to ensure that some survive.

Reading Check An advantage is that the offspring are genetically identical to the parent, and this preserves good genetic traits. A disadvantage is that because all the offspring are identical and there is no genetic diversity, the organism may be less able to adapt to changes in its environment.

Critical Thinking

BL OL AL Predict

ASK STUDENTS: ***If a pond in which turtles and fish are living almost dries up during a drought, what effect will this have on the animals' ability to reproduce?*** Turtles will still be able to reproduce, but fish reproduction rates may drop dramatically. ***Why will the reproductive rates be affected this way?*** Turtles reproduce through internal fertilization. Many fish reproduce through external fertilization and require an aquatic environment although some species can fertilize internally. With less water, fewer fish sperm can reach the eggs and fertilized eggs could dry out.

D Develop Concepts

EL BL OL COOP LEARN

Activity Provide groups of students with clay or salt dough. Salt dough: mix equal parts salt and flour. Add water until the mixture forms a smooth round ball and is not sticky.

SAY TO STUDENTS: ***Make the stages of cell differentiation using this material. Make sure you show the process in sequence with one stage sequencing into the next stage.*** As you check students' work, make sure they understand that the stages do not increase in size from the fertilized egg to the gastrula.

ASK STUDENTS: ***How does the blastula form?*** by cell division ***Why is this process important?*** This is the process of forming different types of tissues in an animal.

Concepts in Motion

Animation

VOCABULARY

WORD ORIGIN

Gastrula

gastr– prefix; from Greek; meaning *stomach* or *belly*

–ula suffix; from Latin; meaning *resembling*

D

■ **Figure 5** The fertilized eggs of most animals follow a similar pattern of development. Beginning with one fertilized egg cell, cell division occurs and a gastrula is formed.

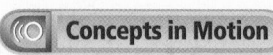

Concepts in Motion

Animation

Early development In most animals, the zygote undergoes mitosis and a series of cell divisions to form new cells. After the first cell division, in which the zygote forms two cells, the developing animal is called an embryo. The embryo continues to undergo mitosis and cell division, forming a solid ball of cells. These cells continue to divide, forming a fluid-filled ball of cells called the **blastula** (BLAS chuh luh), as shown in **Figure 5.** During these early stages of development, the number of cells increases, but the total amount of cytoplasm in the embryo remains the same as that in the original cell. Therefore, the total size of the embryo does not increase during early development.

In animals such as lancelets, the outer blastula is a single layer of cells, while in animals such as frogs, there might be several layers of cells surrounding the fluid. The blastula continues to undergo cell division. Some cells move inward to form a **gastrula** (GAS truh luh), a two-cell-layer sac with an opening at one end. A gastrula looks like a double bubble, one bubble inside another bubble.

Look again at **Figure 5.** Notice how the diagrams of the two-cell stage, the 16-cell stage, and the blastula differ from the photographs of these same stages. The diagrams illustrate early development in embryos that develop inside the adult animal. The photographs illustrate early development in embryos that develop outside of the adult animal. The large ball that does not divide is the yolk sac. It provides food for the developing embryo.

Reading Check **Explain** the differences between the blastula and the gastrula.

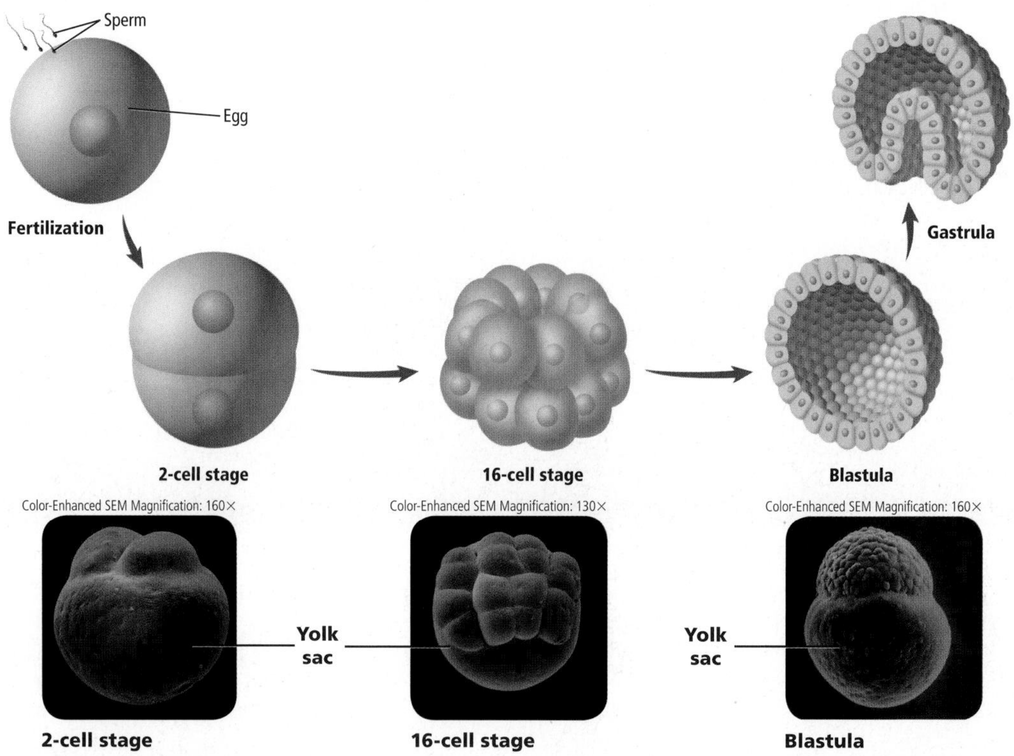

Reading Check A blastula is a fluid-filled ball of cells. A gastrula is a sac with two cell layers and an opening at one end.

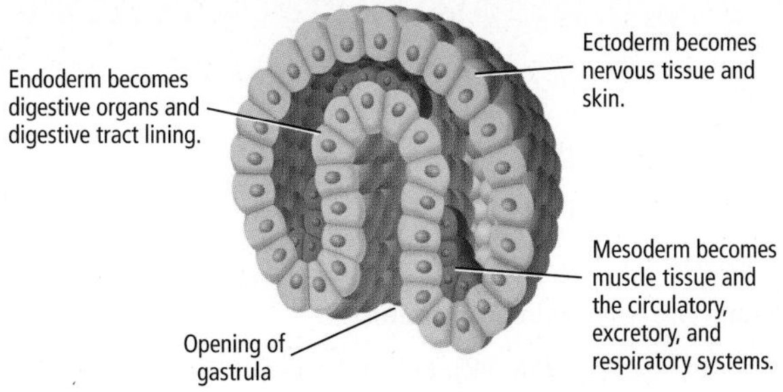
Endoderm becomes digestive organs and digestive tract lining.
Ectoderm becomes nervous tissue and skin.
Mesoderm becomes muscle tissue and the circulatory, excretory, and respiratory systems.
Opening of gastrula

■ **Figure 6** As development continues, each cell layer differentiates into specialized tissues.

Tissue development Notice in **Figure 6** that the inner layer of cells in the gastrula is called the **endoderm.** The endoderm cells develop into the digestive organs and the lining of the digestive tract. The outer layer of cells in the gastrula is called the **ectoderm.** The ectoderm cells in the gastrula continue to grow and become the nervous tissue and skin.

Cell division in some animals continues in the gastrula until another layer of cells, called the **mesoderm,** forms between the endoderm and the ectoderm. In some animals, the mesoderm forms from cells that break away from the endoderm near the opening of the gastrula. In more highly evolved animals, the mesoderm forms from pouches of endoderm cells on the inside of the gastrula. As development continues, mesoderm cells become muscle tissue, the circulatory system, the excretory system, and, in some species of animals, the respiratory system.

Remember that Hox genes might be expressed in ways that give proteins new properties that cause variations in animals. Much of the variation in animal bodies is the result of changes in location, number, or time of expression of Hox developmental genes during the course of tissue development.

Inquiry Launch Lab

Review Based on what you have read about animal characteristics, how would you now answer the analysis questions?

Section 1 Assessment

Section Summary

- Animals are heterotrophs and must get their nutrients from other organisms.
- Animals have diverse means of support and live in diverse habitats.
- Animal cells do not have cell walls, and most have cells that are organized into tissues.
- Most animals undergo sexual reproduction, and most can move.
- During embryonic development, animal cells become tissue layers, which become organs and systems.

Understand Main Ideas

1. MAIN Idea **Infer** why colonial organisms that lived grouped together might have been one of the first steps toward multicellular organisms in the course of evolution.
2. **Infer** how an exoskeleton enables invertebrates to live in a variety of habitats.
3. **Describe** how the evolution of nerve and muscle tissue is related to one of the main characteristics of animals.
4. **Diagram** how an animal zygote becomes a gastrula.

Think Critically

5. **Model** the stages of cell differentiation in embryonic development by comparing them to pushing in the end of a balloon. Draw a diagram of this process and label it with the stages of cell differentiation.

MATH in Biology

6. Biologists have observed that it is common for an animal that doubles its mass to increase its length 1.26 times. Suppose an animal has a mass of 2.5 kg and is 30 cm long. If this animal grows to a mass of 5 kg, how long will it be?

Inquiry Launch Lab

Assess Content Development
Assess how understanding has developed when students revisit the Launch Lab analysis questions.

Formative Assessment

Evaluation Obtain a transparency or picture showing the stages of cell differentiation covered in Figures 5 and 6. (Pages 696 and 697 are available electronically on your eTeacherEdition Online.) Make sure the stages illustrated do not have captions or labels. Cover the labels if projecting images from the book. Project the image for the class to see.

ASK STUDENTS: ***What is this process?*** cell differentiation ***Why is it important?*** Possible Answer: Cell differentiation is important for animals to develop a variety of tissues. Have students list the stages in order and compare answers.

Remediation Have students make flash cards and write the name of each development stage on one side of the card. On the other side, have them draw a picture of the stage to help them review and reinforce knowledge of cell differentiation and tissue development.

Section 1 Assessment

1. Choanoflagellate colonies might have evolved from a group of unicellular protists to a multicellular organism, leading to the multicellular ancestor of animals.
2. Answers will vary but might include that an exoskeleton helps prevent water loss so animals can live in the water and on land.
3. Muscle and nerve tissues enable animals to move. The more advanced the muscular and nervous systems, the more complex the movements.
4. Diagram should show all the stages in Figure 5.
5. A balloon is like a blastula. Pushing in the end represents the formation of the gastrula. Diagrams should have stages properly labeled.
6. $1.26 \times 30 = 37.8$ cm

Assessment Online Quiz

Section 2

MAIN Idea

BL OL AL Evolutionary Tree Using the evolutionary tree in Figure 8 as a model, begin to draw an evolutionary tree on the board. Start with one line and label it *Multicellularity.*

ASK STUDENTS: ***What is the earliest branching point?*** tissues and no true tissues Draw two branches and label them *tissues* and *no true tissues.* ***What is the next branching point?*** radial symmetry and bilateral symmetry Continue to draw branching points, asking students for the next step each time. Explain that the relatedness of animals can be inferred by studying the anatomical features they share and by examining their embryological development.

Develop Concepts

EL BL OL AL

Clarify a Misconception

ASK STUDENTS: ***What are some examples of tissues?*** Students may think tissues are solid sheets or blocks of cells in muscle, bone, and skin. Blood and nerves are also tissues. Have students examine prepared slides of blood and neural tissue under a microscope. Explain the functions of blood and neural tissue.

Section 2

Reading Preview

Essential Questions

- How are animal body plans related to phylogeny?
- How are body cavities related to animal phylogeny?
- What are the two types of coelomate development?

Review Vocabulary

phylogeny: evolutionary history of a species based on comparative relationships of structures and comparisons of modern life-forms with fossils

New Vocabulary

symmetry
radial symmetry
bilateral symmetry
anterior
posterior
cephalization
dorsal
ventral
coelom
pseudocoelom
acoelomate
protostome
deuterostome

Multilingual eGlossary

Animal Body Plans

MAIN Idea Animal phylogeny can be determined, in part, by body plans and the ways animals develop.

Real-World Reading Link People often classify or group things based on what they have in common. If you want to rent an action movie, you would look in the action movie section at the store. You would not find comedies or dramas in this section. In biology, animals generally are classified into groups because they have some of the same features.

Evolution of Animal Body Plans

Recall that the evolutionary tree is organized like a family tree, and the phylogeny of animals is represented by the branches. For example, all of the mammals in **Figure 7** belong on the chordate branch of the tree. The trunk represents the earliest animals and the branches represent the probable evolution of the major phyla of animals from a common ancestor, as shown in **Figure 8.**

Anatomical features in animals' body plans mark the branching points on the evolutionary tree. For example, animals without tissues are grouped separately from animals with tissues, and animals without segments are grouped separately from animals with segments. The relationships among animals on this tree are inferred by studying similarities in embryological development and shared anatomical features. This traditional phylogeny, with animals classified into 35 phyla, is still used by most taxonomists. However, molecular data suggest other relationships among animals. Recent molecular findings, based on comparisons of DNA, ribosomal RNA, and proteins, indicate that the relationships between arthropods and nematodes and between flatworms and rotifers might be closer than anatomical features suggest.

Reading Check **Summarize** the structure of an evolutionary tree.

Figure 7 Although these animals look very different from each other, they all have features that place them on the chordate branch of the evolutionary tree.

Mouse

Ferret

Chimpanzee

Reading Check The base of the tree represents the earliest animals and branches represent the evolution of the major phyla of animals based on scientific evidence.

Development of Tissues

As animals evolved from the first multicellular forms, the first anatomical feature to indicate a major change in body plan was the development of tissues. Therefore, tissues mark the first branching point on the evolutionary tree. Notice in **Figure 8** that the only animals without tissues are sponges. These animals descended from a common ancestor that lacked tissues, and they are on the no-true-tissue branch of the evolutionary tree. Follow the tissue branch of the evolutionary tree, and you will see that all other phyla have tissues.

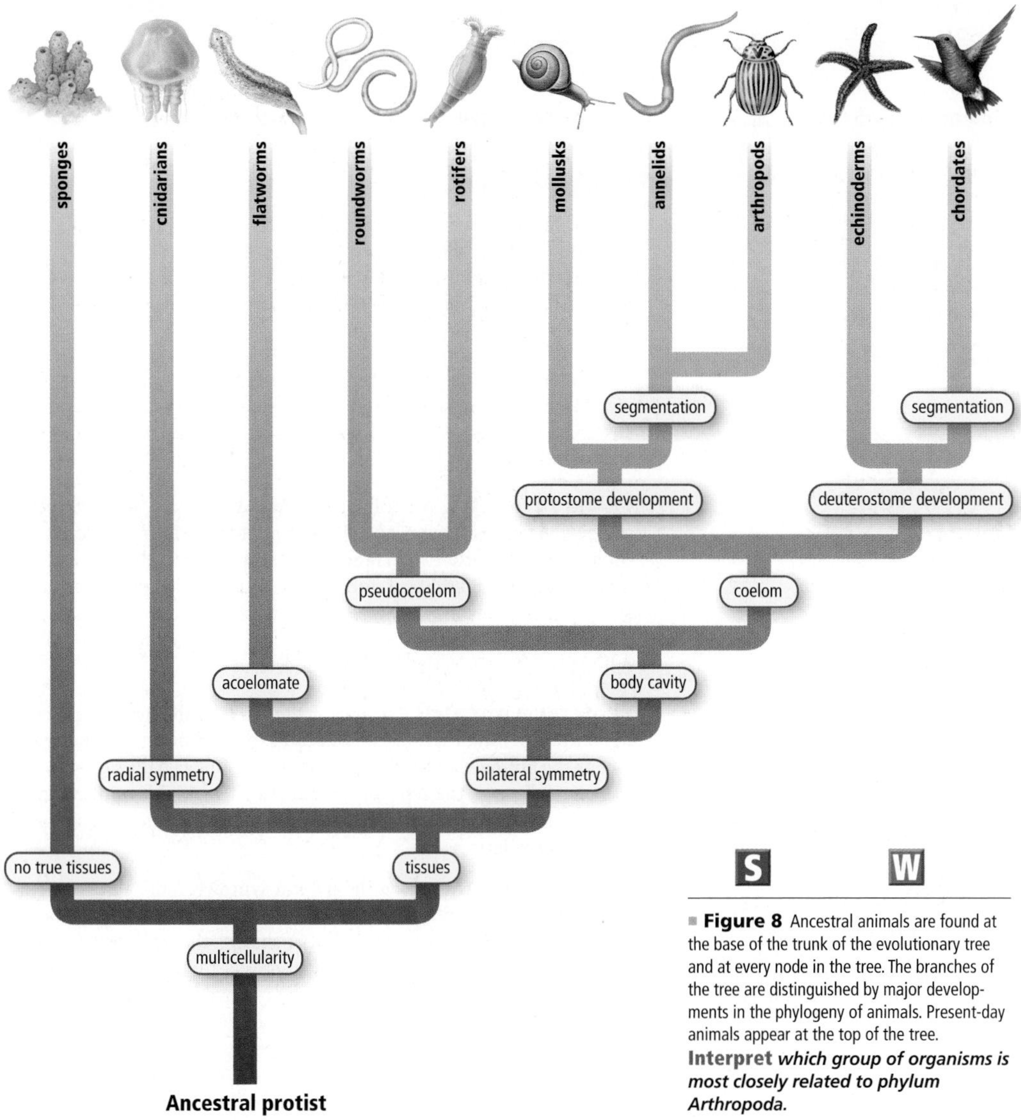

S W

■ **Figure 8** Ancestral animals are found at the base of the trunk of the evolutionary tree and at every node in the tree. The branches of the tree are distinguished by major developments in the phylogeny of animals. Present-day animals appear at the top of the tree.
Interpret ***which group of organisms is most closely related to phylum Arthropoda.***

S Skill Practice

BL OL AL Visual Literacy

ASK STUDENTS: ***How is time shown in Figure 8?*** The lowest branches are the oldest. Branches higher on the page are the most recent. ***What do the branching points represent?*** the significant new features that evolved to produce new animal species ***Which animal group evolved first?*** sponges ***Which animal group is the most recent?*** chordates ***Which animal group evolved just before chordates?*** echinoderms ***Which animal groups have a pseudocoelom?*** roundworms and rotifers ***What do echinoderms and chordates have in common?*** deuterostome development

W Writing Support

OL Technical Writing Have students describe Figure 8 in two paragraphs. In the first paragraph, have them use examples from the diagram to explain how time is represented. In the second paragraph, have them use examples from the diagram to explain how the animal groups evolved and how they are classified.

GOING GREEN When you purchase pens, buy the refillable types. Also, when you loan pens to students, tape a paper flag, a silk flower, or other object to the pen. This will remind students to return the pen at the end of class.

Differentiated Instruction

Visually Impaired When interpreting illustrations as suggested on this page, be sure to make modifications that will allow students who are visually impaired to participate. Verbally describe any visual information that is presented so that students understand the concepts.

For more tips, see pages 14T–15T.

■ **Caption Question Fig. 8** Phylum Annelida is most closely related to phylum Arthropoda because members of these phyla have a common ancestor.

D Develop Concepts

EL BL OL AL COOP LEARN

Discuss Before students read the text under the heading *Symmetry,* put them in groups of three or four and have them agree on a definition of the term *symmetry.* Once they have discussed their definition, have students read the text under the heading *Symmetry.* Students should then compare their definition to what they have read in the text.

ASK STUDENTS: ***What kind of symmetry do a rock and tree branch have?*** asymmetry ***A daisy or dandelion flower and a wheel?*** radial symmetry ***A chair and a table?*** Both have bilateral symmetry.

R Reading Strategy

BL OL COOP LEARN

Question a Partner After reading the text under the heading *Cephalization,* have students form pairs. Give students cards with questions. For example, have Student A ask Student B: ***How does* cephalization *relate to the words* anterior *and* posterior?** Animals with cephalization have a head, or anterior end, where nervous and sensory organs are located, and a tail, or posterior end. Then, have Student B ask Student A: ***What do the terms* dorsal *and* ventral *have to do with bilateral symmetry?*** Bilaterally symmetrical animals have a dorsal surface, or backside, and a ventral surface, or underside.

■ **Caption Question Fig. 9** Answers will vary, but might include desks, chairs, and other people.

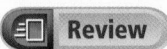

Review Personal Tutor

Listen to a teacher explain symmetry.

Video BrainPOP

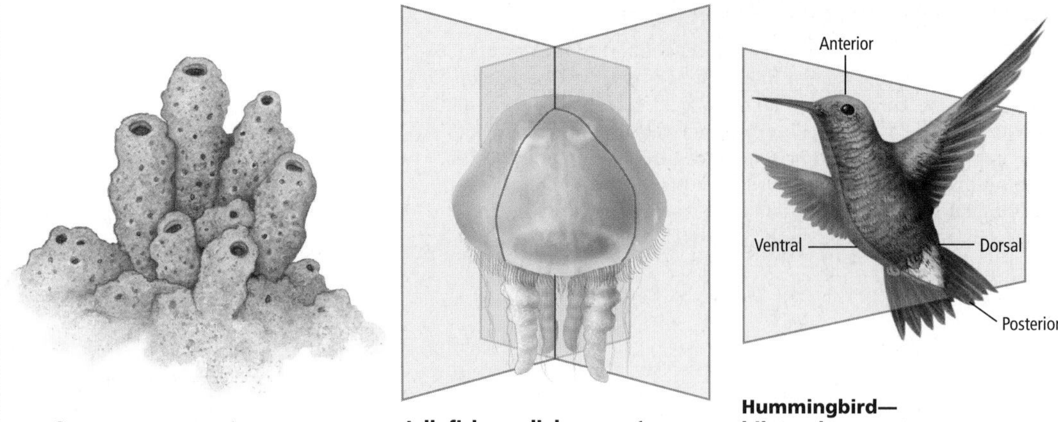

Sponge—asymmetry **Jellyfish—radial symmetry** **Hummingbird—bilateral symmetry**

■ **Figure 9** Animals have different arrangements of body structures. The sponge has an irregular shape and is asymmetrical. The jellyfish has radial symmetry, and the hummingbird has bilateral symmetry.

***List** objects in the classroom that have bilateral symmetry.*

Review Personal Tutor

D Symmetry

Move along the tissue branch on the evolutionary tree in **Figure 8,** and you will find the next branching point to be symmetry. **Symmetry** (SIH muh tree) describes the similarity or balance among body structures of organisms. The type of symmetry an animal has enables it to move in certain ways.

Asymmetry The sponge in **Figure 9** has no tissue and has asymmetry. It is irregular in shape and has no symmetry or balance in its body structures. In contrast, animals with tissues have either radial or bilateral symmetry.

Radial symmetry An animal with **radial** (RAY dee uhl) **symmetry** can be divided along any plane, through a central axis, into roughly equal halves. The jellyfish in **Figure 9** has radial symmetry. Its tentacles radiate from its mouth in all directions, a body plan adapted to detecting and capturing prey moving in from any direction. Jellyfishes and most other animals with radial symmetry develop from only two embryonic cell layers—the ectoderm and the endoderm.

Video BrainPOP

Bilateral symmetry The bird in **Figure 9** has bilateral symmetry. In contrast to radial symmetry, **bilateral** (bi LA tuh rul) **symmetry** means the animal can be divided into mirror image halves only along one plane through the central axis. All animals with bilateral symmetry develop from three embryonic cell layers—the ectoderm, the endoderm, and the mesoderm.

VOCABULARY

SCIENCE USAGE V. COMMON USAGE

Plane

Science usage: an imaginary line that divides a body form into two parts
The dog can be divided into its ventral and dorsal parts by a plane.

Common usage: an aircraft
The pilot flew the plane from Cleveland to Chicago.

Cephalization Animals with bilateral symmetry also have an **anterior,** or head end, and a **posterior,** or tail end. This body plan is called **cephalization** (sef uh luh ZA shun)—the tendency to concentrate nervous tissue and sensory organs at the anterior end of the animal. Most animals with cephalization move through their environments with the anterior end first, encountering food and other stimuli. In addition to cephalization, animals with bilateral symmetry have a **dorsal** (DOR sul) surface, also called the backside, and a **ventral** (VEN trul) surface, also called the underside or belly. R

Demonstration

BL OL Symmetry Bring in household items such as a bowl and a straight drinking straw.

ASK STUDENTS: ***What kind of symmetry do these items have?*** radial symmetry Show them a fork and a spoon. ***What kind of symmetry do these items have?*** bilateral symmetry Explain that symmetry is related to function in objects and animals. For example, a screwdriver with radial symmetry turns to drive in screws and an animal with radial symmetry can obtain food or perceive danger coming from any direction. Est. time: 5 min

Body Cavities

In order to understand the next branching point on the evolutionary tree, it is important to know about certain features of animals with bilateral symmetry. Body plans of animals with bilateral symmetry include the gut, which is either a sac inside the body or a tube that runs through the body, where food is digested. A saclike gut has one opening, a mouth, for taking in food and disposing of wastes. A tubelike gut has an opening at both ends, mouth and an anus, and is a complete digestive system that digests, absorbs, and stores food, and disposes of waste.

Coelomates Between the gut and the outside body wall of most animals with bilateral symmetry is a fluid-filled body cavity. One type of fluid-filled cavity, the **coelom** (SEE lum), shown in **Figure 10,** has tissue formed from mesoderm that lines and encloses the organs in the coelom. You have a coelom, as do insects, fishes, and many other animals. Therefore, you are a coelomate. The coelom was a key adaptation in the evolution of larger and more specialized body structures. Specialized organs and body systems that formed from mesoderm developed in the coelom. As more efficient organ systems evolved, such as the circulatory system and muscular system, animals could increase in size and become more active.

Pseudocoelomates Follow the body cavity branch on the evolutionary tree in **Figure 8** until you come to the pseudocoelomates, which are animals with pseudocoeloms. A **pseudocoelom** (soo duh SEE lum) is a fluid-filled body cavity that develops between the mesoderm and the endoderm rather than developing entirely within the mesoderm as in coelomates. Therefore, the pseudocoelom, as shown in **Figure 10,** is lined only partially with mesoderm. The body cavity of pseudocoelomates separates mesoderm and endoderm, which limits tissue, organ, and system development.

Acoelomates Before the body cavity branch on the evolutionary tree in **Figure 8,** notice that the branch to the left takes you to the acoelomate animals. **Acoelomates** (ay SEE lum ayts), such as the flatworm in **Figure 10,** are animals that do not have a coelom. The body plan of acoelomates is derived from ectoderm, endoderm, and mesoderm—the same as in coelomates and pseudocoelomates. However, acoelomates have solid bodies without a fluid-filled body cavity between the gut and the body wall. Nutrients and wastes diffuse from one cell to

D another because there is no circulatory system.

Review Personal Tutor

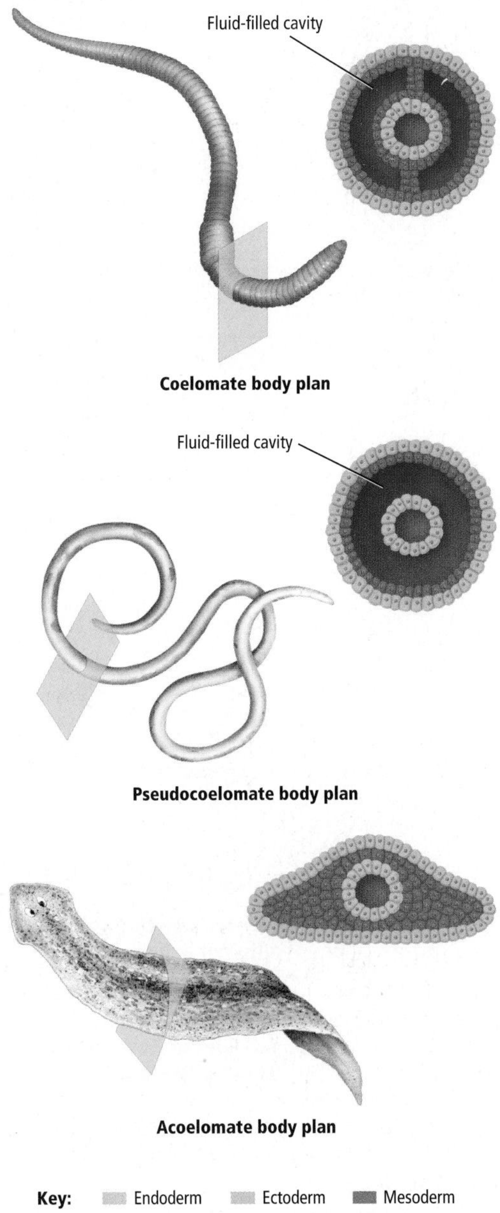

■ **Figure 10** An earthworm has a coelom, a fluid-filled body cavity surrounded completely by mesoderm. The pseudocoelom of a roundworm develops between the mesoderm and endoderm. A flatworm has a solid body without a fluid-filled cavity.

"An education isn't how much you have committed to memory, or even how much you know. It's being able to differentiate between what you do know and what you don't."

—Anatole France

Review Personal Tutor

Listen to a teacher explain body cavities.

FOLDABLES®

RUBRIC A rubric for evaluating Foldables is found on your eTeacherEdition Online.

Going Further Have students draw a Venn diagram on the back of their Foldables to compare and contrast pseudocoelomates and coelomates.

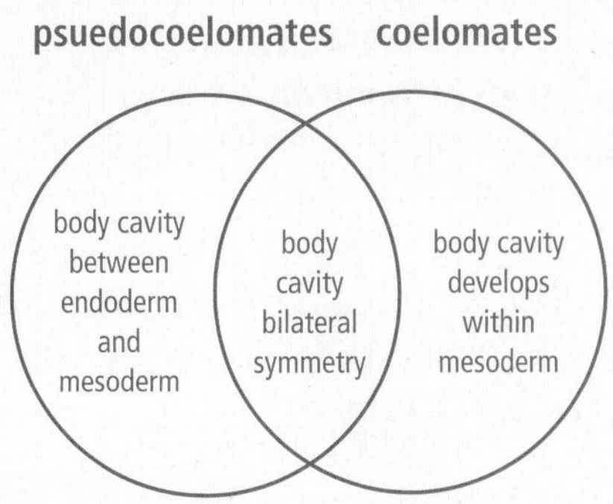

D Develop Concepts

OL AL Scaffolding

ASK STUDENTS: ***What is a coelom?*** It is a fluid-filled body cavity that has tissue formed from mesoderm that lines and encloses the organs in the coelom. ***Explain why it is important.*** A coelom enables animals to develop specialized organ systems, grow large, and move more easily. ***Identify a pseudocoelom.*** It is a fluid-filled body cavity that develops between the mesoderm and the endoderm rather than developing entirely within the mesoderm as in coelomates. The pseudocoelom is only partially lined with mesoderm. ***Analyze its importance.*** Because this body cavity separates mesoderm and endoderm tissue, organ and system development is limited. ***Define the term* acoelomate *and explain its importance.*** Acoelomates, such as flatworms, are animals that do not have a coelom. Their bodies are solid with no fluid-filled cavity to allow space for organ, tissue, and system development.

Critical Thinking

BL OL AL Infer In the early 1900s, German scientist Hans Spemann showed that two normal amphibian embryos form if an area called the gray crescent is divided equally between the eggs at the two-cell stage of development. When the gray crescent is only in one cell, only one normal embryo develops.

ASK STUDENTS: ***Infer why this might happen.*** The gray crescent has something essential for proper development.

MiniLab 2

? Inquiry MiniLab

For a lab worksheet, use your eTeacherEdition Online.

RUBRIC A rubric for evaluating MiniLabs is found on your eTeacherEdition Online.

Est. Time 30 min

Alternative Materials Micrographs of the cross sections

Safety Precaution Approve lab safety forms before work begins.

Teaching Strategy The slides and diagrams might show different portions. Help students compare slides to diagrams.

Analysis

1. The hydra has a gastrovascular cavity but no true body cavity and is acoelomate. The earthworm has a coelom and a digestive tract and is coelomate. They do not share a recent common ancestor.
2. The earthworm, with a coelom, is capable of more complex movement than the hydra.

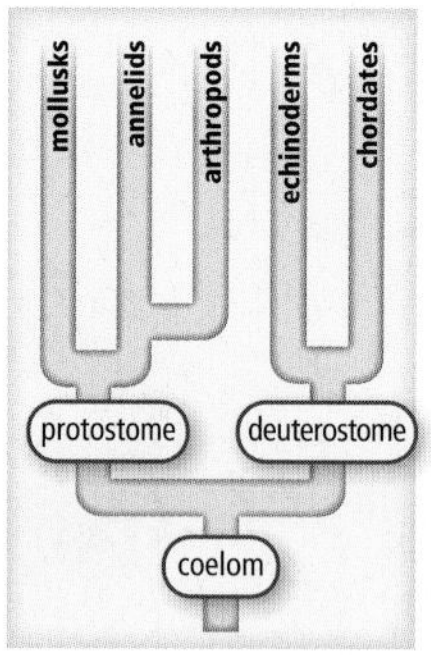

■ **Figure 11** This part of the evolutionary tree shows that protostomes and deuterostomes are branches of coelomate animals.

Development in Coelomate Animals

The evolutionary tree in **Figure 11** begins at the coelomate branch. Notice that two major lines of development have been identified in coelomate animals. One is protostome development, which occurs in animals such as snails, earthworms, and spiders. The other is deuterostome development, which occurs in animals such as sea urchins, dogs, and birds. Biologists can tell if animals are closely related based on their patterns of embryonic development.

Protostomes In organisms that are **protostomes** (PROH tuh stohms), the mouth develops from the first opening in the gastrula. As protostomes develop, the final outcome for each cell in the embryo cannot be altered. If one cell of the embryo is removed, the embryo will not develop into a normal larva, as shown in **Figure 12.** In addition, in the eight-cell stage of embryonic development, the top four cells are offset from the bottom four cells, giving the embryo a spiral appearance. As the embryo continues to develop, the mesoderm splits down the middle. The cavity between the two pieces of mesoderm becomes the coelom.

Deuterostomes In organisms that are **deuterostomes** (DEW tihr uh stohms), the anus develops from the first opening in the gastrula. The mouth develops later from another opening of the gastrula. During the development of deuterostomes, the final outcome for each cell in the embryo can be altered. In fact, each cell in the early embryo, if removed, can form a new embryo, as shown in **Figure 12.** In contrast to protostome development, in the eight-cell stage of embryonic deuterostome development the top four cells are directly aligned on the bottom four cells. As the embryo develops, the coelom forms from two pouches of mesoderm.

Reading Check **Determine** whether you are classified as a protosome or a deuterostome. Explain.

MiniLab 2

Examine Body Plans

? Inquiry MiniLab

What is the importance of a body plan? One way to classify animals is by body plan. Looking at cross sections of different animals can help you distinguish between the different body plans.

Procedure

1. Read and complete the lab safety form.
2. Obtain **prepared slides of cross sections of an earthworm and a hydra.** Using a **microscope,** observe each slide under low-power magnification.
3. Sketch each cross section.
4. Obtain **labeled diagrams of cross sections of each animal** from your teacher. Make a list of how your sketches are like the diagrams and another list of how they are different.

Analysis

1. **Compare and contrast** each animal's type of body cavity. Are they acoelomate or coelomate? What do your observations tell you about the phylogeny of these animals?
2. **Infer** how the body plan of each animal is related to how each of these animals obtains food.

Reading Check Human beings and all other mammals are deuterostomes.

Visualizing Protostome and Deuterostome Development

Figure 12
Developmental differences characterize protostome and deuterostome development.

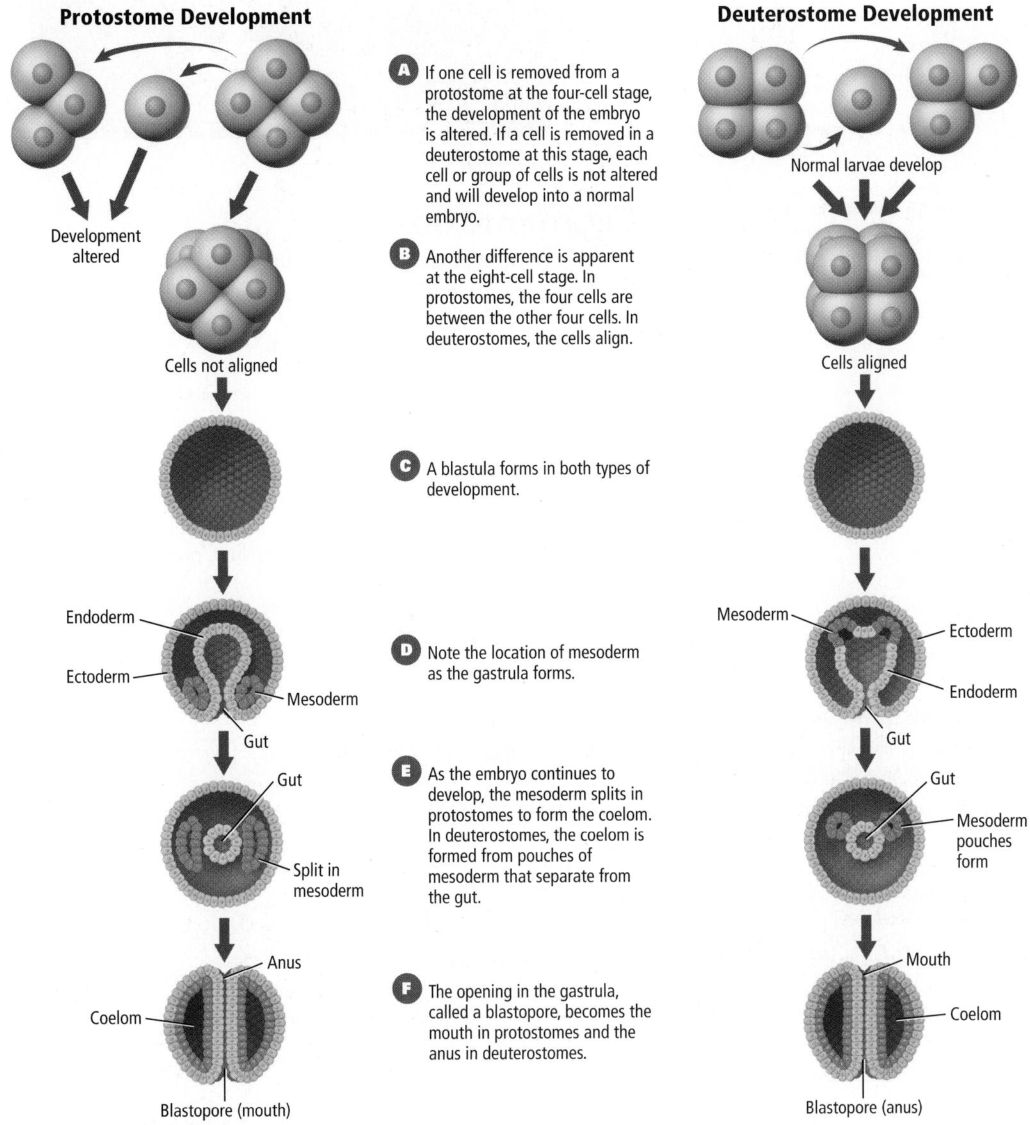

Protostome Development
Deuterostome Development
A If one cell is removed from a protostome at the four-cell stage, the development of the embryo is altered. If a cell is removed in a deuterostome at this stage, each cell or group of cells is not altered and will develop into a normal embryo.
Development altered
Normal larvae develop
B Another difference is apparent at the eight-cell stage. In protostomes, the four cells are between the other four cells. In deuterostomes, the cells align.
Cells not aligned
Cells aligned
C A blastula forms in both types of development.
Endoderm
Ectoderm
Mesoderm
Gut
D Note the location of mesoderm as the gastrula forms.
Mesoderm
Ectoderm
Endoderm
Gut
Gut
Split in mesoderm
E As the embryo continues to develop, the mesoderm splits in protostomes to form the coelom. In deuterostomes, the coelom is formed from pouches of mesoderm that separate from the gut.
Gut
Mesoderm pouches form
Anus
Coelom
Blastopore (mouth)
F The opening in the gastrula, called a blastopore, becomes the mouth in protostomes and the anus in deuterostomes.
Mouth
Coelom
Blastopore (anus)

Concepts in Motion Animation

Visualizing Protostome and Deuterostome Development

Purpose

Students will sequence the development of tissues in protostome and deuterostome animals.
C.1, C.3

Develop Concepts

OL AL COOP LEARN

Activity Divide the class into groups of two or three. Have each group research protostome and deuterostome development in a college-level developmental biology book and make a poster with diagrams of the two types of development and captions that explain the development in depth and detail. Display the posters for all students to examine.

Concepts in Motion
Animation

Research Citation

Formative Assessment Educational research indicates that teachers should assess student understanding on an ongoing basis throughout a lesson. Formative assessments, such as the ones provided at the end of each section, allow teachers to be proactive when modifying their curriculum and instruction to best meet student needs. (Tomlinson, et al., 2003)

Research bibliography on pages 32T–34T

D Develop Concepts

EL BL OL AL Illustrate Have students read the text under the heading *Segmentation.* Then, in pairs, have them make a one-frame cartoon that depicts the advantages of segmentation to the animal mentioned in the reading. Encourage them to be creative, but to be sure to present accurate biology. They might want to make a talking box for the animal to explain what is going on in the cartoon.

Formative Assessment

Evaluation Make three transparencies or pictures of the three body plans shown in Figure 10. (Page 701 is available electronically on your eTeacherEdition Online.) Be sure your images do not contain captions or labels. Project the images for the students to see. Ask the following for each image:

ASK STUDENTS: ***What body plan does this represent?*** Answers should reflect the body plan shown.

Remediation Have students make color diagrams of cross sections of acoelomate, pseudocoelomate, and coelomate body plans, using the same colors as the text for the endoderm, ectoderm, and mesoderm.

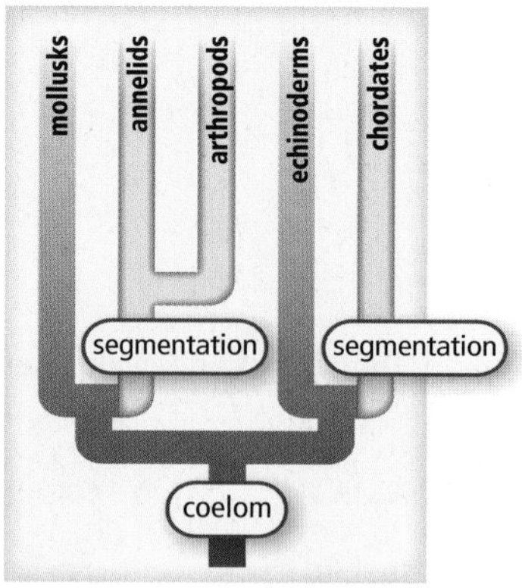

Scorpion

■ **Figure 13** Segmentation enables a scorpion to move its stinger in different directions to attack prey or for defense.

Segmentation

D Examine the next branching point on the evolutionary tree in **Figure 13.** Segmentation is an important feature in the evolution of coelomate animals. Just as a chain is constructed from a series of links, segmented animals can be "put together" from a succession of similar parts.

The segmentation, such as that seen in scorpions, has two advantages. First, segmented animals can survive damage to one segment because other segments might be able to carry out the damaged section's function. Second, movement is more effective because segments can move independently. Therefore, the scorpion in **Figure 13** has more flexibility and can move in ways that are very complex. Segments allow the scorpion to arch its tail over its back to sting prey.

Section 2 Assessment

Section Summary

- Animal phylogeny can be compared to a tree with branches.
- The branches of a phylogenetic evolutionary tree show the relationships among animals.
- Animal phylogeny can be determined, in part, by the animal's type of body cavity or lack of a body cavity.
- After gastrulation, two types of development can occur in coelomate animals.
- Segmentation is an important feature in some coelomate animals.

Understand Main Ideas

1. MAIN Idea **Explain** how body symmetry is related to the phylogeny of animals.
2. **Name** the features marking the main branching points on the evolutionary tree of animals.
3. **Illustrate** how body cavities distinguish branches of development of animals with bilateral symmetry.
4. **Compare and contrast** deuterostome and protostome development.

Think Critically

5. **Diagram** animals not shown in **Figure 9** that have radial and bilateral symmetry. Indicate the type of symmetry by showing planes passing through the animals. Label each animal as having either radial or bilateral symmetry.

WRITING in Biology

6. Write a paragraph summarizing the differences among coelomates, pseudocoelomates, and acoelomates.

Section 2 Assessment

1. The phylogeny can be determined, in part, by body plan symmetry.
2. tissues, types of symmetry, presence and types of body cavities, types of development, segmentation
3. no body cavity—acoelomates; body cavity not completely lined with mesoderm—pseudocoelomates; body cavity completely lined with mesoderm—coelomates
4. Protostome: final outcome of embryo cells cannot be altered, mouth develops from the first opening in the gastrula; deuterostome: outcome of embryo cells can be altered, anus develops from the first opening in the gastrula
5. Answers might include dog, cat, or fish for bilateral symmetry, and medusa stage of a jellyfish for radial symmetry.
6. Paragraphs should define the three types of body cavities.

WRITING in Biology

RUBRIC Use the modifiable rubric found on your eTeacherEdition Online to assess writing assignments.

Assessment Online Quiz

Reading Preview

Essential Questions

- What are the characteristics of sponges and cnidarians?
- How are sponges and cnidarians alike and different?
- What is the ecological importance of sponges and cnidarians?

Review Vocabulary

diploid: cell with two of each kind of chromosome

New Vocabulary

filter feeder
sessile
cnidocytes
nematocyst
gastrovascular cavity
nerve net
polyp
medusa

g Multilingual eGlossary

Sponges and Cnidarians

MAIN Idea Sponges and cnidarians were the first animals to evolve from a multicellular ancestor.

Real-World Reading Link Have you ever double-bagged your groceries? If so, you have an idea of how a sponge is structured—a layer, or sac, of cells within another sac of cells. These sacs of cells are among the first animals to evolve from the common ancestor of all animals.

Sponges

If you examine a living sponge, you might wonder how these animals do so much with so little. They have no tissues, no organs, and most have no symmetry. You can break apart a sponge into its individual cells and those cells will come together again to form a sponge. Other animals cannot do this.

Locate sponges on the evolutionary tree in **Figure 14.** They are in the phylum Porifera (po RIF uh ruh), which contains between 5000 and 10,000 members. Most live in marine environments. Biologists hypothesize that sponges evolved from the colonial choanoflagellates because sponges have cells that look similar to these protist cells.

D **Body structure** Notice the asymmetrical appearance and bright colors of the sponge in **Figure 14.** It is difficult to think that these are animals, especially if you see one washed up on a beach where it might appear as a black blob. Recall that tissues form from ectoderm, endoderm, and mesoderm in a developing embryo. Sponge embryos do not develop endoderm or mesoderm, and, therefore, sponges do not develop tissues. How does a sponge's body function without tissues?

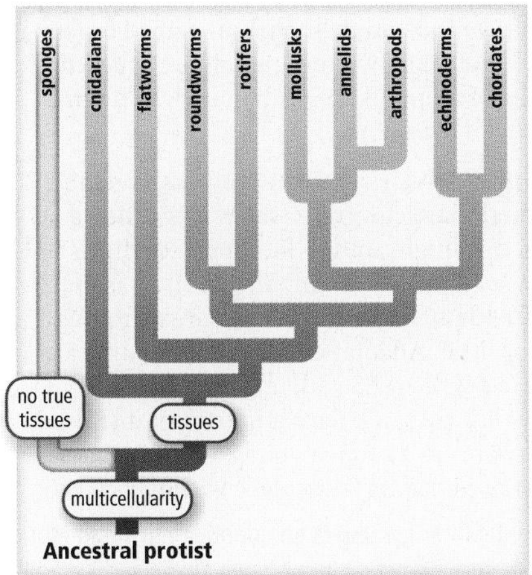

Figure 14 The sponges in the photograph are animals that take in and digest food, grow, and reproduce, even though they lack true tissues.

Section 3

MAIN Idea

BL OL AL

Sponges and Cnidarians

Hold up a dried sea sponge and a preserved jellyfish. Explain that sponges have simpler body plans and structures than jellyfish. **ASK STUDENTS:** ***How are the bodies of sponges and jellyfish adapted to their habitats?*** Most sponges are sessile and take in water and filter out food particles. Most jellyfish drift with currents and capture prey with stinging cells and tentacles. ***What structural features might be simpler in sponges than in cnidarians?*** Sponges do not have true tissues. Individual cells perform specific functions such as digestion.

D Develop Concepts

BL OL AL

Clarify a Misconception

ASK STUDENTS: ***Are sponges more primitive than insects?*** No Students may think that less complex animals are "simpler" in the sense of being more primitive than others. Organs or body systems may be simpler in some animals than in others, but one animal group is not considered to be more primitive than another. All animals are adapted to their habitats and way of life. You can, however, say that sponges evolved earlier than jellyfish or that sponges are ancestral to jellyfish. ***Are jellyfish tentacles simpler than legs?*** Yes. Tentacles do not have the variety of tissues and complex ways of moving as do legs.

Content Background

Real-World Connection Some people like to use natural sponges because they hold so much water and are very soft when wet. Potters use natural sponges for adding water to clay when they are making pottery on a pottery wheel. Painters sometimes use natural sponges for creating unusual patterns in the paint. Sponges also produce a variety of bioactive compounds that are being studied for possible pharmaceutical use.

W Writing Support

OL AL Narrative Writing

Have students make a list of the cell types in a sponge and then write a paragraph describing where each kind of cell is located and the importance of each kind of cell.

Critical Thinking

BL OL AL COOP LEARN

Compare Sponges belong to the phylum Porifera. There are between 5,000 and 10,000 species of sponges. Working in pairs, have students research two or three species of sponges and list their characteristics. Compare two sponge species. Have students prepare oral reports on their findings and include pictures or diagrams.

R Reading Strategy

BL OL AL Clarify the Text

Point out that the term *pore* has several additional meanings. **ASK STUDENTS:** ***What else can the term* pore *refer to?*** opening for sweat on our skin, place on a leaf that lets in carbon dioxide, spaces in soil ***Are there any similarities among these terms?*** All refer to a hole or opening.

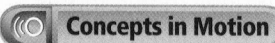

Concepts in Motion

Animation

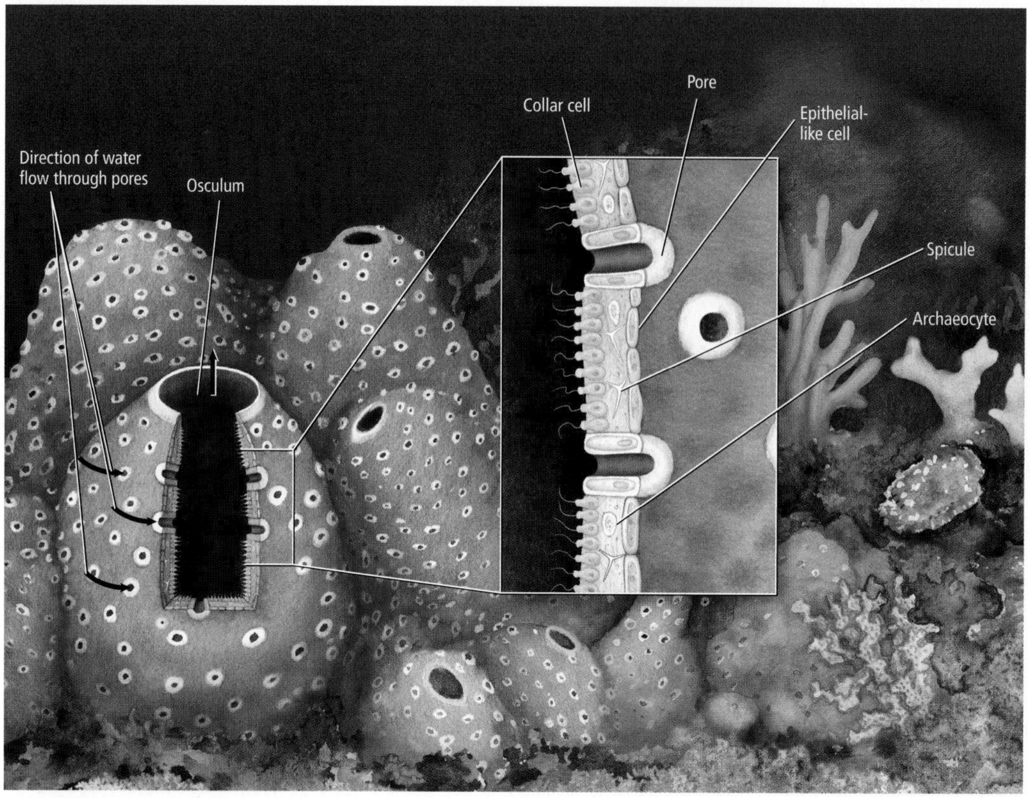

■ **Figure 15** Sponges have no tissues or organs and have a body made of two layers of cells.

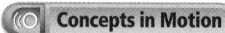

Concepts in Motion

Animation

Two layers of independent cells with a jellylike substance between the layers accomplish all of the life functions of sponges. As illustrated in **Figure 15,** epithelial-like cells cover the sponge and protect it. Collar cells with flagella line the inside of the sponge. As collar-cell flagella whip back and forth, water is drawn into the body of the sponge through pores. These pores give sponges their phylum name Porifera, which means "pore-bearer." Water and waste materials are expelled from the sponge through the osculum (AHS kyuh lum), which is the mouthlike opening at the top of the sponge. W

Feeding and digestion When an organism, such as a sponge, gets its food by filtering small particles from water, it is called a **filter feeder.** Even though this might sound like a process that is not very active, consider that a sponge only 10 cm tall can filter as much as 100 L of water each day. Although sponges have free-swimming larvae, the adults move very little. Adaptations for filter-feeding are common in animals that are **sessile** (SES sul), meaning they are attached to and stay in one place. As nutrients and oxygen dissolved in water enter through the pores in a sponge's body, food particles cling to the cells. Digestion of nutrients takes place within each cell. R

Reading Check **Infer** why filter feeding is an adaptive advantage for sponges.

Study Tip

Think Aloud Read the text and captions aloud. As you read, say aloud your questions and comments. For instance, when you come to the mention of **Figure 15,** look at the figure and say how it relates to the text.

Reading Check Sponges are sessile and cannot move around to catch prey. Instead, a sponge filters food from water that passes through its body.

Demosponge

■ **Figure 16** Bath sponges are harvested from the sea and processed for human use.

Support Within the jellylike material that lies between the two cell layers of a sponge are amoeba-like cells—cells that can move and change shape. These amoeba-like cells are called archaeocytes (ar kee OH sites) and are illustrated in **Figure 15.** These cells are involved in digestion, production of eggs and sperm, and excretion. Archaeocytes also can become specialized cells that secrete spicules (SPIH kyuhls), the support structures of sponges. Spicules are small, needlelike structures made of calcium carbonate, silica, or a tough fibrous protein called spongin.

S **Sponge diversity** Biologists place sponges into three classes based on the type of support system each has. Most sponges belong to class Demospongiae (deh muh SPUN jee uh), the demosponges, and have spicules composed of spongin fibers, silica, or both. Natural bath sponges, like the ones in **Figure 16,** have spongin support. Class Calcarea (kal KER ee uh) consists of sponges with spicules composed of calcium carbonate. Calcareous sponges, like the one in **Figure 17,** often have a rough texture because the calcium carbonate spicules can extend through the outer covering of the sponge. The sponges in class Hexactinellida (heks AK tuh nuh LEE duh) are called glass sponges and have spicules composed of silica. These spicules join together to form a netlike skeleton that often looks like spun glass, as illustrated in **Figure 17.**

Video BrainPOP

■ **Figure 17** Calcareous sponges are small and have a rough texture. The skeletons of glass sponges look like brittle spun glass.

Calcareous sponge

Glass sponge skeleton

Research Citation

Problem Solving Educational research indicates that students will be better able to solve complex problems when they understand the larger context to which the concepts relate. Teachers should make an effort to relate problems to situations that are realistic to students so that they are more relevant and meaningful. (Stanic and Kilpatrick, 1989)

Research bibliography on pages 32T–34T

Writing Support

BL OL AL Technical Writing Have students conduct research on how chemicals produced from sponges are being used in medical and health fields. Have them create a brochure explaining how the chemicals are extracted and the ways in which the chemicals are being used or may be used in the medical field.

Develop Concepts

BL OL AL

Community Connection Have students research information about harvesting sponges. Students should find out where sponges are harvested and the qualifications for a job as a sponge harvester.

SAY TO STUDENTS: ***Assume you are the owner of a boat and wish to go into the sponge-harvesting business. Write a plan for setting up your business that includes job descriptions for workers, instructions for how sponges are stored and processed after harvesting, and how the sponges will be marketed, sold, and shipped.***

S Skill Practice

EL Make a Table Have students make a table with three columns representing classes of sponges. As they read the text under the heading *Sponge diversity,* have them record the features of each class of sponge under the correct column.

Demospongiae	Calcarea	Hexactinellida

Video BrainPOP

D Develop Concepts

EL OL BL COOP LEARN

Activity After students have read the text under the heading *Reproduction,* provide large sheets of butcher paper and markers to groups of two or three.

SAY TO STUDENTS: ***Make a large diagram of a sponge and illustrate the ways in which they can reproduce.*** Remind students to include labels and captions to identify key points.

Develop Concepts

BL OL

Clarify a Misconception

ASK STUDENTS: ***Is a natural bath sponge made from an organism that was once alive?*** Yes, all natural sponges are animals. Students might not be aware that some "sponges" sold as cleaning materials are made of synthetic materials, but all natural sponges are animals. Explain that synthetic sponges are usually in regular shapes, such as rectangles, squares, or ovals, and often are different colors. Reinforce this idea by having students imagine that they are assistant curators working at a natural history museum. They have been asked to prepare an exhibit showing that sponges are animals. Have students create miniature exhibits, in shoe boxes for example, and create a sign displaying information about their exhibit.

AL Have students compare natural and synthetic sponges, listing advantages and disadvantages of each.

A Sperm are released into the water and float on water currents to other sponges.
B Sperm are caught by the collar cells of another sponge, and eggs are fertilized internally. Free-swimming larvae are released.
C The larvae swim using tiny cilia.
D A larva eventually settles on a surface.
E A sessile larva develops into an adult that can reproduce.

■ **Figure 18** Sexual reproduction in sponges requires water currents to carry sperm from one sponge to another.
Evaluate ***whether fertilization is internal or external in sponge sexual reproduction.***

Response to stimuli Sponges do not have nervous systems. They do have epithelial-like cells that detect external stimuli, such as touch or chemical signals, and respond by closing their pores to stop water flow.

Reproduction Sponges can reproduce asexually by fragmentation, through budding, or by producing gemmules (JEM yewlz). In fragmentation, a piece of sponge that is broken off due to a storm or other event develops into a new adult sponge. In budding, a small growth, called a bud, forms on a sponge, drops off, and settles in a spot where it grows into a new sponge. Some freshwater sponges form seedlike particles called gemmules during adverse conditions like droughts or freezing temperatures. Gemmules contain sponge cells protected by spicules that will survive and grow again when favorable conditions occur.

Most sponges reproduce sexually, as illustrated in **Figure 18.** Some sponges have separate sexes, but most sponges are hermaphrodites. Recall that a hermaphrodite is an animal that can produce both eggs and sperm. During reproduction, eggs remain within a sponge, while sperm are released into the water. Sperm released from one sponge can be carried by water currents to the collar cells of another sponge. The collar cells then change into specialized cells that carry the sperm to an egg within the sponge body. After fertilization occurs, the zygote develops into a larva that is free-swimming and has flagella. The larva eventually attaches to a surface, then develops into an adult. **D**

VOCABULARY
ACADEMIC VOCABULARY
Survive
to remain alive
Sponge gemmules survive despite adverse conditions.

Reading Check **Describe** the methods by which sponges reproduce.

Reading Check Most sponges reproduce sexually. During reproduction, sperm are released into the water. When sperm are caught by the collar cells of another sponge, the eggs are fertilized internally. Sponges can reproduce asexually by fragmentation when broken apart or by budding. Some sponges form gemmules that can survive adverse conditions.

■ **Caption Question** **Fig. 18** Fertilization is internal when sponges reproduce sexually.

Sponge ecology Although spicules and toxic or distasteful compounds in sponges discourage most potential predators, sponges are food for some tropical fishes and turtles. Sponges also are common habitats for a variety of worms, fishes, shrimp, and colonies of symbiotic green algae. Some sponges even live on and provide camouflage for mollusks, as shown in **Figure 19.**

Sponges also are beneficial to humans. Sponges with spicules made of spongin fibers often are used for household scrubbing purposes. Medical research is focusing on sponge chemicals that appear to discourage prey and prevent infection. Ongoing studies of these sponge chemicals as possible pharmaceutical agents have shown that they might have antibiotic, anti-inflamatory, or antitumor possibilities. They also might have potential importance as respiratory, cardiovascular, and gastrointestinal medicines.

Connection to Health For example, researchers discovered a powerful antitumor substance in the deep water sponge shown in **Figure 20.** This substance, discodermolide (disk uh DER muh lide), stops cancer cells from dividing by breaking down the nucleus and rearranging the microtubule network. Recall that microtubules are part of a cell's skeleton and help the cell maintain its shape. Note the differences in the nuclei and microtubules between the untreated and treated cancer W cells in **Figure 20.**

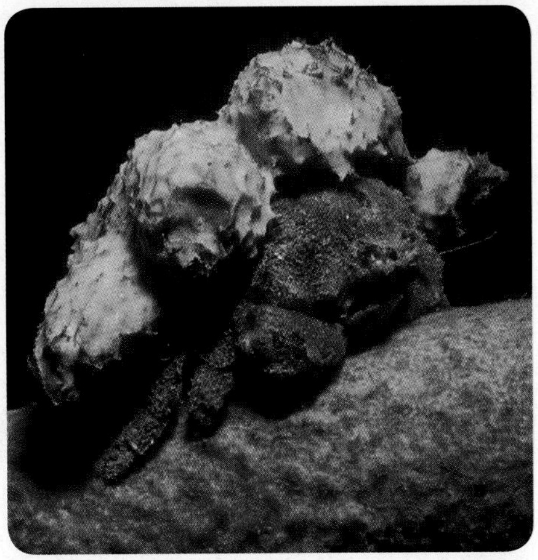

■ **Figure 19** This crab hides from predators by carrying a living sponge on its back. The crab uses two pairs of legs to hold the sponge in place.

■ **Figure 20** Discodermolide, a substance taken from the sponge *Discodermia dissoluta,* breaks down the nucleus in a cancer cell and rearranges its microtubules.

Discodermia dissoluta

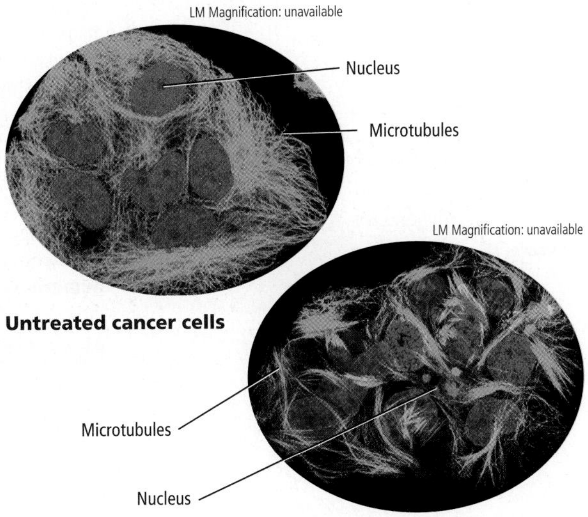

Untreated cancer cells

Treated cancer cells

Develop Concepts

BL OL AL Scaffolding

ASK STUDENTS: ***What is symmetry?*** the arrangement of an animal's body structures ***Explain radial symmetry.*** An animal with radial symmetry can be divided along any plane, through a central axis, into roughly equal halves. ***Explain bilateral symmetry.*** An animal with bilateral symmetry can be divided into mirror-image halves only along one plane through the central axis. ***Compare how symmetry differs from asymmetry.*** An animal with a symmetrical body plan can be divided into roughly equal halves by a plane passing through its center. An asymmetric animal cannot be divided easily into two equal halves by a plane passing through its center. ***Infer the importance of symmetry.*** Symmetry helps with an animal's function. An animal with radial symmetry can find prey or sense danger from any direction. An animal with bilateral symmetry finds food and senses stimuli with its anterior end.

W Writing Support

BL OL AL Journal Writing

Have students imagine that they are on a research ship investigating the ecology of sponges.

SAY TO STUDENTS: ***Write an entry in the ship's log about one day's activities. Include the terms*** **camouflage, spicule, predator,** ***and*** **symbiotic.**

Differentiated Instruction

Physically Disabled When students are working in cooperative learning groups, such as when completing the activities on this page, prepare students to work with others who have physical disabilities. Educate peers about their disability so they will be more understanding and informed about the students' needs.

For more tips, see pages 14T–15T.

S Skill Practice

EL BL OL AL COOP LEARN

Visual Literacy Place students in groups of three or four. After studying Figure 21, have each group of students draw a similar branching tree on a large sheet of paper. On each branch of the tree, have them draw or paste pictures of animals representative of that group. Have them indicate which animals have radial symmetry and which are asymmetrical. Then have the groups compare their selections.

D Develop Concepts

BL OL AL COOP LEARN

Activity Place students into groups of two or three. Have students create a poster describing how a jellyfish or sea anemone uses its stinging cells. Have students include pictures and diagrams of the jellyfish or sea anemone and also pictures of the animals that are its predators or its prey.

Caption Question Fig. 21 Radial symmetry enables cnidarians to detect and capture food from any direction.

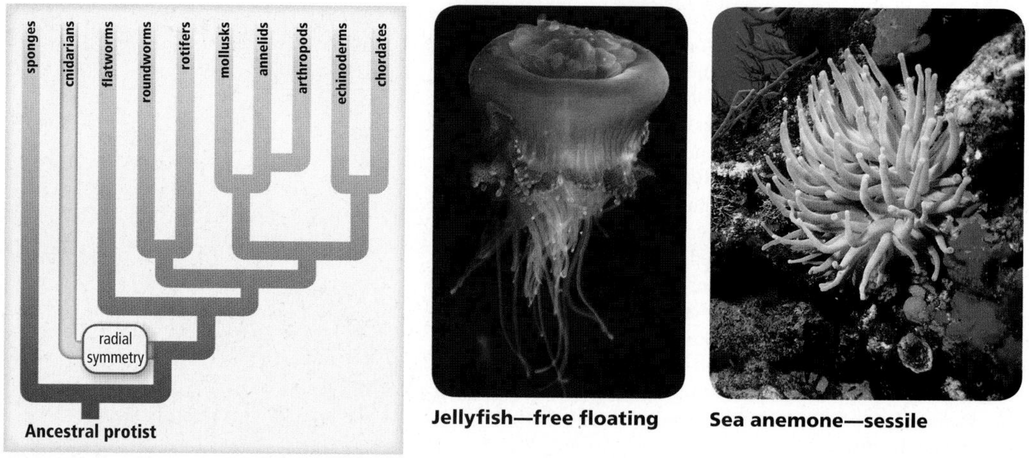

Figure 21 Cnidarians have radial symmetry and can be free floating or sessile.
Explain how radial symmetry helps a cnidarian obtain food.

S

Figure 22 Stinging cells that contain nematocysts are discharged from the tentacles of cnidarians when prey touches them.

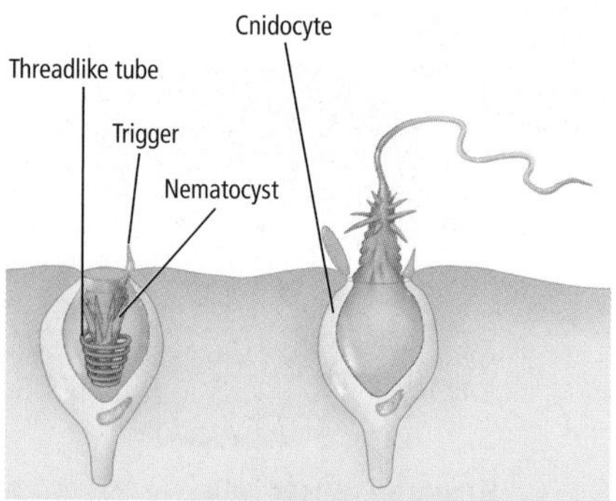

Cnidarians

Imagine that you go snorkeling around a coral reef, and you wear a bodysuit to protect yourself from the stings of jellyfishes that float on the water. Later, when you go ashore to visit a tidepool, you might see colorful sea anemones that look somewhat like flowers. The jellyfish and sea anemone in **Figure 21** belong to phylum Cnidaria (ni DARE ee uh). This phylum consists of about 10,000 species, most of which are marine.

Body structure Like sponges, cnidarians (ni DARE ee uns) have one body opening and most have two layers of cells. However, in cnidarians, the two cell layers are organized into tissues with specific functions. The outer layer functions in protecting the internal body, while the inner layer functions mainly in digestion. Because cnidarians have tissues, they also have symmetry. As shown in **Figure 21,** cnidarian bodies have radial symmetry. Recall that radial symmetry enables slow moving or sessile animals to detect and capture prey from any direction. Cnidarians are adapted to aquatic floating or sessile attachment to surfaces under the water.

Feeding and digestion Cnidarian tentacles are armed with stinging cells called **cnidocytes** (NI duh sites). Cnidarians get their name from these stinging cells. Cnidocytes contain nematocysts, as shown in **Figure 22.** A **nematocyst** (nih MA tuh sihst) is a capsule that holds a coiled, threadlike tube containing poison and barbs. D

Connection to Physics A nematocyst works like a tiny but very powerful harpoon. Remember that osmosis is the diffusion of water through a selectively permeable membrane. The pressure provided by this flow of water is called osmotic pressure. The water inside an undischarged nematocyst is under an osmotic pressure of more than 150 atmospheres. This pressure is about 20 times the pressure in an inflated bicycle tire.

Demonstration

OL **Cnidarians** Collect photos of a variety of jellyfishes, corals, and sea anemones from various sources. Prepare a slideshow presentation that can be shown in class or pass the pictures to the students.
ASK STUDENTS: ***What do these animals have in common? Can you infer by their appearance how they are adapted to their environment?*** Answers will vary but should refer to body plan and symmetry. Est. time: 10 min

In response to being touched or to a chemical stimulus, the permeability of the nematocyst membrane increases, allowing more water to rush in. As the osmotic pressure increases, the nematocyst discharges forcefully. A barb is capable of penetrating a crab shell.

Nematocyst discharge is one of the fastest cellular processes in nature. It happens so quickly—in just 3/1000ths of a second—that it is impossible to escape after touching these cells. After capture by nematocysts and tentacles, the prey is brought to the mouth of the cnidarian.

The inner cell layer of cnidarians surrounds a space called the **gastrovascular** (gas troh VAS kyuh lur) **cavity,** illustrated in **Figure 23.** Cells lining the gastrovascular cavity release digestive enzymes over captured prey. Undigested materials are ejected through the mouth. Recall that digestion occurs within each cell of a sponge. However, in cnidarians, digestion takes place in the gut cavity, a major evolutionary adaptation.

Response to stimuli In addition to cells adapted for digestion, cnidarians have a nervous system consisting of a **nerve net** that conducts impulses to and from all parts of the body. The impulses from the nerve net cause contractions of musclelike cells in the two cell layers. The movement of tentacles during prey capture is the result of contractions of these musclelike cells. Cnidarians have no blood vessels, respiratory systems, or excretory organs. Look at **Table 1** to compare the structures and functions of sponges and cnidarians.

Reading Check **Contrast** a cnidarian's response to stimuli from a sponge's response.

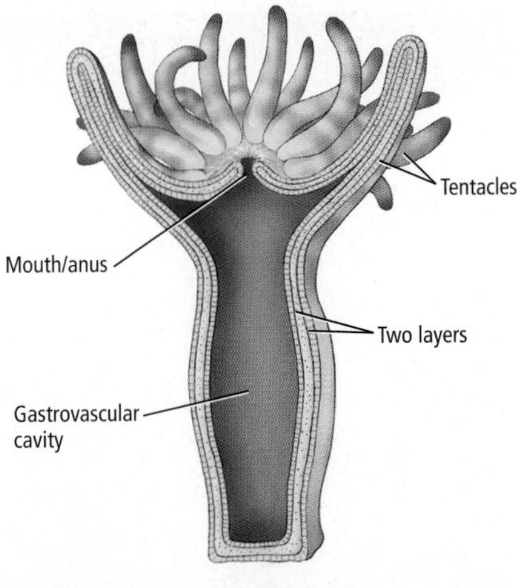

Figure 23 A cnidarian's mouth leads directly into its gastrovascular cavity. Because the digestive tract has only one opening, wastes are expelled through the mouth.

Table 1 **Comparison of Sponges and Cnidarians** — Concepts in Motion Interactive Table

	Sponges	Cnidarians
Example		
Body Plan	• Generally has asymmetry	• Has radial symmetry
Feeding and digestion	• Filter feed • Digestion takes place within individual cells	• Capture prey with nematocysts and tentacles • Digestion takes place in gastrovascular cavity
Movement	• Sessile	• Aquatic floating or sessile
Response to stimuli	• No nervous system • Cells react to stimuli	• Simple nervous system consisting of a nerve net
Reproduction	• Hermaphrodites reproduce sexually • Asexual reproduction by fragmentation, budding, or gemmule production	• Separate sexes reproduce sexually • Polyp stage reproduces asexually by budding

Develop Concepts

BL OL AL Research Have students use the library to research the kinds of prey that cnidarians eat. Have students select one kind of prey and create a hand puppet to represent it with gloves, mittens, or socks. Have students present a puppet show for the class in which the puppet prey describes characteristics about itself, such as size, movement, and body plan. Have the prey also describe how it tries to escape cnidarians.

AL Have students describe evolutionary adaptations that enable cnidarians to catch different types of prey.

Reading Strategy

BL OL Vocabulary Chart Have students make a three-column vocabulary chart. In the first column, have them write the vocabulary terms *gastrovascular cavity, nerve net, cnidocyte, nematocyst, medusa,* and *polyp.* In the second column, have them write the meaning of each term after reading the text. Then have them come up with a memory clue, such as a sketch or word association, to write in the third column.

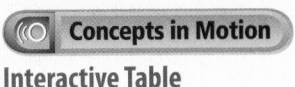

Concepts in Motion
Interactive Table

Reading Check A sponge does not have a nervous system or muscles to react to stimuli. Cnidarians have a nerve net that responds to stimuli and sends signals to musclelike cells, causing tentacles to move.

D Develop Concepts

OL BL AL Activity Provide students with microscopes and prepared slides of budding hydra. Have them draw a diagram of the budding hydra and label the tentacles and the bud.

SAY TO STUDENTS: ***Explain how budding is different from the process shown in Figure 24.*** Budding is asexual, and as shown in the figure, the reproductive cycle of jellyfishes alternates between an asexual stage and a sexual stage.

D Develop Concepts

EL BL OL AL COOP LEARN

Activity Have students form pairs and create a color poster that illustrates the two body forms of cnidarians—the polyp and the medusa. Have them label the parts of each body form and explain how each form contributes to the reproductive cycle.

Concepts in Motion

Animation

Reading Check The larvae of both sponges and cnidarians are free-swimming.

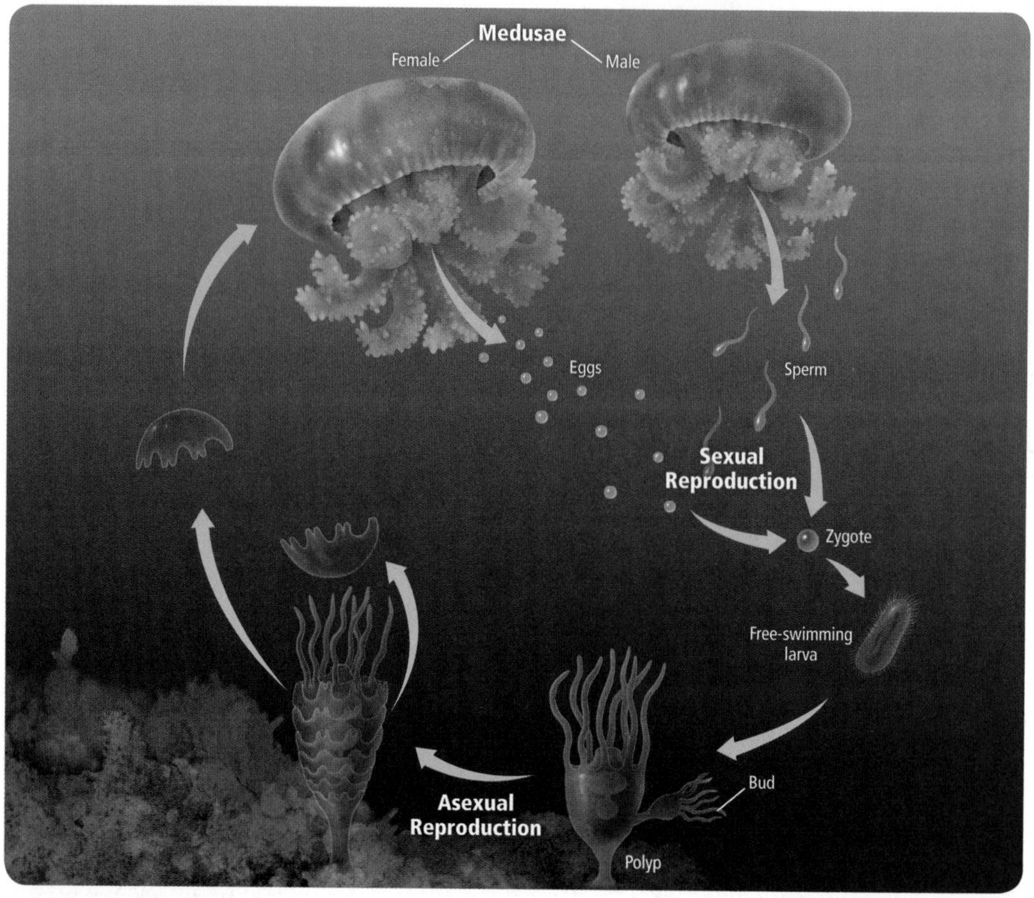

Figure 24 Jellyfishes reproduce by alternating sexual and asexual stages of their life cycle.

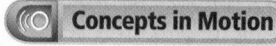

Concepts in Motion

Animation

D

CAREERS IN BIOLOGY

Marine Ecologist Using submersibles and deep-sea robots, a marine ecologist studies the relationships between marine animals and their environments.

Reproduction In addition to stinging cells, cnidarians have another adaptation not seen in most animals of recent origin. Most cnidarians have two body forms: a **polyp** (PAH lup) with a tube-shaped body and a mouth surrounded by tentacles, and a **medusa** (mih DEW suh) (plural, medusae) with an umbrella-shaped body and tentacles that hang down. The mouth of a medusa is on the ventral surface between the tentacles.

The two body forms of cnidarians can be observed in the life cycle of jellyfishes, illustrated in **Figure 24.** To reproduce, jellyfishes in the medusa stage release eggs and sperm into the water where fertilization occurs. The resulting zygotes eventually develop into free-swimming larvae that settle and grow into polyps. These polyps reproduce asexually to form new medusae. It would be easy to confuse the life cycle of cnidarians with the alternation of generations in plants. However, in plants, one generation is diploid and the other is haploid. In cnidarians, both the medusae and polyps are diploid animals. D

Reading Check **Compare** the larvae of sponges and cnidarians.

Demonstration

Cnidarian Diversity Obtain preserved samples of a hydroid colony, a jellyfish, a sea anemone, and a piece of coral. As you hold up each example for the class, have students discuss the kind of symmetry the animal has, how it obtains food, whether it forms colonies, and other distinguishing characteristics. Est. time: 15 min

Cnidarian diversity There are four main classes of cnidarians: Hydrozoa, the hydroids; two classes of jellyfishes, Scyphozoa and Cubozoa (the box jellyfishes); and Anthozoa, the sea anemones and corals.

Hydroids Most of the approximately 2700 known species of hydroids have both polyp and medusa stages in their life cycles. Most hydroids form colonies, such as the Portuguese man-of-war in **Figure 25.** Another well-known hydroid is the freshwater hydra, which is unusual because it has only a polyp stage.

Jellyfishes There are about 200 known species of jellyfishes. They are transparent or translucent in appearance and float near the water's surface. The medusa is the dominant body form, although a polyp stage does exist. They are called jellyfishes because the substance between the outer body covering and the inner body wall is jellylike. The structure of the inner and outer body layers with the jellylike structure between can be compared to a jelly sandwich. The box jellyfishes take their name from the boxlike medusae that are their dominant form. The stings of some box jellyfish species can be fatal to humans.

Sea anemones and corals Generally colorful and inviting, sea anemones and corals still possess stinging cells like all cnidarians. The 6200 known species of sea anemones and corals are different from the jellyfishes because the polyp stage is the dominant stage of their life cycles. Recent research indicates that these anthozoans might have bilateral symmetry. This would alter the evolutionary tree because this adaptation usually is seen only in animal groups that evolved later than cnidarians.

Sea anemones live as individual animals, while corals live in colonies of polyps. Corals secrete protective calcium carbonate shelters around their soft bodies. The living portion of a coral reef is a thin, fragile layer growing on top of the shelters left behind by previous generations. Coral reefs form from these shelters over thousands of years.

Coral polyps extend their tentacles to feed, as shown in **Figure 26.** They also harbor symbiotic photosynthetic protists called zooxanthellae (zoh oh zan THEH lee). The zooxanthellae produce oxygen and food that corals use, while using carbon dioxide and waste materials produced by the corals. These protists are primarily responsible for the bright colors found on healthy coral reefs.

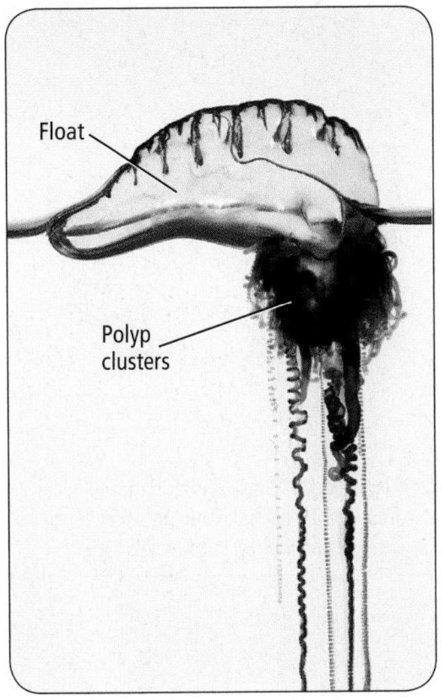

Figure 25 This Portuguese man-of-war is composed of a colony of hydroids. One hydroid polyp forms the large float, while other hydroid polyps cluster beneath the float.

R

Figure 26 Coral polyps capture food by extending their tentacles.

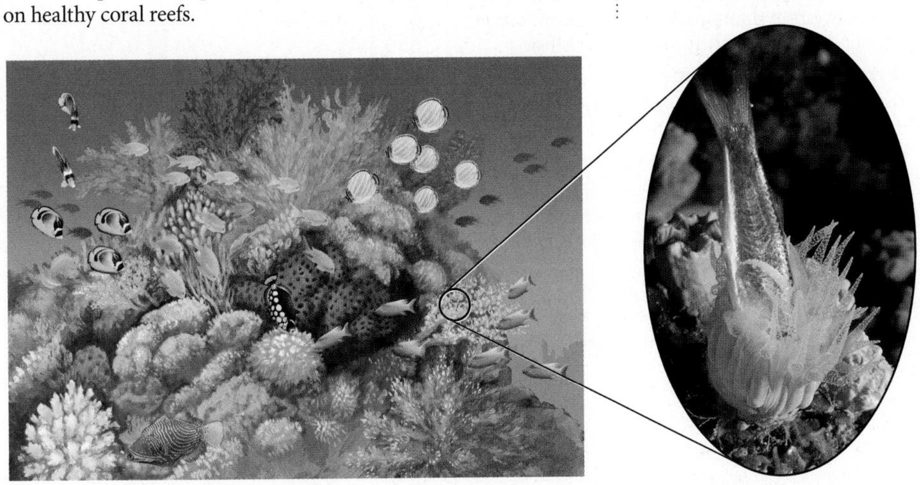

Critical Thinking

AL Hypothesize Few predators will eat the most common coral in the Caribbean, the gorgonian coral. Have students brainstorm possible reasons for this.

SAY TO STUDENTS: ***Form a hypothesis about why most predators avoid the gorgonian coral.*** Have the class share their hypotheses. Then have students gather information about biological research performed on the gorgonian coral.

ASK STUDENTS: ***Summarize the reasons biologists think few predators eat the gorgonian coral.*** Biologists hypothesize that these corals have protective chemical defenses, are protected by their spicules, or are of no nutritive value to predators.

R Reading Strategy

EL OL BL Directed Reading
Have students create a chart with three columns titled *What I know, What I think I'll learn,* and *What I learned.* Have students study Figures 25 and 26 and fill out the first two columns of the chart. After students have read the text under the heading *Cnidarian diversity,* have them fill out the last column on their charts.

Demonstration

Comparative Anatomy Show students dried endoskeletons of a sea urchin and a sea star, a model of a shark skeleton, and a model of a different fish or other vertebrate skeleton.

ASK STUDENTS: ***How are these skeletons different from each other in structure and function?*** Answer: The sea urchin and sea star endoskeletons are on the outside of the body and protect the animals' bodies. These skeletons are made of calcium carbonate. The shark's skeleton is made of cartilage and is internal and supports the body. The bony fish or other vertebrate skeleton is made of bone and is internal support. Est. time: 10 min

DATA ANALYSIS LAB 1

About the Lab

- Explain the meanings of the following terms as related to coral degradation: *Pristine* means no evidence of any human use or damage. *Ecologically extinct* means a species requires human intervention to survive.
- Explain what a bar graph is and how it is used to present information.
- Begin this lesson by preparing slides of pristine and degraded coral reefs and showing them to students.
- Also see Hughes, et al. 2003. Climate change, human impacts, and the resilience of coral reefs. *Science* 301: 929–933.

Think Critically

1. In western Panama and Jamaica reefs have suffered the most damage. The Great Barrier reefs have suffered the least damage.
2. Color coding shows the most degradation in Jamaica and Western Panama and trend toward the least degradation on the Great Barrier Reef.

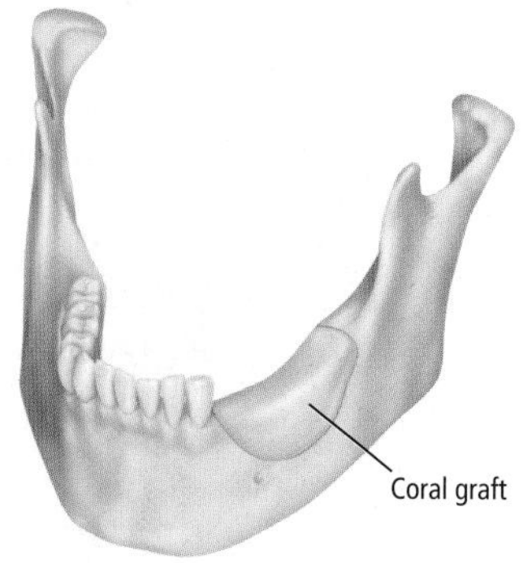

Figure 27 Surgeons use treated hydroxyapatite to make implants for reconstructing facial bones, such as this jaw.

The health of a coral reef depends on proper water temperature, adequate light, and appropriate water depth. If these environmental conditions deteriorate in areas where there are reefs, the health of the reef might also deteriorate. You can examine this problem in **Data Analysis Lab 1.**

Cnidarian ecology Mutualism, a relationship in which both organisms benefit, is common in cnidarians. One species of sea anemone wraps itself around hermit crabs' shells; the anemones obtain food scraps and the crabs are protected. Some sea slugs feed on cnidarians and incorporate the unfired nematocysts into their bodies for their own defense. As shown in the photo at the beginning of the chapter, clown fishes are protected by the tentacles of anemones. One theory as to how clown fishes are protected from the tentacles of anemones is that the fish incorporates mucus from an anemone into its own mucous coating, which prevents the nematocysts from discharging.

People benefit from cnidarians in many ways. Some people enjoy visiting a coral reef. In the medical field, some stony coral species are used in surgical procedures. A calcium phosphate mineral in coral called hydroxyapatite (hi DROX ee ap uh TITE) can be treated so that it has the same structure and chemical composition as human bone. Small pieces of coral are implanted as bone grafts, especially in face and jaw reconstruction and in arm and leg surgery. The grafts anchor to the adjacent bone, as shown in **Figure 27,** and are eventually replaced by new human bone growth.

DATA ANALYSIS LAB 1

Based on Real Data*

Interpret Data

Where are coral reefs being damaged?
Some corals have ejected their symbiotic algae and become bleached, or lost their coloring. Coral reef bleaching is a common response to reef ecosystem damage. However, some corals appear to be recovering from bleaching.

Data and Observations

The graph indicates the percentage of the damage that has occurred to specific reefs.

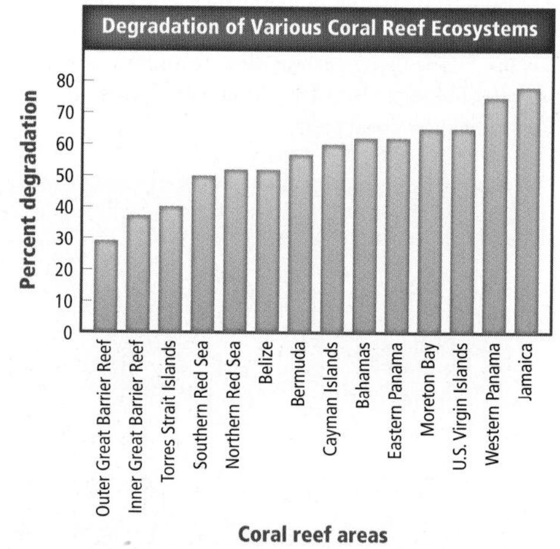

Think Critically

1. **Interpret** What part of the world has suffered the most damage to its coral reefs? What part of the world has suffered the least damage to its reefs?
2. **Model** On a world map, locate the coral reefs noted in the graph. Color code the map based on the percent of degradation.

*Data obtained from: Pandolfi, J.M. et al., 2003. Global trajectories of the long-term decline of coral reef ecosystems. *Science* 301 (5635): 955–958.

Activity

AL COOP LEARN Coral Degradation
Have a group of students give an oral presentation to the class. To prepare, have them find illustrations of the coral reef before and after degradation and research the kinds of measures being taken to restore the reefs. Est. time: 10 min

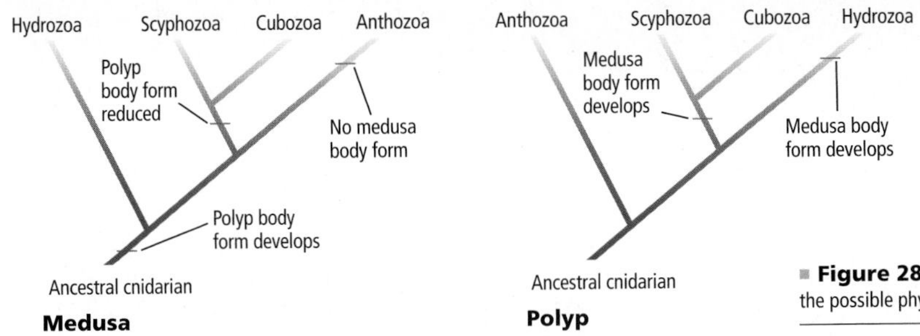

■ **Figure 28** The two cladograms illustrate the possible phylogeny of cnidarians.

Evolution of cnidarians There are two major interpretations of the phylogeny of cnidarians. The fact that cnidarians have two body forms, medusa and polyp, raises the question of whether the ancestral cnidarian had a medusa or a polyp body form. The cladograms in **Figure 28** present both interpretations.

In the cladogram on the left, the ancestral cnidarian has a medusa body form. As cnidarians evolved, a polyp stage developed. The life cycles of hydrozoans have both polyp and medusa stages. As the scyphozoans and cubozoans developed, the medusa stage became the dominant stage in their life cycles. The most highly evolved cnidarians, the anthozoans, have no medusa stage.

In the cladogram on the right, the ancestral cnidarian has a polyp body form. The anthozoans evolved first, and the polyp stage is the dominant stage of their life cycles. The medusa stage evolved independently in hydrozoans and in scyphozoans and cubozoans. Notice how the classes of cnidarians are arranged in each cladogram.

Section 3 Assessment

Section Summary

- Sponges can be described according to animal features they do not have and according to features they do have.
- Sponges do not have tissues, but carry out the same life functions as other animals.
- Cnidarians have unique features that other animals do not have.
- Cnidarians have more highly evolved body forms and structures than sponges.
- Sponges and cnidarians are important to the ecology of their habitats and to humans.

Understand Main Ideas

1. MAIN Idea **Explain** why sponges and cnidarians were the first animals to evolve.
2. **Describe** the differences between the body plans of sponges and cnidarians.
3. **List** two characteristics that are unique to sponges and two characteristics that are unique to cnidarians.
4. **Demonstrate** your knowledge of cnidarians by describing how they affect other marine organisms.

Think Critically

5. **Hypothesize** how nematocysts are an adaptive advantage for cnidarians.

MATH in Biology

6. Review the text under the heading *Cnidarian diversity.* Make a circle graph that shows the proportions of each of the three groups of cnidarians to the total numbers of cnidarians. In addition to the groups in this section, there are 900 species of other cnidarians. Analyze this information and hypothesize why one group is so much smaller than the others.

Develop Concepts

OL AL

Integrate Earth Science
Have students research the early history of Earth.
ASK STUDENTS: ***According to the fossil record, when did cnidarians first appear in abundance?*** during the Cambrian period of the Paleozoic era ***When was the Cambrian period?*** about 570 million to 500 million years ago ***What kinds of cnidarians lived during the early Cambrian period?*** Answers may include sea anemones, corals, and jellyfish.

Formative Assessment

Evaluation Have students make a chart of the four kinds of cnidarians and indicate how each can be identified. hydrozoans: have both polyp and medusa stages, many form colonies; scyphozoans: jellyfishes; cubozoans: jellyfishes with box-shaped medusa; anthozoans: sea anemones with polyp stage dominant, corals with hard body frameworks that form reefs

Remediation Have students make a diagram of each one of the four main kinds of cnidarians. Students should label each diagram with the name of the cnidarian and its major body parts.

Section 3 Assessment

1. Both were the first animals to evolve from a common multicellular ancestor.
2. sponges: no tissues, no organs, and no symmetry; cnidarians: radial symmetry, tissues
3. sponges: no tissues, archaeocytes, spicules; cnidarians: cnidocytes, nematocysts, medusae, and polyps
4. Cnidarians provide camouflage, food, and protection for other marine animals.
5. By providing a "harpoon" to help capture prey, nematocysts make cnidarians more effective at feeding and thus better able to survive.
6. jellyfishes = 2 percent, anthozoans = 62 percent, hydrozoans = 27 percent, other cnidarians = 9 percent. There may be fewer jellyfishes because the stable open ocean environment might not have had as much environmental pressure for evolution to occur.

Purpose

Students will learn what coral reefs are and how human behaviors have put the reefs at risk. They will also learn how people can help preserve coral reefs. C.4, F.4, F.5

Anticipatory Guide

ASK STUDENTS: ***What are corals?*** Tell students that corals are animals that are in the same class (*Anthozoa*) as sea anemones. Corals are in the same phylum (*Cnidaria*) as jellyfish. ***How do you think coral reefs benefit the environment?*** Students might talk about the fishes that live in and around the reefs. Emphasize that many marine species are supported by coral reefs.

Background

Besides the obvious benefits of biodiversity, coral reefs provide many other benefits to humans. Scientists are investigating the biodiversity of coral reefs to find new medicines that can help people suffering from cancers, viruses, and other diseases. In many countries, the fishing industry finds a substantial portion of its catch near coral reefs. Coral reefs drive tourism in some parts of the world, and that tourism provides many people with jobs. Coral reefs also protect coastlines from erosion.

Biology & Society

Beautiful and Endangered: Coral Reefs

Coral reefs dot the coasts around the world and cover over 284,000 square kilometers. People are fascinated by beautiful and delicate corals and by the populations that inhabit reef ecosystems. Ironically, human behaviors have contributed to the endangerment of coral reefs.

What are coral reefs? Not all corals form reefs, but those that do begin the process when individual polyps attach to rocks. They do this by secreting a calcium carbonate exoskeleton that cements the polyps in place. As the polyps die over time, the exoskeletons are left behind and a coral reef forms. Many corals have a symbiotic relationship with the alga zooxanthellae. These algae provide the corals with nutrients gained through photosynthesis, and they use the carbon dioxide produced by the corals.

This healthy coral reef shows no sign of bleaching, disease, or pollution.

Why are coral reefs important? Coral reefs form some of the most diverse ecosystems in the world. About 25 percent of all marine species live in coral reefs, and scientists estimate that reefs also support millions of undiscovered species. The biodiversity of reefs is valuable and irreplaceable.

What is happening to coral reefs? Coral reefs face natural threats, including extreme weather conditions and predation. Many coral reefs have been damaged by human activities, such as fishing practices that employ dynamite or poison. Some polluted runoff stimulates the growth of nonbeneficial algae, which smothers corals. Tourist activities like diving and snorkeling also damage corals. Some divers and snorkelers break off pieces of coral to sell or to take home as souvenirs. Other divers collect live corals to sell for use in aquariums.

Sometimes, corals become so stressed that they expel their symbiotic algae. This is a phenomenon known as "bleaching" because the stressed corals lose their bright colors and appear white. Scientists do not yet completely understand why coral bleaching occurs. They think one of the main causes is rising ocean temperatures. Other possible factors include pollution, bacteria, solar radiation, and changes in salinity. Coral reefs that expel their algae are more likely to become diseased, and the corals will die unless the symbiotic algae are replaced.

VISUAL COMMUNICATION

Make a Movie Research with your classmates what can be done to help keep coral reefs from becoming extinct. Write a script for a short movie about coral reefs. Include facts about what they are, why they are in danger, and what people can do to help. Include visuals such as photographs, maps, and costumes.

Visual Communication Activity

You might decide that your class is too large to have all of the students work on all aspects of the movie. If that is the case, divide the class into groups and assign each a task. If possible, post the movie on a video-sharing website. Choose a video-sharing site that is approved by your school before you post your students' movie online. In the days and weeks after you post the movie, have your students check the site to see how many people have viewed it and left comments.

WebQuest

BIOLAB

Design Your Own

FIELD INVESTIGATION: WHAT CHARACTERISTICS DO ANIMALS HAVE?

Background: A small pond is an ecosystem in which organisms interact to accomplish essential life functions. They exhibit a wide variety of body plans, obtain food in different ways, and use various methods of movement.

Question: *What kinds of animals live in ponds?*

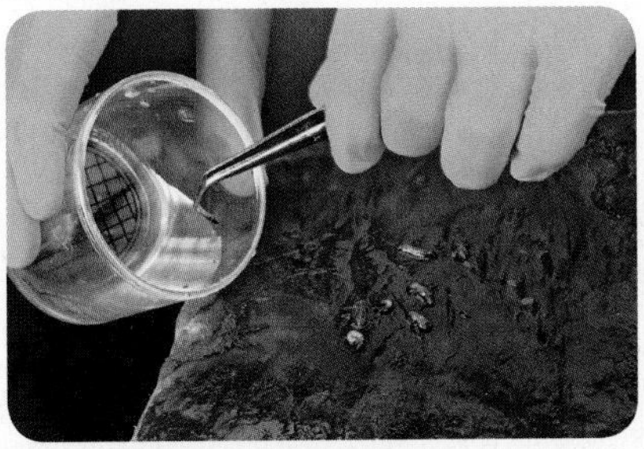

Materials

wading boots
tweezers
aquarium
Petri dishes
dissecting microscopes
Choose other materials that would be appropriate for this lab.

Safety Precautions

WARNING: ***Handle living animals with care.***

Plan and Perform the Experiment

1. Read and complete the lab safety form.
2. Locate a pond to use for your observations and collections. Make sure you have permission to use the pond.
3. Determine methods to observe and record animals that you see at the pond that you do not collect.
4. Design and construct a data table to record your observations.
5. Make sure your teacher approves your plan before you proceed.
6. **Cleanup and Disposal** Wash your hands after handling any live organisms. Return the animals and any pond water to the pond. Wash and return all reusable lab materials and correctly dispose of other materials used in the lab as directed by your teacher.

Analyze and Conclude

1. **Use Scientific Explanations** How were you able to determine if the organisms you observed were animals?
2. **Summarize** the adaptations used for obtaining food that you observed. Were any of the adaptations similar to those you observed in **MiniLab 1?**
3. **Compare and contrast** the methods of movement used by each of the animals you observed.
4. **Interpret Data** Look at drawings or photographs of the animals you observed. What do these illustrations tell you about the body plan of each organism? What gut type does each animal have?
5. **Error Analysis** What other types of observations could you make to verify your conclusions about each organism?

WRITING in Biology

Make a Booklet Choose one of the animals you observed in your pond study. Develop an illustrated booklet that shows how this animal obtains food, how it reproduces, its body plan, and its stages of development. Share the information with your class.

Analyze and Conclude

1. Answers should mention that animals are multicellular, eukaryotic, and heterotrophic.
2. directed movement, presence of a gut, and other adaptations for obtaining food
3. Answers might include the use of flagella, legs, fins, and body movements.
4. The illustrations show whether the organism has both a mouth and an anus, if animal has tubelike gut, i.e., a pseudocoelom or coelom, which helps determine the body plan.
5. Research the life cycle to confirm whether each organism is a coelomate or pseudocoelomate, its type of locomotion, and its adaptations for obtaining food.

WRITING in Biology

RUBRIC Use the modifiable rubric found on your eTeacherEdition Online to assess writing assignments.

BIOLAB

Design Your Own

Inquiry BioLab

For a lab worksheet, use your eTeacherEdition Online.

RUBRIC A rubric for evaluating BioLabs is found on your eTeacherEdition Online.

Est. Time 90 min

Content Background In the small ecosystem of a pond or aquarium, students can observe how animals interact with each other and with other organisms and observe adaptations and characteristics that they share. In this ecosystem, there are animals in different stages of development, from larval forms through adults.

Safety Precautions Approve lab safety forms before work begins. Students should wear protective footwear and use nets and containers to draw samples from the pond. Larger animals such as frogs, salamanders, turtles, fish, ducks, and snakes should be observed rather than collected.

Teaching Strategies

- Some states require a permit for this activity. Obtain local or state permits as needed.
- Prior to taking students to the pond, visit site and use a field guide to become familiar with animals.
- Local or state wildlife agencies often have employees who would be glad to meet you and act as an on-site source of information.
- Be attentive to students who have allergies.

Alternative Teaching Demo One or more aquaria could be set up in the classroom to create an aquatic habitat for observing pond animals.

Chapter 24

Study Guide

ConnectED

Students can use the following to review the chapter.

Review

- Vocabulary eGames
- Vocabulary eFlashcards
- Vocabulary PuzzleMaker

Assessment

- Online Quizzes
- Online Test Practice
- Standardized Test Practice

Use the *ExamView®* *Assessment Suite* CD-ROM to:

- create multiple versions of tests
- create modified tests with one mouse click
- edit existing questions and add your own questions
- build tests aligned with state standards using built-in state curriculum tags
- change English tests to Spanish with one mouse click
- track students' progress using the Teacher Management System

Chapter 24 Study Guide

THEME FOCUS Diversity All animals show some form of symmetry such as radial, bilateral, or asymmetrical symmetry.

BIG Idea Animal phylogeny is determined in part by animal body plans and adaptations.

Section 1 Animal Characteristics

invertebrate (p. 693)
exoskeleton (p. 693)
endoskeleton (p. 693)
vertebrate (p. 693)
hermaphrodite (p. 695)
zygote (p. 695)
internal fertilization (p. 695)
external fertilization (p. 695)
blastula (p. 696)
gastrula (p. 696)
endoderm (p. 697)
ectoderm (p. 697)
mesoderm (p. 697)

MAIN Idea Animals are multicellular, eukaryotic heterotrophs that have evolved to live in many different habitats.

- Animals are heterotrophs and must get their nutrients from other organisms.
- Animals have diverse means of support and live in diverse habitats.
- Animal cells do not have cell walls and most have cells that are organized into tissues.
- Most animals undergo sexual reproduction and most can move.
- During embryonic development, animal cells become tissue layers, which become organs and systems.

Section 2 Animal Body Plans

symmetry (p. 700)
radial symmetry (p. 700)
bilateral symmetry (p. 700)
anterior (p. 700)
posterior (p. 700)
cephalization (p. 700)
dorsal (p. 700)
ventral (p. 700)
coelom (p. 701)
pseudocoelom (p. 701)
acoelomate (p. 701)
protostome (p. 702)
deuterostome (p. 702)

MAIN Idea Animal phylogeny can be determined, in part, by body plans and the ways animals develop.

- Animal phylogeny can be compared to a tree with branches.
- The branches of a phylogenetic evolutionary tree show the relationships among animals.
- Animal phylogeny can be determined, in part, by the animal's type of body cavity or lack of a body cavity.
- After gastrulation, two types of development can occur in coelomate animals.
- Segmentation is an important feature in some coelomate animals.

Section 3 Sponges and Cnidarians

filter feeder (p. 706)
sessile (p. 706)
cnidocyte (p. 710)
nematocyst (p. 710)
gastrovascular cavity (p. 711)
nerve net (p. 711)
polyp (p. 712)
medusa (p. 712)

MAIN Idea Sponges and cnidarians were the first animals to evolve from a multicellular ancestor.

- Sponges can be described according to animal features they do not have and according to features they do have.
- Sponges do not have tissues, but carry out the same life functions as other animals.
- Cnidarians have unique features that other animals do not have.
- Cnidarians have more highly evolved body forms and structures than sponges.
- Sponges and cnidarians are important to the ecology of their habitats and to humans.

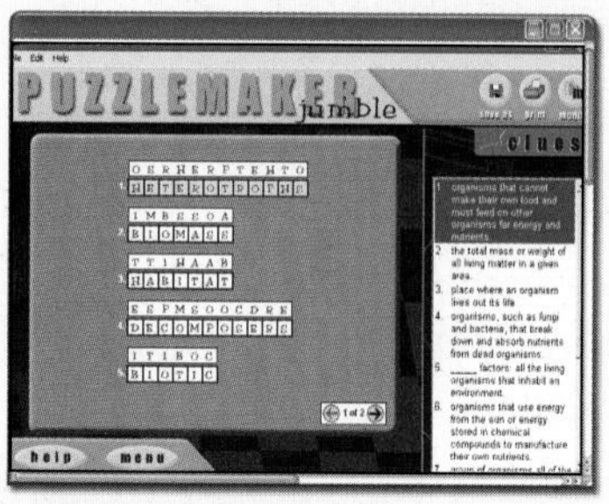

Review Vocabulary PuzzleMaker

For additional practice with vocabulary, have students access the Vocabulary PuzzleMaker online.

Review Vocabulary eGames

Section 1

Vocabulary Review

Match the definitions below with the correct vocabulary terms from the Study Guide page.

1. a hard outer covering that provides support
2. fluid-filled ball of cells formed by miotic cell division of the embryo
3. an animal that produces both eggs and sperm

Understand Main Ideas

Use the diagram below to answer question 4.

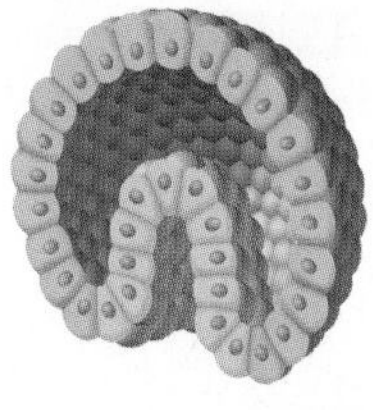

4. The embryo is in which stage of development?
   A. gastrula **C.** egg cell
   B. blastula **D.** zygote
5. Which material is not found in endoskeletons?
   A. calcium carbonate **C.** silica
   B. bone **D.** cartilage
6. Hox genes are active during which process?
   A. cell differentiation **C.** digestion
   B. movement **D.** neural stimulation

Constructed Response

7. MAIN Idea Select an animal and describe its adaptations and characteristics specific to its environment.
8. **Open Ended** Describe the advantages and disadvantages of internal and external fertilization.

Think Critically

9. **Interpret** this statement by Hans Spemann, a biologist who studied embryonic development: "We are standing and walking with parts of our body which could have been used for thinking had they developed in another part of the embryo."
10. **Hypothesize** what might happen to an embryo that suffers damage to some mesoderm cells.

Section 2

Vocabulary Review

Distinguish between the vocabulary terms in each pair.

11. bilateral symmetry and radial symmetry
12. ventral and dorsal
13. coelom and pseudocoelom

Understand Main Ideas

Use the diagram below to answer questions 14 and 15.

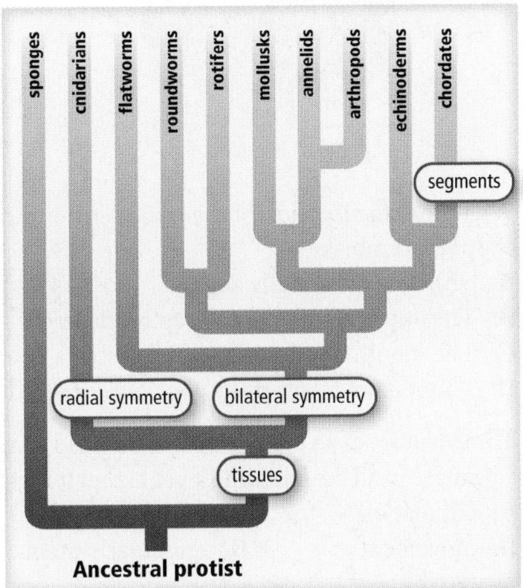

14. Based on the evolutionary tree above, which statement is true?
    A. True tissues evolved after bilateral symmetry.
    B. Segments evolved after bilateral symmetry.
    C. The common animal ancestor was a sponge.
    D. Most animals have radial symmetry.
15. On the evolutionary tree, which animals are related most closely?
    A. an annelids and mollusks
    B. flatworms and annelids
    C. roundworms and annelids
    D. annelids and echinoderms

Chapter 24

Assessment

Section 1

Vocabulary Review

1. exoskeleton
2. blastula
3. hermaphrodite

Understand Main Ideas

4. A
5. C
6. A

Constructed Response

7. Answers will vary. Squirrels have claws to climb with and hold onto trees, strong legs for climbing and jumping, fur for temperature regulation and protection, and a diet of nuts and berries.
8. Possible answer: Internal fertilization ensures that sperm encounter the eggs for fertilization to occur, but mates must first find each other. External fertilization does not require that mates find each other, but eggs and sperm may be washed away in strong waves or currents of water.

Think Critically

9. Certain cells and tissues in specific parts of the embryo are destined to be specific parts of the body. Hox genes and other mechanisms influence how various cells in the embryo will develop.
10. incomplete formation of muscles, circulatory system, or excretory system

Section 2

Vocabulary Review

11. bilateral symmetry: organism can be divided into mirror halves along one plane through central axis
    radial symmetry: organism can be divided into halves along any plane through central axis
12. ventral: underside; dorsal: backside
13. coelom: body cavity completely lined with mesoderm; pseudocoelom: body cavity partially lined with mesoderm

Understand Main Ideas

14. B
15. A

Assessment Online Test Practice

16. B
17. C
18. D
19. C
20. B

Constructed Response

21. Students should first make a large zygote, divide it into two, four, eight, etc. cells and make a hollow ball of these cells, push it in on one side and then create mesoderm in between the two layers. They should understand that the blastula is not a hollow ball of cells—it is fluid-filled.
22. Asymmetry: fiddler crab, amoeba
Bilateral: butterfly, beetle
Radial: sand dollar, flowers

Think Critically

23. Bilateral symmetry may have evolved before the split between animals with bilateral symmetry and cnidarians.
24. Exoskeletons protected animals and enabled them to keep from drying out, thereby enabling them to move to land. Segmentation enabled animals to move more effectively with muscles in segments. Also, segments, each containing similar organs, could be damaged and the animal could still survive with its remaining segments.

Section 3

Vocabulary Review

25. Spicules belong to sponges; other words relate to cnidarians.
26. Nematocysts are cnidarian features; other words relate to sponges.
27. Spongin is a sponge feature; other words relate to cnidarians.

Understand Main Ideas

28. D

Chapter 24 Assessment

16. **CAREERS IN BIOLOGY** An embryologist, a scientist who studies embryos, discovers a new marine animal. When one cell is removed during its early development, this cell develops into a complete animal. This animal is which of the following?
A. acoelomate
B. deuterostome
C. protostome
D. pseudocoelomate

Use the diagram below to answer question 17.

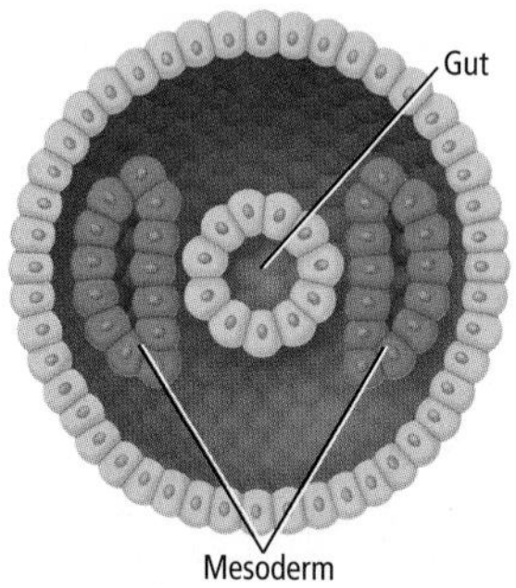

17. What does the location of the mesoderm indicate about this embryo?
A. The cells are directly aligned.
B. The outcome of each cell can be changed.
C. The mouth develops from the gastrula opening.
D. The coelom forms from pouches of mesoderm.

18. The evolution of an internal body cavity had adaptive advantage in all the following areas except for which?
A. circulation
B. movement
C. feeding
D. muscular system

19. Based on the evolutionary tree in **Figure 8,** what characteristics does an annelid have that a flatworm does not?
A. a coelom, a body cavity, bilateral symmetry, and no tissues
B. a coelom and segmentation
C. a coelom, protostome development, and segmentation
D. a pseudocoelom, a body cavity, and bilateral symmetry

20. What is the lighter undersurface of a frog called?
A. dorsal surface
B. ventral surface
C. anterior surface
D. posterior surface

Constructed Response

21. **Open Ended** Construct a working model of cell differentiation using clay, salt dough, or other materials. Make the first stage, then make that stage into the next, and that stage into the next until you have completed the steps.

22. **Open Ended** Describe three examples not discussed in this chapter of each type of symmetry.

Think Critically

23. MAIN Idea Biologists have recently determined that some sea anemones seem to possess bilateral symmetry. Hypothesize how this changes ideas for how and when bilateral symmetry evolved.

24. **THEME FOCUS Diversity** Explain how segmentation and exoskeletons gave some animals an adaptive advantage over those that were not segmented and did not have exoskeletons.

Section 3

Vocabulary Review

For each set of terms below, choose the term that does not belong and explain why it does not belong.

25. cnidocyte, nematocyst, cnidarian, spicule
26. pores, gemmule, filter feeder, nematocyst
27. alternation of generations, polyp, spongin, medusa

Understand Main Ideas

Use the diagram below to answer question 28.

28. The animal in the diagram above possesses which characteristic?
A. cephalization
B. cnidocytes
C. bilateral symmetry
D. asymmetry

29. Cidarians evolved directly from which group?
A. sponges
B. multicellular choanoflagellates
C. flatworms
D. animals with bilateral symmetry

Use the image below to answer question 30.

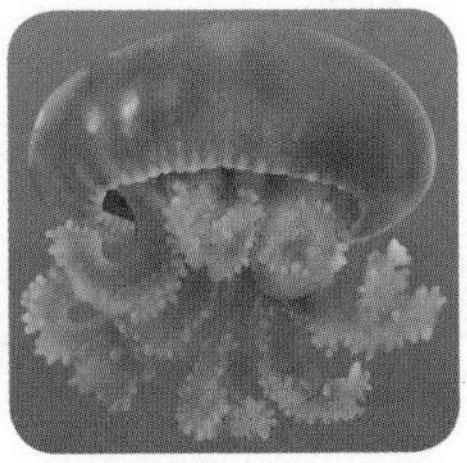

30. How does the animal shown in the image reproduce?
A. fragmentation
B. external fertilization
C. internal fertilization
D. regeneration

31. Which is not a characteristic of sponges?
A. filter feeding
B. digestion inside cells
C. asymmetry
D. tissues

32. Which pair of words is mismatched?
A. sponges, filter feeding
B. cnidarians, nematocysts
C. sponges, free swimming larva
D. cnidarians, spicules

Constructed Response

33. Open Ended Examine the classified section in the newspaper to see how it is organized. Then use your knowledge of cnidarians to write an ad to describe an ideal jellyfish homesite.

Think Critically

34. MAIN Idea Evaluate the importance of sponges and cnidarians in animal phylogeny.

35. Create Make a concept map using the following words: coral, polyp, cnidocyte, reef, calcium carbonatea and zooxanthellae.

Summative Assessment

36. BIG Idea Imagine you are working in a university laboratory. You are given an unknown invertebrate and told to determine its phylogeny. What characteristics would you use to accomplish this?

37. WRITING in Biology Write an editorial for a newspaper advocating protection for coral reefs. Explain the dangers that corals are facing, and make suggestions about what could be done to preserve and protect reefs.

DBQ Document-Based Questions

Transplantation experiments with early embryos of newts show that when tissue responsible for tail development was added into a different fluid-filled gastrula, it caused the effects shown below.

Data obtained from: Niehrs, C. 2003. A tale of tails. *Nature* 424: 375–376.

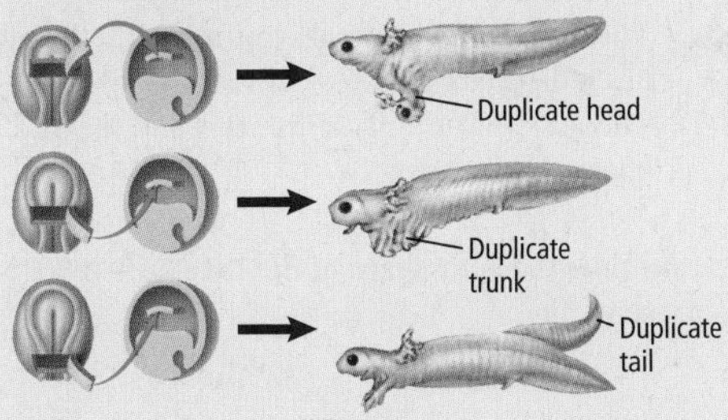

38. When a section from the top of the area was transplanted, where did the new tissue grow?

39. When a section from the bottom of the area was transplanted, where did the new tissue grow?

40. Make a summary statement that describes where new tissue grew when portions of the embryo responsible for tail development were transferred to fluid in the gastrula.

29. B
30. B
31. D
32. D

Constructed Response

33. Ads should express a need for an open ocean with available prey for the medusa stage and a substrate that would be available for the polyp stage. Other amenities will vary.

Think Critically

34. Sponges and cnidarians are the link to the first multicellular animal ancestor.

35.

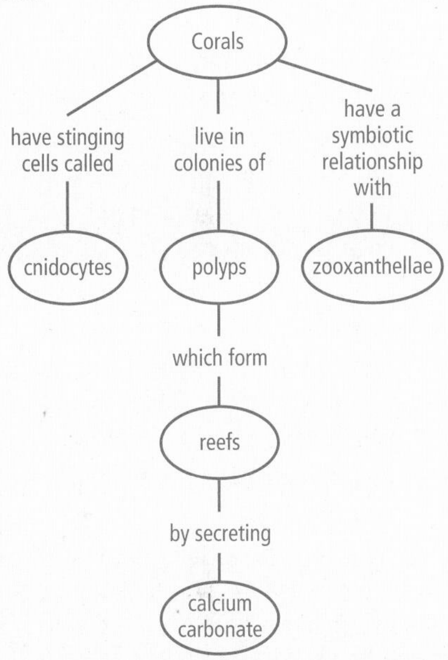

Summative Assessment

36. Answers will vary, but should include the animal's body plan, symmetry, and any adaptations it has, such as nemacysts.

37. Editorial should include destruction of reefs by tourists, coral hunters, and natural disasters. Laws could be passed to protect reefs from human destruction. More research could be done to learn about natural effects, such as hurricanes, on reefs.

DBQ Document-Based Questions

Niehrs, C. 2003. A tale of tails. *Nature* 424: 375–376.

38. in the head area of the animal
39. in the tail area of the animal
40. When cells from the top to the bottom of an area of the developing embryo are transferred into the fluid of the blastula, new tissue forms from the anterior to the posterior of the animal showing that a predetermined gradient exists for where certain cells will express themselves in the embryo.

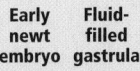

Assessment Online Test Practice

Standardized Test Practice

Multiple Choice

1. D
2. D
3. B
4. C
5. C
6. D
7. D
8. A

Short Answer

9. The student is studying phototropism. Phototropism is a response of plant growth to light.
10. Soft tissues would be best shown in fossils preserved in amber and in fossils preserved by freezing.
11. Spore-producing plants require a film of water on the gametophyte for the sperm to swim through to fertilize the egg.
12. The age of a tree can be estimated by examining the annual growth in the woody stem. Each ring usually represents one year of growth. The tree shown is 15 years old.
13. color, fragrance, pattern, and nectar
14. Answers may vary. Possible answers include the following.
    Embryonic development can show similarities or close relationships.
    Anatomical features can give evidence of similarities or close relationships.
    Molecular data, such as DNA, molecular RNA, and cellular proteins, can show similarities or close relationships

Extended Response

15. Male and female gametes form in mosquitoes from sporozoan cells picked up from the blood of host animals. The gametes fuse to form a zygote. The zygote develops many sporozoites that travel to the salivary glands of the mosquitoes. From the salivary glands, the sporozoites are injected into host animals. The stages of the cycle that occur in mosquitoes allows for genetic recombination and production of infective forms (sporozoites).

Standardized Test Practice

Cumulative

Multiple Choice

1. Which color of flower is most likely to attract nocturnal pollinators such as bats and moths?
   A. blue
   B. red
   C. violet
   D. white

Use the illustration below to answer questions 2 and 3.

2. How would you describe the body symmetry of the animals shown in the above illustration?
   A. Both have bilateral symmetry.
   B. Both have radial symmetry.
   C. The sea star has bilateral symmetry and the bird has radial symmetry.
   D. The sea star has radial symmetry and the bird has bilateral symmetry.

3. How does the body shape of the sea star help with its survival?
   A. It enables the sea star to capture many kinds of prey.
   B. It enables the sea star to capture prey from many directions.
   C. It enables the sea star to move through the water quickly.
   D. It enables the sea star to move through the water feebly.

4. Which structure in nonvascular plants is similar to roots in vascular plants?
   A. chloroplast
   B. mucilage
   C. rhizoid
   D. sporophyte

5. Which hormone stimulates the ripening of fruit?
   A. auxin
   B. cytokinins
   C. ethylene
   D. gibberellins

Use the diagram below to answer question 6.

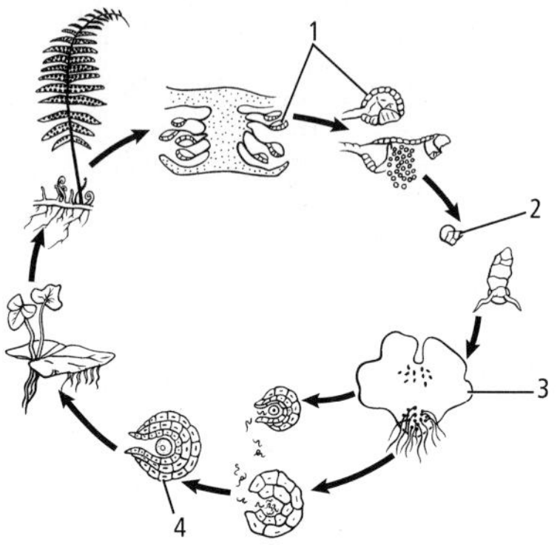

6. At which stage of the fern life cycle does the chromosome number change from haploid to diploid?
   A. 1
   B. 2
   C. 3
   D. 4

7. Which is the role of sclerenchyma cells in plants?
   A. gas exchange
   B. photosynthesis
   C. food storage
   D. support

8. What evidence would help scientists determine that colonial organisms were an early step in the evolution of multicellularity?
   A. similarities in DNA or RNA of early multicellular organisms and colonial unicellular organisms
   B. differences in DNA or RNA of early multicellular organisms and colonial unicellular organisms
   C. similarities of early multicellular organisms and present-day multicellular organisms
   D. differences between early multicellular organisms and present-day multicellular organisms

Short Answer

Use the diagram below to answer question 9.

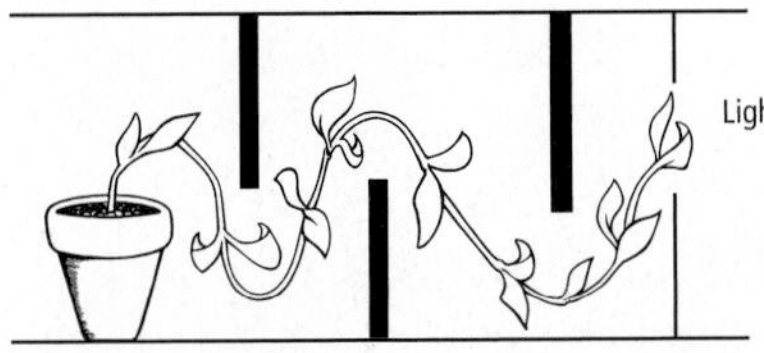

9. A student conducted an experiment using the above set up. Explain the purpose of this experiment.

10. Which type of fossils would tell a paleontologist the most about the soft tissues of an animal?

11. Explain why most spore-producing plants live in moist areas.

Use the diagram below to answer question 12.

12. How is the age of a tree estimated? What is the approximate age of this tree?

13. Name four flower adaptations that attract insects.

14. What are three kinds of evidence that can be used to confirm whether animals with different body structures are related closely?

Extended Response

15. *Plasmodium* is a sporozoan that causes the disease malaria. Identify the different stages of the sporozoan that occur in mosquitoes. Assess the importance of the stages of the life cycle that occur in mosquitoes.

16. Why does Mendel's law of segregation only apply to organisms that reproduce sexually?

17. Summarize egg development and fertilization in flowering plants.

Essay Question

Pollen analysis, or palynology, is an important tool used in archaeology. Palynologists take samples of soil from archaeological sites and analyze the pollen from different soil layers. By examining the changes in pollen types over time, palynologists can learn about historical land use. The pollen in the soil indicates how the land was used—whether it was cultivated, a forest was cleared, or if it was abandoned.

Using the information in the paragraph above, answer the following question in essay format.

18. Scientists have been trying to find the origin of corn. They know that corn was domesticated from a plant called *teosinte* that grew somewhere in the central valley of Mexico between 12,000 and 6,000 years ago. It often is hard to find intact corncobs because they do not fossilize well. How could a palynologist help determine the origin of corn?

NEED EXTRA HELP?																		
If You Missed Question . . .	1	2	3	4	5	6	7	8	9	10	11	12	13	14	15	16	17	18
Review Section . . .	23.1	24.2	24.2	21.2	22.3	23.1	22.1	24.1, 24.3	22.3	14.1	23.1	22.2	23.2	24.1	19.2	10.2	23.2	23.3

16. Mendel's law of segregation has to do with the separation of alleles during gamete formation. Only organisms that reproduce sexually form gametes. Gametes from one organism combine with gametes from another during fertilization. The law of segregation only explains genetic variation found in sexually reproducing organisms.

17. A specialized cell in the ovule undergoes meiosis, producing four megaspores. Three megaspores disintegrate. The nucleus of the remaining megaspore undergoes mitosis. The new nuclei undergo mitosis, and then each of the nuclei undergoes mitosis forming eight nuclei. Three nuclei are at each end of the cell and two nuclei—called polar nuclei—are in the center. One of the nuclei at the end closest to the micropyle becomes the egg. Two sperm enter the ovule. One sperm fertilizes the egg forming a diploid zygote and the other fertilizes the two polar nuclei forming triploid tissue.

Essay Question

18. Archaeologists can identify sites of early habitation and find a date they were occupied. Palynologists can analyze the pollen from soil at the site and gain information about the types of crops that grew there at that time. Pollen spores also can provide information about whether land was being cleared and cultivated then. Because pollen spores contain genetic information and are unique to specific species, palynologists can identify the types of corn found at the sites and study how corn plants changed over time. By working closely with the archaeologists, the changes in pollen can be dated.

Chapter 25 Organizer:
Worms and Mollusks

LabManager™
Customize any lab with the LabManager™ CD-ROM.

Essential Questions	National Science Standards	Materials and Planning: Estimated times include cleanup and disposal, but do not include teacher prep time. For cleanup and disposal guidelines, see page 39T.	Est. Time (min)
Section 1 1. What are the adaptations of free-living flatworms and parasitic flatworms? 2. How do flatworms maintain homeostasis? 3. What are the three classes of flatworms and what are characteristics of each?	UCP.1–3, UCP.5; C.1, C.4, C.5, C.6; F.1; G.1	**Launch Lab,** p. 724: earthworms, magnifying lens	15
		Demonstration, p. 726: 35 mm deep-well slides, slide projector or projecting microscope, planarian	10
		MiniLab 1, p. 728: planaria, observation dish, magnifying lens, cooked egg white	15
Section 2 1. What are the similarities between the features of roundworms and flatworms? 2. How can roundworms be identified based on movement? 3. What are the ways humans risk contracting roundworm parasites?	UCP.1–3, UCP.5; A.1, A.2; C.4, C.5, C.6; F.1, F.3, F.4, F.5, F.6; G.1, G.2, G.3	**Demonstration,** p. 732: binocular microscopes, watch glasses, vinegar eels	15
Section 3 1. What is the importance of the coelum to mollusks? 2. What is the function of the mantle and what are its adaptive advantages to mollusks? 3. What is the importance of mucus and the muscular foot to mollusks?	UCP.1, UCP.2, UCP.5; A.1, A.2; C.3, C.4, C.5, C.6	**Demonstration,** p. 739: corn starch, petri dishes or pieces of clear glass or plastic, snails	10
		Demonstration, p. 742: clam, beaker, water, carmine powder or food coloring	10
Section 4 1. What are the similarities among segmented worms, flatworms, and roundworms? 2. What is the importance of segmentation as an adaptation for survival in segmented worms? 3. What are the features of the three main classes of annelids that make them well-suited for their habitats?	UCP.1–5; A.1, A.2; C.3, C.4, C.5, C.6; D.2; E.1, E.2; F.1; G.1, G.2	**Demonstration,** p. 745: live earthworms, pebbles, clear plastic container, a way to project the image	5
		Activity, p. 747: live earthworms	10
		MiniLab 2, p. 748: blackworms, filter paper, petri dishes, spring water, stereomicroscope or magnifying lens, stopwatch	20
		BioLab, p. 753: mollusks, worms from multiple classes, applicator sticks, classification guides	90

Suggested Time for Each Lesson

Class	Chapter Opener	Section 1	Section 2	Section 3	Section 4	Assessment
Basic	45 min	45 min	45 min	45 min	45 min	45 min
General	20 min	45 min	35 min	45 min	35 min	45 min
Honors	—	45 min	45 min	70 min	45 min	20 min

ConnectED

connectED.mcgraw-hill.com

Access interactive learning opportunities and teaching resources using these icons located throughout your StudentWorks™ Plus Online and eTeacherEdition Online.

Chapter 25 Section Resources	Additional Chapter 25 Resources	Technology
FAST FILE Unit 7 Resources: Launch Lab Worksheet* MiniLab Worksheet* Study Guide (English/Spanish)* Section Quick Check **Reading Essentials 25.1** **Science Notebook 25.1*** **FAST FILE Unit 7 Resources:** Study Guide (English/Spanish)* Section Quick Check **Reading Essentials 25.2** **Science Notebook 25.2*** **FAST FILE Unit 7 Resources:** Study Guide (English/Spanish)* Section Quick Check **Reading Essentials 25.3** **Science Notebook 25.3*** **FAST FILE Unit 7 Resources:** MiniLab Worksheet* BioLab Worksheet* Study Guide (English/Spanish)* Section Quick Check **Reading Essentials 25.4** **Science Notebook 25.4***	**FAST FILE Unit 7 Resources:** Chapter Diagnostic Test Concept Mapping* Real-World Biology Enrichment Chapter Tests A, B, and C **Transparencies:** Bellringer Transparencies* Biology Concepts Transparencies* **Lab Resources:** Laboratory Manual* Probeware Lab Manual* Forensics Lab Manual* Pre-AP Lab Manual* Open Inquiry in Biology* Guided Inquiry in Biology*	**Teaching Tools:** eTeacherEdition Online Classroom Presentation Toolkit CD-ROM* LabManager™ CD-ROM* Video Lab DVD* Virtual Lab CD-ROM* What's BIOLOGY Got To Do With It? StudentWorks™ Plus Online* **Chapter Assessment Tools:** Classroom Presentation Toolkit CD-ROM* *ExamView® Assessment Suite* CD-ROM **Web-Based Resources:** • StudentWorks™ Plus Online • eTeacherEdition Online • Animations* • The Interactive Time Line* • Interactive Tables* • Online Quizzes • Online Test Practice • Standardized Test Practice • Virtual Labs* • Multilingual eGlossary* • Vocabulary eGames* • Vocabulary eFlashcards • WebQuests • Personal Tutors

While all resources listed are appropriate for English learners, the * indicates resources with a strong visual or hands-on component for EL.

Teaching strategies and activities have been coded for differentiated instruction.

AL Activities for students working above grade level	OL Activities for students working on grade level	BL Activities for students working below grade level	EL Activities for English learners (also ELL)	COOP LEARN Activities designed for small cooperative group work

CHAPTER 25

Launch Lab
What do earthworms feel like?

Inquiry Launch Lab

For a lab worksheet, use your eTeacherEdition Online.

RUBRIC A rubric for evaluating Launch Labs is found on your eTeacherEdition Online.

Est. Time 15 min

Additional Materials dissecting pan or tray, moist paper towels

Alternative Materials large photograph, such as the chapter opener photo on this page or poster of an earthworm

Safety Precautions Approve lab safety forms before work begins. Caution students not to focus direct sunlight onto the worm with the magnifying lens.

Procedure

1. Read and complete the lab safety form.
2. Obtain an **earthworm** from your teacher. **REMEMBER:** ***Always treat the earthworm in a humane manner.***
3. Run your finger along the ventral side, or underside, of the worm. Repeat in the opposite direction. Record your observations.
4. Examine the ventral side of the worm with a **magnifying lens**. Record your observations.
5. Wash your hands and return the earthworm to your teacher.

CHAPTER 25

Worms and Mollusks

ConnectED

Your one-stop online resource
connectED.mcgraw-hill.com

- Video
- Audio
- Review
- Inquiry
- WebQuest
- Assessment
- Concepts in Motion
- Multilingual eGlossary

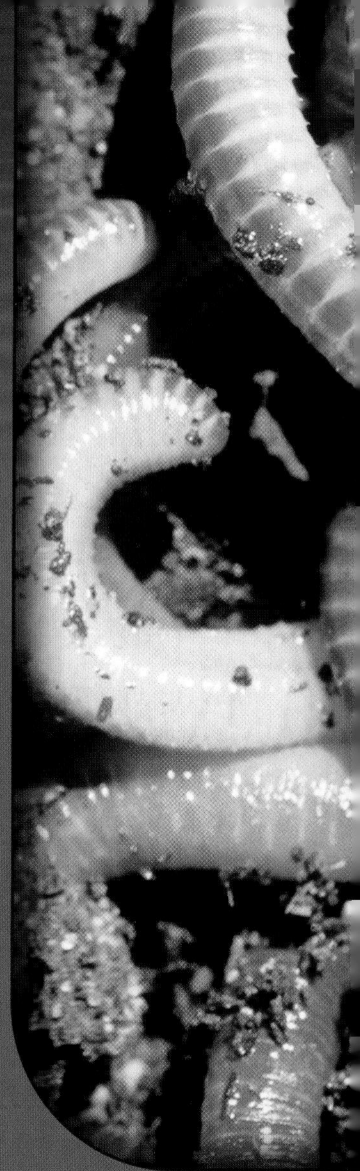

Launch Lab
What do earthworms feel like?

In this lab, you will examine a familiar worm, an earthworm, like the ones in the image above.

For a lab worksheet, use your StudentWorks™ Plus Online.

Inquiry Launch Lab

FOLDABLES®

Make a folded chart using the titles shown. Use it to organize your notes on segmented worms.

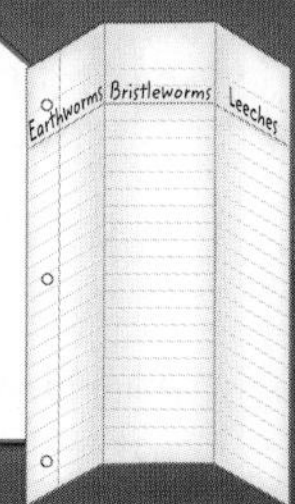

Analysis

1. **Describe** the way the earthworm felt to you when you brushed it in each direction. Students might answer that the earthworm felt rough one way and smooth the other way.
2. **Infer** how any differences you observed might be important adaptations. Possible answers include that the roughness aids in locomotion, it stops the earthworm from going backward, and that the earthworms can use the roughness to anchor themselves to the soil if a predator tries to pull them.
3. **Interpret** what on the worm's ventral side might explain how the worm felt to you. Students should see tiny bristles called setae on the ventral side of the earthworm.

Cleanup and Disposal Have students return earthworms to the approved location, and have them wash their hands thoroughly after handling the worms.

THEME FOCUS Energy
All worms obtain energy from other organisms.

BIG Idea Worms and mollusks have evolved to have a variety of adaptations for living as parasites or for living in water or soil.

THEMES

Scientific Inquiry Biologists study worms and mollusks using field observations, microscopes, and other scientific methods and technology.

Diversity The large number of species of worms have unique adaptations, such as eye spots, that enable them to live in specific habitats.

Energy Worms and mollusks use energy obtained from their food to carry out life functions such as circulation and movement.

Homeostasis Worms and mollusks maintain internal cellular homeostasis by a variety of internal means, such as excretory cells and organs.

Change Over time, natural selection results in the evolution of existing species of worms and mollusks to produce new species.

Introduce the Chapter

Earthworm Adaptations

Have students examine the photo of an earthworm. Have them note the close-up art of setae, the tiny bristles along the worm's body. The setae are an adaptation of an earthworm.

ASK STUDENTS: ***Infer how setae help an earthworm in its habitat.*** Setae help anchor one part of the worm in soil as it pushes the rest of its body through the soil.

BIG Idea

Worms and Mollusks

Show students the Microsoft® PowerPoint® presentation for this chapter on your Classroom Presentation Toolkit CD-ROM. For each image of a flatworm, roundworm, rotifer, mollusk, or segmented worm that you show, ask the following question:

ASK STUDENTS: ***What features do you see in this animal? Describe them.*** Answers may include thin and flat for flatworms, cylinder-shaped and tapered for roundworms, rings of cilia on rotifers, arms or tentacles and a baglike mantle for squid or octopus and a foot for slugs, tube-shaped with rings around the body for segmented worms. Explain that all of these animals have bilateral symmetry and all except for the flatworms have coeloms.

Section 1

MAIN Idea

EL BL OL AL COOP LEARN

Tapeworms Have students gather into groups of five. Pass around preserved tapeworms. **SAY TO STUDENTS:** ***Tapeworms don't have to do anything to survive. They get their food delivered and don't do any work. Make a list of the advantages and disadvantages of being a parasite.*** advantages: no predators, food is easily accessed; disadvantages: parasite cannot live outside host body; if host dies, so does parasite; cannot move away if conditions are not suitable

R Reading Strategy

BL OL Preview the Text

Before they read, have students list the new vocabulary found in bold print in this section. Students should study the figures to find clues to the meaning of each word. **SAY TO STUDENTS:** ***Predict the meaning of each word. As you read the section, revise the meanings as needed.***

Develop Concepts

EL Activity Tape six pieces of chart paper on the wall and title the pages with the headings under *Body Structure* in this section. Have students preview the text. Place them in groups of six. Have them go from sheet to sheet, writing what they recall. Allow them to use their textbooks to fill in their summaries.

Caption Question Fig. 1 The worms have bilateral symmetry, whereas cnidarians have radial symmetry.

Section 1

Reading Preview

Essential Questions

- What are the adaptations of free-living flatworms and parasitic flatworms?
- How do flatworms maintain homeostasis?
- What are the three classes of flatworms and what are characteristics of each?

Review Vocabulary

acoelomate: an animal without any body cavities

New Vocabulary

pharynx
flame cell
ganglion
regeneration
scolex
proglottid

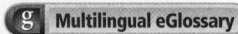

Multilingual eGlossary

Flatworms

R MAIN Idea Flatworms are thin, flat, acoelomate animals that can be free-living or parasitic.

Real-World Reading Link Think about a time when you were caught in an unexpected rain shower without rain gear. If you were wearing layers of clothing, the rain might not have soaked through to your skin. As you read about worms, think about how it is easier for the rain to move through one thin layer than through multiple heavy layers.

Body Structure

The evolutionary tree in **Figure 1,** shows that flatworms are on the acoelomate branch of the tree, while roundworms are on the pseudocoelomate branch. However, flatworms and roundworms both have bilateral symmetry. They can be divided along only one plane into mirror-image halves. Bilateral symmetry is a major evolutionary step that allows parts of the body to evolve different organs. Animals that have bilateral symmetry also have more efficient movement than animals with radial symmetry.

Phylum Platyhelminthes (pla tee HEL min theez)—flatworms—consists of about 20,000 species. **Figure 1** shows some of the variety seen in this phylum. Flatworms range in length from many meters to 1 mm or less. They have thin, flat bodies that resemble ribbons. Unlike sponges and cnidarians, flatworms have a definite head region and body organs. Recall that flatworms are acoelomates and therefore lack a coelom. Their bodies have no cavities.

Most flatworms are parasites living in the bodies of a variety of animals, but some others are free-living in marine, freshwater, or moist land habitats. Freshwater planarians are often seen on the underside of rocks in swiftly flowing streams.

Figure 1 Notice on the evolutionary tree that flatworms, such as flukes and tapeworms, were among the first animals to show bilateral symmetry.
Explain *how the symmetry of flatworms is different from that of cnidarians.*

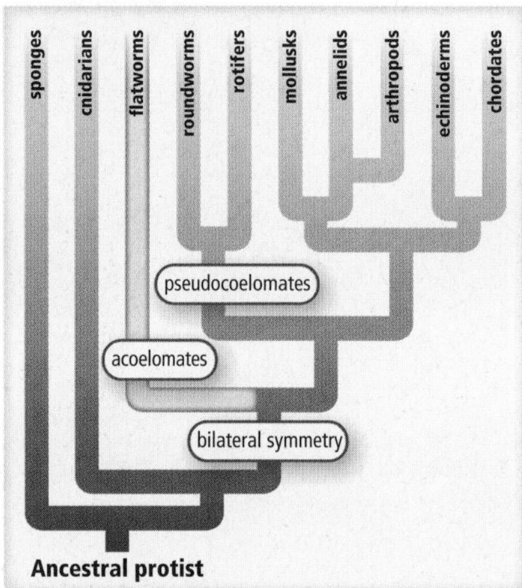

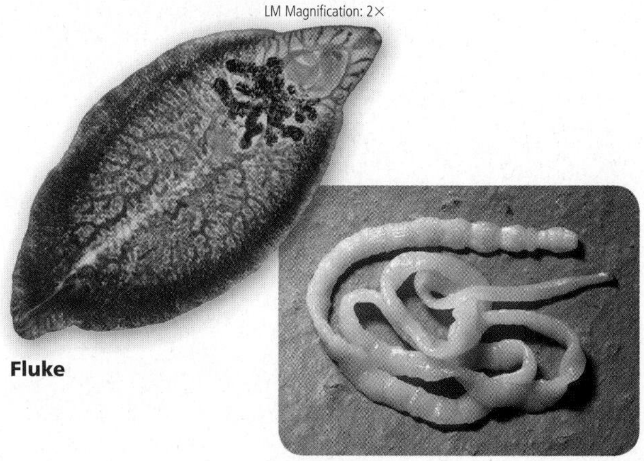

Fluke

Tapeworm

Demonstration

BL OL AL Planarians Place a live planarian in water. Using 35 mm deep-well slides from a biological supply company on a projecting microscope, project the image on a screen. If neither a projector nor microscope are available, have students observe the planarian with a magnifying lens.
ASK STUDENTS: ***How does the planarian move?*** It glides smoothly, sometimes moving its anterior end from side to side. Point out that the planarian has a head area. ***How is the body shape of the planarian different from the body shapes of sponges and cnidarians?*** Planarians have bilateral symmetry. Est. time: 10 min

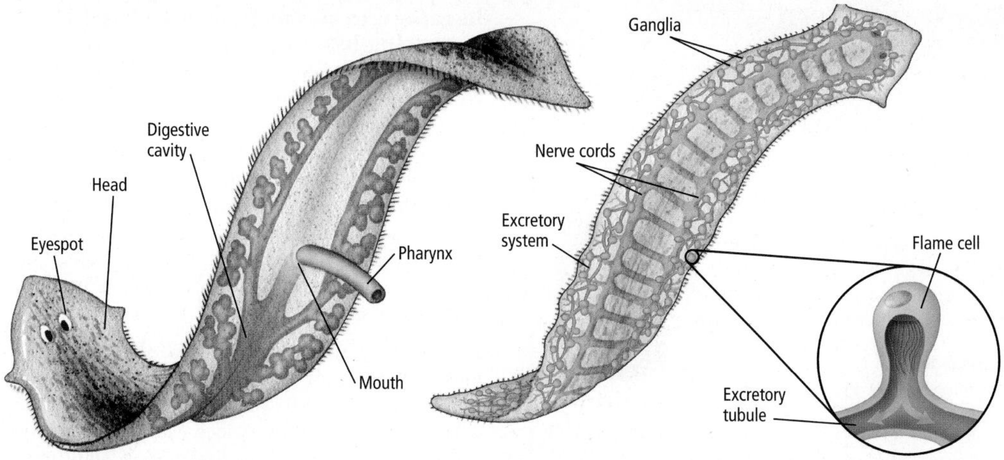

■ **Figure 2** Simple organ systems, such as the excretory and nervous systems, are found in flatworms.

Concepts in Motion
Animation

S

Feeding and digestion Free-living flatworms feed on dead or slow-moving organisms. They extend a tubelike muscular organ, called the **pharynx** (FAHR ingks), out of their mouths. The pharynx, shown in **Figure 2,** releases enzymes that begin the digestion of prey. Then food particles are sucked into the digestive tract, where digestion continues. Because flatworms have only one body opening, wastes are ejected through the mouth.

Parasitic flatworms have modified feeding structures called hooks and suckers, which enable them to stay attached to their hosts. Some parasitic flatworms have a reduced digestive system and feed on blood and other body tissues. Other parasitic flatworms lack a digestive system. Because they are so thin, like a single layer of cloth, and are surrounded by nutrients in their host's intestines, these parasites can absorb directly through their body walls partially or completely digested food eaten by the host.

Inquiry
Video Lab

Reading Check **Compare** feeding and digestion in free-living flatworms and parasitic flatworms.

Respiration, circulation, and excretion Like sponges and cnidarians, flatworms do not have circulatory organs or respiratory organs. Because flatworms are so thin, their cells can use the process of diffusion to move dissolved oxygen and nutrients to all parts of their bodies. Carbon dioxide and other wastes also are removed from flatworm cells by diffusion.

Unlike sponges and cnidarians, flatworms have an excretory system that consists of a network of small tubes that run through the body. On side branches of the tubes, as shown in **Figure 2,** bulblike **flame cells** lined with cilia sweep water and excretory substances into tubules. These substances then exit through pores to the outside of the body. Flame cells were so named because the flickering movements of the cilia inside the cells look like the light of a candle flame. Because flame cells move water out of the body, they keep flatworm cells from becoming waterlogged. In addition to the action of flame cells, flatworms also excrete waste products and maintain homeostatic water balance through their mouths.

VOCABULARY
SCIENCE USAGE V. COMMON USAGE
Host
Science usage: an animal or plant on which or in which a parasite lives
Some parasitic worms live in the intestines of their hosts.

Common usage: a person who entertains guests
Tyler's dad was the host for the football party.

Reading Check Free-living flatworms feed using a pharynx and have a digestive system. Parasitic flatworms feed using hooks and suckers (reduced digestive system) or absorb nutrients through their body walls (no digestive system).

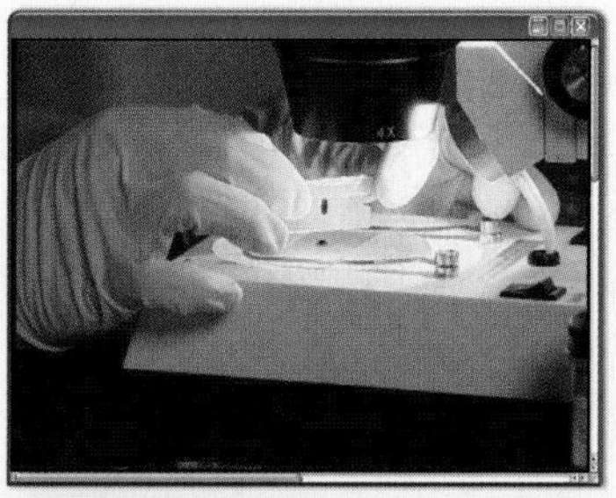

Inquiry **Video Lab** Students will observe an experiment to determine whether or not planarians are capable of regeneration.

Develop Concepts
BL OL AL

Clarify a Misconception
Many people think that anything with a wormlike shape is a worm. **ASK STUDENTS:** ***Is an insect larva a worm?*** no Explain that maggots, caterpillars, and other insect larvae are not true worms. Insect larvae belong to another group of animals called arthropods, which have more complex body structures than worms do. Explain that there are three main groups of true worms: flatworms, roundworms, and segmented worms. In addition, students often think that earthworms are roundworms because they are cylindrical.

Writing Support
EL BL OL **Summary Writing**
Supply students with a full-page diagram of a planarian. Ask them to use their books to label the planarian's body parts and write captions indicating the functions of the parts. Students should label the head and eyespots (light-sensing), pharynx (digestion), flame cells (eliminate water and metabolic wastes), and ganglia (nerve cells).

S Skill Practice
BL OL AL **Visual Literacy**
Have students examine Figure 2. **ASK STUDENTS:** ***In what way do you think the ganglia of the flatworm shown in the diagram are different from or similar to the sensory organs of humans and other mammals?*** Ganglia help the flatworm receive signals about the outside world. The different kinds of sensory organs in mammals receive more information.

Concepts in Motion
Animation

C Critical Thinking

BL OL AL Hypothesize

SAY TO STUDENTS: ***Form a hypothesis about whether or not a planarian can sense its environment.*** Hypotheses may include planaria can see or feel. Have students design an experiment to test their hypothesis by investigating the response of a planarian to light, touch, heat, cold, or other physical variables. Make sure students plan for only one independent variable, a control, and that quantitative data is collected.

MiniLab 1

? Inquiry MiniLab

For a lab worksheet, use your eTeacherEdition Online.

✻RUBRIC A rubric for evaluating MiniLabs is found on your eTeacherEdition Online.

Est. Time 15 min

Safety Precaution Approve lab safety forms before work begins.

Teaching Strategy
Have the planarian in a dish filled with water ready for students to observe.

Cleanup and Disposal Have students return planarians to the approved location, and wash their hands thoroughly.

Analysis

1. flatworms: flat, thin bodies, no segments; earthworms: round bodies with segments
2. Flat body enables it to move between rocks. Mucus enables it to cling to slick surfaces.
3. because they have flat bodies and no segments

LabManager™

Customize this lab with the LabManager™ CD-ROM.

MiniLab 1

? Inquiry MiniLab

Observe a Planarian

LM Magnification: 10×

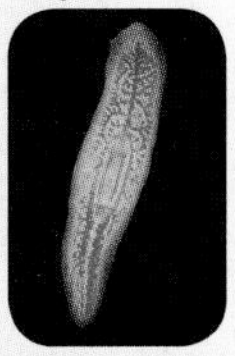

Planarian

How does a planarian behave?
Investigate the physical features and behavior of a planarian by observing this common flatworm.

Procedure

1. Read and complete the lab safety form.
2. Observe the **planarian** in a **water-filled observation dish** by using a **magnifying lens.**
3. Create a data table to record your observations.
4. Record the physical characteristics and behaviors of the flatworm.
5. Place a small piece of **cooked egg white** into the dish, and observe the feeding behavior of the planarian.

Analysis

1. **Compare and contrast** the physical features of the planarian with the features of the earthworm you observed in the Launch Lab.
2. **Analyze** how the body shape and movement of a planarian enables it to live in its environment.
3. **Infer** why scientists classify planaria into a group separate from other worms.

Response to stimuli The nervous system regulates the body's response to stimuli. In most flatworms, the nervous system consists of two nerve cords with connecting nerve tissue that run the length of the body. In most flatworms, the connecting nerve tissue looks like the rungs of a ladder, as illustrated in **Figure 2.** At the anterior end of the nerve cords is a small swelling composed of ganglia, which send nerve signals to and from the rest of the body. A **ganglion** (plural, ganglia) is a group of nerve cell bodies that coordinates incoming and outgoing nerve signals. C

Movement Some flatworms move by contracting muscles in the body wall. To escape predators and to find food, most free-living flatworms glide by using cilia located on their undersides. Mucus lubricates the worms and improves the gliding motion, while muscular action lets the animals twist and turn. If you have ever tried to loosen planaria worms from the bottoms of rocks, you know that their outer mucus covering enables them to stick tightly—an important adaptation in a swiftly moving stream. You can observe the features and behavior of a flatworm in **MiniLab 1.**

Reproduction Flatworms are hermaphrodites because they produce both eggs and sperm. During sexual reproduction, two different flatworms exchange sperm, and the eggs are fertilized internally. In marine flatworms, zygotes in cocoons are released into the water, where they hatch within a few weeks.

Free-living flatworms can reproduce asexually by **regeneration,** a process in which body parts that are missing because of damage or predation can be regrown. A planarian that is cut in half horizontally can grow a new head on the tail end and a new tail on the head end, forming two new organisms, as shown in **Figure 3.**

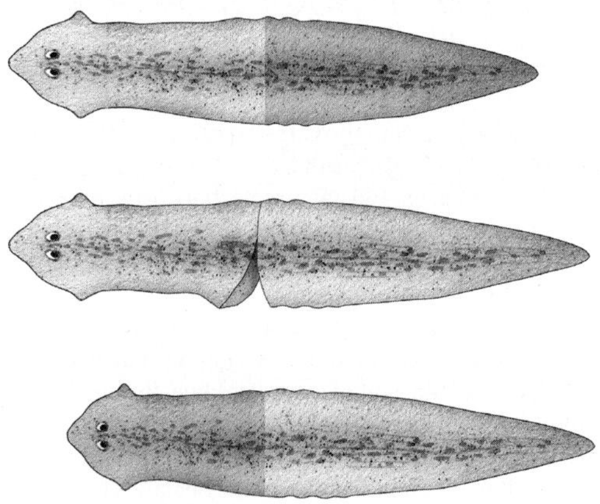

■ **Figure 3** Two new planaria form when one planarian is cut in half horizontally. Some planaria can regenerate from almost any piece of their bodies.

Activity

BL Bulletin-Board Display Ask a group of students to collect illustrations to make a bulletin board display depicting parasitic and free-living flatworms. Est. time: 15 min

Diversity of Flatworms

There are three main classes of flatworms: Turbellaria (tur buh LER ee uh), Trematoda (trem uh TOH duh), and Cestoda (ses TOH duh). Class Turbellaria consists of the free-living flatworms. Class Trematoda and class Cestoda consist of parasitic flatworms.

Turbellarians Members of the class Turbellaria are called turbellarians. Most turbellarians, like planarians, live in marine or freshwater habitats, while some live in moist soils. They vary in size, color, and body shape. As shown in **Figure 4,** turbellarians have eyespots that can detect the presence or absence of light. They also have sensory cells that help them identify chemicals and water movement.

The cells sensitive to chemicals are concentrated on small projections called auricles (OR ih kulz) at the anterior end of the worm. When a planarian hunts, it might wave its head back and forth as it crawls forward, exposing the auricles to chemical stimuli coming from food. At the same time, its eyespots might help it perceive light conditions that would protect it from predators.

Trematodes Flukes belong to class Trematoda—the trematodes. They are parasites that infect the blood or body organs of their hosts. The life cycle of the parasitic fluke *Schistosoma* is shown in **Figure 5.** Notice that this parasite requires two hosts to complete its life cycle.

When humans contract schistosomiasis (shihst tuh soh MI uh sis), the fluke eggs clog blood vessels, causing swelling and eventual tissue damage. Schistosomiasis can be prevented by proper sewage treatment
S and by wearing protective clothing when wading or swimming in infested water. Schistosomiasis infections are not common in the United States.
W

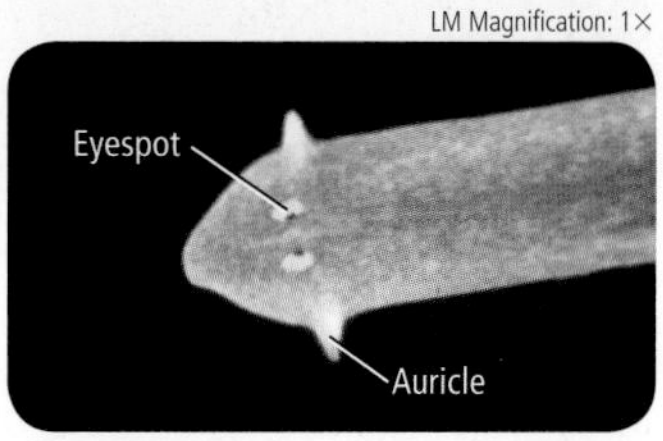

■ **Figure 4** Dark clusters of light-sensitive cells form the eyespots on this planarian. Note the auricles projecting from the same area.

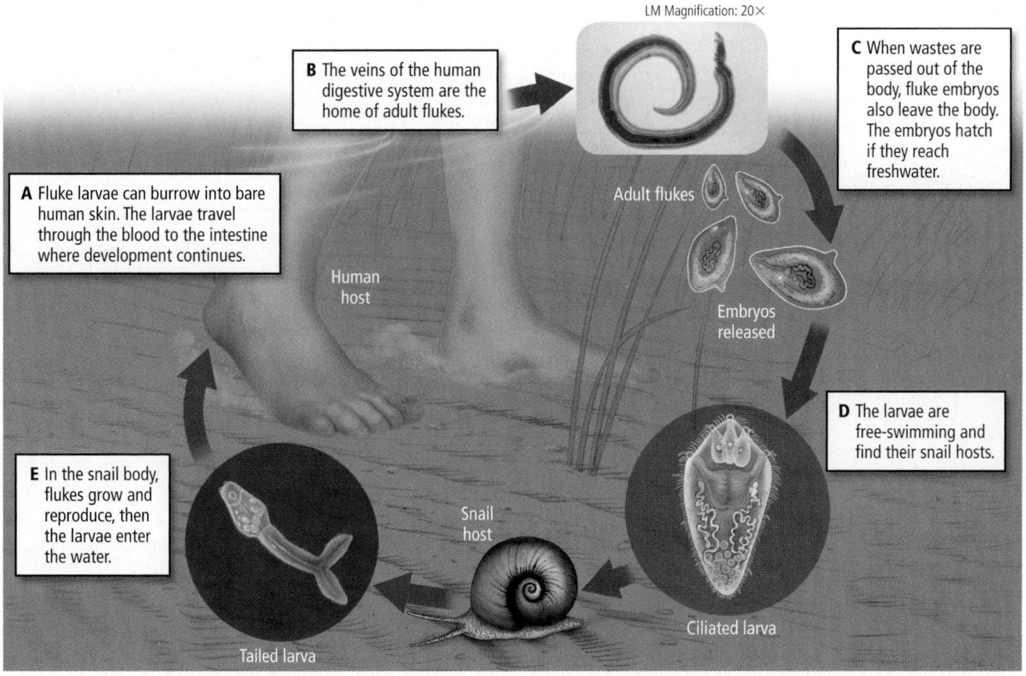

LM Magnification: 20×
B The veins of the human digestive system are the home of adult flukes.
C When wastes are passed out of the body, fluke embryos also leave the body. The embryos hatch if they reach freshwater.
A Fluke larvae can burrow into bare human skin. The larvae travel through the blood to the intestine where development continues.
Adult flukes
Human host
Embryos released
D The larvae are free-swimming and find their snail hosts.
E In the snail body, flukes grow and reproduce, then the larvae enter the water.
Snail host
Ciliated larva
Tailed larva

■ **Figure 5** Two hosts—humans and snails—are needed to complete the life cycle of the fluke *Schistosoma*.

***Infer** why the two larval forms of the fluke are different shapes.*

Develop Concepts

BL OL AL Activity Have students design a one-frame cartoon that will show some of the adaptations of planaria. Show students some cartoons depicting biological topics as examples. Students can use humor, but should keep the cartoon scientifically accurate.

S Skill Practice

OL Compare and Contrast

SAY TO STUDENTS: ***Compare and contrast turbellarian and trematode lifestyle and adaptations.*** Both are flatworms. Turbellarians are mostly free-living while trematodes are parasites. Turbellarians have neural structures that detect stimuli in their environments while trematodes do not have these structures. Trematode parasites need a host, sometimes two, to complete their life cycles.

W Writing Support

AL Narrative Writing Have students research the trematode that causes "swimmer's itch" in humans in many northern states. Have them write a report that explains this parasite's life cycle.

■ **Caption Question Fig. 5** Ciliated larva allows fluke to swim to snail host; tailed larva allows fluke to burrow into skin of human host.

Differentiated Instruction

English Learners Students can deepen their understandings of concepts when they use a variety of writing styles to convey their knowledge. The activity on this page requires students to illustrate with a cartoon. This will assist in language development as well as comprehension of science concepts.

For more tips, see pages 14T–15T.

Develop Concepts

AL Activity Have students research common human flatworm parasite life cycles. College-level textbooks in invertebrate zoology and parasitology are helpful references. Have students make diagrams of life cycles of human flatworm parasites. Have students explain in each case how the life cycle could be interrupted to prevent human infection.

Formative Assessment

Evaluation

SAY TO STUDENTS: ***Make a table that demonstrates the similarities and differences among turbellarians, trematodes, and cestodes.*** Students should include features such as symmetry, habitat, response to stimuli, feeding, digestion, free-living or parasitic, and other adaptations.

Remediation Draw a football field with goalposts and 10-yard lines on the board. Divide the class into two teams. Ask questions of each team about the three classes of flatworms. Draw a circle on the 50-yard line to represent the football. Advance the ball 10 yards toward that team's goal post if the answer is correct. If the answer is wrong, the question goes to the other team. The team that reaches its goalpost first wins. You could also use a soccer goal or a baseball diamond.

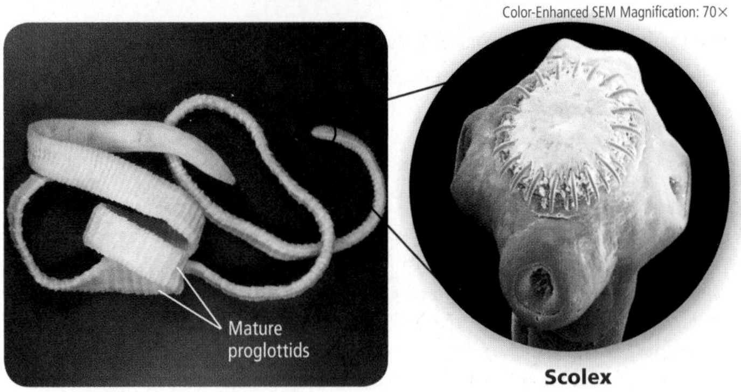

Figure 6 As the proglottids behind the scolex mature, new proglottids form.

Cestodes All tapeworms are members of class Cestoda—the cestodes. They are parasites adapted to life in the intestines of their hosts. Look at the anterior end, or head, of the tapeworm in **Figure 6.** This is the **scolex** (SKOH leks), a knob-shaped structure with hooks and suckers that attach to the intestinal lining of a host, such as a cow or a human.

Behind the scolex of the worm are a series of individual sections called **proglottids** (proh GLAH tihdz), each of which contains muscles, nerves, flame cells, and male and female reproductive organs. Proglottids form continuously; as new ones form near the scolex, older proglottids move farther back and mature. After eggs in the mature proglottids are fertilized, the last segments with developing embryos break off and pass out of the intestines of their hosts. Animals such as cattle might feed on vegetation or drink water contaminated by the tapeworm proglottids, and then the cycle of tapeworm growth is repeated.

When eaten by cattle, tapeworms burrow through intestinal walls, entering blood and muscle. If undercooked infected beef is eaten, human infection by tapeworms is likely. Tapeworm infections are uncommon in industrialized nations because of beef inspections.

Section 1 Assessment

Section Summary

- Flatworms were among the first animals to exhibit bilateral symmetry.
- Flatworms are acoelomates with limited numbers of organs and systems.
- Some flatworms are free-living, and others are parasitic.
- Flatworms that are parasitic have specialized adaptations for parasitic life.

Understand Main Ideas

1. MAIN Idea **Evaluate** the advantages of a flatworm's thin body.
2. **Compare and contrast** the adaptations of free-living flatworms and parasitic flatworms.
3. **Prepare** a chart that compares digestion, respiration, movement, and reproduction in the free-living and parasitic flatworms.
4. **Analyze** the importance of flame cells in a flatworm.

Think Critically

5. **Design** an experiment to determine what habitat conditions planarians prefer.
6. **Evaluate** how the three classes of flatworms are adapted to their habitats. Name the three classes of flatworms in your answer.
7. **Diagram** bilateral symmetry using a planarian as an example. Explain the adaptive advantage of bilateral symmetry to a planarian.

Section 1 Assessment

1. can obtain oxygen and nutrients through diffusion
2. Free-living flatworms have mouths and digestive tracts; parasitic flatworms have hooks for attachment to hosts and reduced digestive systems.
3. digestion: turbellarians—pharynx, mouth; flukes—suckers for blood; tapeworm—none. respiration: turbellarians—diffusion; flukes—diffusion; tapeworm—diffusion. movement: turbellarians—muscles, cilia; flukes—none in adult; tapeworm—none. reproduction: all three groups—hermaphroditic; turbellarians also reproduce asexually by regeneration.
4. move water out of body; keep cells from being waterlogged
5. The answer should include a hypothesis, control, variable, and a plan for data collection.
6. Answers should include adaptations and shapes.
7. divided on one plane into mirror-image halves; organisms with bilateral symmetry can develop organs and have more efficient movement

Assessment Online Quiz

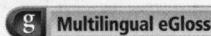

Reading Preview

Essential Questions

- What are the similarities between the features of roundworms and flatworms?
- How can roundworms be identified based on movement?
- What are the ways humans risk contracting roundworm parasites?

Review Vocabulary

cilia: short, numerous projections that look like hairs

New Vocabulary

hydrostatic skeleton
trichinosis

g Multilingual eGlossary

Roundworms and Rotifers

MAIN Idea Roundworms and rotifers have a more highly evolved gut than flatworms.

Real-World Reading Link If you were to guess what animal is one of the most common in the world, what animal would you choose? Would you guess a roundworm? With 20,000 species of roundworms known, scientists estimate that there might be 100 times as many more kinds of roundworms still undiscovered.

R Body Structure of Roundworms

Roundworms are in phylum Nematoda (ne muh TOH duh) and often are called nematodes. Locate roundworms on the evolutionary tree in **Figure 7.** Notice that they are pseudocoelomates. Recall that pseudocoelomates have a fluid-filled body cavity that is partially lined with mesoderm. Roundworms have bilateral symmetry and are cylindrical, unsegmented worms that are tapered at both ends. Roundworms come in a variety of sizes, as shown in **Figure 7.** Most are less than 1 mm long. However, the longest known roundworm, which lives in certain whales, can grow to 9 m in length.

Roundworms are found in both marine and freshwater habitats and on land. Some are parasites that attach to plants or animals. A spadeful of garden soil might contain one million roundworms. One study revealed that a rotting apple contained 1074 roundworms! Dogs and cats can be plagued by roundworms if they are not wormed when they are young and at regular intervals during adulthood. Roundworms have adaptations that enable them to live in many places.

Figure 7 Roundworms are pseudocoelomates with bilateral symmetry.

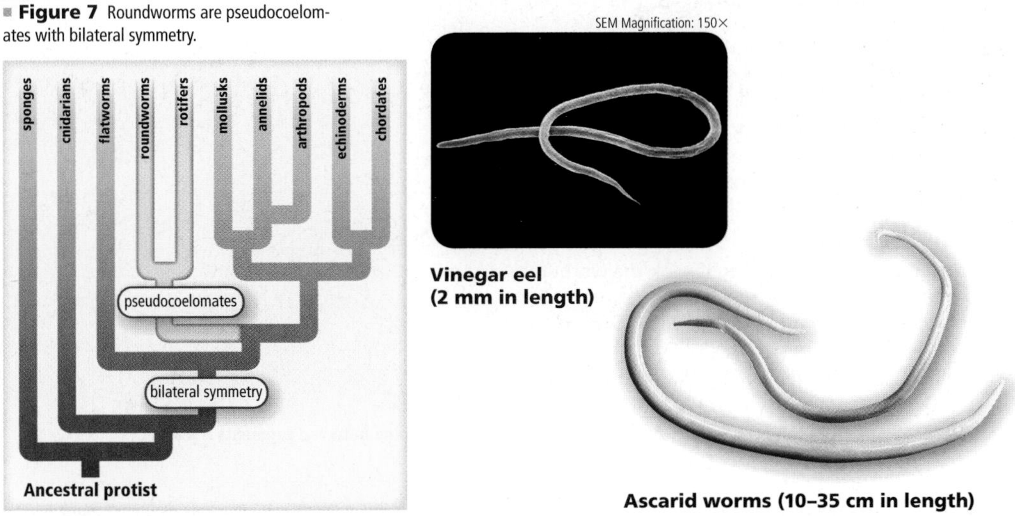

Section 2

MAIN Idea

BL OL AL

Roundworms and Rotifers
Use a projecting microscope and slides or use pictures to show students images of flatworms, roundworms, and rotifers.
ASK STUDENTS: ***What kind of symmetry do these animals have?*** bilateral Explain that flatworms, roundworms and rotifers all have bilateral symmetry. ***What kind of body plan do flatworms have?*** pseudocoelomate Explain that roundworms and rotifers are also pseudocoelomates, but roundworms and rotifers have a more complex gut that will be studied in this section.

R Reading Strategy

BL OL Directed Reading
Have students make a list of the subheadings they will find as they read the text under the heading *Body Structure of Roundworms.* Have them write down their predictions and, as they read the section, revise as needed.
SAY TO STUDENTS: ***As you read, write a list of the important facts under each heading.***

EL Begin the activity by having students form two lines. Have them share and discuss with the student opposite them one thing they learned about flatworms. Have students return to seats and predict what they will learn about roundworms.

Differentiated Instruction

Below Level Educational research indicates that teachers can increase student achievement by providing ample opportunities for hands-on activities. A hands-on activity like the mural on the next page can be used to ensure that students are engaged with the material and develop a deeper understanding of concepts.

For more tips, see pages 14T–15T.

Develop Concepts

EL BL OL COOP LEARN Mural

Have a group of students make a mural that illustrates the main ideas about roundworms and rotifers in this section. The mural should be suitable for bulletin board display.

Writing Support

BL OL AL Creative Writing

Have students research flame cells in some species of roundworms. Have them create a picture map that shows where the flame cells are located and explains how they function and their importance.

DATA ANALYSIS LAB 1

About the Lab

- If possible, provide students with nematode worms for their observation under binocular microscopes.
- Nematode muscle design is adapted to nematodes living in soil, in aquatic sediments, in fruits, and on surface films where the substrate at the air-water interface provides resistance that muscles can push against.
- Also see Pechenik, J. 2005. *Biology of the invertebrates.* New York: McGraw-Hill.

Think Critically

1. 0.33 s
2. (0.5 mm/0.33 s) × 60 s/min × 10 min = 909 mm
3. It would be slower or might not be able to travel forward.

CAREERS IN BIOLOGY

Veterinary Parasitologist As scientists who keep parasites out of the food supply, veterinary parasitologists are responsible for the health of farm and domesticated animals. They determine ways to control and prevent parasites in animals such as cows, pigs, and chickens.

Feeding and digestion Most roundworms are free-living, but some are parasites. Some free-living roundworms are predators of other tiny invertebrates, while others feed on decaying plant and animal matter. Free-living forms have a key evolutionary adaptation in their digestive systems. Recall that in the course of evolution, pseudocoelomate animals were the first to have a body cavity. The pseudocoelom of a nematode separates the endoderm-lined gut from the rest of the body. The movement of food through the gut, or digestive tract, is one-way—food enters through the mouth, and undigested food leaves through an opening at the end of the digestive tract called the anus.

Respiration, circulation, excretion, and response to stimuli Like flatworms, roundworms have no circulatory organs or respiratory organs, and they depend on diffusion to move nutrients and gases throughout their bodies. Most roundworms exchange gases and excrete metabolic wastes through their moist outer body coverings. More complex forms have excretory ducts that enable them to conserve water for living on land, while others have flame cells.

Ganglia and associated nerve cords coordinate nematode responses. Nematodes are sensitive to touch and to chemicals. Some have structures that might detect differences between light and dark.

Movement Roundworms have muscles that run the length of their bodies. These muscles cause the worms' bodies to move in a thrashing manner as one muscle contracts and another relaxes. These muscles also pull against the outside body wall and the pseudocoelom. The pseudocoelom acts as a **hydrostatic skeleton**—fluid within a closed space that provides rigid support for muscles to work against. If you were to observe a roundworm moving, it might resemble a tiny piece of wriggling thread. Learn more about worm movement in **Data Analysis Lab 1.**

DATA ANALYSIS LAB 1

Based on Real Data*

Interpret the Diagram

How does a nematode move? A nematode alternately contracts and relaxes muscles that run lengthwise on each side of its body.

Data and Observations

The diagram sequences the movement of a single nematode. Each segment of time is represented by the space between the dotted lines.

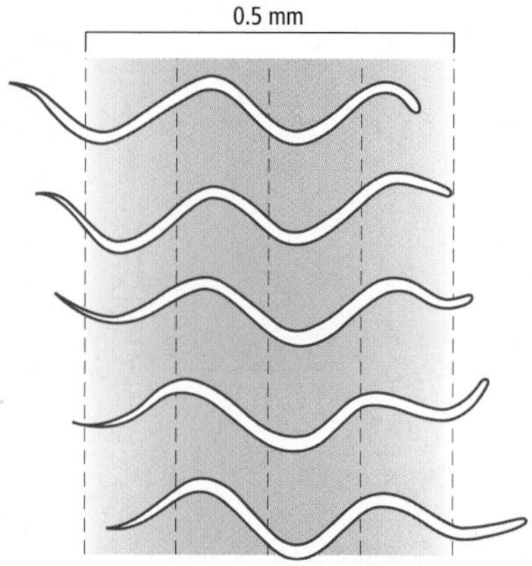

Time between segments is 0.33 s

Think Critically

1. **Interpret** about how long it took the worm to move to its final location.
2. **Calculate** how far the worm could move in 10 min.
3. **Infer** how worm movement might differ if muscles on one side of its body were damaged.

*Data obtained from: Gray, J. and H.W. Lissmann. 1964. The locomotion of nematodes. *Journal of Experimental Biology* 41:135–154.

Demonstration

BL OL AL Vinegar Eels Set up binocular microscopes and watchglasses with vinegar eels in them. Vinegar eels can be purchased from biological supply companies. Have students examine the vinegar eels.

SAY TO STUDENTS: ***Describe the movements of these roundworms and explain this movement in terms of the types of muscles these worms have.*** They move in a thrashing or wriggling manner. They have muscles that run along the length of their bodies. As muscles on one side contract, muscles on the other side relax causing this motion. Est. time: 15 min

Reproduction Roundworms reproduce sexually. The females produce eggs, and the males, which often are smaller than the females, produce sperm. Fertilization is internal. In free-living roundworms, larvae hatch from the fertilized eggs, then grow into adults. In parasitic roundworms, development often is more complicated, involving one or more hosts or different locations in the host's body.

The adult roundworm *Caenorhabditis elegans (C. elegans),* shown in **Figure 8,** contains only 959 cells; zygotes mature to adults in just three days. These characteristics make it an extremely important subject of research on development, aging, and genetics. *C. elegans* was the first multicellular organism to have its entire genome sequenced. The *C. elegans* genome contains 97 million DNA bases encoding more than 19,000 different genes.

W **Reading Check** **Explain** why the features of *C. elegans* make it a good subject for research.

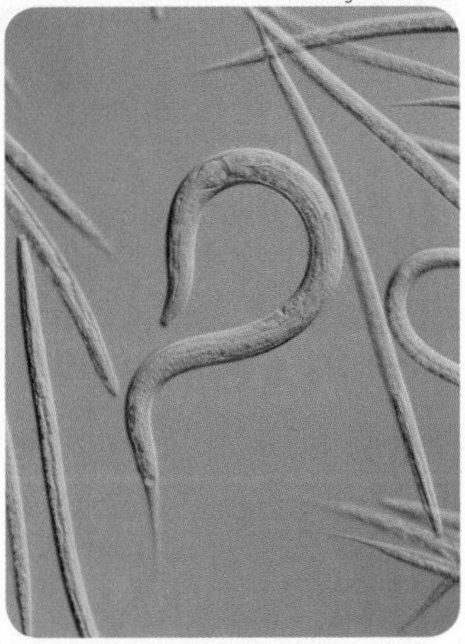

■ **Figure 8** *C. elegans* is the subject of much genetic research. With comparatively few cells and rapid development, scientists can easily research developmental changes.

Diversity of Roundworms

Of the 20,000 known roundworm species, approximately half are parasites. These parasitic roundworms cause a variety of diseases in plants and animals, including humans. Many of these diseases in humans are the result of carelessness, a lack of personal hygiene, or poor sanitation.

Trichinella worms A disease called **trichinosis** (trih keh NOH sis) can be contracted by eating raw or undercooked pork and pork products, or wild game infected with the larvae of *Trichinella,* like the one shown in **Figure 9.** After ingestion by a host organism, the worms mature in one to two days. Female worms with fertilized eggs burrow into the intestinal walls of humans, pigs, and other mammals. After the eggs hatch, the larvae burrow into muscles where they form cysts, causing muscle pain. Trichinosis can be prevented by cooking meat properly.

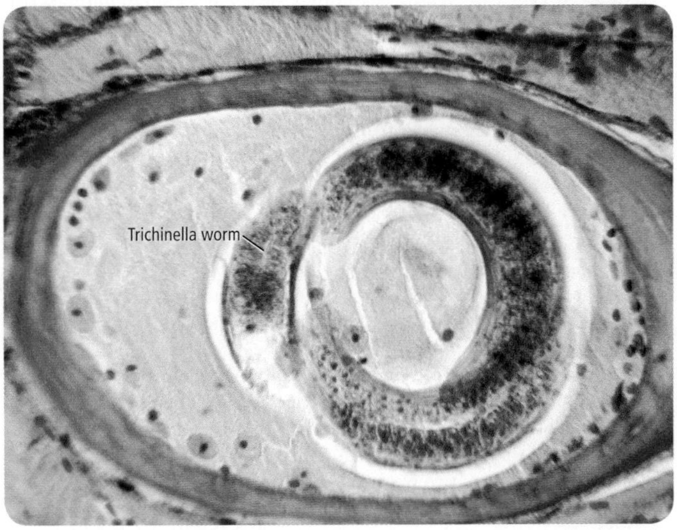

S

■ **Figure 9** A trichinella worm larva is seen curled up inside of a cyst (purple) in pig muscle. **Infer** *what kind of physical symptoms a person with trichinosis might have.*

W Writing Support

AL Informal Writing Have students write a letter to Gregor Mendel explaining what has been learned about the genetics of development by studying *Caenorhabditis elegans.* Have the students research additional discoveries in genetics before writing the letter.

S Skill Practice

BL OL AL Visual Literacy

ASK STUDENTS: ***Infer how the roundworms in Figure 9 are adapted to their parasitic lives.*** They can burrow into muscle, they have hooks or adhesive devices to help attach to the host, they may be very small in large numbers so that their survival will not be jeopardized by the death of a few, and they are thin and can easily absorb food from the host.

GOING GREEN Recycle your old textbooks and reference books. Rather than packaging and shipping, find a local charity that might use books such as a children's shelter, orphanage, detention center, or an organization that provides after school programs for students.

Research Citation

Making Predictions Educational research indicates that teachers can help students extend their thinking by using activities that ask them to make predictions about their reading. Students use clues from the text to anticipate the content, thus practicing valuable critical thinking skills. (Blackowicz, 1986)

Research bibliography on pages 32T–34T

Reading Check They contain only 959 cells and mature in three days.

■ **Caption Question** **Fig. 9** muscle pain and swelling

D Develop Concepts

BL OL

Clarify a Misconception

ASK STUDENTS: ***Are all infections in human beings caused by microscopic germs?*** no Students may believe that only bacteria and viruses cause infections in people. Explain that other organisms, such as ascarid worms, hookworms, and pinworms, can cause intestinal infections. These infections usually result from contact with water or soil contaminated with these worms and from eating contaminated raw and undercooked meat and unwashed vegetables.

Develop Concepts

EL BL OL COOP LEARN

Activity Have students in groups of four design a billboard that will help to educate people about a particular roundworm parasite, such as hookworm or pinworm, that each group chooses.

SAY TO STUDENTS: ***Make sure you indicate how these parasites infect humans and how infection can be prevented.*** Explain that this billboard will be seen by people traveling on a major highway and must be sensitive and not critical of current practices.

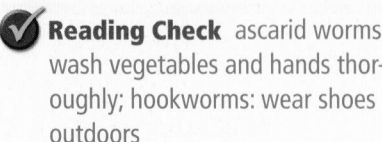

Reading Check ascarid worms: wash vegetables and hands thoroughly; hookworms: wear shoes outdoors

■ **Caption Question Fig. 10** They are round with no segments.

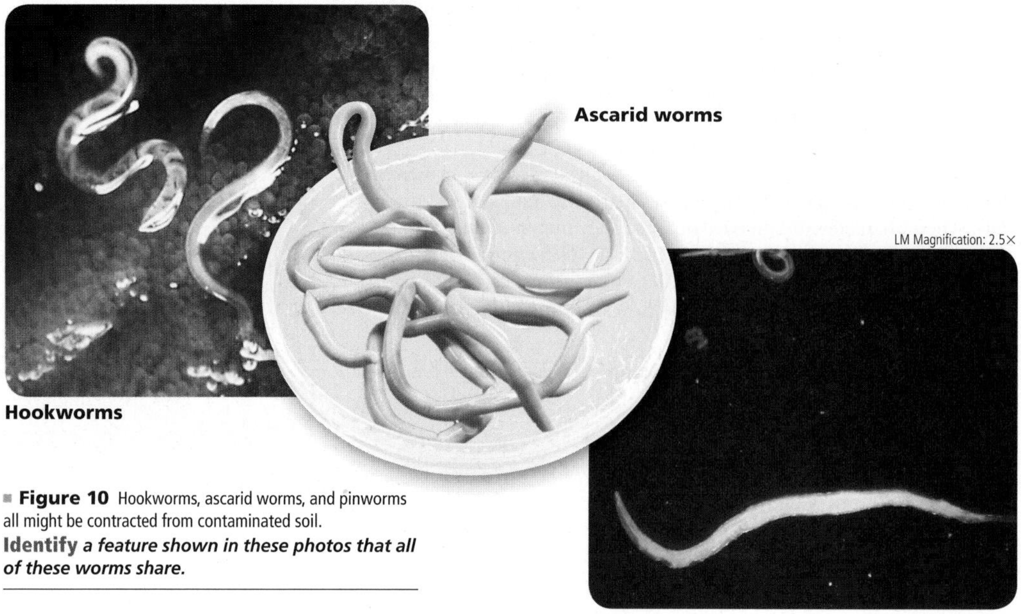

■ **Figure 10** Hookworms, ascarid worms, and pinworms all might be contracted from contaminated soil.
***Identify** a feature shown in these photos that all of these worms share.*

D **Hookworms** Hookworm infections are common in warm climates when people go barefoot on contaminated soil. When a hookworm, shown in **Figure 10,** contacts bare human skin, it cuts its way inside, travels in the bloodstream to the lungs, and then to the windpipe, or esophagus, where it is coughed up and swallowed. The parasite then moves to the small intestine, where it attaches to intestinal walls and feeds on blood and other tissue. Hookworm infection can be prevented by wearing shoes.

Ascarid worms The most common worm infection in humans is ascariasis (AS kuh RI uh sus), which is caused by ascarid (AS kuh rid) worms like the ones shown in **Figure 10.** Eggs of ascarid worms are found in soil in subtropical and tropical areas. They enter the human body through the mouth and live in the intestine. Infection can result when unwashed vegetables from contaminated soil are eaten or when hands contaminated with infected soil are put in the mouth, as young children are likely to do. Infection by ascarid worms can be controlled by carefully washing vegetables and hands.

Reading Check **Explain** how humans can prevent infection from hookworms and ascarid worms.

VOCABULARY
WORD ORIGIN
Nematode
nemato- prefix; from Greek, meaning *thread*
-ode suffix; from the Greek word *oeides,* meaning *similar to*

Pinworms **Figure 10** shows a pinworm, the most common nematode parasite in humans in the United States. The highest incidence of infection occurs in children. At night, female pinworms living in the intestine move out of the anus and lay eggs on nearby skin. When the skin is scratched because of the itching caused by pinworm activity, the eggs are transferred to hands and then to any surface that is touched. These eggs can survive for up to two weeks on surfaces and are ready to hatch if another person ingests them. This infection can spread quickly among children who put toys and other objects in their mouths.

Content Background

Teacher FYI The guinea worm, a nematode parasite of humans in Africa, South America, and Asia, is contracted by drinking water infested with a microscopic crustacean host. The female nematode lives under the skin in humans and releases an ulcer-producing secretion. When the human bathes, the worm releases its young through the open sores, enabling crustaceans to take up the worm and continue the cycle. Prevention requires keeping infected people away from public water supplies and boiling water before drinking it.

Filarial worms Elephantiasis (el uh fun TI uh sus) is a disease caused by filarial (fuh LER ee uhl) worms, which are roundworm parasites that live in tropical areas. A mosquito is the intermediate host of filarial worms. When a mosquito sucks blood from a person who is infected with this roundworm, worm embryos are passed into the insect's bloodstream. The embryos grow into larvae, which then are passed to another person when the mosquito bites again. Adult worms accumulate in the lymphatic system and obstruct the flow of lymph—the tissue fluid in the spaces between cells. This fluid builds up in tissue, causing legs and other body regions to enlarge. Controlling mosquitoes and using mosquito netting at night can aid in preventing this disease.

Another disease caused by a filarial worm—heartworm—is found in dogs and cats throughout the United States. Heartworms are transmitted to dogs and cats through mosquito bites. Once in the bloodstream, the worms travel to the heart and block the flow of blood. Regular doses of oral medications prevent heartworm in dogs and cats.

S

Reading Check **Identify** In what parts of the human body do pinworms and filarial worms live?

Nematodes in plants Some species of roundworms cause diseases in plants. Nematodes can infect and kill pine trees, soybean crops, and food plants such as tomatoes. When they infect plant roots, as shown in **Figure 11,** they damage the plant.

Most species of nematodes are either harmless or beneficial to plants. Certain nematodes are used to control the spread of cabbage worm caterpillars, Japanese beetle grubs, and many other pests of crop plants. Spraying a solution of nematodes and water on areas that are infested with crop pests is most effective when the targeted pest is at the stage in its life cycle when it lives in the soil.

Connection to Health In addition to treating plant pests, nematodes are used to control pests of humans and animals. Nematodes eat flea larvae and thus control the flea population in yards. This reduces or eliminates exposure of humans and animals to traditional chemicals used to treat flea infestations.

C

■ **Figure 11** The growth of the vascular system of plants can be slowed down when nematodes move into the roots and form cysts.

Reading Check Pinworms infect the intestine; filarial worms, the lymphatic cardiovascular systems.

Differentiated Instruction

Above Level Students working above level will perform at a higher level when they understand the content of the material they are learning. Begin each chapter by building on students' prior knowledge.

For more tips, see pages 14T–15T.

S Skill Practice

EL Make Diagrams Have students make three labeled diagrams showing the infection cycle of hookworms, pinworms, and filarial worms.

C Critical Thinking

BL OL AL Analyze

SAY TO STUDENTS: ***Imagine that plants growing in a garden are discovered to have roots covered with cysts containing nematodes. You conduct an experiment to determine whether nematodes are benefiting the plant or harming it. You place one group of plants with root cysts near a sunny window and another group of the same kind of plants that do not have root cysts under artificial grow lights. Each day you measure the height of the plants in both groups.***

ASK STUDENTS: ***Will this experiment give you data to answer your question?*** no ***How can you gather more meaningful data?*** Grow plants with and without cysts under the same conditions, some in sunlight, and some under artificial light. The two different lighting conditions for plants with and without cysts create more than one variable, and a well-designed experiment tests only one variable.

Develop Concepts

EL BL OL AL Activity Have students make a wanted poster for a human roundworm parasite. Have them include a description of the crime (causing infection), the organism's last-known location, a mug shot, and what to do if they come in contact with it. They can research and find additional information and include it as well as information from their textbooks.

D Develop Concepts

EL BL OL AL Activity Provide students with binocular microscopes and have them view prepared slides of a rotifer and a large protist, such as a diatom or protozoans.

SAY TO STUDENTS: ***Draw sketches of the organisms you see.*** Have them list on their sketches differences and similarities between the two. Similarities should include size and cilia; differences should include the fact that rotifers are multicellular and diatoms and protozoans are unicellular.

Formative Assessment

Evaluation

ASK STUDENTS: ***What are some species of roundworms that cause disease in people?*** trichinella, ascarid, and filarial worms, hookworms, and pinworms ***What diseases do they cause?*** trichinella = trichinosis; ascarid = ascariasis; filarial worms = elephantiasis; hookworms and pinworms = intestinal infection

Remediation Form small groups of students and assign each group one disease-causing roundworm. Have them discuss and identify the symptoms, how the disease is transmitted, and how it might be prevented. Write a list of diseases and infections on the board. Have students match the roundworm to the problem.

LM Magnification: 100×

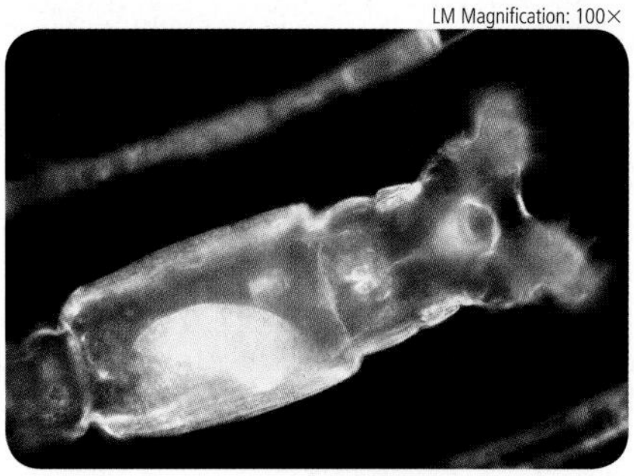

■ **Figure 12** Rotifers have two rings of cilia at their anterior end.

Rotifers

Rotifers are tiny animals only about 0.1 mm to 0.5 mm in length. The phylum Rotifera, meaning *wheel-bearer,* gets its name from the rings of cilia around the mouths of the animals. About 1800 species of rotifers have been studied, mostly from freshwater habitats, including ponds, streams, and lakes. It would not be unusual to find 40 to 500 rotifers in a liter of pond water. A few species are marine. Refer to the evolutionary tree in **Figure 7** and note that although rotifers and roundworms occupy separate branches, both are pseudocoelomates.

Rotifer features and movement Rotifers are similar to roundworms because they have bilateral symmetry and are pseudocoelomates with a gut open at both ends. Unlike roundworms, however, rotifers move through the water by means of their ciliated wheel-like structures, which are shown in **Figure 12.** The posterior end of a rotifer generally has "toes" and glands that secrete an adhesive material that enables a rotifer to attach itself to a surface in the water.

Organ systems of rotifers Rotifers feed by using cilia to gather protists and organic materials into a complete digestive tract, which includes a mouth and an anus. Like other pseudocoelomates, rotifers exchange gases and excrete metabolic wastes by diffusion through body walls. Sensory structures include sensory bristles and eyespots on the head. Some rotifers reproduce sexually, while others have complex life cycles involving diploid eggs producing diploid females and haploid eggs producing haploid males. These life cycles are dependent on environmental conditions, such as spring rains, frost, or the presence of stagnant water. D

Section 2 Assessment

Section Summary

- Roundworms are closely related to flatworms.
- Roundworms, like flatworms, have a limited number of organs and systems.
- Roundworms are either free-living or parasitic.
- Roundworms cause many human and plant diseases.
- Rotifers are pseudocoelomates that appear on a different branch of the evolutionary tree from that of roundworms.

Understand Main Ideas

1. MAIN Idea **Describe** the evolutionary adaptation of the digestive tract of roundworms.
2. **Compare and contrast** the features of flatworms and roundworms.
3. **Explain** how roundworms make their distinctive thrashing movements.
4. **Compare and contrast** the various ways in which humans might risk contracting roundworm parasites.

Think Critically

5. **Hypothesize** Imagine that you are digging in your garden and find some tiny threadlike animals making thrashing movements. Make a hypothesis about what these animals might be. Explain your answer.

MATH in Biology

6. Make a circle graph that shows the number of roundworm species known compared to the estimated number of roundworm species that might exist.

Section 2 Assessment

1. Pseudocoelum separates endoderm-lined gut from the rest of the body.
2. Roundworms: pseudocoelomates with two openings to gut; flatworms: acoelomates with one opening to gut
3. Muscles run the length of their bodies; thrashing occurs as one muscle contracts and another relaxes.
4. Trichinosis: improperly cooked pork, ascarid and hookworms: contaminated soil, pinworms: contaminated surfaces, filararial worms: infected mosquitoes.
5. They might be roundworms because roundworms can be tiny, threadlike, and move with a thrashing motion.
6. 3.6 degrees = known species; divide 360 degrees by 100 (100 times as many species might exist).

Assessment Online Quiz

Reading Preview

Essential Questions

- What is the importance of the coelom to mollusks?
- What is the function of the mantle and what are its adaptive advantages to mollusks?
- What is the importance of mucus and the muscular foot to mollusks?

Review Vocabulary

herbivore: an organism that eats only plants

New Vocabulary

mantle
radula
gill
open circulatory system
closed circulatory system
nephridium
siphon

g Multilingual eGlossary

Mollusks

MAIN Idea **Mollusks are coelomates with a muscular foot, a mantle, and a digestive tract with two openings.**

Real-World Reading Link Have you ever watched a rocket blast off into space? The rocket is powered by jet propulsion—a stream of heated gas is forced out of the engine, pushing the rocket in the opposite direction. Some animals, such as octopuses, also move by jet propulsion, forcefully expelling streams of water to push them away from danger.

R Body Structure

Mollusks are members of the phylum Mollusca. They range from the slow-moving slug to the jet-propelled squid, from scallops and cuttlefish to chitons and nudibranchs. Mollusks range in size from almost microscopic snails to giant squids, which can grow to be 21 m long.

Look at the evolutionary tree in **Figure 13.** Mollusks, such as the nudibranch and the octopus in **Figure 13,** undergo protostome development and might have been the first animals in the course of evolution to have a coelom, which allowed for the development of more complex tissues and organs. There are more than 110,000 known species of mollusks. Many are marine, some live in freshwater, and others live in moist land environments.

Mollusks are coelomate animals with bilateral symmetry, a soft internal body, a digestive tract with two openings, a muscular foot, and a mantle. The **mantle** (MAN tuhl) is a membrane that surrounds the internal organs of the mollusk. In mollusks with shells, the mantle secretes calcium carbonate to form the shell. Other mollusks, including slugs and squids, are adapted to life without a hard outer covering.

■ **Figure 13** Mollusks, such as the nudibranch and octopus, have coeloms.
Infer ***what the main difference is between mollusks and roundworms based on the evolutionary tree.***

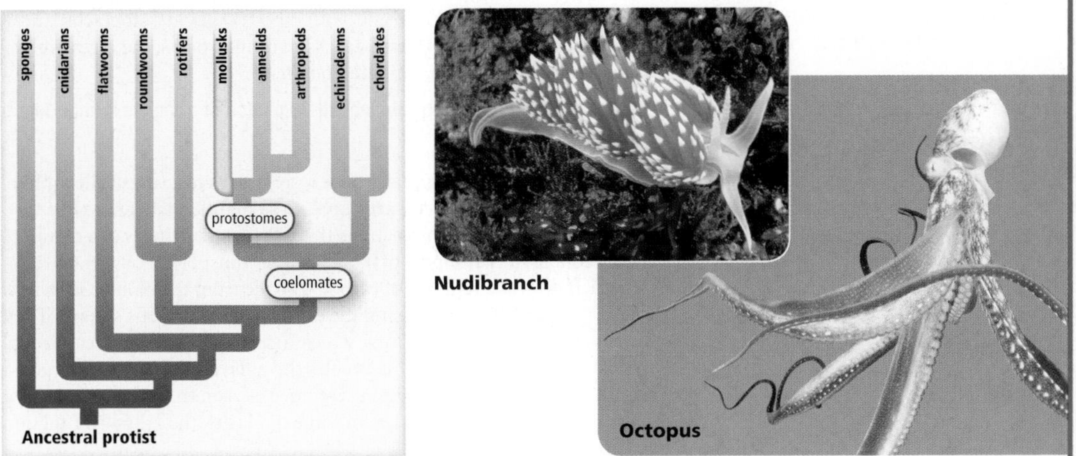

Section 3

MAIN Idea

BL OL AL **Mollusks** Hold a live land snail in a clear container so that students can see it moving.
ASK STUDENTS: ***What do you already know about mollusks?*** Possible answers: Snails are slimy, move slowly, and stick to things. Clams can dig quickly into the sand. ***What kinds have you seen and where have you seen them?*** Answers may include: Have eaten shellfish, have been to beach and seen seashells, have been to a water park or aquarium where there are exhibits of live mollusks such as octopuses and other shellfishes.

R Reading Strategy

EL BL OL COOP LEARN

Determine Importance Hang large sheets of butcher paper around the walls of the room, each sheet representing a heading in this section. Place students in small groups of two to four and assign each group to a different heading. Have them read the text under their heading, noting the most important phrases.
SAY TO STUDENTS: ***As you read the text, choose the important phrases and write them on the posted sheets of paper.***
AL ASK STUDENTS: ***Infer the importance of a closed circulatory system for fast-moving mollusks.*** more specialized and efficient delivery of nutrients

■ **Caption Question Fig. 13** Mollusks have a coelom, and roundworms have a pseudocoelom.

Differentiated Instruction

Visually Impaired Special modifications may be needed for students who are visually impaired when presenting visual materials to the class. Seat these students in the front of the class and verbally describe what is happening so that they may benefit from the demonstration.

For more tips see pages 14T–15T.

C Critical Thinking

BL OL AL COOP LEARN

Hypothesize In pairs, have students develop hypotheses about what plants land snails prefer to eat. Have the students design an experiment with one variable to test their hypotheses by collecting quantitative data. Possible experiment: Introduce 10 snails into a terrarium with one kind of leafy salad vegetable, such as spinach. Time how long the snails spend eating the leaves and record the data. The next day, do the same experiment with a different leafy salad vegetable, such as leaf lettuce.

Develop Concepts

BL OL AL

Clarify a Misconception

ASK STUDENTS: ***Why do biologists classify octopuses and squids as mollusks?*** Students may not realize that octopuses and squids are mollusks because they may think that all mollusks have a shell on the outside of the body.

AL ASK STUDENTS: ***What pieces of evidence do biologists use to classify octopuses and squid as mollusks despite their lack of a shell?*** Students will learn that the definition of a mollusk is an animal that has bilateral symmetry, a coelom, a digestive tract with two openings, a muscular foot, and a mantle. In cephalopods, such as octopuses and squids, the feet have evolved into tentacles with suckers.

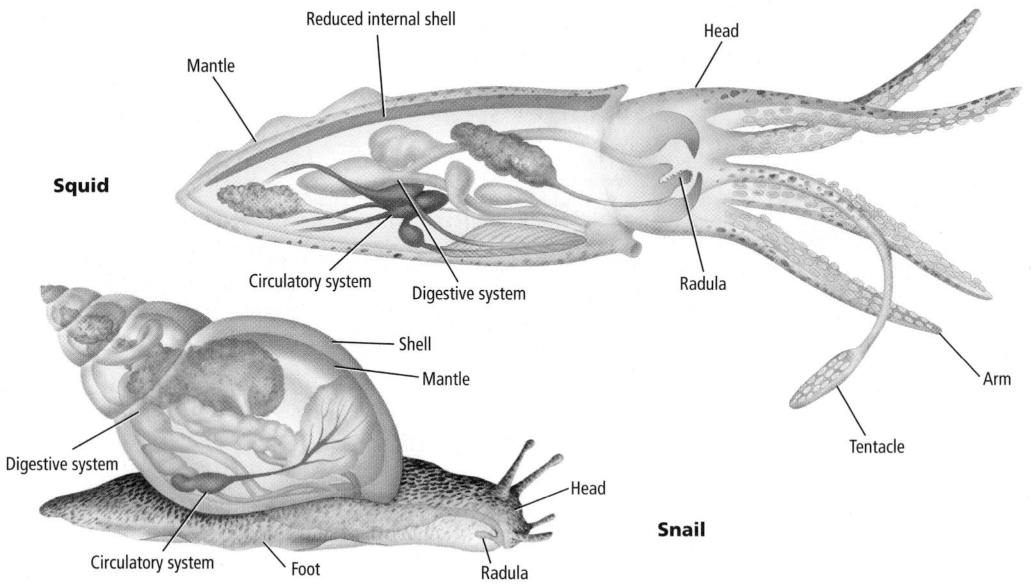

■ **Figure 14** Many mollusks have shells. Inside the shell is a soft body consisting of a foot, organs, and a mantle.
Compare and contrast ***the bodies of the snail and the squid.***

■ **Figure 15** Many mollusks feed using a radula. At the top, the radula is at rest. At the bottom, you can see the toothlike scraping structures on the radula as it is extended to feed.

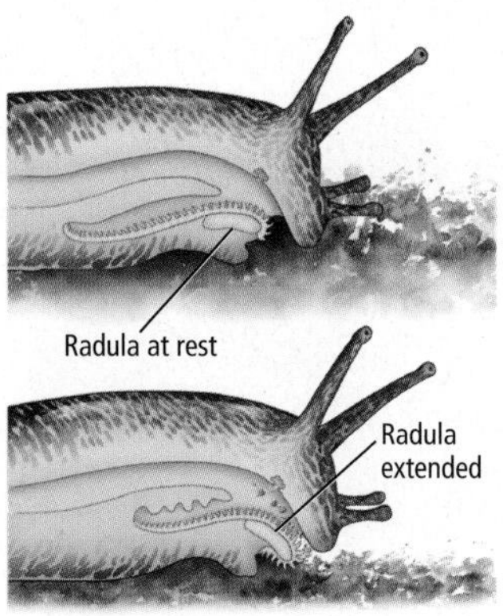

Compare the bodies of the snail and the squid in **Figure 14.** Their external features are very different from each other. However, both have coelomate body plans and highly evolved body systems, such as the digestive system, respiratory system, circulatory system, and nervous system.

Feeding and digestion Many mollusks use a rasping structure called a radula to scrape food into their mouths. Located in a mollusk's mouth, a **radula** (RA juh luh) is a tonguelike organ with rows of teeth, as shown in **Figure 15.** Herbivorous mollusks use their radulas to scrape algae off rocks. Carnivorous mollusks use their radulas to drill into other mollusks and feed on their internal body parts. Some of these predators, such as octopuses and squids, use their radulas to tear up the food they capture with their tentacles. Other mollusks, such as clams, are filter feeders and do not have radulas.

Mollusks have complete guts with digestive glands, stomachs, and intestines, as shown in **Figure 16.** As in roundworms, the digestive system has two openings—a mouth and anus. C

Reading Check **Explain** why the evolution of a coelom is important to mollusks.

Respiration Most mollusks have respiratory structures called gills. **Gills,** shown in **Figure 16,** are parts of the mantle that consist of a system of filamentous projections that are like the fringes of a blanket. Gills contain a rich supply of blood for the transport of oxygen to the blood and for the removal of carbon dioxide from the blood. Gills move water into and through the mantle cavity in a continuous stream. They are highly branched structures, which increase the surface area through which gases can diffuse. This enables the gills to take in more oxygen from water. Land snails and slugs remove oxygen from the air using the lining of their mantle cavities. In some mollusks, the gills also function in filter feeding.

Reading Check More highly evolved body systems, such as digestive and circulatory systems, can develop.

■ **Caption Question** **Fig. 14** Both have soft bodies, organs, mantle; snail has shell and foot; squid has arm, tentacles, and suckers.

D **Circulation** Mollusks have a well-developed circulatory system that includes a chambered heart. Most mollusks have an **open circulatory system,** in which the blood is pumped out of vessels into open spaces surrounding the body organs. This adaptation enables animals to diffuse oxygen and nutrients into tissues that are bathed in blood and also to move carbon dioxide from tissues into the blood. Slow-moving animals, such as snails and clams, utilize this system effectively because they do not need rapid delivery of oxygen and nutrients for quick movements.

Some mollusks, such as squids, move nutrients and oxygen through a closed circulatory system, which was a major adaptation in the evolution of animals. In a **closed circulatory system,** blood is confined to vessels as it moves through the body. A closed system efficiently transports oxygen and nutrients to cells, where they are converted to usable forms of energy. Mollusks that move quickly, such as octopuses and squids, need more energy than slow-moving mollusks, and the closed circulatory system quickly delivers nutrients and oxygen. A closed circulatory system is like the heating ducts in some houses. A furnace is efficient at delivering warm air to the rooms in a house because the air travels through a series **D** of ducts or pipes. Rooms of a house would not be evenly heated if the furnace did not have a delivery system.

Excretion Most mollusks get rid of metabolic wastes from cellular processes through structures called **nephridia** (nih FRIH dee uh), shown in **Figure 16.** After nephridia filter the blood, waste is passed out through the mantle cavity. Nephridia are an evolutionary adaptation enabling mollusks to efficiently maintain homeostasis in their body fluids.

Response to stimuli Mollusks have nervous systems that coordinate their movements and behavior. Mollusks that are more highly evolved, such as octopuses, have brains. In addition, octopuses have complex eyes similar to human eyes with irises, pupils, and retinas. Most mollusks have simple structures in the eyes that reflect light.

CAREERS IN BIOLOGY

Laboratory Assistant Marine biologists depend on laboratory assistants to help collect specimens, such as mollusks, and to maintain databases. These entry-level workers also set up equipment and prepare samples for testing.

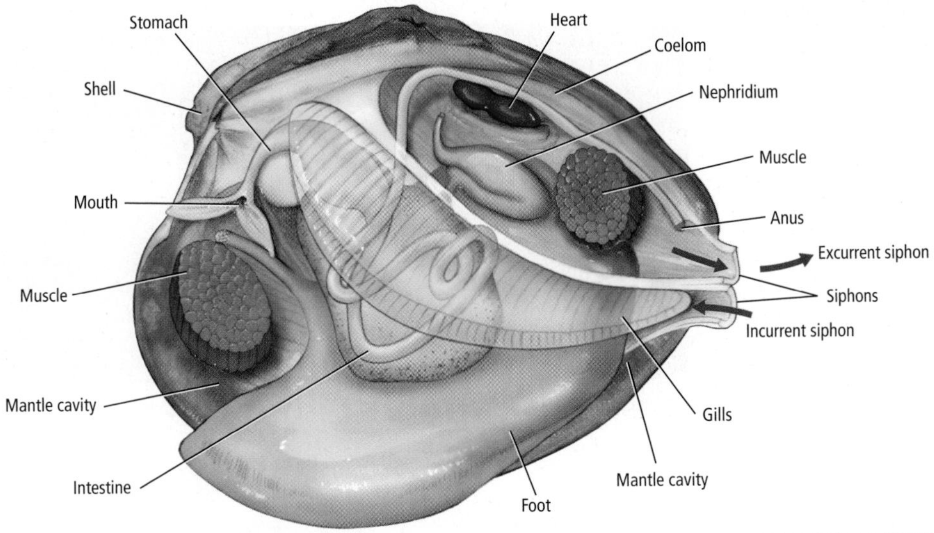

■ **Figure 16** The internal anatomy of a clam illustrates the well-developed organ systems in mollusks.

D Develop Concepts

BL OL Use an Analogy Fill a surgical glove with water, leaving some room near the top, and hold it up for the students to see. Squeeze one of the water-filled fingers.

ASK STUDENTS: ***What happens to the water in the one finger I am squeezing?*** It moves into other parts of the glove. Explain that the glove is a model of an open circulatory system in which blood can move easily into open spaces around the organs of an animal.

AL Have students create an analogy or visual demonstration for an open circulatory system.

D Develop Concepts

BL OL EL Activity

SAY TO STUDENTS: ***Based on what you have learned from reading the text under the heading*** **Circulation,** ***make a diagram of an open circulatory system.***
Diagram should include heart with blood vessels leaving the heart and emptying into open spaces around the organs. The sketch can show heart and organs as simple circles.

Demonstration

BL OL AL COOP LEARN The Radula Mix cornstarch with water and apply a thin layer to the bottom of several petri dishes or other pieces of transparent glass or plastic. Let them dry overnight. Place snails on the glass and have student groups watch as the snails eat the cornstarch. Students should be able to see the snail's radula scrape food off the glass. Have students describe the marks made by the radula and count the number of strokes of the radula per minute. Est. time: 10 min

Visualizing Movement in Mollusks

Purpose
Students will study the form and function of a clam as a representative mollusk.
A.2, C.6

Develop Concepts
Activity Have students make a diagram of a clam that shows the systems of the clam with labels and captions. Students can use color to enhance their diagrams.

Concepts in Motion
Animation

Visualizing Movement in Mollusks

Figure 17
Mollusks move in a variety of ways. The type of movement used often depends on a mollusk's unique adaptations.

Gastropods
A gastropod moves by sending waves of contractions along its muscular foot. A film of mucus lubricates the foot and helps propel the animal forward.

Note the waves of muscle contractions as the snail moves along its mucous trail.

A clam can rapidly bury itself in sand using its muscular foot.

Bivalves
Most bivalves do not move much, unless they are threatened by a predator. Then, a bivalve either uses its muscular foot to burrow into sediment, as shown on the left, or uses jet propulsion to flee, as shown at right.

A scallop pulls its shells together, forcing jets of water toward the shell hinge. The force of the water pushes the scallop in the direction of the shell opening.

Cephalopods
Members of class Cephalopoda, such as octopuses and squids, move by jet propulsion. To avoid predators, a cephalopod draws in water through slits in the body wall. Then the water is pumped rapidly through the siphon, jet-propelling the cephalopod away from danger.

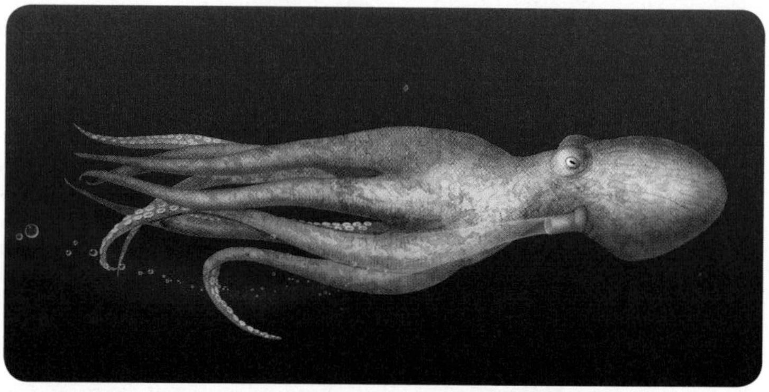
An octopus changes the direction it moves by alternating the direction of its siphon.

Concepts in Motion Animation

Content Background
Cultural Diversity Pearl culture is replacing diving for pearls, but the ama women divers of Japan still carry on this tradition. The ama collect a variety of mollusks for food and oysters that might have a valuable pearl inside. The ama can dive to depths greater than 50 m hundreds of times daily without snorkels or air tanks. They use only masks and fins to assist their dives. It is dangerous work that requires skill and strength to swim in murky water in crevices between rocks prying shellfish from marine surfaces.

Movement The muscular foot of a clam enables it to burrow into wet sand. Mollusks with two shells can clap their shells together for short bursts of rapid swimming. Most slugs and snails creep along moist areas on a slime trail of mucus secreted by glands in the foot. Octopuses and squids take water into the mantle cavity and expel it through a tube called a **siphon.** When threatened, they can eject the water so rapidly that they appear to be jet-propelled. **Figure 17** illustrates the ways mollusks move.

Reading Check **Compare** movement in two-shelled mollusks, snails, and squids.

Reproduction Mollusks reproduce sexually, as illustrated in **Figure 18.** The males and females of most aquatic species release their eggs and sperm into the water at the same time, and fertilization is external. A few bivalves and many gastropods that live on land are hermaphrodites, in which fertilization takes place internally.

All members of the phylum Mollusca share similar developmental patterns, even though their adult forms vary widely. One larval stage of most mollusks, the trochophore (TRO kuh for), looks very similar to the larval stage of segmented worms, which you will study in Section 4. Because the larval forms are similar in both segmented worms and mollusks, scientists hypothesize that segmented worms and mollusks are closely related.

S

Figure 18 The life cycle of a clam illustrates the characteristic developmental stages of all mollusks.

A A female clam releases eggs into the water, where they are then fertilized by sperm released by a male clam.
B After fertilization, the trochophore larvae change into veliger larvae. Both forms are free swimming.
C The veliger larvae shed their velums—the ciliated "sails" that enable them to swim—and settle on a surface.
D The final larval stage, the pediveligers, develop into adult clams.

Develop Concepts

BL OL AL EL **Activity** Have students observe pictures or prepared slides of veliger, the larval stage of freshwater clams.

ASK STUDENTS: ***Did you see anything unusual on the larvae?*** hooks ***What purpose do you think the hooks serve?*** Answers should include that they must be for attachment to something. Have students research to determine the purpose of the hooks, and then have volunteers share their findings with the class. Explain that veliger use the hooks to attach to the fins and gills of fishes. As they mature into juvenile clams, they fall off the fish and resume life in the bottom sediments.

S Skill Practice

BL OL AL EL **Visual Literacy** Have students examine the mollusk life cycle stages shown in Figure 18 and make a list of the stages.

SAY TO STUDENTS: ***Choose another mollusk, such as a squid, and diagram the characteristics of each life-cycle stage.*** Encourage students to research additional characteristics to add to their lists.

Reading Check bivalves: muscular foot burrows in sand, some clap their shells together for short bursts of speed; snails: creep along mucous trails; squids: expel water through a siphon

W Writing Support

BL OL AL Narrative Writing Have students write a description of the escape strategies employed by a gastropod and a bivalve that suddenly perceive danger nearby.

D Develop Concepts

BL OL AL COOP LEARN

Activity Have students form pairs and provide each pair with at least 10 gastropod and bivalve shells and a field guide to shells. Keys to shells may be available at no cost on the Internet. If seashells are not readily available, provide pictures of shells from an area to teach about keys.
SAY TO STUDENTS: ***Identify the shells you have by their common name.*** Have students make a list of the shell names and indicate the habitat the mollusk lived in, such as deep sea, tide pool, or wet beach sand. Also have students note how each species used its foot.

Reading Check Snails have one shell and a foot positioned under the stomach on the ventral surface. Clams have two shells and a foot used for burrowing.

Abalone

Scallop

■ **Figure 19** Most gastropods, such as the abalone, have single shells for protection. Bivalves, such as the scallop, have two shells.

VOCABULARY
WORD ORIGIN
Gastropod
gastro– prefix; from the Greek word *gaster,* meaning *belly*
–pod suffix; from Greek, meaning *foot*

Diversity of Mollusks

Animals in the three major classes of mollusks—gastropods, bivalves, and cephalopods—are grouped based on differences in their shell and foot structures.

Gastropods The largest class of mollusks is Gastropoda, the stomach-footed mollusks. The name comes from the way the animal's large foot is positioned under the stomach on the ventral surface. Most species of gastropods have a single shell, like the abalone in **Figure 19.** Single-shelled gastropods also include snails, conches, periwinkles, limpets, cowries, whelks, and cones. They can be found in aquatic habitats and in moist terrestrial habitats, and they can quickly draw their bodies into their shells for protection when they are threatened. W

Slugs and nudibranchs do not have shells. They secrete a thick mucus that covers their bodies. To protect themselves, land slugs hide in dark locations under forest or garden litter. Nudibranchs incorporate into their own tissues the poisonous nematocysts of the jellyfishes they eat. The presence of nematocysts is advertised to predator fishes by the bright colors of the nudibranchs.

Bivalves One word—*slow*—best describes most behavior of the class Bivalvia, which are the two-shelled mollusks. Bivalves, such as clams, mussels, oysters, and the scallop shown in **Figure 19,** are all aquatic animals. Most are marine, but some are found in freshwater habitats. Bivalves might seem to be inactive, but they are continuously filter feeding and carrying on all bodily functions.

If you have ever been clamming or have seen people clamming, you know that you might have to dig deeply to find clams because they use a muscular foot to burrow far down into wet sand. Mussels attach to rocks with a sticky, gluelike substance called byssal threads. Scallops are more active than other bivalves because they can clap their shells together to move more quickly through water. D

Reading Check Compare the foot and shell of a snail with those of a clam.

Demonstration

BL OL AL Filter Feeding Place a live clam in a beaker with water about 6 cm over the top of the clam. Add two drops of carmine powder suspension or red food coloring near the clam's siphons.
ASK STUDENTS: ***What do you think will happen to the carmine or food coloring in the water?*** The clam will take it in with the water and it will be seen coming out of the siphon of the clam. Est. time: 10 min

Cephalopods *Quick* is a word that best describes some behaviors of the class Cephalopoda. Cephalopods are the head-footed mollusks (from the Greek word *cephalo,* meaning *head*, and from *pod,* meaning *foot*), which includes squids, octopuses, chambered nautiluses, and the cuttlefish shown in **Figure 20.** The chambered nautilus is the only cephalopod with an external shell. Squids and cuttlefishes have an internal shell, while octopuses do not have a shell. The foot of a cephalopod is divided into arms and tentacles with suckers, which are used to capture prey.

Protection Although most cephalopods don't have a hard external shell, they have evolved other protective mechanisms. Octopuses forcefully expel water to propel themselves away from threat. They hide in crevices or caves in the daytime. At night, they creep about in search of prey.

When threatened, an octopus shoots out an inky substance that forms a cloud. Scientists hypothesize that the ink visually confuses predators, and it also might act as a narcotic. Octopuses can change color to blend in with their surroundings. Squids and cuttlefishes also use ink and camouflage to escape predators. A chambered nautilus can pull into its shell for protection. It also uses its shell as camouflage. The dark top of the shell blends in with the ocean bottom when it is seen from above, while the white bottom of the shell blends in with the water above when it is seen from below.

Learning Octopuses are considered to be the most intelligent mollusks. They are capable of complex learning, such as being trained to select an object of a certain shape, color, or texture. See **Data Analysis Lab 2** to study this phenomenon. W

Cuttlefish

■ **Figure 20** Cuttlefish have eight arms and two tentacles. The tentacles often are not visible because they are withdrawn into pouches under the eyes.
***Compare** the differences between cephalopods and gastropods.*

DATA ANALYSIS LAB 2

Based on Real Data*

Interpret the Data

Can untrained octopuses learn to select certain objects? Two groups of octopuses were trained to select either a red ball or a white ball. Each trained group was observed by different groups of octopuses that were not trained.

Data and Observations

The graphs show the results of untrained octopus selection of white or red balls.

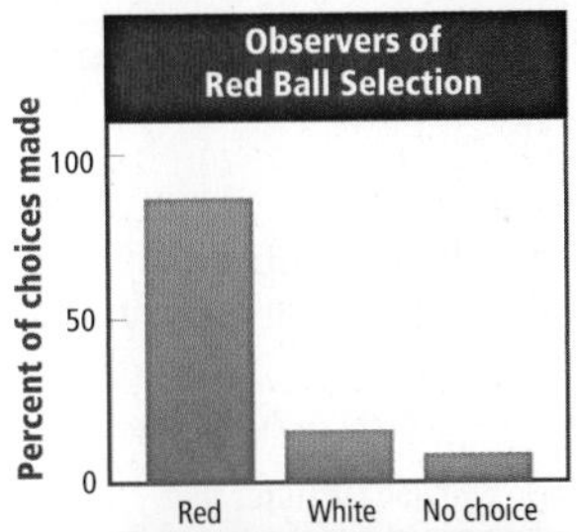

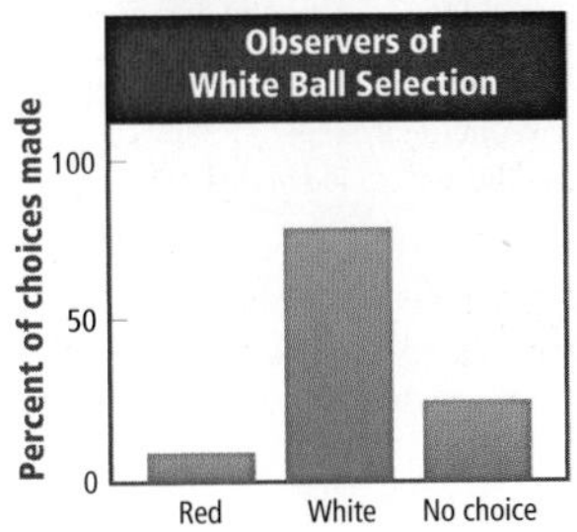

Think Critically

1. **Analyze** What percentage of octopuses selected the red ball or the white ball after observing the red ball being selected?
2. **Analyze** What percentage of octopuses selected the red ball or the white ball after observing the white ball being selected?
3. **Draw Conclusions** Can untrained octopuses learn by observation? Explain.

*Data obtained from: Fiorito, G. and P. Scotto. 1992. Observational learning in *Octopus vulgaris. Science* 256: 545–547.

W Writing Support

AL Formal Writing Have students research octopus learning and write an article for the school or local newspaper on their findings.

DATA ANALYSIS LAB 2

About the Lab

- Also see Hanlon, R., and J. Messenger. 1996. *Cephalopod behavior.* Cambridge: Cambridge Univ. Press.
- Octopuses learn from each other. In fact, they learn more quickly by watching other trained octopuses than they do by being trained by humans. Data from a study showing octopuses learning from each other raises the question of what octopuses learn from each other in their natural habitat.

Think Critically

1. red: 85 percent; white: 10 percent
2. red: 5 percent; white: 75 percent
3. Yes; Octopuses that observed others being trained to select a white ball mostly selected the white ball. Octopuses that observed others being trained to select a red ball mostly selected the red ball.

■ **Caption Question Fig. 20** Most cephalopods have a reduced external shell and can move quickly. Gastropods usually have external shells and move slowly.

Writing Support

OL AL Creative Writing Have students create posters about the spread of zebra mussels in the Great Lakes and other major waterways. Posters should include what features make zebra mussels successful invaders and how this invasion has changed the ecology of U.S. lakes, rivers, and streams.

BL If available, show students a video about zebra mussels and have them summarize it.

AL Have students include in their posters some possible solutions to halt the invasion, such as introducing zebra mussel predators.

Formative Assessment

Evaluation Have students list the three major classes of mollusks. **SAY TO STUDENTS:** ***Explain how the shell and foot structures differ in each class and give examples.*** Gastropods have a large single foot and most have a single shell. Bivalves have two shells and use their feet to dig into sand or cling to rocks. Cephalopod feet evolved into arms or tentacles; shells became reduced in size.

Remediation Organize students into three groups. Have each group make flash cards about one class of mollusk, including pictures and characteristics, to use in a matching or memory game.

■ **Figure 21** Cone snails are prized for their beauty.

Ecology of Mollusks

Mollusks play important roles in aquatic and terrestrial food chains as herbivores, predators, scavengers, and filter feeders. In many areas, certain mollusks are considered keystone species. A keystone is the stone at the top of an arch that holds the arch together, so a keystone species is one whose health influences the health of the entire ecosystem. For example, the hard clam is a keystone species for the Great South Bay in Long Island, New York. These clams filter water, which cleans the ecosystem. If the hard clam population declines, the water isn't filtered. This disrupts the food web, causing algal blooms and a decline in water quality.

The ability of some mussels to accumulate toxins in their body tissues can be useful to scientists who are monitoring water quality. By examining these mollusks, scientists can find out more about water quality than they could by testing the water alone.

Cone snails, as shown in **Figure 21,** are highly prized by collectors for the beauty of their shells. As a result, they might be close to extinction.

Connection to Health Certain cone snails produce powerful venom to kill prey. These venoms are being studied as potential treatments for pain, heart disease, clinical depression, and brain diseases, such as Alzheimer's disease, Parkinson's disease, and epilepsy.

Some mollusks cause damage, while others benefit humans. Some marine bivalve species, such as the shipworm, burrow into wood, causing much damage to wooden marinas and boats. On the other hand, people enjoy beautiful pearls that come from oysters. Pearls result when a grain of sand or a tiny parasite becomes trapped in an oyster. The mantle of the mollusk secretes a coating around the object to protect the mollusk, resulting in a pearl. Cultured-pearl producers implant pieces of shell or tiny plastic spheres in oysters and harvest the cultured pearls in about five to seven years.

Section 3 Assessment

Section Summary

- Mollusks were the first animals in the course of evolution to develop a coelom.
- Mollusks are divided into three main classes based on different characteristics.
- Mollusks have two body features that no other animals have—a mantle and a muscular foot.
- Mollusks have more-developed organ systems than those of roundworms and flatworms.
- Mollusks play important roles in the ecosystems in which they live.

Understand Main Ideas

1. MAIN Idea **Summarize** the main features of the three classes of mollusks.
2. **Evaluate** the ways in which the development of the coelom allowed for adaptations in mollusks that were not possible in earlier animals.
3. **Draw** a diagram of a representative mollusk and show the main evolutionary adaptations common to mollusks.
4. **Analyze** the importance to mollusks of the following adaptations: the mantle, mucus, and the muscular foot.

Think Critically

5. **Design an experiment** A species of bivalves on one beach is a pale color compared to the same species that is a much darker color on a beach 1100 km to the north. Design an experiment that might explain the differences in shell color.
6. **Classify** Make a dichotomous key that would distinguish the differences among the three classes of mollusks.

Section 3 Assessment

1. gastropods: usually one shell and a foot; bivalves: two hinged shells and filter feed; cephalopods: no external shell and a foot divided into tentacles
2. Allowed for development of more complex tissues, organs, and systems such as digestive and circulatory systems.
3. Answers should include coelom and other complex organ systems.
4. mantle: protection of internal organs; mucus: allows movement; muscular foot: burrowing and movement
5. Answers will vary. Make sure students make a hypothesis, have a control, one variable, plan to collect quantitative data, and make a graph.
6. Keys should begin with broad features and end with specific features.

Assessment Online Quiz

Section 4

Segmented Worms

Reading Preview

Essential Questions

- What are the similarities among segmented worms, flatworms, and roundworms?
- What is the importance of segmentation as an adaptation for survival in segmented worms?
- What are the features of the three main classes of annelids that make them well-suited for their habitats?

Review Vocabulary

protostome: an animal with a mouth that develops from the opening in the gastrula

New Vocabulary

crop
gizzard
seta
clitellum

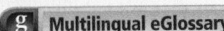

Multilingual eGlossary

MAIN Idea Segmented worms have segments that allow for specialization of tissues and for efficiency of movement.

Real-World Reading Link Suppose that you watch a train as it roars around a curve. The train will follow the curve of the track because it is made up of individual cars that are linked together. The links give the train the flexibility it needs to stay on the track. In the same way, the individual segments that make up a segmented worm enable it to be flexible.

R Body Structure

Earthworms are annelids and belong to phylum Annelida, which is characterized by animals with a body plan consisting of segments. As shown on the evolutionary tree in **Figure 22,** both mollusks and annelids undergo protostome development and therefore are considered close relatives.

There are more than 11,000 known species of annelids, most of which live in the oceans. Most of the remaining species are earthworms. Annelids live almost everywhere, except in the frozen soil of the polar regions and in the sand of dry deserts.

Annelids include earthworms, marine worms, such as the ones shown in **Figure 22,** and parasitic leeches. These worms are different from flatworms and roundworms because they are segmented and have a coelom. Most annelids also have a larval stage that is similar to those of certain mollusks, suggesting a common ancestor. Annelids have bilateral symmetry, like flatworms and roundworms, and have two body openings, like roundworms.

Reading Check Describe two important ways in which segmented worms are different from flatworms and roundworms.

S

Figure 22 Annelids, like these marine worms, show protostome development, have coeloms, and are segmented.

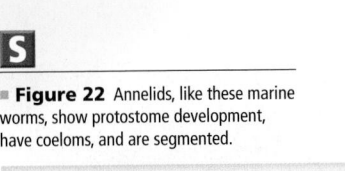

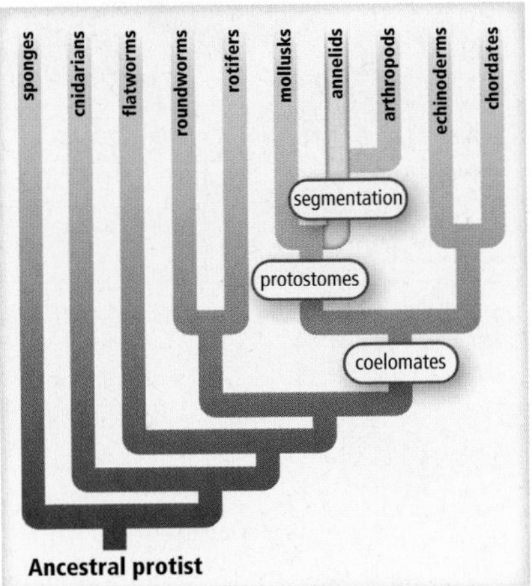

Reading Check Segmented worms have coeloms and segments.

Demonstration

BL OL AL Segmented Worms Place an earthworm and a few pebbles in a clear plastic container and project the image.

ASK STUDENTS: ***How does the earthworm move?*** It pushes the anterior part of its body forward and then pulls up the posterior part. It moves easily around the pebbles as it contacts the pebbles with its most anterior segments. Est. time: 5 min

Section 4

MAIN Idea

BL OL AL Segmented Worms

Show students a live earthworm and a mollusk shell. Students should have moist hands when handling earthworms.

SAY TO STUDENTS: ***Make a list of all the ways in which mollusks and segmented worms are different from each other.*** Answers will vary, but students should point out that earthworms are segmented. Students will learn that the segmentation of these worms is an adaptation that is important in the evolution of the animals they will study in this section.

R Reading Strategy

BL Assessment Preview

Before reading the section, have students read the assessment questions at the end of this section. Have students keep these questions in mind as they read the text under the section heading *Segmented Worms.*

S Skill Practice

EL BL OL AL Visual Literacy

Have students study the evolutionary tree in Figure 22, showing the divergence of segmented worms from the common ancestor that also gave rise to mollusks.

ASK STUDENTS: ***In what ways are mollusks and segmented worms alike?*** They both have coeloms and protostome development. ***How are they different?*** Mollusks are not segmented.

Even though annelids have the same cylindrical body shape as roundworms do, annelid bodies are divided into segments. Externally, the segments look like a stack of thick coins or a stack of donuts. Inside the worm, the segments are divided almost completely from each other by walls of tissue, similar to the way that walls separate the segments of a submarine. Each segment contains structures for digestion, excretion, and locomotion. The fluid within the coelom of each segment makes a rigid support system for the worm similar to the rigidity of a filled water balloon.

This rigidity in annelid segments creates a hydrostatic skeleton that muscles can push against. Segmentation also permits segments to move independently of each other and enables a worm to survive damage to a segment, because other segments with the same functions exist.

Segments can be specialized, and groups of segments might be adapted to a particular function. For example, some segments might be adapted to sensing, while others are adapted to reproduction. As you continue to study annelids, earthworms will be used to show examples of typical annelid features. C

Reading Check **Explain** how segments relate to a hydrostatic skeleton.

Feeding and digestion Running through all earthworm segments from the mouth to the anus is the digestive tract, a tube within a tube. Locate the digestive tract in the earthworm in **Figure 23.** Food and soil taken in by the mouth pass through the pharynx into the **crop,** where they are stored until they pass to the gizzard. The **gizzard** is a muscular sac containing hard particles that help grind soil and food before they pass into the intestine. Nutrients are absorbed in the intestine, then undigested material passes out of the worm's body through the anus. Parasitic annelids have pouches along the digestive tract that hold enough food to last for months. W

Inquiry **Virtual Lab**

Figure 23 As an earthworm pushes through the soil, it takes soil into its mouth. Nutrients are absorbed from the organic matter in the soil as it passes through the intestine.

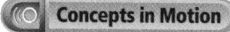

Concepts in Motion **Animation**

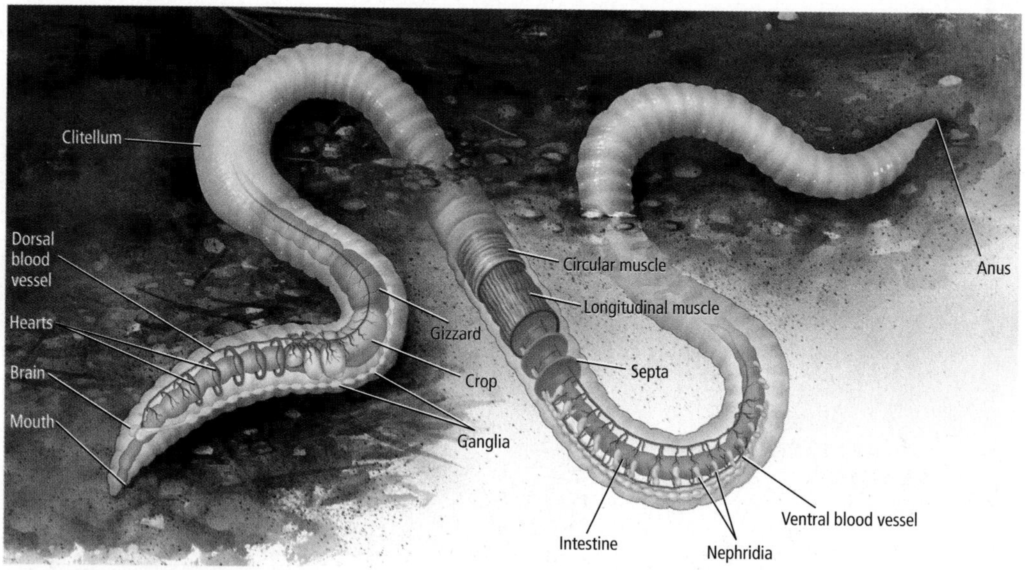

C Critical Thinking

BL OL Compare Have students compare the body structure of segmented worms with the body structure of mollusks.

ASK STUDENTS: ***In what ways are segmented worms and mollusks similar?*** Answers may include: both are protosomes, have a coelom, and are bilaterally symmetrical. ***In what ways are they different?*** Answers may include: most mollusks have shells, a foot for movement and an open circulatory system; segmented worms are made of segments divided from each other by walls of tissue and have a closed circulatory system; earthworms move by contracting muscles around segments.

W Writing Support

BL OL Formal Writing Have students research the importance of earthworms in the field of agriculture. Have them prepare an oral report using pictures and diagrams as visual aids.

BL Have available research material at a reading level appropriate for these students.

Concepts in Motion **Animation**

Reading Check Fluid in the coelom of each segment makes a rigid support system for muscles to push against.

Inquiry **Interactive Dissection**

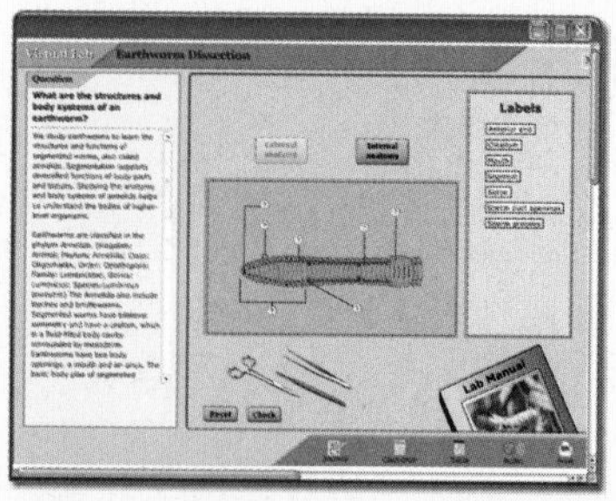

Inquiry **Virtual Lab** Students will perform a virtual dissection on a segmented worm.

Circulation Unlike most mollusks, most annelids have a closed circulatory system. Oxygen and nutrients move to various parts of their bodies through their blood vessels. At the same time, carbon dioxide and metabolic wastes are removed from the blood and excreted. Some of the vessels at the anterior end, or head, are large and muscular, as shown in **Figure 24,** and serve as hearts that pump the blood. The blood moves toward the anterior end of the worm in the dorsal blood vessel and toward the posterior end in the ventral blood vessel.

Respiration and excretion Earthworms take in oxygen and give off carbon dioxide through their moist skin. Some aquatic annelids have gills for the exchange of gases in the water. Segmented worms have two nephridia—similar to those in mollusks—in almost every segment. Cellular waste products are collected in the nephridia and are transported in tubes through the coelom and out of the body. Nephridia also function in maintaining homeostasis of the body fluids of annelids, ensuring that the volume and composition of body fluids are kept constant.

Response to stimuli In most annelids, such as the earthworm, the anterior segments are modified for sensing the environment. The brain and nerve cords, composed of ganglia, are shown in the earthworm in **Figure 23.** You might have seen an earthworm quickly withdraw into its burrow when you shine a flashlight on it or step close to it. These observations show that earthworms can detect both light and vibrations.

Movement When an earthworm moves, it contracts circular muscles surrounding each segment. This squeezes the segment and causes the fluid in the coelom to press outward, like paste in a tube of toothpaste being squeezed. Because the fluid in the coelom is confined by the tissues between segments, the fluid pressure causes the segment to get longer and thinner. Next, the earthworm contracts the longitudinal muscles that run the length of its body. This causes the segment to shorten and return to its original shape, pulling its posterior end forward and resulting in movement.

Many annelids have setae on each segment. **Setae** (SEE tee) (singular, seta), as shown in **Figure 25,** are tiny bristles that push into the soil and anchor the worm during movement. By anchoring some segments and retracting others, earthworms can move their bodies forward and backward, segment by segment.

Reading Check **Describe** how longitudinal and circular muscles work together to enable an earthworm to move.

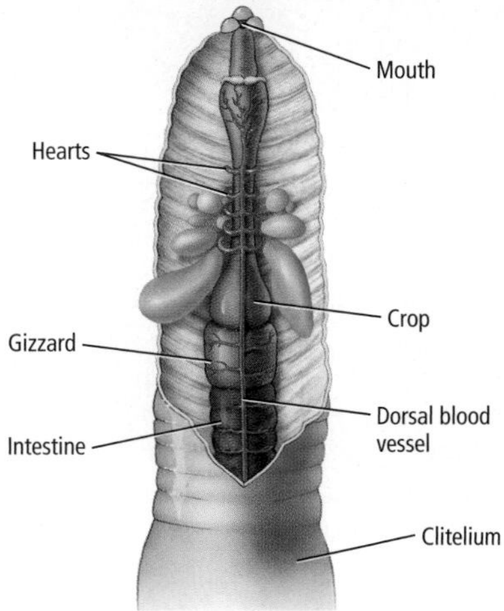

■ **Figure 24** An earthworm has five hearts that pump blood through its circulatory system.

Inquiry Launch Lab

Review **Based on what you've read about earthworm movement, how would you now answer the analysis questions?**

■ **Figure 25** This earthworm cross section shows how the setae extend from the body. Setae dig into soil and anchor the worm as it pushes forward.

Evaluate ***whether an earthworm would move faster on a rough or a smooth surface.***

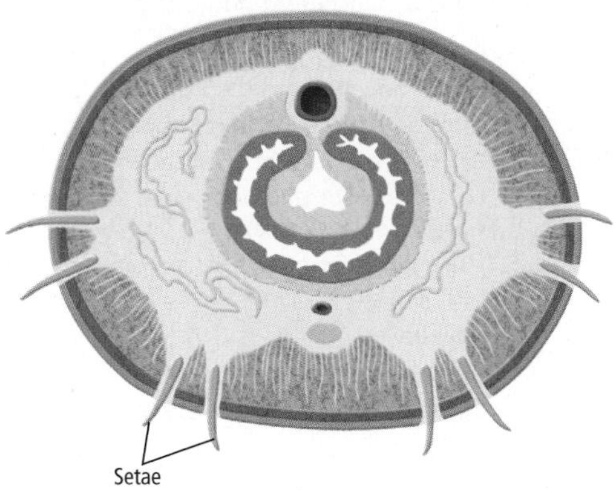

Inquiry Launch Lab

Assess Content Development

Assess how understanding has developed when students revisit the Launch Lab analysis questions.

Develop Concepts

BL OL Activity Provide students with microscopes and prepared slides of earthworm cross-sections. If not available, use pictures of earthworm cross sections, such as Figure 25. Have them make a diagram of what they see and label the parts of the earthworm. They should be able to see muscle layers, gut, ventral nerve cord, dorsal blood vessel.

EL SAY TO STUDENTS: ***You may use the diagram in Figure 25 to help you with your labeling.***

Writing Support

BL OL AL Creative Writing

Read several limericks to students. Have students write a limerick about an earthworm. The limerick may be humorous but also point out details of how they are adapted to their habitat.

Reading Check Circular muscles cause a segment to get longer and thinner. Longitudinal muscles contract making segments return to their original shapes.

■ **Caption Question Fig. 25** Rough because setae act as anchors.

Activity

BL OL AL Earthworms Place students into small groups and provide a live earthworm for each group. Make sure students have moist hands before handling worms and caution them about humane treatment of animals.

SAY TO STUDENTS: ***Write a list of observations about the response of the earthworm to being gently touched on its anterior, posterior, and middle parts. What can you infer from your observations?*** The anterior end is more sensitive to touch. This enables the worm to move around obstacles. Make sure students wash their hands after handling the worms. Est. time: 10 min

MiniLab 2

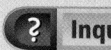

? Inquiry MiniLab

For a lab worksheet, use your eTeacherEdition Online.

RUBRIC A rubric for evaluating MiniLabs is found on your eTeacherEdition Online.

Est. Time 20 min

Alternative Materials aged tap water; magnifying lens

Safety Precautions Approve lab safety forms before work begins. Students should have moist hands for handling earthworms.

Teaching Strategies
- Have students view worms with the lowest light setting possible.
- The worm may need to be encouraged to crawl so that the dorsal blood vessel is in better viewing position.

Cleanup and Disposal Have students wash hands thoroughly after handling worms.

Analysis
1. Blood moves as the muscles in each segment's blood vessel contract and squeeze the blood into the next segment. Blood travels from the posterior (tail) region to the anterior (head) region.
2. Answers will vary. In general, tail regions have a pulse rate ranging from 24–32 beats per min. Due to an occasional loss of a pulse along the length of the worm, the middle portions have a rate of around 8–12 beats per min and head regions will have a similar or even lower rate.

LabManager™
Customize this lab with the LabManager™ CD-ROM.

Figure 26 After developing in the cocoon for two to three weeks, a young earthworm hatches.

FOLDABLES® Incorporate information from this section into your Foldable.

Reproduction Annelids can reproduce both sexually and asexually. Most annelids have separate sexes, but some, such as earthworms and leeches, are hermaphrodites. Sperm are passed between two worms near segments called the clitella (singular, clitellum). Refer to **Figure 23** and notice that the **clitellum** is a thickened band of segments. It produces a cocoon from which young earthworms hatch, as shown in **Figure 26.** Sperm and eggs pass into the cocoon as it slips forward off the body of the worm. After fertilization, the young are protected in the cocoon as they develop. Some annelids reproduce asexually by fragmentation. If a worm breaks apart, the missing parts can be regenerated.

Diversity of Annelids

The phylum Annelida is divided into three classes: class Oligochaeta (ohl ih goh KEE tuh)—the earthworms and their relatives, class Polychaeta (pah lih KEE tuh)—the bristleworms and their relatives, and class Hirudinea (hur uh DIN ee uh)—the leeches.

Earthworms and their relatives Earthworms probably are the best-known annelids. They are used as bait for fishing and are found in garden soil. An earthworm can eat its own mass in soil every day. Earthworms ingest soil to extract nutrients. In this way, earthworms aerate the soil—they break up the soil to allow air and water to move through it.

In addition to earthworms, class Oligochaeta—the oligochaetes (AH lee goh keetz)—includes tubifex worms and lumbriculid worms. Tubifex worms are small, threadlike aquatic annelids that are common in areas of high pollution. Lumbriculid (lum BRIH kyuh lid) worms are freshwater oligochaetes that are about 6 cm long and live at the edges of lakes and ponds. You can observe a feature common to oligochaetes in **MiniLab 2.**

MiniLab 2

Observe Blood Flow in a Segmented Worm

? Inquiry MiniLab

How does blood flow in a segmented worm? The California blackworm has a closed circulatory system and a transparent body. Its blood can be viewed as it flows along the dorsal blood vessel.

Procedure
1. Read and complete the lab safety form.
2. Moisten a piece of **filter paper** with **spring water** and place it in a **Petri dish.**
3. Examine a **blackworm** on the moist paper using a **stereomicroscope.**
4. Locate the dorsal blood vessel in a segment near the midpoint of the worm. Observe how blood flows in each segment.
5. Use a **stopwatch** to record how many pulses of blood occur per minute. Repeat this for two more segments, one near the head and one near the anus of the worm. Record your data in a table.

Analysis
1. **Summarize** how blood moves through each segment, including the direction of blood flow.
2. **Compare and contrast** the rate of blood flow near the head, at the midpoint, and near the anus of the worm.

FOLDABLES®

RUBRIC A rubric for evaluating Foldables is found on your eTeacherEdition Online.

Going Further Have students sketch examples of each of the three classes of segmented worms on the back of their Foldable, and compare and contrast body form and function.

ASK STUDENTS: *How are they similar? Different?*

"The mediocre teacher tells. The good teacher explains. The superior teacher demonstrates. The great teacher inspires."

—William W. Ward

Bristleworm

Fan worms

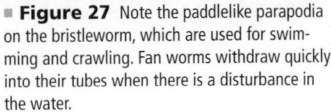

■ **Figure 27** Note the paddlelike parapodia on the bristleworm, which are used for swimming and crawling. Fan worms withdraw quickly into their tubes when there is a disturbance in the water.

Marine annelids Polychaetes (PAH lee keetz), which belong to class Polychaeta, mainly are marine animals. They include bristleworms and fan worms, shown in **Figure 27.** Polychaetes have head regions with well-developed sense organs, including eyes. Most body segments of polychaetes have many setae. Most body segments also have a pair of appendages called parapodia, shown in **Figure 27,** which are used for swimming and crawling. Fan worms are sessile—they stay in one place—and are filter feeders. They trap food in the mucus on their fan-shaped structures. If there is a threat nearby, fan worms retreat into their tubes.

D **Leeches** As shown in **Figure 28,** leeches in class Hirudinea are external parasites with flattened bodies and usually have no setae. Most leeches live in freshwater streams or rivers, where they attach to the bodies of their hosts—including fishes, turtles, and humans. Leeches attach to their hosts using front and rear suckers. When a leech bites, its saliva contains chemicals that act as an anesthetic. Other chemicals in the saliva reduce swelling and prevent the host's blood from clotting. W

Reading Check **Describe** the habitats of the three classes of annelids.

Leech

■ **Figure 28** A leech uses its suckers to attach to its host and feeds by drawing blood into its muscular pharynx.
***Compare and contrast** the feeding methods of leeches and tapeworms.*

D Develop Concepts

BL OL

Clarify a Misconception

ASK STUDENTS: ***What comes to mind when you think of leeches? Do you think they are harmful?*** Answers will vary. Many people are repulsed and afraid of leeches because they think they are poisonous and might cause deadly injury similar to the bite of a poisonous snake. When leeches attach to human skin, they inject anti-clotting agents to keep their blood meal from clotting, analgesic chemicals to prevent pain, and anti-inflammatory agents to prevent swelling. In most cases, this does not harm the human host. Like any other wound to human skin, bacterial infection could result, but not because the leech injects bacteria from its body into the bite. The bite of a leech is not poisonous and causes very little pain.

W Writing Support

OL AL Summary Writing

Have students research how leeches have been used over the course of human history and how they are used in the medical field today. Have them write an illustrated summary about their findings. BL Have students write a report on one way in which leeches were used in history and one way they are used today.

Reading Check Earthworms and their relatives live in soil or water. Polychaetes are marine animals. Leeches are aquatic.

■ **Caption Question Fig. 28** Leeches feed on blood by attaching to external skin with suckers; tapeworms attach to intestines with hooks and suckers.

? Inquiry **BioLab**

The lab at the end of the chapter can be used at this point in the lesson.

Develop Concepts

BL OL Scaffolding

ASK STUDENTS: ***How are earthworms helpful to the ecology of a natural area?*** They aerate soil and mix leaf litter into soil. ***Infer how earthworms can be harmful to a natural area?*** Earthworms introduced into an area where they are not native can destroy the leaf litter on the soil that provides habitat for a variety of native plants and animals. ***Compare the way in which marine polychaetes are like beneficial earthworms.*** They plow the organic debris on the ocean floor so that it decomposes just as earthworms plow the soil.

Skill Practice

BL OL EL

Recognize Cause and Effect

Have students make cross-section diagrams of how a northern forest floor might look before someone who was fishing dumped a can of earthworms in the leaf litter and then how the forest floor might look a few months later. Students should depict thick leaf litter with various invertebrates being eaten by birds and other animals. The "after" illustration should be bare soil with no invertebrates or other animals.

AL Have students explain the sequence of events and infer why soil composition will change.

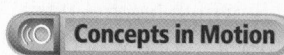

Concepts in Motion

Interactive Table

Reading Check would remove an important food source for marine animals

VOCABULARY

ACADEMIC VOCABULARY

Convert

to change from one form to another

Through photosynthesis, plants convert water and carbon dioxide to sugar and oxygen.

Ecology of Annelids

Segmented worms play important roles in the ecology of ecosystems. Some are beneficial to plants and animals, while others benefit humans.

Earthworms Many different animals, including frogs and birds, eat earthworms as a part of their diets. Earthworms also mix leaf litter into soil, aerating it so that roots can grow easily and water can move through the soil efficiently. Both functions are important for healthy ecosystems. However, nonnative earthworms are moving into areas, especially northern forests, where they are altering ecosystems in harmful ways. The consumption of leaf litter on forest floors by nonnative earthworms removes the shelter and moisture needed by many native plants and animals. Earthworms can be introduced into new habitats inadvertently by fishers and gardeners when the earthworms left from a day's fishing are dumped on the ground, or when a nursery plant from another part of the country is planted in a home garden.

Polychaetes Marine polychaetes help convert the organic debris of the ocean floor into carbon dioxide. Marine plant plankton take in carbon dioxide and use it during photosynthesis. Marine polychaetes are an important part of the diet of many marine predators.

Hirudinea Leeches have been used as medical treatments for centuries. They were used to suck blood out of patients who were believed to be ill because of an excess of blood. Today, leeches are used after microsurgical procedures to prevent blood from accumulating in the surgical area. However, there are drawbacks to using leeches. They have a small feeding capacity and must be replaced often. They can cause bacterial infections, and many people cringe at the thought of having a leech attached to them. To solve these problems, a nonliving mechanical leech has been designed to do the work of the animal. **Table 1** summarizes the ecological benefits of earthworms, polychaetes, and leeches.

Reading Check **Evaluate** the effects of removing polychaetes from oceans.

Table 1 **Ecological Importance of Annelids** Concepts in Motion Interactive Table

Type of Annelid	Example	Characteristics	Habitat	Ecological Benefit
Earthworms	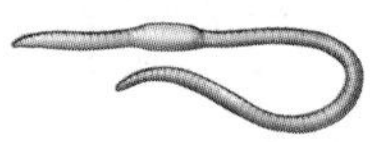	• Few setae on most body segments	Terrestrial	• They aerate soil so roots can grow more easily and water can move efficiently. • They are food for many different animals.
Polychaetes		• Well-developed sense organs • Many setae on most body segments • Parapodia	Mainly marine	• They convert organic debris in oceans into carbon dioxide, which is used by marine plankton for photosynthesis.
Leeches		• Usually no setae on body segments • Front and rear suckers	Mainly freshwater	• They maintain blood flow after microsurgery.

Research Citation

Classify Educational research indicates that teachers can extend students' thinking by asking them to use higher-level thinking skills. Activities such as using dichotomous keys, for example, requires that students identify similarities and differences among objects in order to place them in categories. (English, 1997)

Research bibliography on pages 32T–34T

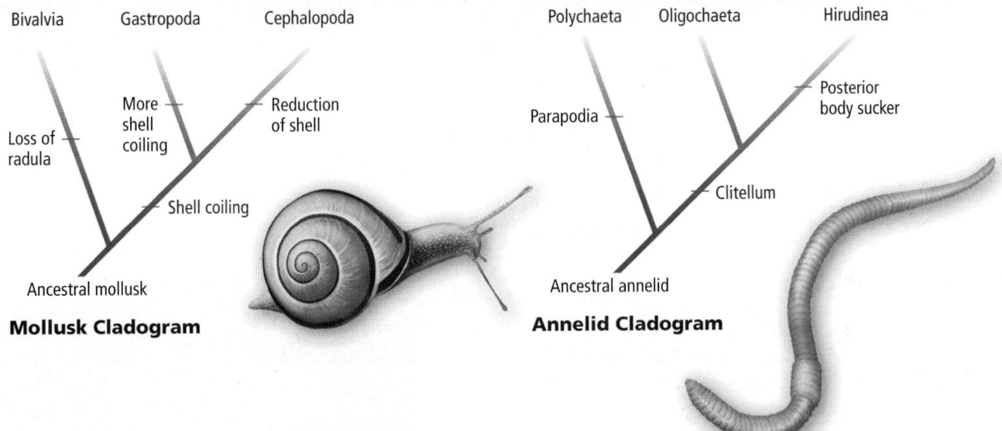

■ **Figure 29** These cladograms show how mollusks and annelids might have evolved.

Evolution of Mollusks and Annelids

In **Figure 29,** the cladogram on the left is one interpretation of the evolution of mollusks. As shown, gastropods have more shell coiling than cephalopods do. In shell coiling, the shell grows in a circular manner, making it more compact and more stable than an uncoiled shell. Cephalopods have a reduced shell. Bivalves are considered to have evolved later than gastropods and cephalopods because they lack a radula.

The cladogram on the right in **Figure 29** is one interpretation of the evolution of annelids. In this interpretation, early segmented worms—the polychaetes—developed parapodia in the course of their evolution. Later annelids—the oligochaetes and leeches—developed clitella. Leeches developed posterior body suckers even later.

D

Section 4 Assessment

Section Summary

- Two main body features characterize annelids and distinguish them from roundworms and flatworms.
- There are three main classes of annelids based on distinctive features.
- Segmentation is an adaptation important to evolution.
- Annelids are important parts of terrestrial and marine habitats.

Understand Main Ideas

1. MAIN Idea **Summarize** how segmentation was an important evolutionary milestone.
2. **Compare and contrast** earthworms to flatworms and roundworms.
3. **Model** Using clay or salt dough, make models of typical examples from the three classes of annelids. Describe the adaptations that enable each annelid to live in its environment.
4. **Summarize** how earthworm muscles interact to cause movement.

Think Critically

5. **Hypothesize** Form a hypothesis about what might happen to a farm field if earthworms suddenly disappeared.
6. **Compare and contrast** circulation in annelids and mollusks.

WRITING in **Biology**

7. Write a paragraph explaining why leeches might be used after microsurgical procedures based on what you know about leech saliva.

D Develop Concepts

EL BL OL Use Models Have students make models of an earthworm and a leech with modeling clay and incorporate all the external features. Earthworm model should include segmentation, setae, and mouth; leech model should include body suckers.

Develop Concepts

AL Diagram Have students make a diagram of a food web, including marine polychaetes. Include at least three other trophic levels. Answers will vary, but should show predator-prey relationships.

Formative Assessment

Evaluation

SAY TO STUDENTS: ***Make a list of the adaptations that make earthworms and leeches suited to their habitats. List the adaptation and its benefit to the animal.*** Answers will vary. Make sure students have indicated features they have studied in the book.

Remediation Have students draw a large diagram of an earthworm and a large diagram of a leech. Ask them to label all the parts that are important adaptations to their habitats and include how the structures are adapted. Have students use figures in their text as reference. earthworm: setae, segments; leech: suckers

Section 4 Assessment

1. enabled annelids to have a rigid muscle support system for efficient movement. Segments can be specialized.
2. earthworms: segmented and have coelom and larval stage; flatworms: lack coelom, unsegmented; roundworms: unsegmented have pseudocoelom; all three have bilateral symmetry
3. Annelids are cylindrical with segments, clitellum, and mouths. Polychaete have parapodia and bristles and segments. A leech should be flattened with suckers.
4. Circular muscles contract and elongate a segment. Longitudinal muscles contract, causing the segment to return to its original shape.
5. Water could not get through the soil as easily, so plants might die. Adequate nutrients might be lacking with no earthworms to break up organic matter.
6. Gastropods and bivalves have open circulatory systems. Annelids and cephalopods have closed circulatory systems.
7. Leech saliva contains an anticoagulant to help keep blood from clotting.

✓ Assessment Online Quiz

In the Field

Purpose

Students will learn about the career of a marine biologist in the context of the work of Dr. Steve O'Shea, who studies giant and colossal squid.
UCP.5, A.2, C.6

Anticipatory Guide

ASK STUDENTS: ***What do marine biologists study?*** Tell students that marine biologists study plants and animals that live in the ocean. They also study factors which affect the ocean and its inhabitants, such as pollution and overfishing. ***What are mollusks?*** Mollusks are coelomates with a muscular foot, a mantle, and a digestive tract with two openings. Squid are mollusks.

Background

Since his voyage that began in 2000, O'Shea has continued to try to collect larval giant squid. He sees the squid as indicative of the oceans' general well-being. "Squid are incredibly good barometers of environmental health," O'Shea said in a 2006 television news program, noting that every year, fewer and fewer giant squid are found near New Zealand. The problem, he said, is "bottom trawling," a kind of industrial fishing that scrapes a weighted net along the sea floor, killing coral and scooping up fish.

At least five species of squid and octopus have become extinct in New Zealand waters because of fishing practices. O'Shea adds, "At the rate we're going, we're not going to have giant squid in ten years."

In the Field

Career: Marine Biologist

The Search for the Giant Squid

For centuries, sailors told stories of encounters with fearsome monsters while on long sea voyages. Today, scientists acknowledge that two species of squid might be the real-life animals lurking behind the old sailors' tales. The giant squid *(Architeuthis dux)* and colossal squid *(Mesonychoteuthis hamiltoni)* are rarely seen in the wild because they live at extreme depths. Most specimens studied by scientists were washed up on beaches or caught in deep-sea fishing nets.

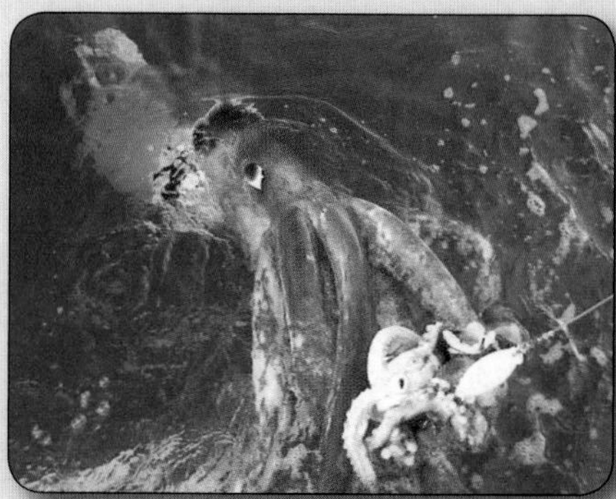

This image, taken by Japanese scientists in 2006, shows a giant squid as it is hauled on board a research vessel.

Marine biologist Steve O'Shea discovered that giant squid can grow up to 12.8 meters in length. They are thought to be the largest invertebrates in the world. Colossal squid are shorter but often weigh more than giant squid. Both species have eight arms and two tentacles covered with sucker rings or hooks for catching prey.

On a research expedition in 2000-2001, O'Shea sailed the waters around South Island, New Zealand. He searched for larval giant squid, which are 9 to 13 mm in size. He intended to raise the squid in captivity to study its life cycle. Although he caught several larval giant squid, none have survived in captivity.

Other scientists have made breakthroughs in the study of giant squid. In September 2004, a ship crewed by two Japanese scientists followed a group of sperm whales, known predators of giant squid, to a spot about 600 miles southeast of Tokyo. The scientists, Tsunemi Kubodera and Kyoichi Mori, lowered a baited fishing line into the ocean and waited.

When a giant squid took the bait, they raised the line and took photos of the squid as it struggled to free itself. The 25-foot-long squid eventually tore itself free, but it left behind one of its tentacles, which scientists later studied.

As O'Shea, Kubodera, and other scientists continue to search for and study giant and colossal squid, they likely will add to our knowledge of these animals. This new knowledge will bring them from the realm of myths into the light of scientific inquiry.

VISUAL COMMUNICATION

Make a Model Research the structure of either the giant squid or the colossal squid. Create a model that accurately shows prey-catching structures and body proportions. Present your model to the class.

Visual Communication

To assist your students with their research, help them find credible, reliable print and online sources. There is a great deal of conflicting information about giant and colossal squid online, so caution them to compare sources and to take their time. Hold a brainstorming session to help students think of materials to use in their models. If possible, give them time in class to work on their models.

WebQuest

BIOLAB

HOW DO WORMS AND MOLLUSKS MOVE?

Background: The worm and mollusk phyla display wide diversity in behavior and physical characteristics. Throughout this chapter, you have been introduced to some of the various species that make up these phyla. In this lab, you will compare the form of movement used by a flatworm (a planarian), a roundworm (a vinegar eel), a mollusk (a land snail), and a segmented worm (a blackworm).

Question: *What kind of motion do worms and mollusks display?*

Materials

plastic droppers (2)
petri dish (1 or 2)
microscope slide (1 or 2)
coverslip (1 or 2)
500-mL beaker
magnifying lens
dissecting microscope
light microscope
spring water or aged tap water (500 mL)
live cultures of planaria, vinegar eels, land snails, and blackworms

Safety Precautions

WARNING: *Be sure to treat live animals in a humane manner at all times. Use caution when working with a microscope, glass slides, and coverslips.*

Procedure

1. Read and complete the lab safety form.
2. Create a data table to record your observations.
3. Observe the movement of a flatworm by placing it in a drop of water in a petri dish or on a slide with no coverslip.
4. Make a wet mount of a vinegar eel and observe its movement under low-power magnification.
5. Place a land snail on a petri dish. Gently tip the dish to observe the snail's movement from underneath.
6. Place a blackworm on a moist paper towel and observe it with a magnifying lens.
7. Place the blackworm in a beaker of aged tapwater and observe its movement.
8. Record your observations in your data table.
9. **Cleanup and Disposal** Wash reusable materials and place them where your teacher directs. Return all live specimens to the cultures provided by your teacher.

Analyze and Conclude

1. **Compare and contrast** the movements of the flatworm, roundworm, land snail, and segmented worm.
2. **Infer** how the forms of the flatworm, roundworm, land snail, and segmented worm are designed to enable the animals to move.
3. **Describe** what happens to each segment of the blackworm as it crawls on land.
4. **Compare** the forward and backward motion of the blackworm on land. How might this be an adaptation for survival?
5. **Infer** how the blackworm might be able to escape from predators in the water.

APPLY YOUR SKILL

Experiment Design an experiment that you could perform to investigate how temperature affects worm and mollusk movement. If you have all the materials you will need, you might want to conduct the experiment.

BIOLAB

Inquiry BioLab

For a lab worksheet, use your eTeacherEdition Online.

RUBRIC A rubric for evaluating BioLabs is found on your eTeacherEdition Online.

Est. Time 90 min

Content Background Students will review and investigate the physical features that distinguish mollusks and the three major groups of worms into separate phyla. They will collect, identify, and classify worms and mollusks into their proper phyla.

Safety Precaution Approve lab safety forms before work begins.

Teaching Strategies

- Assist students with describing the movements they observe, brainstorm possible terms that could be used.
- A flexible probe can be made by attaching a single fiber or eyelash to an applicator stick.

Alternative Teaching Demo Set up four stations around the classroom, each with one representative species. Have students circulate around the room to make measurements and observations. Alternatively, divide the class into research teams to investigate one species and report their findings to the class.

Analyze and Conclude

1. Free-living flatworms move in an undulating motion. Vinegar eels have a sinusoidal or curving motion. Land snails generate waves of muscle movement in the foot. A segmented worm has segments that contract, pushing it forward.
2. The free-living flatworm shape allows it to move by flexing up and down. Roundworms' longitudinal muscles allow them to move in one direction, then the other. The foot of a snail is a large muscle that can contract rhythmically. A segmented worm has longitudinal and circular muscles that work together.
3. Each segment contracts in turn, creating a movement that pushes it forward.
4. When stimulated at the tail, the worm crawls forward. When stimulated near the head, it crawls backward, allowing it to escape from danger at either end.
5. It does not have a reverse-swimming mechanism. When stimulated at the head while in water, it would turn around and swim in the opposite direction.

Chapter 25

Study Guide

ConnectED

Students can use the following to review the chapter.

Review

Vocabulary eGames
Vocabulary eFlashcards
Vocabulary PuzzleMaker

Assessment

Online Quizzes
Online Test Practice
Standardized Test Practice

Use the Exam*View*® *Assessment Suite* CD-ROM to:

- create multiple versions of tests
- create modified tests with one mouse click
- edit existing questions and add your own questions
- build tests aligned with state standards using built-in state curriculum tags
- change English tests to Spanish with one mouse click
- track students' progress using the Teacher Management System

Chapter 25 Study Guide

THEME FOCUS Energy All worms obtain energy from other organisms, though some worms are parasitic and others are free-living.

BIG Idea Worms and mollusks have evolved to have a variety of adaptations for living as parasites or for living in water or soil.

Section 1 Flatworms

pharynx (p. 727)
flame cell (p. 727)
ganglion (p. 728)
regeneration (p. 728)
scolex (p. 730)
proglottid (p. 730)

MAIN Idea Flatworms are thin, flat, acoelomate animals that can be free-living or parasitic.

- Flatworms were among the first animals to exhibit bilateral symmetry.
- Flatworms are acoelomates with limited numbers of organs and systems.
- Some flatworms are free-living, and others are parasitic.
- Flatworms that are parasitic have specialized adaptations for parasitic life.

Section 2 Roundworms and Rotifers

hydrostatic skeleton (p. 732)
trichinosis (p. 733)

MAIN Idea Roundworms and rotifers have a more highly evolved gut than flatworms.

- Roundworms are closely related to flatworms.
- Roundworms, like flatworms, have a limited number of organs and systems.
- Roundworms are either free-living or parasitic.
- Roundworms cause many human and plant diseases.
- Rotifers are pseudocoelomates that appear on a different branch of the evolutionary tree from that of roundworms.

Section 3 Mollusks

mantle (p. 737)
radula (p. 738)
gill (p. 738)
open circulatory system (p. 739)
closed circulatory system (p. 739)
nephridium (p. 739)
siphon (p. 741)

MAIN Idea Mollusks are coelomates with a muscular foot, a mantle, and a digestive tract with two openings.

- Mollusks were the first animals in the course of evolution to develop a coelom.
- Mollusks are divided into three main classes based on different characteristics.
- Mollusks have two body features that no other animals have—a mantle and a muscular foot.
- Mollusks have more developed organ systems than those of roundworms and flatworms.
- Mollusks play important roles in the ecosystems in which they live.

Section 4 Segmented Worms

crop (p. 746)
gizzard (p. 746)
setae (p. 747)
clitellum (p. 748)

MAIN Idea Segmented worms have segments that allow for specialization of tissues and for efficiency of movement.

- Two main body features characterize annelids and distinguish them from roundworms and flatworms.
- There are three main classes of annelids based on distinctive features.
- Segmentation is an adaptation important to evolution.
- Annelids are important parts of terrestrial and marine habitats.

Review Vocabulary PuzzleMaker

For additional practice with vocabulary, have students access the Vocabulary PuzzleMaker online.

Review Vocabulary eGames

Section 1

Vocabulary Review

Use what you know about the vocabulary terms found on the Study Guide page to answer the following questions.

1. What is a group of nerve cell bodies that coordinates ingoing and outgoing messages?
2. What is a tubelike muscular organ that releases digestive enzymes?
3. What structure attaches to the intestinal lining of a host with hooks and suckers?

Understand Main Ideas

Use the diagram below to answer question 4.

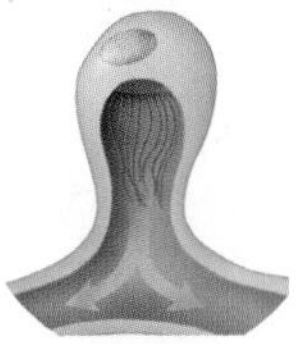

4. What function does the structure in the diagram perform?
   A. digestion **C.** maintains homeostasis
   B. movement **D.** provides support
5. Which animals have proglottids?
   A. flukes **C.** tapeworms
   B. planarians **D.** roundworms
6. Which classification fits a flatworm that is free-living?
   A. Turbellaria **C.** Trematoda
   B. Cestoda **D.** Nematoda
7. Which is not involved in planarian movement?
   A. cilia **C.** mucus
   B. muscles **D.** flame cells

Constructed Response

8. **Open Ended** A certain tapeworm secretes a chemical that slows the intestinal pulsations of its host. This helps to ensure that the tapeworm is not expelled from the body of the host. Explain how adding this chemical to a drug for humans might increase the drug's effectiveness.
9. **MAIN Idea** Design a parasitic worm for an animal that lives in the desert. Remember to consider how the animal will contract the parasite and how the parasite will stay within its host.

Think Critically

10. **THEME FOCUS Energy** Design an experiment that could determine what a planarian prefers to eat.

Section 2

Each of the following sentences is false. Make each sentence true by replacing the italicized word with a vocabulary term from the Study Guide page.

11. Roundworms are bilaterally symmetrical, cylindrical, and have *segmented bodies.*
12. *Schistosomiasis* can be prevented by cooking meat properly.
13. A fluid-filled space that provides rigid suppor for muscles to work against is *an exoskeleton.*

Understand Main Ideas

Use the diagram below to answer questions 14 and 15.

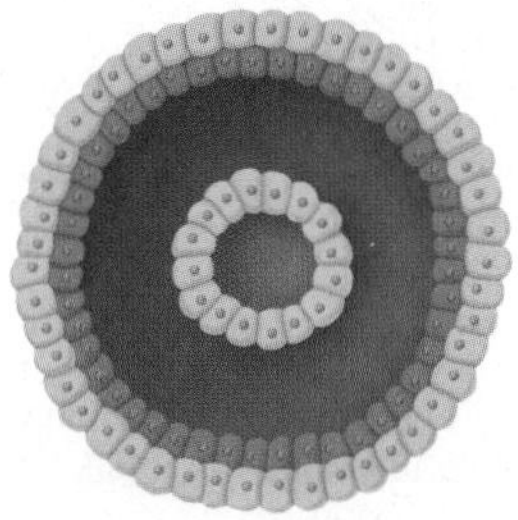

14. Which feature of roundworms is illustrated in the diagram above?
    A. pseudocoelom **C.** circulatory system
    B. scolex **D.** nervous system
15. The feature in the diagram led to which adaptation in roundworms?
    A. a coelom **C.** a mantle
    B. a gut **D.** segments

Chapter 25 Assessment

Section 1

Vocabulary Review

1. ganglion
2. pharynx
3. scolex

Understand Main Ideas

4. C
5. C
6. A
7. D

Constructed Response

8. If the drug stays in the intestine longer, perhaps more of it could be absorbed to combat the disease.
9. The parasite might have only one host and not require water for an intermediate stage. When it is out of the body, it would need to be very small and have a protective covering to keep it from drying out.

Think Critically

10. Students should make a hypothesis, have a control, one variable, plan to collect quantitative data, and make a graph. They might hypothesize that a planarian would eat plant material or some kind of meat.

Section 2

Vocabulary Review

11. hydrostatic skeletons
12. Trichinosis
13. a hydrostatic skeleton

Understand Main Ideas

14. A
15. B

Constructed Response

16. Diagrams should include all stages: the cow feeds on grass and picks up tapeworm proglottides, the tapeworm burrows from the intestine to the muscle of the cow, then the undercooked beef is eaten by a person.

17. Answers will vary but should be both biologically and geographically correct.

Think Critically

18. Make sure the concept map begins with the main idea, which is the nematode, branches off that circle may indicate aspects of a way of life, and off those branches, the structures related to that lifestyle.

19. Compare body shape and structures with features that define a flatworm and a roundworm. Observe movement: roundworms move in a thrashing manner.

Section 3

Vocabulary Review

20. nephridium
21. radula
22. siphon

Understand Main Ideas

23. A
24. B
25. B
26. C

Constructed Response

27. Answers will vary. Make sure students' keys have paired statements, that the statements begin with broader categories and end with more specific features.

Think Critically

28. Answers will vary. Make sure students make a hypothesis, have a control, one variable, plan to gather quantitative data, and make a graph. One experiment might have a large number of zebra mussels in a tank of polluted water and measure the time it takes for the mussels to remove the pollution.

Constructed Response

16. Short Answer Make a diagram that shows the life cycle of a beef tapeworm.

17. Open Ended Select a human parasite and indicate with a key on a map of the world where the parasite is most common. Research online to find information.

Think Critically

18. Concept Mapping Make a concept map that uses the following words: nematode, pseudocoelomate, digestive tract with two openings, parasitic, free-living, lengthwise muscles, host.

19. MAIN Idea Suppose that you find a tiny worm in the garden. How could you determine whether it is a flatworm or a roundworm?

Section 3

Vocabulary Review

An analogy is a comparison relationship between two pairs of words and can be written in the following manner: A is to B as C is to D. In the analogies that follow, one of the words is missing. Complete each analogy with a vocabulary term from the Study Guide page.

20. Kidney is to metabolic waste as __________ is to cellular waste.

21. Tongue is to candy as __________ is to algae.

22. Legs are to running as __________ is to jet-propelled swimming.

Understand Main Ideas

23. If the mantle of a bivalve was damaged, the bivalve would not be able to perform which function?
A. maintain its shell
B. digest food
C. circulate blood
D. excrete wastes

24. Which word pair is related most closely?
A. shell, circulation
B. radula, feeding
C. jet-propelled swimming, bivalve
D. open circulatory system, octopus

Use the diagram below to answer questions 25 and 26.

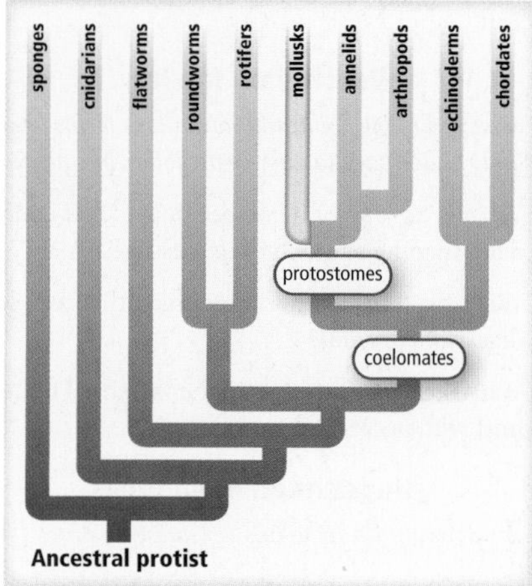

25. MAIN Idea The phylogenetic tree of animals shows that mollusks have which feature?
A. a pseudocoelom
B. a coelom
C. a solid body
D. shells

26. Which group is related most closely to mollusks?
A. nematodes
B. enchinoderms
C. annelids
D. chordates

Constructed Response

27. Open Ended Make a dichotomous key to identify mollusk shells that you find in pictures in books about animals, shells that you have collected, or shells that your teacher supplies.

Think Critically

28. CAREERS IN BIOLOGY Marine biologists know that zebra mussels are pests in many aquatic ecosystems. They form ultradense colonies and can clog pipes leading to water-treatment and industrial plants. However, some marine biologists hypothesize that because the mussels live in such dense groups, they might serve as water-purification systems in places such as zoo ponds and other park ponds that have excessive algal blooms in the summer. Design an experiment that would determine whether zebra mussels could be used to purify water.

Assessment Online Test Practice

Section 4

Vocabulary Review

An analogy is a comparison relationship between two pairs of words and can be written in the following manner: A is to B as C is to D. In the analogies that follow, one of the words is missing. Complete each analogy with a vocabulary term from the Study Guide page.

29. Teeth are to human as __________ is to earthworm.

30. Cocoon is to butterfly as __________ is to earthworm.

31. Vacuole is to protist as __________ is to earthworm.

Understand Main Ideas

Use the diagram below to answer questions 32 and 33.

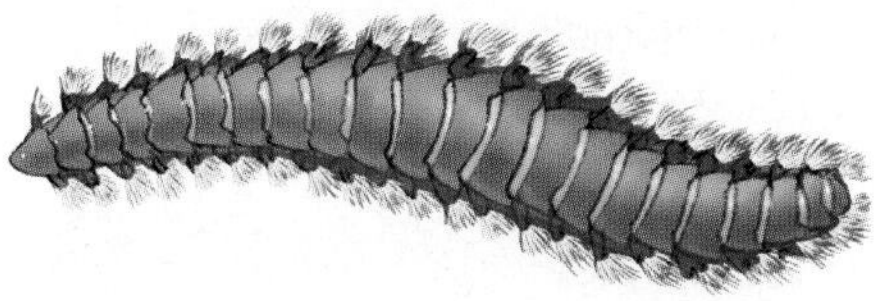

32. Which animal is illustrated in the diagram?
A. roundworm **C.** polychaete
B. leech **D.** earthworm

33. What feature is characteristic of this animal?
A. foot **C.** sucker
B. parapodia **D.** shell

Constructed Response

34. MAIN Idea If global warming continues, predict how earthworms might change as a result of natural selection.

Think Critically

35. CAREERS IN BIOLOGY Rheumatologists, doctors who treat arthritis, have observed that when leeches are applied for a short time to the skin near joints of people affected with arthritis, pain is relieved for up to six months. Design an experiment that could explain this phenomenon.

Summative Assessment

36. BIG Idea Worms have evolved to have a variety of adaptations for living as parasites or for living in water or soil. Give an example of a worm that is parasitic, a worm that lives in soil, and a worm that lives in water. Then, describe a characteristic of each that makes it well suited for that environment.

37. Draw diagrams of a typical example from each of the three classes of mollusks and label the distinctive characteristics.

38. Suggest ways to avoid becoming the host of a flatworm.

39. WRITING in Biology Research mollusks that live in areas of hydrothermal vents. Write a report emphasizing the differences between hydrothermal vent mollusks and those that live in the habitats you studied in this chapter.

Document-Based Questions

The data below represent the percentages of the three main classes of flatworms.

Data obtained from: Pechenik, J. 2005. ***Biology of the Invertebrates***. New York: McGraw-Hill.

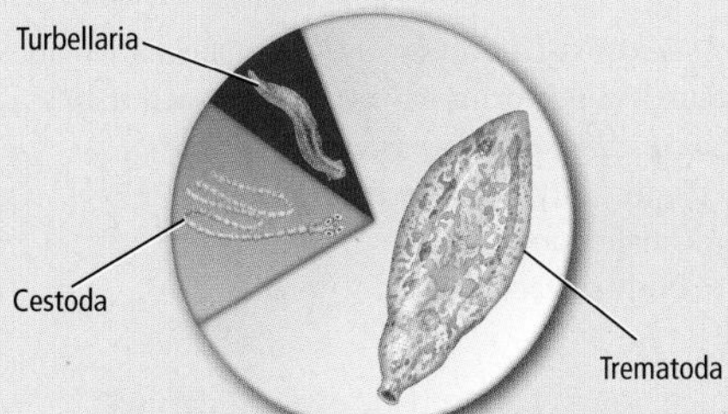

40. Approximately what percentage of flatworms are flukes?

41. Which group of flatworms has the least number of species?

42. Infer why there might be so many more of one kind of flatworm than any other kind.

Section 4

Vocabulary Review
29. gizzard
30. clitellum
31. crop

Understand Main Ideas
32. C
33. B

Constructed Response
34. Accept all reasonable answers such as: Due to more heat and dryness, those with thicker outer coverings might survive in larger numbers and produce more like themselves.

Think Critically
35. Accept all answers in which the student has made a reasonable hypothesis, provided a step by step procedure in which quantitative data are gathered and included a control. It may be that a chemical injected by the leech as it feeds also relieves pain.

Summative Assessment
36. parasite: tapeworm, the scolex attaches to the intestinal lining of a host; water: rotifers, ciliated wheel structures propel them through the water; soil: earthworm, setae anchor the earthworm to the soil
37. Diagrams should illustrate that gastropods have a large foot and one shell (or no shell), bivalves have 2 hinged shells, and cephalopods have tentacles.
38. proper sewage treatment, properly cooking meats, and wearing protective clothing when wading in infested waters
39. Answers will vary but should include difference in water temperature. Make sure students use what they have learned about the habitats of mollusks as they write.

WRITING in Biology

RUBRIC Use the modifiable rubric found on your eTeacherEdition Online to assess writing assignments.

Document-Based Questions

Pechenik, J. 2005. *Biology of the Invertebrates*. New York: McGraw-Hill.

40. 75–80 percent
41. Turbellarians
42. The two-host lifestyle must be a very effective way to live.

Assessment Online Test Practice

Standardized Test Practice

Multiple Choice

1. D 5. C
2. D 6. D
3. A 7. A
4. A 8. B

Short Answer

9. A–seed coat; B–endosperm; C–embryo
10. Seed 1 is a monocot because it has the larger endosperm. Seed 2 has two cotyledons.
11. They have several body structures in common, including a mantle and a muscular foot, which is modified to tentacles in squids. They also have similar digestive and circulatory systems and similar reproductive stages.
12. Answers may vary. Perhaps the most important thing humans can do is make efforts to understand the ecology and the importance of reefs.
13. Ancestral character: vascular tissue; derived character: carpels
14. The haploid gametophyte alternates with the diploid sporophyte. The haploid gametophyte generation produces haploid gametes through mitosis. The gametes unite in the process of fertilization to produce diploid zygotes that develop the diploid sporophyte generation. The diploid sporophyte generation produces haploid spores through meiosis. The haploid spores develop into haploid gametophyte generation.
15. The amoeboid cells come together to form a fruiting body that produces spores. The process is asexual. The advantage of this form of reproduction is that it occurs when food is scarce and allows the organism to form spores that can germinate when conditions are more favorable.

Standardized Test Practice

Cumulative

Multiple Choice

1. During dry weather, pieces of a moss might be scattered by the wind. When it rains, these pieces can grow into new plants. Which process does this display?
A. alternation of generations
B. gametophyte reproduction
C. sporophyte generation
D. vegetative reproduction

Use the diagram below to answer questions 2 and 3.

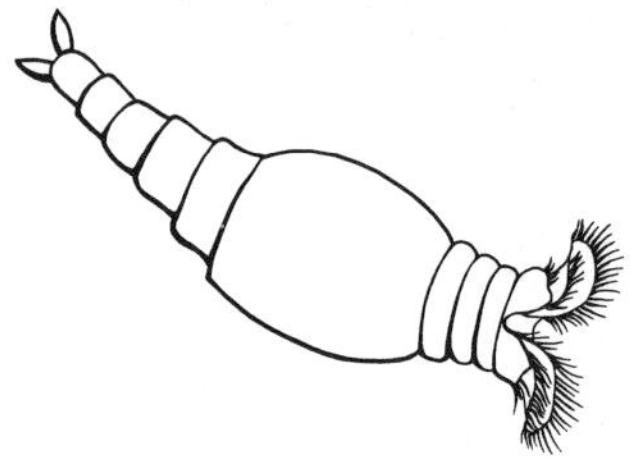

2. In which phylum does the animal shown in the figure belong?
A. Annelida
B. Nematoda
C. Platyhelminthes
D. Rotifera

3. Roundworms differ from the organism shown above because roundworms have which characteristic?
A. a complete digestive tract
B. the inability to live in freshwater
C. a smaller body size
D. a body surface covered with cilia

4. Which is one characteristic of all cnidarians?
A. Their tentacles contain cnidocytes.
B. Their tentacles contain fibroblasts.
C. They live only in freshwater environments.
D. They spend some time as sessile animals.

5. Which is an example of a nastic response?
A. bamboo plants growing toward a light
B. corn plant roots growing downward
C. sunflowers tracking the Sun
D. vines growing up a tree

Use the diagram below to answer question 6.

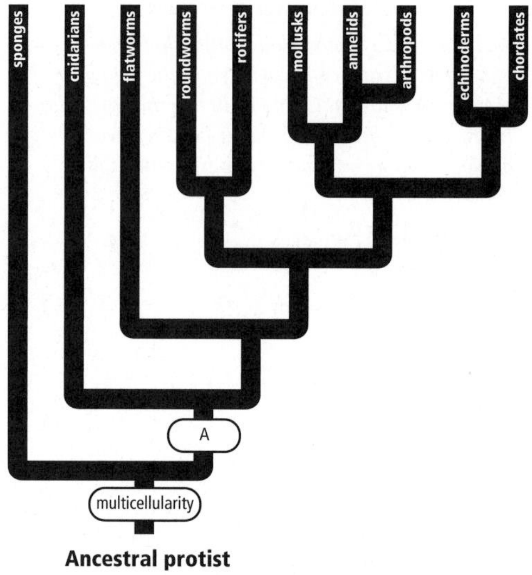

6. Which body structures are typical of all the animals above Point A on the evolutionary tree?
A. cell walls
B. coeloms
C. tentacles
D. tissues

7. How does an aggregate fruit, such as a blackberry or strawberry, form?
A. when a flower has multiple female organs that fuse together
B. when a fruit has multiple seeds that fuse together
C. when multiple flowers from the same plant fuse together
D. when multiple simple fruits fuse together

8. How do hornworts differ from other nonvascular plants?
A. Their cells allow nutrients and water to move by diffusion and osmosis.
B. Their cells can contain a type of cyanobacteria.
C. They can be classified as either thallose or leafy.
D. They have chloroplasts in some of their cells.

Short Answer

Use the diagram below to answer questions 9 and 10.

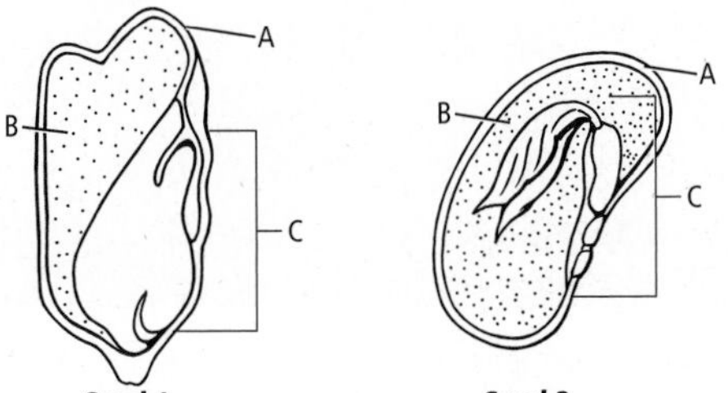

Seed 1 Seed 2

9. Name the parts of these seeds.

10. Which seed is a monocot and which is a eudicot? How do you know?

11. Explain why squids and clams are both included in phylum Mollusca even though they appear to be very different kinds of animals.

12. What is one thing that humans can do to preserve reefs? Explain your reasoning.

13. Specify an example of an ancestral character and a derived character that angiosperms have.

14. Describe the alternation of generations in plants.

15. Describe how cellular slime molds reproduce. Identify whether this process is sexual or asexual. Assess how this form of reproduction is beneficial for cellular slime molds.

Extended Response

16. List two reasons why animals benefit from segmentation. Assess the importance of these benefits.

17. Suppose that you are a scientist trying to determine the water quality of a river where mussels live. What data could you collect from the mussels to determine the quality of the river water?

Essay Question

Schistosomiasis is caused by flukes, which have complex life cycles involving specific freshwater snail species as intermediate hosts. Infected snails release large numbers of minute, free-swimming larvae (cercariae) that are capable of penetrating the unbroken skin of a human host. Even brief exposure to contaminated freshwater, such as wading, swimming, or bathing, can result in infection. Human schistosomiasis cannot be acquired by wading or swimming in salt water (oceans or seas). The cercariae of birds and aquatic mammals can penetrate the skin of humans who enter infested freshwater or salt water in many parts of the world, including cool, temperate areas. The cercariae die in the skin but may elicit a puritic rash ("swimmer's itch" or "clam-digger's itch").

Using the information in the paragraph above, answer the following question in essay format.

18. Schistosomiasis is a disease that is most common in sub-Saharan Africa, the Philippines, southern China, and Brazil. Propose a plan to control this disease in a specific area. What steps would need to be taken to keep people from getting the disease? Develop a plan and explain it in a well-organized essay.

NEED EXTRA HELP?

If You Missed Question . . .	1	2	3	4	5	6	7	8	9	10	11	12	13	14	15	16	17	18
Review Section . . .	23.1	25.3	25.2	24.3	22.3	24.3	23.3	21.2	23.3	23.3	25.3	24.3	18.2	23.1	19.4	24.2	15.2	25.1

Extended Response

16. Answers may vary. Possible answers include the following.
    - A. Segmented animals have several body parts that can all perform the same or similar functions. This benefit enables them to perform life functions more quickly and efficiently.
    - B. Segmented animals have body parts that can respond to stimuli, enabling the animals to respond faster. This trait has survival value.

17. Mussels are filter feeders; toxins build up in their systems more noticeably than in other animals. You could collect samples of mussels, and then test them for different toxins you are interested in studying. The results could be compared with mussels obtained from other areas.

Essay Question

18. Plans can vary, but should show a clear connection between some aspect of the worm's life cycle and intervening in the health of humans. For example, humans could be educated to avoid wading or swimming in possibly contaminated freshwater without proper protection. In a specific community, a campaign could be developed to exterminate the species of snails that host the fluke, either by collecting them manually (as is done in parts of China) or by using some kind of pesticide. Similarly, a pesticide could be used to kill the flukes themselves. The most effective campaign probably would combine all of these methods.

Chapter 26 Organizer:
Arthropods

LabManager™
Customize any lab with the LabManager™ CD-ROM.

Essential Questions	National Science Standards	Materials and Planning Estimated times include cleanup and disposal, but do not include teacher prep time. For cleanup and disposal guidelines, see page 39T.	Est. Time (min)
Section 1 1. What is the importance of exoskeletons, jointed appendages, and segmentation to arthropods? 2. What are some similarities and differences among the organ systems of arthropods? 3. What are the methods used by arthropods to respond to stimuli?	UCP.1–5; A.1, A.2; C.3, C.4, C.5, C.6; F.1, F.5	**Launch Lab,** p. 760: crayfish and pillbug specimens	15
		Demonstration, p. 762: images of local arthropods	15
		Demonstration, p. 763: live or preserved specimens of praying mantises and crayfish	20
		Demonstration, p. 764: bess beetle, tape, washcloth, heavy thread, pennies, plastic petri dish	20
		MiniLab 1, p. 765: magnifying lens or stereomicroscope, mouthparts of preserved specimens of different arthropods (butterfly, mosquito, crayfish, praying mantis)	15
		Activity, p. 767: computers with animation programs	120
		Activity, p. 768: pans of water, crayfishes, dark construction paper	20
Section 2 1. What are the structures and their functions found in the major groups of arthropods? 2. What are the adaptations in the major groups of arthropods? 3. What are characteristics of crustaceans and arachnids?	UCP.1–5; A.1, A.2; C.3, C.4, C.5, C.6; F.1, F.2, F.3, F.4; G.1, G.2, G.3	**Demonstration,** p. 770: arthropod field guides	15
		Activity, p. 772: craft supplies such as twine and duct tape, images of spider webs, picture frames, table tennis balls	55
		MiniLab 2, p. 773: live or preserved arthropod specimens from each of the three major groups	15
Section 3 1. What are characteristics and adaptations of insects? 2. What are similarities and differences between complete and incomplete metamorphosis? 3. How do insects interact and communicate with each other?	UCP.1–5; A.1, A.2; C.3, C.4, C.5, C.6; F.1, F.2, F.3, F.4, F.5, F.6; G.1, G.2, G.3	**Demonstration,** p. 775: live water strider, flat pan, plastic wrap, dechlorinated water	10
		Activity, p. 776: field guides, list of ten most common insect orders of your area	60–120
		Activity, p. 778: preserved specimens of the various life stages of a grasshopper and a moth, goggles, gloves, forceps, microscopes, magnifying lenses	45
		BioLab, p. 783: soil sample, clear funnel, ring stand, gooseneck lamp, wire mesh, beaker, 95% ethanol, plastic collection vials, magnifying lens, arthropod field guide, metric ruler	90

Suggested Time for Each Lesson

Class	Chapter Opener	Section 1	Section 2	Section 3	Assessment
Basic	45 min	45 min	45 min	45 min	45 min
General	20 min	45 min	45 min	70 min	45 min
Honors	—	20 min	70 min	70 min	20 min

ConnectED

connectED.mcgraw-hill.com

Access interactive learning opportunities and teaching resources using these icons located throughout your StudentWorks™ Plus Online and eTeacherEdition Online.

Chapter 26 Section Resources

FAST FILE Unit 7 Resources:
Launch Lab Worksheet*
MiniLab Worksheet*
Study Guide (English/Spanish)*
Section Quick Check

Reading Essentials 26.1
Science Notebook 26.1*

FAST FILE Unit 7 Resources:
MiniLab Worksheet*
Study Guide (English/Spanish)*
Section Quick Check

Reading Essentials 26.2
Science Notebook 26.2*

FAST FILE Unit 7 Resources:
BioLab Worksheet*
Study Guide (English/Spanish)*
Section Quick Check

Reading Essentials 26.3
Science Notebook 26.3*

Additional Chapter 26 Resources

FAST FILE Unit 7 Resources:
Chapter Diagnostic Test
Concept Mapping*
Real-World Biology
Enrichment
Chapter Tests A, B, and C

Transparencies:
Bellringer Transparencies*
Biology Concepts Transparencies*

Lab Resources:
Laboratory Manual*
Probeware Lab Manual*
Forensics Lab Manual*
Pre-AP Lab Manual*
Open Inquiry in Biology*
Guided Inquiry in Biology*

Technology

Teaching Tools:
eTeacherEdition Online
Classroom Presentation Toolkit CD-ROM*
LabManager™ CD-ROM*
Video Lab DVD*
Virtual Lab CD-ROM*
What's BIOLOGY Got To Do With It?
StudentWorks™ Plus Online*

Chapter Assessment Tools:
Classroom Presentation Toolkit CD-ROM*
ExamView® Assessment Suite CD-ROM

Web-Based Resources:
- StudentWorks™ Plus Online
- eTeacherEdition Online
- Animations*
- The Interactive Time Line*
- Interactive Tables*
- Online Quizzes
- Online Test Practice
- Standardized Test Practice
- Virtual Labs*
- Multilingual eGlossary*
- Vocabulary eGames*
- Vocabulary eFlashcards
- WebQuests
- Personal Tutors

While all resources listed are appropriate for English learners, the * indicates resources with a strong visual or hands-on component for EL.

Teaching strategies and activities have been coded for differentiated instruction.

AL Activities for students working above grade level	**OL** Activities for students working on grade level	**BL** Activities for students working below grade level	**EL** Activities for English learners (also ELL)	**COOP LEARN** Activities designed for small cooperative group work

CHAPTER 26

Launch Lab
What structures do arthropods have?

? Inquiry Launch Lab

For a lab worksheet, use your eTeacherEdition Online.

RUBRIC A rubric for evaluating Launch Labs is found on your eTeacherEdition Online.

Est. Time 15 min

Safety Precautions Never release a non native species into the local environment.

Teaching Strategies

- If you have too few aquariums, students can observe their crayfish in large jars.
- Consider having live or preserved specimens of a nonvenomous spider, insect, and shrimp for students to use for comparisons.

Procedure

1. Read and complete the lab safety form.
2. Create a data table to record your observations.
3. Observe the physical characteristics of live or preserved **specimens of a crayfish** and a **pill bug**. Record your observations in your data table. **WARNING: *Treat live animals in a humane manner at all times.***
4. Observe the movements of two of the animals, if possible, and record your observations.

Cleanup and Disposal

Live animals collected from a local environment should be returned to that environment. Purchased animals should be properly housed in the classroom or donated to a pet shop.

CHAPTER 26

Arthropods

ConnectED

Your one-stop online resource
connectED.mcgraw-hill.com

- Video
- Audio
- Review
- Inquiry
- WebQuest
- Assessment
- Concepts in Motion
- Multilingual eGlossary

Launch Lab
What structures do arthropods have?

Arthropods form a group of animals that includes all bees, flies, crabs, millipedes, centipedes, spiders, and ticks. Discover the features arthropods share by observing two different arthropods.

For a lab worksheet, use your StudentWorks™ Plus Online.

? Inquiry Launch Lab

FOLDABLES®

Make a chart and label it as shown. Use it to organize your notes about terrestrial and aquatic arthropods.

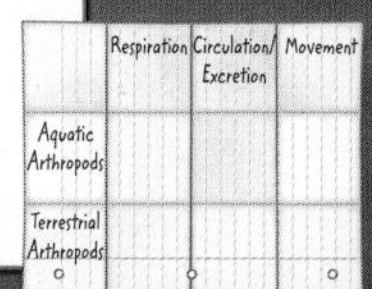

Analysis

1. **Describe** the structures of the two animals that are similar. body segmentation, antennae, eyes, exoskeleton, and jointed appendages
2. **Identify** the defensive structure that the two animals have in common. How does this feature allow them to protect themselves from predators? The exoskeleton is hard and encases the entire body like armor to provide protection for the soft internal structures.

GOING GREEN For the Launch Lab, collect local arthropods and freeze them for a day or two depending on their size for non-living specimens. If you must order preserved specimens, order from a supplier that uses minimal packaging, no bubble wrap, and no polystyrene pellets.

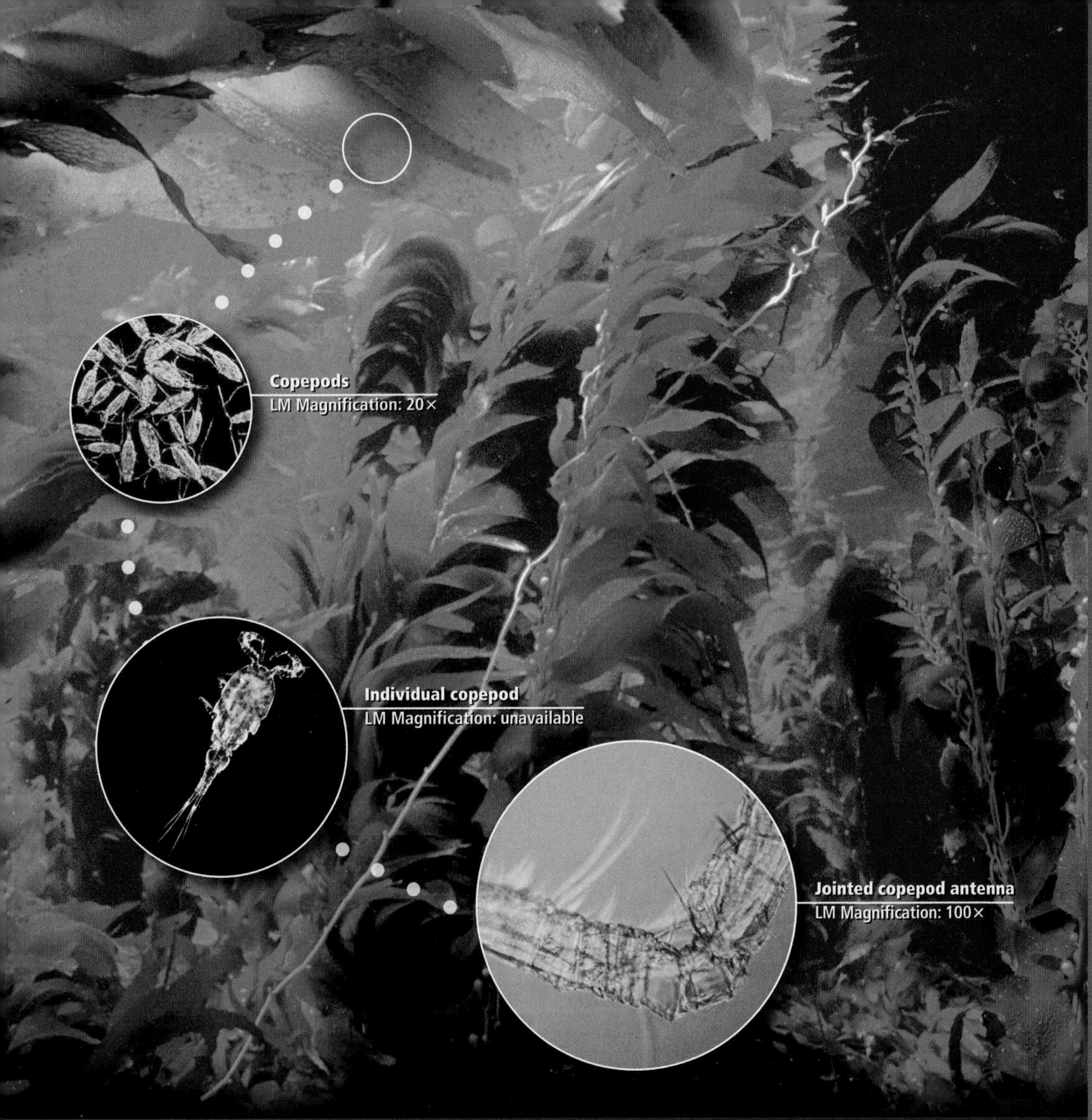

THEME FOCUS Diversity
Arthropods' specific adaptations allow them to live in many habitats.

BIG Idea Arthropods have evolved to have a variety of adaptations for successful diversity, population, and persistence.

Section 1 • Arthropod Characteristics
Section 2 • Arthropod Diversity
Section 3 • Insects and Their Relatives

THEMES

Scientific Inquiry Scientists study arthropods as carriers and transmitters of bacteria and diseases which affect human health.

Diversity Unique adaptations and features enable arthropods to inhabit a wide variety of ecosystems.

Energy Daily body functions, such as, circulation, respiration, and reproduction, require large amounts of energy.

Homeostasis Specific organ systems, such as Malpighian tubules, are used to remove waste and maintain water balance within arthropods.

Change Horseshoe crabs are arthropods that have remained virtually unchanged since the Triassic period.

Introduce the Chapter

Copepods

ASK STUDENTS: ***What type of animal do you think is more numerous than any other?*** Copepods. No one is expected to know that copepods are more numerous than any other type of animal.

SAY TO STUDENTS: ***There are more copepods than any other type of animal. A copepod is a small aquatic crustacean. Examine the photo and infer how their structures are adaptations for survival.*** Accept all reasonable answers. The appendages enable the animal to swim and the antennae enable the copepod to sense its environment as it moves forward.

BIG Idea

What is an arthropod? Show students images of various arthropods such as lobsters, crayfishes, spiders, insects, beetles, or butterflies. As you display the images, ask students to make a list of where they might find these arthropods and infer why they are so diverse in body structure. Students will not know the precise answer, but you can encourage all answers that point out their adaptations for living in a variety of habitats and for ways of getting food. Some may also realize that these are the first animals to take to the air, making an entirely new niche.

Section 1

MAIN Idea

BL OL AL

Arthropod Anatomy Provide students with a variety of preserved or live arthropods.
SAY TO STUDENTS: ***Read the text under the headings*** **Segmentation, Jointed appendages,** ***and*** **Exoskeleton** ***in your books. Draw a sketch of each arthropod and label the segmented body, jointed appendages, and the exoskeleton.*** Sketches should resemble some of the illustrations in this section.

S Skill Practice

BL Visual Literacy
SAY TO STUDENTS: ***Examine Figure 1 and explain how it is similar to other evolutionary trees.*** The trees have a base and branches showing how animals on nearby branches are more closely related than animals that are not on nearby branches.
ASK STUDENTS: ***How are evolutionary trees differentiated?*** Different animal groups are highlighted, and different characteristics are depicted on the branches based upon certain characteristics.

Reading Check Both arthropods and annelids have bilateral symmetry, are coelomates, show protostome development, and have segmentation. Unlike annelids, arthropods have exoskeletons with jointed appendages.

Caption Question Fig. 1
8.6 percent

Section 1

Reading Preview

Essential Questions

- What is the importance of exoskeletons, jointed appendages, and segmentation to arthropods?
- What are some similarities and differences among the organ systems of arthropods?
- What are the methods used by arthropods to respond to stimuli?

Review Vocabulary

ganglion: a group of nerve cell bodies that coordinates messages

New Vocabulary

thorax
abdomen
cephalothorax
appendage
molting
mandible
tracheal tube
book lung
spiracle
Malpighian tubule
pheromone

g Multilingual eGlossary

Arthropod Characteristics

MAIN Idea Arthropods have segmented bodies and tough exoskeletons with jointed appendages.

Real-World Reading Link Think about what animal group might have more individuals than any other group. Did copepods come to mind? Even though copepods are numerous, most people have never seen one. The copepods in the opening photo are tiny arthropods that float in the open ocean and feed on even smaller protists. They can be found almost anywhere there is water.

Arthropod Features

Copepods belong to phylum Arthropoda (ar THRAH puh duh). Between 70 and 85 percent of all named animal species are arthropods (AR thruh pahdz). As shown in the circle graph in **Figure 1,** the majority of arthropods are insects, which includes beetles, butterflies, moths, flies, bees, and wasps.

Find arthropods on the evolutionary tree shown in **Figure 1.** Follow the branches and you will see that, like annelids, arthropods are segmented invertebrates with bilateral symmetry, coelomate body cavities, and protostome development. Unlike annelids, arthropods have exoskeletons with jointed appendages that enable them to move in complex ways. All three of these features—segmentation, exoskeletons, and jointed appendages—are important keys to their success.

Reading Check Compare and contrast arthropods and annelids.

■ **Figure 1** Most arthropods are insects, as shown by the blue segments on the graph. Arthropods are coelomates and show protostome development. S
Interpret *what percentage of arthropods is comprised of crustaceans and spiders.*

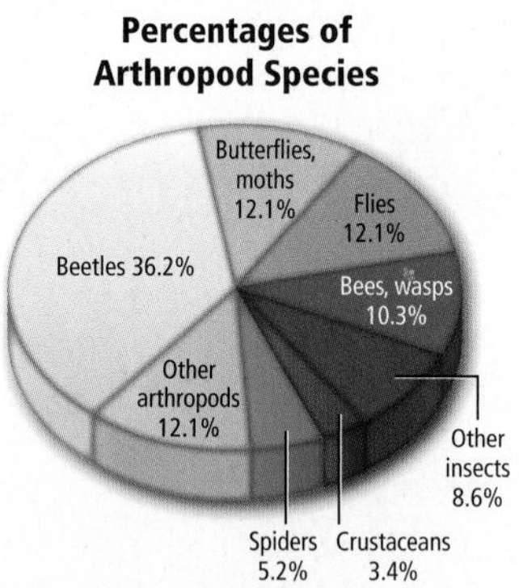

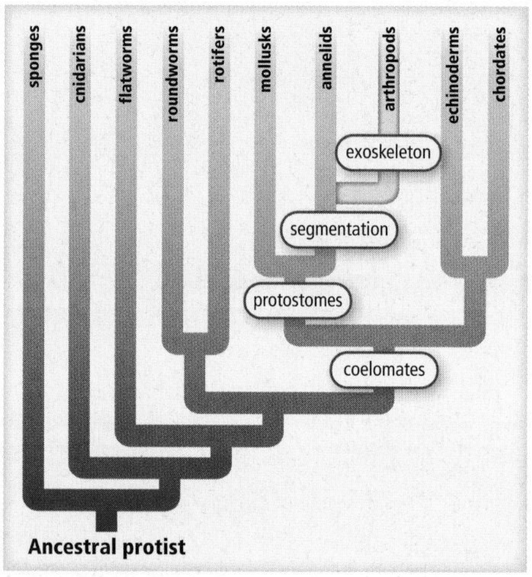

Demonstration

BL OL AL Local Arthropods Show students images of local arthropods. Teach them to identify the ones that are venomous, such as bees and wasps, and others that may live in your area. You might be able to obtain materials about venomous arthropods in your area from the local county extension agent.
ASK STUDENTS: ***How do you think this arthropod senses a potential predator, food, or a mate?*** (Modify your question depending on insect structures such as compound eyes in grasshoppers or feathery antennae of moths.) Possible answers: Some arthropods with compound eyes can sense predators moving toward them. Some arthropods sense food by scent trails and some sense nearby mates with a tympanum that picks up the sound the mate makes. Est. time: 15 min

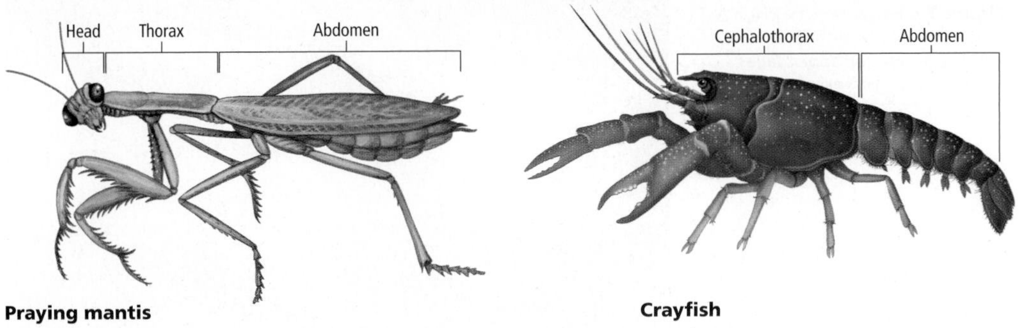

■ **Figure 2** Some segments in arthropods are fused. The praying mantis shows fusion of segments into its head, thorax, and abdomen. The crayfish shows a different fusion of segments into its cephalothorax and abdomen.

Review Personal Tutor

Segmentation Arthropods are segmented, allowing for efficient and complex movements. Notice in **Figure 2** that the praying mantis's segments are fused into three main body regions—a head, a thorax, and an abdomen. The heads of arthropods have mouthparts for feeding and various types of eyes. Many have antennae. Antennae are long sensory structures that contain receptors for smell and touch. The **thorax** is the middle body region, consisting of three fused main segments to which, in many arthropods, the legs and wings are attached. The **abdomen,** which also contains fused segments and is at the posterior end of the arthropod, bears additional legs and contains digestive structures and the reproductive organs. Some arthropods, such as the crayfish in **Figure 2,** have the thorax region fused with the head into a single structure called a **cephalothorax** (sef uh luh THOR aks).

In some groups of arthropods, segmentation is more obvious during early development. For example, a caterpillar has many obvious segments, while the adult butterfly has only three body segments.

Reading Check **Summarize** the main body regions in arthropods.

Exoskeleton Arthropods have hard exoskeletons on the outside of their bodies, similar to a lightweight suit of armor. The exoskeleton provides a framework for support, protects soft body tissues, and slows water loss in animals that live on land. It also provides a place for muscle attachment.

Connection to Chemistry The exoskeleton of an arthropod is made of chitin—a nitrogen-containing polysaccharide bound with protein. While the exoskeleton of a grasshopper is leathery, the exoskeletons of some crustaceans, such as lobsters, incorporate calcium salts that harden them to such an extent that a hammer would be needed to crush them. An arthropod's exoskeleton can be hard in some places and thin and flexible in others, providing for movable joints between body segments and within appendages.

There is a limit to how hard and thick an exoskeleton can be. It is thin in small arthropods, such as the copepod, because tiny muscles pull against it; it is thicker in larger arthropods, such as crabs and lobsters, to bear the pull of larger muscles. Imagine a fly as large as a bird. The fly's exoskeleton would have to be so thick to withstand the pull of the large muscles that the fly would not be able to move under the weight of the exoskeleton.

Demonstration

BL OL AL Praying Mantises and Crayfishes Show students live or preserved specimens of praying mantises and crayfishes. You can often obtain live invertebrate specimens from local pet shops. Before beginning, point out the antenna to students. Explain that the larger ones are called antenna and the smaller are called antennules. **ASK STUDENTS:** ***Where are the antennae and how are they different?*** located on the head of both crayfishes and praying mantises; crayfishes have two pairs, whereas praying mantises have one pair ***Compare the number of main body sections in the praying mantises and crayfishes. How are they different?*** Praying mantises have three body segments; crayfishes have two. ***How are the legs of crayfishes and praying mantises alike and different?*** Praying mantises have three pairs, whereas crayfishes have five pairs. Both have segmented legs. Est. time: 20 min

Skill Practice

OL AL Visual Literacy Have students make a list of all the arthropods pictured in this section, and have them infer from the illustrations how each might be adapted to its environment. After reading the text, ask students to evaluate their inferences.

BL Make a list of how the arthropods pictured in this section are adapted to their environments. Ask students to match the adaptations to the arthropods.

Review Personal Tutor

Listen to a teacher explain arthropods.

Develop Concepts

EL BL OL AL COOP LEARN

Activity Have groups prepare 1-L bottles for use as ant farms. Tell students to fill the bottles half-full with sand and use a needle to make small air holes at the top of the bottles. You can order queened ant colonies, or, weather permitting, students can collect ants by setting food outside and waiting a few hours for ants to arrive. Have students place the ants in the bottle. The ants should be given bread crumbs or other food every few days. Every day, a cotton ball moistened with water should be placed in the farm. Have students cover the sides of the bottle with black paper that will be removed during observations. Students should observe the colony daily and take notes on the construction of tunnels, general ant movement, feeding, and social behavior.

Reading Check head—has eyes and mouth; thorax—has legs and wings; abdomen—has digestive system and reproductive systems Note: Some arthropods have a fused head and thorax called a cephalothorax.

D Develop Concepts

EL BL OL AL COOP LEARN

Activity Provide students with microscopes and prepared slides of arthropod appendages such as legs and antennae. Have students sketch the arthropod appendages. **ASK STUDENTS:** ***How do jointed appendages aid in movement?*** They provide flexible movement for activities such as getting food, escaping predators, and mating. ***What would be an advantage for arthropods to have antennae that are feathery?*** They would provide increased surface area for picking up chemical odors in the air.

C Critical Thinking

BL OL AL **Infer**

ASK STUDENTS: ***How does molting make an arthropod vulnerable?*** Molting makes an arthropod vulnerable because it takes time for the new exoskeleton to harden. Before it does harden, the arthropod is more susceptible to predators.

Inquiry Launch Lab

Assess Content Development
Assess how understanding has developed when students revisit the Launch Lab analysis questions.

Caption Question Fig. 3 Jointed appendages enable animals with exoskeletons to have flexible movements.

Figure 3 Like a door hinge, the joint in this fly's leg can bend in only one direction.
Explain *how jointed appendages benefit animals with exoskeletons.*

D **Jointed appendages** Arthropods have paired appendages. **Appendages** (uh PEN dih juz) are structures, such as legs and antennae, that grow and extend from an animal's body. Appendages of arthropods are adapted for a variety of functions, such as feeding, mating, sensing, walking, and swimming. Notice in **Figure 3** that the appendages of arthropods have joints. To understand how important jointed appendages are, imagine yourself without joints—no finger joints, no wrist, elbow, knee, hip, or ankle joints. Without jointed appendages, you could not play a computer game, sit in a movie theater, shoot a basketball, or even walk. Jointed appendages enable arthropods to have flexible movements and to perform other life functions, such as getting food and mating, that would be impossible without joints.

Inquiry Launch Lab

Review Based on what you have read about arthropod features, how would you now answer the analysis questions?

Molting Because the exoskeleton of arthropods is made of nonliving material and cannot grow, arthropods must shed their outer coverings in order to grow. This process of shedding the exoskeleton is called **molting.** Arthropods make their own new exoskeletons. Glands in the skin make a fluid that softens the old exoskeleton while the new exoskeleton forms underneath. As the fluid increases in volume, the pressure increases and eventually cracks the old exoskeleton. This process is similar to freezing water in a closed glass container. As the water expands, the glass cracks. **Figure 4** shows a tarantula next to its shed exoskeleton. Before the new exoskeleton hardens, blood circulation increases to all parts of the body and the animal puffs up. Some arthropods also take in air, which assists in making the hardening exoskeleton a little larger for "growing room." **C**

Figure 4 Arthropods must molt so that their bodies can continue to grow. This tarantula has just come out of its outgrown exoskeleton.

Demonstration

BL OL **Bess Beetles** Bring to class a bess beetle, tape, a washcloth, a 30-cm long piece of heavy thread, 25 pennies, and half of a plastic petri dish. (Bess beetles can be found in rotting wood in southern climates. They can also be bought from biological supply houses.) Make a slip knot loop on one end of the thread. Place the loop over the beetle's body like a harness. Tape the other end of the thread to the petri dish. Hypothesize how many pennies the beetle will be able to pull on the petri dish "sled." Tape the cloth to the table. Place the beetle on the cloth and add pennies to the dish one at a time until the beetle can no longer pull it.
ASK STUDENTS: ***How does the ability to pull many times its own mass help a beetle survive?*** It enables the beetle to push through decaying wood. Est. time: 20 min

■ **Figure 5** This leafcutter ant uses its mandibles to cut a leaf from a tree. Once fungus grows on the leaf cutting, the ant will feed the fungus to its larvae.

Body Structure of Arthropods

Arthropods have complex organ systems that enable them to live in many diverse habitats. Adaptations in several organ systems, such as the respiratory system and the nervous system, have contributed to the success of these animals.

Feeding and digestion The great diversity of arthropods is reflected in their enormous variety of feeding habits and structures. The mouthparts of most arthropods include a pair of appendages called **mandibles** (MAN duh bulz) that can be adapted for biting and chewing, as shown in **Figure 5.** Depending on their feeding habits, other arthropods have mouthparts modified like feathery strainers, stabbing needles, cutting swords, or sucking straws. Observe the structure of arthropod mouthparts in **MiniLab 1.** Arthropods can be herbivores, carnivores, filter feeders, omnivores, or parasites. To digest food, arthropods have a complete, one-way digestive system with a mouth, gut, and an anus, along with various glands that produce digestive enzymes.

Study Tip

Key Ideas Work with another student to determine this section's key ideas. Notice that the headings often are clues to key ideas. Also, many paragraphs have topic sentences that state the key idea.

MiniLab 1

Compare Arthropod Mouthparts

Inquiry MiniLab

How do the mouthparts of arthropods differ? Arthropods eat a wide variety of foods, from nectar and plants to fish and small birds. Explore how the mouthparts of different types of arthropods are designed for their specific diets.

Procedure

1. Read and complete the lab safety form.
2. Create a data table to record your observations about the mouthparts of the arthropods and your inferences about the function of each type of mouth.
3. Using a **magnifying lens** or a **stereomicroscope,** observe the **mouthparts of preserved specimens of different arthropods**. Record your observations in your data table.
4. Infer the specific function of each type of mouth based on the structure of its parts.

Analysis

1. **Compare and contrast** the different mouthparts that you observed.
2. **Infer** the type of diet each arthropod might eat based upon your observations of their mouthparts.

MiniLab 1

Inquiry MiniLab

For a lab worksheet, use your eTeacherEdition Online.

RUBRIC A rubric for evaluating MiniLabs is found on your eTeacherEdition Online.

Est. Time 15 min

Additional Materials preserved or mounted butterfly with prominent proboscis, preserved or mounted crayfish, preserved or mounted praying mantis, preserved or mounted mosquito

Safety Precaution Approve lab safety forms before work begins.

Teaching Strategy
Students must carefully observe the region beneath the crayfish's head and above the legs to view the small mouthparts (mandible and maxilla).

Analysis

1. The mosquito's mouthparts consist of a long, thin needlelike extension and a second, thicker extension. Those of males also have two feathery extensions. The mouthparts of the crayfish are small and hidden under its head region. The butterfly has a long, curled extension (proboscis), and the mantis has long, thick jaws that are curved inward. The spider has curved fangs.
2. Answers may vary. The mosquito's mouthparts are suited for puncturing and sucking. The crayfish's mouthparts chew small particles without grasping the food, and the butterfly's mouth extends to suck up nectar. The jaws of the mantis grasp and chew prey. Spiders puncture prey with their fangs.

LabManager™

Customize this lab with the LabManager™ CD-ROM.

Content Background

Teacher FYI It has been assumed that predator arthropods, such as ground beetles, wolf spiders, and web-spinning spiders, do not choose their prey to select a balanced diet, but recent research indicates that this is not the case. When the diets of the above predators were manipulated under laboratory conditions to make them either protein or lipid deficient, these animals adjusted their feeding to make up for the deficit either by selecting foods in which the missing nutrients were abundant or by extracting specific nutrients from an individual prey species.

Visualizing Respiratory Structures

Purpose
Students will study the form and function of the respiratory structures of arthropods. Gills, tracheal tubes, and spiracles are featured. UCP.1, UCP.5, C.5

Skill Practice
EL BL OL Make a Table Have students make a three-column table. In the first column, have students write the following list of arthropods: *crayfish, lobster, grasshopper,* and *spider.* Have students label the second column *Respiratory Structure* and the third *How it Works.* Instruct students to fill in the table. crayfishes: gills diffuse oxygen from the water; lobsters: gills diffuse oxygen from the water; grasshopper: tracheal tubes take air in through spiracles and deliver it to cells; spider: book lungs take air in through spiracles

Skill Practice
EL BL Model Provide students with clay, salt dough, or wax-covered yarn. Have students make models of the respiratory systems depicted on this page.

Concepts in Motion
Animation

Visualizing Respiratory Structures

Figure 6
Arthropods take in oxygen by using one of three basic structures: gills, tracheal tubes, or book lungs.

Gills
A crayfish lives in an aquatic environment and uses gills to obtain oxygen. The cross section illustrates how the gills are divided. This provides a large surface area in a small space for the exchange of gases.

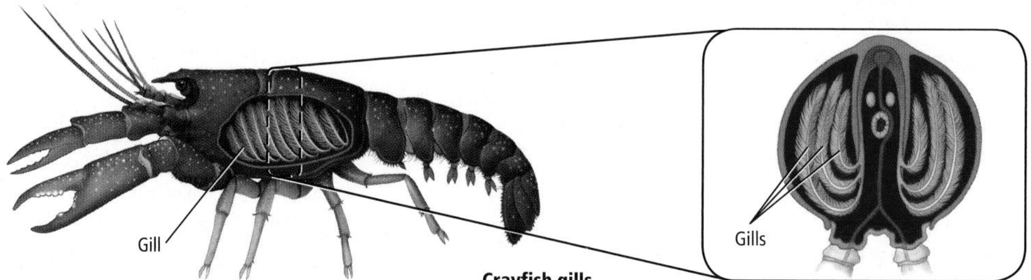

Crayfish gills

Tracheal Tubes
Insects such as this beetle have tracheal tubes that branch into smaller and smaller tubules to carry oxygen throughout the body. Air enters the respiratory system through spiracles, then travels from the tracheal tubes to tracheal tubules until it reaches muscle.

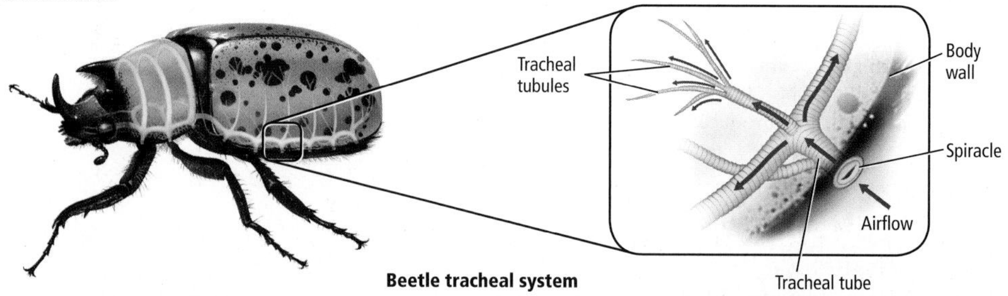

Beetle tracheal system

Book Lungs
This spider uses book lungs to draw in oxygen. As in arthropods with tracheal tubes, air enters the book lungs through spiracles.

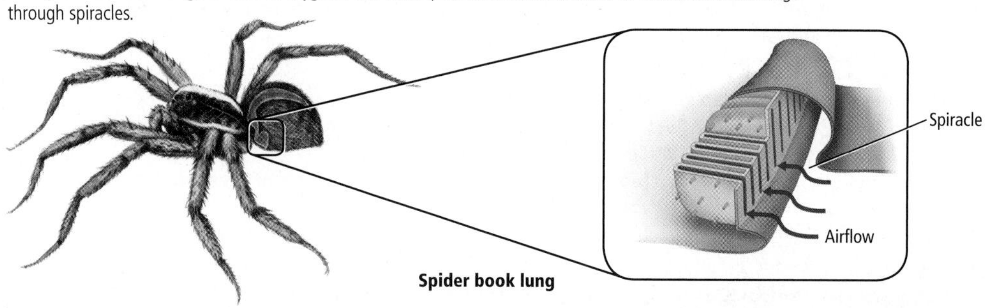

Spider book lung

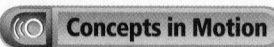

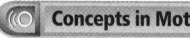

Concepts in Motion **Animation**

Research Citation
Compare Education Research indicates that the ability to identify similarities and differences between pieces of information is an important skill in the development of critical thinking. The activity on the next page, in which students compare methods of respiration, requires that they be able to identify key differences. (Chen, 1996)

Research bibliography on pages 32T–34T

Differentiated Instruction
Behavior Disorders Students with behavior disorders need to be told when they are exhibiting inappropriate behaviors. Communicate directly and honestly with these students about what is acceptable in your classroom.

For more tips, see pages 14T–15T.

Respiration Arthropods obtain oxygen by using one of three structures—gills, tracheal tubes, or book lungs. Maintaining a certain homeostatic balance of oxygen in body tissues enables animals to have energy for a variety of functions. Most aquatic arthropods have gills, like those shown in **Figure 6,** that function in the same way as the gills in mollusks. All terrestrial arthropod body tissues need to be near airways to obtain oxygen.

Terrestrial arthropods depend on respiratory systems rather than circulatory systems to carry oxygen to cells. Most terrestrial arthropods have a system of branching tubes called **tracheal** (TRAY kee ul) **tubes,** as shown in **Figure 6,** that branch into smaller and smaller tubules. These tubules carry oxygen throughout the body.

Some arthropods, including spiders, have **book lungs,** saclike pockets with highly folded walls for respiration. In **Figure 6,** notice how the membranes in book lungs are like the pages in a book. The folded walls increase the surface area of the lungs and allow an efficient exchange of gases. You also can see how both tracheae and book lungs open to the outside of the body of the arthropod in openings called **spiracles** (SPIHR ih kulz).

D **Circulation** Even though most arthropods do not rely on their circulatory systems to deliver oxygen, they do rely on their circulatory systems to transport nutrients and remove wastes. Arthropod blood is pumped by a heart into vessels that carry the blood to body tissues. The tissues are flooded with blood, which returns to the heart through open body spaces. The blood maintains homeostasis in tissues by delivering nutrients and removing wastes.

Excretion In most arthropods, cellular wastes are removed from the blood through **Malpighian** (mal PIH gee un) **tubules.** These tubules also help terrestrial arthropods preserve water in their bodies to maintain homeostatic water balance. In insects, the tubules, as shown in **Figure 7,** are located in the abdomen, unlike in segmented worms, where nephridia exist in each segment. Malpighian tubules are attached to and empty into the gut, which contains the undigested food wastes to be eliminated from the body. Crustaceans and some other arthropods do not have Malpighian tubules. They have modified nephridia, similar to those in annelids, to remove cellular wastes.

FOLDABLES®
Incorporate information from this section into your Foldable.

VOCABULARY
ACADEMIC VOCABULARY
Transport
to transfer from one place to another
Blood transports nutrients to cells throughout the body.

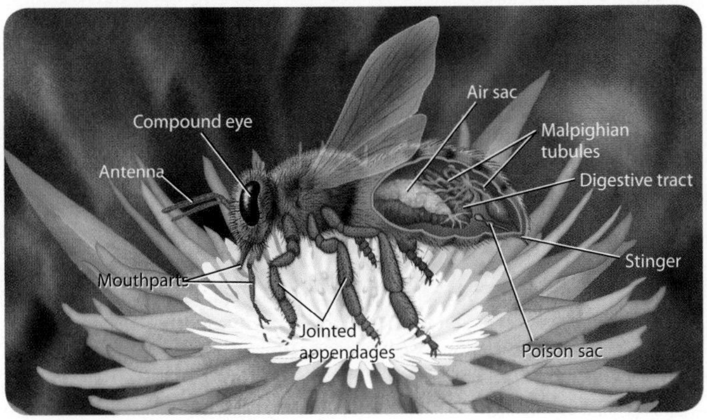

Figure 7 Most arthropods get rid of cellular wastes through Malpighian tubules.
Describe *another function of Malpighian tubules.*

FOLDABLES®

RUBRIC A rubric for evaluating Foldables is found on your eTeacherEdition Online.

Going Further Have students draw a four-part grid on the back of their Foldables. In the top left section, have them choose an arthropod to draw and label. In each of the other three sections, have them describe the form and function of the following: segmented body, jointed appendages, and exoskeleton.

D Develop Concepts

BL OL AL

Clarify a Misconception

ASK STUDENTS: ***Do arthropods have blood?*** yes Some students might think that arthropods don't have blood because most arthropods don't have red blood. This is because arthropod blood does not contain hemoglobin, the protein that gives red blood cells their color.

Reading Strategy

BL Activate Background Vocabulary

ASK STUDENTS: ***How are respiration, circulation, and excretion related?*** During respiration, oxygen is taken in. During circulation, oxygen is delivered to cells where it is used in a chemical reaction (cellular respiration) to convert chemical energy (glucose) into cellular energy (ATP). During excretion, the waste products of cellular activity are eliminated.

■ **Caption Question Fig. 7** to preserve water in terrestrial arthropods

Activity

BL OL AL COOP LEARN Arthropod Respiration Have students work in groups to make a computer animation that explains the differences between the three main methods of respiration in arthropods. If students are not familiar with how to make a computer animation, arrange a tutorial with the school's computer teacher or a technology staff member. Animations should include gills of aquatic mollusks, tracheal tubes of terrestrial arthropods, and book lungs of spiders. Make sure they point out that spiracles are the openings to both book lungs and tracheal tubes. Est. time: 120 min

W Writing Support

OL Narrative Writing Have students describe the sequence in which compound and simple eyes might work together to give an insect important information about its environment. Possible answer: The compound eye of a dragonfly in flight enables it to analyze the landscape with its many lenses. The simple eye can distinguish light from dark and help stabilize flight.

AL Have students write a paragraph discussing the advantages the compound eye has over the simple eye. The compound eye is able to detect movement.

Writing Support

OL AL Technical Writing Have students select an arthropod of interest and research its life cycle. Students should prepare a slideshow presentation about the life cycle of their selected arthropod to share with the class.

BL COOP LEARN Provide research materials that are at an appropriate reading level. Have students work in pairs.

Caption Question Fig. 8 Even though a fly's vision is not as clear as that of a vertebrate, it can still see motion, which enables it to escape from a predator.

Figure 8 Compound eyes enable flying arthropods to see things in motion easily. The image the fly sees might not be as clear as that seen by a vertebrate. That blurry image is all the fly requires for its way of life.
***Infer** how a fly stays safe from predators if it has blurry vision.*

CAREERS IN BIOLOGY

Biochemist As a scientist who determines how biological processes work, a biochemist might study the chemicals in pheromones to develop effective pest-management treatments.

Response to stimuli Most arthropods have a double chain of ganglia throughout their bodies, on the ventral surface. Fused pairs of ganglia in the head make up the brain. Although most behaviors, such as feeding and locomotion, are controlled by the ganglia in each segment, the brain can inhibit these actions.

Vision Have you ever tried to swat a fly with a flyswatter? The fly's accurate vision allows the fly to spot even the slightest movement, and the fly often escapes. Most arthropods have one pair of large compound eyes. A compound eye, as shown in **Figure 8,** has many facets, which are hexagonal in shape. Each facet sees part of an image. The brain combines the images into a mosaic. The compound eyes of flying arthropods, such as dragonflies, enable them to analyze a fast-changing landscape during flight. Compound eyes can detect the movements of prey, mates, or predators, and also can detect colors. In addition, many arthropods have three to eight simple eyes. A simple eye has one lens and functions by distinguishing light from dark. In locusts and some other flying insects, simple eyes act as horizon detectors that help stabilize flight. W

Hearing In addition to having eyes that detect movement and distinguish light from dark, many arthropods also have another sense organ called a tympanum (tihm PA num). A tympanum is a flat membrane used for hearing. It vibrates in response to sound waves. Arthropod tympanums can be located on the forelegs as in crickets, on the abdomen as in some grasshoppers, or on the thorax as in some moths.

Chemicals Imagine ants carrying off potato chip pieces, following each other like soldiers marching in formation. Ants communicate with each other by **pheromones** (FER uh mohnz), chemicals secreted by many animal species that influence the behavior of other animals of the same species. The ants use their antennae to sense the odor of pheromones and to follow the scent trail. Arthropods give off a variety of pheromones that signal behaviors such as mating and feeding.

Activity

EL BL OL AL Crayfish Behavior Provide student groups with a live crayfish inside a pan of water. (If crayfish aren't available, use pillbugs, which can be placed on moist paper towels.) Have students describe the behavior and movements of the crayfish. Have students place a piece of dark construction paper over half of the pan.
ASK STUDENTS: ***What happened when you placed a piece of dark construction paper over half of the pan?*** In general, crayfish will move to the side of the pan that is covered. ***Why do you think the crayfish moved under the paper?*** to hide from predators
Est. time: 20 min

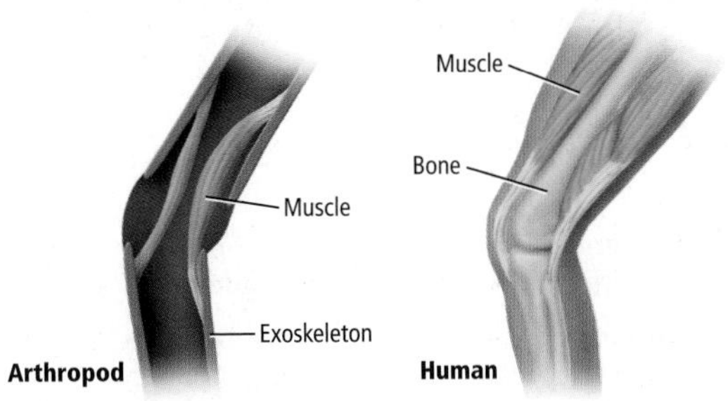

■ **Figure 9** The muscles of an arthropod attach inside of the exoskeleton to each side of the joint. The muscles in a human limb attach to the outer surfaces of the bones.

Movement Think again about the ants carrying the potato chip pieces and how fast they were moving. Arthropods generally are quick, active animals. They are able to crawl, run, climb, dig, swim, and fly because of their well-developed muscular systems. Refer to **Figure 9** to compare muscle attachment in human and arthropod limbs. The muscles in a human leg are attached to the outer surfaces of the bones. The muscles in an arthropod limb are attached to the inner surface of the exoskeleton on both sides of the joint. The strength of muscle contraction in arthropods depends on the rate at which nerve impulses stimulate muscles. In contrast, in vertebrates, the strength of muscle contraction depends on the number of muscle fibers contracting.

Reproduction Most arthropods reproduce sexually and have a variety of adaptations for reproduction. Most arthropods have separate sexes, but a few, such as barnacles, are hermaphrodites and undergo cross-fertilization. Most crustaceans brood, or incubate, their eggs in some way, but they do not care for their hatched offspring. Some spiders and insects also incubate their eggs, and some, such as bees, care for their young.

Section 1 Assessment

Section Summary

- Arthropods can be identified by three main structural features.
- Arthropods have adaptations that make them the most successful animals on Earth.
- Arthropod mouthparts are adapted to a wide variety of food materials.
- In order to grow, arthropods must molt.
- Arthropods have organ system modifications that have enabled them to live in all types of habitats and to increase in variety and numbers.

Understand Main Ideas

1. MAIN Idea **Evaluate** the three main features of arthropods that have enabled them to be successful.
2. **Explain** why jointed appendages are important to an animal with an exoskeleton.
3. **Summarize** the three main methods of respiration in arthropods.
4. **Infer** what might happen to an arthropod that had malformed Malpighian tubules. Be specific.

Think Critically

5. **Design** a model arthropod adapted to conditions on a cold and windy mountaintop with low-growing grasses and arthropod-eating birds.

WRITING in Biology

6. Write a paragraph describing how an arthropod responds to stimuli in its environment. Use a specific example in your paragraph.

Formative Assessment

Evaluation Play a game called "What is it?" Seat students in groups of four. Read a description of a specific structure of an arthropod. Have students decide which organ system it belongs to, its function, and which arthropod has this structure. Have students raise their hands with answers. Give points for correct answers.

Remediation Have students make a table with the following labeled columns: *Arthropod Structure, Function, Organ System,* and *Example of Arthropod with this Structure.* In the first column, students should write *antennae, mandible, tracheal tube, book lung, spiracle, Malpighian tubule, compound eye,* and *tympanum.* Instruct students to fill out the rest of the table using their knowledge about arthropods. Possible answers: Mandible—feeding, digestive system, grasshopper; tracheal tube—breathing, respiratory, grasshopper; book lung—breathing, respiratory, spider; spiracle—breathing, respiratory, grasshopper; malpighian tubule—excretion, excretory, grasshopper; compound eye—sensing movement, nervous system, grasshopper; tympanum—hearing, nervous system, cricket

Section 1 Assessment

1. Segmentation and jointed appendages enable arthropods to have flexible and complex movements. A tough exoskeleton reduces water loss and provides protection.
2. Jointed appendages allow arthropods to move even though their outer body is stiff because of the tough exoskeleton.
3. Aquatic mollusks use gills. Terrestrial arthropods, with the exception of spiders that have book lungs, use tracheal tubes.
4. Possible answer: arthropod might not be able to excrete wastes or might lose too much water and must stay near a water source or die.
5. Possible features are: wingless; mouthparts adapted to feeding on grasses; legs adapted for burrowing into the soil to escape cold and predators; makes loud calls heard by the tympanum to find mates; very small body, covered with a thick exoskeleton to prevent drying by wind; large compound eyes for seeing predator movement; camouflage; short legs for crawling close to the ground to avoid being blown away.
6. Paragraphs will vary. Students should include information about pheremones, insect vision, and insect hearing.

✓ Assessment Online Quiz

Section 2

MAIN Idea

BL OL AL COOP LEARN **Dichotomous Key** Place students in groups of four. Provide them with arthropod field guides and a variety of live or preserved arthropods. Display examples of dichotomous keys for other organisms.

SAY TO STUDENTS: ***To make a dichotomous key for identifying arthropods, first divide the arthropods into two groups based on a yes/no question that reflects characteristics of the arthropods. For example, you could ask, "Does the arthropod have antennae?" Divide each group again based on another yes/no question. Continue to construct your key until you have isolated the arthropods into individuals or groups that are the same. When you are finished, trade your key and arthropods with another group to see if your key works.***

Concepts in Motion
Interactive Table

S Skill Practice

EL BL **Visual Literacy** Have students copy Table 1 on a blank piece of paper. Have them cut the table along the lines, shuffle the pieces, and then put them back together without looking in the book.

Section 2

Reading Preview

Essential Questions

- What are the structures and their functions found in the major groups of arthropods?
- What are the adaptations in the major groups of arthropods?
- What are characteristics of crustaceans and arachnids?

Review Vocabulary

sessile: an organism that is attached to and stays in one place

New Vocabulary

cheliped
swimmeret
chelicera
pedipalp
spinneret

Multilingual eGlossary

Arthropod Diversity

MAIN Idea Arthropods are classified based on the structure of their segments, types of appendages, and mouthparts.

Real-World Reading Link Imagine turning over a rock on the forest floor. The ground beneath the rock suddenly seems to come alive with small animals creeping, crawling, and scurrying every which way. A spider darts under a leaf, a pill bug inches its way out of the light, and ants pour out of a tiny hole. All of these animals are arthropods.

Arthropod Groups

Spiders, pill bugs, and ants are arthropods. In the previous section, you learned why they all are considered arthropods. In the next two sections, you will learn how they differ from one another. Arthropods are classified into groups based on shared similarities, such as the structure of their body segments, appendages, and mouthparts. Taxonomists continue to debate the classification of arthropods. In this section, you will learn about two of the major groups—the crustaceans (krus TAY shunz), such as crabs and lobsters, and the arachnids (uh RAK nids), such as spiders and their relatives. In the next section, you will learn about the third major group—the insects and their relatives. **Table 1** summarizes the common characteristics of the three main groups of arthropods.

S

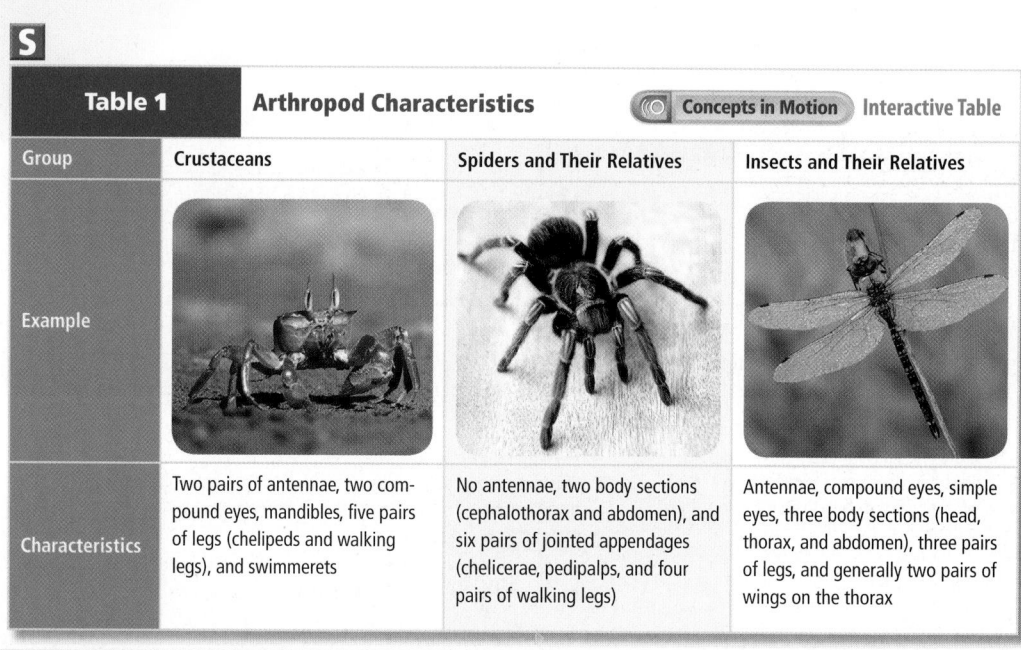

Table 1 Arthropod Characteristics — Concepts in Motion Interactive Table

Group	Crustaceans	Spiders and Their Relatives	Insects and Their Relatives
Example			
Characteristics	Two pairs of antennae, two compound eyes, mandibles, five pairs of legs (chelipeds and walking legs), and swimmerets	No antennae, two body sections (cephalothorax and abdomen), and six pairs of jointed appendages (chelicerae, pedipalps, and four pairs of walking legs)	Antennae, compound eyes, simple eyes, three body sections (head, thorax, and abdomen), three pairs of legs, and generally two pairs of wings on the thorax

Demonstration

BL OL AL COOP LEARN **Arthropod Identification** Bring several arthropod field guides to class. Show students how the guides are organized and how they can be used to identify arthropods. Use a guide to identify an arthropod pictured in the book. Verbalize your thought process so students can use it as a model. Est. time: 15 min

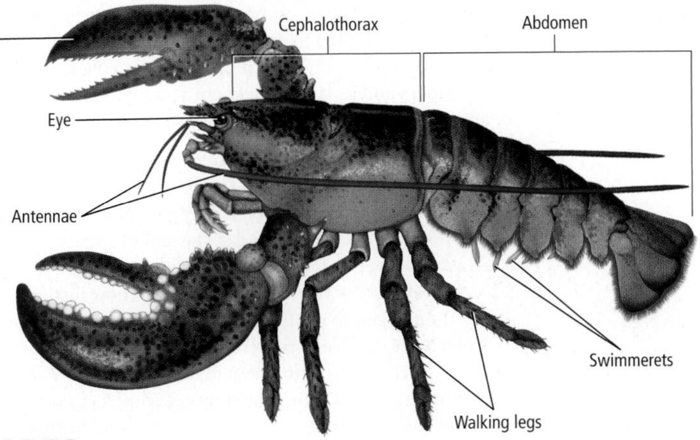

■ **Figure 10** Lobsters are aquatic crustaceans. Note the chelipeds for catching and crushing food, the thick cephalothorax with attached walking legs, the antennae, and the abdomen with attached swimmerets.
Consider ***how else a lobster might use its chelipeds.***

D Crustaceans

Crabs, shrimps, lobsters, crayfishes, barnacles, water fleas, and pill bugs are crustaceans, and they live in marine, freshwater, and terrestrial habitats. Class Crustacea consists of about 35,000 named species. Most are aquatic and have two pairs of antennae, two compound eyes that are often on the tips of slender movable stalks, and mandibles for chewing. Crustacean mandibles open and close from side to side, instead of in an up-and-down movement like human jaws. Crustaceans possess branched appendages and have a free-swimming larval stage called a nauplius (NAW plee us) larva. A larva is an immature form of an animal that is markedly different in form and appearance from the adult.

Most crustaceans, such as crayfishes, lobsters, and crabs, have five pairs of legs. The first pair of legs—the **chelipeds,** shown in **Figure 10**—has large claws adapted to catch and crush food. Behind the chelipeds are four pairs of walking legs used primarily for locomotion. **Swimmerets** are the short legs behind the walking legs. They are used for reproduction and during swimming. If you have ever seen a lobster swim, you might have been surprised at how it can snap its tail beneath its body and move backward quickly. Some crustaceans, such as barnacles, are sessile and use their legs to kick food into their mouths.

Sow bugs and pill bugs are terrestrial crustaceans that live in damp places, such as under logs. They have seven pairs of legs.

Reading Check **Summarize** the functions of a crustacean's appendages.

? Inquiry Virtual Lab

Spiders and Their Relatives

Spiders belong to class Arachnida (uh RAK nuh duh) in which there are about 57,000 named species. Arachnids include spiders, ticks, mites, and scorpions.

Most arachnids have two body sections—a cephalothorax and an abdomen—and six pairs of jointed appendages. They do not have antennae. An arachnid's most anterior pair of appendages is modified into mouthparts called **chelicerae** (kih LIH suh ree) (singular, chelicera). Chelicerae are adapted to function as fangs or pincers and often are connected to a poison gland. Most spiders in the United States are not poisonous to humans. Exceptions include the black widow and the brown recluse shown in **Figure 11.**

C

■ **Figure 11** The inconspicuous brown recluse spider has a violin-shaped mark on its cephalothorax. If a person is bitten by this spider, he or she will require medical treatment because the venom is poisonous to humans.

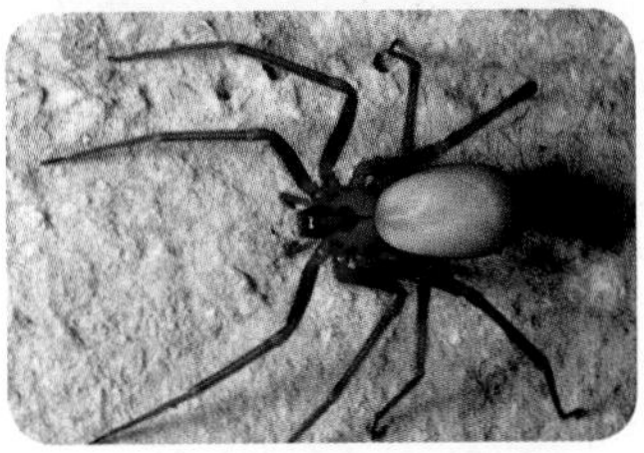

D Develop Concepts

BL OL AL

Clarify a Misconception

ASK STUDENTS: ***How would you classify pill bugs?*** crustaceans Some people think that pill bugs are insects. Pass around a hand lens and a pill bug on a damp paper towel. Point out the pill bug's two pairs of antennae and five pairs of walking legs.

C Critical Thinking

BL OL **Infer**

SAY TO STUDENTS: ***Pill bugs are terrestrial crustaceans. Their outer coverings do not completely protect them from water loss. Infer where pill bugs might live.*** moist areas

Develop Concepts

EL BL OL AL COOP LEARN

Activity Organize students into groups. Provide brine shrimp eggs, containers, and salt solution. Have the groups set up their brine shrimp eggs in solution according to package directions. For each day of one week, have groups observe and draw the developmental stages they see using a binocular microscope. Embryos should hatch in 15–20 h; the embryos will grow and molt around 15 times before reaching adulthood in about 8 days.

■ **Caption Question Fig. 10** Possible answers: fighting with other lobsters, moving objects, such as rocks, and digging in sand

Reading Check Chelipeds—catch and crush food; walking legs—locomotion; swimmerets—reproduction and swimming

Differentiated Instruction

Below Level Struggling students may need additional help when working with dichotomous keys for the activity described on the previous page. Provide these students with models of how the keys are used so they understand the expectations for the activity.

For more tips, see pages 14T–15T.

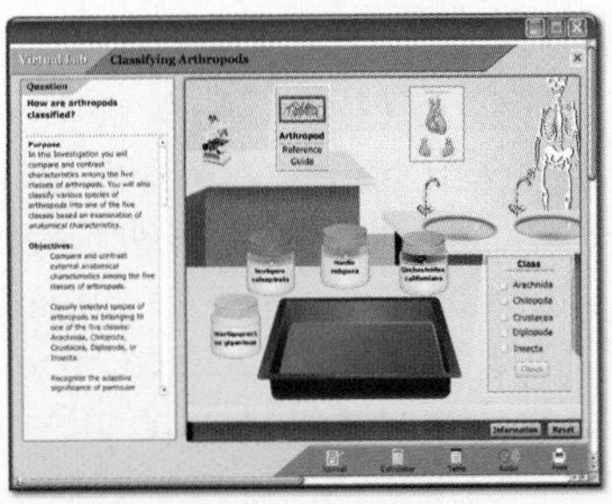

? **Inquiry** **Virtual Lab** Students will classify arthropod species based on anatomical characteristics.

R Reading Strategy

EL BL Word Map Have students write the word *spider* in the center of a piece of paper. As students read the text under the heading *Spiders,* instruct them to write what they learn in a bicycle wheel fashion around the word.

D Develop Concepts

BL OL AL

Clarify a Misconception

ASK STUDENTS: ***How do spiders catch their prey?*** Students might think that all spiders build webs. While many spiders do build webs, some do not build webs—they hunt for prey insects and other invertebrates instead. You can show students images or videos from the school library of wolf spiders or tarantulas hunting and consuming prey animals. They will see that there is no web involved in capturing prey.

W Writing Support

BL OL AL Creative Writing

Have students use the information they have learned about spiders to write a story entitled, "A Day in My Life" from the point of view of a spider. Students might decide to write from the point of view of a garden spider and describe production of silk, building a web, lying in wait for prey, and capturing and eating prey.

Reading Check Both have appendages for holding prey—the crustaceans have chelipeds and the arachnids have pedipalps. Arachnids also have fangs or pincers that are used to inject venom into prey.

VOCABULARY

SCIENCE USAGE V. COMMON USAGE

Weave

Science usage: to spin a web
Spiders weave webs to catch prey.

Common usage: to construct by interlacing strips of material
Artists weave baskets out of reeds and other natural fibers.

In arachnids, the second pair of appendages is called the **pedipalps.** Pedipalps are adapted to carry out various tasks. They are used for sensing and holding prey. The pedipalps are also used for reproduction in male spiders and as large pincers in scorpions. The remaining four pairs of appendages in arachnids are used for locomotion.

R **Spiders** All spiders are carnivores. Some spiders, such as wolf spiders and tarantulas, hunt prey. Other spiders catch prey in silken webs. Silk is D made from a fluid protein secreted by glands and spun into silk by structures called **spinnerets,** located at the end of a spider's abdomen.

Have you ever watched a spider weave a web? If you have, you might have wondered how the spider seemed to know just what to do and where it managed to get the training to do such intricate work.

Spiders are capable of constructing only specific kinds of webs. This instinctive behavior enables them to do this efficiently and effectively time after time. **Figure 12** shows the stages of construction of an orb web.

After catching an insect or other arthropod in their webs, many spiders wrap their prey in a silken cocoon until they are ready to feed. Digestion begins externally, when a spider secretes digestive enzymes onto its prey. After liquification occurs, the spider ingests the softened food. The remaining nutrients are digested internally.

To reproduce, a male spider deposits sperm on a small web he has built, picks up the sperm, and stores it in a cavity on his pedipalps. After a courtship ritual, the male inserts the sperm into the female. The female lays her eggs in a cocoon spun of spider silk. There can be as many as 100 eggs in one cocoon. The young hatch after about two weeks, then molt between five and ten times before reaching their adult size. W

Reading Check **Compare and contrast** the appendages that crustaceans and arachnids use to capture prey.

Figure 12 Orb-weaving spiders usually attach their webs to vegetation. An area of the web that is not sticky enables the spider to pass from one side of the web to the other.

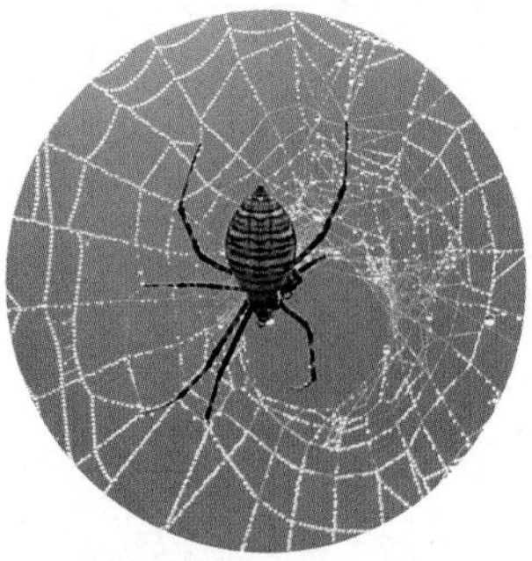

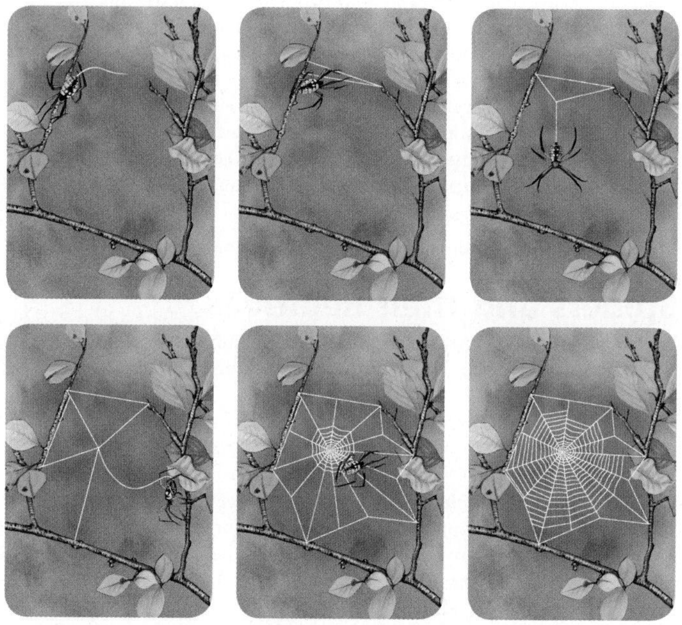

Activity

BL OL COOP LEARN Build a Web Provide groups of students with old picture frames and craft supplies such as twine and duct tape. Provide reference diagrams and photos of various kinds of spider webs. Have students build a spider web that will catch a table tennis ball tossed at it from about 2 m away. The web must be held in a vertical position when the ball is tossed. The table tennis ball represents the flying insect prey of the spider. Tell students that they may use whatever materials they choose, but the web must look like one of those from the references provided. The groups can compete with each other to see whose web catches the most balls. Provide a prize for the winning group. Est. time: 55 min

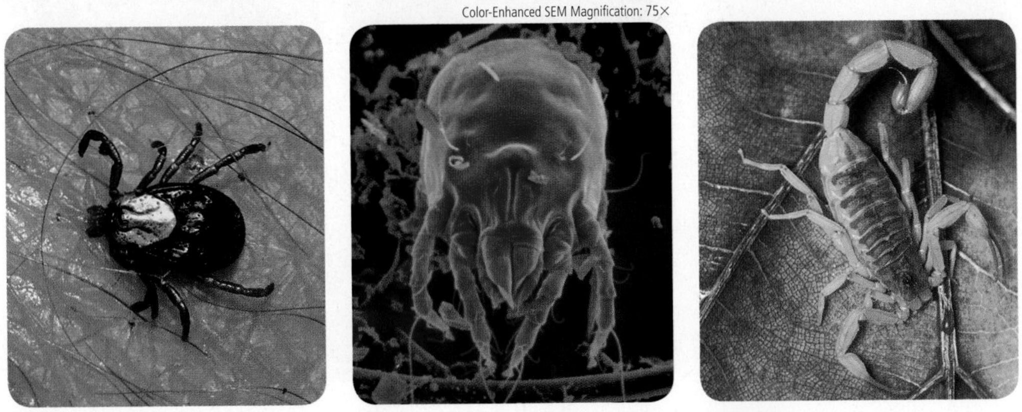

Tick Mite Scorpion

■ **Figure 13** Ticks, mites, and scorpions are in the same class as spiders.
Describe *the characteristics of class Arachnida that can be seen in the photos.*

D **Ticks, mites, and scorpions** Other members of class Arachnida—ticks, mites, and scorpions—are shown in **Figure 13.** Most mites are less than 1 mm long, with the cephalothorax and abdomen fused into one oval-shaped body section. They can be predators or parasites of other animals. Ticks are parasites that feed on blood after attaching themselves to the surface of their hosts. Ticks also frequently harbor disease-causing agents, such as viruses, bacteria, and protozoans, and introduce them to their hosts when they bite. Some of these diseases, such as Lyme disease and Rocky Mountain spotted fever, affect humans.

Scorpions feed on insects, spiders, and small vertebrates that they capture with their pedipalps and tear apart with their chelicerae. They generally are nocturnal, hiding under logs or in burrows during the day. When you think of a scorpion, you might think of the stinger at the end of the abdomen. Most scorpions that live in the United States do not have venom that is dangerous to people, but their stings can be quite painful. Compare different arthropod groups in **MiniLab 2.**

MiniLab 2

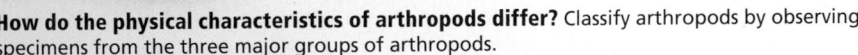

Compare Arthropod Characteristics

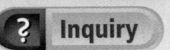

? Inquiry MiniLab

How do the physical characteristics of arthropods differ? Classify arthropods by observing specimens from the three major groups of arthropods.

Procedure

1. Read and complete the lab safety form.
2. Create a data table to record your observations of **live or preserved arthropod specimens.** **WARNING:** ***Treat live specimens in a humane manner at all times.***
3. Observe the arthropod specimens and record your observations about their physical characteristics in your data table.

Analysis

1. **Identify** the physical characteristics your arthropod specimens have in common.
2. **Classify** the arthropods into different taxonomic groups.

Content Background

Real-World Connection Lyme disease is caused by bacteria that are passed to humans when they are bitten by certain ticks that have fed on the blood of deer infected with the bacterium. A bull's-eye-like rash at the site of the bite and rash on other areas of the body within weeks of the bite are the first symptoms. If treated with antibiotics at this time, Lyme disease can be cured, but if left untreated, it can progress to a chronic arthritic condition with neurological symptoms. Preventive measures include wearing protective clothing, checking carefully for ticks attached to the body after being outdoors in areas where there are ticks, and wearing repellent containing the chemical DEET.

D Develop Concepts

BL OL

Clarify a Misconception

ASK STUDENTS: ***How would you classify ticks?*** arachnids Some people think ticks are insects, but they do not have three body sections or six legs.

■ **Caption Question Fig. 13** cephalothorax, abdomen, body segments, pedipalps (scorpion), chelicerae (mite), paired appendages (all three)

MiniLab 2

? Inquiry MiniLab

For a lab worksheet, use your eTeacherEdition Online.

RUBRIC A rubric for evaluating MiniLabs is found on your eTeacherEdition Online.

Est. Time 15 min

Safety Precautions Approve lab safety forms before work begins.

Teaching Strategy Caution students never to release non-native arthropods into a local environment.

Analysis

1. exoskeleton, jointed appendages, bilateral symmetry, and segmented body parts
2. crustaceans–many segmented body parts, branched appendages; spiders–two body parts, eight legs, fangs or pincers; insects–three body parts, six legs, two antennae, often wings

LabManager™

Customize this lab with the LabManager™ CD-ROM.

Writing Support

BL OL COOP LEARN

Creative Writing Have pairs of students write and illustrate a children's book on one type of arthropod of their choice. Students should explain accurate biology in an interesting way. Possible answers: Students might decide to write about scorpions and describe where they live, their nocturnal nature, how they catch and consume prey, and body features that make them arthropods.

Formative Assessment

Evaluation Set up a lab practical. Place representative arthropods, models of arthropods, or microscopic views of arthropod parts at each station. Use numbered tags to mark the structures you want students to identify. Number each station with the same number as the tag. Instruct students to sit at a station and identify the part of the arthropod that is tagged. Tell students to write their answers next to the correct number on their papers. Students should move to the next station on your signal. Use the vocabulary list in this section to help you select the parts you want students to identify.

Remediation Provide students with pictures of arthropods and have them label the same structures as you used for the lab practical.

■ **Figure 14** Horseshoe crabs come to shore to lay eggs in the sand.

Horseshoe crabs Horseshoe crabs are an ancient group of marine animals, related to the arachnids, that have remained basically unchanged since the Triassic period more than 200 million years ago. They have unsegmented heavy exoskeletons in the shape of a horseshoe. The chelicerae, pedipalps, and the next three pairs of legs are used for walking and getting food from the bottom of the sea. The animals feed on annelids, mollusks, and other invertebrates, which they capture with their chelicerae. The posterior appendages are modified with leaflike plates at their tips and can be used for digging or swimming.

Horseshoe crabs, shown in **Figure 14,** come to shore to reproduce at high tide. The female burrows into the sand to lay her eggs. A male adds sperm before the female covers the eggs with sand. Young larvae hatch after a period of being warmed by the Sun and then return to the ocean during another high tide.

Section 2 Assessment

Section Summary

- Arthropods are divided into three major groups.
- Crustaceans have modified appendages for getting food, walking, and swimming.
- The first two pairs of arachnid appendages are modified as mouthparts, as reproductive structures, or as pincers.
- Spiders are carnivores that either hunt prey or trap it in webs that they spin out of silk.
- Horseshoe crabs are ancient arthropods that have remained unchanged for more than 200 million years.

Understand Main Ideas

1. MAIN Idea **Classify** a small, quickly moving arthropod with two pairs of antennae, a segmented body, and mandibles that move from side to side.
2. **Compare and contrast** the ways of life of crustaceans and arachnids, and explain how their body forms are adapted to their environments.
3. **Summarize** the differences in function among the various appendages of spiders.
4. **Identify** the common characteristics among ticks, scorpions, and horseshoe crabs.

Think Critically

5. **Hypothesize** Caribbean spiny lobsters have a navigation system that enables them to return to their original habitat after being moved to an unfamiliar location. Make a hypothesis about what signals the lobsters might use to orient themselves in the direction of their original habitat.
6. **Design an Experiment** A biologist wants to find out what brown recluse spiders eat. After some observation, she hypothesizes that the spiders prefer dead prey to live prey. Design an experiment that would test this hypothesis.

Section 2 Assessment

1. crustacean
2. Most crustaceans are aquatic, whereas most arachnids are terrestrial. Crustaceans have two pairs of antennae and appendages that are modified for catching food in the water, walking, reproduction and swimming. Arachnids have no antennae but have appendages that are modified for catching food on land, walking, and reproduction. Spiders hunt or spin webs to catch their prey.
3. Chelicerae are modified to function as fangs or pincers. Pedipalps are used for catching and holding prey and reproduction in males. Other appendages are used for walking.
4. chelicerae, pedipalps, six pairs of jointed appendages
5. Answers will vary. Accept any that are scientifically based. Spiny lobsters are thought to navigate by using the magnetic field of Earth.
6. Possible answer: Spiders could be placed into individual clear boxes and offered dead and live prey to see which they prefer. The number of spiders preferring dead prey should be compared to the number preferring live prey.

Assessment Online Quiz

Section 3

Reading Preview

Essential Questions

- What are characteristics and adaptations of insects?
- What are similarities and differences between complete and incomplete metamorphosis?
- How do insects interact and communicate with each other?

Review Vocabulary

pollen: a fine powder produced by certain plants when they reproduce

New Vocabulary

metamorphosis
pupa
nymph
caste

Multilingual eGlossary

Insects and Their Relatives

MAIN Idea **Insects have structural and functional adaptations that have enabled them to become the most abundant and diverse group of arthropods.**

Real-World Reading Link Think about a time you were stung by a bee, admired a bright butterfly flitting from flower to flower, or heard a cricket chirp. Insects are everywhere, and they affect your life in many ways.

S Diversity of Insects

Scientists estimate that there are as many as 30 million insect species, which is more species than all other animals combined. Recall that arthropods make up about three-fourths of all named animal species. About 80 percent of arthropods are insects. They are the most abundant and widespread of all terrestrial animals. You can find insects in soil, in forests and deserts, on mountaintops, and even in polar regions.

Insects live in many habitats because of their ability to fly and their ability to adapt. Their small size enables them to be moved easily by wind or water. Diversity of insects also is enhanced by the hard exoskeleton that protects them and keeps them from drying out in deserts and other dry areas. In addition, the reproductive capacity of insects ensures that they are successful in any areas they inhabit. Insects produce a large number of eggs, most of the eggs hatch, and the offspring have short life cycles, all of which can lead to huge insect populations.

External Features

Insects have three body areas—the head, thorax, and abdomen, as shown in **Figure 15.** Head structures include antennae, compound eyes, simple eyes, and mouthparts. Insects have three pairs of legs and generally two pairs of wings on the thorax. Some only have one pair of wings, and others do not have wings at all.

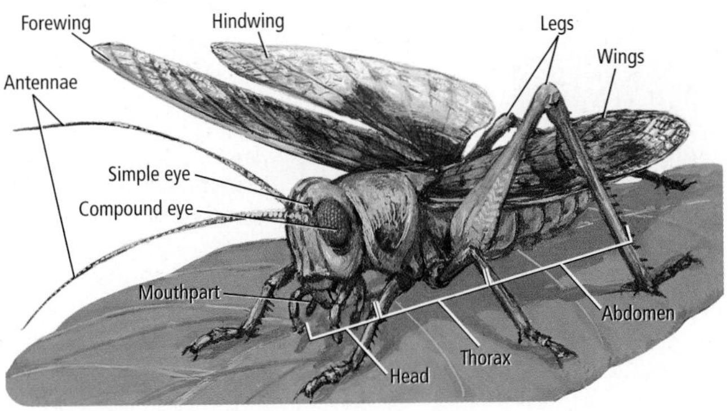

Figure 15 The head, thorax, and abdomen regions of this grasshopper are characteristic of insects.
Compare *how the body regions of insects differ from those of crustaceans.*

Concepts in Motion
Animation

Section 3

MAIN Idea

BL OL AL Insects Provide students with magnifying lenses and a variety of local live or preserved insects. Live insects should be in clear containers for viewing.
SAY TO STUDENTS: ***Observe the insects and make a list of insect structures that may be adaptations to their way of life.*** Answers will vary, but may include mandibles and appendages.

S Skill Practice

BL Make a Graph Have students read the text under the heading *Diversity of Insects* and make a circle graph of the data discussed: There are 30 million insect species. Arthropods make up 3/4 of all animals, and 80 percent of arthropods are insects.

Concepts in Motion
Animation

Caption Question Fig. 15 Crustaceans have a cephalothorax and abdomen; insects have a head, thorax, and abdomen.

Demonstration

BL OL AL Water Strider Movement Place a live water strider (caught from a local stream or bought from a biological supply house) in a clear flat pan with about 4 cm of dechlorinated water (dechlorinate tap water by allowing it to sit out overnight). Cover the top of the pan with plastic wrap and display it for the class. Have students observe the movements of the water strider for 2 min and describe how it moves.
SAY TO STUDENTS: ***Infer how this adaptation might enable a water strider to survive.*** The insect propels itself over the surface of the water with its back legs and steers with its front legs. The ability to "skate" on the surface of the water enables the water strider to utilize a food source on the surface of the water that may not be available to other animals.
Est. time: 10 min

R Reading Strategy

EL BL Illustrate Under the heading titled *Insect Adaptations* there are additional headings that indicate specific adaptations. As students read, have them write these headings and make a labeled sketch of what they read.

S Skill Practice

EL BL OL Visual Literacy

Have students study Table 2. Instruct students to find pictures of mouthparts from at least three different insects. Students should bring copies of the pictures to class. Collect the pictures. Tell students to close their books, then hold up each picture and ask students to identify the type of mouthpart the picture illustrates.

S Skill Practice

EL BL OL

Use Graphic Organizers Have students make an illustrated concept map of the information in Table 2. Students should draw pictures of mouthparts in a center circle and work out from the center as they complete their map.

Concepts in Motion

Interactive Table

Inquiry BioLab

The lab at the end of the chapter can be used at this point in the lesson.

R Insect Adaptations

Structural adaptations to legs, mouthparts, wings, and sense organs have led to increased diversity in insects. These adaptations enable insects to utilize all kinds of food and to live in many different types of environments. Taking advantage of a variety of food sources, insects might be parasites, predators, or plant-sap suckers.

Legs Insect legs are adapted to a variety of functions. Beetles have walking legs with claws that enable them to dig in soil or crawl under bark. Flies have walking legs with sticky pads on the ends that enable them to walk upside down. Honeybee legs have adaptations for collecting pollen, while the hind legs of grasshoppers and crickets are adapted to jumping. Water striders have legs adapted to skimming over the surface of water. On its footpads, a water strider has water-repellent hairs that do not break the surface tension of the water. As it skates over the water, this insect propels itself with its back legs and steers with its front legs, like a rear-wheel-drive car.

Mouthparts Insects' mouthparts are adapted to the food they eat, as shown in **Table 2.** Butterflies and moths have a long tube through which they draw nectar from flowers in a motion similar to sipping through a straw. Different types of flies, such as houseflies and fruit flies, have sponging and lapping mouthparts that take up liquids. Some insects, such as leafhoppers and mosquitoes, have piercing mouthparts for feeding on plant juices or prey. Insects such as beetles and ants cut animal skin or plant tissue with their mandibles to reach the nutrients inside.

S S

Table 2 **Insect Mouthparts** Concepts in Motion Interactive Table

Type of mouthpart	Siphoning	Sponging	Piercing/Sucking	Chewing
Example		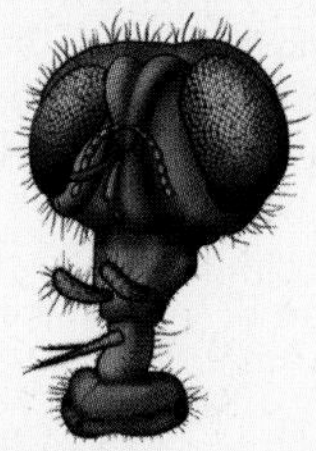	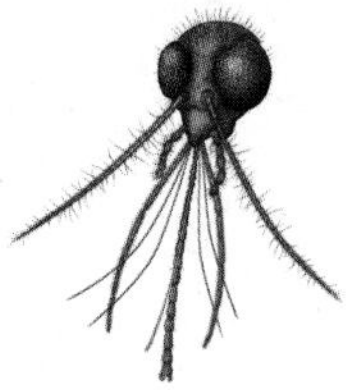	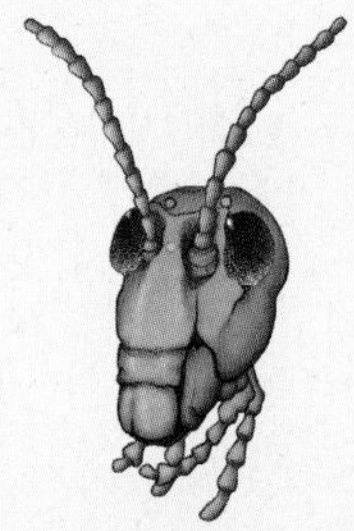
Function	Feeding tube is uncoiled and extended to suck liquids into the mouth.	Fleshy end of mouthpart acts like a sponge to mop up food.	A thin, needlelike tube pierces the skin or plant wall to suck liquids into the mouth.	Mandible pierces or cuts animal or plant tissue, and other mouthparts bring food to the mouth.
Insects with adaptation	Butterflies, moths	Houseflies, fruit flies	Mosquitoes, leafhoppers, stink bugs, fleas	Grasshoppers, beetles, ants, bees, earwigs

Activity

OL Insect Collection For extra credit, instruct students to collect, mount, and identify a variety of insects. Provide students with a list of the ten most common insect orders in your area with brief descriptions. Also have an assortment of field guides with instructions for collecting and mounting insects as well as methods for identifying arthropods. Teach students about the venomous arthropods in your area before beginning this activity.

BL COOP LEARN Have students work in small groups.

AL Ask students to identify the habitat range for each of the collected insects.

Est. time: 1–2 h

Wings Insects are the only invertebrates that can fly. Unlike bird and mammal wings that are modified limbs, insect wings are outgrowths of the body wall. Wings are formed of a thin double membrane of chitin, which is the same material that makes up the exoskeleton, and they have rigid veins that give them strength. Wings can be thin, as in flies, or thick, as in beetles. The wings of butterflies and moths are covered with fine scales, as shown in **Figure 16.** Investigate how butterflies might use their wing scales to attract mates in **Data Analysis Lab 1.** Flying requires complex movements of the wings. Forward thrust, upward lift, balance, and steering are all important. Most insects rotate their wings in a figure-eight pattern.

Reading Check **Compare** how wings are like an exoskeleton.

Sense organs Along with leg, mouthpart, and wing adaptations, insects have a variety of adaptations in their sense organs. Recall how arthropods use their antennae and eyes to sense their environment. Insects also have hairlike structures that are sensitive to touch, pressure, vibration, and odor. In addition to visually detecting motion, a fly detects changes in airflow using the hundreds of hairs that cover its body. It is no wonder that a fly often is long gone before the flyswatter can strike.

Some insects detect airborne sounds with their tympanic organs, while others can detect vibrations coming from the ground. These sensory cells often are located on the legs.

Figure 16 Butterfly wings are covered with fine scales.

DATA ANALYSIS LAB 1

Based on Real Data*

Interpret the Graph

Do butterflies use polarized light for mate attraction? Light waves with electric fields vibrating in the same direction are said to be polarized. Scientists hypothesized that the iridescent wing scales in some butterflies, such as the one shown at right, create polarized light to attract certain males to females. The graph shows the response of males to polarized light versus nonpolarized light from female iridescent butterfly wings.

Think Critically

1. **Interpret the Graph** To which view of wings does the male butterfly respond more often?
2. **Infer** Researchers have noted that forest-dwelling butterflies tend to have iridescent wings, while meadow-dwelling butterflies do not. What might explain this difference?

Data and Observations

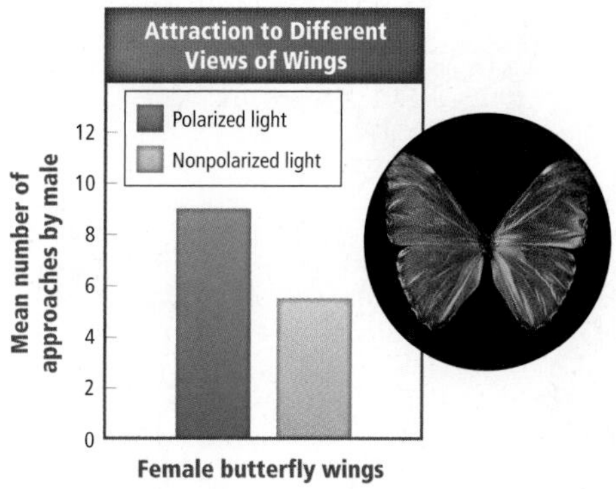

*Data obtained from: Sweeney, A., et al. 2003. Insect communication: polarized light as a butterfly mating signal. *Nature* 423: 31-32.

Develop Concepts

EL BL OL AL COOP LEARN

Activity Divide students into teams. Provide them with modeling clay, salt dough, or wax-covered yarn. Write the names of different types of ecosystems on pieces of paper. Have each team draw the name of an ecosystem from a container and design an insect that would be well adapted to that ecosystem. Students should be prepared to explain their insect and its adaptations to the class.

Reading Check Both are made of chitin.

DATA ANALYSIS LAB 1

About the Lab

- Detection of polarized light in connection with butterfly wings may be important in the visually complicated forest habitat that is inhabited by highly colorful butterflies. Polarized light from iridescent wings is easily recognizable in the unpolarized forest background. The continuing study of the optical properties and colors of butterfly wings will help to explain the ecological diversity of butterflies.
- Also see Yoshioka, et al. 2004. Wavelength-selective and anisotropic light-diffusing scale on the wing of the Morpho butterfly. *Proc. R. Soc. Lond.* B271: 581–587.

Think Critically

1. Males respond more to polarized light from female wings than they do to nonpolarized light.
2. Possible answer: Forest-dwelling butterflies have iridescent wings to reflect any light that filters through the tree leaves. Meadow-dwelling butterflies are exposed to large amounts of light and iridescent wings are not useful.

Content Background

Cultural Diversity Charles Henry Turner (1867–1923) was an African American biologist who conducted a large body of research on the behavior of insects such as ants, bees, and cockroaches. He was very prolific, producing 49 articles in the leading scientific journals of that time period. His experiments were unique and interesting. For example, he was the first scientist to show that insects can hear and distinguish pitch. He also found that roaches can learn by trial and error, and he was a leading authority on the behavioral patterns of ants and spiders.

Critical Thinking

OL AL COOP LEARN

Design an Experiment Organize students into groups of three. Have students design and conduct an experiment with a hypothesis that would help them find out why crickets chirp. Direct students to include a control in their experiment and test only one variable. Direct students to gather quantitative data. Experiments and results will vary. Students might report that the pulse rate of the chirps varies with the temperature, increasing at higher temperatures. Male crickets chirp to attract a female and produce aggressive chirps in the presence of other males.

Writing Support

OL AL Persuasive Writing Have students research the effects of mosquito insecticides. Then instruct students to write an editorial for a local newspaper either for or against the use of insecticides to kill mosquitoes in their community. Possible answers: Students should support their position with sound reasoning such as how spraying will kill mosquitoes that carry West Nile virus or how not spraying will add fewer chemicals to environmental food chains.

S Skill Practice

BL OL Visual Literacy Have students examine Figure 17 and compare and contrast complete metamorphosis and incomplete metamorphosis.

Concepts in Motion

Animation

Reading Check The insect hatches from an egg, becomes a larva, a pupa, and an adult.

Most insects have keen chemical senses. Chemical receptors, or chemoreceptors, for taste and smell are located on mouthparts, antennae, or legs. Some insects, such as moths, can detect odors several kilometers away. Chemical signals in the form of pheromones enable insects to communicate with one another to attract mates or to gather members in large colonies to migrate or survive periods of cold weather.

VOCABULARY
WORD ORIGIN
Metamorphosis
from the Greek word *metamorphoun,* meaning *to transform.*

Metamorphosis Most insects lay their eggs in a specific habitat where the young can survive. For example, a monarch butterfly lays its eggs on milkweed plants, which the young feed on after they hatch. After hatching, most insects undergo **metamorphosis,** a series of major changes from a larval form to an adult form.

Complete metamorphosis Most insects develop through the four stages of complete metamorphosis—egg, larva, pupa, and adult. As shown in **Figure 17,** when the egg of a butterfly hatches, the wormlike larva that appears commonly is called a caterpillar. At this stage, the larva usually has chewing mouthparts and behaves like a feeding machine. The larva molts several times as it grows. A **pupa** (PYEW puh) is a nonfeeding stage of metamorphosis in which the animal changes from the larval form into the adult form. Adult insects are generally specialized for reproduction. Some adult insects do not live long enough to feed—a female adult mayfly only lives for five minutes. If adults feed, they generally do not compete with larvae for food.

S

Reading Check **Summarize** the life cycle of an insect that undergoes complete metamorphosis.

Incomplete metamorphosis Insects that undergo incomplete metamorphosis, as shown in **Figure 17,** hatch from eggs as **nymphs** (NIHMFS)—the immature form of insects that look like small adults without fully developed wings. After several molts, nymphs become adults.

Figure 17 Insects that undergo complete metamorphosis have a resting stage called a pupa. This stage is absent in insects that undergo incomplete metamorphosis.

Concepts in Motion

Animation

Video

BrainPOP

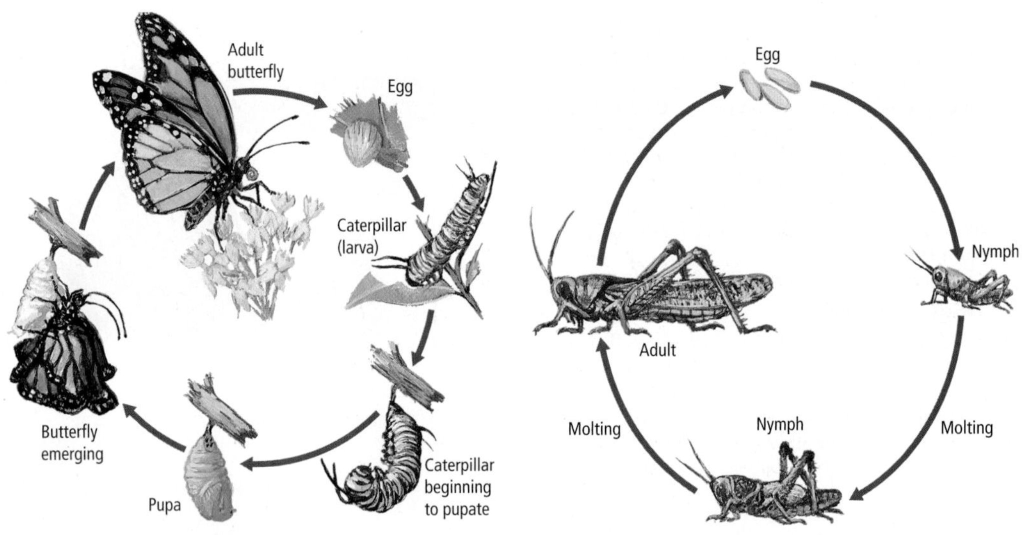

Activity

OL AL Compare Metamorphosis Patterns Provide groups of students with images and preserved specimens of egg, nymph, and adult grasshoppers and egg, larva, pupa, and adult moths. Make sure all the specimens are labeled. Also provide binocular microscopes and magnifying lenses. Make sure students use goggles, disposable protective gloves, and forceps when handling preserved insects. Ask students to make a chart of each stage of the insect life cycles including a diagram of the stage, the insect's method of movement, and its ability to move.

ASK STUDENTS: ***What is the adaptive advantage of metamorphosis?*** Not all stages of the life cycle feed on the same material. This method of utilizing food sources may keep food from being depleted. Est. time: 45 min

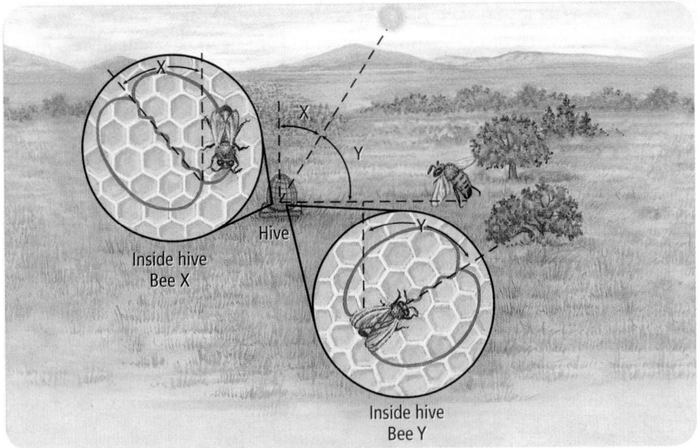

■ **Figure 18** The honeybee's figure-eight waggle dance indicates the direction of the food in relation to the angle of the Sun.
Interpret ***where Bee X has found food.***

Concepts in Motion
Animation

Insect societies The players on a basketball team work together to win the game. Insects such as honeybees, ants, and termites organize into social groups and cooperate in activities necessary for their survival. Honeybees have a complex society, with as many as 70,000 bees in one hive. There are three castes in a hive. A **caste** is a group of individuals within a society that perform specific tasks. Workers are females that do not reproduce. They gather nectar and pollen, build the honeycomb, manufacture honey, care for young, and guard the hive. Drones are the reproductive males. The queen is the only reproductive female.

D

Communication methods Honeybees have evolved an efficient system of communication, using bodily movements to indicate the location of food sources. One of the movements by which honeybees communicate is called the waggle dance, shown in **Figure 18.** This dance is performed when a bee returns to the hive from a faraway food source. First, the returning bee makes a circle with a diameter about three times the bee's length. The bee then moves in a straight line while waggling its abdomen from side to side. The orientation of the line indicates the direction to the food source. Finally, the bee makes another circle in the opposite direction from the first circle. It traces this figure-eight pattern many times. The duration of the dance indicates the distance to the food source.

D

Connection to Math The most significant part of the waggle dance is the straight line because it tells the other bees where the food is in relation to the hive. The direction of the line relative to the vertical indicates the direction of the food relative to the Sun, as shown in **Figure 18.** If food is located 70 degrees to the right of the Sun, the straight line of the dance will be 70 degrees to the right of vertical.

Round dances also convey information about food sources and are used only if the food is close to the hive. In a round dance, the bee traces a clockwise circle followed by a counterclockwise circle and repeats this dance many times. The dance does not indicate distance or direction.

Ants also have evolved various societal behaviors for living in colonies. Females that do not reproduce gather food, care for young, and protect the colony from predators. Like honeybees, the male ants die after mating with the queen, whose sole function is to lay eggs.

CAREERS IN BIOLOGY

Entomologist Scientists who study insects are entomologists. They might study insect life cycles and behaviors, research insect pests and how to control them, or work with beneficial insects like honeybees. A beekeeper cares for bee colonies that are used for crop pollination and honey production.

Concepts in Motion
Animation

D Develop Concepts

BL OL AL Scaffolding

SAY TO STUDENTS: ***Describe a caste.*** a group of individuals within a society that have specialized forms and carry out specific tasks ***Describe the castes in a honeybee society.*** Workers are females that gather nectar and pollen, build honeycombs, care for young, and guard the hive. Drones are the reproductive males. The queen is the only reproductive female. ***How does the caste system help bees?*** They cooperate in doing a variety of activities efficiently. ***Infer why there are so many worker bees and only one queen.*** Possible answer: There are many jobs to be done by the workers and the queen can produce all the eggs needed to sustain the hive. ***What might happen to the hive if the queen suddenly dies?*** Possible answers: The hive might die or obtain a queen from another hive. A new queen is chosen by the workers and fed a particular diet.

D Develop Concepts

OL AL Activity Have students research the details of honeybee dances and make an illustrated slideshow to present to the class. Possible answers: Students may include information about different aspects of bee foraging behavior such as the genetics involved and other kinds of dances such as the tremble dance that bees perform to give information about food sources.

■ **Caption Question Fig. 18** in a field of flowers

Research Citation

Problem Solving Educational research indicates that students are best able to learn new concepts while solving problems. The critical thinking activity described on the previous page asks students to design their own experiments, providing them with the experience solving a problem. (Gouws and Cebulla, 2000)

Research bibliography on pages 32T–34T

Differentiated Instruction

English Learners The scaffolding strategy used on this page can be a valuable tool for developing concepts among English learners. Allow a longer wait time for these students to answer questions so that they are able to organize their thoughts before sharing them with the class.

For more tips, see pages 14T–15T.

D Develop Concepts

BL OL

Clarify a Misconception

ASK STUDENTS: ***Do you think insects are harmful or beneficial to people?*** Students may think insects are harmful and may not be aware of their benefits. Many insects benefit people. For example, some insects are predators that eat harmful insects, many insects are important pollinators, bees produce honey, and silkworms make silk thread that people weave into fabric.

W Writing Support

AL **Formal Writing** Have students research how modern farmers and ranchers use integrated pest management and other strategies to reduce crop loss due to insects. Students should write an article for a magazine that will explain this topic. Answers will vary, but students should discuss crop rotation, tillage techniques, use of biological controls as well as genetically engineered crops, and limited use of chemical insecticides.

BL OL COOP LEARN Include the rest of the class in this activity by having the class put together an entire magazine about integrated pest management. Delegate various tasks, such as writing interviews on the subject with farmers and making advertisements to be placed in the magazine.

■ **Caption Question Fig. 19**

Answers will vary. Insects play roles as both prey and predators in ecosystems.

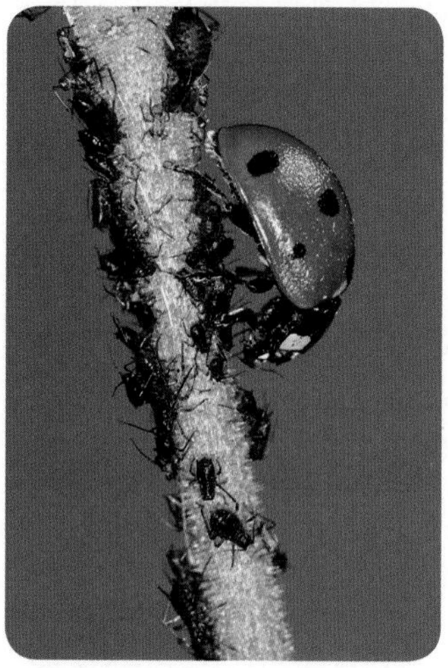

■ **Figure 19** Not only are insects important in pollinating flowers, some are important in feeding on harmful insects. This ladybird beetle feeds on plant pests.

Explain *how insects maintain stability in ecosystems.*

Video

What's BIOLOGY Got To Do With It?

D **Insects and humans** It might be difficult to think of insects as beneficial when a mosquito buzzes around your head or when a bee stings you, but insects are an integral part of all ecosystems on Earth. Most insect species are not harmful to humans. Insects pollinate most flowering plants, including almost ten billion dollars' worth of food crops in the United States. They produce honey and silk used by humans and serve as food for many birds, fishes, and other animals. Insect predators, such as praying mantises and ladybird beetles, feed on plant pests such as aphids and mites, as shown in **Figure 19.**

Insects can also be harmful to humans. Lice and bloodsucking flies are human parasites. Fleas can carry plague, houseflies can carry typhoid fever, and mosquitoes can carry malaria, yellow fever, and the West Nile virus. Weevils, cockroaches, ants, and termites cause property destruction. Grasshoppers, corn borers, and boll weevils destroy agricultural crops. Bark beetles, spruce budworms, and gypsy moths can destroy whole portions of forests.

How is all this insect damage kept in check? In the past, chemicals were used indiscriminately to control insects. However, the overuse of chemicals disrupted food chains, reduced numbers of beneficial insects, and insects developed resistance to the insecticides. Use of biological controls has become increasingly important. Integrated pest management, a technique used by many farmers today, offers long-term control of pests. This strategy employs resistant plant varieties, crop rotation, and critical timing of planting and other agricultural practices along with small amounts of chemicals at critical times to control insect pests. W

Centipedes and Millipedes

The centipedes of class Chilopoda and the millipedes of class Diplopoda are close relatives of insects. Centipedes move quickly and live in moist places under logs, bark, and stones. They have long, segmented bodies, and each segment has one pair of jointed legs. The first pair of appendages is modified to form poisonous claws, which a centipede uses to kill prey. Most species of centipedes are not harmful to humans.

Millipedes have two pairs of appendages on each of their abdominal segments and one pair on each of their thorax segments. Millipedes are herbivorous and live, as centipedes do, in moist places under logs or stones. Unlike centipedes, they do not wriggle quickly, but walk with a slow, graceful motion. Millipedes do not have poisonous claws and feed primarily on damp and decaying vegetation. Compare the centipede and millipede in **Figure 20.**

■ **Figure 20** Centipedes have one pair of appendages on each segment and poison claws on the first segment. Millipedes have two pairs of appendages on each abdominal segment, while the thorax has one pair of appendages on each segment.

Centipede

Millipede

Content Background

Real-World Connection West Nile fever is an infection caused by a virus transmitted from birds to certain mosquitoes that feed on their blood and then, in turn, to humans that are bitten by the infected mosquitoes. In most cases, West Nile virus causes only mild illness in people but can be fatal if the virus enters the brain and causes encephalitis. There is no human vaccination or specific treatment for this disease. Because the larvae of mosquitoes require water for their development, eliminating standing water in drainage ditches and other areas would be an effective preventive measure as well as wearing protective clothing and insect repellent.

Trilobite fossil

Color-Enhanced SEM Magnification: 750×

Tardigrade

■ **Figure 21** Extinct trilobites are considered to be some of the first arthropods. They were abundant in Cambrian times. Tardigrades, belonging to a phylum that might be related to annelids and arthropods, are called water bears and can live in areas that are alternately wet and dry.

Evolution of Arthropods

The relationships of tardigrades, trilobites, and arthropods have been under close scrutiny as new evidence is discovered. Fossil records show that trilobites, abundant in the mid-Cambrian but now extinct, were early arthropods. Trilobites, like the one shown in **Figure 21,** were oval, flattened, and divided into three body sections like some modern arthropods. The large number of identical segments of these ancestral arthropods evolved to more specialized appendages and fewer segments in modern arthropods.

Tardigrades also are related to arthropods, but they appear to be related less closely to arthropods than trilobites are. The tardigrade shown in **Figure 21** illustrates why these tiny animals are known commonly as water bears. The largest are 1.5 mm long with four pairs of stubby legs. They feed on algae, decaying matter, nematodes, and other soil animals. They inhabit freshwater, marine, and land habitats. During temperature extremes and drought, tardigrades can survive for years in a completely dry state with reduced metabolism until favorable conditions return.

Section 3 Assessment

Section Summary

- Insects make up approximately 80 percent of all arthropod species.
- A variety of adaptations have enabled insects to live in almost all habitats on Earth.
- Insect mouthparts reflect their diets.
- Most insects undergo metamorphosis.
- In some insects, social structure, including individual specializations, is necessary for the survival of the colony.

Understand Main Ideas

1. MAIN Idea **Evaluate** three adaptations of insects in terms of the role they played in enabling insects to become so diverse and abundant.
2. **Identify** features common to all insects.
3. **List** adaptations of the mouthparts of insects that feed on three different food sources and explain each one.
4. **Identify** one reason most insects undergo complete metamorphosis.

Think Critically

5. **Design an Experiment** Different species of firefly beetles flash their light in different sequences of short and long flashes. Design an experiment that would explain why fireflies flash their lights.

MATH in Biology

6. There are approximately 1.75 million named animal species. About three-fourths of all known animal species are arthropods, and 80 percent of arthropods are insects. Approximately how many named species are insects?

Develop Concepts

EL BL OL AL Activity Set up stereomicroscope stations. Provide a petri dish containing distilled water and some moss or lichen for each station. Set the petri dish on top of a black background. After 2 h, tardigrades should be visible. Have students view the tardigrades at 40× magnification. Instruct students to make a list of features and behaviors of tardigrades that they observe.

Formative Assessment

Evaluation

SAY TO STUDENTS: ***Explain in detail how the evolution of insect societies with castes contributed to the success of some groups of insects.*** A member of a caste has a specialized function in the society. For example, worker bees gather nectar, build honeycombs, manufacture honey, care for the young, and guard the hive. Drones are reproductive males. The queen is the reproductive female. The division of functions in the society means that one bee does not have to perform all the functions in order for the society to survive.

Remediation Ask students to draw a diagram of an insect hive with a caste system, such as that of ants, termites, or bees. The diagrams should show each caste and should have labels for specific function or functions.

Section 3 Assessment

1. Their exoskeleton provides protection and keeps them from drying out on land. Their wings allow them to fly long distances and take advantage of various food sources and habitats. Their small size allows them to be widely dispersed by wind and water. They lay a large number of eggs, and therefore have large numbers of offspring. They also have a wide variety of leg, mouthpart, and sense organ structures.
2. three body sections, three pairs of legs, and generally two pairs of wings
3. a coiled tube for sucking flower nectar, sponging and lapping mouthparts, needlelike mouthparts that pierce the flesh of animals, and mandibles for cutting
4. Insects that undergo metamorphosis can exploit different food resources during the different stages.
5. Answers will vary. Accept all scientific experimental designs in which a control is included along with a plan to collect quantitative data.
6. 1.05 million

In the Field

Purpose

Students will investigate real-world applications of entomology. UCP.5, C.6

Anticipatory Guide

ASK STUDENTS: ***Have you watched any television shows or movies that feature forensic medicine? Describe what you have seen.*** Possible answer: Scientists using medical facts to provide evidence or hypotheses about crimes. ***Define the term* entomology.** the study of insects ***What do you think a forensic entomologist does?*** Scientists who apply their knowledge of insects to help solve crime. Tell students that while some insects play an important role in decomposition in nature, they also can yield clues about what happened at a crime scene.

Background

Scientists understand the life cycle patterns followed by insects and know how these cycles are influenced by a variety of variables. Knowledge of these patterns and the variables that affect them, like environmental temperature, can allow investigators to establish a range of time during which a death occurred. Forensic entomologists are most frequently consulted in homicide cases. They also contribute to investigations involving improper wound care, which might occur in a nursing home or in a child care situation. They also are called to examine animal deaths and food contamination cases.

In the Field

Career: Forensic Entomologist

Insect Evidence

Insects often are the first to arrive at a crime scene. Blowflies can arrive within minutes. Over time, other insects arrive. As the insects feed, grow, and lay eggs, they follow predictable developmental cycles. For forensic entomologists, scientists who apply their knowledge of insects to help solve crimes, these cycles reveal information about the time and location of death.

Time of death Forensic entomologists use two methods to determine time of death. The first method is used when the victim has been dead for at least one month. While blowflies and houseflies arrive almost immediately, other species arrive later in the decomposition process. Some species arrive to feed on other insects already at the scene. The succession of insects provides information about the time that passed since death occurred.

When death has occurred within a few weeks, a second method used involves the developmental cycle of blowflies. Within a couple of days, the blowflies lay eggs. The next stages of development are determined in part by temperature, as shown in the graph. Based on the stage of insect development and area temperatures, entomologists can determine a range of days in which the first insects laid eggs in the body, establishing a time of death.

Location of death Insects help determine if a body was relocated after death. If insects found on the body are not native to the habitat where the body is found, investigators can assume that the body was moved. The species that are present also provide clues about the area where death took place.

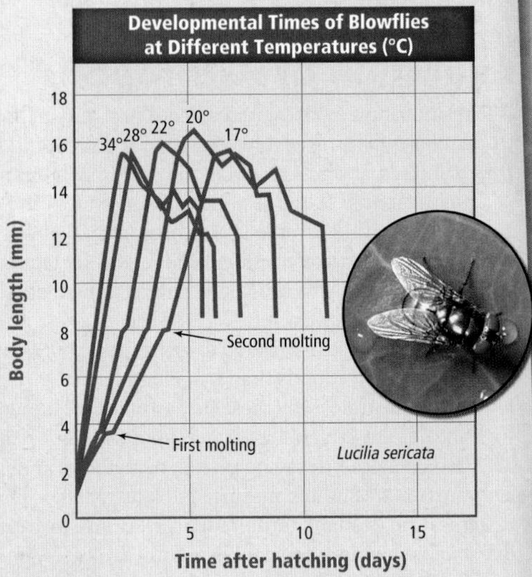

Limitations In many locations, forensic entomology is less useful in winter, when insects are less active and less abundant. In addition, insects might be prevented from invading a body if it is frozen, buried deeply, or wrapped tightly. In many cases, however, insects can give crucial testimony about the details of a crime.

MATH in Biology

Study the graph to solve this problem: Blowfly larvae with a body length of about 6 mm are found on a corpse with a temperature of 22°C. How much time has passed since death?

MATH in Biology

Study the Graph Students should note that as temperature increases, the rate of blowfly development increases. Given these conditions, the time elapsed since death was approximately 2 days.

Follow-Up Discussion Forensic entomology has limitations, which could involve environmental conditions, handling, packaging, and storage of entomological evidence, and the way in which a body was disposed. Discuss factors that could limit the usefulness of insect evidence gathered from a crime scene.

WebQuest

BIOLAB

WHERE ARE MICROARTHROPODS FOUND?

Background: Microarthropods range from 0.1 to 5 mm in size—barely visible to human eyes. Dozens of microarthropod species can be unearthed in one shovelful of soil. Discover these hidden animals during this investigation.

Question: *What types of microarthropods can be found in your local environment?*

Materials

soil sample
clear funnel
ring stand
gooseneck lamp
wire mesh
beaker
95% ethanol
plastic collection vials
magnifying lens
arthropod field guide
metric ruler

Safety Precautions

Procedure

1. Read and complete the lab safety form.
2. Obtain a sample of leaf litter and soil from your teacher.
3. Create a data table to record your observations.
4. Place the funnel in the ring stand.
5. Cut the mesh screen in a circle so it rests inside the funnel.
6. Pour ethanol into the beaker until the beaker is two-thirds full. Set the beaker under the funnel.
7. Remove your soil sample from the bag and place it carefully on the mesh screen in the funnel.
8. Place the lamp at least 10 cm above the sample. Switch on the light and leave it on for several hours. The heat from the lamp dries the soil. This forces the microarthropods downward until they fall through the screen and into the alcohol.
9. Use a magnifying lens to observe the physical characteristics of the microarthropods you collected.
10. **Cleanup and Disposal** Be certain to properly dispose of the alcohol and specimens you collected by following your teacher's instructions.

Analyze and Conclude

1. **Classify** Place the microarthropods you collected into the three major groups of arthropods. Place unidentified specimens into a separate group.
2. **Graph** Use the data you collected to graph the abundances of each type of arthropod.
3. **Describe** Write a description of the physical characteristics of the microarthropod specimens that you could not classify into any of the three major groups.
4. **Hypothesize** How do microarthropods help create a healthy soil ecosystem?
5. **Error Analysis** Check your classifications against those done by other classmates. Did you classify the microarthropods into the same group? If not, explain why.

SHARE YOUR DATA

Report Research microarthropods and write a short report about their role in the food web and ecosystems. Then present your findings to a group of classmates.

Analyze and Conclude

1. Students should use their prior knowledge of arachnid, insect, and crustacean characteristics to classify their collected specimens.
2. Answers will vary, but students should prepare a pie or bar graph showing the percentages of arachnids, crustaceans, insects, and unknown microarthropods collected.
3. Answers will vary. Descriptions could include the color of the body, the number of legs or antenna present.
4. Answers will vary. Microarthropods provide vital links in food chains, and they contribute to the decomposition of organic matter, cycling of essential nutrients, and formation of soil in many terrestrial ecosystems.
5. Answers will vary. Each soil sample is different and so is each specimen. Students might have focused on different characteristics when classifying the microarthropods.

BIOLAB

Inquiry BioLab

For a lab worksheet, use your eTeacherEdition Online.

RUBRIC A rubric for evaluating BioLabs is found on your eTeacherEdition Online.

Est. Time 90 min

Content Background Microarthropods are arthropods measuring 0.1–5 mm in size that live primarily in soil. These animals aid in the decomposition process, nutrient cycling, and the formation of soil.

Alternative Materials an inverted milk jug can be used for the funnel (which eliminates the need for a ring stand), a jar can substitute for the beaker, stereomicroscope, 70% rubbing alcohol, photographs of microarthropods

Safety Precautions Approve lab safety forms before work begins. Students should thoroughly wash their hands after handling the microarthropods. Ethanol is flammable. Keep away from heat and open flame.

Teaching Strategy Encourage students to reserve a column or row in their data tables for unknown microarthropods that they cannot classify into a major arthropod group.

Cleanup and Disposal Properly dispose of the ethanol and microarthropod specimens. Never release nonnative organisms into an environment.

Alternative Teaching Demo Collect microarthropods before class and have groups of students classify them and answer the Analyze and Conclude questions.

Study Guide

ConnectED

Students can use the following to review the chapter.

Review

Vocabulary eGames
Vocabulary eFlashcards
Vocabulary PuzzleMaker

Assessment

Online Quizzes
Online Test Practice
Standardized Test Practice

Use the *ExamView® Assessment Suite* CD-ROM to:

- create multiple versions of tests
- create modified tests with one mouse click
- edit existing questions and add your own questions
- build tests aligned with state standards using built-in state curriculum tags
- change English tests to Spanish with one mouse click
- track students' progress using the Teacher Management System

Chapter 26 Study Guide

THEME FOCUS Diversity Segmented exoskeletons, jointed appendages, and diverse body structures enable arthropods to live in nearly every environment.

BIG Idea **Arthropods have evolved to have a variety of adaptations for successful diversity, population, and persistence.**

Section 1 Arthropod Characteristics

thorax (p. 763)
abdomen (p. 763)
cephalothorax (p. 763)
appendage (p. 764)
molting (p. 764)
mandible (p. 765)
tracheal tube (p. 767)
book lung (p. 767)
spiracle (p. 767)
Malpighian tubule (p. 767)
pheromone (p. 768)

MAIN Idea **Arthropods have segmented bodies and tough exoskeletons with jointed appendages.**

- Arthropods can be identified by three main structural features.
- Arthropods have adaptations that make them the most successful animals on Earth.
- Arthropod mouthparts are adapted to a wide variety of food materials.
- In order to grow, arthropods must molt.
- Arthropods have organ system modifications that have enabled them to live in all types of habitats and to increase in variety and numbers.

Section 2 Arthropod Diversity

cheliped (p. 771)
swimmeret (p. 771)
chelicera (p. 771)
pedipalp (p. 772)
spinneret (p. 772)

MAIN Idea **Arthropods are classified based on the structure of their segments, types of appendages, and mouthparts.**

- Arthropods are divided into three major groups.
- Crustaceans have modified appendages for getting food, walking, and swimming.
- The first two pairs of arachnid appendages are modified as mouthparts, as reproductive structures, or as pincers.
- Spiders are carnivores that either hunt prey or trap it in webs that they spin out of silk.
- Horseshoe crabs are ancient arthropods that have remained unchanged for more than 200 million years.

Section 3 Insects and Their Relatives

metamorphosis (p. 778)
pupa (p. 778)
nymph (p. 778)
caste (p. 779)

MAIN Idea **Insects have structural and functional adaptations that have enabled them to become the most abundant and diverse group of arthropods.**

- Insects make up approximately 80 percent of all arthropod species.
- A variety of adaptations have enabled insects to live in almost all habitats on Earth.
- Insect mouthparts reflect their diets.
- Most insects undergo metamorphosis.
- In some insects, social structure, including individual specializations, is necessary for the survival of the colony.

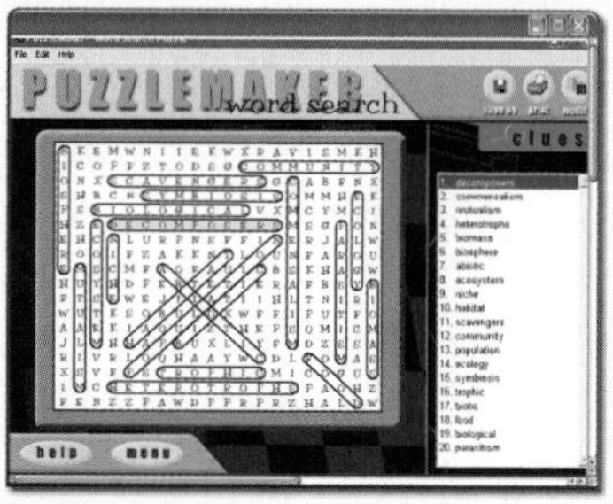

Review **Vocabulary PuzzleMaker**

For additional practice with vocabulary, have students access the Vocabulary PuzzleMaker online.

Review **Vocabulary eGames**

Section 1

Vocabulary Review

An analogy is a relationship between two pairs of words and can be written in the following manner: A is to B as C is to D. *Complete each analogy by providing the missing vocabulary term from the Study Guide page.*

1. Spiracles are to breathing as __________ are to excreting wastes.
2. Compound eye is to sense organ as mandible is to __________.
3. Head is to thorax as __________ is to abdomen.

Understand Main Ideas

Use the diagram below to answer questions 4 and 5.

4. Which labeled structure helps terrestrial arthropods maintain water balance?
   A. 1
   B. 2
   C. 3
   D. 4
5. Which labeled structure would an arthropod use to sense odors in its environment?
   A. 1
   B. 2
   C. 3
   D. 4
6. Which group of words has one that does not belong?
   A. exoskeleton, chitin, molting, growth
   B. mandible, antennae, appendage, leg
   C. cephalothorax, thorax, head, abdomen
   D. simple eye, compound eye, tympanum, thorax
7. The relationship between muscle size and exoskeleton thickness limits which in an arthropod?
   A. diet **C.** motion
   B. habitat **D.** size

Constructed Response

8. MAIN Idea Make a table that lists arthropod structures, their functions, and an analogy of what each structure is like in a world of human-made devices. For example, a particular bird's bill that pulls insects out of bark might be compared to tweezers that can pull a sliver out of skin. Use the following structures in your table: antennae, exoskeleton, mandibles, tracheal tubes, and tympanum.
9. **Open Ended** Katydids are members of the grasshopper family. Most katydids are green, but occasionally both pink and yellow katydids appear. Make a hypothesis to explain why pink and yellow katydids sometimes appear.

Think Critically

Use the diagram below to answer question 10.

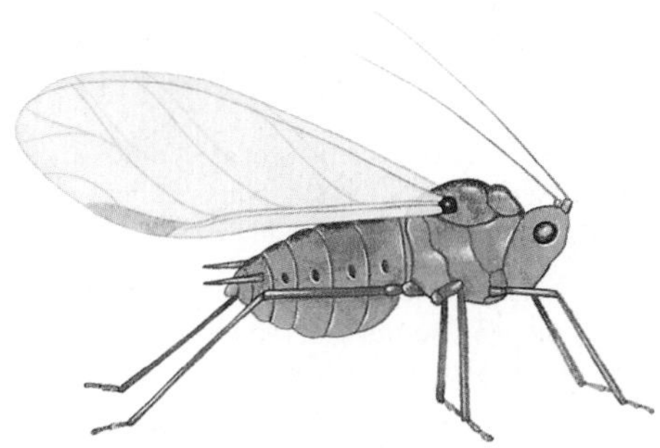

10. **CAREERS IN BIOLOGY** Arborists, people who specialize in caring for trees, sometimes spray horticultural oils on fruit trees to control aphids, the plant pest shown in the diagram. Based on your knowledge of insect anatomy, analyze why oils are an effective treatment to control plant pests.
11. **Infer** Some species of flowers produce heat that attracts certain beetles to live inside the bloom. Infer how the plant and the beetle both benefit from this relationship.

Assessment Online Test Practice

Chapter 26

Assessment

Section 1

Vocabulary Review

1. Malpighian tubules
2. appendage
3. cephalothorax

Understand Main Ideas

4. C
5. B
6. D
7. D

Constructed Response

8. Analogy portion of answers will vary. Possible answers: antennae, sensing, like a thermometer; exoskeleton, protects body, like armor; molting, splitting exoskeleton to allow for growth, like getting new clothes; mandibles, for chewing, like a food processor; tracheal tubes, for breathing, like air moving through heating ducts in a home; tympanum, for hearing, like a vibrating drum; pheromone, chemical communication, like perfume
9. Possible hypotheses: Genetics; pink-yellow food supply can make exoskeleton a different color. In a certain area, there may be a seasonal bloom of a particular color flower that provides camouflage for the katydids that have that particular color; The color could be temporary

Think Critically

10. The oils plug an insect's spiracles, so the insect will suffocate and die.
11. The flower gets pollinated by the beetle and can reproduce and since beetles cannot generate body heat, the beetles are provided with a warm environment in which they can reproduce.

Section 2

Vocabulary Review

12. In crayfishes, lobsters, and crabs, the first pair of legs are called chelipeds, which are large claws. In the same animals, swimmerets are the posterior appendages used for reproduction and swimming.

13. Chelicerae are the most anterior appendages of arachnids, and pedipalps are the second pair of appendages in arachnids.

14. Chelipeds in crustaceans and chelicerae in arachnids are the first pair of appendages modified for feeding in both.

Understand Main Ideas

15. A

16. D

17. B

18. D

19. B

Constructed Response

20. Crustaceans have appendages to walk on the bottom of their aquatic habitat and to swim in it. Arachnids have appendages only to walk on land. Some crustaceans have tails adapted to propel them in the water whereas terrestrial arachnids do not.

21. Crustaceans would be very small because they cannot grow without molting.

Think Critically

22. Answers will vary. Some ideas would be a thicker covering to reduce loss of water from the body due to heat and a smaller body with reduced surface area exposed to potential water loss. They could build webs to capture crawling insects in corners near the floor.

23. chelipeds—catch and crush food; thick exoskeleton—protect body; walking legs—walk along ocean floor; antennae and eyes—sense environment; swimmerets—reproduce and swim

Chapter 26 Assessment

Section 2

Vocabulary Review

For each set of vocabulary terms, explain the relationship that exists.

12. cheliped, swimmeret

13. chelicera, pedipalp

14. cheliped, chelicera

Understand Main Ideas

Use the diagram below to answer question 15.

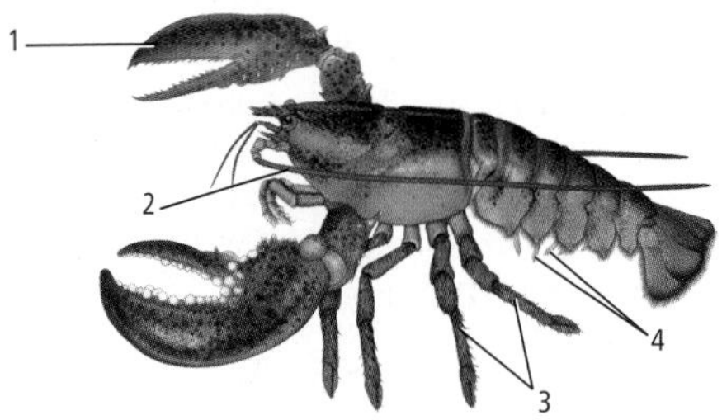

15. Which structure would a lobster use to catch and crush food?

A. 1 **C.** 3
B. 2 **D.** 4

16. Which is not a characteristic of arachnids?

A. chelicerae **C.** spinnerets
B. pedipalps **D.** antennae

17. An animal you found on the forest soil has two body sections, no antennae, and large pincers as the second pair of appendages. What type of animal is it?

A. tick **C.** spider
B. scorpion **D.** lobster

18. In spiders, the spinnerets are involved in which activity?

A. defense **C.** circulation
B. getting rid of waste **D.** spinning silk

19. Which is not a characteristic of mites?

A. one oval-shaped body section
B. carry lyme disease bacteria
C. less than 1 mm long
D. animal parasite

Constructed Response

20. MAIN Idea Compare the body forms of aquatic crustaceans to those of terrestrial arachnids, showing how each is adapted to its environment.

21. **Open Ended** What would happen if crustaceans could not molt?

Think Critically

22. **Formulate Models** Draw and describe a model of a spider that would be adapted to conditions in a hot, dry attic with only crawling insects as a food source.

23. **THEME FOCUS Diversity** Based on the lobster diagram in **Figure 10** and your knowledge of crustaceans, what adaptations enable a lobster to survive in its aquatic enviroment?

Section 3

Vocabulary Review

For each set of vocabulary terms, choose the one term that does not belong and explain why it does not belong.

24. incomplete metamorphosis, pupa, larva, adult

25. complete metamorphosis, nymph, adult, molt

26. pupa, larva, nymph, caste, adult

Understand Main Ideas

Use the diagram below to answer question 27.

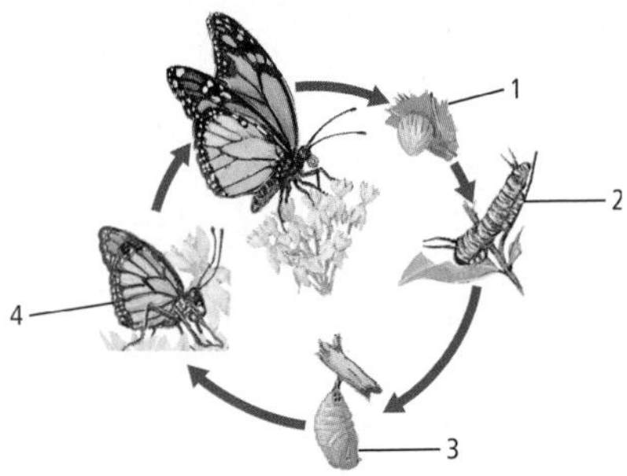

27. Which stage does not belong in the diagram of complete metamorphosis?

A. 1 **C.** 3
B. 2 **D.** 4

Section 3

Vocabulary Review

24. Incomplete metamorphosis does not belong because the other words are ones that would be used in describing complete metamorphosis.

25. Complete metamorphosis does not belong because the other words are ones that would be used in describing incomplete metamorphosis. Alternatively, the word nymph could be removed, as the other words could refer to either incomplete or complete metamorphosis.

26. Caste does not belong because the other words are ones that would be used in describing metamorphosis; caste describes a working position in an insect society.

Understand Main Ideas

27. D

28. If the food is 40 degrees to the right of the Sun, what will be the angle of the straight line of the figure-eight waggle dance?
   A. 60 degrees to the right of vertical
   B. 40 degrees to the right of vertical
   C. 60 degrees to the right of horizontal
   D. 40 degrees to the right of horizontal

29. If a farm field has an infestation of insects, which method would the farmer use to manage it for the long-term?
   A. genetic engineering
   B. insecticides
   C. integrated pest management
   D. pesticide resistance

Constructed Response

Use the diagram below to answer questions 30 and 31.

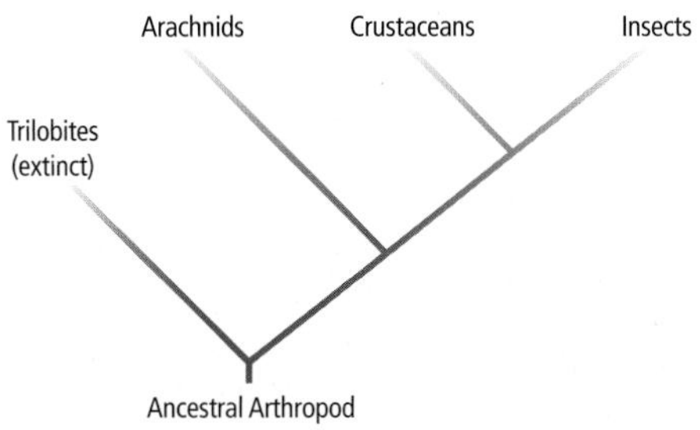

30. **Open Ended** Based on this interpretation of the phylogeny of arthropods, which group developed the earliest? Which group developed most recently?

31. MAIN Idea Examine the cladogram and sequence the order of appearance, from oldest to most modern, of the following features in the evolution of insects: chelicerae, mandibles, body divided into two regions, segmentation. Explain your reasoning.

Think Critically

32. **Hypothesize** A certain species of beetle looks very much like an ant. Make a hypothesis about the advantage to the beetle of looking like a particular ant.

33. **Design** an experiment that would answer this question: Why do crickets chirp?

Summative Assessment

34. BIG Idea Select an arthropod from this chapter. Highlight its adaptations and explain how they help it thrive in its habitat.

35. WRITING in Biology Malaria is spread by mosquitos and is one of the world's worst diseases in terms of numbers of people affected and the difficulties in treating and preventing it. Research and write an essay on how scientists are using fungi to prevent this disease.

DBQ Document-Based Questions

Desert locusts have two distinct phases in their lives: the solitary insect that stays in one area and the social phase in which locusts band together in swarms of billions and move kilometers in search of food. Biologists found that exposing individual insects to jostling by small paper balls induced swarming. Examine the locust below. Each color indicates the percentage of social behavior induced by touching the locust on various parts of the body.

Data obtained from: Enserink, M. 2004. Can the war on locusts be won? *Science* 306 (5703): 1880–1882.

36. What percentage of social behavior resulted from touching the insect's thorax?

37. What part of the insect's body is the most sensitive for generating social activity when it is touched?

38. Draw a conclusion about what physical trigger causes locusts to swarm.

28. B
29. C

Constructed Response

30. earliest—trilobites; most recently—insects and crustaceans

31. Segmentation would appear at the bottom since all arthropods are segmented. Next, chelicerae and cephalothorax since arachnids have them and this group comes before crustaceans and insects. Mandibles would be next since both crustaceans and insects have them. Answers may vary and may be accepted if they make scientific sense.

Think Critically

32. Answers will vary. Mimicry in beetles in which they look like ants may offer protection against certain predators that do not eat the ants. Perhaps the ants are not palatable because of some chemical substance they produce.

33. Answers will vary. Accept all designs that make scientific sense, include a control, and have a plan to collect data. Students may hypothesize that crickets chirp to announce their territories. They might plan to introduce marked crickets into an aquarium and determine how much time the crickets spend in a particular area and count the number of chirps they make in a certain amount of time in a particular area.

Summative Assessment

34. Answers will vary based on arthropod chosen. A possible answer is the walking stick insect from the Phasmida order. Walking sticks have many adaptations including the ability to change color to camouflage itself, the ability to shed and re-grow limbs to avoid predators, they sway while hanging on branches to mimic the wind, and they are nocturnal insects which feed on leaves.

35. Answers will vary. Make sure students explain how the disease is transmitted and include new ideas for prevention and treatment.

WRITING in Biology

RUBRIC Use the modifiable rubric found on your eTeacherEdition Online to assess writing assignments.

DBQ Document-Based Questions

Enserink, M. 2004. Can the war on locusts be won? *Science* 306 (5703): 1880–1882.

36. 0–25 percent
37. upper thigh of jumping leg
38. Locusts that are touching legs of other locusts may begin to swarm. Their legs may be touched more under crowded conditions; or when a certain area no longer has much vegetation, locusts may move more in seeking food and thereby touch the legs of others.

Standardized Test Practice

Multiple Choice

1. C 5. D 9. A
2. B 6. A
3. C 7. B
4. C 8. C

Short Answer

10. (A) stomata—opening for gas exchange, (B) guard cells—open and close stomata, (C) spongy mesophyll—allows gases to pass between the palisade mesophyll and stoma, (D) palisade mesophyll—responsible for photosynthesis, (E) cuticle—waterproofs the leaf, (F) epidermis—protects the inner tissues of the leaf

11. Arthropods differ from other invertebrates because they have an exoskeleton and jointed appendages.

12. Zygote: A new cell forms when an egg is fertilized
Blastula: A fluid-filled, cell-covered ball forms when the cells of the zygote multiply.
Gastrula: A two-cell layered sac forms when some cells from the blastula move inward.

13. All mollusks have a mantle, a muscular foot, a soft internal body, and a digestive tract with two openings.

14. Answers will vary depending on the animal chosen for comparison. Insects have an open circulatory system. In insects, the heart pumps blood through vessels to different tissues. The tissues are flooded with blood that returns to the heart through open spaces. In mammals, for example, the circulatory system is closed. The blood is pumped by the heart through continuous vessels to all parts of the body and back to the heart.

Standardized Test Practice

Cumulative

Multiple Choice

1. Which common function do both the endoskeletons and exoskeletons of animals perform?
- **A.** growing along with the animal
- **B.** preventing water loss
- **C.** supporting the body
- **D.** providing protection from predators

Use the diagram below to answer questions 2 and 3.

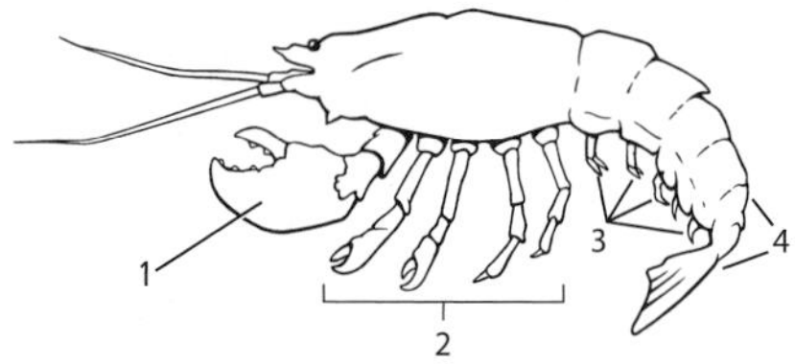

2. In which group does this animal belong?
- **A.** copepods
- **B.** crustaceans
- **C.** insects
- **D.** spiders

3. Which part of the body does this animal use for reproduction?
- **A.** 1
- **B.** 2
- **C.** 3
- **D.** 4

4. How are the organisms in Kingdom Protista different from animals?
- **A.** Some are multicellular.
- **B.** Some are prokaryotes.
- **C.** Some have cell walls.
- **D.** Some have tissues.

5. Which kind of asexual reproduction is possible in flatworms?
- **A.** budding
- **B.** fertilization
- **C.** parthenogenesis
- **D.** regeneration

Use the drawing below to answer question 6.

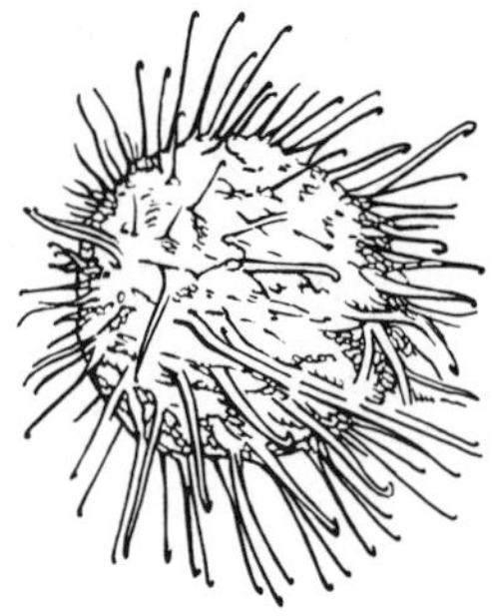

6. Which is the method of seed dispersal for this seed?
- **A.** animals
- **B.** gravity
- **C.** water
- **D.** wind

7. Which process is related to sexual reproduction in animals?
- **A.** budding
- **B.** fertilization
- **C.** fragmentation
- **D.** parthogenesis

8. Which is the role of an earthworm's clitellum in reproduction?
- **A.** It breaks off, allowing fragmentation to occur.
- **B.** It indicates whether or not an earthworm is hermaphroditic.
- **C.** It leaves the earthworm's body and forms a cocoon for developing earthworms.
- **D.** It produces sperm and eggs.

9. Which is used to classify protists?
- **A.** feeding
- **B.** habitat
- **C.** structure
- **D.** reproduction

15. Answers can vary. According to this theory, large prokaryotic cells engulfed smaller prokaryotic cells. These smaller prokaryotic cells lived symbiotically in the larger cell. Eventually, the cells became a single organism. Mitochondria and chloroplasts may represent smaller prokaryotic cells that became part of larger cells. This connection would be supported if the characteristics of mitochondria and chloroplasts were more similar to the characteristics of prokaryotic cells than eukaryotic cells.

Short Answer

Use the diagram below to answer question 10.

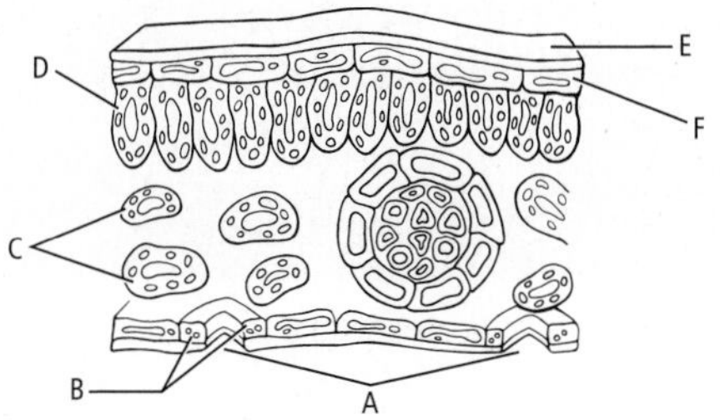

10. Identify the labeled parts of this leaf, and state a function for each part.

11. Which characteristics differentiate arthropods from other invertebrates?

12. Describe embryonic development from a zygote to a gastrula. Provide the name of each stage, and explain how it is unique.

13. What characteristics do all mollusks share?

14. Compare and contrast how blood circulates through an insect with the circulation of blood in another kind of animal.

15. Explain the theory of endosymbiosis as it applies to protists. Assess the possible connection between certain organelles in eukaryotic protists and the structures of prokaryotic organisms.

16. Assess the importance of algae to all living things.

Extended Response

Use the illustrations below to answer question 17.

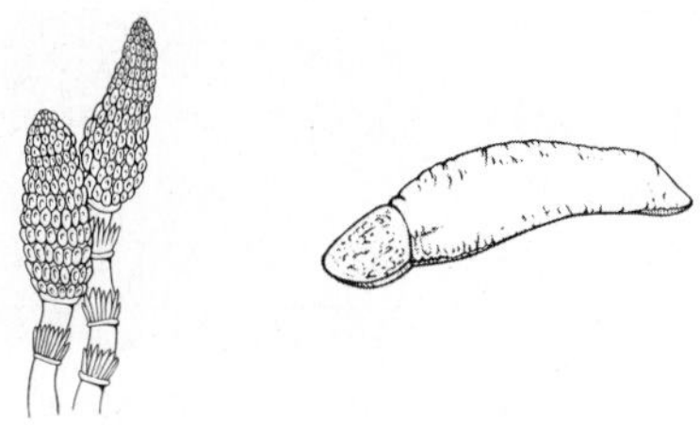

17. The figures above show spores and seeds from different kinds of plants. Explain why one of these structures would have an advantage and would be more likely to be naturally selected.

18. Evaluate the advantages and disadvantages of an exoskeleton.

Essay Question

The world's coral reefs and associated ecosystems are threatened by an increasing array of pollution, habitat destruction, invasive species, disease, bleaching, and global climate change. The rapid decline of these complex and biologically diverse marine ecosystems has significant social, economic, and environmental impacts in the U.S. and around the world. The U.S. Coral Reef Task Force identified two basic themes for national action:

- understand coral reef ecosystems and the processes that determine their health and viability
- reduce the adverse impacts of human activities on coral reefs and associated ecosystems

Using the information in the paragraph above, answer the following question in essay format.

19. *What steps do you think the U.S. should take to preserve coral reef ecosystems?*

NEED EXTRA HELP?																			
If You Missed Question . . .	1	2	3	4	5	6	7	8	9	10	11	12	13	14	15	16	17	18	19
Review Section . . .	24.1	26.2	26.2	24.1	25.1	23.3	24.1	25.4	19.1	22.2	26.1	24.1	25.3	26.1	19.1	19.3	21.3	26.1	24.3

16. Answers can vary. Algae produce much of the oxygen used by marine organisms. Algae are the base organisms of many different food chains because they harvest energy from sunlight. Without algae, there would be very little oxygen in the oceans and many food chains would not exist.

Extended Response

17. Answers can vary. The seed (on the right) has structures that help it survive for longer periods of time including stored food and a thick protective coat. On the other hand, spores are lighter than seeds and would be blown farther from the parent plant by the wind. Spores can remain dormant for a long time and do not germinate unless the conditions are right for growth.

18. The advantages of exoskeletons are that they are tough and impermeable. Consequently, exoskeletons protect arthropods from injury and water loss. The disadvantages of exoskeletons are that they are solid and inflexible. Consequently, they require joints for movement and cause difficulties for growing organisms.

Essay Question

19. Answers can vary depending on needs of coral organisms that a student discusses. In general, taking steps to reduce climate change can help coral reefs because they have to live in a limited temperature range. Because other organisms depend on coral and also contribute to the survival of coral, protecting these organisms could be a useful step. Banning or limiting diving, fishing, and other human activity near coral reefs could be important because the reefs are very fragile. Keeping the water clear and clean, so that the photosynthetic organisms that live symbiotically with coral can survive, is a possible step. A less obvious answer might involve setting up conditions for the formation of new, artificial reefs. However, this option is not covered in the chapter.

Chapter 27 Organizer:
Echinoderms and Invertebrate Chordates

LabManager™
Customize any lab with the LabManager™ CD-ROM.

Essential Questions	National Science Standards	Materials and Planning Estimated times include cleanup and disposal, but do not include teacher prep time. For cleanup and disposal guidelines, see page 39T.	Est. Time (min)
Section 1 1. What are the characteristics common to echinoderms? 2. How do the water-vascular system and tube feet adaptations enable echinoderms to be successful? 3. What distinguishes the classes of echinoderms from each other?	UCP.1–5; A.1, A.2; C.3, C.4, C.5, C.6	**Launch Lab,** p. 790: live sea star, petri dish, salt water, dissecting microscope, glass probe	20
		Demonstration, p. 792: preserved sea urchin and test	7
		Demonstration, p. 793: echinoderm larvae, microprojector	5
		MiniLab 1, p. 793: preserved specimens of sand dollar, sea cucumber, sea star, and sea urchin	45
		Activity, p. 795: droppers	10
		Demonstration, p. 800: live or preserved sea cucumber	10
Section 2 1. What are the features of invertebrate chordates that place them in the phylum Chordata? 2. What are the features of invertebrate chordates that place them with invertebrates? 3. What are the similarities between the adaptations of lancelets and sea squirts?	UCP.1–5; A.1, A.2; B.4; C.2, C.3, C.5, C.6; E.2; G.1, G.2	**Demonstration,** p. 802: snack cakes with white frosting inside	5
		Activity, p. 803: clay, modeling dough, or salt dough	30
		Demonstration, p. 805: slides or illustrations of lancelets, chordates, and their habitats	15
		BioLab, p. 809: Internet access, echinoderm reference book, field journal	45–90

Suggested Time for Each Lesson

Class	Chapter Opener	Section 1	Section 2	Assessment
Basic	45 min	25 min	20 min	45 min
General	20 min	35 min	35 min	45 min
Honors	—	40 min	5 min	45 min

ConnectED

connectED.mcgraw-hill.com

Access interactive learning opportunities and teaching resources using these icons located throughout your StudentWorks™ Plus Online and eTeacherEdition Online.

Chapter 27 Section Resources	Additional Chapter 27 Resources	Technology
FAST FILE Unit 7 Resources: Launch Lab Worksheet* MiniLab Worksheet* Study Guide (English/Spanish)* Section Quick Check **Reading Essentials 27.1** **Science Notebook 27.1*** **FAST FILE Unit 7 Resources:** BioLab Worksheet* Study Guide (English/Spanish)* Section Quick Check **Reading Essentials 27.2** **Science Notebook 27.2***	**FAST FILE Unit 7 Resources:** Chapter Diagnostic Test Concept Mapping* Real-World Biology Enrichment Chapter Tests A, B, and C **Transparencies:** Bellringer Transparencies* Biology Concepts Transparencies* **Lab Resources:** Laboratory Manual* Probeware Lab Manual* Forensics Lab Manual* Pre-AP Lab Manual* Open Inquiry in Biology* Guided Inquiry in Biology*	**Teaching Tools:** eTeacherEdition Online Classroom Presentation Toolkit CD-ROM* LabManager™ CD-ROM* Video Lab DVD* Virtual Lab CD-ROM* What's BIOLOGY Got To Do With It? StudentWorks™ Plus Online* **Chapter Assessment Tools:** Classroom Presentation Toolkit CD-ROM* *ExamView® Assessment Suite* CD-ROM **Web-Based Resources:** • StudentWorks™ Plus Online • eTeacherEdition Online • Animations* • The Interactive Time Line* • Interactive Tables* • Online Quizzes • Online Test Practice • Standardized Test Practice • Virtual Labs* • Multilingual eGlossary* • Vocabulary eGames* • Vocabulary eFlashcards • WebQuests • Personal Tutors

While all resources listed are appropriate for English learners, the * indicates resources with a strong visual or hands-on component for EL.

Teaching strategies and activities have been coded for differentiated instruction.

AL Activities for students working above grade level	**OL** Activities for students working on grade level	**BL** Activities for students working below grade level	**EL** Activities for English learners (also ELL)	**COOP LEARN** Activities designed for small cooperative group work

CHAPTER 27

Launch Lab
Why are tube feet important?

Inquiry Launch Lab

For a lab worksheet, use your eTeacherEdition Online.

RUBRIC A rubric for evaluating Launch Labs is found on your eTeacherEdition Online.

Est. Time 20 min

Alternative Materials an article from a magazine about sea stars on which to base research; preserved sea star specimen

Safety Precaution Approve lab safety forms before work begins.

Teaching Strategies

- Relate the characteristics of the intertidal and subtidal environments in which most sea stars are found to the needs of the sea stars, including avoiding and deterring predators, obtaining food, and remaining upright and steady in moving surf.
- Saltwater tanks and animals can be rented from Gulf of Maine, Inc., P.O. Box 360, Pembroke, ME 04666.

Procedure

1. Read and complete the lab safety form.
2. Place a **live sea star** in a **petri dish** filled with **water from a saltwater aquarium.** WARNING: *Treat the sea star in a humane manner at all times.*
3. Observe the ventral side of the sea star under a **dissecting microscope**. Look for the rows of tube feet that run down the middle of each arm, and draw a diagram of the structures.
4. Gently touch the end of a tube foot with a **glass probe**. Record your observations.
5. Return the sea star and water to the aquarium.

Analysis

1. **Describe** the structure of the sea star's tube feet. The tube feet are small, muscular, fluid-filled tubes that end in suction-cup-like structures.
2. **Infer** Based on your observations, what is the function of an echinoderm's tube feet? Possible answer: The tube feet can be used to anchor the sea star to an object, for mobility, and to obtain food.

CHAPTER 27
Echinoderms and Invertebrate Chordates

ConnectED
Your one-stop online resource
connectED.mcgraw-hill.com

- Video
- Audio
- Review
- Inquiry
- WebQuest
- Assessment
- Concepts in Motion
- Multilingual eGlossary

Launch Lab
Why are tube feet important?

Like all echinoderms, the crown-of-thorns sea star in the opening photo has structures called tube feet. In this lab, you will observe tube feet and determine their function.

For a lab worksheet, use your StudentWorks™ Plus Online.

Inquiry Launch Lab

FOLDABLES®

Make a layered look-book using the titles shown. Use it to organize your notes on invertebrate chordates.

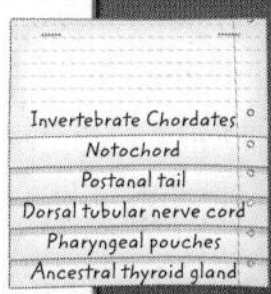

THEME FOCUS Diversity
Echinoderms and invertebrate chordates have diverse adaptations that allow them to live and thrive in their habitats.

BIG Idea Echinoderms and invertebrate chordates have features that connect them to the chordates that evolved after them.

Section 1 • Echinoderm Characteristics

Section 2 • Invertebrate Chordates

THEMES

Scientific Inquiry Scientists continue to study echinoderms and their roles as environmental indicators.

Diversity Echinoderms' and invertebrate chordates' diversity includes over 6,200 distinct species.

Energy The energy obtained from prey gives echinoderms and invertebrate chordates the ability to carry out various life functions.

Homeostasis The simple organ systems of echinoderms effectively maintain homeostasis.

Change The evolution of internal organs link invertebrate chordates to chordates.

Introduce the Chapter

Echinoderm Adaptations

Have students examine the photo of the crown-of-thorns sea star. Point out the organism's spines. Explain that many sea stars have spines and that these are an adaptation to the way of life of an echinoderm.

ASK STUDENTS: ***Based on their shape, how do spines help the sea star survive?*** The pointed spines can penetrate the skin of any predators that try to eat (or pick up) the sea star.

BIG Idea

Two-Column Chart Have students fold a piece of paper in half to make two columns. Have them label the first column *Echinoderms.* Have them label the second column *Invertebrate Chordates.* **SAY TO STUDENTS:** ***In this chapter, you will learn about the features of echinoderms and invertebrate chordates. Read the Main Idea at the beginning of Section 1 and list the features of echinoderms in the first column.*** spiny endoskeleton, water-vascular system, tube feet, radial symmetry in adults Have them then study Figure 16 and list the features of chordates in the second column. dorsal tubular nerve cord, notochord, postanal tail, pharyngeal pouches, early form of thyroid gland Explain to students that invertebrate chordates have these features at some stage of their life. Also remind them that the difference between invertebrates and vertebrates is that invertebrates lack a backbone.

Section 1

MAIN Idea

BL OL AL Echinoderms

Hold a dried, preserved, or live sea star in your hands.

ASK STUDENTS: ***What do you already know about sea stars?*** Possible answers: They live in the sea near the shore. Some may know that they can regenerate an arm. ***Where could you see them?*** Possible answers: They can be seen in tide pools crawling slowly over rocks. ***How do they move?*** They have tiny suction-cup-like structures on their ventral surface that help them move.

R Reading Strategy

EL BL OL Vocabulary Chart

Have students make a three-column chart to fill in as they read Section 1. In the first column, have students write the new vocabulary terms in this section. In the second column, have them write the meaning found in the text. In the last column, instruct students to write a memory clue in the form of a sketch, analogy, or word association.

GOING GREEN Use distilled white vinegar for cleaning lab tables, desk tops and counters. This vinegar is non-toxic and environmentally friendly. Mix one part water and one part distilled white vinegar for general cleaning. For heavy grime, full strength distilled white vinegar can be used to soak the area before wiping it away.

Section 1

Reading Preview

Essential Questions

- What are the characteristics common to echinoderms?
- How do the water-vascular system and tube feet adaptations enable echinoderms to be successful?
- What distinguishes the classes of echinoderms from each other?

Review Vocabulary

endoskeleton: an internal skeleton that provides support and protection and can act as a brace for muscles to pull against

New Vocabulary

pedicellaria
water-vascular system
madreporite
tube foot
ampulla

R

g Multilingual eGlossary

Echinoderm Characteristics

MAIN Idea Echinoderms are marine animals with spiny endoskeletons, water-vascular systems, and tube feet; they have radial symmetry as adults.

Real-World Reading Link To take a blood-pressure reading, a health care professional squeezes a bulb that forces air through a tube and into the blood-pressure cuff around your arm. The cuff remains tight around your arm until the pressure is released when the air is let out. Some animals use similar systems to obtain food and move.

Echinoderms Are Deuterostomes

As shown in the evolutionary tree in **Figure 1,** echinoderms (ih KI nuh durmz) are deuterostomes—a major transition in the phylogeny of animals. Notice how the evolutionary tree branches at deuterostome development.

Recall that mollusks, annelids, and arthropods are protostomes. During development, a protostome's mouth develops from the opening on the gastrula, while a deuterostome's mouth develops from elsewhere on the gastrula. This might not seem important, but consider that only echinoderms and the chordates that evolved after echinoderms have this kind of development. Echinoderms and chordates are related more closely than groups that do not develop in this way. Animals with spinal cords, including humans, are chordates.

The approximately 6000 living species of echinoderms are marine animals and include sea stars, sea urchins, sand dollars, sea cucumbers, brittle stars, sea lilies and feather stars, and sea daisies. Two echinoderms are shown in **Figure 1.**

Figure 1 Echinoderms are marine animals and are the first animals in evolutionary history to have deuterostome development and an endoskeleton.

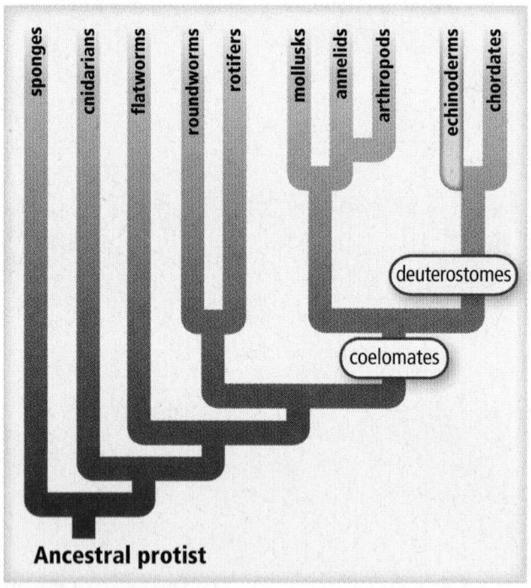

Purple sea urchin

Feather star

Demonstration

BL OL AL Echinoderm Characteristics Hold up a preserved sea urchin and a sea urchin test. If its spines are missing, obtain some spines to show also. Pass the sea urchin, test, and spines around the class.

SAY TO STUDENTS: ***You are more closely related to this sea urchin than to clams or beetles you studied in earlier chapters. Biologists have studied sea urchin development and determined that sea urchin deuterostome development is the same as yours. Infer how the sea urchin's spines are adaptations to its way of life.*** They are used for protection and for boring into rocky areas. Est. time: 7 min

Body Structure

The brittle star is an example of an echinoderm with the spiny endoskeleton that is characteristic of the organisms in this phylum. Echinoderms are the first group of animals in evolutionary history to have endoskeletons. In echinoderms, the endoskeleton consists of calcium carbonate plates, often with spines attached, and is covered by a thin layer of skin. On the skin are **pedicellariae** (PEH dih sih LAH ree ee) (singular, pedicellaria), small pincers that aid in catching food and in removing foreign materials from the skin.

All echinoderms have radial symmetry as adults. In **Figure 2,** you can see this feature in the five arms of the brittle star radiating out from a central disk. However, echinoderm larvae have bilateral symmetry, as shown in **Figure 2.** Bilateral symmetry shows an embryonic link to the vertebrate animals that evolved later.

No other animals with complex organ systems like that of echinoderms have radial symmetry. Scientists theorize that the ancestors of echinoderms did not have radial symmetry. Primitive echinoderms might have been sessile, and radial symmetry developed to enable them to carry on a successful stationary existence. Free-moving echinoderms might have evolved from the sessile animals. Investigate the features of echinoderms in **MiniLab 1.**

Reading Check **Infer** how radial symmetry is important to animals that cannot move quickly.

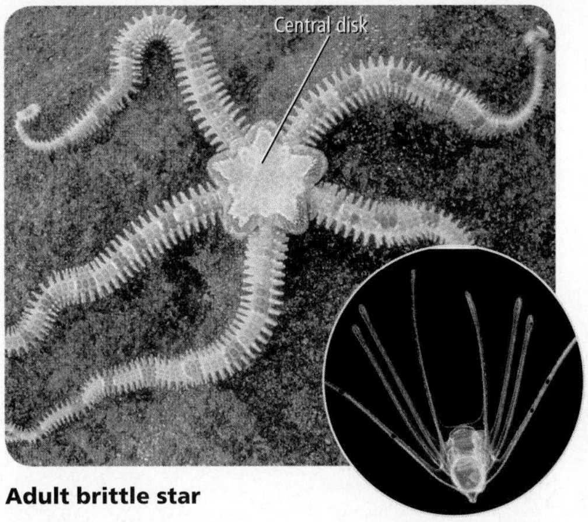

Adult brittle star

Brittle star larva

Figure 2 Brittle star larvae have bilateral symmetry and can be divided along only one plane into mirror-image halves. Adult brittle stars have radial symmetry and can be divided through a central axis, along any plane, into equal halves.

MiniLab 1

Observe Echinoderm Anatomy

Inquiry MiniLab

What are the characteristics of echinoderms? Although they have many shapes and sizes, all echinoderms have some features in common.

Procedure

1. Read and complete the lab safety form.
2. Study preserved specimens of **a sand dollar, a sea cucumber, a sea star,** and **a sea urchin.**
3. Create a data table to record your observations. Complete the table by describing the major features of each specimen. Include a sketch of each specimen.
4. Label any external features you can identify.
5. Clean all equipment and return it to the appropriate place. Wash your hands thoroughly after handling preserved specimens.

Analysis

1. **Compare** the external features of the echinoderms you studied. Can your observations completely justify why these four organisms are classified in the same phylum? Explain.
2. **Infer** which observed features are most important in helping echinoderms avoid being eaten by predators.

MiniLab 1

Inquiry MiniLab

For a lab worksheet, use your eTeacherEdition Online.

RUBRIC A rubric for evaluating MiniLabs is found on your eTeacherEdition Online.

Est. Time 45 min

Alternative Materials This lab could be completed using digital or print photographs of echinoderms, or you can project the figures from this section (found on your eTeacherEdition Online).

Safety Precaution Approve lab safety forms before work begins.

Teaching Strategies

- Specimens may be returned to preservative for future use.
- Limit the number of specimens needed by sharing specimens among student groups.

Analysis

1. Each organism displays radial symmetry, has a hard outer covering, tube feet, and two body openings. Only the sea urchin has extended spines. Only the sea star has rays. While the external features of these organisms show great similarity, they are also classified together based on internal physiology and similarities in development, factors which were not observed in the lab.
2. The hard outer covering, spines, and pedicellariae act as protection.

Demonstration

Echinoderm Larvae Use a microprojector, if available, to show students echinoderm larvae and point out their bilateral symmetry. Remind students that adult echinoderms have radial symmetry. Explain that bilateral larvae demonstrate an embryonic link to vertebrate animals. Est. time: 5 min

Reading Check Radial symmetry enables an animal to detect prey from any direction.

LabManager™

Customize this lab with the LabManager™ CD-ROM.

Visualizing an Echinoderm

Purpose
Students will study form and function of echinoderms using a sea urchin as an example.
UCP.1, UCP.5, C.5

Skill Practice
BL OL AL Visual Literacy
Give students a copy of Figure 3 without labels. Have students study the page and view the Concepts in Motion. Have students close their textbooks and label as many structures as they can on the sea urchin diagram they drew. Also have students explain how the structures are adaptations to this animal's way of life. Have students check their answers with the textbook.
EL Provide students with a list of structures and have them label the structures on their diagram.

Writing Support
OL Creative Writing Have students write and illustrate a story titled "A Day in the Life of a Sea Urchin" from the point of view of a sea urchin.
BL Have students list a sea urchin's activities.

Writing Support
AL Formal Writing Have students write a report on the physics of hydraulic systems. Students should relate what they learn to the tube feet of echinoderms.

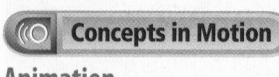

Concepts in Motion
Animation

Visualizing an Echinoderm

Figure 3
Sea urchins can be found in tidal areas of the sea. They burrow into crevices in rocks to hide, and they scrape algae with a hard five-plated structure, called Aristotle's lantern, in their mouths. Imagine that these plates are like teeth that move.

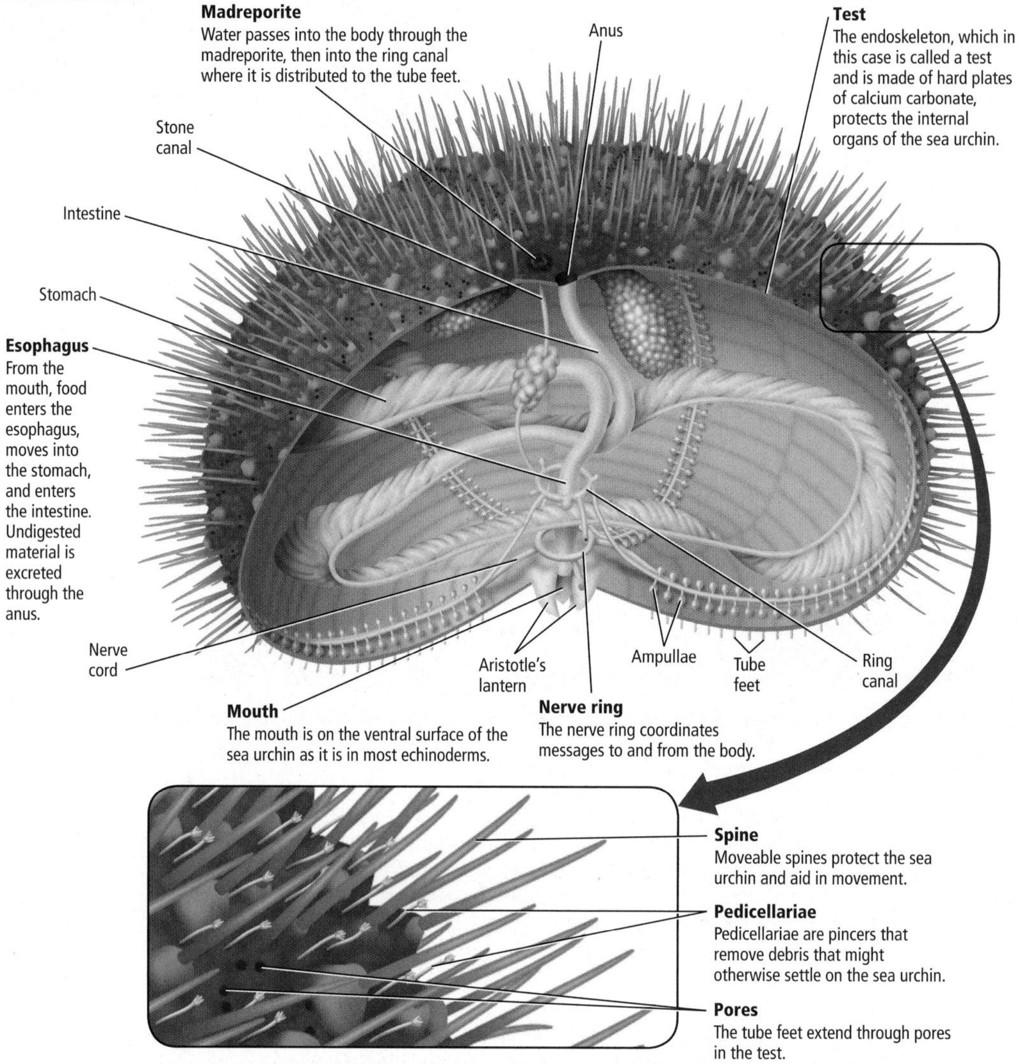

From the mouth, food enters the esophagus, moves into the stomach, and enters the intestine. Undigested material is excreted through the anus.

Ampullae

The nerve ring coordinates messages to and from the body.

Concepts in Motion Animation

Content Background

Cultural Diversity In Japan, sea urchin eggs are eaten as a delicacy. In the United States green sea urchins are harvested in Maine and red urchins are harvested on the Pacific coast to meet the needs of this market. Divers collect sea urchins by hand and dredges mechanically rake the ocean floor for them. Because there are concerns about the decline of sea urchin populations, maximum and minimum size limits have been established so that sea urchins can spawn during many years of their lives. Harvest has been restricted to certain areas, the season has been reduced, and area and individual quotas have been established. In addition, scientists are researching the nutritional requirements of sea urchins in captivity so that they can be farm raised rather than taken from their natural habitat. Pilot farms are currently set up to study the best ways to farm raise sea urchins.

Water-vascular system Another feature of echinoderms is their **water-vascular system**—a system of fluid-filled, closed tubes that work together to enable echinoderms to move and get food. The strainerlike opening to the water-vascular system, shown in **Figure 3,** is called the **madreporite** (MA druh pohr it). Water is drawn into the madreporite, then moves through the stone canal to the ring canal. From there, the water moves to the radial canals and eventually to the tube feet.

D **Tube feet** are small, muscular, fluid-filled tubes that end in suction-cuplike structures and are used in movement, food collection, and respiration. The opposite end of the tube foot is a muscular sac, called the **ampulla** (AM pyew luh). When muscles contract in the ampulla, water is forced into the tube foot and it extends. Imagine holding a small, partly inflated balloon in your hand and squeezing it. The balloon will extend from between your thumb and forefinger, which is similar to the way the tube foot extends. The suction-cuplike structure on the end of the tube foot attaches it to the surface. This hydraulic suction enables all echinoderms to move and some, such as sea stars, to apply a force strong enough to open the shells of mollusks, as illustrated in **Figure 4.** **S**

Feeding and digestion Echinoderms use a great variety of feeding strategies in addition to tube feet. Sea lilies and feather stars extend their arms and trap food. Sea stars prey on a variety of mollusks, coral, and other invertebrates. Many species of sea stars can push their stomachs out of their mouths and onto their prey. They then spread digestive enzymes over the food and use cilia to bring the digested material to their mouths. Brittle stars can be active predators or scavengers, and they can trap organic materials in mucus on their arms. Most sea urchins use teethlike plates, shown in **Figure 3,** to scrape algae off surfaces or feed on other animals. Many sea cucumbers extend their branched, mucus-covered tentacles to trap floating food.

Respiration, circulation, and excretion Echinoderms also use their tube feet in respiration. Oxygen diffuses from the water through the thin membranes of the tube feet. Some echinoderms carry out diffusion of oxygen through all thin body membranes in contact with water. Other echinoderms have thin-walled skin gills that are small pouches extending from the body. Many sea cucumbers have branched tubes, called respiratory trees, through which water passes and oxygen moves into the body.

Circulation takes place in the body coelom and the water-vascular system, while excretion of cellular wastes occurs by diffusion through thin body membranes. Cilia move water and body fluids throughout these systems aided by pumping action in some echinoderms. In spite of the simplicity of these organs and systems, echinoderms maintain homeostasis effectively with adaptations that are suited to their way of life.

Reading Check **Summarize** the functions of an echinoderm's tube feet.

■ **Figure 4** A sea star uses its tube feet to open the two shells of a clam.
Describe *the sea star's feeding method.*

Inquiry Launch Lab
Review Based on what you have read about the water-vascular system, how would you now answer the analysis questions?

Activity

BL OL AL COOP LEARN
Model Tube Feet Divide students into pairs. Provide a dropper to each pair. Have students squeeze the air from the dropper and then touch the dropper to a finger tip and release the bulb. The dropper suction is similar to the suction of tube feet.
Est. time: 10 min

Reading Check Tube feet are used for movement, food collection, and respiration.

■ **Caption Question** **Fig. 4** A sea star uses its tube feet to pry open clams.

D Develop Concepts

BL OL **Activity** Place a live sea star on wet glasslike plastic. Provide students with magnifying lenses to observe the action of tube feet from underneath.

S Skill Practice

BL OL AL
Compare and Contrast
Remind students that scallops and earthworms also use hydraulic pressure for movement. Have students make a diagram that illustrates both the similarities and the differences in how these animals, as well as echinoderms, use hydraulic pressure in movement.

Develop Concepts

BL OL AL **Integrate Geology**
Pass around echinoderm fossils. If you do not have access to echinoderm fossils, use photographs of these fossils. Explain that the parts of an echinoderm that are made of calcium carbonate are the parts that fossilize most readily.
ASK STUDENTS: ***Why do you think it is usually only the hard tissue of an organism that fossilizes?*** Soft tissues decompose more quickly than hard tissue, and hard tissue is able to withstand the weight of layers of sediment over it better than soft tissues.

Inquiry Launch Lab
Assess Content Development
Assess how understanding has developed when students revisit the Launch Lab analysis questions.

Develop Concepts

AL Clarify a Misconception

ASK STUDENTS: ***Which group is more closely related to vertebrates: worms, mollusks, or echinoderms?*** echinoderms Students might think that echinoderm bodies and systems are more complex than those of worms but less complex than those of some mollusks. Some could even think that echinoderms are mollusks because of their hard test that is similar to a shell. Most people do not know that echinoderms, based on similarities in embryological development, are closely related to vertebrates.

Develop Concepts

EL BL OL COOP LEARN Activity

Divide students into pairs. Provide each pair with a microscope and slides of sea urchin development consisting of an unfertilized egg, zygote, 2-cell stage, 4-cell stage, 8-cell stage, blastula, gastrula, and sea urchin larvae. Have students draw diagrams of each stage and label the stage. Students should compare the size of the blastula with that of the zygote, as well as the sizes of the cells in each stage.

Develop Concepts

BL COOP LEARN Activity

Divide students into groups of three and make each group responsible for a bulletin-board display. Provide them with magazines from which to cut pictures of echinoderms, such as sea stars, sand dollars, sea lilies, feather stars, and sea daisies. Instruct students to select pictures of the animals in motion if possible and explain on each picture how the animal moves.

■ **Figure 5** A sea star lifts the end of an arm to sense light and movement.

Response to stimuli Echinoderms have both sensory and motor neurons with varying degrees of complexity in different species. In general, a nerve ring surrounds the mouth with branching nerve cords connecting to other body areas.

Sensory neurons respond to touch, chemicals dissolved in the water, water currents, and light. At the tips of the arms of sea stars are eyespots, clusters of light-sensitive cells, illustrated in **Figure 5.** Many echinoderms also sense the direction of gravity. For example, a sea star will return to an upright position after being overturned by a wave or current.

Movement Echinoderm locomotion is as varied as echinoderm body shapes. The structure of the endoskeleton is important for determining the type of movement an echinoderm can undertake. The movable bony plates in the endoskeletons of echinoderms enable them to move easily. Feather stars move by grasping the soft sediments of the ocean bottom with their cirri—long, thin appendages on their ventral sides—or by swimming with up-and-down movements of their arms. Brittle stars use their tube feet and their arms in snakelike movements for locomotion. Sea stars use their arms and tube feet for crawling. Sea urchins move by using tube feet and burrowing with their movable spines. Sea cucumbers crawl using their tube feet and body wall muscles.

Reading Check **Describe** ways that echinoderms move other than using their tube feet.

VOCABULARY

SCIENCE USAGE V. COMMON USAGE

Structure

Science usage: the arrangement of parts of an organism

The structure of an insect's mouth determines how it functions.

Common usage: something that is constructed, such as a building

The workers built the structure in three months.

Reproduction and development Most echinoderms reproduce sexually. The females shed eggs and the males shed sperm into the water where fertilization takes place. The fertilized eggs develop into free-swimming larvae with bilateral symmetry. After going through a series of changes, the larvae develop into adults with radial symmetry. Recall that echinoderms have deuterostome development, making them an important evolutionary connection to vertebrates.

The sea star in **Figure 6** is regenerating a lost body part. Many echinoderms can drop off an arm when they are attacked, enabling them to flee while the predator is distracted. Others can expel part of their internal organ systems when threatened. This action might surprise and deter predators. The expelled body parts and lost arms can be regenerated.

■ **Figure 6** This sea star is regenerating one of its arms, a process that can take up to one year.
***Explain** how regenerating body parts helps echinoderms survive.*

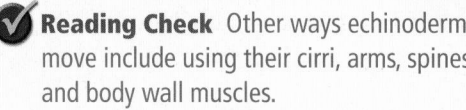

Reading Check Other ways echinoderms move include using their cirri, arms, spines, and body wall muscles.

■ **Caption Question Fig. 6** The lost arm distracts the predator, enabling the sea star or brittle star to escape.

Table 1 **Classes of Echinoderms** Concepts in Motion Interactive Table

Class	Asteroidea	Ophiuroidea	Echinoidea	Crinoidea	Holothuroidea	Concentricycloidea
Examples		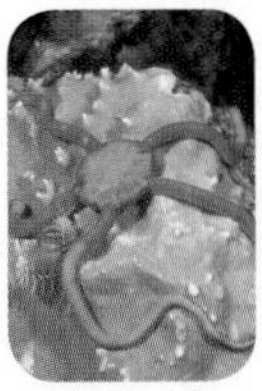			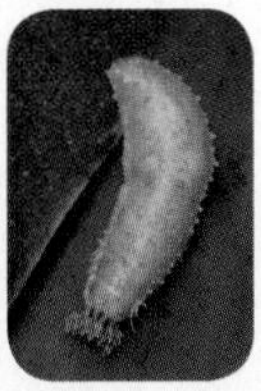	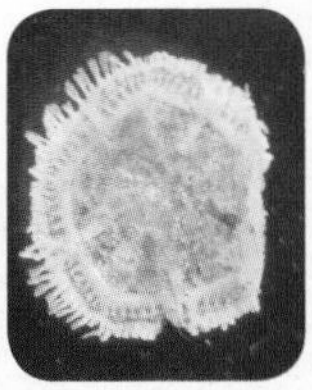
Class Members	Sea stars	Brittle stars	Sea urchins, Sand dollars	Sea lilies, Feather stars	Sea cucumbers	Sea daisies
Distinctive Features	• Often five-armed • Tube feet used for feeding and movement	• Often five-armed • Arms break off easily and can be regenerated • Move by arm movement • Tube feet have no suction cups	• Body encased in a test with spines • Sea urchins burrow in rocky areas. • Sand dollars burrow in sand.	• Sessile for some part of life • Sea lilies have long stalks. • Feather stars have long branching arms.	• Cucumber shape • Leathery outer body • Tube feet modified to tentacles near mouth	• Less than 1 cm in diameter • No arms • Tube feet located around a central disk

Echinoderm Diversity

The major classes of living echinoderms include Asteroidea (AS tuh ROY dee uh), the sea stars; Ophiuroidea (OH fee uh ROY dee uh), the brittle stars; Echinoidea (ih kihn OY dee uh), the sea urchins and sand dollars; Crinoidea (kri NOY dee uh), the sea lilies and feather stars; Holothuroidea (HOH loh thuh ROY dee uh), the sea cucumbers; and Concentricycloidea (kahn sen tri sy CLOY dee uh), the sea daisies. Recall that they all are marine animals with radial symmetry as adults, a water-vascular system with tube feet, endoskeletons often bearing spines, and larvae with bilateral symmetry. The classes of echinoderms are summarized in **Table 1.**

Sea stars If you ever have seen an echinoderm, it probably was a sea star. Most species of sea stars have five arms arranged around a central disk. Some, such as the one in **Figure 7,** have more than five arms. Sea stars can be found in shallow water near the shore and in tide pools when the tide recedes. They can be found in groups clinging to rocks by means of their tube feet. A single tube foot can exert a pull of 0.25–0.30 N. This is equal to the force required to lift 25–30 large paper clips. Because a sea star might have as many as 2000 tube feet, it can exert quite a large force as it crawls or opens mollusks for food. Sea stars are important predators in marine ecosystems, feeding on clams and other bivalves. Because of their spiny skin, sea stars usually are not food for other marine predators.

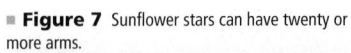

Figure 7 Sunflower stars can have twenty or more arms.

Concepts in Motion
Interactive Table

Skill Practice

EL BL Visual Literacy

Have students make a puzzle of Table 1 by doing the following: Make a copy of the table, cut up the table along the lines, and place all the pieces for one table in an envelope. After students have studied Table 1 and think they understand echinoderm classification, have them close their books and take all the pieces out of the envelope and put them together in the correct positions to reconstruct the table.

Critical Thinking

BL OL AL Hypothesize

ASK STUDENTS: ***What might happen to a marine ecosystem if fishes that eat sea cucumbers died out or were harvested to extinction?*** The population of sea cucumbers would increase, followed by a decrease in the organisms they consume. Sea cucumbers would then probably decrease after their food supply decreased.

> *“Education is not the filling of a bucket, but the lighting of a fire.”*
>
> —William B. Yeats

Research Citation

Reading Strategies Educational research indicates that making predictions is a valuable strategy that students can use to better understand a text. Students learn to anticipate the context of the reading by using the headings as cues and then evaluating their predictions as they read the text. (Blackowicz, 1986)

Research bibliography on pages 32T–34T

R Reading Strategy

EL BL OL **Brainstorm** Before students read this page, have them write a list of what they know about brittle stars, sea urchins, and sand dollars in three columns on their paper. As they read, instruct them to add to the lists and cross out any misconceptions they might have had. Have students share their lists with the class to start a discussion.

C Critical Thinking

OL AL **Hypothesize**

ASK STUDENTS: ***How might brittle stars benefit from having light-gathering sensors on their bodies?*** Possible answer: If they know exactly where the light is, they can easily hide in a dark place away from predators.

D Develop Concepts

BL OL AL COOP LEARN

Role Play Divide students into groups of four. Have the groups stage a debate about whether sea urchins should be harvested or collected and sold for food. In each group, one person will be a diver who makes his/her living harvesting sea urchins. The other three members will be a sea urchin consumer, a scientist studying sea urchins, and a person wanting to protect sea urchins. Have students use research to defend the position assigned to them and then have the teams debate in front of the class.

? Inquiry BioLab

The lab at the end of the chapter can be used at this point in the lesson.

■ **Figure 8** One type of brittle star, the basket star, extends its branched arms into the current to filter feed.
***Analyze** how brittle stars are different from sea stars.*

R **Brittle stars** Like sea stars, most brittle stars have five arms, but the brittle star's arms are thin and very flexible, as shown in **Figure 8.** They do not have suckers on their tube feet, so they cannot use them for movement as sea stars do. Brittle stars move by rowing themselves quickly over the bottom rocks and sediments or by snakelike movements of their arms. When attacked by a predator, a brittle star can release an arm and make a quick getaway. The missing arm will be regenerated later. Brittle stars hide in the crevices of rocks by day and feed at night. They feed on small particles suspended in the water or catch suspended materials on mucous strands between their spines.

Some brittle stars respond to light. The spherical structures covering the body of these brittle stars might function as light-gathering lenses. Brittle stars are more abundant and have more numbers of species than any other class of echinoderm. C

Reading Check **Compare and contrast** the locomotion of sea stars and brittle stars.

Sea urchins and sand dollars Burrowing is a key characteristic of sea urchins and sand dollars. Sand dollars can be found in shallow water burrowing into the sand, while sea urchins burrow into rocky areas. These echinoderms each have a compact body enclosed in a hard endoskeleton, called a test, that looks like a shell. The tube feet extend through pores in the test. Closely fitting plates of calcium carbonate make up the test. Sea urchins and sand dollars lack arms, but their tests reflect the five-part pattern of arms in sea stars and brittle stars. Spines also are an important feature of this class, as seen in **Figure 9.** Some sea urchin spines and pedicellariae contain venom and are used for fending off predators. The poison in pedicellariae can paralyze prey. Sea urchins also can be herbivorous grazers, scraping algae from rocks, while sand dollars filter organic particles from the sand in which they are partially buried. D

■ **Figure 9** Sea urchins burrow themselves into rocky crevices with their sharp, movable spines. Sand dollars burrow themselves into the sand, where they filter out small food particles.

Sand dollar

Sea urchins

Reading Check Both sea stars and brittle stars use their arms for locomotion. Sea stars move using the suction created by their tube feet. Brittle stars move by rowing or snakelike movements of their arms.

■ **Caption Question** **Fig. 8** A brittle star's arms are thinner and more flexible than a sea star's arms. Also, a brittle star does not have suckers on its tube feet, so it moves by rowing with its arms.

Aristotle's lantern **Five-sided lantern**

■ **Figure 10** Aristotle's lantern is a five-sided mouthpart similar in shape to a five-sided lantern. The force of a sea urchin's chewing plates is so strong that it has been known to chew through concrete.

Connection to History Most sea urchins have a chewing apparatus inside their mouths consisting of five hard plates, similar to teeth. This structure, shown in **Figure 10,** is called Aristotle's lantern. It was named after a description written by Aristotle, a Greek philosopher, in his book *Historia Animalium* (The History of Animals). During Aristotle's lifetime in the fourth century B.C., people used five-sided lanterns with side panels made of thin, translucent horn, called horn lanterns. Aristotle thought the mouth of a sea urchin looked like a horn lantern without the panels.

R **Sea lilies and feather stars** Fossil records show that sea lilies and feather stars are the most ancient of the echinoderms and were abundant before other echinoderms evolved. They are different from other echinoderms in that they are sessile for part of their lives. As shown in **Figure 11,** sea lilies have a flower-shaped body at the top of a long stalk, while the long-branched arms of feather stars radiate upward from a central area. Though they might stay in one place for a long time, sea lilies and feather stars can detach themselves and move elsewhere. Both sea lilies and feather stars capture food by extending their tube feet and arms into the water, where they catch suspended organic materials.

Reading Check **Describe** how feather stars and sea lilies are similar.

■ **Figure 11** This fossil illustrates how a sea lily's body is flower-shaped at the tip of a long stalk. The feather star attaches to the sea floor with its cirri while its arms extend from a central point.
***Infer** how the arms of feather stars are adapted to a lifestyle that includes little movement.*

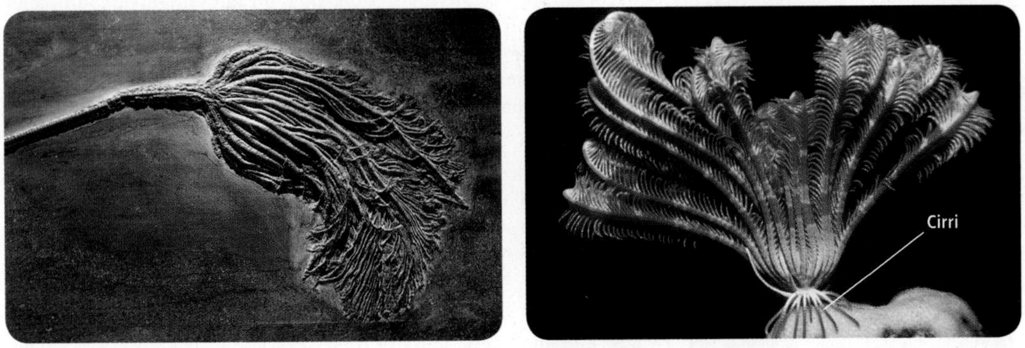

Sea lily **Feather star**

Develop Concepts

BL OL AL Field Trip Plan a field trip to a nearby aquarium or zoo that has displays of saltwater organisms including echinoderms. If there is no local aquarium or zoo, you could visit a nearby pet shop that specializes in saltwater organisms. Plan your visit to coincide with the times that sea stars and sea urchins are being fed. Have students make notes of the feeding behavior they observe. If possible, ask the caretakers to explain the care provided for echinoderms.

Critical Thinking

AL Infer

SAY TO STUDENTS: ***Infer why there are no freshwater echinoderms.*** The sea has a more consistent temperature, chemical makeup, and other consistent abiotic factors than freshwater ponds, lakes, and streams. Echinoderms evolved in saltwater and have not moved to freshwater because their adaptations are very specific to saltwater. Other reasonable answers may also be accepted.

R Reading Strategy

BL COOP LEARN

Find Supporting Details

Divide students into pairs. Have the pairs read the paragraphs under the heads *Sea lilies and feather stars* and *Sea cucumbers.* As they read, have them identify the main idea in each paragraph and list the details that support the main idea. Each pair should present one of their details to the class. Have the pairs add details to their lists as others present.

Reading Check Both are sessile for part or all of their lives, and both feed by catching suspended food with their tube feet and arms.

■ **Caption Question Fig. 11** The long, feathery arms enable feather stars to catch food suspended in the water.

Differentiated Instruction

Physically Disabled If taking students on a field trip, make preparations in advance for students with physical disabilities. Know the students' abilities and talk with them before the field trip about modifications that might be needed.

For more tips, see pages 14T–15T.

Develop Concepts

BL OL AL COOP LEARN

Activity Divide students into groups of three. Have the groups assume that they are in charge of creating a sanctuary for echinoderms on a small section of beach that used to be public. Groups should develop a campaign to educate the public about why this section of the beach is now closed. A variety of media should be used—everything from bumper stickers to TV spots to newspaper articles. Tell students that they must have the scientific evidence to back up what they say about echinoderms. Have students present their campaigns to the class.

Develop Concepts

EL BL OL AL COOP LEARN

Activity Divide students into groups of two or three. Have students make a mobile or diorama that depicts each of the echinoderm groups. Have students identify an important adaptation of each group in their mobile or diorama.

Writing Support

AL Narrative Writing

Have students research the impact of sea stars on the mollusk-fishing industry, then write a newspaper article about a supposed sea star invasion, its economic impact, and what the fishers did to combat it. Detail which measures were effective at controlling the sea stars and which measures (such as chopping up sea stars) made the situation worse.

Figure 12 Some of a sea cucumber's tube feet are modified to form tentacles around its mouth. Look closely to see how these tentacles are used to collect food.

Identify ***what substance coats the tentacles and helps trap food particles.***

CAREERS IN BIOLOGY

Marine Biologist Scientists in this field study plants and animals, such as echinoderms, that live in the ocean. They also study how pollution affects the marine environment.

Sea cucumbers Sea cucumbers do not look like other echinoderms. Some might say they do not even look like animals. Can you guess why they are called sea cucumbers? They look like cartoon cucumbers creeping over the ocean floor. Their elongated bodies move sluggishly by means of tube feet assisted by contractions in their muscular body wall. Their calcium carbonate plates are reduced in size and do not connect as they do in other echinoderms, so their outer bodies generally appear leathery. Some of their tube feet are modified to form tentacles that extend from around their mouths to trap suspended food particles, as shown in **Figure 12.** The tentacles are covered with mucus, which increases their ability to trap food. Once food has been trapped on a tentacle, it is drawn into the mouth where the food is sucked off. This process is similar to licking your finger after putting it in a bowl of pudding.

Sea cucumbers are the only echinoderms to have respiratory organs in the form of respiratory trees. These many-branched tubes pump in seawater through the anus for oxygen extraction. The respiratory tree also functions in excretion by removing cellular wastes.

When a sea cucumber is threatened, it can cast out some of its internal organs through its anus. A potential predator might be confused by this action and move on. The sea cucumber can regenerate its lost parts. Even though the sea cucumber's adaptations might seem odd, it is important to remember that this animal maintains homeostasis with adaptations that fit its way of life in its particular habitat.

Figure 13 Sea daisies are tiny disc-shaped echinoderms.

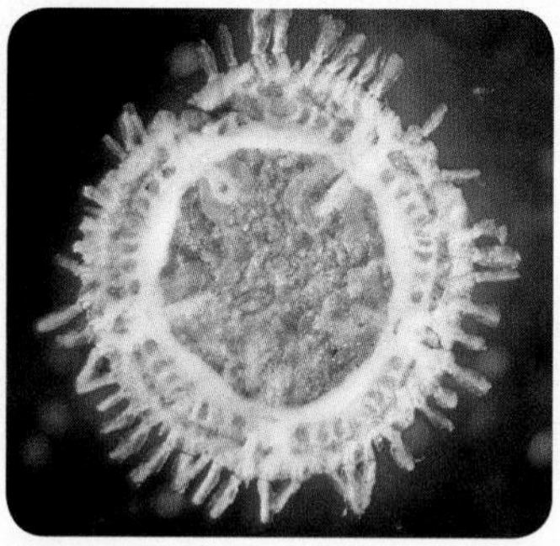

Sea daisies Discovered in 1986 off the coast of New Zealand, sea daisies have been difficult to classify and study, because so few have been found. They are less than 1 cm in diameter and are disc-shaped with no arms. Their tube feet are located around the edge of the disc. **Figure 13** shows that they have five-part radial symmetry, as do other echinoderms. Notice the daisy pattern of petals, or tube feet, around the edges of the disc.

Reading Check **Classify** What characteristics place sea daisies in the phylum Echinodermata?

Demonstration

BL OL AL Sea Cucumbers Pass around a live or preserved sea cucumber for students to observe.

ASK STUDENTS: ***What adaptations to its way of life do you observe in the sea cucumber?*** tentacles that are used to trap food particles, body shape suited to crawling on the ocean floor (could have protective coloration, depending on the species)

Est. time: 10 min

Reading Check They have tube feet and five-part radial symmetry.

Caption Question **Fig. 12** mucus

Ecology of Echinoderms

Sea cucumbers and sea urchins are sources of food for people in some countries. The muscles of certain sea cucumbers are eaten as sushi, and dried sea cucumbers are added to flavor soups, vegetables, and meat. The egg masses of sea urchins are eaten raw or slightly cooked.

Commensal relationships exist between some echinoderms and other marine animals. Recall that commensalism is a relationship in which one organism benefits and the other organism is neither helped nor harmed. For example, some species of brittle stars live inside sponges. The brittle star leaves the protective interior of the sponge and feeds on materials that have settled on the sponge.

Echinoderm benefits Marine ecosystems also depend on some echinoderms. When populations of echinoderms decline, a change in the ecosystem is often noted. For example, a sea urchin species that lives in the Caribbean and the Florida keys declined in numbers by more than 95 percent in 1983 due to disease. After this, algae increased greatly on the coral reefs and virtually destroyed the reefs in many areas. Sea urchins and sea cucumbers are bioturbators—organisms that stir up sediment on the ocean floor. This action is important to the entire marine ecosystem, as it makes nutrients in the seafloor available to other organisms.

Echinoderm harm Some echinoderms can harm marine ecosystems. The crown-of-thorns sea star shown in the photo at the beginning of this chapter feeds on coral polyps. When these sea stars increase in numbers, coral reefs are destroyed. Although the causes of the population explosions of these sea stars continue to be debated, the numbers seem to decline on their own. At a later time, they might increase again with no apparent explanation. Sea urchins are a favorite food of sea otters, as shown in **Figure 14.** The number of sea otters in California has declined in recent years, leading to an increase in the number of sea urchins. The sea urchins are eating the kelp forests, destroying the habitat of fish, snails, and crabs.

Figure 14 Without enough sea otters to keep the sea urchin population under control, sea urchins will continue to increase in number, threatening the kelp forests on which they feed.

W

W Writing Support

AL Technical Writing Have students research and write an illustrated report on the relationship between crown-of-thorns sea stars and coral reefs.

Formative Assessment

Evaluation Conduct a lab practical with 15 stations showing examples of echinoderm features (cirri, sea star arm, spine, pedicellaria, etc.). Place two questions at each station and have students record their answers on a sheet of paper. Give students one minute at each station to answer the questions. (Example questions and answers: Station #1 with dried sea star: 1. Name the structure that is flagged with the pin and labeled. 2. What is its function? 1. madreporite 2. opening to water-vascular system. Use actual specimens or illustrations.

Remediation Have the class list 16 echinoderm structures and brainstorm questions about the structures. Write the questions on the board. Pass out bingo cards made by making copies of a rectangle with 16 squares. Have each student randomly write a structure in each square and then exchange cards with another student. Read the question about each term, allowing students with correct answers to place chips on their cards. Have students play this bingo game until they get a row of four terms vertically, horizontally, or diagonally.

Section 1 Assessment

Section Summary

- Echinoderms are deuterostomes.
- Adult members of phylum Echinodermata have four major common characteristics.
- Larval echinoderms have bilateral symmetry, which is considered an evolutionary link to chordates.
- Echinoderms exhibit great diversity in feeding and digestion, respiration, circulation, and excretion.
- There are six major classes of living echinoderms.

Understand Main Ideas

1. MAIN Idea Identify the four main features that distinguish adult echinoderms.
2. **Explain** how a water-vascular system works.
3. **Sketch** line drawings that represent each of the six classes of echinoderms.
4. **Suggest** how feeding and movement are related to each other in echinoderms.

Think Critically

5. **Hypothesize** A certain species of red-and-white-striped shrimp is often found on a species of colorful brittle stars. Form a hypothesis about the relationship between the shrimp and the brittle stars.

MATH in Biology

6. If it takes a force of 20 N to pull apart a bivalve's shells, how many tube feet will it take to pull apart a bivalve if each tube foot has a pull of 0.25 N?

Section 1 Assessment

1. endoskeletons, radial symmetry, water-vascular system, tube feet
2. Water is drawn in through the madreporite and moves through the stone canal to the ring canal where it moves into radial canals and eventually to tube feet. When muscles contract in the ampulla, water is forced into the tube foot and it extends. Suction is created on the surface where the tube foot attaches.
3. Make sure students' sketches reflect the basic shapes of each of the six classes of echinoderms.
4. Many echinoderms feed by using their tube feet. For example, sea stars use tube feet to pry open bivalves. Sea cucumbers have modified tube feet used to trap food. Both sea stars and sea cucumbers and other echinoderms also use their tube feet for creeping locomotion.
5. Possible answer: The coloring of the shrimp enables it to hide from predators among the colorful arms of the brittle star.
6. 80 tube feet

Section 2

MAIN Idea

BL OL AL Backbones Have students run their fingers up and down their backbones as far as they can with each hand.
ASK STUDENTS: ***Can you feel the separate vertebrae that comprise your vertebral column?*** Answers will vary. Explain that the backbone is a structure that only vertebrate animals have. It is formed from the notochord, a structure that all members of the phylum Chordata have. All chordates have a notochord at some point in their development, but not all adult chordates have backbones.

R Reading Strategy

BL OL Predict Have students study the headings in this section and change them into questions. Students should write down these questions and their predictions for the answers. As students read the text, have them correct their answers.

Skill Practice

BL OL AL

Observe and Compare Place illustrations of echinoderms and invertebrate chordates into two containers. Have students choose one illustration from each container. Instruct students to closely examine the two illustrations. Then have students explain any connections, similarities, or relationships that they can see in the illustrations. Answers will vary depending on the illustrations selected.

Section 2

Reading Preview

Essential Questions

- What are the features of invertebrate chordates that place them in the phylum Chordata?
- What are the features of invertebrate chordates that place them with invertebrates?
- What are the similarities between the adaptations of lancelets and sea squirts?

Review Vocabulary

deuterostome: an animal whose mouth develops from cells other than those at the opening of the gastrula

New Vocabulary

chordate
invertebrate chordate
notochord
postanal tail
dorsal tubular nerve cord
pharyngeal pouch

g Multilingual eGlossary

Invertebrate Chordates

MAIN Idea Invertebrate chordates have features linking them to vertebrate chordates.

Real-World Reading Link Worms, snails, bees, fishes, birds, and dogs are all animals because they share common characteristics. Think about the features these animals have in common and the features that make them different from each other. The animals that share the most features are related more closely than the animals that share only a few features.

R Invertebrate Chordate Features

Look at **Figure 15,** the evolutionary tree of animal phylogeny. Chordates are deuterostomes like echinoderms but they have additional features that echinoderms do not have. Invertebrate chordates include lancelets and tunicates.

Fossil evidence suggests animals such as the lancelet, shown in **Figure 15,** separated from the echinoderms during the Cambrian period. This group of animals is known as the invertebrate chordates. It has become a diverse group over the last 500 million years. The lancelet is also called an amphioxus (am fee AHK sus).

The lancelet is a small eel-like animal that spends most of its life buried in the sand filtering the water for food. They are tiny, headless creatures with translucent, fish-shaped bodies. Fossil and molecular data show that the lancelet is one of the closest living relatives of vertebrates. In 2007, genetic studies showed that tunicates, shown in **Figure 15,** are the closest invertebrate relative to vertebrates. You are more closely related to the lancelet and tunicate than you are to any other invertebrate—yet related very distantly compared to other vertebrates.

■ **Figure 15** Like echinoderms, invertebrate chordates, such as lancelets and tunicates, show deuterostome development.

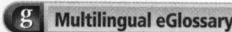

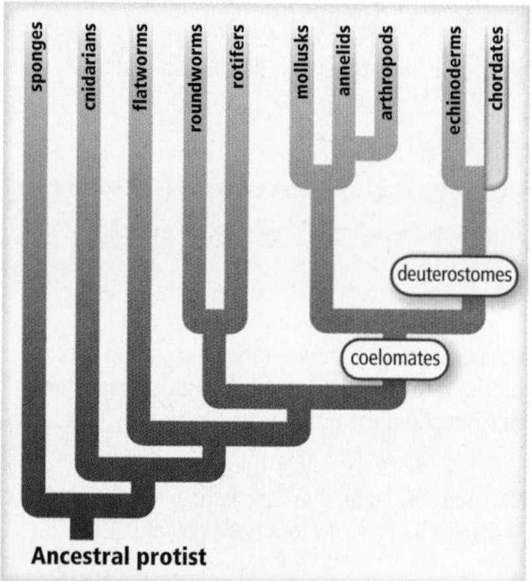

Lancelet

Tunicate

Demonstration

Cross Sections and Longitudinal Sections Review with students the differences between cross sections and longitudinal sections by giving them a store-bought snack cake that has an elongated shape and frosting in the middle. Cut one crosswise and another lengthwise to show the difference in the appearance of the frosting in the two snack cakes. It is best to use a chocolate snack cake that has white frosting. Relate this to the cross and longitudinal sections students will see in chapter illustrations, such as in Figure 16. Est. time: 5 min

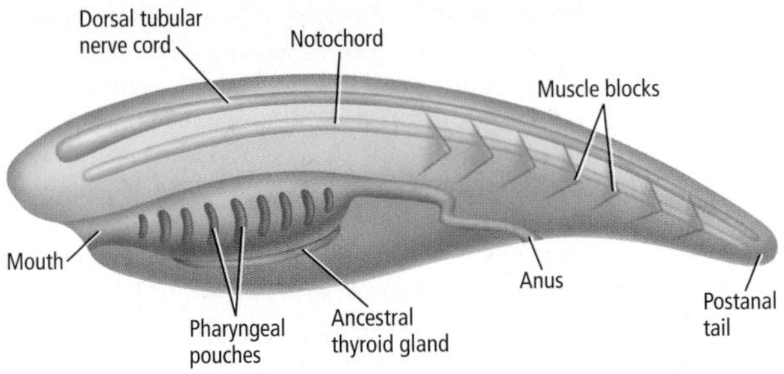

■ **Figure 16** Chordates have a dorsal tubular nerve cord, a notochord, pharyngeal pouches, a postanal tail, and, possibly, some form of a thyroid gland.
***Infer** which of these features you had when you were an embryo.*

Chordates are animals belonging to the phylum Chordata (kor DAH tuh) that have four distinctive features at some point in their development—a dorsal tubular nerve cord, a notochord, pharyngeal pouches, and a postanal tail. Recent evidence suggests that all chordates also might have some form of a thyroid gland. In addition, they have a coelom and segmentation. Study **Figure 16** to see the main features of chordates. Recall that vertebrates are animals with backbones. Most chordates are vertebrates. **Invertebrate chordates,** which belong to two of the subphyla of chordates, Cephalochordata and Urochordata, also have a dorsal tubular nerve cord, a notochord, pharyngeal pouches, a postanal tail, and, possibly, an ancestral thyroid gland. However, they have no backbone.

Notochord The **notochord** (NOH tuh kord) is a flexible, rodlike structure that extends the length of the body. It is located just below the dorsal tubular nerve cord. In most vertebrates, the notochord eventually is replaced by bone or cartilage. In invertebrate chordates, the notochord remains. The flexibility of the notochord enables the body to bend, rather than shorten, during contractions of the muscle segments. An animal with a notochord can make side-to-side movements of the body and tail, the first time in the course of evolution that fishlike swimming is made possible.

Postanal tail A free-swimming animal moves efficiently by using a postanal tail. A **postanal tail** is a structure used primarily for locomotion and is located behind the digestive system and anus. In most chordates, the postanal tail extends beyond the anus. Tails in nonchordates have parts of the digestive system inside and the anus is located at the end of the tail. The postanal tail with its muscle segments can propel an animal with more powerful movements than the body structure of invertebrates without a postanal tail.

Dorsal tubular nerve cord In nonchordates, the nerve cords are ventral to, or below, the digestive system and are solid. Chordates have a **dorsal tubular nerve cord** that is located dorsal to, or above, the digestive organs and is a tube shape. The anterior end of this cord becomes the brain and the posterior end becomes the spinal cord during development of most chordates.

Reading Check **Analyze** how a notochord is important to invertebrate chordates.

VOCABULARY
WORD ORIGIN
Notochord
noto- prefix; from Greek, meaning *back.*
-chord from Greek, meaning *cord* or *string*

FOLDABLES®
Incorporate information from this section into your Foldable.

FOLDABLES®

✻RUBRIC A rubric for evaluating Foldables is found on your eTeacherEdition Online.

Going Further On the back of their Foldables, have students draw a Venn diagram comparing and contrasting invertebrate chordates and vertebrate chordates.

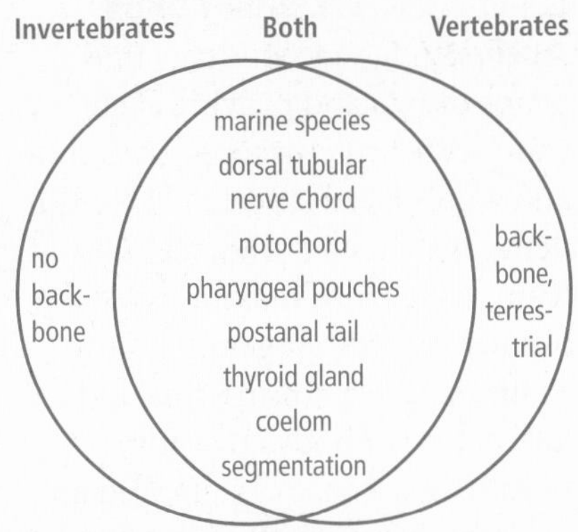

Critical Thinking

OL AL Design an Experiment Have students assume that they found some tadpole-like animals in a tide pool at the seashore and begin to study them in a laboratory. Instruct students to design an experiment in which they could tell if the animals are larvae or adults. Make sure they observe the animals for several weeks and note any changes in their body structures and symmetry and look for reproductive behavior and release of gametes.

Reading Check The notochord allows invertebrate chordates to make side-to-side movements.

■ **Caption Question Fig. 16** dorsal tubular nerve cord, notochord, pharyngeal pouches, postanal tail, and a thyroid gland

Activity

BL COOP LEARN Model Invertebrate Chordates and Echinoderms Divide students into groups of three. Provide groups with clay, modeling dough, or salt dough. Instruct each group to make a sea star, a sea urchin, sand dollar, sea cucumber, lancelet, and a tunicate.

ASK STUDENTS: ***How are these animals adapted to their habitats?*** Echinoderms have tube feet that aid in movement and getting food. They have a spiny endoskeleton that protects them. Lancelets have a shape that enables them to swim, while tunicates have a baglike form that enables them to be sessile filter-feeders. Est. time: 30 min

Writing Support

AL Technical Writing Have students research and write a report on the phylum Hemichordata. Students should describe their habitat, adaptations, and tell how they are related to echinoderms and chordates.

D Develop Concepts

EL BL OL AL COOP LEARN

Activity Divide students into teams of two and provide each team with a microscope, glass slide and a preserved lancelet. Have students sketch what they see. As a team, have them make a list of the following features: general body shape, length (in mm), fins and tail, nature of body covering, mouth area, sense organs, and any other body features they notice. **ASK STUDENTS:** ***In what ways is a lancelet similar to a fish? In what ways is it different from a fish?*** It is like a fish in its shape and tail. Unlike a fish, it does not have gills, fins, or a head.

D Develop Concepts

BL OL AL Scaffolding

SAY TO STUDENTS: ***Describe a lancelet's way of life.*** It burrows its body into the sand and filter feeds. ***Describe filter feeding in a lancelet.*** Water enters the mouth and passes through the pharyngeal gill slits where food is trapped and passed on for digestion. ***How do segmented muscle blocks help a lancelet in its way of life?*** Lancelets can swim with an efficient fishlike motion. ***How is the lancelet's external structure similar to the external structure of a fish?*** It has a streamlined shape. ***Are you more closely related to a lancelet or to a sea star? Explain.*** lancelet, because they have some chordate features that echinoderms do not have, such as a notochord, dorsal, tubular nerve cord, and pharyngeal pouches.

Study Tip

Cooperation Form a group with four other students. Each group member should pick one of the five boldfaced headings under the heading *Invertebrate Chordate Features.* Each group member should read the selected section and then teach the rest of the group the material presented in that section of text.

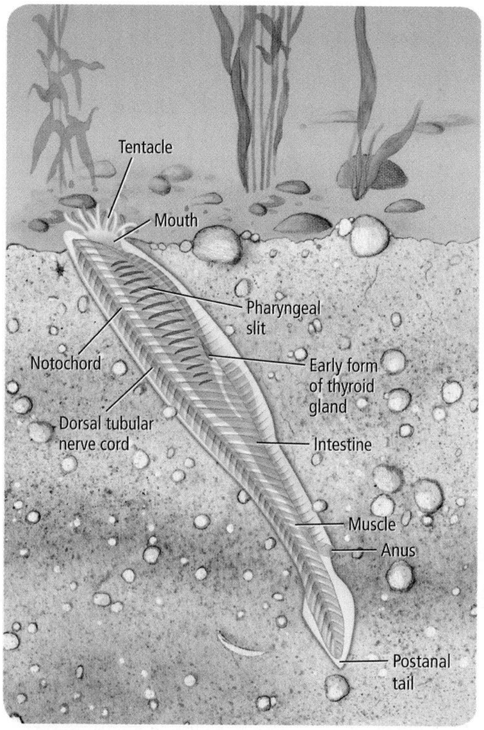

Figure 17 The lancelet is an invertebrate chordate that has the main features of chordates.
Infer *how the short tentacles surrounding the lancelet's mouth might function.*

Pharyngeal pouches In all embryos, paired structures called **pharyngeal pouches** connect the muscular tube that links the mouth cavity and the esophagus. In aquatic chordates, the pouches contain slits that lead to the outside. These structures were used first for filter feeding and later evolved into gills for gas exchange in water. In terrestrial chordates, the pharyngeal pouches do not contain slits and develop into other structures, such as the tonsils and the thymus gland. Pharyngeal pouches are thought to be evidence of the aquatic ancestry of all vertebrates.

Ancestral thyroid gland The thyroid gland is a structure that regulates metabolism, growth, and development. An early form of a thyroid gland had its origins in cells of early chordates that secreted mucus as an aid in filter feeding. Invertebrate chordates have an endostyle—cells in this same area that secrete proteins similar to those secreted by the thyroid gland. Only vertebrate chordates have a thyroid gland.

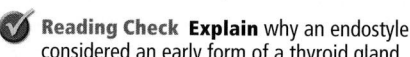

Connection to Health Iodine is concentrated in the endostyle and plays an important role in thyroid gland function. It is essential for the production of thyroid hormones. In the United States, iodine is added to salt to prevent iodine deficiency. Other sources of iodine include fish, dairy products, and vegetables grown in iodine-rich soil.

Reading Check **Explain** why an endostyle is considered an early form of a thyroid gland.

Diversity of Invertebrate Chordates

Like echinoderms, all invertebrate chordates are marine animals. There are about 23 species of lancelets belonging to subphylum Cephalochordata. Tunicates, in subphylum Urochordata, consist of about 1250 species.

Lancelets Recall the amphioxus at the beginning of this section. Most lancelets belong to the genus *Branchiostoma* (formerly *Amphioxus*). They are small, fishlike animals without scales. As shown in **Figure 17,** lancelets burrow their bodies into the sand in shallow seas. D

Lancelets lack color in their skin, which is only one cell layer deep, enabling an observer to view some body functions and structures. Water flowing through the body can be observed as a lancelet filter feeds. To get food, water enters the mouth of the lancelet and passes through pharyngeal gill slits. Food is trapped and passed on to a stomachlike structure to be digested. Water exits through the gill slits. D

Reading Check Endostyles secrete proteins similar to those secreted by the thyroid gland.

Caption Question Fig. 17 Accept all reasonable responses. Possible answer: The tentacles catch food suspended in the water.

Research Citation

Hands-on Activities Educational research indicates that hands-on activities like one described on this page can increase students' engagement in a lesson. Students can use microscopes to observe specimens, thus providing them with concrete visual examples of the concepts being learned.

(Wood and Turner-Vorbeck, 2001)

Research bibliography on pages 32T–34T

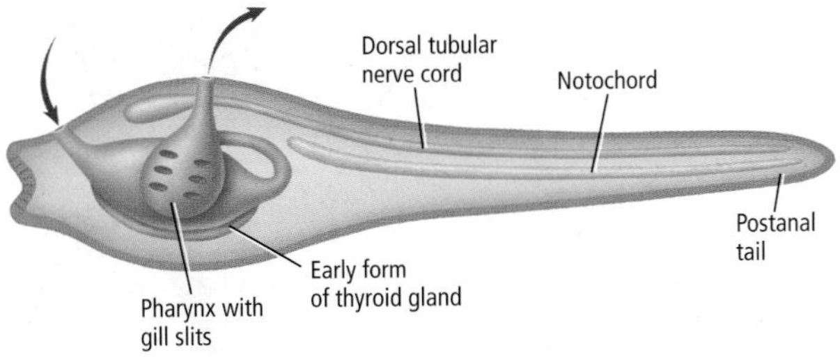

■ **Figure 18** Larval tunicates look like tadpoles and have all of the chordate features. The arrows indicate where water flows into and out of the body.

Just as filter feeding can be observed in the lancelet, its muscles can also be seen. Observe the internal structures of a lancelet in **Figure 17.** The arrangement of segmented muscle blocks is similar to that in vertebrates, enabling lancelets to swim with a fishlike motion. Unlike vertebrates, they have no heads or sensory structures other than light receptors and small sensory tentacles near the mouth. The nervous system consists of main branching nerves and a simple brain at the anterior end of the animal. Blood passes through the body by the action of pumping blood vessels, as there is no true heart. Lancelets have separate sexes, and fertilization is external.

S **Tunicates** Often called sea squirts, tunicates (TEW nuh kayts) are named for the thick outer covering, called a tunic, that covers their small, saclike bodies. Most tunicates live in shallow water; some live in masses on the ocean floor. In general, tunicates are sessile, and only in the larval stages do they show typical chordate features. Locate the notochord, postanal tail, dorsal tubular nerve cord, pharyngeal pouches, and ancestral thyroid gland on the tunicate larva in **Figure 18.**

Water is drawn into the saclike body of an adult tunicate through the incurrent siphon, as shown in **Figure 19,** by the action of beating cilia. Food particles are trapped in a mucous net and moved into the stomach where digestion takes place. In the meantime, water leaves the body, first through gill slits in the pharynx and then out through the excurrent siphon.

Circulation in the body of the tunicate is performed by a heart and blood vessels that deliver nutrients and oxygen to body organs. The nervous system consists of a main nerve complex and branching neurons. Tunicates are hermaphrodites—they produce both eggs and sperm—with external fertilization.

Why are tunicates called sea squirts? When they are disturbed, they eject a stream of water with force through the excurrent siphon, possibly distracting a **D** potential predator.

Reading Check **Compare** tunicates and lancelets.

■ **Figure 19** Adult tunicates look like sacs. The only chordate features that remain in the adult are pharyngeal gill slits and the thyroid gland. The arrows indicate water flow in and out of the body. **Compare** ***other invertebrates that you have studied that are filter feeders.***

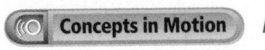

Concepts in Motion **Animation**

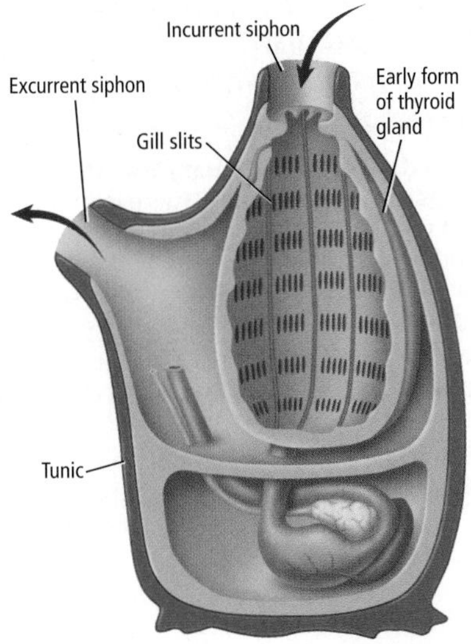

S Skill Practice

OL **COOP LEARN**

Observe and Infer Divide students into teams of two. Provide each team with a preserved or mounted specimen of a tunicate and a binocular microscope. **ASK STUDENTS:** ***What characteristics can you see that make these animals invertebrate chordates?*** cannot see anything in an adult tunicate that indicates that these animals are invertebrate chordates ***What structures do tunicates have that you cannot see that link them to vertebrate chordates?*** In larval stages, notochord and dorsal tubular nerve cord can be found.

Concepts in Motion

Animation

D Develop Concepts

BL **OL**

Clarify a Misconception

ASK STUDENTS: ***Is a tunicate more closely related to a worm or a shark?*** a shark When given an opportunity to see a tunicate, most people would think that it is on the same phylogenetic level as worms and mollusks. They might not know that it is a close relative of vertebrate chordates with notochord and dorsal tubular nerve cord. By showing illustrations of the larvae of tunicates as well as adult planktonic tunicates, pointing out the notochord and dorsal tubular nerve cord of these animals, this misconception can be dispelled.

Reading Check Both are invertebrate chordates that filter feed.

■ **Caption Question** **Fig. 19** sponges, some mollusks

Demonstration

Lancelets and Tunicates Students might not be as familiar with lancelets and tunicates as they are with other groups of animals they have studied. Make an illustrated presentation of lancelets and tunicates in their natural habitat. Point out adaptations such as filter feeding and, in the lancelet, the fishlike form and the baglike structure of tunicates. Explain that of all the invertebrates, these animals are human's closest invertebrate relatives. The term *invertebrate chordate* might seem to be a contradiction to some students. Review the differences between vertebrates and invertebrates.
Est. time: 15 min

S Skill Practice

OL AL Visual Literacy Have students study the cladogram in Figure 20. Ask students to explain, in a few sentences, what the cladogram shows regarding the phylogeny of echinoderms. Possible answer: Echinoderms evolved from ancestors with bilateral symmetry.

DATA ANALYSIS LAB 1

About the Lab

- Review the basics of cladograms with your students.
- Review how cladograms are different from phylogenetic trees.
- Difficulties with understanding phylogenic relationships in echinoderms often result from lack of information about various groups, especially their modes of reproduction.
- Also see Smith, A.B. 2004. Comment on: Paleontology: echinoderm roots. *Nature* 430: 411–412.

Think Critically

1. D
2. *L. Polaris*
3. L, K, M; This group has more divisions, which indicates more diversity.

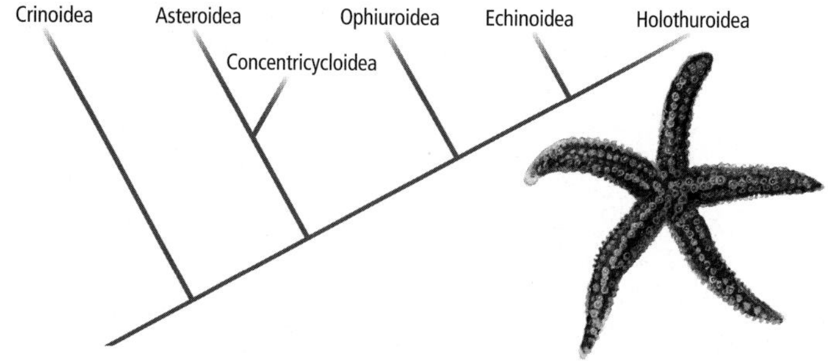

Figure 20 This cladogram shows the phylogeny of echinoderms.
Interpret ***which is the most recent class of echinoderms to evolve.***

S

CAREERS IN BIOLOGY

Evolutionary Biologist Scientists in this field study how organisms have changed and diversified over time. Many evolutionary biologists have specialties that they rely on in the field and in labs.

Evolution of Echinoderms and Invertebrate Chordates

Biologists are studying fossil and molecular evidence to learn how echinoderms and invertebrate chordates are related to the vertebrates that evolved later.

Phylogeny of echinoderms The fossil record of echinoderms extends back to the Cambrian period. Scientists think that they evolved from ancestors with bilateral symmetry because echinoderms have bilaterally symmetrical larvae. Their radial symmetry develops later in the adult stage. Many biologists think that ancient echinoderms were sessile and attached to the ocean floor by a long stalk, just as the sea lily does today.

Echinoderms also undergo deuterostome development. Recall that this type of development links them phylogenetically to chordates, which also have deuterostome development. The cladogram in **Figure 20** shows one interpretation of the evolution of echinoderms.

DATA ANALYSIS LAB 1

Based on Real Data*

Interpret Scientific Illustrations

How does an evolutionary tree show relationships among sea stars? This evolutionary tree is a representation of various species of sea stars and their phylogenetic history based on molecular data. Each letter represents a specific sea star species.

Think Critically

1. **Identify** which sea star is most closely related to sea star A.
2. **Decide** which is the oldest sea star.
3. **Analyze** which group of sea stars has the most diversity—C,G,N or L,K,M. How did you decide?

Data and Observations

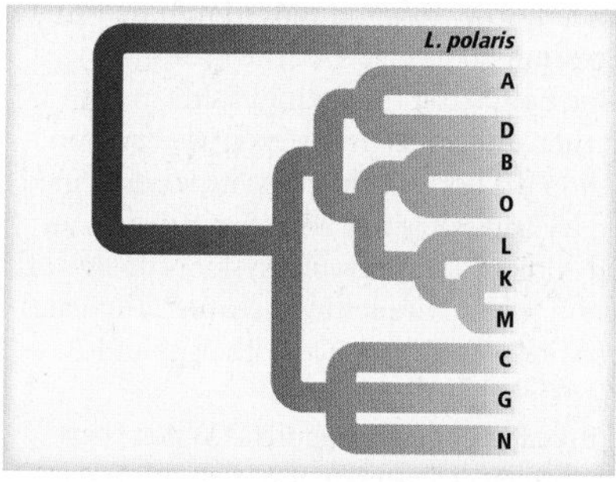

*Data obtained from: Hrincevich, A.W., et al. 2000. Phylogenetic analysis of molecular lineages in a species-rich subgenus of sea stars (*Leptasterias* subgenus *Hexasterias*). *American Zoologist* 40: 365-374.

Caption Question Fig. 20 Holothuroidea

Differentiated Instruction

Visually Impaired Students who are visually impaired might not be able to use the cladogram for the visual literacy activity without assistance. For these students, verbally describe the information that is presented in the diagram so they can draw conclusions about its meaning.

For more tips, see pages 14T–15T.

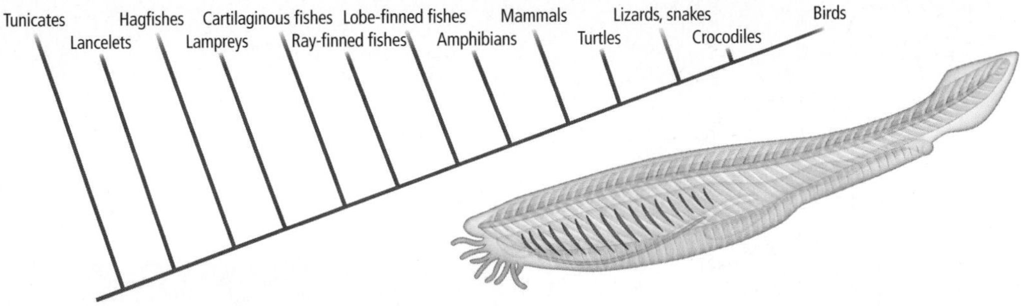

Figure 21 This cladogram shows a possible phylogeny of invertebrate chordates and other chordates that later evolved.

Phylogeny of invertebrate chordates How could sleek, burrowing, fishlike lancelets be close relatives of saclike, sessile sea squirts? They are related because of their dorsal tubular nerve cords, notochords, pharyngeal gill slits, and postanal tails, even if sea squirts have all these features only in their larvae. Beyond this answer, scientists debate about the evolution of these animals and raise still unanswered questions. For example, from which invertebrate chordate did the fishlike tadpole larvae arise? What was the original form of that first fishlike animal?

One thing is certain: the notochord, that flexible tough rod, provided support for the animal, and it also provided a place for muscles to attach. With this arrangement, chordates could swing their backs from side to side and swim through the water, a key development in the evolution of chordates. This advance also led to the first large animals. Examine the cladogram in **Figure 21** to see one interpretation of how chordates are related.

Section 2 Assessment

Section Summary

- Chordates have four main distinguishing features.
- Invertebrate chordates have all of the main features of chordates. They lack a backbone, however, which distinguishes them from vertebrate chordates.
- The notochord is an adaptation which allows invertebrate animals to remain flexible.
- Lancelets are fish-shaped invertebrate chordates that, as adults, have all the main features of chordates.
- Tunicates, or sea squirts, are sac-shaped invertebrate chordates that have chordate features as larvae.

Understand Main Ideas

1. MAIN Idea **Summarize** the main features of invertebrate chordates that show their close relationship to vertebrate chordates.
2. **Draw** a graphic organizer showing the evolution of pharyngeal pouches.
3. **Create** models of a lancelet and a sea squirt from clay or salt dough. Identify features that place these animals in the phylum Chordata.
4. **Compare** the adaptations of sea squirts with those of lancelets that enable them to live in their environments.

Think Critically

5. **Design** an experiment to determine if lancelets prefer a light environment or a dark environment.
6. **Determine** which subphylum of chordates evolved next after the cephalochordates. Use **Figure 21**.

WRITING in Biology

7. Write a paragraph describing how sponges and tunicates are alike. Write another paragraph describing how they are different from each other.

Formative Assessment

Evaluation Have students make a table that compares lancelets and tunicates. Students should be able to point out which characteristics vertebrates and invertebrates share. Column titles could be set up as follows: first column: *Lancelet and Tunicate,* second column: *Body Shape* (lancelet, streamlined; tunicate, bag-shaped), third column: *Ways of Obtaining Food* (lancelet, filter feeder; tunicate, filter feeder), fourth column: *Circulation* (lancelet, pumping blood vessels; tunicate, heart and blood vessels), fifth column: *Reproduction* (lancelet, two sexes, external fertilization; tunicate, hermaphrodites, external fertilization)

Remediation Have students draw diagrams of a lancelet and a tunicate.
SAY TO STUDENTS: ***Describe how lancelet and tunicate body shapes are different on your diagram.*** The lancelet is streamlined; the tunicate is bag-shaped. ***Identify how they take in food.*** They are filter feeders. ***Inside the body are circulatory structures. How are they different in the two animals?*** Lancelets have pumping blood vessels, whereas tunicates have a heart and blood vessels. ***Do these animals have internal or external fertilization?*** external ***Label which of these two animals have male and female counterparts and which is hermaphroditic.*** Lancelets have separate sexes while tunicates are hermaphroditic.

Section 2 Assessment

1. notochord, tubular nerve cord, pharyngeal pouches, postanal tail, and a thyroid gland
2. pharyngeal pouches in filter feeders to gills/gas exchange in water to tonsils and thymus glands
3. lancelet: fishlike shape, no fins, short tentacles around mouth; tunicates: saclike with excurrent and incurrent siphon; both have notochords, nerve cords, pharyngeal pouches, and postanal tails
4. Both have water-vascular systems, enabling them to obtain food.
5. Answers will vary. Accept scientifically sound answers with a control and quantitative data.
6. hagfish
7. Both are filter feeders. Sponge bodies have two layers of cells with no development of tissues, organs, or systems. Tunicates have digestive, circulatory, reproductive, and nervous systems.

WRITING in Biology

RUBRIC Use the modifiable rubric found on your eTeacherEdition Online to assess writing assignments.

Assessment Online Quiz

Purpose
Students will describe three ways echinoderms are used in medical research. Students compare and contrast sea urchins, sea stars, and sea cucumbers and their impact on medical research.
UCP.5, C.5

Anticipatory Guide
Humans can regenerate some cells, such as skin, but not limbs or organs.
ASK STUDENTS: ***How would life be different for humans if we could regenerate tissue/limbs?*** If humans could regenerate tissue, then recovery from heart attacks would be monumental. People would no longer have scar tissue after heart attacks, since new heart tissue would grow in place of the harmed tissue. Organ transplants would no longer be necessary, as individuals would be able to grow new organs. In the event of injuries and accidents, new limbs would grow in place of the lost ones.

Background
Echinoderms have been primarily the focus of research in the area of developmental biology. Millions of dollars have been spent exploring the mysteries of early development when the zygote is in the first few stages of cell division, using the sea urchin as the chosen organism of study. Although sea stars do regenerate, *Hydra*, newts, and zebrafish are currently the more commonly used organisms for study in regeneration by scientists, primarily due to their known genome in the case of *Hydra* and their regeneration of heart tissue in the case of zebrafish.

CUTTING-EDGE BIOLOGY

Echinoderms Aid Medical Research

How did the comic book character the Incredible Hulk increase his body size without ripping his body to pieces?

Believe it or not, producers consulted an expert on echinoderms before creating a film about this character because they wondered if any living creature could perform such feats. Sea cucumbers, specifically, can stretch and then shrink back to their normal size, much like the Incredible Hulk does in the film.

Connective tissue When Greg Szulgit was a graduate student in biology, he discovered the amazing power of sea cucumbers to increase their body size and then shrink back to their normal size. How do sea cucumbers change their body size? It is due to their connective tissue, which is the tissue that connects, supports, and surrounds other tissues and organs in the body.

A sea cucumber's connective tissue is similar to a human's connective tissue. Connective tissue fibers contain a protein called collagen. In humans, collagen is a fixed part of the tissue. Szulgit and other researchers found that the collagen in the connective tissue of echinoderms is not fixed, but instead slides back and forth. When the collagen particles in the endoskeleton are sliding past each other, a sea cucumber's body is soft and flexible. A sea cucumber's cells can release a substance that locks the collagen and stops it from sliding. This stiffens its endoskeleton, making it immobile.

Connective-tissue disorders Szulgit studies the sea cucumber's body-stretching abilities with the hope of someday being able to treat connective-tissue disorders in humans. These disorders include osteogenesis imperfecta, Marfan syndrome, and Ehlers-Danlos syndrome.

Because the collagen in a sea cucumber's connective tissue is not fixed, its body can change from the consistency of liquid gelatin to a rigid structure and back again in seconds.

In osteogenesis imperfecta, the body doesn't produce enough collagen or it produces poor quality collagen, leading to fragile bones that break easily. People with Marfan syndrome have connective tissue that is not as stiff as it should be, causing skeletal abnormalities and weakened blood vessels. People with Ehlers-Danlos syndrome have abnormally fragile connective tissue, resulting in joint problems and weakened internal organs.

By studying the connective tissue in echinoderms such as the sea cucumber, researchers are moving closer to successfully treating debilitating illnesses that prevent people from having freedom of movement in their joints due to connective tissue diseases.

WRITING in Biology

Journal Create a biologist's research journal describing his or her work with an echinoderm. The journal should include thorough descriptions, charts, graphs, and sketches of echinoderms.

WRITING in Biology

RUBRIC Use the modifiable rubric found on your eTeacherEdition Online to assess writing assignments.

Follow-Up Discussion
After the students prepare their journals, have several students share their journals with the class. Start a discussion using the following questions: What are some of the primary research activities of the biologists? How are the echinoderms used in the research? What kinds of research questions do they ask? How interested are the students in studying echinoderms? What did the students learn by doing the research?

WebQuest

BIOLAB

INTERNET: HOW DO ECHINODERMS SURVIVE WITHOUT A HEAD, EYES, OR A BRAIN?

Background: Echinoderms have evolved unlike any other animals on Earth. Lacking eyes and a brain, they also have no heart, and pump seawater through their bodies rather than blood. Some echinoderms can change their endoskeletons from rock hard to nearly liquid within seconds. Some can break off an arm to distract a predator. Sound unusual? Not for echinoderms.

Question: *How do echinoderms survive in the competitive marine environment?*

These sea stars, basket stars, and sea urchins are from the Gulf of Maine.

Materials

Internet access
echinoderm reference book
field journal

Procedure

1. Read and complete the lab safety form.
2. Design and construct a data table for recording the species; physical characteristics; food sources/strategies for obtaining food; predators; defense strategies; reproduction and development; and other interesting facts about six animals.
3. Choose one species from each of the six major classes of echinoderms to study. List the species in your data table.
4. Research the species you chose and fill in information in your data table. Observe the echinoderms in their natural habitat by visiting a local zoo or aquarium. If you cannot observe the animals in their natural habitats, obtain information about the echinoderms from a reference book or the Internet.
5. Record your observations in your field journal. Transfer the information to your data table.

Analyze and Conclude

1. **Describe** some basic physical characteristics shared by echinoderms.
2. **Compare** sexual and asexual reproductive strategies used by echinoderm species.
3. **Think Critically** Echinoderm larvae and mature echinoderms differ in several important ways. Describe the differences and infer the advantages they provide.
4. **Interpret Data** What are the major food sources of the echinoderms you studied?
5. **Draw Conclusions** Are echinoderms well-adapted to survive in the marine environment? Justify your answer.
6. **Error Analysis** Describe advantages and disadvantages of obtaining information about echinoderms from the Internet.

WRITING in Biology

Resource Book Use the data you gathered to create a fact sheet including photos and interesting information about each echinoderm you studied. Combine your fact sheets with those developed by other students to create an echinoderm resource book for your school's media center.

BIOLAB

? Inquiry BioLab

For a lab worksheet, use your eTeacherEdition Online.

RUBRIC A rubric for evaluating BioLabs is found on your eTeacherEdition Online.

Est. Time 45–90 min

Content Background
While some echinoderms can move quickly, most move so slowly that they appear to be stationary. To survive, echinoderms have developed unique strategies for movement, defense, food gathering, and reproduction that have enabled them to thrive in oceans throughout the world.

Alternative Materials This lab could be completed using media center resource materials, allowing students to share information within the classroom.

Safety Precaution Approve lab safety forms before work begins.

Teaching Strategies
- Alert students that their data tables will have to be expanded to accommodate their research findings.
- Optimize available time and prevent overlap of species studied by providing a list of echinoderm species from which to choose and limiting the number of students studying each species.

Alternative Teaching Demo
Through classroom discussion, create a table which illustrates the unique strategies for obtaining food, reproduction, avoiding predators and other survival skills utilized by a few echinoderm species.

Analyze and Conclude

1. radial symmetry with bodies that can be divided into five parts, a water vascular system, an endoskeleton, and a simple nervous system
2. Sexual reproduction: eggs and sperm discharged into the water where fertilization occurs and larva develops. Asexual reproduction: by fragmentation.
3. Echinoderm larvae are free-swimming and display bilateral symmetry. Free-swimming larvae have a greater chance to avoid being eaten by predators. Free-swimming larvae can also disperse farther from the parent's habitat, extending the reach of the species and increasing the chances of genetic mixing.
4. Answers will depend on the organisms studied.
5. Yes. Justifications should be based on abilities to obtain nutrients, avoid predators, or reproduce.
6. Information on the Internet may be unreliable and difficult to verify.

WRITING in Biology

RUBRIC Use the modifiable rubric found on your eTeacherEdition Online to assess writing assignments.

Chapter 27

Study Guide

ConnectED

Students can use the following to review the chapter.

Review

Vocabulary eGames
Vocabulary eFlashcards
Vocabulary PuzzleMaker

Assessment

Online Quizzes
Online Test Practice
Standardized Test Practice

Use the *ExamView®* *Assessment Suite* CD-ROM to:

- create multiple versions of tests
- create modified tests with one mouse click
- edit existing questions and add your own questions
- build tests aligned with state standards using built-in state curriculum tags
- change English tests to Spanish with one mouse click
- track students' progress using the Teacher Management System

Chapter 27 Study Guide

THEME FOCUS Diversity Adaptations such as tube feet enable echinoderms and invertebrate chordates to live in their unique habitats.

BIG Idea Echinoderms and invertebrate chordates have features that connect them to the chordates that evolved after them.

Section 1 Echinoderm Characteristics

pedicellaria (p. 793)
water-vascular system (p. 795)
madreporite (p. 795)
tube foot (p. 795)
ampulla (p. 795)

MAIN Idea **Echinoderms are marine animals with spiny endoskeletons, water-vascular systems, and tube feet; they have radial symmetry as adults.**

- Echinoderms are deuterostomes.
- Adult members of the phylum Echinodermata have four major common characteristics.
- Larval echinoderms have bilateral symmetry and are considered an evolutionary link to chordates.
- Echinoderms exhibit great diversity in feeding and digestion, respiration, circulation, and excretion.
- There are six major classes of living echinoderms.

Section 2 Invertebrate Chordates

chordate (p. 803)
invertebrate chordate (p. 803)
notochord (p. 803)
postanal tail (p. 803)
dorsal tubular nerve cord (p. 803)
pharyngeal pouches (p. 804)

MAIN Idea **Invertebrate chordates have features linking them to vertebrate chordates.**

- Chordates have four main distinguishing features.
- Invertebrate chordates have all of the main features of chordates. They lack a backbone, however, which distinguishes them from vertebrate chordates.
- The notochord is an adaptation which allows invertebrate animals to remain flexible.
- Lancelets are fish-shaped invertebrate chordates that, as adults, have all the main features of chordates.
- Tunicates, or sea squirts, are sac-shaped invertebrate chordates that have chordate features as larvae.

Review Vocabulary PuzzleMaker

For additional practice with vocabulary, have students access the Vocabulary PuzzleMaker online.

Review Vocabulary eGames

Section 1

Vocabulary Review

Distinguish between the terms in each of the following pairs.

1. tube foot, ampulla
2. madreporite, water-vascular system

Understand Main Ideas

3. Which is not an echinoderm?

A. 

C. 

B. 

D. 

A. A
B. B
C. C
D. D

4. Which echinoderm is sessile for part of its life?
   A. sea cucumber
   B. sea lily
   C. brittle star
   D. sea urchin

5. What three functions do tube feet perform?
   A. reproduction, feeding, respiration
   B. feeding, respiration, neural control
   C. feeding, respiration, movement
   D. development, reproduction, respiration

6. What is the function of the water-vascular system?
   A. to remove wastes
   B. to reproduce
   C. for defense
   D. for movement and to obtain food

7. Which are involved in protecting an echinoderm?
   A. endoskeleton, pedicellariae, spines
   B. madreporite, tentacles, endoskeleton
   C. water-vascular system, ampulla, pedicellariae
   D. exoskeleton, pedicellariae, spines

8. What is the main difference between echinoderm larvae and adults?
   A. Larvae are protostomes and adults are deuterostomes.
   B. Larvae are deuterostomes and adults are protostomes.
   C. Larvae have bilateral symmetry and adults have radial symmetry.
   D. Larvae have radial symmetry and adults have bilateral symmetry.

9. Which group of echinoderms has respiratory trees with many branches?
   A. sea cucumbers
   B. sea stars
   C. sea lilies and feather stars
   D. sea urchins and sand dollars

Constructed Response

Use the diagram below to answer questions 10 and 11.

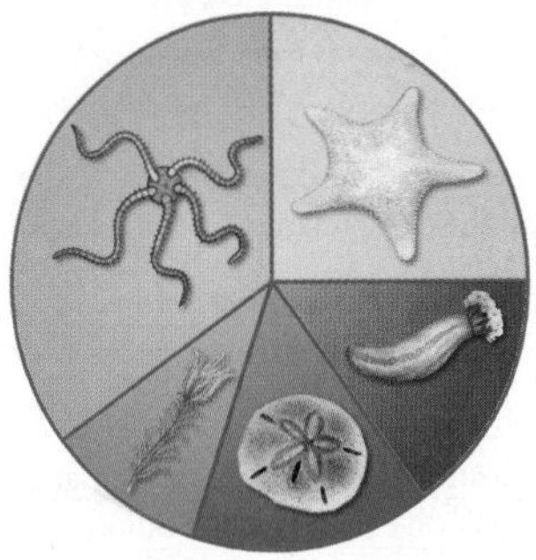

10. **Short Answer** Examine the circle graph and estimate the percentage of echinoderms that are sea cucumbers.

11. **Open Ended** Examine the circle graph and explain why class Concentricycloidea does not appear with the other classes of living echinoderms.

12. MAIN Idea Scientists have discovered a fossil that has the following characteristics: an endoskeleton similar to that of echinoderms, a tail-like structure with an anus at the end of the tail, a structure that might be a gill, and symmetry similar to echinoderms. How might scientists explain this animal in terms of echinoderm classification?

Chapter 27 Assessment

Section 1

Vocabulary Review

1. Tube feet are small, muscular fluid-filled closed tubes that end in a suction-cup-like structure used in movement, getting food, and respiration in echinoderms. An ampulla is a muscular sac at the inner end of the tube foot.
2. The water-vascular system is a system of fluid-filled tubes that work together to enable echinoderms to move and get food. The madreporite is a strainer-like opening to the water-vascular system.

Understand Main Ideas

3. A
4. B
5. C
6. D
7. A
8. C
9. A

Constructed Response

10. Students' estimates should be around 18–20 percent.
11. Scientists have recently discovered them. The density of their population is unknown.
12. Students might say that these are ancestors to echinoderms or larval echinoderms that have not yet become adults with all the echinoderm features.

13. Answers will vary. Accept all answers that make scientific sense. Sea stars are lighter in color than mollusks and therefore might not take on as much heat as the darker colored mussels.

Think Critically

14. There are many different locations in a marine environment that would necessitate the need for unique adaptations. A sand dollar has no need for tube feet because it burrows into the sand and filters organic material for food.
15. Accept all answers that have scientific merit. Sea urchins are protected from predators by long spines. They continue to reproduce all their lives. Older sea urchins are larger and produce more eggs and sperm.

Section 2

Vocabulary Review

16. invertebrate chordates
17. a notochord
18. pharyngeal pouches

Understand Main Ideas

19. D
20. D
21. A
22. B
23. C
24. A
25. B

Chapter 27 Assessment

13. Open Ended Tidal animals suffer when water and air temperatures rise beyond the limits of tolerance of the animals. The temperature of sea stars remains about 18 degrees cooler than those of the surrounding mussels on a hot day. Make a hypothesis about why sea stars have a lower body temperature.

Think Critically

14. **THEME FOCUS Diversity** A marine environment is relatively stable. Formulate a hypothesis using examples to explain why echinoderms have so many unique adaptations.

15. Hypothesize Some sea urchins seem to have relatively long lifespans. Make a hypothesis about why they live so long.

Section 2

Vocabulary Review

Using the vocabulary terms from the Study Guide page, replace the underlined words with the correct term.

16. Animals that are chordates, but do not have backbones are the close relatives of chordates.

17. Located just below the nerve cord is a structure in chordates that enables invertebrate chordates to swim by moving their tails back and forth.

18. The connections between the muscular tube that links the mouth cavity and the esophagus develop slits and are used for filter feeding in some invertebrate chordates.

Understand Main Ideas

19. Chordates have which features at some time in their lives?
A. water-vascular system, notochord, pharyngeal pouches, postanal tail
B. tunic, pharyngeal pouches, dorsal tubular nerve cord, postanal tail
C. tube feet, notochord, pharyngeal pouches, postanal tail
D. dorsal tubular nerve cord, notochord, pharyngeal pouches, postanal tail

20. Which is the main function of a postanal tail?
A. circulation
B. digestion
C. flexibility
D. locomotion

Use the diagram below to answer questions 21 and 22.

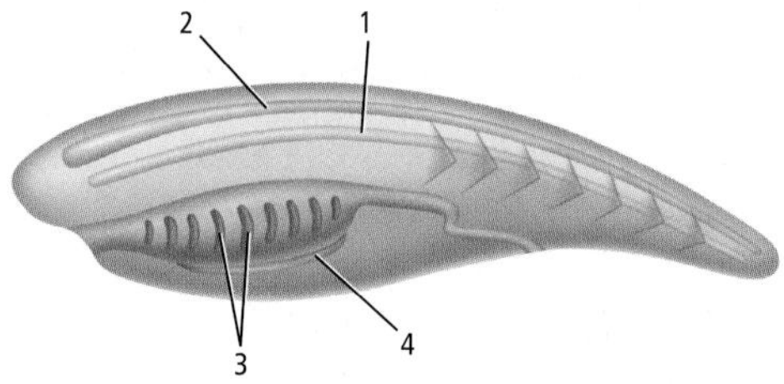

21. Fishlike swimming is made possible by which labeled structure above?
A. 1 **C.** 3
B. 2 **D.** 4

22. Which structure develops into the brain and spinal cord in most chordates?
A. 1 **C.** 3
B. 2 **D.** 4

23. Which describes adult sea squirts?
A. They are bilaterally symmetrical.
B. They have the same adult features as lancelets.
C. As adults, they have only two chordate features.
D. They are actively swimming predators.

24. In invertebrate chordates, what does the endostyle secrete?
A. proteins similar to thyroid hormone
B. mucus
C. the notochord
D. pharyngeal pouches

25. The phylogeny of echinoderms indicates that echinoderms are related to chordates because they both have which feature?
A. pharyngeal pouches
B. deuterostome development
C. protostome development
D. pseudocoeloms

26. Which structure might be an early form of the thyroid gland?
  A. dorsal tubular nerve cord
  B. endostyle
  C. notochord
  D. pharyngeal pouches

27. Which chordate feature enabled large animals to develop?
  A. dorsal tubular nerve cord
  B. notochord
  C. pharyngeal pouches
  D. postanal tail

Constructed Response

28. **Open Ended** Infer why there are no freshwater invertebrate chordates.

29. **Open Ended** What would happen if all lancelets disappeared?

Use the diagram below to answer questions 30 and 31.

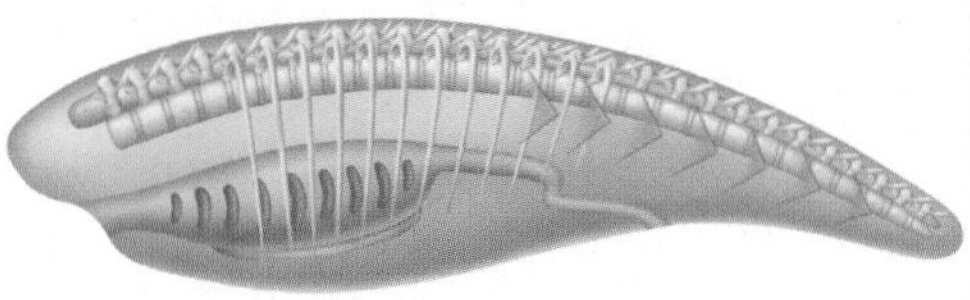

30. **Short Answer** Examine the diagram and explain why this animal could not be an invertebrate chordate.

31. MAIN Idea What features does this animal share with invertebrate chordates?

Think Critically

32. **Analyze** How do the larvae of organisms help scientists classify and determine the phylogeny of animals?

33. **Use the Internet** Make a visual report of the newest information, both molecular and fossil evidence, gathered by scientists on the origins of chordates.

Summative Assessment

34. BIG Idea Explain the evolutionary relationship between echinoderms, invertebrate chordates, and chordates. Provide specific examples from the chapter to support your statement.

35. WRITING in Biology Create a short descriptive story about a human who now has one of an echinoderm's adaptations. Include how this new adaptation would improve or worsen the character's life.

36. Sea cucumbers protect themselves by casting out their internal organs, but other echinoderms cannot. Hypothesize why this adaptation is found only in sea cucumbers.

37. Sketch a typical lancelet and label its main parts.

38. WRITING in Biology Create a poem that describes your favorite echinoderm. Make sure you point out the actual features of the echinoderm.

DBQ Document-Based Questions

Study the illustration of the progression of development of arms in a specific sea star.

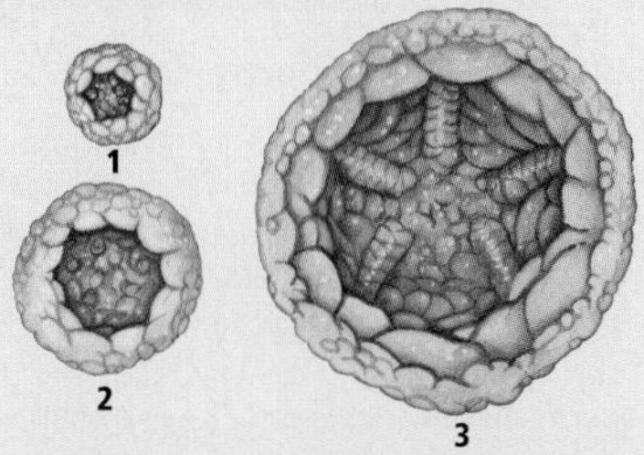

Diagram based on examples from: Sumrall, Colin D., 2005. Unpublished research on the growth stages of *Neoisorophusella lanei*. The University of Tennessee. http://web.eps.utk.edu/Faculty/sumrall/research2.htm

39. What kind of symmetry is shown in the diagram labeled 1?

40. Infer how additional arms might develop.

41. How does the number of arms in diagram 3 reflect the characteristics of all echinoderms?

26. B
27. B

Constructed Response

28. The marine ecosystem is more consistently stable in temperature, chemistry, and other factors than a freshwater ecosystem. The adaptations of invertebrate chordates are specific to marine factors.
29. Animals that feed on lancelets would decline, as would animals that feed on these animals. Food chains would be altered. Since lancelets filter organic materials from the sand, the sand could become unsuitable for other organisms.
30. It has a backbone. Invertebrate chordates do not have backbones.
31. postanal tail, dorsal tubular nerve cord, pharyngeal pouches

Think Critically

32. Larval forms might have features that the adults have lost.
33. Answers will vary. Make sure that students find information about new fossil discoveries as well as molecular data.

Summative Assessment

34. Answers will vary, but should include knowledge about bilateral symmetry, deuterostomes, endoskeletons, (dorsal tubular nerve cord, notochord, pharyngeal pouches, postnatal tail at some point during development), and possibly some form of a thyroid gland.
35. Stories should include a specific adaptation and how their character would use this adaptation.
36. Sea cucumbers split off from the rest of the echinoderms very early. This adaptation evolved in sea cucumbers after they split off from the others.
37. Sketches should resemble Figure 17.
38. Poems will vary, but should be scientifically accurate.

WRITING in Biology

RUBRIC Use the modifiable rubric found on your eTeacherEdition Online to assess writing assignments.

DBQ Document-Based Questions

Data obtained from: Qui, Yin-Long, et al. 1998. The gain of three mitochondrial introns identifies liverworts as the earliest land plants. *Nature* 394: 671.

39. bilateral
40. Accept all scientifically logical answers. The arms divide to form more arms.
41. Most echinoderms show five-part radial symmetry.

Assessment Online Test Practice

Standardized Test Practice

Multiple Choice

1. B 5. B 9. B
2. A 6. B
3. B 7. A
4. C 8. A

Short Answer

10. A sponge uses filter feeding. It takes in water through its pores and then filters food from the water.
11. Sea stars can regenerate whole organisms from parts. Cutting sea stars into pieces may actually increase the sea star population.
12. The two groups of invertebrate chordates have different defense adaptations. Adult lancelets can swim to escape from predators. However, they are usually buried in sand that protects them from predators. Sea squirts are sessile, but they can squirt a jet of water to protect themselves from predators. The defense adaptations are suited to organisms that are mostly sessile as adults.
13. Answers will vary. Echinoderms are deuterostomes and have radial symmetry as adults, endoskeletons, and a water vascular system. Accept answers that list the main characteristics of another phylum and state how the characteristics contrast.
14. Horseshoe crabs and spiders are both chelicerates, while regular crabs and lobsters are in a different group.
15. The trilobites would fit into the phylogenic tree very close to the base of Arthropoda as one of the first branches in this group.

Standardized Test Practice

Cumulative

Multiple Choice

1. In which structure of a flowering plant do eggs develop?
A. anther
B. ovule
C. seed
D. stigma

Use the diagram below to answer question 2.

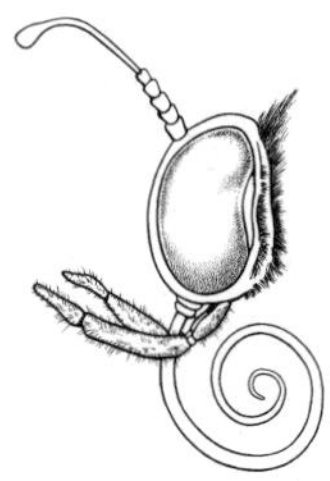

2. Arthropods have specialized mouthparts for feeding. For which type of feeding method is this mouthpart specialized?
A. getting nectar from flowers
B. sponging liquids from a surface
C. sucking blood from a host
D. tearing and shredding leaves

3. Which statement about a group of invertebrates is correct?
A. Cnidarians have collar cells.
B. Flatworms have flame cells.
C. Flatworms have nematocysts.
D. Sponges have a nervous system.

4. Echinoderms have which characteristic that is an evolutionary connection to vertebrates?
A. bilateral symmetry as adults
B. free-swimming larvae
C. deuterostome development
D. radial symmetry as larvae

5. Which special adaptation would be essential for an insect that swims in water?
A. compound eyes
B. modified legs
C. sticky foot pads
D. sharp mouth parts

Use the diagram below to answer questions 6 and 7.

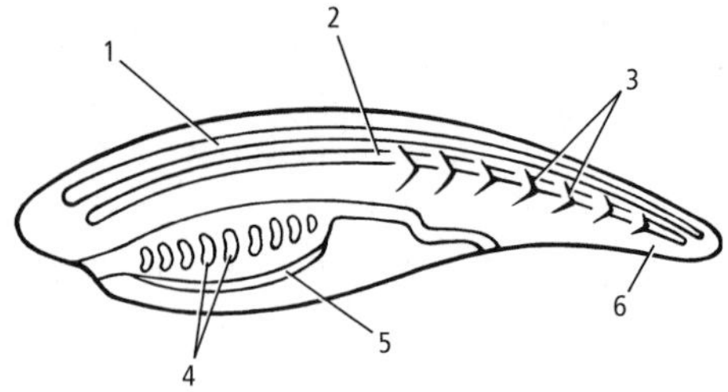

6. Which structure is replaced by bone or cartilage in vertebrate chordates?
A. 1
B. 2
C. 4
D. 5

7. Which structure is a bundle of nerves protected by fluid?
A. 1
B. 3
C. 5
D. 6

8. What kind of body organization or body structure first appeared with the evolution of flatworms?
A. bilateral symmetry
B. coelomic cavity
C. nervous system
D. radial symmetry

9. Suppose a cell from the frond of a fern contains 24 chromosomes. How many chromosomes would you expect to find in the spores?
A. 6
B. 12
C. 24
D. 48

Short Answer

10. Use what you know about the body structure of a sponge to explain how it obtains food.

11. Sea stars are echinoderms that feed on oysters. Justify why oyster farmers should not cut up sea stars and toss the parts back into the water.

12. Evaluate the defense adaptations of the two groups of invertebrate chordates.

13. Contrast the main characteristics of echinoderms with the characteristics of the organisms in another phylum that you already know.

Use the diagram below to answer questions 14 and 15.

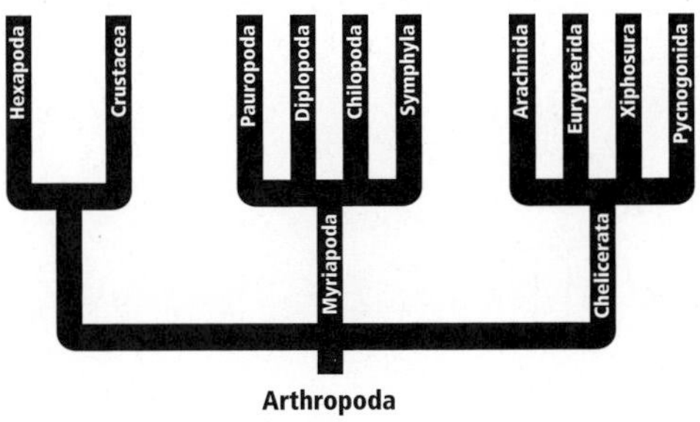

14. Write a hypothesis about why horseshoe crabs (in class Xiphosura) are more closely related to spiders than to regular crabs and lobsters.

15. Write a hypothesis about where trilobites would fit into this phylogenetic tree.

Extended Response

16. Explain how echinoderms and annelids are similar, and how they are different.

17. In animals, how are mitosis and meiosis different?

18. Evaluate the idea that it was not a large evolutionary jump for aquatic arthropods to move onto land.

19. Suppose that one crow in an area's population is hatched with longer claws on its feet than other crows in the same population. According to Darwin's theory of natural selection, under what circumstances would this trait become common in the area's crow population?

Essay Question

In the past, many horror movies have featured giant arthropods attacking major cities. These giant arthropods have included ants, grasshoppers, crabs, and spiders. Actually, the largest living insects are not very big. The longest insect, a walking stick, is about 40 cm long. Some marine arthropods grow larger. The largest arthropod is the Japanese spider crab that can grow up to 4 m wide. Some fossil marine arthropods are even larger. However, none of these are nearly as large as the size of the giant arthropod villains in the movies.

Using the information in the paragraph above, answer the following question in essay format.

20. Write an essay about why real-life arthropods cannot become as large as the giant arthropods shown in horror movies.

NEED EXTRA HELP?

If You Missed Question . . .	1	2	3	4	5	6	7	8	9	10	11	12	13	14	15	16	17	18	19	20
Review Section . . .	23.3	26.1	25.1	27.1	26.3	27.2	27.2	25.1	21.3	24.3	27.1	27.2	27.2	26.2	26.3	24.2	10.1	26.2	15.1	26.1

Extended Response

16. Echinoderms and annelids both have a similar body feature—a coelom. This means they have a fluid-filled body cavity. However, they are different, because annelids are protostomes, and echinoderms are deuterostomes. Protostomes and deuterostomes have different embryonic development. In protostome embryos, the final outcome for each cell cannot be altered, but in deuterostomes, the final outcome can be altered, and any cell could become a new embryo.

17. Mitosis is a process that occurs in all the body cells of an animal to duplicate the chromosomes present in a normal cell. It is a part of the body's growth and repair. Mitosis produces diploid cells. Meiosis, on the other hand, only takes place for the formation of haploid cells. In animals, these haploid cells are gametes, or sex cells. These sex cells—egg and sperm—can join to form a zygote, and this zygote grows into an organism with diploid body cells. Because it produces haploid cells, meiosis requires one more division than mitosis: first the pairs of homologous chromosomes separate, then the sister chromatids separate in another stage.

18. Aquatic arthropods already had many characteristics that were needed for life on land. They already had walking legs and an exoskeleton that would protect them.

19. The longer claws would have to be related to fitness somehow. For example, the longer claws could be more suitable for grasping a certain food that crows eat. Unless the claws contribute directly to crows' fitness for survival, the trait would not be affected by natural selection. It would either remain in the population in small numbers or disappear.

Essay Question

20. Answers will vary. Students may suggest factors such as the weight of the exoskeleton as they increase in size and the need for much larger muscles to move. They might also suggest that the respiratory system and circulatory system are not efficient enough to support a very large arthropod.

UNIT 8

Vertebrates

Preview the Unit

Have students preview the chapters in this unit and make a concept map or graphic organizer relating the Themes, Big Ideas, and Main Ideas. Students' maps should show a hierarchy between Big Ideas and Main Ideas and the interconnectedness of the Themes.

Chapter 28
Fishes and Amphibians
BIG Idea Fishes have adaptations for living in aquatic environments. Most amphibians have adaptations for living part of their lives on land.

Chapter 29
Reptiles and Birds
BIG Idea Reptile and bird adaptations enable them to live and reproduce successfully in terrestrial habitats.

Chapter 30
Mammals
BIG Idea Mammals have evolved to have a variety of adaptations for maintaining homeostasis and living in a variety of habitats.

Chapter 31
Animal Behavior
BIG Idea Many animal behaviors are influenced by both genetics and environmental experiences.

WebQuest
Careers in Biology

UNIT 8 Vertebrates

THEMES

Scientific Inquiry Biologists study the fossil record of vertebrates to understand evolutionary relationships.

Diversity Vertebrate species have unique adaptations, such as gills, that enable them to carry out their lives in specific habitats.

Energy Vertebrates obtain energy from cellular respiration to carry out their life functions, such as digestion, excretion, breathing, circulation, and movement.

Homeostasis Vertebrates maintain internal cellular and systemic homeostasis by using organs such as kidneys, gills, and lungs.

Change Over time, natural selection results in the evolution of existing vertebrate species that produces new species.

WebQuest **CAREERS IN BIOLOGY**

Veterinarians are medical specialists trained to prevent, diagnose, and treat medical conditions in domestic, wildlife, zoo, and laboratory animals. Some veterinarians conduct research to expand knowledge of a particular species, much like this giant panda bear researcher is doing.

5-Minute UNIT LAUNCH

Activity Organize students into groups of four. **SAY TO STUDENTS:** ***Make a list of vertebrate animals, or animals with backbones, that live in your area. Beside the name of each animal, classify it as a fish, an amphibian, a reptile, a bird, or a mammal.*** Students might know that birds, snakes, lizards, fishes, frogs, toads, alligators, and mammals such as dogs, cats, and bears are all vertebrates.

Video

What's BIOLOGY Got To Do With It?
A professor discusses the use of tools by chimpanzees.

Misconceptions

In each section, *Clarify a Misconception* provides you with the information to dispel a common student misconception. A question will help you elicit the misconception, and an explanation will help you correct it.

Below is a preview of misconceptions from each chapter in this unit.

Before studying Chapter 28, students might think that humans can get warts from handling toads. Chapter 28 will explain that warts are not caused by toads; they are caused by a virus (p. 838).

Before studying Chapter 29, students might think that all reptiles lay eggs. Chapter 29 will explain that while all reptiles produce eggs, some incubate the eggs internally and give birth to live young (p. 856).

Before studying Chapter 30, students might think that animals have emotions. Chapter 30 will explain that animals display behavior and do not have human emotions (p. 894).

Before studying Chapter 31, students might think that plants do not communicate. Chapter 31 will explain that plants communicate chemically (p. 920).

SERVICE LEARNING/COMMUNITY SERVICE

State Proclamation Students can write a state proclamation or resolution by going through their mayor or governor's office to find the appropriate format for their state. Their proclamation should proclaim a week of the year designated to campaign for the preservation of local or state habitat that would help a local endangered vertebrate (e.g., Save the Wolves Week). In addition, students should develop an educational campaign for that week. When students help solve community problems, they will be learning to take charge of their own lives as well (Lewis, 1991).

Research bibliography on pages 32T–34T

Chapter 28 Organizer:
Fishes and Amphibians

LabManager™
Customize any lab with the LabManager™ CD-ROM.

Essential Questions	National Science Standards	Materials and Planning: Estimated times include cleanup and disposal, but do not include teacher prep time. For cleanup and disposal guidelines, see page 39T.	Est. Time (min)
Section 1 1. What are the features of vertebrates that make them different from invertebrates? 2. What are the characteristics that most fishes have in common? 3. How are the characteristics of fishes adapted to aquatic life?	UCP.1, UCP.2, UCP.4, UCP.5; A.1, A.2; C.3, C.4, C.5, C.6	**Launch Lab,** p. 818: preserved or live specimens of various fishes	25
		Demonstration, p. 820: vertebrate skeletons such as the skeleton of a cat, fish, and reptile	10
		MiniLab 1, p. 823: fishes in aquarium	40
		Demonstration, p. 823: images of a variety of fish scales, microprojector	10
		Demonstration, p. 824: images of gill filaments	7
		Demonstration, p. 826: movie about salmon reproduction	20
Section 2 1. What are the characteristics of different groups of fishes? 2. What are similarities and differences between the key features of various types of fishes? 3. How is the evolution of fishes explained?	UCP.1, UCP.2, UCP.4, UCP.5; A.1, A.2; C.3, C.4, C.5, C.6; F.4, F.5	**Demonstration,** p. 829: shark teeth	7
		Demonstration, p. 831: slideshow presentation about classes of fishes	15
Section 3 1. What were the kinds of adaptations that were important as animals moved to the land? 2. What are the characteristics of amphibians? 3. What are the differences between the orders of amphibians?	UCP.1-5; A.1, A.2; B.3; C.1, C.3, C.4, C.5, C.6; E.2; F.1, F.3, F.4; G.1, G.2	**Demonstration,** p. 835: variety of frog toys	15
		Activity, p. 836: wax-covered yarn	15
		Demonstration, p. 838: *Xenopus* frog eggs	2 per day
		BioLab, p. 843: thermometers, plastic containers, metric ruler, water, paper towels, sand, soil, high-wattage light bulb and lamp	30

Suggested Time for Each Lesson

Class	Chapter Opener	Section 1	Section 2	Section 3	Assessment
Basic	45 min	20 min	25 min	—	45 min
General	25 min	55 min	55 min	—	45 min
Honors	15 min	50 min	45 min	50 min	20 min

ConnectED

connectED.mcgraw-hill.com

Access interactive learning opportunities and teaching resources using these icons located throughout your StudentWorks™ Plus Online and eTeacherEdition Online.

Chapter 28 Section Resources	Additional Chapter 28 Resources	Technology
FAST FILE Unit 8 Resources: Launch Lab Worksheet* MiniLab Worksheet* Study Guide (English/Spanish)* Section Quick Check **Reading Essentials 28.1** **Science Notebook 28.1*** **FAST FILE Unit 8 Resources:** Study Guide (English/Spanish)* Section Quick Check **Reading Essentials 28.2** **Science Notebook 28.2*** **FAST FILE Unit 8 Resources:** BioLab Worksheet* Study Guide (English/Spanish)* Section Quick Check **Reading Essentials 28.3** **Science Notebook 28.3***	**FAST FILE Unit 8 Resources:** Chapter Diagnostic Test Concept Mapping* Real-World Biology Enrichment Chapter Tests A, B, and C **Transparencies:** Bellringer Transparencies* Biology Concepts Transparencies* **Lab Resources:** Laboratory Manual* Probeware Lab Manual* Forensics Lab Manual* Pre-AP Lab Manual* Open Inquiry in Biology* Guided Inquiry in Biology*	**Teaching Tools:** eTeacherEdition Online Classroom Presentation Toolkit CD-ROM* LabManager™ CD-ROM* Video Lab DVD* Virtual Lab CD-ROM* What's BIOLOGY Got To Do With It? StudentWorks™ Plus Online* **Chapter Assessment Tools:** Classroom Presentation Toolkit CD-ROM* *ExamView® Assessment Suite* CD-ROM **Web-Based Resources:** • StudentWorks™ Plus Online • eTeacherEdition Online • Animations* • The Interactive Time Line* • Interactive Tables* • Online Quizzes • Online Test Practice • Standardized Test Practice • Virtual Labs* • Multilingual eGlossary* • Vocabulary eGames* • Vocabulary eFlashcards • WebQuests • Personal Tutors

While all resources listed are appropriate for English learners, the * indicates resources with a strong visual or hands-on component for EL.

Teaching strategies and activities have been coded for differentiated instruction.

AL Activities for students working above grade level	**OL** Activities for students working on grade level	**BL** Activities for students working below grade level	**EL** Activities for English learners (also ELL)	**COOP LEARN** Activities designed for small cooperative group work

CHAPTER 28

Launch Lab
What are the characteristics of fishes in different groups?

? Inquiry Launch Lab

For a lab worksheet, use your eTeacherEdition Online.

RUBRIC A rubric for evaluating Launch Labs is found on your eTeacherEdition Online.

Est. Time 25 min

Teaching Strategy Have students work in pairs or in small groups, but make sure each student in the team examines specimens.

Procedure

1. Read and complete the lab safety form.
2. Examine **photos** of representatives from each of the three groups of fishes. Look at features such as skin and scales, fin position, fin shape, eyes, mouth shape and teeth, body shape, and tail shape.
3. Construct a table and record information about the external characteristics of the groups of fishes.

Analysis

1. **Summarize** the main external difference among these groups of fishes. Answers should be based on the visual differences in the photos.
2. **Infer** why it is important to examine and compare the internal structures and characteristics of organisms when trying to study them. Internal structures can determine certain characteristics necessary for classifying an organism, and they can help scientists note differences that are not observable to the naked eye.

CHAPTER 28
Fishes and Amphibians

ConnectED
Your one-stop online resource
connectED.mcgraw-hill.com

- Video
- Audio
- Review
- Inquiry
- WebQuest
- Assessment
- Concepts in Motion
- Multilingual eGlossary

Launch Lab
What are the characteristics of fishes in different groups?

Fishes are classified into three main groups: jawless, cartilaginous, and bony. They are classified based on external and internal characteristics. In this lab, you will compare the external characteristics of fishes in three groups.

For a lab worksheet, use your StudentWorks™ Plus Online.

? Inquiry Launch Lab

FOLDABLES®

Make a layered look book using the titles shown. Use it to organize your notes on characteristics of these organisms.

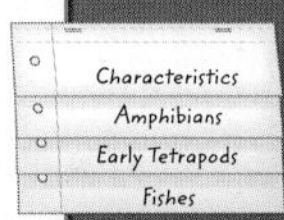

THEME FOCUS Change
Some amphibians go through a major change, called metamorphosis, in their lifetime.

BIG Idea Fishes have adaptations for living in aquatic environments. Most amphibians have adapted to living part of their lives on land.

Section 1 • Fishes

Section 2 • Diversity of Today's Fishes

Section 3 • Amphibians

THEMES

Scientific Inquiry Biologists study fishes and amphibians in the field, as well as in the laboratory.

Diversity Fishes and amphibians have unique adaptations such as gills and moist skin that allow them to inhabit most aquatic ecosystems.

Energy All fishes and amphibians obtain energy from other organisms.

Homeostasis Fishes and amphibians maintain internal cellular and systemic homeostasis by using organs such as kidneys, gills, and lungs.

Change Over time, natural selection results in the evolution of existing species of fishes and amphibians to produce new species.

Introduce the Chapter

Fish Scales Obtain a variety of fish scales from a fish market or grocery store fresh fish counter. Pass them around in a petri dish for students to examine.
SAY TO STUDENTS: ***Examine the fishes in the photo and the scales in the petri dish. Infer how scales help a fish survive.*** possible answers: protection; aid in making the surface of the fish slick so it can pass through the water easily.

BIG Idea

Fishes and Amphibians
Divide students into groups of two or three and assign a manageable portion of the chapter to each group. Provide a large piece of butcher paper and markers to each group. Write *Major Themes, Big Idea,* and *Main Ideas* on the board. You will also need to write the five themes of *Glencoe Biology* on the board for students: *Scientific Inquiry, Diversity, Energy, Homeostasis,* and *Change.*
SAY TO STUDENTS: ***Make a chart with the following columns:* Major Themes, Big Idea, Section 1 Main Idea, Section 2 Main Idea, *and* Section 3 Main Idea. *Skim through the portion of the chapter assigned to your group and find appropriate phrases from the text to place in each column.***

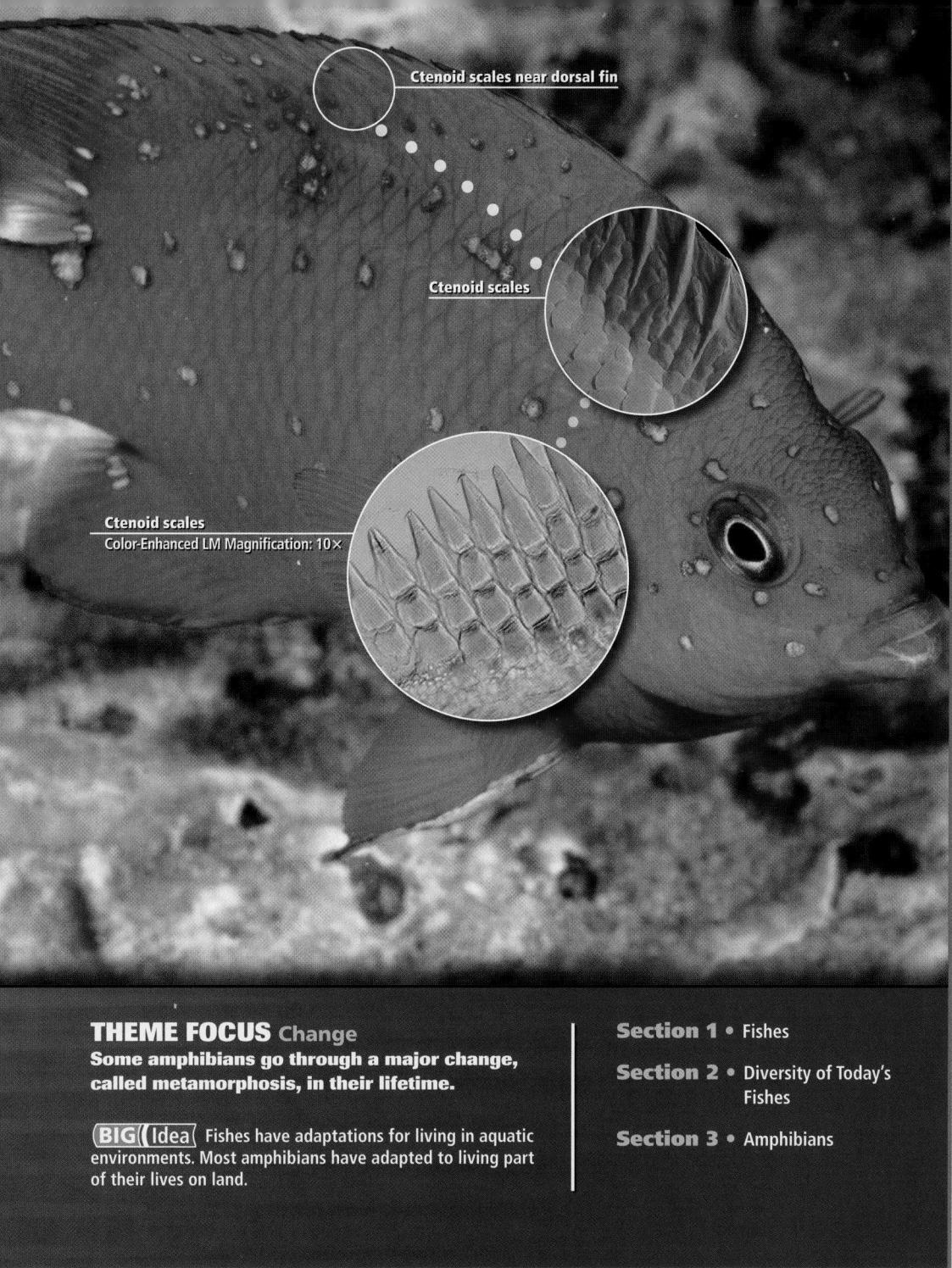

Section 1

MAIN Idea

BL OL AL Fish Adaptations
Have students observe fishes in the classroom aquarium and make a list of their adaptations to life in the water. Answers will depend on the fishes you have. Students might notice tails and fins, the operculum moving water across the gills, feeding behavior of bottom feeders, lateral flattening of fishes that move into small crevices, dorsoventral flattening of bottom feeders, or various positioning of eyes. If you do not have a classroom aquarium, see about the possibility of observing fishes in another class. You can also purchase fishes (such as betas) from a pet store or have students bring fishes from home. Monitor student behavior with the fishes.

C Critical Thinking

BL OL COOP LEARN Infer
Have students choose partners and infer why there are not many large invertebrates, even though some vertebrates, such as elephants and whales, are large. The backbones of vertebrates support larger bodies.

D Develop Concepts

BL OL AL Activity
SAY TO STUDENTS: ***List six common vertebrates and explain how their vertebral columns aid in their activities.*** Answers will vary. In general, the vertebral column provides support and functions as a rod that muscles can pull against during swimming or running. Students might point out the speed of a cheetah, the powerful swimming of a shark, or the jumping of a frog—all of these are made possible because muscles can pull against the vertebral column.

Video BrainPOP

Section 1

Reading Preview

Essential Questions
- What are the features of vertebrates that make them different from invertebrates?
- What are the characteristics that most fishes have in common?
- How are the characteristics of fishes adapted to aquatic life?

Review Vocabulary
notochord: a flexible, rodlike structure that extends the length of the body

New Vocabulary
cartilage
neural crest
fin
scale
operculum
atrium
ventricle
nephron
lateral line system
spawning
swim bladder

g Multilingual eGlossary

Video BrainPOP

Fishes

MAIN Idea Fishes are vertebrates that have characteristics allowing them to live and reproduce in water.

Real-World Reading Link You might have seen an aquarium full of colorful fishes similar to the fish in the photo at the beginning of this chapter. What adaptations do fishes have for living in water? Fishes have unique characteristics that allow them to live and reproduce in water.

Characteristics of Vertebrates

You have studied sponges, worms, and sea stars, which are all invertebrates. Recall that the four main characteristics of chordates are that they have a dorsal nerve cord, a notochord, pharyngeal pouches, and a postanal tail. Animals belonging to subphylum Vertebrata are called vertebrates. Vertebrates have a vertebral column and specialized cells that develop from the nerve cord. The vertebral column, also called a spinal column, is the hallmark feature of vertebrates. Classes of vertebrates include fishes, amphibians, reptiles, birds, and mammals.

C **Vertebral column** In most vertebrates, the notochord is replaced by a vertebral column that surrounds and protects the dorsal nerve cord. The replacement of the notochord happens during embryonic development. Cartilage or bone is the building material of most vertebrate endoskeletons. **Cartilage** (KAR tuh lihj) is a tough, flexible material making up the skeletons or parts of skeletons of vertebrates.

Vertebral columns, two of which are shown in **Figure 1,** are important structures in terms of the evolution of animals. The vertebral column functions as a strong, flexible rod that an animal's muscles can pull against during swimming or running. Separate vertebrae enhance an animal's ability to move quickly and easily. Bones enable forceful contraction of muscles, improving the strength of an animal. D

Figure 1 The vertebral column is present in most vertebrates, including bony fishes and reptiles as shown by the art.

Triggerfish

Sidewinder

Demonstration

BL OL AL Vertebrate Skeletons
Before students read this page, show skeletons or pictures of skeletons of a variety of vertebrates, such as a cat, bird, fish, and reptile.
ASK STUDENTS: ***How do the hardness of the bone and cartilage and flexibility of the vertebrae aid in movement?*** Accept all reasonable answers. Muscles can pull against the skeleton with a great deal of force, and flexibility enables quick movements in a variety of directions. Est. time: 10 min

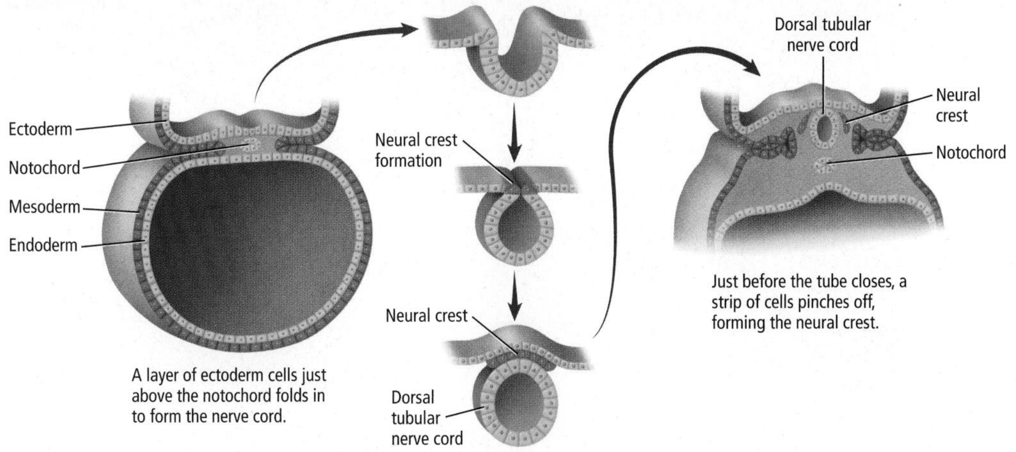

■ **Figure 2** The neural crest of vertebrates develops from the ectoderm of the embryo.

Review Personal Tutor

S

Neural crest As the nerve cord forms during embryonic development in vertebrates, another important process occurs: a neural (NOOR ul) crest forms. A **neural crest** is a group of cells that develop from the nerve cord in vertebrates. The process of neural crest formation is shown in **Figure 2.** Even though this group of cells is small, it is significant in the development of vertebrates because many important vertebrate features develop from the neural crest. These features include portions of the brain and skull, certain sense organs, parts of pharyngeal pouches, some nerve fibers, insulation for nerve fibers, and certain gland cells.

Other features that are characteristic of vertebrates include internal organs, such as kidneys and a liver. A heart and closed circulatory system also are features of all vertebrates.

Reading Check **Explain** why the neural crest is an important vertebrate feature.

Characteristics of Fishes

Fishes live in most aquatic habitats on Earth—seas, lakes, ponds, streams, and marshes. Some fishes live in complete darkness at the bottom of the deep ocean. Others live in the freezing waters of the polar regions and have special proteins in their blood to keep the blood from freezing. There are about 24,600 species of living fishes, more than all other vertebrates combined. They range in size from whale sharks that can be 18 m long to tiny cichlids that are the size of a human fingernail.

The features of fishes provided the structural basis for the development of land animals during the course of evolution. Important characteristics of fishes include the development of jaws and, in some fishes, lungs. As shown in the evolutionary tree in **Figure 3,** there are three groups of fishes, all of which are vertebrates. Although fishes' body shapes and structures vary a great deal, they all have several characteristics in common. Most fishes have vertebral columns, jaws, paired fins, scales, gills, and single-loop blood circulation, and they are not able to synthesize certain amino acids.

■ **Figure 3** The branches of the different groups of fishes are highlighted in this evolutionary tree.

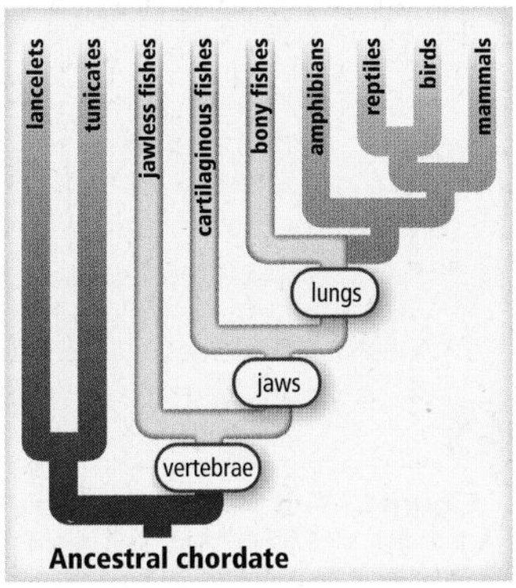

S Skill Practice

EL BL OL AL COOP LEARN

Make Models Organize students into groups of four. Provide groups with clay or salt dough. **SAY TO STUDENTS:** ***Make models of the stages of development of the neural crest. Do not make separate models for the successive stages. Make the first stage, then make that stage into the next stage and continue according to the description shown on this page.*** Ensure that the final models show the key features of Figure 2.

Develop Concepts

BL OL AL COOP LEARN

Activity Organize students into ten groups. Assign each group a different portion of text under the heading *Characteristics of Fishes.* Have the groups study their text and prepare a presentation to teach the key points to the class. Tell them to include props, visuals, and analogies.

Writing Support

BL OL AL **Creative Writing**

SAY TO STUDENTS: ***Write a narrative and descriptive story for children about the life cycle of a species of fish, noting its birth, habitat, and food. Make sure to include a list of predators that might end its life. Include what you are learning about the biology of fishes in your story.*** Stories will vary.

Review Personal Tutor

Listen to a teacher explain neural crest formation.

Differentiated Instruction

Below Level The modeling activity described on this page provides a valuable method for helping students to visualize difficult concepts. Provide step-by-step instructions on how to construct the models. Students will benefit when instructions are clear and detailed.

For more tips, see pages 14T–15T.

Reading Check The neural crest is important because it develops into key vertebrate structures, such as the brain and skull.

Develop Concepts

BL OL AL Activity

SAY TO STUDENTS: ***Observe and describe what fishes do with their fins when they turn and move up and when they move down in the aquarium.*** If you do not have a classroom aquarium, you might be able to borrow a colleague's aquarium, or purchase or borrow fishes from a local pet shop. Answers will depend on the kind of fishes in the aquarium.

S Skill Practice

EL BL Make Models Provide students with clay, wax-covered yarn, or salt dough. Instruct them to make models of fishes that include labels of the caudal, pectoral, and pelvic fins. Models will vary, but should place the caudal, pectoral, and pelvic fins in the correct positions.

Reading Check Jaws enabled fishes to grasp and crush prey more effectively. Fishes could take in more food and grow larger. They could also use the teeth in their jaws to defend themselves.

GOING GREEN Collect clear plastic produce and cake containers that have been cleaned. Large ones can serve as aquariums or terrariums and smaller ones can serve as containers for other specimens or lab supplies. Using these containers for classroom needs will help keep plastic out of landfills.

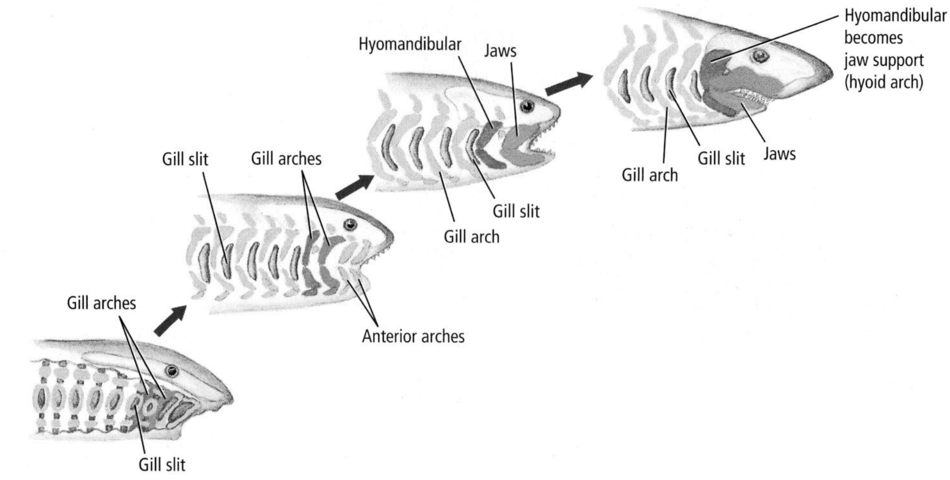

■ **Figure 4** Anterior gill arches evolved into jaws in ancient fishes.

Jaws Most fishes have jaws. The evolution of jaws is shown in **Figure 4,** where you can see that the anterior gill arches evolved to form jaws in ancient fishes. The development of jaws allowed ancient fishes to prey on a larger range of animals. This included the ability to prey on fishes that were larger and more active. Fishes grasp prey with their teeth and quickly crush them using powerful jaw muscles. Jaws also allow for a biting defense against predators.

Reading Check **Describe** why the evolution of jaws in fishes was important.

Paired fins At the same time that jaws were evolving, paired fins were also appearing in fishes. A **fin** is a paddle-shaped structure on a fish or other aquatic animal that is used for balance, steering, and propulsion. Pelvic fins and pectoral fins, like the ones shown in **Figure 5,** give fishes stability. Most fishes have paired fins. Paired fins reduce the chance of rolling to the side and allow for precise steering during swimming.

While fishes in ancient seas moved with precision and skill, they also were able to use their jaws in new ways. Both jaws and paired fins contributed to the evolution of a predatory way of life for some fishes and also enabled them to live in new habitats and produce more offspring.

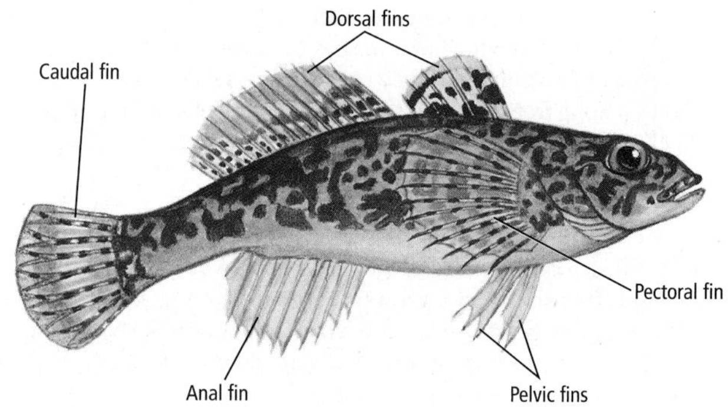

S

■ **Figure 5** Paired fins, such as pelvic and pectoral fins, allow fishes to maintain balance and to steer in the water.

Research Citation

Hands-On Activities Educational research indicates that students who perform hands-on activities will develop a deeper understanding of difficult concepts. The activity described on this page requires that students use clay, yarn, or salt dough to demonstrate their knowledge of fins. Students can refer back to this activity to aid their understanding of the concepts discussed in this chapter. (Sowell, 1989)

Research bibliography on pages 32T–34T

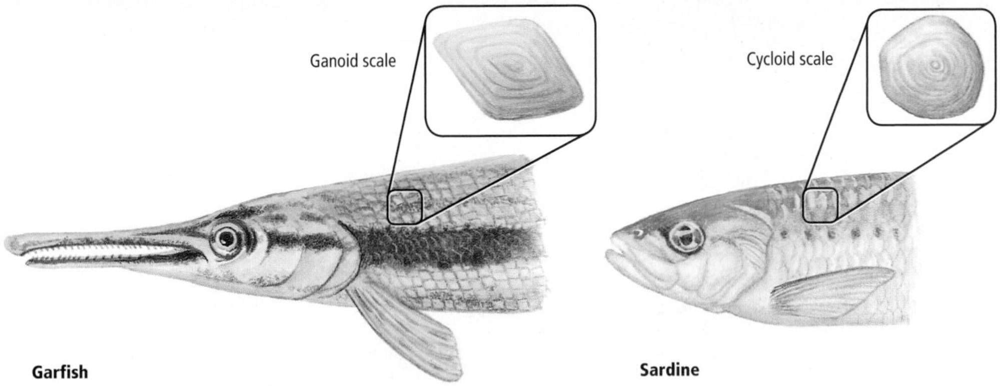

■ **Figure 6** Two types of fishes' scales are shown here—ganoid scales and cycloid scales.
Describe *the difference in the appearance of cycloid and ganoid scales.*

S

Scales Most fishes have at least one of four different types of scales. A **scale** is small, flat, platelike structure near the surface of the skin. There are four types of fish scales. Ctenoid (TEH noyd) scales, shown in the photos at the beginning of the chapter, and cycloid (SY kloyd) scales are made of bone and skin and are thin and flexible. Cycloid scales are shown in **Figure 6.** Placoid (PLA koyd) scales, which can be seen in **Figure 15** in Section 2, are made of toothlike materials and are rough and heavy. Ganoid (GAN oyd) scales, shown in **Figure 6,** are diamond-shaped and made of both enamel and bone.

✓ **Reading Check** **Infer** why different fishes have different kinds of scales.

MiniLab 1

Observe a Fish

? Inquiry MiniLab

What inferences can you make about characteristics of fishes through observation? In this lab, you will observe a fish in its aquatic environment.

Procedure

1. Read and complete the lab safety form.
2. Observe the **fish(es)** in an **aquarium.**
3. Make a diagram of a fish and label the following applicable structures: dorsal fin, caudal fin, anal fin, pectoral fins, pelvic fins, scales, mouth, eye, and gill covering.
4. Observe how the fish moves through the water. Illustrate how the fish moves its body and its fins as it moves forward in the water.

Analysis

1. **Infer** A fish's body is divided into three regions: head, trunk, and tail. Label these regions on your diagram of the fish that you observed.
2. **Apply** Suppose a fish lost one of its pectoral fins when fighting off a predator. How might this affect its ability to move through the water?

S Skill Practice

BL Visual Literacy Organize students into groups of four.
SAY TO STUDENTS: ***Examine the scales shown on page 818, and in Figures 6 and 15. Each student in your group should pick a different scale type, make a large diagram of the scale, and explain it to the rest of the group. Make sure to explain the shape of the scale and what it is made of.*** Check answers against the information provided in sections 1 and 2.

MiniLab 1

? Inquiry MiniLab

For a lab worksheet, use your eTeacherEdition Online.

✱RUBRIC A rubric for evaluating MiniLabs is found on your eTeacherEdition Online.

Est. Time 40 min

Safety Precautions Approve lab safety forms before work begins. Caution students not to put their hands or any objects into the tank with the fish. Use clear plastic tanks if possible.

Teaching Strategy Students could work in small groups.

Analysis

1. A fish's head includes the area between the tip of the mouth to just behind the operculum. The trunk includes the area between the operculum to the anus. The tail includes everything from the anus on.
2. The loss of a pectoral fin while fighting a predator will cause a fish to lose its stability and the ability to steer itself in the water.

LabManager™
Customize this lab with the LabManager™ CD-ROM.

Demonstration

BL OL AL Fish Scales Use a microprojector to show students images of a variety of fish scales.
SAY TO STUDENTS: ***The ages of some fishes can be determined by the number of rings on their scales.***
Est. time: 10 min

■ **Caption Question Fig. 6**
Ganoid scales are thick, nonoverlapping, and shiny, with a diamond-shaped appearance. Cycloid scales are thin, bony, and have a circular-shaped, layered or overlapping appearance.

✓ **Reading Check** Different types of scales are adapted to different life styles.

W Writing Support

BL OL AL COOP LEARN

Informal Writing Have pairs of students write notes to each other explaining what they know about the function of gills and asking questions to clarify what they do not understand. Then have partners exchange notes and write responses to the questions.

Concepts in Motion

Animation

D Develop Concepts

EL BL OL AL COOP LEARN

Model a Fish Heart Divide students into groups of three. Provide them with clay, salt dough, or wax-covered yarn.

SAY TO STUDENTS: ***Make a model of a fish heart that shows the two chambers and explain where the blood leaves the heart and returns to the heart. Label the part of the heart that contains oxygenated blood and the part that contains deoxygenated blood.***

R Reading Strategy

BL OL COOP LEARN

Make an Analogy Divide students into groups of four. Assign half of the groups respiration and the other half circulation. Provide students with markers and sheets of butcher paper.

SAY TO STUDENTS: ***Make an analogy that compares your assigned topic to a process in everyday life. Make a diagram of the everyday process and label it with the biological terms for the fish process.*** An example of an analogy for circulation is a ski lift picking people up at the base of a mountain and dropping them off at the top.

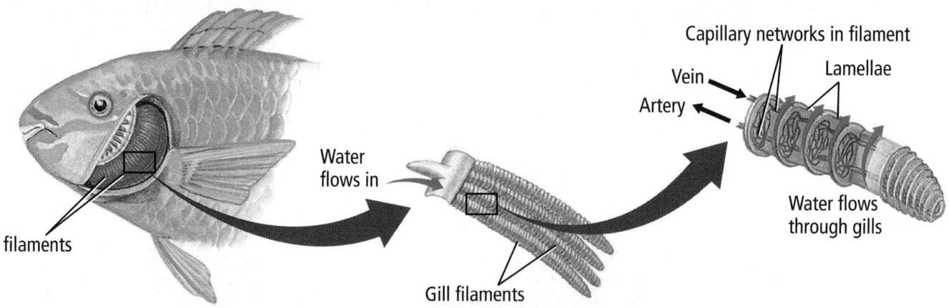

■ **Figure 7** The lamellae in a fish's gills have many blood vessels.
Infer ***why the gills of fishes are made up of very thin tissue.***

VOCABULARY

WORD ORIGIN

Atrium
from the Latin word *atrium,* meaning *central hallway*

D

■ **Figure 8** A fish's heart pumps blood through a closed circulatory system.

Concepts in Motion Animation

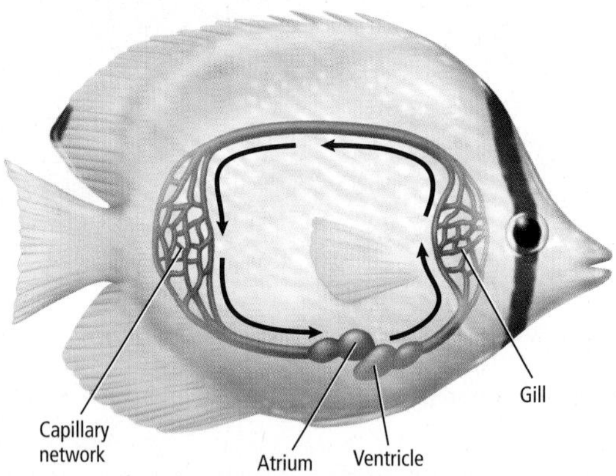

W **Gills** Another adaptation that allows fishes to live in aquatic environments is their ability to get oxygen from the water. Fishes get oxygen when water that enters their mouths flows across their gills, where oxygen from the water diffuses into the blood. Gills are composed of thin filaments that are covered with highly folded, platelike lamellae (luh MEH lee). The gill structure of most fishes is shown in **Figure 7.** The lamellae have many blood vessels that can take in oxygen and give off carbon dioxide.

The flow of blood in the gill is opposite to the flow of water over the gill surface. This countercurrent flow is an efficient mechanism by which oxygen can be removed from water. Up to 85 percent of oxygen dissolved in water is removed as water flows over the gills in one direction and blood in the other. Some fishes have an **operculum** (oh PUR kyuh lum), a movable flap that covers the gills and protects them. An operculum also aids in pumping water coming in the mouth and over the gills. Some fishes, such as lungfishes, can live out of water for short times by using structures resembling lungs. Eels can breathe through their moist skin when they are not in water.

Circulation Vertebrates have a closed circulatory system in which the heart pumps blood through blood vessels. The circulatory system of fishes is shown in **Figure 8.** In most fishes, the blood is passed through the heart in a one-way loop. From the heart, the blood goes to the gills, and then through the body, delivering oxygenated blood to tissues. The blood then returns to the heart. From the heart, blood is pumped back to the gills and then to the body again. Because this system is a complete and uninterrupted circuit, it is called a single-loop circulatory system.

In most fishes, the heart consists of two main chambers that are analogous to parts of your own heart—an atrium and a ventricle. The **atrium** is the chamber of the heart that receives blood from the body. From there, blood is passed to the **ventricle,** a chamber of the heart that pumps blood from the heart to the gills. Once the blood passes over the gills, it travels to the rest of the body. R

Demonstration

BL OL AL **Fish Gills** Project images of gill filaments. Point out that inside the gills, blood moves in the opposite direction from water moving over the gills. The oxygen concentration difference between the blood and the water is large enough that oxygen diffuses from the water into the blood.
Est. time: 7 min

■ **Caption Question Fig. 7** Gills are made up of thin tissue that enables oxygen to diffuse more easily into the blood through the lamellae and allows the carbon dioxide to pass more easily through the gills into the water.

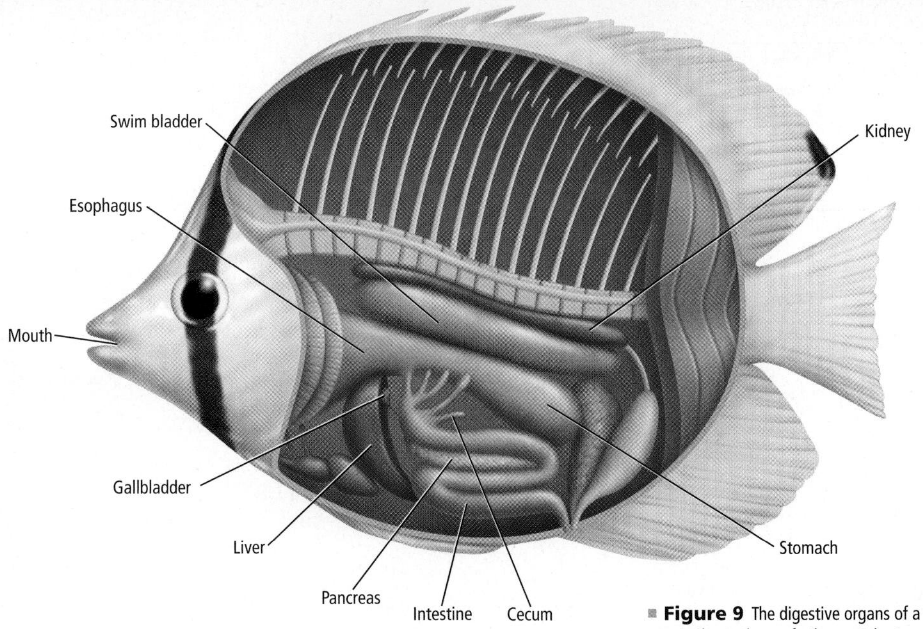

■ **Figure 9** The digestive organs of a fish are similar to those of other vertebrates.
Identify ***the structures that food passes through as it is being digested.***

Feeding and digestion Ancient fishes most likely were filter feeders or scavengers, sucking up organic debris on the ocean floor. With the evolution of jaws, fishes became efficient predators, and the diets of fishes changed dramatically. The digestive tract of fishes, illustrated in **Figure 9,** consists of organs similar to those of other vertebrates.

Most fishes swallow their food whole, passing it through a tube called the esophagus (ih SAH fuh gus) to the stomach, where digestion begins. Food then passes to the intestine, where most digestion occurs. Some fishes have pyloric (pi LOR ihk) ceca (SEE kuh) (singular, *cecum*), which are small pouches at the junction of the stomach and the intestine that secrete enzymes for digestion and absorb nutrients into the bloodstream. The liver, pancreas, and gallbladder add digestive juices that complete digestion.

Fishes are described not only by structures and their functions, but also by one important thing that they cannot do. They are not able to
C synthesize certain amino acids. Therefore, not only fishes, but also all the vertebrates that evolved from them, must get these amino acids
W from the foods they eat.

Excretion Cellular wastes are filtered from fishes' blood by organs called kidneys. The main functional unit of the kidney is the nephron. A **nephron** is a filtering unit within the kidney that helps to maintain the salt and water balance of the body and to remove cellular waste products from the blood. Some cellular wastes are excreted by the gills.

Connection to Chemistry The bodies of freshwater fishes take in water by osmosis because the surrounding water is hypotonic—the water contains more water molecules than the fishes' tissues. The opposite occurs in saltwater bony fishes. Because the surrounding water is hypertonic—the water contains fewer water molecules than their tissues—their bodies tend to lose water. Kidneys, gills, and other internal mechanisms adjust the water and salt balance in the bodies of freshwater and saltwater fishes.

CAREERS IN BIOLOGY

Ichthyologist Researching information about the behavior, ecology, and anatomy and physiology of fishes, both in the field and in the lab, is just one of the jobs an ichthyologist (ihk thee AHL uh jist) might have. Ichthyologists also manage aquariums, organize museum collections, teach at universities, and work to conserve fish populations.

C Critical Thinking

BL OL AL

Design a Fishing Lure Have students choose a game fish and research what it eats. Then have them design a fishing lure or "fly" that would be suited to catching that particular fish. Tell them to make a model or an actual lure and present it to the class. Encourage creativity. Accept any model or lure that relates to the food that fishes eat.

W Writing Support

OL Creative Writing

SAY TO STUDENTS: ***Research what kinds of foods fishes eat, including both common and unusual foods. Write and illustrate an article that would appeal to teenagers about fishes in one particular environment. Describe the fishes, their food, and their adaptations to the area in which they live.*** Articles will depend on the type of fish chosen. Make sure the paper includes a paragraph describing the fish, the type of foods it eats, adaptations to its environment, and one or more illustrations.

Writing Support

AL Persuasive Writing

SAY TO STUDENTS: ***Research to find out which types of fishes we eat are declining in numbers because the natural reproductive rate cannot keep up with the demand for fish as food for humans. Write a persuasive report that advocates measures that would conserve specific fish populations while enabling a reasonable harvest.***

■ **Caption Question Fig. 9** mouth, esophagus, stomach, pyloric ceca, intestine

Research Citation

Creative Writing Educational research indicates that students should be allowed to write in a variety of styles to express their understanding of science concepts. The creative writing activity described on this page provides students with an alternative style of assessment, while providing the teacher with an opportunity to evaluate their understanding of the material. (Fisher and Frey, 2004)

Research bibliography on pages 32T–34T

D Develop Concepts

BL OL AL

Clarify a Misconception

ASK STUDENTS: ***Do sharks give birth to live young, or do they release eggs into the water?*** both

TELL STUDENTS: ***Most sharks give birth to live young, but some release eggs. There are three types of shark development. Viviparous sharks give birth to litters of live shark pups, with eggs hatching inside the female's body and nourished by a placenta.***

Oviparous sharks release egg casings, sometimes called mermaid's purses, into the ocean. The eggs hatch later if predators do not eat them. Ovoviviparous sharks have eggs that hatch within the female's body, but they are not nourished through a placenta. In this case, the shark pups eat unfertilized eggs and also each other.

W Writing Support

AL Technical Writing

Have students conduct research and write an essay describing the three different types of shark egg development, giving one example for each type. Instruct them to include information on the method of reproduction, the amount of eggs per reproductive cycle, and the method of feeding the embryos. Essays will depend on the type of sharks chosen. Examples of viviparous sharks include bull, whale, lemon, blue, mako, and hammerhead sharks. Examples of oviparous sharks include zebra, swell, necklace carpet, and horn sharks. Examples of ovoviviparous sharks include great white, saw, crocodile, cookiecutter, Greenland, gummy, soupfin, Pacific angel, pygmy, nurse, tiger, and sand tiger sharks.

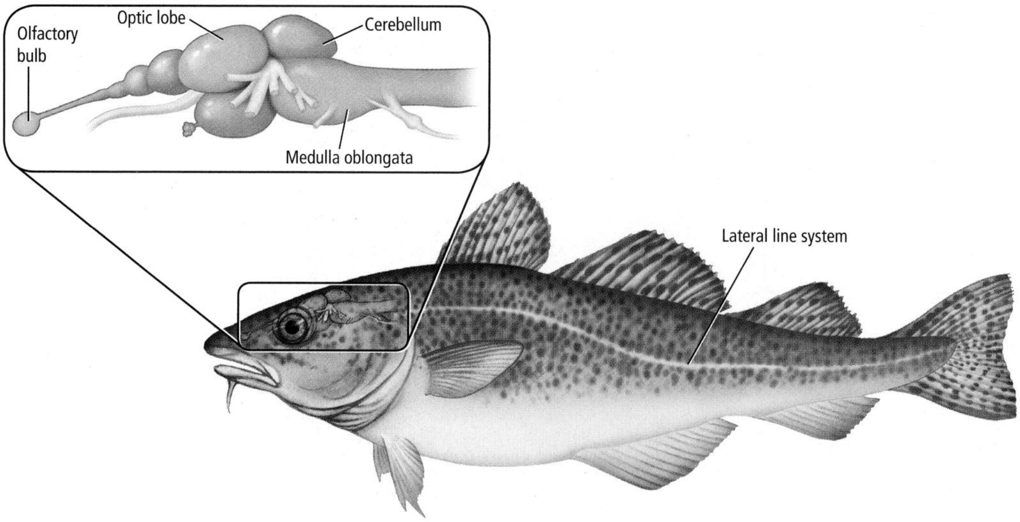

■ **Figure 10** Fishes have a brain that enables them to carry out their life functions. **Infer** ***in what way the brain of a fish that lives passively on the bottom of a pond feeding on organic debris would be different from a predatory fish that has to swim swiftly after prey.***

The brain and senses As in other vertebrates, the nervous system of fishes consists of a spinal cord and a brain. A fish brain is shown in **Figure 10.** The cerebellum is involved in coordinating movement and controlling balance. Fishes have receptors for the sense of smell that enable them to detect chemicals in the water. The olfactory (ohl FAK tree) bulbs record and respond to incoming chemical input. Fishes also have color vision. The optic lobes are responsible for visual input. The cerebrum coordinates input from other parts of the brain. Internal organs are under the control of the medulla oblongata.

If you have spent any time fishing, you know that fishes can detect the slightest movement in the water. Fishes can do this because they have special receptors called the lateral line system. The **lateral line system** enables fishes to detect movement in the water and also helps to keep them upright and balanced. You can see the lateral line system of a fish in **Figure 10.**

D **Reproduction** The majority of fishes reproduce through external fertilization. Male and female fishes release their gametes near each other in the water in a process called **spawning.** Developing embryos get nutrition from food stored in the yolk of the egg. Some fishes, such as sharks, reproduce through internal fertilization. Although fertilization takes place internally, development of the embryo of some fish species might occur outside of the female's body when fertilized eggs are laid. Some species of fishes have internal fertilization as well as internal development of offspring. In these cases, the developing embryos get nutrition from the female's body.

Fishes that reproduce through external fertilization can produce millions of eggs in a single season. Most fishes do not protect or care for their eggs or offspring. As a result, many eggs and juvenile fishes are prey to other animals. The production of large numbers of eggs ensures that some offspring develop and survive to reproduce. One exception is the male sergeant major fish, shown in **Figure 11.** The male fish guards the fertilized eggs from predators until they hatch. W

■ **Figure 11** Most fishes do not care for their young; however, male sergeant majors guard the eggs as the embryos develop.

Demonstration

Salmon Reproduction Show a movie about salmon reproduction, such as *Nature: The Miracle of the Scarlet Salmon* (1998, Time Life Video/BBC).

TELL STUDENTS: ***Salmon live, breed, and die based on their reproductive cycle. Salmon spawn in gravel beds, deposit and fertilize eggs, and most die after spawning one time.***

Est. time: 20 min

■ **Caption Question Figure 10** The cerebellum might be smaller.

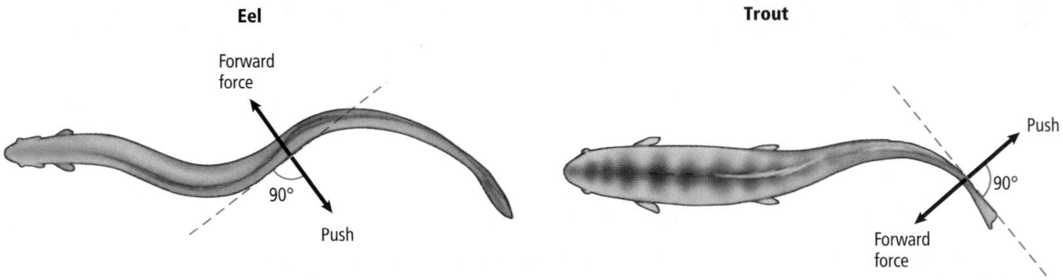

■ **Figure 12** An eel moves its whole body in an S-shaped pattern. Other, faster moving fishes, such as trout, move only their tails as they push forward through the water.

Movement Fishes are well adapted to swimming in water. Most fishes have a streamlined shape. Most also have mucus that lubricates the body surface and reduces friction between the fish and the water. Fins enable fishes to steer and maneuver in a variety of ways. The buoyant force of water reduces the effect of gravity on fishes. In addition, the **swim bladder,** which is shown in **Figure 9,** is a gas-filled space, like a balloon, found in bony fishes that allows a fish to control its depth. When gases diffuse out of the swim bladder, a fish can sink. When gases from the blood diffuse into the swim bladder, a fish can rise in the water column.

Connection to Physics Examine **Figure 12.** Fishes move through the water by contracting muscle groups on either side of their bodies. The arrangement of muscle in a fish allows muscle contraction to bend a large portion of the fish's body. As the body of a fish bends, it pushes against the water, creating an opposing force that moves the fish forward, but at an angle. Alternate contraction of muscles, first on one side of the body and then on the other, keep the fish moving forward in an S-shaped pattern.

Section 1 Assessment

Section Summary

- Vertebrates include fishes, amphibians, reptiles, birds, and mammals.
- All vertebrates have a notochord. In most vertebrates, the notochord is replaced by a vertebral column during embryonic development.
- Fishes share certain characteristics and are therefore classified together.
- The bodies of fishes have unique adaptations that enable them to live their entire lives in water.

Understand Main Ideas

1. MAIN Idea **Describe** the characteristics that fishes have that allow them to live and reproduce in water.
2. **Summarize** the features of vertebrates that make them different from invertebrates.
3. **Evaluate** the importance of the evolution of jaws in fishes.
4. **Identify** the characteristics that most fishes have in common.
5. **Explain** why freshwater and saltwater bony fishes have to adjust the balance of salt and water in their bodies.

Think Critically

6. **Hypothesize** Male three-spined stickleback fishes build nests using bright, shiny materials that are in limited supply and are chosen more frequently by females. Form a hypothesis about why this might ensure that a female is choosing a male that has strong traits of his species.
7. **Infer** How might an injury to a fish's lateral line system affect that fish's ability to escape predation?

Formative Assessment

Evaluation

SAY TO STUDENTS: ***Make a table with the following headings:* Respiration, Circulation, Neural Response, Movement, *and* Reproduction. *Beneath each heading, write the corresponding physical feature of a fish that goes with each topic.*** respiration: gills; circulation: closed circulatory system with two-chambered heart; neural response: brain and associated nerves; movement: muscles pull on vertebral column; reproduction: eggs and sperm with external fertilization

Remediation Prepare flash cards with the following topics labeled on front and the corresponding physical features on the back: *respiration: gills; circulation: closed circulatory system with two-chambered heart; neural response: brain and associated nerves; movement: muscles pull on vertebral column; reproduction: eggs and sperm with external fertilization.* Have students work in pairs to quiz each other.

Section 1 Assessment

1. jaws, paired appendages, gills, single-loop blood circulation, scales, and swim bladder
2. vertebrates have a vertebral column made of cartilage or bone; during development, neural crest develops into many vertebrate features; vertebrates have a closed circulatory system
3. When fishes' jaws evolved, they could feed on a wider variety of food. As a result, new niches became available to them.
4. vertebral column, jaws, paired fins, scales, moist skin for obtaining oxygen, and a single-loop blood circulation
5. Freshwater contains more water molecules than the fishes' tissues, while salt water contains less. Therefore, freshwater fish need less water in their bodies than saltwater fishes.
6. The female chooses a "top-quality" male who is good at obtaining resources that are in limited supply.
7. A fish with a damaged lateral line system will not be able to detect movement in the water.

✓ Assessment **Online Quiz**

Section 2

MAIN Idea

BL OL AL COOP LEARN

Dichotomous Key Organize students into groups of four. Provide them with field guides and pictures of a variety of fishes. Display examples of dichotomous keys for other organisms.

SAY TO STUDENTS: ***To make a dichotomous key for identifying fishes, first divide the fishes into two groups based on a yes-or-no question that reflects characteristics of the fishes. Divide each group again based on a yes-or-no question. Continue to construct your key until you have isolated the fishes into individuals or groups that are the same. When you are finished, trade your key and pictures with another group to see if your key works.***

R Reading Strategy

EL BL OL **Two-Column Notes**

Before they read, have students skim the section and list the classes of fishes on the left side of a piece of paper. As they read, have them fill in two other columns with the specific type of aquatic habitat and the physical adaptations to that habitat.

Skill Practice

BL OL AL **Visual Literacy**

SAY TO STUDENTS: ***Compare and contrast all the figures in this section. Make a chart that indicates the visible adaptations fishes have to their habitat, how they are like other fishes, and how they are different from other fishes.***

Section 2

Reading Preview

Essential Questions

- What are the characteristics of different groups of fishes?
- What are similarities and differences between the key features of various types of fishes?
- How is the evolution of fishes explained?

Review Vocabulary

adaptive radiation: the process of evolution that produces many species from an ancestral species

New Vocabulary

tetrapod

g Multilingual eGlossary

R Diversity of Today's Fishes

MAIN Idea Scientists classify fishes into three groups based on body structure.

Real-World Reading Link You already know that the basic structures and their functions in fishes are similar. Now think about all the different types of fishes you have seen in aquariums, in photos, or on television.

Classes of Fishes

You have read about jellyfish, crayfish, and various shellfish, but none of these are true fishes. True fishes belong to three groups based on their body structure. Hagfishes and lampreys are jawless fishes; sharks, skates, and rays are cartilaginous (kar tuh LAJ uh nus) fishes; and bony fishes include both ray-finned and lobe-finned fishes.

Jawless fishes Hagfishes, as shown in **Figure 13,** are jawless, eel-shaped fishes that do not have scales, paired fins, or a bony skeleton. Members of class Myxini (mik SEE nee), hagfishes have a notochord throughout life. Although they do not develop a vertebral column, they do have gills and many other characteristics of fishes. They live on the seafloor and feed on soft-bodied invertebrates and dead or dying fishes. Even though they are almost blind, their keen chemical sense enables them to locate food. Hagfishes either enter the body of the fish through the mouth or they scrape an opening into the fish with toothlike structures on their tongues. After eating the internal parts of the fish, the hagfish leaves only a sac of skin and bones.

Hagfishes are known for their ability to produce slime. If threatened, they secrete fluid from glands in their skin. When the fluid comes in contact with seawater, it forms a slime that is slippery enough to prevent the hagfishes from being caught by predators.

Figure 13 Hagfishes are jawless fishes that have toothlike structures on their tongues. Lampreys are parasites on other living fishes.
Describe *what adaptations for life on the seafloor you can see in the hagfish photo.*

Hagfish

Lamprey

Differentiated Instruction

Above Level Emphasize the importance of teamwork to gifted students. By requiring that students participate in cooperative learning activities such as the one described on this page, you can help these students develop the skills they need to be productive members of a team.

For more tips, see pages 14T–15T.

Caption Question Fig. 13 no fins, no eyes, wormlike body can easily burrow underneath the sand or mud

Lampreys, like hagfishes, also are jawless, eel-shaped fishes that lack scales, paired fins, or a bony skeleton. Lampreys, members of class Cephalaspidomorphi (ceh fah las pe doh MOR fee), retain a notochord throughout life, as do hagfishes. Lampreys have gills and other characteristics of fishes. An adult lamprey, as shown in **Figure 13,** is a parasite that feeds by attaching itself to other fishes. Lampreys use their sucker-like mouth and tongue with toothlike structures to feed on the blood and bodily fluids of their hosts.

Reading Check **List** the characteristics of jawless fishes.

W D **Cartilaginous fishes** When you hear the word *shark,* the first thing that might come to mind is a large fish with many sharp teeth. In spite of being famous for teeth, a shark's main distinguishing feature is its skeleton. The skeleton of a shark is made of cartilage, which gives the skeleton flexibility, and calcium carbonate, which gives it strength. All cartilaginous fishes have skeletons made of cartilage.

Sharks belong to class Chondrichthyes (kon DRIK thees). Some species of sharks have several rows of sharp teeth, as shown in **Figure 14.** As teeth are broken or lost, new ones move forward to replace them. Most sharks also have a streamlined shape, with a pointed head and a tail that turns up at the end, as shown in **Figure 15.**

These streamlining features, along with strong swimming muscles and sharp teeth, make sharks one of the top predators in the sea. They can sense chemicals in the water, allowing them to detect prey from a distance of one kilometer. As they move in closer, their lateral line systems can detect vibrations in the water. Finally, when they are in the last stages of pursuit, they use their vision and other receptors to detect the bioelectrical fields given off by all animals. An additional adaptation to a predatory life includes tough skin with placoid scales, shown in **Figure 15.**

Not all sharks have rows of teeth. Whale sharks, the largest living sharks, are filter feeders with specialized straining structures in their mouths. Other sharks have mouths adapted to feeding on shelled mollusks.

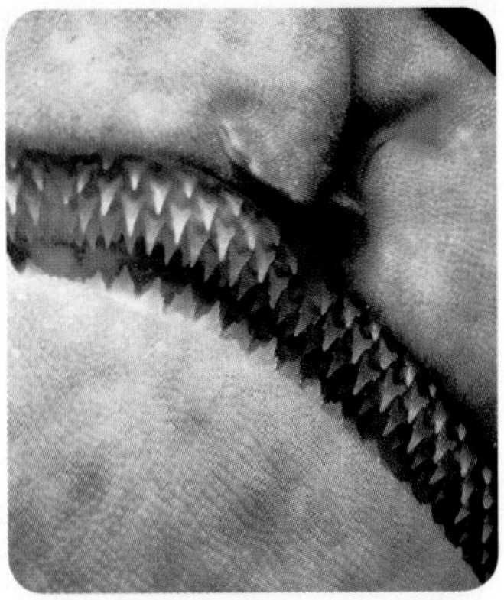

Figure 14 Some sharks have several rows of teeth. As teeth in the front row fall or are pulled out, teeth from the row behind them move up to take their place.

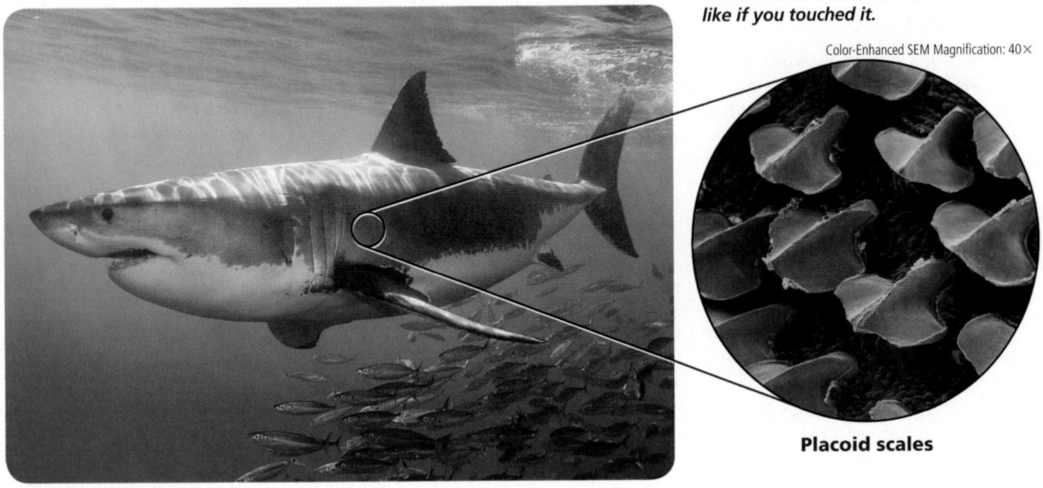

Figure 15 Great white sharks have streamlined bodies and are covered with tough placoid scales.
Infer *what a shark's skin would feel like if you touched it.*

Demonstration

BL OL AL Shark Teeth Obtain some shark teeth (available from biological supply companies) and show them to the class.
ASK STUDENTS: ***How are these teeth adapted to the food sharks eat?*** Sharks are predators. The sharp pointed teeth enable them to seize and tear apart prey.
Est. time: 7 min

Reading Check jawless, eel-shaped, no scales, no paired fins, have a notochord and gills

Caption Question Fig. 15 Answers will vary. Examples: shark skin feels rough like sandpaper, tough, etc.

W Writing Support

BL Summary Writing Have students research one shark and write a summary that includes the following: common name, scientific name, distribution, reproduction information, and size.

D Develop Concepts

BL OL AL

Clarify a Misconception
ASK STUDENTS: ***Are all sharks dangerous to humans?*** no
SAY TO STUDENTS: The three most dangerous sharks to humans are the great white shark, tiger shark, and bull shark. On the average, sharks kill fewer than ten people each year, and cause minor injuries with fewer than 100 nonfatal attacks each year. To put that number into perspective, lightning strikes and bee stings kill more people each year.

Writing Support

BL OL AL Formal Writing
SAY TO STUDENTS: ***Write a report on an endangered fish of your choice. Make sure to explain its habitat needs, its way of life, why it has become endangered, and what can be done to ensure its continued survival.***

Writing Support

BL OL AL Summary Writing
SAY TO STUDENTS: ***Research fish farming and write a summary of your findings. Illustrate your report with appropriate diagrams and illustrations. Include the name of the author, periodical title or book title, publisher (for a book), and publication date from any references you use to write your report.*** Struggling students can make an illustration of a lamnid shark instead.

W Writing Support

AL Technical Writing Scientists refer to bony fishes as being *r*-strategists, which means fishes need to reproduce quickly because they compete with other organisms and have short life spans. Sharks are *k*-strategists, which means they have a large size, longer life span, and lower growth and reproduction rates.

SAY TO STUDENTS: ***Research* r*-strategists and* k*-strategists and write a technical description of these types of fishes. Explain how scientists use this information when planning regulations for fish harvests.***

DATA ANALYSIS LAB 1

About the Lab

- Lamnid sharks include the great white shark and the mako shark. Tunas have a similar shape, as do whales and other large fishes. This convergent evolution of body shape and mechanical design enables these animals to use their tails efficiently for fast propulsion.
- When actively swimming, lamnid sharks confine their body-bending movements to their tails while keeping their midlines in a straight line. When swimming passively, the midline and tail both move from side to side.
- Also see Lingham-Soliar, T. 2005. Caudal fin in the white shark, *Charcharoden carcharias* (Lamnidae): a dynamic propeller for fast, efficient swimming. *Journal of Morphology* 264: 233–252.

Think Critically

1. No, red and white muscles contract at about the same time.
2. Red muscles contract after the white muscles.

■ **Figure 16** Skates have flattened bodies that are adapted for living on the ocean floor.

Skates and rays are cartilaginous fishes adapted to life on the bottom of the sea. In addition to their flattened bodies, their pectoral fins, shown in **Figure 16,** are enlarged and attached to their heads. Their winglike fins flap slowly as they swim along the seafloor in search of mollusks and crustaceans, which they crush with their teeth.

Bony fishes Class Osteichthyes (ahs tee IHK theez) contains two groups of bony fishes: the ray-finned fishes, belonging to subclass Actinopterygii (AK tihn ahp TUR ee jee i), and the lobe-finned fishes, belonging to the subclass Sarcopterygii (SAR kahp TUR ee jee i). Modern ray-finned fishes have a bony skeleton, ctenoid or cycloid scales, an operculum covering the gills, and a swim bladder. The most distinguishing feature of ray-finned fishes is suggested by their name. The thin membranes of these fishes' fins are supported by thin, spinelike rays, which are shown in **Figure 17.** Most fishes alive today, including salmon and trout, are ray-finned fishes.

There are only eight species of lobe-finned fishes living today. Their fins, shown in **Figure 17,** have muscular lobes and joints similar to those of land vertebrates. This makes the fins more flexible than those of ray-finned fishes. Lobe-finned fishes, such as the lungfish, usually have lungs for gas exchange. When drought occurs, a lungfish can burrow with its fleshy fins into the mud and breathe air. When rain returns, lungfishes come out of their burrows.

Coelacanths (SEE luh kanths) are another small group of lobe-finned fishes that many people thought had become extinct about 70 million years ago. However, in 1938, some people fishing off the coast of South Africa caught a coelacanth. Since that time, other coelacanths have been caught. A third group of lobe-finned fishes, now extinct, is thought to be the ancestor of tetrapods. A **tetrapod,** shown in **Figure 17,** is a four-footed animal with legs that have feet and toes that have joints.

DATA ANALYSIS LAB 1

Based on Real Data*

Analyze Data

How do sharks' muscles function? Lamnid sharks have two types of muscles. Red muscle tissue does not tire easily and is used more during cruising. White muscle tissue is used more during short bursts of speed. Both muscles, however, are always used at the same time.

Data and Observations

The peaks of the graph represent when each muscle type contracts.

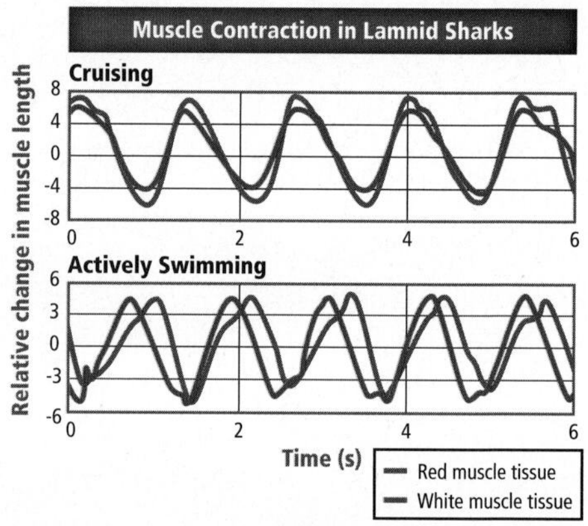

Think Critically

1. **Evaluate** Does the timing of the contractions of the two types of muscle differ when the sharks are cruising?
2. **Compare** How does the timing of the contractions between the two muscle types change when the sharks are actively swimming?

*Data obtained from: Donley, J., et al. 2004 Convergent evolution in mechanical design of lamnid sharks and tunas. *Nature* 429: 61-65.

Content Background

Fishapod In 2004, the first fossil of the fishapod was discovered on Ellesmere Island, Canada. This species, *Tiktaalik roseae*, is thought to be a link between fish and the first tetrapods. It had bony fins that it could push itself up with, and lungs as well as gills, so that it could breathe in and out of the water.

Content Background

Skates and Rays The skate family is often abundant in water that is less than 1000 m deep. Their slender tails often contain electric organs. Rays also contain electric organs that easily can stun an active prey fish. Another group of rays have venom glands at the base of their tails, which they use to defend themselves against predators such as sharks.

Visualizing Bony Fishes

Figure 17

Class Osteichthyes consists of the bony fishes. It can be divided into two subclasses—ray-finned fishes and lobe-finned fishes. An extinct lobe-finned fish is thought to be the ancestor of modern tetrapods.

Ray-finned fish

Ray-finned fishes have thin, spinelike rays that support the membranes of their fins.

Lobe-finned fish

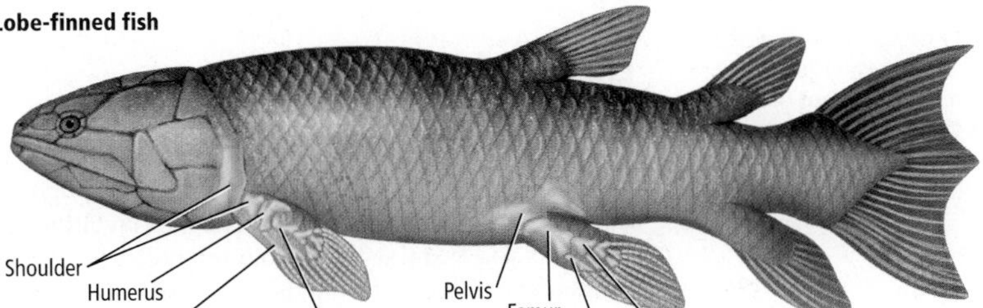

Lobe-finned fishes have muscular lobes and joints similar to those of tetrapods.

Early tetrapod

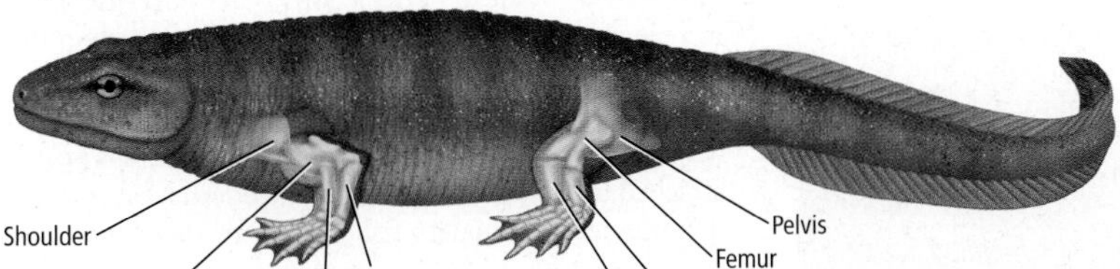

The limbs of tetrapods evolved from the fins of lobe-finned fishes. *Ichthyostega* was a tetrapod that lived about 325 million years ago, had fully formed limbs, and walked on land.

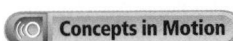

Concepts in Motion Animation

Demonstration

BL OL AL Fish Classes Make a slideshow presentation about the classes of fishes.
ASK STUDENTS: (for each slide) ***What structural adaptations do you see that enable this fish to be successful in its habitat?***
ASK STUDENTS: ***Infer the type of specific water environment this fish might live in.*** examples: rushing stream, in a marsh, on the bottom of a lake, on a coral reef
Est. time: 15 min

Visualizing Bony Fishes

Purpose

Students will study the form and function of a bony fish.
UCP.1, UCP.5, C.5

Develop Concepts

EL BL OL AL COOP LEARN

Activity Organize students into groups of two or three. Provide each group with a fish skeleton or, if they are not available, substitute fish heads obtained from a fish market.

SAY TO STUDENTS: ***Observe the mouths of the fishes and infer what kinds of foods they might eat. Justify your observations. When you are finished with your observation, be prepared to explain your inferences to the class.***

Develop Concepts

BL OL AL

Community Connection Plan a class field trip to a nearby fish hatchery. Talk to the tour guide ahead of time about what students will be seeing and make a list of questions that students can answer to keep them focused on the tour as a learning experience. If a field trip is not possible, you could invite a speaker from a fish hatchery to come to your class, or show a video on the work of a fish hatchery. These are available through the Department of the Interior U.S. Fish and Wildlife Service.

Concepts in Motion
Animation

D Develop Concepts

BL OL AL Discuss Have students make a list of the features of fishes as they evolved, from the earliest fishes to modern fishes. **ASK STUDENTS: *What point on the cladogram would represent the Devonian period?*** where placoderms are represented

S Skill Practice

OL Illustrate Have students research the specific physical appearance of early fishes and make sketches of some of the early forms, such as ostracoderms and placoderms. Students can make additional sketches of other early fishes. Sketches will vary; check for accuracy.

C Critical Thinking

OL AL Infer

ASK STUDENTS: *Infer why modern fishes, unlike early fishes, are not covered with bony armor.* The heavy bony coverings may have prohibited fishes from moving quickly to escape predators, and the ones that survived had less bone and could move with more agility in the water.

■ **Caption Question Fig. 18** hagfishes, lampreys, ostracoderms

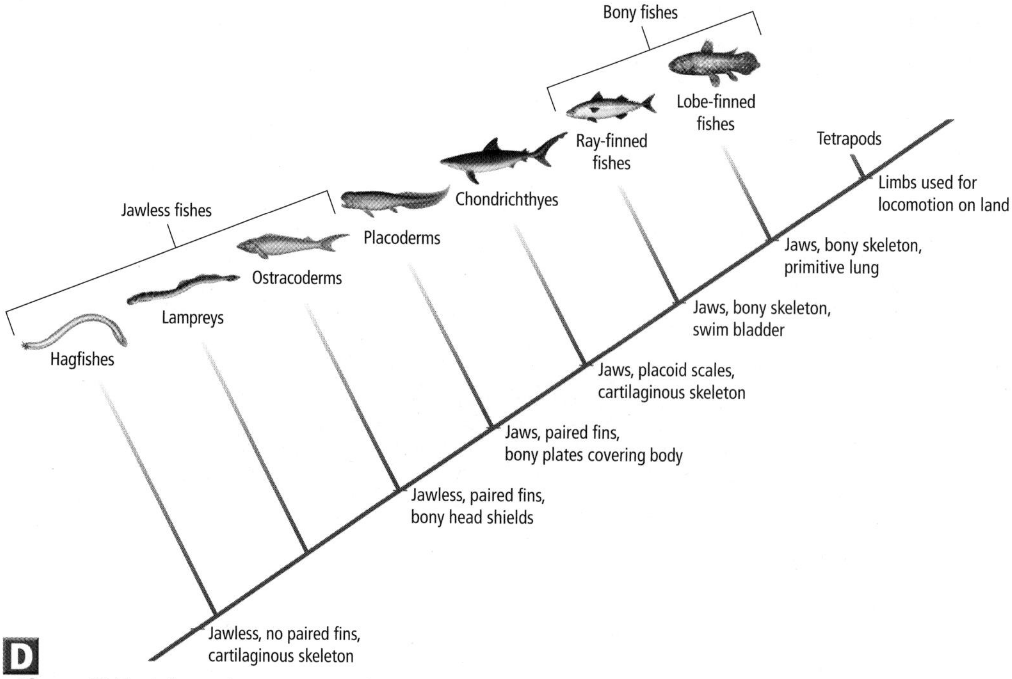

D

■ **Figure 18** The cladogram shows one interpretation of the phylogeny of fishes. ***Identify** which fishes did not have jaws, according to the cladogram.*

■ **Figure 19** *Dinichthys,* also called *Dunkleosteus,* was a placoderm that had armor plating around its head.

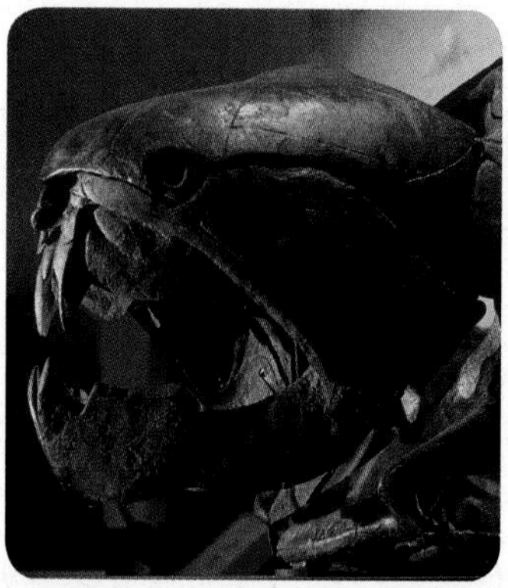

Evolution of Fishes

In the ancient seas of the Cambrian period, the first vertebrates wriggled through the water. They were jawless and toothless, but they did have gills, heads, and tails that moved them through the water. The cladogram shown in **Figure 18** is one interpretation of the phylogeny of fishes. As you examine the cladogram, notice the characteristics of fishes that developed during the course of their evolution.

S **First fishes** These first jawless, toothless fishes sucked up organic materials from the ocean floor as if they were miniature vacuum cleaners. Ostracoderms (OS tra koh dermz) were the next group of fishes to appear in the fossil record, in the Ordovician period. Ostracoderms had head shields made of bone, a bony outer covering, and paired fins. They were jawless filter feeders, many of which rested on the bottom of ancient seas.

The bony armor of ostracoderms was an evolutionary milestone in the development of vertebrates. Stronger movement is possible when muscle is attached to bone. Even though ostracoderms became extinct, scientists hypothesize that modern fishes share an ancestry with ostracoderms.

Age of fishes During the Devonian period, modern fishes had their beginnings. Some were jawless, while some, such as the placoderms, had jaws, a covering of bony plates, paired fins, and an internal skeleton. A fossil of a placoderm fish is shown in **Figure 19.** Recall that three of these features are characteristics of the fishes that eventually replaced the placoderms as they became extinct. The Devonian period often is referred to as the Age of Fishes because of the adaptive radiation of fishes that occurred at that time. C

Content Background

Placoderms The first major group of jawed fishes were the placoderms. Like ostracoderms, they were covered with heavy, bony skeletons. They dominated the seas in the late Devonian period and became extinct in the Carboniferous period. Because they never developed more advanced types of jaw structure and teeth, the Osteichthyes and Chondrichthyes, with these structures, were able to replace the placoderms.

Ecology of Fishes

Fishes are an important source of food in all aquatic ecosystems. Yet their freshwater habitats and saltwater habitats are being changed by human activities, such as the damming of rivers and pollution. Fishes are good bioindicators of the environmental health of an aquatic system. When noncommercial fish populations decrease, the main cause often is habitat alteration. When fishes decline in numbers, not only are there negative human economic impacts, but also, ecosystems can become unbalanced.

Habitat alteration Some fishes, such as salmon, migrate. Salmon spend their adult lives in the ocean but return to freshwater to spawn in the streams where they hatched. In the Pacific Northwest, river and stream habitats have been changed by the construction of dams. Dams interfere with the upstream and downstream migration of salmon, as shown in **Figure 20.** The end result in the Pacific Northwest, for example, is that the number of salmon swimming upstream now is only about three percent of the 10 to 16 million salmon that swam up the rivers 150 years ago.

Pollution The habitats of fishes can be changed by pollution, which can reduce the quality of water in lakes, rivers, and streams. This can result in a decline in both the number and diversity of fishes in an area. In some cases, when the cause of habitat alteration is stopped and suitable conditions return, fishes also return. For example, Atlantic salmon were not observed in the Penobscot River in Maine for ten years during a time when intense pollution altered water quality. When the pollution was stopped, the salmon returned.

Figure 20 Not all salmon are able to get over the dams used to generate hydroelectricity. To spawn, salmon must return to the streams where they hatched.

? Inquiry Launch Lab

Review Based on what you have read about different fishes, how would you now answer the analysis questions?

? Inquiry Launch Lab

Assess Content Development
Assess how understanding has developed when students revisit the Launch Lab analysis questions.

Formative Assessment

Evaluation Organize students into groups of four, then organize each group into pairs for a vocabulary guessing game. Have each group make a set of cards with terms on one side and stack them face down. Have the groups exchange cards with one another. For each round, have the pairs in each group compete with one another to draw hints on paper as their partner guesses the vocabulary term within 1 min or before the other pair in their group. Tell students that the partner who is drawing may not speak or write words, letters, or numbers.

Remediation Have students make a chart with columns labeled *Vocabulary Term, Definition, Diagram,* and *Memory Clue.* Have them work in pairs to fill the chart with the terms from this chapter, the definitions, a diagram that represents each term, and a mnemonic device that will help them remember the term. example: gill, thin filaments that extract oxygen from the water, diagram should be based on Figure 7, Gills Inside Look Lamellar

Section 2 Assessment

Section Summary

- Fishes can be placed into one of three main groups—jawless, cartilaginous, and bony.
- Hagfishes and lampreys are examples of jawless fishes.
- Sharks, rays, and skates are examples of cartilaginous fishes.
- Bony fishes consist of two subclasses—ray-finned fishes and lobe-finned fishes.
- Ancient extinct fishes had features that enabled them to evolve into modern fishes.
- Habitat alteration and pollution can negatively affect fish populations.

Understand Main Ideas

1. MAIN Idea **Compare and contrast** the structures of jawless fishes, cartilaginous fishes, and bony fishes.
2. **Identify** the characteristics of the two subclasses of bony fishes.
3. **Sketch** the basic shape that represents each of the three main groups of fishes.
4. **Describe** the evolutionary sequence of the different groups of fishes.
5. **Hypothesize** Bony fishes have either cycloid or ctenoid scales. Form a hypothesis that explains how scale type is related to diversity.

Think Critically

MATH in Biology

6. The number of fish species often decreases as latitude increases. In fact, the number of fish species in tropical lakes is much greater than the number of fish species in temperate lakes. Suggest a hypothesis that accounts for this mathematical phenomenon.

Section 2 Assessment

1. Jawless fishes are eel-shaped without scales, paired fins, or a bony skeleton; cartilaginous fishes have skeletons made of cartilage and calcium carbonate; bony fishes have fins and a bony skeleton.
2. ray-finned fishes: fins have thin, spinelike rays; lobe-finned fishes: fins have muscular lobes
3. Basic shapes should include jawless fishes: long and slim; cartilaginous fishes: torpedo-shaped and streamlined, or flat, oval or round; bony fishes: round or streamlined with fins and tails.
4. jawless fishes; ostracoderms with bony head shields and paired fins; placoderms with jaws, bony skeletons, and bony head shields; Chondrichthyes with cartilaginous skeletons; and radiation of bony fish
5. Sample answer: Scales are used for external protection. Smaller fishes have ctenoid and cycloid scales made of bone; larger predatorial fishes have placoid scales; gars have ganoid scales.
6. Answers will vary, but might include that the amount of area available for colonization and diversification in the tropics is much greater than that of the temperate regions.

✓ Assessment Online Quiz

Section 3

MAIN Idea

BL OL AL

Amphibian Adaptation Pass around a live frog in a plastic container, or use a plastic specimen with realistic features that you have purchased from a biological supply house.

SAY TO STUDENTS: ***Make a list of the frog's adaptations to land.*** four legs for movement on land, long muscular hind legs that aid in jumping, eyes positioned so the frog can see overhead flying insects for food, long sticky tongue for capturing food, and sensitive eardrum that can hear potential predators approach

R Reading Strategy

EL BL OL AL

Anticipation Guide Before students read, compile a list of ten true/false statements about the content of this section. Have students predict whether the statements are true or false. After students read, have them validate or revise their answers based on what they have learned.

Concepts in Motion

Interactive Table

Reading Strategy

BL OL AL **Foldable**

SAY TO STUDENTS: ***Make a vocabulary Foldable as you have previously learned. Preview this section and rewrite each heading as a question and write it on the front of the tab. As you read, answer the question on the inside of the tab.***

Section 3

Reading Preview

Essential Questions

- What were the kinds of adaptations that were important as animals moved to the land?
- What are the characteristics of amphibians?
- What are the differences between the orders of amphibians?

Review Vocabulary

metamorphosis: a series of developmental changes in the form or structure of an organism

New Vocabulary

cloaca
nictitating membrane
tympanic membrane
ectotherm

Multilingual eGlossary

Amphibians

MAIN Idea Most amphibians begin life as aquatic organisms and then live on land as adults.

Real-World Reading Link Think about the last time you went swimming. How is moving in water different from moving on land? Just as fishes have adaptations for living in water, tetrapods have adaptations for living on land.

R Evolution of Tetrapods

Tetrapods are four-legged vertebrates that first appeared on Earth 360 million years ago. Modern amphibians are descendants of these early tetrapods. Examine the evolutionary tree in **Figure 21** to see how amphibians are related to other vertebrates. As millions of years passed, animals adapted to the conditions of life on land.

The move to land Animals faced several physical challenges in the move from water to land. **Table 1** lists some of the differences between conditions of life in the water and life on land. These differences include buoyancy, oxygen concentration, and temperature. **Table 1** also gives examples of how terrestrial vertebrates adapted to life on land.

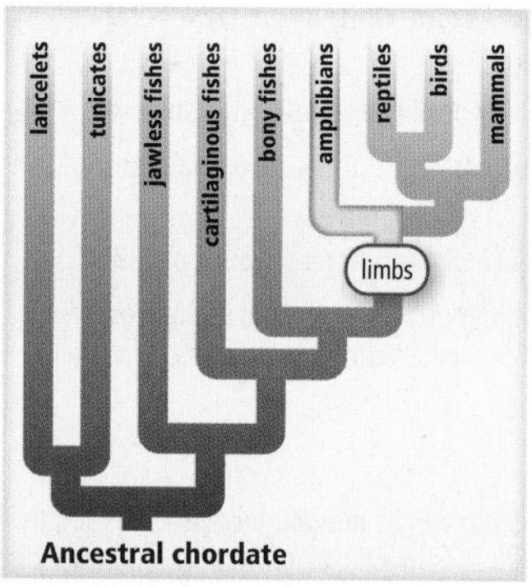

Figure 21 The evolutionary tree shows how amphibians are related to other vertebrates.

Table 1 Adaptations to Land — Concepts in Motion Interactive Table

Conditions in Water	Conditions on Land	Terrestrial Vertebrate Adaptations
Water exerts a buoyant force that counters the force of gravity.	• Air is about 1000 times less buoyant than water. • Animals must move against gravity.	Limbs develop and the skeletal and muscular systems of terrestrial animals become stronger.
Oxygen is dissolved in water and must be removed by gills through countercurrent circulation.	• Oxygen is at least 20 times more available in air than in water.	With lungs, terrestrial animals can get oxygen from air more efficiently than from water.
Water retains heat, so the temperature of water does not change quickly.	• Air temperature changes more easily than water temperature. • Daily temperatures can change by 10°C between day and night.	Terrestrial animals develop behavioral and physical adaptations to protect themselves from extreme temperatures.

FOLDABLES®

RUBRIC A rubric for evaluating Foldables is found on your eTeacherEdition Online.

Going Further Have students research the origins of amphibians and create a time line illustrating changes and adaptations occurring in tetrapods.

"Nine-tenths of education is encouragement."

—Anatole France

In addition to the differences listed in **Table 1,** another difference between conditions in water and on land is that sound travels more quickly through water. Fishes use lateral line systems to sense vibrations, or sound waves, in water. A lateral line system is not effective in air. The ears of terrestrial vertebrates evolved to sense sound waves traveling through air.

Terrestrial habitats In spite of the challenges associated with terrestrial life, there are many habitats available to animals on land. The different biomes on land, including tropical rain forests, temperate forests, grasslands, deserts, taiga, and tundra, provide suitable habitats for animals with appropriate adaptations.

Characteristics of Amphibians

Have you ever watched a tadpole in a jar of pond water? Examine and describe the tadpole in **Figure 22.** A tadpole is the limbless, gill-breathing, fishlike larva of a frog. Day by day, the tadpole undergoes metamorphosis (me tuh MOR fuh sihs)—hind legs form and grow longer, the tail shortens, gills are replaced by lungs, and forelimbs sprout. In just a few weeks or months, depending on the species, the tadpole becomes an adult frog. Most amphibians begin life as aquatic organisms. After metamorphosis, they are equipped to live life on land.

Modern amphibians include frogs, toads, salamanders, newts, and legless caecilians. Most amphibians are characterized by having four legs, moist skin with no scales, gas exchange through the skin, lungs, a double-loop circulatory system, and aquatic larvae.

Feeding and digestion Most frog larvae are herbivores, whereas salamander larvae are carnivores. However, as adults, their diets are similar as both groups become predators and feed on a variety of invertebrates and small vertebrates. Some salamanders and legless amphibians use just their jaws to catch prey. Others, such as frogs and toads, can flick out their long, sticky tongues with great speed and accuracy to catch flying prey. **D**

Food moves from the mouth through the esophagus to the stomach, where digestion begins. From the stomach, food moves to the small intestine, which receives enzymes from the pancreas to digest food. From the intestine, food is absorbed into the bloodstream and delivered to body cells. Food moves from the small intestine into the large intestine before waste material is eliminated. At the end of the intestine is a chamber called the cloaca. The **cloaca** (kloh AY kuh) is a chamber that receives the digestive wastes, urinary waste, and eggs or sperm before they leave the body.

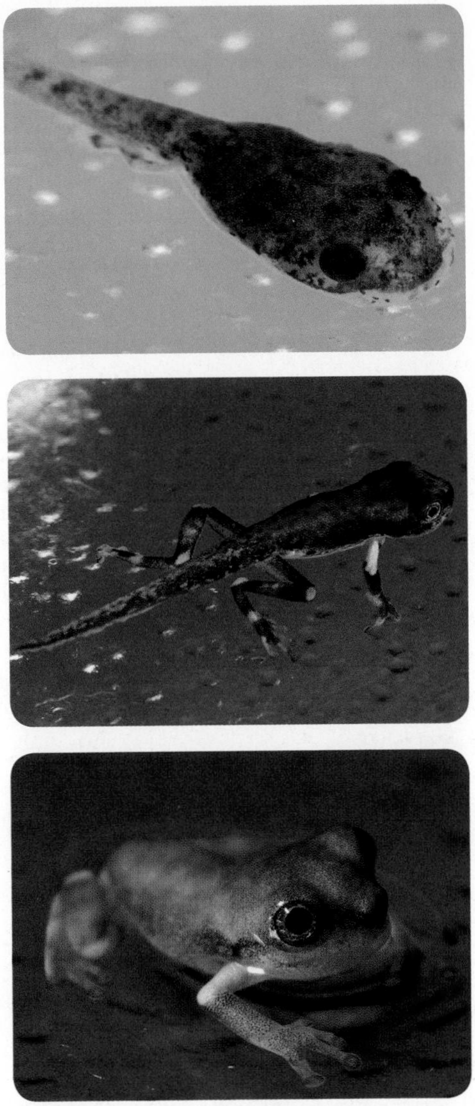

Figure 22 The cayenne slender-legged tree frog is found in South America.
Top: A tadpole is limbless.
Middle: The tadpole is undergoing metamorphosis to become an adult frog. Notice the development of limbs.
Bottom: An adult frog has fully developed limbs and lacks a tail.

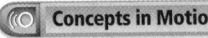

Concepts in Motion **Animation**

S

S Skill Practice

EL BL COOP LEARN

Visual Literacy Obtain or draw diagrams of the three stages of a tree frog (tadpole, metamorphosis, frog) similar to Figure 22, and make several copies. Cut and put all the stages for each copy in separate envelopes. Organize students into pairs and give each pair an envelope. Have partners take the cutouts out of the envelope and put them in the correct sequence.

D Develop Concepts

EL BL OL AL COOP LEARN

Activity Divide students into pairs. Provide each pair with a paper blow-out noisemaker, hook-and-loop tape, and ribbon.

SAY TO STUDENTS: ***Attach a 1-cm square of hook-and-loop tape to the tip of the rolled out noisemaker. Attach the other side of the hook-and-loop tape to a 30-cm piece of 1-cm ribbon. One student should make the ribbon "fly" while the other tries to catch it using the noisemaker "tongue."***
ASK STUDENTS: ***How is this model like a frog's tongue? How is this model not like a frog's tongue?*** Answers will vary, depending on each pair's experience during the experiment.

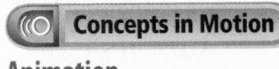

Concepts in Motion **Animation**

Demonstration

BL OL COOP LEARN **Frog Toys** Bring in a variety of frog toys. Pass them around for the class to examine. Divide students into groups of four, and give each student a frog toy.
ASK STUDENTS: ***What characteristics do toy frogs have that are features of live frogs? What characteristics do toy frogs have that are not characteristics of live frogs?*** Answers will vary depending on the kinds of toy frogs you have.
Est. time: 15 min

D Develop Concepts

BL OL AL Scaffolding

ASK STUDENTS: ***Describe the circulatory system of a fish in terms of loops.*** single loop

ASK STUDENTS: ***How does an amphibian's circulatory system compare to that of a fish in terms of loops?*** Amphibians have a double loop system. ***What happens in the first loop?*** Oxygen-poor blood moves from the heart to the lungs and skin, where it picks up oxygen. This blood then goes back to the heart. ***What happens in the second loop?*** Oxygen-rich blood moves from the heart to the body, where oxygen diffuses into cells. ***Where is pressure the greatest?*** in the second loop

S Skill Practice

EL BL Visual Literacy Distribute copies of a diagram of an amphibian circulatory system. Provide each student with a blue marker and a red marker.

SAY TO STUDENTS: ***Study the circulatory system of amphibians in Figure 23 in your text to learn how blood flows through the circulatory system and where oxygen-rich and oxygen-poor blood are located. After you understand the process, close your book and use the red and blue markers to indicate blood flow on the diagram. Use red markers for oxygen-rich blood and blue markers for oxygen-poor blood.***

C Critical Thinking

AL Infer

ASK STUDENTS: ***Why are most frogs and other amphibians so small? Why aren't amphibians the size of dogs such as collies or Labrador retrievers?*** Amphibians have hearts with three chambers that cannot pump enough oxygenated blood to support a large body.

Vocabulary

Science usage v. Common usage

Amphibian

Science usage: any organism that is a member of class Amphibia; most spend part of their lives in water and part on land

A frog is an amphibian.

Common usage: an airplane designed to take off from and land on either land or water

The amphibian landed smoothly on the lake.

Excretion Amphibians filter wastes from the blood through their kidneys and excrete either ammonia or urea as the waste product of cellular metabolism. Ammonia is the end product of protein metabolism and is excreted by amphibians that live in water. Amphibians that live on land excrete urea that is made from ammonia in the liver. Unlike ammonia, urea is stored in the urinary bladder until it is eliminated from the body through the cloaca.

Respiration and circulation As larvae, most amphibians exchange gases through their skin and gills. As adults, most breathe through lungs, through their thin, moist skin, and through the lining of the mouth cavities. Frogs can breathe through their skin either in or out of water. This ability enables them to spend the winter protected from the cold in the mud at the bottom of a pond.

The circulatory system of amphibians is shown in **Figure 23.** It consists of a double loop instead of the single loop you learned about in fishes. The first loop moves oxygen-poor blood from the heart to pick up oxygen in the lungs and skin, and then moves the oxygen-filled blood back to the heart. During circulation in the second loop, blood filled with oxygen moves from the heart through vessels to the body, where the oxygen diffuses into cells.

D Amphibians have three-chambered hearts. The atrium is completely separated into two atria by tissue. The right atrium receives deoxygenated blood from the body, while the left atrium receives oxygenated blood from the lungs. The ventricle of amphibians remains undivided.

S C **Reading Check** **Describe** how the amphibian circulatory system is adapted to life on land.

Inquiry Interactive Dissection

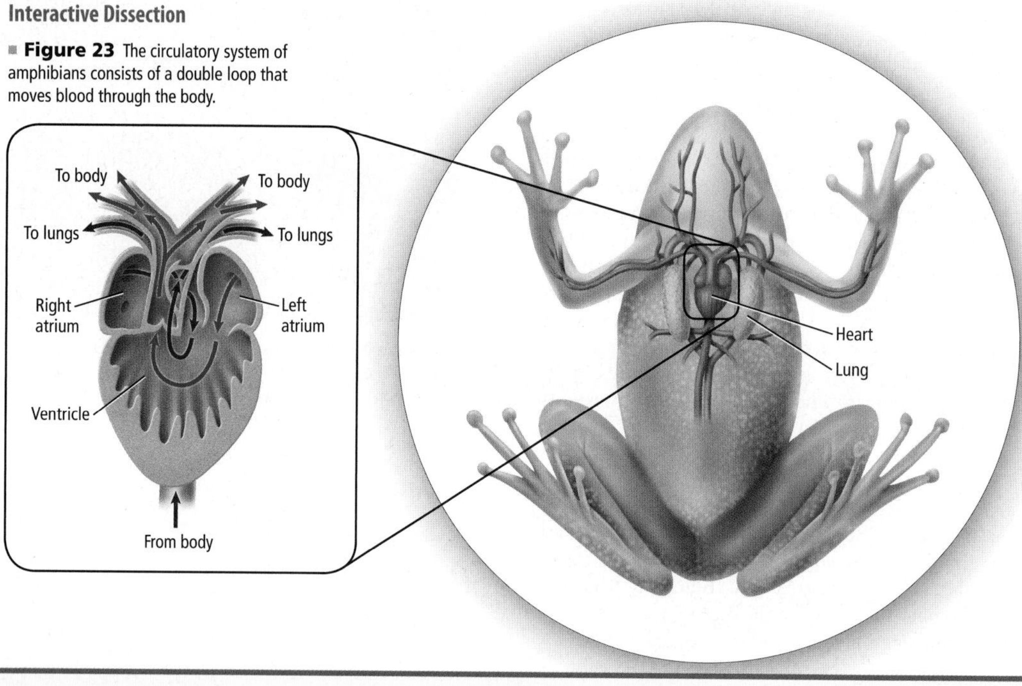

Figure 23 The circulatory system of amphibians consists of a double loop that moves blood through the body.

Activity

BL OL AL COOP LEARN

Model Circulation Divide students into pairs. Provide them with wax-covered yarn. Tell them to make a three-dimensional model of a double-loop circulatory system. Have them use different colors to represent oxygen-poor and oxygen-rich blood. Est. time: 15 min

Reading Check Even though the percentage of oxygen is higher in air than it is in water, blood has to move against the force of gravity. The double-loop circulation ensures that the blood will be under enough pressure to move through the entire body. The heart with two atrial chambers and a ventricle is more efficient for life on land than a two-chambered heart.

Inquiry Interactive Dissection

The brain and senses Like fishes, the nervous systems of amphibians are well developed. The differences in conditions between life in the water and life on land are reflected in the differences between the brains of fishes and those of amphibians. For example, the forebrain of frogs contains an area that is involved with the detection of odors in the air. The cerebellum, which is important in maintaining balance in fishes, is not as well developed in terrestrial amphibians that stay close to the ground.

Vision is an important sense for most amphibians. They use sight to locate and capture prey that fly at high speeds and to escape predators. Frogs' eyes have structures called nictitating (NIK tuh tayt ing) membranes. The **nictitating membrane** is a transparent eyelid that can move across the eye to protect it underwater and keep it from drying out on land.

The amphibian ear also shows adaptation to life on land. The **tympanic** (tihm PA nihk) **membrane** is an eardrum. In frogs, it is a thin external membrane on the side of the head, as shown in **Figure 24.** Frogs use their tympanic membrane to hear high-pitched sounds and to amplify sounds from the vocal cords. Other senses in amphibians include touch, chemical receptors in the skin, taste buds on the tongue, and sense of smell in the nasal cavity.

It is important for amphibians to sense the temperature of their environment because they are ectotherms. **Ectotherms** are animals that obtain their body heat from the external environment. Ectotherms cannot regulate their body temperatures through their metabolism, so they must be able to sense where they can go to get warm or to cool down. For example, if it is cold, a toad can find a warm rock on which to bask and warm itself.

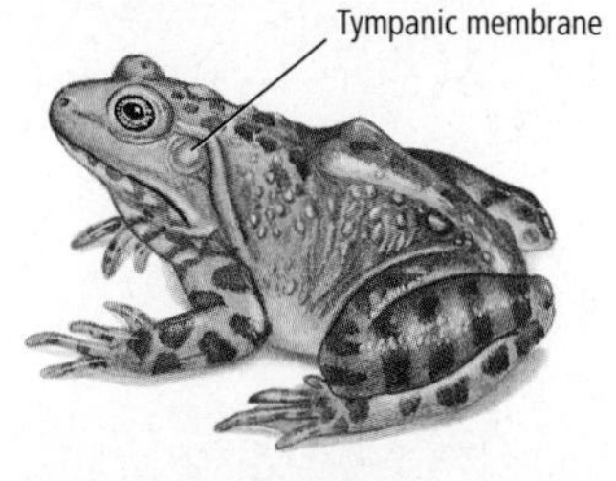

Figure 24 The tympanic membrane is an adaptation for life on land.

Concepts in Motion

Animation

DATA ANALYSIS LAB 2

Based on Real Data*

Interpret a Graph

How does temperature affect the pulse rate of calling in tree frogs? Male tree frogs make calls that females can identify easily based on the rate of the sound pulses in the call.

Data and Observations

The graph shows the pulse rate of two species of frogs versus temperature.

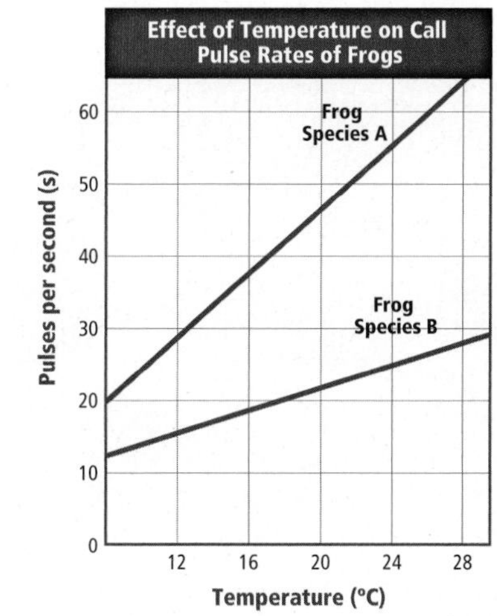

Think Critically

1. **Interpret Data** What is the relationship between sound pulses and temperature?
2. **Compare** How did temperature affect the rate of pulses in species A and in species B?
3. **Infer** Why is it important that the two species of frogs do not have the same pulse rate in their calls at the same temperature?

*Data obtained from: Gerhardt, H.C. 1978. Temperature coupling in the vocal communication system in the grey treefrog *Hyla versicolor. Science* 199: 992–994.

Inquiry BioLab

The lab at the end of the chapter can be used at this point in the lesson.

Differentiated Instruction

Hearing Impaired When playing the recordings of frog calls as suggested on this page, make adjustments to ensure that students who are hearing impaired will be able to participate. Seat these students near the recorder and control the noise level in the classroom.

For more tips, see pages 14T–15T.

Develop Concepts

BL OL AL Activity Obtain a recording of frog calls from the local library or purchase one from a biological supply company. Play it for your class. Have students note the various kinds of calls made by a variety of frogs.

ASK STUDENTS: ***How easy is it to distinguish between different frogs?*** It should be easy for most students.

Concepts in Motion

Animation

DATA ANALYSIS LAB 2

About the Lab

- Changes in temperature affect many life functions of amphibians. Features such as calling rate, call duration, and number of sound pulses depend on temperature.
- Frog communication can be interrupted by background noise. To overcome this, frogs have developed calls that exhibit very little variation and are repeated often. Call rates tend to be highest in noisy environments.
- Also see Prestwich, K.N. 1994. The energetics of acoustic signaling in anurans and insects. *American Zoologist* 34: 625–643.

Think Critically

1. Call pulse rates increase with the rise of temperature.
2. The rate of pulses increases by a ratio of about 2.5:1 with Species A and by a ratio of about 1:1 with Species B. For example, Species B emits 22 pulses per second at 20° C; Species A emits 47 pulses per second at 20° C.
3. The calls of frogs should be specific to the species so the frogs can identify one another.

Develop Concepts

BL OL AL COOP LEARN

Activity Purchase tadpoles from a biological supply company. Divide students into groups of four and give each a tadpole in a plastic container of dechlorinated water. Students will need to feed the tadpoles a pinch of boiled lettuce every few days. Have students observe and describe the changes the tadpole undergoes. It grows lungs and begins to breathe air; it grows two back legs then two front legs; its tail disappears. Have students make observations and sketches of changes in the tadpole's body form every week.

D Develop Concepts

BL OL AL

Clarify a Misconception

Students might have heard that a person can get warts from handling toads.

ASK STUDENTS: ***If you handle a toad, will you get warts?*** no Warts develop as a result of exposure to a virus that causes the wart. Toads do have poison glands in the shape of a kidney bean on their backs. The poison from this gland varies in toxicity from one species to another. It doesn't cause warts, but it can be an irritant and can even cause blindness in humans.

Caption Question Fig. 25 The eggs are covered with a sticky, jellylike substance that helps them anchor to plants in the water.

Reading Check Frogs, unlike toads, have long and powerful legs, their skin is moist, they live close to water sources, and they do not have poison glands.

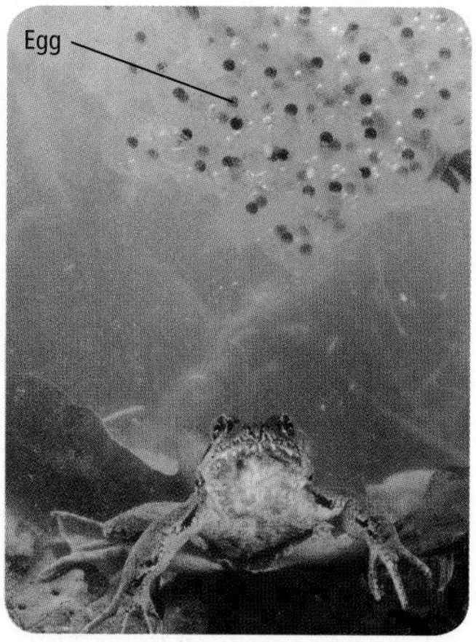

Figure 25 Amphibian eggs do not have shells that would protect them from drying out. **Infer** *what adaptation ensures that amphibian eggs do not dry out.*

Reproduction and development Like many amphibians, female frogs lay eggs in the water to be fertilized by males. The eggs do not have shells or protective coverings to keep them from drying out. The eggs, like the ones shown in **Figure 25,** are covered with a sticky, jellylike substance that helps them stay anchored to vegetation in the water. After fertilization, the developing embryo uses the yolk in the egg for nourishment until it hatches into a tadpole. A tadpole, like the one shown in **Figure 22,** changes from a gill-breathing, legless herbivore with fins and a two-chambered heart into a lung-breathing, four-legged carnivore with a three-chambered heart. The stages of metamorphosis are primarily under the control of chemicals released within the tadpole's body.

Amphibian Diversity

Biologists classify modern amphibians into three orders. Order Anura (a NOOR ah) contains 4200 species of frogs and toads. Order Caudata (kaw DAY tah) has about 400 species of salamanders and newts. One hundred and fifty species of wormlike caecilians make up order Gymnophiona (JIHM noh fee oh nah). Frogs, toads, and salamanders live in moist areas in a variety of habitats, while newts are aquatic. Caecilians are tropical burrowing animals.

D **Frogs and toads** Frogs and toads, shown in **Figure 26,** lack tails and have long legs, enabling them to jump. Frogs have longer and more powerful legs than toads and are able to make more powerful jumps than the small hops of toads. Frogs have moist, smooth skin, while the skin of toads tends to be bumpy and dry. Although both need to be near water to carry out reproduction, toads generally live farther away from water than do frogs. Another difference between frogs and toads is that toads have kidney-bean-shaped glands near the back of their heads that release a foul-tasting poison. The poison discourages predators from eating them.

Reading Check **Compare and contrast** the characteristics of frogs and toads.

Figure 26 The bullfrog has moist, smooth skin compared to the skin of the American toad, which is dry and bumpy.

Bullfrog **American toad**

Demonstration

Frog Egg Development Purchase *Xenopus* frog eggs from a biological supply company and have students observe their development. Set up binocular microscopes with the eggs in a small dish that students can observe briefly each day as they come into class.
Est. time: 2 min each day until hatching occurs

Activity

BL **Frog Greeting Card** Organize students into pairs.
SAY TO STUDENTS: ***Make a greeting card for a particular occasion. Make the card in the shape of frog and present accurate biological information about frogs in an amusing way.***
Est. time: 20 min

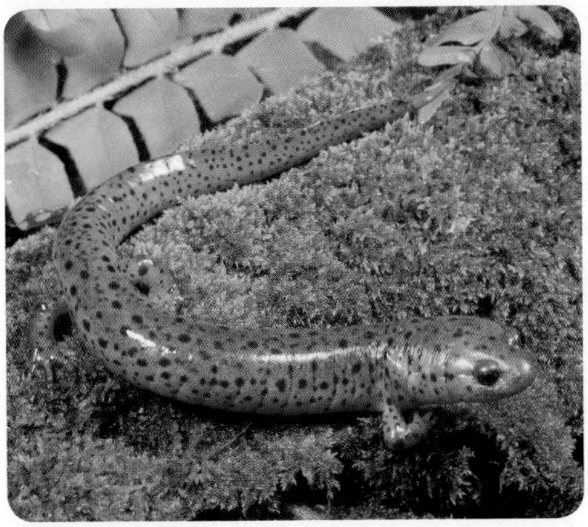

Red salamander

Warty newt

■ **Figure 27** The red salamander is found in the eastern United States. The warty newt breeds in deep ponds that contain aquatic vegetation.

Salamanders and Newts Unlike frogs and toads, salamanders and newts have long, slim bodies with necks and tails, as shown in **Figure 27.** Most salamanders have four legs and thin, moist skin, and they cannot live far from water. Like frogs, most salamanders lay their eggs in water. The larvae look like miniature salamanders, except that they have gills. Newts, like the one in **Figure 27,** generally are aquatic throughout their lives, while most salamanders, as adults, live in moist areas such as under logs or in leaf litter. Salamanders range in size from about 15 cm long to the giant salamander that is 1.5 m long. An adult salamander's diet consists of worms, frog eggs, insects, and other invertebrates.

Caecilians Caecilians (si SILH yenz) are different from other amphibians because they are legless and wormlike, as shown in **Figure 28.** They burrow in the soil and feed on worms and other invertebrates. Skin covers the eyes of many caecilians, so they might be nearly blind. All caecilians have internal fertilization. They lay their eggs in moist soil located near water. Caecilians can be found in the tropical forests of South America, Africa, and Asia.

CAREERS IN BIOLOGY

Animal Curator An animal curator works at a zoo, managing some part of the zoo's animal collection, such as the amphibian exhibit. Curators work together to decide the best way to maintain an animal's habitat in the zoo.

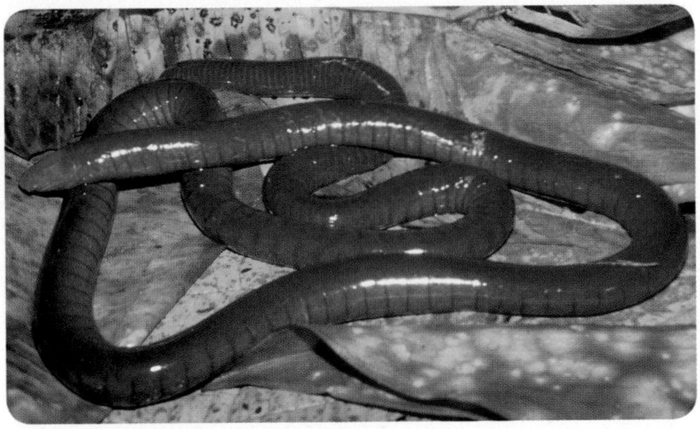

■ **Figure 28** Caecilians do not have ear openings. It is not known if, or how, they can hear sounds.

Reading Strategy

BL Find Supporting Details Have students make a list of the amphibians in this section, including the main features of and supporting details about each amphibian.

Skill Practice

AL Visual Literacy Have students examine the figures depicting amphibians in this section. **SAY TO STUDENTS:** ***Research other species of amphibians that belong to the same groups, especially ones that live in your area. Make a slideshow presentation showing various amphibian species and their habitats.***

Writing Support

BL Creative Writing Have students write a cinquain with an amphibian of their choice as the main subject. Tell them to present scientific information about this amphibian in their cinquain. The cinquain is based on a syllable count:

Line 1 = 2 syllables
Line 2 = 4 syllables
Line 3 = 6 syllables
Line 4 = 8 syllables
Line 5 = 2 syllables

Content Background

Hellbenders The largest living salamanders, which may reach up to 1.5 m in length, undergo incomplete metamorphosis during which adults develop larval features such as lidless eyes, lack of tongue pads, and retention of one gill slit. Hellbenders, as they are called, are completely aquatic salamanders that have an unusual method of suction feeding. They are considered a threatened species because of declining water quality and habitat degradation.

S Skill Practice

BL Visual Literacy Have students examine the cladogram in Figure 29 and make a list of amphibian features as they evolved, from the earliest to the most recent.

W Writing Support

OL Informal Writing

SAY TO STUDENTS: ***Research and report in your journal about* Ichthyostega *and* Acanthostega, *early tetrapod fossils. Draw diagrams based on artists' renditions of what these animals might have looked like.***

W Writing Support

AL Technical Writing Have students research details about the discovery of various fossil tetrapods. Instruct them to write a report that explains the differences between fossil tetrapods and modern amphibians.

Caption Question Fig. 29
caecilians

Reading Check because lobe-finned fishes and tetrapods share characteristics such as bone structure in the skull and limbs, nostril-like openings in the tops of their mouths, and a similar tooth structure

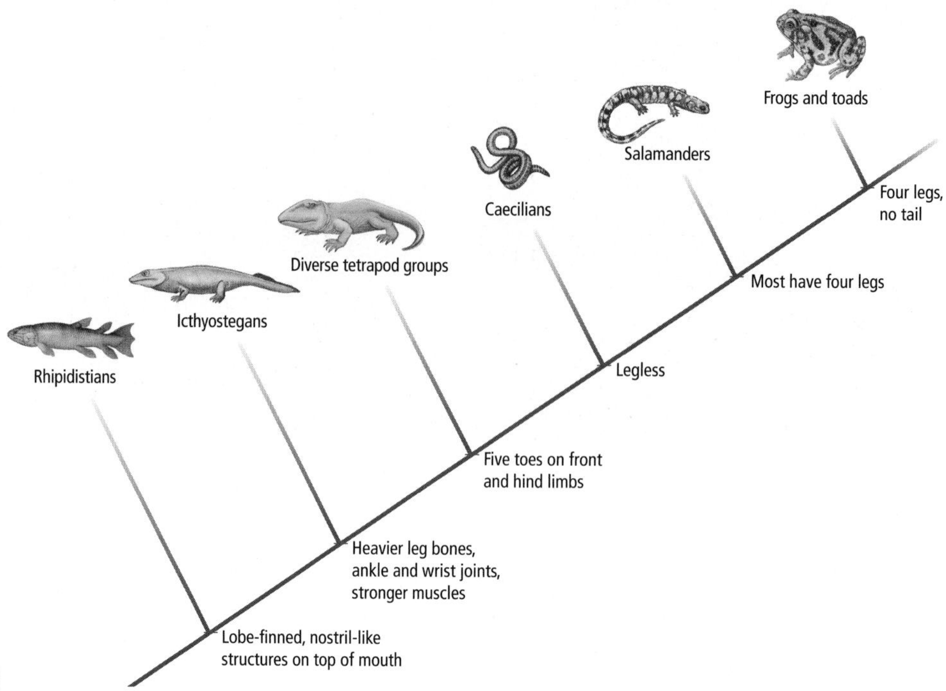

S

Figure 29 The cladogram shows one interpretation of amphibian evolution.
***Interpret** which modern amphibians are more closely related to the first tetrapods.*

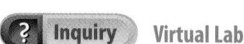

Inquiry Virtual Lab

VOCABULARY

ACADEMIC VOCABULARY

Diversify
to produce variety
The bakery diversified the flavors of doughnuts it made, giving customers more choices.

W Evolution of Amphibians

Fossil evidence shows that the first tetrapods evolved limbs in water before they moved to land. Many adaptations that are useful on land first evolved in water. For example, legs with feet and toes could be helpful in moving through bottom vegetation. Ankles and wrists might have increased maneuverability. The attachment of hip bones to the vertebral column might have helped predators attack prey more easily.

The cladogram shown in **Figure 29** is one interpretation of the evolution of amphibians. Many scientists think that early tetrapods are most closely related to a group of now extinct, lobe-finned fishes called rhipidistians (RI pih dihs tee unz). Characteristics that both early tetrapods and rhipidistians share include similar bone structure in the skull and limbs, nostril-like openings in the tops of their mouths, and a similar tooth structure.

Early tetrapods had defined legs with feet, but the construction of the legs was too weak for these animals to walk easily on land. Ichthyostegans, as shown in **Figure 17,** had more support in the shoulder bones, heavier leg bones, and more muscular features that enabled them to pull themselves onto land and move a little more easily. The skull had the same general shape as the skulls of lobe-finned fishes. Tetrapod groups branched out to produce the three major groups of amphibians alive today, as well as reptiles, birds, and mammals. W

Reading Check Explain why scientists think that tetrapods evolved from rhipidistians.

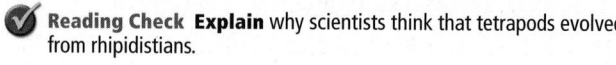

Content Background

Teacher FYI Many older books indicate that tetrapods evolved from lobe-finned fishes that crawled out of the water on their fins, which evolved into legs on land. More recent fossil evidence has discounted this. Legs evolved under water before tetrapods moved to land. A group of lobe-finned fishes called lungfish were most likely ancestral to tetrapods.

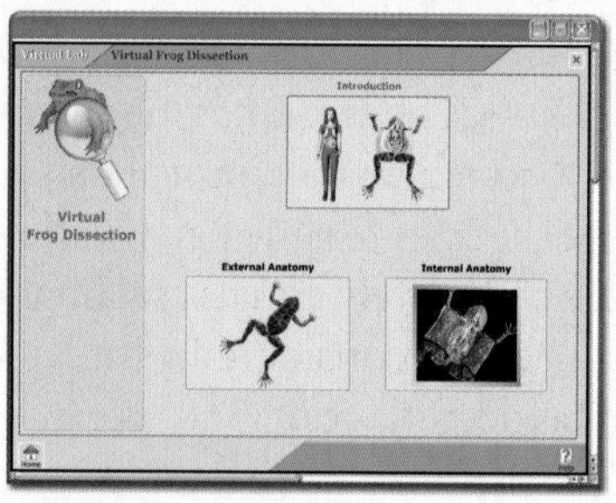

Inquiry Virtual Lab Students will explore the internal and external anatomy of a frog during this virtual dissection.

W Ecology of Amphibians

In recent decades, amphibian populations have been declining worldwide. Scientists have been collecting data to determine possible causes for the decline. The results have varied. In some cases, the cause can be isolated to a local condition. In other cases, the cause might be the result of several factors occurring on a large scale.

Local factors In some cases, such as that of the California red-legged frog, the decline is due to habitat destruction. When wetlands are drained and buildings are built in the areas instead, these areas of water are no longer available to amphibians that must lay eggs in or near water to reproduce successfully. In other areas, the introduction of exotic species—species that are not found in that area naturally—has affected amphibian populations. The exotic species compete with the amphibians for food and habitat space, or they are predators of amphibians. The introduction of trout, which prey on tadpoles, into the high-altitude lakes of California's Sierra Nevada Mountains is thought to have contributed to the near extinction of the mountain yellow-legged frog found in that region.

Global factors In addition to local factors, various global factors might be causing amphibian decline. Aspects of global climate change, such as increased temperature, decreased soil moisture, increased length of the dry season, and changes in rainfall can cause either death or stress to the bodies of amphibians, making them more susceptible to disease.

Figure 30 compares healthy toad eggs with eggs infected by a fungus. Some scientists think that global climate changes that have led to a decreased amount of rainfall leave developing amphibians' eggs in shallow pond water. Because the depth of the water is reduced, the eggs are exposed to more ultraviolet light. Laboratory experiments have shown that increased exposure to UV light leads to an increased risk of fungal infection in amphibian eggs.

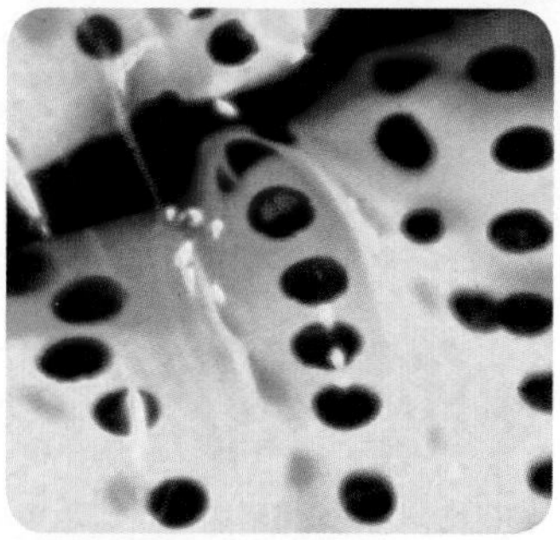

Healthy toad eggs

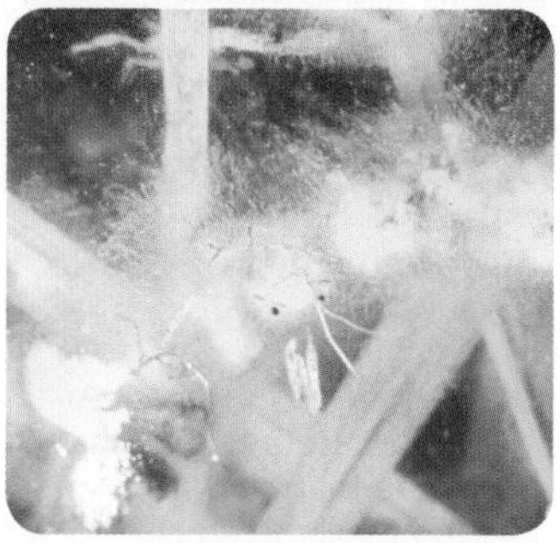

Fungus-infected toad eggs

■ **Figure 30** Healthy toad eggs are laid in single file in the water. Infected toad eggs are covered by fungus; fungal infection might account for a decrease in some toad populations.

Section 3 Assessment

Section Summary

- The transition of animals to land required a variety of adaptations.
- The bodies of amphibians have unique adaptations that enable them to live on land.
- Amphibians belong to three orders based on structural similarities.
- Ancient tetrapods evolved aquatic adaptations that they eventually used on land.
- Amphibian populations are declining worldwide for a variety of reasons.

Understand Main Ideas

1. MAIN Idea **Summarize** the adaptations of amphibians that make them adapted to life on land.
2. **Compare** the conditions of a land environment to that of an aquatic environment.
3. **Analyze** the kinds of adaptations that were important as animals moved to land.
4. **Summarize** the characteristics of each order of amphibians.

Think Critically

5. **Interpret Scientific Illustrations** Examine **Figure 29** and explain which of the three groups of amphibians is the most recent and which is the most ancient.

WRITING in **Biology**

6. On a hike in a marshy area near your home, you find a dead frog with deformed limbs. Hypothesize possible reasons why these deformities might have occurred.

W Writing Support

OL AL Formal Writing

SAY TO STUDENTS: ***Research to find out about an endangered amphibian, preferably one that lives in your area. Write a report that describes the features of the amphibian and its habitat, the causes of its decline, and the potential steps to ensure its survival.***

Formative Assessment

Evaluation Ask students to create a table listing each amphibian order (Anura, Caudata, Gymnophiona). Under each heading, have students list examples of each order and describe their habitat, adaptations, food, protection, reproduction, brain and senses, circulation, and respiration.

Remediation Provide students with clay or salt dough and have them make a model of each order of amphibians: Anura (frogs and toads), Caudata (salamanders and newts), and Gymnophiona (wormlike caecilians).

Section 3 Assessment

1. nostril-like structures, lungs, tympanic membrane, heavier leg bones, ankle and wrist joints, five toes, legless or four legs, no tail
2. Water is more buoyant than land; oxygen is dissolved in water and is 20 times less available than on land; water retains heat.
3. legs with feet and toes; ankles and wrists; attachment of hip bones to the vertebral column; heavier leg bones; stronger limbs and skeletal/muscular systems; development of lungs
4. Order Anura (frogs and toads) lack tails and necks, have muscular legs for jumping; order Caudata (salamanders and newts) have long, slim bodies with necks and tails; order Gymnophiona (caecilians) are legless and wormlike.
5. more recent—caecilians, salamanders, frogs and toads; ancient—rhipidistians, icthyostegans
6. Answers may vary. The limbs could have been deformed due to genetic defect, or due to an animal that killed the frog.

✓ Assessment Online Quiz

Purpose
Students will learn about the fishapod, an evolutionary link between fish and tetrapods. UCP.4, UCP.5, C.3

Anticipatory Guide
ASK STUDENTS: ***What is a tetrapod?*** Tell students that a tetrapod is a four-legged animal with jointed feet and toes. ***When did tetrapods first appear on Earth?*** Tetrapods emerged in the Devonian period, about 359 million years ago, during the Paleozoic era.

Background
The scientists who discovered the fishapod included University of Chicago paleontologist Neil Shubin; Ted Daeschler, chair of vertebrate zoology at Philadelphia's Academy of Natural Sciences; and Farish Jenkins, Jr., of Harvard University. The scientists were on a five-year Arctic fossil-hunting trip, partially funded by the National Geographic Society, when they found the fishapod fossils in 2004. The scientists wrote several articles about their find, which were published in the April 6, 2006, issue of *Nature*.

BioDiscoveries

A Fish... with Legs?

Millions of years ago, a fish braced itself on its fins, pushed its head above water, took a deep breath—and vaulted into evolutionary history. Many scientists hypothesize the "fishapod" (*Tiktaalik roseae*) is a link between fish and the first tetrapods. The fishapod was first discovered in 2004, embedded in a rock formation on Ellesmere Island, a Canadian island in the Arctic Circle. To date, scientists have unearthed 10 separate fishapod fossils.

Why move onto land? At the time of the fishapods, around 375 million years ago, Ellesmere Island was part of a landmass located near the equator. Scientists think the danger of predators and fierce competition for food in deep-water environments favored adaptations that allowed animals to live in shallow water and, eventually, on land.

Not really a fish Although it has fish characteristics, *Tiktaalik roseae* also has a number of features that differentiate it from fish. First, its pectoral fins contain a wrist-like, jointed bone structure and five digit bones. Scientists hypothesize that the fishapod used its strong fins to move through the shallow waters. It also used its fins to push itself above the surface of the water to look for food and to breathe air.

Like many primitive fish, the fishapod had both gills and lungs and it used them both to breathe. It also had a big, strong rib cage that suggests two things: the rib cage made room for and protected lungs, and it supported the fishapod's body when it pushed up on its fins. The fishapod's eyes were located on top of its large, broad head, much like a crocodile. Its head was separated from its shoulders by a neck, while the skulls of fish are connected directly to their shoulders. These characteristics enabled the fishapod to turn and lift its head.

Scientists think that *Tiktaalik roseae* is the evolutionary link between fish and the first tetrapods. The top image shows part of a fishapod fossil. The lower image is an artist's interpretation of how a fishapod may have looked and lived.

Filling in the gaps The discovery of the fishapod has been enormously helpful in detailing the evolution of tetrapods from primitive fish. Scientists hope that in the future, more fossils of other previously unknown species will help answer questions about evolutionary history.

CAREERS IN BIOLOGY
Job Description Research a career in paleontology, which is the study of fossils. What skills does a paleontologist need? What tasks does he or she perform? Write a job description for a paleontology job that you would like. Include where you would travel, what fossils you would like to discover, and what hypothesis you would hope to confirm.

CAREERS IN BIOLOGY
Activity Help students determine credible and reliable sources for research. Tell them that many universities have paleontology departments with Web sites that will provide accurate information about careers in this field. Students can also read about the paleontology research being done at the universities, providing them ideas about the direction in which they would like to take their hypothetical research projects.

BIOLAB

HOW DO SOME ECTOTHERMS REGULATE BODY TEMPERATURE?

Background: Recall that amphibians are ectotherms. Many ectotherms live in habitats where the temperature may fluctuate by 10 or 15°C throughout each day. In this lab, you will investigate the strategies some ectothermic animals use to maintain a suitable body temperature.

Question: *How do ectotherms maintain their body temperature within a specific range?*

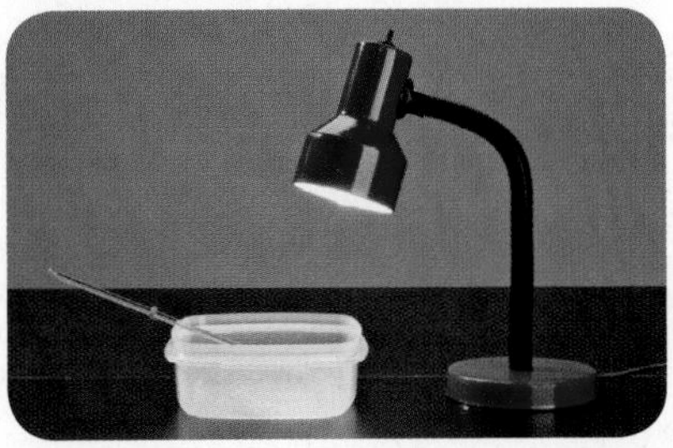

Materials

thermometers (2)	sand
plastic containers (2)	soil
metric ruler	high-wattage light bulb and lamp
room-temperature water	
paper towels	

Safety Precautions

WARNING: *Lamps may become hot when the light bulb is lit.*

Procedure

1. Read and complete the lab safety form.
2. Obtain two thermometers. These will be a model of an ectotherm animal. Record the temperature of each thermometer. Place one thermometer in a plastic container. Place the other thermometer in another container and fill the container so that the thermometer is covered by at least 5 cm of water.
3. Place each container under a lit light bulb. Monitor the temperature of the thermometers. You must maintain the temperature of each thermometer within a range of 36–39°C for the next 15 min. Decide how often you will measure the temperature of the thermometers and record the data in a table. Record what actions you took to maintain the temperature of the thermometers within the given range.
4. Pour the water out of the container and dry the container thoroughly. Allow the thermometers to return to room temperature.
5. Place one thermometer in a container and fill the container with soil so that the thermometer is covered by at least 5 cm of soil. Place the other thermometer in a container and cover it with at least 5 cm of sand.
6. Repeat Step 3.

Analyze and Conclude

1. **Summarize** Did you successfully maintain the temperature within a given range for all steps of the experiment? How did you do this?
2. **Analyze** Were there differences in how you maintained the temperature of the thermometers in water, soil, and sand? In which substance was it easiest to maintain the temperature range? Why?
3. **Draw Conclusions** What are the challenges associated with being an ectothermic animal? Explain.
4. **Think Critically** How do real ectotherms, such as amphibians and reptiles, keep their body temperatures within a specific range?

APPLY YOUR SKILL

Poster Research ectotherms and make a poster that describes the adaptations they require to survive in cold temperatures.

Analyze and Conclude

1. Accept all reasonable answers. Answer should include "yes" or "no," and an explanation.
2. Accept all reasonable answers. Answers should include "yes" or "no," a specific substance, and an explanation.
3. Accept all reasonable answers. Example: ectothermic animals must maintain stable body temperature, limiting time for hunting.
4. Ectothermic animals use the Sun and their surroundings to maintain body temperature.

BIOLAB

Inquiry BioLab

For a lab worksheet, use your eTeacherEdition Online.

RUBRIC A rubric for evaluating BioLabs is found on your eTeacherEdition Online.

Est. Time 30 min

Content Background Fish, amphibians, and reptiles are said to be ectotherms because they cannot regulate their own body temperature. Ectothermic animals usually employ a warm-up strategy early in the day and a cool-down tactic later in the day. By assuming different postures, animals increase or decrease the area of their bodies exposed to the Sun.

Safety Precautions Approve lab safety forms before work begins. Do not use mercury thermometers because they break easily.

Teaching Strategies Discuss with the class some or all of the following temperature tactics:

- Animals might increase their body temperature early in the morning by basking in the Sun, but later in the day they would seek shade from the heat to lower their body temperature.
- The coloration patterns of many animals helps absorb or reflect heat.
- Animals can stay warm on a cool night by moving into water.
- Burrowing can be used for staying warm or cool.

Alternative Teaching Demo If students don't have time to do the entire lab, provide another method for teaching the lab concepts, such as teacher modeling or demonstration, direct instruction, or reading.

Chapter 28

Study Guide

ConnectED

Students can use the following to review the chapter.

Review

Vocabulary eGames
Vocabulary eFlashcards
Vocabulary PuzzleMaker

Assessment

Online Quizzes
Online Test Practice
Standardized Test Practice

Use the *ExamView® Assessment Suite* CD-ROM to:

- create multiple versions of tests
- create modified tests with one mouse click
- edit existing questions and add your own questions
- build tests aligned with state standards using built-in state curriculum tags
- change English tests to Spanish with one mouse click
- track students' progress using the Teacher Management System

Chapter 28 Study Guide

THEME FOCUS Change A tadpole is a fishlike larva that goes through change, called metamorphosis, to become an adult frog.

BIG Idea **Fishes have adaptations for living in aquatic environments. Most amphibians have adaptations for living part of their lives on land.**

Section 1 Fishes

cartilage (p. 820)
neural crest (p. 821)
fin (p. 822)
scale (p. 823)
operculum (p. 824)
atrium (p. 824)
ventricle (p. 824)
nephron (p. 825)
lateral line system (p. 826)
spawning (p. 826)
swim bladder (p. 827)

MAIN Idea **Fishes are vertebrates that have characteristics allowing them to live and reproduce in water.**

- Vertebrates include fishes, amphibians, reptiles, birds, and mammals.
- All vertebrates have a notochord. In most vertebrates, the notochord is replaced by a vertebral column during embryonic development.
- Fishes share certain characteristics and are therefore classified together.
- The bodies of fishes have unique adaptations that enable them to live their entire lives in water.

Section 2 Diversity of Today's Fishes

tetrapod (p. 830)

MAIN Idea **Scientists classify fishes into three groups based on body structure.**

- Fishes can be placed into one of three main groups—jawless, cartilaginous, and bony.
- Hagfishes and lampreys are examples of jawless fishes.
- Sharks, rays, and skates are examples of cartilaginous fishes.
- Bony fishes consist of two subclasses—ray-finned fishes and lobe-finned fishes.
- Ancient extinct fishes had features that enabled them to evolve into modern fishes.
- Habitat alteration and pollution can negatively affect fish populations.

Section 3 Amphibians

cloaca (p. 835)
nictitating membrane (p. 837)
tympanic membrane (p. 837)
ectotherm (p. 837)

MAIN Idea **Most amphibians begin life as aquatic organisms and then live on land as adults.**

- The transition of animals to land required a variety of adaptations.
- The bodies of amphibians have unique adaptations that enable them to live on land.
- Amphibians belong to three orders based on structural similarities.
- Ancient tetrapods evolved aquatic adaptations that they eventually used on land.
- Amphibian populations are declining worldwide for a variety of reasons.

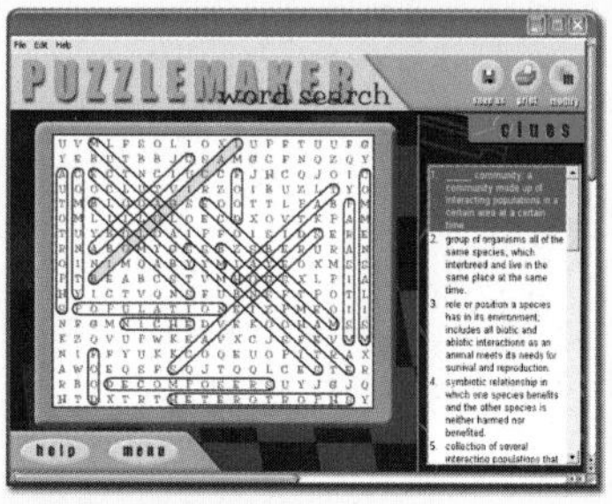

Review **Vocabulary PuzzleMaker**

For additional practice with vocabulary, have students access the Vocabulary PuzzleMaker online.

Review **Vocabulary eGames**

Chapter 28 Assessment

Section 1

Vocabulary Review

Complete each sentence by providing the missing vocabulary term from the Study Guide page.

1. The process by which male and female fishes release their gametes near each other in the water is called __________.
2. The __________ is the chamber of the heart that receives blood from the body.
3. A group of cells that develop from the nerve cord in vertebrates is called a __________.

Understand Main Ideas

Use the diagram below to answer questions 4 and 5.

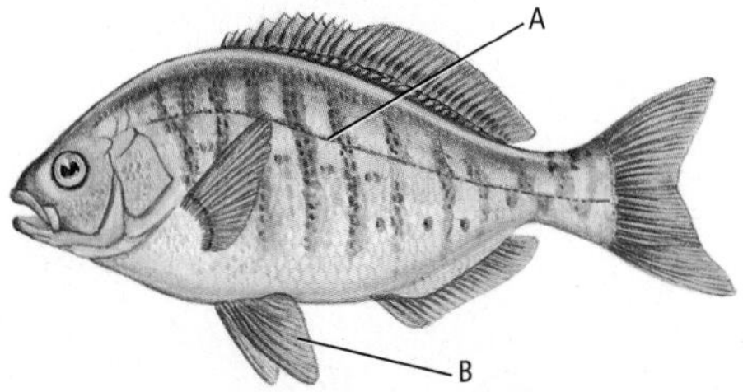

4. Which is the structure labeled A?
   A. ctenoid scales **C.** neural crest
   B. lateral line system **D.** operculum
5. Which is the structure labeled B?
   A. gills
   B. swim bladder
   C. ventricle
   D. pelvic fins
6. Which structure allows fishes to control their depth in an aquatic environment?
   A. operculum
   B. swim bladder
   C. lateral line system
   D. jaws
7. Which adaptation allows fishes to be predators?
   A. paired fins
   B. placoid scales
   C. jaws
   D. gills

Constructed Response

8. MAIN Idea There are more species of vertebrates living in the ocean than there are on land. Form a hypothesis to explain why this is true.
9. **CAREERS IN BIOLOGY** After ichthyologists discovered a new species of deep-sea predatory dragonfish, they were curious about the function of a long, thin, luminescent protrusion called a barbel that was attached under its chin and trailed below its body. Design an experiment that could determine the function of the dragonfish's barbel.

Think Critically

10. **Draw Conclusions** Bluegill males make a nest and protect the eggs and newly hatched offspring. Sometimes intruding males are able to fertilize some of the eggs. The bluegill fathers can identify their biological offspring and will care only for them and not others that might hatch from the same nest. Why is it important for male bluegills to identify their own offspring and care only for them?

Section 2

Vocabulary Review

Complete the sentence by providing the missing vocabulary term from the Study Guide page.

11. A __________ is a four-footed animal with legs that have feet and toes that have joints.

Understand Main Ideas

12. Which illustration shows an external parasite?

A.

C.

B.

D.

Chapter 28

Assessment

Section 1

Vocabulary Review

1. spawning
2. atrium
3. neural crest

Understand Main Ideas

4. B
5. D
6. B
7. C

Constructed Response

8. Because 75 percent of Earth is covered with water, it stands to reason that there are more vertebrates in water than on land. The ocean has a more stable environment than land, with its changes of seasons and climates. Animals living in the sea are not exposed to as many adverse conditions. Also, vertebrates originally evolved in the sea and developed huge diversity there before moving to land.
9. Answers will vary. Students might decide that the barbel helps females identify an appropriate mate in the darkness of the deep sea. The barbel may attract prey to swim near the mouth of the fish.

Think Critically

10. Bluegill males might only have so much energy and capability to care for a limited number of young. A male might care only for his own offspring to ensure that his genes are passed to the next generation.

Section 2

Vocabulary Review

11. tetrapod

Understand Key Concepts

12. B

Assessment Online Test Practice

13. A
14. D

Constructed Response

15. Make sure students sketch an example of jawless fishes, cartilaginous fishes (sharks, skates, rays), and bony fishes (lobe-finned, ray-finned). Students' sketches should indicate that jawless fishes are long and slim; sharks are torpedo-shaped and streamlined; skates/rays are flat, oval, or round; lobe-finned fishes are more muscular with rounded bodies; and ray-finned fishes are typically streamlined with paired fins and tails. Students should explain jaws, scales, skeletons, and fins and how they are adapted to the environment in which the fishes live.

Think Critically

16. in a free-flowing stream
17. behind barrier

Section 3

Vocabulary Review

18. cloaca
19. tympanic membrane
20. nictitating membrane

Understand Main Ideas

21. B
22. A
23. C

---

13. Which ancient extinct fishes are ancestors to modern fishes?
A. ostracoderms
B. ray-finned fishes
C. coelacanths
D. jawless fishes

14. Which are characteristics of sharks?
A. jawless, cartilaginous skeleton, lateral line
B. jawless, cartilaginous skeleton, ray-finned
C. jaws, bony skeleton, swim bladder
D. jaws, cartilaginous skeleton, lateral line

Constructed Response

15. MAIN Idea Sketch the body forms of each of the main groups of fishes. Include and explain external adaptations of fishes to their environment.

Think Critically

Use the diagram below to answer questions 16 and 17.

Biologists have studied muscle activity in trout swimming in a free stream flow compared to trout behind a barrier during the same stream movement. The red dots indicate the most intense muscle activity, orange dots indicates moderate muscle activity, while white dots indicates no muscle activity.

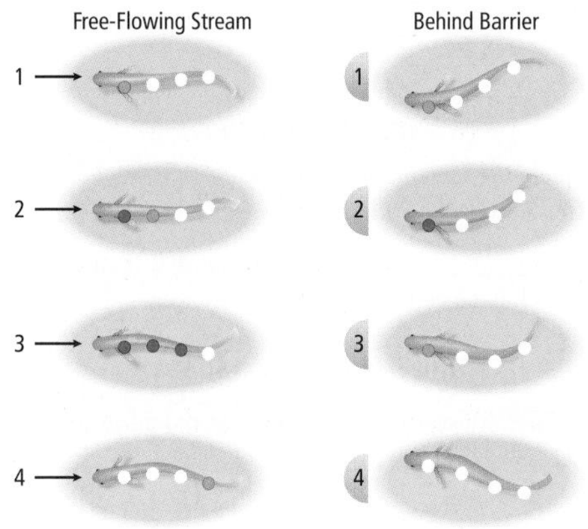

16. Evaluate In which situation does the trout use the most energy?

17. Infer Based on this experiment, if trout are trying to conserve energy, in which part of the stream would they be found?

Section 3

Vocabulary Review

Each of the following sentences is false. Make the sentence true by replacing the italicized word with a vocabulary term from the Study Guide page.

18. The *atrium* is a chamber that receives the digestive wastes, urinary waste, and eggs or sperm before they leave the body.

19. The *nictitating membrane* enables amphibians to hear sounds.

20. Amphibians have *tympanic membranes* to protect their eyes from drying out.

Understand Main Ideas

21. Which is a caecilian?

A.

C.

B.

D.

22. THEME FOCUS Change What does the phylogeny of tetrapods indicate about lobe-finned fishes?
A. Lobe-finned fishes are the ancestors of amphibians.
B. Lobe-finned fishes are similar to amphibians because they both have fins.
C. Lobe-finned fishes are most closely related to hagfishes.
D. Lobe-finned fishes are similar to amphibians because they both have lateral lines as adults.

23. What structures do amphibians use to maintain homeostatic water balance?
A. nictitating membranes **C.** kidneys
B. tympanic membranes **D.** swim bladders

24. Which is not associated with a tadpole?
A. lungs
B. tail
C. gills
D. herbivorous feeding

Constructed Response

25. Open Ended Draw a picture that would illustrate how amphibians could be affected by increased exposure to ultraviolet light.

26. Open Ended Describe how the structure and physiology of amphibians, presently adapted to temperate and tropical climates, might be modified to enable them to live in colder climates.

27. MAIN Idea Describe how the senses of amphibians are adapted to life on land.

Think Critically

28. Design an Experiment Tadpole larvae of certain frogs gather in clusters so close together that the group looks like a moving football in the water. Design an experiment that could test a hypothesis about why the tadpoles exhibit this behavior.

29. Create Read homes-for-sale ads in the newspaper to see how they are written. Write an ad for an amphibian home site based on what you know about the habitat, nutrition, and other needs of frogs.

Use the diagram below to answer question 30.

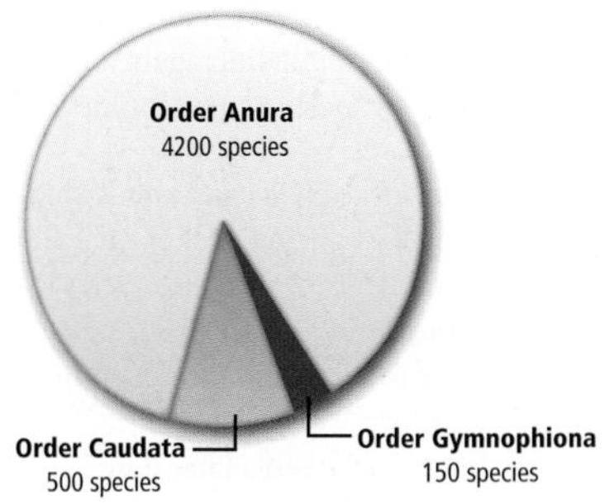

30. Calculate Determine the percent that each order of amphibians contributes to the total amount of amphibians.

Summative Assessment

31. BIG Idea Fishes have adaptations for living in aquatic environments. Most amphibians have adaptations for living part of their lives in water and part on land. Citing specific characteristics of fishes and amphibians, explain how the organisms are similar to each other and how they are different.

32. How did walking change the circulatory needs of an amphibian?

33. WRITING in Biology Research what efforts are being made by scientists to preserve amphibians. Write a newspaper article summarizing what you learned.

Document-Based Questions

Scientists are trying to determine the cause or causes for the decline in amphibian populations over the past few decades. The graph below shows the results of one study in which the survival rate of amphibian embryos was measured against the depth of the water in which they developed.

Data obtained from: Kiesecker, J., et al. 2001. Complex causes of amphibian population declines. *Nature* 410: 681-683.

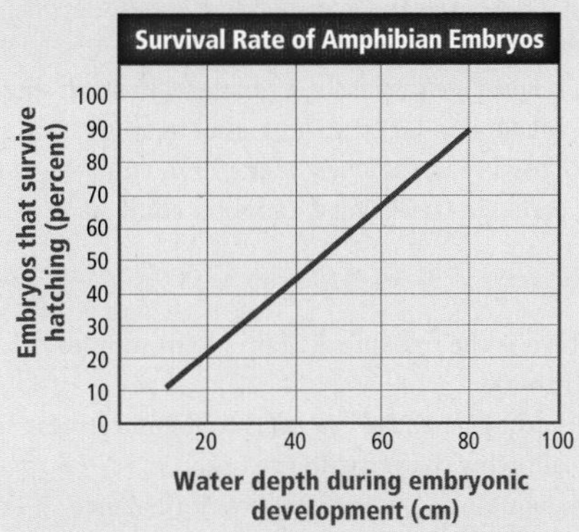

34. Describe the relationship between water depth during development and the survival rate of embryos.

35. Form a hypothesis about the decline of amphibian populations in relation to changes in climate.

24. A

Constructed Response

25. Pictures will vary, but should illustrate that water depth is reduced, leaving eggs exposed to UV light and thereby increasing the risk of fungal infection and malformation.

26. Answers will vary. Make sure students discuss the actual adaptations of amphibians as they add other ideas that would enable survival in cold conditions.

27. Amphibians have adapted through all the senses: smell—the forebrain detects odors in the air; sight—nictitating membrane protects the eyes under water and keeps them from drying out on land; sound—tympanic membrane allows them to hear high-pitched sounds through air; touch—chemical receptors in skin; taste—taste buds on tongue; smell—nasal cavity. Amphibians are also ectothermic—able to sense the temperature of their environment.

Think Critically

28. Answers will vary. Students might hypothesize that the tadpoles swim together for protection. They might plan to "fly" models of predatory birds over a captive group of tadpoles and record how long it takes them to cluster.

29. Answers will depend on students' research. Make sure ads include a water source for reproduction and a moist habitat.

30. There are 4850 total species. Rounding to the nearest .5 of a percent: order Anura—4200/4850 or 86.6 percent, order Caudata—500/4850 or 10.3 percent, Order Gymnophiona 150/4850 or 3 percent.

Summative Assessment

31. Answers may vary but should include specific similarities and differences.

32. Walking on land means the blood has to move against gravity, which requires a double-loop circulation that keeps the blood under enough pressure to move throughout the body.

33. Answers will vary. Make sure students illustrate real science and realistic solutions.

Document-Based Questions

Kiesecker, J. et al. 2001. Complex causes of amphibian population declines. Nature 410: 681–683.

34. Water depth and survival rates are directly related. The higher the water, the higher the survival rate.

35. Answers will vary, but should include an example of a global climate change as it pertains to water depth, ultraviolet light, and the ability of amphibians to reproduce or flourish in their natural habitats.

Standardized Test Practice

Multiple Choice

1. B 5. C 9. A
2. B 6. B
3. C 7. A
4. B 8. D

Open Ended

10. Answers can vary. One possible response: Both a snail and an octopus have a mantle. In the snail, the mantle is inside the shell and it secretes the minerals needed to make the hard shell. In the octopus, the mantle is inside its body.
11. Photosynthesis introduced oxygen to the atmosphere in large quantities. Organisms unable to deal with oxygen became extinct. Oxygen in the atmosphere allowed an ozone layer to form, protecting Earth from UV radiation, which probably reduced mutation rates. The prokaryotes themselves provided a vast new accessible energy source for heterotrophs, based on the huge amount of light energy coming from the Sun.
12. The notochord provides support and muscle attachment for the animal. This allows an animal to swing its back with side-to-side motion.
13. Sharks have a streamlined body, strong muscles, a tail that turns up at the end, and a pointed head. The streamlined body reduces drag. Strong muscles propel the shark rapidly. The turned up tail gives extra thrust to swim movements and extra turning thrust. A pointed head passes through the water more easily than a blunt head.
14. Answers can vary. Lancelets and tunicates are invertebrate chordates. They are both filter feeders. Typically they are sessile organisms, which means that they have to get their food from their immediate surroundings. Filter feeding enables these organisms to get food without moving from place to place.

Standardized Test Practice

Cumulative

Multiple Choice

Use the diagram below to answer question 1.

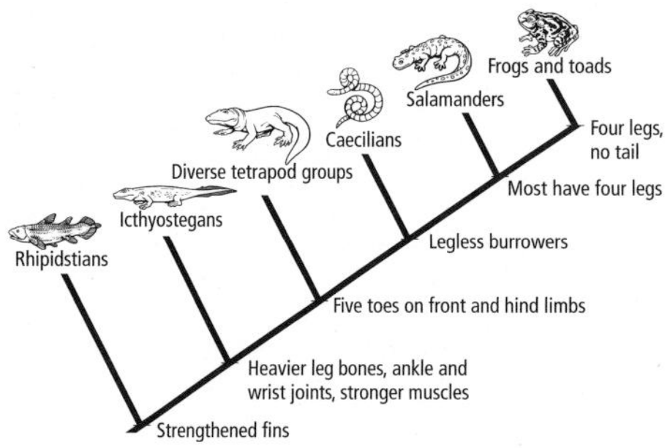

1. According to the cladogram, which is the earliest relative of the amphibians?
A. ichthyostegans
B. rhipidstians
C. rays
D. sharks

2. What describes the symmetry of echinoderms in their larval and adult stages?
A. bilateral in larval stage, bilateral in adult stage
B. bilateral in larval stage, radial in adult stage
C. radial in larval stage, bilateral in adult stage
D. radial in larval stage, radial in adult stage

3. Which is the role of the Malpighian tubules in arthropods?
A. adding digestive enzymes to the intestines
B. allowing oxygen into the body
C. maintaining homeostatic water balance
D. transporting blood to body tissues

4. Which method of communication does a honeybee use to tell others in the hive about the location of food?
A. chemical pheromones
B. complex dances
C. quiet buzzing sounds
D. rapid wing beating

5. What is the function of the simple eye in arthropods?
A. to analyze landscapes during flight
B. to detect colors
C. to distinguish light from dark
D. to see movement

Use the chart below to answer question 6.

Row	Group	Characteristics
1	Invertebrate chordates	Lack a backbone
2	Jawless fishes	Lack a notochord
3	Bony fishes	Have a skeleton made of bone
4	Cartilaginous fishes	Have a skeleton made of cartilage

6. Which row in the chart contains incorrect information?
A. 1
B. 2
C. 3
D. 4

7. Which statement describes the most reasonable way to prevent the disease of trichinosis in humans?
A. Cook pork thoroughly before eating it.
B. Treat infected pigs for trichinosis worms.
C. Vaccinate the population against trichinosis.
D. Wash pork properly before cooking it.

8. Which statement is NOT true about amphibians?
A. Many lack legs during part of their life cycles.
B. Many spend part of their life cycles in the water and part on land.
C. Most depend on outside water sources to keep their bodies moist.
D. Most have developed a lateral line system.

9. Which mutation is often caused by the addition or deletion of a single base pair?
A. frame shift
B. missense
C. substitution
D. tandem repeat

Short Answer

Use the diagrams below to answer question 10.

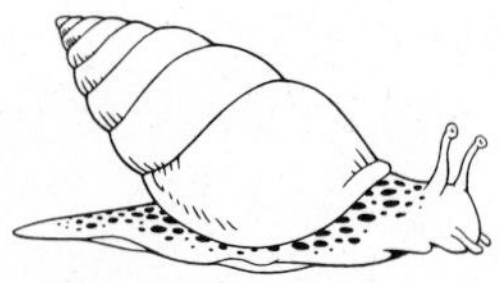

10. Describe a body structure from each of the mollusks shown above, and explain how these structures are related.

11. Sequence the energy transitions that have to take place for the Sun's energy to be used by a heterotroph.

12. Evaluate why the notochord is considered an evolutionary advancement.

13. Analyze which characteristics of a shark enable it to be a fast swimmer. Explain your answer.

14. Name two groups of invertebrate chordates and describe how they feed. Relate their feeding patterns to their way of life.

15. Compare three characteristics of fishes to three characteristics of another group of animals that you have already studied.

Extended Response

16. Create a Venn diagram to organize information about endoderm and ectoderm tissues that form during embryonic development. Then explain how endoderm and ectoderm tissues are similar and different.

17. Explain how energy is converted in photosynthesis and in cellular respiration.

18. Contrast the circulatory systems of lancelets and tunicates. Justify the classification of both kinds of organisms as invertebrate chordates.

19. Hypothesize whether incomplete metamorphosis or complete metamorphosis in insects is more primitive. Explain your reasoning.

Essay Question

Most of the invertebrate animal groups living today trace their evolutionary history back more than 500 million years. Every other group of invertebrates living today expanded from the oceans to freshwater and, in many cases, to land. The fossil record for echinoderms shows that they have changed radically throughout their evolutionary history. Today, there are many diverse forms of echinoderms, yet none have ever left the ocean.

Using the information in the paragraph above, answer the following question in essay format.

20. Hypothesize why echinoderms have continued living only in the ocean while other invertebrate groups have migrated to freshwater and land.

NEED EXTRA HELP?																				
If You Missed Question . . .	1	2	3	4	5	6	7	8	9	10	11	12	13	14	15	16	17	18	19	20
Review Section . . .	28.3	27.1	26.1	26.3	26.1	28.2	25.2	28.3	12.4	25.4	8.2, 8.3,	27.2	28.2	27.2	28.1	24.1	14.2	27.2	26.3	27.1

15. Fishes have an outer covering of scales for protection, paired fins for movement and balance, and gills for breathing. Contrasting characteristics will depend on the animals chosen. For instance, mollusks have an outer tissue called the mantle that produces a protective shell in most species. Mollusks also have a muscular foot for movement and a visceral mass that contains internal organs.

Extended Response

16.

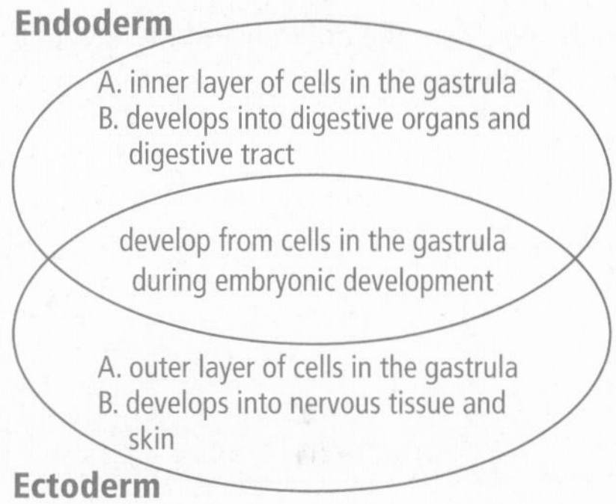

The endoderm and ectoderm are similar because they both develop from parts of the gastrula during embryonic development. The main difference is the kind of tissue they become.

17. Plants, which are autotrophs, use photosynthesis to convert the Sun's light energy to chemical energy stored in glucose. Then, a heterotroph that consumes the plant takes in the chemical energy. The energy in glucose is then converted to ATP molecules during cellular respiration in the heterotroph's body. The energy in ATP molecules can be released as ATP is changed to ADP and the energy can be used for powering cellular activity.

18. A lancelet does not have a heart, but its blood is pumped by blood vessels that contract. A tunicate has a heart that pumps blood through its circulatory system. Both kinds of organisms are classified as invertebrate chordates because the adult lancelets have chordate characteristics and the larval tunicates have chordate characteristics.

19. Incomplete metamorphosis is probably more primitive because it is the simpler of the two life cycles. Complete metamorphosis requires complex changes during the transition from larva to adult.

Essay Question

20. Answers will vary. Students should discuss how the water vascular system depends on a constant supply of water to operate. They also should focus on the idea that the larval stages of echinoderms are free swimming. They also might point out that many echinoderms are sessile or very slow moving. Students should note that the ocean is a stable environment that echinoderms are adapted to.

Chapter 29 Organizer:
Reptiles and Birds

Essential Questions	National Science Standards	Materials and Planning: Estimated times include cleanup and disposal, but do not include teacher prep time. For cleanup and disposal guidelines, see page 39T.	Est. Time (min)
Section 1 1. What is the importance of the amniotic egg in the transition to life on land? 2. What are the characteristics of reptiles? 3. What are the differences between orders of reptiles?	UCP.1–5; C.3, C.5, C.6; G.2	**Launch Lab,** p. 850: library reference materials	45
		Activity, p. 852: polystyrene, plastic food wrap, aluminum foil, clay, salt dough, modeling dough, or gift wrap paper	30
		Demonstration, p. 853: live, nonpoisonous reptile	15
Section 2 1. What are the characteristics of birds? 2. How are the adaptations of birds related to their ability to fly? 3. What are the characteristics of the different orders of birds?	UCP.1–5; C.3, C.5, C.6; G.2	**Demonstration,** p. 864: nutcracker, straw, meat hook, vise, large net, basket, strainer, chisel, hammer, tweezers, toothpick, can opener, tongs, and spatula	20
		Demonstration, p. 865: mounted bird specimens	15
		MiniLab 1, p. 866: binoculars, bird field guide	20
		Demonstration, p. 867: images of birds' feet	15
		Activity, p. 867: binoculars, bird field guides	30
		Demonstration, p. 868: images of early bird fossils	15
		Design Your Own BioLab, p. 871: field guides, sand, soil, cardboard pieces, cardboard box, wooden sticks, toothpicks, glue, scissors, colored markers, dried beans, rocks, pebbles, felt pieces	45

Suggested Time for Each Lesson

Class	Chapter Opener	Section 1	Section 2	Assessment
Basic	45 min	45 min	45 min	45 min
General	25 min	55 min	55 min	45 min
Honors	—	60 min	55 min	20 min

ConnectED

connectED.mcgraw-hill.com

Access interactive learning opportunities and teaching resources using these i
located throughout your StudentWorks™ Plus Online and eTeacherEdition Online

Chapter 29 Section Resources

FAST FILE Unit 8 Resources:
Launch Lab Worksheet*
Study Guide (English/Spanish)*
Section Quick Check

Reading Essentials 29.1
Science Notebook 29.1*

FAST FILE Unit 8 Resources:
MiniLab Worksheet*
BioLab Worksheet*
Study Guide (English/Spanish)*
Section Quick Check

Reading Essentials 29.2
Science Notebook 29.2*

Additional Chapter 29 Resources

FAST FILE Unit 8 Resources:
Chapter Diagnostic Test
Concept Mapping*
Real-World Biology
Enrichment
Chapter Tests A, B, and C

Transparencies:
Bellringer Transparencies*
Biology Concepts Transparencies*

Lab Resources:
Laboratory Manual*
Probeware Lab Manual*
Forensics Lab Manual*
Pre-AP Lab Manual*
Open Inquiry in Biology*
Guided Inquiry in Biology*

Technology

Teaching Tools:
eTeacherEdition
Classroom Presentation Toolkit CD-ROM*
LabManager™ CD-ROM*
Video Lab DVD*
Virtual Lab CD-ROM*
What's BIOLOGY Got To Do With It?
StudentWorks™ Plus Online*

Chapter Assessment Tools:
Classroom Presentation Toolkit CD-ROM*
ExamView® Assessment Suite CD-ROM

Web-Based Resources:

- StudentWorks™ Plus Online
- eTeacherEdition
- Animations*
- The Interactive Time Line*
- Interactive Tables*
- Online Quizzes
- Online Test Practice
- Standardized Test Practice
- Virtual Labs*
- Multilingual eGlossary*
- Vocabulary eGames*
- Vocabulary eFlashcards
- WebQuests
- Personal Tutors

While all resources listed are appropriate for English learners, the * indicates resources with a strong visual or hands-on component for EL.

Teaching strategies and activities have been coded for differentiated instruction.

AL Activities for students working above grade level	**OL** Activities for students working on grade level	**BL** Activities for students working below grade level	**EL** Activities for English learners (also ELL)	**COOP LEARN** Activities designed for small cooperative group work

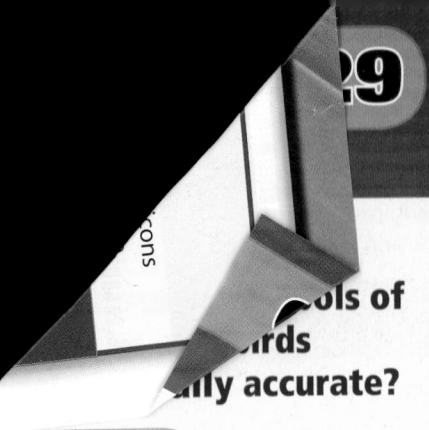

29

ols of
irds
lly accurate?

Inquiry Launch Lab

For a lab worksheet, use your eTeacherEdition.

RUBRIC A rubric for evaluating Launch Labs is found on your eTeacherEdition.

Est. Time 45 min

Additional Materials appropriate references—textbooks, reference books, library resources

Safety Precaution Approve lab safety forms before work begins.

Teaching Strategies
- Have students work in small groups or pairs to research past reptile or bird symbolism.
- Suggest that students work individually on developing their own reptile or bird symbolism.

Procedure
1. Read and complete the lab safety form.
2. Research symbols, stories, or legends about reptiles or birds from different cultures.
3. Analyze the information in the materials that you find from Step 2 for scientific accuracy. Hypothesize as to why a reptile or bird was used as a symbol or legend in each situation.

CHAPTER 29
Reptiles and Birds

ConnectED
Your one-stop online resource
connectED.mcgraw-hill.com

Video
Audio
Review
Inquiry
WebQuest
Assessment
Concepts in Motion
Multilingual eGlossary

Launch Lab

Are cultural symbols of reptiles and birds scientifically accurate?

Throughout history, reptiles and birds have been feared, revered, and symbolized. In this lab, you will review examples of symbolized reptiles and birds and determine whether the representations are scientifically accurate.

For a lab worksheet, use your StudentWorks™ Plus Online.

Inquiry Launch Lab

FOLDABLES®

Make a three-tab Venn diagram using the titles shown. Use it to organize notes on characteristics of reptiles and birds.

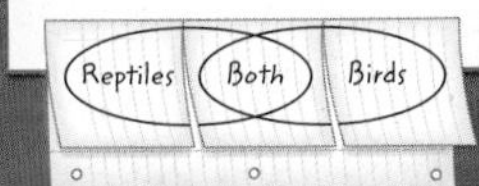

Analysis
1. **Evaluate** How much of the information you analyzed was scientifically accurate? Why do you think some information was inaccurate? Answers will vary. Students should indicate that most of the stories and legends anthropomorphize birds and reptiles. While this portrayal of birds and reptiles is scientifically inaccurate, it is often done to communicate a culture's morals or belief system.
2. **Synthesize** Choose one symbol or legend that contained inaccurate information and modify it so that it is scientifically accurate. Students' answers will vary depending on which symbol or legend they choose to modify.

ConnectED

connectED.mcgraw-hill.com

Access interactive learning opportunities and teaching resources using these icons located throughout your StudentWorks™ Plus Online and eTeacherEdition Online.

Chapter 29 Section Resources	Additional Chapter 29 Resources	Technology
FAST FILE Unit 8 Resources: Launch Lab Worksheet* Study Guide (English/Spanish)* Section Quick Check **Reading Essentials 29.1** **Science Notebook 29.1*** **FAST FILE Unit 8 Resources:** MiniLab Worksheet* BioLab Worksheet* Study Guide (English/Spanish)* Section Quick Check **Reading Essentials 29.2** **Science Notebook 29.2***	**FAST FILE Unit 8 Resources:** Chapter Diagnostic Test Concept Mapping* Real-World Biology Enrichment Chapter Tests A, B, and C **Transparencies:** Bellringer Transparencies* Biology Concepts Transparencies* **Lab Resources:** Laboratory Manual* Probeware Lab Manual* Forensics Lab Manual* Pre-AP Lab Manual* Open Inquiry in Biology* Guided Inquiry in Biology*	**Teaching Tools:** eTeacherEdition Classroom Presentation Toolkit CD-ROM* LabManager™ CD-ROM* Video Lab DVD* Virtual Lab CD-ROM* What's BIOLOGY Got To Do With It? StudentWorks™ Plus Online* **Chapter Assessment Tools:** Classroom Presentation Toolkit CD-ROM* *ExamView® Assessment Suite* CD-ROM **Web-Based Resources:** • StudentWorks™ Plus Online • eTeacherEdition • Animations* • The Interactive Time Line* • Interactive Tables* • Online Quizzes • Online Test Practice • Standardized Test Practice • Virtual Labs* • Multilingual eGlossary* • Vocabulary eGames* • Vocabulary eFlashcards • WebQuests • Personal Tutors

While all resources listed are appropriate for English learners, the * indicates resources with a strong visual or hands-on component for EL.

Teaching strategies and activities have been coded for differentiated instruction.

AL Activities for students working above grade level	**OL** Activities for students working on grade level	**BL** Activities for students working below grade level	**EL** Activities for English learners (also ELL)	**COOP LEARN** Activities designed for small cooperative group work

CHAPTER 29

Launch Lab
Are cultural symbols of reptiles and birds scientifically accurate?

Inquiry Launch Lab

For a lab worksheet, use your eTeacherEdition.

RUBRIC A rubric for evaluating Launch Labs is found on your eTeacherEdition.

Est. Time 45 min

Additional Materials appropriate references—textbooks, reference books, library resources

Safety Precaution Approve lab safety forms before work begins.

Teaching Strategies
- Have students work in small groups or pairs to research past reptile or bird symbolism.
- Suggest that students work individually on developing their own reptile or bird symbolism.

Procedure
1. Read and complete the lab safety form.
2. Research symbols, stories, or legends about reptiles or birds from different cultures.
3. Analyze the information in the materials that you find from Step 2 for scientific accuracy. Hypothesize as to why a reptile or bird was used as a symbol or legend in each situation.

CHAPTER 29

Reptiles and Birds

ConnectED
Your one-stop online resource
connectED.mcgraw-hill.com

- Video
- Audio
- Review
- Inquiry
- WebQuest
- Assessment
- Concepts in Motion
- Multilingual eGlossary

Launch Lab
Are cultural symbols of reptiles and birds scientifically accurate?

Throughout history, reptiles and birds have been feared, revered, and symbolized. In this lab, you will review examples of symbolized reptiles and birds and determine whether the representations are scientifically accurate.

For a lab worksheet, use your StudentWorks™ Plus Online.

Inquiry Launch Lab

FOLDABLES®

Make a three-tab Venn diagram using the titles shown. Use it to organize notes on characteristics of reptiles and birds.

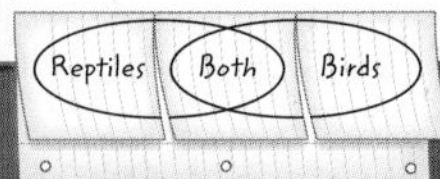

Analysis
1. **Evaluate** How much of the information you analyzed was scientifically accurate? Why do you think some information was inaccurate? Answers will vary. Students should indicate that most of the stories and legends anthropomorphize birds and reptiles. While this portrayal of birds and reptiles is scientifically inaccurate, it is often done to communicate a culture's morals or belief system.
2. **Synthesize** Choose one symbol or legend that contained inaccurate information and modify it so that it is scientifically accurate. Students' answers will vary depending on which symbol or legend they choose to modify.

THEME FOCUS Homeostasis
Reptiles and birds both have a cloaca which helps maintain homeostasis.

BIG Idea Reptile and bird adaptations enable them to live and reproduce successfully in terrestrial habitats.

Section 1 • Reptiles

Section 2 • Birds

THEMES

Scientific Inquiry Biologists study the fossil record to understand how reptiles and birds are related.

Diversity Reptiles and birds are diverse due to the vast number of terrestrial niches available to fill.

Energy Reptiles and birds both obtain energy by ingesting other organisms.

Homeostasis Organs such as kidneys and the cloaca maintain homeostasis in birds and reptiles.

Change Fossil evidence shows that birds and crocodiles evolved from archosaurs.

Introduce the Chapter

SAY TO STUDENTS: ***Study the photo of the rattlesnake in striking position. Note the close-up of the magnified fang. From your prior knowledge and what you can see in the photo, infer how this reptile is adapted to its way of life.*** Possible answers: It has scales that protect it and fangs that aid in protection and getting food. Poison injected by the fangs immobilizes prey that might otherwise get away. Some might know that pit vipers have heat-sensitive pits that enable them to find their warm-blooded prey even in the dark. Some might know that the snake's tongue senses chemicals in the air.

BIG Idea

Make a Chart

SAY TO STUDENTS: ***Make a four-column chart of all the figures in this chapter that show a bird or a reptile. In the first column, list the figure number; in the second column, list the animal or animal group; in the third column, list an adaptation you can see in the illustration that makes the animal or animals suited to its land habitat; in the fourth column, list the theme or themes of the chapter this adaptation is related to. Select from the following themes: energy, homeostasis, change, and diversity.*** Make sure students have identified basic features of reptiles, such as scales, and features of birds, such as feathers and wings. Scales aid in preventing water loss, and feathers and wings aid in flight. Themes of energy are related to wings and feathers, while homeostasis is related to scales.

Section 1

MAIN Idea

BL OL AL

Reptile Adaptations Show students reptile specimens or models.

ASK STUDENTS: ***From what you already know about reptiles, how are these animals adapted to life on land?*** Most will know that all reptiles have scales that help keep them from drying out. Some will know that many lizards are adapted to a hot, dry climate, and that geckos can walk on the ceiling and scoot up window glass. Turtles and alligators swim in the water, but most will know they have lungs, as do other reptiles.

Writing Support

OL AL Journal Writing Have students write two paragraphs describing their personal experiences with reptiles. If students say they have not had any firsthand experience, ask them to describe scenes from videos and movies that could have influenced their feelings about reptiles.

ASK STUDENTS: ***How many of you have had positive experiences with reptiles? How many have had negative experiences with reptiles?*** Answers will vary. Some students might have reptile pets; a snake or other reptile might have frightened others. ***Why do you think reptiles are sometimes associated with negative feelings?*** Answers will vary. Stories, movies, and media often depict reptiles in negative ways.

EL BL Encourage students to list their ideas and then write one paragraph.

Section 1

Reading Preview

Essential Questions

- What is the importance of the amniotic egg in the transition to life on land?
- What are the characteristics of reptiles?
- What are the differences between orders of reptiles?

Review Vocabulary

embryo: the earliest stage of development of plants and animals after an egg has been fertilized

New Vocabulary

amnion
amniotic egg
Jacobson's organ
plastron
carapace

g Multilingual eGlossary

Reptiles

MAIN Idea **Reptiles are fully adapted to life on land.**

Real-World Reading Link Think about the last time you saw a movie in which a reptile was a main character. Maybe it was a giant anaconda or a ferocious *Tyrannosaurus rex.* Maybe it was an animated character that was funny. As you read this section, think about whether the characteristics of the reptile in the movie were scientifically accurate.

Characteristics of Reptiles

Recall that vertebrates with well-developed limbs, circulatory and respiratory systems, and other adaptations moved from water to land. However, amphibians were left vulnerable to the drying effects of life on land with their shell-less eggs and larvae that breathed through gills. In contrast, reptiles, such as the Western fence lizard shown in **Figure 1,** are fully adapted to life on land and were the first completely terrestrial vertebrates. Characteristics that allow reptiles to succeed on land include a shelled egg, scaly skin, and efficient circulatory and respiratory systems.

Amniotic eggs As you can see in the evolutionary tree in **Figure 1,** reptiles have characteristics in common with other groups that have an amnion and other membranes that surround the embryo as it develops. An **amnion** (AM nee ahn) is a membrane that surrounds a developing embryo. It is filled with fluid that protects the embryo during development. Animals that undergo this type of development are called amniotes and include reptiles, birds, and mammals.

Figure 1
Right: This Western fence lizard is one of 7000 species of reptiles belonging to class Reptilia. Reptiles live in a variety of terrestrial and aquatic habitats.
Left: The phylogenetic tree shows that reptiles, along with birds and mammals, have an amnion.

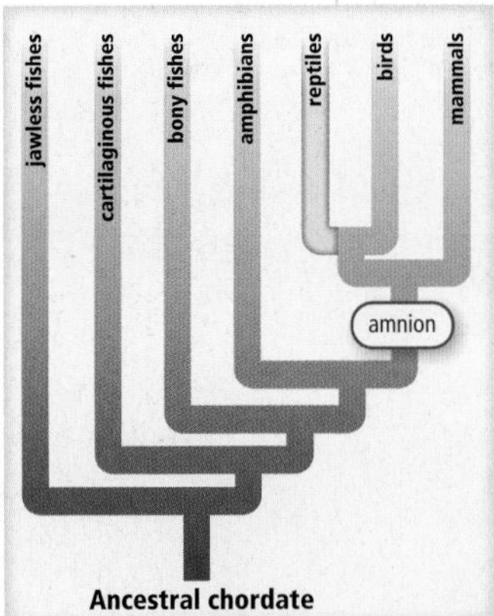

Activity

BL OL AL Model an Amniotic Egg Organize the students into teams of three. Provide them with materials such as polystyrene, plastic food wrap, aluminum foil, clay, salt dough, modeling dough, and gift wrap paper.

SAY TO STUDENTS: ***Make a model of an amniotic egg in cross section. Use the provided materials to represent the egg's membranes.*** Est. time: 30 min

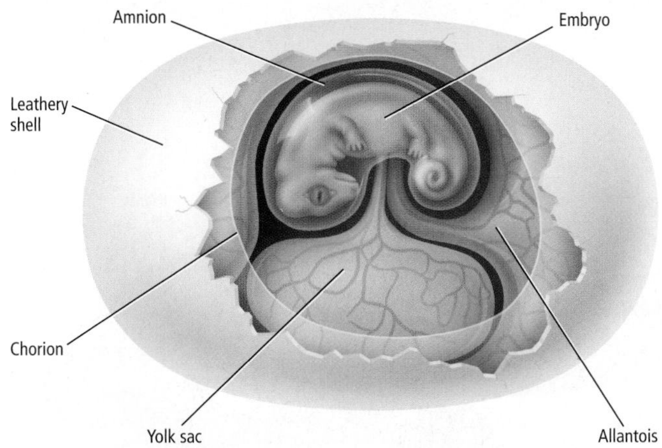

■ **Figure 2** The amniotic egg is protected by a shell and membranes with fluid that help to protect the embryo and keep it from drying out during development.

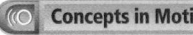

Concepts in Motion
Animation

An **amniotic egg,** like the one shown in **Figure 2,** is covered with a protective shell and has several internal membranes with fluids contained between the membranes. Inside the egg, the embryo is self-sufficient because it gets its nutrition from food in the yolk sac inside the egg. Bathing the embryo within the amnion is amniotic fluid. Amniotic fluid mimics the aquatic environments of fish and amphibian embryos. The allantois (uh LAN tuh wus) is a membrane that forms a sac that contains wastes produced by the embryo. The outermost membrane of the egg is the chorion (KOR ee ahn), which allows oxygen to enter and keeps fluid inside the egg. In reptiles, the leathery shell protects the internal fluids and embryo, and prevents the egg from drying out on land. In birds, the shell is hard instead of leathery.

Dry, scaly skin In addition to keeping fluid in their eggs, reptiles also must keep fluids in their bodies. The dry skin of reptiles keeps them from losing internal fluids to the air. A layer of scales on the exterior of many reptiles also keeps them from drying out. However, one problem with having a tough outer covering is that an organism could have difficulty growing larger. To grow, some reptiles, such as the snake in **Figure 3,** periodically must shed their skins in a process called molting. You might have seen the molt of a snake's skin while hiking on a nature trail.

Respiration Most reptiles, except for some aquatic turtles, depend primarily on lungs for gas exchange. Recall that when amphibians breathe, they squeeze their throats to force air into their lungs. Reptiles are able to suck air into their lungs, or inhale, by contracting muscles of the rib cage and body wall to expand the upper part of the body cavity in which the lungs are held. They exhale by relaxing these same muscle groups. Reptiles exchange gases in lungs that have larger surface areas for gas exchange than the lungs of amphibians. With more oxygen, more energy can be released through metabolic reactions and made available for more complex movements.

Reading Check **Evaluate** why the amniotic egg is important for an animal to be able to live exclusively on land.

■ **Figure 3** Some reptiles molt as they grow larger.
Compare *molting in reptiles to molting in arthropods.*

Concepts in Motion
Animation

Reading Strategy

BL OL AL Change Headings to Questions Have students make a vocabulary Foldable, but instead of using vocabulary terms, have them examine the headings in this section, change them to questions, and write the questions on each tab of the Foldable. As they read, have students answer the questions under each tab. Suggest that students use this Foldable to help them review and study for the chapter assessment.

Writing Support

BL OL AL COOP LEARN

Informal Writing Organize students into groups of three. Have the groups find a children's story that presents a reptile in a negative way. Instruct the groups to rewrite the story so that the reptile is portrayed in a more favorable light. If there is time, have the groups read their stories to the class.

Reading Check The amniotic egg has a shell that keeps it from drying out, membranes and fluid inside that protect the embryo, and a yolk that provides nutrition.

■ **Caption Question Fig. 3** Reptile molting is similar to arthropod molting because both types of animals molt in the process of growing larger.

Demonstration

BL OL AL Scaly Skin of Reptiles If you do not have a reptile display in your classroom, borrow a lizard, snake, or turtle from a pet shop or nature center or ask students who have a pet reptile to bring one or two to school. Point out that the scaly skin is not moist or slimy.

ASK STUDENTS: ***How does scaly skin help a reptile on land?*** reduces water loss from the body Allow students to touch the skin so they can feel that it is not moist or slimy, which is a common misconception. Make sure students wash their hands thoroughly with soap and water after handling reptiles, as some can harbor pathogenic bacteria. Est. time: 15 min

S Skill Practice

BL OL Compare

ASK STUDENTS: ***In what ways are the organs of the digestive systems of reptiles similar to the digestive systems of fishes and amphibians?*** They all have stomachs, intestines, and mouths with jaws.

D Develop Concepts

EL BL OL AL COOP LEARN

Activity Organize students into groups of four. Provide each group with two thick rubber bands, a roll of tape, and a stuffed animal a little larger than the size of two adult fists together. Have one student in each group put their palms together. Have another student tape together the entire two little fingers and the entire two thumbs. Then tell another student in each group to put their palms together. Have someone place the rubber bands over the same fingers as the ones that are taped on the first person. These two pairs of hands are models of a snake's jaws that are loosely hinged and another animal's jaws that are not loosely hinged. Have each set of hands try to "eat" the stuffed animal by opening the three remaining fingers and pushing the animal through the "jaws."

ASK STUDENTS: ***Which type of jaw model is more successful at feeding on its "prey"?*** The model of the snake's jaw with loosely hinged joints (rubber bands) is more successful.

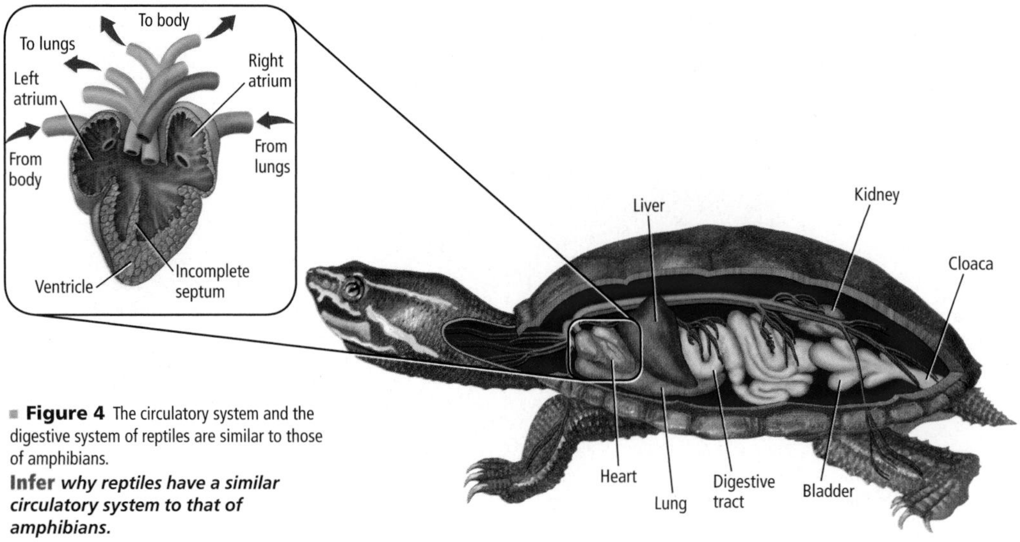

Figure 4 The circulatory system and the digestive system of reptiles are similar to those of amphibians.
***Infer** why reptiles have a similar circulatory system to that of amphibians.*

Figure 5 Snakes can consume a meal that is larger than their mouths because their jaws are loosely jointed, and upper and lower jaws can move independently of each other.

Circulation In most reptiles, oxygen from the lungs enters into a circulatory system that is similar to that of amphibians. Most reptiles have two separate atria and one ventricle that is partially divided by an incomplete septum, as shown in **Figure 4.** In crocodiles, however, the septum in the ventricles is complete, thereby resulting in a four-chambered heart. The separation into two ventricles keeps oxygen-rich blood separate from the oxygen-poor blood throughout the heart.

Because reptiles generally are larger than amphibians, they need to pump blood forcefully enough to reach parts of the body far away from the heart. In an example from the past, the dinosaur *Brachiosaurus* had to pump blood more than 6 m from the heart to the head!

Feeding and digestion The organs of the digestive system of reptiles, shown in **Figure 4,** are similar to those of fish and amphibians. Reptiles have a variety of feeding methods and diets. Most reptiles are carnivores, but some, such as iguanas and tortoises, are herbivores that feed on plants, and some turtles are omnivores. Turtles and crocodiles have tongues that help them swallow. Some lizards, such as chameleons, have long, sticky tongues for catching insects.

Snakes have the ability to ingest prey much larger than themselves. The bones of the skull and jaws of snakes are joined loosely so that they can spread apart when taking in large food materials, as shown in **Figure 5.** To swallow, the opposite sides of the upper and lower jaws can alternately thrust forward and retract to draw in the food. Some snakes have venom that can paralyze and begin digestion of their prey. S D

Excretion The excretory system of reptiles is adapted to life on land. The kidneys, such as the one shown in **Figure 4,** filter the blood to remove waste products. When urine enters the cloaca, water is reabsorbed to form uric acid, which is a semisolid excretion. This method of water reabsorption enables reptiles to conserve water and maintain homeostasis of water and minerals in their bodies.

Content Background

Teacher FYI Ammonia, urea, and uric acid are the nitrogenous waste products of metabolism. Terrestrial species cannot store ammonia, as it is toxic. Instead, they convert ammonia to urea or uric acid. Urine of reptiles contains either urea or uric acid produced after the kidneys filter blood. Reptiles excrete mostly uric acid.

Caption Question Fig. 4 Amphibians and reptiles have a common ancestor, and therefore have similar circulatory systems.

D **The brain and senses** Reptile brains are similar to amphibian brains, except that the cerebrums of reptiles are larger. Because vision and muscle function are more complex, the optic lobes and cerebellum portions in the brains of reptiles are larger than those of amphibians. Vision is the most sensitive sense for most reptiles, and some reptiles even have color vision. Hearing varies in reptiles. Some reptiles have tympanic membranes similar to those of amphibians, while others, such as snakes, detect vibrations through their jaw bones.

The sense of smell is more highly evolved in reptiles than it is in amphibians. You might have seen a snake rapidly flicking its forked tongue. When a snake sticks its tongue out, odor molecules stick to it. The snake then brings the tongue and the odor molecules into its mouth. Inside the mouth, the odor molecules transfer to a pair of saclike structures that sense odors called **Jacobson's organs**. **Figure 6** shows one of these structures. Without Jacobson's organs, snakes would not be able to find prey or mates.

Temperature control Like amphibians, reptiles are ectotherms that cannot generate their own body heat. Because they cannot regulate their body temperatures internally, they must regulate them behaviorally. You might have seen a turtle basking on a rock on a sunny day. Heat from the Sun and the rock raise the turtle's body temperature. Body temperature can be lowered by moving into the shade or a cool burrow. Some reptiles in temperate regions survive winter by burrowing or going into a state of inactivity with lower body metabolism and lower body temperature. Others, such as some snakes, gather together in masses of hundreds during the winter. Heat loss is reduced when the snakes are covering each other.

C **Movement** Compare the leg position of the salamander to the leg position of the crocodile shown in **Figure 7.** Note that the salamander's belly is on the ground, while the crocodile's belly is above the ground. Like amphibians, some reptiles move with limbs sprawled to their sides and push against the ground while swinging their bodies from side to side. Crocodiles, however, have their limbs rotated farther under the body and, as a result, can bear more weight and move faster. To bear more body weight on land, reptiles' skeletons are stronger, with a heavier bone structure. Reptiles also have claws on their toes, which aid in digging, climbing, and gripping the ground for traction.

Reading Check **Compare and contrast** the brain and senses of reptiles to amphibians.

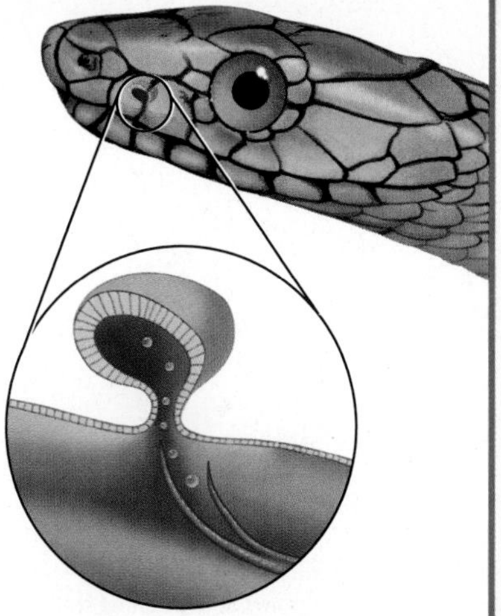

Figure 6 In snakes, Jacobson's organs in the mouth are used to sense odors.

D

Figure 7 Salamanders move with splayed legs pushing against the ground as their bodies drag along. Crocodiles have legs that are rotated underneath their bodies and hold their bodies off the ground.

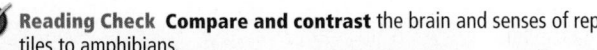

Salamander **Crocodile**

D Develop Concepts

BL OL AL

Clarify a Misconception

ASK STUDENTS: ***Is a snake's tongue dangerous?*** no Explain to students that many people fear that a snake's tongue will sting or hurt them in some way. However, a snake's tongue is nonvenomous. It functions as a chemoreceptor. When a snake flicks its tongue out, odor molecules stick to it. The snake then places its tongue into its pouchlike Jacobson's organs in its mouth to get information about chemicals in its environment. It might help to show students video footage of a snake flicking out its tongue.

C Critical Thinking

EL BL OL AL **Infer** Pass a variety of reptile skulls and skeletons around the classroom.

ASK STUDENTS: ***What can you tell about the movements of these reptiles by studying their skeletons?*** Reptiles have claws on their feet that aid in gripping the ground. The snake does not have legs and must move by undulating its body muscles as it slithers across the ground or through trees. The legs of a tortoise are short and clublike for walking on land. The legs of a turtle are longer and function like paddles in the water.

D Develop Concepts

EL BL **Use Models** Provide students with clay, salt dough, modeling dough, or wax-covered yarn. Have students make three-dimensional models of the leg positions of a salamander and the leg positions of a crocodile. Tell them to make sure that the distinction is clear between the two. The salamander should have legs splayed out to the sides, and the crocodile should have legs underneath the body.

Content Background

Teacher FYI Geckos are noted for their ability to climb up glass windows and scamper across a ceiling with great agility. Gecko feet are covered with microscopic hairlike structures called setae. Each seta branches at the end into about 1000 additional tinier "hairs." Intermolecular attraction between the surface and the "hair" bonds the gecko's foot to the surface.

Reading Check Reptile brains, including the cerebrum, optic lobes, and cerebellum portions, are larger than those of amphibians. Reptile vision and muscle functions are more complex, as is the sense of smell.

D Develop Concepts

BL OL AL

Clarify A Misconception

ASK STUDENTS: ***Do all reptiles lay eggs?*** no Tell students that all reptiles produce eggs, but some reptiles incubate the eggs internally and give birth to live young. Oviparous reptiles lay their eggs. The act of laying eggs is called oviposition. In ovoviviparous reptiles, eggs hatch inside the mother and are born live. Viviparous reptiles also bear live young. The embryos receive nourishment from the female, whereas in ovoviviparous reptiles, the embryos receive nourishment from the yolk sac.

C Critical Thinking

BL OL AL COOP LEARN

Design Organize students into groups of three. Have the groups design a multimedia presentation describing the various ways in which reptiles lay their eggs, highlighting one reptile in depth. Tell the groups to be sure to explain the behavior and functioning of their reptile after oviposition. Examples will vary, but may include: female pythons coil around their eggs until they hatch; some turtles, lizards, cobras, and all crocodiles guard their nests.

Develop Concepts

OL AL **Research** Have students research to find out how to set up a terrarium for a lizard that can be kept as a pet. Tell students to find out about food, light, temperature, humidity, substrate, and size of the terrarium. Have students make a list of all they would need to do to prepare the terrarium and what they would have to do to maintain the terrarium.

BL Direct struggling readers to appropriate reading materials.

D **Reproduction** Recall that amphibian females lay eggs that are later fertilized. Reptile reproduction is significantly different, mainly because reptiles have internal fertilization. After fertilization, an amniotic egg and embryo develop. The yolk of the egg nourishes the embryo. The female reproductive system then produces a leathery shell around the egg. The female usually digs a hole and lays her eggs in the ground or in plant debris. After laying the eggs, most female reptiles leave them unattended to hatch. Alligators and crocodiles build a nest in which to lay eggs and tend to the young after they hatch. Some snakes and lizards keep their eggs in their bodies until they hatch. In this way, the eggs are protected in the mother's body until they are fully developed young. C

Diversity of Modern Reptiles

There are currently four living orders of reptiles—snakes and lizards, belonging to order Squamata (skwuh MAHD uh); crocodiles and alligators, belonging to order Crocodilia; turtles and tortoises, belonging to order Testudinata; and tuataras (tyew ah TAR ahz), belonging to order Sphenodonta (sfee nuh DAHN tuh).

VOCABULARY

WORD ORIGIN

Squamata

squama– from Latin, meaning *scale*

–ata from Latin, meaning *to bear.*

Lizards and snakes Lizards commonly have legs with clawed toes. They usually have movable eyelids, a lower jaw with a movable hinge joint allowing for flexibility in jaw movement, and tympanic membranes. Common lizards include iguanas, chameleons, geckos, and anoles. An iguana is shown in **Figure 8.**

Snakes are legless and have shorter tails than lizards do. Snakes lack movable eyelids and tympanic membranes. Like lizards, however, snakes have joints in their jaws enabling them to eat prey larger than their heads. Some snakes, such as the rattlesnake shown at the beginning of the chapter, have venom that can slow down or even kill their prey. Other snakes, such as the python shown in **Figure 8,** anacondas, and boas, are constrictors. Constrictors generally are very large snakes. They suffocate their prey by wrapping around the prey's body and tightening until the prey dies because it no longer can breathe.

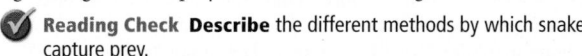

Reading Check **Describe** the different methods by which snakes capture prey.

Figure 8 The green iguana and the green tree python are both members of order Squamata.

Green iguana **Green tree python**

Content Background

Teacher FYI Some male reptiles display certain courtship behaviors to attract a female. For example, head-bobbing displays by some male lizards are meant to show off bright color patterns on the throat. Lizards and snakes use sex pheromones to determine the reproductive condition of a mate.

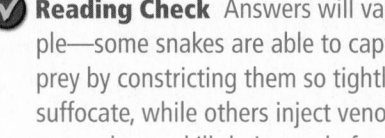

Reading Check Answers will vary. Example—some snakes are able to capture their prey by constricting them so tightly that they suffocate, while others inject venom in order to paralyze or kill their prey before ingesting them.

Eastern box turtle

American alligator

■ **Figure 9** The shell of a turtle helps protect it from predators. An alligator has a broad snout and thick scales covering its body.

Turtles Turtles are unique because they are encased by a protective shell, as shown in **Figure 9.** A turtle can hide from predators by pulling its head and legs inside this hard shell. The ventral part of the shell is called the **plastron** (PLAS trahn), and the dorsal part of the shell is called the **carapace** (KAR ah pays). The vertebrae and the ribs of most turtles are fused to the inside of the carapace. Another unique aspect of turtles is that they do not have teeth. Instead, they have a sharp beak that can deliver a powerful bite. Like other reptiles, there are aquatic turtles and terrestrial turtles. Turtles that live on land are D called tortoises.

Crocodiles and alligators Order Crocodilia includes crocodiles, alligators, and caimans. Unlike most reptiles, crocodilians have a four-chambered heart. Because a four-chambered heart can deliver oxygen more efficiently to their powerful muscles, crocodilians move quickly and aggressively, both in and out of the water. These quick movements help in capturing large prey.

Crocodiles have a long snout, sharp teeth, and powerful jaws. Alligators, like the one in **Figure 9,** generally have a broader snout than crocodiles do. The upper jaw of an alligator is wider than the lower jaw. When an alligator closes its mouth, the upper jaw overlaps the lower jaw and its teeth are almost completely covered. The upper and lower jaws of a crocodile are about the same width. When a crocodile closes its mouth, some teeth in the lower jaw are easily visible. Caimans are closely related to alligators but lack a bony separation between their nostrils. The teeth of crocodiles are similar to those of dinosaurs and the earliest birds.

■ **Figure 10** Tuataras reach a length of about 2 m and can live up to 80 years in the wild.

Tuataras Tuataras look like large lizards, as shown in **Figure 10.** Tuataras have a spiny crest that runs down the back and a "third eye" on top of the head. This structure is covered with scales but can sense sunlight. Biologists think that it might keep the tuatara from overheating in the Sun. One distinguishing feature of tuataras is that they have unique teeth compared to those of other reptiles. Two rows of teeth on the upper jaw shear against one row in the lower jaw, making them effective predators of small vertebrates. The only two living species of tuataras are found exclusively on islands off the coast of New Zealand.

Content Background

Teacher FYI Some reptiles, such as the American alligator, build nests and defend them against predators. After the eggs hatch, the mother might stay near her young for up to two years.

Develop Concepts

BL OL AL COOP LEARN

Activity Organize students into groups of nine. Set up a debate in the form of a radio talk show. Have students debate the best way to protect a beach popular with surfers where sea turtles come ashore to lay eggs. Each student should research sea turtles and assume one of the following positions in each group: mayor of the town, turtle biologist, president of the turtle protection society, teenage surfer, beach concession owner, condo developer, beach homeowner, state wildlife protection officer, and the talk show host. Have each member of the group "call in" to voice an opinion. Others can call in to refute or support arguments and state their own opinion from their assigned point of view. Some will be opposed to protecting the beach, while others will be for protecting the beach.

D Develop Concepts

BL OL AL

Clarify a Misconception

ASK STUDENTS: ***Are alligators and crocodiles the same type of reptile?*** No; both are crocodilian, but they are different species.

TELL STUDENTS: ***Most people do not know the distinction between crocodiles and alligators. The head shape is the best way to distinguish between crocodiles and alligators. Crocodiles have a long narrow snout, while alligators have a broader head and jaws.*** You might wish to show students pictures of alligators and crocodiles and point out these differences.

S Skill Practice

OL AL Visual Literacy Have students examine Figure 11. **ASK STUDENTS:** *Which reptiles are most closely related to tuataras: turtles or crocodiles?* crocodiles *Which reptiles do not have a diapsid skull?* turtles *Which modern reptiles are most closely related to birds?* crocodiles *From what group of reptiles were snakes derived?* tuataras

Critical Thinking

BL OL AL Design

SAY TO STUDENTS: *Assume that you are a genetic engineer of the future, with access to the DNA of all reptiles, past and present. Design a new reptile that would be useful to humans in some way. Draw a diagram of this reptile; label its features and explain what reptile it descended from. Explain how it will be useful to humans.* Diagrams will vary. An example might be a large, lizardlike animal with a turtle shell. This animal might be valuable as a food source.

W Writing Support

EL BL OL AL COOP LEARN

Creative Writing Have students work in pairs to make a diagram of their favorite dinosaur on a large sheet of paper. Tell students to write a poem beside it that describes its biological features. Instruct students to discuss some of the more recent discoveries about dinosaurs in their poems. Students might discuss the incubation of eggs, feathered dinosaurs, colors of dinosaurs, or their body temperatures.

Caption Question Fig. 11 Turtles evolved first. Snakes and lizards evolved most recently.

Reading Check the skull

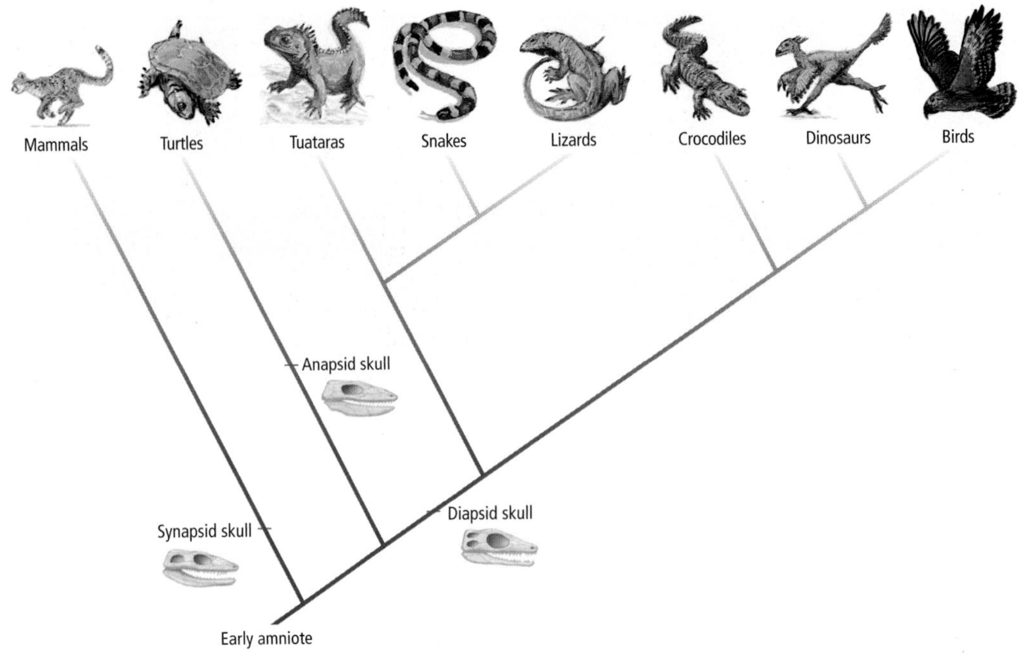

Figure 11 The cladogram shows one interpretation of the relationships between amniotes.
Interpret *Which modern reptiles evolved first? Which evolved most recently?*

S

VOCABULARY

ACADEMIC VOCABULARY

Interpretation
a particular adaptation or version of a work, method, or style
Scientists might make several interpretations of fossil evidence.

Evolution of Reptiles

The cladogram in **Figure 11** shows one interpretation of how early amniotes underwent adaptive radiation, giving rise to reptiles as well as modern birds and mammals. Recall that amniotes are vertebrates in which the embryo is encased in an amniotic membrane. As shown in the cladogram, early amniotes separated into three lines, each having a different skull structure. Anapsids, which might have given rise to turtles, have a skull that has no openings behind the eye sockets. Diapsids, which gave rise to crocodiles, dinosaurs, modern birds, tuataras, snakes, and lizards, have a skull with two pairs of openings behind each eye socket. Synapsids, which gave rise to modern mammals, have one opening behind each eye socket.

Reading Check Identify which part of a reptile fossil would be a major indicator in classifying it as a lizard or a turtle.

Dinosaurs For 165 million years, dinosaurs dominated Earth. Some, such as *Tyrannosaurus rex,* stood almost 6 m high, were 14.5 m long, weighed more than 7 tonnes, and were predatory. Others, such as *Triceratops*, had massive horns and were herbivores. Despite their diversity, dinosaurs can be divided into two groups based on the structure of their hips. A comparison of the two groups is shown in **Figure 12.** Saurischians (saw RISK ee unz) had hip bones that radiated out from the center of the hip area. In Ornithischians, some bones projected back toward the tail.

Like birds and crocodiles, some dinosaurs built nests and cared for eggs and young. Some dinosaurs might have had the ability to regulate their body temperatures. Fossil evidence shows that one group of dinosaurs had feathers and likely evolved into today's birds. W

Research Citation

Problem Solving Educational research indicates that students should be given explicit instruction on how to solve problems. The activity described on this page requires students to think like genetic engineers, teaching them to plan strategies and develop problem solving skills. (Charles and Lester, 1984)

Research bibliography on pages 32T–34T

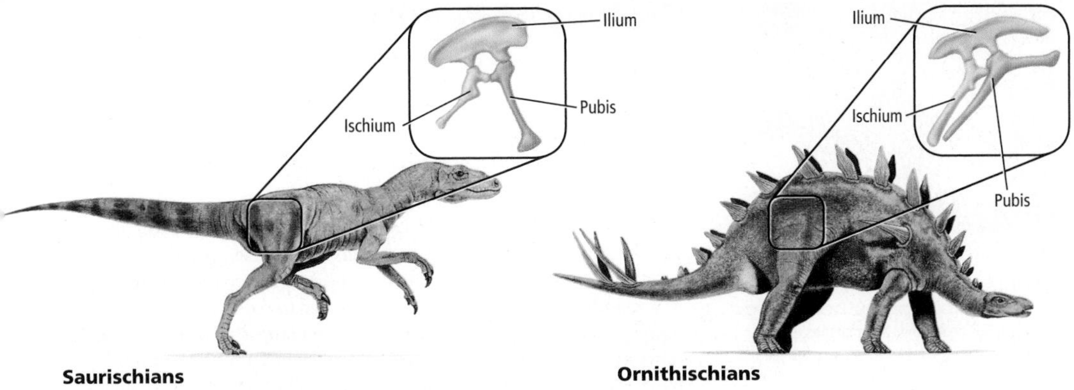

■ **Figure 12** Saurischians had a hip bone that pointed forward. Ornithischians had the same bone pointing back toward the tail end of the animal.

Connection to Earth Science The Cretaceous period is known for worldwide mass extinction of many species, including all dinosaurs. Some scientists hypothesize that a meteorite crashed into Earth and caused this extinction. Clouds of dust might have blocked the Sun, causing a much cooler climate to develop. This change, along with fires, toxic dust, and gases, could have caused the death of many plants and animals at this time. When dinosaurs disappeared, the niches that they had occupied were made available for other vertebrates to evolve and fill. **W**

DATA ANALYSIS LAB 1

Based on Real Data*

Interpret the Data

How fast did dinosaurs grow? Scientists study thin sections of fossilized bone tissue to determine how rapidly the bone grew. By studying how quickly dinosaurs grew, scientists have learned about their populations and ecology.

Think Critically

1. **Compare** During what age span did the dinosaurs experience the greatest growth? Explain.
2. **Analyze Data** Which dinosaur grew at the slowest rate? The fastest rate?
3. **Infer** Fast-growing bones have many blood vessels. How would the bones of *Tyrannosaurus* compare to those of *Daspletosaurus*?

Data and Observations

The graph shows bone-based growth curves comparing several dinosaurs.

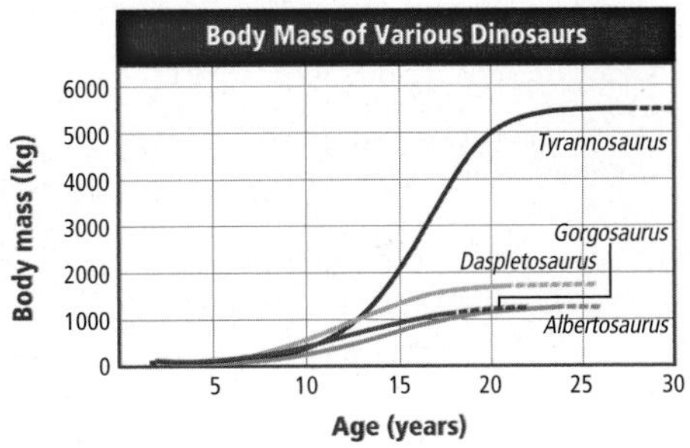

*Data obtained from: Stokstad, E. 2004. Dinosaurs under the knife. *Science* 306: 962-965.

W Writing Support

AL Creative Writing

SAY TO STUDENTS: ***Imagine you are a journalist living during the Cretaceous period. Write a newspaper article reporting on a cataclysmic event that extinguished many dinosaurs and other species.*** Encourage students to use a different cataclysmic event than the one most commonly believed, or devise one that sounds reasonable.

DATA ANALYSIS LAB 1

About the Lab

- **ASK STUDENTS:** ***What do you think was the function of the bony "collar" around the head of triceratops?*** Powerful jaw muscles were attached to this bone.
- Organize students into groups of three and provide each group with a different plastic dinosaur. Ask them to describe in terms of Darwin's theory of evolution how the dinosaur could have developed a particular structure.
- Also see Erickson, et al. 2004. Gigantism and comparative life-history parameters of tyrannosaurid dinosaurs. *Nature,* 430: 772–775.

Think Critically

1. The greatest increase in body mass per year occurred between 10–20 years of age.
2. *Albertosaurus; Tyrannosaurus*
3. *Tyrannosaurus* bones would have many more blood vessels than *Daspletosaurus.*

Differentiated Instruction

Below Level Students will benefit when they are familiar with the schedule and structure of the classroom. Give students several reminders, several minutes apart, before changing from one activity to another. This will allow students time to finish their current work and prepare for the next assignment.

For more tips, see pages 14T–15T.

GOING GREEN When using paper for classroom activities, encourage students not to use colored paper. When paper is colored, the dyes that are used become pollutants. Use recycled, unbleached paper whenever possible.

Develop Concepts

BL OL AL

Community Connection Invite a local reptile expert to discuss a local endangered reptile, explain their own current research on reptiles, or bring in reptile specimens to show students.

Formative Assessment

Evaluation

SAY TO STUDENTS: *Make a chart titled* **Reptile Features** *with the following reptiles in the first column:* **lizard, snake, alligator, turtle,** *and* **tuatara.** *In the next column, indicate means of respiration; in the third column, circulation; in the fourth column, feeding adaptations; and in the last column, temperature control. Fill in the chart.* All have lungs and all have three-chambered hearts (except the alligator, which has four). Some are carnivores, some are herbivores. All are ectotherms.

Remediation Have students write a note to a friend that says: "What I already understand about the features of reptiles is ______. What I don't understand about reptiles is ______." Tell students to base their note on the concepts or text they had difficulty understanding. Have them trade notes with a partner and explain in writing what their partner doesn't understand by referencing their books.

Figure 13 The San Francisco garter snake *(Thamnophis sirtalis tetrataenia)* lives in wetlands or grasslands near ponds and marshes.

Ecology of Reptiles

Reptiles are important parts of food chains both as prey and as predators. The balance of an ecosystem can be disrupted when a reptile species is removed. For example, when certain snakes are removed from an environment, rodent populations can increase. Loss of habitat and the introduction of exotic species are factors that contribute to the decline in populations of some reptile species.

Habitat loss Both the American alligator *(Alligator mississippiensis)* and the American crocodile *(Crocodylus acutus)* have been affected by habitat loss in the Florida Everglades. The destruction and fragmentation of wetlands for building development has led to reduced numbers of these reptiles. The American crocodile remains endangered, with only 500-1200 remaining in Florida. With the passage of laws to protect wetlands in certain areas, the American alligator population has rebounded enough so that its status has been changed from endangered to threatened.

Introduction of exotic species An exotic species is a species that is not naturally found in an area, and when introduced, the local animals might suffer due to predation or competition for resources. For example, when the mongoose, a small mammal, was introduced into Jamaica to kill rats in sugarcane fields, the mongoose fed on several lizard species, which are now endangered. This includes the Jamaican iguana, which was thought to have become extinct due to the introduction of the mongoose. In 1990, a small population of the iguanas was discovered in a remote area of Jamaica.

Some species, such as the San Francisco garter snake shown in **Figure 13,** have suffered a population decline due to both habitat loss and the introduction of exotic species. The use of land for building and agriculture has led to habitat loss for this snake. The American bullfrog, which is not native to California, eats both the garter snake and the red-legged frog, a food source of the garter snake.

Section 1 Assessment

Section Summary

- Reptiles have several types of adaptations for life on land.
- Eggs of reptiles are adapted to development on land.
- Reptiles belong to four living orders: Squamata, Crocodilia, Testudinata, and Sphenodonta.
- Modern reptiles evolved from early amniotes. Many ancient reptiles, including dinosaurs, became extinct.

Understand Main Ideas

1. MAIN Idea **Identify** features that allow reptiles to live on land successfully.
2. **Describe** the parts of an amniotic egg. How did this structure allow reptiles to move to land?
3. **Compare and contrast** members of order Squamata with members of order Sphenodonta.
4. **Explain** the differences among anapsids, diapsids, and synapsids. Which gave rise to groups of reptiles?

Think Critically

5. **Formulate Models** Make a model of the amniotic egg shown in **Figure 2.** Relate the function of each membrane.

MATH in Biology

6. The biting force of alligators is directly proportional to their lengths. An alligator that is 1 m long has a biting force of 2653 N. What is the biting force of a larger alligator that is 3.6 m long?

Section 1 Assessment

1. Amniotic eggs and dry, scaly skin allow reptiles to live on land. Reptiles have lungs with larger surface area than those of amphibians. The ventricle in the heart of reptiles is partially separated and in crocodiles is completely separated. Reptiles have higher blood pressure than amphibians, and they excrete uric acid.
2. The amniotic egg has a leathery shell and internal membranes. The shell prevents the egg from drying out on land.
3. Accept any reasonable answer. Answers may include that some members of Squamata look like members of Sphenodonta, but members of Sphenodonta have a "third eye."
4. anapsids—no openings behind the eye sockets; diapsids—two pairs of openings behind each eye socket; synapsids—one opening behind each eye socket; reptiles are diapsids.
5. The model should show a shell and amnion (protection), the allantois (waste products), the yolk sac (nutrition), and the chorion (keeps the fluid in the egg and lets oxygen in).
6. Multiply 2653 by 3.6, which is about 9551N.

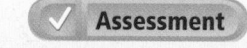

Assessment Online Quiz

Reading Preview

Essential Questions

- What are the characteristics of birds?
- How are the adaptations of birds related to their ability to fly?
- What are the characteristics of the different orders of birds?

Review Vocabulary

terrestrial: living on or in land

New Vocabulary

endotherm
feather
contour feather
preen gland
down feather
sternum
air sac
incubate

Multilingual eGlossary

Birds

MAIN Idea Birds have feathers, wings, lightweight bones, and other adaptations that allow for flight.

Real-World Reading Link You probably have heard the sayings: "Free as a bird," "Birds of a feather flock together," or "Light as a feather." As people talk, listen for "bird words." As you read, see if these sayings refer to real science.

Characteristics of Birds

Suppose your teacher asked you to describe a bird. You might respond that birds have feathers and that they fly. Birds belong to class Aves and include about 8600 species, making them the most diverse of all terrestrial vertebrates. Birds range in size from tiny hummingbirds hovering over bright flowers to large flightless ostriches running across the African plains. Birds are found in deserts, forests, mountains, prairies, and on all seas.

As shown on the evolutionary tree in **Figure 14,** birds and reptiles have a common ancestor. Birds have many characteristics that demonstrate their reptilian roots. For example, birds lay amniotic eggs. In addition, scales similar to those of reptiles cover the legs of birds.

You can think of a bird as a collection of adaptations to a lifestyle that includes flight. The adaptations include being able to generate their own body heat internally, feathers, and lightweight bones. The respiratory and circulatory systems of birds are also adapted to provide more oxygen to working muscles to support flight.

Endotherms Unlike reptiles, birds are endotherms. An **endotherm** is an organism that generates its body heat internally by its own metabolism. The high metabolic rate associated with endothermy generates a large amount of ATP that can be used to power flight muscles or for other purposes. Endotherms generate heat from their normal body metabolism. The body temperature of a bird is about 41°C. Your body temperature is about 37°C. A high body temperature enables the cells in a bird's flight muscles to use the large amounts of ATP needed for rapid muscle contraction during flight.

Reading Check Explain why endothermy is an important adaptation for flight.

Feathers Birds are the only living animals to have feathers. **Feathers** are specialized outgrowths of the skin of birds. They are made of keratin (KER ah tihn), a protein in the skin that also makes up hair, nails, and horns of other animals. Feathers have two main functions: flight and insulation. Feathers keep heat generated during metabolism from escaping from the body of the bird. When a bird fluffs its feathers, it creates a dead air space that traps the heat. Similarly, if you are covered with a quilt while you sleep, the quilt creates dead air space between you and the cool air in the room so that you do not lose body heat.

Figure 14 The evolutionary tree shows that feathers are a unique characteristic of birds.

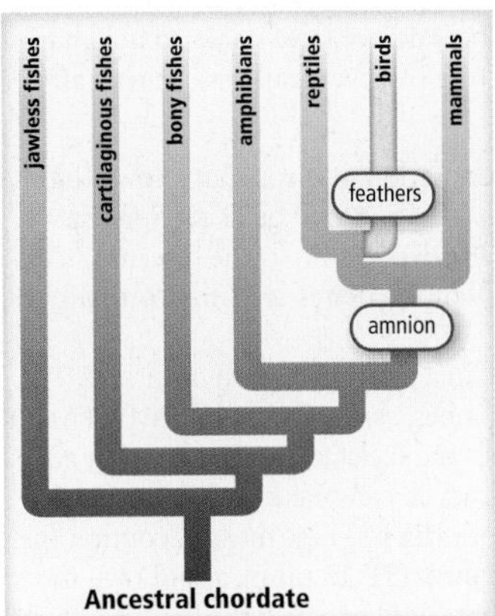

Section 2

MAIN Idea

EL BL OL AL Birds Show students a bird specimen, model, or picture.

ASK STUDENTS: ***How do you think this bird is adapted to flight?*** From their previous knowledge, students may already know that feathers, wings, and lightweight bones are adaptations for flight.

TELL STUDENTS: ***Other structures, such as the four-chambered heart, endothermy, air sacs, and good vision, also contribute to the ability to fly. You will study these features in this section.***

Skill Practice

EL BL OL AL

Observe and Infer Have students cut a strip of notebook paper 4 cm wide by 28 cm long and tape one end of the paper to the middle of a pencil so that it is at right angles to the pencil. Have students hold the pencil near their mouth so that the paper is hanging down from the pencil away from their mouths. Have them blow across the top of the pencil where the paper is and observe what happens to the paper.

ASK STUDENTS: ***How does this result apply to the wings of a bird in flight?*** Lower air pressure and density on the top of a bird's wing causes the wing to rise. Birds will not have to generate as much energy in flight if their wings are shaped to use this principle.

Reading Check Endothermy allows for the production of enough energy to make flight possible.

Research Citation

Skill Practice Educational research indicates the value of providing ample opportunities for students to practice skills as described on this page. This practice will reinforce understanding of main ideas and improve student achievement. (Good et al., 1983)

Research bibliography on pages 32T–34T

Differentiated Instruction

Behavior Disorders Students with behavior disorders need to know that while certain behaviors are unacceptable, they are important members of the class. Communicate to these students that you accept and value them while continuing to correct inappropriate behavior.

For more tips, see pages 14T–15T.

C Critical Thinking

EL BL OL AL COOP LEARN

Differentiate Organize students into groups of four. Have them examine a contour feather and a down feather using 10× magnifiers and compare and contrast them.

ASK STUDENTS: ***Based on the structure you see, what is the difference in function of a down feather compared to a contour feather?*** The streamlining of contour feathers makes them suited for flight, while down feathers can trap air. This makes them better insulators.

Concepts in Motion

Animation

D Develop Concepts

EL BL OL AL **Activity** Using a mounted skeleton of a bird and a skeleton of a human, frog, cat, or snake, point out the large size of the sternum of the bird in comparison to the rest of its body as opposed to that of the other skeleton. Also, point out that bird bones are very thin but structurally strong.

Develop Concepts

BL OL AL **Activity** Have students make a flipbook that simulates a bird's wing in flight. Tell them to cut eight 3" × 5" index cards in half and draw a sequence of a bird in flight on the 16 cards. Have them place the cards in sequence and staple them on one side so that when they flip them quickly they see the sequence of a wing flapping.

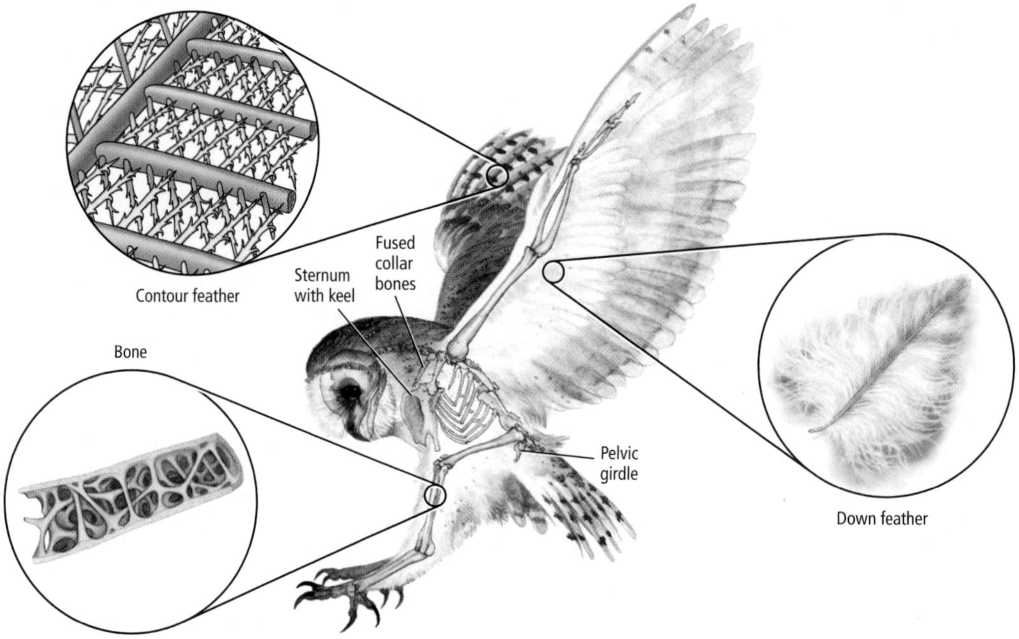

Figure 15 Birds have contour feathers, down feathers, and lightweight bones.

Concepts in Motion

Animation

VOCABULARY

SCIENCE USAGE V. COMMON USAGE

Preen

Science usage: to maintain or repair using a bill (of a bird)

The bluejay was preening its feathers before it flew away.

Common usage: to gloat or congratulate oneself on an achievement

Jim was preening over his victory at the track meet.

Feathers that cover the body, wings, and tail of a bird are called **contour feathers.** Examine the contour feathers shown in **Figure 15.** A contour feather consists of a shaft with barbs that branch off. Barbules branch off barbs and are held together by hooks. If two adjoining barbs become separated, they can be rejoined like the teeth of a zipper. Birds repair broken links when they preen their feathers. They use their bills to preen their feathers, drawing the length of the feather through the bill to zip up broken links. Birds spend a large amount of time maintaining their feathers. Many birds have a **preen gland,** a gland located near the base of the tail that secretes oil. During preening, birds spread oil from the preen gland over their feathers, thereby adding a waterproofing coating. **Down feathers,** shown in **Figure 15,** are soft feathers located beneath contour feathers. Down feathers do not have hooks to hold barbs together. As a result, the looser structure of down feathers can trap air that acts as insulation. C

Lightweight bones Another adaptation of birds that allows flight is their strong, lightweight skeletons. The bones of birds are unique because they contain cavities of air. **Figure 15** shows the internal structure of a bird bone. Despite the fact that the bones are filled with air, they are still strong.

Have you ever found the wishbone in a piece of chicken or turkey? The wishbone is formed from fused collarbones, as shown in **Figure 15.** Fusion of bones in the skeleton of a bird makes the skeleton sturdier, another adaptation for flight. Large breast muscles, which can make up 30 percent of a bird's total weight, provide the power for flight. These muscles connect the wing to the breastbone, called the **sternum** (STUR num), also shown in **Figure 15.** The sternum is large and has a keel to which the muscles attach. D

Content Background

Teacher FYI Wings of birds provide propulsion and lift and are adapted to different habitat conditions. Broad elliptical wings provide maneuverability in forested habitats for birds such as chickadees and sparrows. High-speed wings sweep back with pointed wing tips that are aerodynamically suited to high-speed flight. Birds that feed on insects during flight, such as swallows, or birds that migrate long distances, benefit from this type of wing. Most soaring wings are long and narrow, adapted for high lift. Albatrosses that live over the sea have this type of wing.

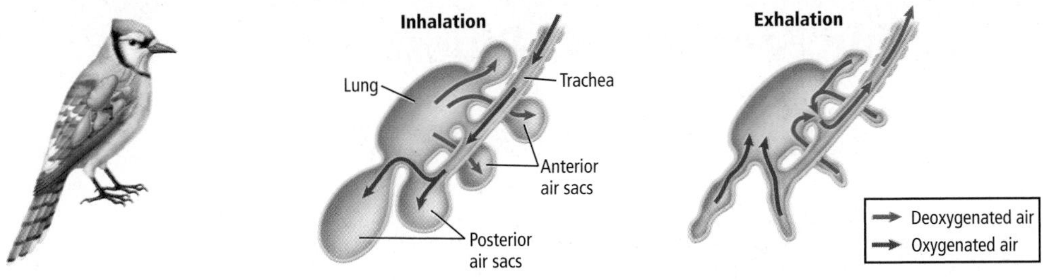

■ **Figure 16** When a bird breathes, air always flows in a single direction, and highly efficient gas exchange can be achieved.

R **Respiration** Flight muscles use a large amount of oxygen, and the respiratory systems of birds are well-adapted to provide it. Not only do birds have much more space for air in their respiratory system than reptiles, but birds also have one-way air circulation. When a bird inhales, oxygenated air moves through the trachea into posterior **air sacs,** shown in **Figure 16.** Other air already within the respiratory system is drawn out of the lungs, where gas exchange occurs, and into the anterior air sacs. When a bird exhales, the deoxygenated air in the anterior air sacs is expelled from the respiratory system and oxygenated air from the posterior air sacs is sent to the lungs. The net result is that only oxygenated air is moved through the lungs, and it is moved in a single direction relative to blood flow. D

Circulation A bird's circulatory system also helps it maintain high levels of energy by efficient delivery of oxygenated blood to the body. Recall that crocodiles are the only reptiles to have a heart ventricle completely divided by a septum. Birds also have a four-chambered heart, as shown in **Figure 17.** Having two ventricles keeps the oxygenated and deoxygenated blood separated and makes delivery of oxygenated blood more efficient. The left atrium receives blood from the lungs. This blood is pumped into the left ventricle and out to the body. Blood returning from the body is delivered to the right atrium, then moves into the right ventricle and on to the lungs, where it will pick up more oxygen.

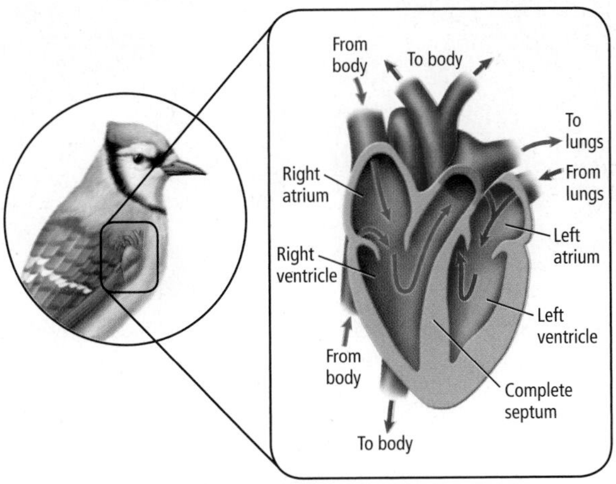

■ **Figure 17** Birds have a four-chambered heart that keeps oxygenated and deoxygenated blood separate.
Compare ***the heart of a bird to that of the reptile shown in Figure 4.***

R Reading Strategy

BL OL Active Comprehension
Have a student volunteer read aloud the text below the heading *Respiration.*
ASK STUDENTS: ***What more would you like to know about bird respiration?*** Answers will vary. Write student questions on the board.
AL Have students research answers to the class's questions.

D Develop Concepts

BL OL AL Scaffolding
ASK STUDENTS: ***When you breathe, does air go in and out through the same pathway?*** yes ***Do your lungs get oxygen when you breathe out or when you breathe in?*** when you breathe in ***When a bird breathes in, where does the air go, including the oxygen-depleted air?*** Entering air goes into the posterior air sacs, and oxygen-depleted air into the anterior air sacs. ***What happens to the air in a bird's body when the bird breathes out?*** Air in the posterior air sacs moves to the lungs, and air in the anterior air sacs moves out of the bird. ***What advantage is there to this system compared to the human system of respiration?*** Only oxygen-rich air is in the bird's lungs, making oxygen extraction very efficient. ***Infer why this system of respiration evolved in birds.*** Birds need a great deal of energy to maintain the high level of endothermic metabolism required for flight.

Content Background

Teacher FYI When birds migrate, they generally travel the same routes each year. Birds generally fly north, where they breed and raise young. They fly south to feed in the winter. Birds that summer in the far north, such as the high Arctic, go south to the northern United States in the winter. The stimulus for bird migration might be the change in day length. The change in the number of hours of light causes a series of physiological changes that stimulate migratory behavior. Some birds travel extraordinary distances. For example, a bobolink commutes 22,500 km between its breeding grounds in North America and its winter range in Argentina. The circulatory and respiratory systems of birds are adapted to these long flights.

■ **Caption Question Fig. 17**
The bird's heart has a divided ventricle, which keeps oxygenated blood separated from deoxygenated blood. This system is more efficient in delivering oxygen to the body and results in the availability of higher levels of energy.

Visualizing Feeding and Digestion

Purpose
Students will study the organs in the digestive system of a bird. UPC.1, UPC.5, C.5

Concepts in Motion
Animation

Skill Practice
EL BL OL AL
Observe and Infer
SAY TO STUDENTS: ***Obtain a large plastic milk carton and cut a large hole in one side. Place birdseed in the bottle and hang it with wire in a tree. Observe and use a field guide to identify which birds come to your feeder. Use a different seed each week, to see if you attract different birds with each type of seed.*** Students' observations will vary. Sunflower seeds attract a large variety of birds. Mourning doves are attracted to millet. Students might observe jays, nuthatches, juncos, chickadees, sparrows, finches, cardinals, and a variety of other birds, depending on where they live.

Writing Support
OL AL **Formal Writing** Have students research one of the capture/release programs for birds and write a news article about how it was accomplished and about its success or lack of success. Students could write about the success of the whooping crane, California condor, peregrine falcon, or others.

Visualizing Feeding and Digestion

Figure 18
Examine the organs in the digestive system of a bird. Aside from having unique adaptations to their digestive systems, birds have beaks that are adapted to the type of food they eat.

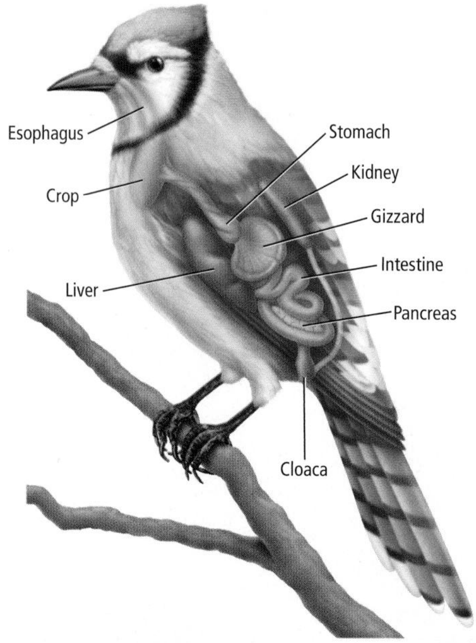

Herons use their long, thin, sharp bills to stab and capture fish and small amphibians as prey.

Hummingbirds have long, thin beaks shaped for drinking nectar from flowers.

An eagle uses its sharp beak to tear flesh from its prey.

A pelican uses its beak to scoop fish out of the water.

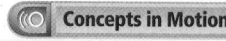

Concepts in Motion Animation

Demonstration
EL BL OL AL **Bird Diet** Bring in the following items: nutcracker, straw, meat hook, vise, large net, basket, strainer, chisel, hammer, tweezers, toothpick, key-type can opener, tongs, spatula. Use these items as models of a bird's beak. Hold up each of the items one at a time and ask the following:
ASK STUDENTS: ***What type of food would a bird eat if it had a beak like these tools?*** Answers will vary. Examples include sipping nectar with the straw, breaking nuts with the nutcracker, and opening bivalve mollusks with the can opener. If time permits, provide students with field guides to birds and have them find actual birds with beaks that might be like each of the models. Est. time: 20 min

Feeding and digestion Birds require large amounts of food to maintain their high metabolic rate. Once they have taken in food, birds process it with unique adaptations of their digestive systems, shown in **Figure 18.** Many birds have a storage chamber, called the crop, at the base of their esophagus. The crop stores food that the bird is ingesting. From the crop, food moves to the stomach. The posterior end of the stomach is a thick, muscular sac called the gizzard (GIH zurd). The gizzard often contains small stones that, together with the muscular action of the gizzard, crush food the birds have swallowed. The smaller food particles that result are easier to digest. Birds have no teeth and cannot chew their food. Digestion and absorption of food occurs primarily in the small intestine, where secretions from the pancreas and liver aid the digestive process.

Excretion As in reptiles, bird kidneys filter wastes from the blood and convert it to uric acid. Birds also have a cloaca, shown in **Figure 18,** where the water is reabsorbed from the uric acid. Birds do not have urinary bladders to store urine. Stored urine would add weight during flight, so having no urinary bladder can be considered an adaptation for flight. Birds excrete uric acid in the form of a white, pasty substance.

The brain and senses The brain of a bird, shown in **Figure 19,** is large compared to the body size of the bird. The cerebellum is large because birds need to coordinate movement and balance during flight. The optic lobes coordinate visual input. The core of the cerebrum also is large because it is the primary integrating center of the brain. This area of the brain controls eating, singing, flying, and instinctive behavior. The medulla oblongata controls automatic functions such as respiration and heartbeat.

Birds generally have excellent vision. Birds of prey, such as the hawk shown in **Figure 19,** have a focusing system that instantaneously enables them to stay focused on moving prey as they make a dive for their food. The position of a bird's eyes on its head relates to its life habits. Birds of prey have eyes that are at the front of the head. This enables them to recognize the distance of an object because both eyes can focus on the object. A pigeon has eyes on the sides of its head. This enables
C the bird to see nearly 360 degrees of the space nearby, with each eye focusing on different areas. A pigeon eats grain and seeds and does not pursue prey. Its eyesight is adapted to scout out predators that might be nearby. Birds also have a good sense of hearing. Owls can hear the faintest sound of a scurrying mouse in the night. Even as the mouse runs for cover, the owl can catch it by following just the sound.

FOLDABLES®
Incorporate information from this section into your Foldable.

? Inquiry Launch Lab
Review Based on what you have read about reptiles and birds, how would you now answer the analysis questions?

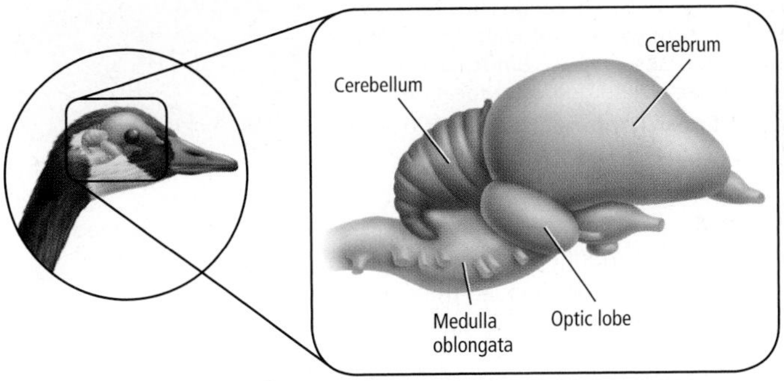

Figure 19
Left: Birds have large cerebellums that enable them to balance and coordinate movements. The medulla oblongata controls automatic processes.
Right: A hawk's eyes stay focused on moving prey as it dives.

FOLDABLES®

RUBRIC A rubric for evaluating Foldables is found on your eTeacherEdition Online.

Going Further Have students draw a large Venn diagram on the back of their Foldable, and use it to compare and contrast bird eggs and reptile eggs. Have them indicate whether the eggs are similar or different and give reasons for their answers.

? Inquiry Launch Lab

Assess Content Development
Assess how understanding has developed when students revisit the Launch Lab analysis questions.

Develop Concepts
EL BL OL AL COOP LEARN

Activity Organize students into groups of three and provide a sterile owl pellet, paper plate, tweezers, rubber gloves, and a ruler to each group. Have one student handle the owl pellet while the others write down information. Sterile owl pellets are available from biological supply houses.

SAY TO STUDENTS: ***After measuring your owl pellet, carefully tear it apart and look for bones of an animal inside the pellet. Take the bones and reconstruct the animal to determine what type of animal the owl ate and regurgitated.***
Answers will depend on the contents of the owl pellet.

Demonstration

BL OL AL **Birds' Eyes** Obtain mounted specimens of birds. You might be able to borrow them from local nature centers, museums, or taxidermy shops. Show birds of prey, such as owls, that have eyes at the front of their heads and binocular vision that aids in hunting prey. Show other birds, such as pigeons, that have eyes on the sides of their heads that enable them to be on the lookout for potential predators in a wide field of view. Est. time: 15 min

C Critical Thinking
BL OL **Infer**

ASK STUDENTS: ***If you saw a bird with eyes in the front of its head, would you infer that it is a predator or a herbivore? Why?***
a predator, because predators must be able to see potential prey from a distance and estimate how far away the prey is

Develop Concepts

BL OL AL

Clarify a Misconception

ASK STUDENTS: ***Have you ever eaten like a bird? What does that phrase mean?*** Students might think that eating like a bird means a person doesn't eat very much. Point out that the intended meaning behind the expression "to eat like a bird" is inaccurate. Some birds eat the equivalent or more of their body weight in a short period of time.

MiniLab 1

Inquiry MiniLab

For a lab worksheet, use your eTeacherEdition Online.

RUBRIC A rubric for evaluating MiniLabs is found on your eTeacherEdition Online.

Est. Time 20 min

Safety Precaution Approve lab safety forms before work begins.

Teaching Strategies

- Use tapes of bird songs to help attract more birds for identification.
- Have students work with a partner for ease of identification and for safety in the neighborhood.
- Compile student data into a class data table.

Analysis

1. Number of species will probably be 5-10.
2. Most birds will probably be native.
3. Students will probably observe the same species.
4. Answers will depend on your region. In most cases, the species living near homes will differ from those living near commercial buildings.

LabManager™

Customize this lab with the LabManager™ CD-ROM.

Reproduction The reproductive activities of birds are complex. They include establishing territories, locating mates, courtship behavior, mating, constructing nests, incubating eggs, and feeding young. During breeding season, many birds gather in large colonies where they breed and take care of young. All birds have internal fertilization. Generally, after fertilization, the amniotic egg develops and is encased within a hard shell while still within the body of the female. After the shell forms, the egg or eggs are released through the cloaca to a nest, where the male or female or both birds incubate the egg or eggs and feed the young after hatching. To **incubate** means to maintain favorable conditions for hatching. Birds sit on their eggs to incubate them.

Diversity of Modern Birds

Modern birds are divided into about 27 orders, depending on the classification system used. Anatomical differences, specific behaviors, songs, and the habitats occupied distinguish the orders. In **Table 1,** you will study the most common orders of birds and their adaptations. The largest order of birds is the Passeriformes, which often are called perching birds or songbirds. There are more than 5000 species in order Passeriformes. Flightless birds, including ostriches, emus, and kiwis, have reduced or no wings. The kiwi, a bird about the size of a chicken found in New Zealand, lays an egg that is extremely large given the size of the bird. Some birds, such as penguins, geese, and ducks, have adaptations that allow them to swim. Penguins use their wings as paddles to swim through the water. Ducks and geese have webbed feet.

MiniLab 1

Inquiry MiniLab

Survey Local Birds

What birds live in your local area? A variety of birds can be found in almost any environment. Explore the area around your school to survey the different birds that live there.

Procedure

1. Read and complete the lab safety form.
2. Predict the number of different kinds of birds you can observe in the area around your school. Make a data table to keep track of birds that you observe.
3. Go for a 10-min walk in the area near your school. Be sure to follow your teacher's instructions about where you are allowed to go. Record information about the birds that you observe. Use **binoculars** if necessary. If you cannot identify a bird, use a **field guide** for local birds.
4. Compile your findings as a class. Research information about the birds that you observed.

Analysis

1. **Count** the number of bird species that you observed. List the types of birds that you observed.
2. **Identify** Were the birds you saw native to your area or have they been introduced?
3. **Analyze** whether any patterns emerged as you compiled the data.
4. **Predict** Would this list differ if you surveyed the area around your home? If so, how?

Activity

BL OL AL COOP LEARN

Birds in the School Yard Divide students into groups of three. Have students make a map of the school grounds and research how the habitat of the grounds could be improved for local birds. Have students add these features to their map and present their ideas to the rest of the class. Est. time: 30 min

Table 1	Diversity of Bird Orders		S Concepts in Motion Interactive Table
Order	**Example**	**Members**	**Distinguishing Characteristics**
Passeriformes Perching song-birds; about 5000 species		Thrushes, warblers, mockingbirds, crows, blue jays, nuthatches, finches	Members of this order have feet that are adapted to perching on thin stems and twigs. Many birds in this order sing. The vocal organ, called the syrinx, is well-developed in these birds. Other species, such as crows and ravens, do not sing.
Piciformes Cavity-nesters; about 380 species		Woodpeckers, toucans, honeyguides, jacamars, puffbirds	Members of this order have highly specialized bills that are related to their feeding habits. They all build nests in cavities—for example, a hole in a dead tree. The feet have two toes that extend forward and two toes that extend backward, allowing them to cling to tree trunks.
Ciconiiformes Wading birds and vultures; about 90 species		Herons, egrets, bitterns, storks, flamingoes, ibises, vultures	Members of this order are medium- to large-sized birds that have long necks and long legs. Most are wading birds that live in large colonies in wetlands. Vultures are closely related to storks but are detritovores.
Procellariiformes Marine birds; about 100 species		Albatrosses, petrels, shearwaters, storm-petrels	All members of this order are marine birds. They have hooked beaks that aid in feeding on fish, squid, and small crustaceans. They all have tube-shaped nostrils located on the top of their beaks. Many have webbed feet.
Sphenisciformes Penguins; about 17 species		Penguins	Penguins are marine birds that use their wings as flippers to swim through the water rather than fly. The bones of penguins are solid, lacking the air spaces of other birds. All species are found in the southern hemisphere.
Strigiformes Owls; about 135 species		Owls	Owls are nocturnal birds with large eyes, strong, hooked beaks, and large, sharp talons on their feet. All of these adaptations aid in capturing prey. Many species have feathers on their legs. Owls are found worldwide except for Antarctica.
Struthioniformes Flightless birds; 10 species		Ostriches, kiwis, cassowaries, emus, rheas	All members of this order have reduced wings and are flightless birds. The ostrich is the largest living bird, reaching a height of more than 2 m and a weight of 130 kg. All species are found in the southern hemisphere.
Anseriformes Waterfowl; about 150 species		Swans, geese, ducks	Members of this order live in aquatic environments. They have webbed feet that aid in moving them through the water. Many have broad, round beaks. They feed on aquatic plants and sometimes crustaceans or small fish.

Demonstration

BL OL AL Bird Feet Show students a slideshow of various birds' feet. Have students identify which are climbers, graspers, swimmers, runners, perchers, or predators.

ASK STUDENTS: ***What is your justification for your answer?*** Accept all answers that make scientific sense.

Est. time: 15 min

Activity

BL OL AL COOP LEARN

Birdwatching Take the class to the school grounds or a nearby field, marsh, or forest and invite a local bird expert to help in identifying birds by their songs and using field guides. Organize students into teams and provide each team with a field guide to local birds and one pair of binoculars per team. Est. time: 30 min

Concepts in Motion

Interactive Table

S Skill Practice

BL OL AL Visual Literacy

SAY TO STUDENTS: ***Summarize the similarities you observe in the birds pictured in Table 1. Select two characteristics of one of the birds pictured and explain how they are adaptations to their way of life.*** Possible answers: All have feathers, beaks, two eyes, two legs, wings. Songbirds have grasping feet for perching and beaks adapted to their food source. Woodpeckers have beaks adapted to getting insects from trees and feet adapted to clinging to tree bark. Wading birds have long legs that keep their bodies out of the water and beaks adapted to their food source. Marine birds have large strong wings for continual soaring and beaks that can capture fishes on the fly.

Develop Concepts

BL OL AL COOP LEARN

Activity Obtain information from the Internet about the Audubon Christmas Bird Count in your area. Provide this information to students in the form of a handout. Organize students into teams and have the teams participate in the Audubon Christmas Bird Count. Instruct teams to use a field guide to help identify birds. Have the teams follow the instructions on the handout and report to the class on the kinds and numbers of birds the team saw. Answers will depend on your area. Those in the Northeast might find cardinals and chickadees, while those in the Southeast might see Canada geese and great blue herons. Those in the Midwest might see finches, and those in the West might see magpies.

S Skill Practice

BL Visual Literacy Help students relate the words in the text to an illustration. Have them examine Figure 20. Call on one student to read the first paragraph under the heading *Feathered dinosaurs.* As the paragraph is read aloud, point out the features described in the illustration.

Critical Thinking

BL OL AL Infer

ASK STUDENTS: ***Infer why, in general, birds did not evolve poisonous venom as many snakes did.*** Birds can easily escape predators by flying and evolved other mechanisms for getting food. For example, specialized beaks of predators can capture and tear apart prey.

W Writing Support

BL OL AL Narrative Writing

Have students research how the feathered dinosaurs were discovered in the Chinese fossil beds and write a description about the details of the discovery. Students could write about the immense numbers of fossils that have been found in this area, how the initial lack of government regulations created problems, and about additional feathered dinosaur discoveries.

Inquiry BioLab

The lab at the end of the chapter can be used at this point in the lesson.

Archaeopteryx

Caudipteryx

■ **Figure 20** *Archaeopteryx* had a long, reptilelike tail, clawed fingers, teeth, and feathers. This artist's rendering of *Caudipteryx* shows long feathers that might have been used for insulation and balance.

S

Evolution of Birds

Fossil evidence shows that birds descended from archosaurs, the same line from which crocodiles and dinosaurs evolved, as you saw in **Figure 11.** Similarities between birds and reptiles are apparent. They have similar skeletal features, kidney and liver function, amniotic eggs, and behaviors such as nesting and caring for young.

Feathered dinosaurs Three different species of birdlike dinosaurs from Chinese fossil beds have been carefully studied. *Sinosauropteryx* had a coat of downy, featherlike fibers. *Protoarchaeopteryx* and *Caudipteryx,* illustrated in **Figure 20,** had long feathers on their front appendages and on their tails. The downy dinosaur feathers might have functioned as insulation, and the front appendage feathers might have served as balancing devices as the dinosaurs ran along the ground.

Connection to History In 1861, in southern Germany, paleontologist Hermann von Meyer discovered what is now known to be the oldest bird fossil—*Archaeopteryx. Archaeopteryx,* illustrated in **Figure 20,** lived about 150 million years ago. This ancient bird had a long reptilelike tail, clawed fingers in the wings, and teeth. These are features that modern birds do not have. Yet, like modern birds, its body was covered with feathers. The feathers were asymmetrical, like those found only in modern birds that fly. Recent fossil evidence also shows that the brain of *Archeopteryx* was much like that of modern birds. W

Recent discoveries In 2006, a new fossil bird, *Gansus yumenensis,* was discovered. It lived 110 mya and might be the link between *Archaeopteryx* and modern birds. *Gansus* had webbed feet, leading some scientists to think that modern birds evolved from aquatic birds. Scientists say that *Gansus* likely would have looked a lot like a modern duck.

CAREERS IN BIOLOGY

Paleontologist Scientists who learn more about the history of life on Earth by studying fossils are paleontologists. Many paleontologists teach at colleges and conduct research in the field by uncovering fossils. Some work at museums, managing fossil exhibits.

Content Background

Teacher FYI Birds are appreciated by many people, including bird watchers and naturalists. Birds are the subject of symbols, myth, art, poetry, sport, music, and science. Yet birds can also cause problems for people. For example, they damage crops and carry diseases such as West Nile virus and bird flu.

Demonstration

Fossil Birds Show students images of early bird fossils. Show artists' renditions of *Sinornis* and *Eoalulavis.* In addition, show birdlike feathered dinosaurs. Point out birdlike features and reptile-like features. Est. time: 15 min

Ecology of Birds

Birds are important parts of food chains as predators of small mammals, arthropods, and other invertebrates. For example, you probably have seen a robin pulling a worm out of the ground. Birds are also important parts of food chains and food webs as prey of larger birds and mammals.

Birds play an important role in the dispersal of seeds. Birds eat seeds or fruits and berries, and, after digestion, eliminate them in a different location. Seeds also get caught on the feathers and drop off as birds move from one location to another. Some birds, such as hummingbirds, feed on the nectar of flowers and pollinate the flowers as they feed.

Habitat destruction Many birds are threatened with extinction as the habitat they require either disappears or is degraded by pesticides and other chemical pollutants. Waterfowl populations depend on wetlands—a habitat that is disappearing rapidly as wetlands are drained for development. Deforestation of tropical rain forests has also led to some species of birds being endangered.

Illegal trade Illegal pet-bird trade is increasing. Many pet birds are raised in captivity, but other exotic birds are taken from the wild in a multibillion dollar industry. In some cases, illegal capture has led to the disappearance of rare birds in the wild. The little blue macaw, shown in **Figure 21,** exists only in captivity. An international trade agreement was enacted in 1975 to ensure that the buying and selling of wild animals does not endanger their survival. Currently, 160 countries participate in the agreement; however, illegal wildlife trade continues.

Figure 21 There are no little blue macaws left in the wild. Only about 70 of these birds remain in captivity.

Formative Assessment

Evaluation Have students use their book to write three questions about bird adaptations and exchange them with a partner. Tell students that their questions must deal with main ideas under a heading rather than minute details. Have students answer their partners' questions without looking at their books. Tell students to check with their partner to see if their answers are correct. Answers will vary. Questions may be about bird adaptations for flight, feeding, digestion, excretion, reproduction, or other topics.

Remediation Have students make a list of bird adaptations for each heading in this section, beginning with the heading *Endotherms* and ending with the heading *Reproduction.* For each adaptation, have students describe how the adaptation helps the bird survive. Examples of answers: Endothermy, higher metabolic rate aids flight; feathers aid flight and prevent body-heat loss; lightweight bones aid flight; sternum aids flight; air sacs provide more efficient oxygen delivery; four-chambered heart provides high levels of oxygen to cells to maintain energy for flight.

Section 2 Assessment

Section Summary

- Birds have characteristics that make them well-adapted for flight.
- The shape of a bird's beak is related to the type of food it eats.
- Birds generally have excellent vision.
- Birds belong to about 27 orders.
- Modern birds evolved from dinosaurs.
- Habitat destruction and illegal trade can negatively affect some species of birds.

Understand Main Ideas

1. MAIN Idea **Identify** the characteristics of birds that make them adapted for flight.
2. **Compare and contrast** contour feathers and down feathers.
3. **Explain** how respiration and circulation in birds are adapted for flight.
4. **Compare and contrast** reproduction in birds and reptiles.
5. **Describe** how the characteristics of birds in order Strigiformes are different from those of birds in order Anseriformes.
6. **Describe** how scientists have been able to conclude that birds evolved from dinosaurs.

Think Critically

7. **Scientific Illustrations** Draw and label the parts of a bird's brain. Explain the function of the different parts of the brain.

WRITING in **Biology**

8. Most small land birds that feed their young lay from 2 to 12 eggs in their nests. Some larger birds, such as waterfowl, have young that are able to care for themselves after hatching and are not fed by parents. These birds lay up to 20 eggs in their nests. Write a detailed hypothesis that explains why some bird species might lay fewer eggs than other species do.

Section 2 Assessment

1. feathers, wings, lightweight bones
2. Contour feathers are on the outside of the bird, consist of barbs and hooks, and keep water away from the body. Down feathers are soft, found under contour feathers, and help generate and hold warmth.
3. The respiratory system is a one-way loop. Oxygen is more efficiently moved into the bloodstream, enabling birds to have more energy available for flight muscles.
4. Birds and most reptiles lay amniotic eggs, but bird eggs are hard, whereas reptile eggs are leathery.
5. Strigiformes—nocturnal, large eyes, hooked beaks, sharp talons; Anseriformes—webbed feet, round beaks
6. Fossil evidence shows that some dinosaurs had feathers and other skeletal structures that are similar to birds.
7. cerebellum—movement and balance; optic lobes—visual input; core of cerebrum—integrating center of the brain; cerebral cortex—intelligence
8. Answers will vary. Accept all that have a scientific basis.

Purpose

Students will explain how invasive species impact a native environment and differentiate between invasive and noninvasive species. UCP.4, F.3

Anticipatory Guide

ASK STUDENTS: ***When I say the words* invasive species, *what comes to mind?*** Student responses will vary. Some students might have heard of invasive species before and could respond that they are organisms that choke out, devour, and destroy native wildlife and their habitat. ***Do you know of any invasive species that exist in our area?*** Some students who work at nurseries, have forestry backgrounds, live on farms, or have a background in biology may know of some invasive species from your area. ***What do you think the term* biological pollution *means?*** *Biological pollution* is another term for invasive species. Burmese pythons, African clawed frogs, and honeysuckle plants are all invasive species.

Background

One of the first recorded invasive species in America occurred in 1868 with garlic mustard, *Alliaria petiolata,* found in Long Island. This European invasive species is a low-growing weed living in wooded areas that prevents biodiversity by invading the understory of forests.

Biology & Society

Invasive Species Run Wild

What happens when pet owners buy infant Burmese pythons and then decide when the pythons grow to be 4–5 m long that they no longer can care for them? Scientists have discovered that pet owners are dumping these large snakes in the Everglades. In the Everglades, Burmese pythons now are considered an invasive species that is causing increasing problems in the area. Other invasive species cause similar problems for their host environments around the country.

What are invasive species? Invasive species are organisms that are introduced, by human action, to an area where they do not naturally live and where they do not naturally breed. They successfully breed, become pests in the new area, and threaten biodiversity. The Burmese python is just one of thousands of nonnative species that are now in the United States. The rooting of feral pigs, which have spread throughout Florida, is destructive to native vegetation and the nests of sea turtles. Officials actively have been removing feral pigs from Florida state parks in an effort to reduce their impact. The image to the right shows a feral pig.

What are the costs of invasive species? Invasive species can cause billions of dollars of damage annually to crops, rangelands, and waterways throughout the United States. The presence of invasive species is the second-leading cause of species endangerment and extinction. Invasive plant species can threaten bird populations by causing habitat loss at their breeding or wintering grounds. Invasive animal species prey on animals native to an area. Competing for space and prey is another major way in which invasive species overrun the native species.

Solutions Invasive species can be controlled through various methods, including legislation such as the National Invasive Species Act established in 1996. Research is ongoing by scientists who are constantly examining invasive species to understand methods to control their spread, life cycle, and behavior. Public education can provide people with knowledge to make informed decisions to vote on important policies. Legislation related to environmental issues also can help improve situations involving invasive species.

Feral pigs have been removed from Florida State Parks since 1993.

COMMUNITY INVOLVEMENT

Lesson Plan Develop a lesson plan about an invasive species of your choice that is affecting your state. The lesson plan should be geared toward the elementary school children in your district. Be sure that you involve the elementary students in an activity.

Discussion

After the students conduct their lesson plans with the elementary students, ask them what kinds of questions the elementary children asked. What were the reactions of the children to the lessons? How did teaching the lesson help their own understanding of invasive species? Did they find that by teaching about invasive species they learned even more about them? What additional questions do they have about invasive species as a result of teaching about them?

WebQuest

BIOLAB

Design Your Own

HOW CAN YOU MODEL A HABITAT FOR REPTILES AND BIRDS?

Background: Your class has been asked to help plan a new zoo exhibit about adaptations in birds and reptiles. In this lab, you will research a variety of birds and reptiles to understand how their body structures are adapted to habitats and food sources. You will use this information to help make a model habitat in which reptiles and birds would live in the zoo.

Question: *How can you make a model habitat based on what you know about an organism's adaptations to its environment?*

Materials

field guides for birds and reptiles
sand
soil
cardboard pieces
cardboard box
wooden sticks
toothpicks
glue
scissors
colored markers
dried beans
rocks/pebbles
felt pieces

Safety Precautions

Plan and Perform the Experiment

1. Read and complete the lab safety form.
2. Choose one reptile species and one bird species. Research the adaptations of each species. Find out information about the habitat in which they live, the food they eat, and their behavior. Examine how their body structures and behaviors give them a competitive advantage in the habitats in which they live.
3. Use the information you collected to make a detailed description of the habitat that should be set up in the exhibit for each reptile and bird that you investigated.
4. Make sure your teacher approves your plan before you proceed.
5. Use the materials available to make a model habitat for the reptile species and a model habitat for the bird species that they would live in at the zoo.
6. Present and explain your models to the class.

Analyze and Conclude

1. **Describe** how the differences between reptiles and birds lead to differences in the models you made for each habitat.
2. **Identify** any weaknesses in your model. Would your model habitats support the needs of each species? What changes would you make to your model?
3. **Describe** how the structures and behaviors of the organisms give them a competitive advantage in their habitat.

WRITING in Biology

Take-Home Pamphlet Write and illustrate a pamphlet that people visiting your exhibit could take home. Include informational text about the animals in the exhibit as well as illustrations of their natural habitats.

Analyze and Conclude

1. Answers will vary, but could include the difference between how reptiles and birds move, how they mate and reproduce, what they eat, and how they regulate internal body temperature.
2. Answers will vary, but should focus on some aspect of the model that does not meet the needs of the animals.
3. Answers will vary, depending on the species studied, but may include that animals are good at finding or capturing food or that they are successful at reproduction and offspring are equipped to survive until maturity.

WRITING in Biology

RUBRIC Use the modifiable rubric found on your eTeacherEdition to assess writing assignments.

BIOLAB

Design Your Own

Inquiry BioLab

For a lab worksheet, use your eTeacherEdition.

RUBRIC A rubric for evaluating BioLabs is found on your eTeacherEdition.

Est. Time 45 min

Content Background In recent years, veterinarians, zoo personnel, and other scientists have realized the importance of providing an appropriate habitat for animals in the zoo. Many zoos have implemented techniques to help provide mental and physical stimulation for captive animals. These include allowing animals to search for and capture their own food; designing exhibits that allow animals to move to other areas of the zoo; and rotating exhibits to avoid having animals living in the same space day after day.

Teaching Strategy Encourage students to thoroughly research and design their exhibit, working in groups for enhanced creativity.

Alternative Teaching Demo Obtain pamphlets from the local zoo or download information from a zoo Web site about exhibits and how they are built and maintained. Discuss with students the importance of providing an appropriate habitat for captive animals. Have students choose a reptile or bird and design an exhibit for it. Have them illustrate the exhibit on paper and remind them to include the "behind-the-scenes" part of the exhibit, including how the animal is fed, how it can reproduce, and how the habitat is maintained (plants kept healthy, water, and cleaning).

Chapter 29

Study Guide

ConnectED

Students can use the following to review the chapter.

Review

Vocabulary eGames
Vocabulary eFlashcards
Vocabulary PuzzleMaker

Assessment

Online Quizzes
Online Test Practice
Standardized Test Practice

Use the *ExamView® Assessment Suite* CD-ROM to:

- create multiple versions of tests
- create modified tests with one mouse click
- edit existing questions and add your own questions
- build tests aligned with state standards using built-in state curriculum tags
- change English tests to Spanish with one mouse click
- track students' progress using the Teacher Management System

Chapter 29 Study Guide

THEME FOCUS Homeostasis Reptiles and birds both have a cloaca where water is reabsorbed from urine, which helps maintain homeostasis of water and minerals.

BIG Idea Reptile and bird adaptations enable them to live and reproduce successfully in terrestrial habitats.

Section 1 Reptiles

amnion (p. 852)
amniotic egg (p. 853)
Jacobson's organ (p. 855)
plastron (p. 857)
carapace (p. 857)

MAIN Idea Reptiles are fully adapted to life on land.

- Reptiles have several types of adaptations for life on land.
- Eggs of reptiles are adapted to development on land.
- Reptiles belong to four living orders: Squamata, Crocodilia, Testudinata, and Sphendonta.
- Modern reptiles evolved from early amniotes. Many ancient reptiles, including dinosaurs, became extinct.

Section 2 Birds

endotherm (p. 861)
feather (p. 861)
contour feather (p. 862)
preen gland (p. 862)
down feather (p. 862)
sternum (p. 862)
air sac (p. 863)
incubate (p. 866)

MAIN Idea Birds have feathers, wings, lightweight bones, and other adaptations that allow for flight.

- Birds have characteristics that make them well-adapted for flight.
- The shape of a bird's beak is related to the type of food it eats.
- Birds generally have excellent vision.
- Birds belong to about 27 living orders.
- Modern birds evolved from dinosaurs.
- Habitat destruction and illegal trade can negatively affect some species of birds.

Review Vocabulary PuzzleMaker

For additional practice with vocabulary, have students access the Vocabulary PuzzleMaker online.

Review Vocabulary eGames

Section 1

Vocabulary Review

Each of the sentences below is false. Make each sentence true by replacing the italicized word with the correct vocabulary term from the Study Guide page.

1. Several membranes are inside a(an) *carapace.*

2. The ventral part of a turtle's shell is called the *Jacobson's organ.*

3. The *plastron* is responsible for the sense of smell in snakes.

4. The dorsal part of a turtle's shell is the *amniotic egg.*

Understand Main Ideas

5. Which is not a reptile?

A.

C.

B.

D.

6. Which is not true about respiration in reptiles?
- **A.** Most reptiles use lungs for gas exchange.
- **B.** As reptiles inhale, the muscles of the rib cage relax.
- **C.** As reptiles exhale, the muscles of the body wall relax.
- **D.** The lungs of reptiles have a larger surface area than those of amphibians.

7. In which structure in reptiles can uric acid be found?
- **A.** the lungs
- **B.** the cloaca
- **C.** the heart
- **D.** the stomach

8. Which statement best represents scientists' understanding of early reptiles?
- **A.** Dinosaurs evolved into modern-day reptiles such as lizards, snakes, and turtles.
- **B.** Birds and crocodiles are the closest relatives of dinosaurs.
- **C.** The earliest reptiles did not have amniotic eggs.
- **D.** Dinosaurs became extinct because they were too big.

Constructed Response

9. MAIN Idea Make a table that lists the following structures, their functions, and an analogy of what that structure is like in the world of human-made devices: amnion, ventricle, bladder, Jacobson's organ, carapace and plastron, kidney.

10. Open Ended Make a dichotomous key that would allow a person to determine which order of reptile he or she is examining.

Think Critically

Use the figure below to answer question 11.

11. Apply Concepts The feet of a gecko are covered by billions of tiny hairlike structures that stick to surfaces. When the hairs contact a surface, attractions between molecules bond the gecko's feet to the surface. These structures can support up to 400 times the body weight of the gecko. How could scientists use the way in which a gecko's feet stick to surfaces to make a tool that would be useful to people?

Chapter 29 Assessment

Section 1

Vocabulary Review

1. amniotic egg
2. plastron
3. Jacobson's organ
4. carapace

Understand Main Ideas

5. A
6. B
7. B
8. B

Constructed Response

9. Answers will vary. Amnion: protects embryo, like bubble-wrap around a figurine being shipped; ventricle: pumps blood to body, like a bicycle pump; bladder: holds uric acid waste, like a trash can; Jacobson's organ: senses smell, like chemical detectors at crime scenes; carapace and plastron: shells that protect turtles, like a helmet; kidney: filters blood, like a coffee filter
10. Answers will vary. Make sure student keys consist of paired statements that lead to identification.

Think Critically

11. Tape could be fashioned after gecko foot pads; gloves and shoes could be made that would support human movement across ceilings and into areas that currently can't be reached except by ladders. Accept all answers that show critical-thinking skills.

12. The brown, four-fingered skink has increased in number, and the Marianas blue-tailed skink has decreased in number.

13. Answers will vary, but students might suggest that the introduced skink outcompeted the native skink.

14. They are similar, but the hearts of most reptiles need to be more powerful than the hearts of most amphibians.

15. Accept any reasonable depiction. The illustration should communicate a decrease in snake population.

Section 2

Vocabulary Review

16. Birds are endotherms, which means they generate their own heat. Down feathers trap the warm air between a bird's skin and the contour feathers.

17. Birds have both contour feathers and down feathers. Contour feathers cover most of a bird's body and are used for flight. Down feathers provide insulation.

18. A preen gland allows birds to spread oil from the gland over their contour feathers to add a waterproof coating.

19. The sternum and air sacs are both adaptations to flight. The large sternum is the attachment point for breast muscles that power flight. Air sacs are a part of the respiratory system that is a one-way loop in birds. This system enables birds to have more oxygen available for powering flight.

Understand Main Ideas

20. D
21. B
22. A
23. A
24. C

Use the graph below to answer questions 12 and 13. The brown four-fingered skink was introduced to the Pacific island of Guam in the early 1950s.

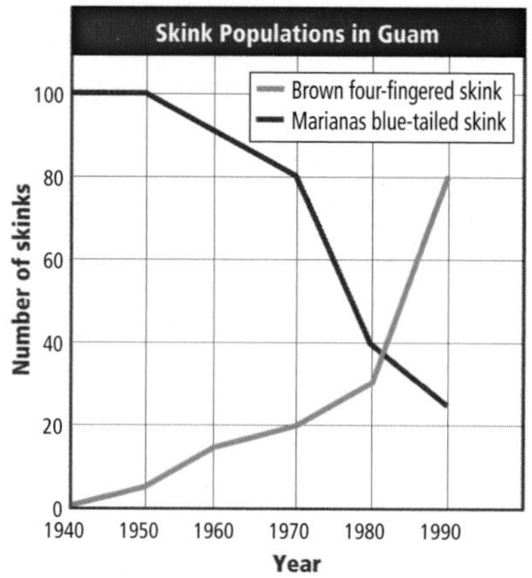

12. Analyze Data How have the populations of the brown four-fingered skink and the Marianas blue-tailed skink changed since the 1950s?

13. Hypothesize Form a detailed hypothesis that might explain the decline in population of the Marianas blue-tailed skink.

14. Compare How does circulation in reptiles compare to circulation in amphibians?

15. Illustrate Make a diagram, flowchart, concept map, or illustration that shows how the loss of habitat and the introduction of exotic species have affected the population of the San Francisco garter snake.

Section 2

Vocabulary Review

Explain the relationship that exists between the vocabulary terms in each pair.

16. endotherm, down feather

17. contour feather, down feather

18. preen gland, contour feather

19. sternum, air sac

Understand Main Ideas

20. Which group of words has a word that does not belong?
- **A.** ventricle, atrium, oxygenated blood, deoxygenated blood
- **B.** kidney, nitrogenous waste, uric acid, cloaca
- **C.** cerebellum, cerebrum, optic lobes, medulla
- **D.** amniotic egg, cloaca, kidney, amnion

Use the figure below to answer question 21.

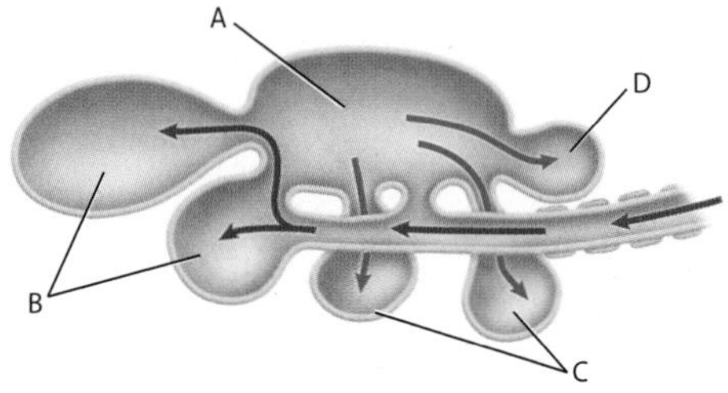

21. When a bird breathes in, oxygenated air goes into which structure(s)?
- **A.** Structure A
- **B.** Structure B
- **C.** Structure C
- **D.** Structure D

22. To which system do the kidney and cloaca belong?
- **A.** excretory
- **B.** nervous
- **C.** digestive
- **D.** reproductive

23. What type of beak would a bird need if it feeds on aquatic plants?
- **A.** broad and flat
- **B.** large and scooped
- **C.** sharp and hooked
- **D.** long, thin, and pointed

24. What does fossil evidence in dinosaurs show?
- **A.** Dinosaurs were not related to birds.
- **B.** Dinosaurs were not warm-blooded.
- **C.** Dinosaurs were not flying animals.
- **D.** Dinosaurs were not feathered.

Constructed Response

25. CAREERS IN BIOLOGY Ornithologists hypothesized that the long-term memory of certain migratory birds is better than that of nonmigrants. To test this hypothesis, two rooms were decorated differently. Food was placed in only one room. Both migrant and nonmigrant birds explored both of the rooms. One year later, the same birds were allowed to explore the rooms. Migrant birds spent significantly more time exploring the room that had contained food than the nonmigrants did. Draw a conclusion about the long-term memories of these birds.

Think Critically

26. Hypothesize Biologists have discovered that the larger a bird's eyes are, the earlier in the day it sings. Form a hypothesis about why eye size might be correlated to how early birds begin to sing.

27. THEME FOCUS Homeostasis Biologists know that the young of modern birds curl up their bodies in their nests to conserve body heat. Recently, fossils of dinosaurs' young have been found in a curled position in their nests. This particular line of dinosaurs is one with a direct lineage to birds. Infer what this curled-up position might mean about the bodies of these dinosaurs.

28. MAIN Idea Birds have many adaptations for flight. Identify three of these adaptations and explain how each contributes to making flight possible.

Use the figure below to answer question 28.

29. Infer What type of food does this bird eat? How does it use its beak during feeding?

Summative Assessment

30. BIG Idea Review the different adaptations that enable reptiles and birds to live on land. Which adaptation do you think is the most important for living on land? Support your answer scientifically.

31. WRITING in Biology Write a summary for a yearbook page about the Ornithology Club, in which students went bird watching, recorded observations of species, and conducted species counts.

DBQ Document-Based Questions

Sea snakes have highly toxic venom that they inject into prey. In many cases, the toxin paralyzes the muscles that pump water across the gills of fishes. The graph shows the rate of mortality of five species of fish when given different doses of venom from an olive sea snake.

Data obtained from: Zimmerman, K.D., et al. 1992. Survival times and resistance to sea snake *(Aipysurus laevis)* venom by five species of prey fish. *Toxicon* 30: 259–264.

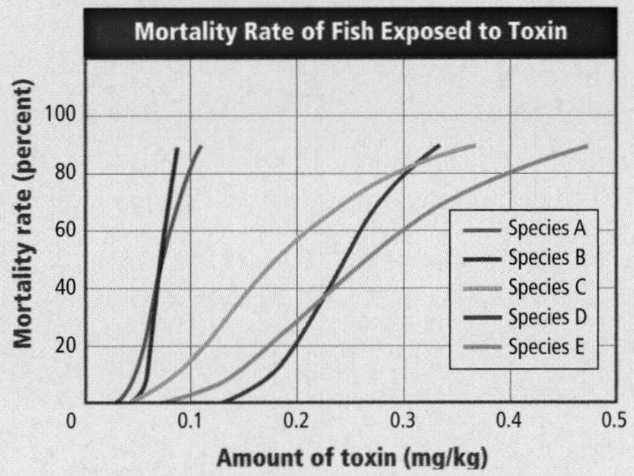

32. Which fish species is most affected by the venom? Which species is least affected? Explain how you know this.

33. The species of fish least affected by the venom have the ability to respire through their skin as well as through their gills. Why would this ability be important to surviving a bite by a sea snake?

Constructed Response

25. Migratory birds have better long-term memories. They remained in the room longer trying to find the food that had been there originally.

Think Critically

26. Larger eyes can take in more of the available light and the bird would be able to see better than a bird with smaller eyes. Because singing might attract a potential predator, it would be important that a bird be able to see the approach of a potential predator.

27. This type of dinosaur may have been warm-blooded, and curling up may have conserved body heat.

28. Possible answer: high metabolic rate associated with endothermy generates enough ATP to power flight muscles; lightweight bones are strong but do not add a lot of mass to lift; large breast muscles provide power for flight

29. meat; tearing and picking

Summative Assessment

30. Possible answer: An amniotic egg is the most important adaptation for living on land because it protects the embryo and keeps it from drying out.

31. Answers will be based on students' experience.

WRITING in Biology

✱RUBRIC Use the modifiable rubric found on your eTeacher-Edition Online to assess writing assignments.

DBQ Document-Based Questions

Zimmerman, K. D., et al. 1992. Survival times and resistance to sea snake *(Aipysurus laevis)* venom by five species of prey fish. *Toxicon* 30: 259–264.

32. Species B; Species E; Species B has the highest mortality rate with relatively low exposure and Species E has the lowest mortality rate with relatively high exposure

33. Because the venom often affects the muscles that pump water across the gills, a snake bite inhibits respiration. Fishes that can respire through their skin as well have a higher rate of survival because the snake bite does not completely inhibit their respiration.

Assessment Online Test Practice

Standardized Test Practice

Multiple Choice

1. A
2. A
3. C
4. C
5. B
6. A
7. B
8. C

Short Answer

9. The structures of the water vascular system are (1) ring canal, (2) stone canal, (3) ampulla, (4) tube foot, (5) madreporite. Sea stars use their water vascular system to move. The tube feet have suction cups that attach to a surface and the sea star pulls itself along as the muscles contract.
10. The sea star puts its arms on opposite sides of the oyster. It attaches its tube feet to the oyster's shell with suction from the water vascular system. Then the sea star contracts its muscles. The tube feet pull on opposite sides of the oyster and force the oyster to open.
11. Answers can vary. Viruses need to find a specific receptor site on the surface of a host cell that will enable them to enter the host cell. One possible reason that this might be important for research is that most kinds of viruses are limited to one, or a few kinds, of host cells.
12. The lobe-finned fishes have fins with jointed bones similar to the bones in the legs of amphibians. One of the lobe-finned fishes, the lungfish, has lungs.
13. Reptiles bask in the sun if they are cold to raise their body temperature or they cool off in the shade or burrow if they are too hot.
14. Birds have strong muscles to maintain flight. They need an efficient respiratory system to supply oxygen to their muscles.
15. The tadpole begins growing legs as its tail reduces in size. The tadpole develops lungs as it loses its gills.

Standardized Test Practice

Cumulative

Multiple Choice

1. The word *echinoderm* means "spiny skin." Which describes the skin of an echinoderm?
   A. calcium carbonate plates with spines covered with a thin skin
   B. calcium carbonate spines that protrude through the skin
   C. silicon plates with spines covering the entire surface
   D. silicon spines that protrude through the skin

Use the figure below to answer questions 2 and 3.

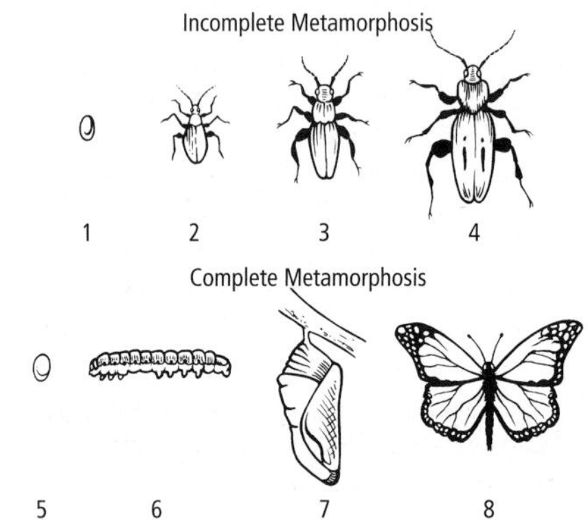

2. Which of these stages are identical in both of the processes?
   A. 1, 5
   B. 2, 7
   C. 3, 8
   D. 4, 7

3. During which stages do immature insects feed?
   A. 1, 5
   B. 1, 7
   C. 2, 6
   D. 4, 8

4. How do pseudocoelomates take in gases and excrete metabolic wastes?
   A. The digestive tract is used for gas exchange.
   B. Gas exchange occurs through the endoderm tissue.
   C. Materials diffuse through their body walls.
   D. Materials exchange in the primitive respiratory system.

5. Which is a function of the lateral line system in fishes?
   A. detecting chemicals in the water
   B. detecting water pressure changes
   C. keeping a fish upright and balanced
   D. sending signals between fishes

Use the diagram below to answer questions 6 and 7.

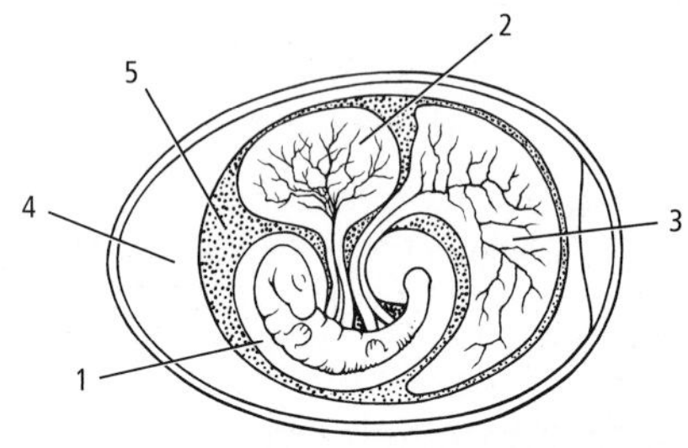

6. Which number represents the fluid-filled membrane that prevents dehydration and cushions the pictured embryo?
   A. 1
   B. 2
   C. 4
   D. 5

7. Which number represents the main food supply for the pictured developing reptile embryo?
   A. 1
   B. 2
   C. 3
   D. 4

8. Which structures are used in most adult amphibians to take in oxygen and transport it to body cells?
   A. gills and a closed circulatory system
   B. gills and an open circulatory system
   C. lungs and a closed circulatory system
   D. lungs and an open circulatory system

Short Answer

Use the diagram to answer questions 9 and 10.

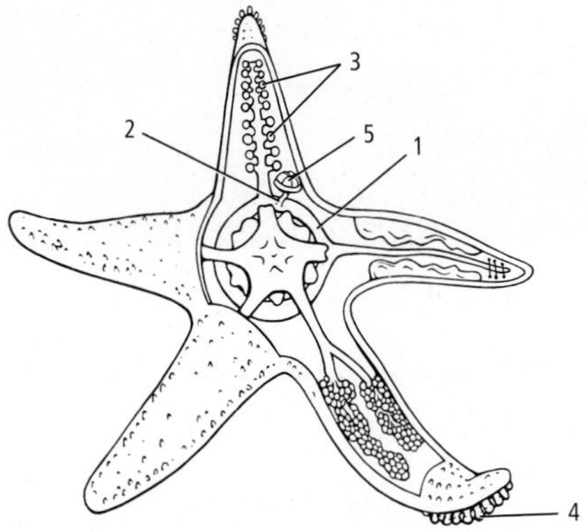

9. Name each of the numbered structures, and describe how it enables a sea star to move.

10. Analyze how a sea star opens an oyster by relating the process to the above numbered structures.

11. Give a reason why most viruses are limited to attacking only a few types of cells, and hypothesize why this might be important information for a medical researcher.

12. Relate evidence that scientists use to propose that the lobe-finned fishes are the ancestors of the amphibians.

13. Describe how reptiles regulate their body temperatures.

14. Explain why birds need an efficient respiratory system.

15. Generalize changes that a tadpole goes through before becoming a frog.

Extended Response

16. Contrast the circulatory system of a frog with the circulatory system of a fish, and assess the importance of those differences.

17. Select a technology that has changed the way in which scientists learn about genetics, and describe how that technology has brought about the change.

Essay Question

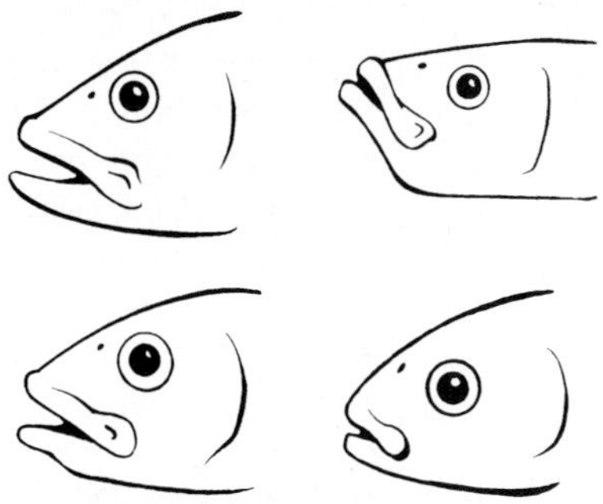

The evolution of a jaw was an important advancement in fish structure. The evolution of the jaw was a specialized adaptation for feeding. The jaw of fishes continued to evolve as fishes became more specialized in their feeding behaviors. The shape of the jaw gives important information about how a fish feeds and, in some cases, what it feeds on. By studying the different shapes of the jaw, scientists can understand how different species became adapted for their particular environments.

Using the information in the paragraph above, answer the following question in essay format.

18. Justify how each of these four types of jaws is suited for the food that fishes eat.

NEED EXTRA HELP?

If You Missed Question . . .	1	2	3	4	5	6	7	8	9	10	11	12	13	14	15	16	17	18
Review Section . . .	27.1	26.3	26.3	25.1, 25.2	28.1	29.1	29.1	28.3	27.1	27.1	18.2	28.2	29.1	29.2	28.3	28.3	13.1	28.1

Extended Response

16. A frog has a double loop circulatory system and a three-chambered heart. The double loop system passes blood to the body and separately to the lungs. That allows for the separation of oxygen-rich blood from oxygen-poor blood. In the three-chambered heart, oxygen-rich blood is partially separated from oxygen-poor blood. A fish has a single loop circulatory system and a two-chambered heart. One chamber receives the blood and the other pumps it out. A two-chambered heart is simpler than a three-chambered heart but allows the oxygen-rich and oxygen-poor blood to mix. Other answers are possible.

17. Answers can vary. The response should show an understanding of an experiment, finding, or lab technique in genetics/genomics that is possible only because of a technological development. For example, the discovery of bacteria that exist at high temperatures made it possible to find a DNA polymerase that could be used in PCR to replicate DNA rapidly. Lab replication of DNA through the process of PCR changes the way researchers can work.

Essay Question

18. Fishes with large mouths are able to eat large prey or large chunks of food. The big mouth lets the fish eat quickly. The upward pointing mouth is an advantage for fishes that eat off the surface because they can grab their food while maintaining a swimming position. An anterior mouth lets a fish catch its food while swimming because it is in a position where the fish can see it. The small mouth is well suited for nibbling plants because small bites need to be taken to aid in digesting the plants.

Chapter 30 Organizer: Mammals

LabManager™
Customize any lab with the LabManager™ CD-ROM.

Essential Questions	National Science Standards	Materials and Planning: Estimated times include cleanup and disposal, but do not include teacher prep time. For cleanup and disposal guidelines, see page 39T.	Est. Time (min)
Section 1 1. What are the characteristics of mammals? 2. How do mammals maintain a constant temperature? 3. How does respiration in mammals differ from that of other vertebrates?	UCP.1, UCP.2, UCP.5; A.1, A.2; C.4, C.5, C.6; F.1; G.1	**Launch Lab,** p. 878: specimens or photographs of mammals	15
		Demonstration, p. 880: microprojector, prepared slides of hair strands	10
		Demonstration, p. 882: fur-lined leather glove, unlined leather glove, two test tubes, hot water, thermometer	10
		MiniLab 1, p. 884: photographs or posters of mammalian skulls, prepared skulls of mammals	20
		Demonstration, p. 885: sheep or calf heart	10
		Demonstration, p. 886: preserved sheep brain or plastic model of brain	10
Section 2 1. What are the characteristics of mammals in each of the three subgroups of living mammals? 2. What are the adaptations that contribute to the diversity of mammals and enable them to live in a variety of habitats? 3. How might mammals have evolved?	UCP.1, UCP.2, UCP.4, UCP.5; C.3, C.4, C.5, C.6	**Demonstration,** p. 891: maps depicting geographic ranges of placental mammals	10
		Demonstration, p. 892: skulls of placental mammals	15
		Demonstration, p. 893: illustrations or photos of rodent skulls	10
		Demonstration, p. 894: specimens of endangered species parts	10
		Demonstration, p. 895: slideshow on endangered mammals or video from library	15
		BioLab, p. 899: North American mammal identification field guide, binoculars, field journal	90

Suggested Time for Each Lesson

Class	Chapter Opener	Section 1	Section 2	Assessment
Basic	45 min	45 min	45 min	45 min
General	25 min	100 min	55 min	45 min
Honors	—	25 min	45 min	20 min

ConnectED

connectED.mcgraw-hill.com

Access interactive learning opportunities and teaching resources using these icons located throughout your StudentWorks™ Plus Online and eTeacherEdition Online.

Chapter 30 Section Resources	Additional Chapter 30 Resources	Technology
FAST FILE Unit 8 Resources: Launch Lab Worksheet* MiniLab Worksheet* Study Guide (English/Spanish)* Section Quick Check **Reading Essentials 30.1** **Science Notebook 30.1*** **FAST FILE Unit 8 Resources:** BioLab Worksheet* Study Guide (English/Spanish)* Section Quick Check **Reading Essentials 30.2** **Science Notebook 30.2***	**FAST FILE Unit 8 Resources:** Chapter Diagnostic Test Concept Mapping* Real-World Biology Enrichment Chapter Tests A, B, and C **Transparencies:** Bellringer Transparencies* Biology Concepts Transparencies* **Lab Resources:** Laboratory Manual* Probeware Lab Manual* Forensics Lab Manual* Pre-AP Lab Manual* Open Inquiry in Biology* Guided Inquiry in Biology*	**Teaching Tools:** eTeacherEdition Online Classroom Presentation Toolkit CD-ROM* LabManager™ CD-ROM* Video Lab DVD* Virtual Lab CD-ROM* What's BIOLOGY Got To Do With It? StudentWorks™ Plus Online* **Chapter Assessment Tools:** Classroom Presentation Toolkit CD-ROM* *ExamView® Assessment Suite* CD-ROM **Web-Based Resources:** • StudentWorks™ Plus Online • eTeacherEdition Online • Animations* • The Interactive Time Line* • Interactive Tables* • Online Quizzes • Online Test Practice • Standardized Test Practice • Virtual Labs* • Multilingual eGlossary* • Vocabulary eGames* • Vocabulary eFlashcards • WebQuests • Personal Tutors

While all resources listed are appropriate for English learners, the * indicates resources with a strong visual or hands-on component for EL.

Teaching strategies and activities have been coded for differentiated instruction.

AL Activities for students working above grade level	**OL** Activities for students working on grade level	**BL** Activities for students working below grade level	**EL** Activities for English learners (also ELL)	**COOP LEARN** Activities designed for small cooperative group work

CHAPTER 30

Launch Lab
What is a mammal?

Inquiry Launch Lab

For a lab worksheet, use your eTeacherEdition Online.

RUBRIC A rubric for evaluating Launch Labs is found on your eTeacherEdition Online.

Est. Time 15 min

Safety Precaution Approve lab safety forms before work begins.

Teaching Strategies
Encourage students to consider mammals not depicted in the photographs when answering their questions and making inferences.

Procedure

1. Read and complete the lab safety form.
2. Examine **specimens or photographs of mammals**, including the red fox shown on this page.
3. Identify characteristics that the mammals in the photographs share.
4. Create a data table to record your observations.

CHAPTER 30

Mammals

ConnectED
Your one-stop online resource
connectED.mcgraw-hill.com

- Video
- Audio
- Review
- Inquiry
- WebQuest
- Assessment
- Concepts in Motion
- Multilingual eGlossary

Launch Lab
What is a mammal?

You see mammals every day—the neighborhood dog, a squirrel scampering across the grass, and the people with whom you live. What characteristics do mammals share?

For a lab worksheet, use your StudentWorks™ Plus Online.
Inquiry Launch Lab

FOLDABLES®

Make a trifold book using the titles shown. Use it to organize your notes on subgroups of mammals.

Analysis

1. **Infer** the function of each physical characteristic shared by mammals. Mammary glands provide milk to nourish developing young. Fur insulates against cold climates, preventing heat loss and enabling mammals to live in colder regions. Mammals have different types of specialized teeth designed for eating a specific diet. Sweat glands secrete fluids that evaporate and draw heat away from the body to regulate body temperature and maintain an internal homeostasis.
2. **Describe** the wide diversity of mammalian characteristics and behaviors using the photographs and your experiences with other mammals. Answers will vary. Mammals vary in size from 100 tons (whales) to a few grams (shrews). The habitats of mammals vary widely from aquatic environments to deserts to polar regions. Mammals also vary in many physical features such as teeth, limbs, and fur. They display a wide variety of behaviors.
3. **Infer** how scientists would use different characteristics to classify mammals into specific groups. Answers will vary. Different types of extremities, such as wings and flippers, are used to classify bats and aquatic mammals. Specialized teeth are used to classify carnivores and rodents. Horses, deer, hippos, and pigs are classified based on the structure of their feet. Shrews, hedgehogs, and moles are classified by what they eat.

THEME FOCUS Energy
Mammals' metabolisms need large amounts of energy to sustain their body temperatures.

BIG Idea Mammals have evolved to have many adaptations for maintaining homeostasis and living in a variety of habitats.

Section 1 • Mammalian Characteristics

Section 2 • Diversity of Mammals

THEMES

Scientific Inquiry Biologists study mammalian characteristics as a way to classify species more efficiently.

Diversity Mammal diversity exploded at the end of the Mesozoic era.

Energy The endothermic metabolisms of mammals require large amounts of energy.

Homeostasis Consistent body temperatures are maintained by the circulatory systems.

Change Mammals evolved over millions of years from early mammals, such as therapsids and cynodonts.

Introduce the Chapter

Mammalian Characteristics

Obtain animal furs from a local department of fisheries and wildlife division of education to introduce and discuss the photo.

TELL STUDENTS: ***Mammalian hair is an important adaptation of mammals.***

ASK STUDENTS: ***What does the photo show you about the hair of this fox?*** Possible answer: Foxes have more than one type of hair. ***Are the different types of hair visible in the photo?*** Answers will vary. ***Red foxes live in areas that can be very cold. Infer how thick hair might help a fox survive.*** Possible answer: Thick hair provides insulation from the cold.

BIG Idea

Outline

SAY TO STUDENTS: ***You will learn about the characteristics of mammals in Section 1. In Section 2, you will learn more details about the three subclasses of mammals. Before you begin reading, preview the chapter by making an outline based on the bold headings in the chapter. As you read the chapter, fill in details under each head in your outline.***

Sample outline:

I. Mammalian Characteristics
   A. Hair and Mammary Glands
      1. Functions of hair
      2. Structure of hair
   B. Other Characteristics
      1. Endothermy
      2. Feeding and digestion
         a. Trophic categories
         b. Ruminant herbivores
         c. Teeth
      3. Excretion
      4. Respiration
      5. Circulation

Section 1

MAIN Idea

BL OL AL

Mammalian Characteristics Provide students with photos of a variety of mammals. Outdoor and nature magazines are good sources.

ASK STUDENTS: ***What characteristics do these mammals have that the fox in the chapter opening photo has?*** Possible answers: fur, hair, teeth, eyes, ears, four legs, brain, learning ability, bear live young, feed young milk, breathe air with lungs, heart Have students group the mammals that live in similar habitats. ***What kinds of adaptations can you see in the photos that make each mammal suited to its habitat?*** Possible answers: flippers in aquatic mammals, long legs in mammals that live in prairies or savannas Students will learn that the characteristics of mammals enable them to live in a variety of habitats. The specific features of mammals, such as hair, enable them to maintain homeostasis in spite of extreme and/or changing environmental conditions.

R Reading Strategy

EL OL **SQ3R**

SAY TO STUDENTS: ***Before you read this section, Survey the section and make a list of headings. Write under each section a list of Questions related to the key headings. Next, Read the section, making notes related to your questions. Then, Recite vocabulary and Review the meanings of the words.***

Section 1

Reading Preview

Essential Questions

- What are the characteristics of mammals?
- How do mammals maintain a constant temperature?
- How does respiration in mammals differ from that of other vertebrates?

Review Vocabulary

metabolic rate: the rate at which all the chemical reactions that occur within an organism take place

New Vocabulary

mammary gland
diaphragm
cerebral cortex
cerebellum
gland
uterus
placenta
gestation

g Multilingual eGlossary

Mammalian Characteristics

MAIN Idea **Mammals have two distinct characteristics: hair and mammary glands.**

Real-World Reading Link Think about the characteristics of the other classes of vertebrates that you have studied. Think about how you are different from the animals in the other classes. The characteristics you have as a mammal allow you to carry out your daily life functions and activities.

R Mammary Glands and Hair

Two characteristics that distinguish members of class Mammalia from other vertebrate animals are mammary glands and hair. **Mammary glands** produce and secrete milk that nourishes developing young. Recall that if an animal has feathers, it is a bird. In a similar way, if an animal has hair, it is a mammal. As you can see on the evolutionary tree in **Figure 1,** mammals have their own branch labeled *hair and mammary glands.*

Functions of hair Mammals' hair has several functions, including:

1. Insulation: One of the most important functions of hair is to insulate against the cold. Mammals benefit from having fur or hair that traps their body heat and prevents it from escaping.
2. Camouflage: The striped coat of a Bengal tiger allows it to blend into its natural habitat—the jungle.
3. Sensory devices: In some cases, hair has been modified into sensitive whiskers. Seals use the whiskers on their snouts to track prey in murky water by sensing changes in water movements when a fish is nearby.
4. Waterproofing: You might know how cool it feels when you come out of a swimming pool on a hot day. As the water evaporates from your skin, your body loses heat. Many aquatic mammals, such as the sea otter shown in **Figure 2,** have hair that keeps water from reaching their skin. This helps them maintain their body temperature.

Figure 1 Hair and mammary glands are two characteristics that distinguish mammals from other vertebrates.

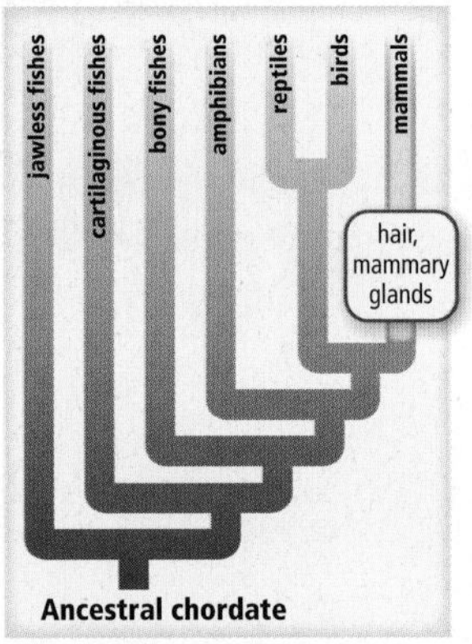

Figure 2 The hair covering this sea otter helps keep water from reaching its skin.

Content Background

Teacher FYI Most mammals shed their hair once or twice each year. For example, foxes shed their coat each summer. Weasels shed in the spring and fall. Summer coats are generally thinner and might be a different color. Snowshoe hares, for example, have a white coat in the winter and a brown coat in the summer.

Demonstration

Hair Using a microprojector, show prepared slides of the cuticle, cortex, and medulla of a strand of hair. You can also show hair from a variety of mammals. You might be able to obtain hair from a local zoo and mount it in glycerin on slides. Very thin hair might not have a medulla, and the thickness of the cuticle and cortex will vary from one species to another. Est. time: 10 min

Signaling

Defense

■ Figure 3
Left: The white hair on the tails of these deer signal them to follow each other as they run from predators.
Right: The quills of a porcupine are modified hairs that are used as protection from predators.

5. Signaling: Hair can function as a signaling device. The white-tailed deer in **Figure 3** raise their tails, the undersides of which are white, when they run so that other deer can follow.
6. Defense: Hair also can function as a defense against predators. The porcupine in **Figure 3** has sharp quills, which are modified hairs, that are easily detached when the animal is threatened by a predator. The quills stick to and stab predators that touch the porcupine.

Structure of hair The hair in a bushy fox tail and the hair on your head contains a tough, fibrous protein called keratin, which is a protein that also makes up nails, claws, and hooves. A coat of hair usually consists of two kinds of hair, long guard hairs that protect a dense layer of shorter insulating underhair. The air trapped in the thick underhair layer provides insulation against the cold and retains body heat.

Reading Check **Explain** why hair is important to mammals.

Other Characteristics

In addition to having hair and mammary glands, mammals share other characteristics. These include a high metabolic rate, which supports endothermy; specialized teeth and digestive systems; a diaphragm to aid in respiration; a four-chambered heart; and a highly developed brain.

Endothermy Mammals are endotherms, which means they produce their body heat internally. The source of body heat is internal, the result of heat produced by a high metabolic rate. Body temperature is regulated by internal feedback mechanisms that send signals between the brain and sensors throughout the body.

For example, when some mammals become warm as a result of exertion or because the air is warm, sweat glands in the skin are stimulated to secrete sweat that evaporates from the skin. As the sweat evaporates, it draws heat away from the body and cools it. When body temperature lowers, sweating stops. For other mammals that do not sweat, panting cools the body. You might have seen a dog panting in the summer heat. During panting, water evaporates from the mouth and nose. Because mammals can regulate their body temperatures internally to maintain homeostasis, they can live in a range of ecosystems from the frigid temperatures of polar regions to the sweltering heat of deserts and the tropics.

D

Study Tip

Prediction Preview this section by looking at the bold titles and the photos. Predict the distinguishing characteristics of mammals. Use the titles and photos to help anticipate how to take notes on this section.

D Develop Concepts

OL Activity

SAY TO STUDENTS: ***Hair generally is made of three layers. The outer layer is the cuticle, which consists of flat, overlapping structures like shingles or tiles on a roof. You can feel the cuticle on your own hair by pinching a single long hair between your thumb and forefinger at the root and pulling your finger and thumb down the hair. Then, while still pinching the hair, move in the opposite direction back toward the root.***

ASK STUDENTS: ***How does moving from tip to root feel different? Why?*** Possible answer: As you pull from root to tip you are moving your finger in the same direction as cuticle layers, so it feels smooth, while in the opposite direction it will feel rough.

SAY TO STUDENTS: ***The cuticle protects the inner layers of hair. Inside the cuticle, the cortex is made up of long twisted proteins that can stretch. Try stretching a hair gently. What do you notice?*** Possible answer: The hair stretches. When a person gets split ends, this means that the cuticle has worn away and the cortex has frayed.

Reading Check Hair provides insulation, camouflage, protection against predators, and it is used to signal other animals and sense air or water movements.

> *"I am not a teacher, but an awakener."*
>
> —Robert Frost

Content Background

Cultural Diversity Ancient Egyptians shaved their heads to help keep cool and wore cotton-fiber wigs that symbolized social and spiritual status. The ancient Greeks did not mandate class structure and used hot irons to create curls. The Spartans kept their hair long as a symbol of fierceness. Headdresses, braiding, and threading hair with fabric originated on the African continent.

Develop Concepts

AL COOP LEARN

Community Connection
Assign students to groups and have them visit a nearby zoo, wild-animal park, nature preserve, wildlife rehabilitation center, or wildlife refuge and take photos of animals living there. Have students create a computer-generated presentation of their photos that includes text boxes indicating what the animals eat, how much it costs to feed them, and what their adaptations are for getting food in the wild. Encourage the groups to ask the staff ahead of time if they can assist in food preparation and/or animal feeding. Have each group prepare a presentation for the class.

R Reading Strategy

BL OL COOP LEARN

Find Supporting Details
Put students in groups of three and have each read one of the paragraphs on this page.
SAY TO STUDENTS: ***Take notes indicating the main idea and supporting details of your paragraph. Devise a way to teach what you have learned in your paragraph to other group members.***
BL Provide struggling students with an outline to fill in.

Reading Check The relationship is an example of symbiosis, specifically mutualism. Bacteria have a place to live and are getting food and the ruminant is able to digest cellulose.

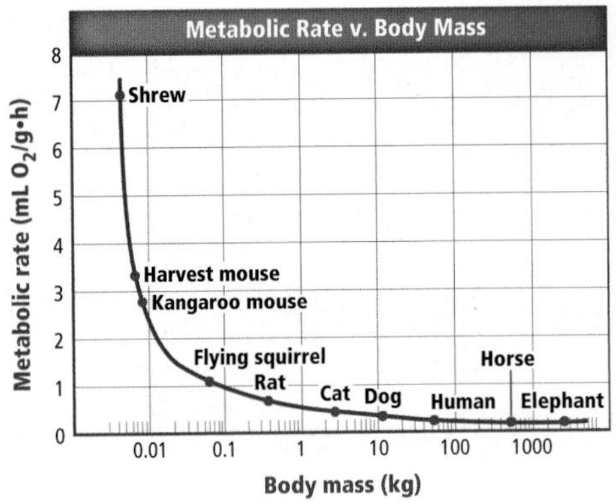

Figure 4 Due to their high metabolic rates, some small mammals, such as mice and shrews, must eat food masses that are equivalent to their body masses each day in order to maintain temperature homeostasis.

CAREERS IN BIOLOGY

Mammalogist The branch of biology that focuses on the study of mammals is mammalogy. A mammalogist might research the behavior, anatomy, or ecology of one or more species of mammals, or he or she can compare characteristics, such as digestion, in many species of mammals.

Feeding and digestion Maintaining an endothermic metabolism requires large amounts of energy. Mammals get the energy they need from the breakdown of food. Much of an endotherm's daily intake of food is used to generate heat to maintain a constant body temperature. **R**

Examine the graph in **Figure 4.** The graph shows the relationship of a mammal's metabolic rate to its body mass. Small mammals, including shrews, bats, and mice, have high metabolic rates relative to their body mass. As a result, these small mammals must hunt and eat food almost constantly in order to fuel their metabolisms.

Trophic categories Mammalogists divide mammals into four trophic categories based on what they eat.

1. Insectivores, such as moles and shrews, eat insects and other small invertebrates.
2. Herbivores, such as rabbits and deer, feed on vegetation.
3. Carnivores, such as foxes and lions, mostly feed on herbivores.
4. Omnivores, such as raccoons and most primates, feed on both plants and animals.

A mammal's adaptations for finding, capturing, chewing, swallowing, and digesting food all influence the mammal's structure and life habits. The fibers of plants are more difficult to digest and take longer than the digestion of meat. As a result, mammals that eat plant material have a larger cecum and longer digestive tracts than those that eat meat, as shown in **Figure 5.**

Ruminant herbivores Cellulose, a component of the cell walls of plants, can be a source of nutrition and energy. However, the enzymes in the digestive system of mammals cannot digest cellulose. Instead, some herbivores have bacteria in the cecum, a pouch where the small intestine meets the large intestine. Other herbivores have bacteria in their stomachs that break down the cellulose and release nutrients the animals can use. These mammals, called ruminants, have large, four-chambered stomachs. Cattle, sheep, and buffalo are all ruminants. As a ruminant feeds, plant material passes into the first and second stomach chambers. Plants are partially digested by bacteria into a material called cud. The ruminant brings the cud back up into the mouth and chews the cud for a long period of time. This further crushes the grass fibers. Once the cud is swallowed, it eventually reaches the fourth chamber of the stomach where digestion continues.

Reading Check **Infer** the type of relationship that exists between a ruminant and the bacteria in its stomach.

Demonstration

OL Insulation Obtain an authentic, fur-lined leather glove and a similar leather glove that is unlined. Pour hot water into two test tubes that can be sealed. Measure the temperature of the water before sealing the test tubes. Place the test tubes in the gloves at the beginning of the class period. Write the temperature of each of the test tubes on the board.
AL Have students suggest how to set up the demonstration.
ASK STUDENTS: ***What do you think the temperature of the water in the test tubes will be at the end of the class period?*** Possible answer: lower temperature for each, but less change in fur-lined glove Measure the temperature in each test tube at the end of the class period and write it on the board. Est. time: 10 min

Visualizing the Digestive Systems of Mammals

S **Figure 5**

The digestive systems of mammals are adapted to maximize the digestion and absorption of food. The protein consumed by carnivores and insectivores is readily digestible. Plant materials contain cellulose, which resists digestion, water, and some carbohydrates. Compare the structure of each digestive system below.

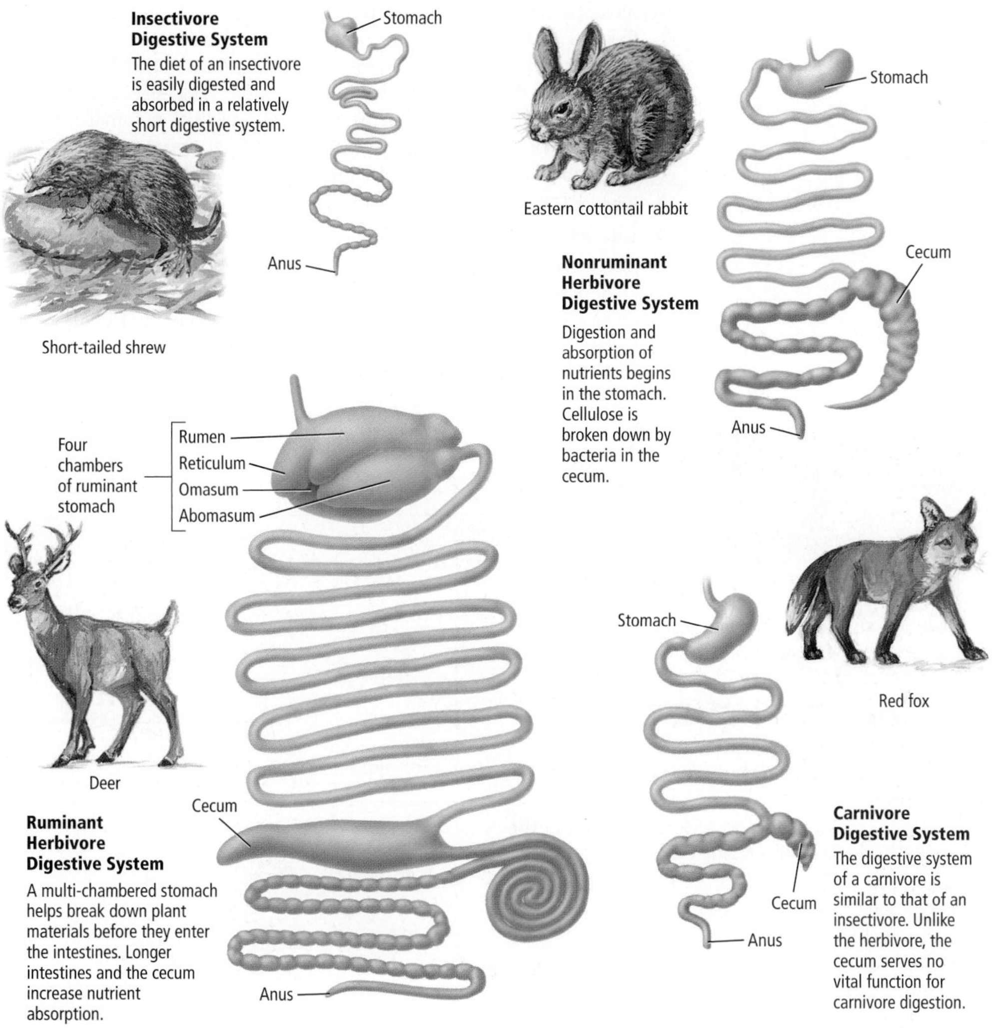

The diet of an insectivore is easily digested and absorbed in a relatively short digestive system.

Short-tailed shrew
Eastern cottontail rabbit

Abomasum

Concepts in Motion Animation

Research Citation

Compare and Contrast Educational research indicates that when students are asked to compare and contrast as they are on this page, they will learn to gather and organize data into categories. These skills help them to organize their thinking and learning.

(Horowitz, 1985)

Research bibliography on pages 32T–34T

Visualizing the Digestive Systems of Mammals

Purpose

Students will examine a diagram displaying form and function in the digestive systems of different types of mammals.
UCP.1, UCP.5

S Skill Practice

OL AL Visual Literacy

SAY TO STUDENTS: ***Compare and contrast the digestive systems of the four types of mammals shown here.*** Answers will vary. Possible similarities include that all four animals have a stomach, intestines, and an anus. Possible differences include the fact that herbivores have a cecum, ruminants have a four-chambered stomach, carnivores have a smaller cecum and intestine than herbivores and ruminants, and insectivores have the simplest system with a short intestine and no cecum.

Skill Practice

OL AL Visual Literacy

Brainstorm with students about the digestive systems of other animals in this chapter in order to familiarize students with animal digestion.

SAY TO STUDENTS: ***Make a list of other mammals pictured in this section and indicate how their digestive systems might look based on what they eat.*** animals pictured include: fox—carnivore, deer—herbivore, porcupine—herbivore, mole—insectivore, and bat—herbivore (fruits) or insectivore (insects). Answers will depend on students' prior knowledge.

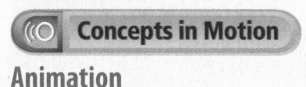

Concepts in Motion Animation

MiniLab 1

Inquiry MiniLab

For a lab worksheet, use your eTeacherEdition Online.

RUBRIC A rubric for evaluating MiniLabs is found on your eTeacherEdition Online.

Est. Time 20 min

Alternative Materials photographs or posters of mammalian skulls, prepared skulls of mammals

Safety Precaution Approve lab safety forms before work begins.

Teaching Strategy Consider showing models or prepared specimens of mammal skulls to your class for close observation.

Analysis

1. Incisors are sharp and pointed and normally used for biting and cutting; canines are pointed for puncturing and tearing; premolars are slightly pointed for shearing and shredding food; and molars are flat for grinding and crushing.
2. molars
3. Answers may vary. Carnivores bite, hold, and kill their prey using canines and incisors. They also tear flesh from prey using canines and incisors. They use premolars to shred large pieces of meat into smaller pieces, and molars to grind the meat into particles.
4. Answers may vary. Carnivores are classified together for their ability to tear flesh. Insectivores are classified together because their incisors are designed for trapping and spearing insects. Rodents have modified incisors that never stop growing and are used for gnawing.

LabManager™

Customize this lab with the LabManager™ CD-ROM.

VOCABULARY

ACADEMIC VOCABULARY

Retain
to keep in possession or use
You can retain your teeth throughout adulthood by brushing and flossing.

Teeth In addition to adaptations of the digestive system, teeth, perhaps more than any other physical characteristic, reveal the life habits of a mammal. Generally, in fish and reptile species, all teeth in the mouth look very much alike. This is because these animals use all of their teeth in similar ways, for seizing prey or for tearing prey apart before swallowing. In contrast, mammals have different types of teeth that are specialized for various functions. Examine the four types of mammalian teeth—canines, incisors, premolars, and molars—as illustrated in **MiniLab 1**.

A fox's canines are long and sharp. Carnivores use canines to stab and pierce their prey. The canines of herbivores often are reduced in size. This is illustrated in the cow skull shown in **MiniLab 1.** The premolars and molars of carnivores are used to slice and shear meat from the bones of their prey, while crushing and grinding are the functions of premolars and molars in herbivores. The incisors of insectivores are long and curved, functioning as pincers in seizing insect prey. The chisel-like incisors of beavers are modified for gnawing. Because the teeth of mammals reflect their feeding habits, biologists can determine what a mammal eats by examining its teeth. Complete **MiniLab 1** to see what inferences you can make about a mammal's diet based on its teeth.

Excretion The kidneys of mammals excrete metabolic wastes and maintain the homeostatic balance of body fluids. Kidneys filter urea, an end product of cellular metabolism, from the blood. Mammalian kidneys excrete or retain the proper amount of water in body fluids as well. Kidneys enable mammals to live in extreme environments, such as deserts, because they can control the amount of water in body fluids and cells.

MiniLab 1

Inquiry MiniLab

Compare Mammalian Teeth

How are the teeth of mammals specialized? Explore how the teeth of different mammal species are related to their diets.

Procedure

1. Read and complete the lab safety form.
2. Observe **teeth from the skulls of different mammal species.**
3. List the similarities and differences among the teeth of the different mammal species.

Analysis

1. **Infer** the function of each type of tooth based on its shape.
2. **Identify** the type of tooth common to all of the mammals that you have studied.
3. **Describe** how each mammal that you have studied uses its teeth to obtain and ingest food.
4. **Explain** how scientists might use the differences in mammalian teeth to classify mammals.

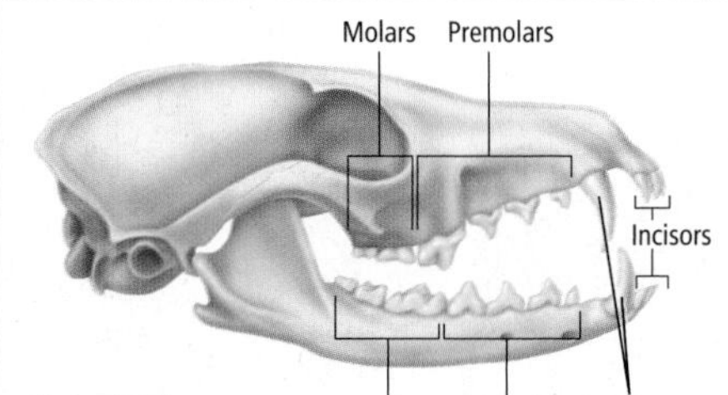

Fox skull

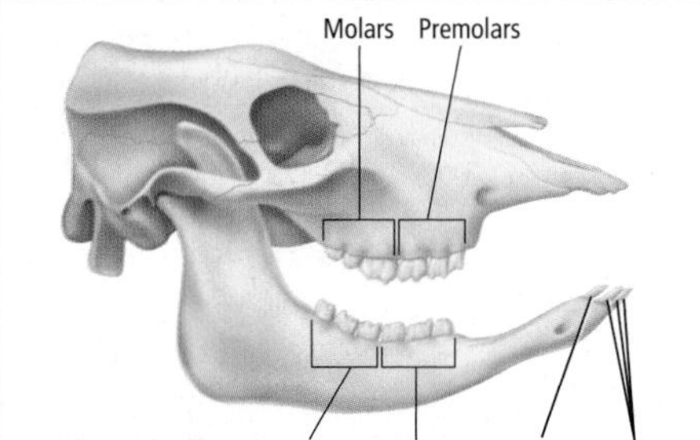

Cow skull

GOING GREEN When purchasing lab and classroom supplies, look for the greenest options. This might mean buying recycled materials, buying from local businesses, or seeking out sustainable resources.

Differentiated Instruction

Below Level Provide students with alternative ways by which to demonstrate their proficiency. Students performing below grade level will benefit when they can express their learning orally, with art and music, or by using technology.

For more tips, see pages 14T–15T.

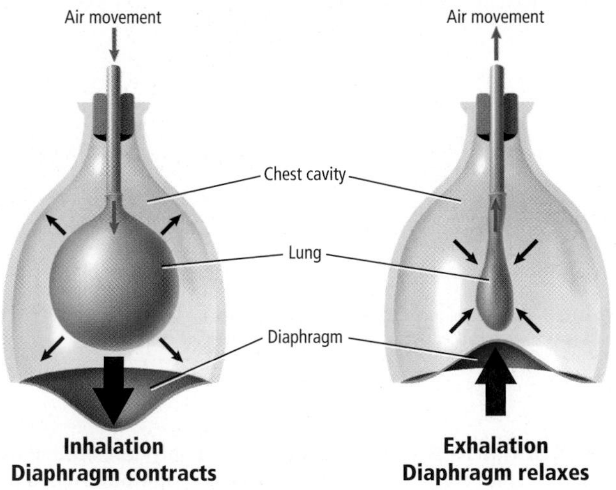

■ **Figure 6** The flask with the balloon is an analogy of how the diaphragm aids breathing in mammals.
Describe *what happens to the chest cavity as the diaphragm contracts and relaxes.*

D **Respiration** The food a mammal eats is used to maintain high energy levels. High levels of oxygen also are required to maintain a high level of metabolism. Oxygen is taken into the lungs of mammals during respiration. Although other animals, such as birds and reptiles, have lungs, mammals are the only animals that have a diaphragm. A **diaphragm** is a sheet of muscle located beneath the lungs that separates the chest cavity from the abdominal cavity where other organs are located. As the diaphragm contracts, it flattens, causing the chest cavity to enlarge, as shown in **Figure 6.** Once air enters the lungs, oxygen in the air moves by diffusion into blood vessels. When the diaphragm relaxes, the chest cavity becomes smaller and air is exhaled.

Reading Check **Describe** how the respiratory system of mammals is different from other animals.

Circulation Once oxygen is in the blood, vessels carry it to the heart, which pumps it out to the body. Like birds, mammals have a four-chambered heart. Also as in birds, oxygenated blood is kept entirely separate from deoxygenated blood in mammals. This is illustrated in **Figure 7.** Because most mammals are physically active and all are endotherms, they require a consistent supply of nutrients and oxygen to maintain homeostasis. Keeping oxygenated and deoxygenated blood separate makes the delivery of nutrients and oxygen more efficient.

Connection to Physics The circulatory system of a mammal also functions to help maintain a constant internal temperature. When body temperature increases, the blood vessels near the surface of the skin dilate, or expand, and deliver more blood than usual. Heat moves from the blood to the surface of the skin by conduction. At the skin's surface, W heat is lost from the body by radiation and the evaporation of sweat. When body temperature decreases, blood vessels near the surface of the skin contract and do not deliver as much blood as usual. This action reduces the loss of body heat.

Review Personal Tutor

■ **Figure 7** The circulatory system of mammals has a four chambered heart that keeps oxygen–rich and oxygen–poor blood separate. Oxygen–rich blood is represented by the color red, while oxygen–poor blood is the color blue.

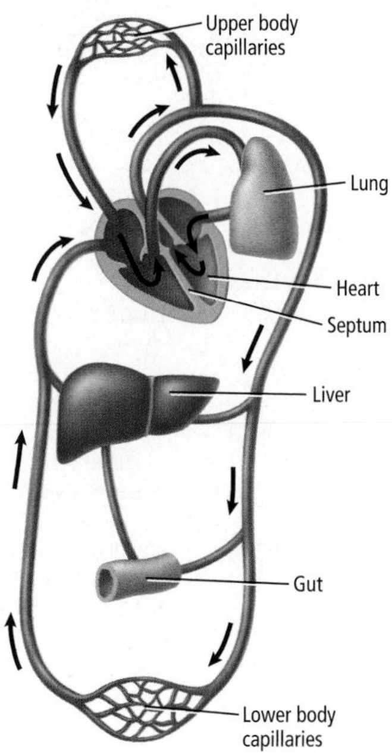

D Develop Concepts

OL AL Integrate Math The total volume of air inhaled and exhaled each minute can be calculated by multiplying the respiratory rate (number of breaths per min) by the tidal volume (volume of one breath). The respiratory rate for the average adult human is 12 breaths per min. The tidal volume is about 500 mL. The total volume of air inhaled and exhaled each minute is 6 L.
SAY TO STUDENTS: ***Calculate the total volume of air inhaled and exhaled per min for a horse, which has a respiratory rate of 14 breaths per min and a tidal volume of about 6000 mL.*** 84 L

Develop Concepts

OL Clarify a Misconception Students might think that the largest part of a tooth is what appears above the gum.
ASK STUDENTS: ***What percentage of a tooth is above the gum line?*** Only 10 percent of a tooth is above the gumline. Students might be surprised to discover how long teeth really are; the root is often longer than the portion of the tooth above the gum. You can show students some human teeth obtained from a dentist. Make sure they have been cleaned, soaked in hydrogen peroxide, and sterilized in an autoclave prior to bringing them into school. Keep them in a sealed clear container so that students can see them easily.

Demonstration

OL Mammalian Heart Obtain a fresh sheep or calf heart from a meat-packing facility. Show students how oxygenated and deoxygenated blood are separated from each other by the septum, making delivery of oxygen and nutrients to the body efficient. Project a diagram of blood circulation through the heart to help explain the movement of blood through the heart. Est. time: 10 min

Reading Check Mammals are the only animals that have a diaphragm.

■ **Caption Question Fig. 6** diaphragm contracts—chest cavity enlarges; diaphragm relaxes—chest cavity becomes smaller

Review Personal Tutor
Listen to a teacher explain four-chambered hearts.

W Writing Support

AL Creative Writing Imagine you are a red blood cell. Write a story about your journey through the four chambers of the heart and how you deliver oxygen to the body.

C Critical Thinking

OL AL COOP LEARN Design

SAY TO STUDENTS: ***Many large mammals in zoos tend to exhibit unnatural behavior, such as pacing back and forth for hours in their enclosures. One reason for this behavior might be a lack of stimulation in the captive environment. In the wild, most mammals are exposed to a variety of stimuli each day, thereby keeping their brains active and alert.*** Have students work in groups of three or four to design a toy for a large zoo animal that would enable it to engage in stimulating behavior using its paws or feet and mouth and teeth. Encourage students to research the natural behavior of the animal they choose and base their toy design on these natural behaviors.

Develop Concepts

BL OL AL COOP LEARN Activity

TELL STUDENTS: ***Wolves are complex social animals that express highly developed audible signals such as howls, barks, whimpers, and growls. Pack members communicate to locate each other, assemble, indicate danger, announce or defend a fresh kill, mark their territory, promote pack unity in a group howl, indicate submission, and show positive acceptance of another wolf.*** Have students work in groups of four to research what scientists know about wolf communication or develop a wolf language that can be used to communicate these and other wolf messages.

Reading Check Accept all reasonable responses. The folds in the cerebral cortex can be compared to the folds in the inner membrane of the mitochondria; they both increase surface area.

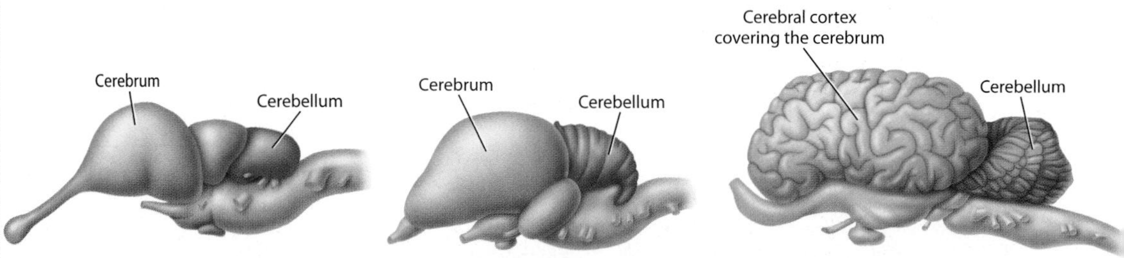

Figure 8 The cerebral cortex is the most complex part of the brain and is the part that has increased in size and changed most during the course of vertebrate evolution.

C

The brain and senses Mammals have highly developed brains, especially the cerebrum. The **cerebral cortex,** shown in **Figure 8,** is the highly folded outer layer of the cerebrum. The foldings allow the brain to have a larger surface area for nerve connections while allowing it to still fit inside the skull. The cerebral cortex is responsible for coordinating conscious activities, memory, and the ability to learn.

Another area of the mammalian brain that is well-developed is the cerebellum. The **cerebellum** is responsible for balance and coordinating movement. Compare the size and structure of the cerebellums of a reptile, a bird, and a mammal that are shown in **Figure 8.** A well-developed cerebellum allows an animal to have precise motor movements and to make complex movements in three dimensional space.

Complex behavior The mother fox on the opening page of the chapter will teach her young to hunt. Because mammals can learn and teach their young survival skills, they have an increased chance of survival. Mammals can carry out complex behaviors, such as learning and remembering what they have learned. Many mammals can get information about their environment and retain it. This information can then be used later. For example, mice that have had a chance to explore a habitat are able to avoid predators better than mice that have not had a chance to explore and learn about the same habitat.

Senses The importance of the senses varies from one group of mammals to the next. In some mammals, such as humans, vision is extremely important, while hearing is most important to mammals such as bats. Bats produce high-frequency sounds that bounce off objects and return to them. In this way a bat can detect objects in its path. This process is called echolocation. If you have seen how a dog sniffs people and objects in its surroundings, you recognize the importance of the sense of smell to this mammal. In some cases, a dog's sense of smell is one million times more sensitive than a human's sense of smell.

VOCABULARY

SCIENCE USAGE V. COMMON USAGE

Sense

Science Usage: a specialized animal function that involves a sense organ and a stimulus

Dogs use their sense of smell to get information about their environments.

Common Usage: an intended meaning

As I read the paragraph, I tried to get a sense of the main idea.

Reading Check **Describe** the advantage of having folds in the outer layer of the cerebral cortex using an analogy.

Demonstration

OL Mammalian Brains Show students a preserved sheep brain or a plastic model of the brain. Point to the cerebral cortex.

ASK STUDENTS: ***What is the function of this part of the brain?*** possible answer: coordinating conscious activity, memory, and the ability to learn ***What is the function of the cerebellum?*** possible answer: to coordinate movement and balance ***What part of the brain would be highly developed in mammals that possess high levels of intelligence?*** cerebral cortex ***If a mammal had the ability to jump from limb to limb in a tree and pick up objects with its fingers, what part of the brain would be highly developed?*** cerebellum
Est. time: 10 min

Glands A system of glands secretes a variety of fluids that helps to regulate a mammal's internal environment. A **gland** is a group of cells that secrete fluid to be used elsewhere in the body. Sweat glands help maintain body temperature. Mammary glands produce and secrete milk that nourishes developing young. Milk contains water, carbohydrates in the form of the sugar lactose, fat, and protein. The proportion of these nutrients differs according to species.

Examine **Table 1** to see the proportions of nutrients in the milk of various mammals. The proportion of nutrients is highly variable among different species of mammals. For example, fat amounts can range from one percent to 50 percent. Aquatic mammals, which use a layer of fat to help keep warm, usually have the highest percent of fat in their milk.

Scent glands produce substances that mammals use to mark their territories or attract mates. Oil glands in the skin maintain the quality of the animal's hair and skin. Other glands produce hormones that regulate internal processes, such as growth and release of eggs from ovaries.

Reading Check **Explain** why the fat content in milk would be higher in aquatic mammals.

Reproduction In mammals, the egg is fertilized internally. In most mammals, development of the embryo takes place in the female uterus. The **uterus** is a saclike muscular organ in which embryos develop. In most mammals, the developing embryo is nourished by the **placenta,** an organ that provides food and oxygen and removes waste from the developing young. The amount of time the young stay in the uterus before they are born is called **gestation.** Gestation periods in mammals vary by species, the shortest being that of the Virginian opossum which can be only 12 days. The longest gestation period occurs in the African elephant, which is an average of 660 days and can be as long as 760 days. In general, the larger the mammal, the longer the gestation period. After birth, the offspring of mammals drink milk for nourishment from the mother's mammary glands.

VOCABULARY
WORD ORIGIN
Gestation
gest– from the Latin word *gestare,* meaning *to bear*
–ation suffix; from Latin meaning *action* or *process*

R

S

Table 1 **Proportion of Nutrients in the Milk of Mammals** Concepts in Motion Interactive Table

Nutrient	Dog	Dolphin	Harp Seal	Rabbit	Zebra
Water	76.3	44.9	43.8	71.3	86.2
Protein	9.3	10.6	11.9	12.3	3.0
Fat	9.5	34.9	42.8	13.1	4.8
Sugar	3.0	0.9	0.0	1.9	5.3

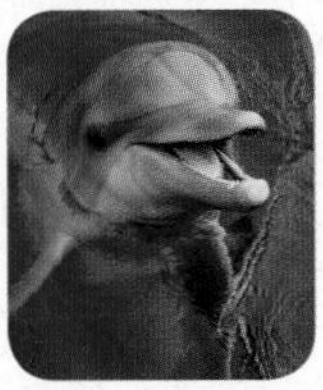

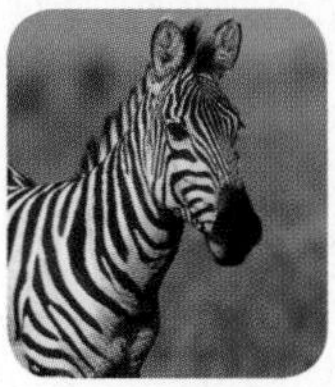

S Skill Practice

OL AL Make a Graph

SAY TO STUDENTS: ***Make a graph of the data in Table 1. Decide if a bar graph or a line graph would be best. Decide which variable will go on the x-axis and which will go on the y-axis.***

ASK STUDENTS: ***What is more obvious in the graph at a first glance that might not have been as obvious in the table?*** Possible answer: The amount of water in milk is very significant and the amount of fat varies significantly between species of mammals. It is easier to see the comparisons in a graph.

R Reading Strategy

OL Clarify the Text

SAY TO STUDENTS: ***The terms* uterus *and* placenta *can be confused easily as they both support developing young. The uterus contains the placenta. The embryo is attached to the placenta, which is attached to the inside of the uterus.***

Concepts in Motion
Interactive Table

Research Citation

Formative Assessments Educational research indicates that using formative assessment activities, like the one on page 888, helps teachers monitor their students' thinking throughout a lesson. These assessments allow teachers to modify the lesson in order to address the learning needs of their students.
(Tomlinson et al., 2003)

Research bibliography on pages 32T–34T

Reading Check In order to keep warm, aquatic animals need to have more fat than other mammals.

Develop Concepts

EL OL AL Activity Provide students with animal-track guidebooks to find tracks of local and non-local mammals and trace them onto paper. Specify the mammals with pads/claws, webbing, or hooves.

ASK STUDENTS: ***How does the structure of a mammal's foot relate to the type of movement they exhibit?*** possible answers: rabbits—powerful legs for jumping, defense; bear—claws for tearing prey; elephant —large surface area to distribute weight

Formative Assessment

Evaluation

SAY TO STUDENTS: ***Summarize the adaptations of mammals that enable them to live anywhere.*** Mammal adaptations include hair, mammary glands, a high metabolic rate supporting endothermy, specialized teeth and digestive systems, a diaphragm, a four-chambered heart, and a highly developed brain.

Remediation Give students pictures of mammal teeth and limbs. **ASK STUDENTS:** ***How do teeth and limbs provide adaptations to a particular way of life?*** Answers should include information on teeth that are adapted for capturing and/or chewing food and limbs for swimming, running, and digging.

Limbs used for digging and burrowing

Limbs used for flying

Figure 9
Left: The mole has powerful, short forelimbs that are adapted to digging and burrowing in the ground.
Right: The bat can fly with thin membranes spread between the elongated arm and hand bones.

Movement Mammals must find food, shelter, and escape from predators. They have evolved a variety of limb types that enable them to carry out these essential behaviors. Some mammals, such as coyotes and foxes, run. The cheetah, which is the fastest land mammal, can reach speeds as fast as 110 km/h.

Other mammals, such as kangaroos, leap. Some mammals, including dolphins, swim. Bats are the only mammals that fly. The structure of the skeletal and muscular systems in animals reflects the type of movement that an animal uses. Examine **Figure 9,** which shows the forelimbs of a mole and those of a bat. How does the structure of these limbs reflect the habitat and behavior of these animals?

Section 1 Assessment

Section Summary

- Mammals are successful in a wide variety of habitats.
- Mammals have specialized teeth that are adapted to their diets.
- Respiratory, circulatory, and nervous systems have complex adaptations that enable mammals to have the extra energy they need and to maintain homeostasis.
- Mammals have internal fertilization and, in most mammals, offspring develop within the female uterus.

Understand Main Ideas

1. MAIN Idea **Identify** two characteristics unique to mammals.
2. **Explain** how mammals maintain a constant body temperature.
3. **Classify** the mammals that live in your area as herbivores, carnivores, omnivores, or insectivores.
4. **Summarize** how the respiratory and circulatory systems of mammals work together to enable mammals to have high energy levels.
5. **Compare and contrast** how respiration occurs in mammals to respiration in birds.

Think Critically

6. **Hypothesize** While working at an excavation site, an archeologist finds an intact skull fossil, including the teeth, of a mammal. Why are the teeth important to the archeologist?

MATH in Biology

7. Suppose a hare spotted a coyote and tried to run away. Coyotes can run at a speed of 70 km/h. Hares can run at a speed of 65 km/h. How far could the hare run before the coyote catches up? Assume that the hare is 25 m from the coyote.

Section 1 Assessment

1. hair, mammary glands
2. Mammals are endothermic. Hair provides insulation from the cold, and sweating and panting help animals keep cool in the heat.
3. Answers will vary.
4. Mammals have lungs that take in oxygen. The diaphragm contracts, expanding the chest cavity so that large amounts of air can be drawn in. Newly oxygenated blood is pumped by the four-chambered heart and kept separate from deoxygenated blood. Large amounts of oxygen are available to cells for aerobic respiration.
5. Mammals have a diaphragm, enabling them to inhale and exhale. Birds breathe in one direction through anterior and posterior air sacs.
6. The type, amount, and placement of the teeth will identify the diet and location on the food chain.
7. $65{,}000t + 25 = 70{,}000t$
$25 = 5000t$
$t = \frac{1}{200}\text{h}$
$70{,}000\text{m/h}\left(\frac{1}{200}\text{h}\right) = 350\text{m}$

Assessment Online Quiz

Reading Preview

Essential Questions

- What are the characteristics of mammals in each of the three subgroups of living mammals?
- What are the adaptations that contribute to the diversity of mammals and enable them to live in a variety of habitats?
- How might mammals have evolved?

Review Vocabulary

chromosome: cell structure that carries genetic material that is copied and passed from generation to generation of cells

New Vocabulary R

monotreme
marsupial
placental mammal
therapsid

Multilingual eGlossary

Diversity of Mammals

MAIN Idea Class Mammalia is divided into three subgroups based on reproductive methods.

Real-World Reading Link Think about the mammals that you see every day, such as dogs or squirrels. They are only a small part of the 4500 living species of mammals found on Earth. Scientists have developed zoos and wild animal parks that offer opportunities to learn about and enjoy the great variety of mammal species found in the world today.

Mammal Classification

Class Mammalia is divided into three subgroups based on methods of reproduction—monotremes, marsupials, and placental mammals.

Monotremes The animal shown in **Figure 10** with its duck bill and webbed feet might not look like any mammal you have seen. However, it has hair and mammary glands, which makes it a mammal. The duck-billed platypus is a monotreme that lays eggs similar to those of reptiles. **Monotremes** are mammals that reproduce by laying eggs. The only other living monotremes besides the duck-billed platypus are echidnas. An adult echidna and an echidna egg are shown in **Figure 10.** Both the duck-billed platypus and the echidna only live in Australia, Tasmania, and New Guinea. Besides laying eggs, other unique features of these mammals include reptilian bone structure in the shoulder area, lower body temperature than most mammals, and a unique mix of chromosomes with characteristics similar to both mammals and reptiles.

Reading Check **Identify** how monotremes are different from other subgroups of mammals.

Figure 10 The echidna, like the duck-billed platypus, is an egg-laying mammal. Once an egg hatches, the offspring receive nourishment from the mother's mammary glands.

Duck-billed platypus

Echidna

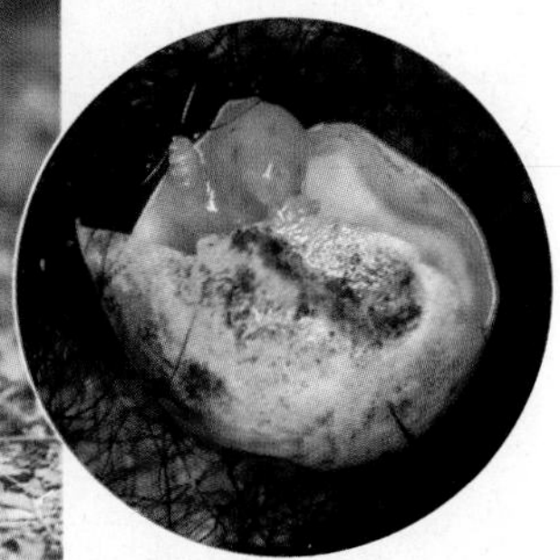
Echidna hatching from egg

Content Background

Teacher FYI Monotremes have distinctive characteristcs. An Aboriginal legend says that the platypus is the offspring of a duck and a water-rat. It has short, dense fur covering its body except for its bill, feet, and underside of its tail. The bill is soft and pliable with nostrils at the tip. This bill can detect electrical fields given off by muscle contractions of their prey. Unlike platypuses, echidnas, which are also called spiny anteaters, are terrestrial and have a short, beaklike structure that they use to probe for ants or worms, which they then capture with their sticky tongue. The spiny anteater's guard hairs on its back and sides are modified to form spines that it can erect when threatened.

Section 2

MAIN Idea

BL OL AL

Diversity of Mammals Display mounted taxidermy specimens or skins of a variety of mammals. Nature centers, museums, colleges, or taxidermists might loan these to you. Fish and game departments usually have an education division with specimens and/or guest speakers.

ASK STUDENTS: ***In what ways are these mammals diverse in their adaptations?*** Answers will vary depending on the specimens you provide. They could range in size, amount of fur or hair, length of extremities, length of ears, positioning of eyes on the head, size of the tail, and kinds of teeth.

R Reading Strategy

OL **Brainstorm** Have students read the new vocabulary terms on this page.

SAY TO STUDENTS: ***Write down what comes to mind for the meaning of each term. Correct and add to these ideas as you read this section.***

Develop Concepts

EL OL

Activate Prior Knowledge

Show students pictures of monotremes, marsupials, and placentals. Write these words on the board and have students place the animals you are showing in one of the three groups. Have them write this information in their science journals and correct or add to it while reading this section.

Reading Check Monotremes reproduce by laying eggs, unlike marsupials or placental mammals.

Writing Support

OL AL Formal Writing Show students photographs of a variety of marsupials from a book such as *Walker's Mammals of the World* by Ronald Nowak (1999). Have students select a marsupial to write an article about for an illustrated nature magazine for children. Make sure student articles are appropriate for the elementary school level and include artwork depicting the chosen animal. Another source for photographs is in magazines focused on nature and the outdoors.

W Writing Support

AL COOP LEARN

Technical Writing Ask a group of students to research the origins of marsupials and their eventual isolation in Australia and New Guinea. In addition to a written report on these details, have students prepare a large bulletin-board display that illustrates the movements of marsupials over the course of history.

■ **Figure 11** Opossums are the only marsupials in North America. Most opossums spend much of their time in the trees.

Marsupials Pouched mammals that have a very short gestation period are **marsupials.** Immediately following birth, the offspring crawl into a pouch made of skin and hair on the outside of the mother's body. Within the pouch, the offspring continue development while being nourished by milk from the mother's mammary glands. In some species of marsupials, offspring are born and crawl into the mother's pouch only eight days after fertilization occurs.

The only North American marsupial is the opossum, shown hanging by its tail in **Figure 11.** Other marsupials include the koala, wallaby, kangaroo, and cuscus, some of which are shown in **Figure 12.** Australia and its nearby islands are home to most marsupials.

Connection to Earth Science Why marsupials are limited mostly to Australia is still a subject for debate among scientists. One theory, based on fossil evidence, is that marsupials originated in North America, then spread to South America and Europe while the continents were still connected as one giant landmass. From South America, marsupials moved across Africa to Antarctica then to Australia. Then, about 200 million years ago, the continents separated due to the movement of Earth's tectonic plates. This isolated the ancestors of today's marsupials to Australia and nearby islands.

Australian marsupials thrived because they were isolated from competing placental mammals. In North and South America, however, placental mammals had competitive adaptive advantages. For example, placental mammals evolved highly social behavior, had more variety in food sources, and evolved greater diversity in form and function than marsupials.

Marsupials in Australia and New Guinea fill the niches occupied by placental mammals elsewhere in the world. For example, kangaroos are the grazers in Australia. They fill the niche that deer, antelope, and buffalo fill in other areas of the world.

■ **Figure 12** The cuscus is a nocturnal marsupial that is found in northern Australia and New Guinea. The red kangaroo, shown here with a joey in its pouch, has a development period of only 33 days, after which the newborn begins nursing in the pouch.

Cuscus

Red kangaroo

Research Citation

Write Educational research indicates that writing can be used as a tool to promote language development. The writing activities on this page require students to write in a variety of ways, providing them with different methods to use in expressing their knowledge.

(Carrasquillo and Rodriguez, 1996)

Research bibliography on pages 32T–34T

Humpback whale

Pygmy shrew

Placental mammals Most mammals living today, including humans, are placental mammals. **Placental mammals** have a placenta, the organ that provides food and oxygen to and removes waste from developing young. Placental mammals give birth to young that do not need further development within a pouch.

Placental mammals are represented by 18 orders. Some orders are represented only by a few species. For example, there are only two species of flying lemurs in order Dermoptera. The aardvark, a termite-eating mammal found in Africa, is the only species in its order. Other orders, such as Rodentia, which includes squirrels and rats, have almost 2000 species. Sizes of placental mammals range from 1.5-g pygmy shrews to 100,000-kg whales, both of which are shown in **Figure 13.** Placental mammals range from marine dolphins with adaptations for swimming to moles adapted to subterranean life and bats equipped with wings and ultrasonic echolocation for flying in the dark. **Table 2** on page 894 describes some of the different orders of placental mammals.

Scientists have hypothesized several reasons why there are greater numbers and kinds of placental mammals compared to marsupials. One hypothesis is that marsupial young must cling to their mother's fur at birth. Limbs, therefore, are limited in their ability to evolve into structures such as the flippers and wings of some placental mammals. Another hypothesis that explains the success of placental mammals points out that the cerebral cortex of placental mammals is larger and more complex than that of marsupials. This might be due to the more stable, oxygen-rich environment they experience inside the uterus. D According to this hypothesis, this might have enabled placental mammals to develop more complex social behaviors that led to their success.

Reading Check **Identify** how placental mammals differ from marsupials.

Figure 13
The humpback whale, weighing 100,000 kg, is one of the largest mammals. The pygmy shrew, weighing 1.5 g, is one of the smallest mammals. Notice the size of the pygmy shrew by comparing it to the size of the earthworm it is eating.

FOLDABLES®
Incorporate information from this section into your Foldable.

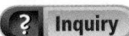

? Inquiry Virtual Lab

? Inquiry Launch Lab

Review Based on what you have read about mammal classification, how would you now answer the analysis questions?

FOLDABLES®

✱RUBRIC A rubric for evaluating Foldables is found on your eTeacherEdition Online.

Going Further On the back of their Foldables, have students list examples of each mammalian subclass and note the continent or habitat of their origin.

D Develop Concepts

OL Scaffolding

ASK STUDENTS: ***What are the two main characteristics of mammals?*** hair and mammary glands ***In addition, mammals have four other distinguishing features. What are they?*** specialized teeth, a diaphragm, a four-chambered heart, and large cerebral hemispheres ***What is a placental mammal?*** a mammal with a placenta that nourishes an embryo and gives birth to young that do not continue development in a pouch after birth ***What are some possible reasons for the higher numbers of placental mammals compared to marsupials?*** They have young that do not need their limbs to grasp their mother's fur, so these limbs evolved for other functions. Also, development in the uterus provided a more stable, oxygen-rich environment that led to the development of a larger cerebral cortex.

? Inquiry Launch Lab

Assess Content Development
Assess how understanding has developed when students revisit the Launch Lab analysis questions.

Reading Check Placental mammals have a placenta, and the young of placental mammals do not need further development in a pouch.

Demonstration

Ranges of Mammals Obtain current maps of the geographic ranges of various placental mammals from books and/or magazines on mammals of the world, such as *Walker's Mammals of the World.* Project these images to show students the huge areas of the world where placental mammals live. Est. time: 10 min

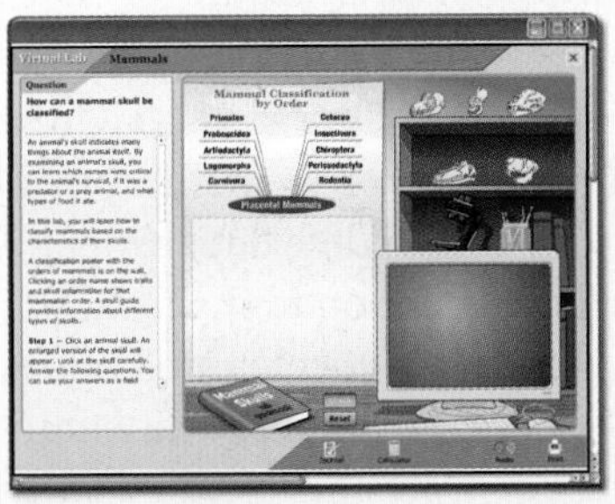

? Inquiry **Virtual Lab** Students will classify placental mammal skulls by studying the skulls' features.

Skill Practice

EL OL Visual Literacy

SAY TO STUDENTS: ***Make a five-column table listing all the mammals pictured in this section. The columns should be labeled left to right:*** **Figure Number, Name of Mammal, Subclass, Identifying Features,** ***and*** **Adaptations to Habitat.**

Develop Concepts

AL COOP LEARN Activity Ask a group of students to find out what types of bats live in your area. Have them make a bat house that could be placed on the school grounds or in a nearby public park. Talk to school or park officials before installing the bat house.

D Develop Concepts

EL OL COOP LEARN Activity

SAY TO STUDENTS: ***Ask a partner to tape your thumbs to the palms on the same hand. Then use this hand to try to open a peanut in a shell.*** Remind students that primates have opposable thumbs, whereas most other mammals do not.

AL Have students list typical activities that require an opposable thumb to complete. dressing, opening screw top containers, finger snapping

ASK STUDENTS: ***How difficult was this task without an opposable thumb?*** difficult, if not impossible For students with peanut allergies, you can substitute a jar with a lid and ask them to try to open the jar.

Caption Question Fig. 15 Some examples are monkeys, apes, and humans.

Order Insectivora—shrew

Order Chiroptera—flying fox

Figure 14 Shrews are members of order Insectivora. The flying fox is a bat that is a member of order Chiroptera.

VOCABULARY

ACADEMIC VOCABULARY

Modify
to make changes that result in a new purpose
The wings of a bat are modified forelimbs for flying.

Figure 15 Golden lion tamarins are omnivores that live in the coastal forests of Brazil.
Identify *other animals that are members of order Primates.*

Order Insectivora As the name implies, these mammals' main food source is insects. The shrew, shown in **Figure 14,** is an insectivore, as are hedgehogs and moles. Members of order Insectivora usually are small and have pointed snouts that allow them to capture insects easily. Shrews include the smallest of all mammals. Shrews can be found in almost all parts of the world and spend most of their lives underground.

Order Chiroptera There are about 925 species in order Chiroptera (ky RAHP ter uh), all of which are bats. As mentioned previously, bats are the only mammals that truly can fly. Their wings are thin membranes supported by modified forelimbs. Bats feed on a variety of foods. Some eat insects, some eat fruit, and others feed on blood. The most common North American bat is the little brown bat which you might have seen swooping and darting at dusk to catch insects. The flying fox, shown in **Figure 14,** is the largest of all bats. It lives in tropical regions worldwide and feeds on fruit.

Order Primates Monkeys, apes, and humans are all examples of primates. Primates' brains, with large cerebral hemispheres, are the most developed brains of all mammals. Most primates are tree dwellers. This leads scientists to hypothesize that the need to perform complex movements while in trees, such as those involved in capturing food and avoiding enemies, led to advances in the brain structure of primates. Primate forelimbs often are adapted for grasping and most have nails instead of claws. The golden lion tamarin in **Figure 15** is grasping with its hands the branch on which it is sitting. D

Order Xenarthra Animals in order Xenarthra (zen AR thra) either have no teeth or have simple, peglike teeth. Anteaters, like the one shown in **Figure 16,** are toothless. Anteaters have a spiny tongue and sticky saliva that allow them to easily capture ants and termites in their nests. Sloths and armadillos both have peglike teeth. Sloths mostly feed on leaves, and armadillos feed on insects. Most mammals in this order live in Central America and South America with the exception of the armadillo, which also can be found in the southern United States.

Demonstration

OL Mammalian Skulls If you do not have skulls of placental mammals to display, you might be able to borrow them from a local museum, nature center, taxidermy shop, college, or fish and wildlife department. Show students a variety of placental mammal skulls while calling attention to the features of each skull, especially the teeth. If possible, get a bear skull. Many students think of bears as meat eaters and don't realize that the bulk of a bear's diet is vegetation. Point out the large, flat molars—perfect for grinding plant material. For each skull, **ASK STUDENTS:** ***What do you think this animal eats?*** Answers will depend on the skull. Est. time: 15 min

Giant anteater

Beaver

■ **Figure 16** The giant anteater, the largest anteater, is found throughout Central and South America. The second largest rodent is the beaver, weighing as much as 80 kg.
Describe *the characteristics of members of order Xenarthra.*

S

Order Rodentia The gnawing mammals in order Rodentia, called rodents, include the beaver, which is shown in **Figure 16,** rats, woodchucks, marmots, squirrels, hamsters, and gerbils. Rodents make up nearly 40 percent of all mammalian species. Two pairs of razor-sharp incisor teeth continue to grow throughout the life of a rodent. They use their sharp teeth to gnaw through wood, seed pods, or shells to get food. The ability of rodents to invade all land habitats and their successful reproductive behavior have made them ecologically important in all terrestrial ecosystems.

Order Lagomorpha Like rodents, members of the the order Lagomorpha—rabbits, pikas, and hares—have long sharp incisors that continue to grow. Lagomorphs also have a pair of peglike incisors that grow behind the first pair. These mammals are herbivores that eat grasses, herbs, fruits, and seeds. The pika shown in **Figure 17** lives in high latitude or high altitude environments in which the ground is covered with snow for parts of the year. The grasseaters adapt to these conditions by harvesting grass during the warm months and storing it. The pikas then eat the grass during the winter when no fresh vegetation is available.

VOCABULARY
WORD ORIGIN
Lagomorpha
lago– from the Greek word *lagos,* meaning *hare*
–morph, from the Greek word *morphe,* meaning *form*

Order Carnivora You might have a pet dog or cat. It, along with wolves, bears, seals, walruses, coyotes, skunks, otters, minks, and weasels, belongs to the order Carnivora. All of these carnivores are predators with teeth adapted to tearing flesh. The lion, shown in **Figure 17,** feeds on antelope, giraffes, and even crocodiles. After she captures her prey, she uses her incisors to tear off chunks of meat.

■ **Figure 17** The American pika can be found in alpine regions of the western U.S. and southwestern Canada. The lion uses her canines to stab and pierce her prey.

Pika

Lion

Demonstration

OL Rodent Skulls and Teeth Show students a variety of illustrations of rodent skulls in field guides, or download photos from the Internet.
ASK STUDENTS: ***How does the variety of teeth in the skulls of rodents contribute to their success in making up nearly 40 percent of all mammalian species?*** Possible answer: The variety in teeth of rodents enables them to live in many different habitats and occupy a variety of environments. Est. time: 10 min

Develop Concepts

OL Activity
SAY TO STUDENTS: ***Assume that you are a zookeeper at a zoo that will be opening a new mammal exhibit. Research to determine what elements would need to be incorporated into this exhibit and what type of food the mammal would need. Make a large diagram of the exhibit, with captions explaining the details about the design of the exhibit, an exhibit sign, and a daily diet for the animal.***
BL Have students build a diorama of the zoo habitat using shoe boxes or other suitable containers.

S Skill Practice

OL Visual Literacy
SAY TO STUDENTS: ***Study Figures 16 and 17 and describe the habitats of the giant anteater and the pika. Infer what kinds of adaptations they have to help them be successful in their environment.*** Anteaters live in fairly dry areas where they can dig up ants and other insects. Their head is adapted to probing for insects in the ground, and their tongue is sticky to capture the insects. Pikas live in mountainous areas where it is cold in the winter. Their bodies have short extremities, including short ears, that slow the loss of body heat in the cold.

Writing Support

BL AL Persuasive Writing
SAY TO STUDENTS: ***Find out about a local or nearby mammal that is endangered and write a persuasive essay about measures that could be taken to preserve the mammal's habitat. Also include any other measures that could be taken to prevent the demise of this mammal.*** Answers will depend on the mammal chosen.

■ **Caption Question Fig. 16** no teeth or simple, peglike teeth; anteaters have a spiny tongue and sticky saliva

Develop Concepts

OL AL

Clarify a Misconception

ASK STUDENTS: ***Have you ever seen a dog that seems happy, or annoyed, or a cat that appears to be sad?*** Answers will vary. Students will generally think that animals have emotions.

TELL STUDENTS: ***When human traits are given to nonhuman things or other animals, this is called* anthropomorphism. *Many people think that animals have human feelings and thoughts. It might seem that your dog is happy or worried and that your cat is sad, but correctly stated in terms of science and the behavior of animals, you could say that your dog is displaying a positive response or a negative response, or that the cat is sleeping longer than normal and is slow to respond.***

SAY TO STUDENTS: ***Reword the following sentences to make them scientifically accurate. My dog is outraged.*** My dog is displaying aggression. ***My dog is surprised.*** My dog is displaying a startled response. Students will learn that animals display behavior and do not have human emotions.

Concepts in Motion
Interactive Table

Reading Check Answers will vary, but may include: artiodactyla and perissodactyla are both hooved plant eaters, but artiodactyla have an even number of toes and perissodactyla have an odd number of toes.

■ **Figure 18** The trunk of an elephant is called a proboscis. Trunks are unique to members of order Proboscidea.

Order Proboscidea Elephants are the largest living land mammals. They have flexible trunks adapted to gathering plants and taking in water. Two upper incisors are modified as tusks for digging up roots and tearing bark from trees. Some elephants are trained to help lift heavy objects. The elephant shown in **Figure 18** is helping remove debris that washed ashore during a tsunami in Indonesia on December 26, 2004. Ancient mastodons and mammoths are the extinct relatives of today's African and Asian elephants.

Order Sirenia Manatees and dugongs are members of the order Sirenia. They are large, slow-moving mammals with big heads and no hind limbs. Their forelimbs are modified into flippers that aid in swimming. These animals are herbivores, feeding on seagrasses, algae, and other aquatic plants. Depending on their size, manatees can consume as much as 50 kg of vegetation per day. Sirenians can be found cruising the surface of warm tropical rivers and lagoons. Because they are so slow and prefer the surface of the water, they often are injured or killed by the propellers of speedboats. Notice the scars on the back of the manatee in **Figure 19.**

Order Perissodactyla These hoofed mammals include horses, zebras, and rhinoceroses. Members of this order have an odd number of toes, either one or three on each foot. These mammals are herbivores and have teeth that are adapted for grinding plant material. Perissodactyls can be found on all continents except Antarctica.

Reading Check **Compare** placental mammals using **Table 2.**

Table 2 **Orders of Placental Mammals** — Concepts in Motion Interactive Table

Order	Example	Characteristics
Insectivora	Shrews, hedgehogs, moles	Pointed snouts, smallest mammals, live underground, insect-eaters
Chiroptera	Bats	Nocturnal, use sonar, adapted to flight, fruit and insect-eaters
Primates	Monkeys, apes, humans	Binocular vision, large brains, most are tree-dwellers, opposable thumb
Xenarthra	Anteaters, sloths, armadillos	Toothless or peg-like teeth, insect-eaters
Rodentia	Beavers, rats, woodchucks, marmots, squirrels, hamsters, and gerbils	Sharp continuously growing incisor teeth, plant-eaters
Lagomorpha	Rabbits, pikas, hares	Back legs longer than front legs, adapted to jumping, incisors that continually grow, herbivores
Carnivora	Dogs, cats, wolves, bears, seals, walruses, coyotes, skunks, otters, minks, and weasels	Teeth adapted to tear flesh, meat-eaters
Proboscidea	Elephants	Long trunks, incisors become long tusks, largest land animal
Sirenia	Manatees and dugongs	Slow moving, big heads, no hind limbs, adapted to aquatic environment
Perissodactyla	Horses, zebras, rhinoceroses	Hoofed, odd number of toes, plant-eaters
Artiodactyla	Deer, cattle, pigs, hippopotamuses	Hoofed, even number of toes, plant-eaters that chew cud
Cetacea	Whales, dolphins, porpoises	Front limbs that are flippers, no hind limbs, nostril forms a blowhole

Demonstration

Carnivores Show students specimens of endangered species parts such as teeth, tusks, and fur of endangered carnivores and elephants. You can obtain this material at no cost from federal government labs after the material has been confiscated, processed, and criminals have been convicted. These materials are available to teachers for educational purposes at the following address: U.S. Fish and Wildlife Service National Forensics Lab, 1490 E. Main St., Ashland, Oregon 97520-1310. Point out to students that demand for these materials has contributed to the demise and near extinction of many animals. Est. time: 10 min

Manatee

Humpback whale

■ **Figure 19** The West Indian manatee is endangered. Wildlife managers help rescue manatees that have been injured by boat propellers. The baleen of a whale is similar to a sieve.

Order Artiodactyla Members of the order Artiodactyla also are hoofed mammals. They differ from perissodactyls in that they have an even number of toes, either two or four, on each limb. Deer, antelopes, cattle, sheep, pigs, goats and hippopotamuses are all artiodactyls. Many cattle, sheep, and deer have horns or antlers. Mammals in this order are herbivorous and most chew cuds as part of their digestive processes.

Order Cetacea Whales, dolphins, and porpoises have front limbs modified into flippers that aid in swimming. They have no hind limbs and the tail consists of fleshy flukes. Nostrils are modified into a single or double blowhole on top of the head. Except for a few muzzle hairs, their bodies are hairless. Some whales are predators. Others, like the blue whale, have a specialized structure inside their mouths called a baleen that is used to filter plankton for food. The baleen of a humpback whale is shown in **Figure 19.**

DATA ANALYSIS LAB 1

Based on Real Data*

Analyze and Conclude

How does boat noise affect whales? Killer whales might coordinate their cooperative hunting and other social behavior with certain calls that have meaning to the pod, or group of whales with which they travel. The number of boats in the area of study increased by about five times from 1990–2000.

Data and Observations

Biologists examined the duration of whales' calls in three different pods for several years. Examine the graphs to the right.

Think Critically

1. **Evaluate** the trend in call duration of whales in J, K, and L pods from 1977 to 2003. What might account for this trend?
2. **Hypothesize** what the researchers were investigating in this study.

*Data obtained from: Foote, A., et al. 2004. Whale-call response to masking boat noise. *Nature* 428: 910.

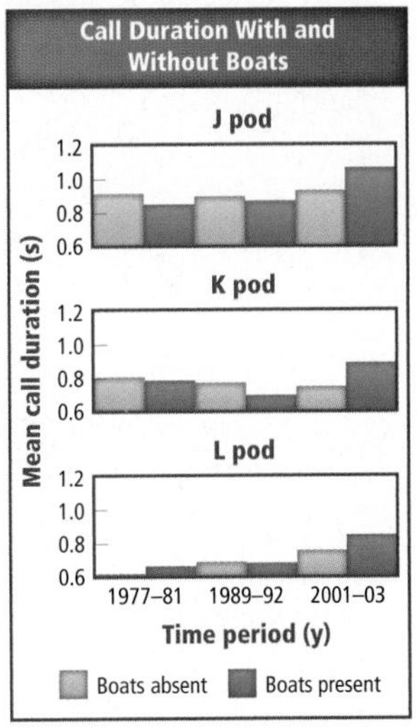

Writing Support

OL AL Persuasive Writing

SAY TO STUDENTS: ***Zoos serve three main purposes:***

- ***to provide educational experiences that will help people become better informed about the plight of endangered species and the need for habitat preservation,***
- ***to captively breed animals that are on the road to extinction,***
- ***to preserve biodiversity through research on the genetic makeup of animals.***

Some people think that rather than keeping animals in zoos, this money should be spent on preserving wild habitats. Research and write a report defending one viewpoint or the other.

DATA ANALYSIS LAB 1

- Killer whales are the largest dolphins and live in pods that stay together for decades. They emit vocal sounds that are specific to the pod. To compensate for the background noise of boats, whales could increase the frequency, amplitude, or duration of their sounds. This experiment tested only the duration of the sounds.
- Also see Williams et al. 2002. Behavioural responses of killer whales *(Orcinus orca)* to whale-watching boats: opportunistic observations and experimental approaches. *Journal of Zoology* 256: 255–270.

Think Critically

1. The boat noise interferes with the whale calls.
2. As the amount of boat noise increased, the duration of the calls increases.

Demonstration

Endangered Mammals Prepare a slideshow presentation of endangered mammals. Focus on carnivores, elephants, and the order Sirenia. Emphasize the demands that have brought about the animals' endangered status. For example, many endangered cats have been hunted for their fur. Elephants have been hunted for their ivory tusks. Manatees have been killed in boating accidents. As an alternative, consider showing a video on the current status of elephants and the measures that have been taken to prevent their extinction. Films are available in public libraries. Est. time: 15 min

R Reading Strategy

EL Anticipatory Guide

SAY TO STUDENTS: *Before you read this page, decide whether the following statements are true or false. After you read, validate or revise your answers.* ***1. Mammals evolved from reptiles.*** True ***2. Mammals did not live at the same time as dinosaurs.*** False ***3. The first mammals were very large.*** False ***4. When flowering plants appeared, mammals decreased in number.*** False ***5. Therapsids are extinct.*** True ***6. The Cenozoic Era is called the "Age of Mammals."*** True ***7. Mammals had higher metabolic rates than dinosaurs.*** True

C Critical Thinking

AL Interpret

SAY TO STUDENTS: ***Examine the cladogram in Figure 20 and determine the trend in mammalian size during the course of evolution.*** Mammals generally became larger. ***Infer why this trend occurred.*** Answers will vary. One reason might be that when mammals first evolved, dinosaurs roamed Earth. In order to escape dinosaur predators, mammals that were small had an advantage because they could hide easily. After dinosaur predators no longer existed, mammals that were larger were no longer at a disadvantage.

Caption Question Fig. 20 monotremes

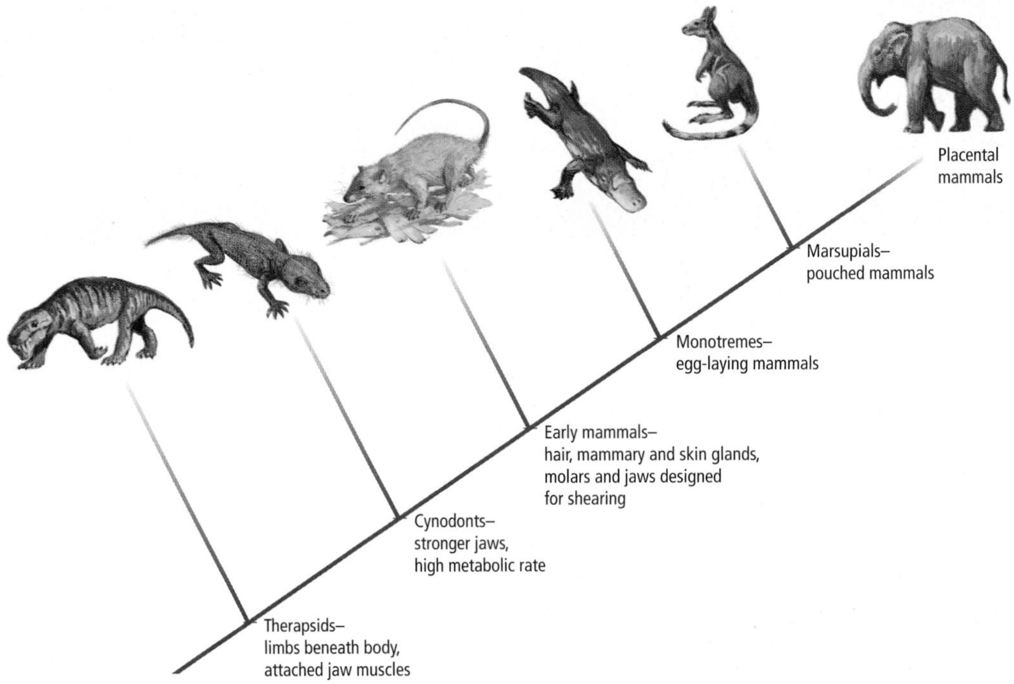

Figure 20 Fossil evidence has enabled scientists to make this cladogram that reflects the evolution of living placental mammals. **Interpret** *which present-day mammals are the oldest group?*

C

Evolution of Mammals

R

The first mammals probably evolved from reptiles in the mid-Triassic period about 220 million years ago. A few lived side by side with the dinosaurs, but mammals did not become common until the dinosaurs disappeared. The cladogram in **Figure 20** shows one interpretation of the evolution of mammals.

Therapsids Fossil evidence indicates that the first mammals probably arose from a group of mammal-like reptiles called therapsids. A **therapsid** is an extinct vertebrate with both mammalian and reptilian features. Therapsids had some characteristics of mammals today, including a pair of holes in the roof of the skull that allowed for the attachment of jaw muscles. Therapsids also had limbs positioned beneath their bodies that allowed for more efficient movement.

Evidence shows that therapsids might have been endotherms. They ate more food than their ancestors, which might have provided them with the energy to produce their own body heat. Being endothermic would have given therapsids an advantage over other ectothermic vertebrates in that they would have been able to be more active during the winter. Therapsids went extinct about 170 million years ago. One subgroup of therapsids called cynodonts continued to evolve more mammalian characteristics, including a high metabolic rate, stronger jaws, and a structure in the mouth that allowed them to breathe while holding food or nursing. A cynodont is shown in **Figure 21.**

Research Citation

Think Critically Educational research indicates that students should be provided with direct instruction on how to think critically. For example, before asking students to examine the cladogram on this page, model the strategies of interpreting a diagram and finding patterns. (Suydam, 1980)

Research bibliography on pages 32T–34T

Differentiated Instruction

Hearing Impaired If you show a video or presentation on endangered animals as suggested on page 895, provide hearing impaired students with a summary before the movie is shown in class or use captioning if available.

For more tips, see pages 14T–15T.

Cynodont

Eomaia

■ **Figure 21** Cynodonts were animals that had some characteristics of mammals and were about the size of a weasel. *Eomaia* is the oldest placental mammal fossil discovered.

The Age of Mammals According to fossil evidence, the first placental mammals might have been mouse-sized animals such as *Eomaia,* shown in **Figure 21.** Recently unearthed fossils show some mammals were larger. One was 1m in length with a squat body and predatory teeth. Another had a beaverlike tail adapted to swim. When dinosaurs disappeared at the end of the Mesozoic Era, mammals underwent extraordinary adaptations to the environment. As flowering plants flourished, new sources of nutrition and new habitats became available. Mammals had new environments to fill. For example, fast-moving herbivores and their predators evolved to fill the niches in the drier prairies. The huge expansion in mammalian diversity and numbers led some scientists to call the Cenozoic Era the "Age of Mammals."

D

Section 2 Assessment

Section Summary

- Of the three subgroups of mammals, only members of one lay eggs.
- Members of one of the mammalian subgroups have pouches in which the young spend most of their development time.
- Placental mammals have young that are nourished by the placenta as they develop in the uterus.
- Mammals might have evolved from reptilian ancestors called therapsids.
- There was a huge expansion in the diversity of mammals in the Cenozoic era.

Understand Main Ideas

1. MAIN Idea **Describe** the three subgroups of mammals and their features.
2. **Identify** the order or orders to which the following mammal might belong and explain your reasoning: it has reddish-brown fur, two pairs of incisors in the upper jaw (one pair behind the other), claws, a body that is a little smaller than a basketball, and it can jump easily.
3. **Compare and contrast** the characteristics of mammals in order Perissodactyla to those in order Artiodactyla.
4. **Explain** how evidence suggests that mammals evolved from reptiles.

Think Critically

5. **Hypothesize** The bill of a platypus can detect the electrical fields of muscle contraction of other animals. This is how the platypus searches for prey. Form a hypothesis about how this complicated adaptation developed in place of simply searching visually for prey.

WRITING in **Biology**

6. Some people have the misconception that marsupials are inferior to placental mammals. Analyze and explain the faulty reasoning of this idea.

D Develop Concepts

OL AL COOP LEARN Activity

Divide students into small groups. **SAY TO STUDENTS:** ***Research what the environment and habitat were like during the "Age of Mammals." Make a travel brochure for "time travelers" who would like to take a trip back in time to the "Age of Mammals."***

Formative Assessment

Evaluation

SAY TO STUDENTS: ***Create and complete a table with the following columns:*** **Placental mammal orders, Diagram of mammal, Adaptations to habitat.** For example, Cetacea, dolphin diagram, tail modified for swimming.

Remediation Divide students into teams of three. Have them make cards with the names of mammalian groups and vocabulary terms from this section. Have one person take a card from the deck and draw a diagram of the term on the back of the card. As the diagram is being drawn, the other two members of the team have one minute to try to guess the term from the diagram. If the team guesses the term, award them a point. The team with the most points wins.

Section 2 Assessment

1. Monotremes lay eggs. Marsupials have pouches for the development of young. The young of placental mammals develop in the uterus, where they get nourishment from the placenta.
2. Rodentia. They have two pairs of incisors and make up 40 percent of mammals.
3. Both are hoofed mammals and herbivores with specialized teeth adapted for chewing. Perissodactyls have an odd number of toes, and members of order Artiodactla have an even number of toes.
4. Fossil evidence shows that the first mammals probably arose from a group of mammal-like reptiles. These organisms may have been endotherms and had limbs positioned beneath their bodies.
5. Platypuses might hunt in muddy water where prey cannot be found visually.
6. Marsupials are well adapted to their environments. They occupy the same environments as their placental counterparts. Their reproductive methods are successful.

Assessment Online Quiz

In the Field

Purpose

Students will learn that scientists, including comparative anatomist Joy Reidenberg, perform whale necropsies in order to understand how whales live and what causes their deaths.
C.6, F.5

Anticipatory Guide

ASK STUDENTS:

What do you know about whale beachings? Students probably have heard about whale beachings; they might have seen the topic reported on a TV news program. They might know that scientists are not sure why live whales beach themselves. ***Why don't scientists know more about this phenomenon?*** Students might say that because whales are so large and because they live in deep ocean waters, scientists have not been able to study them very closely.

Background

Whales are not always found on a beach. Sometimes, they are found floating dead in the ocean, and then the necropsy must take place at sea. In 2005, Woods Hole Oceanographic Institution biologist Michael Moore was called to perform a necropsy on a finback whale found floating near Nantucket, Massachusetts. His ship scared away hundreds of mako, blue, and dusky sharks that were gathering to feed on the whale's body. Moore had planned to perform the whale necropsy from a small rubber boat put into the water by the larger ship on which he had traveled to the scene. However, several of the sharks refused to leave and continued to feed on the whale's body, so Moore was forced to climb onto the whale's body and perform the necropsy there.

In the Field

Career: Comparative Anatomist

Necropsies Help Scientists Study Whales

It is a disturbing sight: A whale beaches itself and, unable to return to the ocean, dies. Scientists do not fully understand why whales beach themselves, and so they often perform a necropsy, an examination of the body to determine the cause of death. Comparative anatomist Dr. Joy Reidenberg has devoted her career to necropsies of whales and dolphins, a smelly, slimy job that reaps valuable data for scientists.

Whales live so much of their lives in deep ocean waters that scientists have not been able to study them closely. Dr. Reidenberg and other scientists who perform necropsies want to find out how whales died, but they also want to learn more about how they live.

Usually, whales are too large to move and so necropsies are performed where the whales beach. This was the situation in January 2009, when an adult fin whale beached itself and died in a bay off the south coast of Ireland. Dr. Reidenberg and other scientists struggled against rain, hail, and wind to perform a necropsy.

Dr. Reidenberg began by cutting the whale to let out gases caused by decomposition. Once the gases had dispersed, she stripped the blubber off the whale's underside and removed the digestive tract. Dr. Reidenberg found that several chambers of the whale's stomach held nothing but liquid, which meant the whale had not been feeding. Dr. Reidenberg suspected the whale had been sick.

Dr. Reidenberg examined the other organs too. She checked the whale for cuts, bruises, and broken bones, but she found none.

She hypothesized that the sick whale had moved into the shallows of the bay to rest; but when the tide went out, gravity caught up with it. Without water to support it, the whale suffocated under its own weight.

As smelly, slimy, and difficult as it is, whale necropsy is important. If scientists can figure out why whales beach themselves and die, they can work to protect them and other marine animals from conditions that cause premature death. That is not bad for a messy day's work.

WRITING in Biology

News Blog Imagine that you are a journalist for a local newspaper. A dead whale has just washed up on a beach in your town. For your newspaper's Web site, write a blog entry that describes the work of the scientists who perform a necropsy on the beach.

WRITING in Biology

RUBRIC Use the modifiable rubric found on your eTeacherEdition Online to assess writing assignments.

Activity

Students might not be aware that journalists write blogs for the Web sites of newspapers, magazines, and TV news programs. Help them find several local news blogs so that they can see the kind of information contained in the blogs and the styles in which they are written. Encourage students to do more research on whale necropsy so that their fictional blog entries contain factual information about the process.

WebQuest

BIOLAB

HOW DO WE IDENTIFY MAMMALS?

Background: The physical characteristics that all mammals share, such as fur and mammary glands, have enabled them to adapt to nearly every ecosystem in the biosphere. Mammals thrive in rain forests, deserts, and polar regions, and they have adapted to the environment near your home or school as well.

Question: *What diversity of mammals can be found in your area?*

Materials

North American mammal identification field guide
binoculars
field journal

Safety Precautions

Procedure

1. Read and complete the lab safety form.
2. List the mammals you have observed in your area of the country.
3. Predict how these species of mammals would be classified.
4. Design and construct a data table for recording the species; physical characteristics, such as size, body shape, and unique features; and taxonomic classifications of the mammals you have observed.
5. Research the mammals to fill in information in your data table. Either observe the animals in their natural habitat in your local area, such as a park or wetlands, or visit the zoo. If you cannot observe the animals in their natural habitats, obtain information about local mammals from a guide book.
6. Record your observations in your field journal and transfer the information to your data table.
7. Share your results with classmates.

Analyze and Conclude

1. **Describe** basic characteristics shared by all mammals that you have observed.
2. **Compare and contrast** the mammals from your study to those of other students around the country.
3. **Compare and contrast** the physical characteristics scientists could use to separate the mammals into different taxonomic orders.
4. **Infer** how the mammals from your list have adapted to and survived in their environments.
5. **Describe** other observation strategies that could be used to conduct a more comprehensive mammal search of your chosen search area.
6. **Error Analysis** Compare your list of identified mammal species with the lists compiled by other students to determine possible identification errors.

POSTER SESSION

Make a Presentation Collect photographs of the mammals from another area of the country and create a poster to present to your class. Include information about the specific characteristics and adaptations of each mammal.

Analyze and Conclude

1. Answers will vary, but could include fur, mammary glands, and teeth.
2. Answers will vary, but should include the names of several mammals not included in the student's study. Also, students should hypothesize why those mammals may not live in their region.
3. Answers will vary, but scientists could classify mammals based on teeth, type of food eaten, or shape of limbs.
4. Answers will vary but may include thick fur and hibernation to survive cold winters, specialized teeth for obtaining local foods, and coloration for camouflage
5. Answers will vary, but may include setting up an observation blind, using a variety of foods to attract mammals, nighttime observation of nocturnal mammals, and tree-top observation platforms.
6. Student answers will vary, but should include an explanation of which animals differ and why the findings are different.

BIOLAB

? Inquiry BioLab

For a lab worksheet, use your eTeacherEdition Online.

RUBRIC A rubric for evaluating BioLabs is found on your eTeacherEdition Online.

Est. Time 90 min

Content Background Students will review the common characteristics all mammals share, and they will explore the diversity of mammals found in their area. Students also will observe mammal characteristics used to classify the mammals they discover into their proper taxonomic orders.

Safety Precautions Approve lab safety forms before work begins. Caution students entering wild areas to follow proper precautions to guard against ticks, poisonous snakes, and plants. Tell students not to conduct their surveys in wilderness areas unless accompanied by an expert wilderness guide. Students should never handle or approach wild animals.

Teaching Strategy Instruct students to consider searching for mammals early in the morning or at dusk, when some mammals might be more active. Bats, for example, can be observed in the early evening.

Alternative Teaching Demo Ask permission to make a video of the mammals found in a large pet store or a zoo. The class can watch the video and fill out their data tables based on their observations of the mammals in the store or zoo.

Chapter 30 Study Guide

THEME FOCUS Energy High metabolic rates of mammals require the consumption of large quantities of food to obtain the energy needed for daily life.

BIG Idea **Mammals have evolved to have many adaptations for maintaining homeostasis and living in a variety of habitats.**

Section 1 Mammalian Characteristics

mammary gland (p. 880)
diaphragm (p. 885)
cerebral cortex (p. 886)
cerebellum (p. 886)
gland (p. 887)
uterus (p. 887)
placenta (p. 887)
gestation (p. 887)

MAIN Idea **Mammals have two distinct characteristics: hair and mammary glands.**

- Mammals are successful in a wide variety of habitats.
- Mammals have specialized teeth that are adapted to their diets.
- Respiratory, circulatory, and nervous systems have complex adaptations that enable mammals to have the extra energy they need and to maintain homeostasis.
- Mammals have internal fertilization and, in most mammals, offspring develop within the female uterus.

Section 2 Diversity of Mammals

monotreme (p. 889)
marsupial (p. 890)
placental mammal (p. 891)
therapsid (p. 896)

MAIN Idea **Class Mammalia is divided into three subgroups based on reproductive methods.**

- Of the three subgroups of mammals, only members of one lay eggs.
- Members of one of the mammalian subgroups have pouches in which the young spend most of their development time.
- Placental mammals have young that are nourished by the placenta as they develop in the uterus.
- Mammals might have evolved from reptilian ancestors called therapsids.
- There was a huge expansion in the diversity of mammals in the Cenozoic era.

Chapter 30 Study Guide

ConnectED

Students can use the following to review the chapter.

Review

Vocabulary eGames
Vocabulary eFlashcards
Vocabulary PuzzleMaker

Assessment

Online Quizzes
Online Test Practice
Standardized Test Practice

Use the *ExamView®* *Assessment Suite* CD-ROM to:

- create multiple versions of tests
- create modified tests with one mouse click
- edit existing questions and add your own questions
- build tests aligned with state standards using built-in state curriculum tags
- change English tests to Spanish with one mouse click
- track students' progress using the Teacher Management System

Review **Vocabulary PuzzleMaker**

For additional practice with vocabulary, have students access the Vocabulary PuzzleMaker online.

Review **Vocabulary eGames**

Section 1

Vocabulary Review

In the analogies that follow, one of the words is missing. Complete each analogy by filling in the blank with a vocabulary term from the Study Guide page.

1. A yolk is to a bird as a ________ is to a mammal.
2. Incubation period is to a bird as a ________ period is to a mammal.
3. The nucleus is to the cell as the ________ is to the brain.

Understand Main Ideas

Use the diagram below to answer questions 4 and 5.

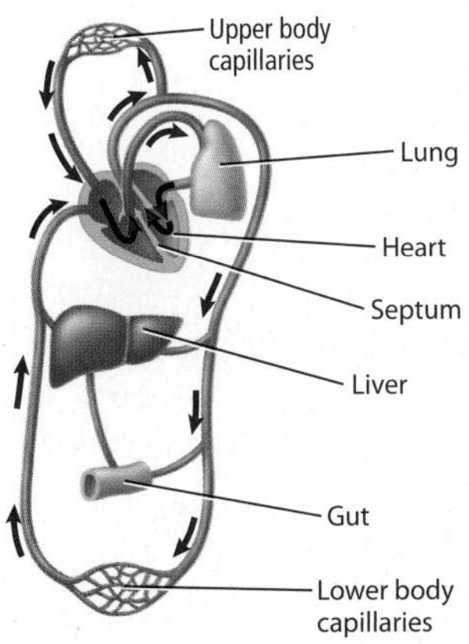

4. Which body system is illustrated in the diagram?
   A. excretory system **C.** circulatory system
   B. skeletal system **D.** reproductive system

5. Which best explains how this system supports endothermy in mammals?
   A. Oxygenated blood is separated from deoxygenated blood.
   B. The heart has three chambers and is able to pump more blood.
   C. This system moves oxygenated blood to the lungs.
   D. This system moves deoxygenated blood from the heart to the body.

6. Which is the least involved in maintaining homeostasis in mammals?
   A. kidneys **C.** sweat glands
   B. heart **D.** claws

7. Oil glands, sweat glands, and mammary glands are responsible for which functions?
   A. hair and skin maintenance, temperature regulation, milk production
   B. reproduction, hair and skin maintenance, temperature regulation
   C. temperature regulation, milk production, reproduction
   D. milk production, oxygen delivery, hair and skin maintenance

Use the diagram below to answer questions 8 and 9.

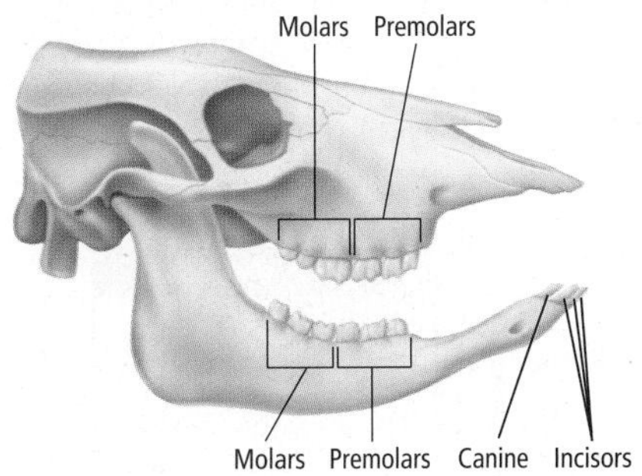

8. In what way did having a variety of tooth types contribute to the presence of mammals in all habitat types?
   A. They could eat a variety of foods.
   B. They could hunt effectively.
   C. They could digest their food more easily.
   D. Their digestive tracts were modified.

9. In which trophic category does this mammal belong?
   A. herbivore **C.** carnivore
   B. insectivore **D.** detritivore

Constructed Response

10. **THEME FOCUS Energy** Examine **Table 1** and form a hypothesis that explains why there are such big differences in the nutrient content of the milk from different mammals.

Chapter 30

Assessment

Section 1

Vocabulary Review

1. placenta
2. gestation
3. cerebral cortex

Understand Main Ideas

4. C
5. A
6. D
7. A
8. A
9. A

Constructed Response

10. Different amounts of nutrients provide different levels of energy to the young. This needed energy is determined by the mammal's metabolic and endothermic rates.

11. cetacea and sirenia – both are aquatic, neither have hind limbs, both have flippers; sirenia tend to be herbivores, cetacean can be carnivores or omnivores, cetacean move quickly through the water

Think Critically

12. Obtain two small pieces of clear glass through which UV light can freely pass. Place the fluid on one piece of glass and place beads that are UV-sensitive behind the glass. Place the plain glass adjacent to it with more UV-sensitive beads behind this piece. Hold a UV light in front of the pieces of glass for 10 min. If a UV light is not available, expose the set-up to outdoor light.

13. Pacing behavior increased in captivity when mammals had larger home ranges in the wild.

Section 2

Vocabulary Review

14. placental mammal
15. therapsids
16. Monotremes
17. Marsupials

Understand Main Ideas

18. B
19. D
20. C
21. C
22. C

Constructed Response

23. Answers will vary.
24. Answers will vary, but can be based on diet, location, and adaptation of hair.
25. Debate assertions will vary, depending on the student's thoughts about testing with animals.

11. MAIN Idea Refer to **Table 2** which organizes twelve orders of placental mammals. Compare and contrast two of the orders' characteristics.

Think Critically

12. **Design an Experiment** Hippopotamuses secrete a fluid from glands deep in their skin that may function as sweat but can have other functions as well. Biologists hypothesize that this fluid might act as a sunscreen for the skin of the hippopotamus. Design an experiment using beads that absorb ultraviolet light that would test if the fluid on the skin of this mammal provides protection from the Sun.

13. **Analyze and Conclude** Biologists hypothesized that carnivores with large home range sizes, when in captivity in small spaces, had higher incidences of pacing behavior. They studied the arctic fox, the polar bear, and the lion. Analyze the graph below and make conclusions about the effect of confinement on pacing behavior.

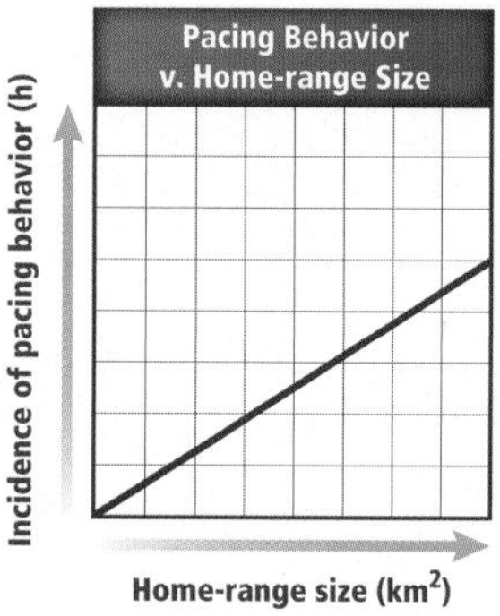

Section 2

Vocabulary Review

Each of the following sentences is false. Make the sentence true by replacing the italicized word with a vocabulary term from the Study Guide page.

14. An elephant is an example of a *marsupial.*
15. Mammals might have evolved from *monotremes.*
16. *Therapsids* are egg-laying mammals.
17. *Monotremes* are mammals that have a pouch.

Understand Main Ideas

18. Which mammal is a member of order Cetacea?
    A. beaver
    B. whale
    C. zebra
    D. manatee

19. Which is a benefit of the development of young within a uterus?
    A. Young are born alive.
    B. Predation of the young is less likely.
    C. Predation of the young is more likely.
    D. Young are more fully developed at birth.

20. Which mammal is not a marsupial?
    A. opossum
    B. kangaroo
    C. echidna
    D. wallaby

21. Which is not a characteristic of the duck-billed platypus?
    A. webbed feet
    B. egg-laying ability
    C. three-chambered heart
    D. small, reptilelike chromosomes

22. Examine **Figure 20.** Which mammal evolved first?
    A. elephant
    B. opossum
    C. echidna
    D. blue whale

Constructed Response

23. **Open Ended** Sketch and explain the ideal adaptations of a mammal that lives in 1-m deep marsh water, much underwater vegetation, and predatory snakes.

24. MAIN Idea Suggest an alternative organization of mammal subgroups.

25. **Open Ended** Arrange for a debate in your class about the use of animals for testing medicines and cosmetics.

Think Critically

26. **Infer** Fossil evidence indicates that mammals lived at the same time as dinosaurs for many millions of years. During this time, mammals were very small compared to the dinosaurs. Infer why it might have been an advantage for mammals to remain so small when dinosaurs roamed Earth.

27. **CAREERS IN BIOLOGY** Find out what mammals are endangered in your area. Assume that you will be the zookeeper responsible for providing and maintaining a space for a new animal that is locally endangered and will be kept on exhibit at the zoo. Design a space, feeding routine, and other care instructions for maintaining this animal in your local zoo. Prepare a sign for the space that will alert people of the importance of protecting this endangered species and ways in which individuals can participate in conservation measures.

28. **Research** Select your favorite group of mammals. Make a map that shows its world distribution. Reflect on ecological factors that might currently be limiting its potential range or might affect the group in the future. Make recommendations about what should be done to insure the success of your favorite mammal group.

Use the table below to answer question 29.

Birth Weight and Protein Content of Milk

Mammal	Days Needed to Double Birth Weight	Protein Content of Milk (g/1000)
Human	180	12
Horse	60	26
Cow	47	33
Pig	18	37
Sheep	10	51
Cat	9	101

29. **Analyze Data** Explain the relationship between the number of days it takes to double birth weight and the protein content of milk. Make a graph of this table.

Summative Assessment

30. **BIG Idea** Choose a specific mammal and describe several adaptations that help the mammal maintain homeostasis in their habitat.

31. **WRITING in Biology** Research which mammal genomes have been sequenced. Write a summary paragraph describing what you learned.

DBQ Document-Based Questions

A specific type of ground squirrel was found to have the ability to produce ultrasonic calls that could not be heard by other mammals as well as calls that could be heard (audible). Biologists exposed ground squirrels to the ultrasonic call, background noise, a tone similar to the ultrasonic calls, and an audible call. Then they observed the portion of time the animals spent in vigilant behavior (looking for predators) during each sound. Use this graph to answer the questions below.

Data obtained from: Wilson, D. and Hare, F. 2004. Ground squirrel uses ultrasonic alarms. *Nature* 430: 523.

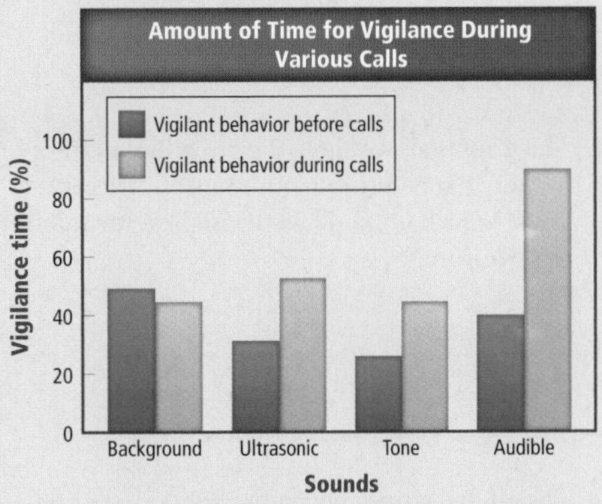

32. Under which conditions did ground squirrels exhibit the most vigilant behavior overall?

33. Under which conditions might an ultrasonic signal be more effective as a warning?

34. What is the percent difference between vigilant behavior before and after the ultrasonic call?

Think Critically

26. Mammals could eat different food than what the dinosaurs were eating. Also, by remaining small, they most likely could hide easily from predatory dinosaurs.
27. Answers will depend on the animal chosen.
28. Answers will depend on the animal chosen.
29. As the number of days needed to double birth weight increases, the amount of protein in milk decreases.

Summative Assessment

WRITING in Biology

RUBRIC Use the modifiable rubric found on your eTeacherEdition Online to assess writing assignments.

30. Descriptions will depend upon animal chosen; snow leopard—long, thick fur, large paws, strong legs.

31. Make sure students describe the mammals that have had their genomes sequenced, such as the mouse and the dog, and how this led to scientific understanding. They might also describe DNA analysis that has led to reclassification of a variety of mammals.

DBQ Document-Based Questions

Wilson, D. and Hare, F. 2004. Ground squirrel uses ultrasonic alarms. *Nature* 430: 523.

32. when an audible call was heard
33. When a ground squirrel sees a predator close by, it emits an ultrasonic call. The predator will not hear it and the squirrel can remain unobserved while still warning other squirrels of the danger.

34. 55% – 30% = 25% difference

Standardized Test Practice

Multiple Choice

1. B 4. C
2. B 5. C
3. A 6. D

Short Answer

7. Answers may vary. Accept all reasonable responses.
   A. Blood vessels close to the surface of the body can dilate or contract, releasing more or less heat to the surroundings.
   B. Mammals can sweat or pant, releasing heat and moisture to the surroundings.
   C. Mammals can shiver, an involuntary muscle response that generates heat in the body.
   D. Hair on the body can stand up, trapping more heat near the surface of the body.
8. Contour feathers cover the body, wings, and tail of birds. They give birds a smooth and streamlined body. Down feathers are soft feathers found under the contour feathers. They trap air that acts as insulation to keep birds warm.
9. Answers can vary. Accept all reasonable responses.
   A. The mother's milk contains the best blend of protein, fat, and other nutrients for the animal's environment and growth needs.
   B. The baby does not have to hunt for food or find food until later in life.
10. Crocodiles are the modern reptiles most closely related to dinosaurs. They are the modern reptiles on the closest branch to the dinosaurs.
11. Birds are very adaptable and can move easily over broad areas. They have adapted to a wide variety of habitats and become very specialized in their feeding habits.

Standardized Test Practice

Cumulative

Multiple Choice

Use the graphs below to answer questions 1 and 2.

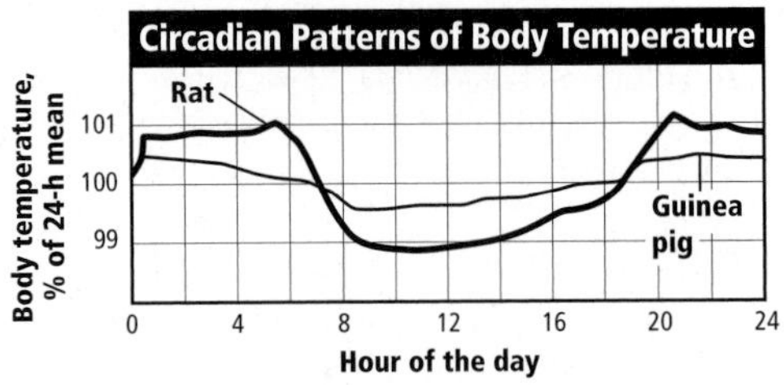

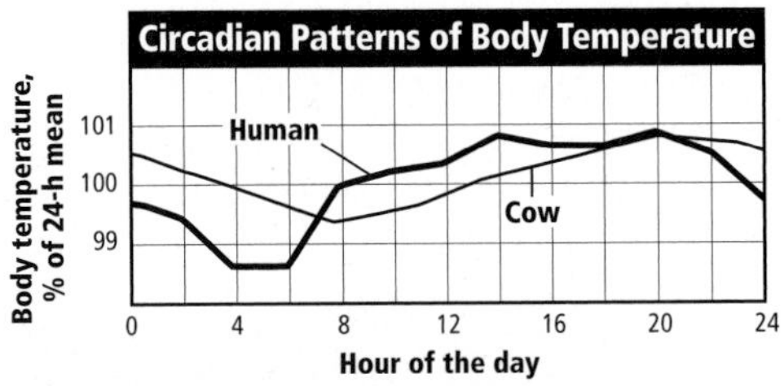

1. The graphs above show the circadian pattern of body temperature in animals of different sizes. Which animal has the highest mean body temperature?
   A. cow
   B. guinea pig
   C. human
   D. rat

2. The rat and guinea pig on the graph above are mainly nocturnal animals. What can you infer from this graph about the body temperatures of nocturnal animals?
   A. They have higher body temperatures than animals that are active during the day.
   B. They have more extreme temperature changes than animals that are active during the day.
   C. They have lower body temperatures than animals that are active during the day.
   D. They have less extreme temperature changes than animals that are active during the day.

3. Which statement describes the difference between invertebrate chordates and the rest of the phylum Chordata?
   A. Invertebrate chordates lack a backbone.
   B. Invertebrate chordates lack a notochord.
   C. Other members of the phylum lack a backbone.
   D. Other members of the phylum lack a notochord.

Use the table below to answer question 4.

Row	Group	Some Components of the Digestive System
1	Amphibians	Has gizzard, stomach, intestines
2	Reptiles	Has crop, large and small intestines
3	Birds	Has crop, gizzard, intestines
4	Fishes	Has swim bladder, stomach, intestines

4. Which row of information in the table contains correct information about the digestive system?
   A. 1
   B. 2
   C. 3
   D. 4

5. Pharyngeal pouches are defined as which of the following?
   A. cavities that hold food as it is digested
   B. sacs that hold the coiled digestive system in place
   C. structures that link the mouth cavity and the esophagus
   D. structures that regulate metabolism, growth, and development

6. How many pairs of jointed appendages do spiders have?
   A. 3
   B. 4
   C. 5
   D. 8

Short Answer

7. Describe four different characteristics or processes that enable mammals to maintain homeostatic temperature control.

8. Compare and contrast the two types of bird feathers.

9. Describe two benefits for young mammals receiving milk from their mothers.

Use the diagram below to answer question 10.

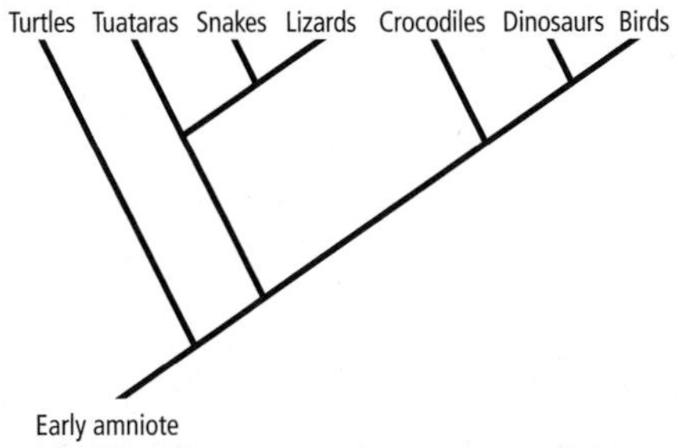

10. Assess which group of modern reptiles is most closely related to dinosaurs.

11. Hypothesize why there are so many different types of birds living today.

12. List two ways in which seedless vascular plants are better adapted than nonvascular plants to survive in a changing environment.

Extended Response

13. Sea cucumbers protect themselves by casting out their internal organs, but other echinoderms cannot. Hypothesize why this adaptation is found only in sea cucumbers.

14. Assess how the skeleton of a bird is adapted for flight.

15. Critique why an *r*-strategist population might be better suited to live in an unpredictable climate than a *k*-strategist population.

Essay Question

In most bird species, both parents care for the young. The parents come together during mating season to mate and raise their young. In some bird species, one parent builds the nest and then attracts a mate. In other bird species, the parents build the nest together. The parents often take turns guarding the eggs and keeping them warm. When the young hatch, the parents bring food that is similar to what young birds will eat as adults. This parental care continues until the chicks are ready to fly away. After they leave the nest, young birds are on their own and seldom have any more contact with their parents.

Using the information in the paragraph above, answer the following question in essay format.

16. Young birds usually are cared for by both parents. In mammals, the mother often raises the young by herself. Propose a hypothesis that explains why both bird parents care for the young while only the mammalian mother cares for her young. Discuss how the hypothesis could be tested.

NEED EXTRA HELP?																
If You Missed Question . . .	1	2	3	4	5	6	7	8	9	10	11	12	13	14	15	16
Review Section . . .	30.1	30.1	27.2	29.2	27.2	26.2	30.1	29.2	30.1	29.1	29.2	21.2	27.1	29.2	4.1	29.2

12. Answers may vary. Possible answers include the following.
   A. They can grow taller, allowing better photosynthesis, because they have a vascular system.
   B. They can survive without water for some time, because a vascular system allows them to store water.

Extended Response

13. Sea cucumbers split off from the rest of the echinoderms very early. This adaptation evolved in sea cucumbers after they split off from the others.
14. Birds have lightweight skeletons that are strong. Their bones are hollow and air filled. Many of the bones are fused together to make them stronger.
15. An *r*-strategist population reproduces and grows rapidly. When conditions are favorable, the population quickly increases. A *k*-strategist population requires a long time to reach maturity and grows slowly. The population usually cannot adapt to rapidly changing conditions.

Essay Question

16. Answers will vary. Possible answers include that male and female birds can help take care of offspring or only female mammals are capable of producing milk for their young. Students may suggest using observations of success rates for both birds and mammals as a way of testing the hypothesis.

Chapter 31 Organizer: Animal Behavior

LabManager™
Customize any lab with the LabManager™ CD-ROM.

Essential Questions	National Science Standards	Materials and Planning: Estimated times include cleanup and disposal, but do not include teacher prep time. For cleanup and disposal guidelines, see page 39T.	Est. Time (min)
Section 1 1. How are animal behaviors related to evolution by natural selection? 2. What are the differences between innate and learned behaviors? 3. What are the different types of animal behavior and what are examples of each?	UCP.1–5; A.1, A.2; C.2, C.3, C.4, C.6	**Launch Lab,** page 906: video or photos of bird behaviors	20
		Demonstration, page 910: photographs or videos showing animal behaviors	10
		MiniLab 1, page 912: earthworms, tray, paper towel, aged tap water, gloves, paint brush	15
		Activity, page 912: writing utensil	5
Section 2 1. What are different types of competitive behaviors and what are examples of each? 2. What is the importance of foraging, migration, and biological rhythms? 3. What are the different types of communication, nurturing, and cooperative behaviors? 4. What are the advantages and disadvantages of behavior in terms of survival and reproductive success?	UCP.1–5; A.1, A.2; C.3, C.4, C.5, C.6; F.3, F.4, F.5	**Demonstration,** page 922: ant farm or tank with fish	10
		Activity, page 924: coiled spring toy	10
		Design Your Own BioLab, page 925: clear plastic food wrap, forceps, petri dishes with lids, cardboard boxes or trays, small paper plates, aged tap water, black paper, isopods, scissors, light source, filter paper, paper towels, tape, graph paper	90

Suggested Time for Each Lesson

Class	Chapter Opener	Section 1	Section 2	Assessment
Basic	45 min	45 min	45 min	45 min
General	25 min	100 min	55 min	45 min
Honors	—	25 min	20 min	45 min

ConnectED

connectED.mcgraw-hill.com

Access interactive learning opportunities and teaching resources using these icons located throughout your StudentWorks™ Plus Online and eTeacherEdition Online.

Chapter 31 Section Resources

FAST FILE Unit 8 Resources:
- Launch Lab Worksheet*
- MiniLab Worksheet*
- Study Guide (English/Spanish)*
- Section Quick Check

Reading Essentials 31.1

Science Notebook 31.1*

FAST FILE Unit 8 Resources:
- BioLab Worksheet*
- Study Guide (English/Spanish)*
- Section Quick Check

Reading Essentials 31.2

Science Notebook 31.2*

Additional Chapter 31 Resources

FAST FILE Unit 8 Resources:
- Chapter Diagnostic Test
- Concept Mapping*
- Real-World Biology
- Enrichment
- Chapter Tests A, B, and C

Transparencies:
- Bellringer Transparencies*
- Biology Concepts Transparencies*

Lab Resources:
- Laboratory Manual*
- Probeware Lab Manual*
- Forensics Lab Manual*
- Pre-AP Lab Manual*
- Open Inquiry in Biology*
- Guided Inquiry in Biology*

Technology

Teaching Tools:
- eTeacherEdition Online
- Classroom Presentation Toolkit CD-ROM*
- LabManager™ CD-ROM*
- Video Lab DVD*
- Virtual Lab CD-ROM*
- What's BIOLOGY Got To Do With It?
- StudentWorks™ Plus Online*

Chapter Assessment Tools:
- Classroom Presentation Toolkit CD-ROM*
- *ExamView® Assessment Suite* CD-ROM

Web-Based Resources:
- StudentWorks™ Plus Online
- eTeacherEdition Online
- Animations*
- The Interactive Time Line*
- Interactive Tables*
- Online Quizzes
- Online Test Practice
- Standardized Test Practice
- Virtual Labs*
- Multilingual eGlossary*
- Vocabulary eGames*
- Vocabulary eFlashcards
- WebQuests
- Personal Tutors

While all resources listed are appropriate for English learners, the * indicates resources with a strong visual or hands-on component for EL.

Teaching strategies and activities have been coded for differentiated instruction.

AL Activities for students working above grade level	**OL** Activities for students working on grade level	**BL** Activities for students working below grade level	**EL** Activities for English learners (also ELL)	**COOP LEARN** Activities designed for small cooperative group work

CHAPTER 31

Launch Lab
How do scientists observe animal behavior in the field?

? Inquiry Launch Lab

For a lab worksheet, use your eTeacherEdition Online.

RUBRIC A rubric for evaluating Launch Labs is found on your eTeacherEdition Online.

Est. Time 20 min

Teaching Strategies
- If a video of bird behavior is not available, photos showing bird behavior, without the captions displayed, can be substituted. Alternatively, any video showing behavior in a large group of seals, prairie dogs, or other colonial animals could be used.
- Depending on school location, live birds may also be observed, such as gulls on the shore, ducks in a park, or pigeons in a city school yard.
- Some resources that may be useful include the film *Winged Migration* by filmmaker Jacques Perrin, and *March of the Penguins*, a National Geographic film directed by Luc Jacquet, both of which includes scenes of birds exhibiting mating, territorial, nurturing, and migratory behavior.

Procedure
1. Read and complete the lab safety form.
2. Record a description of all the different behaviors you observe in the **video** or **photos**.
3. Review your list and infer why the birds might have exhibited each type of behavior.

CHAPTER 31

Animal Behavior

ConnectED
Your one-stop online resource
connectED.mcgraw-hill.com

- Video
- Audio
- Review
- Inquiry
- WebQuest
- Assessment
- Concepts in Motion
- Multilingual eGlossary

Launch Lab
How do scientists observe animal behavior in the field?

Observing animals in their natural habitat is one way that scientists can study animal behavior. The photo shows a colony of emperor penguins in Antarctica. Penguins exhibit behavior associated with courtship, care of their young, grooming, and defending territories. In this lab, you will watch a short video or view photos of bird behavior.

For a lab worksheet, use your StudentWorks™ Plus Online.

? Inquiry Launch Lab

FOLDABLES®

Make a five tab book and label it with the types of learned behavior. Use it to organize your notes on the five types of learned behavior.

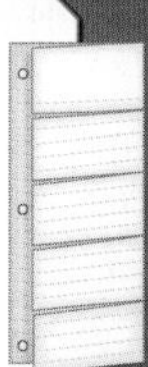

Analysis

1. **Explain** If you want to understand penguin behavior, you need to study many birds under various conditions. Why is this? Students' answers should include ideas such as the need to study both males and females, and both young birds and adult birds. Birds should be studied under different conditions since they would have various behaviors for different activities; for example: territorial behavior differs from mating behavior.
2. **Infer** Some of the behaviors you noticed might have been competitive behaviors. For what resources might animals compete? How could competitive behaviors benefit any animal? Birds and other colonial animals must compete for mates, nesting space, food, and water. Animals that are able to compete successfully will be more likely to survive and produce offspring.

THEME FOCUS Scientific Inquiry
Biologists study animals, their behavior, and their environment to learn about their interactive relationships.

BIG Idea Many animal behaviors are influenced by both genetics and environmental experiences.

Section 1 • Basic Behaviors

Section 2 • Ecological Behaviors

THEMES

Scientific Inquiry Biologists study animal behavior to learn about their interactive relationships.

Diversity Animal behaviors depend on the situation and the action required.

Energy Different behaviors have different energy requirements. Some behaviors might specifically conserve energy.

Homeostasis Migratory behaviors and biological rhythms maintain homeostasis in populations through reproduction, food consumption, and land use.

Change Animals adapt and change their behaviors to meet changes in their environment.

Introduce the Chapter

Identify Behavior Animals exhibit behaviors necessary for species survival. As students will learn in this chapter, some behaviors are group oriented and some are individual. Have students study the photos of the penguins on this page.

ASK STUDENTS: ***What behaviors are being exhibited by the penguins?*** possible answers: feeding young, defending territory, greeting a mate

BIG Idea

Concept Map Have students read the headings in the chapter. From the New Vocabulary lists, select three or four behavior terms and write them on the board. sample terms: dominance hierarchy, language, migratory behavior, foraging behavior, nurturing behavior Also write "innate" and "learned."

SAY TO STUDENTS: ***Create a concept map of animal behaviors. As you read the text, write a brief definition of the behavior, then indicate on your map whether the behavior is innate, learned, or both.*** Have students also include an animal example of the behavior.

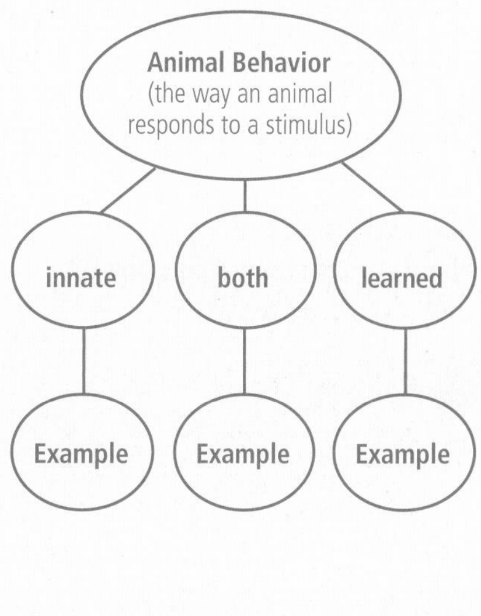

Section 1

MAIN Idea

OL AL Behavior of Animals

ASK STUDENTS: ***How do you think animal behavior in nature differs from behavior of the same species in a zoo?*** Nurturing and grooming might be the same in nature and in a zoo; competing for resources such as food, space, and mates might be different. ***Why do you think these behaviors were altered or remained the same?*** Some behaviors might remain the same because they have a genetic basis. Other behaviors might be altered because they are influenced by the environment, which is different in a zoo than in the wild.

R Reading Strategy

OL AL Vocabulary Chart

Have students create a chart like the one below. As students read Section 1, have them look for definitions for each vocabulary term and record the definition and an example in their charts.

Term	Definition	Example
Behavior		
Innate behavior		
Fixed action pattern		
Learned behavior		
Habituation		
Classical conditioning		
Operant conditioning		
Imprinting		
Cognitive behavior		

EL BL COOP LEARN

Have students work in pairs as they do this activity.

Reading Check After a cool night, the lizard would need to warm up. It increases its body temperature by lying on the warm rock because it cannot generate body heat on its own.

Section 1

Reading Preview

Essential Questions

- How are animal behaviors related to evolution by natural selection?
- What are the differences between innate and learned behaviors?
- What are the different types of animal behavior and what are examples of each?

Review Vocabulary

natural selection: population process by which heritable traits that result in the greatest number of offspring eventually become the most common traits in the population

New Vocabulary

behavior
innate behavior
fixed action pattern
learned behavior
habituation
classical conditioning
operant conditioning
imprinting
cognitive behavior

g Multilingual eGlossary

R Basic Behaviors

MAIN Idea Animal behaviors can be innate or learned, and they evolve through natural selection.

Real-World Reading Link Think about what happens when you smell your favorite food as you walk by a restaurant. Whether you are hungry or not, your mouth might start to water and you might start thinking about how good that food tastes. Other animals have similar behaviors.

Behavior

You might have seen a lizard lying on a rock in the sunlight. The lizard is regulating its body temperature through its behavior. In order to raise its body temperature, the lizard absorbs the Sun's heat. If the lizard's body temperature starts to get too high, it will move into the shade. This is an example of behavior. **Behavior** is the way an animal responds to a stimulus. A stimulus (STIHM yuh lus) is an environmental change that directly influences the activity of an organism.

Behavior can occur in response to an internal stimulus, which is a stimulus that comes from inside the body, as in the case of the lizard. Behavior can also be caused by an external stimulus—a stimulus that comes from outside the body. An external stimulus could be the smell of food, someone calling your name, or the sight of a predator.

Reading Check Summarize why a lizard might lie on a warm rock in the morning.

Figure 1
Studying Animal Behavior
The study of animal behavior only began about 100 years ago.

Concepts in Motion
The Interactive Timeline

1923 Austrian zoologist Karl von Frisch discovers that bees communicate by performing rhythmic dances.

1935 Konrad Lorenz describes and names the behavior of imprinting in baby ducks and goslings.

1900 — 1920 — 1970

1898 Ivan Pavlov, a Russian physiologist, conditions a dog to salivate in response to the stimulus of a ringing bell.

1971 British zoologist Jane Goodall first documents that chimpanzees use tools.

Concepts in Motion
The Interactive Timeline

Research Citation

Main Ideas Educational research indicates that students will benefit when they understand the main idea of a lesson. By making the big ideas explicit, a teacher can help students understand the context of what they are learning and gain more meaning from the knowledge that is presented. (National Research Council, 2005)

Research bibliography on pages 32T–34T

What influences behavior? For many years, scientists asked whether behavior was genetically based or a result of experiences. Studies have shown that some behavior is based solely on genetics and is not influenced by experience. Other behaviors, such as a finch learning the song of its species, are known to result from a combination of genetics and environmental influences. Today, many behaviors are considered to be the result of both genes and experience. In many cases, behavior results from the interaction of genetically based behaviors and behaviors based on experience. **Figure 1** shows some important discoveries about animal behavior.

D **The evolution of behavior** Two general questions are asked when studying animal behavior. The first question focuses on what triggers an animal to react to specific stimuli. For example, what triggers a male bird, like the one shown in **Figure 2,** to sing during breeding season? The answer usually is found by studying the internal biology of an animal. Scientists now know that some male birds sing during breeding season in response to the internal stimulus of increased levels of the hormone testosterone.

The second question focuses on what advantages certain behaviors provide animals. The answers to this question are tied to the evolution of behavior through natural selection. What advantage does singing during breeding season provide the male bird? Perhaps the singing helps the male bird keep other male birds away. Perhaps the singing helps the male attract a mate.

You already have learned that animals with traits giving them a competitive advantage over other animals that do not possess those traits are more likely to reproduce and pass their genes on to future generations. In the past, birds that sang tended to have more offspring than birds that did not sing. Over a number of generations, birds that sang became the only birds contributing to the population's gene pool. The behavior has been naturally selected.

■ **Figure 2** The male black-breasted zebra finch sings during mating season to attract a female.

Inquiry Virtual Lab

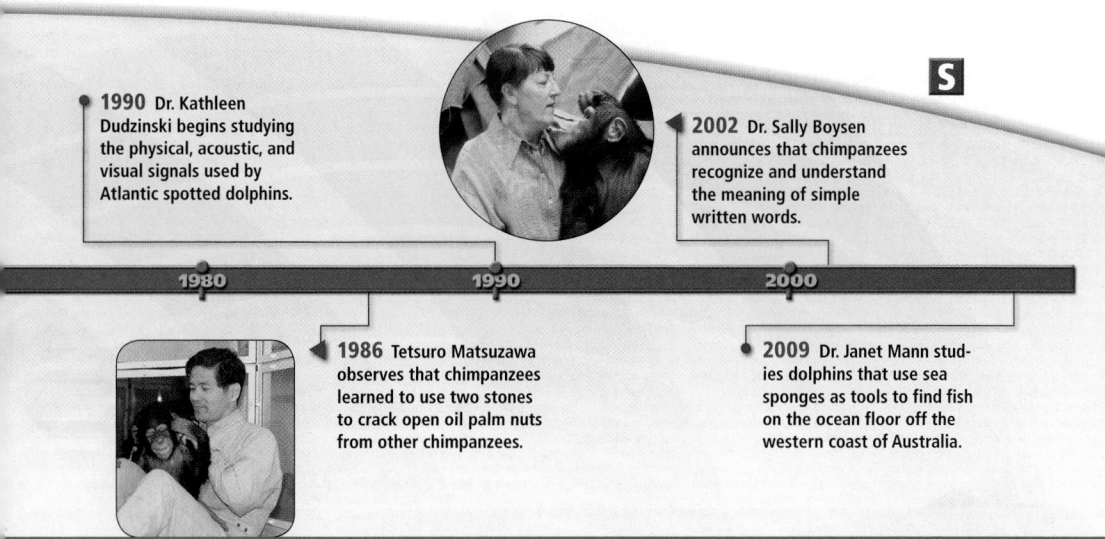

1990 Dr. Kathleen Dudzinski begins studying the physical, acoustic, and visual signals used by Atlantic spotted dolphins.

2002 Dr. Sally Boysen announces that chimpanzees recognize and understand the meaning of simple written words.

S

1980 — 1990 — 2000

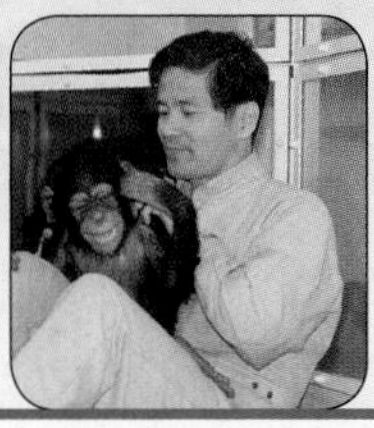

1986 Tetsuro Matsuzawa observes that chimpanzees learned to use two stones to crack open oil palm nuts from other chimpanzees.

2009 Dr. Janet Mann studies dolphins that use sea sponges as tools to find fish on the ocean floor off the western coast of Australia.

Content Background

Teacher FYI When trying to breed his first whooping crane, which was a female, George Archibald, director of the International Crane Foundation, discovered that his crane had imprinted on humans and would not perform the breeding dance. To encourage the crane to lay eggs, George learned the mating dance. In 1975, George began dancing with the crane. In 1981, the crane successfully laid fertile eggs and an offspring, a male, was produced from one of the eggs through artificial insemination.

S Skill Practice

BL OL AL Visual Literacy

Have students examine the important milestones in the time line of the study of animal behavior shown in Figure 1.

SAY TO STUDENTS: ***Choose one of the milestones in animal studies. Imagine that you live during the time period and are a reporter for a local newspaper. Write a newspaper article explaining the importance of the project.*** Articles should be based on the value of the project's specific findings.

D Develop Concepts

BL OL AL

Clarify a Misconception

ASK STUDENTS: ***How long does it take for a species to develop or lose a characteristic?*** Natural selection depends on generation time length. It can occur relatively quickly if the generation length of a species is short, such as in bacteria or fruit flies. In other species, such as humans, where generation length is longer, natural selection occurs more slowly. Many students think natural selection is an overnight process that causes behaviors to immediately appear or disappear.

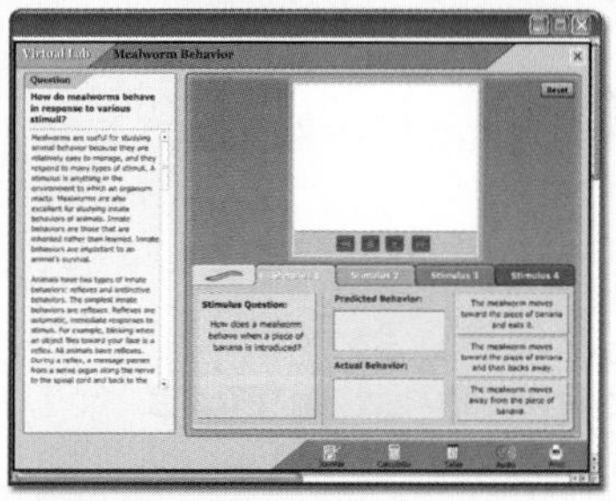

Inquiry Virtual Lab

Students will predict, observe, and describe the responses of mealworms to various stimuli.

C Critical Thinking

BL OL AL Analyze

ASK STUDENTS: ***If humans have to learn to walk, why is the behavior innate?*** Every human is genetically programmed to walk erect. Even without the aid of an adult, each human would eventually walk. ***If you take the same path home from school every day, is this a fixed action pattern?*** No; your path can be consciously altered.

S Skill Practice

OL AL Illustrate Have students research animal examples of fixed action patterns. Have them draw a three-frame cartoon illustrating a fixed action pattern behavior. possible answer: aggressive behavior of the stickleback when exposed to the color red

Writing Support

BL OL AL Journal Writing

Have students keep a journal of their behaviors for one day. Tell students to list the behavior, the type of behavior, and time of occurrence. Do not collect or read the journals. Have students write a summary paragraph differentiating which of their behaviors were innate and which were learned.

Reading Check A fixed action pattern is not influenced by the environment. It is genetically based.

Caption Question Fig. 3 The goose would still carry out the fixed action pattern.

CAREERS IN BIOLOGY

Animal Behaviorist Scientists that study the causes, development, and evolution of behavior are animal behaviorists. Animal behaviorists might work at zoos, aquariums, or museums, or they might teach or conduct research at a university.

Innate Behavior

Behaviors that are genetically based and not linked to past experiences are called **innate** (ih NAYT) **behaviors.** However, you might say that all animal behaviors occur in and are influenced by the environment. Behaviors are referred to as innate, or instinct, when the same behavior commonly is observed among a large number of individuals within a population, even if the environments are different. For example, in some species, newly hatched birds will make innate chirping sounds while opening their mouths in an upward direction when a parent lands in the nest. As part of an innate response to the chick's open mouth, the parent will feed the chirping bird. In addition, members of a particular group of mammals typically begin to walk at the same age, depending on their species. Therefore, walking is generally considered an innate behavior. C

Fixed action patterns The goose in **Figure 3** is exhibiting innate behavior. When an animal carries out a specific set of actions in sequence, in response to a stimulus, it is called **fixed action pattern.** The goose is responding to the stimulus of an egg that is out of the nest. The set of actions carried out is usually the same and usually in the same order. The goose will extend its neck toward the egg and then stand up. It will then roll the egg back to the nest with a side-to-side motion of its neck with the egg held beneath its bill. The stimulus, finding that the egg is out of the nest, triggers the innate behavior, and the entire sequence of actions is carried out. Even if the egg is removed midway through the retrieval process, the goose will continue the behavior without the egg. This is the key to a fixed action pattern. The stimulus triggers an innate response that the animal does not control and is not directly influenced by environmental conditions or past experiences. Another example of a fixed action pattern is shown in **Figure 4.** S

Reading Check **Explain** why a fixed action pattern is an example of innate behavior.

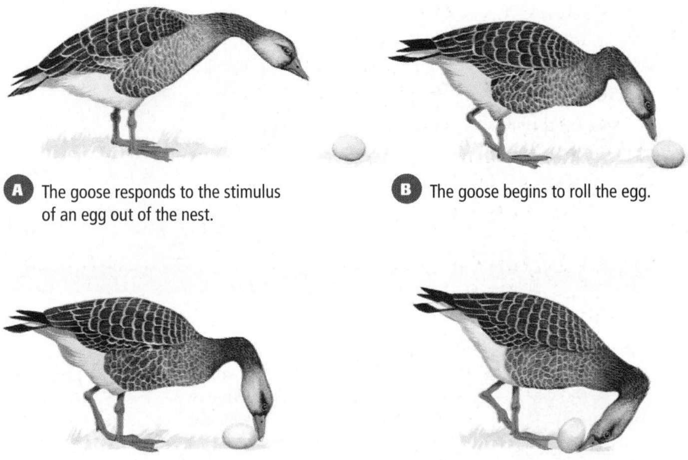

A The goose responds to the stimulus of an egg out of the nest.

B The goose begins to roll the egg.

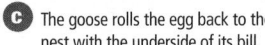

C The goose rolls the egg back to the nest with the underside of its bill.

D The goose continues to roll the egg until it is in the nest.

Figure 3 The goose is carrying out a fixed action pattern.
Infer *what would happen if the egg were replaced with a similarly shaped object, such as a small rubber ball.*

Demonstration

BL OL AL Animal Behavior Project photographs or videos of different types of animal behavior on a screen. Figures 3 (innate behavior), 4 (habituation), and 6 (classical conditioning) are available as Biology Concepts transparencies. Use these images to facilitate a discussion of natural selection's role in animal behavior.

ASK STUDENTS: How does the behavior pictured aid in species survival? possible answers: defending territory, courtship, nurturing What role do you think natural selection played in the development of the behaviors? Possible answer: Animals who could not defend themselves were killed or unable to reproduce. Est. time: 10 min

Visualizing Types of Behavior

S Figure 4
Animal behavior is either innate or learned. Fixed action pattern behavior is innate because it is genetically based and is not linked to past experience. Habituation and operant conditioning are learned behaviors because each results from situations that the animal experiences.

Fixed Action Pattern This newly hatched cuckoo is carrying out a fixed action pattern. An adult female cuckoo lays her eggs in the nests of other bird species. When the baby cuckoo hatches, it ejects the other eggs from the nest before its eyes are even open. The process of ejection is a fixed action pattern.

Habituation These birds have become habituated to the scarecrow. Although they might have avoided it when it was first placed in the field, they learned that there were no positive or negative effects associated with it.

Operant Conditioning These ducks have learned to associate the presence of humans near the edge of the pond with the reward of food.

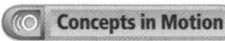

Concepts in Motion Animation

Differentiated Instruction

English Learners If you have several English learners in your classroom, allow them to form small groups and discuss, in their first language, the concept of learned behavior. This will allow them to organize their ideas before joining a larger class discussion.

For more tips, see pages 14T–15T.

Visualizing Types of Behavior

Purpose

Students will distinguish between types of animal behaviors.
UCP.5, C.6

S Skill Practice

BL OL AL Visual Literacy Have students study Figure 4. **ASK STUDENTS:** Identify a learned behavior shown in these photographs. birds sitting on a scarecrow, ducks eating food provided by people in a park Distinguish what type of learned behavior it is. habituation; operant conditioning Infer why the animal is exhibiting the behavior. Possible answer: The bird became aware that the scarecrow poses no threat; ducks learned to associate people with food.

Writing Support

OL AL Formal Writing Generate a list of animals. Have students pick an animal and write a one-page report discussing the types of behavior the animal can exhibit, suggesting how natural selection might have influenced the behavior.

Concepts in Motion
Animation

MiniLab 1

Inquiry MiniLab

For a lab worksheet, use your eTeacherEdition Online.

RUBRIC A rubric for evaluating MiniLabs is found on your eTeacherEdition Online.

Est. Time 15 min

Safety Precaution Approve lab safety forms before work begins.

Teaching Strategies

- Make sure students handle worms with wet hands, because dry hands can damage the mucus membrane of the worms.
- Students will find it easier to work with medium- to large-size worms.

Analysis

1. Answers will vary because individual worms may vary in their responses; however, students should notice that the worm's withdrawal reflex decreases.
2. Because all of the worms exhibited the same withdrawal reflex in response to touch, this is likely an innate behavior in earthworms. In its natural environment, a predator, such as a bird, might touch a worm and this behavior could help the worm escape.

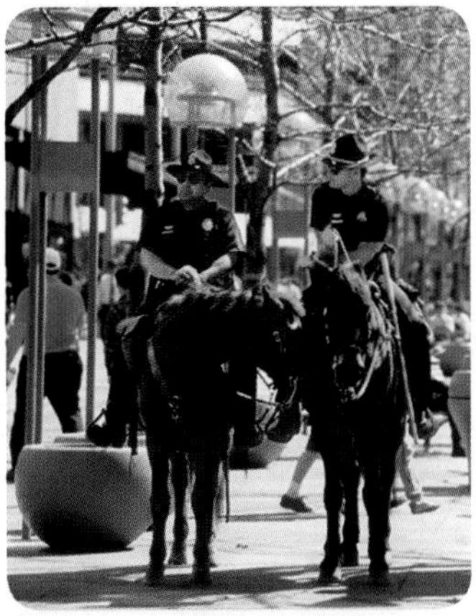

Figure 5 Police horses become habituated to noise from crowds and traffic.
Recall *a time when you became habituated to a stimulus.*

FOLDABLES® Incorporate information from this section into your Foldable.

Learned Behavior

Which activities do you enjoy—playing a sport, driving a car, playing video games or a musical instrument? These activities are examples of learned behaviors. **Learned behaviors** result from an interaction between innate behaviors and past experiences within a particular environment. Examples of learned behavior include habituation, conditioning, imprinting, and cognitive behavior.

Habituation Sometimes, animals learn over time that a potentially important stimulus deserves little or no attention. For example, baby birds in a nest see many types of objects moving overhead. At first, they might respond to these stimuli by crouching down and staying still. Some of the objects, such as falling leaves or members of their own species flying by, often are seen and have no positive or negative effects to the birds. Over time, the birds will stop responding to these stimuli. This is referred to as **habituation** (huh bit choo AY shun), which is a decrease in an animal's response after repeatedly being exposed to a stimulus that has no positive or negative effects.

The horses shown in **Figure 5** have become habituated to street and crowd noise. Habituation can be thought of as learning not to respond to a stimulus. Habituation is important to an animal's success because it allows an animal to ignore unimportant stimuli and focus on and respond to important stimuli, such as the presence of food, a mate, or a predator. Another example of habituation is shown in **Figure 4.** Birds often become habituated to a scarecrow because they learn that it has no positive or negative effects.

MiniLab 1

Inquiry MiniLab

Explore Habituation

Does an earthworm habituate to touch? In this lab, you will observe whether an earthworm will learn that a stimulus can be ignored.

Procedure

WARNING: *Treat the earthworm in a humane manner at all times.*

1. Read and complete the lab safety form.
2. Line a small narrow **tray** with a **paper towel** moistened with **aged tap water.** Put on a pair of **gloves** and wet them with aged tap water.
3. Use your gloved hand to pick up an **earthworm** and gently transfer it to your tray. Allow the worm to rest for 1 min.
4. Determine which is the anterior end (head) of your worm. Lightly touch the anterior of the worm with the bristles of a small **paintbrush.**
5. After the worm recovers from its withdrawal reflex, touch it lightly again.

6. Repeat Step 5 five more times and record any changes in the worm's behavior.

Analysis

1. **Explain** Did the earthworm become habituated to the stimulus? How do you know?
2. **Think Critically** Why is the earthworm's withdrawal reflex likely an innate behavior? How does this behavior help the worm survive in its natural environment?

Caption Question Fig. 5 Answers will depend on what stimulus the student learned to ignore.

Activity

BL OL AL Learned Behavior Help students learn a behavior. Have them place the middle of their writing utensil between their index and middle fingers at the first knuckle. Teach students to twirl the utensil by grasping it with their ring finger while releasing their index finger. Have them repeat this with the little finger, releasing the middle finger. Est. time: 5 min

FOLDABLES®

RUBRIC A rubric for evaluating Foldables is found on your eTeacherEdition Online.

Going Further On the back of their Foldables, have students list and illustrate an example for each type of learned behavior.

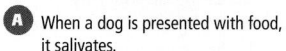

A When a dog is presented with food, it salivates.

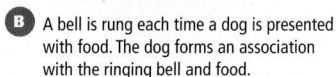

B A bell is rung each time a dog is presented with food. The dog forms an association with the ringing bell and food.

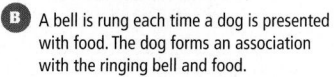

C Eventually, the dog will salivate to the sound of the bell alone. It has been conditioned to respond to the ringing bell.

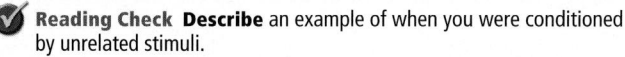

Figure 6 Through classical conditioning, the dog learns to associate the sound of a ringing bell with food.

Classical conditioning Ivan Pavlov, a Russian scientist who conducted experiments in the late 1890s and early 1900s, noticed that after he presented meat powder to a dog, the animal produced saliva. Later, Pavlov rang a bell each time he presented the meat powder. After repeated trials, the dog salivated when it heard the bell alone, without smelling or tasting meat powder.

Pavlov concluded that the dog related the sound of the ringing bell with the meat powder. Animal behaviorists refer to this type of learning as classical conditioning, which is illustrated in **Figure 6.** **Classical conditioning** occurs when an association is made between two different kinds of stimuli. In Pavlov's experiment, the dog learned to associate the sound of the bell with the unrelated stimulus of meat D powder. The sound of the bell could produce the response of salivation.

Reading Check **Describe** an example of when you were conditioned by unrelated stimuli.

Operant conditioning B.F. Skinner, an American psychologist, carried out experiments on operant conditioning. In **operant conditioning,** an animal learns to associate its response to a stimulus with a reward or a punishment. In Skinner's experiment, a rat was placed in a box. As the rat explored the box, it accidentally would hit a lever, causing a food pellet to be released into the box. At first, the rat ignored the lever. It would eat the pellet and continue to move around the box. Eventually, the rat learned to associate pressing the lever with getting food. The animal was rewarded positively (receiving the food pellet) for its response (pressing the lever) to the stimulus (the lever).

In some cases, animals learn to associate their response with a negative reward. Monarch butterflies, which have a bright orange color pattern, are toxic to many predators. When a young blue jay eats a monarch butterfly for the first time, the bird becomes ill and vomits the butterfly. The bird quickly associates eating the butterfly with illness. In the future, the bird avoids eating monarch butterflies and other butterflies with a similar color pattern.

VOCABULARY
SCIENCE USAGE V. COMMON USAGE
Trial
Science usage: one of a number of repetitions in an experiment
The biologist collected data for 50 trials during her study of behavior.

Common usage: a formal examination of a matter in a civil or criminal court
The defendant was found innocent at the end of the trial.

Video BrainPOP

D Develop Concepts

BL OL AL Discuss Discuss with students why Pavlov's dog salivated. **ASK STUDENTS:** ***When do occurrences similar to this happen in your life?*** Possible answers: When the phone rings, your heart might start beating fast because you think a certain person might be calling; the smell of a pie baking could make you feel hungry.

Writing Support

OL AL Formal Writing Have students research and write a short biography about the life and work of either Ivan Pavlov or B.F. Skinner.

Skill Practice

BL OL AL Classify Have students draw two columns on a sheet of paper. Provide students with a list of animals to write in the first column. Have students use the second column to identify behaviors of that animal influenced by natural selection. Answers will vary depending on the animal. Possible answer: lizard defending territory

Video BrainPOP

Reading Check Answers will vary, but could include leaving or entering the classroom when the bell rings.

Content Background

Teacher FYI Earthworms typically move head-first, so watching the worm as it moves helps distinguish the head end. Earthworms have a centralized nervous system with a segmented brain in the head region. A ventral nerve cord with peripheral nerves runs from the brain down the length of the worm. Each segment contains ganglia (a collection of nerve cell bodies) that help coordinate a worm's movements. Worms have cells that sense touch, light, vibration, moisture, and chemical receptors. In addition to habituation and classical conditioning, earthworms have also displayed operant conditioning. Worms can learn to navigate a T-maze to avoid an unpleasant stimulus and instead find the side of the maze associated with food or moisture.

D Develop Concepts

BL OL AL COOP LEARN

Activity Divide students into groups of four. Have the groups create bulletin board displays demonstrating either classical conditioning or operant conditioning. Encourage students to include at least four animal examples of each behavior with illustrations.

S Skill Practice

OL AL **Visual Literacy** Have students study Figure 7.

ASK STUDENTS: ***Why do scientists not release the whooping cranes at the southernmost point of migration?*** because their reproductive cycle would be disrupted

C Critical Thinking

BL OL AL **Conclude**

ASK STUDENTS: ***What role does imprinting play in species survival?*** Possible answer: Enabling an individual of a species to identify with a role model early in life usually ensures that the individual will learn behaviors needed to survive and reproduce. ***How does imprinting help a bird learn to sing its species-specific song?*** The song of other individuals of its species heard by the nestling bird forms a template for use when learning to sing.

Operant conditioning is a more powerful, long-lasting kind of learning that dominates much of everyday learning of humans and other vertebrates. For example, animals, including humans, learn ways of finding food by exploring a variety of locations. When certain locations prove to be a good source of food, animals are positively reinforced. Research shows that such animals are more likely to seek food the next time in the same location or locations that appear similar. D

Imprinting Learning that can only occur within a specific time period in an animal's life and is permanent is called **imprinting.** The time during which an animal imprints is called the *sensitive period.* In some animals, the sensitive period occurs immediately after birth. Newborn offspring can form a strong bond with another animal, such as a parent, during this time. Some animals, such as whooping cranes, form a social attachment to the first object that they see after birth. Other animals, such as salmon, imprint on the chemical composition of the water in which they are hatched. The salmon use this imprint to return to this location when it is time for them to spawn.

Evidence of the influence of genetics on imprinting comes from experiments with newly hatched birds. In nature, the first object the offspring sees most likely will be its parent. This ensures that the offspring will have a higher chance of survival by being nurtured by a parent. Experiments have shown that newly hatched birds will imprint on whatever object they see first, whether it is an animal of a different species, such as a human, or an inanimate object, such as a box.

Connection to History In 1999, only one flock of 180 migratory whooping cranes existed naturally. Scientists created a plan to introduce a second migratory flock of cranes to help ensure the species would not become extinct. Crane chicks were hatched in Wisconsin at the northernmost point of their migratory path. The chicks were imprinted using an ultralight plane like the one shown in **Figure 7.** Each year since 2001, a group of newly hatched chicks is imprinted by an ultralight. They follow it to the winter migration site in Florida and back to Wisconsin in the spring. In doing this, a second population of migratory cranes has been established successfully. C

VOCABULARY

ACADEMIC VOCABULARY

Migratory
characterized by moving from one location to another
Migratory birds fly south for the winter.

S

Figure 7 The first flock of whooping cranes to be imprinted using the ultralight arrived at their winter destination on December 3, 2001. Each year since then, a new flock has been imprinted, with all the cranes following the ultralight back to Wisconsin in the spring.

***Infer** what would happen if newly hatched cranes imprinted using a crane from the first flock.*

Content Background

Teacher FYI The team members of Operation Migration used puppets shaped like Canada geese and whooping cranes when handling the baby birds to keep the birds from imprinting on humans. Tapes of the aircraft engine were played often so that the baby birds would imprint on the sound of the aircraft engine.

Caption Question Fig. 7 The newly hatched cranes would follow the adult on its migratory path.

■ **Figure 8**
The chimpanzee uses a stone to crack open nuts. Some scientists interpret this as cognitive behavior.

Cognitive behavior Thinking, reasoning, and processing information to understand complex concepts and solve problems are **cognitive behaviors.** Humans exhibit cognitive behaviors when they solve problems, make decisions, and plan for the future. Some experimental evidence supports the idea that other animals, such as chimpanzees, exhibit cognitive behavior.

Observations made by scientists of animals in their natural habitats also seem to show examples of cognitive behavior. Chimpanzees, like the one shown in **Figure 8,** have been observed using rocks to break open nuts. This behavior suggests that the chimpanzees are thinking and using tools to solve problems. Experiments are being conducted to find out if some primates purposely deceive, or lie to, other animals in their group, which is another sign of cognitive behavior.

W

W Writing Support

AL Narrative Writing Have students research how cognitive behavior differs throughout the animal kingdom and write an essay describing their findings. Essays will vary, but should explain that low-level organisms possess little or no cognitive behaviors.

Formative Assessment

Evaluation Provide students with descriptions of various types of animal behaviors. Have students identify whether the type of behavior exhibited in each example is innate or learned. Possible examples include walking—innate; finding food sources—learned.

Remediation Have students use information from this section to create flash cards with a description of a behavior on one side and whether it is innate or learned on the other. Have students use the flash cards to quiz one another.

Section 1 Assessment

Section Summary

- Behavior can be influenced by both genes and experience.
- Successful behaviors are those that give individuals an advantage for survival and reproduction.
- Behavior can be innate or learned.
- Learned behavior includes habituation, conditioning, and imprinting.
- Cognitive behavior involves thinking, reasoning, and problem solving.

Understand Main Ideas

1. MAIN Idea **Explain** how behavior could evolve.
2. **Explain** the difference between an internal stimulus and an external stimulus. Give an example of each.
3. **Compare and contrast** innate and learned behavior.
4. **Illustrate** specific examples of two types of learned behavior.

Think Critically

5. **Infer** A toad eats a bumblebee and receives a painful sting on its tongue. From then on, the toad avoids feeding on bumblebees or any other yellow and black insects. What kind of behavior is the toad exhibiting?

WRITING in Biology

6. Explain how you would train an animal, such as a dog, to do tricks. Use the terms *classical conditioning* and *operant conditioning.*

Section 1 Assessment

1. Behavior can evolve because it is genetically based. Individuals that engage in beneficial behavior live to reproduce and pass their genes on to future generations.
2. An internal stimulus originates within the body, such as a stomach growling when a person is hungry. An external stimulus originates outside the body, such as someone calling your name.
3. Both behaviors are exhibited by animals. Innate behaviors are genetically based and not influenced by the environment. Learned behaviors are influenced by an environment.
4. A mouse races through a maze to find the piece of cheese at the end (operant conditioning); a cat runs to greet its owner when it hears the garage door open (classical conditioning)
5. operant conditioning
6. Answers should include the idea of having the dog associate a response to a stimulus.

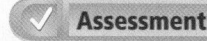

Assessment Online Quiz

Section 2

MAIN Idea

BL OL AL Species Survival
Show students a picture of an animal such as a bear.
ASK STUDENTS: ***What behaviors could this animal use for survival?*** Possible answers: Bear—winter sleep allows it to survive the winter and lack of food; competition for mates enables reproduction. Inform students that in this section they will learn about behaviors that allow species to survive and reproduce.

R Reading Strategy

EL OL Assessment Preview
Prior to reading Section 2, have students read the section assessment questions.
SAY TO STUDENTS: ***Keep the assessment questions in mind while you read the section.***

■ **Caption Question Fig. 9** Sparring sheep will lead to only the strongest males passing on their genetic information.

Section 2

Reading Preview

Essential Questions
- What are different types of competitive behaviors and what are examples of each?
- What is the importance of foraging, migration, and biological rhythms?
- What are the different types of communication, nurturing, and cooperative behaviors?
- What are the advantages and disadvantages of behavior in terms of survival and reproductive success.

Review Vocabulary
colony: a group of unicellular or multicellular organisms that live together in a close association

New Vocabulary
agonistic behavior
dominance hierarchy
territorial behavior
foraging behavior
migratory behavior
circadian rhythm
language
courting behavior
nurturing behavior
altruistic behavior

g Multilingual eGlossary

R Ecological Behaviors

MAIN Idea **Animals that engage in complex behaviors might survive and reproduce because they have inherited more favorable behaviors.**

Real-World Reading Link Think about the advantages and disadvantages of owning a car. You would be able to drive yourself and your friends around town. However, you would also have to pay for gasoline, car insurance, and repairs. In a similar way, there are advantages and disadvantages to every type of animal behavior.

Types of Behaviors

All animal behaviors are somewhat ecologically based. Ecology is the study of the interactions of living things with each other and with their environment. These interactions can occur between members of the same species or between members of different species. Animals that engage in complex behaviors survive and reproduce because they have inherited genes that allow them to be successful in a particular environment.

Examine **Figure 9,** which shows two bighorn sheep fighting over a mate. Although it looks painful, the thick horns of the sheep protect them from injury when they butt heads. One of the sheep eventually will give up the contest, leaving the other the winner. What are the survival and reproductive advantages and disadvantages of this behavior? The winner is able to court and mate with a female without interference from the other male. The genes of the winner most likely will be passed on to future generations. Genes that provide adaptive advantages will increase in relative frequency according to the principles of evolution by natural selection. Genes that do not help an individual animal survive and produce offspring are likely to decrease in frequency in the gene pool of future generations. As you read about different types of behavior in this section, think about why a particular behavior might have evolved.

■ **Figure 9** These bighorn sheep spar until one sheep gives up. The winner will be able to court a mate without interference from the other male.
Explain ***why this behavior favors natural selection.***

Content Background

Cultural Diversity The spiny-tailed iguana is a territorial creature inhabiting Mexico, Central America, and islands adjacent to Panama. Living within colonies ruled by a dominance hierarchy, each male iguana will defend its territory against every other male except the leader. This behavior protects the iguana's food supply and the females with which he mates in the territory. While defending his territory, the iguana might exhibit color changes, body inflation, jaw gaping, rapid nodding of the head, and sometimes, biting and tail-thrashing fights.

■ **Figure 10** Polar bears engage in agonistic behavior. They spar until one bear leaves.
Infer *some advantages of agonistic behavior.*

Competitive behaviors Competition for food, space, mates, and other resources occurs between individuals within a population. Competitive behaviors, like the example shown in **Figure 9,** allow individuals to establish dominance or control of an area or resource. Animals that are successful at competitive behaviors are more likely to obtain resources needed for survival and reproduction. Successful animals are therefore more likely to reproduce and pass their traits to the next generation. Types of competitive behaviors include agonistic
D behavior, dominance hierarchies, and territorial behavior.

Agonistic behavior The polar bears in **Figure 10** are engaging in behavior in which one bear will be the winner and will have control over resources such as food or potential mates. This type of threatening or combative interaction between two individuals of the same species is called **agonistic** (ag oh NIHS tihk) **behavior.** Although the bears look as though they might hurt each other, agonistic behavior usually does not result in serious injury or death to either individual. The challenge will end when one animal eventually stops participating and leaves.

Dominance hierarchies A hierarchy is a grouping in which objects or individual animals are ranked in order from highest to lowest. Some animals living in groups develop **dominance hierarchies** (DAH muh nunts • HI rar keez) in which a top-ranked animal has access to resources without conflict from other animals in the group. This ranking system helps reduce hostile behaviors among animals. These hostile behaviors would take time and energy away from finding food or a mate, or caring for offspring. Higher-ranked animals are more likely to get what they need to survive and reproduce. Female
C wolves, baboons, some songbirds, and the chickens shown in **Figure 11,** establish dominance hierarchies.

Study Tip

Flashcards Make flashcards of the vocabulary terms in this section. Use the flashcards to review the terms with a partner or small group.

■ **Figure 11** Female chickens, called hens, establish hierarchies in which one hen is dominant over the others. The dominant hen pecks other hens to maintain dominance.

D Develop Strategies

BL OL AL COOP LEARN

Brainstorm Place students in groups of three. Have groups think of competitive behaviors, and then share their ideas with the class. Write their ideas on the board.

ASK STUDENTS: ***What competitive behaviors do humans and other animals exhibit?*** Possible answers: Animals compete for food when it is scarce, and people look for the shortest checkout line at the grocery store. ***Do zoo animals exhibit competitive behaviors?*** With food being plentiful, many competitive behaviors are reduced. Animals raised in captivity often will not adapt once released into the wild. Zoo animals may compete for things such as space to nap.

C Critical Thinking

OL AL Conclude

ASK STUDENTS: ***Where did the term* pecking order *originate?*** Students might associate the term with chickens. Point out that chickens use their beaks to peck at each other to establish dominance. ***What does the term mean?*** *Pecking order* refers to the ranking of animals within the same species living in close proximity, otherwise known as the dominance hierarchy.

BL ASK STUDENTS: ***Have you heard of the phrase* pecking order?** If they have siblings, have them give examples of pecking order and what it might mean.

> *"At the desk where I sit, I have learned one great truth. The answer for all our national problems—the answer for all the problems of the world—comes to a single word. That word is "education."*"
>
> –Lyndon B. Johnson

■ **Caption Question Fig. 10** The dominant animal wins mates or food. Competition does not usually result in serious injury or death.

S Skill Practice

BL Classify Have students make a list of ten vertebrate and invertebrate animals.

SAY TO STUDENTS: ***Next to each animal, indicate whether it is territorial. If so, write how they defend and mark their territory.*** Answers will vary but may include: Cat: yes; rubs items in the territory and hisses. Bee: yes; will sting.

D Develop Concepts

OL AL Discuss

ASK STUDENTS: ***How are territorial and foraging behaviors linked?*** Possible answers: Within the territory, animals have limited the area of food searching, which conserves energy.

DATA ANALYSIS LAB 1

About the Lab

- Project the graph from your eTeacherEdition Online during class discussion.
- Also see Carpenter, F.L. and R.E. MacMillen. 1976. Energetic cost of feeding territories in an Hawaiian Honeycreeper. *Oecologia* 26:213-223.

Think Critically

1. Each set of data shows the feeding rate of the fishes over time.
2. The fishes that engage in territorial behavior feed more often than fishes that do not.
3. Fishes that defend territories have more success at reproducing. Their genes are passed on to future generations. Fishes that do not defend territories are not as successful at reproducing; their genes are not passed on.

■ **Figure 12** Gannets breed in large colonies. They establish a small area of territory in which to make a nest. Territorial behaviors include fighting, jabbing at each other, and biting each other's necks.

Territorial behaviors Many animals establish a territory. A territory is a specific area that contains resources, such as food or potential mates, that an individual continually defends against other individuals of the same species. The size of territories varies widely, depending on the animal and the particular environment. **Territorial behaviors** are attempts to adopt and control a physical area against the other animals of the same species. Territorial behaviors include verbal signals, such as the singing of birds or chattering of squirrels, as well as chemical signals, such as a male cheetah's urine. Birds, such as the North American gannets shown in **Figure 12,** that gather in large colonies to breed engage in territorial behavior by fighting and jabbing to maintain space in the nesting colony. Territories usually are defended by males in order to increase their chance of obtaining adequate food, mates, and places to rear their offspring. S

Foraging behaviors Finding and eating food are examples of **foraging behaviors.** These behaviors have obvious advantages for animals. Foraging successfully means obtaining needed nutrients, while avoiding predators and poisonous foods. Foraging involves a trade-off between a food's energy content and the cost of finding, pursuing, and eating it. Scientists theorize that natural selection favors individual animals whose foraging behaviors use the least amount of energy to obtain the maximum amount of energy possible. These are the animals that will be most able to reproduce successfully and pass genes on to future generations. D

Reading Check **Identify** some of the disadvantages of foraging behaviors.

DATA ANALYSIS LAB 1

Based on Real Data*

Interpret the Data

Can the advantages of territorial behavior be observed? Surgeonfish are algae-eating fishes that vigorously defend their territory against other algae-eating fishes. They maintain a territory of about 2–3 m^2.

Data and Observations

The graph shows the results of a study that compared the feeding rates of territorial surgeonfish to those of nonterritorial surgeonfish.

Think Critically

1. **Interpret** the meaning of each set of graphed data.
2. **Interpret** the advantage of the surgeonfishes' territorial behavior.
3. **Hypothesize** why this behavior has evolved.

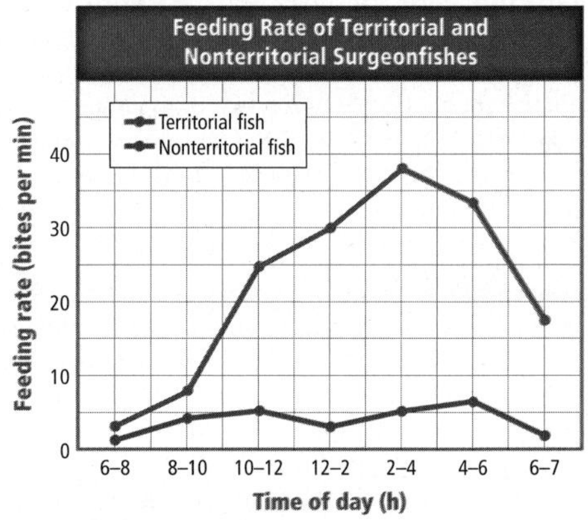

*Data obtained from: Craig, P. 1996. Intertidal territoriality and time-budget of the surgeonfish), *Acanthurus lineatus*, in American Samoa. *Environmental Biology* 46: 27–36.

Reading Check spending energy looking for food, getting injured while hunting prey

Migratory behaviors Some animals, such as birds and grazing mammals, engage in **migratory behaviors**, moving long distances seasonally to new locations increasing their chances of survival. Land animals, like the wildebeest and zebra in East Africa, migrate almost continuously as different areas receive the rain needed for their food sources to grow. Each fall in North America, about two-thirds of bird species fly south to areas such as South America where food is available during the North American winter. The birds fly north in the spring to areas where they feed and breed during the summer.

How do the snow geese, shown in **Figure 13,** and other birds know which direction to fly? Sometimes migrations cover thousands of kilometers each year, with seemingly little navigational information. Recent studies show that the first migration of some birds is guided innately by both the position of the stars and Earth's magnetic field. Future migrations are influenced by external cues that the bird learns while flying that help it navigate more precisely.

Biological rhythms Many animals, including humans, repeat behaviors in a rhythmic cycle. A **circadian** (sur KAY dee uhn) **rhythm** is a cycle, such as sleeping and waking, that occurs daily. Other biological cycles are seasonal or yearly. These cycles are influenced by environmental factors such as temperature changes, the increase or decrease of daylight hours, and the availability of food and water. These factors act as cues for animals to move into another phase of the cycle.

The daily cycle of sleeping and waking is influenced by external cues in animals. However, experiments have shown that many animals have an internal clock, often referred to as a biological clock, that maintains the daily rhythm of the sleep/wake cycle of about 24 hours. The graphs in **Figure 14** show the results of an experiment in which the activity level of nocturnal squirrels was monitored under two sets of conditions for 23 days—one in which a squirrel was exposed to a light cycle of 12 hours of light followed by 12 hours of darkness, and one in which a squirrel was kept in continual darkness. The biological clock of the squirrel maintained a sleep/wake cycle of 24 hours and 21 minutes in the absence of an external light and dark cycle. Controlled experiments show that the human biological clock has a cycle length of about 24 hours and 11 minutes.

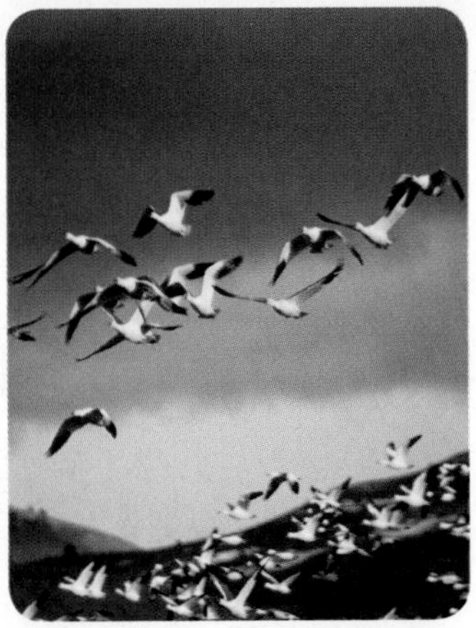

Figure 13 Snow geese are one of the many bird species that migrate to find better weather conditions and food sources as seasons change.
Explain *why animals may engage in migratory behaviors.*

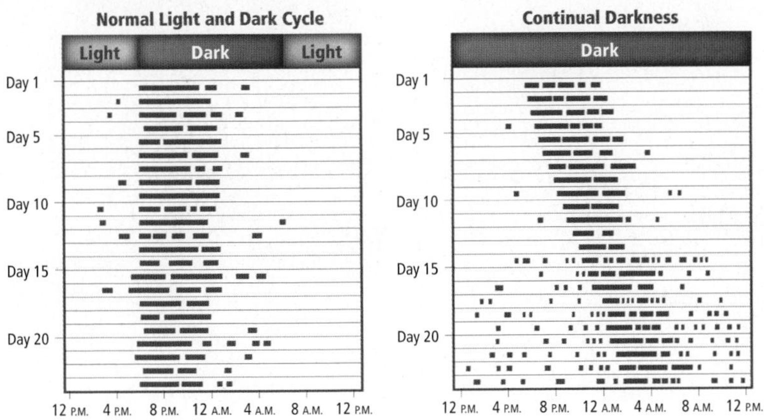

Figure 14 The green bars represent periods of the squirrels' activity, confirming that they have a sleep/wake cycle of about 24 h. **Left:** When exposed to a normal cycle of light and dark, the nocturnal squirrel was active when it was dark. It slept while it was light. **Right:** When in the dark all of the time, the squirrel maintained a sleep/wake cycle of 24 h 21 min, instead of 24 h.

S Skill Practice

BL OL AL Diagram Supply students with a black-line map that includes North America and Central America. Have students research and map the migration route of the monarch butterfly.
ASK STUDENTS: ***What reproductive advantage is gained by the monarch butterfly in migrating?*** possible answers: warm weather, larger mating pool ***To what dangers might an animal with migratory behaviors be exposed?*** possible answers: different predators, disappearing habitats, storms

W Writing Support

BL OL AL Journal Writing Have students imagine taking a week-long field trip to Alaska during the months when there are 24 hours of daylight.
SAY TO STUDENTS: ***Keep a log of your trip. Write how it feels to go to bed and get up in daylight. Describe how this affects your internal clock.***

C Critical Thinking

BL OL Hypothesize
ASK STUDENTS: ***How would spending five days in a cave, without any knowledge of time or sunrise and sunset, affect your internal clock?*** Possible answers: You might not be on a 24-hour cycle and might become hungry and sleepy at unusual times.

AL ASK STUDENTS: ***How would a job that requires rotation between day and night shifts affect your internal clock?*** Possible answers: You might have difficulty sleeping at some times and staying awake at others.

Differentiated Instruction

Visually Impaired Prepare and announce the assignment to research and map the migration of butterflies described on this page in advance. This will allow visually impaired students to make any accommodations that are necessary.

For more tips, see pages 14T–15T.

Caption Question Fig. 13 Migration might allow an animal to more easily find food year-round.

D Develop Concepts

BL OL COOP LEARN Activity

Have students work in pairs to create a poster showing methods of communication that are unique to humans and methods of communication that other animals use. Possible answers: Animals, including humans, use body movements, vocalizations, pheromones, and eye contact. Humans are unique in using speech, writing, and art.

D Develop Concepts

BL OL AL

Clarify a Misconception

ASK STUDENTS: ***What organisms communicate chemically?*** Students might answer animals. Many people do not think of plants as communicators. Point out that plants also communicate chemically. The sweet smell of flowers and fruits is an example. These chemical communications enable the plant to attract insects and other animals that carry pollen, aiding in successful reproduction.

C Critical Thinking

BL OL AL Evaluate

ASK STUDENTS: ***What are the advantages and disadvantages of visual communication?*** possible answers: advantages = can change quickly, easily produced; disadvantages = requires light, must have the attention of receiver ***What are the advantages and disadvantages of chemical or auditory communication?*** possible answers: advantages = chemical lasts longer, allows animal to define territory without being present, auditory can change quickly; disadvantages = chemical is difficult to change; auditory disappears quickly

BL Have students explain the advantages and disadvantages of visual, auditory, and chemical communication by drawing a picture map.

VOCABULARY

WORD ORIGIN

Auditory

audio– from Latin, meaning *relating to sound*

–ory suffix; from Latin, meaning *producing*

D Communication Behaviors

Dogs bark, birds chirp, wolves howl, and lions roar. These are all examples of animal communication. Wolves howl to communicate information over long distances, including letting other wolves know their location, attracting mates, and signaling the presence of a predator. Such communication behaviors are critical to the survival and reproductive success of animals. Animals have several types of communication behaviors.

D **Pheromones** Some animals communicate by spreading highly specific chemicals called pheromones. These chemicals are specific to species, ensuring that individuals within a population receive important information. An advantage of species-specific pheromones is that predators cannot detect them, unlike other more noticeable communication behaviors, such as barks or howls. Pheromones often are used to relay messages between males and females about reproduction. For example, female silk moths produce a pheromone that is used to attract male moths for mating. Pheromones also can be used to relay messages of alarm in response to a predator attack. The cheetah in **Figure 15** is leaving its scent to communicate with other cheetahs.

Auditory communication If you ever have spent an evening outside in a park or a forest, you might have heard many animals using auditory communication. Howls, hoots, barks, and chirps are just a few of the sounds you might have heard. Auditory communication permits animals to send and receive sound messages that move faster than chemical messages. Male crickets, frogs, birds, and the howler monkey shown in **Figure 15** communicate information about mating, predators, and territory to others in the population using auditory communication. Humans use language to communicate complex information. **Language** is a form of auditory communication in which animals use vocal organs to produce groups of sounds that have shared meanings. C

Figure 15 Some animals, like this cheetah, use pheromones to communicate and mark their territory. Male howler monkeys defend their territories with howls that can be heard over 4 km through dense forest.
***Identify** which communication behavior sends a message the farthest distance.*

Cheetah

Howler monkey

Research Citation

Classify Educational research indicates that students benefit when they learn the skill of classification. By identifying similarities and differences, students are able to group items into categories based on their characteristics, an important higher-level thinking skill. (English, 1997)

Research bibliography on pages 32T–34T

Caption Question Fig. 15 auditory communication

■ **Figure 16** Male frigate birds on the Galapagos Islands inflate and display red throat sacs to attract females during breeding season.

Courting and Nurturing Behaviors

Certain behaviors displayed by animals are directly related to the reproductive success of an individual animal. Attracting a mate and caring for offspring are important aspects of reproductive success.

Courting behaviors An animal engages in **courting behaviors** in order to attract a mate. An example of courting behavior is shown in **Figure 16.** The male frigate bird has inflated its bright red throat sac and is displaying it to attract the attention of female frigate birds. Courtship signals, whether they are a display of brightly colored feathers or a series of movements or sounds, are species specific. This is important in ensuring the reproductive success of a species. Courting behavior can last for minutes or months, depending on the species.

Selecting a male is often the female's role in the courtship process. Females often choose to mate with males that appear relatively larger and healthier than others. Thus, males with desired traits have a competitive advantage over other males and typically have a better chance **D** of mating and successfully producing offspring.

Nurturing behaviors When parents provide care to their offspring in the early stages of development, they are engaging in **nurturing behaviors.** This includes providing food, protection, and skills needed for survival. Nurturing behaviors cost parents energy because of the extra work required to sustain offspring until they can take care of themselves. Animal species that spend time nurturing young often produce fewer offspring than animals that do not nurture.

For example, a female cod can produce as many as nine million eggs during a single reproductive period. Only a small percentage of these eggs will survive. Reproductive energy can be spent producing millions of eggs, with little if any energy spent on nurturing. In contrast to the cod, animals that nurture, such as primates, produce far fewer eggs and offspring. A female orangutan, like the one shown in **Figure 17,** will give birth to one baby that she will nurse for up to three years. The baby will stay with the mother for five to seven years. In this case, more energy is spent nurturing young after birth to ensure they successfully reach a reproductive age. Although each reproductive strategy uses energy differently, they both usually result in the survival of at least one mature, **W** reproductive offspring.

Reading Check **Compare and contrast** courting and nurturing behaviors.

■ **Figure 17** Nursing is an example of a nurturing behavior.
Describe *other examples of nurturing behaviors.*

D Develop Concepts

OL AL Activity Have students create a three-column chart. Supply the names of several animals to write in the first column, such as whooping cranes, frogs, whales, spiders, or insects. Have them research the courtship behaviors of these animals and, in the second column, describe the type of behavior. In the third column, have them write the type of communication involved, i.e., visual, auditory, or chemical.

W Writing Support

BL OL AL COOP LEARN

Creative Writing Organize students into pairs. Assign each pair an animal such as a cod, frog, sparrow, or cat. Have partners research the animal's reproductive and nurturing behaviors and compose a poem that links the number of offspring to the animal's nurturing behavior. Invite students to share their poems with the class.

Inquiry BioLab

The lab at the end of the chapter can be used at this point in the lesson.

Reading Check Both behaviors increase chances for reproductive success: courting behavior attracts a mate; nurturing behavior cares for and protects young.

■ **Caption Question Fig. 17** making a nest, defending a nest, grooming, teaching young to hunt

Content Background

Teacher FYI Is behavior influenced by genetics or nurturing? For many years, scientists believed that nurturing controlled behavior. In 2001, researchers at Duke University Medical Center used mice to link genetics to nurturing and provide insight into whether nurturing controlled animal behavior. The research concluded that genes impact behavior, including the nurturing behavior of mother and offspring. By the end of 2005, researchers were studying genetic links to other behaviors, such as foraging among bees and communication among mice. The nurture v. nature debate, however, is far from over. Some research indicates that a combination of genes and environmental factors influence behaviors.

D Develop Concepts

BL OL AL COOP LEARN

Activity Organize students into groups of three. Have groups create a new social insect species that is ideal for its environment. Create a system of conduct for this new society to allow for successful species survival. Students might model the behavior of their insect species on that of ants or honeybees.

W Writing Support

OL AL **Persuasive Writing**

There are many examples of altruistic behavior in individuals of other animal species.

SAY TO STUDENTS: ***Think of an example of altruistic behavior in humans. Write a paragraph that explains in what way this act is beneficial, and whether you think the altruistic behavior is learned or genetically based.***

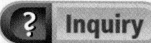

Inquiry Launch Lab

Assess Content Development

Assess how understanding has developed when students revisit the Launch Lab analysis questions.

GOING GREEN Buy bath board from a local building supply that is cut into 30-cm^2 pieces. If you purchase a class set of boards and fine tipped washable markers, you can reuse these materials for years. Have students use these materials instead of paper for making tables, charts, and diagrams in class.

CAREERS IN BIOLOGY

Evolutionary Psychologist The social behavior of animals, including human social behavior and altruistic behavior, is studied by evolutionary psychologists.

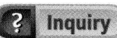

Inquiry Launch Lab

Review Based on what you have read about animal behavior, how would you now answer the analysis questions?

Cooperative Behaviors

Cooperative behaviors can exist in groups of same-species animals. Cooperative behaviors can benefit all members of the group. However, some examples of cooperative behavior lead to an individual animal performing altruistic (al trew IHS tihk), or self-sacrificing, behaviors.

Altruistic behavior Sometimes an animal will perform an action that benefits another individual at a cost to itself. This type of behavior is called **altruistic behavior.** One example of altruistic behavior occurs in naked mole rats. Naked mole rats live underground in colonies. Each colony consists of one female that reproduces, called the queen, several males with whom the queen mates, called kings, and between 75–250 other males and females that do not reproduce. The nonreproductive members of the colony forage for food and care for and protect the queen, kings, and newborn offspring. **Figure 18** shows the nonreproductive individuals of a colony surrounding a queen and her offspring. By huddling around her, they are helping to keep the offspring warm.

Scientists have wondered what the advantage of altruistic behavior would be to an individual animal. Why should behavior that might hurt the individual animal ever be selected? D W

Kin selection One theory that has been presented to explain some types of altruistic behavior is kin selection. According to the idea of kin selection, altruistic behavior evolves because it increases the number of copies of a gene that is common to a population. It does not matter which individual passes the gene on to future generations. In the case of the mole rats, scientists have discovered through DNA analysis that all of the individuals in a colony of naked mole rats are closely related. The nonreproductive members of the colony will not pass on their genes. However, genes that are similar, if not identical, to their own will be passed on by the queen. As the nonreproductive members work to protect the queen and bring her food, they are ensuring that genes similar to their own will be passed on to future generations.

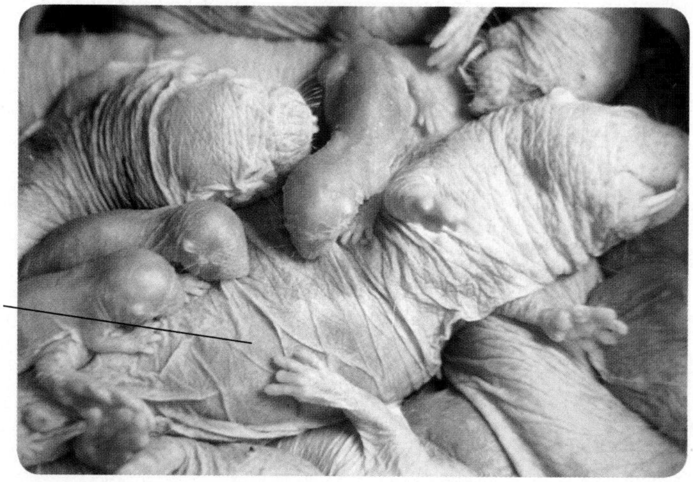

Figure 18 The nonreproductive members of a colony of naked mole rats exhibit altruistic behavior. They forage for food, protect the queen, and huddle around her to provide warmth while she nurses her offspring.

Demonstration

BL OL AL **Observe Animal Behavior** Use ants in an ant farm or fish in a fish tank to provide students an opportunity to observe animal behavior. Have students view the tank or farm for 5 minutes and record the behaviors they observe. Once the observation period is complete, have students identify the behavior types they observed. Possible answers: social insects performing tasks, fish moving to surface searching for food

Est. time: 10 min

Table 1 **Effects of Behaviors** Concepts in Motion Interactive Table

Behavior	Example	Advantage	Disadvantage
Migration		Animals that migrate increase their chance of survival by moving to a location that has better climate conditions and more food.	A large amount of energy is needed to move long distances and there is the possibility of increased predation while moving.
Pheromone communication		Pheromones provide a species-specific form of communication, which works without alerting predators.	Pheromones have a more limited range of communication than auditory or visual cues.
Nurturing		Nurturing increases an offspring's chance of survival. Genes of the parents continue to be present in future generations.	Parents spend increased amounts of energy on caring for offspring, possibly at the cost of the parents' health or safety.

S

Advantages and Disadvantages

Many behaviors have benefits and disadvantages related to survival and reproductive success. A cost-benefit analysis examines the advantages and disadvantages of a particular behavior in terms of survival and reproductive success. **Table 1** shows the cost-benefit analysis of some types of animal behavior.

Section 2 Assessment

Section Summary

- Behavior evolves when genes from successfully reproductive animals remain in a gene pool.
- Competitive behaviors allow animals to establish dominance without serious injury or death to other individuals.
- Behaviors such as foraging, migrating, and maintaining a biological rhythm are important activities in animals' lives.
- Communication behaviors are critical to the survival and reproductive success of animals.
- Certain behaviors, such as courting and nurturing, are directly related to the reproductive success of an individual animal.

Understand Main Ideas

1. MAIN Idea **Explain** how the behavior of an animal relates to its survival and reproductive success.
2. **Define** agonistic behavior. Give one example of this type of behavior.
3. **Analyze** the advantages and disadvantages of nurturing behaviors.
4. **Describe** how animals can communicate using pheromones.
5. **Explain** why migration is advantageous for some animals.

Think Critically

6. **Expand Table 1** by providing examples of the advantages and disadvantages of three other behaviors presented in this section.

MATH in Biology

7. The data in **Figure 14** show that the squirrel kept in continual darkness shifted the time of its activity slightly each day. After 23 days, the squirrel's activity cycle had shifted by eight hours. On average, how much, in minutes, did the activity cycle change each day?

S Skill Practice

BL OL AL COOP LEARN

Visual Literacy Have students study the information in Table 1, then organize them into groups of three. Have each group research a behavior in a specific animal, such as altruistic behavior in ants or migratory behavior in whales or monarch butterflies. Have the teams discuss advantages and disadvantages of the behavior and then share their conclusions with the class.

Concepts in Motion
Interactive Table

Formative Assessment

Intervention Provide students with a written list of competitive, foraging, migratory, and communicative behaviors. Have students identify each type of behavior exhibited. Example: whooping cranes dance to attract a mate = communicative behavior

Remediation Show students photos of animals exhibiting specific behaviors. For example, show a photo of a peacock plumage with feathers exposed.
ASK STUDENTS: ***What is happening in this photo?*** The peacock has his feathers spread to attract a mate. Discuss the types of behaviors shown in each picture.

Section 2 Assessment

1. The behaviors of an animal allow it to survive to reproductive age and to attract and successfully reproduce with a mate.
2. Agonistic behavior is threatening or combative interaction between two individuals of the same species. Examples include polar bears sparring or bighorn sheep butting heads.
3. Advantages include an increased chance of offspring survival, which means that genes of the parents remain in the gene pool. Disadvantages include high energy input from parents.
4. Pheromone chemicals relay messages about reproduction readiness between males and females and sometimes warn of danger.
5. Migration allows animals to locate food sources and better weather conditions year round.
6. Possible answers include altruistic behavior, courting behavior, foraging behavior, and competitive behavior.
7. 21 min

Assessment Online Quiz

Purpose

Students will learn how scientists study auditory communication among elephants in the wild.
C.6, G.1, G.2, G.3

Anticipatory Guide

ASK STUDENTS: ***What is infrasound?*** sound waves below the audible range for humans ***Why would infrasound communication be helpful for elephants?*** Because it travels over long distances, it can keep groups of elephants in touch with each other. The lower the sound, the farther it travels. ***How do you analyze infrasound if you cannot hear it?*** Record it, and then speed up the tape (typically 3×).

Background

Animal communication is the transmission of information from one animal to another by means of sound, behavior, taste or odor, electrical impulse, touch, or a combination of these mediums. Communication is employed by animals to attract or repel other individuals of particular groups and to establish and maintain distinct forms of social organization. There are distinct evolutionary benefits in being able to communicate, from attracting a mate to signaling approaching danger to a fellow animal.

BioDiscoveries

Eavesdropping on Elephants

Elephant ESP? Humans can hear many of an elephant's calls, from the loud, shrill trumpet to low moans and grumbles. However, people used to believe that elephants also used Extra Sensory Perception (ESP) to communicate with each other. ESP might include the ability to read other's minds or know their thoughts. ESP was used to explain how a male elephant, traveling for kilometers, avoids other male elephants but finds a female that is ready to mate, which occurs once every few years.

Solving the mystery Enter Katy Payne, a bioacoustics researcher at Cornell University. In 1984, she was visiting the elephant display at the Washington Park Zoo in Portland, Oregon, when she realized that the air throbbed near the elephants. Was something going on that people could not hear? She recorded "elephant talk" and found that the low rumbles that people could hear were only a small part of an elephant's way of communicating. The elephants were using infrasonic sound waves to communicate. Infrasonic sound is produced by sound waves that are below the range of human hearing. Those deep elephant sounds people could hear actually were the overtones of sounds so low and powerful they could travel without interference over long distances. In fact, these calls can be heard by other elephants and felt as vibrations in the ground many kilometers away.

Copy cat Not only do elephants use infrasonic sound to communicate, they also are capable of vocal learning and mimicry. Scientists hypothesize that vocal imitation is used within complex social groups to enhance bonds between individuals.

Most infrasonic calling occurs within family groups, and females with young tend to be the most vocal.

Just why exactly do elephants need to communicate? And why is it important to biology? The way animals communicate can reveal some evolutionary secrets, such as how "talking" to each other can increase the chances of survival of individuals in a species. The wide variety of communication methods that have evolved demonstrates the importance of communication among all creatures. Future research might enhance our understanding of animal communication, as well as uncover many more methods of communication.

WRITING in Biology

Time Line Research at least four scientists from the past and present who have made discoveries about animal communication. Create a time line with your results. Detail the research that they conducted, including their hypotheses, scientific methods, data, and results.

WRITING in Biology

RUBRIC Use the modifiable rubric found on your eTeacherEdition Online to assess writing assignments.

Activity

Sound travels as a compression wave through the air, but the air does not travel. This fact can be demonstrated using a coiled spring toy. Stretch the spring toy to almost its full length. Have a student hold the far end of the toy. Holding your end of the spring, give a rapid push on the spring, followed by an equally rapid pull. This will produce a compression wave that travels the length of the spring. Take care not to let go of the spring.

WebQuest

BIOLAB

Design Your Own

HOW DOES THE EXTERNAL STIMULUS OF LIGHT AFFECT BEHAVIOR?

Background: A response to light can be an important part of an animal's ecological behavior in that it might help make an animal more successful in finding food, escaping predators, or maintaining homeostasis. In this lab, you will design a testing chamber and use it to test how isopods respond to light.

Question: *How do isopods respond to light?*

Materials

clear plastic food wrap
forceps
plastic Petri dishes with lids
cardboard boxes or trays
small paper plates
aged tap water
black paper
isopods
scissors
light source
filter paper
paper towels
tape
graph paper

Safety Precautions

WARNING: ***Be careful when working with a light source that can become hot. Treat the isopods in a humane manner at all times.***

Plan and Perform the Experiment

1. Read and complete the lab safety form.
2. Form a hypothesis about how the isopods will respond to light.
3. Plan how you will build a testing chamber, and then design an experiment to test your hypothesis. Keep in mind that isopods need to be kept moist at all times. Make sure your experiment has a control group of isopods. Identify the variables and ensure that your experiment tests only one variable at a time. What will you measure? How will you measure it?
4. Design and construct a data table you can use to record the data you collect concerning the behavior of the isopods in response to light.
5. Make sure your teacher approves your plan before you proceed.
6. Collect material needed for your experiment and construct your testing chamber. Handle isopods gently and carefully.
7. Carry out your experiment.
8. **Cleanup and Disposal** Return isopods to their classroom habitat. Disassemble any equipment you put together and return any reusable materials to their proper storage area. Be sure to wash your hands thoroughly.

Analyze and Conclude

1. **Organize data** by creating a graph to illustrate your findings.
2. **Explain** what your graph shows about the response of isopods to light.
3. **Draw Conclusions** Did the data you collected from your observations of the control and experimental groups of isopods support your hypothesis?
4. **Use Scientific Explanations** What types of complex ecological behaviors of isopods might involve their response to light?
5. **Think Critically** Isopods also respond to the stimulus of low moisture by crowding together. Predict how this behavior would maximize their fitness and success.
6. **Error Analysis** What variables in your experiment would affect your data if they were not well controlled?

APPLY YOUR SKILL

Field Investigation Look for isopods in their natural habitat. How do the data you collected in this lab help you select places to begin your search? Write a summary describing your observations of isopods in their natural habitat.

Analyze and Conclude

1. Graphs should compare the control group with the experimental group.
2. Answers will depend on experiment results.
3. Answers will depend on hypothesis. Students should notice that isopods were active in a lighted area but inactive on the dark side.
4. survival behavior, because darkness may help protect them from predators; foraging behavior; possibly reproductive behavior
5. Students should indicate that loss of moisture would be higher for a single isopod than for a group crowded together.
6. Variables may include: temperature differences between the experimental and control group or between the dark and light side of the chamber, differences in humidity, the number of isopods, or the intensity of the light. If isopods are not healthy, they may not respond as quickly or at all to stimuli. There might be differences in how isopods respond by age or size.

BIOLAB

Design Your Own

? Inquiry BioLab

For a lab worksheet, use your eTeacherEdition Online.

RUBRIC A rubric for evaluating BioLabs is found on your eTeacherEdition Online.

Est Time 90 min

Content Background Isopods are arthropods that are more closely related to crabs and lobsters than to insects. Isopods breathe using gills that must be kept moist. Isopods have a well-developed nervous system and sensory organs that include eyes and antennae. They respond strongly to moisture, temperature, and light.

Safety Precautions Approve lab safety forms before work begins. Remind students to be careful using scissors.

Teaching Strategies

- Use a spoon to pick up and transfer isopods.
- A damp filter disk or paper towel in the bottom of the chamber will keep isopods moist.
- If students use a paper towel, they may need to tape the towel edges down to prevent the isopods from crawling under the towel.

Alternative Teaching Demo This entire experiment may be run as a teacher demo. Each student can come up with a hypothesis concerning how isopods will respond to light. Students can work together to design a testing chamber that you would then build and use. Students can collect the data using a common table. Then copy and distribute the data to all students and have them use it to develop a graphic display.

Chapter 31 Study Guide

ConnectED

Students can use the following to review the chapter.

Review

Vocabulary eGames
Vocabulary eFlashcards
Vocabulary PuzzleMaker

Assessment

Online Quizzes
Online Test Practice
Standardized Test Practice

Use the *ExamView®* *Assessment Suite* CD-ROM to:

- create multiple versions of tests
- create modified tests with one mouse click
- edit existing questions and add your own questions
- build tests aligned with state standards using built-in state curriculum tags
- change English tests to Spanish with one mouse click
- track students' progress using the Teacher Management System

Chapter 31 Study Guide

THEME FOCUS Scientific Inquiry Scientific studies have taught us about many types of animal behaviors—from Pavlov's dogs to teaching sign language to chimpanzees.

BIG Idea Many animal behaviors are influenced by both genetics and environmental experiences.

Section 1 Basic Behaviors

behavior (p. 908)
innate behavior (p. 910)
fixed action pattern (p. 910)
learned behavior (p. 912)
habituation (p. 912)
classical conditioning (p. 913)
operant conditioning (p. 913)
imprinting (p. 914)
cognitive behavior (p. 915)

MAIN Idea Animal behaviors can be innate or learned, and they evolve through natural selection.

- Behavior can be influenced by both genes and experience.
- Successful behaviors are those that give individuals an advantage for survival and reproduction.
- Behavior can be innate or learned.
- Learned behavior includes habituation, conditioning, and imprinting.
- Cognitive behavior involves thinking, reasoning, and problem solving.

Section 2 Ecological Behaviors

agonistic behavior (p. 917)
dominance hierarchy (p. 917)
territorial behavior (p. 918)
foraging behavior (p. 918)
migratory behavior (p. 919)
circadian rhythm (p. 919)
language (p. 920)
courting behavior (p. 921)
nurturing behavior (p. 921)
altruistic behavior (p. 922)

MAIN Idea Animals that engage in complex behaviors might survive and reproduce because they have inherited more favorable behaviors.

- Behavior evolves when genes from successfully reproductive animals remain in a gene pool.
- Competitive behaviors allow animals to establish dominance without serious injury or death to other individuals.
- Behaviors such as foraging, migrating, and maintaining a biological rhythm are important activities in animals' lives.
- Communication behaviors are critical to the survival and reproductive success of animals.
- Certain behaviors, such as courting and nurturing, are directly related to the reproductive success of an individual animal.

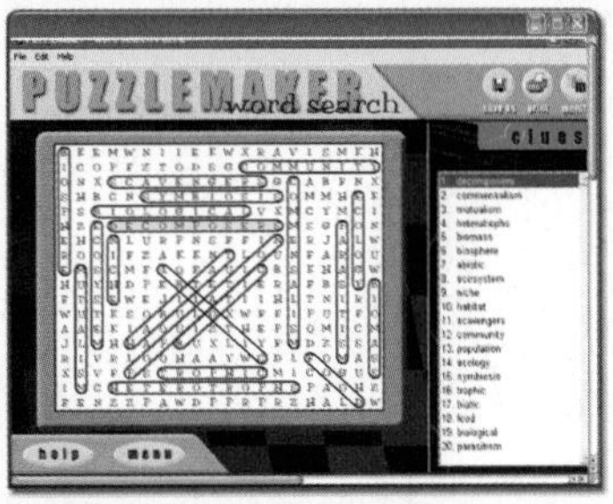

Review **Vocabulary PuzzleMaker**

For additional practice with vocabulary, have students access the Vocabulary PuzzleMaker online.

Review Vocabulary eGames

Section 1

Vocabulary Review

Use what you know about the vocabulary terms found on the Study Guide page to answer the following questions.

1. What type of behavior is carried out in a sequence of specific actions in response to a stimulus?
2. What type of behavior occurs when an association is made between two different kinds of stimuli?
3. What type of learning is permanent and occurs within a specific time period of an animal's life?
4. What type of behavior leads to a decrease in an animal's response after being exposed repeatedly to a stimulus that has no positive or negative consequences?
5. What type of behavior involves an animal associating its response with a reward or punishment?

Understand Main Ideas

6. Which behavior is genetically based and not linked to past experience?
   A. habituation **C.** fixed action pattern
   B. classical conditioning **D.** operant conditioning
7. Which is an example of imprinting?
   A. salmon returning to the water in which they hatched to spawn
   B. a rat learning to press a lever to get food
   C. a baby lion learning how to hunt
   D. baby birds getting used to seeing objects above them
8. An animal that solves a problem is engaging in what type of behavior?
   A. fixed action pattern
   B. cognitive behavior
   C. imprinting
   D. conditioning
9. Seasonal movement is an example of which type of behavior?
   A. migratory behavior
   B. classical conditioning
   C. cognitive behavior
   D. imprinting

Use the figure below to answer question 10.

10. Which type of behavior is shown above?
    A. imprinting **C.** habituation
    B. fixed action pattern **D.** operant conditioning
11. What is the time during which an animal imprints?
    A. nurturing period
    B. cognitive period
    C. sensitive period
    D. learning period

Constructed Response

12. **Short Answer** Compare and contrast classical conditioning and operant conditioning.
13. **Open Ended** What difficulties might scientists have when trying to determine if animals engage in cognitive behaviors?
14. MAIN Idea Describe how the evolution of animal behaviors is affected by natural selection.

Think Critically

15. **Hypothesize** why a behavior of an animal would cause it not to spend energy and time caring for its offspring.
16. **CAREERS IN BIOLOGY** Animal behaviorists observed that one species of lovebird carries nest-building materials in its beak. Another species of lovebird carries the material under its feathers. Hybrid offspring are produced by breeding these two species. The hybrids repeatedly shift the material between their beaks and their feathers while carrying it. What conclusion can be drawn about the influence of genetics on behavior from the results of this experiment?

Assessment Online Test Practice

Chapter 31

Assessment

Section 1

Vocabulary Review

1. fixed action pattern
2. classical conditioning
3. imprinting
4. habituation
5. operant conditioning

Understand Main Ideas

6. C
7. A
8. B
9. A
10. B
11. C

Constructed Response

12. Both are types of learned behavior that involve an animal making an association. Classical conditioning occurs when an animal forms an association between two different stimuli. Operant conditioning occurs when an animal forms an association with its response and a punishment or a reward.
13. Scientists cannot know what another animal is thinking or communicate with the animal to find out.
14. The evolution of animal behaviors is directly related to natural selection; the behaviors of the winning mate are more desirable and will be passed on to future generations.

Think Critically

15. The behavior does not benefit the parent or the offspring.
16. The behavior of nest building is genetically based.

Section 2

Vocabulary Review

17. language
18. dominance hierarchy
19. pheromone
20. territorial behavior
21. agonistic behavior

Understand Main Ideas

22. C
23. B
24. C
25. D
26. B
27. C

Constructed Response

28. The courting behaviors of many animals are linked to genetic inheritance; the brighter a peacock's tail feathers are, the better his chances of obtaining a peahen.
29. A dominance hierarchy occurs when animals in groups establish a ranking order from highest to lowest. Territorial behavior occurs when animals are trying to establish and maintain a territory. Territorial behaviors include verbal cues, chemical messages, and fighting.
30. Answers should include disruption of certain patterns, such as sleep and wakefulness, and disrupted mating cycles.

Think Critically

31. If a sibling survives, genes similar to that of the sacrificed individual remain in the gene pool to be passed on to future generations.
32. The higher the rank, the more successful the male is at mating.
33. The highest-ranking individual may be stronger or better at finding food than other individuals. Those genes may be passed on more often with increased mating success.

Chapter 31 Assessment

Section 2

Vocabulary Review

Use the vocabulary terms found on the Study Guide page to answer the following questions.

17. What is a form of auditory communication in which animals use vocal organs to produce groups of sounds which have shared meanings?

18. In which situation does a top-ranked individual get access to resources without conflict from other individuals in the group?

19. What is a specific chemical spread by animals in order to communicate?

20. Which type of behavior results in an animal adopting and controlling a physical area against other animals of the same species?

21. Which type of behavior results in a threatening or combative interaction between two individuals of the same species?

Understand Main Ideas

22. Which behavior usually is concerned with finding and eating food?
A. nurturing
B. courting
C. foraging
D. migration

23. Which behavior is directly related to reproductive success within a species?
A. altruism
B. courting
C. foraging
D. migration

Use the figure below to answer question 24.

24. What is shown in the figure above?
A. agonistic behavior
B. migration
C. dominance hierarchy
D. nurturing behavior

25. What behavior is linked with pheromones?
A. agonistic
B. migration
C. nurturing
D. communication

26. Which is an example of a circadian rhythm?
A. migration
B. sleep/wake cycle
C. hibernation
D. reproductive cycle

27. Ensuring that offspring have an increased chance of survival is an example of which type of behavior?
A. agonistic
B. migration
C. nurturing
D. territorial

Constructed Response

28. MAIN Idea Provide an example that illustrates how animal behavior is related to genetic inheritance.

29. Short Answer Distinguish dominance hierarchy from territorial behaviors.

30. Open Ended Hypothesize what would happen if circadian rhythms disappeared.

Think Critically

31. THEME FOCUS Scientific Inquiry Hypothesize the successful evolutionary advantages of an animal sacrificing itself for its sibling in a competitive battle with a predator.

Use the graph below to answer questions 32 and 33.

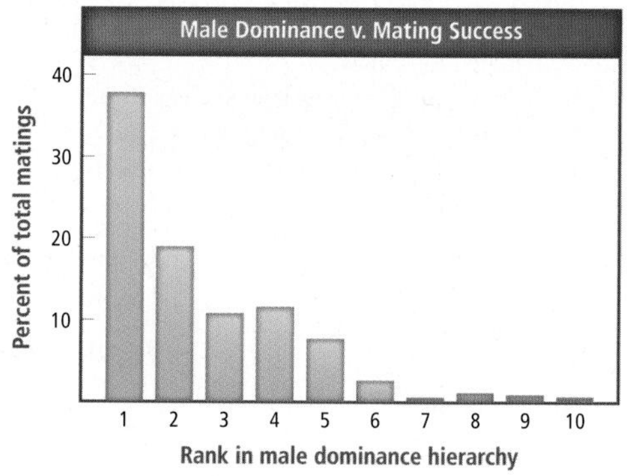

32. Draw conclusions about the relationship between the order of male seals in the dominance hierarchy and their number of matings.

33. Hypothesize a reason for this behavior.

34. **Infer** how an animal might starve if its parents failed to teach it competitive behaviors.

35. **Infer** If an individual animal no longer was able to learn, how might this condition affect its ability to engage in competitive behaviors in the near future?

36. **Compare and contrast** two strategies of spending reproductive energy—producing large numbers of eggs with little or no parental care, and producing a smaller number of eggs and engaging in nurturing behavior. Give an example of animals that use each strategy.

37. **Conclude** Of the three animals you have observed in this chapter—emperor penguins, earthworms, and isopods, which has the most complex ecological behavior? Based on what you know about these animals, why do you think this might be?

Use the figure below to answer questions 38 and 39.

A species of marine isopods lives in sponges in intertidal zones. The males of this species exist in three different sizes—alpha, beta, and gamma. Females of this species are similar in size to the beta males. Each size of male has a different strategy for mating.

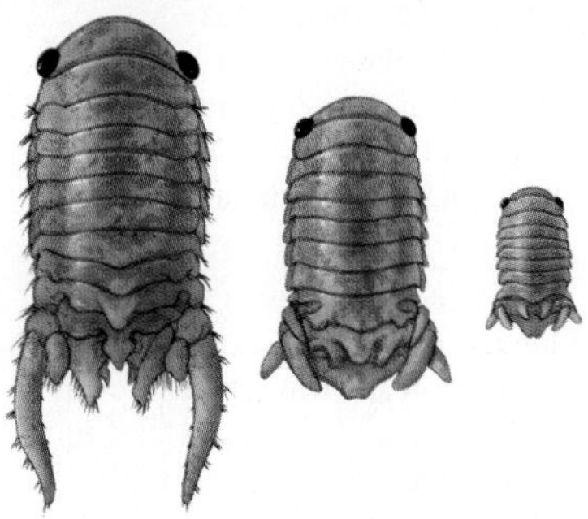

Alpha Beta Gamma

38. **Identify** which size of male would use the mating strategy that involves avoiding the alpha-sized males and hiding in a sponge to mate with a female. Explain your answer.

39. **Identify** which size of male would use the mating strategy that involves fighting with an alpha-sized male until one isopod wins. What is this type of behavior called?

Summative Assessment

40. **BIG Idea** Choose an animal and create a graphic organizer showing how genetics and environmental factors have influenced its daily needs and activities.

41. **WRITING in Biology** Write a persuasive paragraph on why altruistic behavior by an individual animal might result in the animal's genes appearing in future generations.

DBQ Document-Based Questions

Oystercatchers are small shore birds that eat mussels as one of their primary foods. The birds must spend time and effort to hammer or stab the mussels to open them.

Use this graph to answer the questions below.

Data obtained from: Meire, P.M., and Ervynck, A. 1986. Are oystercatchers *(Haematopus ostralegus)* selecting the most profitable mussels *(Mytilus edulis)*? *Animal Behaviour* 34: 1427-1435.

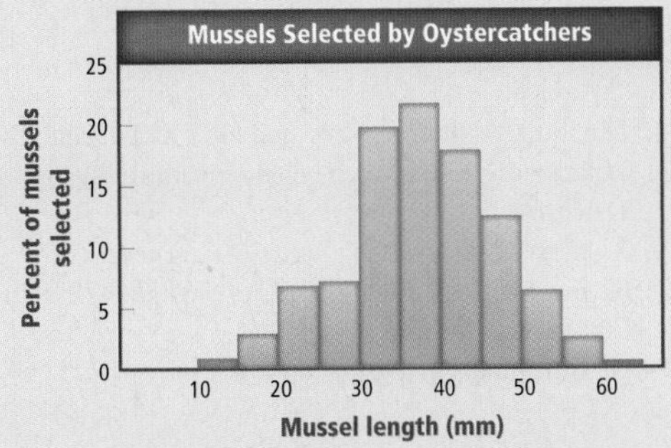

42. Which mussel size do the oystercatchers prefer?

43. The 10-mm mussels are the most abundant. Hypothesize why oystercatchers often do not forage for them.

44. Larger mussels provide many more calories than smaller mussels. The larger the mussel, the more it tends to be encrusted with barnacles that make it harder to open. Hypothesize why oystercatchers do not forage for the largest, most energy-rich mussels.

34. If an individual does not learn to engage in competitive behaviors, it may not be able to obtain enough food to survive.

35. The animal may be at a disadvantage for competition if it could no longer learn.

36. Both are successful reproductive strategies, as they are used throughout the animal kingdom. More energy can be spent on producing large numbers of eggs and less on nurturing. This may result in the death of many offspring, but some will survive. Less energy can be spent on producing eggs and fewer offspring will be produced. The reproductive energy is spent on nurturing the offspring, increasing their chances of survival. Many fish produce large numbers of eggs. Humans spend a large amount of energy on nurturing behaviors.

37. Emperor penguins have the most complex ecological behaviors of the three organisms observed. Students should recognize from their previous studies that the nervous system and sense organs of birds are much more highly developed than that of the worm or isopod. This, along with their more developed musculature and other systems, allows the penguins to respond in more complex ways than the other two animals.

38. The gamma male, being the smallest, would employ this method. The individuals are small enough to sneak into the sponges undetected by the larger males.

39. other alpha-sized males; agonistic behavior

Summative Assessment

40. Answers will vary based upon the chosen animal. Answers should include knowledge about the environment and habitat in which their animal lives and the daily life and activities carried out by the animal.

41. When displaying altruistic behavior, an individual may sacrifice its own life in order for other individuals in a colony or population to survive. By trying to help a related individual survive, there is a better chance that the same or similar genes will be passed on to future generations.

WRITING in Biology

RUBRIC Use the modifiable rubric found on your eTeacherEdition Online to assess writing assignments.

DBQ Document-Based Questions

Meire, P.M., and Ervynck, A. 1986. Are oystercatchers (Haematopus ostralegus) selecting the most profitable mussels (Mytilus edulis)? Animal Behaviour 34: 1427–1435.

42. between 30 and 40 mm

43. The mussels do not provide enough calories for the effort or the birds' beak size is too big to handle the smaller mussels.

44. It takes too much energy to try to break through the barnacles. The cost outweighs the benefits.

Assessment Online Test Practice

Standardized Test Practice

Multiple Choice

1. A
2. A
3. D
4. C
5. A
6. A
7. B
8. A

Short Answer

9. The bones of the jaw evolved from pharyngeal pouches. As the strength and shape of the jaw changed, the diets of the fish diversified. The jaw enabled fishes to grab and crush their prey allowing them to eat larger prey.
10. By migrating, the birds can use food sources that are in different places and not overuse them in one place during the year.
11. Answers can vary. Accept logical answers.
    - They have a high metabolic rate that enables them to generate enough heat if the surroundings are too cold.
    - They can use fur or hair to stay warm if the surroundings are too cool.
    - They have a four-chambered heart that promotes effective circulation and makes cooling and heating mechanisms in the body more effective.
12. Both circulatory systems bring nutrients to parts of the body and carry waste matter away. In an open circulatory system, blood is simply pumped through open spaces in the body. In a closed circulatory system, blood vessels carry the blood from one place to another.
13. Order Rodentia is the largest order of mammals and includes beavers, chipmunks, guinea pigs, mice, rats, and squirrels. Order Lagomorpha includes hares, pikas, and rabbits. Animals of both orders are herbivores. Rodents have a pair of long sharp teeth that continue to grow throughout their lifetime. Lagomorphs have teeth that are structurally different from those of rodents.
14. Having a dominance hierarchy would reduce aggression among the animals in the area when feeding and searching for mates.

Standardized Test Practice

Cumulative

Multiple Choice

1. Which describes a function of feathers?
   A. insulation
   B. nesting
   C. conserving water
   D. swimming

Use the diagram below to answer questions 2 and 3.

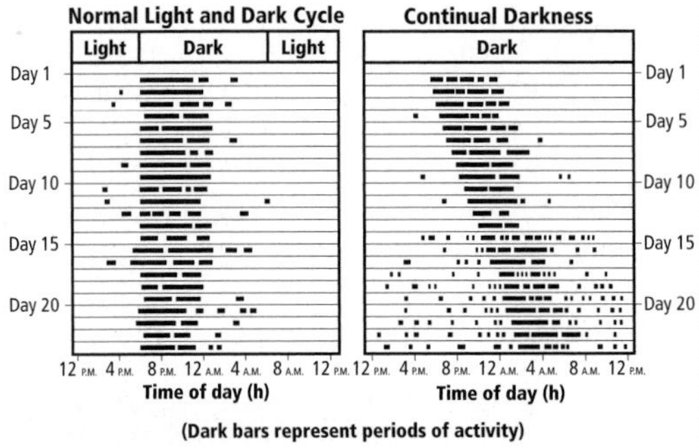

2. The squirrels that were exposed to 12 h of daylight each day displayed which behavior pattern during the 24-h cycles?
   A. most activity during hours of darkness
   B. most activity during hours of daylight
   C. constant sleeping
   D. continuous activity

3. Squirrels that were exposed to 24 h of darkness displayed which circadian rhythm?
   A. cycles of exactly 12 h
   B. cycles of less than 12 h
   C. cycles of exactly 24 h
   D. cycles of more than 24 h

4. How did the earliest fishes obtain their food?
   A. by grazing on phytoplankton at the water surface
   B. by living as parasites inside larger marine animals
   C. by sucking up organic matter off the ocean floor
   D. by using sharp teeth to break apart mollusks

Use the diagram below to answer question 5.

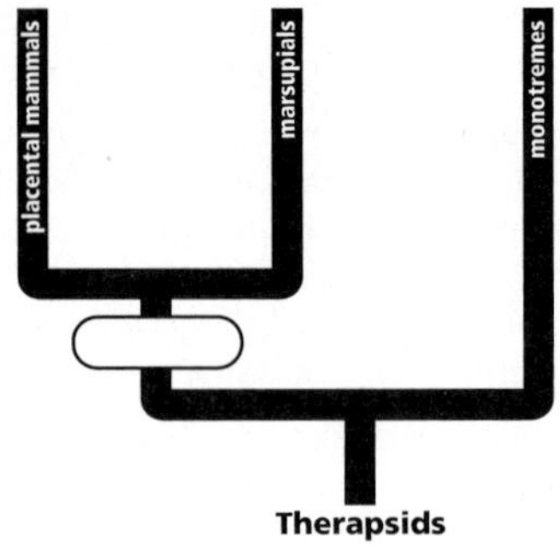

5. What information belongs in the bubble in the diagram?
   A. Adults give birth to live young.
   B. Adults lay eggs.
   C. Offspring live in mother's pouch after birth.
   D. Offspring receive milk from their mother.

6. Which structures are used by fishes to take in oxygen and transport it to body cells?
   A. gills and a closed circulatory system
   B. gills and an open circulatory system
   C. lungs and a closed circulatory system
   D. lungs and an open circulatory system

7. Echinoderms, such as sea stars, use their tube feet for locomotion and what else?
   A. reproduction
   B. respiration
   C. sensing gravity
   D. sensing light

8. Which characteristic is used to classify dinosaurs into two groups?
   A. structure of the hipbones
   B. structure of the skull and jaw
   C. whether they are ectotherms or endotherms
   D. whether they are herbivores or carnivores

Short Answer

Use the diagram below to answer question 9.

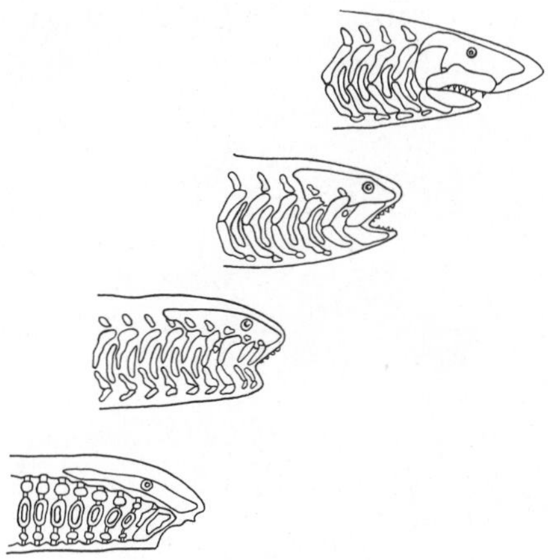

9. Describe the evolution of the jaw. Explain how it was an important advancement for fishes.

10. Hypothesize why some birds migrate thousands of miles each year.

11. Identify three traits of mammals. Explain why they are necessary for endotherms.

12. Compare and contrast an open circulatory system and a closed circulatory system.

13. Compare and contrast organisms in the order Rodentia with those in order Lagomorpha.

14. Hypothesize how an animal would benefit from a dominance hierarchy if it does not defend a territory.

Extended Response

15. Suppose a plant with adaptations for survival in a tropical rain forest is transplanted to a tropical desert. What adaptations in the rain forest plant could cause it to have trouble surviving in the new environment?

16. A certain type of insect uses pheromones to attract mates. The insect is most active during the day. Propose the advantages and disadvantages of this type of behavior for attracting mates.

Essay Question

The ring-tailed lemur is an herbivore. It eats a variety of plants and plant materials. Ring-tailed lemurs eat up to three dozen species of vegetation, but one of their favorites is the kily tree.

Groups of ring-tailed lemurs are led by a dominant female. A group usually contains between 15 and 30 lemurs. They can travel over a large area, some days more than 4 km. When the lemurs aren't eating, they often bathe in the Sun, groom each other, or play. Ring-tailed lemurs sleep under large trees. Settling down for the night is usually preceded by a loud whooplike call from all the lemurs.

Using the information in the paragraph above answer the following question in essay format.

17. The passage above describes the diet and behavior of ring-tailed lemurs. Suppose you want to do a study of lemur behavior. In an organized essay, explain what your research question would be and how you would study the behavior of ring-tailed lemurs.

NEED EXTRA HELP?																	
If You Missed Question . . .	1	2	3	4	5	6	7	8	9	10	11	12	13	14	15	16	17
Review Section . . .	29.2	31.1	31.2	28.2	30.2	28.1	27.1	29.1	28.2	31.2	30.1	25.3	30.2	31.2	21.1	31.2	30.2

Extended Response

15. Plants in a rainy or wet climate would not have adaptations, such as a thick cuticle, to prevent water loss in dry weather. They also would lack structures for storing water. Too much water would leave the plant through transpiration and it would probably die.

16. Answers can vary. Pheromones are an effective method for insects to attract mates because pheromones are specific for each species and therefore do not attract other organisms. Also, pheromones do not depend on visual recognition. Using pheromones to attract mates also enables insects that are normally active during the day to remain in concealed locations and not be exposed to predators. On the other hand, pheromones only are effective in a limited area. Insects that use pheromone attractants can attract potential mates only in a small area. Also, pheromones can be dissipated by strong breezes.

Essay Question

17. Answers can vary depending on the aspect of lemur life that students plan to study. Questions should involve mammalian characteristics covered in the chapter, such as the following. How do lemurs care for their young? What environmental conditions influence lemurs to be nocturnal or diurnal? How is their behavior related to their diet? The research plan can involve tracking the daily patterns of a community of lemurs, noting their means of communication, or videotaping or audiotaping their behavior.

UNIT 9

The Human Body

Preview the Unit

Have students preview the chapters in this unit and make a concept map or graphic organizer.

Chapter 32

Integumentary, Skeletal, and Muscular Systems

BIG Idea These systems work together to maintain homeostasis by protecting, supporting, and moving the body.

Chapter 33

Nervous System

BIG Idea The nervous system is essential for communication among cells, tissues, and organs.

Chapter 34

Circulatory, Respiratory, and Excretory Systems

BIG Idea These systems function together to maintain homeostasis by delivering important substances to the body's cells while removing wastes.

Chapter 35

Digestive and Endocrine Systems

BIG Idea The digestive system breaks down food to provide energy and nutrients for the body. The endocrine system produces hormones that regulate body functions.

Chapter 36

Human Reproduction and Development

BIG Idea Human reproduction involves the joining together of sperm and egg.

Chapter 37

Immune System

BIG Idea The immune system attempts to protect the body from contracting an infection through pathogens.

WebQuest

UNIT 9

The Human Body

THEMES

Scientific Inquiry Scientists investigate human body systems to develop better treatments for diseases.

Diversity Tremendous diversity within human cells allows for highly specialized systems.

Energy The chemical bonds of ATP provide stored energy for daily bodily functions.

Homeostasis Human body systems work together to maintain homeostasis.

Change Human body systems react to internal and external environmental changes.

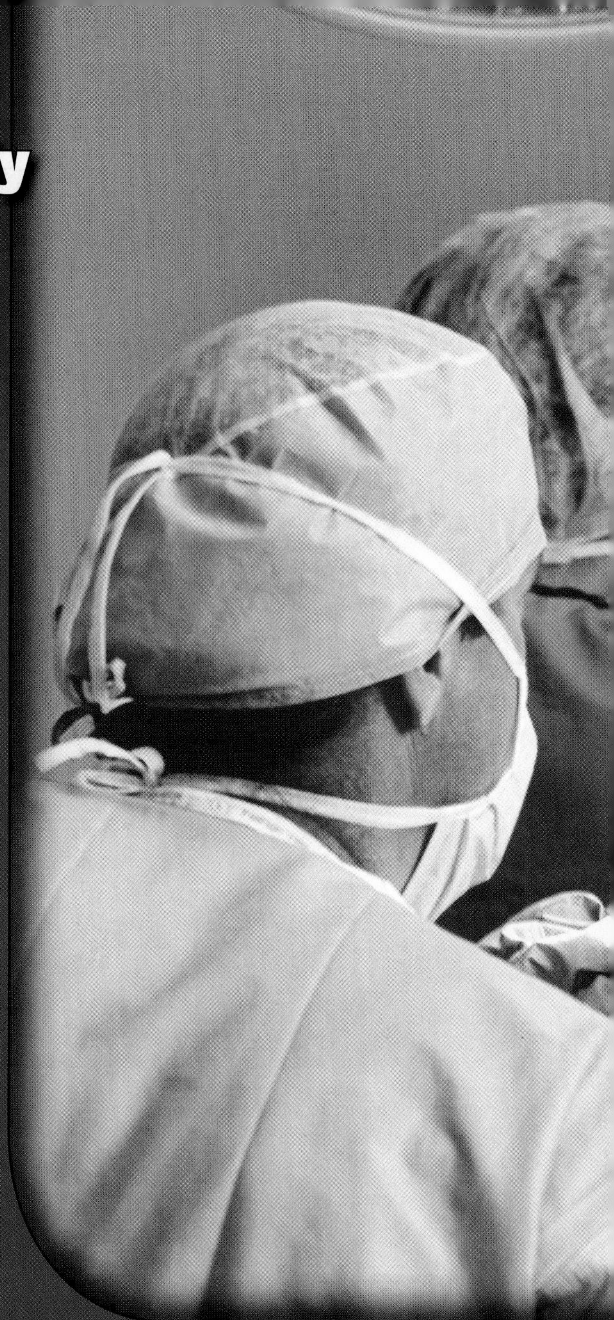

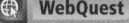

WebQuest **CAREERS IN BIOLOGY**

Orthopedic surgeons are medical doctors that concentrate on the treatment of the musculoskeletal system. Orthopedic surgeons perform procedures such as bone grafting, joint replacement, and arthroscopic surgery.

5-Minute UNIT LAUNCH

Before and After Review the meaning of the term *homeostasis* with the students. On a sheet of paper, have students make two columns. For each body system covered in Unit 9, have students fill in the first column describing in one sentence how each system contributes to homeostasis. After studying the unit, have them revisit their charts and revise their sentences in the second column.

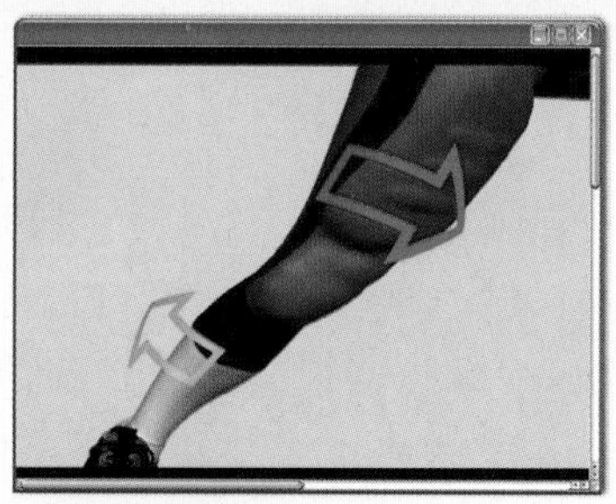

Video

What's BIOLOGY Got To Do With It?

This video describes sports injuries and the treatment of them.

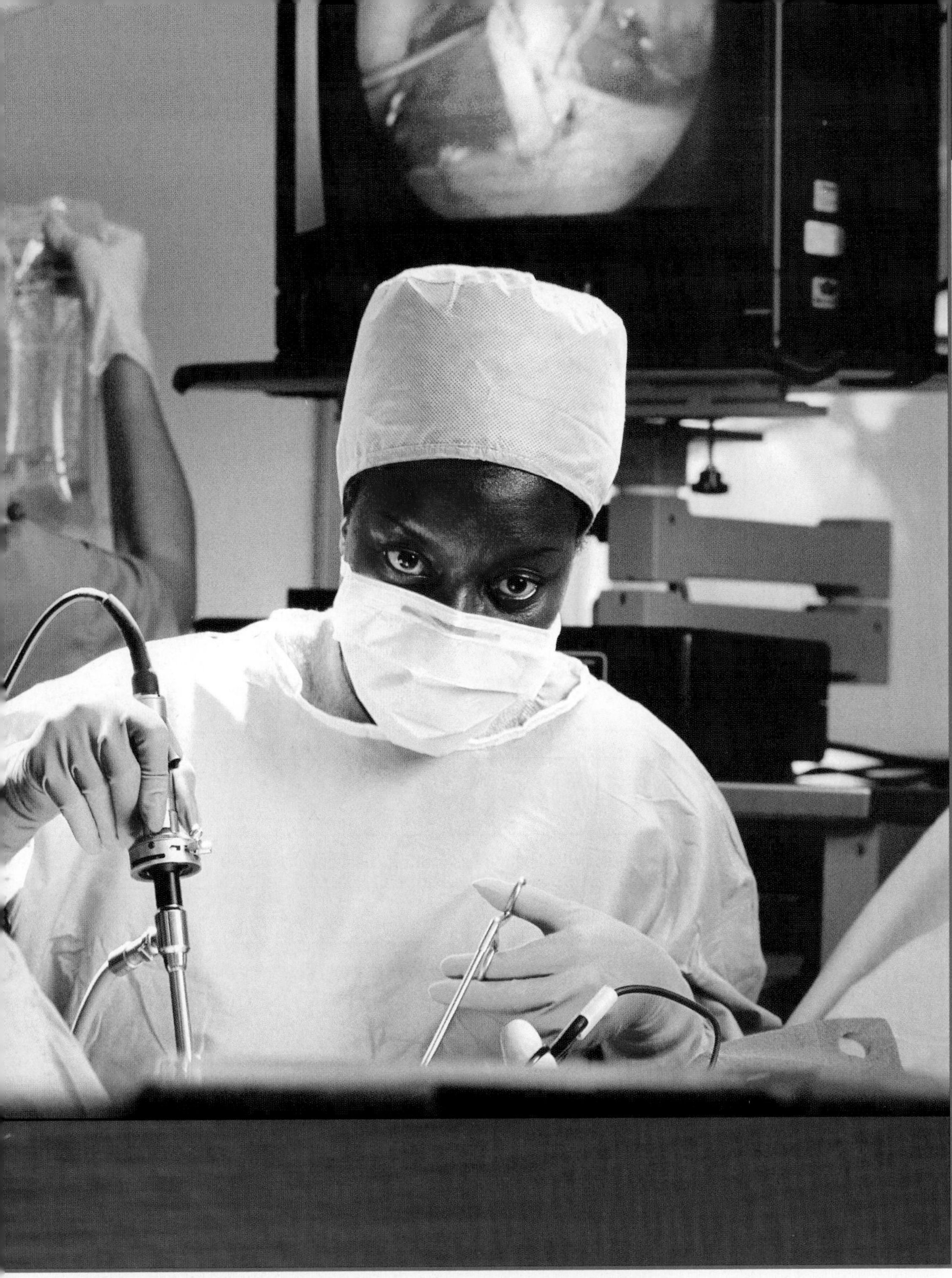

Misconceptions

In each section, *Clarify a Misconception* provides you with the information to dispel a common student misconception. A question will help you elicit the misconception and an explanation will help you correct it.

Before studying Chapter 32, students might think that bones are dead. Chapter 32 will explain that bones are made of living cells that are organized into tissues (p. 943).

Before studying Chapter 33, students might think that over-the-counter drugs are safer than prescription drugs. Chapter 33 will explain that all drugs are danderous if misused (p. 979).

Before studying Chapter 34, students might think that the heart is on the left side of the chest. Chapter 34 will explain that the heart is in the center of the chest, but we feel the beat on the left side because that's where the stronger-pumping ventricle is located (p. 994).

Before studying Chapter 35, students might think that ulcers are caused by stress or certain foods. Chapter 35 will explain that ulcers are caused by a bacterium, but food and stress could aggravate the symptoms (p. 1021).

Before studying Chapter 36, students might think that the sex of an embryo is determined when the genitals begin to develop. Chapter 36 will explain that sex is determined at conception by genetics (p. 1059).

Before studying Chapter 37, students might think that the tonsils and appendix serve no function. Chapter 37 will explain that both function as part of the immune system (p. 1086).

SERVICE LEARNING/COMMUNITY SERVICE

Public Service Agencies Students can volunteer to work for public service agencies such as the Muscular Dystrophy Association, the American Heart Association, and the March of Dimes. Students will be exposed to a large amount of information about various human conditions and can get first-hand experience working with individuals needing assistance. Educational research indicates that most students who participate in service learning feel more empowered and develop more overt leadership skills (Swick et al., 2002).

Research bibliography on pages 32T–34T

Chapter 32 Organizer: Integumentary, Skeletal, and Muscular Systems

LabManager™
Customize any lab with the LabManager™ CD-ROM.

Essential Questions	National Science Standards	Materials and Planning: Estimated times include cleanup and disposal, but do not include teacher prep time. For cleanup and disposal guidelines, see page 39T.	Est. Time (min)
Section 1 1. What are the four tissue types that are found in the integumentary system? 2. What are the functions of the integumentary system? 3. What are the two layers of skin composed of? 4. What are the events that occur when skin is repaired?	UCP.1, UCP.2, UCP.5; A.1, A.2; C.5; F.1, F.5; G.1, G.2	**Launch Lab,** p. 934: treated chicken wings, self-sealing sandwich bags, bleach	15
		Activity, p. 937: rubber gloves, pen	10
		MiniLab 1, p. 938: treated chicken wings, dissecting tools, plastic disposable gloves, dissecting tray, warm soapy water	25
		Demonstration, p. 939: UV-sensitive nail polish, beads, disks, sunglasses, sunscreen	20
Section 2 1. What are the differences between the bones of the axial and appendicular skeletons? 2. How is new bone formed? 3. What are the functions of the skeletal system?	UCP.1, UCP.2, UCP.5; A.1, A.2; D.1; E.1; F.1, F.5, F.6; G.2	**Demonstration,** p. 941: chicken bones, vinegar, water	5 per day
		Demonstration, p. 942: lengthwise cut of a beef bone	10
		Activity, p. 945: tennis ball	5
		MiniLab 2, p. 945: lab gloves, skinned chicken wing, dissection pan, dissection scissors	25
Section 3 1. What are the three types of muscle tissue? 2. What are the events involved in muscle contraction at the cellular and molecular levels? 3. What are the differences between slow-twitch and fast-twitch muscle fibers?	UCP.1–3, UCP.5; A.1, A.2; B.6; C.1, C.5; E.1, E.2; F.1, F.5, F.6; G.1, G.2, G.3	**Demonstration,** p. 949: door with reachable doorframe	10
		BioLab, p. 953: impressions of three unknown bones, set of clues, various animal skeletons, magnifying lens, metric ruler, string	60–90

Suggested Time for Each Lesson

Class	Chapter Opener	Section 1	Section 2	Section 3	Assessment
Basic	45 min	45 min	45 min	45 min	45 min
General	25 min	45 min	65 min	90 min	45 min
Honors	5 min	45 min	55 min	55 min	20 min

ConnectED

connectED.mcgraw-hill.com

Access interactive learning opportunities and teaching resources using these icons located throughout your StudentWorks™ Plus Online and eTeacherEdition Online.

Chapter 32 Section Resources	Additional Chapter 32 Resources	Technology
FAST FILE Unit 9 Resources: Launch Lab Worksheet* MiniLab Worksheet* Study Guide (English/Spanish)* Section Quick Check **Reading Essentials 32.1** **Science Notebook 32.1*** **FAST FILE Unit 9 Resources:** MiniLab Worksheet* Study Guide (English/Spanish)* Section Quick Check **Reading Essentials 32.2** **Science Notebook 32.2*** **FAST FILE Unit 9 Resources:** BioLab Worksheet* Study Guide (English/Spanish)* Section Quick Check **Reading Essentials 32.3** **Science Notebook 32.3***	**FAST FILE Unit 9 Resources:** Chapter Diagnostic Test Concept Mapping* Real-World Biology Enrichment Chapter Tests A, B, and C **Transparencies:** Bellringer Transparencies* Biology Concepts Transparencies* **Lab Resources:** Laboratory Manual* Probeware Lab Manual* Forensics Lab Manual* Pre-AP Lab Manual* Open Inquiry in Biology* Guided Inquiry in Biology*	**Teaching Tools:** eTeacherEdition Online Classroom Presentation Toolkit CD-ROM* LabManager™ CD-ROM* Video Lab DVD* Virtual Lab CD-ROM* What's BIOLOGY Got To Do With It? StudentWorks™ Plus Online* **Chapter Assessment Tools:** Classroom Presentation Toolkit CD-ROM* *ExamView® Assessment Suite* CD-ROM **Web-Based Resources:** • StudentWorks™ Plus Online • eTeacherEdition Online • Animations* • The Interactive Time Line* • Interactive Tables* • Online Quizzes • Online Test Practice • Standardized Test Practice • Virtual Labs* • Multilingual eGlossary* • Vocabulary eGames* • Vocabulary eFlashcards • WebQuests • Personal Tutors

While all resources listed are appropriate for English learners, the * indicates resources with a strong visual or hands-on component for EL.

Teaching strategies and activities have been coded for differentiated instruction.

AL Activities for students working above grade level	**OL** Activities for students working on grade level	**BL** Activities for students working below grade level	**EL** Activities for English learners (also ELL)	**COOP LEARN** Activities designed for small cooperative group work

CHAPTER 32

CHAPTER 32

Integumentary, Skeletal, and Muscular Systems

ConnectED

Your one-stop online resource
connectED.mcgraw-hill.com

Video
Audio
Review
Inquiry
WebQuest
Assessment
Concepts in Motion
Multilingual eGlossary

Launch Lab
How is a chicken's wing like your arm?

Inquiry Launch Lab

For a lab worksheet, use your eTeacherEdition Online.

RUBRIC A rubric for evaluating Launch Labs is found on your eTeacherEdition Online.

Est. Time 15 min

Alternative Materials Students whose cultures or dietary restrict them from handling meat could use photographs or drawings of a chicken combined with video footage of a living chicken as it flaps its wings and moves.

Safety Precautions Although students should not be handling the chicken directly, they should still wash their hands when they have completed this exercise.

Teaching Strategies

- Treat the raw chicken with bleach before putting it in the bags for this lab.
- Along with making the diagram of the chicken wing, you might wish to have students make a diagram of their arm and compare the two.

Launch Lab
How is a chicken's wing like your arm?

Chickens have structures similar to ours. They have skin, muscles, and bones. In this lab, you will examine a chicken wing and begin to explore it.

For a lab worksheet, use your StudentWorks™ Plus Online.

Inquiry Launch Lab

FOLDABLES

Make a layered look-book using the labels shown. Use it to organize your notes on skin.

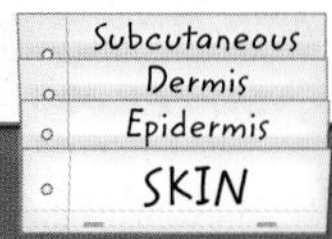

Procedure

1. Read and complete the lab safety form.
2. Obtain a **treated chicken wing** in a **self-sealing sandwich bag.** Observe the skin of the wing.
3. Without removing the wing from the bag, manipulate the wing to determine how it moves and where the joints are located.
4. Lay the bag on a flat surface and gently press and massage the wing to determine where bones and muscles are located.
5. Based on your observations, draw the wing as you imagine it if the skin was removed. Show the bones and muscles.

Analysis

1. **Label** your drawing to show which parts correspond to your upper arm, elbow, wrist, and hand. The section before the first joint is homologous to a human's upper arm. The first joint down from the cut is the elbow, the next joint is the wrist, and the lower third of the wing is homologous to the hand.
2. **Differentiate** How are the parts that make up your arm different from the chicken wing? Observations might include that the skin shows points for attachment of feathers in chickens and hairs in humans, that chickens do not have fingers, and that the part of the chicken homologous to the hand is longer than the part that is homologous to the lower arm.

Introduce the Chapter

Body Structure

ASK STUDENTS: ***What does the illustration on this page tell you about the organization of your body?*** The human body is made of multiple organs and tissue layers. These organs and tissues work together. Students will learn later in this chapter that while bone and muscles are tissues, skin is an organ.

BIG Idea

Homeostasis

ASK STUDENTS: ***How do skin, muscles, and bones work together to maintain homeostasis?*** The skin protects the body against physical trauma and disease-causing organisms. Muscles attach to the skeleton and enable body movement. Bones provide support. Most blood cells are made in the bones. These processes together help keep the body stable within its environment.

THEME FOCUS Homeostasis

Specialized functions of the integumentary, skeletal, and muscular systems maintain homeostasis within the human body.

BIG Idea These systems work together to maintain homeostasis by protecting, supporting, and moving the body.

THEMES

Scientific Inquiry Scientific studies involving human integumentary, skeletal, and muscular systems provide insight into new treatments.

Diversity The variety of bones in the human skeleton provide specialized protection for internal organ systems.

Energy Muscles metabolize energy both in the presence and absence of oxygen.

Homeostasis The integumentary system provides protection from outside pathogens and regulates body temperature.

Change Over time the body can repair damaged bones.

Section 1

MAIN Idea

BL OL AL Skin Functions

ASK STUDENTS: ***Why is skin considered an organ rather than a tissue?*** Tissues are made of cells that work together to perform specific functions. An organ is made of two or more tissues organized to perform activities within an organism. Skin is made of more than one type of tissue. **AL** Have students conduct research on genetic disorders that affect the structure of the skin, including how treatments supplement the function of missing tissues.

R Reading Strategy

EL BL OL Anticipation Guide Before reading Section 1, present 10–15 statements that you have developed from the content of this section and have students predict whether each is true or false. For example: The skin is an organ. T Skin is thicker than a piece of paper. F Some of the dust in your house is really dead skin cells. T Hair and fingernails belong to the same body system. F People sweat to help the body stay cool. T After they read, have students validate or revise their answers based on the information in the text.

S Skill Practice

OL Visual Literacy Have students examine Figure 1 and make a Venn diagram comparing the structures found in the epidermis to those found in the dermis.

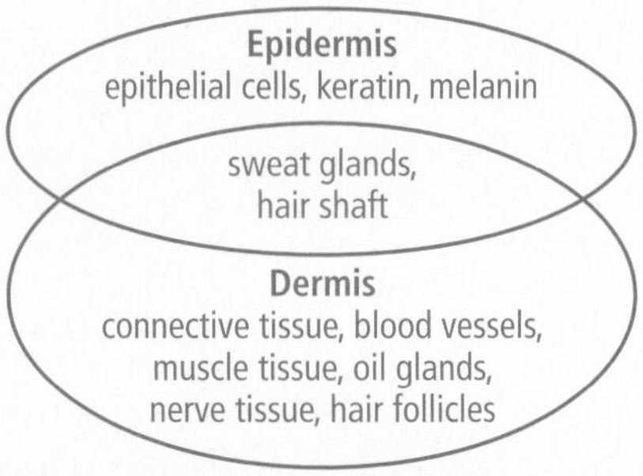

Section 1

Reading Preview

Essential Questions

- What are the four tissue types that are found in the integumentary system?
- What are the functions of the integumentary system?
- What are the two layers of skin composed of?
- What are the events that occur when skin is repaired?

Review Vocabulary

integument: an enveloping layer of an organism

New Vocabulary

epidermis
keratin
melanin
dermis
hair follicle
sebaceous gland

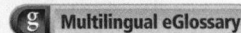

Multilingual eGlossary

R The Integumentary System

MAIN Idea **Skin is a multilayered organ that covers and protects the body.**

Real-World Reading Link The skin on the tips of fingers and toes is thick and is composed of curving ridges that form the basis of fingerprints. Fingerprints were first used in criminal investigations in 1860 by Henry Faulds, a Scottish medical missionary. Your skin is not just a simple covering that keeps your body together. It is complex and is essential for your survival. Your ridges are uniquely yours!

The Structure of Skin

The integumentary (ihn TEG yuh MEN tuh ree) system is the organ system that covers and protects the body. Skin is the main organ of the integumentary system and is composed of four types of tissues: epithelial tissue, connective tissue, muscle tissue, and nerve tissue. Epithelial tissue covers body surfaces, and connective tissue provides support and protection. Muscle tissue is involved in body movement. Nerve tissue forms the body's communication network. You will learn more about muscle tissue in Section 3.

FOLDABLES® Incorporate information from this section into your Foldable.

The epidermis Refer to **Figure 1,** which illustrates the two main layers of skin as seen through a microscope. The outer superficial layer of skin is the **epidermis.** The epidermis consists of epithelial cells and is about 10 to 30 cells thick, or about as thick as this page. The outer layers of epidermal cells contain **keratin** (KER uh tun), a protein which waterproofs and protects the cells and tissues that lie underneath. These dead, outer cells are constantly shed. **Figure 2** shows that some of the dust in a house are dead skin cells. As much as an entire layer of skin cells can be lost each month.

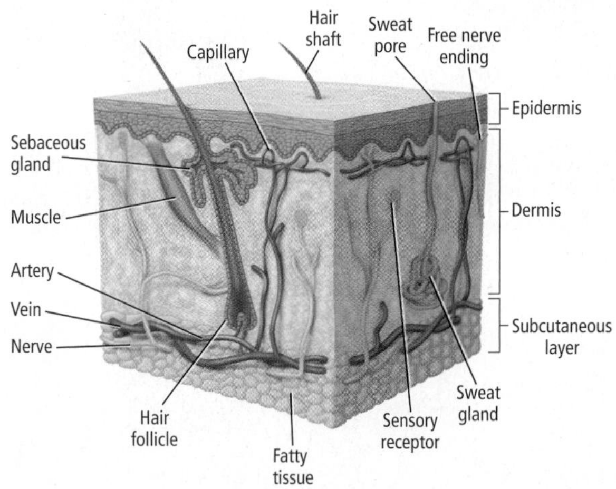

S

■ **Figure 1** Skin is an organ because it consists of different types of tissues joined together for specific purposes.
***Summarize** what types of tissues make up the skin.*

FOLDABLES®

RUBRIC A rubric for evaluating Foldables is found on your eTeacherEdition Online.

Going Further On the back of their Foldables, have students explain the importance of fat deposits in the subcutaneous layers. store food, retain heat, and help protect the body from impact

■ **Caption Question Fig. 1** All four tissue types are present in the skin, including epithelium, muscle, nervous, and connective tissues.

The inner layer of the epidermis contains cells that continually are dividing by mitosis to replace cells that are lost or die. Some cells in the inner layer of the epidermis provide protection from harmful ultraviolet radiation by making a pigment called melanin. **Melanin** is a pigment that absorbs light energy, which protects deeper cells from the damaging effects of ultraviolet rays of sunlight. The amount of melanin that is produced also influences the color of a person's skin. A suntan results when melanin is produced in response to exposure to the ultra-
C violet radiation in sunlight.

The dermis Directly beneath the epidermis is the **dermis,** the second layer of skin. The thickness of the dermis varies but usually is 15–40 times thicker than the epidermis. The dermis consists of connective tissue, a type of tissue that prevents the skin from tearing and also enables the skin to return to its normal state after being stretched. This layer contains other structures including nerve cells, muscle fibers, sweat glands, oil glands, and hair follicles. Beneath the dermis is the subcutaneous layer, a layer of connective tissue that stores fat and helps the body retain heat.

Hair and nails Hair, fingernails, and toenails also are parts of the integumentary system. Both hair and nails contain keratin and develop from epithelial cells. Hair cells grow out of narrow cavities in the dermis called **hair follicles.** Cells at the base of a hair follicle divide and push cells away from the follicle, causing hair to grow.

D Hair follicles usually have sebaceous or oil glands associated with them, as shown in **Figure 3. Sebaceous glands** lubricate skin and hair. When glands produce too much oil, the follicles can become blocked. The blockage can close the opening of a follicle, causing a whitehead, blackhead, or acne—an inflammation of the sebaceous glands.

Reading Check **Summarize** the differences in structure and function of the epidermis and the dermis.

Color-Enhanced SEM Magnification: 187×

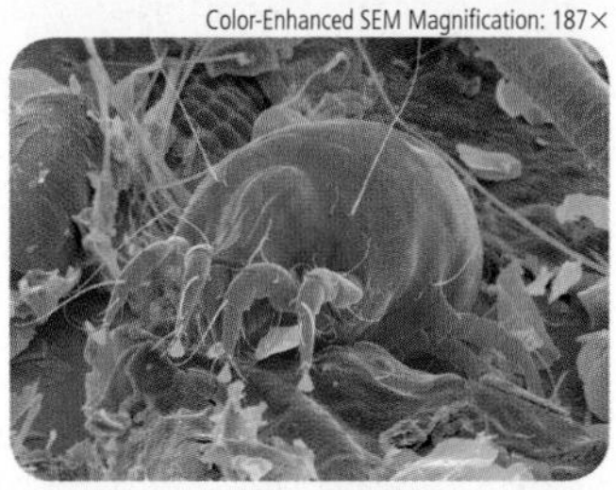

Figure 2 The dust mite pictured here is feeding on dead skin cells—a major component of dust.

Study Tip

Chart Make a chart with *Skin, Bones,* and *Muscles* as row labels, and *Components and structure* and *Function and purpose* as the column labels. Work in small groups to complete your chart as you review the text.

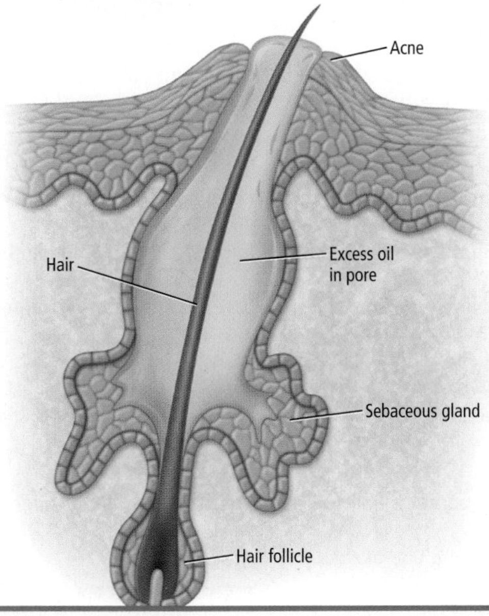

Figure 3 Oil, dirt, and bacteria can become trapped in follicles and erupt and spread to the surrounding area, causing localized inflammation.

C Critical Thinking

AL Analyze

ASK STUDENTS: ***Why do skin cells respond to harmful ultraviolet radiation by making the skin darker?*** Sunlight induces cells to produce more melanin. Since dark colors absorb more light, the melanin absorbs the damaging UV rays and helps protect the skin cells. Have students write an editorial for the school newspaper about the dangers of tanning beds.

D Develop Concepts

BL OL AL

Clarify a Misconception

ASK STUDENTS: ***What causes acne?*** Acne occurs when sebaceous glands produce too much oil, which blocks the pores. One factor causing acne, especially among teenagers, is an increase in the male sex hormone testosterone. This hormone causes sebaceous glands to produce more oil. Certain medicines may also cause acne. Acne may be aggravated by friction on the skin caused by such things as bike helmets or backpacks. Some students may say chocolate and greasy foods or stress cause acne, but research does not support this.

Skill Practice

EL BL OL Visual Literacy

Have students examine the figures in Section 1 and list concepts they think they will be studying. skin features, skin cells, acne, skin muscles, skin cancer English learners may find it easier to generate their lists in their first language. After they read, they can revise their lists.

Reading Check epidermis—outer superficial layer, waterproofs and protects cells and tissues that lie underneath; dermis—15–40 times thicker than epidermis, contains nerves, sweat glands, and hair follicles, protects skin from tearing

Activity

BL OL AL Functions of Skin Provide a pair of rubber gloves. Ask two volunteers to each put on a glove. Place a pen in the gloved hand of each volunteer.
ASK STUDENTS: ***Why does the tip not feel sharp on your hand under the glove?*** The glove serves as a model of another layer of skin, offering protection. Instruct each volunteer to squeeze the tip gently. ***What would you feel if you squeezed the tip hard?*** pokes, jabs, or pressure Receptors in the skin help us perceive the environment. Next, have the volunteers remove the gloves. Ask the students to describe what their hands feel like after removing the gloves. Their hands are probably sweaty. This demonstrates a third function of skin—temperature regulation. Est. time: 10 min

MiniLab 1

Inquiry MiniLab

For a lab worksheet, use your eTeacherEdition Online.

RUBRIC A rubric for evaluating MiniLabs is found on your eTeacherEdition Online.

Est. Time 25 min

Alternative Materials Waterproof trays that resist cutting can be used in place of dissecting pans. Small, sharp scissors can substitute for dissecting scissors, and the handle of a metal spoon can be used as a probe. A scalpel is not necessary.

Safety Precaution Approve lab safety forms before work begins.

Teaching Strategy The skin can be very difficult to remove, especially skin near the tip of the wing, so encourage students to take their time and work carefully.

Cleanup and Disposal Have students place chicken skin in a special container, and dispose of this with kitchen wastes instead of in the regular trash. Have students wash all dissecting tools and the dissecting tray with warm, soapy water. Collect and refrigerate skinned wings for use in the next MiniLab; however, be sure to use them within two or three days. Have students wash their hands.

Analysis

1. feather follicles
2. so it doesn't tear as the body bends and twists

Figure 4 Muscles in the skin cause the hair of some mammals to stand on end, and cause "goose bumps" on human skin.
Relate *what environmental changes produce "goose bumps."*

Fingernails and toenails grow from specialized epithelial cells at the base of each nail. As cells at the base of a nail divide, older dead cells are compacted and pushed out. Nails grow about 0.5 to 1.2 mm per day. You might have heard that nails and hair continue to grow for several days after death. This is a myth; cells surrounding the nail and hair cells dehydrate causing the cells to shrink and pull away from nails and hair. This makes both appear longer.

Functions of the Integumentary System

Skin serves several important functions including regulation of body temperature, production of vitamin D, protection, and perception of one's surroundings.

Temperature regulation What happens when a person is working outside on a hot summer day? In order to regulate body temperature, the person sweats. As sweat evaporates it absorbs body heat, thereby cooling the body. What happens to skin when a person gets cold or frightened? "Goose bumps" are caused by the contraction of muscle cells in the dermis. In other mammals, when these muscles contract, the hair (fur) stands on end.

Notice the frightened cat in **Figure 4.** The cat appears larger, perhaps as a way to scare off enemies. This also is a mechanism for trapping air, which insulates or warms the mammal. Humans do not have as much hair as most other mammals, but "goose bumps" are caused by the same type of muscles that make a cat's fur stand on end. Humans rely on fat in the subcutaneous layer instead of hair to keep warm.

MiniLab 1

Inquiry MiniLab

Examine Skin

How is chicken skin similar to human skin? The skin of chicken has characteristics similar to human skin. Using the chicken wing from the Launch Lab, you will further examine the characteristics of skin.

Procedure

1. Read and complete the lab safety form.
2. Wear disposable **lab gloves.** Remove the **chicken wing** from the **self-sealing bag** and place it in a **dissecting pan.**
3. Use a **dissecting kit** to remove the skin from the wing. Use **scissors** to carefully snip a hole in the skin that is loosely attached to the wing.
4. Make a cut about 6 cm in length. Pull the skin away from the wing. Use scissors and the **scalpel** to cut through the transparent membrane that attaches the skin to the muscles.
5. Try to remove the skin without making any more holes. Look for pockets of fat, blood vessels, and muscle fibers attached to the skin. Note the strength of the skin.
6. Dispose of the skin and used gloves as directed by your teacher. Clean your dissecting tools and dissecting pan with **warm, soapy water.** Save the skinned wing to use in the next MiniLab.

Analysis

1. **Think Critically** about follicles. Human skin contains hair follicles. What type of follicles might you find on chicken skin?
2. **Explain** why it is important for skin to be strong and elastic.

Caption Question Fig. 4 decrease in temperature or the appearance of a frightening stimulus (e.g. predator)

Differentiated Instruction

Hearing Impaired When giving directions for the MiniLab, use visual cues for students who are hearing impaired. Write any important terms or helpful information on the board or an overhead.

For more tips, see pages 14T–15T.

Vitamin production Skin also responds to exposure to ultraviolet light rays from the Sun by producing vitamin D. Vitamin D increases absorption of calcium into the bloodstream and is essential for proper bone formation. Many food products are now fortified with vitamin D.

Protection and senses Intact skin prevents the entry of microorganisms and other foreign substances. Skin helps maintain body temperature by preventing excessive water loss. Melanin in the skin protects **D** against ultraviolet rays. Information about changes in the environment, such as pain, pressure, and temperature changes, is relayed to the brain.

VOCABULARY
ACADEMIC VOCABULARY
Function
action, purpose
One function of the skin is to protect the body.

Damage to the Skin

Skin has the remarkable ability to repair itself. Without a repair mechanism, the body would be subject to invasion by microbes through breaks in the skin.

Cuts and scrapes Sometimes, as in the case of a minor scrape, only the epidermis is injured. Cells deep in the epidermis divide to replace the lost or injured cells. When the injury is deep, blood vessels might be injured, resulting in bleeding. Blood flows out of the wound and a clot is formed. Blood clots form a scab to close the wound, and cells beneath the scab multiply and fill in the wound. At the same time, infection-fighting white blood cells will help get rid of any bacteria that might have entered the wound.

Effects of the Sun and burns As people age, the elasticity of their skin decreases and they start to get wrinkles. Exposure to ultraviolet rays from the Sun accelerates this process and can result in burning of the skin and other damage.

Connection to Health Burns, whether caused by the Sun, heat, or chemicals, usually are classified according to their severity. The types of burns are summarized in **Table 1**. First-degree burns generally are mild and involve only cells in the epidermis. A burn that blisters or leaves a scar is a second-degree burn and involves damage to both the epidermis and dermis. Third-degree burns are the most severe. Muscle tissue and nerve cells in both the epidermis and dermis might be destroyed, and skin function is lost. Healthy skin might have to be transplanted from another place on the body in order to restore the protective layer of the body.

CAREERS IN BIOLOGY

Physical Therapist A physical therapist helps injured or disabled people to improve or regain physical functions using techniques such as exercise and massage.

Table 1 Classification of Burns — Concepts in Motion Interactive Table

Severity of burn	Damage	Effect
First-degree	Cells in the epidermis are injured and may die.	• Redness and swelling • Mild pain
Second-degree	Cells deeper in the epidermis die. Cells in the dermis are injured and may die.	• Blisters • Pain
Third-degree	Cells in the epidermis and dermis die. Nerve cells and muscles cells are injured.	• Skin function lost • Healthy skin needs to be transplanted • No pain because of nerve cell damage

Demonstration

BL OL AL Effects of UV Radiation Ultraviolet-sensitive plastic flying disks and nail polishes are available at toy and discount stores. Inexpensive UV-sensitive beads are available online. Test the disks, polish, or beads indoors to make sure they don't change color before performing the demonstration. Set up the UV-sensitive articles in a variety of situations, such as in full sun, in the shade, under sunglasses, or covered with sunscreen. Students working above level might wish to develop hypotheses related to UV strength, use the disks to test them, and report results to the class.
ASK STUDENTS: ***What differences do you see between the situations? What might account for those differences?*** The disks, polish, and beads should change color when exposed to UV light, even in the shade. Color intensity might vary with light intensity. Est. time: 20 min

D Develop Concepts

EL BL OL COOP LEARN Activity Make two sets of index cards. On one set, write the name of a different skin structure on each card. On the other set, write the corresponding function of each structure. Give each student one card and have them find the student with the corresponding card. Structures might include: epidermis, oil gland, sweat gland, dermis, hair follicle, erector pili, and subcutaneous layer.

Critical Thinking

AL Analyze Review with students the two main layers of the skin.
ASK STUDENTS: ***What if these two layers of skin were reversed? What if a particular tissue type were missing?*** Have students predict the outcome of any missing tissue. If the dermis were the outer layer, nerve endings would be exposed, resulting in pain. Cells and tissues associated with this layer would not be protected, so physical trauma and burns would be more severe.

Writing Support

AL Creative Writing Have students imagine the skin as a well-oiled machine. Each structure of the skin represents a part of the machine. Have students write an owner's manual for the skin. Tell them to include the function and importance of each structure and how to properly care for it.

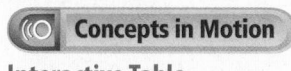

Concepts in Motion
Interactive Table

Develop Concepts

EL BL OL COOP LEARN

K-W-L Chart Divide students into groups. Provide each group with a poster board and have them divide it into three columns labeled *What I Know* (K), *What I Want to Know* (W), and *What I Learned* (L). Have the groups brainstorm what they know about sunburns. Then direct the groups to write down what they want to know about sunburns. After discussion about sunburns, have students record what they learned. Some topics may include UVA and UVB radiation and how they affect skin; skin cancer, sunscreen (and SPF ratings), seasonal and geographical differences of sunburn, and ways to minimize sunburn.

Formative Assessment

Evaluation Determine whether or not students understand the four tissue types and their functions. Have students describe the four tissue types found in the integumentary (skin) system.

Remediation Help students visualize the four tissue types and their functions by using models or illustrations of the skin. Review each tissue and its function orally.

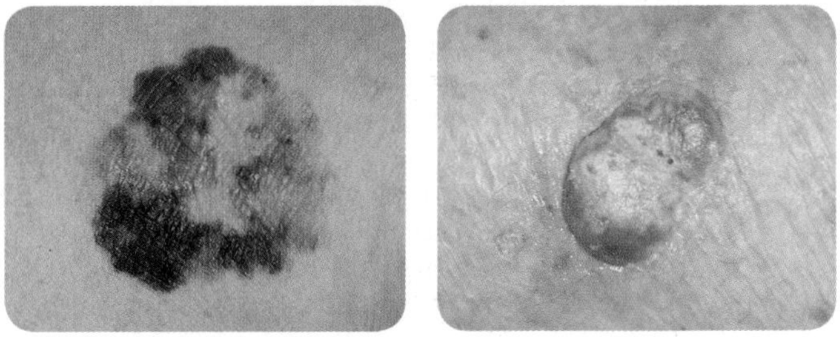

Figure 5 Warning signs of skin cancer include any obvious change in a wart or mole, or moles that are irregularly shaped, varied in color, or are larger than the diameter of a pencil.

Skin cancer Exposure to ultraviolet radiation, whether it is from the Sun or from artificial sources such as tanning beds, is recognized as an important risk factor for the development of skin cancer. Ultraviolet radiation can damage the DNA in skin cells, causing those cells to grow and divide uncontrollably. When this happens, skin cancer results. Refer to **Figure 5** to see some warning signs of skin cancer.

Skin cancer is the most common cancer in the United States. There are two main categories of skin cancer: melanoma and nonmelanoma. Melanoma begins in melanocytes, the cells that produce the pigment melanin. Melanoma is the deadliest form of skin cancer. Melanoma can spread to internal organs and the lymphatic system. It is estimated that one person dies from melanoma every hour in the United States. Teens are at greater risk for melanoma because as they grow, their skin cells divide more rapidly than they will when they reach adulthood.

Anyone can get skin cancer. However, individuals with light skin, light-colored eyes, light hair color, and a tendency to burn or freckle are at the greatest risk. Everyone should try to avoid prolonged exposure to the Sun, especially between 10 A.M. and 4 P.M. when the Sun's rays are the strongest. Other preventative measures include wearing protective clothing or sunscreen with a Sun Protection Factor (SPF) of at least 15.

Section 1 Assessment

Section Summary

- The skin is the major organ of the integumentary system.
- Maintaining homeostasis is one function of the integumentary system.
- There are four types of tissues in the integumentary system.
- Hair, fingernails, and toenails develop from epithelial cells.
- Burns are classified according to the severity of the damage to skin tissues.

Understand Main Ideas

1. MAIN Idea **Diagram** the two layers of the skin.
2. **Summarize** the types of tissues in the integumentary system and their functions.
3. **Generalize** different ways the integumentary system helps a human survive.
4. **Sequence** the process of skin repair in response to a cut.
5. **Compare** effects of first-degree, second-degree, and third-degree burns.

Think Critically

6. **Evaluate** the labels of two name-brand skin creams to compare how the two products claim to benefit the skin.

MATH in Biology

7. To determine how long an SPF will protect a person from burning in the Sun, multiply the amount of time the person can spend in the Sun before starting to burn by the SPF rating. If an individual who usually burns in 10 min uses a product with an SPF of 15, how long will the protection last?

Section 1 Assessment

1. Diagrams should include epidermis and dermis.
2. epithelium—regulation of body temperature, vitamin D production, protection from desiccation and UV light; muscle—movement of hair and constriction and dilation of blood vessels; connective tissue—elasticity, nourishment, and flexibility; nerve—perception of one's environment
3. Sensory receptors respond to the environment (temperature and pain). Vitamin D production provides an essential nutrient. Regulation of body temperature, protection from UV radiation, and protection from foreign invaders are essential to homeostasis.
4. blood flows, clots and scabs form, cells beneath the scab multiply and fill in the wound
5. first-degree—redness and swelling; second-degree—blisters, pain, scarring; third-degree—both skin layers damaged with serious long-lasting loss of function
6. Note specific benefits, short-term and long-term.
7. 150 min

Assessment Online Quiz

Reading Preview

Essential Questions

- What are the differences between the bones of the axial and appendicular skeletons?
- How is new bone formed?
- What are the functions of the skeletal system?

Review Vocabulary

cartilage: tough, flexible connective tissue that forms the skeletons of embryos and later covers the surface of bones that move against each other in joints

New Vocabulary

axial skeleton
appendicular skeleton
compact bone
osteocyte **R**
spongy bone
red bone marrow
yellow bone marrow
osteoblast
ossification
osteoclast
ligament

g Multilingual eGlossary

The Skeletal System

MAIN Idea The skeleton provides a structural framework for the body and protects internal organs such as the heart, lungs, and brain.

Real-World Reading Link Framing is an early stage of building a house. A person can walk through a house at that stage and know the plan of the house because of the framework. The skeletal system can be compared to the framework of a house. The framework provides structure and protection.

Structure of the Skeletal System

Notice all the bones in the adult skeleton pictured in **Figure 6.** If you counted them, you would find that there are 206 bones. The human skeleton consists of two divisions—the axial skeleton and the appendicular skeleton. The **axial skeleton** includes the skull, the vertebral column, the ribs, and the sternum. The **appendicular skeleton** includes the bones of the shoulders, arms, hands, hips, legs, and feet.

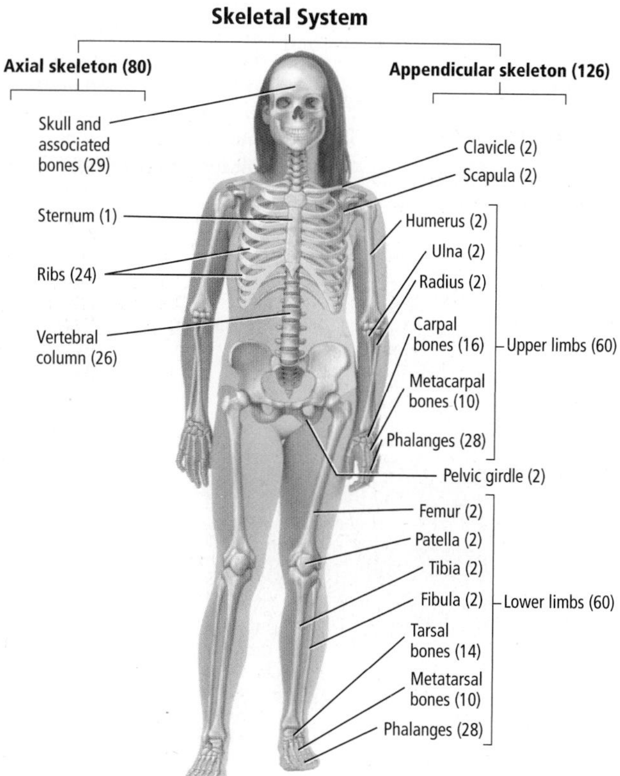

S

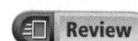

Review Personal Tutor

Figure 6 The axial skeleton includes the bones of the head, back, and chest. Bones in the appendicular skeleton are related to movement of the limbs.

Demonstration

Minerals in Bone Obtain two clean chicken bones. Boil chicken bones to completely clean them of their meat. For 5–7 days, soak one in vinegar and the other in water. Students can observe bubbles of carbon dioxide from the bone in the vinegar. The bone soaked in vinegar will be softer than the one soaked in water because vinegar has leached the calcium salts out of the bone. Relate this to the importance of calcium in the diet for strong bones, bone growth, and bone repair. Est. time: 5 min per day

Section 2

MAIN Idea

BL OL AL Endoskeleton Hold up an earthworm or other segmented worm. (Do not handle worms with dry hands.)

ASK STUDENTS: ***What limitations does the lack of a bony skeleton impose on this worm?*** Answers may vary, but should include lack of protection of internal organs, limited size, and limited movement.

R Reading Strategy

EL BL OL Vocabulary Chart Have students construct a chart with three columns and 11 rows. Instruct students to write the vocabulary terms from this section in the first column. In the second column, have them write a definition of the vocabulary term. In the last column, have students make a memory clue in the form of a sketch or word association that will help them remember what each term means.

AL Have students break the words down into prefixes and suffixes and define the parts.

S Skill Practice

BL OL Visual Literacy Ask students to examine Figure 6. Have students list the bones of the axial skeleton using one color of ink. Then have them differentiate the skeletons by listing the bones of the appendicular skeleton in a second color of ink. axial skeleton: skull, sternum, ribs, vertebrae; appendicular skeleton: clavicle, scapula, humerus, ulna, radius, carpals, metacarpals, phalanges, pelvis, femur, patella, tibia, fibula, tarsals, metatarsals

Review Personal Tutor

Listen to a teacher explain the skeletal system.

Develop Concepts

EL BL OL AL COOP LEARN

Activity Play the game "Simon Says" using names of bones. Provide students with three index cards and ask them to write the scientific names of three bones and their locations on the body on the card. Use these cards to play the game.

SAY TO STUDENTS: ***Simon says touch your patella.*** Have students who did not touch their kneecap sit down. ***Simon says place your left ulna across your right femur.*** Students should touch their right thigh with their left forearm.

The last student standing wins the game.

Develop Concepts

EL BL OL COOP LEARN **Activity**

Obtain cardboard skeletons from a local store; these usually are available around Halloween. Cut out the individual bones. Hand out one set of bones to each pair of students. Have students reassemble the skeletons.

Writing Support

EL BL OL **Technical Writing**

Have students write a classified ad for a specific bone. The ad should include a description of the bone, its location, and function. Ads will vary, but should be appropriate for the specific bone.

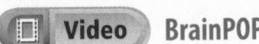

Video BrainPOP

■ **Caption Question Fig. 7** Compact bone provides strength and protection to the outer layers of all bones. Spongy bone contains the marrow cavities and is located at the center of short or flat bones and at the end of long bones.

CAREERS IN BIOLOGY

Medical Illustrator A medical illustrator combines a talent in art with an interest in biology to illustrate procedures or to create teaching models.

Compact and spongy bone Bone is a connective tissue that has many shapes and sizes. Bones are classified as long, short, flat, or irregular. Refer to **Figure 6.** Arm and leg bones are examples of long bones, and wrist bones are examples of short bones. Flat bones make up the skull. Facial bones and vertebrae are irregular bones.

The outer layers of all bones are composed of compact bone. **Compact bone** is dense and strong; it provides strength and protection. Running the length of compact bones are tubelike structures called osteons, or Haversian systems, which contain blood vessels and nerves. The blood vessels provide oxygen and nutrients to **osteocytes**—living bone cells.

The centers of bones can differ greatly, as illustrated in **Figure 7.** As the name suggests, **spongy bone** is less dense and has many cavities that contain bone marrow. Spongy bone is found in the center of short or flat bones and at the end of long bones. Spongy bone is surrounded by compact bone and does not contain Haversian systems.

There are two types of bone marrow—red and yellow. Red and white blood cells and platelets are produced in **red bone marrow.** Red bone marrow is found in the humerus bone of the arm, the femur bone of the leg, the sternum and ribs, the vertebrae, and the pelvis. The cavities of an infant's bones are composed of red marrow. Children's bones have more red marrow than adult bones. **Yellow bone marrow,** found in many other bones, consists of stored fat. The body can convert yellow bone marrow to red bone marrow in cases of extreme blood loss or anemia.

Formation of bone The skeletons of embryos are composed of cartilage. During fetal development, cells in fetal cartilage develop into bone-forming cells called **osteoblasts.** The formation of bone from osteoblasts is called **ossification.** Except for the tip of the nose, outer ears, discs between vertebrae, and the lining of movable joints, the human adult skeleton is all bone. Osteoblasts also are the cells responsible for the growth and repair of bones.

Video BrainPOP

■ **Figure 7** Bone is either compact bone or spongy bone.
Classify *how spongy bone and compact bone differ in location and function.*

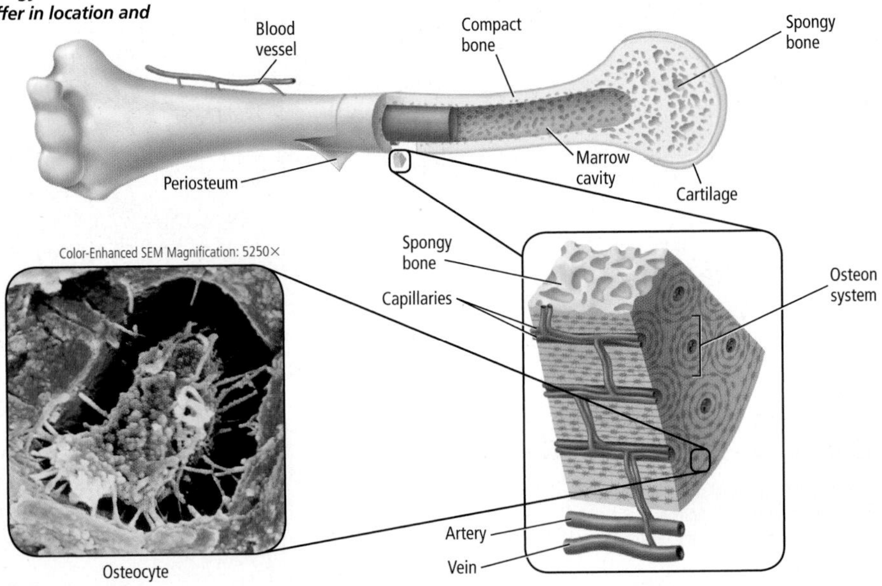

Demonstration

Compact and Spongy Bone Obtain a long bone, such as a beef femur, from a local grocery store or butcher shop. Have the butcher saw the bone in half lengthwise. Use this bone to illustrate compact bone and spongy bone.

ASK STUDENTS: ***What would be possible consequences if all bones were made completely of compact bone?*** Possible answers include that blood cells would not be produced and bones might be more likely to break under trauma because spongy bone can provide a cushion for the bone. Est. time: 10 min

D **Remodeling of bone** Bones constantly are being remodeled, which involves replacing old cells with new cells. This process is continual throughout life and is important in the growth of an individual. Cells called **osteoclasts** break down bone cells, which are then replaced by new bone tissue. Bone growth involves several factors, including nutrition and physical exercise. For example, a person with insufficient calcium can develop a condition known as osteoporosis that results in weak, fragile bones that break easily.

Reading Check **Compare** the roles of osteoblasts and osteoclasts.

W **Repair of bone** Fractures are very common bone injuries. When a bone breaks but does not come through the skin, it is a simple fracture. A compound fracture is one in which the bone protrudes through the skin. A stress fracture is a thin crack in the bone. When a bone is fractured, repair begins immediately. Refer to **Figure 8,** which illustrates the steps in the repair of a broken bone.

Fracture Upon injury, endorphins, chemicals produced in the brain and sometimes called "the body's natural painkillers," flood the area of the injury to reduce the amount of pain temporarily. The injured area quickly becomes inflamed, or swollen. The swelling can last for two or three weeks.

Within about eight hours, a blood clot forms between the broken ends of the bone and new bone begins to form. First, a soft callus, or mass, of cartilage forms at the location of the break. This tissue is weak, so the broken bone must remain in place.

Callus formation About three weeks later, osteoblasts form a callus made of spongy bone that surrounds the fracture. The spongy bone is then replaced by compact bone. Osteoclasts remove the spongy bone while osteoblasts produce stronger, compact bone.

Splints, casts, and sometimes traction can ensure that the broken bone remains in place until new bone tissue has formed. Broken fingers often are kept in place by being taped to an adjacent finger.

Remodeling Bones require different amounts of time to heal. Age, nutrition, location, and severity of the break are all factors. A lack of calcium in a person's diet will slow down bone repair. Bones of younger people usually heal more quickly than bones of older people. For example, a fracture might take only four to six weeks to be repaired in a toddler, but it might take six months in an adult.

Video What's BIOLOGY Got To Do With It?

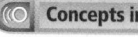

Concepts in Motion Animation

■ **Figure 8** Bone repair requires several steps. First, a mass of clotted blood forms in the space between the broken bones. Then connective tissue fills the space of the broken bone. Eventually, osteoblasts produce new bone tissue.

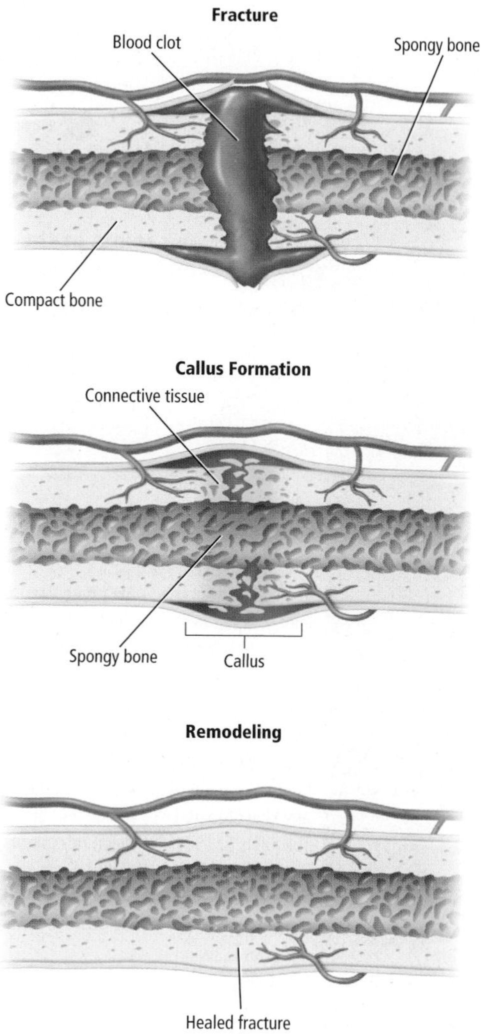

D Develop Concepts

BL OL AL

Clarify a Misconception Students might think bones are dead because they are hard and because they often associate bones with fossil remains.

ASK STUDENTS: ***Are bones made of living cells or dead cells?*** Bones are made of living cells organized into tissues. Bones continue to grow until adulthood because they are made of living cells.

W Writing Support

OL AL **Creative Writing** Have students imagine that they are microscopic engineers in charge of repairing a broken bone. Have them write directions to their building crew describing what processes need to occur to repair the bone.

Critical Thinking

AL **Assess** Have students research anatomical ratios for human bones. For example, the arm span of a human is about equal to the height of the human. **ASK STUDENTS:** ***How can forensic scientists predict the height of a human if only a few bones are available?*** Scientists can predict the height and form of a person by using anatomical ratios, even if all there is to work with are the bones of arms and shoulders. Show students a picture of Leonardo da Vinci's Vitruvian Man.

Differentiated Instruction

English Learners For the creative writing activity on this page, encourage English learners to write their first draft in their first language. They can refer to this draft as they prepare their final draft in English.

For more tips, see pages 14T–15T.

Reading Check Osteoblasts are cells that form bone. Osteoclasts are cells that break down bone cells.

Concepts in Motion Animation

GOING GREEN When you leave school, shut down your computer. This action will save energy, lower mechanical stress on your computer, and prolong the life of your computer. Encourage students to do the same with their home computers.

Inquiry Launch Lab

Assess Content Development
Assess how understanding has developed when students revisit the Launch Lab analysis questions.

Develop Concepts

OL AL Discuss

ASK STUDENTS: ***How many of you have broken a bone?*** Answers will vary. Have students describe their experiences from the initial injury to final treatments. ***Why shouldn't you move a person with a broken bone?*** The injured bone may injure a nerve, and this could cause permanent loss of movement or feeling. There is also a risk of injuring blood vessels. ***Why does a cast have to be left on for a certain amount of time?*** A cast needs to be left on long enough for the osteoblasts and osteoclasts to complete the repair. If the cast is removed too early, there is a greater risk of the bone being broken again in the same place.

C Critical Thinking

OL AL Analyze Have students analyze what would be the result if a given joint were replaced with a different type of joint. For example, what impact would there be on arm movement if the shoulder joint were a hinge joint rather than a ball-and-socket joint? Answers will depend on the specific joints being discussed. In this example, the arm would be able to move only up and down or side to side instead of in circles.

Concepts in Motion
Interactive Table

Inquiry BioLab

The lab at the end of the chapter can be used at this point in the lesson.

Inquiry Launch Lab
Review Based on what you have read about joints, how would you now answer the analysis questions?

Video BrainPOP

Joints

Joints occur where two or more bones meet. Except for the joints in the skull, they can be classified according to the movement they allow and the shapes of their parts. **Table 2** identifies five kinds of joints—ball-and-socket, pivot, hinge, gliding, and sutures. Study **Table 2** to identify the type of movement that each kind of joint allows and also the bones involved in each example.

Not all joints are movable. The joints between some skull bones are fixed. At birth, however, skull bones are not all fused together. They become fused by the time a baby is about three months old. Gliding joints, like those found in the hand, have limited movement. Other joints, such as the hinge joint of the elbow and the pivot joint in the lower arm, allow back-and-forth movement and twisting. The ball-and-socket joints of the hips and shoulders have the widest range of motion.

The bones of joints are held together by ligaments. **Ligaments** are tough bands of connective tissue that attach one bone to another. You will learn more about ligaments and tendons, which attach muscle to bone, in the following section.

Reading Check **Review** the types of joints and how joints are classified.

C

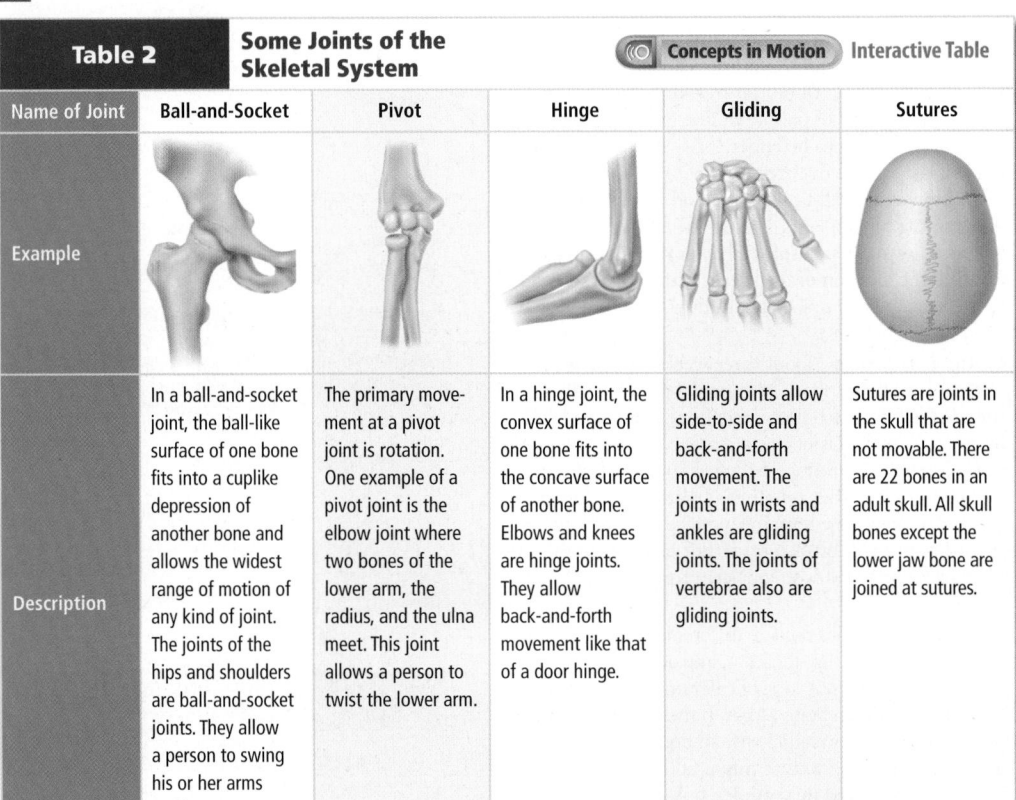

Table 2 **Some Joints of the Skeletal System** — **Concepts in Motion** Interactive Table

Name of Joint	Ball-and-Socket	Pivot	Hinge	Gliding	Sutures
Example	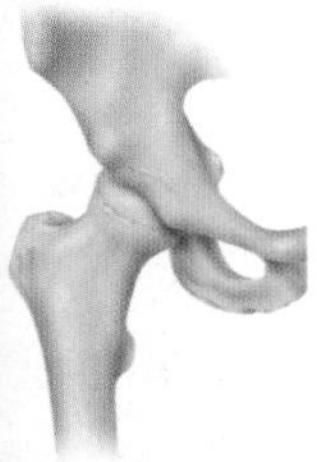	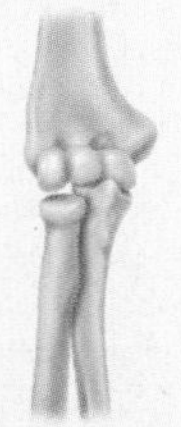	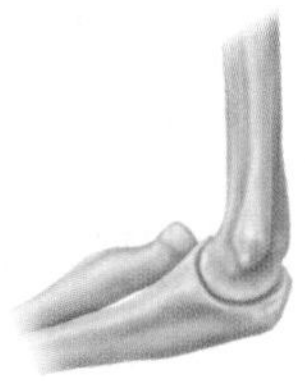	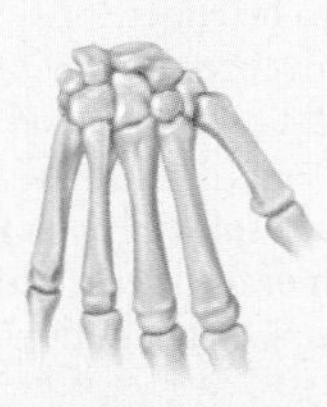	
Description	In a ball-and-socket joint, the ball-like surface of one bone fits into a cuplike depression of another bone and allows the widest range of motion of any kind of joint. The joints of the hips and shoulders are ball-and-socket joints. They allow a person to swing his or her arms and legs.	The primary movement at a pivot joint is rotation. One example of a pivot joint is the elbow joint where two bones of the lower arm, the radius, and the ulna meet. This joint allows a person to twist the lower arm.	In a hinge joint, the convex surface of one bone fits into the concave surface of another bone. Elbows and knees are hinge joints. They allow back-and-forth movement like that of a door hinge.	Gliding joints allow side-to-side and back-and-forth movement. The joints in wrists and ankles are gliding joints. The joints of vertebrae also are gliding joints.	Sutures are joints in the skull that are not movable. There are 22 bones in an adult skull. All skull bones except the lower jaw bone are joined at sutures.

Reading Check Joints are classified by the type of movement they allow and the shapes of their parts. See Table 2 for a list of joints.

Video BrainPOP

Research Citation

Real-World Applications Educational research indicates that when connections are made between the lesson and the community outside the classroom, students will better retain what they learn. They are better able to understand material that connects to their own interests.
(Steen and Forman, 1995)

Research bibliography on pages 32T–34T

Osteoarthritis (ahs tee oh ar THRI tus) The ends of bones in movable joints, such as the knee, are covered by cartilage, which serves as a cushion and allows smooth movement of the joint. Osteoarthritis is a painful condition that affects joints and results from the deterioration of the cartilage. It is a very common condition in knees and hips and also affects the neck and back. Osteoarthritis affects about ten percent of Americans and the frequency increases with age. A young person who has a joint injury is at risk to develop osteoarthritis later in life.

Rheumatoid arthritis Rheumatoid (roo MAH toyd) arthritis is another form of arthritis that affects joints. Rheumatoid arthritis is not the result of cartilage deterioration or of wear and tear on the joint. Affected joints lose strength and function and are inflamed, swollen, and painful. Fingers can look deformed, as illustrated in **Figure 9.**

Bursitis Shoulders and knees also have fluid-filled sacs called bursae that surround these joints. Bursae decrease friction and act as a cushion between bones and tendons. Bursitis is an inflamation of the bursae and can reduce joint movement and cause pain and swelling. Perhaps you have heard of "tennis elbow" which is a form of bursitis. Treatment usually involves resting the joint involved.

Sprains A sprain involves damage to the ligaments that hold joints together. It is caused when a joint is twisted or overstretched and usually causes the joint to swell and be tender and painful.

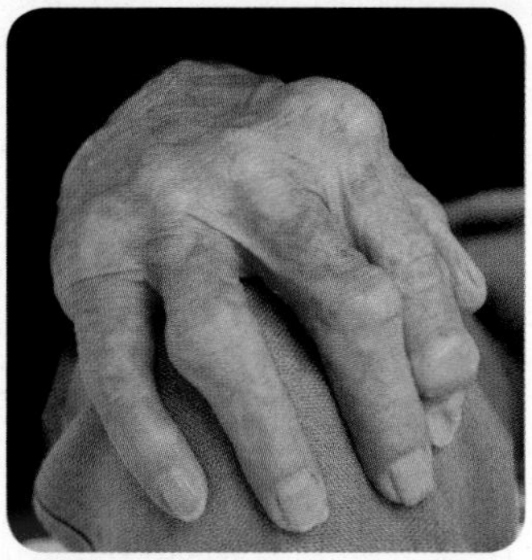

Figure 9 Rheumatoid arthritis can cause loss of strength and function and involves severe pain.
Compare *how rheumatoid arthritis differs from the more common osteoarthritis.*

MiniLab 2

Inquiry MiniLab

Examine Bone Attachments

How are bones attached to muscles and other bones? Tendons attach muscle to bone, and ligaments attach bone to bone. You will examine these attachments using a skinned chicken wing.

Procedure

1. Read and complete the lab safety form.
2. Wear disposable **lab gloves.** Put the **skinned chicken wing** in a **dissection pan.**
3. Choose one muscle and use a pair of **dissection scissors** to cut the muscle away from the bone, leaving each end intact. Look for the long, white, tough tendons that connect the muscle to the bone.
4. Move the bones at the joint and notice how the tendon moves as the bones are pulled.
5. Carefully cut away all the muscles from the bones. The bones will still be attached to each other. Look for the white ligaments that hold them together. Examine the ends of each bone.
6. Draw a diagram of the wing without the muscles showing how the bones are attached to each other. Compare this drawing to the one you made in the Launch Lab.

Analysis

1. **Explain** how the drawing that you made in the Launch Lab is different from the drawing that you made of the wing in this lab.
2. **Observe and Infer** Did you notice how a muscle is attached at one end to a bone and then how the ligament at the other end runs across a joint to attach that end of the muscle to the next bone? Use a diagram to explain why this is important.
3. **Think critically** about the color of the ends of the bones at moveable joints. What do you think this material is?

Caption Question Fig. 9
Rheumatoid arthritis causes inflammation of the joints, whereas osteoarthritis is the result of wear and tear (deterioration) of the joint. Both are painful conditions.

Activity

BL OL Joints and Flexibility
Obtain a tennis ball or other object that can be picked up using one hand. Have a student try to pick up the ball without bending any of the joints in their hand. Next, have a student try to pick up a ball without using a hinge joint. Finally, have a student try to pick up a ball without using a ball-and-socket joint. Est. time: 5 min

MiniLab 2

Inquiry MiniLab

For a lab worksheet, use your eTeacherEdition Online.

RUBRIC A rubric for evaluating MiniLabs is found on your eTeacherEdition Online.

Est. Time 25 min

Alternative Materials Waterproof trays that resist cutting can be used instead of dissecting pans. Small, sharp scissors can substitute for dissecting scissors.

Safety Precaution Approve lab safety forms before work begins.

Teaching Strategies

- Help students recognize the difference between ligaments and tendons.
- You may save, clean, and dry the bones from one of the wings to review with later.

Cleanup and Disposal Have students place dissected muscles and the remaining bones in a special container, and dispose of this with kitchen wastes instead of in the regular trash. Used gloves can be disposed of in the regular trash. Have students wash all dissecting tools and the dissecting tray with warm, soapy water. Have students also wash their hands.

Analysis

1. There are many more bones than those depicted in the drawings in the Launch Lab.
2. To form a lever and cause movement, a muscle must be attached to two different bones.
3. white; cartilage

Concepts in Motion
Interactive Table

Skill Practice

BL OL AL Make a Table Have students construct a table to organize the different types of joints found in the human body. Have students give examples of the different types of joints.

Formative Assessment

Evaluation Prepare a set of flash cards containing the names of major bones on one side and the corresponding function on the other. Hold up one card at a time listing the name of the bone facing students. Have them take turns identifying the corresponding function.

Remediation Have students make their own set of flash cards listing the bones and their functions. Have students practice their flash cards with a partner.

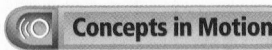

Concepts in Motion Interactive Table

Table 3 Functions of the Skeletal System

Function	Description
Support	• Legs, pelvis, and vertebral column hold up the body • Mandible supports the teeth • Almost all bones support muscles
Protection	• Skull protects the brain • Vertebrae protect the spinal column • Rib cage protects the heart, lungs, and other organs
Formation of blood cells	• Red bone marrow produces red blood cells, white blood cells, and platelets
Reservoir	• Stores calcium and phosphorus
Movement	• Attached muscles pull on bones of arms and legs • Diaphragm allows normal breathing

Functions of the Skeletal System

You might think that the only purpose of a skeleton is to serve as a framework to support the body. The bones of the legs, pelvis, and the vertebral column hold up the body. The mandible supports the teeth, and almost all bones support muscles. Many soft organs are directly or indirectly supported by nearby bones.

The skeletal system serves other functions besides support, as shown in **Table 3.** The skull protects the brain, vertebrae protect the spinal cord, and the rib cage protects the heart, lungs, and other organs.

The outer layers of bone tissue also protect the bone marrow found inside bones. In addition to forming red blood cells and white blood cells, red bone marrow forms platelets, which are involved in blood clotting. Red blood cells are produced at the rate of more than two million per second.

Until a person reaches about seven years of age, all bone marrow is red bone marrow. Then, fat tissue replaces some red marrow and gives the marrow a yellowish appearance, which gives it its name. Fat is an important source of energy.

Bones are reservoirs for the storage of minerals such as calcium and phosphorus. When blood calcium levels are too low, calcium is released from bones. When blood calcium levels are high, excess calcium is stored in bone tissue. In this way, the skeletal system helps to maintain homeostasis.

Bones that have muscles attached to them allow movement of the body. For example, as muscles pull on the bones of the arms and legs, they cause movement. Muscles that are attached to your ribs allow you to breathe normally.

Section 2 Assessment

Section Summary

- The human skeleton consists of two divisions.
- Most bones are composed of two different types of tissue.
- Bones are being remodeled constantly.
- Bones work in conjunction with muscles.
- The skeleton has several important functions.

Understand Main Ideas

1. MAIN Idea **Identify** and describe the functions of the axial skeleton and the appendicular skeleton.
2. **Compare** the compositions of red bone marrow and yellow bone marrow.
3. **Compare** the body's mechanism for repairing a fractured bone with the original development of bone.
4. **Construct** a classification scheme for all of the bones shown in **Figure 6.**

Think Critically

5. **Consider** what the result might be if osteoblast and osteoclast cells did not function properly both in a developing fetus and in an adult.
6. **Distinguish** between compact and spongy bone based on appearance, location, and function.

Section 2 Assessment

1. axial skeleton—skull, vertebral column, ribs, and sternum provide support and protection; appendicular skeleton—arms, hands, legs, feet, shoulders, and hips provide support and reservoir for blood-forming elements
2. red—red and white blood cells and platelets; yellow—fat
3. Bone formation and bone repair both require osteoblasts and osteoclasts to lay down and resculpt bone.
4. Bones could first be classified as part of the appendicular or axial skeleton. Bones within each group would then be further classified as part of the legs, arms, hands, feet, skull or vertebral column.
5. In a developing fetus, improper bone formation and sculpturing would result in deformities in the fetus. In the adult, bone weakening and lack of phosphorous and calcium would cause ailments including motor weakness and muscle malfunction.
6. Compact bone is dense and found where support is important. Spongy bone is porous and found where marrow cavities give rise to blood elements.

Assessment Online Quiz

Reading Preview

Essential Questions

- What are the three types of muscle tissue?
- What are the events involved in muscle contraction at the cellular and molecular levels?
- What are the differences between slow-twitch and fast-twitch muscle fibers?

Review Vocabulary

anaerobic: chemical reactions that do not require the presence of oxygen

New Vocabulary

smooth muscle
involuntary muscle
cardiac muscle
skeletal muscle
voluntary muscle
tendon
myofibril
myosin
actin
sarcomere

Multilingual eGlossary

The Muscular System

MAIN Idea The three major types of muscle tissue differ in structure and function.

Real-World Reading Link Leonardo da Vinci contributed a great amount of knowledge to the scientific community. He studied the human body by examining cadavers. Da Vinci replaced muscles with string and learned that muscles shorten and pull on bones to make them move.

R Three Types of Muscle

A muscle consists of groups of fibers or muscle cells that are bound together. When the word muscle is used, many people immediately think of skeletal muscle. Examine **Figure 10** to see that there are three types of muscle: smooth muscle, cardiac muscle and skeletal muscle. Muscles are classified according to their structure and function.

Smooth muscle Many hollow internal organs such as the stomach, intestines, bladder, and uterus are lined with **smooth muscle.** Smooth muscle is called **involuntary muscle** because it cannot be controlled consciously. For example, food moves through the digestive tract because of the action of smooth muscles that line the esophagus, stomach, and small and large intestines. Under a microscope, smooth muscle does not appear striated, or striped, and each cell has one nucleus.

Cardiac muscle The involuntary muscle present only in the heart is called **cardiac muscle.** Cardiac muscle cells are arranged in a network, or web, that allows the heart muscle to contract efficiently and rhythmically. This arrangement gives strength to the heart. Cardiac muscle is striped, or striated, with light and dark bands of cells with many nuclei. Cells usually have one nucleus and are connected by gap junctions.

Figure 10 When magnified, differences in muscle shape and appearance can be seen. Smooth muscle fibers appear spindle-shaped; cardiac muscle appears striated or striped; skeletal muscle also appears striated.
***Explain** how muscles are classified, in addition to their appearance.*

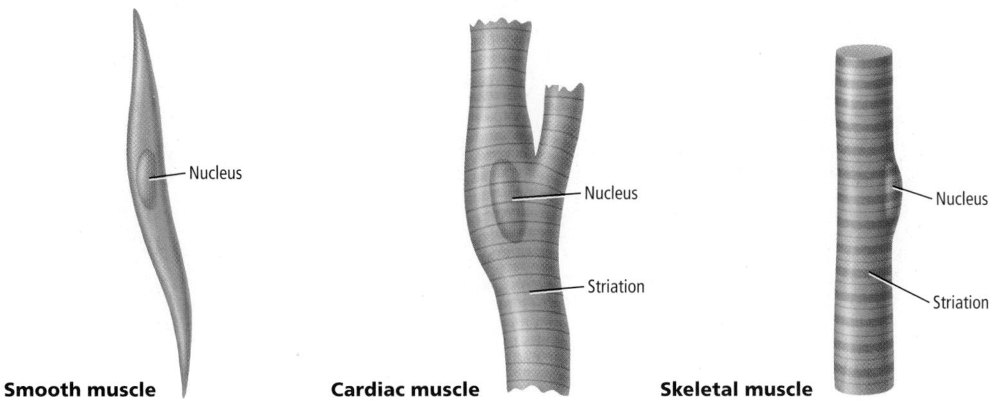

Section 3

MAIN Idea

BL OL AL Muscle Types

SAY TO STUDENTS: ***Think about what you know regarding the purposes or functions of muscles.***

ASK STUDENTS: ***Why might the body need muscles with different structures?*** Answers will vary. Possible answers: Moving an arm requires different muscles than blinking an eyelid. Digestion requires special muscles, as does giving birth.

R Reading Strategy

OL AL COOP LEARN Predict

ASK STUDENTS: ***Describe what you know about muscles.*** Answers should include information about the types of muscles, their functions, and how muscles move. Place students in groups based on their answers. Have students discuss what they've written and identify and address any discrepancies among the predictions.

Develop Concepts

OL Clarify a Misconception

Students may think that muscles push and pull.

ASK STUDENTS: ***How do muscles move parts of the body?*** Muscles can only contract or relax. When a muscle contracts, it pulls on a body part. When a muscle relaxes, it does not move a body part or exert force on it.

AL Have students make a list of muscles and their antagonists.

Caption Question Fig. 10 In addition to their appearance, muscles are classified by their function (i.e., voluntary or involuntary).

Content Background

Teacher FYI Skeletal, cardiac, and smooth muscles are each stimulated in different ways. Skeletal muscle fibers are innervated by a neuron, so each cell is stimulated independently. This is not the case with smooth muscle. Only a few smooth muscle cells can be stimulated by a nerve; the action potential can spread from cell to cell. In some cases, a physical event, such as stretching, can cause the contraction of a smooth muscle. Nervous system stimulation is not needed. Cardiac muscle cells are under the control of the SA node in the heart. The action potential can travel from cell to cell in a manner similar to smooth muscle.

S Skill Practice

BL OL AL Diagram Have each student prepare a Venn diagram comparing the features of skeletal, cardiac, and smooth muscle.

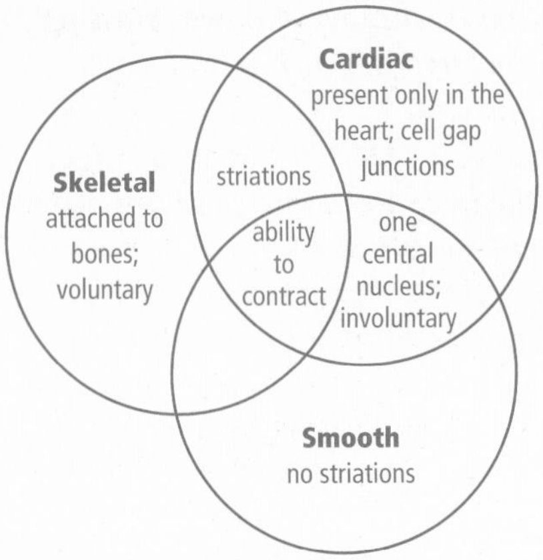

D Develop Concepts

AL Scaffolding

ASK STUDENTS: ***Describe the structure of a myofibril.*** small contractile unit made of two kinds of protein—thick myosin and thin actin filaments ***What physical events are associated with skeletal muscle contraction?*** A nerve impulse releases calcium, causing attachment of actin and myosin, and sliding of the actin filaments toward one another in the direction of the center of the sarcomere, shortening the fiber. ***What role do calcium ions and ATP play in muscle contraction?*** Calcium promotes connections between myosin and actin filaments. ATP is broken down and provides energy for the muscle contractions. ***What would happen to muscles if ATP or calcium were not present?*** If ATP was not present, the actin filaments would not be pulled over the myosin and the muscle would not contract. If calcium was not present, actin and myosin could not interact. If ATP was not present later in the process, calcium could not be actively transported out of the muscle cell, and the muscle would not relax.

Concepts in Motion
Animation

VOCABULARY
SCIENCE USAGE V. COMMON USAGE
Contract
Science usage: to tighten or to shorten
Muscles contract and cause movement.

Common usage: to become affected with
If you are exposed to the flu, you may contract the illness.

Inquiry **Virtual Lab**

Skeletal muscle Most of the muscles in the body are skeletal muscles. **Skeletal muscles** are muscles attached to bones by tendons and when tightened, or contracted, cause movement. Skeletal muscles are **voluntary muscles** that are consciously controlled to move bones. **Tendons,** which are tough bands of connective tissue, connect muscles to bones. Under a microscope, skeletal muscles also appear striated. S

Reading Check **Compare and contrast** the three types of muscles.

Skeletal Muscle Contraction

Most skeletal muscles are arranged in opposing, or antagonistic pairs. **Figure 11** illustrates muscles that you use to raise your arm and opposing muscles that you use to lower your arm. Skeletal muscle is arranged into fibers, which are fused muscle cells. Muscle fibers consist of many smaller units called **myofibrils.** Myofibrils consist of even smaller units, **myosin** and **actin,** which are protein filaments. Myofibrils are arranged in sections called sarcomeres. A **sarcomere** is the functional unit of a muscle and the part of the muscle that contracts as illustrated in **Figure 12.** The striations of skeletal muscles are a result of the sarcomeres, which run Z line to Z line. Z lines are where actin filaments attach within a myofibril. The overlap of actin and myosin filaments results in a dark band called the A band. The M line consists of only myosin filaments. The arrangement of the components of a sarcomere causes a muscle to shorten and then relax.

Sliding filament theory The sliding filament theory is also illustrated in **Figure 12**. This theory states that once a nerve signal reaches a muscle, the actin filaments slide toward one another, causing the muscle to contract. Notice that the myosin filaments do not move. There are many skeletal muscles involved in a simple motion.

Connection to Chemistry When the nerve impulse reaches the muscle, calcium is released into the myofibrils causing the myosin and actin to attach to each other. The actin filaments are pulled toward the center of the sarcomere, resulting in muscle contraction. ATP is necessary for this step of muscle contraction. As the muscle relaxes, the filaments return into their original positions. D

Figure 11 Skeletal muscles are arranged in antagonistic pairs.

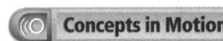

Concepts in Motion
Animation

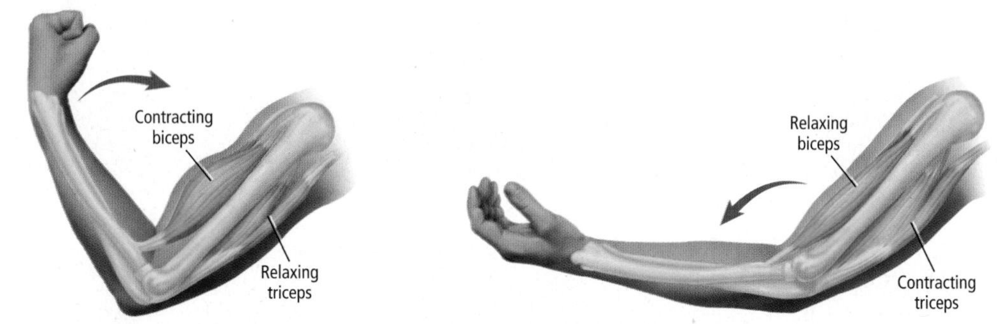

When the biceps muscle contracts, the lower arm is moved upward.

When the triceps muscle on the back of the upper arm contracts, the lower arm moves downward.

Reading Check Smooth muscles are a type of involuntary muscle found in internal organs and do not have striations. Cardiac muscles are specialized involuntary muscles, like smooth muscles, but are only found in the heart and are striated. Skeletal muscles are voluntary muscles attached to bones by tendons. Skeletal muscles are also striated like cardiac muscles.

Visualizing Muscle Contraction

Figure 12
A muscle fiber is made of myofibrils. The protein filaments actin and myosin form myofibrils.

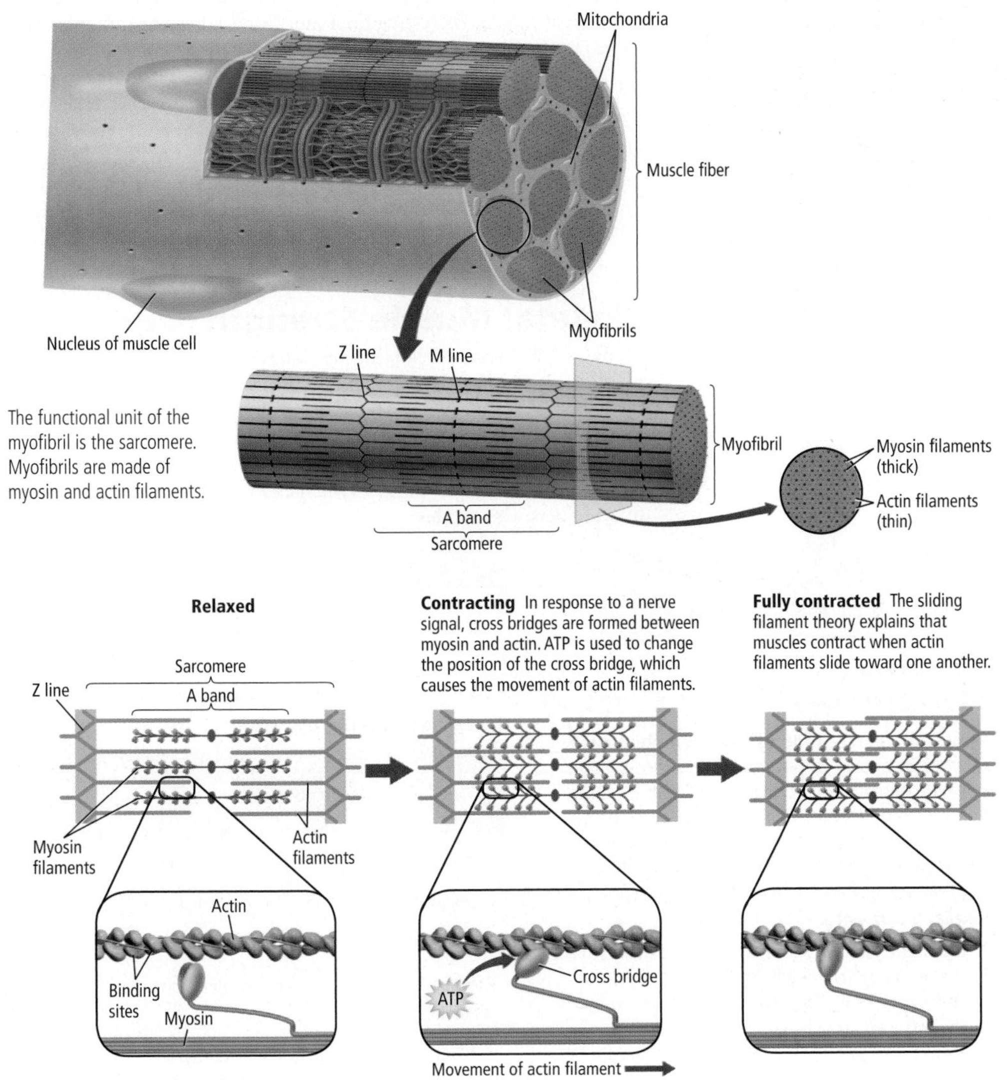

Mitochondria
Muscle fiber
Nucleus of muscle cell
Myofibrils
Z line
M line
The functional unit of the myofibril is the sarcomere. Myofibrils are made of myosin and actin filaments.
Myofibril
Myosin filaments (thick)
Actin filaments (thin)
A band
Sarcomere
Relaxed
Contracting In response to a nerve signal, cross bridges are formed between myosin and actin. ATP is used to change the position of the cross bridge, which causes the movement of actin filaments.
Fully contracted The sliding filament theory explains that muscles contract when actin filaments slide toward one another.
Sarcomere
Z line
A band
Myosin filaments
Actin filaments
Actin
Binding sites
Myosin
Cross bridge
ATP
Movement of actin filament

Concepts in Motion Animation

Demonstration

Resistance to Muscle Contraction Have a student volunteer stand inside a doorframe, arms at sides. Have the student lift his or her arms out to the side until the back of each hand is in contact with the doorframe. Instruct the student to press hard against the doorframe for about 40 s. Then have the student step out of the doorframe and observe the result. The student's arms should raise up. Inform students that the muscles are in a state of sustained contraction or prolonged activation. Calcium ions are being continually released into the muscle cells, but not completely returned to the sarcoplasmic reticulum. When the student moves away from the doorframe, there is still enough calcium in the muscle cells to maintain muscle contraction, even though the impulse from the nervous system has ceased. Est. time: 10 min

Visualizing Muscle Contraction

Purpose

Students will learn the cellular and molecular basis for muscle contraction.
C.1, C.5

Skill Practice

BL OL Sequence Have students make a list of events that occur when a muscle contracts, using vocabulary words from this chapter. Have them include the roles of calcium and ATP.

Critical Thinking

OL AL Infer

ASK STUDENTS: ***Based on what you have learned about the cellular basis for muscle contraction, what do you think rigor mortis is? What causes it?*** At death, no ATP is available, so the actin-myosin complex becomes stable and causes extreme muscle rigidity.

Concepts in Motion
Animation

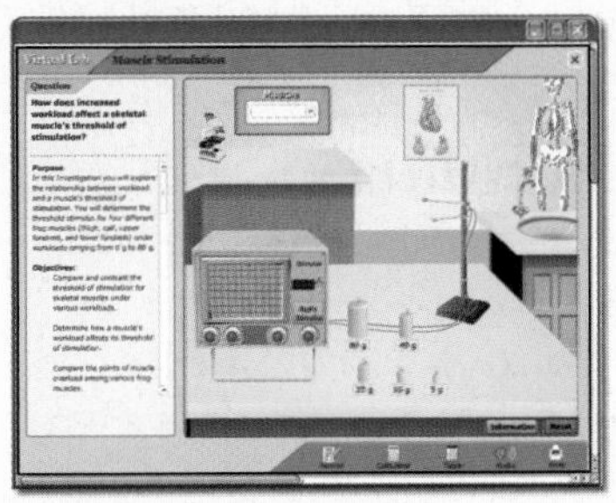

Inquiry Virtual Lab

Students will explore the relationship between workload and a muscle's threshold of stimulation.

Writing Support

BL OL AL Narrative Writing

Have students write a play-by-play description of a muscle contracting and then relaxing by simulating a sports broadcast. Give students the opportunity to share their broadcasts with the class.

C Critical Thinking

OL Predict

ASK STUDENTS: *What can you infer about the composition or ratio of muscle fiber types in the bodies of famous long-distance marathoners?* They most likely have a higher percentage of slow-twitch muscles in their legs than fast-twitch muscles.

DATA ANALYSIS LAB 1

About the Lab

- A brief amount of material might need to be presented about muscle biopsies and staining for ATPase activity.
- Also see Thayer, R., J. Collins, E. G. Noble and A. W. Taylor. 2000. A decade of aerobic endurance training: histological evidence for fibre type transformation. *Jour Sports Med Phys Fitness* 40(4):284–289.

Think Critically

1. The soleus must sustain a contraction for long periods of time. The orbicularis oculi have more fast-twitch fibers because they are not endurance muscles but require quick movements.
2. Fast-twitch muscles would be those that move the head, neck, and face.

Caption Question Fig. 13 During exercise, lactic acid buildup stimulates rapid breathing. After resting, adequate oxygen is restored to the body and muscles and lactic acid is broken down.

Figure 13 Crossing the finish line is a moment of intense energy.
Explain *why normal breathing is important after intense exercise.*

Energy for muscle contraction All muscle cells metabolize aerobically and anaerobically. When sufficient oxygen is available, aerobic cellular respiration occurs in muscle cells.

Recall that cellular respiration process provides ATP for energy. After a period of intense exercise, muscles might not get enough oxygen to sustain cellular respiration, limiting the amount of ATP that is available. Muscles, like those of the athlete in **Figure 13,** then must rely on the anaerobic process of lactic acid fermentation for energy.

During exercise, lactic acid builds up in muscle cells, causing fatigue. Excess lactic acid enters the bloodstream and this stimulates rapid breathing. After resting for a short time, adequate amounts of oxygen are restored and lactic acid is broken down.

You probably have seen a dead animal along the side of the road. When an animal dies, rigor mortis sets in. Rigor mortis is a state of prolonged muscular contraction. ATP is required to pump the calcium back out of the myofibrils, which causes the muscles to relax. In rigor mortis, the dead animal cannot produce ATP, so the calcium remains in the myofibrils and the muscle remains contracted. After 24 hours, cells and tissues begin degrading and the muscle fibers cannot remain contracted.

Skeletal Muscle Strength

Many people do not develop the physiques of champion bodybuilders, no matter how often they work out in the weight room. A person might be the fastest sprinter on the track team, but quickly becomes fatigued in a long-distance race. What might be the reason for these differences? The reason in both cases is the ratio of slow-twitch muscle fibers to fast-twitch muscle fibers. Both slow-twitch and fast-twitch fibers are present in every person's muscles. C

DATA ANALYSIS LAB 1

Based on Real Data*

Interpret the Data

How is the percentage of slow-twitch muscle related to action of a muscle? The proportion of slow-twitch to fast-twitch muscle fibers can be determined by removing a small piece of a muscle and staining the cells with a dye called *ATPase stain.* Fast-twitch muscle fibers with a high amount of ATP activity stain dark brown.

Think Critically

1. **Hypothesize** why a muscle such as the soleus has more slow-twitch muscle fibers than a muscle such as the orbicularis oculi.
2. **Classify** muscles by giving examples of muscles that have a high proportion of fast-twitch muscle fibers.

Data and Observations

Muscle	Action	Percent Slow Twitch
Soleus (leg)	Elevates the foot	87
Biceps femoris (leg)	Flexes the leg	67
Deltoid (shoulder)	Lifts the arm	52
Sternocleidomastoideus (neck)	Moves the head	35
Orbicularis oculi (face)	Closes the eyelid	15

*Data adapted from: Lamb, D.R. 1984. *Physiology of Exercise* New York: Macmillan Co.

Research Citation

Reading and Writing Educational research indicates that students need to be able to write in ways that demonstrate their reasoning. The creative writing activity on this page has students communicate and use language in ways other than repetition.

(Lampert and Cobb, 2003)

Research bibliography on pages 32T–34T

Differentiated Instruction

Physically Disabled Be sure that all students can participate in group activities such as this chapter's BioLab. The lab may need to be modified for students with physical disabilities. Hold a private conference before the lab to determine which accommodations will be needed.

For more tips, see pages 14T–15T.

Slow-twitch muscles Muscles vary in the speeds at which they contract. Slow-twitch muscles contract more slowly than fast-twitch muscle fibers. Slow-twitch muscle fibers have more endurance than fast-twitch muscle fibers. The body of the triathlete in **Figure 14** has many slow-twitch fibers. These kinds of muscle fibers function well in long-distance running or swimming because they resist fatigue more than fast-twitch muscle fibers.

Slow-twitch muscle fibers have many mitochondria needed for cellular respiration. They also contain myoglobin, a respiratory molecule that stores oxygen and serves as an oxygen reserve. Myoglobin causes the muscles to have a dark appearance. Exercise increases the number of mitochondria in these fibers, but the overall increase in the size of the muscle is minimal.

Fast-twitch muscles Fast-twitch muscle fibers fatigue easily but provide great strength for rapid, short movements. Fast-twitch muscle fibers are adapted for strength. They function well in exercises requiring short bursts of energy such as sprinting or weightlifting, as illustrated in **Figure 14.**

Fast-twitch fibers are lighter in color because they lack myoglobin. Because they have fewer mitochondria, they rely on anaerobic metabolism, which causes a buildup of lactic acid. This causes these muscles to fatigue easily. Exercise increases the number of myofibrils in a muscle, thereby increasing the diameter of the entire muscle.

Most skeletal muscles contain a mixture of slow-twitch and fast-twitch muscle fibers. The ratio of these fibers is determined genetically. If there is a very high ratio of slow-twitch to fast-twitch, a person might be a champion cross-country runner. Champion sprinters have a high proportion of fast-twitch muscle fibers. Most people are somewhere in between. **D**

■ **Figure 14** Triathletes have a high proportion of slow-twitch muscle fibers. Weight lifters have a high proportion of fast-twitch muscle fibers.

Section 3 Assessment

Section Summary

- There are three types of muscle tissue.
- Skeletal muscles are arranged in antagonistic pairs that work opposite to each other.
- Smooth muscles line many internal organs.
- Cardiac muscle is present only in the heart.
- All muscle cells metabolize both aerobically and anaerobically.

Understand Main Ideas

1. MAIN Idea **Construct** a chart that lists similarities and differences among the three types of muscles.
2. **Identify** which type of muscles are voluntary and which are involuntary.
3. **Explain** why aerobic respiration occurs before lactic acid fermentation in most muscles.
4. **Compare** the role of mitochondria in slow-twitch and fast-twitch muscle fibers.

Think Critically

5. **Infer** Wild turkeys have a higher ratio of dark meat (muscle) to white meat than farm-raised turkeys. Why does this allow wild turkeys to fly longer distances than domesticated turkeys?

WRITING in **Biology**

6. Write a short story that describes the sequence of events involved in skeletal muscle contraction. Tell your story from the point of view of a calcium ion.

D Develop Concepts

OL AL

Community Connection

Have students make a list of athletic events for which it would be favorable to have a high proportion of slow-twitch muscle fibers. endurance events: 500-m swim, marathon, cross-country skiing, long-distance biking Have them list activities for which fast-twitch muscle fibers would be favorable. short events that require short bursts of energy: 50-m dash, sprints, weight lifting, long jump

Formative Assessment

Evaluation Have students compare the three types of muscle tissue. Answers will vary, but may include that some muscles contain striations and some don't. Some muscle cells work together, others work independently; some muscles work involuntarily, others require conscious control (voluntary).

Remediation Have students construct a four-column chart. Have them list the three types of muscle tissue in the first column. skeletal, smooth, cardiac In the second column, have students indicate whether the cells are single or multinucleated; in the third column, voluntary or involuntary; and in the fourth column, the location(s) of each muscle type.

Section 3 Assessment

1. skeletal—multinucleated, voluntary, all over the body, attached to bones and skin; smooth—single nucleus, involuntary, in the walls of organs and blood vessels; cardiac—single nucleus, involuntary, heart
2. skeletal—voluntary; smooth and cardiac—involuntary
3. Aerobic respiration occurs when plenty of oxygen is available. Lactic acid fermentation occurs when oxygen supplies are low, such as during strenuous exercise.
4. Slow-twitch muscle fibers have many mitochondria, whereas fast-twitch muscle fibers have fewer mitochondria and must rely on anaerobic metabolism.
5. Myoglobin gives muscles a dark appearance. Myoglobin stores oxygen, which can be used for activities that require endurance, such as flying long distances.
6. Answers will vary, but should include that calcium is released into the myofibrils and causes the myosin and actin to attach to each other.

Assessment Online Quiz

Biology & Society

Purpose

Students will understand that UV rays can damage skin and cause skin cancer. They will also learn about sunscreens, SPF ratings, and how to protect themselves from the Sun's rays.
F.1, F.5

Anticipatory Guide

ASK STUDENTS: ***What is skin?*** Tell students that skin is a multilayered organ that covers and protects the body. ***How is skin structured, and how do the layers react to sunlight?*** The epidermis is the outer superficial layer of skin. In the inner layer of the epidermis, melanin is produced. Melanin works to absorb UV rays and protect the skin cells beneath it. When the skin increases its production of melanin, it is an indication that the skin is being damaged by the Sun.

Background

Explain that some of the ingredients in sunscreens, such as titanium oxide or zinc oxide, scatter UV rays, keeping them from penetrating the skin. Other ingredients, such as oxygenzone or octyl methoxycinnamate, absorb the Sun's rays, turn them into heat, and scatter them.

Some people's skin is irritated by the products in some sunscreens, but there are other ways to avoid UV damage. Clothing does not block all UV rays. However, clothing can provide some protection from UV rays. Dark-colored, tightly woven pants, long skirts, and shirts with long sleeves provide the best protection.

Biology & Society

SPFs and Sunscreens

When you are outside playing sports or hanging out with your friends, the Sun is a welcome companion. Its warm rays are a staple of summertime fun. But are you adequately protecting yourself from the potentially harmful effects of the Sun? Retailers display many shelves of sun-protection products, but how much protection do these products provide?

Damaged skin It is important to understand that tanned skin is damaged skin. Skin cells that have been exposed to and injured by the Sun's ultraviolet (UV) rays produce melanin in order to absorb the rays. The melanin causes the "tanned" look. There are two kinds of UV rays that can reach Earth. UVB rays cause sunburns. UVA rays, which penetrate skin more deeply than UVB rays, cause other kinds of skin damage, such as wrinkles and sunspots. The same problems can result from using tanning beds or sunlamps, both of which emit UV rays. Even if you do not become sunburned, exposure to both kinds of UV rays can increase your risk of skin cancers—especially melanoma, the most serious kind of skin cancer.

To protect skin from the Sun's rays, people can wear sunscreen. Many sunscreens are labeled with a number marked "SPF," which stands for "Sun Protection Factor." However, SPF only measures protection from UVB rays. Sunscreens that are labeled "broad-spectrum" offer some protection from UVA rays, but scientists have not yet developed a system of measuring how well a sunscreen protects from UVA rays.

Understanding SPF Using the best product may be difficult because SPF numbers can be misleading. For example, one might think that a sunscreen with an SPF of 30 would have twice the protection against UVB rays than a sunscreen with an SPF of 15.

These students should all be wearing sunscreen with at least SPF 15 on all skin surfaces exposed to the Sun's rays.

However, that is not the case. A sunscreen with an SPF of 15 protects against 93 percent of UVB rays, while a sunscreen with an SPF of 30 protects against 97 percent of UVB rays.

The American Cancer Society recommends that when outdoors, people of all ethnicities should wear a water-resistant sunscreen with an SPF of at least 15. About one ounce of sunscreen should be applied 15 to 30 minutes before going outside, even on cloudy days. Sunscreen should be reapplied every two hours. This simple habit goes a long way to protect skin from the Sun's rays. And for people who miss having that golden glow, there are always self-tanning products.

WRITING in Biology

Create a skit Write a skit that explains SPF ratings and why wearing sunscreen is important to one's health. Research other steps that people can take to protect themselves from the Sun, and include those steps in the skit. If time allows, perform your skit for other classes.

WRITING in Biology

Activity You might want to split your class into several groups and have each group create its own skit. To each member of a group, assign a job such as writer, actor, prop handler, etc. (Or you might want to let each groups decide internally who will handle each task.) Make sure that each skit includes information on how people can best protect themselves from UV rays. If time allows, have your class perform their skits for other classes or for students in elementary or middle school.

BIOLAB

FORENSICS: HOW CAN SKELETONS HELP YOU SOLVE A "CRIME"?

Background: Imagine there is a National Museum of Domestic Chickens and it has been robbed. Several bones from the first chicken eaten in America are missing. Three dogs are suspects. Your job is to examine impressions of bones that were found in mud near the doghouse of each dog and to determine if any of the bones came from a chicken. You will be given a clue for each unknown bone.

Question: *Can the structure and form of a bone tell you from which animal it came?*

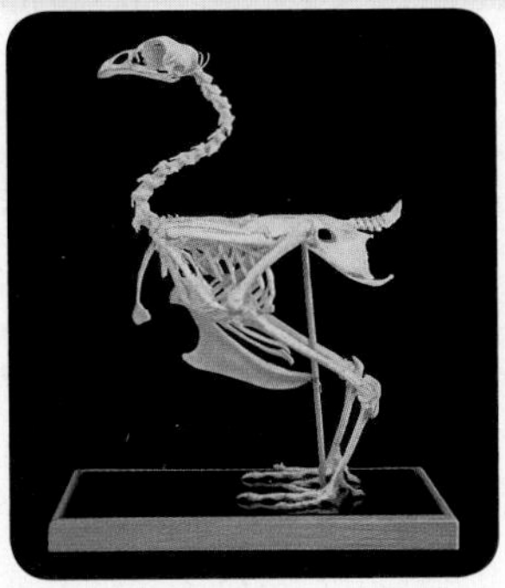

Materials

impressions of three unknown bones
set of clues
various animal skeletons
hand lens
metric ruler
string

Safety Precautions

Procedure

1. Read and complete the lab safety form.
2. Collect materials you will use to measure and examine the skeletons. Determine what types of measurements you will make.
3. Obtain impressions of three bones and a set of clues from your teacher. Do not open the clues until you are told to do so.
4. Design a data table to record your measurements.
5. Examine the skeletons. Compare them to the impressions.
6. Make measurements and record the data.
7. Open the clues you were given and reexamine your data and answers.
8. **Cleanup and Disposal** Return any reusable materials to their proper storage areas.

Analyze and Conclude

1. **Analyze Data** Based on your observations and measurements, determine which one of the impressions came from a chicken.
2. **Interpret Data** How did you use information concerning the size and shape of each impression to help you determine from which animal it came?
3. **Evaluate** Did your conclusions change after you opened the clues? Explain your reasoning if your conclusions changed.
4. **Compare and Contrast** What similarities did you notice between each impression and bones in the human skeleton? What differences did you notice?
5. **Relate** Which skeletons seem to share the most characteristics with a human skeleton?
6. **Draw Conclusions** Which dog stole the chicken bones?

SHARE YOUR DATA

Poster Session Paleontologists are scientists who study fossils. Through their studies of fossil bones they have found evidence that birds had a dinosaur ancestor. Research the evidence that has been found and create a poster that shows what you learned.

Analyze and Conclude

1. Answers will depend on which impressions students had.
2. Answers will vary, but should include that after students opened the clues and found the bone on the human skeleton, they then examined the other skeletons to find the homologous bones.
3. Students might say that their answers changed with this additional information.
4. Answers will depend on the bone impressions each group had. Similarities include shape and comparative size of many of the bones. Differences include the fact that the human bones are much larger than those of the other animals.
5. The cat and rabbit skeletons share the most characteristics with the human skeleton. All of the animals in this lab are vertebrates, but the cat, rabbit, and human are all mammals and more closely related in an evolutionary sense.
6. Answers will vary, but will be based on the students' findings.

BIOLAB

Inquiry BioLab

For a lab worksheet, use your eTeacherEdition Online.

RUBRIC A rubric for evaluating BioLabs is found on your eTeacherEdition Online.

Est. Time 60–90 min

Content Background Skeletons of all vertebrate animals, including humans, chickens, cats, and frogs, share many of the same bones, although the structure and function of many of these bones might be quite different. The more closely related the animals, the smaller the differences are likely to be. For example, the skeletons of mammals have more in common with the human skeleton than the bird (chicken) and amphibian (frog) skeletons. Quadruped animals (cat and frog) share some structural forms that are not seen in the bipedal animals (chicken and human). The chicken skeleton is different largely because it is modified for flight.

Alternative Materials Skeletons of other vertebrate animals can be substituted. If skeletons are not available, high-quality photos or diagrams of skeletons can be used. The unknown bones would then need to be cut out from a second copy of these photos.

Safety Precaution Approve lab safety forms before work begins.

Teaching Strategies

- Give each group a different set of three impressions.
- Remind students to handle skeletons gently.

Alternative Teaching Demo Make overheads or a slideshow presentation of each skeleton and unknown bone. Have the class try to guess the identity of each bone.

Chapter 32 Study Guide

THEME FOCUS **Homeostasis** Specialized functions such as temperature regulation, conversion of yellow bone marrow to red bone marrow in times of need, and lactic acid fermentation maintain homeostasis in the human body.

BIG Idea **These systems work together to maintain homeostasis by protecting, supporting, and moving the body.**

Section 1 The Integumentary System

epidermis (p. 936)
keratin (p. 936)
melanin (p. 937)
dermis (p. 937)
hair follicle (p. 937)
sebaceous gland (p. 937)

MAIN Idea **Skin is a multilayered organ that covers and protects the body.**

- The skin is the major organ of the integumentary system.
- Maintaining homeostasis is one function of the integumentary system.
- There are four types of tissues in the integumentary system.
- Hair, fingernails, and toenails develop from epithelial cells.
- Burns are classified according to the severity of the damage to skin tissues.

Section 2 The Skeletal System

axial skeleton (p. 941)
appendicular skeleton (p. 941)
compact bone (p. 942)
osteocyte (p. 942)
spongy bone (p. 942)
red bone marrow (p. 942)
yellow bone marrow (p. 942)
osteoblast (p. 942)
ossification (p. 942)
osteoclast (p. 943)
ligament (p. 944)

MAIN Idea **The skeleton provides a structural framework for the body and protects internal organs such as the heart, lungs, and brain.**

- The human skeleton consists of two divisions.
- Most bones are composed of two different types of tissue.
- Bones are being remodeled constantly.
- Bones work in conjunction with muscles.
- The skeleton has several important functions.

Section 3 The Muscular System

smooth muscle (p. 947)
involuntary muscle (p. 947)
cardiac muscle (p. 947)
skeletal muscle (p. 948)
voluntary muscle (p. 948)
tendon (p. 948)
myofibril (p. 948)
myosin (p. 948)
actin (p. 948)
sarcomere (p. 948)

MAIN Idea **The three major types of muscle tissue differ in structure and function.**

- There are three types of muscle tissue.
- Skeletal muscles are arranged in antagonistic pairs that work opposite to each other.
- Smooth muscles line many internal organs.
- Cardiac muscle is present only in the heart.
- All muscle cells metabolize both aerobically and anaerobically.

Chapter 32

Study Guide

ConnectED

Students can use the following to review the chapter.

Review

Vocabulary eGames
Vocabulary eFlashcards
Vocabulary PuzzleMaker

Assessment

Online Quizzes
Online Test Practice
Standardized Test Practice

Use the *ExamView® Assessment Suite* CD-ROM to:

- create multiple versions of tests
- create modified tests with one mouse click
- edit existing questions and add your own questions
- build tests aligned with state standards using built-in state curriculum tags
- change English tests to Spanish with one mouse click
- track students' progress using the Teacher Management System

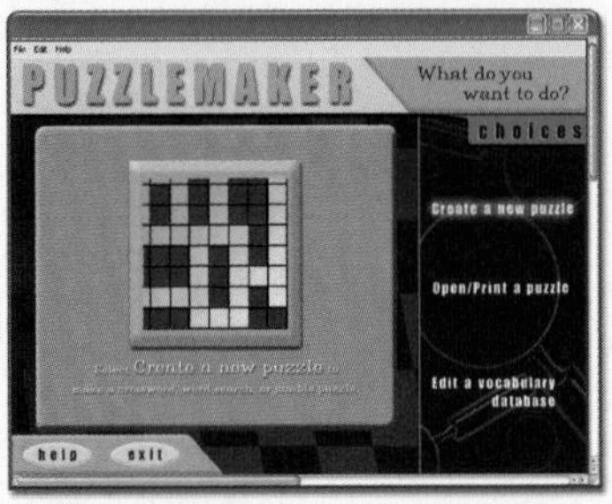

Review **Vocabulary PuzzleMaker**

For additional practice with vocabulary, have students access the Vocabulary PuzzleMaker online.

Review **Vocabulary eGames**

Section 1

Vocabulary Review

Explain the difference between the terms in each set.

1. epidermis, dermis

2. melanin, keratin

3. sebaceous glands, hair follicles

Understand Main Ideas

Use the diagram below to answer question 4.

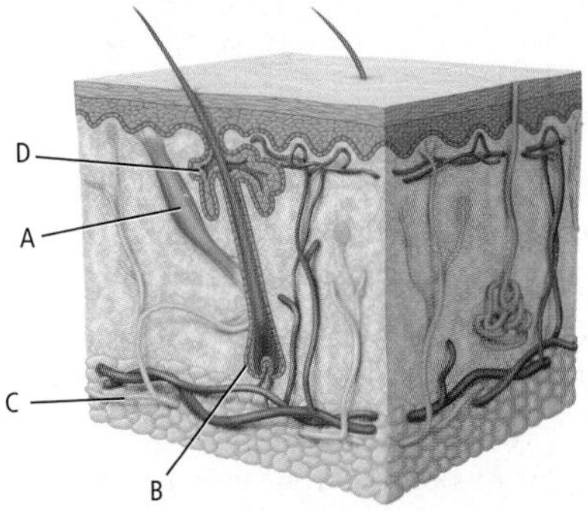

4. Which tissue type is responsible for "goose bump" formation?
A. A **B.** B **C.** C **D.** D

5. When are blackheads formed?
A. when sebaceous glands become clogged
B. when grooves in the epidermis gather dirt
C. when hair follicles grow inward rather than outward
D. when there is an excess of keratin produced

6. How does the skin regulate body temperature?
A. by increasing sweat production
B. by retaining water
C. by producing vitamin D
D. by regulating fat content in the epidermis

7. Which are not found in the dermis?
A. muscles
B. sweat and oil glands
C. fat cells
D. nerve cells

8. What could be inferred from suntans?
A. Sunning for the purpose of tanning produces healthier skin.
B. A tan might indicate sun damage to the skin.
C. Tanning strengthens the elastic in the skin making the skin feel tight.
D. Tanning promotes skin that has a more youthful appearance.

Constructed Response

9. MAIN Idea What possible effects on the body might there be if the epidermis was absent?

10. **Open Ended** What possible effects on the body might there be if the dermis was absent?

11. **THEME FOCUS Homeostasis** Describe how the integumentary system contributes to homeostasis.

Think Critically

12. **Explain** why it does not hurt when you get a haircut.

13. **Assess** the reason why people with third degree burns do not feel pain at the site of the burn.

Section 2

Vocabulary Review

Explain the difference between the terms in each set.

14. spongy bone, compact bone

15. tendons, ligaments

16. osteoblasts, osteoclasts

Understand Main Ideas

Use the figure below to answer question 17.

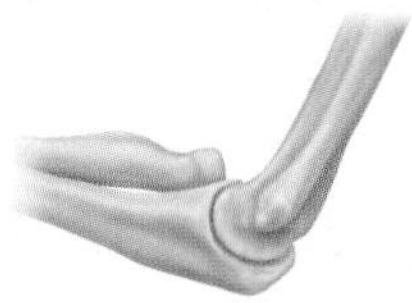

17. Where would you find the type of joint shown above?
A. hip **B.** vertebrae **C.** elbow **D.** skull

Chapter 32

Assessment

Section 1

Vocabulary Review

1. The epidermis is the outer layer of the skin; it is made of epithelial cells and its primary purpose is protection. The dermis is found directly beneath the epidermis; it contains several tissue types, including connective, epithelial, muscle, and nerves that perform many functions.
2. Melanin is the pigment that gives the skin its color. It protects the skin from ultraviolet light. Keratin is a protein found in the epidermis that waterproofs and protects the underlying cells and tissues.
3. Hair follicles are narrow cavities in the dermis from which hair cells grow. Sebaceous glands produce an oily secretion, and are found at the base of hair follicles.

Understand Main Ideas

4. A
5. A
6. A
7. C
8. B

Constructed Response

9. If the epidermis was absent, underlying cells would be susceptible to damage from environmental factors and physical trauma.
10. If the dermis was absent or damaged, the body could not sweat, sense pain, vitamin D synthesis would be impaired, heat retention would be lessened, and tissue underlying the dermal layer would be susceptible to injury.

Short Answer

11. The integumentary system assists in the regulation of body temperature, prevents water loss, senses changes in the environment, and protects against physical trauma and ultraviolet damage.

Think Critically

12. Hair does not contain nerve cells or pain receptors.
13. A third-degree burn can destroy nerve endings in the skin.

Section 2

Vocabulary Review

14. Compact bone is much more dense than spongy bone.
15. Tendons connect muscles to bone, and ligaments connect bones to other bones.
16. Osteoblasts form bone, and osteoclasts break it down.

Understand Main Ideas

17. C

18. A
19. B
20. B
21. C
22. C
23. A

Constructed Response

24. It would diminish the strength of the skeleton and reduce protection of internal organs.
25. Blood cells would have no space for their production.
26. Osteoblasts form bone, thereby decreasing blood calcium, and osteoclasts break bone down and increase blood calcium levels.

Think Critically

27. The ankle should be examined for damage to bones, muscles, tendons, and ligaments.
28. She would deprive herself and her fetus of needed calcium, possibly resulting in osteoporosis.

Section 3

Vocabulary Review

29. Melanin does not belong; it is a pigment. Actin and myosin are proteins involved with muscle contraction.
30. Fast-twitch muscle does not belong. Cardiac and smooth muscle are two of the three types of major muscle types. Fast-twitch muscle is a type of skeletal muscle fiber.
31. Myoglobin does not belong, as it is a molecule associated with oxygen storage. Sarcomeres and myofibrils are parts of a muscle.

18. Which is not a function of bone?
A. production of vitamin D
B. internal support
C. protection of internal organs
D. storage of calcium

Use the diagram below to answer question 19.

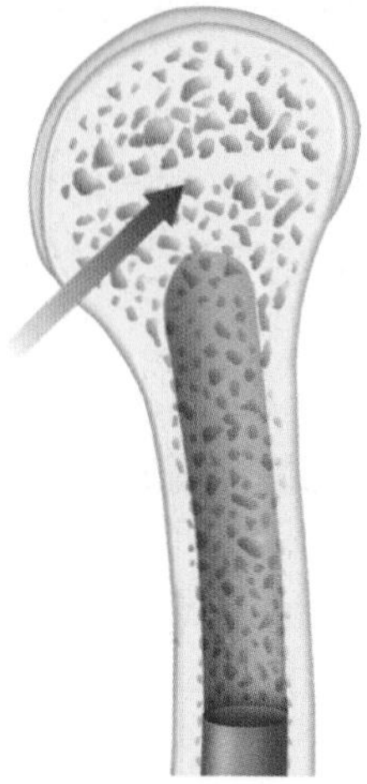

19. What is a characteristic of the portion of the bone indicated by the arrow?
A. It contains no living cells.
B. It contains bone marrow.
C. It is the only type of bone tissue in long bones.
D. It is made of overlapping osteon systems.

20. Which pair of terms is mismatched?
A. cranium, sutures
B. wrist, pivot joint
C. shoulder, ball-and-socket joint
D. knee, hinge joint

21. What are the cells that remove old bone tissue called?
A. osteoblasts
B. osteocytes
C. osteoclasts
D. osteozymes

22. Which is not part of the axial skeleton?
A. skull
B. ribs
C. hip bone
D. vertebral column

23. Which is part of the appendicular skeleton?

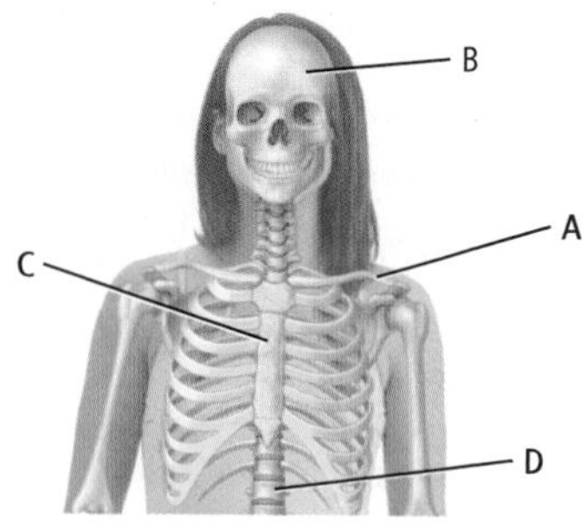

A. A
B. B
C. C
D. D

Constructed Response

24. MAIN Idea Describe potential consequences if all bone tissue in humans was comprised of spongy bone and there was no compact bone.

25. **Open Ended** Describe potential consequences if all bone tissue in humans was comprised of compact bone and there was no spongy bone.

26. **Short Answer** Compare the function of osteoclasts and osteoblasts.

Think Critically

27. **Analyze** the following scenario. A person enters the emergency room with an ankle injury. What structures of the patient's ankle need to be examined to determine the proper treatment?

28. **Hypothesize** what might happen to a woman's bones if she did not increase her intake of calcium during pregnancy?

Section 3

Vocabulary Review

For each set of terms below, choose the one term that does not belong and explain why it does not belong.

29. actin, melanin, myosin

30. cardiac muscle, smooth muscle, fast-twitch muscle

31. sarcomere, myofibril, myoglobin

Assessment Online Test Practice

Understand Main Ideas

32. Which requires ATP?
- **A.** muscle contraction
- **B.** muscle relaxation
- **C.** both muscle contraction and relaxation
- **D.** neither muscle contraction nor relaxation

Use the diagram below to answer question 33.

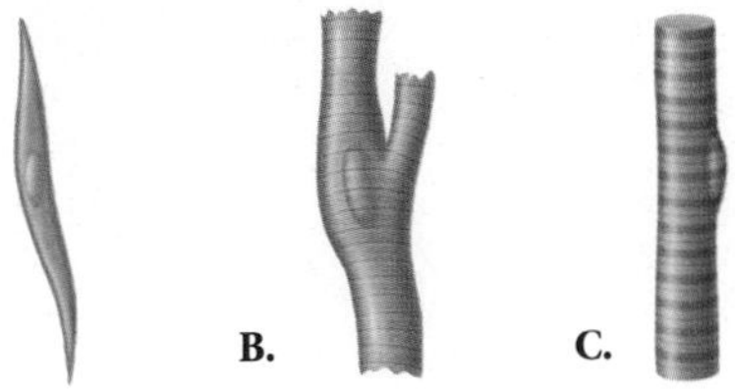

33. What muscles shown above are classified as voluntary muscles?
- **A.** the muscle type shown in A
- **B.** the muscle type shown in B
- **C.** the muscle type shown in C
- **D.** all muscles

34. Which is a characteristic of fast-twitch muscle fibers?
- **A.** They contain more myoglobin than slow-twitch fibers.
- **B.** They are resistant to fatigue.
- **C.** They have fewer mitochondria than slow-twitch fibers.
- **D.** They require high amounts of oxygen in order to function.

Constructed Response

35. MAIN Idea Compare and contrast the structure of skeletal, smooth, and cardiac muscle.

36. Short Answer Explain, based on the structure of the muscle fibers, why skeletal muscles can contract but not lengthen.

Think Critically

37. Predict any possible consequences if cardiac and smooth muscle had the same structure as skeletal muscle.

38. Infer why it is important that no muscle contains solely slow-twitch or fast-twitch fibers.

Summative Assessment

39. BIG Idea Explain how the loss of the integumentary body system would cause a breakdown of homeostasis.

40. WRITING in Biology Imagine you are a writer for a health and fitness magazine. Write a brief article about the need for calcium in order for the skeletal and muscular systems to function correctly.

Document-Based Questions

Athletes burn fat at a maximum rate when they exercise at an intensity near the lactate threshold—the point at which lactic acid starts to build up in the muscles. In addition, athletes who consume the greatest amounts of oxygen during intense exercise [VO_{2peak}] burn the most fat. Researchers compared the lactate threshold and oxygen consumption of overweight subjects who did not exercise to those of highly-trained athletes.

Data obtained from: Bircher, S. and Knechtle, B. 2004. Relationship between fat oxidation and lactate threshold in athletes and obese women and men. Journal of Sports Science and Medicine 3:174–181.

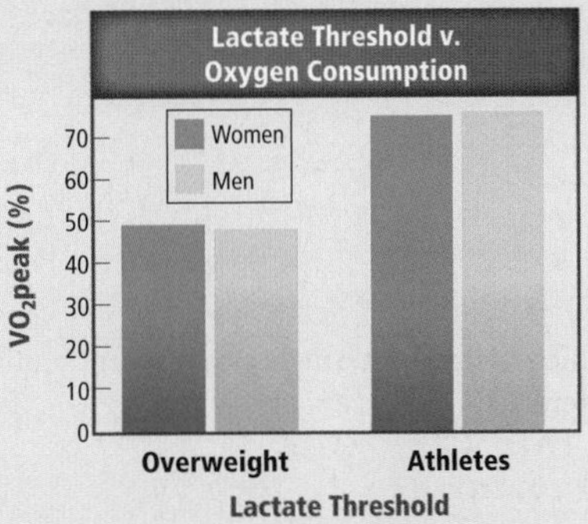

41. At what percent of VO_{2peak} was the lactate threshold reached in overweight subjects?

42. How might an overweight person who does not exercise increase his or her VO_{2peak} and, therefore, his or her lactate threshold?

Understand Main Ideas

32. C
33. C
34. C

Constructed Response

35. Skeletal muscle fibers are striated; smooth muscle cells have a single nucleus and are not striated; cardiac muscle cells are striated and have a single nucleus.

36. The heads on the myosin filaments are designed to pull the actin filaments only toward each other.

Think Critically

37. Cardiac muscle fibers are webbed and act as a syncytium (coordinated movement critical for heart muscle); smooth muscle cells are laid down in sheets (important in organs that require stretch); skeletal muscle is made for voluntary responses, heavy lifting, and support of the skeleton.

38. A muscle with only one type of fiber would lack necessary versatility.

Summative Assessment

39. Loss of skin—no temperature regulation, no protection from infections

WRITING in Biology

RUBRIC Use the modifiable rubric found on your eTeacherEdition Online to assess writing assignments.

40. Key points include that calcium is an important structural component of bone and is necessary for muscle contractions. Bones can act as a reservoir for calcium storage. If blood calcium levels are low, calcium can be released from bones. A lack of sufficient calcium can lead to osteoporosis and improper muscle function.

Document-Based Questions

Bircher, S. and Knechtle, B. 2004. Relationship between fat oxidation and lactate threshold in athletes and obese women and men. *Journal of Sports Science and Medicine* 3:174–181.

41. 50 percent
42. take in oxygen

Assessment Online Test Practice

Standardized Test Practice

Multiple Choice

1. B 5. C
2. B 6. C
3. C 7. C
4. A 8. B

Short Answer

9. A fish with an S-shaped pattern moves its entire body in the shape of an S. A fish that moves its tail only swishes its tail with a strong motion that propels the fish forward.
10. A fish with an S-shaped pattern would be found swimming around between rocks and seaweed because it can easily move between obstacles.
11. Butterflies go through complete metamorphosis. The butterfly begins as an egg. It hatches as a larva and eats and grows. It spins a cocoon in its pupal stage and emerges from the cocoon as an adult butterfly. Grasshoppers undergo incomplete metamorphosis. The grasshopper begins as an egg. It hatches into an immature nymph that lacks wings and reproductive organs. The nymphs go through several molts in which the nymphs become increasingly like adults. The final molt results in an adult grasshopper with wings and reproductive organs.
12. They are using auditory communication. Because they are using their calls to mark their territory, they are exhibiting both communicative behavior and territorial behavior.
13. Cells in fetal cartilage called osteoblasts form bone. Bone is formed through a process called ossification during which calcium salts are deposited around collagen protein fibers.
14. It is a learned behavior that results from an interaction between innate behaviors and the chimpanzee's past experience. It might also be a form of cognitive learning.

Standardized Test Practice

Cumulative

Multiple Choice

1. Which describes the circulatory system of most reptiles?
   A. double loop, four-chambered heart
   B. double loop, three-chambered heart
   C. single loop, three-chambered heart
   D. single loop, two-chambered heart

Use the figure below to answer question 2.

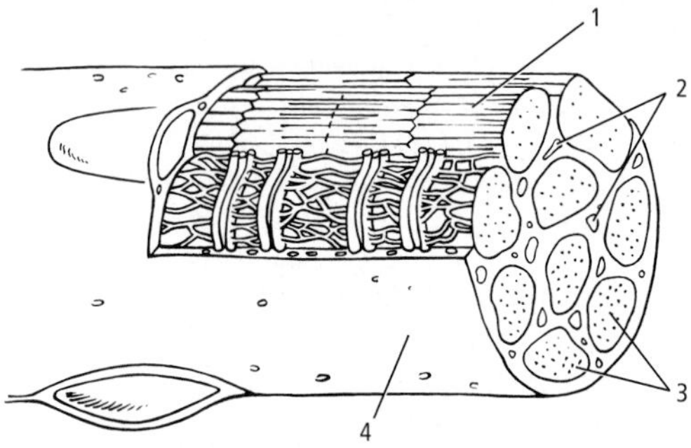

2. Which part of a muscle is used for cellular respiration?
   A. 1
   B. 2
   C. 3
   D. 4

3. Which characteristic makes bats unique among mammals?
   A. eyesight
   B. feathers
   C. flight
   D. teeth

4. Which learned behavior occurs only at a certain critical time in an animal's life?
   A. classical conditioning
   B. fixed action pattern
   C. habituation
   D. imprinting

Use the figure of the joint below to answer question 5.

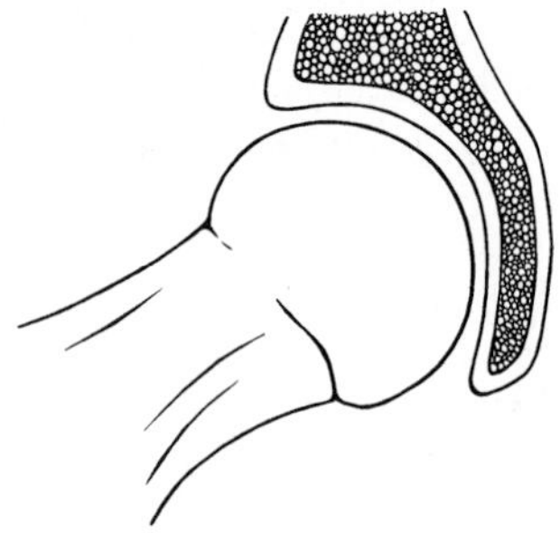

5. Where is the type of joint shown in the figure found?
   A. elbows and knees
   B. fingers and toes
   C. hips and shoulders
   D. wrists and ankles

6. Which describes the characteristics of a bird's brain?
   A. Birds have a large medulla to process their vision.
   B. Birds have a large cerebellum to control respiration and digestion.
   C. Birds have a large cerebrum to coordinate movement and balance.
   D. Birds have a large cerebral cortex to control flight.

7. Which type of bone is classified as irregular?
   A. leg bones
   B. skull
   C. vertebrae
   D. wrist bones

8. Which adaptation helps stop fishes from rolling side to side in the water?
   A. ctenoid scales
   B. paired fins
   C. placoid scales
   D. swim bladders

Short Answer

Use the diagram below to answer questions 9 and 10.

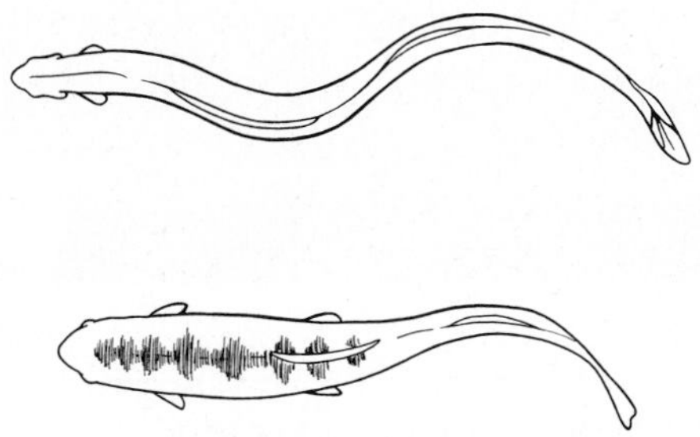

9. Describe the difference between how a fish with an S-shaped pattern swims and a fish that moves its tail only.

10. Decide where a fish with an S-shaped pattern would be likely found swimming.

11. Relate the key events in the life cycle of a butterfly to the key events in the life cycle of a grasshopper.

12. Howler monkeys are the loudest land animals. Their calls are heard for miles across the jungle. They use their calls to mark their territory. Assess this type of behavior.

13. Describe how fetal cartilage becomes bone.

14. A chimpanzee picks up a blade of grass and sticks it in an anthole. When it pulls the blade of grass out, it has ants on it. The chimpanzee eats the ants. The chimpanzee continues doing this because it is an easy way to get ants. Assess this activity as it relates to animal behaviors.

15. Describe two types of joint conditions.

Extended Response

Use the diagram to answer questions 16 and 17.

Pigeon Eagle

16. Evaluate what the location of the eyes on these two birds reveals about their behavior.

17. Explain how the beaks of these two birds give evidence of what they eat.

Essay Question

Whooping cranes are an endangered species. One of the reasons for this is that they hatch in nesting areas and then migrate south for the winter. Humans can raise chicks, but teaching them to migrate is a different problem. Operation Migration solved this problem in 2001. Operation Migration used ultralight aircraft to lead a migration of human-raised whooping cranes on a 2000-km migration from Wisconsin to Florida. The whooping cranes followed the ultralight aircraft that used recorded calls to learn the migration route.

Using the information in the paragraph above, answer the following question in essay format.

18. Migratory behavior has been shown to be an innate behavior. Evaluate why it is necessary to use ultra-light aircraft to guide the birds so they can learn the migration route.

NEED EXTRA HELP?																		
If You Missed Question . . .	1	2	3	4	5	6	7	8	9	10	11	12	13	14	15	16	17	18
Review Section . . .	29.1	32.3	30.1	31.1	32.2	29.2	32.2	28.1	28.1	28.1	26.3	31.2	32.2	31.1	32.2	29.2	29.2	31.2

15. Osteoarthritis is a painful condition that results from deterioration of cartilage. Rheumatoid arthritis is a type of arthritis that causes swelling and pain at the joints. Other answers are possible.

Extended Response

16. The eagle has forward-looking eyes that enable it to see prey at a distance. The pigeon has eyes on the sides of its head that enable it to see all around and watch for predators.
17. The eagle has a strong beak that is made for tearing flesh from its prey. The pigeon has a thin beak for picking up small bits of food.

Essay Question

18. The navigation ability of the birds is innate behavior. However, the birds must learn the route to know where they are going. Once the route is learned, their innate navigation ability can guide them back and forth between the winter and summer areas.

Chapter 33 Organizer:
Nervous System

LabManager™

Customize any lab with the LabManager™ CD-ROM.

Essential Questions	National Science Standards	Materials and Planning: Estimated times include cleanup and disposal, but do not include teacher prep time. For cleanup and disposal guidelines, see page 39T.	Est. Time (min)
Section 1 1. What are the major parts of a neuron and what is the function of each part? 2. How is a nerve impulse similar to an electrical signal, and how does it move along a neuron?	UCP.1, UCP.2, UCP.5; A.1, A.2; B.3; F.1	**Launch Lab,** p. 960: paper, pencil	20
		Demonstration, p. 962: projecting compound microscope, prepared microscope slide of a neuron	10
		Demonstration, p. 963: battery; switch; electrical wires; lightbulb, horn, or buzzer	5
		Demonstration, p. 964: dominoes	5
		MiniLab 1, p. 965: 1-m^2 acrylic, table tennis ball	25
		Activity, p. 966: two green tennis balls, two white tennis balls	5
Section 2 1. How can the major divisions of the nervous system be illustrated? 2. What are the similarities and differences between the somatic nervous system and the autonomic nervous system?	UCP.1, UCP.2, UCP.5; A.1, A.2; F.1; G.3	**Demonstration,** p. 969: calf's brain or sheep's brain	10
		Demonstration, p. 970: child's helmet, standard pillowcase	5
Section 3 1. What are the different sensory structures and what are each of them able to detect? 2. How is each sense organ able to transmit a nerve impulse? 3. What is the relationship between smell and taste?	UCP.1, UCP.2, UCP.5; A.1, A.2; F.1, F.2, G.2	**MiniLab 2,** p. 975: plastic bottlecaps in several colors, stopwatches	25
		Demonstration, p. 975: rotating stool	5
Section 4 1. What are the four ways that drugs can affect the nervous system? 2. What are different ways that drugs can harm the body or cause death? 3. How, at the cellular level, can a person become addicted to a drug?	UCP.1, UCP.2, UCP.3, UCP.5; A.1, A.2; C.5; F.1, F.5; G.1, G.2	**Demonstration,** p. 978: rubber tubing or garden hose, faucet, clamp	10
		Activity, p. 980: six tennis balls	10
		BioLab, p. 983: graph paper, paper, pencil, calculator	60

Suggested Time for Each Lesson

Class	Chapter Opener	Section 1	Section 2	Section 3	Section 4	Assessment
Basic	45 min	45 min	45 min	45 min	45 min	45 min
General	25 min	90 min	65 min	45 min	45 min	45 min
Honors	5 min	45 min	30 min	30 min	50 min	20 min

ConnectED

connectED.mcgraw-hill.com

Access interactive learning opportunities and teaching resources using these icons located throughout your StudentWorks™ Plus Online and eTeacherEdition Online.

Chapter 33 Section Resources	Additional Chapter 33 Resources	Technology
FAST FILE Unit 9 Resources: Launch Lab Worksheet* MiniLab Worksheet* Study Guide (English/Spanish)* Section Quick Check **Reading Essentials 33.1** **Science Notebook 33.1*** **FAST FILE Unit 9 Resources:** Study Guide (English/Spanish)* Section Quick Check **Reading Essentials 33.2** **Science Notebook 33.2*** **FAST FILE Unit 9 Resources:** MiniLab Worksheet* Study Guide (English/Spanish)* Section Quick Check **Reading Essentials 33.3** **Science Notebook 33.3*** **FAST FILE Unit 9 Resources:** BioLab Worksheet* Study Guide (English/Spanish)* Section Quick Check **Reading Essentials 33.4** **Science Notebook 33.4***	**FAST FILE Unit 9 Resources:** Chapter Diagnostic Test Concept Mapping* Real-World Biology Enrichment Chapter Tests A, B, and C **Transparencies:** Bellringer Transparencies* Biology Concepts Transparencies* **Lab Resources:** Laboratory Manual* Probeware Lab Manual* Forensics Lab Manual* Pre-AP Lab Manual* Open Inquiry in Biology* Guided Inquiry in Biology*	**Teaching Tools:** eTeacherEdition Online Classroom Presentation Toolkit CD-ROM* LabManager™ CD-ROM* Video Lab DVD* Virtual Lab CD-ROM* What's BIOLOGY Got To Do With It? StudentWorks™ Plus Online* **Chapter Assessment Tools:** Classroom Presentation Toolkit CD-ROM* *ExamView® Assessment Suite* CD-ROM **Web-Based Resources:** • StudentWorks™ Plus Online • eTeacherEdition Online • Animations* • The Interactive Time Line* • Interactive Tables* • Online Quizzes • Online Test Practice • Standardized Test Practice • Virtual Labs* • Multilingual eGlossary* • Vocabulary eGames* • Vocabulary eFlashcards • WebQuests • Personal Tutors

While all resources listed are appropriate for English learners, the * indicates resources with a strong visual or hands-on component for EL.

Teaching strategies and activities have been coded for differentiated instruction.

AL Activities for students working above grade level	**OL** Activities for students working on grade level	**BL** Activities for students working below grade level	**EL** Activities for English learners (also ELL)	**COOP LEARN** Activities designed for small cooperative group work

CHAPTER 33

Launch Lab
How does information travel in the nervous system?

Inquiry Launch Lab

For a lab worksheet, use your eTeacherEdition Online.

RUBRIC A rubric for evaluating Launch Labs is found on your eTeacherEdition Online.

Est. Time 20 min

Safety Precaution Approve lab safety forms before work begins.

Teaching Strategies
- This activity works well when students are in groups of four.
- Be prepared to offer guidance as groups begin to brainstorm situations in step 2 of the procedure.

Procedure

1. Form groups of four and assign one student to each of the following roles: a sensor a relayer, an interpreter, and an actor.
2. Brainstorm situations, such as touching a hot object, in which your senses receive information and you respond.
3. Model one situation. The sensor should describe what he or she sensed to the relayer, who passes the information to the interpreter, who decides on a body response. The relayer then passes the response to the actor to act out the response.
4. Repeat step 3 using different situations.

CHAPTER 33

Nervous System

ConnectED
Your one-stop online resource
connectED.mcgraw-hill.com

- Video
- Audio
- Review
- Inquiry
- WebQuest
- Assessment
- Concepts in Motion
- Multilingual eGlossary

Launch Lab
How does information travel in the nervous system?

Your body is bombarded by sounds, odors, sights, tastes, and physical contact almost constantly. The nervous system makes sense of these stimuli, and reacts in ways that promote your survival. In this lab, you will model that communication process.

For a lab worksheet, use your StudentWorks™ Plus Online.

Inquiry Launch Lab

FOLDABLES®

Make a three column chart using the labels shown. Use it to record how drugs affect the nervous system.

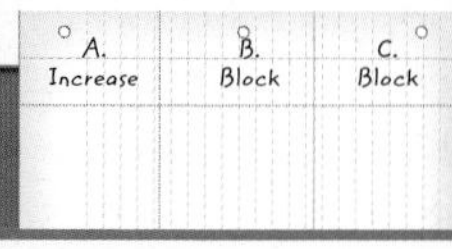

Analysis

Explain what factors could cause the situations that you modeled to vary in speed.
A situation perceived as dangerous or one that caused pain might result in a more rapid nervous system response.

GOING GREEN Try using small print classified ads from the newspaper or copy paper that still has one side clean for making Foldables instead of using new paper each time. Use markers instead of pens if you use newspaper pages.

THEME FOCUS Energy
Energy is required for a nerve impulse to travel the length of a neuron.

BIG Idea The nervous system is essential for communication among cells, tissues, and organs.

Introduce the Chapter

Nervous System Have students examine the chapter opener photo, paying particular attention to the callout of the spinal cord and nerves.

ASK STUDENTS: ***Why do you think the nervous system has so many branches?*** Answers will vary. Students might say that the nervous system is responsible for many reactions.

TELL STUDENTS: ***Nerves in the body enable organisms to interpret the environment around them. The nervous system needs to be in contact with all parts of the body to ensure communication.***

BIG Idea

Maintain Homeostasis

ASK STUDENTS: ***How does the nervous system work with other systems to maintain homeostasis?*** Answers will vary. The nervous system detects changes in both the internal and external environment. The nervous system communicates the nature of these changes with other systems so they can respond appropriately.

THEMES

Scientific Inquiry Scientific investigations are underway to gain better understanding of the nervous system and the diseases that afflict it.

Diversity There's a large diversity of stimuli to which the nervous system can react.

Energy Energy is required for a nerve impulse to travel the length of a neuron.

Homeostasis The nervous system is important for the coordination of other body systems.

Change Changes in the body's internal or external environment can cause an action potential to be produced.

Section 1

MAIN Idea
BL OL AL

Nerve Cell Communication
ASK STUDENTS: ***How do cells communicate with each other?*** through the nervous system
TELL STUDENTS: ***The nervous system is only one way that cells communicate. Some cells communicate when they are physically contacting each other. The endocrine system enables cells to communicate using hormones. The nervous system functions by sending small electrical currents through nerve cells.***

D Develop Concepts
BL OL COOP LEARN

Use Models Have students work in groups of three to five to design and make a model of a neuron. Have a variety of materials available; some suggested items include modeling clay, wax-coated yarn, plastic straws, pipe cleaners, cardboard tubing, marshmallows, and small pieces of candy. Instruct students to include dendrites, the cell body, and an axon in their models. AL This activity can be extended to include other organelles found in nerve cells. Have students use their models to explain how a nerve impulse travels along the nerve cell. Have students arrange their model with other student models to show a nerve network.

Reading Check Neurons are composed of dendrites, axons, and cell bodies. Dendrites receive impulses from other neurons and transmit the signal to the cell body. Axons carry nerve impulses from the cell body to other cells.

Section 1

Reading Preview

Essential Questions

- What are the major parts of a neuron and what is the function of each part?
- How is a nerve impulse similar to an electrical signal, and how does it move along a neuron?

Review Vocabulary

diffusion: the random movement of particles from an area of higher concentration to an area of lower concentration resulting in even distribution

New Vocabulary

neuron
dendrite
cell body
axon
reflex arc
action potential
threshold
node
synapse
neurotransmitter

Multilingual eGlossary

D

Structure of the Nervous System

MAIN Idea Neurons conduct electrical impulses that allow cells, tissues, and organs to detect and respond to stimuli.

Real-World Reading Link Imagine that you wake up in the middle of the night and get out of bed. On your way to the kitchen, you stub your toe. You know right away what happened. Was it one second before you said, "Ouch"? Or was it less than that? How did your brain get the message so quickly?

Neurons

Electricity and chemistry were both involved as your brain received the message that you stubbed your toe. **Neurons** are specialized cells that help you gather information about your environment, interpret the information, and react to it. Neurons make up an enormous communication network in your body called the nervous system.

Figure 1 shows that a neuron consists of three main regions: the dendrites, a cell body, and an axon. **Dendrites** receive signals called impulses from other neurons and conduct the impulses to the cell body. Each neuron contains several dendrites. The nucleus of the neuron and many of the cell organelles are found in the **cell body.** Lastly, an **axon** carries the nerve impulse from the cell body to other neurons and muscles.

Reading Check **Relate** dendrites, axons, and cell bodies.

Figure 1 There are three main parts of a neuron: the dendrites, a cell body, and an axon. Neurons are highly specialized cells that are organized to form complex networks.

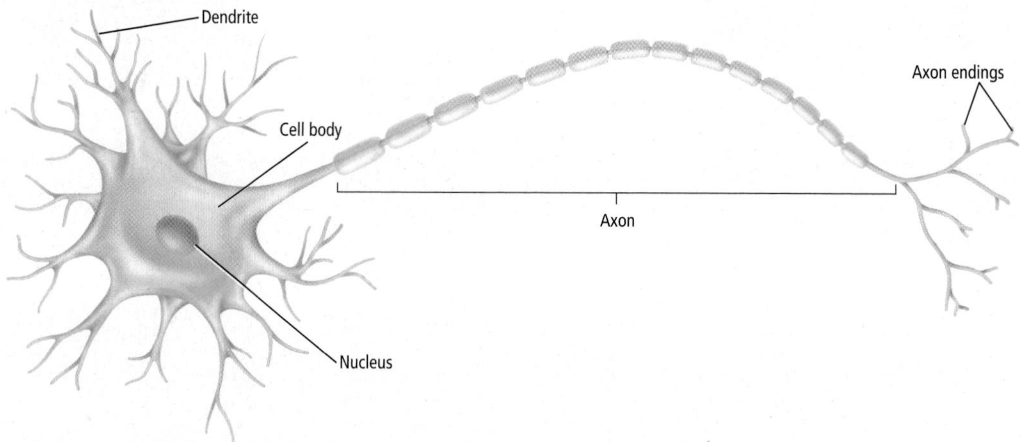

Demonstration

BL OL AL **Nerve Cells** Using a projecting compound microscope, show students a prepared microscope slide of a neuron. Point out the different parts of the neuron: the dendrites, the cell body, and the axon.
ASK STUDENTS: ***Where do you expect to find a synapse?*** before the dendrite or after the axon ***Where are most cell organelles, such as mitochondria and the nucleus, found in a neuron?*** in the cell body Est. time: 10 min

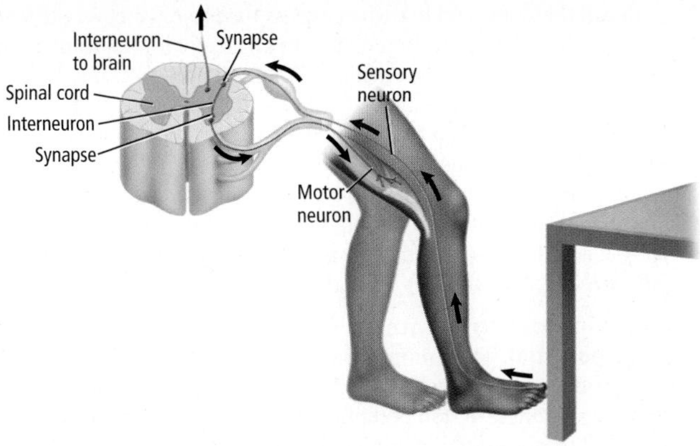

■ **Figure 2** A simple reflex involves a sensory neuron, an interneuron, and a motor neuron. Interneurons can also carry impulses to the brain.
Explain ***how a reflex might be completed before the brain interprets the event.***

Concepts in Motion
Animation

There are three kinds of neurons: sensory neurons, interneurons, and motor neurons. Sensory neurons send impulses from receptors in the skin and sense organs to the brain and spinal cord. Sensory neurons signal interneurons, which are found in the spinal cord and brain. Interneurons carry the impulse to motor neurons, which carry impulses away from the brain and spinal cord to a gland or muscle, which results in a response. Refer to **Figure 2** to follow the path of an impulse for a simple involuntary reflex. The nerve impulse completes what is called a reflex arc. A **reflex arc** is a nerve pathway that consists of a sensory neuron, an interneuron, and a motor neuron. Notice that the brain is not involved. A reflex arc is a basic structure of the nervous system.

A Nerve Impulse

C Connection to Physics A nerve impulse is an electrical charge traveling the length of a neuron. An impulse results from a stimulus, such as a touch or perhaps a loud bang, which causes a person to jump.

A neuron at rest When a neuron is at rest, as shown in **Figure 3,** it is not conducting an impulse. Notice that there are more sodium ions (Na^+) outside the cell than inside the cell. The reverse is true for potassium ions (K^+)—there are more potassium ions inside the cell than outside the cell.

■ **Figure 3** The distribution of Na^+ and K^+ ions, and the presence of negatively charged protein molecules in the cytoplasm, keep the inside of the cell more negatively charged than the outside when a neuron is at rest.

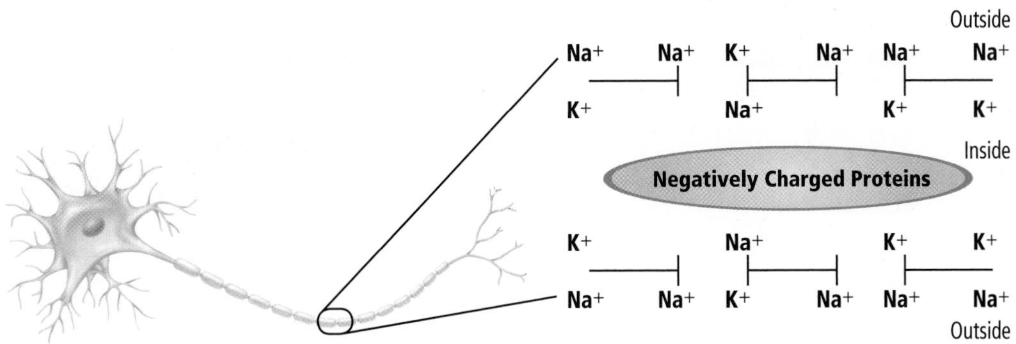

Reading Strategy

EL OL Vocabulary Chart Have students create a three-column chart. In the first column, have students write the vocabulary word from this section. In the second column, have them write the word's meaning as found in the text. In the last column, have students create a memory clue in the form of a sketch or word association that will help them remember what each term means. Example: first column—neurotransmitter; second column—chemical released by a nerve cell that will affect a neighboring cell; third column—*transmit* means to send a signal, *neuro* means nerve.

C Critical Thinking

BL OL Assess
ASK STUDENTS: ***How do you respond when you touch a hot object?*** jerk away from, or drop the object Many reflexes are fast so that they occur before the brain can interpret the situation.
ASK STUDENTS: ***What would be a possible consequence if you had to wait for the brain to interpret the stimulus and signal an appropriate response?*** In this short amount of time, a severe burn could occur.

Concepts in Motion
Animation

■ **Caption Question Fig. 2** The impulse reaches the spinal cord, which sends an impulse to motor neurons in response.

Demonstration

BL OL AL Neural Circuit Prepare a simple electrical circuit using a battery, a switch, electrical wires, and a lightbulb, horn, or buzzer. Press the switch and observe that the light goes on or the horn or buzzer sounds. Point out that this is similar to a simple reflex arc. The switch represents the stimulus, the wires represent neurons, and the lightbulb represents the response.
ASK STUDENTS: ***How does this demonstration differ from an actual neural circuit?*** There are no separate sensory and motor neurons in the demonstration. The demo uses a battery for energy; cells use ATP. ***If I press harder on the switch, does the light get brighter?*** no This is analogous to the all-or-none principle in a nerve cell. Est. time: 5 min

Develop Concepts

OL AL Scaffolding

ASK STUDENTS: ***Describe the distribution of ions inside and outside of a resting neuron.*** There are more sodium ions outside the neuron and more potassium ions inside the neuron. The distribution of these ions is unequal. There are more negative ions in the cytoplasm than there are outside the cell. So, the inside of the neuron is negatively charged in relation to the outside of the neuron. **ASK STUDENTS:** ***Explain the reversal of electrical charges that occurs as an action potential travels along the neuron.*** An action potential results in the opening of channels in the plasma membrane. Positively charged sodium ions rush into the cytoplasm, causing a reversal of charges. ***Analyze what would be the effect if the sodium/potassium pump carried equal numbers of sodium and potassium ions across the plasma membrane.*** There would not be much of a difference in electrical charges inside and outside the neuron. ***Develop a mechanism that would prevent an action potential from traveling along the neuron.*** Accept any mechanism that prevents the influx of sodium ions; some drugs bind to specific receptors on the dendrites, blocking a substance that could trigger an action potential.

Concepts in Motion

Animation

VOCABULARY

SCIENCE USAGE V. COMMON USAGE

Channel

Science usage: a path along which information in the form of ions or molecules passes

Nerve impulses move through neurons as channels open in the plasma membrane.

Common usage: the deeper part of a river, harbor, or strait

Large ships move through a harbor channel.

Recall that ions tend to diffuse across the plasma membrane from an area of high concentration of ions to an area of low concentration of ions. Proteins found in the plasma membrane work to counteract the diffusion of the sodium ions and potassium ions. These proteins, called the sodium-potassium pump, actively transport sodium ions out of the cell and potassium ions into the cell.

For every two potassium ions pumped into a neuron, three sodium ions are pumped out. This maintains an unequal distribution of positively charged ions, resulting in a positive charge outside the neuron and a negatively charged cytoplasm inside the neuron.

An action potential Another name for a nerve impulse is an **action potential.** The minimum stimulus to cause an action potential to be produced is a **threshold.** However, a stronger stimulus does not generate a stronger action potential. Action potentials are described as being "all or nothing," meaning that a nerve impulse is either strong enough to travel along the neuron or it is not strong enough.

When a stimulus reaches the threshold, channels in the plasma membrane open. Sodium ions rapidly move into the cytoplasm of the neuron through these channels, causing a temporary reversal in electrical charges. The inside of the cell then has a positive charge, which causes other channels to open. Potassium ions leave the cell through these channels, restoring a positive charge outside the cell. **Figure 4** shows that this change in charge moves like a wave along the length of the axon.

Figure 4 Follow as an action potential moves along an axon from left to right. Notice what happens to the Na^+ and K^+ and how this changes the relative electrical charges inside and outside the neuron.

Concepts in Motion Animation

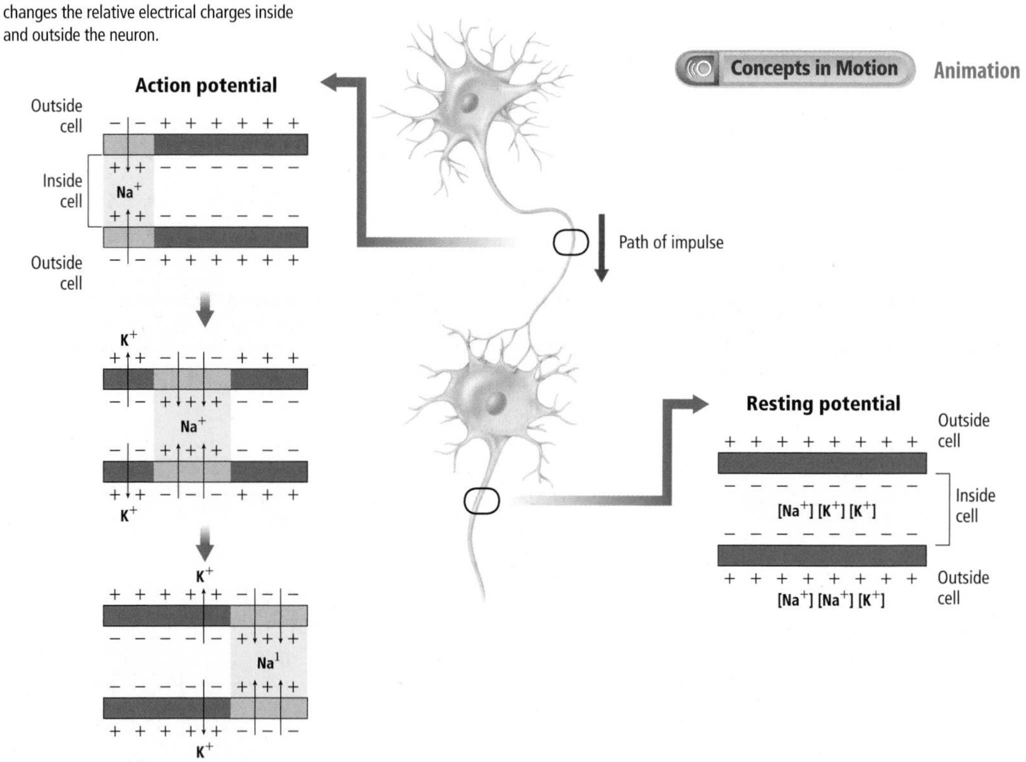

Research Citation

Question Educational research indicates that teachers can use questioning techniques, such as the scaffolding technique described on this page, to challenge students' thinking. These methods require students to move beyond simple recall of information and deepen their understanding of concepts. (Heibert et al., 1997)

Demonstration

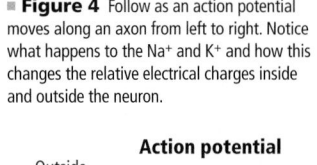

BL OL Sodium Channels Line up dominoes on a table. Push over the first domino, which will cause the remaining dominoes to fall in sequence. **ASK STUDENTS:** ***How does this resemble an action potential?*** When a threshold stimulus causes the first sodium channel to open, this begins a series of events that causes the next sodium channel to open. Est. time: 5 min

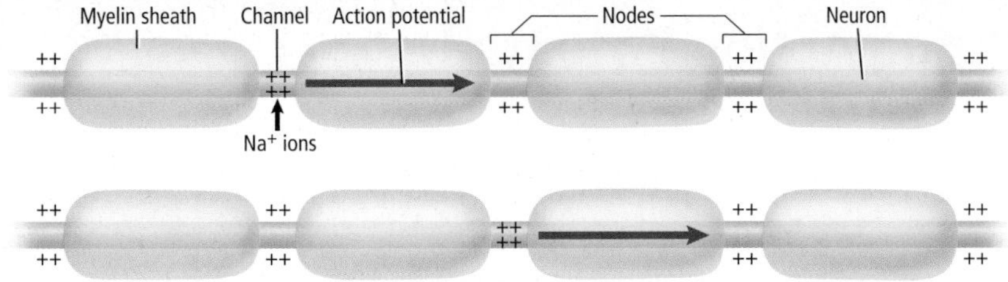

■ **Figure 5** A nerve impulse moves from node to node along myelinated axons.
Explain *what happens at a node when an impulse moves along a myelinated axon.*

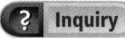

Speed of an action potential The speed of an action potential varies. Many axons have a covering of a lipid called myelin, which forms an insulating layer, called a sheath, around the axon. The myelin sheath has many gaps, called **nodes,** along the length of the axon, as shown in **Figure 5.** Sodium ions and potassium ions cannot diffuse through myelin, but they can reach the plasma membrane at these nodes. This allows the action potential to jump from node to node, greatly increasing the speed of the impulse as it travels the length of the axon.

In the human body, there are neurons that have myelin, and neurons that do not have myelin. Neurons with myelin carry impulses that are associated with sharp pain; neurons that lack myelin carry impulses associated with dull, throbbing pain. The action potentials in these neurons travel much more slowly than they do in neurons with myelin. When you stub your toe, which kind of neurons are involved?

Reading Check **Explain** the relationship of a threshold to an action potential.

Inquiry Launch Lab
Review Based on what you've read about action potentials, how would you now answer the analysis questions?

Mini Lab 1

Investigate the Blink Reflex

Inquiry MiniLab

What factors affect the blink reflex? Have you ever been in a car when an object hit the windshield? You probably blinked. The blink reflex, in which the eye closes and opens again rapidly, is an involuntary response to stimuli that the brain interprets as harmful. Nerve impulses associated with the blink reflex travel short, simple pathways in milliseconds, allowing for rapid reaction time that can prevent eye damage.

Procedure

1. Read and complete the lab safety form.
2. Form a group of three. One person, the subject, should sit behind a 1 m^2 piece of **acrylic.** A second person will monitor and record the subject's responses.
3. The third person should stand 1 m from the barrier and gently toss a **table-tennis ball** so that it hits the barrier.
4. Repeat Step 3 and record the subject's response after each trial.
5. Brainstorm variables that might affect the subject's response. Predict the effect of each on the blink reflex.

Analysis

Interpret Data Did the subject perceive the stimuli in each trial the same way? Explain.

■ **Caption Question** **Fig. 5** Sodium ions and potassium ions cannot diffuse through myelin, but reach the plasma membrane at these nodes. This allows the action potential to jump from node to node, greatly increasing the speed of the impulse as it moves along a motor neuron.

Reading Check The minimum energy required to begin an action potential is a threshold. Once the threshold is reached, the action potential begins.

■ **In-Text Question** Students probably experienced a sharp pain when they stubbed a toe, so some nerves involved would have myelin. The throbbing pain they experienced involved neurons that lack myelin.

Mini Lab 1

Inquiry MiniLab

For a lab worksheet, use your eTeacherEdition Online.

RUBRIC A rubric for evaluating MiniLabs is found on your eTeacherEdition Online.

Est. Time 25 min

Safety Precaution Approve lab safety forms before work begins.

Alternative Materials
1-m^2 transparent barrier of different material, such as thick plastic or wire screen; plastic, perforated ball

Teaching Strategies
- Have students create flowcharts to introduce/reinforce the reflex arc concept and compare experimental trials.
- Have students brainstorm other reflex responses, and reinforce the importance of reflexes to organism survival.

Cleanup and Disposal Students should return equipment to the designated location.

Analysis
Answers will vary based on subject response. Depending on the variable tested, the subject probably will have blinked with greater or less frequency as compared to the initial trial.

Inquiry Launch Lab
Assess Content Development
Assess how understanding has developed when students revisit the Launch Lab analysis questions.

Visualizing Potential Action

Purpose

Students will examine how nerve cells transmit information to other cells.
B.3, C.1

Develop Concepts

BL OL AL

Clarify a Misconception

ASK STUDENTS: ***Are nerve cells in direct contact with other types of tissues?*** Answers will vary. Students might be familiar with the term *synapse,* but they might only associate the term as the junction of two nerve cells. The term *synapse* also refers to a junction of a neuron and other types of cells, such as muscle cells. This type of communication relies on neurotransmitters, not direct contact.

Concepts in Motion
Animation

Writing Support

BL OL **Creative Writing** Have students write a short story about "Ach" the neurotransmitter. The story should start with how Ach is formed, and then describe the cellular events that occur as Ach is released into a synapse and binds to a postsynaptic cell. The story should end with what happens to Ach when it is time for it to be removed from the synapse. A neurotransmitter is formed in a neuron; a vesicle takes it to the end of an axon. When an action potential reaches the end of the axon, the neurotransmitter is released by exocytosis. The neurotransmitter binds to receptors on the postsynaptic cell. The neurotransmitter is then either taken up by the cell that released it, or enzymes in the synapse break it down.

Visualizing Action Potential

Figure 6
To cause the voluntary contraction of a muscle, a signal from the brain creates an action potential in a motor neuron. This action potential travels along the motor neuron, which leads to the release of a neurotransmitter that signals the fibers of the muscle to contract.

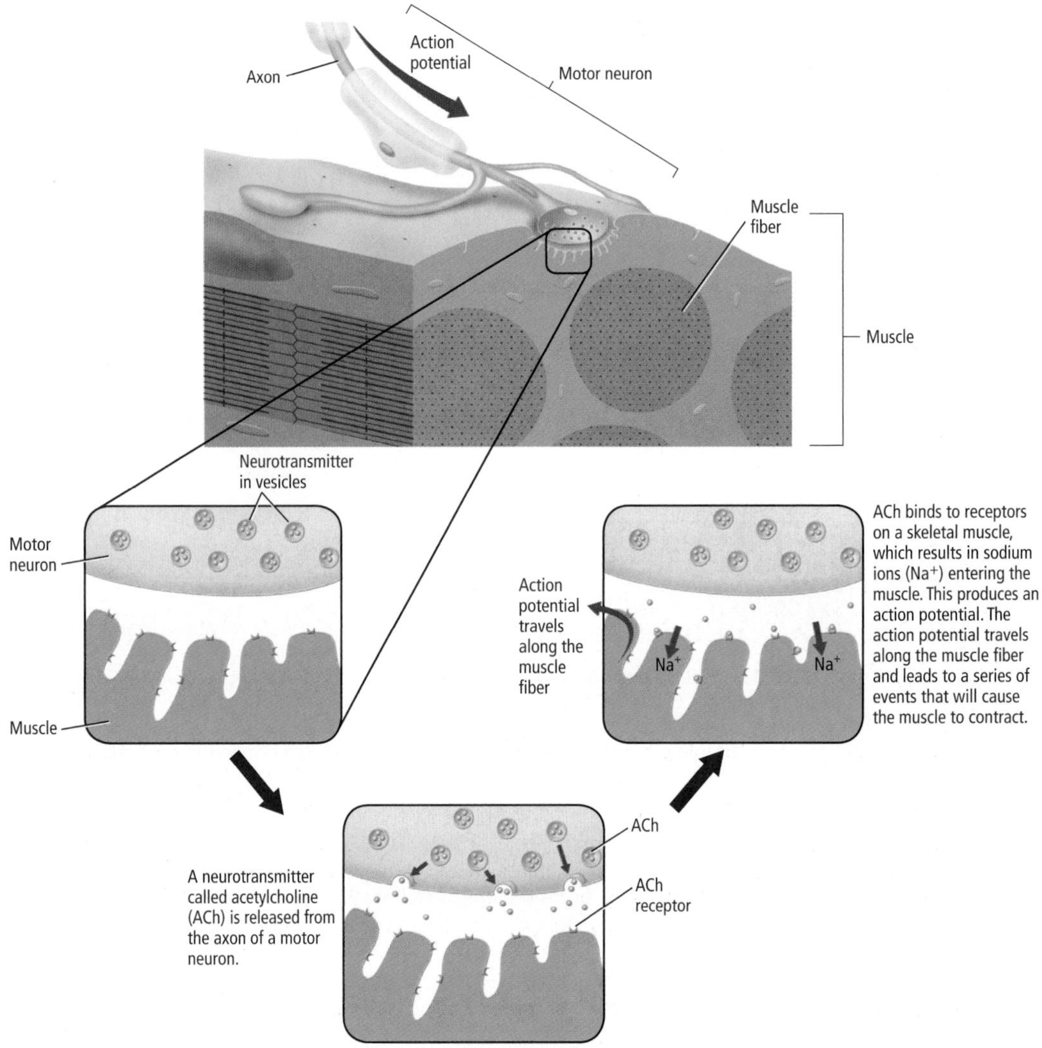

Axon
Action potential
Motor neuron
Muscle fiber
Muscle
Neurotransmitter in vesicles
Motor neuron
Muscle
Action potential travels along the muscle fiber
Na+
Na+
ACh binds to receptors on a skeletal muscle, which results in sodium ions (Na+) entering the muscle. This produces an action potential. The action potential travels along the muscle fiber and leads to a series of events that will cause the muscle to contract.
A neurotransmitter called acetylcholine (ACh) is released from the axon of a motor neuron.
ACh
ACh receptor

Concepts in Motion Animation

Activity

BL OL AL **Presynaptic and Postsynaptic Neurons** Recruit two student volunteers. Have Student A stand on one side of the room. Give Student A two white and two green tennis balls. Have Student B stand on the other side of the room. Student A represents a presynaptic neuron; Student B represents a postsynaptic neuron. The tennis balls represent neurotransmitters. Quietly tell Student B to catch only the white balls, and to let the green ones fall to the floor. Instruct Student A to gently toss the balls to Student B one at a time, in any order.
ASK STUDENTS: ***If the students represent neurons, why is the postsynaptic neuron (Student B) responding only to the white ball (neurotransmitter)?*** This neuron does not have receptors for the neurotransmitter represented by the green ball. Est. time: 5 min

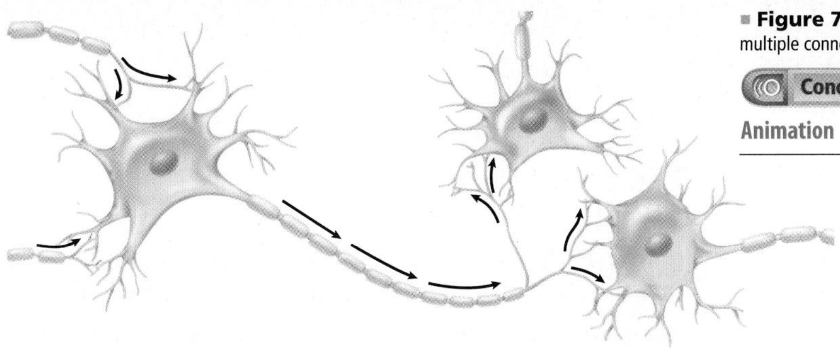

■ **Figure 7** A single neuron can have multiple connections with other neurons.

Concepts in Motion
Animation

The synapse A small gap exists between the axon of one neuron and the dendrite of another neuron. This gap is called a **synapse** (SIH naps). When an action potential reaches the end of an axon, small sacs called vesicles carrying neurotransmitters fuse with the plasma membrane and release a neurotransmitter by exocytosis. When a motor neuron synapses with a muscle cell, as illustrated in **Figure 6,** the released neurotransmitter crosses the synapse and causes a muscle to contract.

Connection to Chemistry A **neurotransmitter** is a chemical that diffuses across a synapse and binds to receptors on the dendrite of a neighboring neuron. This causes channels to open on the neighboring cell and creates a new action potential.

There are more than 25 known neurotransmitters. Once a neurotransmitter has been released into a synapse, it does not remain there for long. Depending on the neurotransmitter, it might simply diffuse away from the synapse, or enzymes might break it down. Some neurotransmitters are recycled and used again. **Figure 7** shows that a single neuron can communicate with many other neurons.

Section 1 Assessment

Section Summary

- There are three major parts of a neuron.
- There are three basic types of neurons.
- A nerve impulse is an electric charge and is called an action potential.
- Neurons use chemicals and electricity to relay impulses.

Understand Main Ideas

1. MAIN Idea **Compare** How is the nervous system similar to the Internet as a communication network?
2. **Infer** why energy is necessary to counteract the diffusion of Na^+ and K^+ ions across the plasma membrane of a neuron.
3. **Predict** If the sensory nerves in a person's foot are nonfunctional, would the person feel pain if the foot was severely burned?

Think Critically

4. **Plan an experiment** that neurobiologists could use to show that an action potential travels faster along a myelinated axon than along a nonmyelinated axon.

MATH in Biology

5. The sciatic nerve extends from the lower spinal cord to the foot. If a person's sciatic nerve is 0.914 m in length and the speed of an action potential is 107 m/s, how long will it take for a nerve impulse to travel the full distance of this nerve?

Concepts in Motion
Animation

S Skill Practice

OL AL Visual Literacy Ask a student volunteer to read aloud the first paragraph on the page. Project the page (available on eTeacherEdition Online) on a screen. As the student describes each step of the events that occur at a synapse, have another student point to the corresponding place on Figure 7.

BL Ask students to list the steps a neurotransmitter goes through.

Formative Assessment

Evaluation

ASK STUDENTS: ***How does an action potential travel along a neuron?*** Action potentials move down the axon. A threshold stimulus produces an action potential, and sodium channels in the plasma membrane open. This causes a reversal of electrical charges, which causes neighboring sodium channels to open. This continues until the action potential reaches the end of the neuron.

Remediation Have students review the text on action potentials and refer to Figure 4. Have them construct a flipbook of the events associated with an action potential.

Section 1 Assessment

1. The Internet and the nervous system are both vast networks used for sending and receiving information. The Internet uses computers and data lines to communicate. The nervous system uses neurons and neurotransmitters to communicate.
2. The ions would naturally move from areas of high concentration to areas of low concentration. The opposite occurs across the cell membrane of a neuron. Forcing ions to concentrate on one side of the membrane takes energy.
3. No. If the sensory neurons do not send impulses to the brain, a person would not feel the pain of the burn.
4. Accept all reasonable experimental designs. Student answers should demonstrate an understanding of how experiments are conducted and should realistically demonstrate how nerves could be tested.
5. $0.914\ m \div 107\ m/s = 0.0085\ s$

Assessment Online Quiz

Section 2

MAIN Idea

BL OL AL Divisions of the Nervous System

ASK STUDENTS: ***How would you divide the billions of neurons in the nervous system into subunits or categories?*** The nervous system can be divided into smaller divisions according to the function and location of nerve cells. **TELL STUDENTS:** ***For classification purposes, the nervous system is separated into two major divisions: the central nervous system and the peripheral nervous system. These two divisions can be further subdivided based on factors such as the direction of the action potential in the neurons or the organs or structures that the neurons contact.***

R Reading Strategy

EL OL Two-Column Notes

Before reading, have students skim the section and list the major headings on the left-hand side of a piece of paper. As they read, have them write key words and phrases from the text under the head on the right side of their paper. **BL** Provide students with a graphic organizer that has the major headings filled in.

Reading Check The CNS is made up of the brain and spinal cord. It coordinates the body's activities.

Section 2

Reading Preview

Essential Questions

- How can the major divisions of the nervous system be illustrated?
- What are the similarities and differences between the somatic nervous system and the autonomic nervous system?

Review Vocabulary

sensory: conveying nerve impulses from the sense organs to the nerve centers

New Vocabulary

central nervous system
peripheral nervous system
cerebrum
medulla oblongata
pons
hypothalamus
somatic nervous system
autonomic nervous system
sympathetic nervous system
parasympathetic nervous system

g Multilingual eGlossary

Organization of the Nervous System

R **MAIN Idea The central nervous system and the peripheral nervous system are the two major divisions of the nervous system.**

Real-World Reading Link Imagine that you are taking a test. When you look at the first question, you are not sure how to answer it. You picture your notes. Your memory clicks and you answer the question. How does this happen?

The Central Nervous System

The nervous system consists of two major divisions. The interneurons of the brain and the spinal cord make up the **central nervous system** (CNS). The **peripheral nervous system** (PNS) consists of the sensory neurons and motor neurons that carry information to and from the CNS.

The function of the CNS is the coordination of all the body's activities. It relays messages, processes information, and analyzes responses. When sensory neurons carry information about the environment to the spinal cord, interneurons might respond via a reflex arc, or they might relay this information to the brain. Some brain interneurons send a message by way of the spinal cord to motor neurons, and the body responds. Other neurons in the brain might store the information.

Reading Check **Describe** the function of the central nervous system.

Figure 8
Brainstorm

For thousands of years, scientists have studied the brain and investigated ways to treat neurological diseases.

Concepts in Motion

The Interactive Timeline

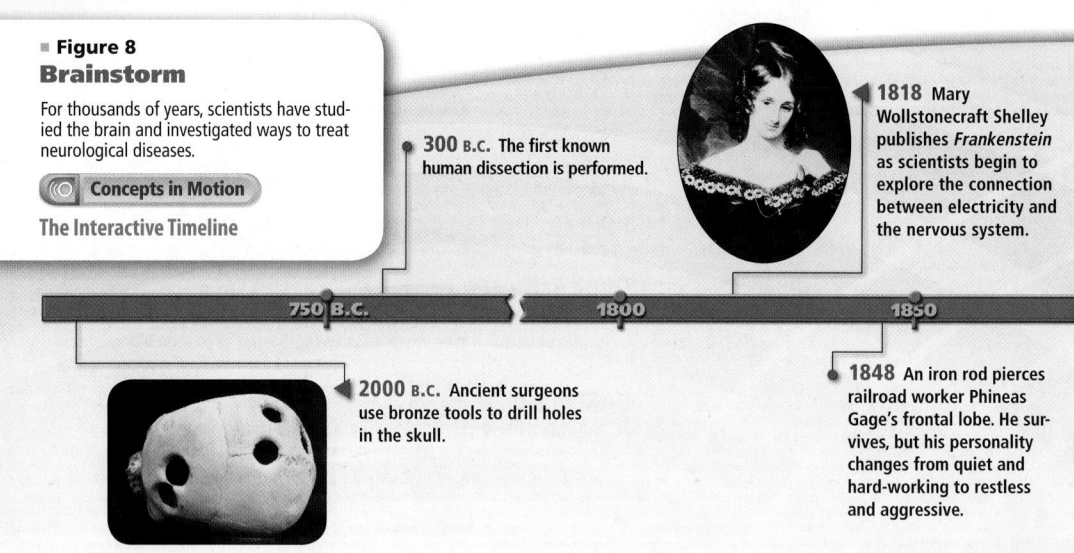

300 B.C. The first known human dissection is performed.

1818 Mary Wollstonecraft Shelley publishes *Frankenstein* as scientists begin to explore the connection between electricity and the nervous system.

750 B.C. — 1800 — 1850

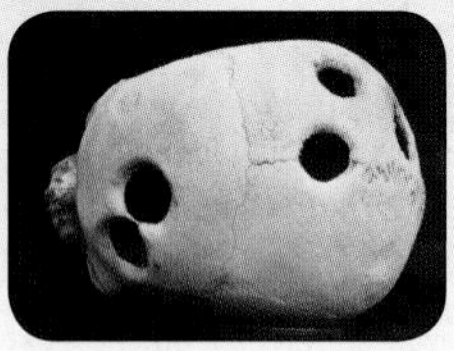

2000 B.C. Ancient surgeons use bronze tools to drill holes in the skull.

1848 An iron rod pierces railroad worker Phineas Gage's frontal lobe. He survives, but his personality changes from quiet and hard-working to restless and aggressive.

Content Background

Teacher FYI Italian scientist Luigi Galvani (1737–1798) was one of the first scientists to make the connection between electricity and nerve impulses. Galvani was dissecting a frog near a spark machine in his lab. The frog's leg touched the spark machine and the leg twitched. Galvani conducted many experiments over the next few years investigating the relationship between electricity and muscle movement. He concluded that all animals have "animal electricity" that causes muscles to move.

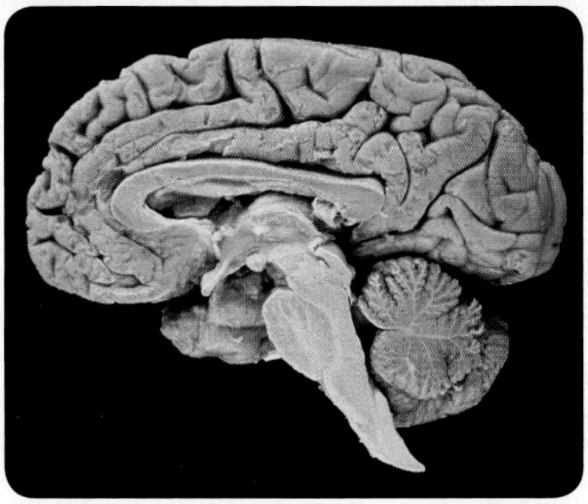

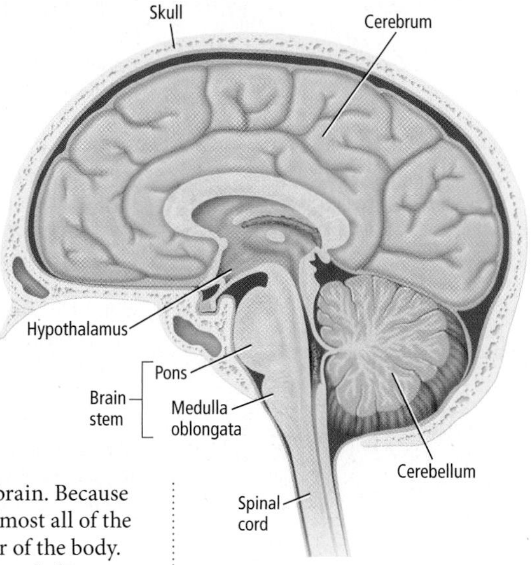

The brain Over 100 billion neurons are found in the brain. Because the brain maintains homeostasis and is involved with almost all of the body's activities, it is sometimes called the control center of the body. Refer to **Figure 8** to learn about important events that have led to understanding of the functions of the brain.

Refer to **Figure 9.** The **cerebrum** (suh REE brum) is the largest part of the brain and is divided into two halves called hemispheres. The two hemispheres are not independent of each other; they are connected by a bundle of nerves. The cerebrum carries out thought processes involved with learning, memory, language, speech, voluntary body movements, and sensory perception. Most of these higher thought processes occur near the surface of the brain. The folds and grooves on the surface of the cerebrum, as shown in **Figure 9,** increase the surface area and allow more complicated thought processes.

Figure 9
Left: A photograph of a human brain shows distinct sections.
Right: The major sections of the brain are the cerebrum, the cerebellum, and the brain stem.

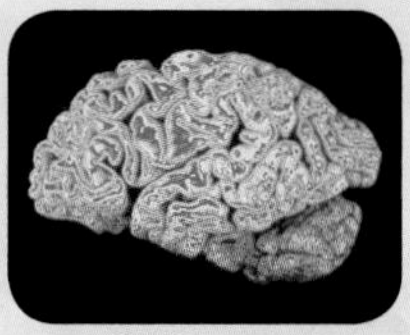

1885 Knee-jerk response becomes one of the principle elements of a neurological exam after the absence of a knee-jerk response is described in syphilis patients.

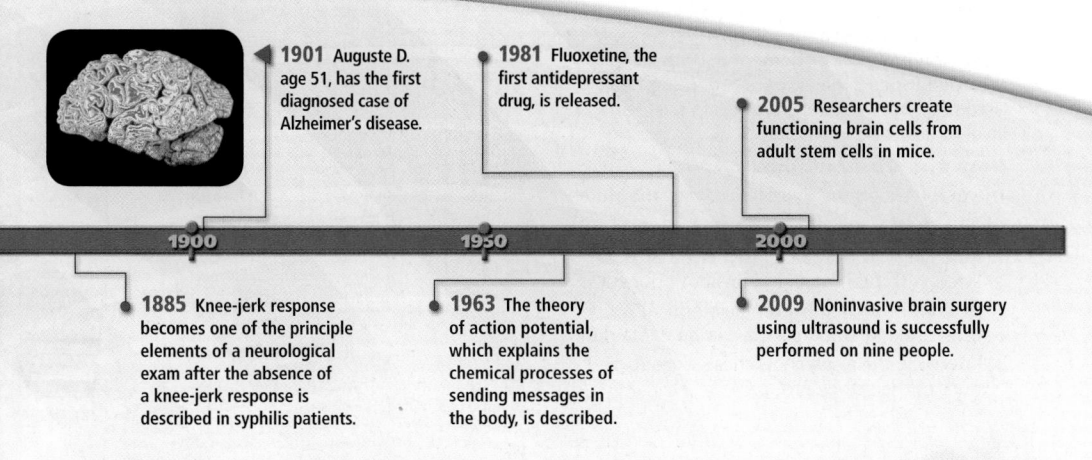

1901 Auguste D. age 51, has the first diagnosed case of Alzheimer's disease.

1963 The theory of action potential, which explains the chemical processes of sending messages in the body, is described.

1981 Fluoxetine, the first antidepressant drug, is released.

2005 Researchers create functioning brain cells from adult stem cells in mice.

2009 Noninvasive brain surgery using ultrasound is successfully performed on nine people.

1900 | 1950 | 2000

Reading Strategy
BL OL AL

Metacognitive Strategies

As students read this page, ask them to think about the way they read and learn information. They should try to identify what helps them understand what they read, such as looking at visuals or rereading the text. Have students share different strategies they use to help them process what they learn.

ASK STUDENTS: ***Do illustrations such as Figures 8 and 9 help you understand the text better? Do you reread paragraphs to grasp key points? What other strategies do you use?*** Answers will vary. Students should express which strategies help them learn.

Develop Concepts
BL OL AL

Clarify a Misconception

ASK STUDENTS: ***Are* nerve *and* neuron *(or* nerve cell*) two terms for the same structure?*** Answers will vary. Some students might think the terms are synonymous. Others might think that a nerve is like a piece of string that carries an impulse. A nerve consists of bundles of nerve cells called neurons. You could illustrate this by having students compare a single string (representing a neuron) to a bundle of strings (representing a nerve).

Concepts in Motion
The Interactive Timeline

Demonstration

BL OL AL **Observe a Brain** Obtain a calf's or sheep's brain from a meat market, butcher, or slaughterhouse. Cut the brain to divide it into two hemispheres, using a scalpel or sharp knife. Show students that the brain has two hemispheres, connected by bundles of neurons.

ASK STUDENTS: ***Why does the brain have so many folds and grooves on its surface?*** They increase the surface area of the cerebellum, which allows for more complex thought processes. Est. time: 10 min

DATA ANALYSIS LAB 1

About the Lab

- Some additional studies suggest that people with less education are more prone to cardiovascular disease. Cardiovascular disease could be associated with reduced blood flow.
- Also see Ott et al. 1995. Prevalence of Alzheimer's disease and vascular dementia: association with education. *British Medical Journal* 310: 970–973.

Think Critically

1. The data shows that the nuns who had lower levels of education and smaller head circumference were more likely to suffer from dementia.
2. Low education attainment might be related to exposures that increase the risk of dementia later in life; greater education might be related to greater neuron connectivity, neuron growth, and mental stimulation throughout the lifetime.
3. Nuns live stable, relatively similar lives without factors that contribute to illness, such as smoking cigarettes or using alcohol or other drugs. Also, they do not experience physical changes related to pregnancy.

Develop Concepts

BL OL AL COOP LEARN

Make a Poster Organize students into small groups. Have students brainstorm a list of possible factors that could contribute to dementia. Students could list factors such as genes, trauma, or chemicals. Have each student in the group select one possible cause of dementia and research it further. Then have each group prepare a poster about risk factors that contribute to dementia.

Reading Check The CNS coordinates all of the body's activities by relaying messages, processing information, and analyzing responses.

CAREERS IN BIOLOGY

EEG Technologist EEG technologists operate electroencephalographs, instruments that record the brain's activity (brain waves). Hospitals and community colleges offer training for people who want to be eligible to work in hospitals and clinics.

The cerebellum controls balance, posture, and coordination, and is located at the back of the brain. The cerebellum is responsible for the smooth and coordinated movement of skeletal muscles and is also involved with motor skills, such as playing the piano or riding a bike.

The brain stem connects the brain to the spinal cord and is made up of two regions called the medulla oblongata and the pons. The **medulla oblongata** relays signals between the brain and the spinal cord. It also helps control breathing rate, heart rate, and blood pressure. The **pons** relays signals between the cerebrum and the cerebellum. The pons also helps control the rate of breathing. Have you ever felt a gagging sensation when your doctor put a tongue depressor in your mouth? The medulla oblongata contains the interneurons responsible for the swallowing, gagging, vomiting, coughing, and sneezing reflexes.

Located between the brain stem and the cerebrum, the hypothalamus is essential for maintaining homeostasis. The **hypothalamus** (hi poh THA luh mus) regulates body temperature, thirst, appetite, and water balance. It also partially regulates blood pressure, sleep, aggression, fear, and sexual behavior. It is about the size of a fingernail and performs more functions than any other brain region of comparable size.

The spinal cord The spinal cord is a nerve column that extends from the brain to the lower back. It is protected by the vertebrae. Spinal nerves extend from the spinal cord to parts of the body and connect them to the central nervous system. Reflexes are processed in the spinal cord.

Reading Check **Review** the functions of the CNS.

DATA ANALYSIS LAB 1

Based on Real Data*

Interpret the Data

Is there a correlation between head size, level of education, and the risk of developing dementia? In a ten-year study, 294 Catholic nuns were assessed annually for severe loss of mental function, or dementia. Data were recorded for each participant regarding head circumference—a measure of brain size—and level of education completed.

Data and Observations

The graph shows the overall results of the study.

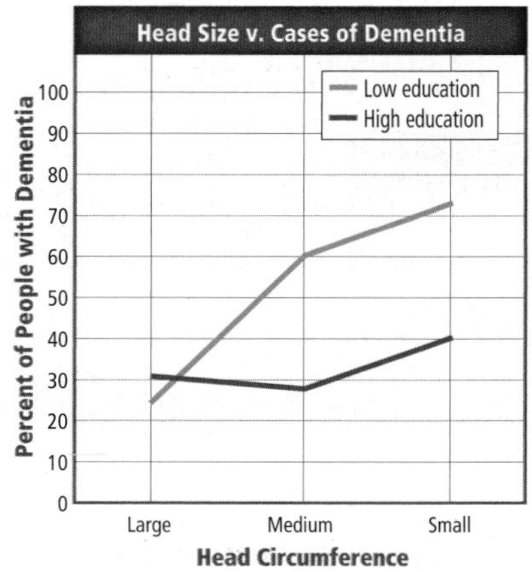

Data obtained from: Mortimer, James A., et al. 2003. Head circumference, education and risk of dementia: findings from the nun study. *Journal of Clinical & Experimental Neuropsychology* 25: 671–679.

Think Critically

1. **Analyze** how the risk of dementia is correlated with brain size and level of education.
2. **Explain** how the difference in education level and risk of dementia can be explained.
3. **Infer** why the researchers chose a group of nuns as their study group.

Demonstration

OL **Brain Surface Area** Hold up a child's football helmet, a child's bicycle helmet, or some similar type of children's helmet. Tell students that the inside surface of the helmet is roughly the same dimensions as the cerebral hemispheres. Now hold up a standard pillowcase. Inform students that the surface area of the brain is approximately the same size as the pillowcase.

ASK STUDENTS: ***How can something as large as the pillowcase fit into something as small as the helmet?*** The pillowcase can be folded so it fits. Fold the pillowcase as many times as it takes to line the inside of the helmet. The large surface area of the brain fits into the smaller cerebral hemispheres because it's folded. Est. time: 5 min

The Peripheral Nervous System

When you hear the word *nerve,* you might initially think of a neuron. However, a nerve is a bundle of axons. Many nerves contain both sensory and motor neurons. For example, there are 12 cranial nerves that lead to and from the brain and 31 spinal nerves (and their branches) that lead to and from the spinal cord, as shown in **Figure 10.** You could think of nerves as two-way streets. Information travels to and from the brain through these sensory and motor neurons.

Refer to **Figure 11** as you read about the peripheral nervous system. This system includes all neurons that are not part of the central nervous system, including sensory neurons and motor neurons. Neurons in the peripheral nervous system can be classified further as being either part of the somatic nervous system or part of the autonomic nervous system.

The somatic nervous system Nerves in the **somatic nervous system** relay information from external sensory receptors to the central nervous system. Somatic motor nerves relay information from the central nervous system to skeletal muscles. Usually, this is voluntary. However, not all reactions of the central nervous system are voluntary. Some responses are the result of a reflex, which is a fast response to a change in the environment. Reflexes do not require conscious thought and are involuntary. Most signals in reflexes go only to the spinal cord and not to the brain. Remember the example of stubbing your toe? Refer to **Figure 2** and note that the illustrated reflex is part of the somatic nervous system.

W **The autonomic nervous system** Remember the last time you had a scary dream? You might have awakened and realized that your heart was pounding. This type of reaction is the result of the action of the autonomic nervous system. The **autonomic nervous system** carries impulses from the central nervous system to the heart and other internal organs. The body responds involuntarily, not under conscious control. The autonomic nervous system is important in two different kinds of situations. When you have a nightmare or find yourself in a scary situation, your body responds with what is known as a fight-or-flight C response. When everything is calm, your body rests and digests.

Reading Check **Compare and contrast** voluntary responses and involuntary responses.

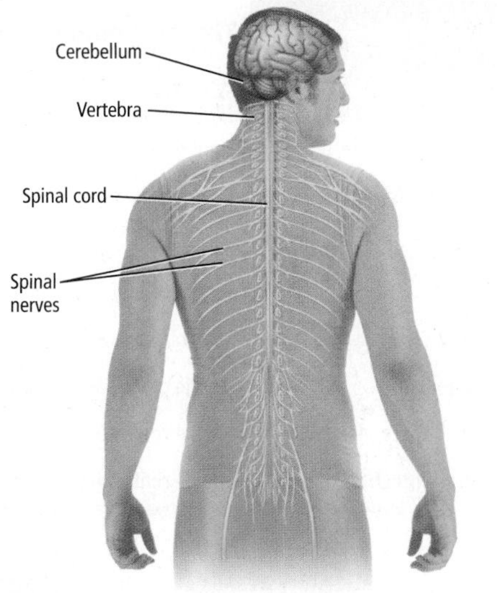

■ **Figure 10** Thirty-one pairs of spinal nerves extend from the spinal cord.
Differentiate *how a neuron is related to a nerve.*

Review Personal Tutor S

■ **Figure 11** Each division of the nervous system functions in the control of the body and the communication within the body.

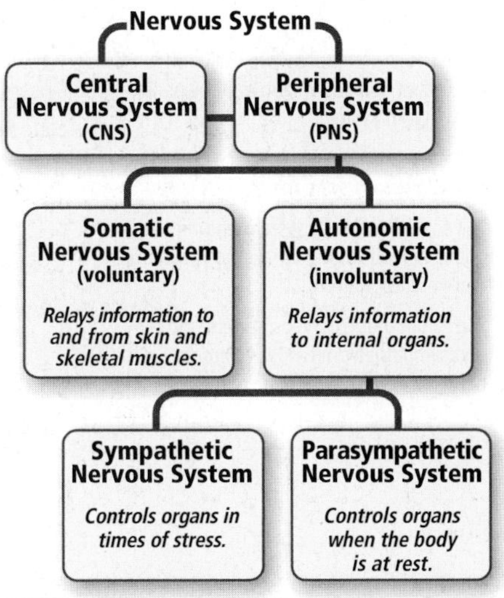

W Writing Support

BL OL AL Make a List Before students read about the autonomic nervous system, discuss what is meant by the "fight or flight" response. Have students make a list of the physiological reactions that they might have experienced when they've been frightened. Compile a master list of all responses, and compare this list to Table 1.

S Skill Practice

BL OL AL Visual Literacy
Have students study Figure 11.
ASK STUDENTS: ***Why are the boxes for CNS and PNS connected directly?*** because the CNS and PNS share information ***Why aren't the boxes containing the somatic nervous system and autonomic nervous system directly connected?*** because those systems are relatively independent of each other

Review
Personal Tutor
Listen to a teacher explain the nervous system.

C Critical Thinking

BL OL AL Compare
ASK STUDENTS: ***When you stub your toe, why is only the somatic nervous system involved in detecting the stimulus but both the somatic and autonomic nervous systems are involved in the response?*** Sensory neurons in the somatic nervous system transmit the nerve impulses from the sensory receptors in your foot to the central nervous system (CNS). Somatic motor neurons carry impulses from the CNS to your skeletal muscles, which make you jerk your foot. The autonomic nervous system transmits nerve impulses from the CNS to organs and glands; in this case, your heart rate might increase and tears might form.

Reading Check Both are the result of impulses carried by neurons. Voluntary responses are under conscious control; involuntary responses do not require conscious thought.

■ **Caption Question Fig. 10** Nerves are made of neurons bundled together.

Differentiated Instruction

Visually Impaired To help students who are visually impaired understand the divisions of the nervous system illustrated in Figure 11, verbally describe the information that is being presented in the figure.

For more tips, see pages 14T–15T.

Concepts in Motion

Interactive Table

Formative Assessment

Evaluation

ASK STUDENTS: ***What are the major divisions of the nervous system and what are the functions of each division?*** The central nervous system integrates stimuli and coordinates body actions and movements. The brain enables thought processes. The peripheral nervous system can be divided into the somatic nervous system and the autonomic nervous system. The sympathetic and parasympathetic nervous systems are divisions of the autonomic system.

Remediation Have students draw an outline of a human body. On the drawing, have students add lines representing the central nervous system and peripheral nervous system. Have them then create a two-column by four-row chart. In the left column, have students indicate the divisions of the peripheral nervous system. In the right column, have them give an example of how each division could be stimulated.

Table 1 **The Autonomic Nervous System** Concepts in Motion Interactive Table

Structure	Sympathetic Stimulation	Parasympathetic Stimulation
Iris (eye muscle)	Pupil dilation	Pupil constriction
Salivary Glands	Saliva production reduced	Saliva production increased
Oral/Nasal Mucosa	Mucus production reduced	Mucus production increased
Heart	Heart rate and force increased	Heart rate and force decreased
Lung	Bronchial muscle relaxed	Bronchial muscle contracted
Stomach	Muscle contractions reduced	Gastric juice secreted; motility increased
Small Intestine	Muscle contractions reduced	Digestion increased
Large Intestine	Muscle contractions reduced	Secretions and motility increased

Connection to Health There are two branches of the autonomic nervous system, and they act together. The **sympathetic nervous system** is most active in times of emergency or stress, when the heart rate and breathing rate increase. The **parasympathetic nervous system** is most active when the body is relaxed. It counterbalances the effects of the sympathetic system and restores the body to a resting state after a stressful experience. **Table 1** compares and contrasts the two systems. Both the sympathetic and parasympathetic systems relay impulses to the same organs, but the overall response depends on the intensities of the opposing signals.

Section 2 Assessment

Section Summary

- The nervous system has two major divisions: the central nervous system and the peripheral nervous system.
- The brain and spinal cord make up the central nervous system.
- The somatic nervous system and the autonomic nervous system make up the peripheral nervous system.
- The sympathetic nervous system and the parasympathetic nervous system are branches of the autonomic nervous system.

Understand Main Ideas

1. MAIN Idea **Compare** the structures of the central nervous system with the structures of the peripheral nervous system and explain their relationships.
2. **Assess** the similarities and differences between the somatic nervous system and the autonomic nervous system.
3. **Explain** Which part of the nervous system is involved in a fight-or-flight response? Why is such a response important?

Think Critically

4. **Hypothesize** what types of tests a researcher could perform to check whether different sections of the brain were functioning.
5. **Design an experiment** to demonstrate the actions of the sympathetic and parasympathetic nervous systems on the iris of the eye.

WRITING in Biology

6. Write a short story that describes a situation involving the heart when the sympathetic and parasympathetic nervous systems work together to maintain homeostasis.

Section 2 Assessment

1. The central nervous system is made up of the brain and spinal cord. The brain has 100 billion connected neurons. The spinal cord is a column of nerves extending from the brain to the lower back. The peripheral nervous system is made of bundles of neurons that branch out to all parts of the body to send information to and from the central nervous system.
2. Both systems are part of the peripheral nervous system. The somatic nervous system communicates sensory information to the brain and instructions from the brain to the skeletal muscles. The autonomic nervous system carries impulses from the brain to the internal glands and organs.
3. The autonomic nervous system. This response is important because it helps respond to danger.
4. Sample answer: Check the cerebellum by testing balance.
5. Answers will vary, but should indicate that parasympathetic response is most active when the body is relaxed.
6. Accept all stories that demonstrate accurate knowledge.

Assessment Online Quiz

Section 3

The Senses

Reading Preview

Essential Questions

- What are the different sensory structures and what are each of them able to detect?
- How is each sense organ able to transmit a nerve impulse?
- What is the relationship between smell and taste?

Review Vocabulary

stimulus: anything in the internal or external environment that causes an organism to react

New Vocabulary

taste bud
lens
retina
rods
cones
cochlea
semicircular canal

g Multilingual eGlossary

MAIN Idea Sensory receptors allow you to detect the world around you.

Real-World Reading Link Who can resist the smell of chocolate-chip cookies baking in the oven? When the aroma travels from the kitchen, you are responding to chemicals in the air. Your senses allow you to be aware of changes in your environment. You are interpreting the environment around you every second. You even were reacting to environmental stimuli before you were born.

D Taste and Smell

Specialized neurons in your body called sensory receptors enable you to taste, smell, hear, see, and touch, and to detect motion and temperature.

The senses of taste and smell are stimulated by chemicals and often function together. Specialized receptors located high in the nose respond to chemicals in the air and send the information to the olfactory bulb in the brain. **Taste buds** are areas of specialized chemical receptors on the tongue that detect the tastes of sweet, sour, salty, and bitter. These receptors detect the different combinations of chemicals in food and send this information to another part of the brain.

The receptors associated with taste and smell are shown in **Figure 12.** Signals from these receptors work together to create a combined effect in the brain. Try eating while holding your nose. You will find that your food loses much of its flavor.

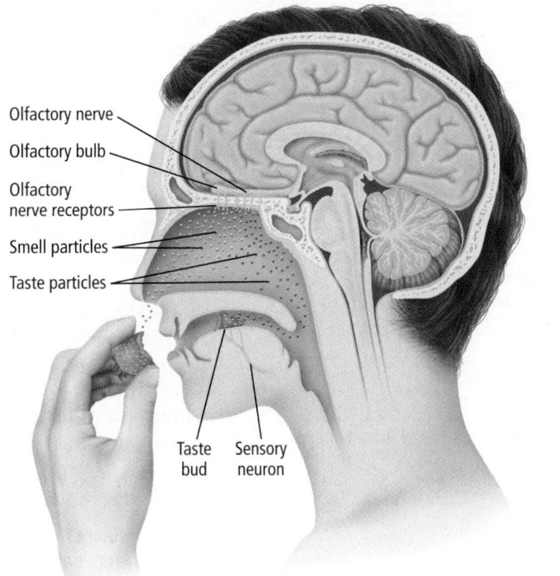

Figure 12 The receptors of taste and smell function together and are stimulated in similar ways. Food is often smelled as it is tasted.

Section 3

MAIN Idea

BL OL AL The Senses

ASK STUDENTS: ***How does the transfer of information or stimuli from the environment to the central nervous system happen?*** An environmental stimulus must trigger action potentials in sensory neurons. The central nervous system can interpret these stimuli and respond accordingly.

TELL STUDENTS: ***Our sensory structures, which include the skin, nose, mouth, eyes and ears, all have specialized structures called receptors.***

D Develop Concepts

BL OL COOP LEARN Activity

Have students work in pairs to try to interpret stimuli. Have one student close his or her eyes and pinch his or her nostrils closed. Instruct the other student to hand a piece of fruit-flavored candy to the first student. Tell this student to taste the candy and try to guess the flavor. Then have the student release the nostrils and guess the flavor again. Students may be able to detect that the candy is sweet or sour, but usually cannot correctly guess the flavor without having the nasal passages open, as one cannot determine specific tastes without also using the sense of smell.

Develop Concepts

BL OL AL

Clarify a Misconception

ASK STUDENTS: ***Do our senses provide a complete and accurate picture of the world?*** Many students will say yes, but others might make a connection that senses are interpreted by the brain. Human sense organs are not capable of detecting all stimuli. One example of stimuli not detected by a human brain would be the low-frequency sound waves given off by some species of whales.

Differentiated Instruction

English Learners Students with limited English language proficiency could require additional resources during lectures or demonstrations. Use visuals or manipulatives to help clarify information.

For more tips, see pages 14T–15T.

"Without education, you're not going anywhere in this world."

—Malcolm X

Video BrainPOP

S Skill Practice

EL BL OL Visual Literacy

Obtain a diagram of the parts of the eye similar to Figure 13. Remove any labels. Have students label the parts of the eye and then use a highlighter to trace the path of light through the eye on their diagrams.

C Critical Thinking

BL OL AL Analyze

ASK STUDENTS: ***What would be the consequence if the retina had less than the usual number of cones?*** Color blindness can result from a deficiency of the cones. ***What would be the consequence if the retina had less than the usual number of rods?*** Poor night vision might be the result.

R Reading Strategy

EL OL COOP LEARN

Question a Partner Organize students into pairs. Have Student A ask Student B to list the structures of the eye in the order that light would pass through them. Allow one minute for a response. cornea, pupil, iris, lens, retina, rods, cones, and optic nerve Have Student B ask Student A to briefly state the function of each structure in the eye. Cornea focuses light through the pupil; pupil lets light into eye; iris regulates size of pupil; lens inverts image and projects it onto retina; retina contains receptors called rods and cones; rods help see in dim light; cones are specialized for color perception; optic nerve carries nerve impulses to the brain

AL Provide students with a diagram of a camera and have them match parts of the camera to analogous parts of the eye.

■ **Figure 13** Light travels through the cornea and the pupil to the lens, which focuses the image on the retina. Rods and cones in the retina send information to the brain through the optic nerve.

S

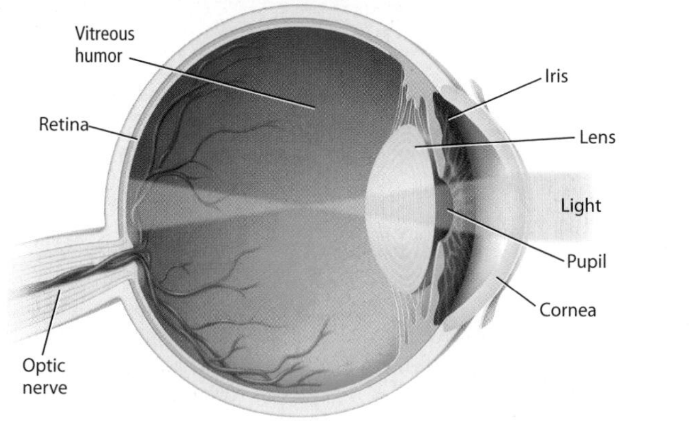

Video BrainPOP

Sight

Figure 13 shows the path of light as it travels through the eye. Light first enters the eye through a transparent, yet durable, layer of cells called the cornea. The cornea helps to focus the light through an opening called the pupil. The size of the pupil is regulated by muscles in the iris—the colored part of the eye. Behind the iris is the **lens,** which inverts the image and projects it onto the retina. The image travels through the vitreous humor, which is a colorless, gelatinlike liquid between the lens and the retina. The **retina** contains numerous receptor cells called rods and cones. **Rods** are light-sensitive cells that are excited by low levels of light. **Cones** function in bright light and provide information about color to the brain. These receptors send action potentials to the brain via the neurons in the optic nerve. The brain then interprets the specific combination of signals received from the retina and forms a visual image. C R

CAREERS IN BIOLOGY

Ophthalmologist An ophthalmologist is a medical specialist who deals with the structure, functions, and diseases of the eye. Four years of specialized training after medical school are required to become an opthalmologist.

Hearing and Balance

Hearing and balance are the two major functions of the ear. From a soft sound, such as whispering, to a loud sound, such as a crowd cheering at a sporting event, specialized receptors in the ear can detect both the volume and the highness and lowness of sounds. Canals in the inner ear are responsible for your sense of balance, or equilibrium.

Hearing Vibrations called sound waves cause particles in the air to vibrate. **Figure 14** illustrates the path of sound waves as they travel through the ear.

VOCABULARY

ACADEMIC VOCABULARY

Interpret

to explain or tell the meaning of

Our senses help us interpret our environment.

Connection to Physics Sound waves enter the auditory, or ear, canal and cause a membrane, called the eardrum or tympanum, at the end of the ear canal to vibrate. These vibrations travel through three bones in the middle ear: the malleus (also called the hammer), the incus (anvil), and the stapes (stirrup). As the stapes vibrates, it causes the oval window, a membrane that separates the middle ear from the inner ear, to move back and forth. In the inner ear, a snail-shaped structure called the **cochlea** (KOH klee uh) is filled with fluid and lined with tiny hair cells. Vibrations cause the fluid inside the cochlea to move like a wave against the hair cells. The hairs cells respond by generating nerve impulses in the auditory nerve and transmitting them to the brain.

Reading Check **Summarize** how each sense organ detects changes in the environment.

Reading Check Taste buds and receptors in the nasal cavity have chemical receptors that detect tastes. Specialized neurons located high in the nose respond to chemicals in the air. Receptors in the retina detect colors and light intensity and send this information to the brain. Sound waves enter the ear and cause its structures to vibrate. When the cochlea vibrates, its fluid moves against tiny hair cells. The hair cells send nerve impulses through the auditory nerve to the brain.

Research Citation

Reading Strategies Educational research indicates that the reciprocal teaching strategy used on this page can help promote independent learning. Students question each other about what they have read, encouraging them to develop a deeper understanding of the material and to practice higher-order thinking skills. (Palinscar and Brown, 1986)

Research bibliography on pages 32T–34T

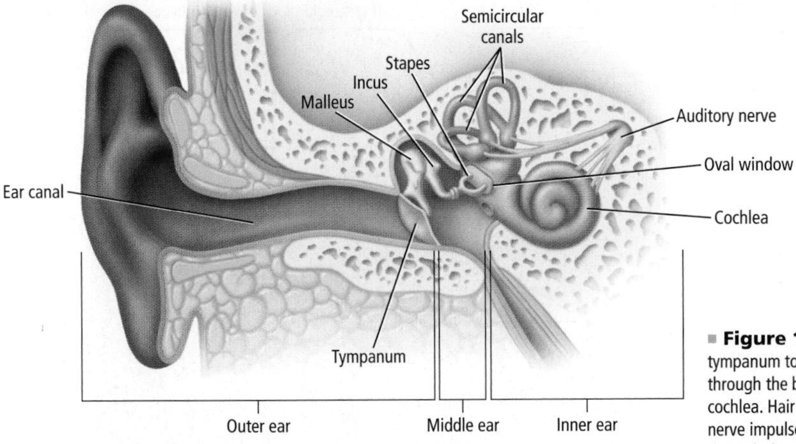

■ **Figure 14** Sound waves cause the tympanum to vibrate, and the vibrations travel through the bones of the middle ear to the cochlea. Hair cells in the cochlea generate nerve impulses, which are sent to the brain through the auditory nerve.

Balance The inner ear also contains organs for balance, including three semicircular canals. **Semicircular canals** transmit information about body position and balance to the brain. The three canals are positioned at right angles to one another, and they are fluid-filled and lined with hair cells. When the position of your head changes, fluid within the semicircular canals moves. This causes the hair cells to bend, which in turn sends nerve impulses to the brain. The brain then is able to determine your position and whether your body is still or in motion.

MiniLab 2

Investigate Adaptations to Darkness

? Inquiry MiniLab

How fast do light receptors in the retina adapt to low-light conditions? The retina contains two types of receptor cells. Cones, adapted for vision in bright light, allow you to perceive color. Rods, adapted for vision in dim light, help you detect shape and movement. The brain combines and interprets nerve impulses received from these cells, making it possible for you to see in various light conditions.

1. Work with a partner. Using a **stopwatch,** time how long it takes to separate 30 **plastic bottle caps** into groups based on color.
2. Record the time, the number of caps in each group, and the percent accuracy of the grouping.
3. Predict changes in the data if the experiment is repeated in dim light.
4. Mix the caps into one group. Dim the lights. Immediately repeat Step 1.
5. Restore light conditions and record the data.
6. Discuss the data with your group. Predict changes in the data if the experiment is repeated after five minutes in dim light. Dim the lights.
7. Wait five minutes and repeat Step 1. Restore the light and record data.

Analysis

1. **Analyze** Graph the time required and the percent accuracy in each trial. How do these variables compare across trials?
2. **Think Critically** Based on the data, compare the action of the blink reflex (**MiniLab 1**) to the action of the eyes in adjusting to low-light conditions.

MiniLab 2

? Inquiry MiniLab

For a lab worksheet, use your eTeacherEdition Online.

RUBRIC A rubric for evaluating MiniLabs is found on your eTeacherEdition Online.

Est. Time 25 min

Safety Precaution Approve lab safety forms before work begins.

Teaching Strategy Demonstrate percent accuracy calculations for students. To calculate, divide the number of caps correctly grouped by the total number of caps, then multiply the result by 100.
Suggested colors for bottle caps: white, yellow, blue, green, and red.

Alternative Materials Math counter chips

Analysis

1. The accuracy was 100 percent in the first trial. It likely decreased in the second trial, then increased in the third trial. The sorting time likely increased in the second trial, then decreased in the third trial.
2. The blink reflex is a more efficient and rapid response than that of adjusting to low-light conditions.

Demonstration

BL OL AL Nystagmus This is a condition which is characterized by rapid, involuntary eye movement, which usually results in some loss of vision. A significant characteristic of nystagmus (nih STAG mus) is that it involves two different physiological systems. One form of this condition causes a person to perceive rotation when there is none, and the eyes rotate to adjust. This phenomenon can be simulated in the classroom. Ask a volunteer to sit on a rotating stool. Rotate the volunteer five to ten times and stop abruptly with the volunteer's eyes facing the class. Have students observe the volunteer's eyes. There should be a temporary jerking movement of the eyes.
ASK STUDENTS: ***What is the sensory structure responsible for the detection of rotation?*** semicircular canals Est. time: 5 min

W Writing Support

OL Narrative Writing Have students examine Figure 15 and write a paragraph describing the different types of receptors in the skin, and give an example of a stimulus to which each type of receptor would respond.

AL Have students write a story about the differences among walking on sand, grass, or hot concrete.

Formative Assessment

Evaluation

ASK STUDENTS: ***How can the body detect a change in position?*** Answers will vary. Sample answer: When the head changes direction, the moving fluid in canals of the inner ear causes hair cells to bend and send nerve impulses to the brain, enabling the brain to determine body position.

Remediation

Have students mark an X about a third of the way down from the top of an empty beaker. The X represents hair cells. Have students pour water into the beaker until it is half full, and then tilt the beaker until the water reaches the X. Explain that the hair cells (X) are stimulated only when touched by the fluid.

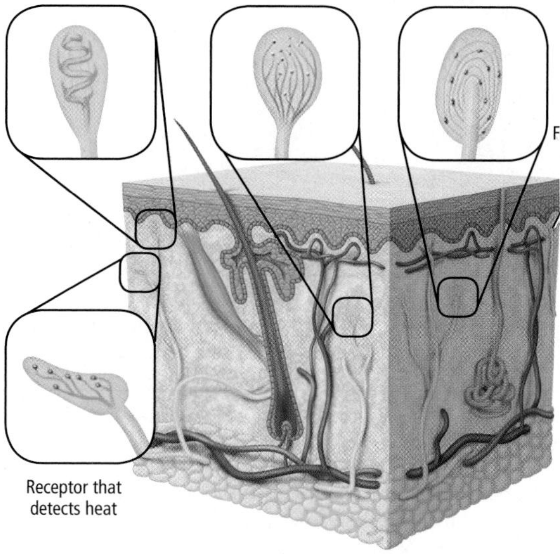

■ **Figure 15** Many types of receptors are found in the skin. A person can tell if an object is hot or cold, sharp or smooth.

W

Touch

Many types of sensory receptors that respond to temperature, pressure, and pain are found in the epidermis and dermis layers of the skin. **Figure 15** illustrates the different types of receptors—some that respond to light touches and others that respond to heavy pressure.

Distribution of receptors is not uniform in all areas of the body. The tips of the fingers have many receptors that detect light touch. The soles of the feet have many receptors that respond to heavy pressure. Pain receptors are simple, consisting of free nerve endings that are found in all tissues of the body except the brain. The brain constantly receives signals from these receptors and responds appropriately.

Section 3 Assessment

Section Summary

- The senses of taste and smell work together.
- The eye has two types of receptors.
- The ear is involved in both hearing and balance.
- The skin has many types of sensory receptors.

Understand Main Ideas

1. MAIN Idea **Diagram** the route of a sound wave from the auditory canal until it causes a nerve impulse to be generated.
2. **Predict** what might be the result if the cornea was damaged.
3. **Analyze** the importance of the kind of receptors found in the fingers.
4. **Explain** why it might be difficult to taste when you have a cold and your nasal passages are clogged.

Think Critically

5. **Construct** an experiment to test the idea that certain areas of the tongue are taste-specific.
6. **Develop a hypothesis** as to why people who have lost their sense of sight still experience sight occasionally. People who once could hear occasionally experience sound. Why might these phenomena occur?

Section 3 Assessment

1. Student diagrams should include all the structures in Figure 14 (except the semicircular canals) in order from the outside of the ear to the inside and describe the function of each structure.
2. Sample answer: Light might be distorted as it enters the eye, causing the image formed in the brain to be distorted.
3. The variety of receptors are important because the fingers encounter many kinds of stimuli.
4. The sense of taste comes from receptors in the mouth and the nasal cavity. If the nasal cavity is blocked, the brain does not get all the information needed to identify a particular taste.
5. Accept all reasonable experiments. Sample experiment: Obtain foods that have one of the distinctive tastes. Using a cotton swab, dab each area of the tongue with each of the tastes. Record which tastes each area can detect.
6. Possible answer: Sight and sound are realized in the brain. People who have lost these senses but occasionally experience images or sounds, may be experiencing a phenomenon in which the brain generates sounds or images without stimuli.

Assessment Online Quiz

Section 4

Reading Preview

Essential Questions

- What are the four ways that drugs can affect the nervous system?
- What are different ways that drugs can harm the body or cause death?
- How, at the cellular level, can a person become addicted to a drug?

Review Vocabulary

threshold: the minimum strength of a stimulus that causes an action potential to be generated

New Vocabulary

drug
dopamine
stimulant
depressant
tolerance
addiction

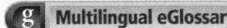

g Multilingual eGlossary

Effects of Drugs

MAIN Idea Some drugs alter the function of the nervous system.

Real-World Reading Link What is a drug? Some people think of illegal substances such as heroin or cocaine when they hear the term *drug*. However, some drugs are common, everyday substances. When you have a headache and take aspirin, you are taking a drug.

How Drugs Work

R A **drug** is a substance, natural or artificial, that alters the function of the body. There are many types of drugs, some of which are illustrated in **Table 2.** Drugs range from prescriptions such as antibiotics, which fight bacterial infections, to over-the-counter pain relievers. There are also illegal drugs, such as cocaine and heroin, which can cause addiction and death. Common substances such as caffeine, nicotine, and alcohol are also drugs.

Drugs affect a person's body in many different ways. Drugs that affect the nervous system work in one or more of the following ways:

- A drug can cause an increase in the amount of a neurotransmitter that is released into a synapse.
- A drug can block a receptor site on a dendrite, preventing a neurotransmitter from binding.
- A drug can prevent a neurotransmitter from leaving a synapse.
- A drug can imitate a neurotransmitter.

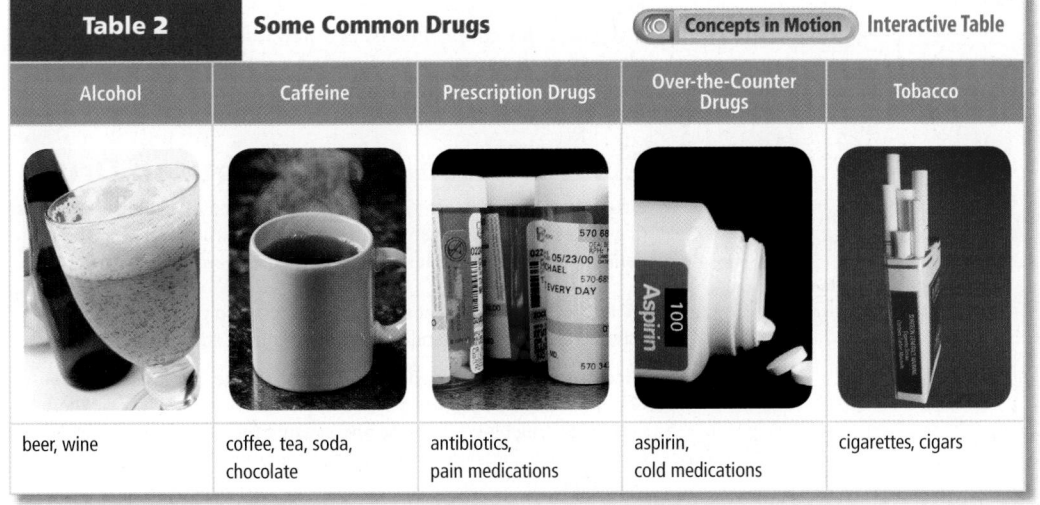

Table 2 Some Common Drugs Concepts in Motion Interactive Table

Alcohol	Caffeine	Prescription Drugs	Over-the-Counter Drugs	Tobacco
		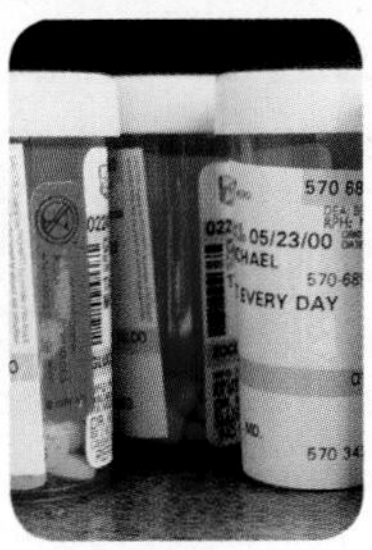	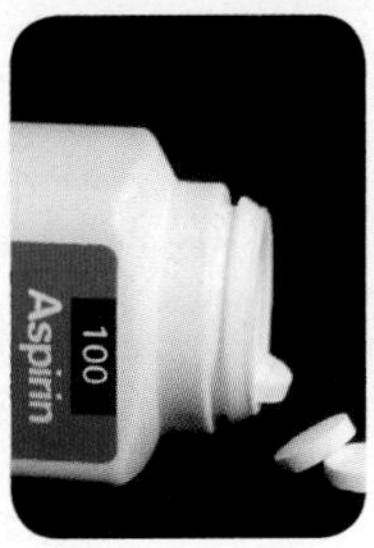	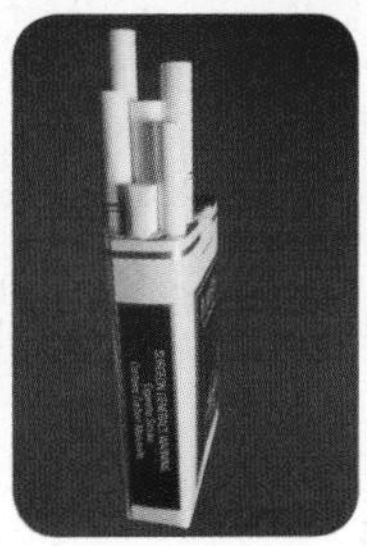
beer, wine	coffee, tea, soda, chocolate	antibiotics, pain medications	aspirin, cold medications	cigarettes, cigars

Section 4

MAIN Idea

BL OL AL Effects of Drugs
ASK STUDENTS: ***What types of substances are considered drugs?*** Possible answers could include types of prescription medications, over-the-counter substances, illegal substances, and common substances such as caffeine. ***Why are these different substances all considered drugs?*** They all affect cells or body functions in certain ways. Inform students that all drugs influence a biological process, but many drugs influence the nervous system. Furthermore, many drugs have hazardous effects when they are combined with other drugs.

R Reading Strategy

BL OL AL K-W-L Chart Have students divide a sheet of paper into three columns. From left to right, the column heads should be *What I* **K***now, What I* **W***ant to Know,* and *What I've* **L***earned.* Instruct students to fill in the left and middle columns before reading this section. After they read, have students fill in the right-hand column.

FOLDABLES®

RUBRIC A rubric for evaluating Foldables is found on your eTeacherEdition Online.

Going Further
SAY TO STUDENTS: ***On the back of your Foldables chart, draw another chart and use it to investigate and report on three commonly abused drugs. How are they obtained? What hazards do they present?***

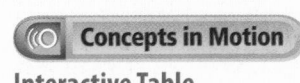

Concepts in Motion
Interactive Table

S Skill Practice
BL OL AL COOP LEARN

Visual Literacy Organize students into groups of three. Have one student in each group examine Figure 4, have another student look at Figure 5, and have the third student examine Figure 16. Have the group members explain their individual figures, then discuss how the figures are related. Have each group prepare a written summary of how the figures are related. Figure 4 describes an action potential, which is necessary for a neurotransmitter to be released into a synapse, as shown in Figure 5. Figure 16 shows how dopamine crosses the synapse to transmit the impulse from one neuron to the next.

Critical Thinking

BL OL AL Analyze

ASK STUDENTS: ***What factors make it difficult for researchers to determine the effects of some types of drugs in humans?*** Answers will vary. Some students may say that it is unethical to conduct controlled experiments with human beings.

TELL STUDENTS: ***Very strict controlled experiments are conducted on humans before a prescription drug is legalized. Controlled studies are not often possible with illegal drugs.***

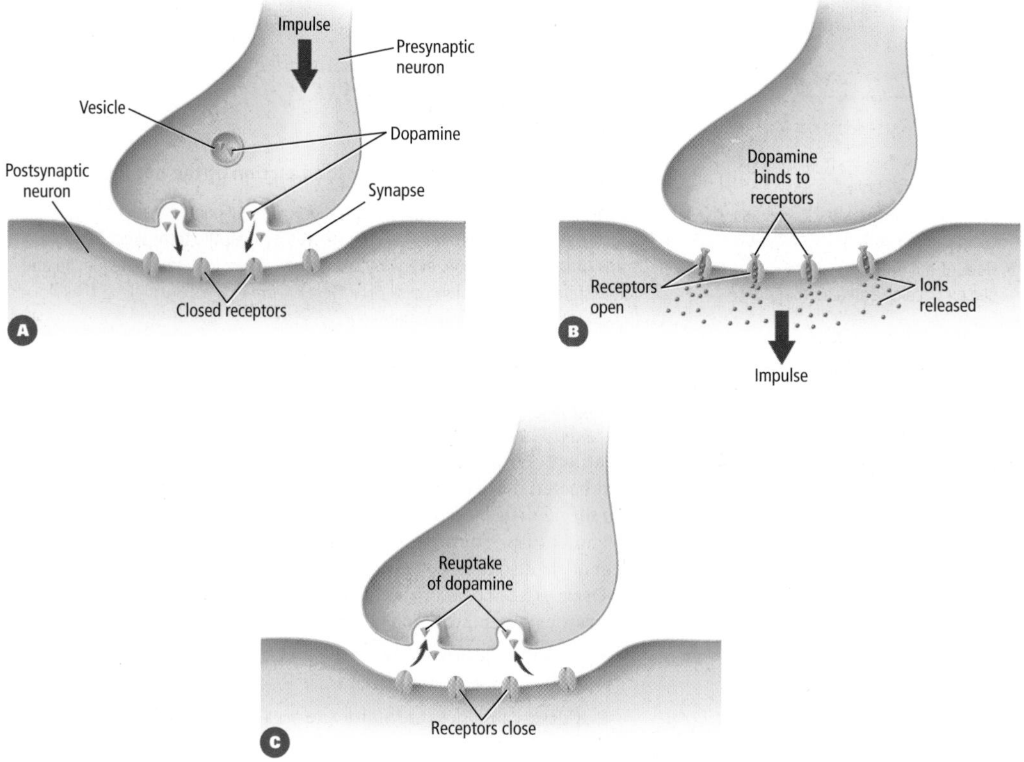

Figure 16 Dopamine crosses the gap from one neuron and binds to receiver sites, or receptors, on the membrane of another neuron. This occurs at a synapse.

S

VOCABULARY
WORD ORIGIN
dopamine
dopa– refers to an amino acid
–amine refers to a derivative of ammonia

Many drugs that affect the nervous system influence the level of a neurotransmitter called dopamine. **Dopamine** (DOH puh meen) is a neurotransmitter found in the brain that is involved with the control of body movements and other functions. Dopamine also is strongly involved with feelings of pleasure or reward. Dopamine normally is removed from a synapse by being reabsorbed by the neuron that released it, as illustrated in **Figure 16.**

Classes of Commonly Abused Drugs

Drug abuse does not necessarily involve the use of illegal drugs. Any use of a drug for reasons other than legitimate medical purposes, whether deliberate or unintentional, can be considered abuse of that drug.

Stimulants Drugs that increase alertness and physical activity are **stimulants. Figure 17** indicates some common stimulants.

Nicotine Nicotine in cigarette and cigar smoke increases the amount of dopamine released into a synapse. Nicotine also constricts blood vessels, raising blood pressure and causing the heart to work harder than normal. Cigarette smoking has been linked to about 90 percent of all lung cancer cases.

Demonstration

BL OL AL Vasoconstriction Attach a small length of rubber tubing or garden hose to a water faucet. Turn on the faucet part way and let water flow freely through the tube. Then partially clamp the tube so the water flow is restricted but not completely shut off. Do not adjust the faucet. Inform students that the hose represents a blood vessel; the clamp has the same effect as nicotine.

ASK STUDENTS: ***What harmful effect may nicotine have on the body?*** Answers may vary. Possible answer: Nicotine can reduce blood flow. Reduced blood flow reduces the amount of oxygen getting to cells and increases blood pressure. Est. time: 10 min

Caffeine The most commonly used, and often abused, stimulant is caffeine. Caffeine is found in coffee, tea, some soft drinks, and even some foods such as chocolate. Caffeine works by binding to adenosine receptors on neurons in the brain. Adenosine slows down neural activity, causing drowsiness. When caffeine binds to these receptors, it has the opposite effect. It makes users feel awake and alert. Caffeine also temporarily raises epinephrine (adrenaline) levels in the body, giving a quick burst of energy that soon wears off.

Depressants Drugs that tend to slow down the central nervous system are **depressants.** These drugs can lower blood pressure, interrupt breathing, and slow the heart rate. Depressants can relieve anxiety, but they also can cause the noticeable effect of sedation.

Alcohol Alcohol is a depressant. It affects the central nervous system and is one of the most widely abused drugs in the world today. It is produced by the fermentation of grains and fruits. Alcohol is known to affect at least four different neurotransmitters, resulting in a feeling of relaxation and sluggishness. Short-term alcohol use impairs judgment, coordination, and reaction time. Long-term effects of alcohol abuse include a reduction in brain mass, liver damage, stomach and intestinal ulcers, and high blood pressure. Consumption of alcohol during pregnancy is the cause of fetal alcohol syndrome, which can result in damage to a baby's brain and nervous system.

Inhalants Inhalants are chemical fumes that have an influence on the nervous system. Exposure to inhalants might be accidental as a result of poor ventilation. Inhalants generally work by acting as a depressant on the central nervous system. Inhalants might produce a short-term effect of intoxication, as well as nausea and vomiting. Death can occur. Long-term exposure to inhalants can cause memory loss, hearing loss, vision problems, peripheral nerve damage, and brain damage. **D**

Study Tip

Chart Create a three-column chart titled *The Effects of Drugs.* Before reading this section, check the section heads, the boldfaced terms, and figures. Identify what you know about drugs in the first column. In the second column, list what you would like to know. In the third column, write what you have learned after studying this section.

■ **Figure 17** There are many common stimulant drugs, such as coffee, tea, cocoa, and chocolate.

D Develop Concepts

BL OL AL

Clarify a Misconception

ASK STUDENTS: ***Are over-the-counter drugs safer than prescription drugs?*** no Students might answer yes because over-the-counter drugs are easier to obtain. Students will learn that both over-the-counter drugs and prescription drugs can have serious side effects and can even result in death. Also, combining drugs can cause hazardous side effects. Not all the potential side effects or risk factors are listed on the packaging of over-the-counter drugs. Since over-the-counter drugs can be purchased without a doctor's instruction, many are misused.

Develop Concepts

BL OL AL **Make a Poster** As a class, brainstorm a list of drugs that are known to cause harm to the body. Alcohol, nicotine, marijuana, cocaine, and methamphetamine are mentioned in the text, others can be added to the list. Have each student select one drug from the list and make an educational poster clearly emphasizing the health risks of the drug. Posters can be displayed and discussed as space and time permit.

? Inquiry **Video Lab** In this lab, students test the effects of drugs on *Daphnia*.

Differentiated Instruction

Hearing Impaired During class discussions like the one described on this page, take measures to ensure that students who are hearing impaired can take part in and benefit from class discussion. Be sure to look at students when you speak, use visual cues, and write any terms or helpful information on the board.

For more tips, see pages 14T–15T.

C Critical Thinking

AL Create a Model Dopamine is a neurotransmitter associated with many types of addiction. Have students create a model that explains the dopamine cycle as it relates to addiction. Then have students propose a possible therapy technique that could help addicts recover from their reliance on dopamine. Dopamine is associated with pleasure. Many drugs increase the amount of dopamine in the body, resulting in the addict's getting used to the higher levels. When dopamine levels start to drop, the person uses more of the drug to get the same level of pleasure. One line of therapy could be to increase pleasure in the addicted person's life rather than relying on drugs to achieve this. **EL COOP LEARN** Have students work in cooperative groups to complete the activity.

DATA ANALYSIS LAB 2

About the Lab

- Also see Ling, et al. 2003. Effects of alcohol on subjective ratings of prospective and everyday memory deficits. *Alcohol Clin Exp Res* 27: 970–974.

Think Critically

1. The amount of brain activity is lower in the heavy drinkers than in the nondrinkers.
2. There could be long-term damage to areas of the brain that involve memory.

Reading Check A neurotransmitter diffuses across a synapse and binds to the receptors on the dendrite of a neighboring neuron. This initiates an action potential.

Illegal drugs Amphetamines and cocaine both increase dopamine levels, and both prevent dopamine from being reabsorbed, so it remains in the synapses. This ultimately increases the levels of dopamine in the brain, which results in a feeling of pleasure and well-being.

The use of cocaine and amphetamines has short-term and long-term effects. Cocaine abuse might result in disturbances in heart rhythm, heart attacks, chest pain, respiratory failure, strokes, seizures, headaches, abdominal pain, and nausea. Abuse of amphetamines might result in rapid heart rate, irregular heartbeat, increased blood pressure, and irreversible, stroke-producing damage to small blood vessels in the brain. Elevated body temperature, called hyperthermia, and convulsions can result from an amphetamine or cocaine overdose, and if not treated immediately, this can result in death. Abusers also can experience episodes of violent behavior, paranoia, anxiety, confusion, and insomnia. It can take a year or longer for users of methamphetamine—the strongest type of amphetamine—to recover after quitting the drug.

Marijuana is the most-used illegal drug in the United States. The active chemical in marijuana is tetrahydrocannabinol, or THC. Smoking marijuana quickly gets THC into the bloodstream, where it is carried to the brain. THC binds to receptors on neurons in the brain, which produces the effect of intense pleasure. These receptors are found on neurons associated with many body activities. Short-term effects of marijuana use include problems with memory and learning, loss of coordination, increased heart rate, anxiety, paranoia, and panic attacks. Long-term smoking of marijuana might also cause lung cancer. C

Reading Check **Explain** the function of a neurotransmitter.

DATA ANALYSIS LAB 2

Based on Real Data*

Interpret the Data

Can the effects of alcohol use be observed? Two groups of students, ages 15–16, were given memory tasks to perform. Group 1 included heavy drinkers. Group 2 were nondrinkers. The images indicate typical results of comparing students from each group. The amount of the red-pink color indicates the amount of brain activity associated with performing the memory tasks.

Think Critically

1. **Describe** the difference between the brain activity of heavy drinkers and the brain activity of nondrinkers.
2. **Analyze** what long-term consequences might result from drinking as a teen. Base your answer on these results.

Data and Observations

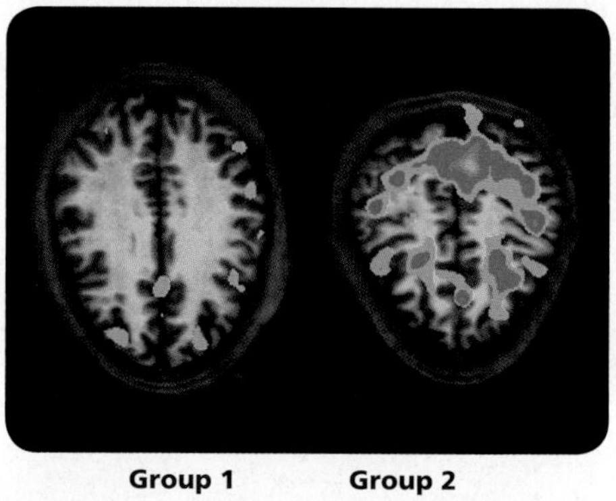

*Data obtained from: Brown, S.A., et al. 2000. Neurocognitive functioning of adolescents: effects of protracted alcohol use. *Alcoholism: Clinical and Experimental Research*. 24:164-171.

Activity

BL OL AL Effects of Drug at a Synapse Have two student volunteers stand on opposite sides of the room. Student A represents a pre-synaptic neuron, and Student B a postsynaptic neuron. Give Student A six tennis balls. Instruct Student A to gently toss a ball to Student B. Have Student B hold on to the ball for a moment, and then toss it back. Have students repeat this several times. This represents the reuptake of a neurotransmitter. Next, have Student A toss all the balls, one by one, to Student B. Instruct Student B to catch the balls and then toss them back to Student A. Have Student A refuse to pick them up. This represents a drug that blocks the reuptake of a neurotransmitter. Est. time: 10 min

Tolerance and Addiction

Tolerance occurs when a person needs more and more of the same drug to get the same effect. The dosage needs to increase because the body becomes less responsive to the drug. Drug tolerance can lead to addiction.

Addiction The psychological and physiological dependence on a drug is **addiction.** Current research suggests that the neurotransmitter dopamine is involved with most types of physiological addiction. Recall that dopamine normally is removed from a synapse as it is reabsorbed by the neuron that released it. However, certain drugs prevent that reabsorption, which results in an increase of dopamine in the brain. A person addicted to drugs derives pleasure from increased levels of dopamine and builds up a tolerance to the drug. As a result, the person takes more of the drug. When people who are addicted try to quit, the levels of dopamine decrease, making it difficult to resist going back to the drug.

Addictions can also be psychological. An individual with a psychological dependence on a drug such as marijuana has a strong desire to use the drug for emotional reasons. Both physiological and psychological dependence can affect emotional and physical health. Both types are strong, making it difficult to quit a drug.

Treatment People who are either psychologically or physiologically dependent on a drug experience serious withdrawal symptoms without it. It is very difficult for dependent users to quit on their own. They might be able to quit for short periods of time, but they are likely to use the drug again. Medical supervision is necessary when people who are psychologically and physiologically dependent on a drug try to quit.

The best way to avoid an addiction is never to use drugs in the first place, even when pressured to use them. Encourage people who abuse drugs to seek treatment for drug dependency. Physicians, nurses, counselors, clergy, and social workers are trained to direct people to the resources they need to get help, as illustrated in **Figure 18.** W

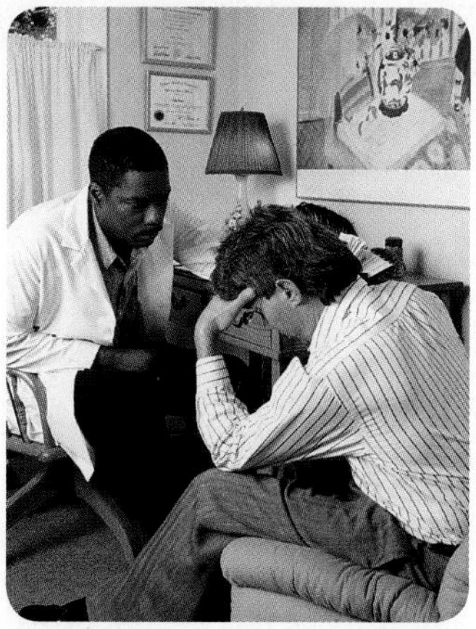

Figure 18 Counseling often is necessary to break an addiction.

Section 4 Assessment

Section Summary

- Drugs can affect the nervous system in four ways.
- Common substances such as caffeine and alcohol are considered drugs.
- Many addictive drugs increase levels of dopamine.
- Drug abuse has many negative consequences.
- A person can become psychologically and physiologically addicted to drugs.

Understand Main Ideas

1. MAIN Idea **Describe** four ways that drugs can influence the nervous system.
2. **Compare** the actions of cocaine, amphetamines, and nicotine.
3. **Explain** why the effects of stimulants and depressants do not necessarily counteract each other.
4. **Infer** why students who abuse amphetamines are likely to experience failing grades.
5. **Discuss** how, on a cellular level, a person can become addicted to a drug.

Think Critically

6. **Design an experiment** Drugs affect people in different ways and at different rates. How would you design an experiment to determine the rate at which a drug is delivered to different body tissues?

W Writing Support

OL AL COOP LEARN

Persuasive Writing In small groups or as a class, discuss the regulations banning smoking. Have each student write a persuasive letter that could be sent to a local government official supporting or opposing smoking bans. Students should use one reference book in addition to their textbooks when they conduct their research. The potential biological effects and health risks of cigarette smoke and the rights of individuals need to be discussed in the letters.

Formative Assessment

Evaluation

ASK STUDENTS: ***What are two ways drugs can increase the concentration of a neurotransmitter in a synapse?*** A drug can cause a neuron to increase its production, and release of a neurotransmitter or a drug might block the reuptake of a neurotransmitter so it remains in the synapse.

Remediation Have students make a two-column chart. In the left column, have them list cocaine, nicotine, alcohol, and caffeine. In the right column, have them indicate the mechanism of each drug, using their textbooks for reference.

Section 4 Assessment

1. A drug can increase the amount of a neurotransmitter released into a synapse; block a neurotransmitter receptor site on a dendrite; prevent a neurotransmitter from leaving a synapse; and imitate a neurotransmitter.
2. Cocaine and amphetamines prevent dopamine from being reabsorbed, so dopamine remains in the synapse. Nicotine and some amphetamines increase the release of dopamine.
3. Stimulants and depressants are not biological opposites. Common stimulants increase the level of dopamine. Depressants might not affect dopamine levels at all.
4. Students abusing amphetamines quickly become addicted and suffer from insomnia, paranoia, anxiety, and confusion.
5. Some drugs prevent reabsorption of dopamine, therefore increasing the amount of dopamine in the brain. As a result, a person needs more of the drug to derive pleasure.
6. Accept all reasonable responses. Sample answer: The experiment could use a mildly radioactive version of the drug. After administering the drug, its movement could be monitored.

Assessment Online Quiz

Purpose
Students will describe the science behind brain-controlled limb technology. Students analyze the process by which a brain-controlled implant works.
E.2

Anticipatory Guide
ASK STUDENTS: ***How many of you have seen movies that feature creatures with bionic limbs?*** Many students probably will have seen them. ***What is realistic and unrealistic about these limbs?*** Students might say that the limbs are stiff-looking or perhaps very strong.
SAY TO STUDENTS: ***Brainstorm possibilities for creating new limbs.*** Make a list of students' ideas. Accept any reasonable ideas at this point.

Background
Currently, the technology of this brain-controlled device involves about 500 neurons. If the device were applied to people, it would help them grasp a cup of coffee or brush their teeth. However, if a pianist who suffered a spinal-cord injury wanted to play the piano again, then 500 neurons would not be nearly enough.

CUTTING-EDGE BIOLOGY

BRAIN-CONTROLLED LIMBS: NO LONGER SCIENCE FICTION

For centuries, the only recourse for a person who loses an arm or leg to accident or disease has been a prosthetic, or artificial, limb. These limbs help people regain some of the functions of real arms or legs. However, their effectiveness is limited because the limbs are not controlled by the brain. Scientific research is changing such limits.

What are brain-controlled prostheses?
Scientists are developing thought-controlled robotic arms with fully mobile shoulders and elbows. Each hand is in the shape of a gripper that functions much like a real hand. Used primarily with monkeys and now with humans in research, these arms are connected to the brain using implants.

The implants are collections of hundreds of electrodes that are as thin as a human hair. The electrodes are placed in the motor cortex of the brain 3 mm beneath the skull to pick up nerve signals in the brain. The implant transmits these signals to a computer. A mathematical procedure translates them into instructions for the arm. For example, within 30 milliseconds of the command, the arm is able to pick up food and bring it to the mouth. The arm is equipped with several motors and moves in three dimensions, just like a real arm. The arm responds and brings food to the patient when the patient thinks about the food.

How were the arms tested? While testing the robotic arms, patients used his or her own arms to experiment with a joystick and to get used to working with the robotic arm. Once a patient had practiced with the joystick, the scientists removed it and gently restrained the patient's own arm. To the scientists' amazement, the robotic arm began to move as a result of the patient's thoughts.

Scientists want to refine the technology so the system is completely wireless. One concern is that the current electrodes last only about six months.

How might these brain-controlled devices help society? Scientists plan to continue researching and using these devices with humans in the next few years. The hope is that these brain-computer interfaces (BCI) will help people who are parapalegic regain some movement or ability to communicate with others. Brain implants could also allow hand-free control of small robots that could perform everyday tasks. BCIs also might benefit people who are not paralyzed or who have not lost a limb. BCIs could also be used to perform tasks in dangerous environments or war zones.

MAKE A MODEL
Create a model of a device similar to that described in this feature. Use materials provided by your teacher or from your home. Write a 200-word description of your invention, how it works, and some benefits of this invention.

WRITING in Biology

RUBRIC Use the modifiable rubric found on your eTeacherEdition Online to assess writing assignments.

Follow-Up Discussion
Organize students into groups. Have each group discuss ideas, conduct research on their ideas, pick the best idea, and collaborate on writing a newspaper article about their model. Assign roles to each person so each contributes equally to the article. Have the groups conduct further research online. Group members can email their findings to one another and compile their article electronically. Have students read the news articles of other groups, and work together to compile them into a newsletter.

BIOLAB

HOW DO NEURAL PATHWAYS DEVELOP AND BECOME MORE EFFICIENT?

Background: Imagine forging a narrow path through a wooded area. As the path is traveled over time, it becomes more defined and easier to follow. In a similar manner, neural pathways are developed in the brain when you learn something new. As you practice what you have learned, connections between neurons strengthen, causing nerve impulses to pass more quickly and efficiently along the circuit.

Question: *What effect do learning strategies have on the efficiency of a neural circuit?*

Materials

graph paper
paper
pencil
calculator

Procedure

1. Read and complete the lab safety form.
2. Work with one student in your group to write a list of 20 concrete words that describe specific physical objects. Assign a number, 1 to 20, to each word.
3. Read the list aloud to three other members of your group who are the test subjects. Immediately, and without discussion, have them write down as many words as they can remember from the list.
4. Calculate and record the percent recall for each word: divide the number of subjects who recalled each word by the total number of subjects. Multiply by 100.
5. Graph the percent recall for each word. Note patterns in the data.
6. Calculate the average percent recall: add the percent recall for each word, divide by 20, and multiply by 100.
7. Brainstorm techniques to increase the average percent recall. Choose one technique. Predict how it will affect the average percent recall. Design an experiment to test the prediction.
8. Once your teacher approves the plan, implement it with the same test subjects, using another list of 20 concrete words that describe specific physical objects.
9. Repeat Steps 4–6 to evaluate changes in the average percent recall.

Analyze and Conclude

1. **Identify** patterns in the percent recall data after the list was read the first time. Which words were most likely to be remembered?
2. **Interpret Data** by describing the technique used to increase the average percent recall and by comparing the average percent recall before and after the technique was used.
3. **Analyze** whether the technique strengthened the neural circuits responsible for remembering the list of words as well as you had predicted. Explain.
4. **Error Analysis** Identify factors, other than the technique that you used, that might have affected the average percent recall.

APPLY YOUR SKILL

Design an experiment to determine whether a specific learning strategy is equally effective with different test subjects. Consider how sample size would impact your results.

Analyze and Conclude

1. The data likely show a decrease in percent recall in the middle of the list. The first and last words on the list likely have the highest percent recall.
2. Techniques will vary. The data should show an increase in the average percent recall.
3. Answers will vary. Students should compare the prediction to the average percent recall calculated after the technique was employed.
4. Some words might have existing associations for students that make them easier to recall. Words from the second list might have been shorter or easier to remember than words from the first list.

BIOLAB

? Inquiry BioLab

For a lab worksheet, use your eTeacherEdition Online.

RUBRIC A rubric for evaluating BioLabs is found on your eTeacherEdition Online.

Est. Time 60 min

Content Background
When learning occurs, new connections among brain neurons form. As the new knowledge or skill is reviewed or practiced, synapses become more efficient in passing nerve impulses along the new circuit. Techniques to strengthen connections include repetition, grouping small pieces of information into larger chunks, visualization, and using acrostic words or phrases.

Safety Precautions Approve lab safety forms before work begins.

Alternative Materials Provide a list of 20 concrete terms for students to use rather than having them develop a list: orange, car, apple, house, body, desk, shirt, square, iron, hat, candle, tripod, tile, monkey, bottle, juice, stapler, tack, sunshine, pen.

Teaching Strategies
- This activity works well when students are in groups of five.
- Discuss the difference between concrete words (such as *dog* and *pencil*) and abstract terms (such as *anger* and *wealthy*). Make sure student lists contain only concrete terms.

Alternative Teaching Demo
This lesson could be conducted as a large group activity using student volunteers and analyzing data as a class.

Chapter 33

Study Guide

ConnectED

Students can use the following to review the chapter.

Review

Vocabulary eGames
Vocabulary eFlashcards
Vocabulary PuzzleMaker

Assessment

Online Quizzes
Online Test Practice
Standardized Test Practice

Use the *ExamView® Assessment Suite* CD-ROM to:

- create multiple versions of tests
- create modified tests with one mouse click
- edit existing questions and add your own questions
- build tests aligned with state standards using built-in state curriculum tags
- change English tests to Spanish with one mouse click
- track students' progress using the Teacher Management System

Chapter 33 Study Guide

THEME FOCUS Energy The sodium-potassium pump uses energy to pump ions against the gradient so that a nerve impulse can travel the length of a neuron.

BIG Idea **The nervous system is essential for communication among cells, tissues, and organs.**

Section 1 Structure of the Nervous System

neuron (p. 962)
dendrite (p. 962)
cell body (p. 962)
axon (p. 962)
reflex arc (p. 963)
action potential (p. 964)
threshold (p. 964)
node (p. 965)
synapse (p. 967)
neurotransmitter (p. 967)

MAIN Idea **Neurons conduct electrical impulses that allow cells, tissues, and organs to detect and respond to stimuli.**

- There are three major parts of a neuron.
- There are three basic types of neurons.
- A nerve impulse is an electric charge and is called an action potential.
- Neurons use chemicals and electricity to relay impulses.

Section 2 Organization of the Nervous System

central nervous system (p. 968)
peripheral nervous system (p. 968)
cerebrum (p. 969)
medulla oblongata (p. 970)
pons (p. 970)
hypothalamus (p. 970)
somatic nervous system (p. 971)
autonomic nervous system (p. 971)
sympathetic nervous system (p. 972)
parasympathetic nervous system (p. 972)

MAIN Idea **The central nervous system and the peripheral nervous system are the two major divisions of the nervous system.**

- The nervous system has two major divisions: the central nervous system and the peripheral nervous system.
- The brain and spinal cord make up the central nervous system.
- The somatic nervous system and the autonomic nervous system make up the peripheral nervous system.
- The sympathetic nervous system and the parasympathetic nervous system are branches of the autonomic nervous system.

Section 3 The Senses

taste bud (p. 973)
lens (p. 974)
retina (p. 974)
rod (p. 974)
cone (p. 974)
cochlea (p. 974)
semicircular canal (p. 975)

MAIN Idea **Sensory receptors allow you to detect the world around you.**

- The senses of taste and smell work together.
- The eye has two types of receptors.
- The ear is involved in both hearing and balance.
- The skin has many types of sensory receptors.

Section 4 Effects of Drugs

drug (p. 977)
dopamine (p. 978)
stimulant (p. 978)
depressant (p. 979)
tolerance (p. 981)
addiction (p. 981)

MAIN Idea **Some drugs alter the function of the nervous system.**

- Drugs can affect the nervous system in four ways.
- Common substances such as caffeine and alcohol are considered drugs.
- Many addictive drugs increase levels of dopamine.
- Drug abuse has many negative consequences.
- A person can become psychologically and physiologically addicted to drugs.

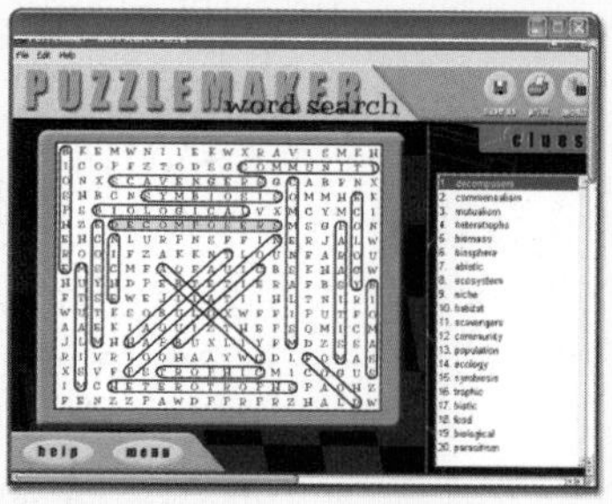

Review **Vocabulary PuzzleMaker**

For additional practice with vocabulary, have students access the Vocabulary PuzzleMaker online

Review **Vocabulary eGames**

Section 1

Vocabulary Review

For each set of terms below, choose the one term that does not belong and explain why it does not belong.

1. axon, dendrite, reflex arc
2. cell body, synapse, neurotransmitter
3. myelin, node, threshold

Understand Main Ideas

Use the diagram below to answer question 4.

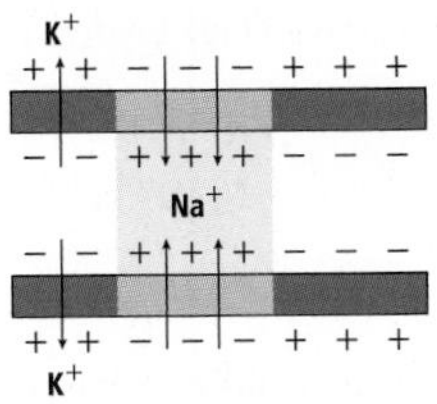

4. What is occurring in the diagram above?
   A. K^+ ions are entering the neuron.
   B. Negatively charged proteins are leaving the neuron.
   C. Na^+ ions are entering the neuron.
   D. The myelin coat has broken down, allowing ions to freely cross the plasma membrane.

5. Which is the correct path that a nerve impulse will follow in a reflex arc?
   A. motor neuron → interneuron → sensory neuron
   B. interneuron → motor neuron → sensory neuron
   C. motor neuron → sensory neuron → interneuron
   D. sensory neuron → interneuron → motor neuron

Constructed Response

6. **THEME FOCUS Energy** Hypothesize why it takes more energy for a nerve impulse to travel along an axon that lacks myelin as opposed to an axon that has myelin.

7. **MAIN Idea** Explain the following analogy: A neuron is like a one-way street, while a nerve is like a two-way street.

Think Critically

8. **Infer** In most animals, an action potential will travel only in one direction along a neuron. Infer what the result might be in humans if nerve impulses could travel in both directions on a single neuron.

Section 2

Vocabulary Review

For each set of terms below, choose the one term that does not belong and explain why it does not belong.

9. somatic system, parasympathetic system, sympathetic system
10. cerebrum, pons, medulla oblongata
11. autonomic nervous system, somatic nervous system, central nervous system

Understand Main Ideas

12. Which is characteristic of the sympathetic division of the autonomic system?
    A. stimulates digestion
    B. dilates the bronchi
    C. slows the heart rate
    D. converts glucose to glycogen

Use the diagram below to answer question 13.

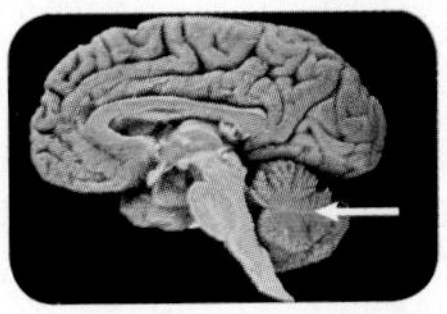

13. If the portion indicated by the arrow was damaged as a result of trauma, what effect would this person most likely experience?
    A. partial or complete memory loss
    B. body temperature fluctuations
    C. trouble maintaining balance
    D. rapid breathing

14. Which nervous system is the hypothalamus most involved in regulating?
    A. voluntary **C.** sensory
    B. peripheral **D.** autonomic

Chapter 33 Assessment

Section 1

Vocabulary Review

1. reflex arc; it is not a part of a neuron
2. cell body; it is not part of the space between neurons
3. threshold; it is not part of a myelinated neuron

Understand Main Ideas

4. C
5. D

Constructed Response

6. Ions can cross the membrane only at the nodes. The myelin insulates the rest of the membrane so the cell does not need to use energy to regulate the ion flow.
7. Each neuron receives a signal in an axon and transmits a signal through a dendrite. The flow goes only one way. A nerve is a bundle of neurons; some neurons in the nerve go one way and some go the opposite way.

Think Critically

8. Possible answer: Since the action potential could not flow in opposite directions at the same time, a neuron might need to have several axons and several dendrites to allow for action potential flowing both ways.

Section 2

Vocabulary Review

9. somatic system; it is not part of the autonomic nervous system
10. cerebrum; it is not part of the brain stem
11. central nervous system; it is not part of the peripheral nervous system

Understand Main Ideas

12. B
13. C
14. D

Constructed Response

15. Possible answer: The autonomic nervous system regulates many involuntary functions necessary for homeostasis. For example, the autonomic nervous system regulates breathing, even while you are asleep. It also regulates heartbeat and digestion.

Think Critically

16. Students should show an understanding that we use all of our brain.

17. increased ability to learn, process language, form speech, and retain memories

Section 3

Vocabulary Review

18. Rods detect low light. Cones provide information about color.

19. The cochlea is a fluid-filled vessel in the ear. When sound waves cause the cochlea to vibrate, hairs inside the cochlea cause neurons to send information about sound to the brain. The semicircular canals also are fluid-filled organs, but they assist in maintaining balance.

20. The retina senses light energy. The taste buds detect chemicals and transmit information about taste to the brain.

Understand Main Ideas

21. A

22. B

23. C

24. A

Constructed Response

25. Undesirable. Pain warns the body of danger. If a person cannot sense pain, he or she could be seriously injured.

Think Critically

26. because the body gets used to constant levels of light pressure

27. Answers will vary, but students should have logical answers for the way they have rated the senses.

Constructed Response

15. MAIN Idea Suppose you are on the debate team at school. You must support the following statement: The autonomic nervous system is more involved with homeostasis than the somatic nervous system. Build your case.

Think Critically

16. Critique You might have heard the statement, "Humans use only ten percent of their brains." Use the Internet or other sources to compile evidence that either supports or refutes this idea.

17. Analyze The human cerebrum is disproportionately large compared to the cerebrum of other animals. What advantage does this give to humans?

Section 3

Vocabulary Review

Distinguish between the terms in each of the following sets.

18. rods, cones

19. cochlea, semicircular canals

20. retina, taste buds

Understand Main Ideas

21. If there was a power outage in a movie theater and only a few dim emergency lights were lit, which cells of the retina would be most important for seeing your way to the exit?
A. rods
B. cones
C. Rods and cones are equally important.

22. Which represents the correct sequence as sound waves travel in the ear to trigger an impulse?
A. cochlea, incus, stape, eardrum
B. tympanum, bones in the middle ear, cochlea, hair cells
C. auditory canal, tympanum, hair cells, cochlea
D. hair cells, auditory canal, cochlea, malleus

23. With which sense are free nerve endings associated?
A. taste **C.** touch
B. hearing **D.** sight

Use the diagram below to answer question 24.

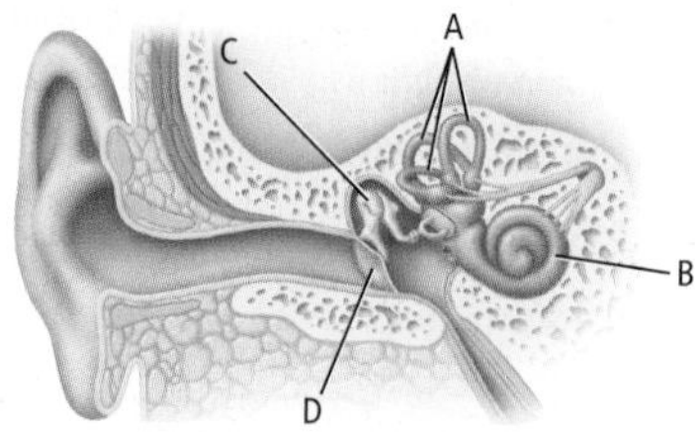

24. Some rides at amusement parks cause a person to become dizzy when the ride stops. Which structure in the diagram is most likely involved with the dizzy feeling?
A. A **C.** C
B. B **D.** D

Constructed Response

25. Open Ended A rare condition exists in which a person cannot feel pain. Is this desirable or undesirable? Explain your response.

Think Critically

26. Explain You have receptors for light (soft) touch all over your body. In terms of what you know about the nervous system, why are you not always conscious of things such as wearing clothes or a wristwatch?

27. MAIN Idea Rate the senses from 1 to 5 in order of importance (with 1 representing the most important.) Be prepared to debate this issue with other students in the class.

Section 4

Vocabulary Review

Explain the difference between the terms in each set. Then explain how the terms are related.

28. stimulants, depressants

29. tolerance, addiction

30. dopamine, drug

Section 4

Vocabulary Review

28. Stimulants make people more alert. Depressants make people drowsy. Both affect the central nervous system.

29. Tolerance is adapting to a certain level of a drug in the body. Addiction is becoming psychologically and/or physically dependent on a drug. A person addicted to a drug builds up a tolerance to the drug.

30. Dopamine is a neurotransmitter involved with feelings of pleasure and reward. A drug is a substance that alters the function of the body. Many drugs affect levels of dopamine.

Assessment Online Test Practice

Understand Main Ideas

31. Which decreases brain activity?
A. nicotine
B. amphetamines
C. cocaine
D. alcohol

32. MAIN Idea What is the most likely function of amphetamines?
A. to stimulate the sympathetic nervous system
B. to stimulate the parasympathetic nervous system
C. to stimulate the sympathetic and parasympathetic systems equally
D. not to affect either the sympathetic or parasympathetic nervous system

Use the diagram below to answer question 33.

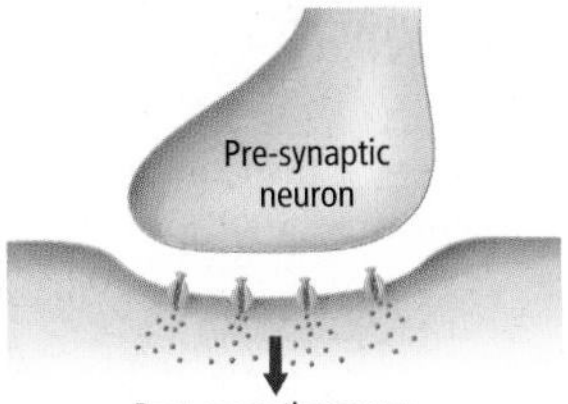

33. If a person is suffering from depression, which drug is one recommended treatment of the presynaptic neuron?
A. one that increases the reuptake of dopamine
B. one that increases the production of dopamine
C. one that decreases the receptors for dopamine
D. one that decreases the reuptake of dopamine

Constructed Response

34. Short Answer What does it mean when someone is addicted to a drug?

35. Open Ended Discuss what consequences might arise if a person's gene for the production of dopamine is defective.

Think Critically

36. Defend Form a conclusion about the following statement: "It is more difficult for someone to get addicted to drugs than it is to stop using drugs." Defend your position.

Summative Assessment

37. BIG Idea The nervous system is essential for communication among cells, tissues, and organs. Predict the results if nerve impulses are interrupted due to injury or destruction of nerve fibers and the myelin sheath.

38. WRITING in Biology Write a short story about a person who heard a loud noise and became afraid. Make sure to include in your story all of the events that might occur in each division of the nervous system during such an experience.

39. Imagine that you are a scientist who is developing a new drug. Explain how your drug works on the nervous system and what disease the drug treats. How could you determine what side effects the drug might have?

DBQ Document-Based Questions

Data obtained from: Blinkov, S.M., and Glezer, I.I. 1968. *The human brain in figures and tables: a quantitative handbook*. New York: Plenum Press.
Nieuwenhuys, R., Ten Donkelaar, H.J., and Nicholson, C. 1998. *The central nervous system of vertebrates*. Vol. 3. Berlin: Springer.
Berta, A., et al. 1999. *Marine mammals: evolutionary biology*. San Diego: Academic Press.

Average Brain Mass (in grams)

Species	Mass (g)	Species	Brain Mass (g)
Fin whale	6930	Dog (beagle)	72
Elephant	6000	Cat	30
Cow	425–458	Turtle	0.3–0.7
Adult human	1300–1400	Rat	2

40. Does there appear to be a correlation between body size and brain mass?

41. Discuss possible explanations (in terms of adaptations) that would account for your response to question 40.

DBQ Document-Based Questions

Blinkov, S.M. and Glezer, I.I. 1968. *The human brain in figures and tables: a quantitative handbook*. New York: Plenum Press.Nieuwenhuys, R., Ten Donkelaar, H.J., and Nicholson, C.
1998. *The central nervous system of vertebrates*. Vol. 3. Berlin: Springer.
Berta, A., et al. 1999. *Marine mammals: evolutionary biology*. San Diego: Academic Press.

40. with some exceptions, yes, as body weight increases, brain size increases

41. Larger animals need larger brains to control more muscles and bigger systems.

Understand Main Ideas
31. D
32. A
33. D

Constructed Response
34. It means someone is physically and or psychologically dependent on a drug.
35. Answers will vary. Some students may say that the person may suffer from depression or that control of bodily movements might be affected.

Think Critically
36. Students will probably conclude that becoming addicted is easier than stopping. Student answers should include biological support for their conclusion.

Summative Assessment

37. When nerve fibers and myelin sheaths are injured or damaged, nerve impulses are distorted or interrupted. This results in a variety of symptoms ranging from tingling and numbness in the limbs to paralysis or loss of vision.

WRITING in Biology

RUBRIC Use the modifiable rubric found on your eTeacher-Edition Online to assess writing assignments.

38. Stories will vary, but should involve the autonomic nervous system and sympathetic responses to danger, and parasympathetic responses to the return to equilibrium.

39. Answers will vary, but should include a description of the chemical or drug they have developed and how it works on the body. Answers should also include a brief summary of an experiment that could be done to determine side effects.

Assessment Online Test Practice

Standardized Test Practice

Multiple Choice

1. A
2. B
3. A
4. A
5. D
6. A
7. C
8. C

Short Answer

9. Answers can vary, but should include information similar to the following. The animal with incisors and teeth that continue growing (Animal A) probably has to chew/gnaw on vegetation constantly. It might be a rodent. The things it chews on wear down its teeth. Animal B has more sharp teeth towards the front, but these teeth do not continue growing. It probably needs sharp teeth for eating meat, but it does not need to gnaw on food like Animal A. This animal is probably a carnivore.
10. Answers can vary, as long as they accurately point out some similarity between human teeth and the animal teeth in the figure. Students might point out that Animal A has similar teeth, in that humans also lack extra sharp teeth in front that could be used for tearing meat. Or, students might point out that Animal B is closer, since humans' teeth do not grow indefinitely, and the canine and molar teeth are well suited for chewing on meat.
11. Answers can vary, depending on the organism chosen for comparison. Spiders capture their prey either in a web or by other means. They wrap their prey in silk and then secrete digestive enzymes into the prey. After the prey is liquefied, spiders take in the already digested food. One possible organism for comparison is the grasshopper. The grasshopper chews leaves and digests them in its internal digestive system. The adaptations of the grasshopper include chewing mouthparts and a digestive system that can process the components of leaves and then absorb the nutrients.

Standardized Test Practice

Cumulative

Multiple Choice

1. Which characteristic is unique to mammals?
   A. hair
   B. endothermy
   C. four-chambered heart
   D. internal fertilization

Use the diagram below to answer questions 2 and 3.

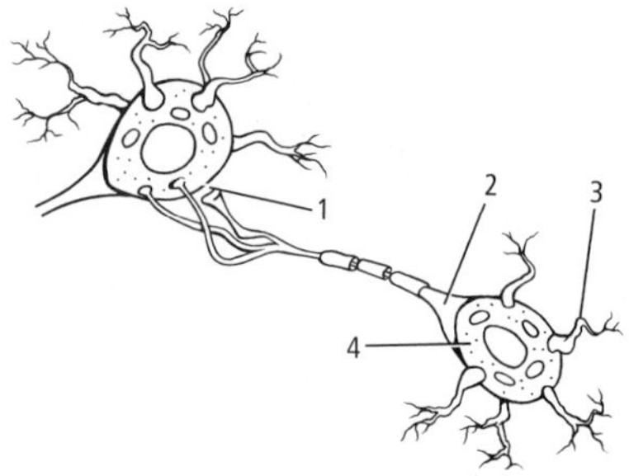

2. In which part of the diagram above would you expect to find myelin?
   A. 1
   B. 2
   C. 3
   D. 4

3. In which part of the diagram above would you expect to find neurotransmitters when an action potential reaches the end of the neuron?
   A. 1
   B. 2
   C. 3
   D. 4

4. What is the purpose of the epithelial tissue in the integumentary system?
   A. cover the body surface and protect its tissues
   B. move joints and bones
   C. provide a structural framework for the body
   D. transmit nerve signals

5. Which animal is a placental mammal?
   A. hummingbird
   B. kangaroo
   C. duck-billed platypus
   D. whale

Use the diagram below to answer questions 6 and 7.

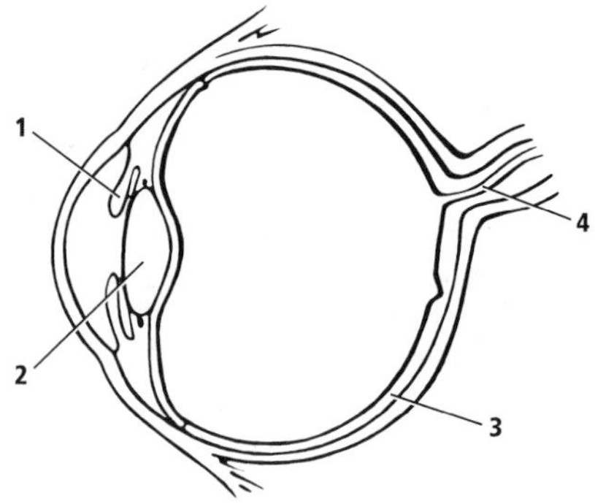

6. Which part of the eye is made of muscles that respond to stimuli?
   A. 1
   B. 2
   C. 3
   D. 4

7. If a person cannot see certain colors, what part of the eye might be damaged?
   A. 1
   B. 2
   C. 3
   D. 4

Use the graph below to answer question 8.

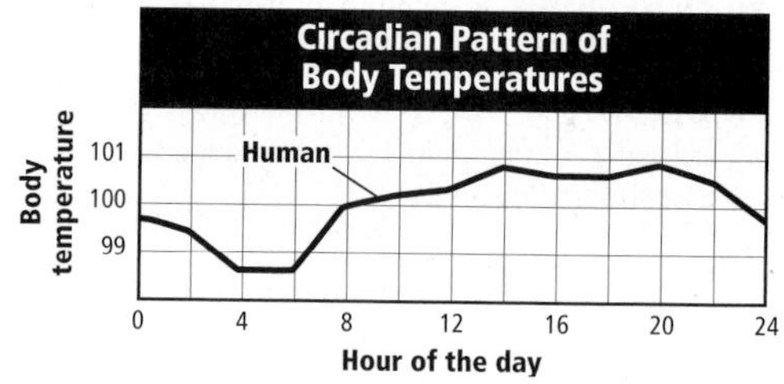

8. The graph above shows the circadian pattern of body temperature in humans. When does the body temperature of humans seem to be the lowest?
   A. after eating
   B. in the afternoon
   C. just before dawn
   D. late at night

Short Answer

Use the diagram below to answer questions 9 and 10.

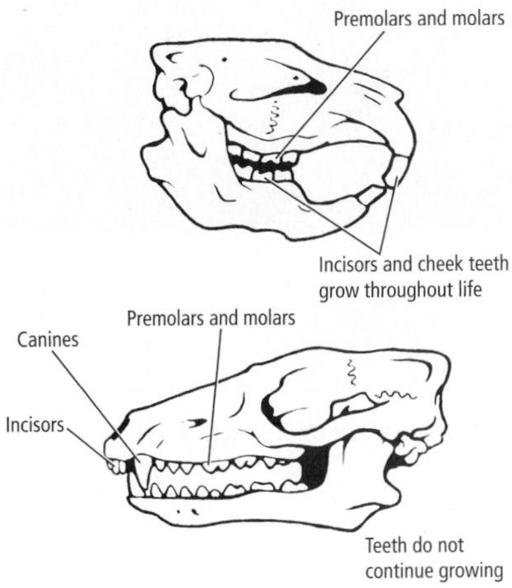

9. The figure above shows the teeth of two different types of mammals. From these teeth, what can you infer about the diets of these mammals?

10. Which animal's teeth most closely resemble those of humans? Explain your answer.

11. Explain how spiders predigest their food. Compare this process to the digestion process of another animal with which you are familiar.

12. Suppose that a person who used to drink one cup of coffee to stay awake at night finds that she needs to drink two cups. What is the name of this phenomenon and what causes it?

13. What is the role of the gametophyte generation in seed plants?

Extended Response

14. Two abandoned whooping crane chicks are found several days after they hatched. A scientist wants to raise the chicks. To make the chicks feel comfortable, the scientist uses a hand puppet that looks like a whooping crane. The scientist offers the chicks mealworms, but they will not take them. Formulate a hypothesis that gives a possible explanation of the actions of the chicks.

15. How are the actions of myosin and actin fibers related to the contraction of a muscle?

16. What is the main difference between segmented worms and other worms? What is the importance of this difference?

Essay Question

Each year, doctors perform more than 450,000 joint repair and replacement surgeries. These surgeries reduce pain and increase movement in the joints. Joint repair surgery involves removing any debris or excess bone growth from around the joint. This restores the functioning of the joint. Joint replacement surgery involves replacing the joint with a synthetic joint. The synthetic joint is made of polyethylene, ceramic, or metal. Joint replacement enables the joint to function in the same way as a natural joint. Joint replacements usually are performed on the knee, hip, or shoulder.

Using the information in the paragraph above, answer the following question in essay format.

17. Doctors usually replace only knee or hip joints on older patients who are less active than younger patients. Suggest why doctors recommend this.

NEED EXTRA HELP?																	
If You Missed Question . . .	1	2	3	4	5	6	7	8	9	10	11	12	13	14	15	16	17
Review Section . . .	30.1	33.1	33.1	32.1	30.2	33.3	33.3	30.1	30.2	30.2	26.1	33.2	21.4	31.1	32.3	25.1	32.2

12. The phenomenon is increased tolerance. When a person uses a stimulant regularly, such as caffeine in coffee, the body gets used to the stimulant and its effectiveness decreases in time. Consequently, it takes more of the stimulant to produce the original effect.
13. The gametophyte generation is the male sex cells, in pollen, and the female sex cells, in the plant's eggs or ovary, that join during fertilization to form seeds.

Extended Response

14. Answers will vary. Possible hypotheses include that the chicks are not imprinted for the hand puppet, the mealworms are not a food they have eaten before, or the hand puppet does not look real enough to the chicks.
15. The myosin and actin filaments attach to each other. The actin filaments are pulled toward the sarcomeres, causing the muscle to contract.
16. Segmented worms have a true coelom, which is a body cavity completely lined with mesoderm. Other kinds of worms have no coelom or a false coelom. The importance of this difference is that the digestive tract and other internal organs develop within the coelom.

Essay Question

17. Knee and hip joints receive much stress and strain in their daily use by an active person. In time, joints can wear out and may need to be replaced through surgeries. Older patients have used their joints longer than younger patients so they are more likely to have worn out their joints.

Chapter 34 Organizer: Circulatory, Respiratory, and Excretory Systems

LabManager™
Customize any lab with the LabManager™ CD-ROM.

Essential Questions	National Science Standards	Materials and Planning: Estimated times include cleanup and disposal, but do not include teacher prep time. For cleanup and disposal guidelines, see page 39T.	Est. Time (min)
Section 1 1. What are the main functions of the circulatory system? 2. How does the blood flow through the heart and body? 3. What are the similarities and differences between the major components of the blood?	UCP.1, UCP.2, UCP.5; A.1, A.2; F.1, F.5; G.1	**Launch Lab,** p. 990: pencil, paper	20
		MiniLab 1, p. 996: blood-pressure cuff, blood-pressure chart, stopwatch or clock	25
		Demonstration, p. 996: faucet, 3-m rubber tube, 1000-mL beaker	5
Section 2 1. What is the difference between internal and external respiration? 2. What is the path of the air through the respiratory system? 3. What changes occur in the body during breathing?	UCP.1, UCP.2, UCP.5; A.1, A.2; F.1	**Demonstration,** p. 1001: fish tank, water, aquarium pump, filter	10
		MiniLab 2, p. 1002: stopwatch or clock, graph paper	25
		Demonstration, p. 1002: three balloons	10
Section 3 1. What is the function of the kidney in the body? 2. What are the steps of the excretion of wastes from the Bowman's capsule to the urethra? 3. What is the difference between filtration and reabsorption in the kidneys?	UCP.1, UCP.2, UCP.3, UCP.5; A.1, A.2; F.1, F.5, F.6; G.1, G.2	**Demonstration,** p. 1005: sand, pebbles, red food coloring, water, a 100-mL graduated cylinder, filter paper, funnel, a 250-mL beaker	10
		BioLab, p. 1011: resource materials about health choices from the school library or classroom	90

Suggested Time for Each Lesson

Class	Chapter Opener	Section 1	Section 2	Section 3	Assessment
Basic	45 min	45 min	45 min	45 min	45 min
General	25 min	55 min	55 min	45 min	45 min
Honors	5 min	60 min	60 min	45 min	45 min

ConnectED

connectED.mcgraw-hill.com

Access interactive learning opportunities and teaching resources using these icons located throughout your StudentWorks™ Plus Online and eTeacherEdition Online.

Chapter 34 Section Resources	Additional Chapter 34 Resources	Technology
FAST FILE Unit 9 Resources: Launch Lab Worksheet* MiniLab Worksheet* Study Guide (English/Spanish)* Section Quick Check **Reading Essentials 34.1** **Science Notebook 34.1*** **FAST FILE Unit 9 Resources:** MiniLab Worksheet* Study Guide (English/Spanish)* Section Quick Check **Reading Essentials 34.2** **Science Notebook 34.2*** **FAST FILE Unit 9 Resources:** BioLab Worksheet* Study Guide (English/Spanish)* Section Quick Check **Reading Essentials 34.3** **Science Notebook 34.3***	**FAST FILE Unit 9 Resources:** Chapter Diagnostic Test Concept Mapping* Real-World Biology Enrichment Chapter Tests A, B, and C **Transparencies:** Bellringer Transparencies* Biology Concepts Transparencies* **Lab Resources:** Laboratory Manual* Probeware Lab Manual* Forensics Lab Manual* Pre-AP Lab Manual* Open Inquiry in Biology* Guided Inquiry in Biology*	**Teaching Tools:** eTeacherEdition Online Classroom Presentation Toolkit CD-ROM* LabManager™ CD-ROM* Video Lab DVD* Virtual Lab CD-ROM* What's BIOLOGY Got To Do With It? StudentWorks™ Plus Online* **Chapter Assessment Tools:** Classroom Presentation Toolkit CD-ROM* *ExamView® Assessment Suite* CD-ROM **Web-Based Resources:** • StudentWorks™ Plus Online • eTeacherEdition Online • Animations* • The Interactive Time Line* • Interactive Tables* • Online Quizzes • Online Test Practice • Standardized Test Practice • Virtual Labs* • Multilingual eGlossary* • Vocabulary eGames* • Vocabulary eFlashcards • WebQuests • Personal Tutors

While all resources listed are appropriate for English learners, the * indicates resources with a strong visual or hands-on component for EL.

Teaching strategies and activities have been coded for differentiated instruction.

AL Activities for students working above grade level	**OL** Activities for students working on grade level	**BL** Activities for students working below grade level	**EL** Activities for English learners (also ELL)	**COOP LEARN** Activities designed for small cooperative group work

CHAPTER 34

Launch Lab
What changes take place in the body during exercise?

? Inquiry Launch Lab

For a lab worksheet, use your eTeacherEdition Online.

RUBRIC A rubric for evaluating Launch Labs is found on your eTeacherEdition Online.

Est. Time 20 min

Safety Precautions Approve lab safety forms before work begins. This lab involves physical activity. Assign a spotter to each group to make sure the exercising student is not in physical distress during or after exercise.

Teaching Strategies
- Review the concept of homeostasis prior to beginning the lab.
- Do not compare fitness levels or body types of students.

Procedure
1. Read and complete the lab safety form.
2. Do a rhythmic exercise, such as jogging or marching in place, for two minutes. As you exercise, note how your body responds.
3. Make a list of the body system responses you identified as you exercised.

CHAPTER 34
Circulatory, Respiratory, and Excretory Systems

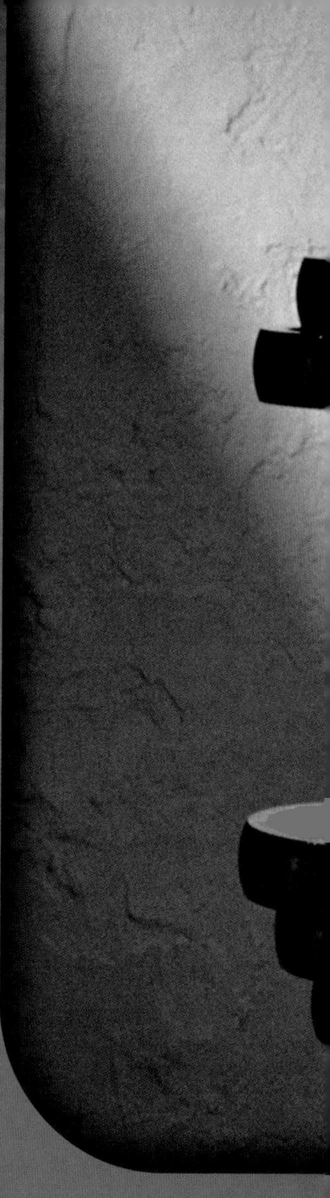

ConnectED

Your one-stop online resource
connectED.mcgraw-hill.com

- Video
- Audio
- Review
- Inquiry
- WebQuest
- Assessment
- Concepts in Motion
- Multilingual eGlossary

Launch Lab
What changes take place in the body during exercise?

Body systems, including the respiratory and circulatory systems, function together to meet the demands of exercise and to maintain homeostasis. For example, red blood cells circulate throughout the body to deliver oxygen to cells, where it is used to help produce the energy required for exercise. In this lab, you will investigate how body system responses to exercise might be related to each other.

For a lab worksheet, use your StudentWorks™ Plus Online.

? Inquiry Launch Lab

FOLDABLES®

Make a four-door book and label it as shown. Use it to organize your notes about the ABO blood group.

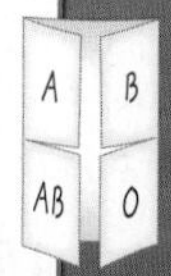

Analysis
1. **Create** a flowchart showing how these body responses might be related to each other. Student charts may show increased heartbeat, increased breathing rate, and sweating.
2. **Analyze** how one of the body system responses on your list helps regulate the body's internal environment. Student answers should indicate a plausible connection between the response and its role in regulation. For example, an increased breathing rate supplies the body with more oxygen and removes more carbon dioxide than a slow breathing rate.

THEME FOCUS Homeostasis
The circulatory, respiratory, and excretory systems regulate the internal environment of the human body to maintain conditions needed for life.

BIG Idea These systems function together to maintain homeostasis by delivering important substances to the body's cells while removing wastes.

Section 1 • Circulatory System
Section 2 • Respiratory System
Section 3 • Excretory System

Introduce the Chapter

Identify Surgeons take great care to maintain the support systems of the body. Tell students that the circulatory, respiratory, and excretory systems are three of the main systems maintained during surgery.

ASK STUDENTS: ***Why do you think it is important to maintain these systems?*** These systems provide materials or processes needed to sustain life.

BIG Idea

Concept Map Have students make a concept map showing the relationships among the circulatory, respiratory, and excretory systems, including the major components of each system. Sample concept map:

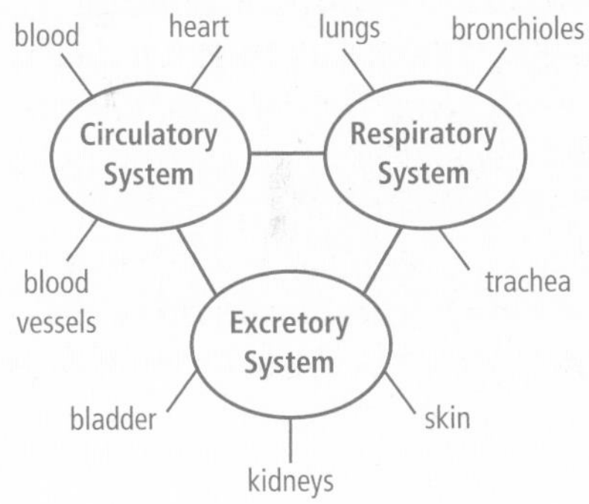

THEMES

Scientific Inquiry Research is underway to find a way to grow new hearts for transplants.

Diversity The large diversity of cells in the human body allows for specialized systems.

Energy Energy is used by the body for life processes such as respiration and circulation.

Homeostasis The circulatory, respiratory, and excretory systems are integral to maintaining homeostasis.

Change The human body is able to respond quickly to change in the environment, due to these body systems.

Section 1

MAIN Idea

BL OL AL

Transporting Material

ASK STUDENTS: ***How do your cells obtain nutrients and dispose of waste products?*** Blood carries important material, such as oxygen, to cells and removes wastes, such as carbon dioxide, from the cells. Inform students that Section 1 will help them understand how these transactions take place.

Reading Strategy

BL OL **Take Notes** As students read, have them write questions about any concepts they do not understand. Have a class discussion using these questions as a guide. Possible question: *What is the relationship between arteries and capillaries?*

Develop Concepts

OL AL

Activate Prior Knowledge

ASK STUDENTS: ***What do you recall about the definition of homeostasis?*** regulation of an organism's internal environment to maintain conditions needed for life ***What benefits do you think are derived when the body maintains homeostasis?*** Homeostasis maintains stability in the body and allows the body to survive. Then cells can carry out life processes.

D Develop Concepts

BL OL AL COOP LEARN

Analogy Have pairs of students think of an analogy of the circulatory system, such as a pool, a radiator heating system, or a water and sewage treatment system. Have them draw a diagram of their analogy. A successful analogy will demonstrate a complete cycle.

Section 1

Reading Preview

Essential Questions

- What are the main functions of the circulatory system?
- How does the blood flow through the heart and body?
- What are the similarities and differences between the major components of the blood?

Review Vocabulary

muscle contraction: muscle cells or fibers shorten in response to stimuli

New Vocabulary

artery
capillary
vein
valve
heart
pacemaker
plasma
red blood cell
platelet
white blood cell
atherosclerosis

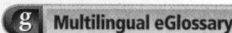

Multilingual eGlossary

Circulatory System

MAIN Idea **The circulatory system transports blood to deliver important substances, such as oxygen, to cells and to remove wastes, such as carbon dioxide.**

Real-World Reading Link Fast-moving highway traffic gets people to and from work quickly. Similarly, blood flowing in your body supplies nutrients and removes waste products quickly. When either traffic or blood flow is blocked, normal functions slow down or stop.

Functions of the Circulatory System

Cells must have oxygen and nutrients and must also get rid of waste products. This exchange is accomplished by the circulatory system—the body's transport system. The circulatory system consists of blood, the heart, blood vessels, and the lymphatic system. Blood carries important substances to all parts of the body. The heart pumps blood through a vast network of tubes inside your body called blood vessels. The lymphatic system is considered part of the circulatory and immune systems. All of these components work together to maintain homeostasis in the body.

The circulatory system transports many important substances, such as oxygen and nutrients. The blood also carries disease-fighting materials produced by the immune system. The blood contains cell fragments **D** and proteins for blood clotting. Finally, the circulatory system distributes heat throughout the body to help regulate body temperature.

Figure 1
From Cadavers to Artificial Hearts
The human circulatory system has been studied for thousands of years, leading to great advances in medical technology.

Concepts in Motion
The Interactive Timeline

350 B.C. Greek physician Praxagoras recognizes that veins and arteries are two different kinds of vessels.

1628 The first accurate description is made of the human heart—a pump that circulates blood in a one-way system.

1500 — 1600 — 1900

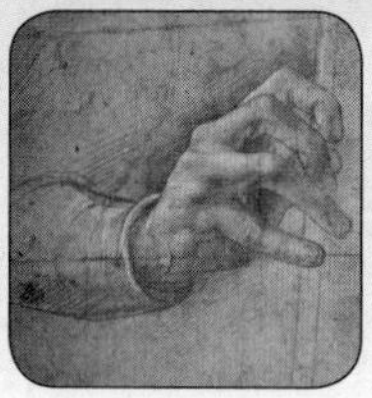

1452–1519 Leonardo da Vinci conducts extensive research on human cadavers. It is believed that he dissected about 30 corpses in his lifetime.

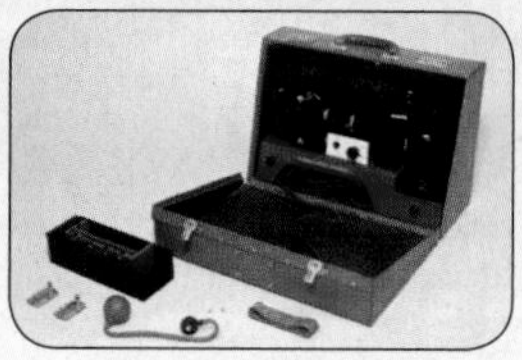

1903 The first electrocardiograph records the electrical activity of the heart.

Content Background

Teacher FYI Today, stents are used to open arteries narrowed by plaque build up. A stent is a small, meshlike, metal tube that acts like scaffolding once inserted into the artery. The stent is inserted into the body using a tiny balloon catheter that enters though a blood vessel in the groin area or the arm. The catheter, balloon, and stent travel through the blood vessels to the spot where the stent is needed. Once at the correct spot, the balloon pushes the plaque away, and the stent is put into place. The stent holds the artery open so that blood can flow through.

Blood Vessels

Highways have lanes that separate traffic. They also have access ramps that take vehicles to and from roads. Similarly, the body has a network of channels—the blood vessels. Blood vessels circulate blood throughout the body and help keep the blood flowing to and from the heart. The fact that there are different kinds of blood vessels was first observed by the Greek physician Praxagoras, as noted in **Figure 1.** The three major blood vessels are arteries, capillaries, and veins, as illustrated in **Figure 2.**

Arteries Oxygen-rich blood, or oxygenated blood, is carried away from the heart in large blood vessels called **arteries.** These strong, thick-walled vessels are elastic and durable. They are capable of withstanding high pressures exerted by blood as it is pumped by the heart.

As shown in **Figure 2,** arteries are composed of three layers: an outer layer of connective tissue, a middle layer of smooth muscle, and an inner layer of endothelial tissue. The endothelial layer of the artery is thicker than that of the other blood vessels. The endothelial layer of arteries needs to be thicker because blood is under higher pressure when it is pumped from the heart into the arteries.

Capillaries Arteries branch into smaller vessels called arterioles, which become smaller in diameter as they grow farther away from the main vessel. The smallest branches are capillaries. **Capillaries** are microscopic blood vessels where the exchange of important substances and wastes occurs. Capillary walls are only one cell thick, as illustrated in **Figure 2.** This permits the easy exchange of materials between the blood and body cells through the process of diffusion. Capillaries are so small that red blood cells move single-file through these vessels.

The diameter of blood vessels changes in response to the needs of the body. For example, when you are exercising, muscle capillaries expand, or dilate. This increases blood flow to working muscles, which brings more oxygen to cells and removes extra wastes from cells.

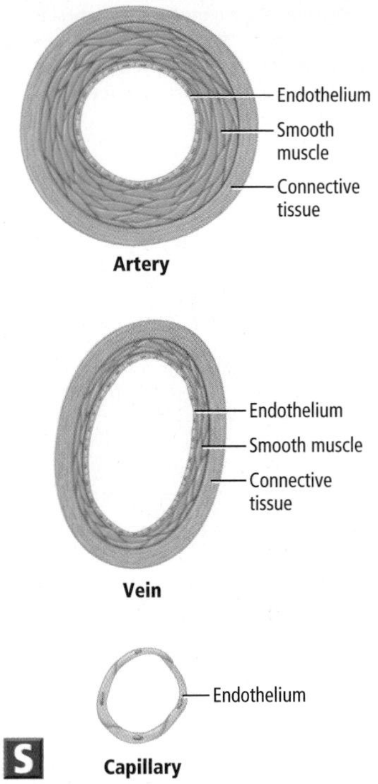

Figure 2 The three major blood vessels in the body are arteries, veins, and capillaries.
Predict *By what process do you think materials cross the walls of capillaries?*

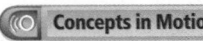

Concepts in Motion
Animation

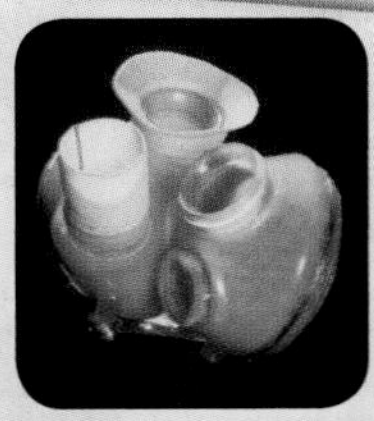

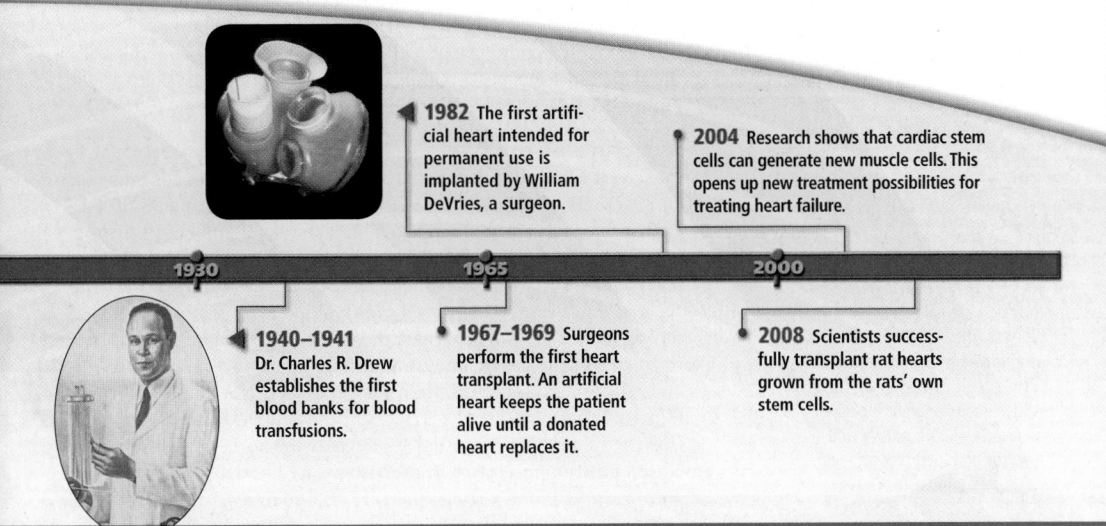

1982 The first artificial heart intended for permanent use is implanted by William DeVries, a surgeon.

2004 Research shows that cardiac stem cells can generate new muscle cells. This opens up new treatment possibilities for treating heart failure.

1930 — 1965 — 2000

1940–1941 Dr. Charles R. Drew establishes the first blood banks for blood transfusions.

1967–1969 Surgeons perform the first heart transplant. An artificial heart keeps the patient alive until a donated heart replaces it.

2008 Scientists successfully transplant rat hearts grown from the rats' own stem cells.

Caption Question Fig. 2 Materials move across the walls of capillaries by diffusion.

Differentiated Instruction

Above Level When introducing a chapter, connect what will be learned to the broader themes of science. Gifted students will perform at a higher level when they understand the larger context into which facts fit.

For more tips, see pages 14T–15T.

S Skill Practice
EL OL AL

Compare and Contrast
Have students construct a three-column chart comparing and contrasting blood vessel types. Have them label the columns *Arteries, Veins,* and *Capillaries.* Tell students to identify the structure, function, type of blood carried, and other unique features in each row. Student charts should be organized to allow students to easily compare and contrast the structure and function of different blood vessels.

Concepts in Motion
Animation
The Interactive Timeline

C Critical Thinking
BL OL AL **Evaluate**

ASK STUDENTS: ***Why do arteries contain smooth muscle and not skeletal or cardiac muscle?*** Smooth muscles allow for involuntary control of the arteries. Skeletal muscle would be inefficient for monitoring the blood flow because it is so energy consuming. Cardiac muscle is located only in the heart.

Develop Concepts

BL OL AL COOP LEARN

Scaffolding Have students work in groups of four to generate answers.

ASK STUDENTS: ***When giving blood, is an artery or vein used?*** vein ***Why?*** the larger supply of blood in the veins, thinner walls, less pressure ***What color is the blood?*** dark red ***If you bleed from the same area, what indicates you cut a vein?*** Blood flow from a cut vein is steady. A cut artery will spurt blood.

D Develop Concepts

BL OL

Clarify a Misconception

ASK STUDENTS: ***Where in your chest is your heart located? What does it look like?*** Students might think that the heart is located on left side and has a "heart" shape. The heart is actually located in the center of the chest, using the sternum for protection. The stronger pumping ventricle is on the left side, hence we can feel the beat on the left side. Emphasize that the heart, while resembling the commonly seen heart shape, is not symmetrical. You might want to obtain a beef heart from a butcher to show the class.

Video BrainPOP

Caption Question Fig. 3 Blood vessels that have a large diameter have a large surface area from which to radiate and lose heat from the blood. This can cool the body. Blood vessels that have a narrow diameter have a smaller surface area and cannot radiate heat from the blood and body as effectively.

Figure 3 Blood circulates throughout the body inside blood vessels.
Hypothesize *how body temperature can be regulated by the diameter of blood vessels.*

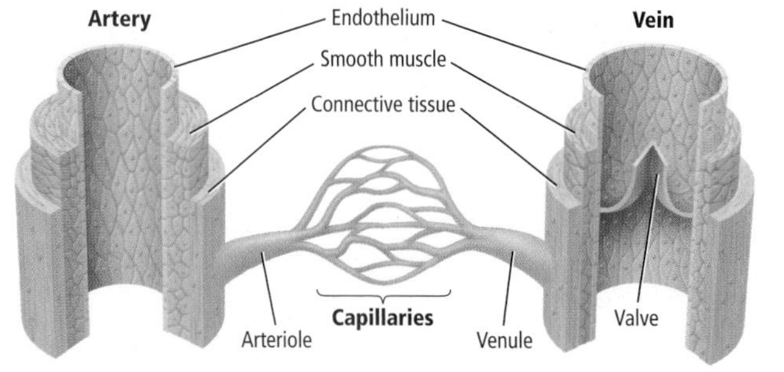

Inquiry Virtual Lab

Video BrainPOP

Veins After blood moves through the tiny capillaries, it enters the larger vessels called venules, and then enters the largest blood vessels, called veins. **Veins** carry oxygen-poor blood, or deoxygenated blood, back to the heart. The endothelial walls of veins are much thinner than the walls of arteries. The pressure of the blood decreases when the blood flows through capillaries before it enters the veins. By the time blood flows into the veins, the heart's original pushing force has less effect on making the blood move. So how does the blood keep moving? Many veins are located near skeletal muscles, and the contraction of these muscles helps keep the blood moving. Larger veins in the body also have flaps of tissue called **valves,** such as the one in **Figure 3,** which prevent blood from flowing backward. Lastly, breathing movements exert a squeezing pressure against veins in the chest, forcing blood back to the heart.

Reading Check **Describe** the differences in structure among arteries, capillaries, and veins.

D

The Heart

The **heart** is a muscular organ that is about as large as your fist and is located at the center of your chest. This hollow organ pumps blood throughout the body. The heart performs two pumping functions at the same time. The heart pumps oxygenated blood to the body, and it pumps deoxygenated blood to the lungs.

Structure of the heart Recall that the heart is made of cardiac muscle. It is capable of conducting electrical impulses for muscular contractions. The heart is divided into four compartments called chambers, as illustrated in **Figure 4.** The two chambers in the top half of the heart, the right atrium and the left atrium (plural, atria), receive blood that is returning to the heart. Below the atria are the right and left ventricles, which pump blood away from the heart. A strong muscular wall separates the left side of the heart from the right side of the heart. The right and left atria have thinner muscular walls and do less work than the ventricles. Notice the valves in **Figure 4** that separate the atria from the ventricles and keep blood flowing in one direction. Valves, such as the aortic valve shown in a closed position in **Figure 4,** are also located between each ventricle and the large blood vessels that carry blood away from the heart.

CAREERS IN BIOLOGY

Exercise Physiologist Scientists who study the effects of exercise on the body are called exercise physiologists. They develop exercise programs and administer medical tests, such as stress tests. Their responsibilities might include monitoring heart activity and monitoring blood pressure levels.

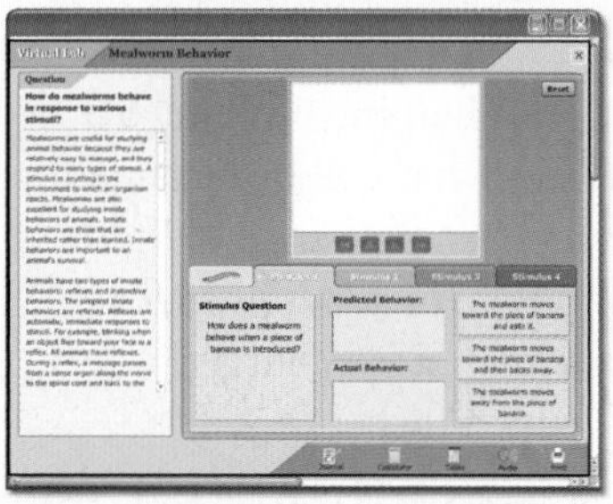

Inquiry Virtual Lab In this lab, students will examine factors that affect the likelihood of hypertension.

Reading Check Veins are the largest blood vessels, but have thinner endotheliums than arteries. The largest veins contain valves to prevent blood from flowing backward. Arteries are large blood vessels with thick endotheliums to withstand high blood pressure. Capillaries are microscopic blood vessels with walls that are only one cell thick.

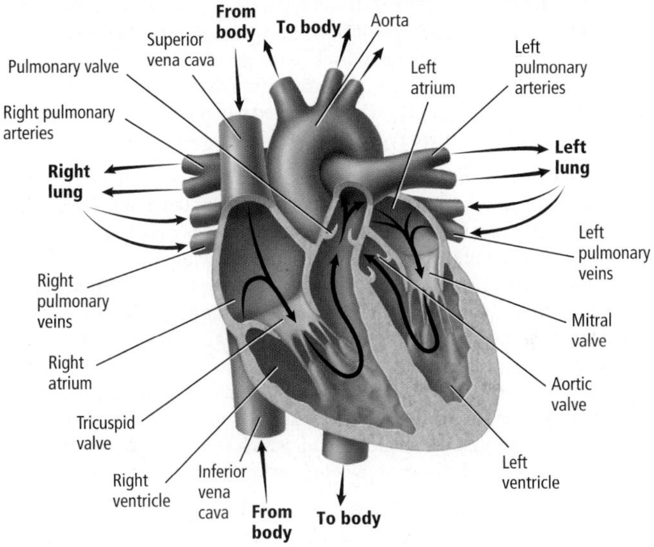

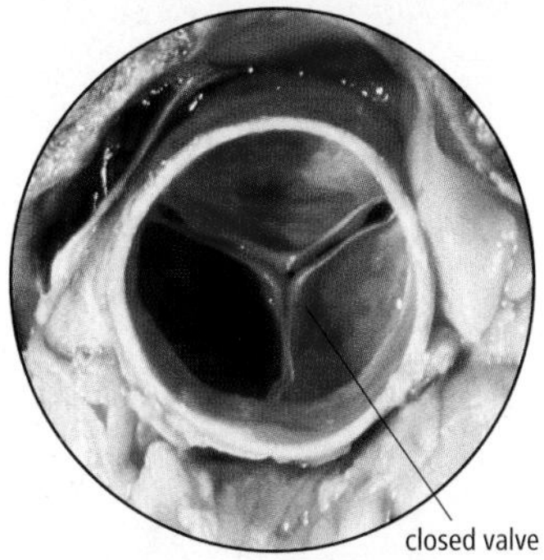

Aortic valve in a closed position

■ **Figure 4** The arrows map the path of blood as it circulates through the heart.
***Diagram** the path of blood through the heart.*

S

How the heart beats The heart acts in two main phases. In the first phase, the atria fill with blood. The atria contract, filling the ventricles with blood. In the second phase, the ventricles contract to pump blood out of the heart, into the lungs, and forward into the body.

The heart works in a regular rhythm. A group of cells located in the right atrium, called the **pacemaker** or sinoatrial (SA) node, send out signals that tell the heart muscle to contract. The SA node receives internal stimuli about the body's oxygen needs, and then it responds by adjusting the heart rate. The signal initiated by the SA node causes both atria to contract. Then the signal travels to another area in the heart called the atrioventricular (AV) node, as illustrated in **Figure 5.** The signal moves through fibers, causing both ventricles to contract. This two-step contraction makes up one complete heartbeat.

D

■ **Figure 5** The SA node initiates the contraction of the heart, which spreads through both atria to the AV node. The AV node transmits the signal through excitable fibers that stimulate both ventricles.

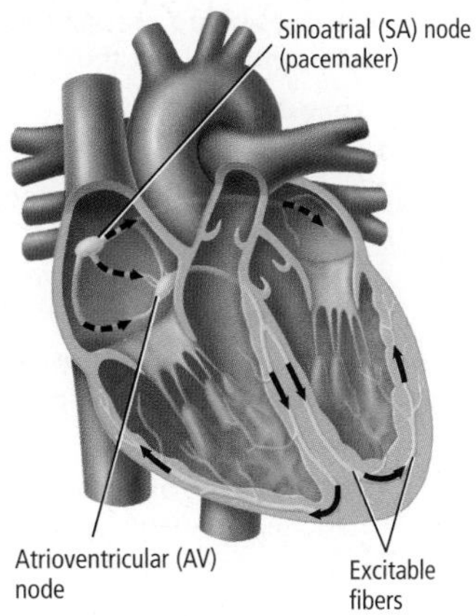

Pulse The heart pulses about 70 times each minute. If you touch the inside of your wrist just below your thumb, you can feel a pulse in the artery in your wrist rise and fall. This pulse is the alternating expansion and relaxation of the artery wall caused by the contraction of the left ventricle. The number of times the artery in your wrist pulses is the number of times your heart beats.

Blood pressure Blood pressure is a measure of how much pressure is exerted against the vessel walls by the blood. Blood-pressure readings can provide information about the condition of arteries. The contraction of the heart, or systole (SIS tuh lee), causes blood pressure to rise to its highest point, and the relaxation of the heart, or diastole (di AS tuh lee), brings blood pressure down to its lowest point. The ideal normal blood-pressure reading for a healthy adult is 120 (systolic pressure)/80 (diastolic pressure).

Content Background

Real-World Connection The implantable cardiac pacemaker was invented in Buffalo, New York, by Wilson Greatbatch during the late 1950s and was patented in 1962. The pacemaker uses electrical signals to maintain the proper heartbeat and is credited with savings thousands of lives. Each year, 600,000 pacemakers are implanted into people. About three million people worldwide have pacemakers. The life expectancy of people with pacemakers is about the same as it is for people without pacemakers. Once inserted, the pacemaker battery is monitored frequently and usually lasts five to eight years.

S Skill Practice

EL BL OL AL Visual Literacy

Have students review Figure 4 and then diagram the heart, labeling each major area and denoting blood flow with arrows.

D Develop Concepts

BL OL AL Discuss

ASK STUDENTS: ***Why is it important for both atria to beat at the same time and for both ventricles to contract together?*** This provides consistent flow of blood through the heart.

Writing Support

BL OL AL Technical Writing

Have pairs or small groups of students write a product guide and care instructions for the heart. This guide should detail the heart functions to someone unfamiliar with how the heart works. Illustrations may be used. Sample guide should be similar to product instructions. Items might include a diagram with labeled parts, flow of blood, and location.

Skill Practice

EL BL OL AL Use Math Skills

Have students calculate their heart beats per minute. First, show students how to find their pulse on their wrist below their thumb. Have students count the number of beats they feel in 15 seconds. Then have students multiply that number by 4 to calculate their heartbeats per minute.

■ **Caption Question Fig. 4** The blood follows the following path:

1. superior and inferior vena cava
2. right atrium
3. right ventricle
4. pulmonary arteries
5. lungs
6. pulmonary veins
7. left atrium
8. left ventricle
9. aorta
10. body

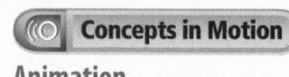

Concepts in Motion

Animation

MiniLab 1

Inquiry MiniLab

For a lab worksheet, use your eTeacherEdition Online.

RUBRIC A rubric for evaluating MiniLabs is found on your eTeacherEdition Online.

Est. Time 25 min

Safety Precaution Approve lab safety forms before work begins.

Teaching Strategies

- Make sure students are comfortable using the blood pressure cuff prior to the lab. Cuff pressure that is too high or a cuff left inflated for more than a few seconds can cause severe bruising. Review with students how to measure both systolic and diastolic pressure.
- Ask a school nurse to demonstrate or monitor the MiniLab.

Analysis

1. The control sample should be a blood pressure reading taken while the test subject is at rest. Students should hold as many factors constant as possible, including the way the sphygmomanometer is used. The independent variable is the activity undertaken by the test subject. The dependent variable is the blood pressure of the test subject after engaging in the activity.
2. Answers should explain how the data relates to the hypotheses.

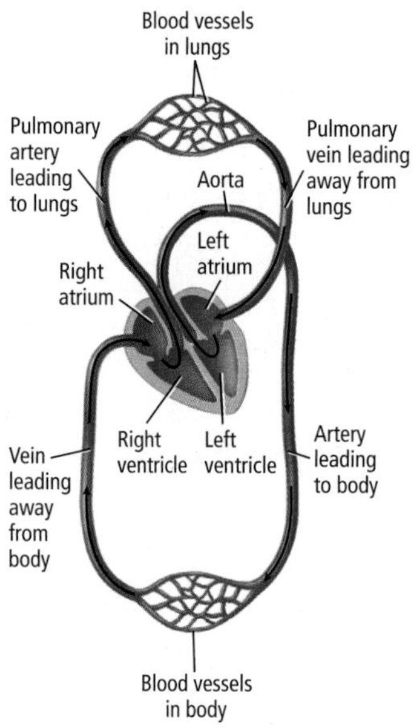

Figure 6 Blood flow through the body consists of two different circulatory loops.

Concepts in Motion

Animation

Blood flow in the body If you follow the flow of blood shown in **Figure 6,** you will notice that it flows in two loops. First, the blood travels from the heart to the lungs and back to the heart. Then, the blood is pumped in another loop from the heart through the body and back. The right side of the heart pumps deoxygenated blood to the lungs, and the left side of the heart pumps oxygenated blood to the rest of the body.

To the lungs and back When blood from the body flows into the right atrium, it has a low concentration of oxygen but a high concentration of carbon dioxide. This deoxygenated blood is dark red. The blood flows from the right atrium into the right ventricle and is pumped into the pulmonary arteries that lead to the lungs, as shown in **Figure 6.**

Eventually, blood flows into capillaries in the lungs that are in close contact with the air that enters the lungs. The air in the lungs has a greater concentration of oxygen than the blood in the capillaries does, so oxygen diffuses from the lungs into the blood. At the same time, carbon dioxide diffuses in the opposite direction—from the blood into the airspace in the lungs. Oxygenated blood, which is now bright red, flows to the left atrium of the heart to be pumped out to the body.

To the body and back The left atrium fills with oxygenated blood from the lungs, beginning the second loop. As shown in **Figure 6,** the blood then moves from the left atrium into the left ventricle. The left ventricle pumps the blood into the largest artery in the body called the aorta. Eventually, blood flows into the capillaries that branch throughout the body. Importantly, the capillaries are in close contact with body cells. Oxygen is released from the blood into the body cells by diffusion, and carbon dioxide moves from the cells to the blood by diffusion. The deoxygenated blood then flows back to the right atrium through veins.

MiniLab 1

Investigate Blood Pressure

Inquiry MiniLab

How does blood pressure change in response to physical activity? Blood pressure changes from day to day and throughout the day. It is affected by physical, psychological, behavioral, and inherited factors.

Procedure

1. Read and complete the lab safety form.
2. Watch the instructor demonstrate how to safely measure blood pressure. Practice using a **blood-pressure cuff** to measure a partner's blood pressure. Refer to a **blood-pressure chart** to interpret the reading.
3. Predict how exercise will affect systolic and diastolic blood pressure.
4. Take the resting blood-pressure reading of one of your classmates.
5. Have the person whose blood pressure you took do a rhythmic exercise for one minute.
6. Take a second blood-pressure reading and compare it to the resting blood-pressure reading.

Analysis

1. **Identify** the experimental constants, the independent and dependent variables, and the control in your experiment.
2. **Conclude** whether your prediction was supported. Explain.

Demonstration

BL OL AL Heart Valves Use your sink's faucet, a 3-m rubber tube, and a 1000-mL beaker to demonstrate valves. Connect one end of the rubber tubing to your sink's rubber tube connector and place the other end in the beaker. Slowly turn on the water so it is running out of the tube at a low-to-medium rate. Using your fingers, pinch the hose to stop the water from traveling down the tube. Count to two and release your fingers. Continue to pinch and release the tube.

ASK STUDENTS: ***What happens when I pinch the tube?*** The water stops flowing. Point out to students that pinching the tube with your fingers simulates the action of the heart valves in stopping the flow of blood. Est. time: 5 min

Blood Components

Blood is the fluid of life because it transports important substances throughout the body. Blood is made up of a liquid medium called plasma, red blood cells, platelets, and white blood cells.

Plasma The clear, yellowish fluid portion of blood is the **plasma.** More than 50 percent of blood is plasma. Ninety percent of plasma is water, and nearly 10 percent is dissolved materials. Plasma carries the broken-down products of digested food, such as glucose and fats. Plasma also transports vitamins, minerals, and chemical messengers including hormones that signal body activities, such as the uptake of glucose by the cells. In addition, waste products from the cells are carried away by plasma.

There are three groups of plasma proteins that give plasma its yellow color. One group helps to regulate the amount of water in blood. The second group, produced by white blood cells, helps fight disease. The third group helps to form blood clots.

Reading Check **Explain** the functions of plasma.

Red blood cells The **red blood cells** carry oxygen to all of the body's cells. Red blood cells resemble discs with pinched-in centers, as shown in **Figure 7.** Recall that red blood cells develop in the marrow—the center portion of large bones. Red blood cells have no nuclei and live for only about 120 days.

C

D

Red blood cells mostly consist of an iron-containing protein called hemoglobin. Hemoglobin chemically binds with oxygen molecules and carries oxygen to the body's cells.

Platelets Have you ever cut your finger? If so, you probably noticed that in a short while, the blood flowing from the cut slowed down and then stopped as a blood clot formed a scab. **Platelets** are cell fragments, shown in **Figure 7,** that are important in forming blood clots.

When a blood vessel is cut, platelets collect and stick to the vessel at the site of the wound. The platelets then release chemicals that produce a protein called fibrin. Fibrin weaves a network of fibers across the cut that traps blood platelets and red blood cells, as shown in **Figure 8.** As more and more platelets and blood cells are trapped, a blood clot forms.

W

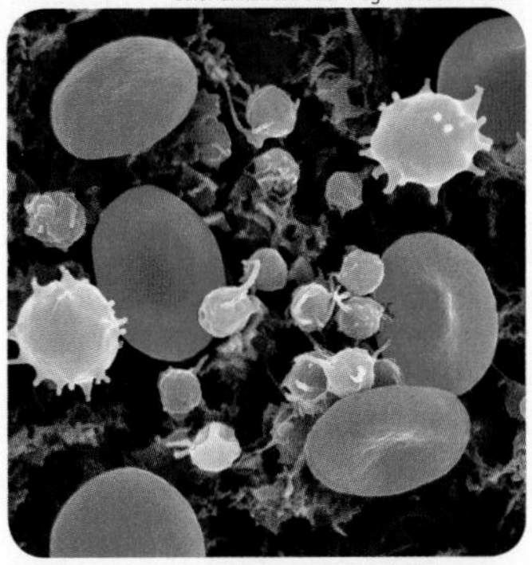

Figure 7 Blood is composed of liquid plasma, red blood cells (dimpled discs), white blood cells (irregularly shaped cells), and platelets (flat fragments).
Infer *What might be occurring if there are too many white blood cells?*

S

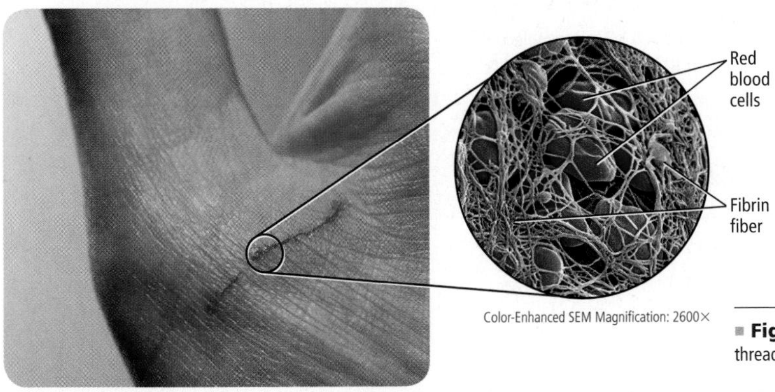

Figure 8 A scab forms as fibrin threads trap blood cells and platelets.

Caption Question Fig. 7 A high number of white blood cells might indicate an infection.

Reading Check Plasma transports vitamins and carries waste products away from cells.

S Skill Practice

BL OL AL Visual Literacy

Have students examine Figure 7. **ASK STUDENTS:** ***Why are red blood cells concave in shape?*** This shape allows a maximum surface area for the transfer of gases and to give them the flexibility they need to travel and fit through capillaries.

C Critical Thinking

BL OL AL Hypothesize

ASK STUDENTS: ***What is the advantage of the red blood cell not having a nucleus?*** A nucleus decreases the space available for gas transport. Having more space leaves more room for hemoglobin to transport oxygen. A nucleus also adds cell mass. Tell students that this increases the heart's workload by about 20 percent. If every red blood cell had a nucleus, the heart would have to work 20 percent harder.

D Develop Concepts

BL OL AL Discuss

ASK STUDENTS: ***Have you ever bitten your lip and noticed that your blood had a specific taste?*** Some will say yes. ***Why do you think this is?*** The iron of hemoglobin within the red blood cell is responsible for the specific taste.

Writing Support

OL AL Creative Writing Have students imagine they are a red blood cell and write an autobiography entitled *120 Days of Life.*

W Writing Support

BL OL AL Technical Writing

Have students write an ingredient label for a vial of blood. Sample label: plasma (10 percent is dissolved materials—glucose, fats, vitamins, minerals—and 90 percent is water), red blood cells, white blood cells, and platelets

FOLDABLES®

✻RUBRIC A rubric for evaluating Foldables is found on your eTeacherEdition Online.

Going Further On the back of their Foldables, have students list the type of marker associated with each blood type.

Critical Thinking

BL OL AL Infer

ASK STUDENTS: ***Why is it difficult to pull a gauze strip away from a cut?*** Blood clots within the gauze, making the gauze part of the clot. The blood uses the gauze network much like the fibrous structure it forms on its own.

D Develop Concepts

BL OL AL Discuss

ASK STUDENTS: ***Why can people who have type O blood donate blood to people who have other types of blood?*** Type O blood does not have the marker molecules that would cause rejection in the recipient. Recently researchers have discovered that the immune response to blood transfusions is increasingly complicated. Type O blood is given when blood type is unknown, but type-specific blood is preferred over type O if the patient is not type O.

Review Personal Tutor

Listen to a teacher explain blood groups.

Concepts in Motion

Interactive Table

Study Tip

Graphic Organizer Make a word map with the word *blood* in a large circle in the middle. Place the words *components, blood groups, circulation,* and *heart* in smaller circles around the large circle. Find information you learned in the chapter and add it to the appropriate smaller circles.

White blood cells The body's disease fighters are the **white blood cells.** Like red blood cells, white blood cells are produced in bone marrow. Some white blood cells recognize disease-causing organisms, such as bacteria, and alert the body that it has been invaded. Other white blood cells produce chemicals to fight the invaders. Still, other white blood cells surround and kill the invaders.

White blood cells are different from red blood cells in important ways. Many white blood cells move from the marrow to other sites in the body to mature. Unlike red blood cells, there are fewer white blood cells—only about one white blood cell for every 500 to 1000 red blood cells. Also, white blood cells have nuclei. Finally, most white blood cells live for months or years.

Review Personal Tutor

Blood Groups

How do you know what type of blood you have? There are marker molecules attached to red blood cells. These markers are called blood groups, which determine blood type.

FOLDABLES® Incorporate information from this section into your Foldable.

ABO blood group There are four types of blood: A, B, AB, and O. If your blood type is A, you have A markers on your blood cells. If your blood type is B, you have B markers on your blood cells. If your blood type is AB, you have both A and B markers. If your blood type is O, you do not have A or B markers.

D

Importance of blood type If you ever need a blood transfusion, you will be able to receive only certain blood types, as shown in **Table 1.** This is because plasma contains proteins called antibodies that recognize red blood cells with foreign markers and cause those cells to clump together. For example, if you have blood type B, your blood contains antibodies that cause cells with A markers to clump. If you received a transfusion of type-A blood, your clumping proteins would make the type-A cells clump together. Clumping of blood cells can be dangerous because it can block blood flow.

Table 1 **Blood Types** — Concepts in Motion Interactive Table

Blood type	A	B	AB	O
Marker molecule and antibody	Marker molecule: A Antibody: anti-B	Marker molecules: B Antibody: anti-A	Marker molecules: AB Antibody: none	Marker molecules: none Antibodies: anti-A, anti-B
Example	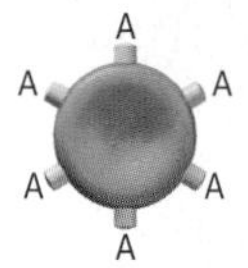	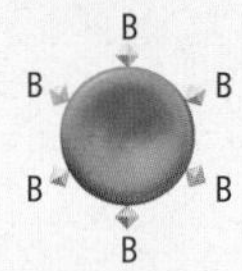	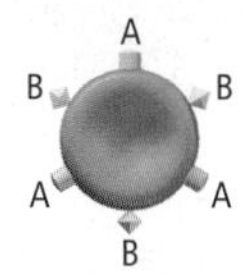	
Can donate blood to:	A or AB	B or AB	AB	A, B, AB, or O
Can receive blood from:	A or O	B or O	A, B, AB, or O	O

Research Citation

Question Educational research indicates that good questioning challenges students to think beyond simple recall. As suggested on this page, students should be asked to use higher level thinking skills when considering the main ideas of a lesson in order to deepen their understanding. (Heibert et al., 1997)

Research bibliography on pages 32T–34T

Rh blood group Another marker found on the surface of red blood cells is called the Rh factor. A person with A positive blood has A markers and Rh markers on their blood cells. The Rh marker can cause a problem when an Rh-negative person, someone without the Rh factor, receives a transfusion of Rh-positive blood that has the Rh marker. This can result in clumping of red blood cells, because Rh-negative blood contains Rh antibodies against Rh-positive cells.

The Rh factor can cause complications during some pregnancies. If the Rh-positive blood of a fetus mixes with the mother's Rh-negative blood, the mother will make anti-Rh antibodies. If the mother becomes pregnant again, these antibodies can cross the placenta and can destroy red blood cells if the fetus has Rh-positive blood. Rh-negative mothers are given a substance that prevents the production of Rh antibodies in the blood so that these problems can be avoided.

Circulatory System Disorders

Several disorders of the blood vessels, heart, and brain are associated with the circulatory system. Blood clots and other matter, such as fat deposits, can reduce the flow of oxygen-rich and nutrient-rich blood traveling through arteries. Physicians refer to the condition of blocked arteries as **atherosclerosis** (a thuh roh skluh ROH sus). When blood flow is reduced or blocked, the heart must work even harder to pump blood, and vessels can burst.

Atherosclerosis can lead to a heart attack or stroke. A heart attack occurs when blood does not reach the heart muscle. This can result in damage to the heart, and can even result in death if not treated. A stroke occurs when clots form in the blood vessels that supply oxygen to the brain. This can lead to ruptured blood vessels and internal bleeding, as shown in W **Figure 9.** Parts of the brain die because brain cells are deprived of oxygen.

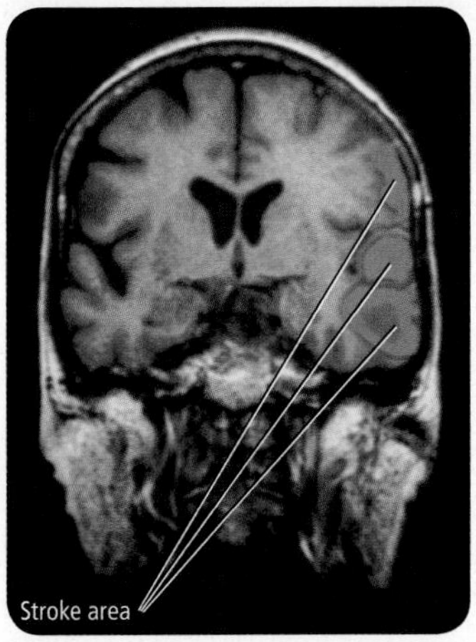

Figure 9 A stroke is associated with ruptured blood vessels in the brain, as shown in red.

Section 1 Assessment

Section Summary

- Blood vessels transport important substances throughout the body.
- The top half of the heart is made up of two atria, and the bottom half is made up of two ventricles.
- The heart pumps deoxygenated blood to the lungs, and it pumps oxygenated blood to the body.
- Blood is made up of plasma, red blood cells, white blood cells, and platelets.
- Blood is classified by the following four blood types: A, B, AB, and O.

Understand Main Ideas

1. MAIN Idea **Explain** the main functions of the circulatory system.
2. **Diagram** the path of blood through the heart and body.
3. **Compare and contrast** the structure of arteries and the structure of veins.
4. **Calculate** the average number of red blood cells for every 100 white blood cells in the human body.
5. **Summarize** the functions of the four components of blood.

Think Critically

6. **Cause and Effect** If a pacemaker received faulty signals from the brain, what would happen?
7. **Hypothesize** why exercise helps to maintain a healthy heart.

MATH in Biology

8. Count the number of times your heart beats during 15 seconds. What is your heart rate per minute?

W Writing Support

OL AL Technical Writing

Have students research and write a brochure about preventing heart disease. Have students present their finished piece to the class.

Formative Assessment

Evaluation Give students two diagrams of the circulatory system with blood flow labeled. One diagram will be labeled correctly, the other will be labeled incorrectly. **ASK STUDENTS:** ***Which diagram is correct? What is incorrect on the other diagram?*** Answers should demonstrate correct understanding of how blood flows through the circulatory system.

Remediation Provide students with an unlabeled diagram of the circulatory system. Have them use the diagrams in the book to label the direction of blood flow on the diagram which you have given them.

Section 1 Assessment

1. The circulatory system supplies the cells of the body with oxygen and nutrients, and it removes wastes such as carbon dioxide.
2. Diagrams will reflect Figures 4 and 6.
3. Arteries have a thicker endothelial wall than veins have. Veins have valves and arteries do not.
4. For every 100 white blood cells, there would be 50,000–100,000 red blood cells.
5. Plasma is the liquid portion of the blood. Red blood cells carry oxygen to cells and carry carbon dioxide away from cells. White blood cells defend the body from disease. Platelets are cell fragments that help form blood clots.
6. The heart might beat irregularly.
7. People who exercise strengthen their cardiac muscle.
8. Students should multiply their count by four to calculate their heart rate per minute.

Assessment Online Quiz

Section 2

MAIN Idea

BL OL AL Respiratory System

ASK STUDENTS: ***How does oxygen reach a car engine to mix with an energy source, providing energy for the car?*** Possible answers: through the air intake, carburetor, or in the fuel injection.

SAY TO STUDENTS: ***Powering a car takes oxygen and fuel. Your body also requires oxygen and fuel for cellular respiration.***

R Reading Strategy

BL OL

Monitor Comprehension

Help students practice monitoring their comprehension as they read. As they read the text on this page, remind them to slow down and make note of any concepts that they do not understand. Help them practice the habits of rereading or reviewing to clarify what is unclear.

S Skill Practice

BL OL AL Identify

ASK STUDENTS: ***How would the two processes of respiration be affected if you were running a 400-m race?*** Breathing and respiration rates would increase. ***What if you were sleeping?*** They would slow down. ***Walking to school?*** They would increase.

Caption Question Fig. 10

Inhaled air has more O_2; exhaled air has more CO_2.

Video BrainPOP

Section 2

Reading Preview

Essential Questions

- What is the difference between internal and external respiration?
- What is the path of the air through the respiratory system?
- What changes occur in the body during breathing?

Review Vocabulary

ATP: biological molecule that provides the body's cells with chemical energy

New Vocabulary

breathing
external respiration
internal respiration
trachea
bronchus
lung
alveolus

Multilingual eGlossary

Video BrainPOP

Respiratory System

R **MAIN Idea** **The function of the respiratory system is the exchange of oxygen and carbon dioxide between the atmosphere and the blood and between the blood and the body's cells.**

Real-World Reading Link Air filters separate dust and other particles from the air before they enter a car's engine. This prevents engine problems and helps ensure good air flow. Similarly, your respiratory system has features that ensure that enough clean air gets into your lungs.

The Importance of Respiration

Your body's cells require oxygen. Recall that oxygen and glucose are used by cells to produce energy-rich ATP molecules needed to maintain cellular metabolism. This process is called cellular respiration. In addition to releasing energy, cellular respiration releases carbon dioxide and water.

Breathing and respiration The respiratory system sustains cellular respiration by supplying oxygen to body cells and removing carbon dioxide waste from cells. The respiratory system can be divided into two processes: breathing and respiration. First, air must enter the body through breathing. **Breathing** is the mechanical movement of air into and out of your lungs. **Figure 10** illustrates air being released from the lungs into the air. Second, gases are exchanged in the body. **External respiration** is the exchange of gases between the atmosphere and the S blood, which occurs in the lungs. **Internal respiration** is the exchange of gases between the blood and the body's cells.

Figure 10 Exhaled air from a person's lungs can be seen on a chilly evening.
Infer *how the air that you inhale is different from the air that you exhale.*

Content Background

Real-World Connection Irritants enter the respiratory system daily, and the body has protective reflexes, such as coughing and sneezing, to fight them. Both involve a temporary period of apnea, which is a period when respiration is suspended. Sneezing is triggered by the irritation of the nasal cavity wall, while coughing is triggered by irritation of the larynx, trachea, or bronchi. The air forced out of the larynx during a sneeze can travel up to 160 km/h, carrying mucus, foreign particles, and the irritant out of the respiratory tract.

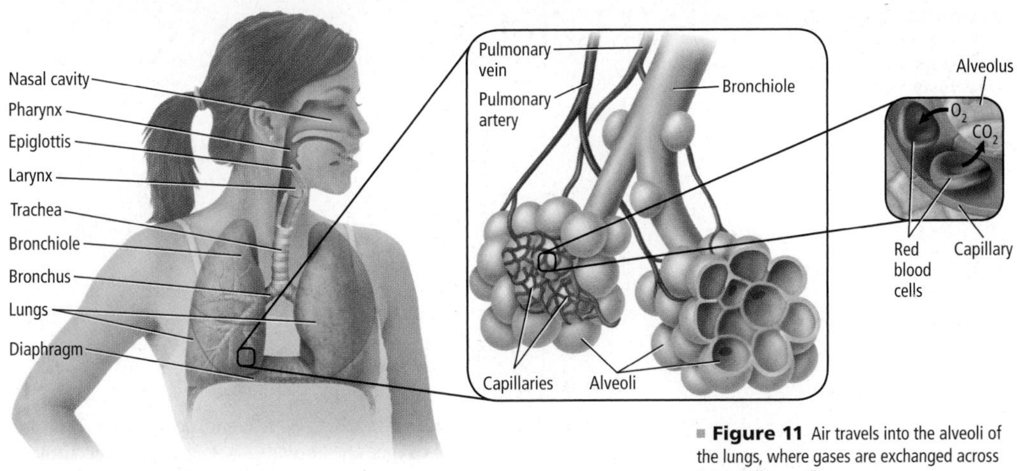

■ **Figure 11** Air travels into the alveoli of the lungs, where gases are exchanged across thin capillary walls.
Diagram ***Trace the path of oxygen from the atmosphere to the alveoli in the lungs.***

The Path of Air

The respiratory system is made up of the nasal passages, pharynx (FER ingks), larynx (LER ingks) or voice box, epiglottis, trachea, lungs, bronchi, bronchioles, alveoli (al VEE uh li), and diaphragm. Air travels from the outside environment to the lungs, where it passes through the alveoli, as shown in **Figure 11.**

First, air enters the mouth or nose. Hairs in the nose filter out dust and other large particles in the air. Hairlike structures called cilia, shown in **Figure 12,** also line the nasal passages, as well as other respiratory tubes. Cilia trap foreign particles from the air and sweep them toward the throat so that they do not enter the lungs. Mucous membranes beneath the cilia in C the nasal passages, also shown in **Figure 12,** warm and moisten the air while trapping foreign materials.

Filtered air then passes through the upper throat, called the pharynx. A flap of tissue called the epiglottis, which covers the opening to the larynx, prevents food particles from entering the respiratory tubes. The epiglottis allows air to pass from the larynx to a long tube in the chest cavity called the **trachea,** or windpipe. The trachea branches into two large tubes, called **bronchi** (BRAHN ki) (singular, bronchus), which lead to the lungs. The **lungs** are the largest organs in the respiratory system, and gas exchange takes place in the lungs. Each bronchus branches into smaller tubes called bronchioles (BRAHN kee ohlz), which continue to branch into even smaller passageways. Each of these ends in an individual air sac called an **alveolus** (plural, alveoli). Each alveolus has a thin wall—only one cell thick—and is surrounded by very thin capillaries.

Gas exchange in the lungs Air travels to individual alveoli, where oxygen diffuses across the moist, thin walls into capillaries and then into red blood cells. The oxygen is then transported to be released to tissue cells in the body during internal respiration. Meanwhile, carbon dioxide in the blood crosses capillary walls and diffuses into the alveoli to be returned to the atmosphere during external respiration. Carbon dioxide in the blood is found as carbonic acid in the red blood cells, dissolved in plasma, and bound to hemoglobin in plasma.

VOCABULARY
WORD ORIGIN
Alveolus
comes from the Latin word *alveus,* meaning *belly* or *hollow space*

■ **Figure 12** Hairlike cilia line the mucous membranes of the nasal cavity.

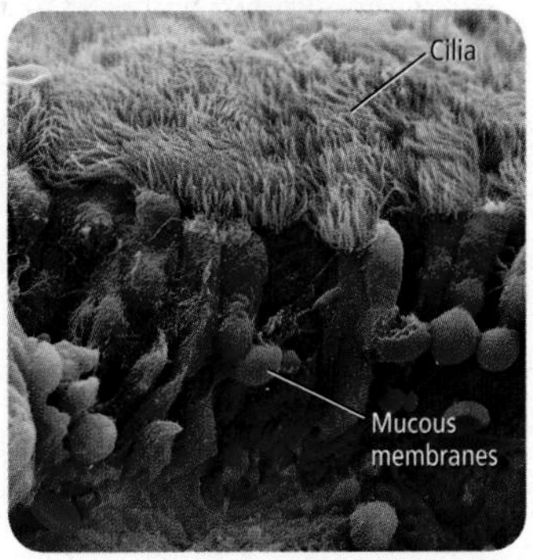

Color-Enhanced SEM Magnification: 2000×

Inquiry BioLab
The lab at the end of the chapter can be used at this point in the lesson.

GOING GREEN If you bring your lunch to school, place items in reusable containers. Encourage students to do the same. Also be conscious of the packaging used for single serving snack-sized packages.

C Critical Thinking
BL OL AL Hypothesize
ASK STUDENTS: ***What role does mucus play when you have a cold?*** Mucus is the body's first line of defense against foreign particles. Often, more mucus is developed during a cold in an attempt to rid the body of the invaders in the respiratory system.

Develop Concepts
BL OL AL
Clarify a Misconception
ASK STUDENTS: ***When you get a cold, can you visit the doctor and obtain medication to cure the cold?*** Some students might say yes. Colds are a respiratory infection caused by viruses, not by bacteria. Medication does not exist to cure the cold but medication can be used to treat its symptoms. Antibiotics are often prescribed to fight secondary bacterial infections resulting from the cold. Overuse and unnecessary use of antibiotics might lead to resistant strains of bacteria.

■ **Caption Question Fig. 11**
Air travels into the body through the mouth and nose, past the pharynx, down the trachea, down the bronchi, through the bronchioles, and into the alveoli.

Demonstration
BL OL Circulation and Respiration Use a fish tank, water, and an aquarium pump with a filter to demonstrate how a circulatory system and respiratory system work together. Fill the aquarium with water and hook up the filter/pump system. Turn the pump on and have the water pass through the filter.
ASK STUDENTS: ***Where are the gases being exchanged?*** The gases are exchanged as the water passes over the edge back into the aquarium. Point out that the filter acts like cilia in the respiratory tract, the water acts similar to the blood, and the pump acts like the heart. Est. time: 10 min

Inquiry Launch Lab

Assess Content Development
Assess how understanding has developed when students revisit the Launch Lab analysis questions.

MiniLab 2

Inquiry MiniLab

For a lab worksheet, use your eTeacherEdition Online.

RUBRIC A rubric for evaluating MiniLabs is found on your eTeacherEdition Online.

Est. Time 25 min

Safety Precaution Approve lab safety forms before work begins.

Teaching Strategy Ask students who cannot walk if they can participate using another form of exercise.

Analysis

1. Students will probably find that as heart rate increases, breathing increases also.
2. Exercise does affect metabolism. The increase in breathing indicates that more oxygen is being used and more carbon dioxide is being produced.
3. Different bodies require different amounts of oxygen.

LabManager™
Customize this lab with the LabManager™ CD-ROM.

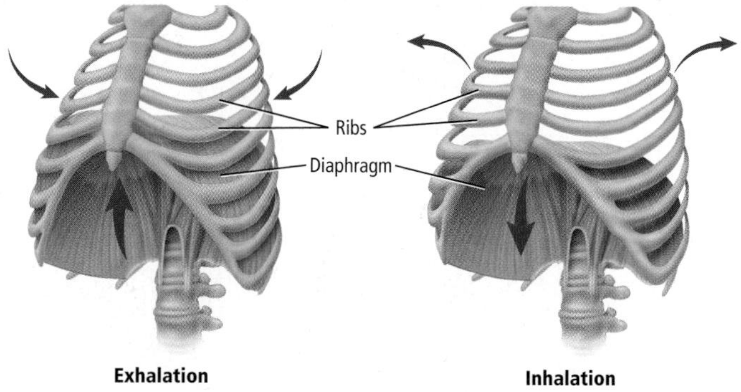

■ **Figure 13** Rib and diaphragm muscles contract and relax during breathing.
***Analyze** how air pressure is involved in breathing.*

Inquiry Launch Lab
Review Based on what you've read about respiration, how would you now answer the analysis questions?

Breathing

The brain directs the rate of breathing by responding to internal stimuli that indicate how much oxygen the body needs. When the concentration of carbon dioxide in the blood is high, the breathing rate increases because cells need more oxygen.

Inhalation is the act of taking air into the lungs. During inhalation, as shown in **Figure 13,** the diaphragm contracts. This causes the chest cavity to expand as the diaphragm moves down, allowing air to move into the lungs. During exhalation, the diaphragm relaxes and returns to its normal resting position. This reduces the size of the chest cavity as the diaphragm moves up. Air naturally flows out from the greater pressure of the lungs. Follow **Figure 14** to learn how circulation and respiration work together to supply the needed oxygen and to get rid of carbon dioxide.

MiniLab 2

Recognize Cause and Effect

Inquiry MiniLab

Does exercise affect metabolism? Most of the chemical reactions that occur in your cells make up your metabolism. In this lab, you will explore how exercise affects the circulatory and respiratory systems and infer how this affects metabolism.

Procedure

1. Read and complete the lab safety form.
2. Record the number of heartbeats and number of breaths per minute for ten classmates.
3. Instruct the same students to walk in place for five minutes. At the end of that time, record each person's heartbeat per minute and the number of breaths per minute.
4. After students have rested for five minutes, instruct them to jog or walk briskly in place for five minutes. Then record each person's heartbeat per minute and the number of breaths per minute.
5. Plot your results on **graph paper.** Each coordinate point should indicate breaths per minute on the horizontal axis and heartbeats per minute on the vertical axis.

Analysis

1. **Interpret** the relationship between the two dependent variables of your experiment—heart rate and breathing rate.
2. **Conclude** whether exercise affects metabolism. Why?
3. **Hypothesize** why students might have different numbers of heartbeats per minute and breaths per minute even though they all walked or jogged for the same amount of time.

Skill Practice

BL OL AL Sequence

TELL STUDENTS: ***Create a list of events that take place when a force "knocks the air out of you."*** Force hits the abdominal region, forcing the diaphragm up, which in turn compresses the lungs and releases the air inside the lungs.

■ **Caption Question Fig. 13** Air flows from areas of greater to lesser pressure during inhalation and exhalation.

Demonstration

BL OL AL Lung Capacity Use three balloons to demonstrate the different volume levels of lung capacity. Demonstrate the resting tidal volume by taking a normal breath and blowing up a balloon while exhaling, tying the balloon upon completion. Demonstrate expiratory reserve volume by taking a normal breath and exhaling as much as possible into another balloon, and then tying the balloon. Demonstrate inspiratory reserve volume by inhaling as deeply as possible and exhaling normally into a third balloon, and then tying the balloon. Explain that residual volume is what remains in the lungs after exhaling as much as possible. **ASK STUDENTS:** ***Why do we not use our total inhalation capacity?*** Our resting tidal volume provides the oxygen we need at rest; however, we need our extra capacity when we are active. Est. time: 10 min

Visualizing Gas Exchange

S

Figure 14
Gases are exchanged in the lungs and in the tissue cells of the body.

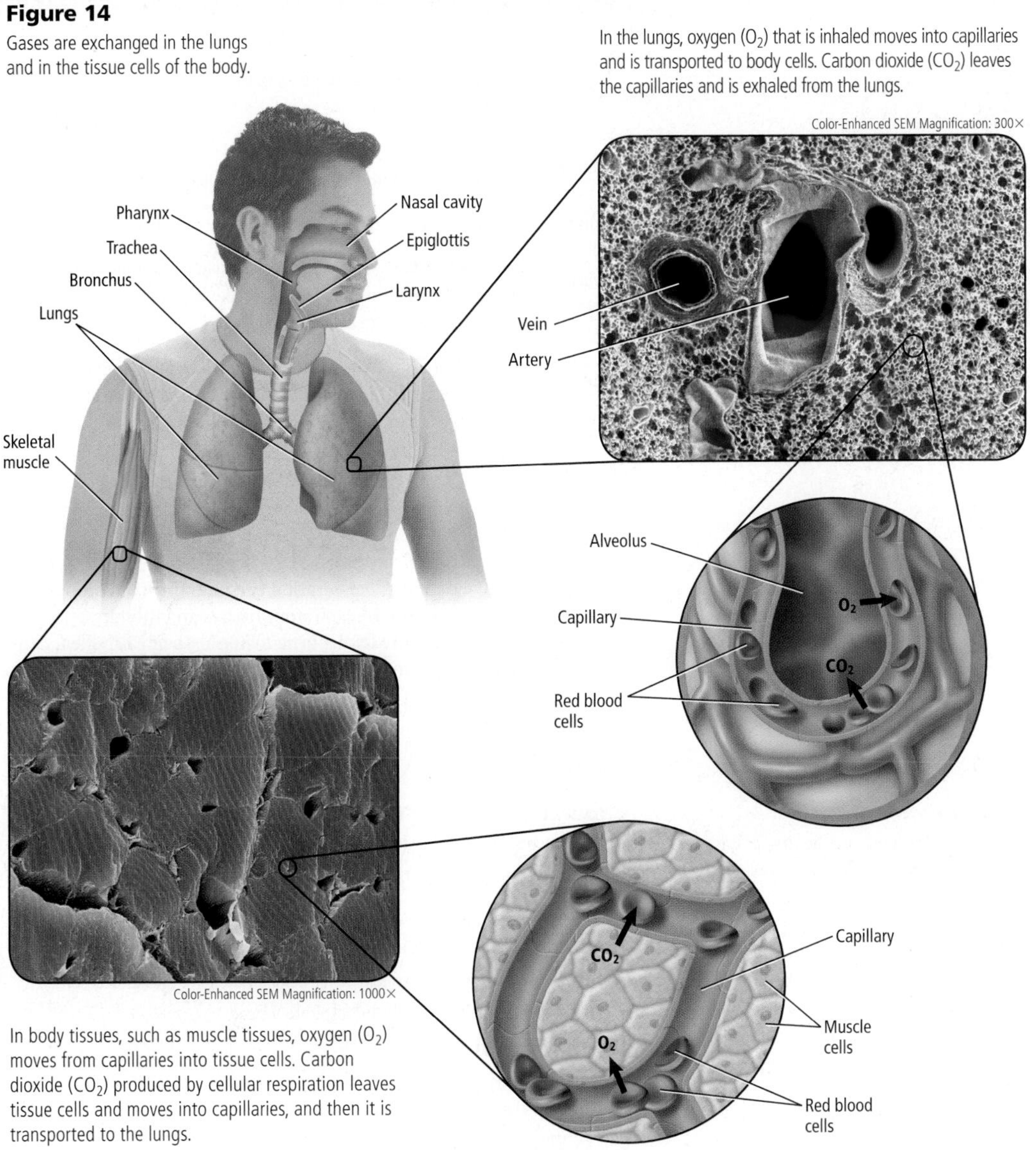

In body tissues, such as muscle tissues, oxygen (O_2) moves from capillaries into tissue cells. Carbon dioxide (CO_2) produced by cellular respiration leaves tissue cells and moves into capillaries, and then it is transported to the lungs.

Concepts in Motion Animation

Differentiated Instruction

Behavior Disorders Students with behavior disorders might require additional support during hands-on activities like the MiniLab on the previous page. Present the instructions for appropriate behavior during these activities in a manner that will increase the likelihood of compliance.

For more tips, see pages 14T–15T.

Research Citation

Formative Assessment Educational research indicates that assessment should be ongoing, strategic, and purposeful. The results can then benefit students by allowing the teacher to adapt curriculum and instruction to meet individual needs. **(Bredekamp and Copple, 1997)**

Research bibliography on pages 32T–34T

Visualizing Gas Exchange

Purpose

Students will understand organisms accommodate the need for obtaining, transforming, and transporting the matter and energy used to sustain the organism.
C.5

S Skill Practice

BL OL Visual Literacy Have students review the figure on this page examining the gases exchanged within the lungs.
ASK STUDENTS: ***What part of the figure is responsible for gas exchange in the respiratory and circulatory systems?*** alveoli, capillaries, and blood ***Are they similar?*** Yes, both alveoli and capillaries contain one thin layer of tissue. ***What is the mechanism for gas exchange?*** diffusion

Writing Support

EL BL OL AL

Narrative Writing
SAY TO STUDENTS: ***Suppose you are an oxygen molecule traveling into a human body. Write a narrative describing what you see and what is happening to you as you travel to the alveoli. Then write a sentence describing each stage.*** A possible narrative may include the following chain of events: An oxygen molecule might pass into the nose, passing cilia and mucus, through the trachea, passing dust and other foreign particles into the bronchi, to a bronchiole, to an alveolus, and into a red blood cell.

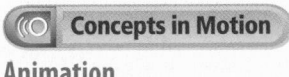

Concepts in Motion
Animation

Concepts in Motion

Interactive Table

W Writing Support

BL OL AL Informal Writing Have students work in groups of four to research, write, and produce a public service announcement (PSA) about a respiratory disease. The PSA should include the name of the disease, symptoms, causes, possible cures, and how to prevent it. If time permits, have students act out their commercials in front of class.

Formative Assessment

Evaluation Have students examine a diagram of the lungs and describe the exchange of oxygen and carbon dioxide in the lungs. Oxygen flows into the lungs to individual sacs called alveoli, in which oxygen and carbon dioxide are exchanged with the capillaries of the circulatory system.

Remediation Have students work in pairs to write a skit about how the body obtains oxygen and removes carbon dioxide using their books as a reference. If time permits, have students present their skits to the class. Each individual could play multiple roles to demonstrate the parts and processes of the respiratory system.

Table 2 Common Respiratory Disorders

Concepts in Motion Interactive Table

Lung Disorder	Brief Description
Asthma	Respiratory pathways become irritated, and bronchioles constrict.
Bronchitis	Respiratory pathways become infected, resulting in coughing and production of mucus.
Emphysema	Alveoli break down, resulting in reduced surface area needed for gas exchange with the alveoli's blood capillaries.
Pneumonia	Infection of the lungs causes the alveoli to collect mucous material.
Pulmonary tuberculosis	A specific bacterium infects the lungs, resulting in less elasticity of the blood capillaries surrounding the alveoli, thus decreasing effective gas exchange between the air and blood.
Lung cancer	Uncontrolled cell growth in lung tissue can lead to a persistent cough, shortness of breath, bronchitis, or pneumonia, and can lead to death.

Respiratory Disorders

Some diseases and disorders irritate, inflame, or infect the respiratory system, as described in **Table 2.** These disorders can produce tissue damage that reduces the effectiveness of the bronchi and alveoli. When these tissues become damaged, respiration becomes difficult. Smoking also causes chronic irritation to respiratory tissues and inhibits cellular metabolism. Finally, exposure to airborne materials, such as pollen, can W produce respiratory problems in some people who have allergic reactions.

Section 2 Assessment

Section Summary

- Alveoli in the lungs are the sites of gas exchange between the respiratory and circulatory systems.
- The pathway of air starts with the mouth or nose and ends at the alveoli located in the lungs.
- Inhalation and exhalation are the processes of taking in and expelling air.
- Respiratory disorders can inhibit respiration.

Understand Main Ideas

1. MAIN Idea **Identify** the main function of the respiratory system.
2. **Distinguish** between internal and external respiration.
3. **Sequence** the path of air from the nasal passages to the bloodstream.
4. **Describe** the mechanics of inhalation and exhalation.
5. **Infer** how the respiratory system would compensate for a circulatory disorder.
6. **Describe** three disorders of the respiratory system.

Think Critically

7. **Hypothesize** an advantage of heating and moisturizing air before it reaches the alveoli.

MATH in Biology

8. The total surface area of the alveoli tissue in your lungs is approximately 70 m^2. This is more than 40 times the surface area of the skin. What is the surface area of your skin?

Section 2 Assessment

1. to provide oxygen to the body and to remove carbon dioxide
2. Internal respiration is the exchange of gases between the blood and the body's cells; external respiration is the exchange of gases between the atmosphere and the blood.
3. Air travels in through the nose, past the pharynx, down the trachea, down the bronchi, through the bronchioles, and into the alveoli where oxygen from the air passes through capillaries to the bloodstream.
4. When the diaphragm contracts, the chest cavity expands, the diaphragm moves down, and air is pulled into the lungs. When the diaphragm rises and the chest cavity shrinks, air is pushed out of the lungs.
5. Sample answer: The respiratory system might have to work harder to compensate for a circulatory disorder.
6. Student answers should include information from Table 2.
7. Warm, moist air helps keep the lining of the alveoli moist and able to diffuse gases.
8. The surface area of the skin is approximately 1.75 m^2.

Assessment Online Quiz

Section 3

Reading Preview

Essential Questions

- What is the function of the kidney in the body?
- What are the steps of the excretion of wastes from the Bowman's capsule to the urethra?
- What is the difference between filtration and reabsorption in the kidneys?

Review Vocabulary

pH: the measure of acidity or alkalinity of a solution

New Vocabulary

kidney
urea

g Multilingual eGlossary

Excretory System

R **MAIN Idea** **The kidneys maintain homeostasis by removing wastes and excess water from the body and by maintaining the pH of blood.**

Real-World Reading Link Suppose that you cleaned your bedroom by first moving everything except large items into the hallway. You then return only the items that you will keep in your bedroom and leave the items that you do not want any longer in the hallway for later disposal. This is similar to how your kidneys filter materials in your blood.

Parts of the Excretory System

The body collects wastes, such as toxins, waste products, and carbon dioxide, that result from metabolic functions of the body. The excretory system removes these toxins and wastes from the body. In addition, the excretory system regulates the amount of fluid and salts in the body, and it maintains the pH of the blood. All of these functions help to maintain homeostasis.

The components that make up the excretory system include the lungs, skin, and kidneys, as illustrated in **Figure 15.** The lungs primarily excrete carbon dioxide. The skin primarily excretes water and salts contained in sweat. The kidneys, however, are the major excretory organs in the body.

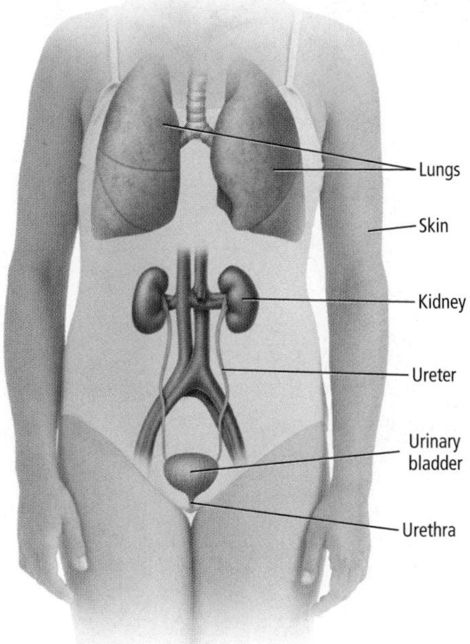

Figure 15 The organs of excretion work together to eliminate wastes from the body. These organs include the lungs, skin, and kidneys.

Section 3

MAIN Idea

BL OL AL Removing Waste
ASK STUDENTS: ***How does the water in a swimming pool stay clean?*** pump, filters, vacuum
TELL STUDENTS: ***Water circulates around the pool through a series of pipes and filters, a cleaning agent is added, and the water is pumped back into the pool. The pH is monitored and agents are added to maintain a balance in the water, similar to the excretory system you will read about in Section 3.***

R Reading Strategy

BL OL Assessment Preview
Before students read Section 3, have them read the section assessment questions.
SAY TO STUDENTS: ***As you read this section, attempt to develop answers to these questions.***

Critical Thinking

BL OL AL Predict
ASK STUDENTS: ***What is a good indicator of the hydration level of your body?*** One indicator is the color of urine. Dark urine usually indicates the kidneys are reabsorbing water and is a key indicator of dehydration. Drinking enough water to produce light-colored urine is a good rule to follow since this indicates that the body has enough water.

Demonstration

BL OL AL Function of a Kidney Use sand, pebbles, red food coloring, water, a 100-mL graduated cylinder, filter paper, funnel, and a 250-mL beaker to demonstrate the function of a kidney. Place the filter paper in the funnel and set the funnel on top of the beaker. Fill the graduated cylinder with 65 mL of water, add food coloring until the water is light red. Add 10 mL of sand and 10 mL of pebbles to the 65 mL of water in the graduated cylinder. Pour the water mixture into the funnel, and allow the water to filter into the beaker.
ASK STUDENTS: ***What does this process represent?*** the kidneys filtering the blood
TELL STUDENTS: ***The particles in the water represent waste material in the blood. As the blood (colored water) passes through the kidney (filter paper/funnel), the waste is removed and the blood is returned to the body (beaker).*** Est. time: 10 min

W Writing Support

BL OL AL Creative Writing Have students write a paragraph describing life as a molecule of urea in the excretory system. Students working at a higher level could write a one-page essay. All paragraphs or essays should begin by discussing the renal artery and conclude with the urethra. Each essay should describe what happens to substances, such as red blood cells, that molecules meet along the way.

D Develop Concepts

BL OL AL

Clarify a Misconception

ASK STUDENTS: ***Where is urea formed?*** liver Many students will associate urea filtration with urine formation. Urea is a toxic waste produced by the liver during breakdown of excess amino acids. Urea is removed from the blood by the kidneys and excreted in urine.

AL ASK STUDENTS: ***What is ammonia? What would happen to the body if ammonia were to be ingested?*** Ammonia is a toxic waste product, which is part of urea. If a person ingested ammonia in large amounts, they would die.

S Skill Practice

EL BL OL AL COOP LEARN

Visual Literacy Have students work in pairs and construct a flowchart of the excretory system and its processes based on the information they see in Figure 16. Sample chart:

blood
↓
kidney
↓
Bowman's capsule
↓
urine
↓
ureter
↓
urinary bladder
↓
urethra

The Kidneys

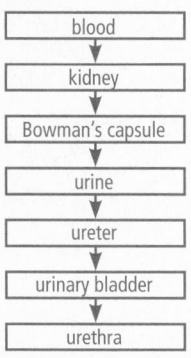

As shown in **Figure 16,** the **kidneys** are bean-shaped organs that filter out wastes, water, and salts from the blood. The kidneys are divided into two distinct regions, also illustrated in **Figure 16.** The outer portion is called the renal cortex and the inner region is called the renal medulla. Each of these regions contains microscopic tubes and blood vessels. In the center of each kidney is a region called the renal pelvis, where urine collection occurs. Follow **Figure 16** as you read about how the kidneys function.

Nephron filtration Each kidney contains approximately one million filtering units called nephrons. Blood enters each nephron through a long tube that is surrounded by a ball of capillaries called the glomerulus (gluh MER uh lus) (plural, glomeruli). The glomerulus is surrounded by a structure called the Bowman's capsule.

The renal artery transports nutrients and wastes to the kidney and branches into smaller and smaller blood vessels, eventually reaching the tiny capillaries in the glomerulus. The walls of the capillaries are very thin, and the blood is under great pressure. As **W** a result, water and substances dissolved in the water, such as the nitrogenous waste product called **urea,** are pushed through the capillary walls into the Bowman's capsule. Larger molecules, such **D** as red blood cells and proteins, remain in the bloodstream.

S

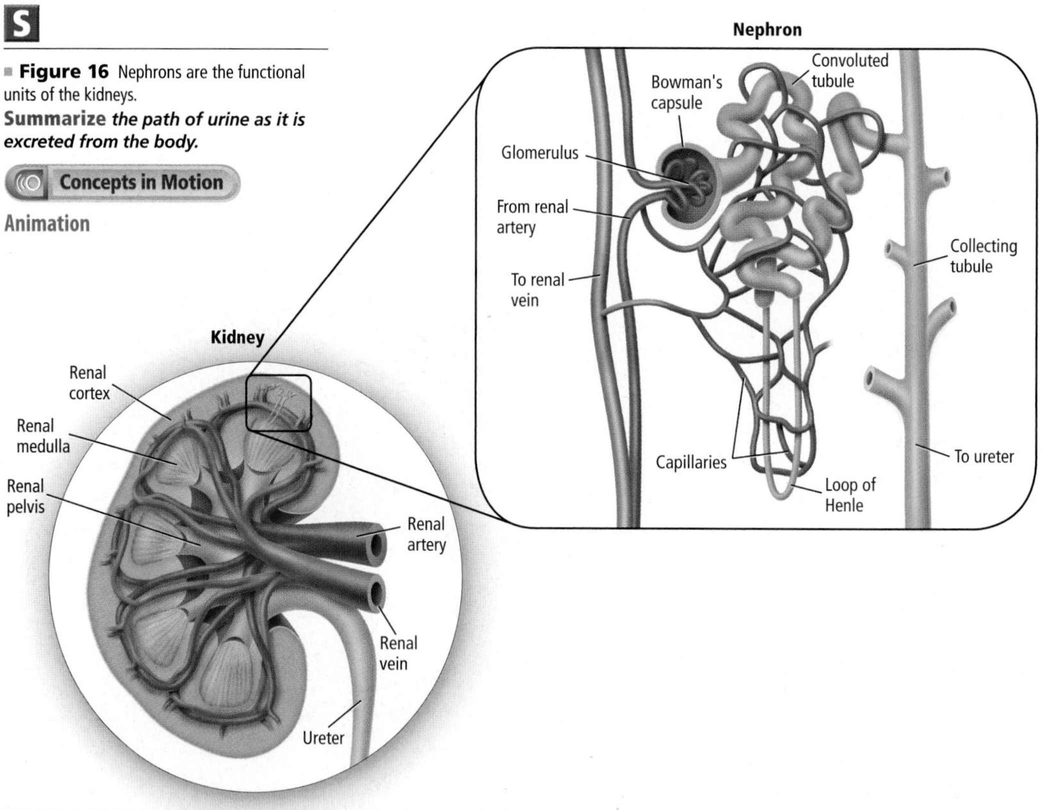

■ **Figure 16** Nephrons are the functional units of the kidneys.
Summarize *the path of urine as it is excreted from the body.*

Concepts in Motion
Animation

Concepts in Motion
Animation

■ **Caption Question Fig. 16** The filtrate collected in the Bowman's capsule flows through the renal tubule. Capillaries reabsorb useful materials and water back into the bloodstream. Waste products drain from the capillaries into the tubule. The urine leaves the kidneys through ureters and flows into the bladder. The urine exits the body through the urethra.

Reabsorption and the formation of urine The filtrate collected in the Bowman's capsule flows through the renal tubule, which consists of the convoluted tubule, the loop of Henle, and the collecting tubule, as illustrated in **Figure 16.** Much of the lost water and useful substances, such as glucose and minerals, are reabsorbed into the capillaries surrounding the renal tubule. This process is called reabsorption. At the same time, excess fluids and toxic substances in the capillaries are passed to the collecting tubules. This waste product is called urine. Urine leaves the kidney through ducts called the ureters (YOO ruh turz), as shown in **Figure 16.** Urine is then stored in the urinary bladder and exits the body through the urethra.

The kidneys filter about 180 L of blood each day in adults but produce only about 1.5 L of urine. The processes of filtration and reabsorption from the blood require large amounts of energy. Although kidneys account for only one percent of body weight, **S** they use 20 to 25 percent of the body's oxygen intake for their internal energy requirements.

Connection to Chemistry The kidneys can help maintain a normal pH in the blood by adjusting the acid-base balance. Recall that low pH results when there is an abundance of H^+. When the blood pH is too low, the kidneys can increase pH levels in the body by excreting hydrogen (H^+) ions and ammonia into the renal tubules. The kidneys can decrease pH levels by reabsorbing buffers such as bicarbonate (HCO_3^+) and sodium (Na^+) ions. Because biological processes normally require pH between 6.5 and 7.5, the kidneys help to maintain homeostasis by keeping pH levels within the normal range.

CAREERS IN BIOLOGY

Urologist A urologist is a medical doctor who has specialized knowledge about problems of the male and female urinary systems. Responsibilities can include examining patients, performing laboratory tests, interpreting test results and examination findings, and treating injuries and disorders.

DATA ANALYSIS LAB 1

Based On Real Data*

Interpret the Data

How do extreme conditions affect the average daily loss of water in the human body? The body obtains water by absorbing it through the digestive tract. The body loses water primarily by excreting it in urine from the kidneys, through sweat, and through the lungs.

Think Critically

1. **Identify** what the major source of water loss is during normal temperatures.
2. **Hypothesize** why more water is lost in sweat during rigorous exercise than in urine.
3. **Calculate** the percent of water loss for each of the three conditions.

Data and Observations

The table shows data collected for normal temperatures, for high temperatures, and during rigorous exercise.

Average Daily Water Loss in Humans (in mL)

Source	Normal Temperatures	High Temperatures	Rigorous Exercise
Kidneys	1500	1400	750
Skin	450	1800	5000
Lungs	450	350	650

*Data obtained from: Beers, M. 2003. *The Merck Manual of Medical Information, Second Edition* West Point, PA.: Merck & Co. Inc.

"The aim of education should be to convert the mind into a living fountain, and not a reservoir."

—John Mason

S Skill Practice

OL AL Use Math Skills

ASK STUDENTS: ***What percent of the material passing through each kidney is filtered as urine?*** less than 1% (0.833%) Have students calculate the percentage of urine generated compared to the total liquid passing through each kidney by using the numbers in this section: 180 L of blood, 1.5 L of urine.
1.5 L/180 L x 100 = 0.833%

DATA ANALYSIS LAB 1

About the Lab

- Graph the data, placing urine, sweat, lungs, and digestive tract along the *x*-axis and increments of 200 mL along the *y*-axis. Project the graph on a screen. Use the following colors for lines:

Green	Normal temperature
Red	High temperature
Yellow	Rigorous exercise

- Also see research by Shirreffs, Susan M., and, Maughan, Ronald J. 1998. Urine osmolality and conductivity as indices of hydration status in athletes in the heat. *Medicine & Exercise* 30 (11): 1958–1602.

Think Critically

1. urine
2. The body sweats to cool itself and maintain a constant temperature. During rigorous exercise, the body sweats heavily to counteract the heat generated in the muscles.
3.

Source	Normal Temps	High Temps	Rigorous Exercise
Urine	62%	39%	12%
Sweat	19%	51%	78%
Lungs	19%	10%	10%

R Reading Strategy

Panel Discussion Have students read the material under the heading *Kidney Disorders* and create a panel of students to act as scientists willing to explain kidney problems and treatments to the class. Instruct other students to ask questions as though they are in a conference.

D Develop Concepts

BL OL AL

Integrate Chemistry Kidney stones form by precipitation—the condensation of a solid. The two most common kinds of kidney stones are calcium stones and uric acid stones. Calcium stones form when excess calcium in the kidneys combines with other substances, such as phosphates, to precipitate and form stones. Uric acid stones form when uric acid is so concentrated in the kidneys that it precipitates and forms crystals. The presence of solid objects in a system that can only process liquids creates a medical problem. **ASK STUDENTS:** ***Why do you think stones in the kidneys are usually painful?*** The stones are painful because the kidneys process liquids by passing the liquids through membranes and very small openings. Even small stones are much too large to pass easily through the kidneys.

Concepts in Motion
Interactive Table

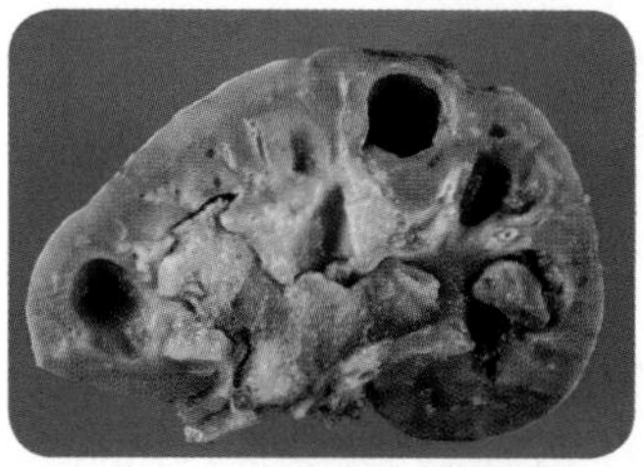

Figure 17 Kidney stones form as minerals, such as calcium, become solid masses.

VOCABULARY

ACADEMIC VOCABULARY

Inhibit
to hold back, restrain, or block the action or function of something
The concentration of the protein in the blood inhibited the organ from producing more of the same protein.

R Kidney Disorders

Sometimes kidney function can be inhibited or impaired by infections or disorders. When kidney function is impaired, the body cannot rid itself of wastes and homeostasis might be disrupted.

Infections Symptoms of a kidney infection include fever, chills, and mid- to low-back pain. Kidney infections often start as urinary bladder infections that spread to the kidneys. Obstructions in the kidneys also can cause an infection. If the infection is not treated, the kidneys can become scarred and their function might be permanently impaired. Antibiotics usually are effective in treating bacterial infections.

Nephritis Another common kidney problem is nephritis (nih FRIH tus), which often is caused by inflammation or painful swelling of some of the glomeruli, as listed in **Table 3.** This occurs for many reasons, such as when large particles in the bloodstream become lodged in some of the glomeruli. Symptoms of this condition include blood in the urine, swelling of body tissues, and protein in the urine. If this condition does not improve on its own, the patient may need a special diet or prescription drugs to treat the infection.

D **Kidney stones** Kidney stones are another type of kidney disorder, as listed in **Table 3** and shown in **Figure 17.** A kidney stone is a crystallized solid, such as calcium compounds, that forms in the kidney. Small stones can pass out of the body in urine; this can be quite painful. Larger stones often are broken into small pieces by ultrasonic sound waves. The smaller stones then can pass out of the body. In some cases, surgery might be required to remove large stones.

Kidneys also can be damaged by other diseases present in the body. Diabetes and high blood pressure are the two most common reasons for reduced kidney function and kidney failure. In addition, kidneys can be damaged by prescription and illegal drug use.

Table 3 **Common Excretory Disorders** Concepts in Motion Interactive Table

Excretory Disorder	Brief Description
Nephritis	Inflammation of the glomeruli can lead to inflammation of the entire kidneys. This disorder can lead to kidney failure if it is left untreated.
Kidney stones	Hard deposits form in the kidneys that might pass out of the body in urine. Larger kidney stones can block urine flow or irritate the lining of the urinary tract, leading to possible infection.
Urinary tract blockage	Malformations present at birth can lead to blockage of the normal flow of urine. If it is untreated, this blockage can lead to permanent damage of the kidneys.
Polycystic (pah lee SIHS tihk) kidney disease	This is a genetic disorder distinguished by the growth of many fluid-filled cysts in the kidneys. This disorder can reduce kidney function and lead to kidney failure.
Kidney cancer	Uncontrolled cell growth often begins in the cells that line the tubules within the kidneys. This can lead to blood in the urine or a mass in the kidneys, or it can affect other organs as the cancer spreads, which can lead to death.

Research Citation

Reading Strategies Educational research indicates that reading strategies such as the one described on this page can be beneficial to students. As students participate in the panel discussion, they will gain experience in forming and answering higher-order questions, deepening their understanding of the lesson. (Manzo, 1969)

Research bibliography on pages 32T–34T

Differentiated Instruction

Physically Disabled When students who have physical disabilities are in your class, avoid viewing them as less capable than other students. Expect the same academic and social standards from every student.

For more tips, see pages 14T–15T.

Kidney Treatments

A large percentage of kidney function can be lost before kidney failure becomes apparent. If kidney problems are left untreated, the buildup of waste products in the body can lead to seizures, a comatose state, or death. However, modern medicine offers two possible treatments for reduced kidney function or complete kidney failure.

Dialysis Dialysis (di AH luh sus) is a procedure in which an artificial kidney machine filters out wastes and toxins from a patient's blood. There are two different types of dialysis, one of which is illustrated in **Figure 18.** Blood is passed through a machine that temporarily filters and cleanses the blood. The filtered blood is then returned to the patient's body. The procedure lasts about three to four hours and requires three sessions per week.

In the second type of dialysis, the membrane lining the abdomen acts as an artificial kidney. The abdominal cavity is injected with a special fluid through a small tube attached to the body. The patient's fluid, which contains wastes from the blood, is drained. This procedure is performed on a daily schedule for 30 to 40 minutes.

W **Kidney transplant** A kidney transplant is the surgical placement of a healthy kidney from another person, called a donor, into the patient's body. Kidney transplants have shown increasing success in recent years. However, there is a limited supply of donated kidneys. The number of patients waiting for kidney transplants far exceeds the organs available for transplant.

The major complication of a transplant is possible rejection of the donated organ. Rejection is prevented with medications such as steroids and cyclosporine. Cyclosporine is a drug given to transplant recipients to help prevent organ rejection. Many transplant patients also need blood-pressure medication and other drugs to prevent infections.

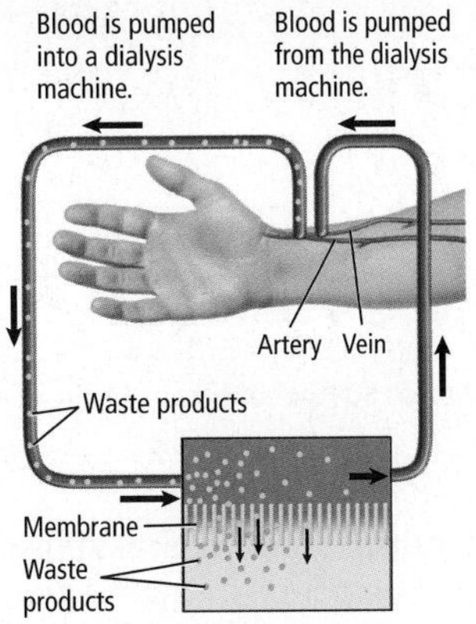

Blood is pumped into a dialysis machine.
Blood is pumped from the dialysis machine.
Artery
Vein
Waste products
Membrane
Waste products
In the dialysis machine, waste products are filtered from the blood through an artificial membrane.

Figure 18 Dialysis is used to filter wastes and toxins from a patient's blood.

Review Personal Tutor

Section 3 Assessment

Section Summary

- The kidneys are the main excretory organs in the body.
- Nephrons are independent filtration units in the kidneys.
- Water and important substances are reabsorbed into the blood after filtration.
- The kidneys produce a waste product called urine.

Understand Main Ideas

1. MAIN Idea Explain how the kidneys help maintain homeostasis.
2. **Diagram** the excretion of waste from the Bowman's capsule to the urethra.
3. **Compare and contrast** filtration and reabsorption in a nephron.
4. **Identify** three types of kidney disorders.

Think Critically

5. **Hypothesize** why kidney failure without dialysis can result in death.

WRITING in Biology

6. Research the effects of a high-protein diet on the excretory system. Summarize your findings in a public service announcement.

MATH in Biology

7. Calculate the average amount of urine that the body produces in a week.

W Writing Support

BL OL AL Summary Writing
Have students research the history of the dialysis machine and write a paper summarizing their findings.

Review **Personal Tutor**

Listen to a teacher explain dialysis.

Formative Assessment

Evaluation Have students write each step of the excretory process on an index card. Tell them to shuffle the cards and then put the steps in order. Putting the sequence number on the back of each card will help students check their accuracy.

Remediation Have students examine diagrams of excretory system processes.
ASK STUDENTS: *What are the steps of the excretory process?* Students should be able to write down the steps of the excretory process in chronological order.

Section 3 Assessment

1. The kidneys help maintain homeostasis by removing wastes, conserving water, and regulating the amount of salt in the body.
2. Diagrams should contain the information in Figure 16.
3. Filtration is the process of removing wastes from the blood. Reabsorption is the process of returning useful materials, such as glucose and water, to the bloodstream.
4. kidney infections, nephritis, and kidney stones
5. Kidney failure can lead to death because without kidneys, toxic wastes can build up in the blood and poison the body.
6. Students may find that a high-protein diet can lead to kidney stones and other medical problems. Public service announcements should be engaging and informative.
7. 1.5 L/day $\times$ 7 days = 10.5 L

Assessment Online Quiz

Purpose

To teach students about Tissue Engineering and its potential uses. E.1, E.2, F.1

Anticipatory Guide

ASK STUDENTS: ***What is a scaffold?*** A scaffold is a framework. Your bones are a scaffold for the other tissues and organs in your body. ***What are stem cells?*** Stem cells are unspecialized cells that can develop into specialized cells under the right conditions. Several sources of potent stem cells have been identified in the human adult—ranging from bone marrow to peripherally-derived stem cells in blood. Recently, discoveries of uncommitted stem cells in various tissues (including heart!) have been identified. This suggests that adult tissues have "intelligent" stem cells within themselves throughout life that can respond to stress or disease.

Background

Currently, there are about 5 million people living with heart failure in the United States. Fewer than 3,000 heart transplants are performed annually in the United States, while up to 50,000 patients die waiting for an organ.

Other human organs that can be transplanted include kidneys, livers, lungs, pancreases, and intestines. Tissues such as heart valves, corneas, tendons, and skin can also be transplanted.

Additional definitions

Biocompatible: able to co-exist with life. Biocompatible materials allow cells to attach and grow without damaging or killing them.

Bioreactor: a complex machine that allows scientists to apply normal physiologic conditions to an isolated organ in the lab, including temperature, pH, and fluid flow.

CUTTING-EDGE BIOLOGY

ENGINEERING HEARTS

By Thomas Matthiesen, Tissue Engineer, Chicago, IL

Heart disease is a global killer—with over 22 million people affected worldwide. For many people with heart failure the only treatment option is to seek cardiac transplantation. However, because a there is a severe shortage of donor organs, most patients die waiting for a new heart.

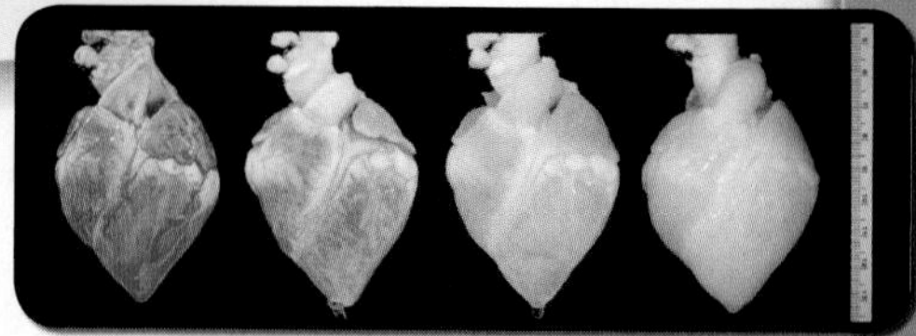

Figure 1 Detergent Perfusion Decellularization: The image on the far left is a freshly-isolated heart from a 20 kg swine. Over time, cells are removed, leaving a decellularized extracellular matrix (far right). The scale bar is in centimeters. *Photos: Thomas Matthiesen*

Can science build organs? In the relatively new field of *Tissue Engineering* scientists are studying methods to generate new tissues in the lab by combining scaffolds and stem cells. Underlying nearly any biological tissue is a scaffold of proteins that forms the basis of its shape, structure, and support. This support scaffold is a major component of the *extracellular matrix* and allows for proper cell alignment and function. To-date, scientists have successfully engineered small vessels, hollow organs, and two-dimensional cardiac patches by stacking together plastics or polymer sheets to form a scaffold and coating them with cells.

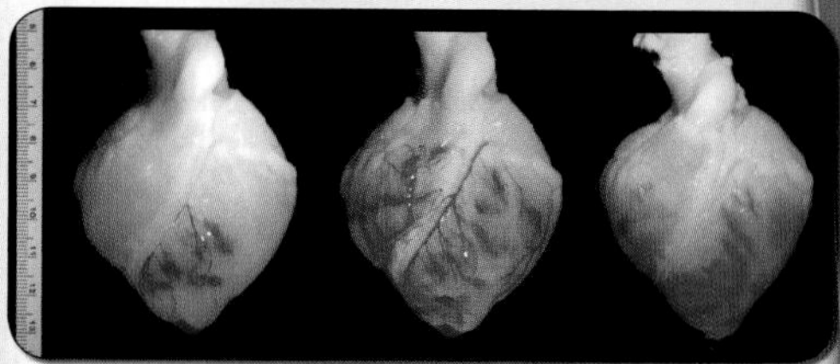

Figure 2 Whole Heart Recellularization: The left and middle images depict cells newly placed into the decellularized heart matrix seen in Figure 1. Seven days after cell placement, recellularization is underway (far right). The scale bar is in centimeters. *Photos: Thomas Matthiesen and Sudhish Sharma*

In 2008, **Dr. Harald Ott** and colleagues published an article on how the extracellular matrix of a rat heart could be isolated by a process called *detergent perfusion decellularization,* (Figure 1). This technique removes all cellular components from a cadaver organ, but keeps intact its natural vessel system and three-dimensional architecture. This vital network of vasculature (arteries and veins) can then be used to deliver nutrients to cells placed back into the matrix in a process called *recellularization,* (Figure 2).

An important milestone On April 10, 2006, Ott and Matthiesen first observed that when they placed immature cardiac cells back into the extracellular matrix, and then delivered nutrients and a small electric charge, the recellularized heart began to beat! Using these biocompatible scaffolds gives the potential to use a patient's own stem cells and bioengineer a custom organ. This means that a patient's immune system would not recognize the bioengineered organ as a foreign object and reject it.

Looking forward, tissue engineering offers hope, yet holds many mysteries. Cells, scaffolds, and special machines called *bioreactors* must be optimized to allow scientists to develop this technology in years to come.

WRITING in Biology

Research Investigate donor organ shortages in the United States—especially heart. What is a donor organ wait list? Which organs can be harvested and transplanted? How could tissue engineering help solve some of the donor shortages?

WRITING in Biology

RUBRIC Use the modifiable rubric found on your eTeacherEdition Online to assess writing assignments.

Activity

Help students find reliable, credible sources for their research. Remind students that not all online sources are credible. Peer-reviewed research is the most credible. Students may enjoy seeing heart drawings, cartoons, and hearing heart sounds of the many types of cardiac problems at the site:

www.cincinnatichildrens.org/health/heart-encyclopedia/anomalies/default.htm

BIOLAB

INTERNET: MAKE POSITIVE HEALTH CHOICES

Background: Both heredity and lifestyle choices affect overall health. Achieving optimal health involves making wise choices regarding exercise, nutrition, drugs and alcohol, stress management, and smoking. Because body systems function together to maintain homeostasis, changes in one system can impact overall health. In this lab, you will design a presentation that focuses on how specific health choices influence the functionality of body systems.

Question: *How do lifestyle choices affect the function of the circulatory, respiratory, and excretory systems?*

Materials

Choose materials that would be appropriate for creating the type of presentation that you create. Possible materials include:

resource materials about health choices from the school library or classroom

Procedure

1. Read and complete the lab safety form.
2. Develop an outline of information that you would like to include in your presentation. Include information about how specific health choices affect the respiratory, circulatory, and excretory systems.
3. Use resources and data that you collected in this chapter's labs to determine the effects of specific health choices on your body.
4. Choose a presentation medium. Ideas include a multimedia presentation, video, poster, or pamphlet. The medium you choose should appeal to a specific audience.
5. Share your presentation with your target audience. If this is not possible, share your presentation with your class or another group of people from your school.
6. Use the evaluation information provided by your teacher to evaluate the effectiveness of the presentation.

Analyze and Conclude

1. **Describe** What is the intended audience for your presentation? How did you modify the information included to target this audience?
2. **Summarize** Identify the key points of your presentation.
3. **Explain** How do the health choices you described affect multiple body systems?
4. **Evaluate** Do you think your presentation will influence the health choices of your target audience? Explain.
5. **Critique your presentation** How could you increase the effectiveness of your presentation?

COMMUNITY INVOLVEMENT

Create Choose one or more health-promoting behaviors from your presentation. Design a survey to gather data about the choices that members of your target audience make regarding this health-promoting behavior. If possible, use the Internet to distribute your survey to members of your community and gather data.

BIOLAB

Inquiry BioLab

For a lab worksheet, use your eTeacherEdition Online.

RUBRIC A rubric for evaluating BioLabs is found on your eTeacherEdition Online.

Est. Time 90 min

Content Background Information can be effectively presented using a variety of formats, including posters, pamphlets, and multimedia presentations.

Safety Precaution Approve lab safety forms before work begins.

Teaching Strategy Students may need help narrowing the scope of information in their presentations.

Alternative Teaching Demo Students could examine prepared pamphlets, videos, and posters from a variety of health organizations and evaluate their effectiveness in communicating information using the rubric provided.

Analyze and Conclude

1–5. Answers will vary based on presentations. Students' presentations should demonstrate solid research skills and original work, should be well organized and accessible to the target audience. The presentation rubric below may help in your evaluations.

RUBRIC Presentation Evaluation Rubric: Rate each category according to the following scale: *excellent—9–10 points; very good—7–8 points; good—5–6 points; satisfactory—3–4 points; poor—1–2 points; and unsatisfactory—0 points.*

Categories	Points Possible	Self-Assessment	Target Audience Member Assessment
The presentation flows well from one topic to another and is easy to follow.	10		
The presentation includes diagrams and photographs that provide visual interest.	10		
The presentation provides information about the importance of making positive health choices.	10		
The presentation conveys the interconnected nature of body systems.	10		
Information in the presentation is helpful to someone who is trying to establish and/or follow a healthy lifestyle.	10		

Chapter 34

Study Guide

ConnectED

Students can use the following to review the chapter.

Review

Vocabulary eGames
Vocabulary eFlashcards
Vocabulary PuzzleMaker

Assessment

Online Quizzes
Online Test Practice
Standardized Test Practice

Use the *ExamView®* *Assessment Suite* CD-ROM to:

- create multiple versions of tests
- create modified tests with one mouse click
- edit existing questions and add your own questions
- build tests aligned with state standards using built-in state curriculum tags
- change English tests to Spanish with one mouse click
- track students' progress using the Teacher Management System

Chapter 34 Study Guide

THEME FOCUS Homeostasis The circulatory, respiratory, and excretory systems regulate the pH of the blood as well as amounts of wastes and oxygen in the body, to maintain conditions needed for life.

BIG Idea These systems function together to maintain homeostasis by delivering important substances to the body's cells while removing wastes.

Section 1 Circulatory System

artery (p. 993)
capillary (p. 993)
vein (p. 994)
valve (p. 994)
heart (p. 994)
pacemaker (p. 995)
plasma (p. 997)
red blood cell (p. 997)
platelet (p. 997)
white blood cell (p. 998)
atherosclerosis (p. 999)

MAIN Idea The circulatory system transports blood to deliver important substances, such as oxygen, to cells and to remove wastes, such as carbon dioxide.

- Blood vessels transport important substances throughout the body.
- The top half of the heart is made up of two atria, and the bottom half is made up of two ventricles.
- The heart pumps deoxygenated blood to the lungs, and it pumps oxygenated blood to the body.
- Blood is made up of plasma, red blood cells, white blood cells, and platelets.
- Blood is classified by the following four blood types: A, B, AB, and O.

Section 2 Respiratory System

breathing (p. 1000)
external respiration (p. 1000)
internal respiration (p. 1000)
trachea (p. 1001)
bronchus (p. 1001)
lung (p. 1001)
alveolus (p. 1001)

MAIN Idea The function of the respiratory system is the exchange of oxygen and carbon dioxide between the atmosphere and the blood and between the blood and the body's cells.

- Alveoli in the lungs are the sites of gas exchange between the respiratory and circulatory systems.
- The pathway of air starts with the mouth or nose and ends at the alveoli located in the lungs.
- Inhalation and exhalation are the processes of taking in and expelling air.
- Respiratory disorders can inhibit respiration.

Section 3 Excretory System

kidney (p. 1006)
urea (p. 1006)

MAIN Idea The kidneys maintain homeostasis by removing wastes and excess water from the body and by maintaining the pH of blood.

- The kidneys are the main excretory organs in the body.
- Nephrons are independent filtration units in the kidneys.
- Water and important substances are reabsorbed into the blood after filtration.
- The kidneys produce a waste product called urine.

Review **Vocabulary PuzzleMaker**

For additional practice with vocabulary, have students access the Vocabulary PuzzleMaker online.

Review **Vocabulary eGames**

Section 1

Vocabulary Review

Match each of the following definitions with the correct vocabulary term from the Study Guide page.

1. a vessel carrying oxygen-rich blood
2. involved in blood vessel repair
3. stimulates the heart to contract

Understand Main Ideas

4. When blood leaves the heart, where does it exit?
   A. the aorta
   B. the capillaries
   C. the lungs
   D. the pulmonary vein

Use the diagram below to answer questions 5 and 6.

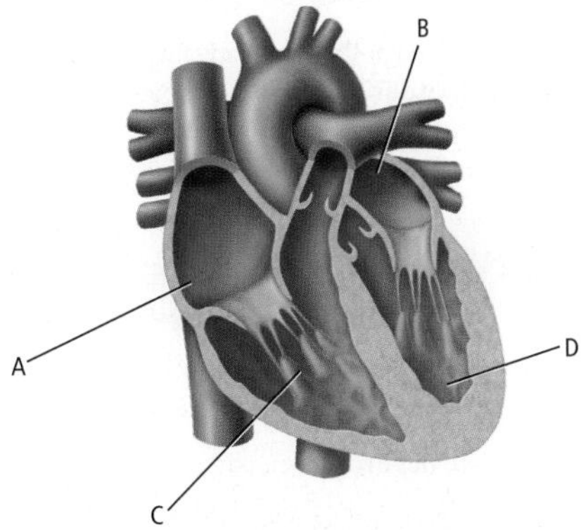

5. Which represents the right ventricle?
   A. A
   B. B
   C. C
   D. D
6. Into what part of the heart does oxygen-rich blood enter?
   A. A
   B. B
   C. C
   D. D
7. If a teenager with type A blood is injured in an auto accident and needs a blood transfusion, what type of blood will he or she receive?
   A. only type A
   B. type A or type O
   C. only type AB
   D. only type O
8. Where are one-way valves in the circulatory system located?
   A. arteries
   B. capillaries
   C. veins
   D. white blood cells
9. When a small blood vessel in your hand is cut open, which plays an active defensive role against possible disease?
   A. plasma
   B. platelets
   C. red blood cells
   D. white blood cells

Constructed Response

10. MAIN Idea Differentiate between the function of the atria and the function of the ventricles.

Use the diagram to answer question 11.

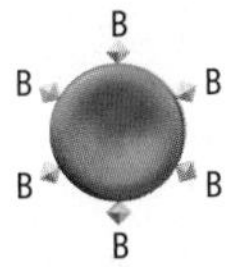

11. **Short Answer** A person has the blood type represented above. What type of blood can the person receive in a transfusion? Explain.

Think Critically

12. **Hypothesize** an advantage of your heart containing two pumping systems within the same organ, rather than two separate pumping organs.
13. **Deduce** which ABO blood type—A, B, AB or O—is the most valuable to medical personnel in an extreme emergency situation and explain why.

Section 2

Vocabulary Review

Use the vocabulary terms from the Study Guide page to answer the following questions.

14. In what structure does external respiration take place?
15. Which term defines the exchange of gases between the blood and the body's cells?
16. Which part of the air pathway branches off the trachea?

Chapter 34 Assessment

Section 1

Vocabulary Review

1. artery
2. platelets
3. pacemaker

Understand Main Ideas

4. A
5. C
6. B
7. B
8. C
9. D

Constructed Response

10. The atria receive blood into the heart and the ventricles deliver blood from the heart to tissue cells outside the heart.
11. The person can receive only blood type B or type O. This is because the person contains antibodies that react with A markers, which can lead to blood cell clumping.

Think Critically

12. Sample answer: A heart with its two separate pumps in one is likely to use less energy compared to two separate pumping organs.
13. Type O would be the most valuable because people with all other blood types can receive this blood type.

Section 2

Vocabulary Review

14. alveoli
15. internal respiration
16. bronchi

Assessment Online Test Practice

Understand Main Ideas
17. A
18. B
19. D
20. B
21. D
22. C

Constructed Response
23. Emphysema is a dysfunction of the alveoli. Bronchitis is an infection of the bronchi. Asthma is caused by an irritation that causes the lining of the bronchi to constrict.
24. Mucous membranes beneath the cilia in the nasal passages warm and moisten the air while trapping foreign materials. Cilia trap foreign materials and sweep them toward the throat so that they do not enter the lungs. These structures line the nasal passages as well as other respiratory tubes.

Think Critically
25. People who breathe more deeply can more efficiently exchange gases and ultimately transport more needed oxygen to muscle tissue and more carbon dioxide away from muscle tissue, thus permitting muscle tissue to work more efficiently and effectively.

Section 3

Vocabulary Review
26. in the kidneys
27. urea

Understand Main Ideas
28. A
29. C
30. C

Understand Main Ideas

Use the diagram below to answer questions 17 and 18.

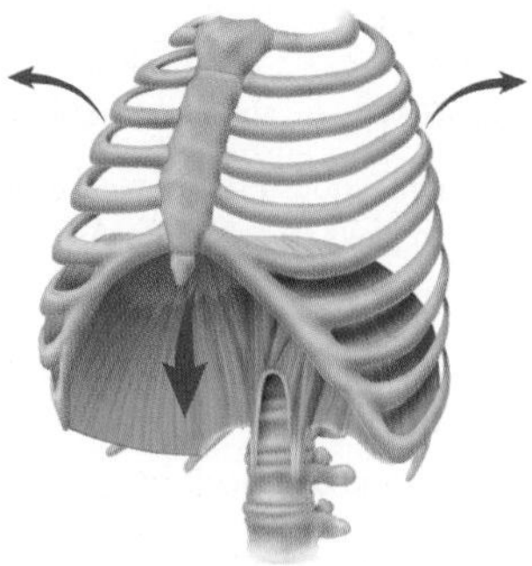

17. Which process is shown above?
A. inhalation
B. exhalation
C. cellular respiration
D. filtration

18. Which structure moves down as its muscles contract?
A. trachea
B. diaphragm
C. pharynx
D. ribs

19. Which process occurs inside the tissue cells in your legs?
A. filtration
B. breathing
C. external respiration
D. internal respiration

20. Which process causes the diaphragm to move back up?
A. cellular respiration
B. exhalation
C. inspiration
D. internal respiration

21. Which gas is needed by all cells?
A. sulfur
B. hydrogen
C. carbon dioxide
D. oxygen

22. How many breaths will a person take in one day if he or she takes 12 breaths per minute?
A. about 1000
B. about 10,000
C. about 17,000
D. about 1,000,000

Constructed Response

23. Short Answer Differentiate between asthma, bronchitis, and emphysema.

Use the photo below to answer question 24.

24. Short Answer Describe the function of the structures above. Where would these structures be found?

Think Critically

25. MAIN Idea Hypothesize an advantage in breathing more deeply during exercise compared to another person engaged in similar exercise breathing at a normal rate.

Section 3

Vocabulary Review

Review the vocabulary terms found on the Study Guide page. Use the terms to answer the following questions.

26. Where are nephrons located?

27. Which waste product is found in urine?

Understand Main Ideas

28. Where is the loop of Henle?
A. renal tubule
B. glomerulus
C. Bowman's capsule
D. urethra

29. THEME FOCUS Homeostasis Which one of the kidney functions conserves water in the body?
A. absorption
B. filtration
C. reabsorption
D. breathing

30. Which process returns glucose to the blood?
A. excretion
B. filtration
C. reabsorption
D. exhalation

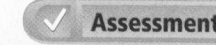

Assessment Online Test Practice

Use the table below to answer questions 31, 32, and 33.

Reabsorption of Some Substances in the Kidneys

Chemical substance	Amount Filtered by Kidneys (g/day)	Amount Excreted by Kidneys (g/day)	Percent of Filtered Chemical Reabsorbed (per day)
Glucose	180	0	100
Urea	46.8	23.4	50
Protein	1.8	1.8	0

31. Based on the data from the table above, how much urea is reabsorbed by the kidneys?
A. 0.50 g/day
B. 23.4 g/day
C. 46.8 g/day
D. 50.0 g/day

32. Based on the table data above, what happens to glucose in the kidneys?
A. It is reabsorbed into the blood.
B. It is permanently filtered out of the blood.
C. It is treated in the kidney like creatinine.
D. It is treated in the kidney like urea.

33. Infer why proteins are not removed by nephrons.
A. The collecting ducts are too small.
B. Proteins cannot be filtered.
C. Proteins never enter the nephron.
D. Proteins are reabsorbed by nephrons.

Constructed Response

34. Short Answer How many liters of blood flow through your kidneys in one hour?

35. MAIN Idea Explain the differences between filtration and reabsorption in the kidneys.

36. Open Ended Infer why kidneys require so much energy to function.

Think Critically

37. CAREERS IN BIOLOGY Formulate a list of questions one might ask a a urologist regarding urinary problems.

Summative Assessment

38. BIG Idea What are the important substances that the circulatory and respiratory systems deliver to body cells? Why are these substances important? Give two examples of wastes that the excretory system removes from the body.

39. WRITING in Biology Construct an analogy about the circulatory system that is based on your local highway system in your town, city, or rural area.

Document-Based Questions

The following data compare the state of five subjects whose circulation was monitored. (The weight, age, and sex of all five subjects were the same.) All of Subject A's data were within normal limits; the other four were not.

Data obtained from: Macey, R. 1968. *Human Physiology*. Englewood Cliffs, NJ: Prentice Hall.

Subject	Hemoglobin (Hb) content of blood (Hb/100 mL blood)	Oxygen contents of blood in arteries (mL O_2/100 mL blood)	Oxygen content of blood in veins (mL O_2/100 mL blood)
A	15	19	15
B	15	15	12
C	8	9.5	6.5
D	16	20	13
E	15	19	18

40. Which subject might be suffering from a dietary iron deficiency? Explain your choice.

41. Which subject might have lived at a high altitude where the atmospheric oxygen is low? Explain your choice.

42. Which subject might have been poisoned by carbon monoxide that prevents tissue cells from using oxygen? Explain your choice.

Assessment Online Test Practice

31. B
32. A
33. B

Constructed Response

34. 180 L/24 hr = 7.5 L/hr

35. Filtration removes huge quantities of selected chemicals from blood capillaries. Reabsorption is the process of returning material to the blood.

36. Sample answer: There is a great deal of active transporting of chemicals from one location to another. Active transport takes energy.

Think Critically

37. Questions will vary, but should reflect realistic concerns about urinary and reproductive health.

Summative Assessment

38. The respiratory and circulatory systems deliver oxygen and nutrients. Oxygen is important for cellular respiration; nutrients are important for energy and cell function. The excretory system removes carbon dioxide and excess salt.

39. Answers may include comparisons of arteries and veins to highways, and red blood cells to cars.

Document-Based Questions

Macey, R. 1968. *Human Physiology*. Englewood Cliffs, NJ: Prentice Hall.

40. most likely Subject C because his or her hemoglobin content of the blood is the lowest

41. most likely Subject B because the oxygen content of Subject B's blood in the arteries is the lowest (except for Subject C, whose low oxygen content is due to another reason)

42. most likely Subject E because the difference between the oxygen content of his or her arteries and veins is the smallest

Standardized Test Practice

Multiple Choice

1. A 5. B
2. B 6. A
3. A 7. A
4. D 8. B

Short Answer

9. When the biceps muscle contracts, the lower arm is moved upward. When the triceps muscle contracts, the lower arm is pulled downward.
10. Muscles only do work when they contract. Muscles need to be in pairs that work against each other to create movement.
11. Answers can vary depending on the drug chosen. For example, cocaine causes an increased level of dopamine in the nerve synapses. The increased dopamine level causes general excitement and a sense of heightened awareness.
12. Answers may vary.

	Autonomic nervous system	Somatic nervous system
Type of response	Involuntary	Voluntary and involuntary
Systems affected	Internal organs and glands	Skeletal muscles
Example	CNS sends impulses to digestive system to proceed with digestion	Brain sends a signal to move leg muscles when running

13. Monotreme characteristics that are reptilian: webbed feet, lay eggs, and lower body temperature than most mammals.
Monotreme characteristics that are mammalian: hair and fur on the body and mammary glands that provide milk to young.

Standardized Test Practice

Cumulative

Multiple Choice

1. What happens to a skeletal muscle when the actin fibers are pulled toward the center of the sarcomeres?
   A. It contracts.
   B. It grows.
   C. It relaxes.
   D. It stretches.

Use the diagram to answer questions 2 and 3.

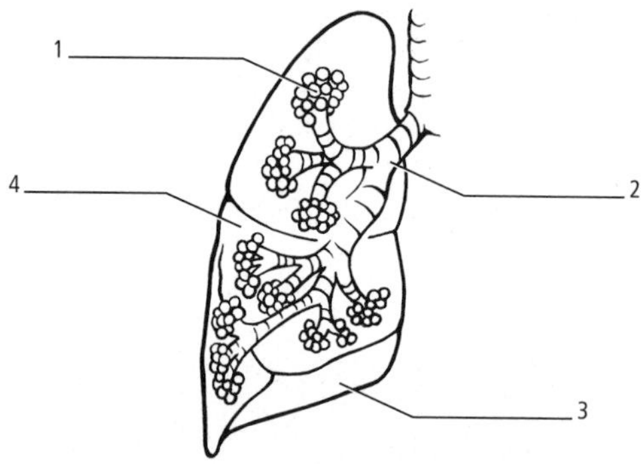

2. Which part of the respiratory system has hairs to filter particles from the air?
   A. 1
   B. 2
   C. 3
   D. 4

3. In which numbered location does gas exchange take place?
   A. 1
   B. 2
   C. 3
   D. 4

4. Which is an example of operant conditioning?
   A. A dog salivates when it hears a bell.
   B. A horse becomes accustomed to street noises.
   C. A newborn forms an attachment to the first animal seen after birth.
   D. A rat learns that it can get food by pulling a lever.

5. Which is an example of nurturing behavior?
   A. An animal in a colony spots a predator and warns the whole colony.
   B. A female chimpanzee takes care of her infant for three years.
   C. A male peacock displays its feathers in front of a female.
   D. A squirrel chatters at another squirrel to drive it away.

Use the table below to answer question 6.

Muscle Type	Function
Skeletal muscles	attached to bones and tighten when contracted causing movement
Smooth muscles	line the hollow internal organs such as stomach, intestines, bladder, and uterus
Cardiac muscles	

6. Where is the muscle type that is missing a description in the table located?
   A. in the heart
   B. in the kidneys
   C. lining the blood vessels
   D. lining the lymph vessels

7. Which answer choice is a result of parasympathetic stimulation?
   A. decreased heart rate
   B. decreased mucus production
   C. increased digestive activity
   D. increased pupil size

8. Which characteristic directly affects homeostatic temperature control in mammals?
   A. four-chambered heart
   B. high metabolic rate
   C. milk production
   D. signaling devices in fur

Short Answer

Use the diagram below to answer questions 9 and 10.

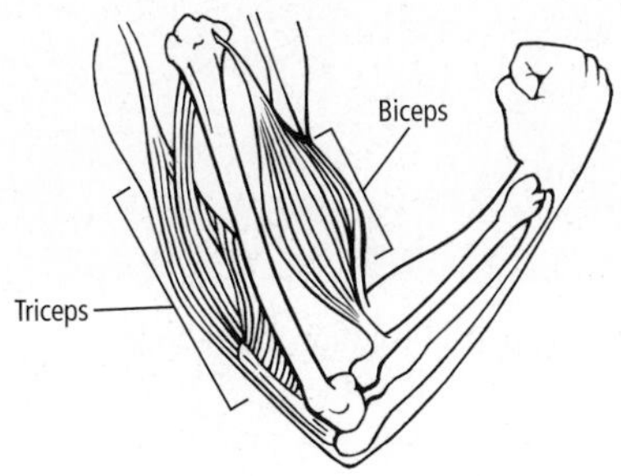

9. Describe how the biceps and triceps allow movement in the arm.

10. Explain why muscles are always in antagonistic pairs.

11. Some drugs cause an increased level of dopamine in nerve synapses. Name one of these drugs and relate the increased dopamine level to other effects that result from using the drug.

12. Use a table to organize information about the autonomic and somatic nervous systems. List the types of responses, systems affected, and include an example.

13. Monotremes are mammals that are similar to reptiles in some ways. Classify monotreme characteristics as similar to reptiles or similar to mammals.

14. A rare disease called amyotrophic lateral sclerosis (ALS) causes motor neurons in the body to lose myelin. What do you think would be the initial symptoms a person with ALS would have?

15. Explain how nephrons filter blood.

Extended Response

Use the illustration below to answer question 16.

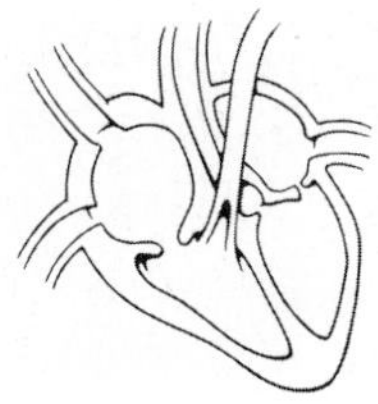

16. The illustration above shows a four-chambered mammalian heart. Write an explanation of the role of the four-chambered heart in circulating oxygenated blood throughout the body.

17. Compare and contrast apical meristems and lateral meristems in plants.

18. The invention of the microscope allowed scientists to discover hundreds of tiny living organisms that were never seen before. Distinguish, in a written statement, between an advance in technology and an advance in science using this historical example.

Essay Question

The human nervous system consists of a complex arrangement of voluntary and involuntary responses and activities. The presence of these different types of responses has evolved in humans to help with survival.

Using the information in the paragraph above, answer the following question in essay format.

19. From what you know about different nervous system responses, write a well-organized essay explaining how different types of involuntary response systems in humans are helpful for survival.

NEED EXTRA HELP?																			
If You Missed Question . . .	1	2	3	4	5	6	7	8	9	10	11	12	13	14	15	16	17	18	19
Review Section . . .	32.3	34.2	34.2	31.1	31.2	32.3	33.2	30.1	32.3	32.3	33.4	33.2	22.1	33.1	34.3	30.2	22.1	1.2	33.2

14. Since myelin provides insulation on neurons, early symptoms would be related to the loss of control of muscles, for example, trouble with walking, moving, picking up things.

15. Blood enters nephron units in the kidney through the renal artery. The renal artery enters the kidney and branches into smaller and smaller blood vessels, eventually ending in the tiny capillaries in the glomerulus. The walls of the capillaries are very thin. As a result, water and substances dissolved in the blood, and the waste product urea, pass through the capillary walls into the Bowman's capsule. Larger molecules and red blood cells are too large to pass through the capillary walls and remain in the bloodstream.

Extended Response

16. Blood from each atrium flows into the ventricle below, and then is pumped either to the lungs, or to the body. A four-chambered heart separates oxygen-rich and oxygen-poor blood, making it possible to pump highly oxygenated blood to the body.

17. Both types of meristems are regions in a plant that have rapidly dividing cells. Apical meristems occur at the tips of roots and stems. These tissues cause roots and stems to grow longer. Lateral meristems occur along roots and stems. They are responsible for the lateral growth, or increase in diameter, of roots and stems.

18. Inventing microscopes was an advance in technology because the microscope is a tool that is useful for seeing tiny objects that are invisible to the unaided eye. The discovery of hundreds of microscopic organisms was an advance in science that came from observations by many researchers using microscopes. That advance in science could not have happened without an advance in technology.

Essay Question

19. The involuntary responses involved with "fight or flight" responses may seem useless today because they include pupil dilation, decreased activity of the digestive system, and faster heart rate. In the past, these responses may have been useful for survival when humans often were hunting for food or in danger from predatory animals. These responses are not typically needed by humans in today's high-stress activities, such as having to perform in front of other people, that might still stimulate the "fight or flight" response. Other involuntary responses, however, include reflexes that cause a person to pull away from a hot stove. This response is useful because it occurs much faster than a voluntary response could. Moreover, the processes of whole organ systems such as digestion, respiration, and circulation are controlled by involuntary actions of the nervous system. This control is important so that these systems can work constantly together.

Chapter 35 Organizer:
Digestive and Endocrine Systems

LabManager™
Customize any lab with the LabManager™ CD-ROM.

Essential Questions	National Science Standards	Materials and Planning: Estimated times include cleanup and disposal, but do not include teacher prep time. For cleanup and disposal guidelines, see page 39T.	Est. Time (min)
Section 1 1. What are the three main functions of the digestive system? 2. What are the structures of the digestive system and what are their functions? 3. What is the process of chemical digestion?	UCP.1, UCP.2, UCP.5; A.1, A.2; B.2, B.3, B.4; C.5; E.2; F.1; G.1	**Launch Lab,** p. 1018: test tubes, HCl solution, pepsin solution, hard-boiled egg whites, knife, incubator	20
		Demonstration, p. 1022: banana, cucumber, knife, potassium iodide solution, Gram's iodine, or iodine from pharmacy	10
		MiniLab 1, p. 1023: three test tubes, vegetable oil, phenolphthalein, NaOH solution, water, 250-mL beaker, stopper, distilled water, bile salt, pancreatic solution	40
		Activity, p. 1023: four different colors of yarn, scissors, rulers, metersticks	15
Section 2 1. Depending on activity level, what caloric intake is needed to maintain proper body weight? 2. How are proteins, carbohydrates, and fats used by the body? 3. What are the roles of vitamins and minerals in maintaining homeostasis? 4. How can you apply the information in MyPyramid and on food labels to establishing healthy eating habits?	UCP.1–3, UCP.5; A.1, A.2; B.2, B.3; C.5, C.6; F.1	**Demonstration,** p. 1026: several different snack foods, some of which contain fat and some that do not—potato chips, fruit slices, cookies, cheese, etc.; paper	5
		Demonstration, p. 1028: cooking oil, water, dishwashing detergent, dish	5
Section 3 1. What are the functions of the glands that make up the endocrine system? 2. What is the role of the endocrine system in maintaining homeostasis? 3. What are the feedback mechanisms that regulate hormone levels in the body?	UCP.1–3, UCP.5; A.1, A.2; B.2, B.3; B.6; C.1, C.5, C.6; F.1; G.1, G.2	**Demonstration,** p. 1031: tape or CD of soothing music or sounds, tape player or CD player	10
		Design Your Own BioLab, p. 1039: variety of crackers, mortar and pestle, test tubes and test tube rack, filter paper, funnels, balance, beaker, Bunsen burner, graduated cylinder, iodine solution, droppers, watch glasses, amylase solution, stopwatch or clock	90

Suggested Time for Each Lesson

Class	Chapter Opener	Section 1	Section 2	Section 3	Assessment
Basic	45 min	45 min	90 min	45 min	45 min
General	25 min	45 min	65 min	45 min	45 min
Honors	5 min	75 min	20 min	60 min	20 min

ConnectED

connectED.mcgraw-hill.com

Access interactive learning opportunities and teaching resources using these icons located throughout your StudentWorks™ Plus Online and eTeacherEdition Online.

Chapter 35 Section Resources	Additional Chapter 35 Resources	Technology
FAST FILE Unit 9 Resources: Launch Lab Worksheet* MiniLab Worksheet* Study Guide (English/Spanish)* Section Quick Check **Reading Essentials 35.1** **Science Notebook 35.1*** **FAST FILE Unit 9 Resources:** Study Guide (English/Spanish)* Section Quick Check **Reading Essentials 35.2** **Science Notebook 35.2*** **FAST FILE Unit 9 Resources:** MiniLab Worksheet* BioLab Worksheet* Study Guide (English/Spanish)* Section Quick Check **Reading Essentials 35.3** **Science Notebook 35.3***	**FAST FILE Unit 9 Resources:** Chapter Diagnostic Test Concept Mapping* Real-World Biology Enrichment Chapter Tests A, B, and C **Transparencies:** Bellringer Transparencies* Biology Concepts Transparencies* **Lab Resources:** Laboratory Manual* Probeware Lab Manual* Forensics Lab Manual* Pre-AP Lab Manual* Open Inquiry in Biology* Guided Inquiry in Biology*	**Teaching Tools:** eTeacherEdition Online Classroom Presentation Toolkit CD-ROM* LabManager™ CD-ROM* Video Lab DVD* Virtual Lab CD-ROM* What's BIOLOGY Got To Do With It? StudentWorks™ Plus Online* **Chapter Assessment Tools:** Classroom Presentation Toolkit CD-ROM* *ExamView® Assessment Suite* CD-ROM **Web-Based Resources:** • StudentWorks™ Plus Online • eTeacherEdition Online • Animations* • The Interactive Time Line* • Interactive Tables* • Online Quizzes • Online Test Practice • Standardized Test Practice • Virtual Labs* • Multilingual eGlossary* • Vocabulary eGames* • Vocabulary eFlashcards • WebQuests • Personal Tutors

While all resources listed are appropriate for English learners, the * indicates resources with a strong visual or hands-on component for EL.

Teaching strategies and activities have been coded for differentiated instruction.

AL Activities for students working above grade level	**OL** Activities for students working on grade level	**BL** Activities for students working below grade level	**EL** Activities for English learners (also ELL)	**COOP LEARN** Activities designed for small cooperative group work

CHAPTER 35

CHAPTER 35

Digestive and Endocrine Systems

ConnectED

Your one-stop online resource
connectED.mcgraw-hill.com

- Video
- Audio
- Review
- Inquiry
- WebQuest
- Assessment
- Concepts in Motion
- Multilingual eGlossary

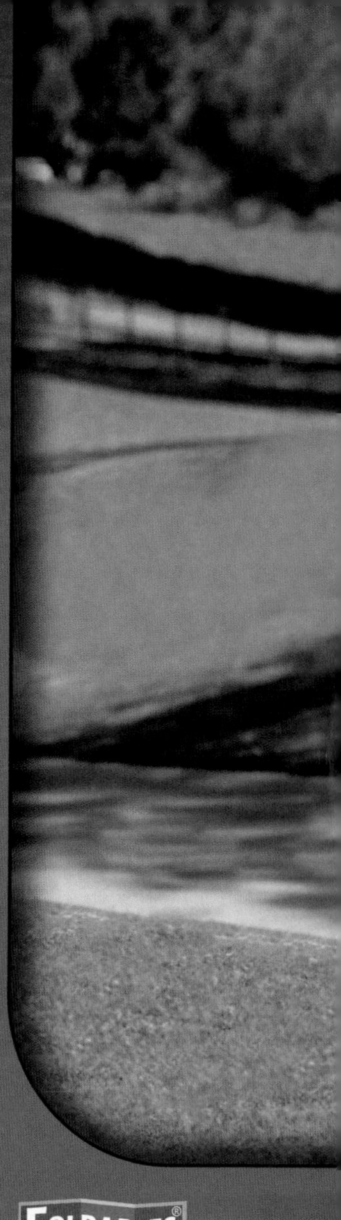

Launch Lab
How does the enzyme pepsin aid digestion?

The acidic digestive juices in the stomach contain the enzyme pepsin. In this lab, you will investigate the role of pepsin in digestion.

For a lab worksheet, use your StudentWorks™ Plus Online.

Inquiry Launch Lab

FOLDABLES®

Make a folded chart using the titles shown. Use it to organize your notes on hormones.

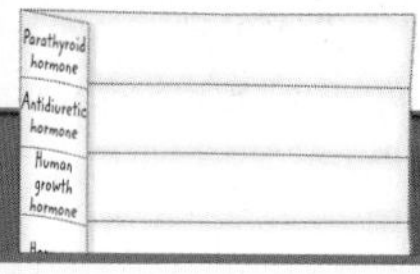

Launch Lab
How does the enzyme pepsin aid digestion?

Inquiry Launch Lab

For a lab worksheet, use your eTeacherEdition Online.

RUBRIC A rubric for evaluating Launch Labs is found on your eTeacherEdition Online.

Est. Time 20 min

Safety Precautions Remind students to add acid to water, rather than water to acid, to limit the possibility of acid burn.

Teaching Strategies
- Introduce the location and role of the stomach in the digestive process, describe the chemical environment of the stomach, and help students understand that digestion is both a physical and chemical process.
- Students should understand that enzymes are proteins that speed up chemical reactions.

Procedure
1. Read and complete the lab safety form.
2. Label and prepare **three test tubes**.
   - **A.** 15 mL water
   - **B.** 10 mL water, 5 mL **HCl solution**
   - **C.** 5 mL each water, HCl solution, and **pepsin solution**
3. Cut **hard-boiled egg white** portions into pea-sized chunks with a **knife**.
4. Add equal amounts of egg white to each tube. Predict the relative amount of digestion in each test tube.
5. Place test tubes in an **incubator** overnight at 37°C. Record observations the next day.

Cleanup and Disposal Have students dispose of test tube contents in a designated container, clean and return all glassware and equipment to the appropriate location, and wash hands thoroughly.

Analysis
1. **Evaluate** Rank the test tubes based on the amount of digestion that occurred. According to your results, describe the roles of pepsin and pH in digestion of proteins. The test tube containing pepsin showed the greatest digestion. The test tube containing only water showed the least digestion. While HCl and pepsin both digest proteins in the stomach, pepsin speeds up the digestion of protein.

THEME FOCUS Homeostasis
Homeostasis is maintained by negative feedback in the endocrine system.

BIG Idea The digestive system breaks down food to provide energy and nutrients for the body. The endocrine system produces hormones that regulate body functions.

Section 1 • The Digestive System
Section 2 • Nutrition
Section 3 • The Endocrine System

THEMES

Scientific Inquiry Researchers continue to investigate the effect of hormones on the body.

Diversity A wide diversity of nutrients is vital for the proper function of the body.

Energy The digestive system breaks down food to obtain energy.

Homeostasis Negative feedback in the endocrine system maintains homeostasis.

Change Hormones can cause quick changes in body processes.

Introduce the Chapter

Intestinal Lining

ASK STUDENTS: ***Why does the surface lining of the small intestine appear to be rough rather than smooth?*** The wall of the small intestine contains projections called villi. ***What would be the effect if there were no villi?*** The small intestine would not be able to absorb nearly as many nutrients because the villi greatly increase the small intestine's surface area, and thus its capacity to absorb nutrients.

BIG Idea

Directed Reading Have students make a three-column chart and label the left column *Digestive System,* the middle column *Nutrition,* and the third column *Endocrine System.* As students study the material in this chapter, instruct them to list main ideas in the appropriate columns. Then have them draw arrows between main ideas in different columns as they make connections between the three sections of this chapter. Answers will vary. One possible table is shown below.

Digestive System	Nutrition	Endocrine System
esophagus	sugar	thyroxine
stomach	fats	aldosterone
small intestine	proteins	insulin

Section 1

MAIN Idea

BL OL AL Energy From Food
ASK STUDENTS: ***Why do you eat?*** to obtain the energy and nutrients necessary to keep alive ***What is digestion?*** Students might say that digestion is the process of breaking down food into the smallest component molecules. ***How is energy stored in food?*** in chemical bonds in the food molecules

R Reading Strategy

EL BL OL AL

Anticipatory Guide Develop 10–15 true/false statements relating to the content under the heading *Functions of the Digestive System.* Sample statements:

- Most absorption of nutrients occurs in the stomach. False
- A main function of the large intestine is to absorb water from the remaining food from the small intestine. True

Have students indicate which statements they think are true and which ones they think are false. As students read, have them validate or correct their answers based on the information in the text.

S Skill Practice

OL Visual Literacy Have students examine Figure 1 and record the body parts indicated on the labels. As they read the text under the heading *Functions of the Digestive System,* have them write descriptions of the role of each body part in digestion.

Concepts in Motion
Animation

Section 1

Reading Preview

Essential Questions

- What are the three main functions of the digestive system?
- What are the structures of the digestive system and what are their functions?
- What is the process of chemical digestion?

Review Vocabulary

nutrient: vital component of foods that provides energy and materials for growth and body functions

New Vocabulary

mechanical digestion
chemical digestion
amylase
esophagus
peristalsis
pepsin
small intestine
liver
villus
large intestine

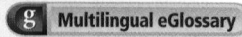

Multilingual eGlossary

Inquiry Video Lab

The Digestive System

MAIN Idea The digestive system breaks down food so nutrients can be absorbed by the body.

Real-World Reading Link During an average lifespan, as much as 45 tons of food can pass through a person's digestive system. The food will travel almost 9 m through the digestive tract. What happens as food passes through this long tube?

R Functions of the Digestive System

There are three main functions of the digestive system. The digestive system ingests food, breaks it down so nutrients can be absorbed, and eliminates what cannot be digested. Refer to **Figure 1** and **Figure 2** as you learn about the structure and function of the digestive system.

Digestion Supose on Friday night, you and your friends meet to have pizza. You bite into a slice and begin to chew. How does your body digest that pizza?

Mechanical digestion involves chewing food to break it down into smaller pieces. It also includes the action of smooth muscles in the stomach and small intestine that churn the food. **Chemical digestion** involves the breakdown of large molecules in food into smaller substances by enzymes. The smaller substances can be absorbed into the body's cells. Enzymes are proteins that speed up biological reactions. When you chew the bites of pizza, **amylase,** an enzyme found in saliva, begins the process of chemical digestion by breaking down starches into sugars.

S

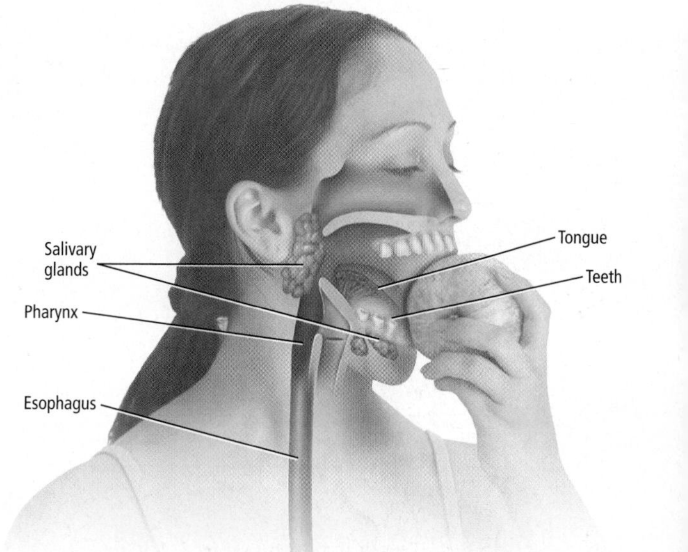

Figure 1 Mechanical digestion starts in the mouth. Secretions from the salivary glands keep food moist and begin the process of chemical digestion. Food moves through the pharynx into the esophagus.

Concepts in Motion
Animation

In-Text Question You chew each bite to break down food into smaller pieces. An enzyme in saliva then breaks carbohydrates down into these smaller pieces, beginning the process of chemical digestion.

Differentiated Instruction

English Learners When using the reading strategy described on this page, allow students with limited English proficiency to read the material in their first language before reading it in English.

For more tips, see pages 14T–15T.

Esophagus When the tongue pushes chewed food to the back of the mouth, the swallowing reflex is stimulated. The food is forced by the action of the tongue into the upper portion of the esophagus. The **esophagus** (ih SAH fuh gus) is a muscular tube that connects the pharynx, or throat, to the stomach, as illustrated in **Figure 2.** The wall of the esophagus is lined with smooth muscles that contract rhythmically to move the food through the digestive system in a process called **peristalsis** (per uh STAHL sus). Peristalsis continues throughout the digestive tract. Even if a person were upside down, food would still move toward the stomach.

When a person swallows, the small plate of cartilage called the epiglottis covers the trachea. If this opening is not closed, food can enter the trachea and cause a person to choke. The body responds to this by initiating the coughing reflex in an attempt to expel the food to keep the food from entering the lungs.

D **Stomach** When food leaves the esophagus, it passes through a circular muscle called a sphincter, and into the stomach. The sphincter between the esophagus and stomach is the cardiac sphincter. The walls of the stomach are composed of three overlapping layers of smooth muscle that are involved with mechanical digestion. As the muscles contract, they further break down the food and mix it with the secretions of glands that line the inner wall of the stomach.

Connection to Chemistry Recall that pH is a measure of a solution's acidity. The environment inside the stomach is very acidic. Stomach glands, called gastric glands, secrete an acidic solution, which lowers the pH in the stomach to about 2. This is about the same level of acidity as lemon juice. If the sphincter in the upper portion of the stomach allows any leakage, some of this acid might move back into the esophagus, causing what is commonly known as heartburn.

The acidic environment in the stomach is favorable to the action of **pepsin,** an enzyme involved in the process of the chemical digestion of proteins. Cells in the lining of the stomach secrete mucus to help prevent damage from pepsin and the acidic environment. Although most absorption occurs in the small intestine, some substances, such as alcohol and aspirin, are absorbed by cells that line the stomach. While empty, the capacity of the stomach is about 50 mL. When full, it can expand to 2–4 L.

The muscular walls of the stomach contract and push food farther along the digestive tract. The consistency of the food resembles tomato soup as it passes through the pyloric sphincter at the lower end of the stomach into the small intestine. **Figure 3** illustrates peristalsis in the small intestine.

Reading Check **Compare** digestion in the mouth with digestion in the stomach.

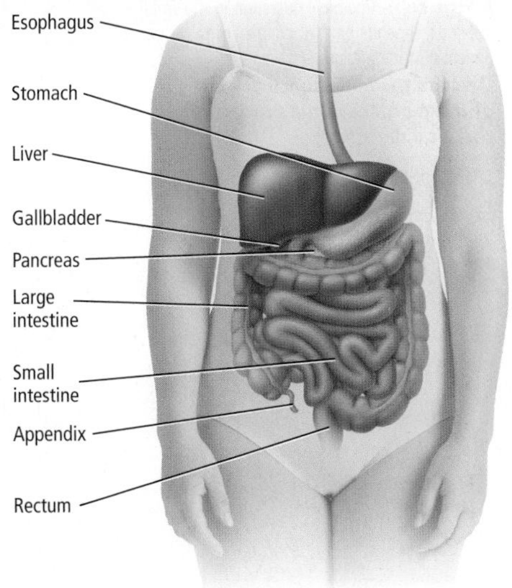

■ **Figure 2** The esophagus extends from the pharynx to the stomach and is approximately 25 cm long.
Describe *why humans are classified as coelomates.*

C

■ **Figure 3** The smooth muscles in the walls of the digestive tract contract in the process of peristalsis.

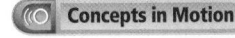

Concepts in Motion Animation

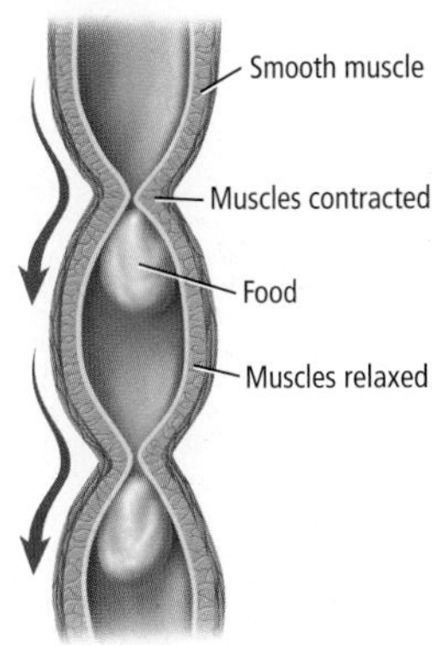

D Develop Concepts

OL AL

Clarify a Misconception

ASK STUDENTS: ***Do spicy foods cause stomach ulcers?*** no ***Does stress cause stomach ulcers?*** no Stomach ulcers are usually caused by the bacterium *Helicobacter pylori.* Heavy use of medications such as aspirin or ibuprofen can increase the risk of developing ulcers. Some types of cancer can also cause ulcers. However, stress and spicy foods may aggravate the symptoms of a stomach ulcer and even delay healing because the stomach lining is already compromised. Students might need an explanation of what an ulcer is—any open sore that doesn't heal. A stomach ulcer is an open sore in the lining of the stomach or upper intestine.

C Critical Thinking

OL AL **Analyze** Tell students to suppose that a newborn's stomach has a pH between 5 and 6.
ASK STUDENTS: ***How would this stomach pH affect the breakdown of protein?*** Pepsin, found in the stomach, works best at a pH of 2, and functions to catabolize proteins. An infant with a stomach pH of 5 or 6 might have a hard time breaking down proteins. ***How might the stomach of infants be adapted to break down proteins?*** Accept all reasonable responses. Inform students that infants produce an enzyme called rennin, which breaks down milk proteins. Rennin works well at a pH of 5 to 6.

Concepts in Motion
Animation

Reading Check In the mouth, mechanical digestion is accomplished by chewing and chemical digestion by saliva. In the stomach, mechanical digestion is accomplished by muscles in the stomach walls and chemical digestion by hydrochloric acid and the enzyme pepsin.

■ **Caption Question** **Fig. 2** Humans are coelomates because they contain the fluid-filled cavity called the coelom.

Inquiry **Video Lab** Students will observe how the enzyme amylase acts on breakfast cereals.

Develop Concepts

BL OL AL COOP LEARN

Activity Have students work in groups of three to create a quiz show. Have them write questions for their show based on the digestive system, its parts, and their functions. Sample question: What is the tube that connects the throat to the stomach? Esophagus Have student volunteers act as contestants on the shows.

Writing Support

BL OL AL COOP LEARN

Formal Writing Have students work in groups to research one of the accessory organs listed—pancreas, liver, or gallbladder. Students should individually write summaries of their findings in a report.

ASK STUDENTS: ***Based on your reports, where is the accessory organ you researched located in the body?*** pancreas—along the small intestine near the stomach; liver—under the diaphragm on the right side of the body; gallbladder—under the liver ***How does the organ aid in digestion?*** pancreas—secretes fluid to raise the pH in the small intestine; liver—produces bile; gallbladder—stores bile ***What are some medical complications that can affect the organ?*** Answers will vary. Students might mention gallstones, cirrhosis of the liver, or pancreatic cancer.

■ **Caption Question Fig. 4** The liver produces bile, which helps break down fats; the pancreas produces enzymes that digest carbohydrates, proteins, and fats and a fluid that raises pH of intestine; the gallbladder stores excess bile.

Video BrainPOP

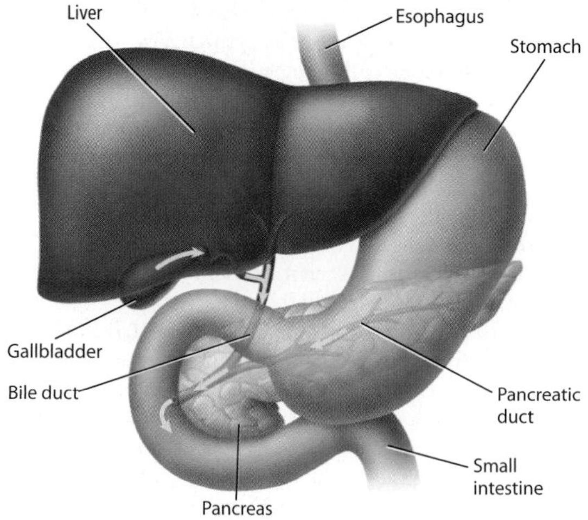

■ **Figure 4** Chemical digestion in the small intestine depends on the activities of the liver, pancreas, and gallblader.
Discuss ***the importance of each of these organs in the process of chemical digestion.***

Video BrainPOP

Small intestine The **small intestine** is approximately 7 m in length and is the longest part of the digestive tract. It is called *small* because its diameter is 2.5 cm compared to the 6.5 cm diameter of the large intestine. The smooth muscles in the wall of the small intestine continue the process of mechanical digestion and push the food farther through the digestive tract by peristalsis.

The completion of chemical digestion in the small intestine depends on three accessory organs—the pancreas, liver, and gallbladder, as illustrated in **Figure 4.** The pancreas serves two main functions. One is to produce enzymes that digest carbohydrates, proteins, and fats. The other is to produce hormones, which will be discussed later in this chapter. The pancreas secretes an alkaline fluid to raise the pH in the small intestine to slightly above 7, which creates a favorable environment for the action of intestinal enzymes.

The **liver** is the largest internal organ of the body and produces bile, which helps to break down fats. About 1 L of bile is produced every day, and excess bile is stored in the gallbladder to be released into the small intestine when needed. **Figure 5** shows gallstones, which are cholesterol crystals that can form in the gallbladder.

Study Tip

Sequence and Order Using your notes, work with a partner to review the sequence of the organs in the digestive system. Then, practice retelling the sequence without your notes. Ask questions of one another for deeper learning.

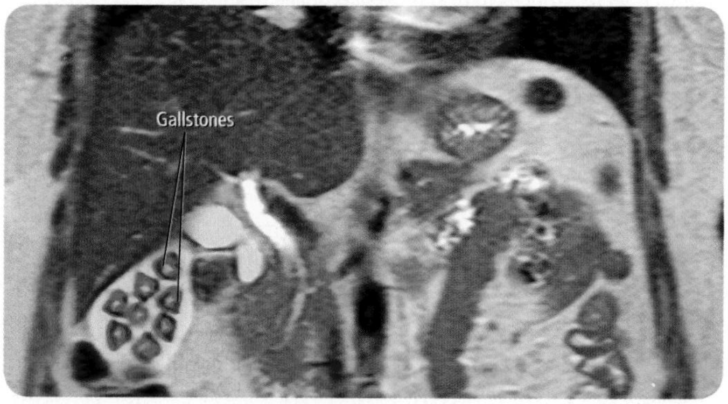

■ **Figure 5** Gallstones can obstruct the flow of bile from the gallbladder. Note the gallstones on this MRI film of a gallbladder.

Demonstration

BL OL AL **Presence of Starch** Show students that iodine turns dark in the presence of starch. Cut a slice of banana and a slice of cucumber. Add several drops of iodine (potassium iodide solution) to each. Gram's iodine or the iodine available from a pharmacy will also work.

ASK STUDENTS: ***What do you observe?*** The iodine on the cucumber remains relatively unchanged; the iodine on the banana turns dark. ***What do these results indicate about the starch content of these foods?*** There is more starch in a banana than in a cucumber.

Est. time: 10 min

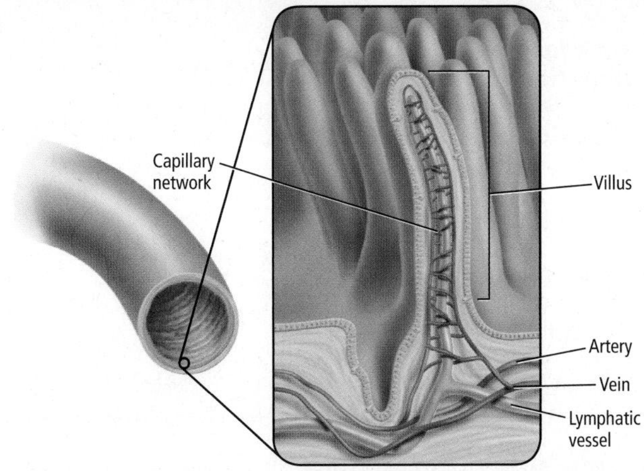

■ **Figure 6** A villus is a fingerlike extension of the lining of the small intestine. Nutrients diffuse into capillaries in the villi and reach body cells by means of circulating blood.

Chemical digestion is completed and most of the nutrients from food are absorbed from the small intestine into the bloodstream through fingerlike structures called **villi** (VIH li) (singular, villus). Villi, illustrated in **Figure 6,** increase the surface area of the small intestine, giving the small intestine approximately the same surface area as a tennis court.

Refer again to **Figure 1** and **Figure 2** to follow the movement of digested food through the digestive system. Once digestion is complete, the remaining food, now in a semiliquid form called chyme (KIME), moves into the large intestine. Chyme is made up of materials that cannot be digested or absorbed by villi in the small intestine.

MiniLab 1

Investigate Digestion of Lipids

Inquiry MiniLab

How do bile salts and pancreatic solution affect digestion? Lipids, or fats, are not water soluble. The body compensates by producing bile, a chemical that breaks apart fat and helps the molecules mix with the watery solution in the small intestine. In this lab, you will investigate the breakdown of lipids.

Procedure

1. Read and complete the lab safety form.
2. Study the lab procedure and construct a data chart.
3. Label **three test tubes.** Add 5 mL **vegetable oil** and 8-10 drops **phenolphthalein** to each. Shake well. If the color is not pink, add **NaOH solution** one drop at a time until the solution turns pink.
4. Add 125 mL **water** to a **250-mL beaker.** Warm to about 40°C.
5. Prepare the test tubes as follows, then seal each with a **stopper.**
   Test Tube A: 5 mL **distilled water,** pinch of **bile salt**
   Test Tube B: 5 mL **pancreatic solution,** pinch of bile salt
   Test Tube C: 5 mL pancreatic solution
6. Shake each tube to mix the contents and gently place in the beaker. Record your observations.
7. Dispose of test tube contents in the designated container.

Analysis

1. **Analyze** What did a color change inside a test tube indicate? What caused the change?
2. **Draw conclusions** based on your results. Describe the roles of bile and pancreatic solution in digestion.

Activity

BL OL COOP LEARN Length of the Digestive Tract Give pairs of students four different colors of yarn and one pair of scissors. Tell them one color of yarn represents the esophagus; another, the stomach; a third, the small intestine; and the fourth, the large intestine. Have students cut each piece of yarn into lengths they think represent the length of each digestive-tract structure and then tie the pieces together to represent the total length of the digestive tract. Have them compare their models to one based upon the actual length: esophagus = 25 cm, stomach = 20 cm, small intestine = 7 m, large intestine = 1.5 m.

AL Have students use the four different colors of yarn to create a model of the four parts of the digestive tract that is based on the actual length. Est. time: 15 min

MiniLab 1

Inquiry MiniLab

For a lab worksheet, use your eTeacherEdition Online.

RUBRIC A rubric for evaluating MiniLabs is found on your eTeacherEdition Online.

Est. Time 40 min

Alternative Material Phenol red could be used as an indicator rather than phenolphthalein.

Safety Precaution Approve lab safety forms before work begins.

Teaching Strategies

- Make sure students understand that phenolphthalein changes from pink to colorless as a solution goes from alkaline to acidic.
- Tell students that the pancreatic solution is the source of the enzyme lipase in the lab.
- Make sure students understand that lipids are broken down into fatty acids which, because of their acid properties, will cause phenothalein to become colorless.

Cleanup and Disposal Have students dispose of test tube contents in a designated container, clean and return equipment to the appropriate location, and wash hands thoroughly.

Analysis

1. A color change showed that the solution was becoming acidic. As fatty acids were produced through the digestion of fat, the pH of the solution decreased.
2. Bile and pancreatic solution break down lipids, such as the vegetable oil in the experiment.

LabManager™

Customize this lab with the LabManager™ CD-ROM.

Concepts in Motion

Interactive Table

Inquiry BioLab

The lab at the end of the chapter can be used at this point in the lesson.

Formative Assessment

Evaluation Have students list the order of structures of the digestive tract and indicate what digestive processes occur in each. mouth: mechanical (chewing) and chemical (amylase) digestion; esophagus: peristalsis moves food from mouth to stomach; stomach: mechanical (muscles contract) and chemical (pepsin) digestion; small intestine: mechanical and chemical digestion (enzymes from pancreas and liver break down carbohydrates, fats, and proteins); large intestine: absorbs water in food; chemical digestion (peristalsis) moves waste products to rectum

Remediation Have pairs of students draw a diagram of the digestive tract, label each part, and list the digestive processes that occur in each.

Table 1 Time for Digestion — Concepts in Motion Interactive Table

Digestive Structure	Primary Function	Time Food in Structure
Mouth	Mechanical and chemical digestion	5–30 s
Esophagus	Transport (swallowing)	10 s
Stomach	Mechanical and chemical digestion	2–24 h
Small intestine	Mechanical and chemical digestion	3–4 h
Large intestine	Water absorption	18 h–2 days

Large intestine The **large intestine** is the end portion of the digestive tract. It is about 1.5 m long and includes the colon, the rectum, and a small saclike appendage called the appendix. Although the appendix has no known function, it can become inflamed and swollen, resulting in appendicitis. If inflamed, the appendix will likely have to be removed surgically.

Some kinds of beneficial bacteria are normal in the colon. These bacteria produce vitamin K and some B vitamins available to the body.

A primary function of the colon is to absorb water from the chyme. The indigestible material then becomes more solid and is called feces. Peristalsis continues to move feces toward the rectum, causing the walls of the rectum to stretch. This initiates a reflex that causes the final sphincter muscle to relax, and the feces are eliminated from the body through the anus. Refer to **Table 1** to review the primary function of each structure of the digestive system and how long food usually remains in each structure as it is being digested.

Section 1 Assessment

Section Summary

- The digestive system has three main functions.
- Digestion can be categorized as mechanical or chemical.
- Most nutrients are absorbed in the small intestine.
- Accessory organs provide enzymes and bile to aid digestion.
- Water is absorbed from chyme in the colon.

Understand Main Ideas

1. MAIN Idea **Describe** the process that breaks down food so that nutrients can be absorbed by the body.
2. **Analyze** the difference between mechanical digestion and chemical digestion. Explain why chemical digestion is necessary for the body.
3. **Summarize** the three main functions of the digestive system.
4. **Analyze** what the consequence might be if the lining of the small intestine were completely smooth instead of having villi.

Think Critically

5. **Design** an experiment to gather data about the effect of pH on the digestion of different types of food.

MATH in Biology

6. A can of carbonated beverage typically holds about 354 mL of fluid. Compare this amount with the volume of an empty stomach. Give a ratio.
7. **Explain** why the pH in the digestive system changes. Give examples and explain the importance of these changes.

Section 1 Assessment

1. Digestion begins in the mouth and continues in the stomach. Next, nutrients are absorbed in the small intestine. Digestion ends in the large intestine where water is absorbed before excretion.
2. Mechanical digestion, such as chewing in the mouth, grinds food into smaller particles. Chemical digestion by acids and enzymes changes foods chemically and enables cells to absorb nutrients.
3. ingest food, break it down so nutrients can be absorbed, and eliminate what cannot be digested
4. Fewer nutrients could be absorbed by the decreased surface area.
5. Possible answer: Add an equal amount of high-carbohydrate foods to three beakers containing solutions with various pH levels. Repeat with high-protein foods and fatty foods.
6. empty stomach vol. = 50 mL; pop-to-stomach ratio = 7:1
7. Stomach glands lower the pH to about 2, which helps the enzyme pepsin to chemically digest proteins. The pancreas secretes an alkaline fluid to raise the pH in the small intestine to about 7, which helps intestinal enzymes to act.

Assessment Online Quiz

Reading Preview

Essential Questions

- Depending on activity level, what caloric intake is needed to maintain proper body weight?
- How are proteins, carbohydrates, and fats used by the body?
- What are the roles of vitamins and minerals in maintaining homeostasis?
- How can you apply the information in MyPyramid and on food labels to establishing healthy eating habits?

Review Vocabulary

amino acid: the basic building block of proteins

New Vocabulary

nutrition
Calorie
vitamin
mineral

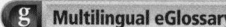

g Multilingual eGlossary

R Nutrition

MAIN Idea **Certain nutrients are essential for the proper function of the body.**

Real-World Reading Link There is a saying, "You are what you eat." What do you think that means? Much of the time, you have freedom to choose what you eat. However, your choices have consequences. What you eat can affect your health now and in the future.

D Calories

Nutrition is the process by which a person takes in and uses food. Foods supply the building blocks and energy to maintain body mass. The daily input of energy from food should equal the amount of energy a person uses daily. A **Calorie** (with an uppercase C) is the unit used to measure the energy content of foods. A Calorie is equal to 1 kilocalorie, or 1000 calories (with a lowercase c). A calorie is the amount of heat needed to raise the temperature of 1 mL of water by 1°C.

The energy content of a food can be measured by burning the food and converting the stored energy to heat. Not all foods have the same energy content. The same mass of different foods does not always equal the same number of Calories. For example, one gram of carbohydrate or protein contains four Calories. One gram of fat contains nine Calories. To lose weight, more Calories must be used than consumed. The opposite is true to gain weight. In 2005, the United States Department of Agriculture released new guidelines for nutrition and suggested that people should become more active and use more Calories. **Table 2** compares average Calorie usage with different activities. The exact number of calories burned will vary depending on weight and gender.

Table 2 Activities and Average Calorie Usage — Concepts in Motion Interactive Table

Activity	Calories Used Per Hour	Activity	Calories Used Per Hour
Baseball	282	Hiking and backpacking	564
Basketball	564	Hockey (field and ice)	546
Bicycling	240–410	Jogging	740–920
Cross-country skiing	700	Skating	300
Football	540	Soccer	540

Differentiated Instruction

Below Level When assigning the cooperative learning activity described on this page, break the assignment down into smaller tasks. The assignment will be more manageable for students if they are able to accomplish one small goal at a time.

For more tips, see pages 14T–15T.

GOING GREEN Use biodegradable, phosphate free detergent to clean lab equipment. Also keep "green" soap on hand for student hand washing. "Green" soap does not contain antimicrobials or harsh chemicals such as lauryl sulfate. Look for vegetable oil based soaps.

Section 2

MAIN Idea

BL OL AL **Nutrition**

ASK STUDENTS: ***In addition to obtaining energy, why is it important to eat a variety of food types?*** Different foods provide the variety of nutrients that are necessary to sustain life.

SAY TO STUDENTS: ***Nutrients are the compounds in foods that are essential for life. They include carbohydrates, fats, and proteins. They also include vitamins and minerals, which your body needs to function properly.***

R Reading Strategy

EL BL OL AL

Directed Reading On a sheet of paper, have students make three columns and label them *What I Know, What I Want to Know*, and *What I've Learned.* Have students fill in the columns labeled *What I Know* and *What I Want to Know* before reading Section 2. After they read the text, have students fill in the final column.

D Develop Concepts

EL BL OL AL COOP LEARN

Activity Place students in groups of three or four. Have groups develop an exercise program consisting of team sports and individual activities that will cause an average individual to burn at least 2000 calories per week.

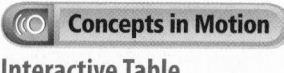

Concepts in Motion
Interactive Table

D Develop Concepts

EL BL OL Activity Have students create a recipe for a single dish that contains simple and complex carbohydrates and saturated and unsaturated fats. Have English learners work in pairs. Possible example: a lettuce salad that also contains tomatoes and orange slices (simple carbohydrates); sliced, grilled chicken breast (saturated fats); and is topped with a salad dressing made from olive oil (unsaturated fat) and vinegar. Serve with whole-grain bread (complex carbohydrates).

AL Have students design a week's worth of meals that are nutritionally sound.

W Writing Support

AL Create Posters Have students research what foods are high in saturated fats and the health effects of a diet that is high in saturated fats. Have each student choose a disease or disorder, such as heart disease or obesity, that can result from a high-fat diet, as well as what percentage of people have the disease or disorder they choose. Have them find out among which group or groups of people the disease is most prevalent. Then have them use this information to create a poster that warns of the dangers. The poster should include healthful alternative eating habits that can help people avoid the risks of a high-fat diet.

Figure 7 Your body needs carbohydrate-rich foods like these every day.

VOCABULARY
SCIENCE USAGE V. COMMON USAGE
Consume
Science usage: to eat or drink
We consume Calories when we eat food.

Common usage: to destroy
The fire consumed several buildings.

Carbohydrates

Cereal, pasta, potatoes, strawberries, and rice all contain a high proportion of carbohydrates. Recall that sugars, such as glucose, fructose, and sucrose, are simple carbohydrates that are found in fruits, soda pop, and candy. Complex carbohydrates are macromolecules such as starches, which are long chains of sugars. Foods such as those shown in **Figure 7** have a high starch content, as do some vegetables.

Complex carbohydrates are broken down into simple sugars in the digestive tract. Simple sugars are absorbed through villi in the small intestine into blood capillaries and circulated throughout the body to provide energy for cells. Excess glucose is stored in the liver in the form of glycogen. Cellulose, sometimes called dietary fiber, is another complex carbohydrate found in plant foods. Although humans cannot digest fiber, it is important because fiber helps keep food moving through the digestive tract and helps with the elimination of wastes. Bran, whole-grain breads, and beans are good sources of fiber.

Reading Check Compare simple and complex carbohydrates.

Fats

In proper amounts, fats are an essential part of a healthful diet. Fats are the most concentrated energy source available to the body, and they are building blocks for the body. Fats also protect some internal organs and help maintain homeostasis by providing energy and by storing and transporting certain vitamins. However, not all fats are beneficial.

Connection to Health Recall that fats are classified according to their chemical structure as saturated or unsaturated. Meats, cheeses, and other dairy products are sources of saturated fats. A diet high in saturated fats might result in high blood levels of cholesterol, which can lead to heart problems. Plants are the main source of unsaturated fats. They are not associated with heart disease, although excessive consumption of any type of fat can lead to weight gain.

A general rule is that saturated fats are solid and unsaturated fats are liquid at room temperature. The olive oil in **Figure 8** contains less saturated fat than the butter, which is why the olive oil is liquid at room temperature. Fats are digested in the small intestine and broken down into fatty acids and glycerol. Fatty acids can be absorbed through the villi and circulated in the blood throughout the body. D W

Figure 8 The way in which naturally low-fat foods are cooked and served can increase saturated fat content. Olive oil may be a better cooking option than butter for this reason.

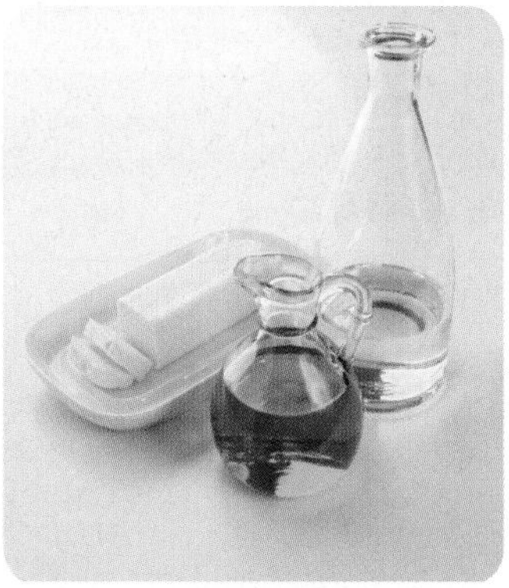

Reading Check Simple carbohydrates are sugars found in fruit and candy. Complex carbohydrates, found in cereal grains and other starchy foods, are broken down into simple sugars in the digestive tract.

Demonstration

Presence of Fats Bring snack foods such as potato chips, fruit slices, cheese, and cookies to class. Test for fat content by rubbing each item on a separate piece of brown paper. Remove the food and let the papers dry. Hold each paper up to a light. Point out that if the area of the paper exposed to the food is translucent, the substance contains fat. Est. time: 5 min

Proteins

You have learned that proteins are basic structural components of all cells, and that amino acids are the building blocks of proteins. Enzymes, hormones, neurotransmitters, and membrane receptors are just a few important proteins in the body.

During the process of digestion, proteins in foods are broken down to their subunit amino acids. The amino acids are absorbed into the bloodstream and carried to various body cells. These body cells, through the process of protein synthesis, assemble the amino acids into proteins needed for body structures and functions.

Humans require 20 different amino acids for protein synthesis. The human body can produce 12 of the 20 amino acids needed for cellular function. Essential amino acids are the eight amino acids that must be included in a person's diet. Animal products, such as meats, fish, poultry, eggs, and dairy products, are sources of all eight essential amino acids. Vegetables, fruits, and grains contain amino acids, but no single plant food source contains all eight essential amino acids. However, certain combinations, such as the beans and rice shown in **Figure 9,** provide all of the essential amino acids.

W

Figure 9 Beans and rice can be combined to provide all the essential amino acids.
Explain ***why it is important to eat foods that contain the essential amino acids.***

Food Pyramid

In 2005, the United States Department of Agriculture published a new food pyramid, MyPyramid, which replaces the old pyramid that had been a symbol of good nutrition since 1992. **Figure 10** shows a version of the new pyramid. Notice that the orange and green sections are wider than the purple and yellow sections. The message of the pyramid is that a person needs more nutrients from grains and vegetables than from meats and oils.

D

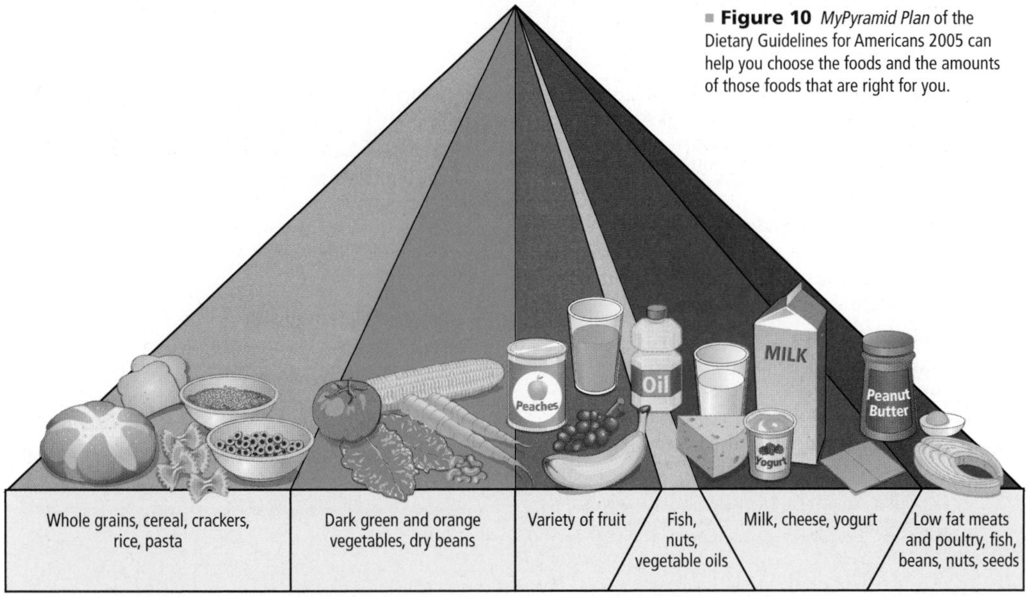

Figure 10 *MyPyramid Plan* of the Dietary Guidelines for Americans 2005 can help you choose the foods and the amounts of those foods that are right for you.

W Writing Support

BL OL Technical Writing

Have students create a bookmark listing the major groups of nutrients (carbohydrates, fats, proteins, vitamins, and minerals) and a brief description of why each group is important to the functioning of the human body. Encourage them to decorate their bookmark with pictures of food from each group.

EL COOP LEARN Have students work in pairs.

D Develop Concepts

EL BL OL AL COOP LEARN

Activity Have students keep a food journal in which they record everything they eat in one week. Then, have them share their lists with a partner. Have the pairs identify sources of carbohydrates, fats, proteins, vitamins, and minerals in their diets. Nutrition labels on prepared foods can help students determine the serving size and the nutrient value of each serving. Calorie books or other sources can help them determine nutrients in other foods, such as produce. Then, have each pair get together with another pair, share their lists, and create one group list. **ASK STUDENTS:** ***Which groups of nutrients provided the most calories in your diet? Are there any groups of nutrients that were lacking in your diet?*** Answers will vary, but students should be specific about each food they consumed and categorize each food into the proper group.

Research Citation

Cooperative Learning Educational research indicates that student achievement can be improved when they work in groups with their peers. These activities allow students to be more involved in a lesson and to question and listen to each other rather than rely only on information from the teacher. (Wood and Turner-Vorbeck, 2001)

Research bibliography on pages 32T–34T

Caption Question Fig. 9 The essential amino acids are needed for body structures and functions, and your body cannot make them.

C Critical Thinking

BL OL AL COOP LEARN

Assess Have students identify and bring to school newspaper or magazine ads that claim or imply that the advertised food has nutritional benefits. Have pairs of students state the claim and any evidence used by the ad to support the claim, and then critique the claim. Students should analyze the sources of Calories in the food as well as vitamin and mineral content, then assess whether the food actually provides the implied or claimed nutritional benefits.

DATA ANALYSIS LAB 1

About the Lab

- Some students might have the misconception that the nutrient information on the food label is for the entire package. Packaged food labels carry information about calories and nutrients for one serving of the food. The label also states how many servings the package contains.
- Also see France, K.R., and P.F. Bone. 2005. Policy makers' paradigms and evidence from consumer interpretations of dietary supplement labels *Journal of Consumer Affairs* 39: 27–51.

Think Critically

1. Percent difference = (actual mass –label mass)/actual mass × 100 cereal, bran flakes = 28%; cereal, toasted grains = 42%; cookie = 15%; mini danish = 22%; mini donut = 14%
2. All actual masses were greater than the label masses. Cereals have the highest percent difference.

CAREERS IN BIOLOGY

Registered Dietician A registered dietician addresses a variety of health issues by showing patients how to make healthful decisions about their diets.

? Inquiry Virtual Lab

Vitamins and Minerals

In addition to carbohydrates, fats, and proteins, your body needs vitamins and minerals to function properly. **Vitamins** are organic compounds that are needed in small amounts for metabolic activities. Many vitamins help enzymes function properly. Some vitamins are produced within the body. Vitamin D is made by cells in your skin. Some B vitamins and vitamin K are produced by bacteria living in the large intestine. However, sufficient quantities of most vitamins cannot be made by the body, but a well-balanced diet can provide the vitamins that are needed. Some vitamins that are fat-soluble can be stored in small quantities in the liver and fatty tissues of the body. Other vitamins are water-soluble and cannot be stored in the body. Foods providing an adequate level of these vitamins should be included in a person's diet on a regular basis.

Minerals are inorganic compounds used by the body as building materials, and they are involved with metabolic functions. For example, the mineral iron is needed to make hemoglobin. Recall that oxygen binds to hemoglobin in red blood cells and is delivered to body cells as blood circulates in the body. Calcium, another mineral, is an important component of bones.

Vitamins and minerals are essential parts of a healthy diet. **Table 3** on the next page lists some important vitamins and minerals, their benefits, and some food sources that can provide these necessary nutrients. Over-the-counter vitamins are also available. Taking more than the recommended daily allowance, however, can be dangerous and should not be done without consulting a doctor. C

DATA ANALYSIS LAB 1

Based on Real Data*

Compare Data

How reliable are food labels? In a study conducted at the U.S. Department of Agriculture Human Nutrition Research Center, scientists measured the mass of 99 single-serving food products.

Data and Observations

The table compares the mass listed on the food package label with the actual mass of the food in five single-serving packages.

Food (1 serving)	Label Mass (g)	Actual Mass (g)
Cereal, bran flakes with raisins (1 box)	39	54.2
Cereal, toasted grains with supplement (1 box)	23	39.6
Cookie, chocolate sandwich (1 pkg)	57	67.0
Mini danish, apple (1 per serving)	35	44.8
Mini donut, chocolate covered (4 per serving)	100	116.5

Think Critically

1. **Calculate** the percent difference in mass between the label mass and the actual mass of the cookies.
2. **Compare** the trend in the percent differences.

*Data obtained from: Conway, J.M., D.G. Rhodes, and W.V. Rumpler. 2004. Commercial portion-controlled foods in research studies: how accurate are label weights? *Journal of the American Dietetic Association* 104: 1420–1424.

Demonstration

BL OL **Emulsification of Lipids** Place a small amount of cooking oil and water in a dish. Add a few drops of dishwashing detergent.
AL Have students work in pairs at their seats to carry out the demonstration.
ASK STUDENTS: ***What has happened to the oil?*** The oil has broken down into smaller particles. Inform the students that bile secreted by the liver, and also stored in the gallbladder, breaks down fats in a similar manner. These smaller fat molecules can be absorbed into the bloodstream and carried throughout the body. Once they enter the blood, the fat particles can combine with other molecules. Est. time: 5 min

S

Table 3 Major Roles of Some Vitamins and Minerals

Concepts in Motion Interactive Table

Vitamin	Major Role in the Body	Possible Sources	Mineral	Major Role in the Body
A	• Vision • Health of skin and bones		Ca	• Strengthening of teeth and bone • Nerve conduction • Contraction of muscle
D	• Health of bones and teeth		P	• Strengthening of teeth and bone
E	• Strengthening of red blood cell membrane		Mg	• Synthesis of proteins
Riboflavin (B_2)	• Metabolism		Fe	• Synthesis of hemoglobin
Folic Acid	• Formation of red blood cells • Formation of DNA and RNA		Cu	• Synthesis of hemoglobin
Thiamine	• Metabolism of carbohydrates		Zn	• Healing of wounds
Niacin (B_3)	• Metabolism		Cl	• Balance of water
Pyridoxine (B_6)	• Metabolism of amino acids		I	• Synthesis of thyroid hormone
B_{12}	• Formation of red blood cells		Na	• Nerve conduction • Balance of pH
C	• Formation of collagen		K	• Nerve conduction • Contraction of muscle

S Skill Practice

EL OL Visual Literacy Have students study the information provided in Table 3.

SAY TO STUDENTS: ***Use this information to develop a meal plan for one day that includes all of the listed vitamins and minerals. Devise an alternative method to visually present the meal plan.***

BL COOP LEARN Have students work in pairs.

AL Have students develop a plan that not only includes all of the vitamins and minerals, but that is also nutritionally sound based on the food pyramid guidelines. Ideas will vary, but one example is a pie chart that resembles a dinner plate; another could be a picnic basket filled with foods that represent the vitamins and minerals.

Develop Concepts

OL AL

Activate Prior Knowledge

ASK STUDENTS: ***In what processes are the following minerals involved: calcium, iron, potassium, and sodium?*** Calcium is important in bone formation and muscle contraction; iron is a component of hemoglobin; potassium and sodium are involved in the transmission of an action potential.

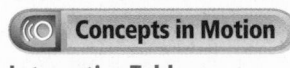

Concepts in Motion
Interactive Table

Content Background

Real-World Connection One reason why the U.S. government developed a new food pyramid was the mounting concern about rising obesity rates among children and adults in the United States. Exercise is a key component of the new food pyramid. Exercise was not addressed in previous food-pyramid models.

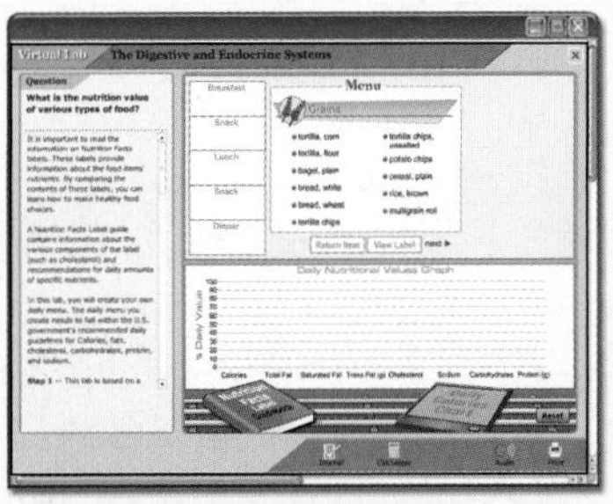

Inquiry Virtual Lab Students will plan a daily menu by analyzing nutrition labels on foods.

Develop Concepts

OL AL

Clarify a Misconception

ASK STUDENTS: ***Will a diet low in carbohydrates (or sugars or fats) cause weight loss?*** It is not the energy source itself that is responsible for weight gain or loss, although different energy sources are metabolized differently in different individuals. To lose weight, a person needs to expend more Calories than they consume, and a balance of food types is necessary for good health.

Formative Assessment

Evaluation

ASK STUDENTS: ***What are the respective functions of carbohydrates, fats, proteins, vitamins, and minerals?*** Carbohydrates can be used for "fast energy." Fats are concentrated sources of energy and are building blocks for the body. Proteins, when digested, are broken down into amino acids, which the body reassembles into other proteins that it needs. Vitamins are organic compounds, and minerals are inorganic compounds needed for many metabolic functions.

Remediation Have students make a three-column chart. In the left column, have them list carbohydrates, fats, proteins, vitamins, and minerals. In the middle column, have them list food sources for each nutrient. In the right-hand column, have students indicate why the body needs each type of nutrient.

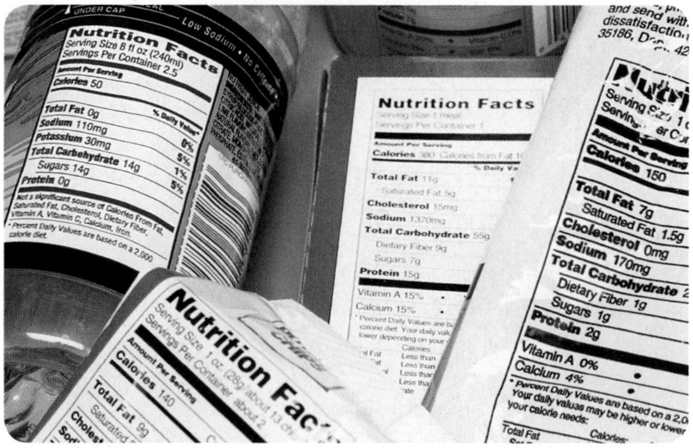

Figure 11 Notice how many servings are in each food container. The percent daily values are based on an individual serving, not the entire package.

Nutrition Labels

Nutrition labels are provided on commercially packaged foods like those shown in **Figure 11.** These labels are based on a 2000-Calorie-per-day diet. Labels can be especially useful for monitoring fat and sodium intake, which are two nutrients that need to be consumed in moderation. The FDA requires that food labels list the following information.

- name of the food
- net weight or volume
- name and address of manufacturer, distributor, or packager
- ingredients
- nutrient content

Section 2 Assessment

Section Summary

- The energy content of food is measured in Calories.
- Carbohydrates, fats, and proteins are three major groups of nutrients.
- Carbohydrates are a major source of energy for the body.
- Fats and proteins provide energy and are important building blocks for the body.
- Vitamins and minerals are essential for proper metabolic functioning.
- The *MyPyramid Plan* and food labels are tools that you can use to eat healthfully.

Understand Main Ideas

1. MAIN Idea **Explain** the roles of vitamins and minerals in the process of maintaining homeostasis.
2. **Describe** what proteins, carbohydrates, and fats are used for in the process of digestion.
3. **Recommend** what nutrients a vegetarian should add to his or her diet.
4. **Explain** why keeping a count of Calories consumed and Calories used is important in maintaining proper functioning of the body.

Think Critically

5. **Summarize** how many Calories you consume during one day by recording everything you eat or drink. Compare this to how many Calories you burn in an average day.

WRITING in **Biology**

6. Write a short article for your school newspaper describing what is needed for a well-balanced diet.

Section 2 Assessment

1. Vitamins help enzymes to function well, and minerals are used by the body as building material and are involved in essential metabolic functions.
2. carbohydrates = quick energy; proteins and fats = energy and molecular building blocks
3. Because meat and other animal products contain some of the 20 amino acids that humans need for protein synthesis, vegetarians should add foods such as rice and beans that provide these essential amino acids.
4. Balancing Calories consumed with Calories used maintains body weight.
5. Answers will vary, but nutritional data and Calorie estimators are available online. Nutritional data can also come from nutrition labels, cookbooks, and other resources.
6. Answers will vary, but should include the basic ingredients for a well-balanced diet. Students can base their answers on the food pyramid in this section.

Assessment Online Quiz

Section 3

The Endocrine System

Reading Preview

Essential Questions

- What are the functions of the glands that make up the endocrine system?
- What is the role of the endocrine system in maintaining homeostasis?
- What are the feedback mechanisms that regulate hormone levels in the body?

Review Vocabulary

homeostasis: the regulation of an organism's internal environment to maintain life

New Vocabulary

endocrine gland
hormone
pituitary gland
thyroxine
calcitonin
parathyroid hormone
insulin
glucagon
aldosterone
cortisol
antidiuretic hormone

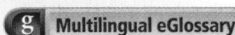

Multilingual eGlossary

MAIN Idea Systems of the human body are regulated by hormonal feedback mechanisms.

Real-World Reading Link When driving a car, everyone usually maintains a similar speed. When cars go faster or slower than the accepted speed, the chance of an accident increases. Similarly, hormones must stay in the proper balance to maintain homeostasis in the body.

R Action of Hormones

The endocrine system is composed of glands and functions as a communication system. **Endocrine glands** produce hormones, which are released into the bloodstream and distributed to body cells. A **hormone** is a substance that acts on certain target cells and tissues to produce a specific response. Hormones are classified as steroid hormones and nonsteroid or amino acid hormones, based on their structure and mechanism of action.

Steroid hormones Estrogen and testosterone are two examples of steroid hormones. Both of these hormones affect the human reproductive system. All steroid hormones work by causing the target cells to initiate protein synthesis, as illustrated in **Figure 12.**

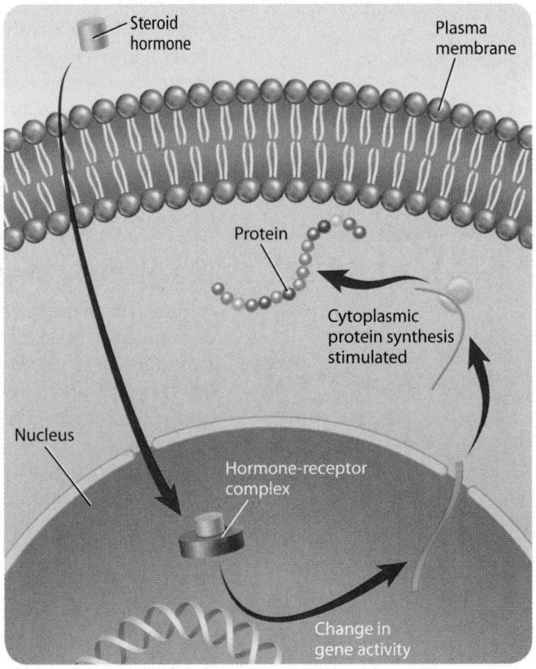

■ **Figure 12** A steroid hormone passes through a cell membrane, binds to a receptor within the cell, and stimulates protein synthesis.

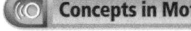

Concepts in Motion
Animation

Section 3

MAIN Idea

BL OL Homeostasis

ASK STUDENTS: ***What is the endocrine system? How does the endocrine system help to maintain homeostasis in the body?*** Answers will vary. The endocrine system is made up of glands and provides one way by which cells in the body can communicate. Endocrine glands secrete hormones, which are chemical signals. Hormone levels are regulated by feedback mechanisms.

AL ***What do hormones control?*** Answers will vary. Hormones control a wide variety of body functions—regulation of calcium and blood sugar levels, growth, and reproduction, to name a few.

R Reading Strategy

EL OL SQ3R Have students **S**urvey Section 3, focusing on subheadings. Next, have students write **Q**uestions about key points made in this section. Then have students **R**ead the section and make notes related to the questions. Finally, have them **R**ecite vocabulary and **R**eview for meaning.

Concepts in Motion
Animation

Demonstration

BL OL Fight or Flight

SAY TO STUDENTS: ***We are going to cover some complex material next, so everyone needs to be alert and ready to learn. Take some deep breaths and relax.*** Create a relaxing atmosphere for 5 min by dimming the lights and playing soothing sounds. Without warning, make a loud, startling noise. Turn on the lights.

ASK STUDENTS: ***How did your body respond to the noise?*** Possible answers include increased heart rate, sweating, or jumping. Point out that the hormone epinephrine is responsible for these reactions. Est. time: 10 min

Note: If there is a student who has cardiac problems or is easily frightened, use caution or do not complete this activity.

C Critical Thinking

OL AL Analyze

ASK STUDENTS: ***Why would an amino-acid hormone not have any effect on a steroid hormone receptor?*** Amino acids are not lipid soluble and cannot pass through the plasma membrane. Receptors for steroid hormones are in the cytoplasm of a cell.

S Skill Practice

OL Visual Literacy Have students study Figures 14 and 17. Have them write a paragraph describing the events occurring in Figure 14, beginning with a temperature of 20°C. The thermostat is set for 21°C, and when the temperature drops below that setting, the furnace turns on; when it rises above, the furnace turns off. Then have them write a paragraph comparing this negative feedback loop with the loop shown in Figure 17. When blood calcium drops below a certain level, glands produce parathyroid hormone, which causes blood calcium to rise.

BL Have students create a flowchart to illustrate the processes.

AL Have students describe the processes verbally.

D Develop Concepts

OL AL Brainstorm Have students think of analogies of negative feedback similar to the example in Figure 14. One example is that some cars have cruise control to maintain a constant speed. If the car goes down a hill and begins to go faster than the speed at which the cruise control is set, the cruise control will slow down the car. If the car is going slower than the preset speed, the cruise control will cause the car to go faster.

Concepts in Motion

Animation

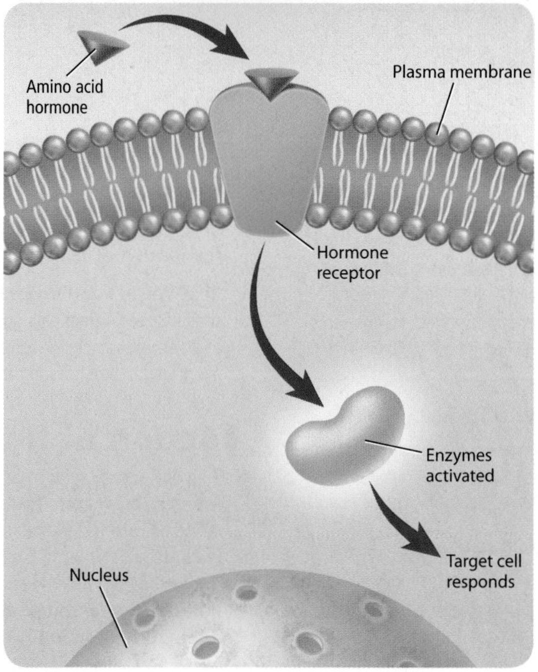

■ **Figure 13** An amino acid hormone binds to a receptor on the plasma membrane before entering the cell.
Explain ***the difference between amino acid hormones and steroid hormones.***

Concepts in Motion

Animation

Steroid hormones are soluble in lipids and therefore can diffuse through the plasma membrane of a target cell. Once inside a target cell, they bind to a receptor in the cell. The hormone and the receptor that are bound together bind to DNA in the nucleus, which activates specific genes.

Amino acid hormones Insulin and growth hormones are two examples of nonsteroid, or amino acid, hormones. As the name implies, these hormones are composed of amino acids. Amino acid hormones must bind to receptors found on the plasma membrane of a target cell because they cannot diffuse through the plasma membrane. Once the hormone binds to the receptor, the receptor activates an enzyme found on the inside of the membrane. This usually initiates a biochemical pathway, eventually causing the cell to produce the desired response, as illustrated in **Figure 13.** C

S D

■ **Figure 14** A furnace turns on or off based on the relationship of the detected room temperature and the set point.

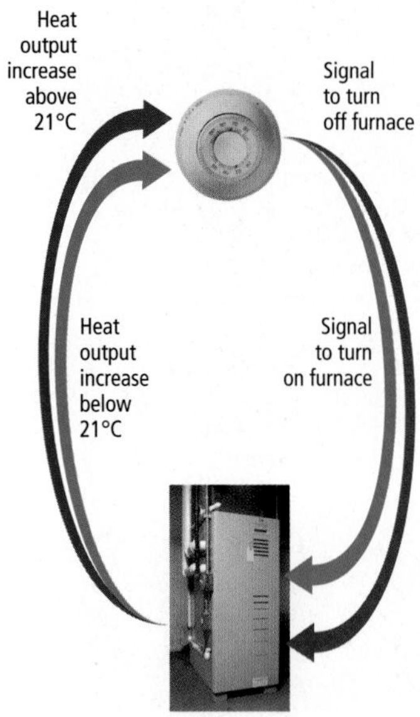

Negative Feedback

Homeostasis in the body is maintained by internal feedback mechanisms called negative feedback. Negative feedback returns a system to a set point once it deviates sufficiently from that set point. As a consequence, the system varies within a particular range. You already might be familiar with an example of a negative feedback system in your own home, as illustrated in **Figure 14.**

For example, the temperature in a house might be maintained at 21°C. The thermostat in the house detects the temperature, and when the temperature drops below 21°C, the thermostat sends a signal to the heat source, which turns it on and produces more heat. Soon the temperature rises above 21°C, and the thermostat sends a signal to the heat source to shut off. The heat source will not turn on again until the room temperature drops below 21°C and is detected by the thermostat. Because this process can go on indefinitely, negative feedback often is described as a loop.

■ **Caption Question Fig. 13** Steroid hormones are soluble in lipids and can pass through the plasma membrane to a receptor inside a cell. Amino acid hormones cannot pass through the plasma membrane and must bind to receptors on the membrane.

Differentiated Instruction

Visually Impaired Provide visually impaired students with audio reinforcement. This will enable these students to participate in activities and discussions for which it is necessary to have read the text. Audio for the complete text is available on your StudentWorks™ Plus Online.

For more tips, see pages 14T–15T.

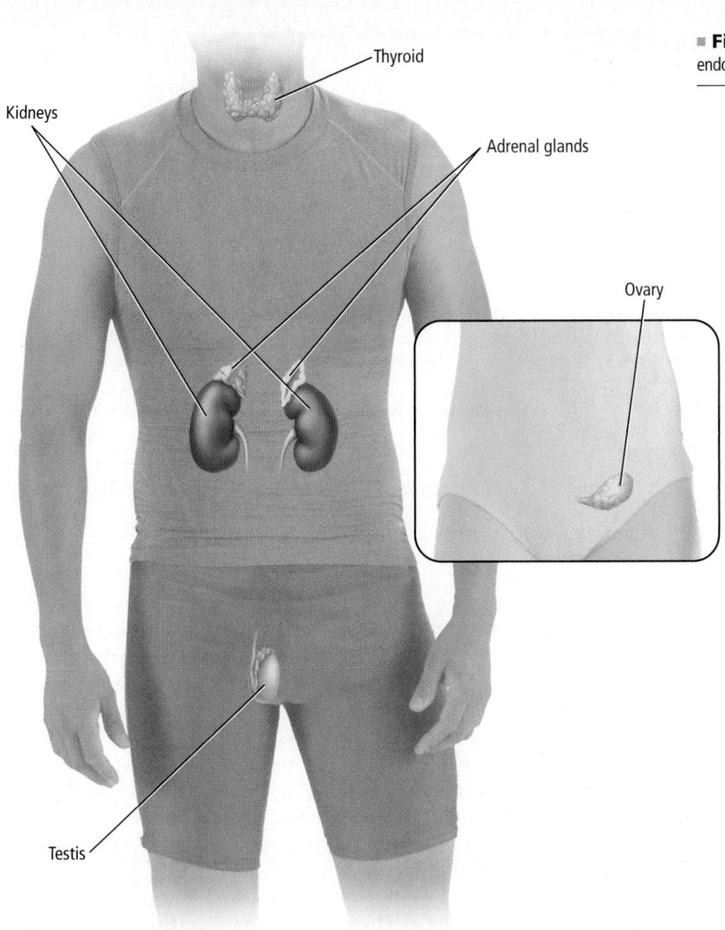

■ **Figure 15** The principal glands of the endocrine system are located throughout the body.

Endocrine Glands and Their Hormones

The endocrine system, shown in **Figure 15,** includes all the glands that secrete hormones—pituitary, thyroid, parathyroid, and adrenal glands, the pancreas, ovaries, testes, pineal gland, and the thymus gland.

Pituitary gland The pituitary gland is situated at the base of the brain, as illustrated in **Figure 16.** This gland is sometimes called the "master gland" because it regulates so many body functions. Despite its small size, it is the most important endocrine gland. The **pituitary gland** secretes hormones that not only regulate many body functions but also regulates other endocrine glands, such as the thyroid gland, the adrenal glands, the testes, and the ovaries.

A few pituitary hormones act on tissues rather than on specific organs. Human growth hormone (hGH) regulates the body's physical growth by stimulating cell division in muscle and bone tissue. This hormone is especially active during childhood and adolescence.

■ **Figure 16** The pituitary gland is located at the base of the brain. This gland has a diameter of approximately 1 cm and weighs 0.5–1 g.

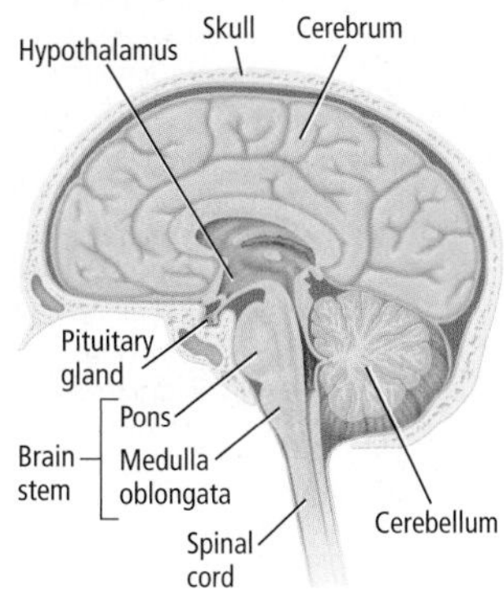

Content Background

Teacher FYI Located within the brain is an endocrine gland called the pineal body or pineal gland. The pineal gland produces the hormone melatonin. Melatonin levels increase at night and are low during the daylight hours. Evidence suggests that the pineal gland influences sleep-wake cycles. Research also suggests melatonin may be involved with the regulation of sexual development. In children whose pineal gland has been destroyed by a tumor, early sexual development can result.

Critical Thinking

BL OL AL Analyze Point out that when a person who is allergic to bees gets stung, they might experience wheezing, shortness of breath, and a sudden drop in blood pressure.

ASK STUDENTS: ***Why is the treatment for this an injection of epinephrine?*** Epinephrine increases the overall metabolic rate, including increasing breathing rate and raising blood pressure. This counteracts some of the harmful reactions caused by the bee sting.

Develop Concepts

OL AL Scaffolding

ASK STUDENTS: ***Explain how a hormone is transported through the body.*** Hormones are secreted by an endocrine gland into the bloodstream and the blood distributes the hormone to its target cells. ***Identify how a hormone influences the activity of a target cell.*** A hormone first binds to a receptor on a target cell. Steroid hormones pass through the plasma membrane and bind to receptors in the cytoplasm, causing the cell to synthesize certain proteins. Nonsteroid hormones bind to receptors on the plasma membrane, activating an enzyme. ***Infer how the body with a normally functioning hormonal system would respond if the level of a hormone became too low.*** Hormones are usually regulated by a negative-feedback mechanism. When the level of a certain hormone is low, the gland that produces this hormone increases the release of the hormone. When the level of the hormone is high, the gland decreases the release of the hormone.

EL Before asking the above questions, show students an illustration that depicts how a hormone is transported.

C Critical Thinking

OL AL Infer

ASK STUDENTS: ***How might a condition that is caused by low levels of a hormone be treated?*** A drug could be prescribed to stimulate an endocrine gland to produce more of the low hormone, or a synthetic form of the hormone could be given. For example, human growth hormone is manufactured using recombinant DNA technology to treat dwarfism.

Tell students that acromegaly (ak roh ME guh lee) is a condition caused by too much growth hormone being produced.

ASK STUDENTS: ***How might acromegaly be treated?*** with a drug to slow down the production of growth hormone or a drug to block the receptors on target cells, preventing growth hormone from binding to them

BL Before asking the questions above, have students first look for commercials on television for prescription drugs that help regulate certain hormones.

W Writing Support

AL Summary Writing Have students research the effects of a hormone produced by one of the endocrine glands, such as the thyroid gland, and write a summary about the gland and its hormone and what disorders can occur if the hormone is not produced in sufficient quantities.

Review Personal Tutor

Listen to a teacher explain insulin feedback.

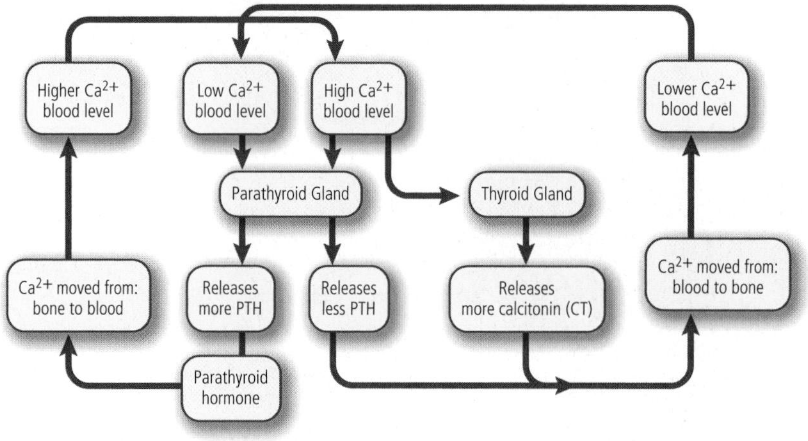

■ **Figure 17** Parathyroid hormone (PTH) and calcitonin (CT) regulate the level of calcium in the blood.
Explain ***how PTH and CT illustrate negative feedback.***

Review Personal Tutor

Thyroid and parathyroid glands Identify the thyroid and parathyroid glands in **Figure 17.** One hormone produced by the thyroid gland is thyroxine. Like hGH, **thyroxine** does not act on specific organs; rather, it causes cells of the body to have a higher rate of metabolism. The thyroid gland also produces calcitonin. **Calcitonin** (kal suh TOH nun) is a hormone that is partly responsible for the regulation of calcium, an important mineral for bone formation, blood clotting, nerve function, and muscle contraction. Calcitonin lowers blood calcium levels by signaling bones to increase calcium absorption and also signaling the kidneys to excrete more calcium.

When blood calcium levels are too low, the parathyroid glands increase production of parathyroid hormone. **Parathyroid hormone** increases blood calcium levels by stimulating the bones to release calcium. The action of this hormone also causes the kidneys to reabsorb more calcium and the intestines to absorb more calcium from food. The thyroid and parathyroid glands have opposite effects on blood calcium levels. However, as they work together, they maintain homeostasis. C W

Reading Check Explain how negative feedback is important in maintaining homeostasis.

■ **Figure 18** Glucagon and insulin work together to maintain the level of sugar in the blood.

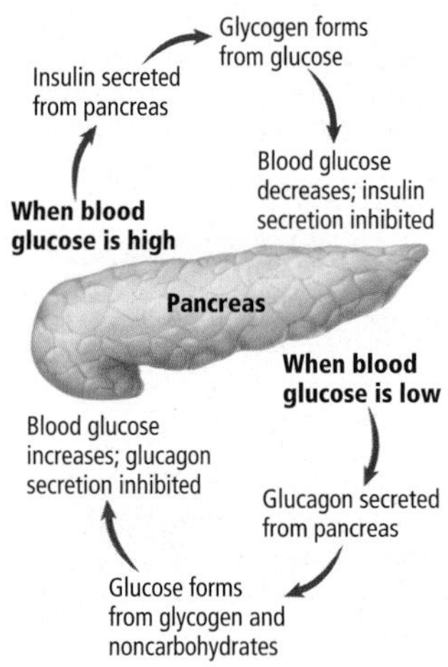

Pancreas As discussed in Section 1, the pancreas has a crucial role in the production of enzymes that digest carbohydrates, proteins, and fats. The pancreas also secretes the hormones insulin and glucagon, which work together to maintain homeostasis, as illustrated in **Figure 18.** When blood glucose levels are high, the pancreas releases insulin. **Insulin** signals body cells, especially liver and muscle cells, to accelerate the conversion of glucose to glycogen, which is stored in the liver. When blood glucose levels are low, glucagon is released from the pancreas. **Glucagon** (GLEW kuh gahn) binds to liver cells, signaling them to convert glycogen to glucose and release the glucose into the blood.

■ **Caption Question Fig. 17** When blood calcium levels drop, the parathyroid gland releases PTH, setting off events that raise blood calcium levels. When blood calcium levels are high, the parathyroid gland releases less PTH and the thyroid gland releases more CT to remove calcium from the blood.

Reading Check Responding to negative feedback, when levels of a substance in the body rise too high, glands secrete a regulating hormone that causes the level of the substance to drop. When levels of the substance drop too low, the regulating hormone causes more of the substance to be released. Often described as a feedback loop, this process of maintaining homeostasis can go on indefinitely.

Diabetes is a disease that results from the body not producing enough insulin or not properly using insulin. Type 1 diabetes, which usually appears in people by the age of 20, occurs when the body cannot produce insulin. Type 2 diabetes occurs in 70–80 percent of people diagnosed with diabetes, and usually occurs after the age of 40. It results from the cells of the body becoming insensitive to insulin. Complications from diabetes include coronary heart disease, retinal and nerve damage, and acidosis, or low blood pH. In both types of diabetes, the blood glucose levels must be monitored and maintained to prevent complications from the disease.

Adrenal glands Refer again to **Figure 15.** The adrenal glands are located just above the kidneys. The outer part of the adrenals is called the cortex, which manufactures the steroid hormone aldosterone and a group of hormones called glucocorticoids. **Aldosterone** (al DAWS tuh rohn) primarily affects the kidneys and is important for reabsorbing sodium. **Cortisol,** another glucocorticoid, raises blood glucose levels and also reduces inflammation.

The body has different mechanisms for responding to stress, such as those concerning the role of the nervous system and the "fight or flight response." The endocrine system also is involved with these types of responses. An "adrenaline rush" occurs when there seems to be a sudden burst of energy during a stressful situation. The inner portions of the adrenal glands secrete epinephrine (eh puh NEH frun), also called adrenaline, and norepinephrine. Together, these hormones increase heart rate, blood pressure, breathing rate, and blood sugar levels, all of which are important in increasing the activity of body cells.

CAREERS IN BIOLOGY

Endocrinologist An endocrinologist studies glands that secrete hormones and the diseases involving those glands.

FOLDABLES®
Incorporate information from this section into your Foldable.

MiniLab 2

Inquiry MiniLab

Model the Endocrine System

How do hormones help the body maintain homeostasis? Activities such as taking a test or running a race place demands on your body. Your body's responses to these demands cause changes in your body. Your endocrine and nervous systems work together to ensure a stable internal environment.

Procedure

1. Read and complete the lab safety form.
2. Identify a sport or activity. Brainstorm what body actions occur as you prepare for, take part in, and recover from the activity.
3. Imagine that you are writing a computer program that your body will follow to complete the activity. Sequence the steps that you brainstormed in Step 2.
4. Review your program. Insert steps where the endocrine system might secrete hormones to maintain homeostasis. Use your knowledge and available resources to identify the specific hormones involved. Include body responses to these hormones as separate steps.
5. Compare your program with those developed by other students.

Analysis

1. **Think Critically** Did some of the same hormones appear in most of the other programs that you studied in Step 5? Why or why not?
2. **Draw conclusions** by describing the major body systems represented in your program. What does this show about the range of body functions controlled by the endocrine system?

FOLDABLES®

RUBRIC A rubric for evaluating Foldables is found on your eTeacherEdition Online.

Going Further On the back of their Foldables, have students compare the endocrine system to the nervous system—both carry information and coordinate activities throughout the body, but hormones move much more slowly than nerve impulses.

MiniLab 2

Inquiry MiniLab

For a lab worksheet, use your eTeacherEdition Online.

RUBRIC A rubric for evaluating MiniLabs is found on your eTeacherEdition Online.

Est. Time 25 min

Safety Precaution Approve lab safety forms before work begins

Teaching Strategies

- Encourage students to think of activities such as riding a bike, speaking before an audience, running to catch the bus, playing basketball.
- Discuss parameters that might change during the activity, including water concentration in the blood, blood sugar levels, blood pressure, heart rate, rate of respiration, and blood calcium levels.

Analysis

1. Antidiuretic hormone, insulin, glucagon, aldosterone, epinephrine, norepinephrine, thyroxine, calcitonin, and parathyroid hormone would likely be named by most student programs. A variety of activities require similar body responses, which are controlled by a relatively small number of hormones.
2. Body systems that appear in the programs might include the nervous, circulatory, skeletal, muscular, respiratory, and excretory systems. The endocrine system plays an important role in the functions of all body systems.

LabManager™
Customize this lab with the LabManager™ CD-ROM.

Visualizing the Endocrine System

Purpose

Students will understand the differences between the anterior and posterior pituitary glands.
C.5, C.6

Critical Thinking

OL Analyze

ASK STUDENTS: ***Why shouldn't the pituitary gland be described as a single gland?*** There are two distinct portions to the pituitary: an anterior and a posterior lobe. ***Why do some scientists not consider the posterior lobe to be a gland?*** The anterior pituitary manufactures hormones, whereas the posterior lobe does not actually make any hormones.

AL ***How are ADH and oxytocin made and released?*** ADH and oxytocin are made by neurons in the hypothalamus. These hormones travel down axons through the posterior pituitary gland, where they are released into the bloodstream.

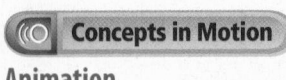

Concepts in Motion
Animation

Visualizing the Endocrine System

Figure 19

The hypothalamus maintains homeostasis by serving as a link between the nervous system and the endocrine system. The pituitary releases growth hormone, ADH, and oxytocin as needed by the body. The pituitary gland also manufactures and secretes hormones that regulate the testes, the ovaries, and the thyroid and adrenal glands.

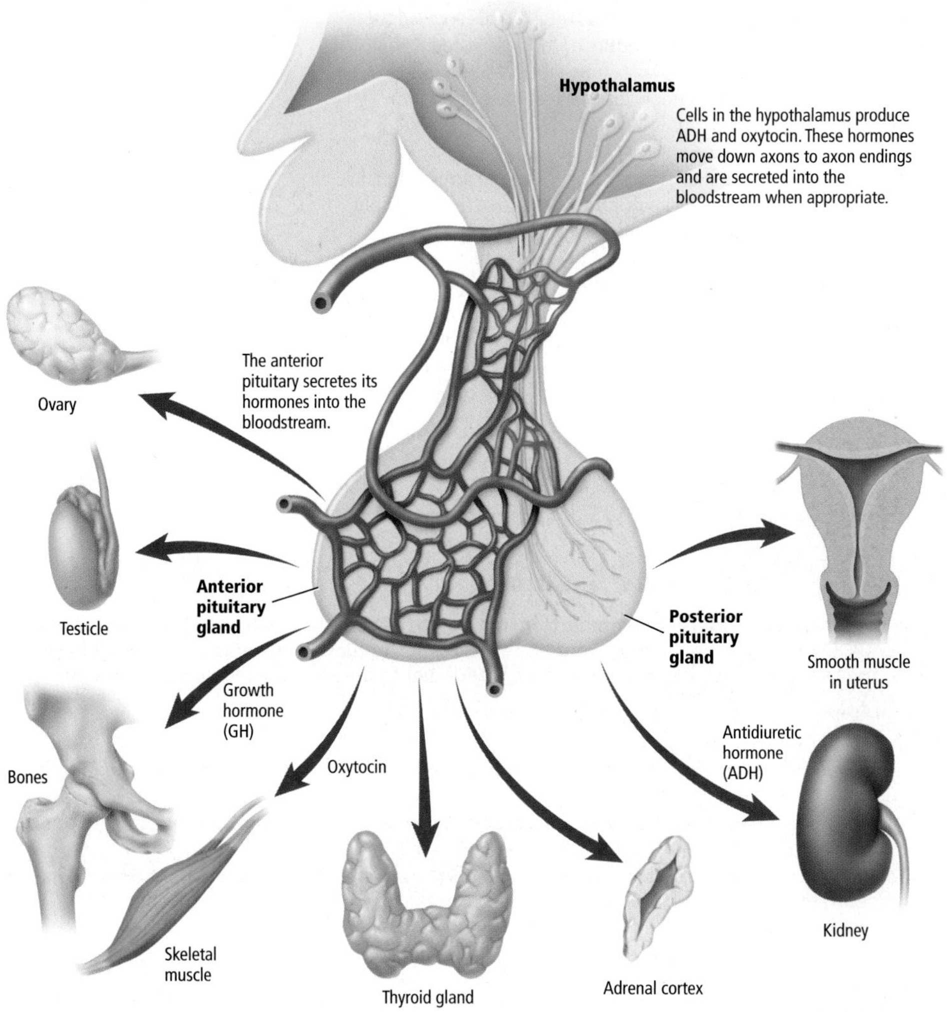

Concepts in Motion Animation

"Who dares to teach must never cease to learn."
—John Cotton Dana

Link to the Nervous System

The nervous and endocrine systems are similar in that they both are involved in regulating the activities of the body and maintaining homeostasis. Refer to **Figure 19** to study the role of the hypothalamus in homeostasis. Recall that this part of the brain is involved with many aspects of homeostasis. The hypothalamus produces two hormones, oxytocin (ahk sih TOH sun) and antidiuretic hormone (ADH). These hormones are transported through axons and stored in axon endings located in the pituitary gland.

The **antidiuretic** (AN ti DY yuh REH tic) **hormone** (ADH) functions in homeostasis by regulating water balance. ADH affects portions of the kidneys called the collecting tubules. Think back to the last time you were working outside on a hot summer day. You produced a lot of sweat to help keep you cool, and you might have become dehydrated. When this happens, cells in your hypothalamus detect that you are dehydrated—that the level of water in the blood is low—and respond by releasing ADH from axons in the pituitary gland that have been storing the hormone.

As illustrated in **Figure 20,** ADH travels in the blood to the kidneys, where it binds to receptors on certain kidney cells. This causes the kidneys to reabsorb more water and decrease the amount of water in the urine, increasing the water level in the blood. If there is too much water in a person's blood, the hypothalamus decreases the release of ADH, and the urine tends to be more dilute. ADH production is stimulated by nausea and vomiting, both of which cause dehydration. Blood loss of 15 or 20 percent by hemorrhage results in the release of ADH.

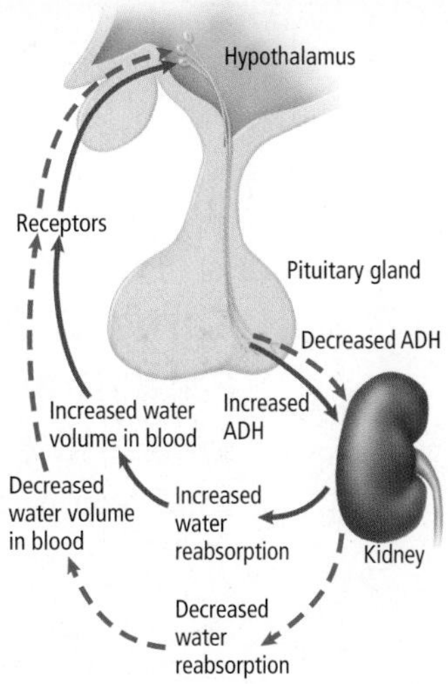

■ **Figure 20** Antidiuretic hormone (ADH) helps to control the concentration of water in the blood.

Section 3 Assessment

Section Summary

- Endocrine glands produce substances called hormones.
- Hormones travel throughout the body in the bloodstream.
- Hormones are classified as steroid hormones or amino acid hormones.
- Hormone levels are influenced by feedback systems.
- The endocrine system helps to maintain homeostasis with signals from internal mechanisms called negative feedback.

Understand Main Ideas

1. MAIN Idea **Assess** the reasons why hormone feedback systems are referred to as "negative feedback."
2. **Predict** when you would expect to find high levels of insulin in a person's blood and when you would expect to find high levels of glucagon in a person's blood.
3. **Explain** how the endocrine and nervous systems work together to maintain homeostasis.
4. **Identify** and describe the functions of pituitary, thyroid, parathyroid, pancreas, and adrenal glands.

Think Critically

5. **Research** Iodine is essential for thyroid gland function. Fetal and childhood iodine deficiency is a major cause of mental retardation in the world, yet the deficiency is preventable. Predict how iodine deficiency might lead to mental retardation or other health issues. Research what has been and what is being done to alleviate this concern. Include information about sources of iodine in your response.
6. **Analyze** how a malfunction in a negative feedback mechanism can lead to the death of an organism.

Develop Concepts

BL OL

Clarify a Misconception

Students might associate the term *negative* with something bad or detrimental.

ASK STUDENTS: ***Is negative feedback good for the body or bad?*** good

AL ***What does the negative in negative feedback mean?*** In this case, *negative* refers to counteracting a situation, or bringing it back to normal range.

Formative Assessment

Evaluation

ASK STUDENTS: ***Describe the basis of a negative feedback loop.*** Hormone levels are regulated by a negative feedback mechanism. If the level of a hormone is too high, it is detected and the gland that manufactures the hormone will slow down its production. If hormone levels are too low, the gland will increase production of the hormone.

Remediation As an example of a hormonal negative feedback loop, have students list the steps of regulating antidiuretic hormone (ADH), which acts on kidney tubules to reabsorb water. If a body becomes dehydrated, the hypothalamus will increase production of ADH. Traveling through the bloodstream, the ADH will bind to cells of the kidney tubules, causing them to retain water. Water levels in the body will increase, rehydrating the body.

Section 3 Assessment

1. Hormones work in the opposite direction of the stimulus; therefore the feedback system is described as negative.
2. Insulin is secreted when sugar levels are high. Glucagon is secreted when blood glucose levels are low.
3. Both systems help maintain homeostasis. For example, the hypothalamus, a part of the brain, secretes ADH, which regulates the balance of water in the body.
4. Pituitary hormones regulate many body functions as well as other endocrine glands. Thyroid hormones increase metabolism and regulate calcium. Parathyroid hormones increase blood calcium levels. The pancreas aids digestion and produces hormones that regulate blood sugar levels. Adrenal hormones aid in reabsorbing sodium, raising blood sugar levels, and reducing inflammation.
5. Lack of thyroxin from iodine deficiency will slow metabolism in neurons in the brain. Iodized table salt can eliminate the problem.
6. Answers will vary. Example: malfunction of the ADH water-regulation negative-feedback loop could lead to fatal dehydration.

Assessment Online Quiz

In the Field

Purpose

Students will identify and describe specific tools and methods used by forensic pathologists to determine the circumstances surrounding a death.
A.2, C.5, E.2, F.6

Anticipatory Guide

ASK STUDENTS: ***If someone examined your stomach contents now, what might they discover?*** Answers will depend on what students have recently consumed. ***How could knowing what is in a person's stomach help investigators determine how that person died?*** This information could indicate when and where the person last ate; drugs or chemicals could indicate poisoning.

Background

One of the most important questions a forensic pathologist attempts to answer is: "When did death occur?" Data from an analysis of stomach contents would never be used by itself to determine time of death. Other factors used by forensic pathologists include the temperature of the body and the rate of cooling, body discoloration caused by pooled blood, the degree of stiffening of the muscles, degree of decomposition, and any insect activity on or near the body. A pathologist does not base an estimate of time of death on any one factor alone.

In the Field

Careers: Forensic Pathologist and Forensic Toxicologist

Tools and Techniques of Forensic Pathology

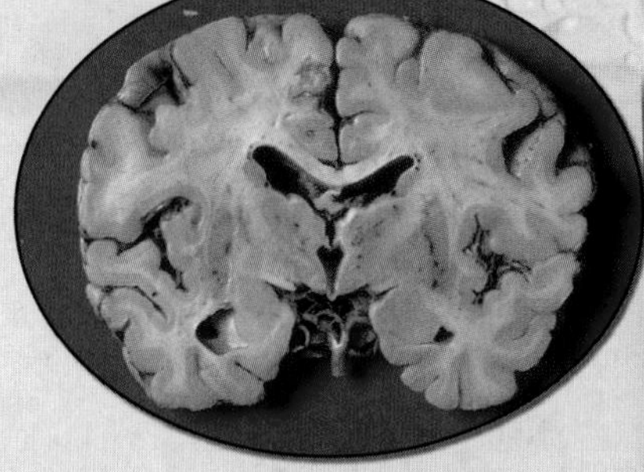

A brain slice might be used to determine a cause of death.

Can a dead person talk? In a way, yes. The condition of a dead body can speak volumes about the circumstances surrounding the death. Forensic pathologists gather data from a body, then analyze it to determine when and how a person died. The tools, techniques, and scientific methods that forensic pathologists use help investigators plot the last hours of a person's life, as well as the events that led to death.

Clues from an autopsy The purpose of an autopsy is to make a permanent legal record of a body's characteristics. A forensic pathologist is trained to examine victims of sudden, unexpected, or violent deaths. During an autopsy, the pathologist examines and weighs the lungs, brain, heart, liver, and stomach. He or she uses a scalpel to slice thin sections of the organs, such as the brain slice shown at the right. The slices are chemically preserved to prevent further decay.

Digestion and time of death During the autopsy, the pathologist examines the victim's stomach contents. Why is this important? At the moment of death, digestion stops. The pathologist can use the condition of the stomach to estimate a time line. If the stomach is entirely empty, the victim probably died at least three hours after he or she last ate. If the small intestine also is empty, death likely occurred at least ten hours after the last meal.

Is it possible to identify the type of food in the stomach? In some cases, yes. A scanning electron microscope can be used to identify food particles. A stomach sample that matches the last known meal also can help investigators establish a time period.

Stomach contents can reveal poisoning Toxic substances such as household products, poisons, and drugs can be involved in a death. A forensic toxicologist, a specialist who can identify foreign chemicals that can lead to death, might be called.

While one piece of evidence rarely serves as conclusive proof, forensic pathologists are trained to note specific details. These details can add up and sometimes help tell the story of the final hours of a person's life.

WRITING in Biology

Classifieds Your city has an opening for a forensic pathologist. Write an advertisement for the job. Be sure to include specific techniques and procedures with which applicants should be familiar, as well as general skills and characteristics applicants should have.

WRITING in Biology

RUBRIC Use the modifiable rubric found on your eTeacherEdition Online to assess writing assignments.

Discussion

Foods are digested at different rates: Starches—30 min to 2 hours; proteins—between 1.5 and 6 hours; fatty foods—at the rate of about 10 g per h. Fiber is not digested at all. Have students write down their favorite meal. Then discuss what foods in this meal would help a forensic pathologist estimate time of death if this were the last meal a deceased person had eaten.

BIOLAB

Design Your Own

HOW DOES THE RATE OF STARCH DIGESTION COMPARE AMONG CRACKERS?

Background: **Starch digestion begins in the mouth. The enzyme amylase, present in saliva, catalyzes the breakdown of starch into sugar molecules, the smallest of which is glucose, an important energy source. Foods, including crackers, vary in starch content. In this lab, you will compare how quickly starch is digested in several types of crackers to determine the relative amount in each.**

Question: *How does the amount of time required for starch digestion by amylase compare among various types of crackers?*

Possible Materials

variety of crackers
mortar and pestle
test tubes and test tube rack
filter paper
funnels
balance
beaker
Bunsen burner or hot plate
graduated cylinder
iodine solution
droppers
watch glasses
amylase solution
glass markers or wax pencil

Safety Precautions

WARNING: *Iodine can irritate and will stain skin.*

Plan and Perform the Experiment

1. Read and complete the lab safety form.
2. Examine three types of crackers. Design an experiment to compare the amount of time required to digest the starch in each. You will use the enzyme amylase to stimulate the digestion of starch. Iodine, a chemical indicator that turns blue-black when starch is present, will indicate when starch digestion is complete.
3. Construct a data chart to record your observations.
4. Consider these points with your group and modify the plan as necessary.
   - What factors will be held constant?
   - Have you established a control sample?
   - How will you know when starch digestion is complete in each sample?
   - How will you keep constant the amount of each type of cracker tested?
   - Will the chart accommodate your data?
5. Make sure your teacher approves your plan before you proceed.
6. Carry out your experiment.
7. **Cleanup and Disposal** Dispose of test tube contents as directed. Clean and return glassware and equipment. Wash your hands thoroughly after handling chemicals and glassware.

Analyze and Conclude

1. **Analyze** how the amylase affected the starch in the crackers.
2. **Observe and Infer** In which cracker was starch digested most quickly? What does this indicate about the amount of starch in this cracker compared to the others?
3. **Think Critically** What variations among human mouths might affect the action of amylase on starch? Explain.
4. **Error Analysis** Did any steps in your procedure introduce uncontrolled variables into the experiment? Explain how the procedure could be redesigned to make these factors constant.

APPLY YOUR SKILL

Design an experiment to determine how varying a condition such as temperature or pH would affect the digestion of starch by amylase in one of the crackers.

Analyze and Conclude

1. The amylase caused the starch to break down into simple sugars.
2. The cracker with the lowest starch concentration should have required the least amount of time to digest.
3. pH, temperature, and other chemicals might vary among mouths. Temperature and pH were controlled by dissolving the crackers in solutions with constant conditions. However, different crackers might contain different compounds that could have an effect on starch digestion, which was an uncontrolled variable.
4. Answers will vary, but can include controlling the water temperature and the amount of cracker in each sample.

BIOLAB

Design Your Own

Inquiry BioLab

For a lab worksheet, use your eTeacherEdition Online.

RUBRIC A rubric for evaluating BioLabs is found on your eTeacherEdition Online.

Est. Time 90 min

Content Background Starch is a polymer that is made from thousands of sugar molecules joined chemically into one large chain-like molecule. When starch breaks down, smaller sugar molecules, including glucose, are produced. The enzyme amylase, found in saliva, begins starch digestion. The pancreas also secretes amylase in the small intestine.

Safety Precautions Approve lab safety forms before work begins. Warn students that iodine can irritate skin and eyes.

Teaching Strategies

- Discuss iodine as an indicator for starch. Tell students that iodine is dark blue or black in the presence of starch.
- Have students consider grinding cracker samples into a powder, then filtering hot water over the powder to obtain a sample in a test tube. They can add amylase and test for starch by combining drops of the sample and drops of iodine.

Alternative Teaching Demo Complete this lab as a demonstration using student helpers.

Chapter 35

Study Guide

ConnectED

Students can use the following to review the chapter.

Review

Vocabulary eGames
Vocabulary eFlashcards
Vocabulary PuzzleMaker

Assessment

Online Quizzes
Online Test Practice
Standardized Test Practice

Use the *ExamView® Assessment Suite* CD-ROM to:

- create multiple versions of tests
- create modified tests with one mouse click
- edit existing questions and add your own questions
- build tests aligned with state standards using built-in state curriculum tags
- change English tests to Spanish with one mouse click
- track students' progress using the Teacher Management System

Chapter 35 Study Guide

THEME FOCUS Homeostasis Homeostasis is maintained by negative feedback in glands such as the thyroid, parathyroid, pancreas, and adrenal glands.

BIG Idea The digestive system breaks down food to provide energy and nutrients for the body. The endocrine system produces hormones that regulate body functions.

Section 1 The Digestive System

mechanical digestion (p. 1020)
chemical digestion (p. 1020)
amylase (p. 1020)
esophagus (p. 1021)
peristalsis (p. 1021)
pepsin (p. 1021)
small intestine (p. 1022)
liver (p. 1022)
villus (p. 1023)
large intestine (p. 1024)

MAIN Idea The digestive system breaks down food so nutrients can be absorbed by the body.

- The digestive system has three main functions.
- Digestion can be categorized as mechanical or chemical.
- Most nutrients are absorbed in the small intestine.
- Accessory organs provide enzymes and bile to aid digestion.
- Water is absorbed from chyme in the colon.

Section 2 Nutrition

nutrition (p. 1025)
Calorie (p. 1025)
vitamin (p. 1028)
mineral (p. 1028)

MAIN Idea Certain nutrients are essential for the proper function of the body.

- The energy content of food is measured in Calories.
- Carbohydrates, fats, and proteins are three major groups of nutrients.
- Carbohydrates are a major source of energy for the body.
- Fats and proteins provide energy and are important building blocks for the body.
- Vitamins and minerals are essential for proper metabolic functioning.
- The *MyPyramid Plan* and food labels are tools you can use to eat healthfully.

Section 3 The Endocrine System

endocrine gland (p. 1031)
hormone (p. 1031)
pituitary gland (p. 1033)
thyroxine (p. 1034)
calcitonin (p. 1034)
parathyroid hormone (p. 1034)
insulin (p. 1034)
glucagon (p. 1034)
aldosterone (p. 1035)
cortisol (p. 1035)
antidiuretic hormone (p. 1037)

MAIN Idea Systems of the human body are regulated by hormonal feedback mechanisms.

- Endocrine glands produce substances called hormones.
- Hormones travel throughout the body in the bloodstream.
- Hormones are classified as steroid hormones or amino acid hormones.
- Hormone levels are influenced by feedback systems.
- The endocrine system helps to maintain homeostasis with signals from internal mechanisms called negative feedback.

Review Vocabulary PuzzleMaker
For additional practice with vocabulary, have students access the Vocabulary PuzzleMaker online.

Review Vocabulary eGames

Chapter 35 Assessment

Section 1

Vocabulary Review

For each set of terms, choose the one term that does not belong and explain why it does not belong.

1. esophagus, pancreas, large intestine

2. pepsin, glycogen, glucose

3. bile, amylase, peristalsis

Understand Main Ideas

4. Which action takes place in the stomach?
- **A.** Large fat molecules are digested into smaller molecules.
- **B.** Proteins are broken down.
- **C.** Amylase breaks down starches into smaller sugar molecules.
- **D.** Insulin is secreted for use in the small intestine.

5. Which row in the chart contains the words that best complete this statement? The (1) produces (2), which is secreted into the (3).

Row	1	2	3
A	liver	bile	small intestine
B	gallbladder	pepsin	stomach
C	pancreas	acid	large intestine
D	villi	amylase	mouth

- **A.** Row A
- **B.** Row B
- **C.** Row C
- **D.** Row D

6. A person complaining of digestion problems is not digesting fats well. Which is a reasonable explanation for this condition?
- **A.** The pyloric sphincter is blocked.
- **B.** The bile duct is blocked.
- **C.** The person is secreting excess bile.
- **D.** The stomach is secreting too much acid.

Use the graph to answer question 7.

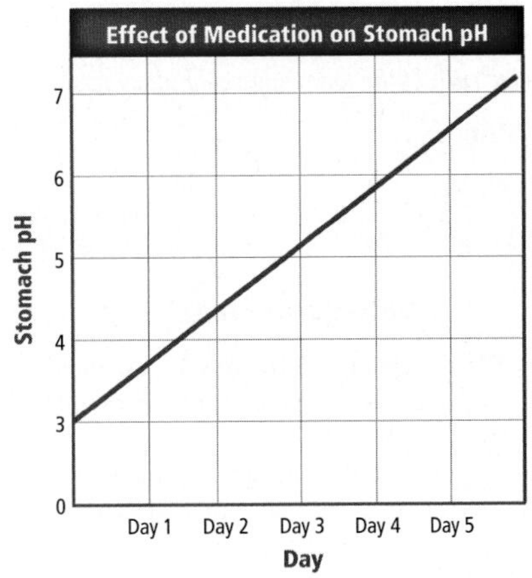

7. A person has been taking a medication for 5 days. Which of the following is likely to be a consequence of this medication?
- **A.** Pepsin would not be able to break down proteins.
- **B.** Amylase would not be able to break down starch.
- **C.** Bile would not be able to be produced.
- **D.** Enzymes secreted by the pancreas would not function well.

Constructed Response

8. Short Answer Explain why the term *heartburn* is an inaccurate description of this condition.

9. MAIN Idea Refer to **Table 1** to summarize the digestive processes that occur in the following structures: mouth, large intestine, stomach, small intestine, and esophagus.

10. Open Ended Why can a person live without a gall bladder? Assess the effects, if any, that this would have on the person's ability to digest food.

Think Critically

11. Explain why a drug manufacturer might add vitamin K to some antibiotics in tablet or pill form.

12. Hypothesize why the human body has an appendix if the appendage has no known useful function.

Chapter 35

Assessment

Section 1

Vocabulary Review

1. pancreas; food moves through esophagus and large intestine—not the pancreas
2. pepsin; glycogen and glucose are energy-storage molecules; pepsin is a digestive enzyme
3. peristalsis; bile and amylase are digestive enzymes, peristalsis describes a physical process

Understand Main Ideas

4. B
5. A
6. B
7. A

Constructed Response

8. Heartburn has nothing to do with the heart. It is caused by stomach acid moving up into the esophagus.
9. mouth: physical digestion (chewing) and chemical digestion (starches broken into smaller molecules); large intestine: water reabsorption; stomach: food broken into smaller pieces and proteins broken down; small intestine: digestion is completed, nutrients are absorbed into cells; esophagus: food moves from mouth to stomach.
10. The gallbladder is a storage organ for bile. Without it, bile from the liver flows directly into the small intestine instead of being stored. There are usually no adverse effects on a person's ability to digest food.

Think Critically

11. Bacteria that live in the colon secrete vitamin K. If the antibiotic kills some of these bacteria cells, a vitamin K deficiency could arise. The addition of vitamin K to the antibiotic minimizes the deficiency.
12. Answers will vary, but students should suggest that the presence of an appendix is an evolutionary "leftover" of the larger cellulose-digesting cecum found in precursors to modern humans.

Assessment Online Test Practice

Section 2

Vocabulary Review

13. Nutrition is the process by which people take in and use food.
14. A vitamin is an organic compound needed in small amounts for the body to function.
15. A Calorie is a unit used to measure energy content in food.

Understand Main Ideas

16. C
17. D
18. A
19. D

Constructed Response

20. Diets high in proteins and fats suggest a large amount of animal products being consumed; therefore, the diet might be lacking in nutrients obtained from fruits and vegetables. A diet high in fats can lead to problems with the cardiovascular system.
21. Eating foods lacking in essential nutrients, such as protein, vitamins, or minerals, could cause malnourishment.

Think Critically

22. A high-fiber diet keeps materials moving through the digestive tract. If there are cancer-causing substances in the diet, they may be eliminated before they have the opportunity to cause harm.
23. One possible reason is that people are less active now than 30 years ago. Modern conveniences and indoor jobs have led to a more sedentary lifestyle. Another possible cause may be the availability of processed foods, which are usually high in Calories and saturated fats.

Chapter 35 Assessment

Section 2

Vocabulary Review

Describe each of the following vocabulary terms.

13. nutrition

14. vitamin

15. Calorie

Understand Main Ideas

16. Which are characteristics of saturated fats?
- **A.** liquid at room temperature and found in vegetable oils
- **B.** mostly absorbed in the large intestine
- **C.** derived from animal sources and are solid at room temperature
- **D.** tend to lower blood cholesterol

17. Which carbohydrate is not digestible and provides fiber in your diet?
- **A.** sucrose
- **B.** starch
- **C.** glycogen
- **D.** cellulose

18. Which combinations in the stomach break down high-protein foods?
- **A.** a low pH and pepsin
- **B.** a high pH and bile
- **C.** a high pH and pepsin
- **D.** a low pH and bile

Use the image below to answer question 19.

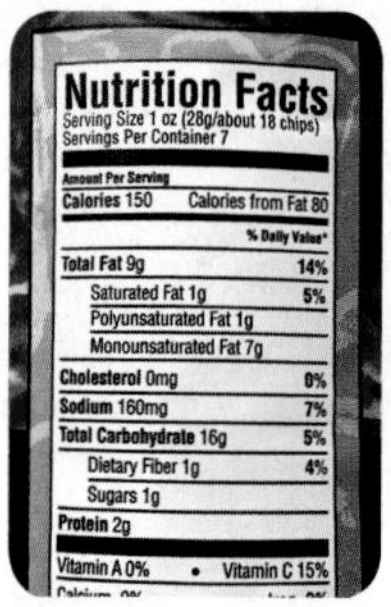

19. If you ate the entire bag of chips, what percent of the recommended daily value of saturated fat would you consume?
- **A.** 14 percent
- **B.** 28 percent
- **C.** 5 percent
- **D.** 35 percent

Constructed Response

20. **CAREERS IN BIOLOGY** According to dieticians, low-carbohydrate diets are usually high in fat and protein. Evaluate what health risks might be associated with a long-term intake of foods high in fats and proteins.

21. MAIN Idea Describe what factors, besides not having enough food, might cause a person to be malnourished.

Think Critically

22. **Explain** why a diet high in fiber might reduce the chance of colon cancer.

23. **Infer** the reasons why obesity rates in the United States have continued to rise steadily for at least the past 30 years.

Section 3

Vocabulary Review

Explain the difference between the terms in each pair. Then explain how the terms are related.

24. insulin, glucagon

25. estrogen, growth hormone

26. cortisol, epinephrine

Understand Main Ideas

Use the graph below to answer question 27.

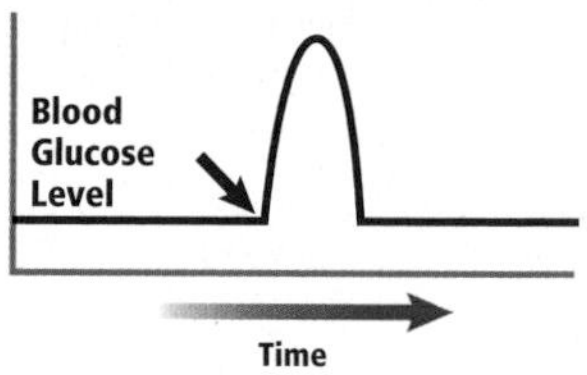

27. The graph shows blood glucose levels over a period of time. Which hormone might have caused a sudden surge as indicated by the arrow?
- **A.** antidiuretic hormone
- **B.** growth hormone
- **C.** glucagon
- **D.** insulin

Section 3

Vocabulary Review

24. The effects of insulin and glucagon are opposite, but both hormones regulate blood sugar levels.
25. Both are important for growth; each hormone is produced by different endocrine glands.
26. Both hormones raise blood sugar levels, but they are secreted by different regions of the adrenal glands.

Understand Main Ideas

27. C

Assessment Online Test Practice

28. Which hormones are released from nerve cells rather than from endocrine glands?
A. antidiuretic hormone and oxytocin
B. growth hormone and thyroxine
C. insulin and glucagon
D. norepinephrine and epinephrine

29. Which pairs of hormones have opposite effects?
A. calcitonin and parathyroid hormone
B. epinephrine and norepinephrine
C. growth hormone and thyroxine
D. aldosterone and cortisol

Use the photos below to answer question 30.

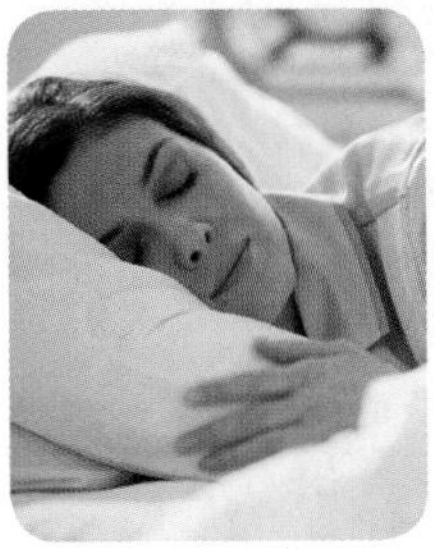
A.

B.

30. Which person is likely to have high levels of epinephrine?
A. person A **C.** both persons
B. person B **D.** neither person

Constructed Response

31. **THEME FOCUS Homeostasis** What would be the direct effect of overproduction of calcitonin? Analyze how this might disrupt homeostasis in systems other than the endocrine system.

32. **Short Answer** Assess how the long-term use of cortisol would impact a person's ability to fight infection.

Think Critically

33. **MAIN Idea** Create an analogy using a balance describing the relationship between calcitonin and parathyroid hormone.

34. **Hypothesize** Why is insulin usually injected instead of taken orally?

Summative Assessment

35. **BIG Idea** Breakfast is considered the most important meal of the day. Based on the food pyramid, plan a balanced breakfast and explain why the nutrients are important. Then describe the processes that will take place in your digestive and endocrine systems after you have eaten. Why is breakfast so important?

36. **WRITING in Biology** This chapter began with a situation where you were eating a pizza. Write a short story describing the events that occur as the food moves through your digestive tract. *Hint: Be sure to include all major groups of nutrients.*

DBQ Document-Based Questions

Source: *Dietary Guidelines for America 2005*

Estimated Calorie Requirements in Gender and Age Groups

Gender	Age	Moderately Active	Active
Female	9–13	1600–2000	1800–2200
	14–18	2000	2400
	19–30	2000–2200	2400
	31–50	2000	2200
	51+	1800	2000–2200
Male	9–13	1800–2200	2000–2600
	14–18	2400–2800	2800–3200
	19–30	2600–2800	3000
	31–50	2400–2600	2800–3000
	51+	2400	2400–2800

37. According to the chart, which gender needs more Calories?

38. Describe the general trend regarding the number of Calories needed to maintain energy balance in relation to age.

39. Why do individuals in the 19–30-year-old group need the most Calories?

28. A
29. A
30. B

Constructed Response

31. Overproduction of calcitonin will lower blood calcium levels. If calcium levels are low, the parathyroid gland increases production of parathyroid hormone, which will cause the release of calcium from bones, potentially weakening them.

32. Cortisol reduces inflammation, a defense mechanism against disease. Long-term use of cortisol may reduce one's ability to fight infection.

Think Critically

33. Students may make the connection that while insulin and glucagon both regulate blood sugar, they have opposing effects. When insulin levels are high, glucagon levels are low. The same is true for calcitonin and parathyroid hormone in regulating calcium levels.

34. Insulin is a protein, so the pepsin in the stomach would break it down quickly.

Summative Assessment

35. Answers will vary. Breakfasts should include a variety of nutrients. For example: scrambled eggs, whole wheat toast, and a glass of milk; protein is a molecular building block, carbohydrates are quick energy, and calcium strengthens teeth and bones. Digestive responses should include mechanical and chemical digestion in the mouth and stomach, and chemical digestion and absorption in the small and large intestines. Endocrine responses could include the release of parathyroid hormone so that the small intestine absorbs more calcium, or the pancreas releasing insulin so that body cells can absorb glucose from the blood. Breakfast provides the body with the first source of nutrients and calories for the day.

WRITING in Biology

RUBRIC Use the modifiable rubric found on your eTeacherEdition Online to assess writing assignments.

36. Answers will vary, but should include the processes of mechanical and physical digestion, digestive enzymes, pH, and the structures of the digestive tract as they relate to carbohydrates, fats, proteins, vitamins, and minerals.

DBQ Document-Based Questions

Dietary Guidelines for America 2005

37. males
38. Generally, Calories consumed need to increase from childhood into the early twenties. From the mid-twenties, Calorie consumption should decrease.
39. They tend to expend more energy.

Assessment Online Test Practice

Standardized Test Practice

Multiple Choice

1. A 4. D
2. A 5. C
3. C 6. A

Short Answer

7. Answers will vary. Possible answers include the following. The territorial fish showed much more feeding activity during the day than the nonterritorial fish. The territorial fish showed a strong peak of feeding activity in the period from 2 to 4 p.m., while the nonterritorial fish showed a lower, but more consistent, feeding activity throughout the day.
8. Answers will vary. One possible answer is that the graph of the feeding behavior of the territorial fish, during the season of nonterritorial behavior, would be similar to the graph of the nonterritorial fish.
9. Proteins are needed in the diet to supply the amino acids that the cells of the body use to make their own proteins. Without proteins, no cells in the body could exist.
10. Answers can vary. Accept logical answers.
    The mother's milk contains the best blend of protein, fat, and other nutrients for the animal's environment and growth needs.
    The baby does not have to hunt for food or find food until later in life.
11. Roundworms move as some muscles in their body contract and others relax. They wriggle along by these muscle movements. Annelids, on the other hand, have circular muscles in their segments and also longitudinal muscles. They can extend their bodies, then return to their original shape again. They also have setae that act as bristles pushing the ground to aid with movement.

Standardized Test Practice

Cumulative

Multiple Choice

1. What is the function of melanin in the epidermis?
   - A. to protect tissue from ultraviolet radiation
   - B. to provide support for blood vessels
   - C. to stimulate the growth of hair in the follicles
   - D. to waterproof and protect the skin surface

Use the diagram below to answer questions 2 and 3.

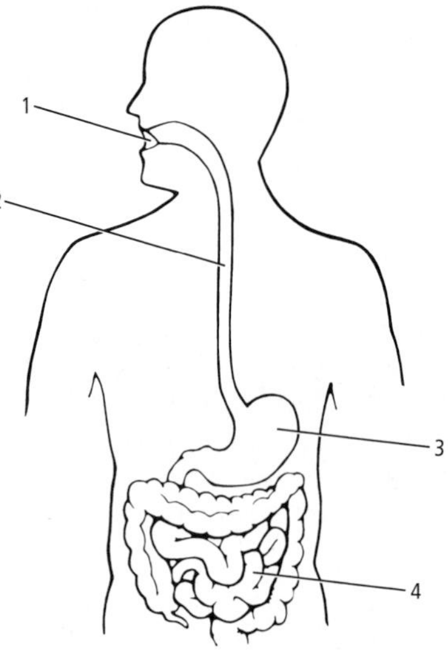

2. In which part of the digestive system do chemical and mechanical digestion first occur?
   - A. 1
   - B. 2
   - C. 3
   - D. 4

3. Which process happens first in a nerve cell when a stimulus reaches its threshold?
   - A. Potassium channels in the cell membrane open.
   - B. Neurotransmitters are released into the synapse.
   - C. Sodium ions move into the nerve cell.
   - D. The cell becomes negatively charged.

4. Where would fat stored in bones be found?
   - A. compact bone
   - B. osteocytes
   - C. red marrow
   - D. yellow marrow

Use the diagram below to answer question 5.

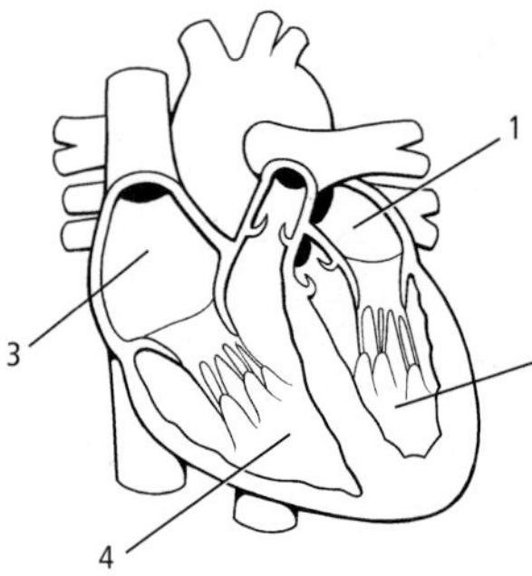

5. Which is the path that blood follows as it flows through the heart immediately after returning from the head and body?
   - A. 1 → 2
   - B. 2 → 1
   - C. 3 → 4
   - D. 4 → 3

6. Which describes how filtering occurs in the excretory system?
   - A. Blood enters nephrons of the kidneys, and excess water and wastes are filtered from the blood.
   - B. Urine leaves the kidneys through ureters.
   - C. Water and nutrients are absorbed back into the blood.
   - D. Water is added to excess nitrogenous wastes from the digestive system to form urine.

Short Answer

Use the graph below to answer questions 7 and 8.

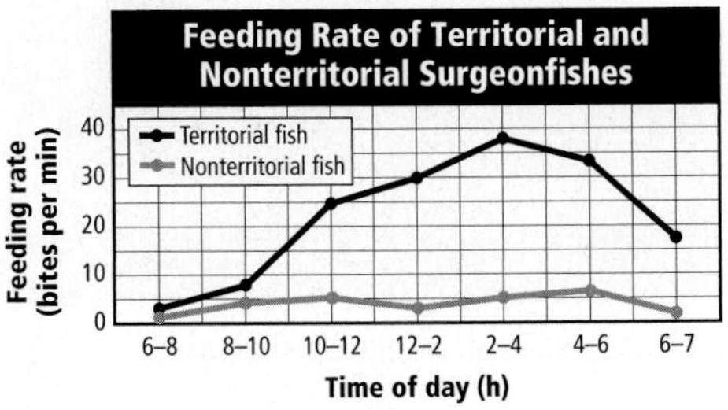

7. Compare and contrast the feeding behavior of the fishes shown in the graph.

8. Predict how the graph might appear if the territorial fish showed territorial behavior only during one season of the year.

9. Assess why a diet with no protein would be unhealthy.

10. What are two benefits to the young of mammals in receiving milk from their mothers?

11. Explain how the different body structures in roundworms and annelids enable them to move.

12. A person who exercises in extreme heat can lose salts that contain potassium and sodium through his or her sweat. What can you infer about the effect of overexertion on the nervous system?

13. Differentiate the three main vessels through which blood flows as it goes from the heart through the body and returns to the heart.

Extended Response

14. Evaluate how a swim bladder helps a fish maintain its depth.

15. Evaluate how high blood pressure and kidney damage could be related.

16. Name three components of sympathetic stimulation, and assess how they could be helpful to a human's survival.

Essay Question

Humans need vitamin C in their diets because it strengthens the function of the immune system and prevents a disease called scurvy. Vitamin C is water-soluble, so it is not stored in the body. Vitamin C is often suggested for someone who is just getting sick or is already sick. Some people recommend taking very high doses of vitamin C, sometimes even thousands of times higher than the recommended dose. Medical researchers disagree about the effectiveness of taking large doses of vitamin C. Some think that it does nothing, while others think that it is helpful. However, almost all medical researchers agree that taking large doses of vitamin C for short periods of time is probably not harmful.

Using the information in the paragraph above, answer the following question in essay format.

17. Formulate a hypothesis about whether taking large doses of vitamin C for a cold is helpful. Explain one way this hypothesis could be tested.

NEED EXTRA HELP?

If You Missed Question . . .	1	2	3	4	5	6	7	8	9	10	11	12	13	14	15	16	17
Review Section . . .	32.1	35.1	33.1	32.2	34.1	34.3	31.1	31.1	35.2	30.1	25.3	33.1	34.1	28.2	34.3	33.2	35.2

12. Neurons need potassium and sodium ions to send action potentials. Without enough of these ions in the system, a person who overexerts may have problems with the nervous system. This could cause loss of coordination and difficulty in moving or sensing things properly.
13. Blood leaves the heart in arteries. The arteries branch out to form capillaries. The capillaries come back together to form veins that return the blood to the heart.

Extended Response

14. The swim bladder is a gas-filled sac that a fish uses to maintain buoyancy. By increasing or decreasing the amount of gas in the swim bladder, a fish moves up or down in the water column.
15. Answers can vary but might include that high blood pressure can affect the kidney because it may cause the thin-walled vessels in the nephrons to rupture.
16. Heart rate increase allows for better circulation in case it is necessary to run/flee. Reduced function of digestive system allows for blood to be directed to muscles involved in flight, instead of to digestion. Pupil dilation allows for better sight that is helpful to deal with an emergency. Sympathetic stimulation has to do with "fight or flight" syndrome, so it causes changes that make the body ready to deal with emergency situations. Other answers are possible.

Essay Question

17. Answers will vary. One hypothesis is that taking extra large doses of vitamin C is not effective in helping people heal quickly from a cold. This hypothesis could be tested by doing a double-blind experiment. In the experiment, participants with colds would be given either extra large doses of vitamin C or a placebo. Negative results from the extra large doses of vitamin C would support the hypothesis.

Chapter 36 Organizer:
Human Reproduction and Development

LabManager™
Customize any lab with the LabManager™ CD-ROM.

Essential Questions	National Science Standards	Materials and Planning: Estimated times include cleanup and disposal, but do not include teacher prep time. For cleanup and disposal guidelines, see page 39T.	Est. Time (min)
Section 1 1. What are the structures of the male and female reproductive systems and what are the functions of each? 2. How do hormones regulate the male and female reproductive systems? 3. What are the events that take place during a menstrual cycle?	UCP.1–3, UCP.5; A.1, A.2; C.1; F.1	**Launch Lab,** p. 1046: compound microscope, slide of sperm cell, slide of egg cell	20
		Demonstration, p. 1048: compound microscope, slide of cross section of testis, labeled diagram of testis cross section	10
		Demonstration, p. 1051: compound microscope, slide of cross section of ovary, labeled diagram of ovary cross section	10
		MiniLab 1, p. 1052: two lumps of clay	25
Section 2 1. What are the events that take place during the first week following fertilization? 2. What are the major changes that occur during each trimester of development? 3. How are female hormone levels altered during pregnancy?	UCP.1–3, UCP.5; A.1, A.2; C.1; E.2; F.1, F.5; G.1, G.2	**Demonstration,** p. 1056: compound microscope, prepared slides of stages of sea star or sea urchin embryonic development	10
		MiniLab 2, p. 1060: images on pages 1058 and 1059	25
Section 3 1. What are the events that occur during the three stages of birth? 2. What are the stages of human development from infancy to adulthood? 3. What are the hormones necessary for growth?	UCP.1–3, UCP.5; A.1, A.2; C.1; E.2, F.1, F.2, F.5; G.1,G.2, G.3	**Demonstration,** p. 1064: growth charts for boys 2–20 years old and girls 2–20 years old	10
		BioLab, p. 1067: computer with Internet access, labeled and unlabeled ultrasound images	45

Suggested Time for Each Lesson

Class	Chapter Opener	Section 1	Section 2	Section 3	Assessment
Basic	45 min	45 min	45 min	90 min	45 min
General	25 min	55 min	55 min	90 min	45 min
Honors	5 min	60 min	65 min	30 min	20 min

ConnectED

connectED.mcgraw-hill.com

Access interactive learning opportunities and teaching resources using these icons located throughout your StudentWorks™ Plus Online and eTeacherEdition Online.

Chapter 36 Section Resources	Additional Chapter 36 Resources	Technology
FAST FILE Unit 9 Resources: Launch Lab Worksheet* MiniLab Worksheet Study Guide (English/Spanish)* Section Quick Check **Reading Essentials 36.1** **Science Notebook 36.1*** **FAST FILE Unit 9 Resources:** MiniLab Worksheet* Study Guide (English/Spanish)* Section Quick Check **Reading Essentials 36.2** **Science Notebook 36.2*** **FAST FILE Unit 9 Resources:** BioLab Worksheet* Study Guide (English/Spanish)* Section Quick Check **Reading Essentials 36.3** **Science Notebook 36.3***	**FAST FILE Unit 9 Resources:** Chapter Diagnostic Test Concept Mapping* Real-World Biology Enrichment Chapter Tests A, B, and C **Transparencies:** Bellringer Transparencies* Biology Concepts Transparencies* **Lab Resources:** Laboratory Manual* Probeware Lab Manual* Forensics Lab Manual* Pre-AP Lab Manual* Open Inquiry in Biology* Guided Inquiry in Biology*	**Teaching Tools:** eTeacherEdition Online Classroom Presentation Toolkit CD-ROM* LabManager™ CD-ROM* Video Lab DVD* Virtual Lab CD-ROM* What's BIOLOGY Got To Do With It? StudentWorks™ Plus Online* **Chapter Assessment Tools:** Classroom Presentation Toolkit CD-ROM* *ExamView® Assessment Suite* CD-ROM **Web-Based Resources:** • StudentWorks™ Plus Online • eTeacherEdition Online • Animations* • The Interactive Time Line* • Interactive Tables* • Online Quizzes • Online Test Practice • Standardized Test Practice • Virtual Labs* • Multilingual eGlossary* • Vocabulary eGames* • Vocabulary eFlashcards • WebQuests • Personal Tutors

While all resources listed are appropriate for English learners, the * indicates resources with a strong visual or hands-on component for EL.

Teaching strategies and activities have been coded for differentiated instruction.

AL Activities for students working above grade level	**OL** Activities for students working on grade level	**BL** Activities for students working below grade level	**EL** Activities for English learners (also ELL)	**COOP LEARN** Activities designed for small cooperative group work

CHAPTER 36

Launch Lab
Sex Cell Characteristics

? Inquiry Launch Lab

For a lab worksheet, use your eTeacherEdition Online.

RUBRIC A rubric for evaluating Launch Labs is found on your eTeacherEdition Online.

Est. Time 20 min

Alternative Materials
Students could complete this exercise using digital or print images of sex cells. Make sure the images are proportional so the size differential between eggs and sperm can be observed.

Safety Precaution Approve lab safety forms before work begins.

Teaching Strategy Help students understand that all egg cells and all sperm cells share some general characteristics, regardless of the animal species that produces them.

Procedure

1. Read and complete the lab safety form.
2. Observe the **slide of the egg cell** under the **microscope** and identify its characteristics. Make a sketch.
3. Observe the **slide of the sperm cell** under the microscope and identify its characteristics. Make a sketch.

CHAPTER 36

Human Reproduction and Development

ConnectED
Your one-stop online resource
connectED.mcgraw-hill.com

- Video
- Audio
- Review
- Inquiry
- WebQuest
- Assessment
- Concepts in Motion
- Multilingual eGlossary

Launch Lab
Sex Cell Characteristics

How are sex cells specialized for the formation of a zygote? Reproduction is a process that follows a predictable pattern. The production of sex cells is a crucial step in reproduction. Sperm and egg cells have specific characteristics that support their roles in reproduction. In this lab, you will investigate how the design of sex cells supports their function.

For a lab worksheet, use your StudentWorks™ Plus Online.

? Inquiry Launch Lab

FOLDABLES®
Make a two door book and label it as shown. Use it to organize your notes about sperm and egg production.

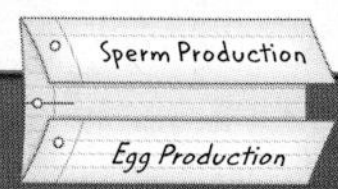

Analysis

1. **Compare and contrast** the sperm and egg cells that you studied. How do they differ? Sperm and egg cells differ in shape and size. Sperm cells are smaller than egg cells and have three distinct sections. Eggs are rounded and are much larger than sperm.
2. **Identify** the structures and characteristics you observed, which might affect each cell's role in reproductions. The whiplike tails of sperm cells allow them to move to the egg's location. The large, rounded shape of the egg cell allows access for many sperm for possible penetration.

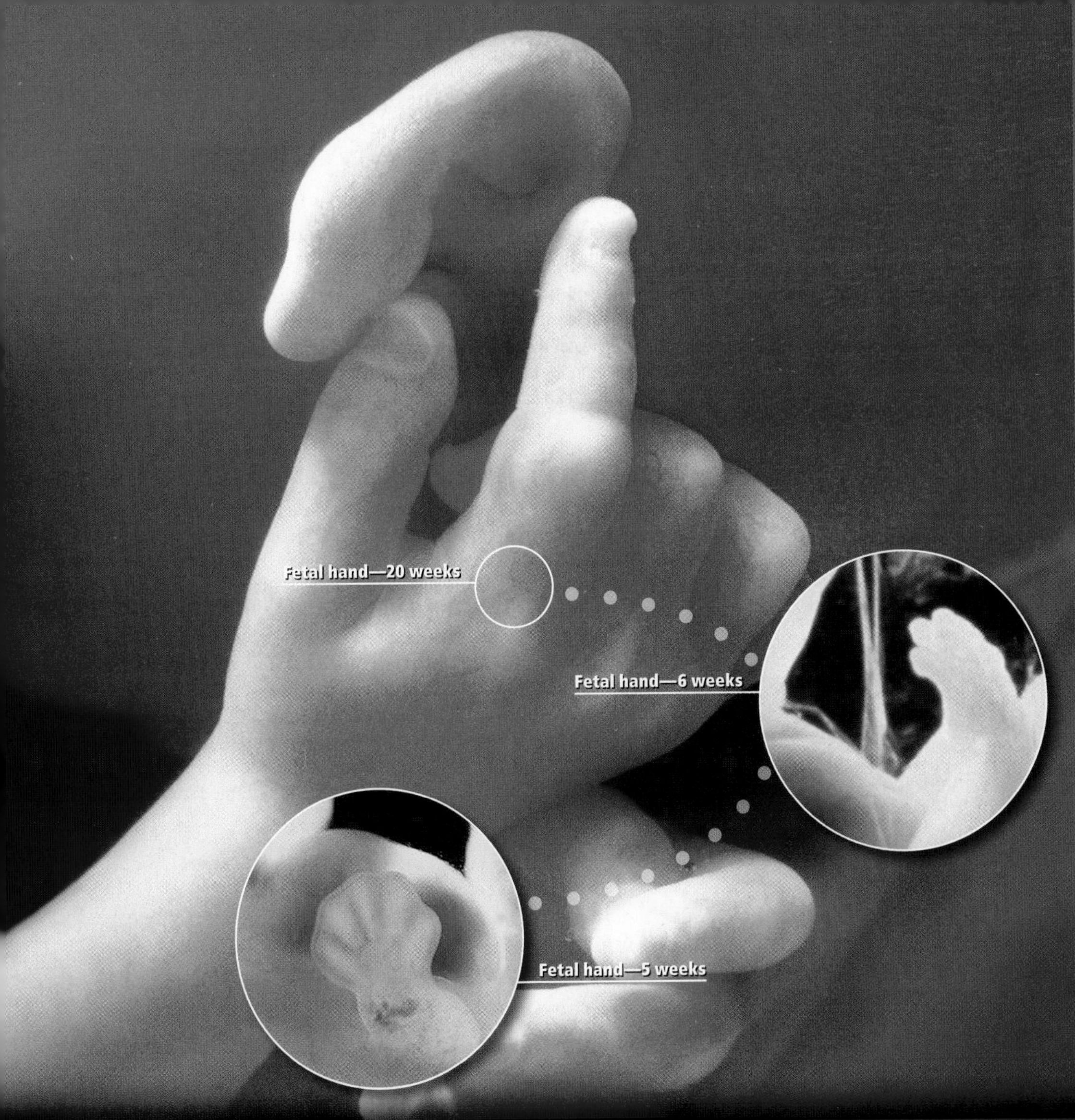

THEME FOCUS Change
The human body changes throughout life.

BIG Idea Human reproduction involves the joining together of sperm and egg.

Section 1 • Reproductive Systems

Section 2 • Human Development Before Birth

Section 3 • Birth, Growth, and Aging

THEMES

Scientific Inquiry Scientists continue to research early development to ensure the health of the fetus.

Diversity Prior to birth, cells differentiate to perform highly specialized functions.

Energy A growing fetus gets all energy from the mother through the placenta.

Homeostasis Wastes are removed from the fetus through the placenta to maintain homeostasis.

Change The human body goes through changes such as puberty and aging throughout life.

Introduce the Chapter

Human Development

ASK STUDENTS: ***How old is the fetus shown in the picture?*** 20 weeks ***What do the smaller pictures tell you about human development?*** Hands and fingers begin developing early in the womb.

BIG Idea

Outline Have students outline major developmental events or changes that occur in the life of a human.

This sample outline is less detailed than what students should provide:

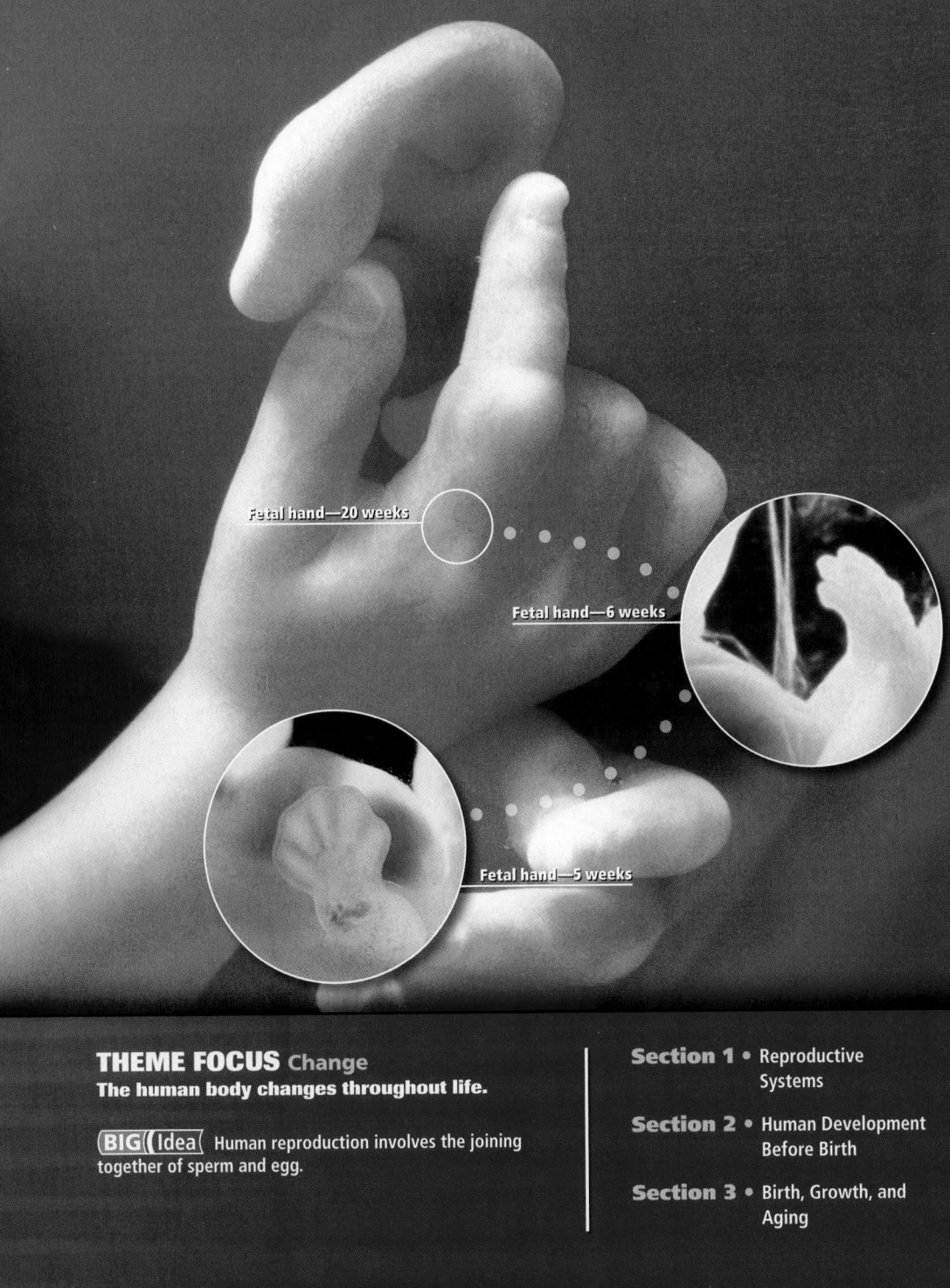

I. Fertilization
   A. Sperm cell meets egg cell
II. Development in the womb
   A. Placenta forms
   B. Heart begins to beat
   C. Fetus can move
III. Birth
   A. Baby functions on its own
IV. Childhood
V. Teenage years
   A. Hormone levels increase
VI. Adulthood
VII. Old age

Section 1

MAIN Idea

BL OL AL

Reproductive Hormones
ASK STUDENTS: ***What hormones are involved in human reproduction?*** Student responses likely will be limited to testosterone in males and estrogen and progesterone in females. Use a model or diagram to teach students about the reproductive hormones made by the anterior pituitary gland.

Reading Strategy

BL OL **SQ3R** This five-step process helps promote active reading. Have students first **S**urvey the section, focusing on the headings. Students should then write **Q**uestions about key concepts. Next, students should **R**ead the section, making notes related to the questions. Then have students **R**ecite the vocabulary and **R**eview for meaning.

R Reading Strategy

BL OL **Preview the Text**
Instruct students to note the new vocabulary terms in this section. Have the students define each term either by reading the text or by studying the figures on this page.

Section 1

Reading Preview

Essential Questions

- What are the structures of the male and female reproductive systems and what are the functions of each?
- How do hormones regulate the male and female reproductive systems?
- What are the events that take place during a menstrual cycle?

Review Vocabulary

hypothalamus: portion of the brain that connects the endocrine and nervous systems, and controls the pituitary gland

New Vocabulary

seminiferous tubule
epididymis
vas deferens
urethra
semen
puberty
oocyte
oviduct
menstrual cycle
polar body

g Multilingual eGlossary

Reproductive Systems

MAIN Idea **Hormones regulate human reproductive systems, including the production of gametes.**

Real-World Reading Link You might have noticed how the temperature of a room affects the thermostat that controls furnace activity. If the room is warm, the thermostat will not allow the furnace to run. Similarly, male and female hormones in the human body have effects on body structures and influence human reproduction.

R Human Male Reproductive System

Reproduction is necessary to ensure continuation of a species. The result of the human reproductive process is the union of an egg cell and a sperm cell, development of the fetus, and the birth of an infant. The organs, glands, and hormones of the male and female reproductive systems are instrumental in meeting this goal.

Figure 1 illustrates the male reproductive structures. The male reproductive glands are called the testes (tes TEEZ) (singular, testis) and are located outside of the body cavity in a pouch called the scrotum (SKROH tum). A temperature lower than 37°C—the average body temperature—is required for the development of sperm. Because the scrotum is located outside of the body cavity, it is several degrees cooler. This makes the environment suitable for the normal development of sperm.

■ **Figure 1** The male reproductive system produces gametes called sperm in the testes.

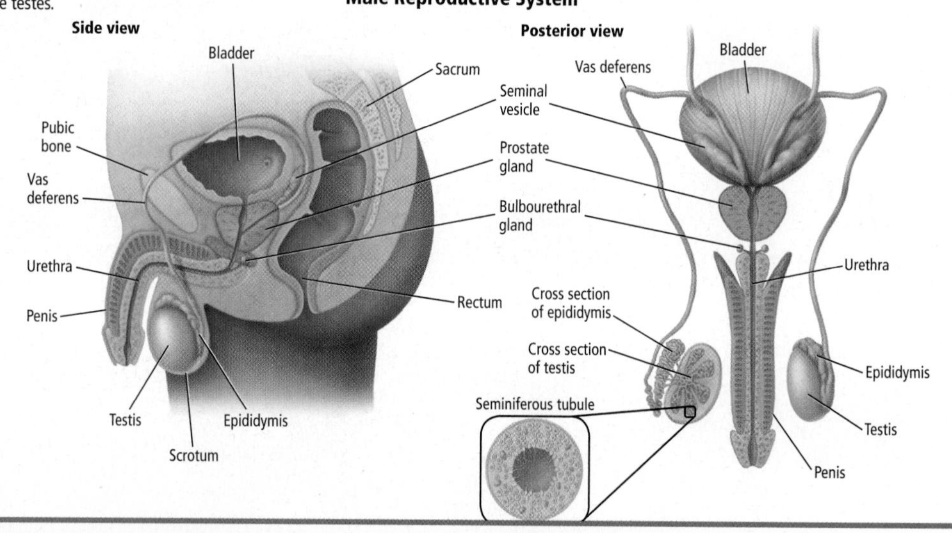

Demonstration

Formation of Sperm Set up a microscope slide of a cross section of a testis using the high-power objective. Next to the microscope, provide a labeled diagram of the image showing a seminiferous tubule, spermatogonium, primary spermatocyte, secondary spermatocyte, spermatid, and sperm. You could also use posters or images from the Internet for this activity. Est. time: 10 min

Sperm cells The male reproductive cells, called sperm cells, are produced in the testes. Follow the path that sperm travel in **Figure 1** as you read about the structures in the male reproductive system. Sperm, like the one shown in **Figure 2,** develop in the testes in the **seminiferous tubules** (se muh NIHF rus • TEW byulz). These tubules produce 100–200 million sperm each day. Next, sperm travel to the **epididymis** (eh puh DIH duh mus), a structure located on top of each testis where sperm mature and are stored. When the sperm are released from the body, they travel through the **vas deferens** (VAS • DEF uh runz), a duct leading away from the testis. There are two vas deferens, one leading away from each testis. The two vas deferens join together and enter the **urethra** (yoo REE thruh), the tube that carries both semen and urine outside of the body through the penis.

Sperm require a nourishing fluid to survive long enough to fertilize an egg. **Semen** (SEE mun) refers to the fluid that contains sperm, the nourishment, and other fluids from the male reproductive glands. The seminal vesicles contribute over half of the semen and secrete sugar into the fluid, which provides energy, other nutrients, proteins, and enzymes for the sperm. The prostate gland and bulbourethral glands contribute an alkaline solution to the fluid to neutralize acidic conditions that sperm might encounter in the urethra and the female reproductive tract.

Male hormones Testosterone (tes TAHS tuh rohn), which is made in the testes, is a steroid hormone that is necessary for the production of sperm. It also influences the development of male secondary sex characteristics that begin to appear at **puberty,** the period of growth when sexual maturity is reached. These characteristics include hair on the face and chest, broader shoulders, increased muscle development, and a deeper voice. Recall that the larynx contains the vocal cords. Because the vocal cords are longer in males than in females, the male voice is deeper. Later in life, testosterone might lead to a receding hairline or baldness.

Three hormones influence testosterone production. **Figure 3** indicates that the hypothalamus produces gonadotropin-releasing hormone (GnRH), which acts on the anterior pituitary gland. GnRH increases the production of follicle-stimulating hormone (FSH) and luteinizing (LEW tee uh ni zing) hormone (LH). Both FSH and LH travel from the anterior pituitary gland through the bloodstream and to the testes. In the testes, FSH promotes the production of sperm and LH stimulates the production and secretion of testosterone.

Levels of the male hormones are regulated by a negative feedback system that starts with the hypothalamus. Increased levels of testosterone in the blood are detected by cells in the hypothalamus and anterior pituitary, and the production of LH and FSH **C** is decreased. When testosterone levels in the blood drop, the body responds by making more LH and FSH, as shown in **D** **Figure 3.**

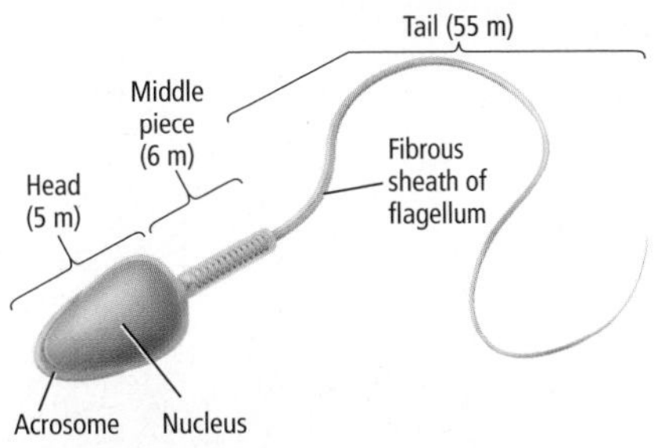

■ **Figure 2** A sperm is a flagellated cell composed of a head, midpiece, and tail.
Identify, ***in correct sequence, the structures that a sperm cell passes through or encounters as it makes its way out of the body.***

■ **Figure 3** The hypothalamus produces gonadotripin, the releasing hormone, which travels to the pituitary gland. GnRH influences the rate of LH and FSH production. The levels of LH and FSH are regulated by a negative feedback pathway.

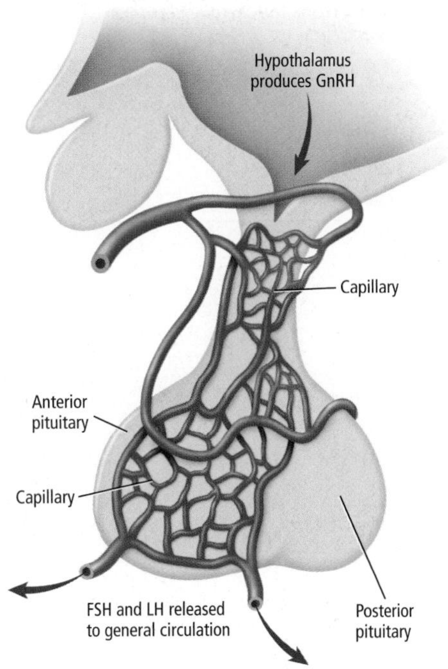

C Critical Thinking

OL AL Hypothesize Students may be aware that, although most athletic accrediting organizations outlaw it, some athletes use laboratory-manufactured versions of steroid hormones—mainly testosterone. While these steroids can increase muscle mass, they also cause the testicles to shrink and cause a decrease in sperm-cell production and other issues. **ASK STUDENTS:** ***Why might steroid use decrease sperm production?*** FSH promotes the production of sperm cells. When testosterone levels are high, FSH and sperm production decrease; when testosterone levels are low, FSH and sperm production increase. This is an example of negative feedback. If synthetic testosterone is introduced into the body, levels of FSH will decrease, resulting in fewer sperm cells being formed.

D Develop Concepts

OL Activate Prior Knowledge **SAY TO STUDENTS:** ***Describe how the endocrine, circulatory, and reproductive systems are involved with the production of gametes.*** FSH, LH, and testosterone are produced by the endocrine glands. These hormones travel through the bloodstream and participate in the production of sperm cells.

■ **Caption Question Fig. 2** Sperm cells travel through the seminiferous tubules, epididymis, vas deferens, and urethra.

Content Background

Teacher FYI Testosterone and derivatives of testosterone are commonly abused anabolic steroids. These drugs can make muscles bigger, but steroid abuse has many harmful consequences. These consequences can include stunted growth, dramatic mood swings, severe acne, and even death. Anabolic steroids can give girls a masculine appearance, including increased body hair. In boys, anabolic steroids can cause the testicles to shrink, sperm production to drop, and breasts to develop—a condition called gynecomastia.

![FOLDABLES]

RUBRIC A rubric for evaluating Foldables is found on your eTeacherEdition Online.

Going Further On the back of their Foldables, have students sketch a Venn diagram and use it to compare and contrast male and female reproductive hormones.

Concepts in Motion

Animation

S Skill Practice

EL BL OL Visual Literacy

Project this page from your eTeacherEdition Online. Point out that Figure 4 and many other figures in this section are illustrations. **ASK STUDENTS:** ***Why is it helpful to have illustrations as well as photographs?*** Illustrations can help show some features better than photographs. This figure clearly shows the organs inside the female body, an enlarged detail of the oviduct and ovary, and also shows the development of an egg over time.

W Writing Support

BL OL Narrative Writing

SAY TO STUDENTS: ***Give directions to an ovum as it leaves a follicle so it can find its way out of a female's body.*** Answers should demonstrate an understanding that the egg is released into an oviduct; from there it travels to the uterus, the cervix, and finally the vagina.

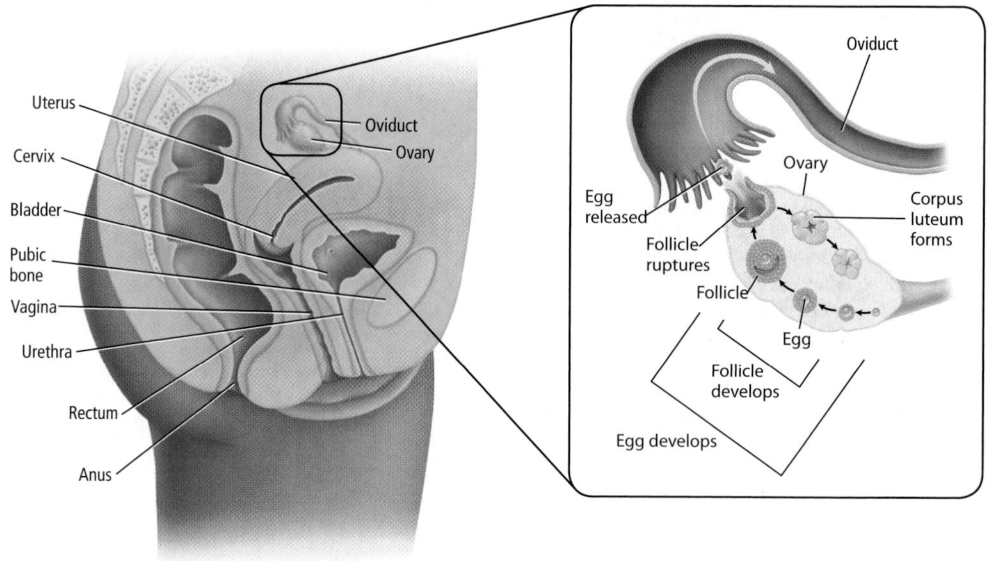

Figure 4
Left: The main structures of the female reproductive system are the vagina, uterus, and ovaries.
Right: During every menstrual cycle, one follicle fully matures and releases an egg. The follicle is then called the corpus luteum.
***Predict** what the result might be if more than one follicle fully develops during a cycle.*

Concepts in Motion
Animation

Review
Personal Tutor

S

Human Female Reproductive System

A female's reproductive system is specialized to produce egg cells, receive sperm, and provide an environment that is right for fertilization of an egg and the development of an embryo. Refer to **Figure 4** as you read about the structures of the female reproductive system.

Egg cells The female reproductive cells, called egg cells, are produced in the ovaries, also illustrated in **Figure 4.** Each ovary is about the size of an almond. Inside each ovary are **oocytes** (OH uh sites), which are immature eggs. Approximately once every 28 days, oocyte development is stimulated and an egg, called an ovum, is formed. The ovum is surrounded by follicle cells that provide protection and nourishment.

After the egg is released from the ovary, it travels through an **oviduct** (OH vuh duct), a tube that connects to the uterus. The uterus, or womb, is about the size of an average human fist and is where a baby develops before birth. The cervix, at the lower end of the uterus, has a narrow opening into the vagina, which leads to the outside of the female's body. **W**

Female hormones Estrogen and progesterone (proh JES tuh rohn) are steroid hormones made by cells in the ovaries. A female's anterior pituitary gland also produces LH and FSH, which influence estrogen and progesterone levels in a negative feedback loop. Effects of LH and FSH are different in males and females. During puberty, an increase in estrogen levels causes a female's breasts to develop, her hips to widen, and her amount of fat tissue to increase. During puberty, a female also will experience her first **menstrual** (MEN stroo ul) **cycle,** the events that take place each month in the human female to help prepare the female body for pregnancy.

Caption Question Fig. 4 If the eggs are all released and fertilized, multiple births can result.

Review **Personal Tutor**

Listen to a teacher explain sperm and egg formation.

Differentiated Instruction

Above Level When introducing a new chapter, make connections to previous lessons and discuss future applications of what is being learned. Gifted students will benefit when they see how information is built upon previous lessons throughout the year.

For more tips, see pages 14T–15T.

Sex Cell Production

Through meiosis one cell in the male or female gonads—called testes and ovaries in humans—gives rise to four sex cells called gametes. In the human male, sperm are produced daily from primary spermatocytes, beginning at puberty and continuing throughout a male's lifetime.

The production of eggs in the human female differs, as illustrated in **Figure 5.** A female is born with all of her eggs already beginning to develop. The genetic material has replicated in primary oocytes before birth, and the process of meiosis stops before the first meiotic division is completed. Then, once each menstrual cycle during the reproductive years, meiosis continues for a single developing oocyte. The resulting structures at the end of the first meiotic division of the oocyte are of unequal size. The smaller of the two structures is called a **polar body.** The chromosomes have segregated, but there is an unequal division of the cytoplasm. Most of the cytoplasm from the original cell goes to the cell that eventually will become the egg, and the polar body disintegrates.

During the second meiotic division, a similar process takes place. During metaphase of the second meiotic division, an egg ruptures through the ovary wall in a process called ovulation. The second meiotic division is completed only if fertilization takes place. Then, the zygote and the second polar body are formed, as shown in **Figure 5.** The second polar body also disintegrates.

Thus, the two meiotic divisions have yielded only one egg instead of four. If four eggs were formed and released midway through a female's menstrual cycle, more multiple births would be expected.

D The Menstrual Cycle

The length of the menstrual cycle can vary from 23 to 35 days, but it typically lasts around 28 days. The entire menstrual cycle can be divided into three phases: the flow phase, the follicular phase, and the luteal phase.

Flow phase Day one of the menstrual cycle is when menstrual flow begins. Menstrual flow is the shedding of blood, tissue fluid, mucus, and epithelial cells from the endometrium—the tissue that lines the uterus. The endometrium is where the embryo will implant if fertilization of the egg occurs. Because an embryo will need oxygen and nutrients, the endometrium has a good supply of blood. During menstruation, bleeding occurs because the outer layers of the endometrium tear away, and blood vessels that supply the endometrium are ruptured. Around day five, repair of the endometrial lining begins, and it becomes thicker as the cycle continues.

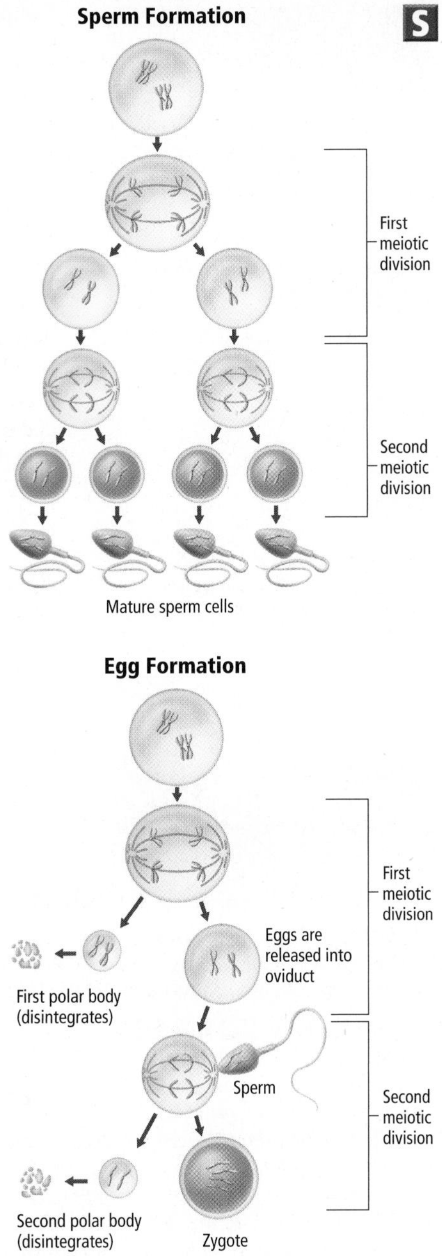

Figure 5
Top: The human male sex cell production follows the general pattern of meiosis and results in many sperm.
Bottom: Meiosis in the human female results in one egg. The second division in meiosis will not be completed in a human female unless the egg is fertilized.

Demonstration

Formation of Eggs Set up a microscope slide of a cross section of an ovary using the high-power objective. Next to the microscope provide a labeled drawing of the image showing a primary oocyte, a mature follicle, a ruptured follicle, a secondary oocyte, and a corpus luteum. You could also use posters or images from the Internet for this demonstration. Est. time: 10 min

S Skill Practice

OL Visual Literacy Direct students to Figure 5.

SAY TO STUDENTS: ***Compare and contrast meiosis in a human female and a human male.*** Meiosis in both genders involves two cell divisions. The genetic material replicates and segregates in an identical manner. Meiosis in a human male results in four sperm cells. Meiosis in a human female results in one viable ovum and three nonviable polar bodies.

Develop Concepts

BL OL AL Scaffolding

ASK STUDENTS: ***What is the generalized process of meiosis?*** Students should be able to outline the steps of meiosis. ***What is the advantage of the formation of four gametes each time meiosis occurs in the human male?*** The more sperm cells a male produces, the greater the chances of successfully fertilizing an egg. ***Why does the process of meiosis in a human female result in only one viable gamete?*** In a human female, most of the contents from the cytoplasm of the cell about to undergo meiosis are concentrated into one cell (the ovum). This helps ensure a stronger egg. Also, this process reduces the chance of multiple births.

D Develop Concepts

BL OL AL

Clarify a Misconception

ASK STUDENTS: ***Is the reproductive cycle the same length for all females?*** Some students might answer yes. In reality, most menstrual cycles range from 21–40 days. The length of a menstrual cycle is not always constant for any one female. Help students understand that a 28-day cycle generally is used as an example because it is an *average* length.

MiniLab 1

? Inquiry MiniLab

For a lab worksheet, use your eTeacherEdition Online.

RUBRIC A rubric for evaluating MiniLabs is found on your eTeacherEdition Online.

Est. Time 25 min

Safety Precaution Approve lab safety forms before work begins.

Teaching Strategy Encourage students to view reproduction as a multistep process that they are observing at various points. Have students develop a time line of events, beginning with the production of sex cells and ending with the birth of offspring. Students can add to the time line as they complete lab exercises and engage in chapter content.

Analysis

1. Student drawings should accurately depict the steps being modeled.
2. Concentrating most of the cytoplasm into one egg provides the egg with plenty of materials and organelles, such as mitochondria, for the rapid growth of the zygote.

LM Magnification: 10×

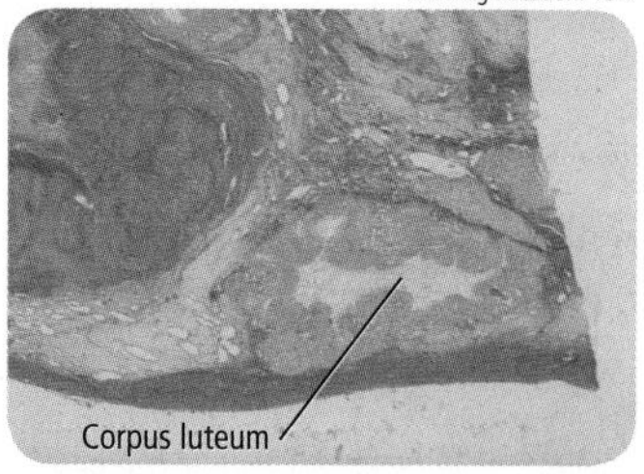

■ **Figure 6** The corpus luteum produces progesterone and some estrogen.

VOCABULARY
WORD ORIGIN
Corpus luteum
corpus from Latin, meaning *body*
luteum from Latin, meaning *yellow*.

Follicular phase During the menstrual cycle, changes also occur in the ovaries as a result of changing hormone levels, as illustrated in **Table 1.** At the beginning of a menstrual cycle, when estrogen levels are low, the anterior pituitary begins to increase production of LH and FSH. This stimulates a few follicles to begin to mature in the ovary. Cells in the follicles then begin to produce estrogen and a small amount of progesterone. Inside each follicle is an immature egg, the oocyte. After about a week, usually only one of the growing follicles remains. This remaining follicle continues to grow and secrete estrogen, which keeps levels of LH and FSH low, an example of negative feedback.

On about day 12, the high level of estrogen causes the anterior pituitary gland to release a surge of LH. This rapid release of a large quantity of LH causes the follicle to rupture, and ovulation occurs.

Luteal phase After ovulation, the cells of the follicle change, and the follicle is transformed into a structure called the corpus luteum (KOR pus • LEW tee um), as illustrated in **Figure 6.** The corpus luteum slowly degenerates as the menstrual cycle continues. The corpus luteum produces high amounts of progesterone and some estrogen, which keep levels of LH and FSH low through negative feedback. Recall that FSH and LH stimulate new follicles to develop, but when these hormones are kept at low levels, new follicles are temporarily prevented from maturing. Toward the end of the cycle, the corpus luteum breaks down, and it no longer produces progesterone and estrogen. This results in a rapid decrease in progesterone and estrogen levels. A rapid decrease in hormones triggers detachment of the endometrium, and the flow phase of a new menstrual cycle will begin.

MiniLab 1

Model Sex Cell Production

? Inquiry MiniLab

Why does meiosis produce four sperm but only one egg? The difference in the division of cytoplasm is the major reason why meiosis is different in human males and females. Use clay to model how the sex cells are produced during meiosis.

Procedure

1. Read and complete the lab safety form.
2. Choose **two lumps of clay,** each of a different color. Choose one to represent a primary spermatocyte and the other a primary oocyte.
3. Use the primary spermatocyte to simulate the meiotic divisions as they occur in males.
4. Simulate maturation of the sperm by removing about half of the clay from each sperm and using a small part of it to add a flagellum to each cell.
5. Next, simulate the first meiotic division in females.
6. Use one of the sperm and mold it to one side of the large cell. Now simulate the second meiotic division.

Analysis

1. **Model** Make drawings of each step above. Label the following: primary spermatocyte and oocyte, egg, sperm, first polar body, second polar body, fertilized egg, and zygote.
2. **Explain** the benefit of meiosis concentrating most of the cytoplasm into one egg.

Content Background

Teacher FYI The number of ovarian follicles decreases throughout a female's life. When a female is in the fourth month of development, her ovaries contain five million oogonia (cells that can develop into oocytes). By birth, the number has been reduced to two million oocytes (immature eggs). By puberty, only 400,000 oocytes remain. A woman will ovulate approximately 400 eggs in her lifetime.

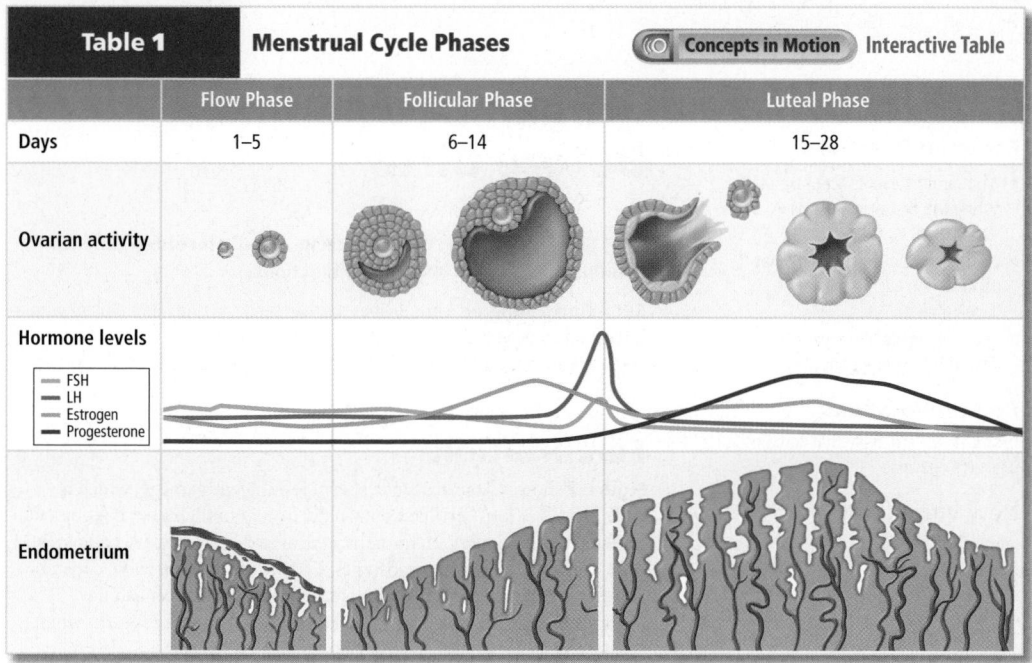

Table 1 Menstrual Cycle Phases — Concepts in Motion Interactive Table

	Flow Phase	Follicular Phase	Luteal Phase
Days	1–5	6–14	15–28
Ovarian activity	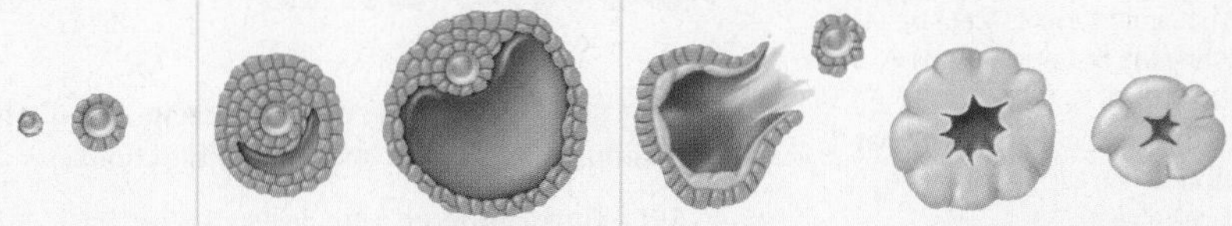		
Hormone levels	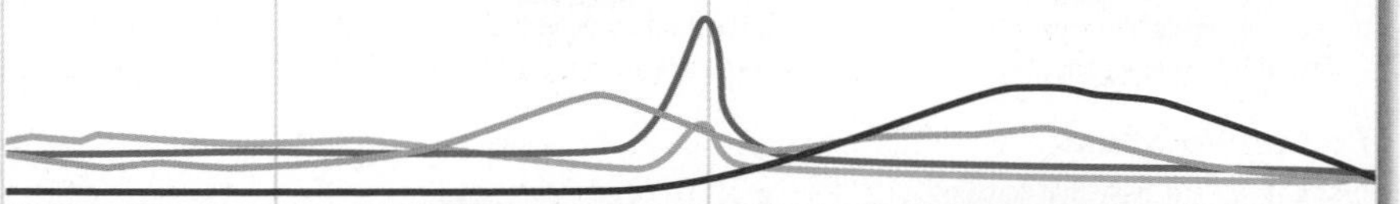		
Endometrium	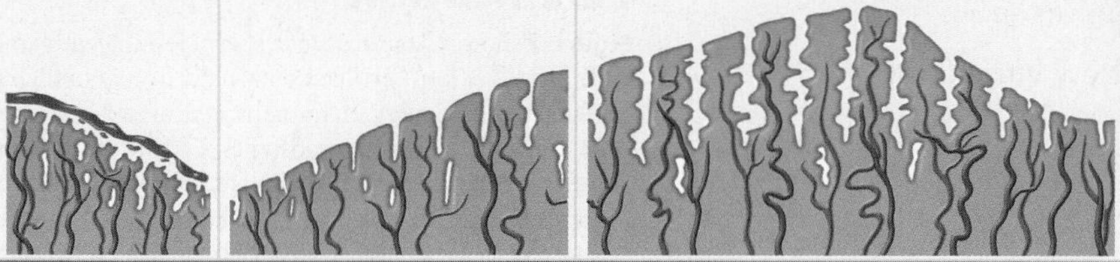		

If the egg is fertilized, a different chain of events occurs, and a new menstrual cycle does not begin. The progesterone levels remain high and increase the blood supply to the endometrium. The corpus luteum does not degenerate and hormone levels do not drop. The endometrium accumulates lipids and begins secreting a fluid rich in nutrients for the developing embryo.

D

Section 1 Assessment

Section Summary

- Levels of male and female hormones are regulated by negative feedback systems.
- The human male produces millions of sperm cells every day.
- The number of sex cells resulting from meiosis differs in males and females.
- The human female has a reproductive cycle called the menstrual cycle.
- The menstrual cycle has three phases: the flow phase, the follicular phase, and the luteal phase.

Understand Main Ideas

1. MAIN Idea **Describe** how hormones regulate sperm and egg cells.
2. **Summarize** the structures of the reproductive systems and their functions.
3. **Describe** the origin and importance of substances found in semen.
4. **Explain** the major events that take place in the endometrium and in the ovary during the menstrual cycle.

Think Critically

5. **Infer** On about day 12, estrogen levels cause a sharp increase in the amount of LH that is released. According to a negative feedback model, what would you expect to happen?

MATH in Biology

6. Suppose a female began menstruating at age 12 and stopped menstruating at age 55. If she never became pregnant and her menstrual cycles averaged 28 days, how many eggs did she ovulate during her reproductive years?

Concepts in Motion

Interactive Table

D Develop Concepts

AL Discuss

ASK STUDENTS: ***What would happen if the corpus luteum did not degenerate and continued to function?*** Progesterone and estrogen levels would remain high. This would prevent the menstrual cycle from continuing.

Formative Assessment

Evaluation

ASK STUDENTS: ***How does the level of testosterone influence levels of follicle-stimulating hormone and luteinizing hormone?*** When testosterone levels are low, FSH and LH levels are high. These are regulated by a negative-feedback loop.

Remediation

Students struggling to understand the relationship among these hormones might benefit from a graphic. Draw a rectangle on the board. Write "T" near the top and "FSH" or "LH" near the bottom. Divide the rectangle in half horizontally to demonstrate equal hormone levels.

ASK STUDENTS: ***What happens to the hormone levels if I move the line up?*** Testosterone decreases, FSH or LH increases.

Section 1 Assessment

1. FSH and LH are regulated by negative feedback processes involving testosterone, estrogen, and progesterone. These hormones regulate sex cell production.
2. Student summaries should include all structures and functions shown in Figure 1 and Figure 4.
3. Sugar is produced by the seminal vesicles and provides energy for sperm cells. An alkaline solution is produced by the prostate gland and bulbourethral glands to neutralize any acidic conditions sperm cells may encounter in the urethra and vagina.
4. The endometrium sheds the blood, tissue fluid, mucus, and epithelial cells. About five days later, the endometrium begins to repair itself. After about 12 days, ovulation occurs. The follicle is changed to the corpus luteum, which produces high amounts of progesterone and some estrogen. Late in the cycle, the corpus luteum breaks down and stops producing hormones. The endometrium detaches and the cycle starts over.
5. When estrogen levels rise, LH levels will decrease.
6. 559 egg cells (43 years × 13 cycles per year)

Assessment Online Quiz

Section 2

MAIN Idea

BL OL AL

Development Before Birth

A human begins as a unicellular zygote, but an adult body consists of trillions of specialized cells. **ASK STUDENTS:** ***What processes account for the formation of many specialized cells?*** All body cells are a result of mitosis; gene expression determines the specificity of each type of cell.

R Reading Strategy

EL OL **Vocabulary Chart** Have students create a three-column chart. In the first column, have them write the vocabulary terms associated with this section. In the second column, have them write a definition of each term. In the last column, have students make up a phrase that will help them remember what each term means.

C Critical Thinking

OL **Analyze**

ASK STUDENTS: ***If only one sperm cell fertilizes an egg, why is it important that millions of sperm cells are released in each ejaculation?*** Most sperm cells never reach the oviduct; it takes several hundred sperm cells to weaken the barrier around the egg.

S Skill Practice

BL OL **Visual Literacy**

SAY TO STUDENTS: ***Examine Figure 7. Which part of an egg cell and a sperm cell fuse together?*** The nucleus of both cells fuse together to form a diploid zygote.

Video BrainPOP

Section 2

Reading Preview

Essential Questions

- What are the events that take place during the first week following fertilization?
- What are the major changes that occur during each trimester of development?
- How are female hormone levels altered during pregnancy?

Review Vocabulary

lysosome: organelle that contains digestive enzymes

New Vocabulary

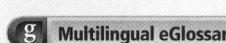

morula
blastocyst
amniotic fluid

R

g Multilingual eGlossary

Video BrainPOP

Human Development Before Birth

MAIN Idea **A human develops from a single fertilized cell into trillions of cells with specialized functions.**

Real-World Reading Link Just as a single seed can grow into a plant with a beautiful flower, your complex body began as a single cell at the union of an egg and a sperm at fertilization.

Fertilization

Figure 7 shows the process of a sperm joining with an egg, which is called fertilization. Fertilization usually occurs in the upper portion of an oviduct near the ovary. In humans, sperm and eggs each are haploid, and each normally has 23 chromosomes. Fertilization brings these chromosomes together, restoring the diploid number of 46 chromosomes.

Sperm enter the vagina of the female's reproductive system when strong muscular contractions ejaculate semen from the male's penis during intercourse. Some sperm can exit through the penis before ejaculation without the male's knowledge. As a result, sexual activity that does not result in ejaculation can lead to the release of sperm, fertilization, and pregnancy.

Sperm can survive for 48 hours in the female reproductive tract, but an unfertilized egg can survive for only 24 hours. Fertilization can happen if intercourse occurs anytime from a few days before ovulation to a day after ovulation. Overall, there is a relatively short time when fertilization can occur successfully. However, it is important to remember that the length of the menstrual cycle can vary and ovulation can occur at any time.

C

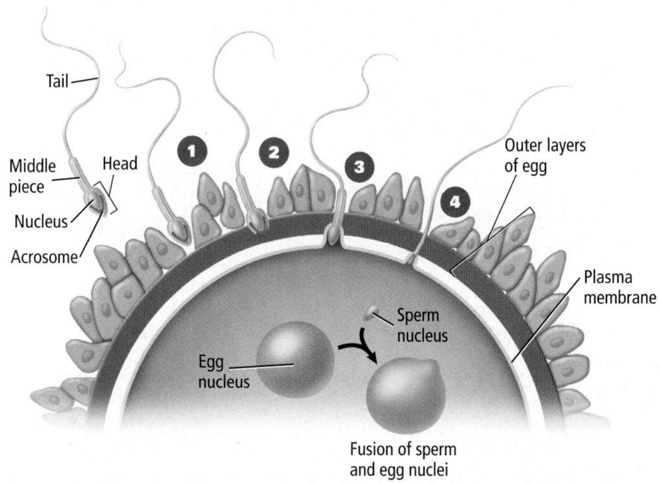

S

■ **Figure 7** Although many sperm are needed to weaken the barrier that surrounds the egg, only one sperm fertilizes an egg (steps 1-4). Fertilization is complete when the sperm nucleus fuses with the egg nucleus.

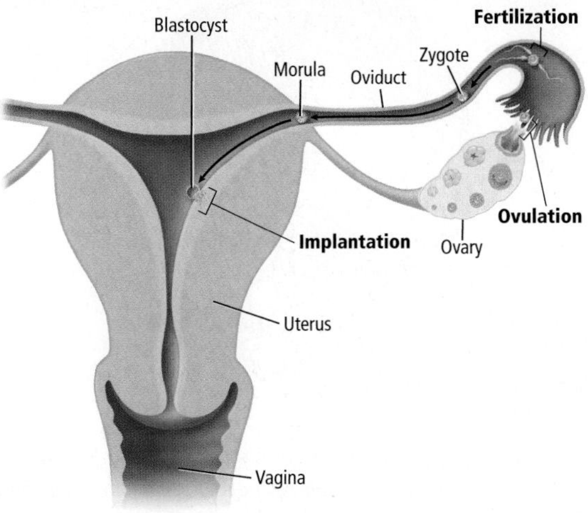

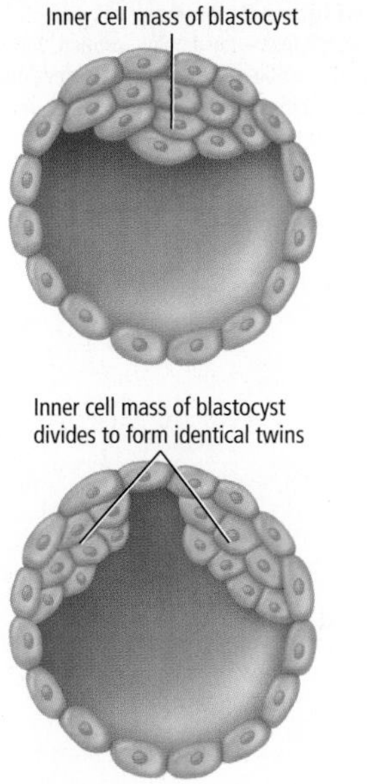

■ **Figure 8**
Left: During the first week of development, many changes occur as the zygote travels through the oviduct.
Right: The inner cell mass of the blastocyst will develop into a fetus (top). If the inner cell mass divides, identical twins might form (bottom).

About 300 million sperm are released into the vagina during intercourse. Only several hundred of them will successfully complete the journey to the egg. Many never make it out of the vagina, some are attacked by white blood cells, and many simply die along the way. Only one sperm can fertilize an egg, but it takes several hundred to participate in the process.

Connection to Chemistry A single sperm cannot penetrate the plasma membrane that surrounds the human egg. Recall that lysosomes are organelles that contain digestive enzymes. Notice in **Figure 7** that the tip of each sperm is a specialized lysosome called an acrosome. As each of several hundred sperm bombard the egg, the enzymes inside of the acrosome weaken the plasma membrane surrounding the egg. Eventually the plasma membrane becomes weak enough that one sperm can penetrate the egg.
D Immediately following this penetration, the egg forms a barrier to prevent other sperm from entering the now-fertilized egg.

Reading Check **Explain** why hundreds of sperm are necessary for fertilization to take place.

W Early Development

Figure 8 illustrates the first week of human development. The fertilized egg, which is called a zygote (ZI goht), moves through the oviduct propelled by involuntary smooth muscle contractions and by the cilia lining the oviduct. Around 30 hours after fertilization, the zygote undergoes its first mitosis and cell division. Cell division continues, and by the third day, the embryo leaves the oviduct and enters the uterus. At this point, the embryo is described as a **morula,** a solid ball of cells.

By the fifth day, the morula has developed into a **blastocyst,** which can be described as a hollow ball of cells. The blastocyst attaches to the endometrium around the sixth day and is fully implanted by day 10. **Figure 8** shows that the blastocyst is not completely hollow. Inside the blastocyst is a group of cells called the inner cell mass. The inner cell
C mass eventually will become the embryo. Sometimes, the inner cell mass splits, and identical twins might form.

CAREERS IN BIOLOGY

Reproductive Endocrinologist
Physicians who have advanced training in the treatment of infertility and disorders involving the reproductive hormones are called reproductive endocrinologists. A reproductive endocrinologist also might conduct research or train medical students.

Reading Check A protective barrier surrounds the egg. Hundreds of sperm cells release enzymes from their acrosomes to weaken this barrier.

D Develop Concepts

OL AL

Activate Prior Knowledge
ASK STUDENTS: ***What might be the result if two sperm cells fertilized the same egg?*** It would result in a zygote that is trisomic for all 23 pairs of chromosomes. This usually results in the death of the embryo or fetus—a miscarriage. ***Why don't scientists know how often this occurs?*** Possible answers: the embryo may die before there are any effects on the female cycle; the female might not know that fertilization had occurred; often the causes of miscarriages are never investigated.

W Writing Support

BL OL AL Informal Writing
SAY TO STUDENTS: ***Create a diary that describes the events and changes that occur during the first week of embryonic development.*** After fertilization, cell replication begins to occur. The zygote replicates into two identical cells, which then become four cells. Eventually, a morula and then a blastocyst are formed. The embryo travels through the oviduct and attaches to the endometrium around Day 6.

C Critical Thinking

OL AL Hypothesize
ASK STUDENTS: ***How do you think conjoined twins form?*** Conjoined twins form in a similar way as identical twins form, except that there is a bridge of cells connecting the two inner cell masses. You may have to help students understand the meaning of the term *conjoined.*

D Develop Concepts

OL Clarify a Misconception

ASK STUDENTS: ***Are the functions of the placenta and the umbilical cord the same?*** no Students might need help understanding the difference. Explain that a placenta is an organ that regulates what passes from mother to fetus and from fetus to mother. The umbilical cord actually transfers the materials from placenta to fetus and from fetus to mother.

Develop Concepts

OL Activate Prior Knowledge

Have students review the four extraembryonic membranes in nonplacental mammals.

ASK STUDENTS: ***How might the functions of these layers differ in humans?*** Student responses likely will be that chorion and the yolk sac are not necessary since nutrient and gas exchange occurs in the placenta. Students may make a connection with formation of the placenta. Students likely will not know the function of the yolk sac. Students will learn that the yolk sac is the site of red blood cell formation.

Develop Concepts

OL Analogy

SAY TO STUDENTS: ***Make an analogy comparing the dimensions of a familiar object with the dimensions of a placenta.*** A completely formed placenta is about the same size as a personal pizza or a flying disc.

■ **Figure 9** Four extraembryonic membranes—the amnion, chorion, yolk sac, and allantois—are important in development. ***Identify** the role of the yolk sac in humans.*

Extraembryonic membranes The membranes that extend beyond an embryo are called the extraembryonic membranes. You also might have learned about the development of the amniotic egg, and how this enabled animals to reproduce on land. Developing humans have these membranes, as shown in **Figure 9.** But because humans and most other mammals develop inside the mother's body, these membranes have somewhat different functions.

Early in human development, four extraembryonic membranes form. These membranes are the amnion, the chorion (KOR ee ahn), the yolk sac, and the allantois (uh LAN tuh wus), as illustrated in **Figure 9.** The amnion is a thin layer that forms a sac around the embryo. Inside this sac is the **amniotic fluid** (am nee AH tihk • FLU id), which protects, cushions, and insulates the embryo. Outside of the amnion is the chorion, which, together with the allantois, contributes to the formation of the placenta. The yolk sac in humans does not contain any yolk but serves as the first site of red blood cell formation for the embryo.

VOCABULARY

ACADEMIC VOCABULARY

Enable
to make able or feasible
Amniotic eggs enable reproduction on land.

The placenta About two weeks after fertilization, tiny fingerlike projections of the chorion, called chorionic villi (VIH li), begin to grow into the wall of the uterus. The placenta (pluh SEN tuh), the organ that provides food and oxygen and also removes waste, begins to form and is fully formed by the tenth week. The placenta has two surfaces—a fetal side that forms from the chorion and faces the fetus and a maternal side that forms from uterine tissue. When completely formed, the placenta is 15–20 cm in diameter, 2.5 cm thick, and has a mass of about 0.45 kg. The umbilical cord, a tube containing blood vessels, serves as the connection between the fetus and the mother. **Figure 10** illustrates the connection between the mother and fetus.

The placenta regulates what passes from the mother to the fetus and from the fetus to the mother. Oxygen and nutrients can travel from the mother to the fetus. Alcohol, drugs, various other substances, and the human immunodeficiency virus (HIV) also can pass through the placenta to the developing fetus. D

Metabolic waste products and carbon dioxide travel from the fetus to the mother. Because the mother and the fetus have their own separate circulatory systems, blood cells do not pass through the placenta. However, the mother's antibodies pass to the fetus and help protect the newborn until its immune system is functioning.

Study Tip

Time Line Create a time line showing the development of a human being from fertilization to adulthood. Use average ages for various stages of development. Include major characteristics of each stage of development.

Demonstration

Fertilization and Early Development Set up a series of microscopes with prepared slides of early embryonic development. Slides of sea stars or sea urchins work well. Stages of development that can be shown to students include the fertilized egg, 2-, 4-, and 8-cell stages, morula, blastula, and gastrula. Est. time: 10 min

■ **Caption Question Fig. 9** The yolk sac serves as first site of red blood cell formation.

Visualizing a Placenta

Figure 10
A growing fetus exchanges nutrients, oxygen, and wastes with the mother through the placenta. The placenta contains tissue from both mother and fetus.

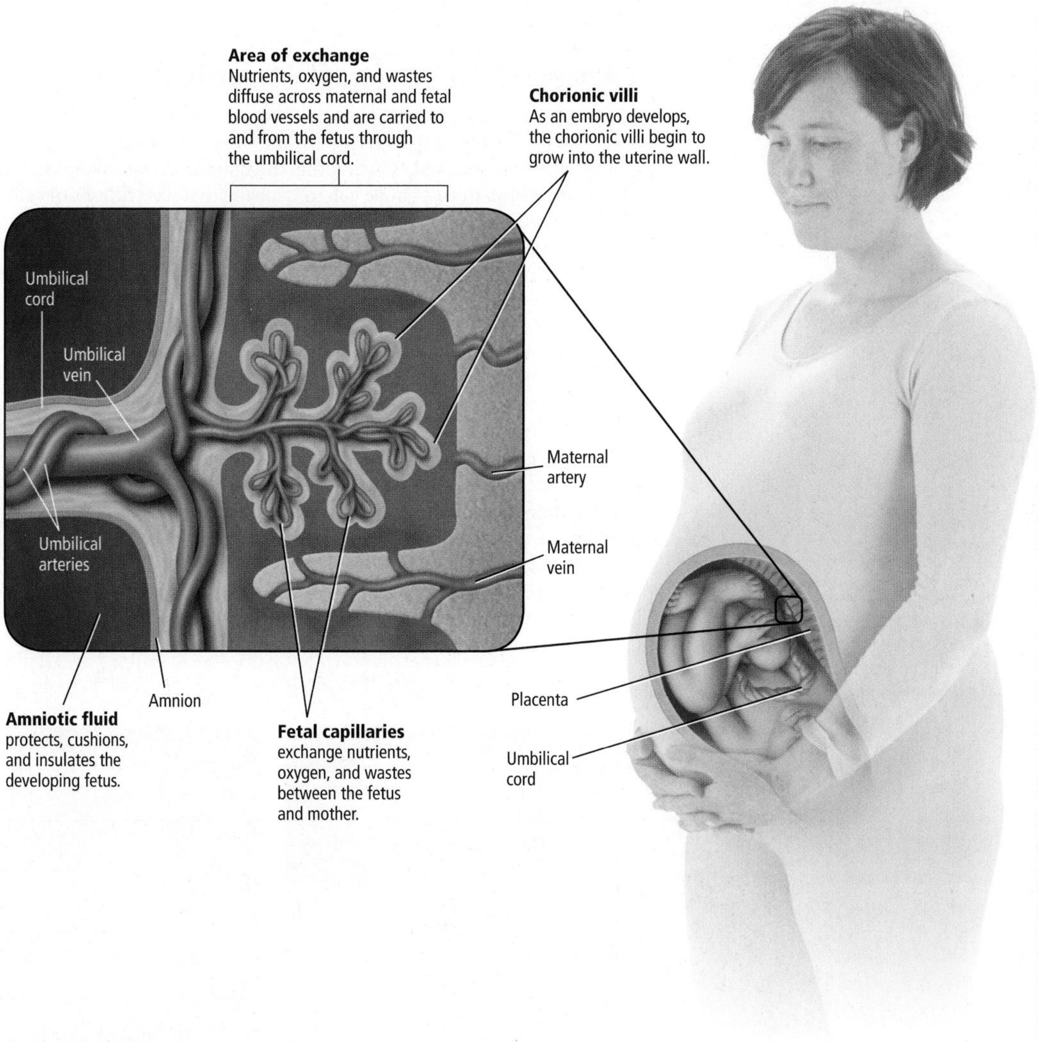

Concepts in Motion Animation

Research Citation

Make Predictions Educational research indicates that students can benefit from making predictions prior to reading as suggested by the critical thinking activity on this page. These activities help readers anticipate the content of the material and activate any background information they have about the subject. (Readance, Bean, and Baldwin, 1985).

Research bibliography on pages 32T–34T

Visualizing a Placenta

Purpose

Students will examine how substances are transferred between the maternal bloodstream and the fetal bloodstream.
C.5, F.1

Critical Thinking

OL Predict Have students make a two-column chart, labeling one side *fetus* and the other side *mother*. The line separating the two columns represents placental membranes. Before they read the Figure 10 caption, ask students the following questions.
ASK STUDENTS: ***What substances will travel from the mother to the fetus?*** oxygen, nutrients, alcohol, drugs, some viruses ***Which substances will travel from the fetus to the mother?*** carbon dioxide and metabolic wastes, such as water or salts

Develop Concepts

OL Clarify a Misconception
ASK STUDENTS: ***Does blood flow directly from the mother's circulatory system into the fetal circulatory system?*** Many students will think a mother and fetus share a common circulatory system that separates at the time of birth. Students will learn that the mother and fetus have separate circulatory systems. Blood cells do not cross the placenta. If they did, there would be a risk of adverse immune reactions.

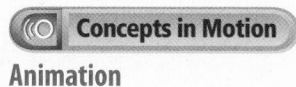

Concepts in Motion
Animation

C Critical Thinking

OL AL Analyze

ASK STUDENTS: ***If a doctor wanted to confirm that a woman is pregnant, for which hormone would he or she most likely test?*** The embryo makes hCG (human chorionic gonadotropin). Some of this hormone will enter the mother's body and be filtered out by the kidneys. The hormone then will be present in the mother's urine. The doctors test for the presence of hCG to confirm pregnancy.

Skill Practice

OL AL Use Math Skills

ASK STUDENTS: ***If you were able to pinpoint the day an embryo was conceived, how could an initial due date be predicted?*** Using a calendar, determine what date is 266 days after conception. This provides only an early estimate; more reliable estimates can be determined later in pregnancy by growth of the fetus and other factors.

GOING GREEN Make note pads from scrap paper. Cut into a convenient size and staple together blank side up.

Hormonal regulation during pregnancy During the first week of development, the embryo begins to secrete a hormone, called human chorionic gonadotropin (hCG) (kor ee AH nihk • go na duh TROH pen), which keeps the corpus luteum from degenerating. If the corpus luteum remains active, progesterone levels, and to a lesser extent estrogen levels, remain high. Remember from the previous section that the decline of progesterone triggers a new menstrual cycle. If levels of these hormones remain high, a new menstrual cycle will not begin. Two to three months into development, the placenta secretes enough progesterone and estrogen to maintain the proper conditions for pregnancy. C

Reading Check **Compare** two functions of the placenta.

Three Trimesters of Development

On average, human development takes around 266 days from fertilization to birth. This time span is divided into three trimesters, each around three months long. During this time, many events take place. The zygote grows from a single cell into a baby that has trillions of cells. These cells develop into tissues and organs with specialized functions. Follow **Figure 11,** which shows different stages of human development during the first trimester.

The first trimester In the first trimester, all tissues, organs, and organ systems begin to develop. During this time of development, the embryo is especially vulnerable to the effects of alcohol, tobacco, drugs, and other environmental influences, such as environmental pollutants. During the first two weeks of development, the mother might not realize that she is pregnant because she has not yet missed a menstrual period. A lack of certain essential nutrients during this time might cause irreversible damage to the developing embryo. A few of the major causes of preventable birth defects are listed in **Table 2.**

At the end of eight weeks, the embryo is called a fetus. All of the organ systems have begun to form. By the end of the first trimester, the fetus can move its arms, fingers, and toes and make facial expressions. Fingerprints also are present.

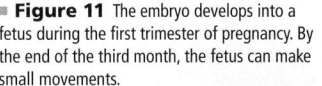

■ **Figure 11** The embryo develops into a fetus during the first trimester of pregnancy. By the end of the third month, the fetus can make small movements.

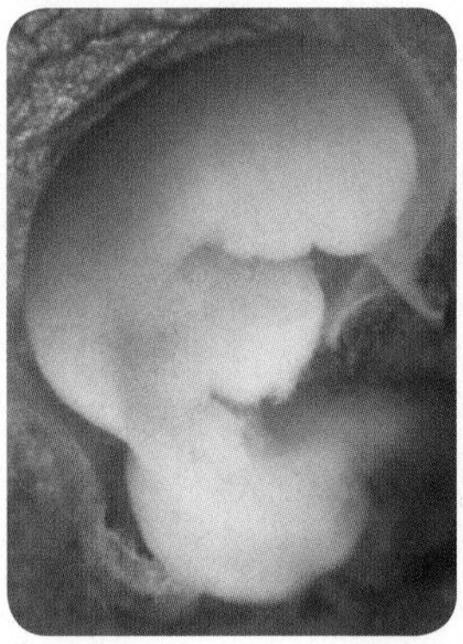
4 weeks

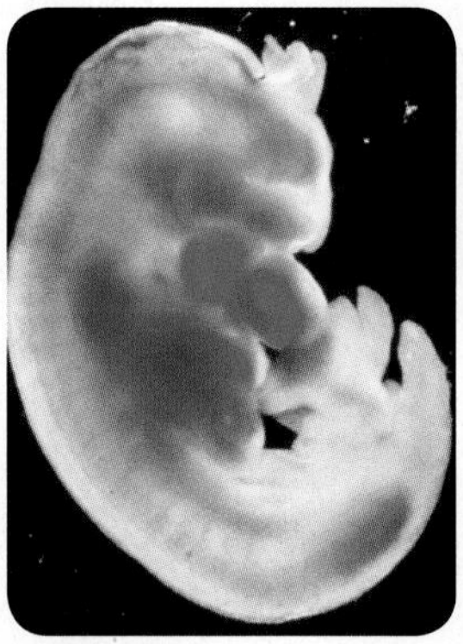
5–6 weeks

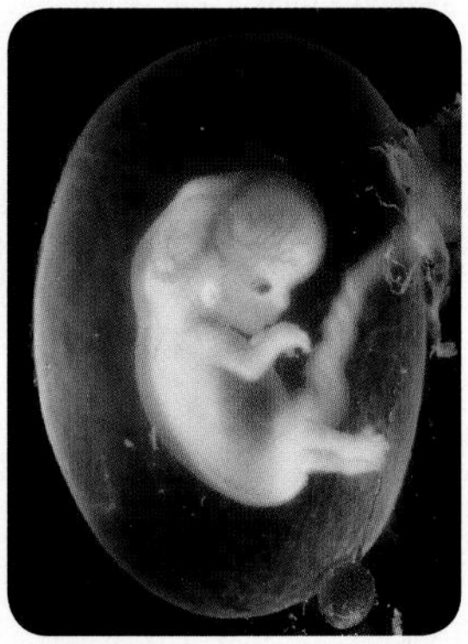
7–8 weeks

Reading Check The placenta regulates the passage of materials from mother to fetus and from fetus to mother. The placenta also secretes progesterone and estrogen to maintain pregnancy.

Table 2	Preventable Causes of Birth Defects — Concepts in Motion Interactive Table
Cause	Defect
Alcohol consumption	• Mental retardation
Cigarette smoking	• Health problems related to premature births and underweight babies
Lack of folic acid in diet	• Anencephaly (head and brain do not completely form) • Spina bifida (nerve cells from the spinal cord are exposed, leading to paralysis)
Cocaine	• Low birth weight • Premature birth • Possible permanent brain damage and behavioral disorders
Methamphetamine	• Premature birth • Extreme irritability

The second trimester The second trimester primarily is a period of growth. Around 18 to 20 weeks, the fetal heartbeat might be heard using a stethoscope. The developing fetus is capable of sucking its thumb and can develop the hiccups. The mother might feel a fluttering sensation or might even feel light kicks. Hair usually forms, and the fetal eyes will open during this period. At the end of this trimester, the fetus might be able to survive outside the mother's uterus with the aid of medical intervention, but the chances for survival are not very high. If born this early, the baby cannot maintain a constant body temperature. The baby's lungs have not developed fully, so respiratory failure is a great risk. Also, the baby is very likely to become seriously ill because its immune system is not fully functional.

The third trimester During the third trimester, the fetus continues to grow at a rapid rate. Fat accumulates under the skin to provide insulation for the fetus once it is born. Adequate protein intake by the mother is important during this time. Protein is essential for the rapid amount of brain growth that occurs. New nerve cells in the brain are forming at a rate of 250,000 cells per minute. The fetus now might respond to sounds in the environment, such as music or the sound of its mother's voice. **S**

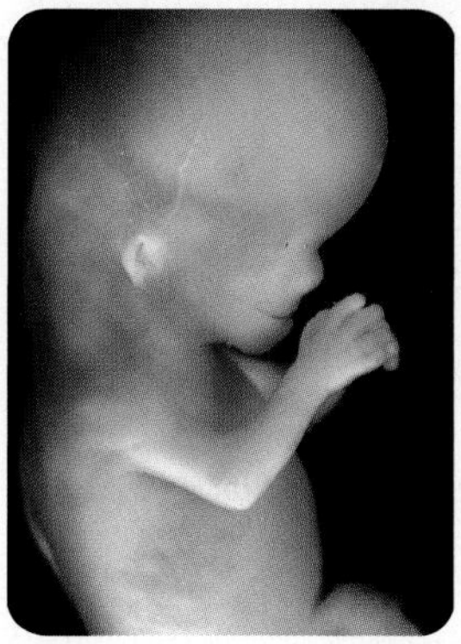

9–10 weeks

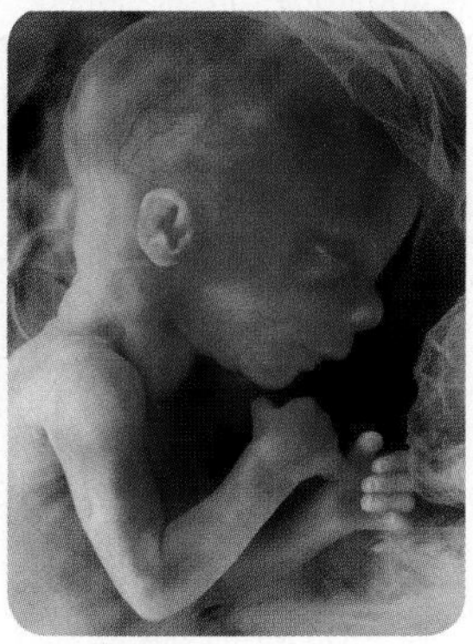

12 weeks

Differentiated Instruction

Below Level Graphic organizers, such as the table suggested on this page, are useful for students who are working below level. Organizing information this way can help these students make connections and retain the information presented.

For more tips, see pages 14T–15T.

Concepts in Motion
Interactive Table

Develop Concepts

OL Clarify a Misconception

ASK STUDENTS: ***When does a developing embryo become a female or male?*** Students may respond that it is when the external genitals become visible (by ultrasound). Students may have heard statements such as "everyone starts out as female." It is true that physical changes may not be observable until development is well underway; however, the gender of an individual is determined at conception by whether the sperm carried an X or a Y chromosome.

S Skill Practice

EL BL OL Make A Table

Instruct students to make a two-column table. In the left column, have them list the three trimesters of pregnancy. In the right column, instruct students to fill in developmental events or milestones that occur during each trimester. 1st trimester: organ systems begin to form, the fetus begins to move its arms, fingers, and toes; 2nd trimester: primarily a time of growth, the fetal heartbeat can be heard; 3rd trimester: a period of rapid brain growth; the fetus will respond to external stimuli

Develop Concepts

OL AL Extension Have students research events in human development other than those discussed in the text.

MiniLab 2

Inquiry MiniLab

For a lab worksheet, use your eTeacherEdition Online.

RUBRIC A rubric for evaluating MiniLabs is found on your eTeacherEdition Online.

Est. Time 25 min

Alternative Materials Additional images can be found online, however these should be located by the teacher as some images may be unsuitable for students.

Safety Precaution Approve lab safety forms before work begins.

Teaching Strategies

- Human embryonic development is a predictable process that follows an expected time line. Students can add information gained from this exercise to the time lines they started in MiniLab 1.
- Help students understand the critical nature of the first eight weeks following fertilization. During this period, the embryo is more sensitive to outside factors, including environmental toxins and drugs, than at any other time during development.

Analysis

1. Answers will vary based on the characteristic chosen.
2. Answers will vary. In general, although all organ systems have been formed by this time, changes in body growth, metabolism, skin, and lungs that occur during the remainder of the development period are crucial to survival of the offspring.

Figure 12 In amniocentesis, fluid and cells lost from the fetus are removed from the amniotic fluid and analyzed.

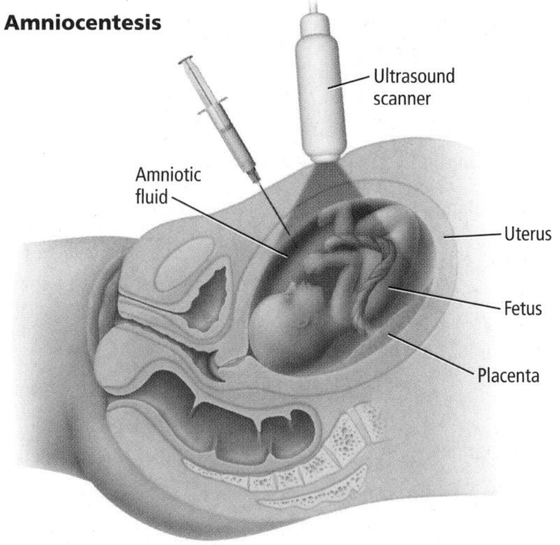

CAREERS IN BIOLOGY

Ultrasound Technician
Technical skills are needed in biology. An ultrasound technician obtains ultrasound images that are interpreted by a physician.

Diagnosis in the Fetus

Many conditions can be diagnosed before a baby is born. Identifying certain conditions as early as possible increases the chance for proper medical treatment to help a newborn baby have the highest quality of life possible.

Ultrasound One way to identify conditions in the fetus is by using ultrasound, a procedure in which sound waves are bounced off the fetus. These sound waves are converted into light images that can be seen on a video monitor. Ultrasound can be used to determine if the fetus is growing properly, the position of the fetus in the uterus, and the gender of the fetus.

MiniLab 2

Inquiry MiniLab

Sequence Early Human Development

What developmental changes occur during the first eight weeks of life? Fertilization begins when a sperm penetrates the egg. The zygote undergoes predictable developmental changes. Cell division produces increasing numbers of cells. Cells move and arrange themselves to form specific organs, making it possible for cells to perform specific functions.

Procedure

1. Refer to **Figure 11** to see **images of embryos.**
2. Study the images for the first trimester of pregnancy. Choose one factor to track through this developmental period. Factors might include embryonic size, overall structural changes, specific organ or organ system development, or others.
3. Chart the development of this factor along a time line through the first trimester of pregnancy.

Analysis

1. **Analyze** the time line you created. Identify developmental milestones related to this factor during the ten-week period.
2. **Summarize** the level of development of the factor you examined by the end of the first twelve weeks.

Inquiry BioLab

The lab at the end of the chapter can be used at this point in the lesson.

"We need to add to the three R's, namely Reading, 'Riting and 'Rithmetic, a fourth—Responsibility."

—Herbert Hoover

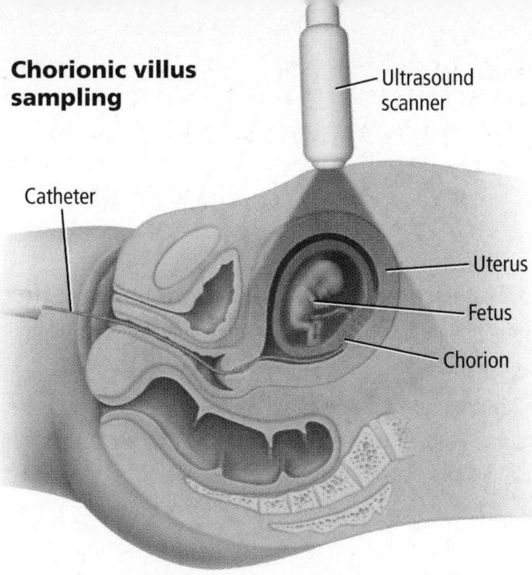

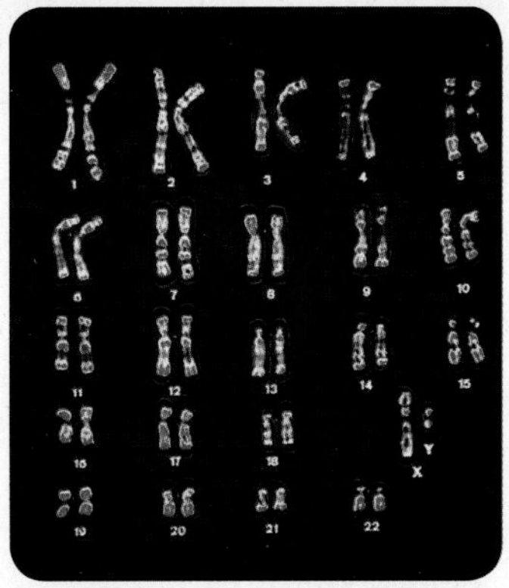

Karyotype

■ **Figure 13**
Left: Chorionic villus sampling involves removing cells from the chorion and analyzing them. This procedure carries a small risk of a miscarriage.
Right: Karyotypes can be analyzed to help with diagnosis.

Amniocentesis and chorionic villus sampling Amniocentesis (am nee oh sen TEE sus) and chorionic villus sampling are prenatal tests. During amniocentesis—usually performed in the second trimester—a needle is inserted through the abdomen of the pregnant female, illustrated in **Figure 12.** Fluid from the amniotic sac is removed and analyzed. Tests that measure enzyme levels associated with certain conditions can be performed. Fetal cells can be examined by a karyotype or even by DNA analysis. Remember a karyotype is a chart of chromosome pairs, shown in **Figure 13,** that is valuable in identifying unusual chromosome numbers or the sex of the fetus.

In chorionic villus sampling—usually performed during the first trimester—a small tube, called a catheter, is inserted through the vagina and cervix of the mother, as illustrated in **Figure 13.** Cells from the chorion are removed and analyzed by karyotyping. The chromosomes in the cells of the chorion are identical to those of the cells in the fetus.

Section 2 Assessment

Section Summary

- Fertilization is the joining of egg and sperm.
- Four extraembryonic membranes are associated with a human embryo.
- The placenta regulates what substances can be exchanged between a fetus and its mother.
- Hormone regulation during pregnancy is different from hormone regulation during the menstrual cycle.
- Preganancies are divided into three trimesters.
- Some medical conditions of a baby can be detected before it is born.

Understand Main Ideas

1. MAIN Idea Describe the changes that the zygote undergoes during the first week following fertilization.
2. **Describe** how defective acrosomes would affect the process of fertilization.
3. **Summarize** the development that occurs during each trimester in a concept map.
4. **Compare and contrast** hormonal regulation during pregnancy with hormonal regulation during the menstrual cycle.

Think Critically

WRITING in Biology

5. Write a paragraph explaining the functions of the extraembryonic membrane in humans, and contrast those functions with the functions in other animals.

MATH in Biology

6. Determine the due date (predicted birth date) of a baby if the egg was fertilized on January 1.

Develop Concepts

OL AL Make a List Have students make a list of other possible uses of ultrasounds and share their answers with the class. Ultrasound use is not limited to prenatal diagnoses. Other common uses are examining blood flow through a vessel, examining heart valves, and looking for the presence of kidney stones or gallstones.

Formative Assessment

Evaluation

ASK STUDENTS: ***What keeps a female from continuing to ovulate while she is pregnant?*** The embryo produces human chorionic gonadotropin (hCG). This hormone enters the mother's bloodstream and then exerts its influence on the corpus luteum. The corpus luteum, which usually degenerates, keeps producing progesterone and estrogen. High levels of estrogen and progesterone keep FSH and LH levels low. This prevents ovulation.

Remediation Students who struggle to understand the hormone changes that occur during pregnancy may benefit from creating a step-by-step chart that outlines the changes. Have students review the material from fertilization through hormonal regulation during pregnancy (pages 1054–1058) to create their chart.

Section 2 Assessment

1. The zygote divides via mitosis, becoming a morula. The morula hollows out and becomes a blastocyst.
2. The barrier surrounding the egg could not be penetrated and fertilization would not occur.
3. Concept maps will vary, but many maps are likely to be linear because development is a sequential process. The maps should account for all the major developments in all three trimesters.
4. During pregnancy, progesterone and estrogen levels remain high, preventing another menstrual period. During a normal menstrual cycle, levels of progesterone and estrogen drop near the end of the cycle.
5. Paragraphs should note that, in humans, there are four extraembryonic membranes: the amnion holds the fluid around the embryo, the chorion and allantois contribute to forming the placenta, the yolk sac serves as the first site of red blood cell formation.
6. September 24 (September 23 in a leap year), based on a 266-day pregnancy

Section 3

MAIN Idea

BL OL AL Life Development
SAY TO STUDENTS: ***List what you feel are the major phases in a human life span and changes that occur in each.*** Possible responses may include: infancy during which a person learns to crawl, talk, and eat solid food; childhood, a time of rapid growth; teenage years during which puberty occurs; adulthood, a time for reproduction and professional growth; and old age during which some body processes begin to slow down.

R Reading Strategy

OL SQ3R Have students first **S**urvey Section 3, focusing on headings. Next have students write **Q**uestions about key points made in this section. Then tell them to **R**ead the section and make notes related to the questions. Finally, have students **R**ecite vocabulary and **R**eview for meaning.

S Skill Practice

BL OL AL Visual Literacy
Have students examine Figure 14 and write predictions about what they will be studying in the first part of Section 3. After they read this section, have students reexamine Figure 14 and revise their initial predictions.

Caption Question Fig. 14
Answers will vary. Possible answer: It might result in bleeding in the mother.

Section 3

Reading Preview

Essential Questions

- What are the events that occur during the three stages of birth?
- What are the stages of human development from infancy to adulthood?
- What are the hormones necessary for growth?

Review Vocabulary

growth: increase in the amount of living material and formation of new structures in an organism

New Vocabulary

labor
dilation
expulsion stage
placental stage
adolescence
infancy
adulthood

Multilingual eGlossary

Birth, Growth, and Aging

MAIN Idea Developmental changes continue throughout the stages of life.

Real-World Reading Link You know from looking at your family photo album that you have grown and changed since you were born. Your bones, teeth, eyes, and muscles have changed. You can look forward to continued changes in your face and body structure throughout your life.

R Birth

Birth occurs in three stages: dilation, expulsion, and the placental stage, as shown in **Figure 14.** Just before giving birth, the posterior pituitary gland releases the hormone oxytocin (ahk sih TOH sun), which stimulates involuntary muscles in the wall of the uterus to contract. This is the beginning of the birthing process called **labor.**

Another sign that the baby is going to be born is the **dilation** (di LAY shun), or opening, of the cervix. The cervix must open to allow the baby to leave the uterus. Contractions of the uterus become stronger and more frequent, and at some point the amniotic sac tears. The amniotic fluid flows out of the vagina, which is sometimes described as the "water breaking."

After a period of time that could be as short as a few hours or as long as a couple of days, the cervix fully dilates to around 10 cm. The uterine contractions are now very strong. The mother consciously will contract her abdominal muscles to help push the baby, usually head first, through the vagina in the **expulsion stage.** When the baby is out of the mother's body, the umbilical cord is clamped and cut. A small piece of the cord still attached to the baby soon will dry up and fall off, forming the navel, or belly button.

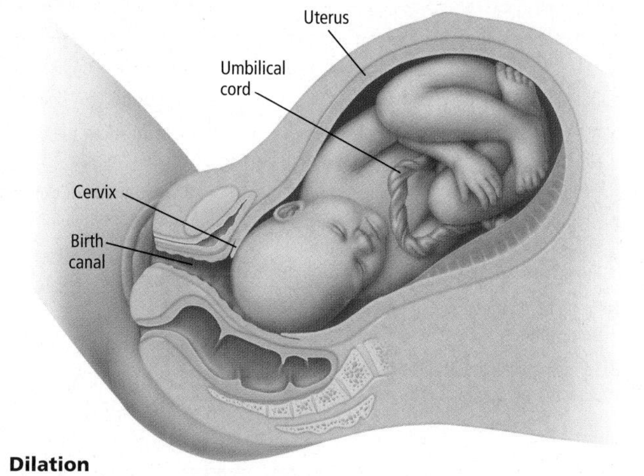

S

Figure 14 Note the three stages of birth.
Dilation stage: Contractions open the cervix.
Expulsion stage: The baby rotates as it moves through the birth canal, making expulsion easier.
Placental stage: The placenta and umbilical cord are expelled.
Hypothesize *what might happen if the placenta was not expelled quickly.*

Research Citation

Reading Strategies Education research indicates that helping students use a reading strategy such as SQ3R will help them understand the purpose of the material they are reading. Knowing the purpose leads to a deeper understanding of the text and higher retention of information. (McKeown, Beck, Sinatra, and Loxterman, 1992).

Research bibliography on pages 32T–34T

Shortly after the baby is delivered, the placenta detaches from the uterus and leaves the mother's body along with extraembryonic membranes. This is the **placental stage** of the birthing process.

Sometimes, complications prevent the baby from being born through the vagina. In these cases, an incision is made through the mother's abdomen and uterus, and the baby is removed from the mother's body. This process is called a cesarean section.

During the first four weeks of life, the baby is called a newborn. Human newborns vary in size. However, on average, a newborn human baby has a mass of 3300 g and is 51 cm long.

Reading Check **Describe** major events that occur during each stage of labor.

Growth and Aging

W Humans go through many stages of growth during their lives. After you were born, you were in your infancy, but soon you will enter adulthood. You now are in a major development phase called **adolescence** (a dul ES unts), which began with puberty and ends at adulthood.

Hormones, such as human growth hormone, thyroxine, and steroids, influence growth. Human growth hormone stimulates most areas of the body to grow as cells replicate by the process of mitosis. This hormone works by increasing the rates of protein synthesis and the breakdown of fats. Thyroxine from the thyroid increases the overall metabolic rate and is essential for growth to occur. Steroid hormones, such as estrogen and testosterone, are also important for growth. Recall that testosterone and estrogen pass through the plasma membrane and into the nucleus of a target cell. The hormones activate certain genes that promote the formation of proteins. In this way, testosterone, and to a lesser extent, estrogen, cause an increase in the size of cells.

Reading Check **Summarize** the roles of human growth hormone and thyroxine.

VOCABULARY

SCIENCE USAGE V. COMMON USAGE

Labor

Science usage: the process of giving birth

There are three stages of labor: dilation, expulsion, and the placental stage.

Common usage: the use of physical or mental effort

Lifting the heavy bags of soil requires labor.

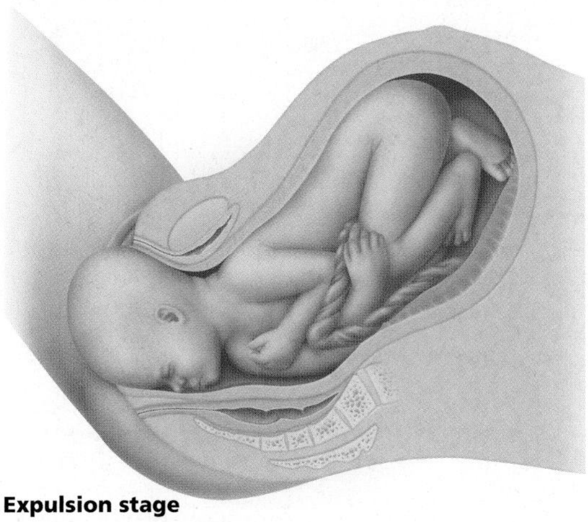

Expulsion stage

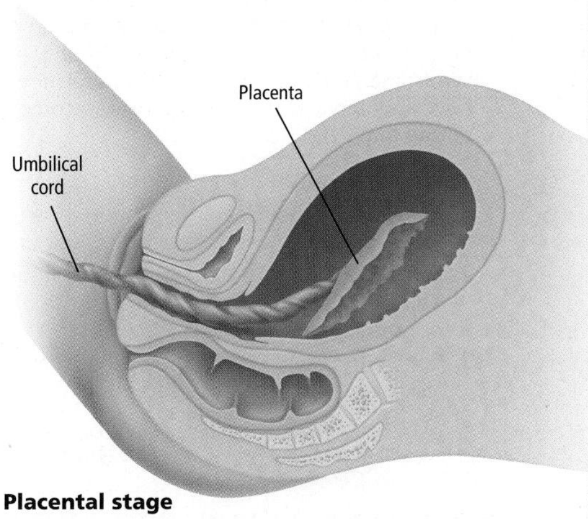

Placental stage

Develop Concepts

BL OL K-W-L Chart Have students make three columns on a sheet of paper. From left to right, have students write *What I Know, What I Want to Know,* and *What I've Learned.* Ask students to fill in the left and middle columns before reading a selection. After reading an assignment, have them fill in the right column.

EL Have English learners write in their first language about what they know and want to know. Then, after reading, the students can return to their chart and write concepts and vocabulary terms that they have learned in English.

W Writing Support

BL OL AL Narrative Writing Have students write an autobiography describing their lives from birth to the present. They should focus on biological changes—although they may incorporate other memories if they wish. Students will need to ask questions of parents or other adults who knew them when they were infants.

BL OL AL Extension Ask students to extend their story into the future and incorporate changes they expect will happen as they age. Encourage discussion by allowing students to share their stories with the class.

Reading Check During dilation, the opening to the cervix widens and uterine contractions become stronger. The amniotic sac may tear, releasing the amniotic fluid. During the expulsion phase, the baby is born. During the placental phase, the placenta is delivered.

Reading Check HGH stimulates most areas of the body to grow. Thyroxin increases the overall metabolic rate.

Differentiated Instruction

English Learners The K-W-L chart and other graphic organizers can benefit English learners. Use these tools to provide an overview of the information presented during a lesson.

For more tips, see pages 14T–15T.

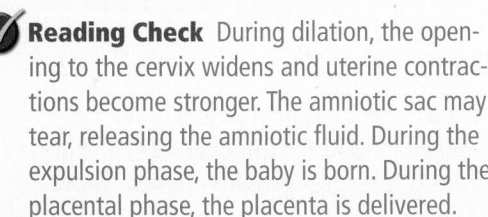

Skill Practice

OL Make a Graph Have students construct a line graph using the data presented in the data analysis lab.

DATA ANALYSIS LAB 1

About the Lab

- The National Institute of Child Health and Human Development (NICHD) is a part of the National Institutes of Health.
- NICHD endorses the American Academy of Pediatrics's policy on reducing the risk of SIDS.
- The *Back to Sleep* campaign informs parents and infant caregivers about the importance of infants sleeping on their backs.
- Also see Kiely, K. S., and Kiely, J. 1992. Relationship of sudden infant death syndrome to maternal smoking during and after pregnancy. *Pediatrics* 90(6): 905–908.

Think Critically

1. Yes; overall numbers of SIDS deaths dropped.
2. 70.7 percent; 68.8 percent; 65.9 percent; 67.5 percent; 73.7 percent; 67.6 percent; 77.1 percent; 66.3 percent; 83.4 percent; 82.9 percent
3. Although the numbers of SIDS deaths dropped, the percentage of deaths of babies of mothers who smoked remained high.

Infancy The first two years of life are known as **infancy.** Many changes take place during these years. An infant learns how to roll and crawl, grasp objects, and perform simple tasks. By the end of the first year, the infant likely is walking and might be uttering a few words. An enormous amount of mental development also occurs during these first two years.

In the first year, a baby typically grows about 25 cm in length and weighs three times more than when the baby was born. The child's growth slows during the second year; children grow at a rate of around 6 cm per year until the beginning of puberty.

Childhood and adolescence Childhood is the period of growth and development that extends from infancy to adolescence. The child's ability to reason and solve problems develops progressively during childhood. Puberty marks the beginning of adolescence, the period of growth between childhood and adulthood. Puberty usually begins between ages 8 to 13 in girls and ages 10 to 15 in boys.

In addition to the hormonal and sexual development that occur during this time, other physical changes also take place. An adolescent experiences a growth spurt—girls grow approximately 6–11 cm and boys grow approximately 7–13 cm—in one year. In girls, the hips become wider and the waist might become narrower. In boys, the shoulders usually become broader. At the end of adolescence, physical growth is complete, marking the beginning of **adulthood.** The transition between adolescence and adulthood can be hard to define because of physical, emotional, and behavioral changes.

S

DATA ANALYSIS LAB 1

Based on Real Data*

Form a Conclusion

Is SIDS linked to smoking? Researchers studied the annual SIDS rate per 1000 infants for mothers who smoked and mothers who did not smoke during pregnancy. In 1994, doctors began to recommend that infants sleep on their backs to reduce the risk of Sudden Infant Death Syndrome (SIDS). Use the table to determine how smoking and the Back to Sleep recommendation impacted SIDS.

Think Critically

1. **Analyze** whether sleeping position affects SIDS. Explain.
2. **Calculate** the percentage of SIDS for babies born to smoking mothers and to those of nonsmoking mothers each year.
3. **Conclude** how this data shows that some SIDS cases might be linked to smoking.

SIDS Deaths		
Year	Smoke Exposed	Unexposed
1989	3.21	1.33
1990	2.96	1.34
1991	3.32	1.72
1992	2.93	1.41
1993	3.28	1.17
1994	1.65	0.79
1995	2.19	0.65
1996	1.61	0.82
1997	3.21	0.64
1998	1.80	0.37

*Data obtained from: Anderson, M.E., et al. 2005. Sudden Infant Death Syndrome and prenatal maternal smoking: rising attributed risk in the Back to Sleep era. *BMC Medicine* 3: 4.

Demonstration

Understand Growth Charts Obtain growth charts from a local pediatrician or health clinic. Ask for the charts for boys ages 2–20 years and for girls ages 2–20 years. Demonstrate to students how to plot data points and interpret growth curves. Show students how these charts can help to predict a person's adult height, and where they are in height and weight compared to averages. A comparison of the chart for boys and chart for girls shows the difference in ages when periods of fast growth occur. Est. time: 10 min

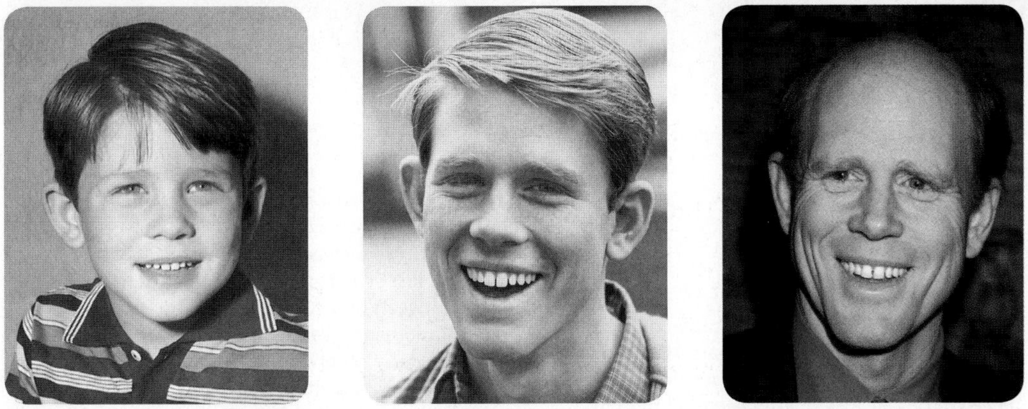

■ **Figure 15** These photos show actor and director Ron Howard in various stages of life.
Summarize *changes that occur in adulthood.*

Adulthood There are a number of theories on why people age. However, scientists do agree that the body goes through many changes as it ages, as shown in **Figure 15.** Physical changes perhaps are the most noticeable signs of aging, such as hair turning gray or white as pigment production declines. An individual might lose as much as two centimeters of height during the aging process because the discs between the vertebrae in the spine become flattened. Other changes include a decrease in muscle mass, a slowing of overall metabolism, and a decreased pumping ability of the heart. The skin loses its elasticity, and sensory perceptions might diminish somewhat. In women, the ability to have children ends with menopause (MEN uh pawz). Sperm production decreases in men.

Despite all of the potential challenges of aging, many people continue to be physically and mentally active as they grow older. Some older adults even begin new careers. Anna Mary Robertson Moses, known as Grandma Moses, became a famous artist when she was in her late 70s. C

C Critical Thinking

OL AL Hypothesize

ASK STUDENTS: ***What advantages might an older person have in developing a new career?*** Sample answer: perhaps lots of experience or lots of friends who may help develop the career.

Formative Assessment

Evaluation

SAY TO STUDENTS: ***Describe the events associated with each stage of birth.*** During dilation, the cervix widens. The amniotic sac may tear causing the loss of amniotic fluid. Uterine contractions will increase in intensity. In the expulsion stage, the baby exits the mother's body. The placenta and extraembryonic membranes are expelled in the placental stage.

Remediation Students struggling with the stages of birth should review the stages under the heading Birth in this section. Then, students can write each stage on an index card. Have students shuffle their cards and then put them back in order.

Section 3 Assessment

Section Summary

- Humans go through many changes throughout the stages of life.
- There are three stages of the birthing process.
- Levels of several hormones influence human growth.
- The first year of life is a time of learning motor skills and of rapid growth.
- Puberty causes many changes in the body, and changes continue to occur as an adult grows older.

Understand Main Ideas

1. MAIN Idea **Construct** a chart that illustrates major changes that occur during the stages of human growth and aging.
2. **Identify** two signs that tell a pregnant woman she is almost ready to give birth.
3. **Name** the events that occur during the three stages of birth.
4. **Describe** how the human growth hormone causes a person to grow.

Think Critically

5. **Hypothesize** Robert Wadlow, the tallest human being on record, was 272 cm tall and weighed 220 kg when he died at age 22. He was an average-sized newborn but developed a tumor in his anterior pituitary gland. Develop a hypothesis to explain how this tumor led to his great height.
6. **Infer** How do you think scientists determine which specific substances cause birth defects?

Section 3 Assessment

1. Charts should include the following information: infancy—a great deal of growth occurs, motor skills develop; adolescence—puberty begins, another period of rapid growth occurs; adulthood—muscle mass might decrease, the person might become shorter, metabolism slows, the senses might dull, menopause occurs in women.
2. Uterine contractions become stronger and more frequent; amniotic fluid leaks out.
3. Dilation: cervix opens, amniotic fluid leaves mother's body; expulsion: baby delivered; placental stage: placenta detaches and leaves mother's body
4. HGH increases protein production and stimulates cells to grow.
5. Possible answer: The tumor caused the anterior pituitary to make too much growth hormone.
6. Researchers backtrack cause and effect. When a baby is born with a specific birth defect, scientists gather information about the mother. Then they look for a common link found among mothers of babies born with condition in question.

Purpose
Students will describe the process by which growth hormone is made in the body; students will propose a solution for a person facing a height-challenging situation and the possibility of using HGH therapy.
C.1, F.1

Anticipatory Guide
ASK STUDENTS: ***What is a hormone?*** a chemical signal in the body excreted by a gland ***What do hormones do?*** Hormones trigger particular responses. ***Which hormones affect development?*** Answers will vary. Students may know that estrogen and testosterone cause changes during puberty.

Background
Genetic engineering has made HGH readily available for those who need it for health reasons, such as those with pituitary deficiencies and those with debilitating illnesses such as AIDS. HGH therapy can help AIDS patients build muscle, restore strength, and gain weight.

Biology & Society

HGH: The Tall and Short of It

Terry is a 157.5-cm tall high school senior. He has not grown in the last two years. His dad is 190.5 cm, and his other three brothers are 177.8 cm or taller. He doesn't seem to mind his height—or lack of it. His mom, though, wonders if he might have a disadvantage in sports because he is short. She suggests that he take growth hormones to become taller. She thinks that they might help him be more successful in sports—and in life. What should he do?

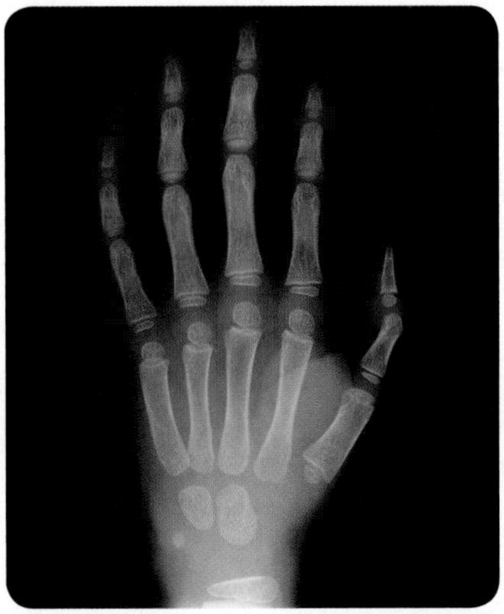

The oval bones are the growth plates, where bone growth occurs. If the growth plate is no longer visible, no more growth can occur.

What is human growth hormone? Human growth hormone (HGH) is a protein produced in the pituitary gland found in the brain. It is plentiful during the growth period of youth. Children with a lack of HGH are known as pituitary dwarfs and generally do not reach a height of over 135 cm.

What is HGH therapy? During adolescence, pituitary dwarfs can receive injections of synthetic HGH to increase their growth 10–12 cm during the first year. Less growth occurs during subsequent years. In 2003, the Food and Drug Administration approved HGH therapy for children who are otherwise healthy, but are predicted to reach adult heights of 160.0 cm or shorter for males and 149.9 cm or shorter for females. For these children, HGH therapy adds an average of 4–7 cm of height by adulthood. Using X-rays, a child's bone age—and therefore their growth potential—can be determined.

Therapy v. enhancement Sometimes HGH therapy can be used by physicians for individuals who are short and want to be taller or stronger athletes; however, this type of treatment is rare. There have been instances in which HGH drugs have been sold illegally and obtained by professional athletes to enhance their performance. These athletes were fined heavily or suspended because the drugs were in their systems.

HGH supplements sold in health food stores have less than one percent of HGH in them. Based on numerous scientific studies, they show no significant impact on human performance. Only HGH injections can improve growth and increase one's metabolism.

DEBATE in Biology

Debate Should HGH therapy be permissible when a teen is dissatisfied with his or her height for primarily cosmetic or athletic reasons? Consider Terry's situation, where he is feeling pressured to use HGH to become taller simply because the option exists. Conduct additional research about HGH and HGH therapy.

DEBATE in Biology

The students' debate will likely focus on whether the risk of using the hormone outweighs a student's desire or right to attain a certain height. If students need prompting, ask them if HGH therapy is comparable to any of the following scenarios: an actor getting face lift surgery, an athlete using performance enhancing steroids, or a diabetic taking insulin.

Discussion
After the debate, have the groups go online to evaluate various claims made by companies trying to sell HGH products. Have the students examine the science and pseudoscientific claims made in the ads. You might want to pre-screen a few specific Web sites to use for this activity.

WebQuest

BIOLAB

INTERNET: HOW ARE ULTRASOUND IMAGES USED TO TRACK FETAL DEVELOPMENT?

Background: **Ultrasound is a medical imaging technique that uses high-frequency sound waves and their echoes to produce an image of something inside the body. While two-dimensional images are the current standard, technology capable of producing three-dimensional fetal images and four-dimensional, or moving images, is now available.**

Question: *How are ultrasound images used to assess fetal characteristics and development?*

Materials
computer with Internet access
labeled ultrasound images showing embryos and fetuses at various developmental stages
ultrasound images showing embryos and fetuses at unknown stages of development

Procedure
1. Read and complete the lab safety form.
2. Visit the Internet to examine fetal development from the second trimester through week 40. Use this information to complete the development time line you started in **MiniLab 2.**
3. Study the ultrasound images of fetuses during identified stages of development provided by your teacher. Compare these to your time line, and identify as many features as possible. As you study the images, choose a body structure that you would like to examine further.
4. Study the ultrasound images provided by your teacher of fetuses at unknown stages of development. Use your time line and what you have learned to determine the approximate stage of fetal development. Look for clues based on the development of the system you choose.

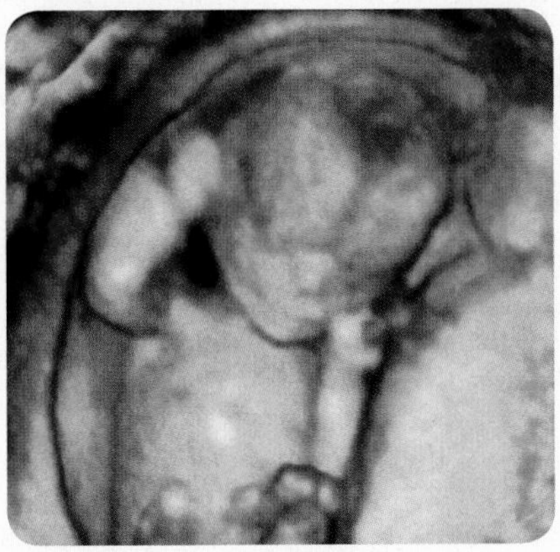

Analyze and Conclude
1. **Interpret Data** During which time period does the developing embryo or fetus change the most? Justify your answer.
2. **Analyze** What physical characteristics were most helpful in identifying the level of fetal development? Explain.
3. **Compare** two- and three-dimensional ultrasound images. Which are easiest to interpret?
4. **Think Critically** What advantages are provided by four-dimensional imaging?
5. **Error Analysis** How accurate were your estimates of fetal development? Explain how your estimates could have been improved.

WRITING in Biology

Poster Session Create a flowchart that illustrates the reproductive process. Begin with the creation of sex cells and end with a fetus at full term.

Analyze and Conclude
1. The first eight weeks are a time of rapid development: all internal and external structures are formed. The greatest changes in size occur during the second and third trimesters.
2. Answers will vary. first eight weeks—changes in shape and structure, development of organs and physical features; second and third trimesters—changes in size
3. Grainy, flat two-dimensional images are more difficult to interpret; three-dimensional images show features in relief and detail.
4. Four-dimensional ultrasounds provide several advantages: allow detection of bone and skeletal abnormalities, better correlation of fetal heart development and function, overall fetal well-being, and can aid precision biopsies as needed.
5. Answers will vary. Students might suggest having multiple images of the same feature from different perspectives using three- or four-dimensional images.

BIOLAB

Inquiry BioLab

For a lab worksheet, use your eTeacherEdition Online.

RUBRIC A rubric for evaluating BioLabs is found on your eTeacherEdition Online.

Est. Time 45 min

Content Background
Ultrasound imaging can provide information about a multitude of fetal characteristics, including size, position, sex, stage of development, skeletal and organ formation, and potential physical abnormalities. This is a noninvasive technique that utilizes high-frequency sound waves. Ultrasound machines that can produce three-dimensional images are now widely available. New technology also can produce video images of a fetus in real time (referred to as 4-D) showing a true image of the fetus as it moves and develops in the womb.

Safety Precautions Approve lab safety forms before work begins.

Teaching Strategies
- Pre-screen the Web sites that students will be using to make sure that the images and content are suitable.
- Provide labeled and unlabeled ultrasound images at various stages of embryonic and fetal development.
- Students will benefit from graphed information showing the relationship between fetal size and fetal development. Students should record this information in their time lines.

Alternative Teaching Demo
Make this a teacher-directed learning activity, omitting research.

Chapter 36

Study Guide

ConnectED

Students can use the following to review the chapter.

Review

Vocabulary eGames
Vocabulary eFlashcards
Vocabulary PuzzleMaker

Assessment

Online Quizzes
Online Test Practice
Standardized Test Practice

Use the *ExamView®* *Assessment Suite* CD-ROM to:

- create multiple versions of tests
- create modified tests with one mouse click
- edit existing questions and add your own questions
- build tests aligned with state standards using built-in state curriculum tags
- change English tests to Spanish with one mouse click
- track students' progress using the Teacher Management System

Chapter 36 Study Guide

THEME FOCUS Change Once fertilization occurs, human growth and development involve constant changes in structures and processes.

BIG Idea Human reproduction involves the joining together of sperm and egg.

Section 1 Reproductive Systems

seminiferous tubule (p. 1049)
epididymis (p. 1049)
vas deferens (p. 1049)
urethra (p. 1049)
semen (p. 1049)
puberty (p. 1049)
oocyte (p. 1050)
oviduct (p. 1050)
menstrual cycle (p. 1050)
polar body (p. 1051)

MAIN Idea Hormones regulate human reproductive systems, including the production of gametes.

- Levels of male and female hormones are regulated by negative feedback systems.
- The human male produces millions of sperm cells every day.
- The number of sex cells resulting from meiosis differs in males and females.
- The human female has a reproductive cycle called the menstrual cycle.
- The menstrual cycle has three phases: the flow phase, the follicular phase, and the luteal phase.

Section 2 Human Development Before Birth

morula (p. 1055)
blastocyst (p. 1055)
amniotic fluid (p. 1056)

MAIN Idea A human develops from a single fertilized cell into trillions of cells with specialized functions.

- Fertilization is the joining of egg and sperm.
- Four extraembryonic membranes are associated with a human embryo.
- The placenta regulates what substances can be exchanged between a fetus and its mother.
- Hormone regulation during pregnancy is different from hormone regulation during the menstrual cycle.
- Pregnancies are divided into three trimesters.
- Some medical conditions of a baby can be detected before it is born.

Section 3 Birth, Growth, and Aging

labor (p. 1062)
dilation (p. 1062)
expulsion stage (p. 1062)
placental stage (p.1063)
adolescence (p. 1063)
infancy (p. 1064)
adulthood (p. 1064)

MAIN Idea Developmental changes continue throughout the stages of life.

- Humans go through many changes throughout the stages of life.
- There are three stages of the birthing process.
- Levels of several hormones influence human growth.
- The first year of life is a time of learning motor skills and of rapid growth.
- Puberty causes many changes in the body, and changes continue to occur as an adult grows older.

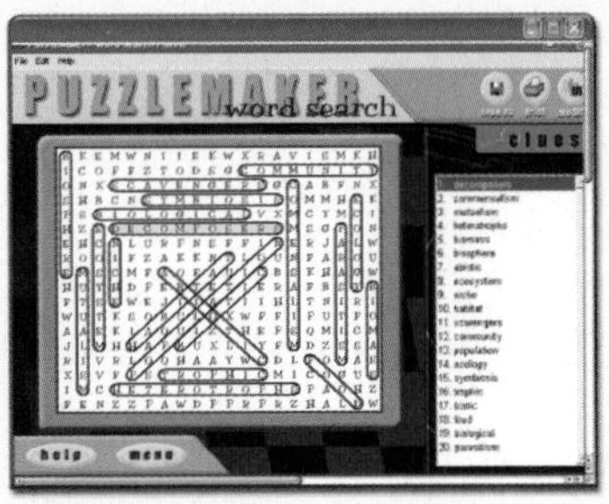

Review Vocabulary PuzzleMaker

For additional practice with vocabulary, have students access the Vocabulary PuzzleMaker online.

Review Vocabulary eGames

Section 1

Vocabulary Review

Explain the difference between the terms in each pair below, and then explain how the terms are related.

1. urethra, semen
2. oocyte, oviduct
3. menstrual cycle, polar body

Understand Main Ideas

4. What would happen if the testes were located inside the body cavity?
   A. Sperm would not be produced because it is too warm.
   B. Testosterone levels would increase because of the warm temperature.
   C. The seminal vesicles would no longer be needed.
   D. Hormones from the testes would have difficulty entering the bloodstream.

Use the diagram below to answer questions 5 and 6.

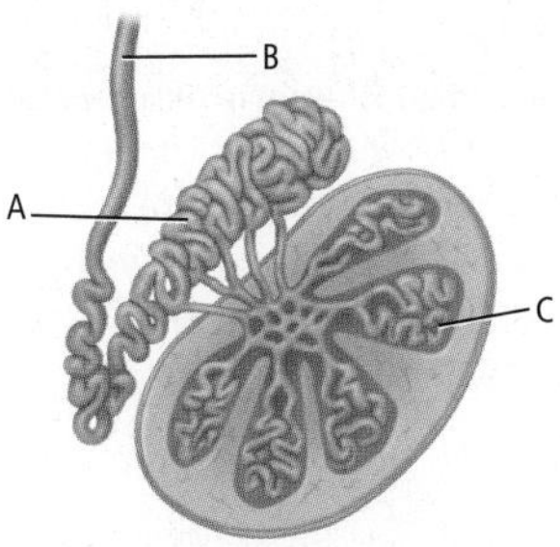

5. What occurs in the structure labeled C in the illustration?
   A. sperm cell storage and maturation
   B. sperm cell production
   C. secretion of sugar
   D. production of FSH

6. What is the function of the structure labeled A in the illustration?
   A. sperm cell storage and maturation
   B. sperm cell production
   C. secretion of sugar
   D. production of FSH

Constructed Response

7. **Short Answer** Why are the secretions of the male reproductive glands so important to sperm?

8. MAIN Idea Compare the actions of FSH and LH in the ovaries and testes.

9. **Short Answer** What advantages are there for the formation of one egg and polar bodies as compared to four eggs?

Think Critically

Use the diagram below to answer question 10.

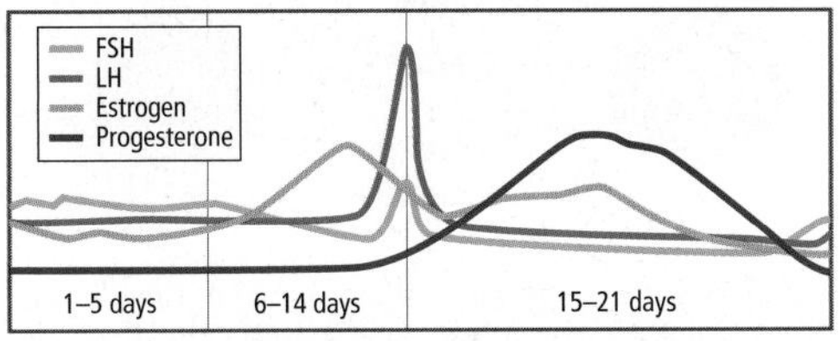

10. **Cause and Effect** Based on what you know about the hormonal control of a woman's reproductive cycle shown above, explain the hormonal basis of why a woman cannot get pregnant again while she is pregnant.

11. **Hypothesize** All of the reproductive hormones in a human male are present at birth. Develop a hypothesis to explain why the hormones have a greater influence on the body once puberty begins.

Section 2

Vocabulary Review

For questions 12–14, describe each of the following vocabulary terms.

12. morula
13. blastocyst
14. amniotic fluid

Understand Main Ideas

15. Where in the human female reproductive tract does fertilization usually occur?
   A. in the uterus
   B. in the vagina
   C. in the corpus luteum
   D. in an oviduct

Chapter 36

Assessment

Section 1

Vocabulary Review

1. The urethra is a tube and semen is a fluid. Semen travels through the urethra.
2. An oocyte is an immature egg, and an oviduct is a tube that leads to the uterus. The oviduct is the organ that permits the egg to get to the uterus.
3. The menstrual cycle includes all the events in the female body that prepare the body for pregnancy. The polar body is the smaller product of meiosis (the larger product goes on to become the egg). The polar body is formed during the menstrual cycle.

Understand Main Ideas

4. A
5. B
6. A

Constructed Response

7. The secretions provide a substance in which sperm can travel, an energy source, such as sugar, and an alkaline solution to neutralize acidic conditions.
8. FSH and LH influence oocyte development. Follicle cells then make estrogen and progesterone. LH surges result in ovulation. In males, FSH stimulates formation of sperm; and LH causes testosterone to be made.
9. Cytoplasm from the original cell is conserved in one cell rather than equally divided among four cells. This concentrates sugar and other substances into the egg, helping ensure survival of the ovum. One egg released each cycle helps prevent multiple births.

Think Critically

10. Progesterone and estrogen levels remain high, which inhibits production of LH and FSH (responsible for follicle development and ovulation).
11. Answers will vary, but students should suggest that some factor must cause a change in hormonal levels.

Section 2

Vocabulary Review

12. early stage in animal development, described as a solid ball of cells
13. early stage in human development, described as a hollow ball of cells
14. fluid inside the amniotic sac that cushions, protects, and insulates the embryo

Understand Main Ideas
15. D
16. C
17. B
18. C
19. B

Constructed Response
20. The endometrium is where the embryo will attach and implant; it is important to have a fresh tissue layer available.
21. Possible answers could include low sperm count, defective sperm, or a failure to ovulate due to hormonal imbalances.
22. The first trimester is when the body systems begin to form and function; damaging them early can adversely affect later stages of development.

Think Critically
23. In normal development, the cells of the inner cell mass divide but the mass stays connected. In the development of identical twins, the inner cell mass splits and each mass develops into an individual.
24. Possible solutions include administering hCG to the woman or increasing her levels of progesterone and estrogen (there are several ways to do this: shots, pills, etc.).

Section 3

Vocabulary Review
25. labor before birth, placental stage after birth: associated with birth
26. dilation before birth, expulsion is actual birth of baby: stages of birth
27. adolescence is the stage directly before adulthood: stages of life

Understand Main Ideas
28. C
29. A
30. B
31. C
32. A

16. Which of the following describes the proper sequence of development?
    A. zygote, blastocyst, morula
    B. morula, zygote, blastocyst
    C. zygote, morula, blastocyst
    D. morula, blastocyst, zygote

17. Which is produced by the placenta?
    A. human chorionic gonadotropin
    B. estrogen and progesterone
    C. oxytocin
    D. endometrial birth hormone

Use the diagram below to answer question 18.

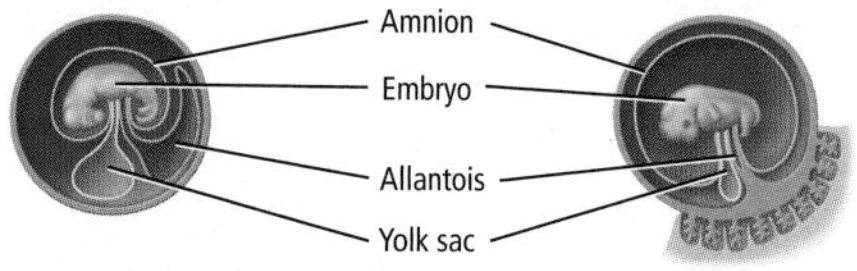

18. Why is the human yolk sac shown in the illustration smaller than that of the chick?
    A. The yolk in humans is converted into muscle.
    B. The yolk sac in chicks keeps the embryo warm.
    C. Developing humans get their nourishment from the placenta.
    D. The yolk sac serves no purpose for a developing human.

19. When can a pregnant woman first feel the movements of her fetus?
    A. in the first trimester
    B. in the second trimester
    C. in the third trimester
    D. in the last month only

Constructed Response

20. **Short Answer** Why is it important that the endometrium is refreshed each cycle?

21. **CAREERS IN BIOLOGY** Some couples consult with a reproductive endocrinologist because they are having difficulty conceiving a child. What are some possible biological reasons that could contribute to this difficulty?

22. MAIN Idea What do you think are the reasons that the greatest amount of harm to an embryo or fetus caused by alcohol or drugs occurs in the first trimester?

Think Critically

23. **Compare and contrast** the division of the inner cell mass during normal development and during the development of identical twins.

24. **Formulate a Model** A woman is carrying an embryo, but not enough hCG is getting into her system. Propose a possible treatment that might allow the embryo to be saved.

Section 3

Vocabulary Review

Explain the difference between the terms in each pair below. Then explain how the terms are related.

25. labor, placental stage
26. dilation, expulsion
27. adolescence, adulthood

Understand Main Ideas

28. At which measurement is the cervix fully dilated?
    A. 10 mm
    B. 2 cm
    C. 10 cm
    D. 20 cm

29. When a pregnant woman tells her doctor that "her water broke," what does she mean?
    A. The amniotic sac has torn.
    B. There is a lot of pressure on her bladder.
    C. The yolk sac has torn.
    D. The placenta is leaking.

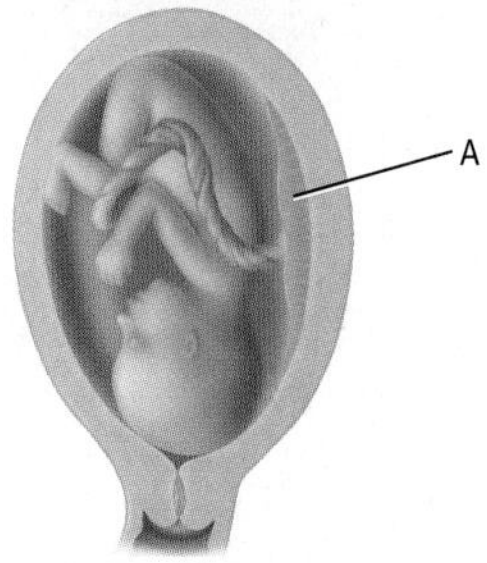

Use the diagram below to answer questions 30 and 31.

30. What is the name of the structure labeled A in the illustration?
    A. uterus
    B. placenta
    C. fetus
    D. cervix

31. During which stage of birth does structure A leave the female's body?
 A. first
 B. second
 C. third
 D. fourth

32. During which year of a person's life does the most rapid rate of growth occur?
 A. the first year of infancy
 B. the first year of puberty
 C. the second year of puberty
 D. the first year of adulthood

Constructed Response

33. Open Ended What biological reasons can you think of to explain why women go through menopause and stop producing eggs, while men can produce sperm all their lives?

34. MAIN Idea Compare puberty in females with puberty in males.

35. CAREERS IN BIOLOGY During rare occasions, a pediatrician examines a newborn baby who does not produce enough thyroxin. What are some possible results of this? Suggest a treatment for this condition.

Think Critically

Use the graph below to answer question 36.

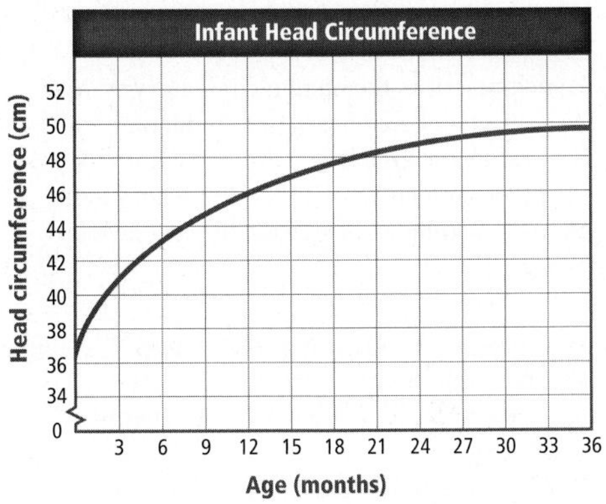

36. Change During which period shown on the graph is the rate of change in head circumference greatest?

Summative Assessment

37. BIG Idea Human reproduction involves the joining together of sperm and egg. What is the result of human reproduction? What is the ultimate goal of human reproduction? Construct your answer from a scientific point of view.

38. WRITING in Biology Prepare a pamphlet for pregnant women on health and lifestyle issues during pregnancy. Include a chart about the major events of fetal development.

DBQ Document-Based Questions

To reduce the chances of brain and spine birth defects, the U.S. Public Health Service recommended in 1992 that women of childbearing age increase folic acid in their diets. The U.S. Food and Drug Administration required all cereal products be enriched with folic acid beginning in January 1998 (an optional period began in March 1996).

Below is a table showing the rate per 100,000 births of anencephaly—incomplete head and brain development—from 1991–2002.

Year	Rate	Year	Rate
1991	18.38	1997	12.51
1992	12.79	1998	9.92
1993	13.50	1999	10.81
1994	10.97	2000	10.33
1995	11.71	2001	9.42
1996	11.96	2002	9.55

Data obtained from: Mathews, T.J. Trends in Spina Bifida and Anencephalus in the United States, 1991–2002. National Center for Health Statistics/Centers for Disease Control and Prevention/Department of Health and Human Services.

39. Construct a graph to represent these data and describe the relationship between the variables that you observe.

40. Explain the overall trend in the number of cases of anencephaly during this time period.

Constructed Response

33. Possible answer: Females carry the fetus; physical stress might be too great in older women. Eggs are about the same age as the woman. Older eggs could be more likely to produce offspring with birth defects or may be nonviable.

34. Both females and males develop into adults. Male shoulders and female hips become broader. Female breasts develop. Both develop other secondary sex characteristics, such as body hair. Females begin their menstrual cycles, males begin to produce sperm. Puberty usually begins earlier in females.

35. Thyroxin increases metabolic rate. Possible results: becoming overweight, slow growth, slow heart rate, mental retardation. Treatment is oral synthetic thyroid hormone.

Think Critically

36. birth to three months

Summative Assessment

37. result: development of a fetus, birth of an infant; goal: continuation of the species

WRITING in Biology

RUBRIC Use the modifiable rubric found on your eTeacher-Edition Online to assess writing assignments.

38. To create the pamphlet, students can use the general information in the chapter and additional information from health clinics, physicians, and organizations such as the March of Dimes.

DBQ Document-Based Questions

Mathews, T. J. Trends in Spina Bifida and Anencephalus in the United States, 1991–2002. National Center for Health Statistics/Centers for Disease Control and Prevention/Department of Health and Human Services.

39. Students should graph the rate on a bar or line graph.

40. The overall decrease in cases of anencephaly corresponds to increased intake of folic acid.

Standardized Test Practice

Multiple Choice

1. A 5. C 9. C
2. D 6. A
3. D 7. B
4. B 8. B

Short Answer

10. Parathyroid hormone causes the release of calcium and phosphorus from bone tissue so that bone mass is reduced and bones are weakened.
11. Answers may vary. The thyroid regulates calcium and phosphate levels in the blood through opposing effects of two hormones: parathyroid hormone and calcitonin. Without these hormones, the calcium levels in the blood would rise and fall depending on diet and whether bones were releasing or depositing calcium.
12. Pavlov rang a bell and gave dogs meat powder at the same time. After repeating this procedure, the dogs began to salivate as soon as Pavlov rang the bell because they had associated the sound with meat powder.
13. Emphysema causes damage to the alveoli, so the exchange of gases is affected. When the body is working hard, such as when a person is climbing stairs, more oxygen is needed. Because of the damage to the alveoli, the person suffers shortness of breath.
14. The axial skeleton includes the skull, the vertebral column, the ribs, and the sternum. The appendicular skeleton includes the bones of the arms, hands, legs, feet, shoulders, and hips. One reason the division is useful is because the axial skeleton protects organs such as the brain, heart, and lungs. The appendicular skeleton enables a person to walk, run, and do other actions.

Standardized Test Practice

Cumulative

Multiple Choice

1. Which is the role of arteries in the circulatory system?
   A. to carry blood away from the heart
   B. to carry blood back to the heart
   C. to provide individual cells with nutrients
   D. to prevent blood from flowing backward

Use the diagram below to answer question 2.

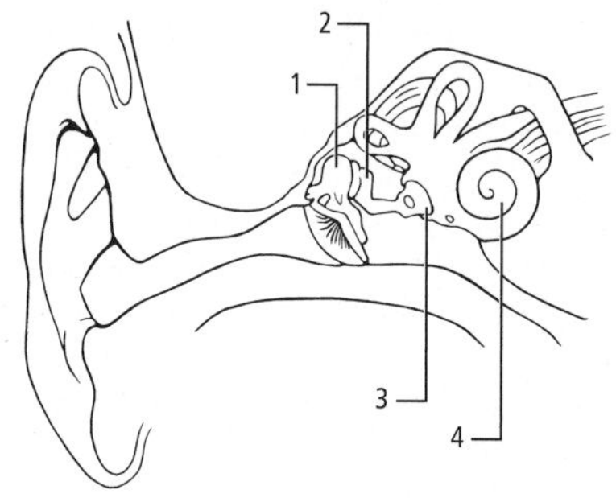

2. Which contains sensors for the auditory nerve?
   A. 1
   B. 2
   C. 3
   D. 4

3. What is the role of hormones in the body?
   A. They act as reaction catalysts.
   B. They control the breathing process.
   C. They help synthesize proteins.
   D. They regulate many body functions.

4. Which is the sequence of human development during the first week?
   A. egg → morula → blastocyst → zygote
   B. egg → zygote → morula → blastocyst
   C. morula → blastocyst → egg → zygote
   D. morula → egg → zygote → blastocyst

5. What is the function of the kidneys?
   A. to deplete carbon dioxide from the blood
   B. to eliminate undigested foods from the body
   C. to remove excess water and wastes from the blood
   D. to rid excess proteins from the blood

Use the diagram below to answer question 6.

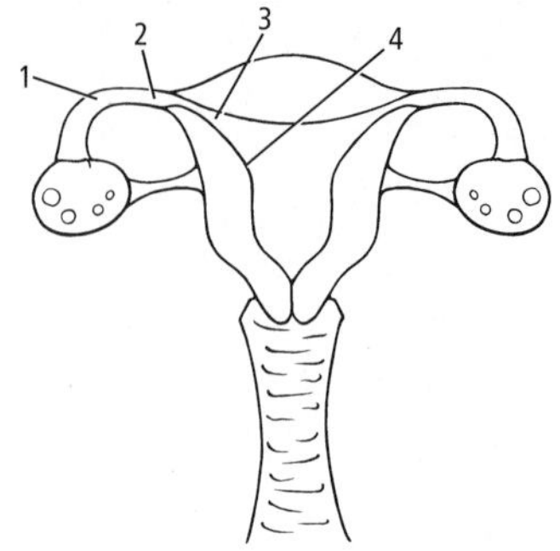

6. Where does fertilization take place?
   A. 1
   B. 2
   C. 3
   D. 4

7. When blood glucose levels are very high, what does the pancreas secrete?
   A. glycogen
   B. insulin
   C. insulin and glycogen
   D. neither insulin nor glycogen

8. Which describes the human circulatory system?
   A. four-chambered heart, one circulatory loop
   B. four-chambered heart, two circulatory loops
   C. two-chambered heart, one circulatory loop
   D. two-chambered heart, two circulatory loops

9. Which statement describes what happens during internal respiration?
   A. Carbon dioxide is used to derive energy from glucose.
   B. Gases are exchanged between the atmosphere and the blood.
   C. Gases are exchanged between the blood and the body's cells.
   D. Oxygen is used to derive energy from glucose.

Short Answer

Use the diagram below to answer questions 10 and 11.

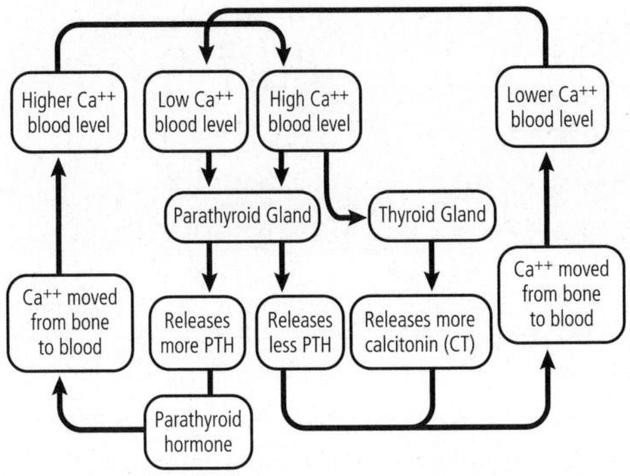

10. Assess how the parathyroid hormone affects bone tissue.

11. Evaluate how a person's blood calcium levels would be affected if his or her thyroid gland stopped working.

12. Analyze how Ivan Pavlov conditioned dogs to salivate when they heard a bell.

13. Assess how emphysema would cause difficulty for a person when climbing stairs.

14. Name and describe the two divisions of the human skeleton. Critique this division of the skeleton.

15. Think about the structure of the middle and inner ear. Infer why people might experience a temporary hearing loss after attending a loud concert.

16. Explain how the villi in the small intestine affect the rate of absorption.

Extended Response

17. A student did an experiment in a sunny room using unripe bananas. He found that bananas ripened faster in a paper bag than on top of a plate. Based on these results, what conclusion could the student make about the ripening of the bananas? Give one example of a way to improve the experiment.

18. Muscles in the legs tend to store large amounts of glycogen and fat. Muscles in the arms do not. When the muscles are used repeatedly, why do the muscles in the arm fatigue more quickly?

19. Different kinds of mammals have different digestive systems. Explain how the digestive systems of ruminant herbivores differ from other herbivores.

Essay Question

As elevation increases, air pressure decreases. At sea level, air pressure is about 760 mmHg. The percentage of oxygen in the atmosphere is about 21 percent. At 3200 m in elevation, the air pressure is 30 percent less than that at sea level; however, the percentage of oxygen is the same. The difference in pressure occurs because the molecules of gas are spread farther apart. As altitude continues to increase, the pressure continues to decrease. Mountain climbers face the problems of decreased pressure when they climb a mountain. When climbers go to the summit of the highest mountains, they carry oxygen tanks with them to help them breathe.

Using the information in the paragraph above, answer the following question in essay format.

20. Evaluate why breathing oxygen would enable a mountain climber to reach a higher altitude.

NEED EXTRA HELP?

If You Missed Question . . .	1	2	3	4	5	6	7	8	9	10	11	12	13	14	15	16	17	18	19	20
Review Section . . .	34.1	33.3	35.1	36.2	34.3	36.2	35.3	34.3	34.2	35.3	35.3	31.1	34.2	32.2	33.3	35.1	1.3	32.3	30.2	34.2

15. The small parts of the middle ear are very sensitive. They could be damaged if the vibrations are too great, as they could be at a loud concert. Also, big vibrations from loud sounds could damage the small hairs in the cochlea.

16. The villi increase the surface area of the small intestine so absorption occurs more quickly.

Extended Response

17. The conclusion is that bananas ripen faster in a closed container than in the open air. One possible way to improve the experiment is to put some unripened bananas in an opaque bag and some in a transparent bag in a sunny room. The rate of ripening of the two groups of bananas could be compared for the effect of light on the process. Other answers are possible.

18. The leg muscles have a large supply of energy that can be quickly broken down as needed. The arm muscles lack this source of energy so they fatigue quicker than leg muscles.

19. Ruminant herbivores, unlike other herbivores, have several stomachs. They bring partially digested food (cud) back to their mouths to chew and break it down further. This allows them to break down even complex compounds in vegetation so they can get more nutrients from the food.

Essay Question

20. At high altitude, the air is very thin and air pressure is low. Although the oxygen concentration in the air is the same as at lower elevations, there are not enough oxygen molecules in the air to supply the body's needs. Breathing oxygen enables the blood cells to pick up needed oxygen and carry it throughout the body to allow the body to function properly.

Chapter 37 Organizer:
The Immune System

LabManager™
Customize any lab with the LabManager™ CD-ROM.

Essential Questions	National Science Standards	Materials and Planning: Estimated times include cleanup and disposal, but do not include teacher prep time. For cleanup and disposal guidelines, see page 39T.	Est. Time (min)
Section 1 1. What are Koch's postulates? 2. How are diseases transmitted and how do reservoirs play a role in disease dispersal? 3. What are the symptoms and treatment of infectious diseases? 4. What are disease patterns?	UCP.1, UCP.2, UCP.5; A.1, A.2; C.1, C.4; F.1, F.5; G.1–3	**Launch Lab,** p. 1074: poster board	25
		Activity, p. 1076: chalk	15
		MiniLab 1, p. 1082: dollar bill, photos of a rusted nail and a sample of pond water, plastic container filled with soapy water, science textbook, new dish cloth, a petition or sign-up sheet with 50 names, used cutting board, new plastic wrap, soil sample	20
		Demonstration, p. 1082: raw meat juice, sterile water, nutrient agar plate, masking tape	10
Section 2 1. What are the similarities and differences between nonspecific and specific immunity? 2. What is the structure and function of the lymphatic system? 3. What is the importance of B cells and T cells? 4. What are the differences between passive and active immunity?	UCP.1–3, UCP.5; A.1, A.2; C.1, C.4; E.2, F.1, F.5, F.6; G.1–3	**Demonstration,** p. 1084: sterile swab or tape, nutrient agar plate, masking tape	10
		Activity, p. 1089: a young child's puzzle with large pieces	5
Section 3 1. What are the five categories of noninfectious diseases? 2. What is the role of allergens in allergies? 3. What is the difference between allergies and anaphylactic shock?	UCP.1, UCP.2, UCP.5; A.1, A.2; C.1, C.2, C.5; F.1, G.1–3	**MiniLab 2,** p. 1093: compound microscope, glass slides of normal liver and liver with cancer	10
		Demonstration, p. 1094: photos of common allergens	10
		BioLab, p. 1097: Pasteur pipets, numbered test tubes of water, NaOH, test tube racks, small paper cups, pencil and paper, testing indicator	45

Suggested Time for Each Lesson

Class	Chapter Opener	Section 1	Section 2	Section 3	Assessment
Basic	45 min	90 min	45 min	45 min	45 min
General	25 min	90 min	65 min	90 min	45 min
Honors	5 min	40 min	90 min	45 min	45 min

ConnectED

connectED.mcgraw-hill.com

Access interactive learning opportunities and teaching resources using these icons located throughout your StudentWorks™ Plus Online and eTeacherEdition Online.

Chapter 37 Section Resources	Additional Chapter 37 Resources	Technology
FAST FILE Unit 9 Resources: Launch Lab Worksheet* MiniLab Worksheet* Study Guide (English/Spanish)* Section Quick Check **Reading Essentials 37.1** **Science Notebook 37.1*** **FAST FILE Unit 9 Resources:** Study Guide (English/Spanish)* Section Quick Check **Reading Essentials 37.2** **Science Notebook 37.2*** **FAST FILE Unit 9 Resources:** MiniLab Worksheet* Study Guide (English/Spanish)* Section Quick Check **Reading Essentials 37.3** **Science Notebook 37.3***	**FAST FILE Unit 9 Resources:** Chapter Diagnostic Test Concept Mapping* Real-World Biology Enrichment Chapter Tests A, B, and C **Transparencies:** Bellringer Transparencies* Biology Concepts Transparencies* **Lab Resources:** Laboratory Manual* Probeware Lab Manual* Forensics Lab Manual* Pre-AP Lab Manual* Open Inquiry in Biology* Guided Inquiry in Biology*	**Teaching Tools:** eTeacherEdition Online Classroom Presentation Toolkit CD-ROM* LabManager™ CD-ROM* Video Lab DVD* Virtual Lab CD-ROM* What's BIOLOGY Got To Do With It? StudentWorks™ Plus Online* **Chapter Assessment Tools:** Classroom Presentation Toolkit CD-ROM* *ExamView® Assessment Suite* CD-ROM **Web-Based Resources:** • StudentWorks™ Plus Online • eTeacherEdition Online • Animations* • The Interactive Time Line* • Interactive Tables* • Online Quizzes • Online Test Practice • Standardized Test Practice • Virtual Labs* • Multilingual eGlossary* • Vocabulary eGames* • Vocabulary eFlashcards • WebQuests • Personal Tutors

While all resources listed are appropriate for English learners, the * indicates resources with a strong visual or hands-on component for EL.

Teaching strategies and activities have been coded for differentiated instruction.

AL Activities for students working above grade level	**OL** Activities for students working on grade level	**BL** Activities for students working below grade level	**EL** Activities for English learners (also ELL)	**COOP LEARN** Activities designed for small cooperative group work

CHAPTER 37

Launch Lab
How do you track a cold?

Inquiry Launch Lab

For a lab worksheet, use your eTeacherEdition Online.

RUBRIC A rubric for evaluating Launch Labs is found on your eTeacherEdition Online.

Est. Time 25 min

Safety Precautions Caution students to follow proper hygiene procedures when interviewing classmates who have cold symptoms.

Teaching Strategies

- Caution students not to use any names in this exercise. Have them list students as Student A, Student B, etc.
- To save class time, consider having a small group of students who are not exhibiting infectious disease symptoms interview a student who has recently had a cold or other disease. Groups can rotate from person to person after a short interview period.

Procedure

1. Read and complete the lab safety form.
2. Create a series of questions you can ask your classmates about the last time they had a cold: their symptoms, other family members and friends who had the same symptoms, and the hygiene precautions they used to avoid illnesses.
3. Interview your classmates using your list.
4. Design a concept map that organizes the data you have collected to trace the paths the colds in your classmates took as they passed from person to person.

Analysis

1. **Describe** how your concept map distinguishes between different cold symptoms present in your classmates. Answers will vary, but students may use different-colored circles or different shapes on their maps to distinguish between the different colds present.
2. **Infer** what paths the different colds might have taken as they passed from person to person among your classmates and their friends and family. Answers will vary, but may include sharing drinking glasses or breathing in droplets from the sneeze of an infected person.

CHAPTER 37
The Immune System

ConnectED

Your one-stop online resource
connectED.mcgraw-hill.com

- Video
- Audio
- Review
- Inquiry
- WebQuest
- Assessment
- Concepts in Motion
- Multilingual eGlossary

Launch Lab
How do you track a cold?

Colds and many other illnesses are caused by pathogens that can pass from person to person. In this lab, you will trace the path of a cold.

For a lab worksheet, use your StudentWorks™ Plus Online.

Inquiry Launch Lab

FOLDABLES®

Make a layered-look book using the titles shown. Use it to organize your notes on immunity.

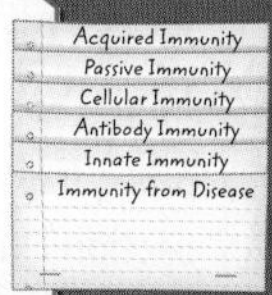

THEME FOCUS Scientific Inquiry
Scientists learn how the immune system responds to disease through research and experimentation.

BIG Idea The immune system attempts to protect the body from contracting an infection through pathogens.

Section 1 • Infectious Diseases
Section 2 • The Immune System
Section 3 • Noninfectious Disorders

THEMES

Scientific Inquiry Continuing scientific research has led to new treatments and medicines.

Diversity The variety of pathogens has caused the necessity of many different treatments.

Energy The immune system uses a large amount of energy when fighting disease.

Homeostasis The human body uses nonspecific and specific immunities to maintain a healthy balance in the body.

Change As bacteria evolve, the need for new and stronger antibiotics becomes a concern.

Introduce the Chapter

Disease and the Body

Review the functions of macrophages.

SAY TO STUDENTS: ***Using your previous knowledge, infer the function of the tonsils, which are shown in the opening photo.*** Tonsils are in the back of the throat. They help protect the openings of the respiratory and digestive systems against pathogens.

BIG Idea

Think-Pair-Share Have students in pairs choose one of the themes of the chapter.

SAY TO STUDENTS: ***Hypothesize how this theme applies to the immune system.*** After students discuss their ideas in pairs, call on groups to share with the class how the themes relate to the immune system. Answers will vary, but might include that scientific inquiry was used to discover what we know about the immune system and diseases. It is being used to discover more about the immune system and diseases such as avian flu, AIDS, Ebola, and West Nile Virus. The function of the immune system is to maintain homeostasis of the body, protecting the body from disease. Diversity is shown by the number of disease-producing organisms as well as the various ways the body protects against disease.

Section 1

MAIN Idea

EL BL OL AL

Disease Transmission Show a picture of, or ask students to describe, people in a restaurant or people at a picnic.

ASK STUDENTS: ***How might disease organisms be spread to a person in the setting shown?*** Possible answers include: from person to person, from food to people, from items in the environment such as cooking utensils to people, and from insects to people.

Develop Concepts

BL OL AL

Activate Prior Knowledge

ASK STUDENTS: ***Which organisms have we studied that cause diseases?*** Bacteria, fungi, protozoans, and worms (tapeworms, flukes, and roundworms) all cause disease. Viruses are not organisms, but they do cause diseases.

D Develop Concepts

BL OL

Clarify a Misconception

ASK STUDENTS: ***How do you catch a cold?*** Students might think that people acquire colds from being cold (for example, after getting wet in the rain). Although being cold might lower the resistance of the immune system, colds are caused by contagious strains of viruses.

AL ***How is this misconception perpetuated?*** Possible answer: Cold and flu season typically arrives during the fall and winter months, so people may associate being cold with cold and flu viruses.

Reading Check Koch was able to isolate the bacteria in infected cattle.

Section 1

Reading Preview

Essential Questions

- What are Koch's postulates?
- How are diseases transmitted and how do reservoirs play a role in disease dispersal?
- What are the symptoms and treatment of infectious diseases?
- What are disease patterns?

Review Vocabulary

protozoan: unicellular, heterotrophic, animal-like protist

New Vocabulary

infectious disease
pathogen
Koch's postulates
reservoir
endemic disease
epidemic
pandemic
antibiotic

g Multilingual eGlossary

Figure 1 These rodlike bacteria cause the disease anthrax.

Color-Enhanced SEM Magnification: 50×

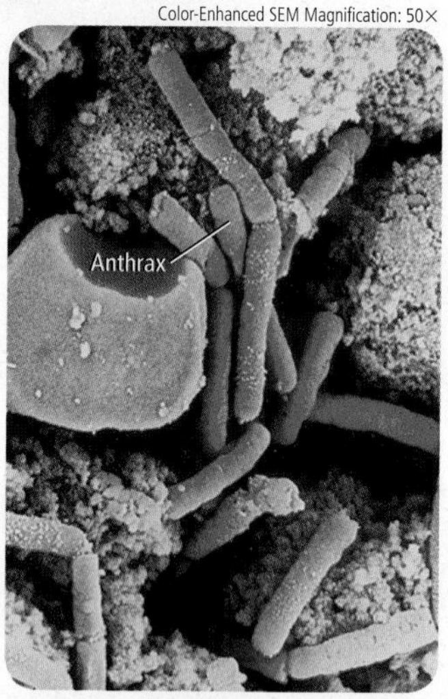

Infectious Diseases

MAIN Idea **Pathogens are dispersed by people, other animals, and objects.**

Real-World Reading Link Have you ever gotten something sticky on your hands? As you touched other objects, they too became sticky. In a similar manner, viruses transfer to objects that you touch. When these objects are touched by someone else, the virus can be picked up by another person.

Pathogens Cause Infectious Disease

D What do a cold and athlete's foot have in common? They are both examples of an infectious disease. An **infectious disease** is a disease that is caused by a pathogen passed from one organism to another, disrupting homeostasis in the organism's body. Agents called **pathogens** are the cause of infectious diseases. Some but not all types of bacteria, viruses, protozoans, fungi, and parasites are pathogens.

Many types of these organisms are present in the world around us without causing infectious diseases. Your body benefits from organisms, such as certain types of bacteria and protozoans, that normally live in your intestinal and reproductive tracts. Other bacteria live on your skin, especially in the shafts of your hair follicles. These organisms keep pathogens from thriving and multiplying on your body.

Germ Theory and Koch's Experiments

Before the invention of the microscope, people thought "something" passed from a sick person to a well person to cause an illness. Then, scientists discovered microorganisms and Louis Pasteur demonstrated that microorganisms from the air are able to grow in nutrient solutions. With the knowledge gained from these and other discoveries, doctors and scientists began to develop the germ theory. The germ theory states that some microorganisms are pathogens. However, scientists were not able to clearly demonstrate this theory until Robert Koch developed his postulates.

Identification of the first disease pathogen In the late 1800s, Robert Koch, a German physician, was studying anthrax (AN thraks)—a deadly disease that affects cattle and sheep and can also affect people. Koch isolated bacteria, like those in **Figure 1,** from the blood of cattle that had died from anthrax. After growing the bacteria in the laboratory, Koch injected the bacteria into healthy cattle. These animals developed the disease anthrax. He then isolated bacteria from the blood of newly infected cattle and grew the bacteria in the laboratory. The characteristics of the two sets of cultures were identical, indicating that the same type of bacteria caused the illness in both sets of cattle. Thus, Koch demonstrated that the bacteria he originally isolated were the cause of anthrax.

Reading Check **Explain** how Koch proved the germ theory correct.

Activity

Disease Transmission Have students role play how disease spreads. Use chalk to cover several students' hands. Then have those students shake hands with several more students (some of the chalk will transfer to the other students' hands). Then have the second group of students shake hands with several more students. This demonstrates how pathogens spread through direct contact. Est. time: 15 min

"Develop a passion for learning. If you do, you will never cease to grow."

—Anthony J. D'Angelo

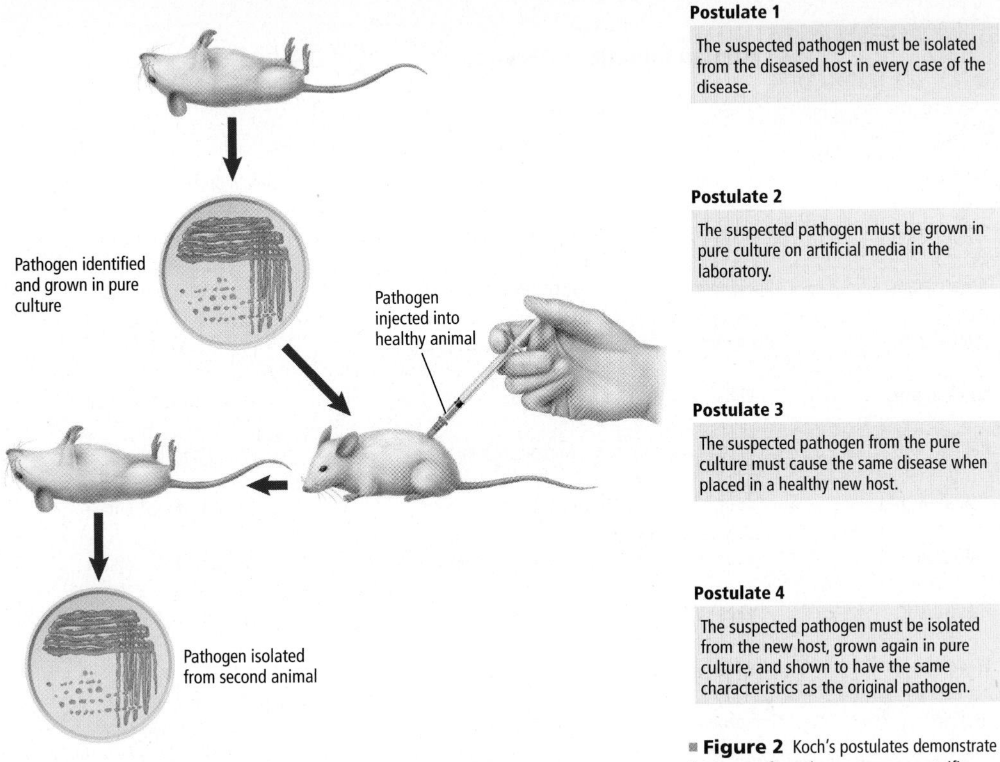

■ **Figure 2** Koch's postulates demonstrate that a specific pathogen causes a specific disease.
Infer ***what Koch demonstrated when he isolated the same bacteria from the cattle the second time.***

S

Koch's postulates Koch established and published experimental steps known as **Koch's postulates,** which are rules for demonstrating that an organism causes a disease. These steps are followed today to identify a specific pathogen as the agent of a specific disease. Follow the steps in **Figure 2** as you read each of the four postulates.

Postulate 1: The suspected pathogen must be isolated from the diseased host in every case of the disease.

Postulate 2: The suspected pathogen must be grown in pure culture on artificial media in the laboratory. A pure culture is a culture that contains no other types of microorganisms—only the suspected pathogen.

Postulate 3: The suspected pathogen from the pure culture must cause the disease when placed in a healthy new host.

Postulate 4: The suspected pathogen must be isolated from the new host, grown again in pure culture, and shown to have the same characteristics as the original pathogen.

Some exceptions to Koch's postulates do exist. Some pathogens, such as the pathogen that is thought to cause syphilis (SIH fuh lus), cannot be grown in pure culture on artificial media. Artificial media are the nutrients that the bacteria need to survive and reproduce. Pathogens are grown on this media in the laboratory. Also, in the case of viruses, cultured cells are needed because viruses cannot be grown on artificial media.

Study Tip

Purposeful Reading Before reading, predict how the information you learn about diseases can be applied to your daily life. Scan the chapter and focus on the boldfaced headings to get an idea about what you will study. Record your ideas. Refer to the list as you study the chapter.

■ **Caption Question Fig. 2** The same bacteria caused the same disease in the second host, demonstrating that the bacteria was the cause of the disease.

S Skill Practice

BL OL AL Visual Literacy Use Figure 2 to help students apply Koch's postulates to a new scenario. Have students imagine that a suspected disease-causing organism was brought to Earth by a returning spacecraft. Have students write one question for each of the four postulates in the figure. The question should address how Koch's postulates could be used to see if the organism is a pathogen. Sample answer: 1) Can the organism be isolated from the diseased host in every case of the disease? 2) Can the suspected pathogen be grown in pure culture in the lab? 3) Does the suspected pathogen grown in pure culture cause disease when placed in healthy hosts? 4) Does the suspected pathogen isolated from new hosts have the same characteristics as the original suspected pathogen?

Critical Thinking

BL OL AL Predict Anthrax is caused by *Bacillus anthracis.* Anthrax is a disease that usually affects herbivores. Humans are an accidental host. When conditions for reproduction are unfavorable, *Bacillus anthracis* can form very tough spores. These spores can survive for many years under tough conditions in soil. When conditions improve or a host appears, the spores can return to a developing state of bacteria, grow, and reproduce.
ASK STUDENTS: ***How might spore formation make anthrax a difficult problem for cattle ranchers?*** Possible answer: Because the spores are very tough, they are difficult to destroy. They survive in the soil for many years. Even after an outbreak is over, pathogens are still in the environment and can infect cattle.

Concepts in Motion

Interactive Table

S Skill Practice

BL OL Visual Literacy

Have students read the information in Table 1.

SAY TO STUDENTS: ***Identify four kinds of pathogens.*** bacteria, viruses, protozoa, and fungi

ASK STUDENTS: ***What is the difference between a pathogen and a disease?*** Sample answer: A pathogen is a virus or organism that can cause disease. The disease is the result of the pathogen living, growing, or replicating in or on another organism.

R Reading Strategy

BL OL AL

Metacognitive Strategies

As students read this page, ask them to think about the way they read and learn information.

ASK STUDENTS: ***Do you understand the text better when visuals are involved? Do you read the paragraphs first or try to understand the figure first? Do you reread paragraphs to help you grasp key points?*** Discuss different strategies as a class.

Table 1 Human Infectious Diseases Concepts in Motion Interactive Table

Disease	Cause	Affected Organ System	How Disease is Spread
Tetanus	Bacterium	Nervous system	Soil in deep puncture wound
Strep throat	Bacterium	Respiratory system	Droplets/direct contact
Tuberculosis	Bacterium	Respiratory system	Droplets
Lyme disease	Bacterium	Skeletal and nervous system	Vector (tick)
Chicken pox	Virus	Skin	Droplets/direct contact
Rabies	Virus	Nervous system	Animal bite
Common cold	Virus	Respiratory system	Droplets/direct contact
Influenza	Virus	Respiratory system	Droplets/direct contact
Hepatitis B	Virus	Liver	Direct contact with exchange of body fluids
West Nile	Virus	Nervous system	Vector (mosquito)
Giardia	Protozoan	Digestive tract	Contaminated water
Malaria	Protozoan	Blood and liver	Vector (mosquito)
Athlete's foot	Fungus	Skin	Direct contact or contaminated objects

S

R

Spread of Disease

Of the large number of microorganisms that coexist with humans, only a few cause disease. The pathogens vary as much as the diseases themselves. Some might cause mild diseases, such as the common cold. Others cause serious diseases, such as meningitis (men in JI tus), an infection of the coverings of the brain and spinal cord. **Table 1** lists some of the human infectious diseases you might know.

For a pathogen to spread, it must have both a reservoir and a way to spread. A disease **reservoir** is a source of the pathogen in the environment. Reservoirs might be animals, people, or inanimate objects, such as soil.

Human reservoirs Humans are the main reservoir for pathogens that affect humans. They might pass the pathogen directly or indirectly to other humans. Many pathogens might be passed on to other hosts before the person even knows he or she has the disease. An individual that is symptom-free but capable of passing the pathogen is called a carrier. Pathogens that cause colds, influenza (commonly referred to as the flu), and sexually transmitted diseases, such as human immunodeficiency (ih MYEWN noh dih fih shun see) virus (HIV), can be passed on without the person knowing he or she is infected.

VOCABULARY

SCIENCE USAGE V. COMMON USAGE

Carrier

Science usage: person who spreads germs while remaining well

Typhoid fever was spread by a carrier known as "Typhoid Mary."

Common usage: a person or corporation in the transportation business

Freight is shipped by carriers.

Content Background

Integrate History The bubonic plague caused by *Yersinia pestis* has been a devastating disease throughout history. The word *plague* now refers to any devastating disease or infestation. The bubonic plague spread through Egypt and Africa in A.D. 541. Another pandemic began in the 1320s and killed more than 25 million people in Europe during a five-year period. Sporadic cases of bubonic plague still occur today. The United States has an average of ten reported cases each year, primarily spread to humans by fleas from wild animals such as rats.

Animal reservoirs Other animals also are reservoirs of pathogens that can be passed to humans. Influenza and rabies are examples of human diseases listed in **Table 1** that are caused by pathogens passed to humans from other animals. Influenza can infect pigs and various types of birds. Rabies is found in domestic dogs and many wild animals, such as bats, foxes, skunks, and raccoons.

Other reservoirs Some bacteria normally found in the soil, such as tetanus bacteria, can cause disease in humans. The tetanus bacteria can cause a serious infection if it contaminates a deep wound in the body. Contamination of wounds by bacteria was a major cause of death during wars before the development of antibiotics and vaccinations.

Contaminated water or food is another reservoir of pathogens for human disease. One of the main purposes of sewage treatment plants is the safe disposal of human feces, which prevents contamination of the water supply by pathogens. Contaminated water used in growing or preparing food can transfer pathogens. Food also can become contaminated through contact with humans or insects such as flies.

Transmission of pathogens Pathogens mainly are transmitted to humans in four ways: direct contact, indirectly through the air, indirectly through touching contaminated objects, or by organisms called vectors that carry pathogens. **Figure 3** illustrates some of the ways pathogens can be transmitted to humans.

Direct Contact Direct contact with other humans is one of the major modes of transmission of pathogens. Diseases such as colds, infectious mononucleosis (mah noh new klee OH sus)(commonly referred to as mono, or the "kissing disease"), herpes (HUR peez), and sexually transmitted diseases are caused by pathogens passed through direct contact.

CAREERS IN BIOLOGY

Epidemiologist An epidemiologist studies disease patterns to help prevent and control the spread of diseases. An epidemiologist might track the spread of a new strain of influenza and advise the public on safety concerns.

S

■ **Figure 3** Diseases can be transmitted to humans in various ways.
Identify *ways to prevent contracting diseases if contact cannot be avoided.*

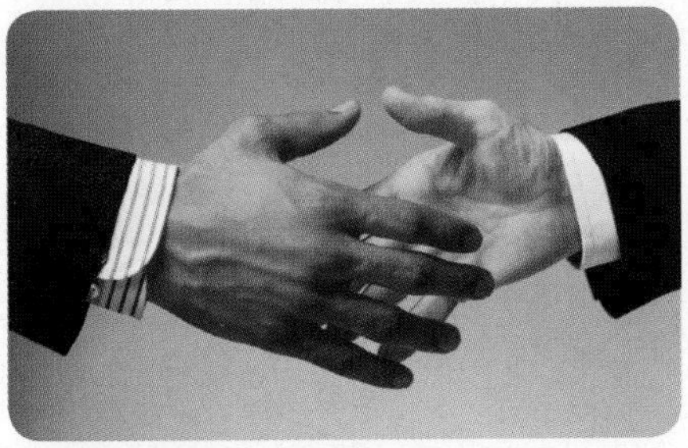

Direct contact

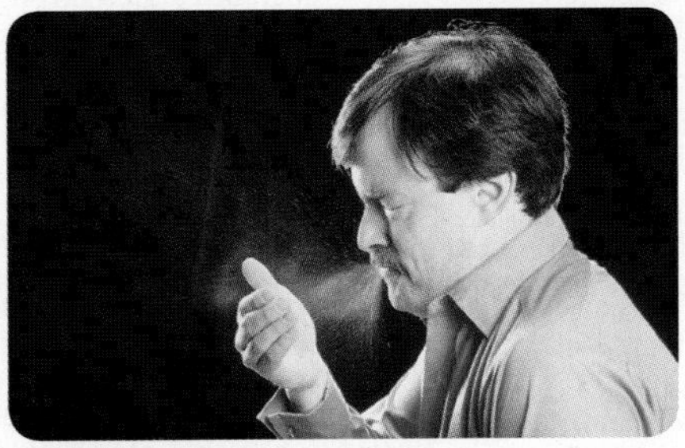

Indirect contact through air

Indirect contact by objects

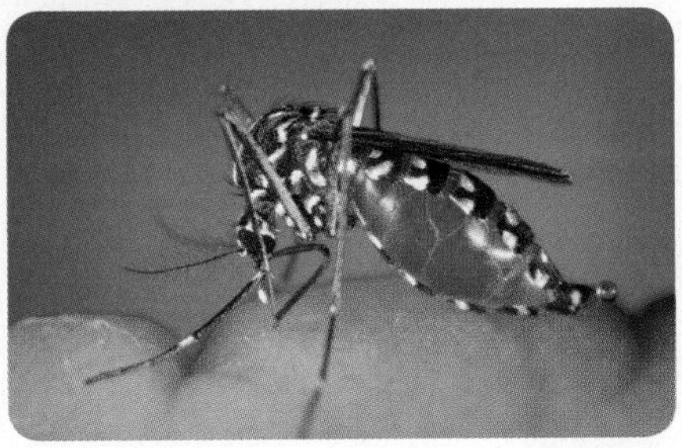

Vectors

Develop Concepts

Integrate Health Syphilis is a complicated bacterial disease of the reproductive tract. The only natural hosts of syphilis bacteria are humans. Syphilis infection occurs worldwide and is treated with antibiotics, most often penicillin. A person treated for syphilis must be reported to the CDC, and health departments will contact and treat any infected sexual partners.

S Skill Practice

BL OL AL Illustrate Have students look at Figure 3. Then have them draw other examples of each type of transmission. Possible examples: direct contact: kissing, holding hands; indirectly through touching contaminated objects: drinking from cup that someone else has used, using someone else's phone; indirectly through the air: contaminated ventilation systems; by organisms: mammals with rabies, cats transferring ringworm

GOING GREEN Colds and flu are often passed around a classroom. People often use tissues for their cold symptoms, which can create a lot of landfill waste. Brainstorm greener alternatives that are still sanitary and avoid spreading germs. Implement the alternatives in your classroom.

Content Background

Teacher FYI The expression "typhoid Mary" comes from Mary Mallon, a seemingly healthy woman who was a carrier of typhoid fever caused by the bacteria *Salmonella typhi.* This bacteria is passed from human to human by a fecal-oral route. Contaminated water often is a source of infection. Once New York health officials identified that she was spreading disease in the early 1900s, she was forced to live in seclusion on a small island near the Bronx, New York.

■ **Caption Question Fig. 3** Answers may vary but may include washing hands, covering mouth when coughing or sneezing, cleaning/sterilizing objects, cooking food, not drinking contaminated water, caring for wounds, and wearing insecticide when around insects.

C Critical Thinking

AL COOP LEARN Hypothesize

Group students into threes.

SAY TO STUDENTS: ***Research an infectious disease. Draw a cycle of transmission and hypothesize various ways to interrupt the disease transmission cycle. Then present your cycle to the class, pointing out ways of interrupting the disease cycle.*** Drawings should show disease transmission cycles and offer concrete ways of interrupting the cycle to stem the spread of the disease. For example, West Nile virus can be controlled, in part, by controlling the mosquitoes that serve as the vector for that virus.

W Writing Support

BL OL AL Technical Writing

Help students understand that, in many cases, host or vector organisms transfer other organisms. For example, malaria is caused by a protist. When a mosquito takes blood from a person infected with the protist that causes malaria and bites a second person, that second person becomes infected with the protist. The mosquito carried the protist, but the protist causes the disease.

Have students create an informative pamphlet about various ways that diseases can be transmitted from one organism to another. Students' pamphlets should show both the carriers of the disease and the organisms that cause the disease.

D Develop Concepts

OL Community Connection

Ask representatives from the school cafeteria, a restaurant, hospital, or health department to speak to the class about how their facility tries to prevent the spread of disease.

C **Indirect contact** Some pathogens can be passed through the air. When a person with an infectious disease sneezes or coughs, pathogens can be passed along with the tiny mucus droplets. These droplets then can spread pathogens to another person or to an object.

Many organisms can survive on objects handled by humans. Cleansing of dishes, utensils, and countertops with detergents as well as careful hand-washing help prevent the spread of diseases that are passed in this manner. As a result, there are various food rules that restaurants must abide by that are based on preventing the spread of disease.

Vectors Certain diseases can be transmitted by vectors. The most common vectors are arthropods, which include biting insects such as mosquitoes and ticks. Recall from **Table 1** that Lyme disease, malaria, and West Nile virus are diseases that are passed to humans by vectors. The West Nile virus, which is currently spreading across the United States, is transmitted from horses and other mammals to humans by mosquitoes. Flies can transmit pathogens by landing on infected materials, such as feces, and then landing on materials handled or eaten by humans. W D

Inquiry Launch Lab

Review Based on what you have read about the spread of disease, how would you now answer the analysis questions?

Reading Check **Describe** how diseases are spread to humans.

Symptoms of Disease

When you become ill with a disease such as the flu, why do you feel aches and pains, and why do you cough and sneeze? The pathogen, such as an influenza virus or bacteria, has invaded some of the cells of your body. The virus multiplies in the cells and leaves the cells either by exocytosis or by causing the cell to burst. Thus, the virus damages tissues and even kills some cells. When pathogenic bacteria invade the body, harmful chemicals or toxins might be produced. The toxins can be carried throughout the body via the bloodstream and damage various parts of the body.

Figure 4

Immunology Through Time

For centuries, scientists have struggled to learn about the human immune system. Today, scientists are working to stop HIV, a virus that has attacked the immune system of over 40 million people worldwide.

Concepts in Motion The Interactive Timeline

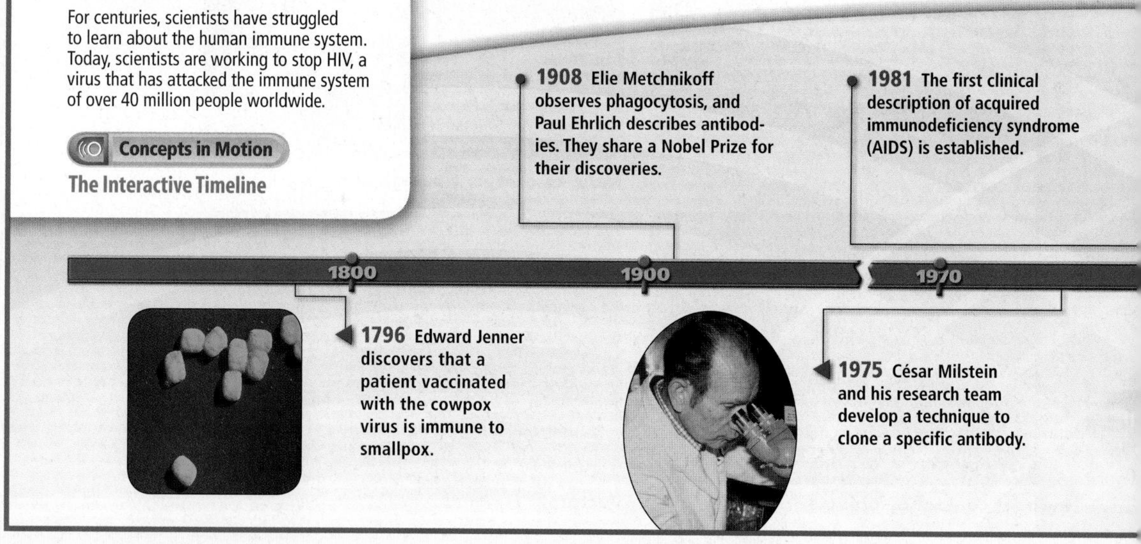

1908 Elie Metchnikoff observes phagocytosis, and Paul Ehrlich describes antibodies. They share a Nobel Prize for their discoveries.
1981 The first clinical description of acquired immunodeficiency syndrome (AIDS) is established.
1800
1900
1970
1796 Edward Jenner discovers that a patient vaccinated with the cowpox virus is immune to smallpox.
1975 César Milstein and his research team develop a technique to clone a specific antibody.

Inquiry Launch Lab

Assess Content Development

Assess how understanding has developed when students revisit the Launch Lab analysis questions.

Reading Check Diseases are spread by direct contact, indirect contact through air or objects, or are carried by vectors.

Toxins produced by pathogens can affect specific organ systems. The tetanus bacteria produce a potent toxin that causes spasms in the voluntary muscles. The disease botulism (BAH chuh lih zum) usually is caused when a person consumes food in which the botulism bacteria have grown and produced a toxin. This toxin paralyzes nerves. The toxin from the botulism bacteria can cause disease in humans even when no bacteria are present.

Some types of bacteria, some protozoans, and all viruses invade and live inside cells, causing damage. Because the cells are damaged, they might die, causing symptoms in the host. Some disease symptoms, such as coughing and sneezing, are triggered by the immune system, as discussed later in this chapter. For a closer look at research on the immune system, examine **Figure 4.**

Disease Patterns

As outbreaks of diseases spread, certain patterns are observed. Agencies such as community health departments, the Centers for Disease Control and Prevention (CDC), and the World Health Organization (WHO) continually monitor disease patterns to help control the spread of diseases. The CDC, with headquarters in Atlanta, Georgia, receives information from doctors and medical clinics and publishes a weekly report about the incidence of specific diseases, as shown in **Figure 5.** The WHO similarly watches disease incidence throughout the world.

Some diseases, such as the common cold, are known as **endemic diseases** because they continually are found in small amounts within the population. Sometimes, a particular disease will have a large outbreak in an area and afflict many people, causing an **epidemic.** If an epidemic is widespread throughout a large W region, such as a country, continent, or the entire globe, it is described as **pandemic.**

TABLE 2. Reported cases of notifiable diseases,* by geographic division and area — United States, 2003

Area	Total resident population (in thousands)	AIDS†
UNITED STATES	287,974	44,232**
NEW ENGLAND	14,134	1,697
Maine	1,295	52
N.H.	1,274	37
Vt.	616	16
Mass.	6,422	757
R.I.	1,068	102
Conn.	3,459	733
MID. ATLANTIC	40,038	10,142
Upstate N.Y.	11,385	1,589
N.Y. City	7,749	5,133
N.J.	8,575	1,514
Pa.	12,329	1,906
E.N. CENTRAL	45,635	3,875
Ohio	11,409	775
Ind.	6,157	506
Ill.	12,586	1,734
Mich.	10,043	676
Wis.	5,440	184
W.N. CENTRAL	19,464	844
Minn.	5,025	179
Iowa	2,936	75
Mo.	5,670	404
N. Dak.	634	2
S. Dak.	760	13
Nebr.	1,728	60
Kans.	2,712	111
S. ATLANTIC	53,564	12,191
Del.	806	216
Md.	5,451	1,572
D.C.	569	961

■ **Figure 5** The Centers for Disease Control and Prevention publish reports on the incidence of certain diseases.
Infer ***how these reports are helpful in understanding disease patterns.***

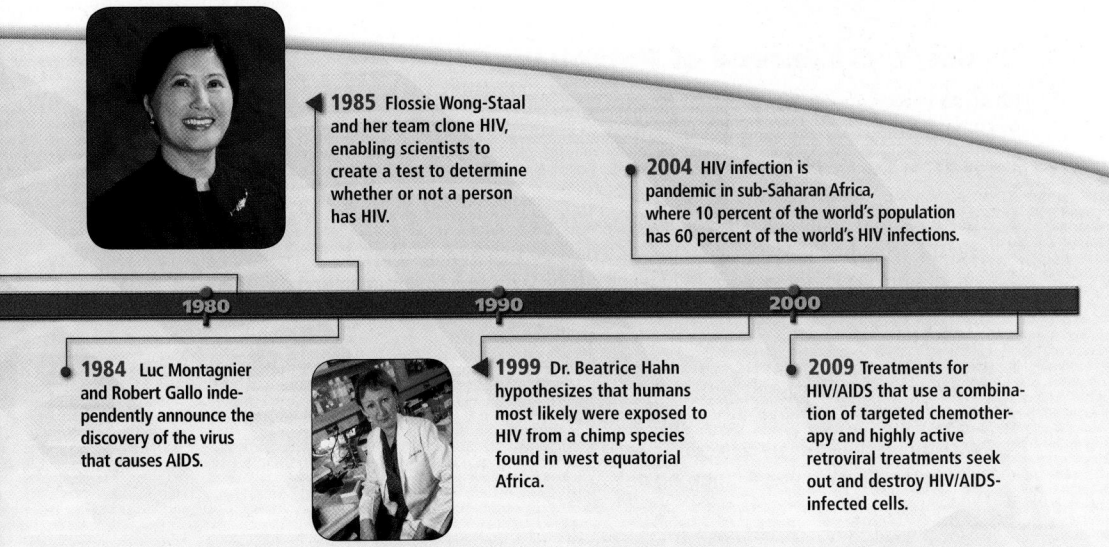

1985 Flossie Wong-Staal and her team clone HIV, enabling scientists to create a test to determine whether or not a person has HIV.

2004 HIV infection is pandemic in sub-Saharan Africa, where 10 percent of the world's population has 60 percent of the world's HIV infections.

1980 — 1990 — 2000

1984 Luc Montagnier and Robert Gallo independently announce the discovery of the virus that causes AIDS.

1999 Dr. Beatrice Hahn hypothesizes that humans most likely were exposed to HIV from a chimp species found in west equatorial Africa.

2009 Treatments for HIV/AIDS that use a combination of targeted chemotherapy and highly active retroviral treatments seek out and destroy HIV/AIDS-infected cells.

■ **Caption Question Fig. 5** Reports monitor diseases in order to recognize new and reemerging diseases. Tracking the number of cases of a disease also helps determine if there is an outbreak or epidemic and may help control spread of the disease.

Concepts in Motion
The Interactive Timeline

Develop Concepts

BL OL Scaffolding

ASK STUDENTS: ***How does plane travel benefit people?*** People can get to places more quickly, and visit more places in a shorter period of time. ***How might plane transportation also aid in the faster spread of diseases?*** People traveling from a place where a disease begins can easily carry the pathogen to other places. ***Should people who are sick be allowed to travel to other countries?*** Students may say that it depends on the severity of illness, and how easily the disease can spread. ***How might the United States government address the problem of people traveling from other countries bringing dangerous infectious diseases into this country?*** Students may say that our government might insist that people traveling from other countries known to have a prevalence of certain diseases should be tested for those diseases before they are allowed to enter the United States.

W Writing Support

OL AL Formal Writing

SAY TO STUDENTS: ***Write a newspaper article about a fictional epidemic spreading across the United States.*** The students can create the name, kind of disease, and how it spreads.

MiniLab 1

Inquiry MiniLab

For a lab worksheet, use your eTeacherEdition Online.

RUBRIC A rubric for evaluating MiniLabs is found on your eTeacherEdition Online.

Est. Time 20 min

Additional Materials items such as: a dollar bill; photos of a rusted nail and a sample of pond water; science textbook; new dish cloth; a petition or sign-up sheet with 50 names; a used cutting board; soil sample

Safety Precaution Approve lab safety forms before work begins.

Teaching Strategy Have students complete the lab while working in small groups.

Analysis

1. viruses, bacteria, fungi, and protozoans
2. Pond water, soil, and garbage
3. Students' answers should demonstrate an understanding of disease transmission. Table 1 shows many likely sources of pathogens.
4. Students' answers should reflect an understanding of how to avoid contact with pathogens. Good personal hygiene, proper food preparation, and a clean environment help prevent contact with pathogens.

LabManager™
Customize this lab with the LabManager™ CD-ROM.

■ **Caption Question Fig. 6** Various antibiotics are needed because bacteria are diverse and many bacteria have become resistant to antibiotics.

■ **Figure 6** Penicillin, a widely used antibiotic, is secreted by the mold called *Penicillium,* shown growing on these oranges.
Determine *why many strengths and varieties of penicillin and other antibiotics are needed.*

Treating and Fighting Diseases

A medical professional may prescribe a drug to help the body fight a disease. One type of prescription drug is an **antibiotic** (an ti bi AH tihk), which is a substance that can kill or inhibit the growth of microorganisms. Penicillin is secreted by the fungus *Penicillium,* which is shown in **Figure 6.** This fungus secretes the chemical penicillin to kill competing bacteria that grow on the fungal food source. Penicillin was isolated, purified, and first used in humans during World War II. Many other fungal secretions are used as antibiotics, such as erythromycin, neomycin, and gentamicin. Synthetic antibiotics also have been developed by pharmaceutical companies.

Chemical agents also are used in the treatment of protozoan and fungal diseases. Some antiviral drugs are used to treat herpes infections, influenza in the elderly, and HIV infections. Most viral diseases are handled by the body's built-in defense system—the immune system.

Connection to Health Over the last 60 years, the widespread use of antibiotics has caused many bacteria to become resistant to particular antibiotics. Natural selection occurs when organisms with favorable variations survive, reproduce, and pass their variations to the next generation. Bacteria in a population might have a trait that enables them to survive when a particular antibiotic is present. These bacteria can reproduce quickly and pass on the variation. Because reproduction can occur so rapidly in bacteria, the number of antibiotic-resistant bacteria in a population can increase quickly, too.

MiniLab 1

Evaluate the Spread of Pathogens

Inquiry MiniLab

How can you evaluate the spread of disease? Investigate what possible diseases might be transmitted by common items.

Procedure

1. Read and complete the lab safety form.
2. Observe all the items given to you by your teacher.
3. Infer the types of diseases each item could pass on to a human (if any).
4. Evaluate the likelihood of each item transmitting a disease to a human and devise a scale for assessing each item's probability for transmitting an infectious disease.

Analysis

1. **Identify** the types of pathogens that might be transmitted by the items you were given and the methods of transmission of each pathogen.
2. **Infer** the items most likely to be disease reservoirs.
3. **Describe** possible disease patterns of each pathogen.
4. **Infer** how you could prevent getting diseases from these possible pathogens.

Demonstration

Bacteria in Food Obtain a small sample of liquid (1 mL or less) from raw meat. Spread it on a nutrient agar plate. Seal the plate with masking tape. Incubate the plate at 37°C for one or two days at room temperature. Do not let students touch the plate. After the incubation period, students should be able to see bacteria growing on the plate. Some of the bacteria growing on the plate might be harmless, but some might be pathogenic. *Salmonella* is one common genus of pathogenic bacteria found on many foods. *Salmonella* can cause food poisoning in people. Est. time: 10 min
WARNING: ***Wash hands with soap and water after handling, and thoroughly clean all surfaces used during the demonstration.***

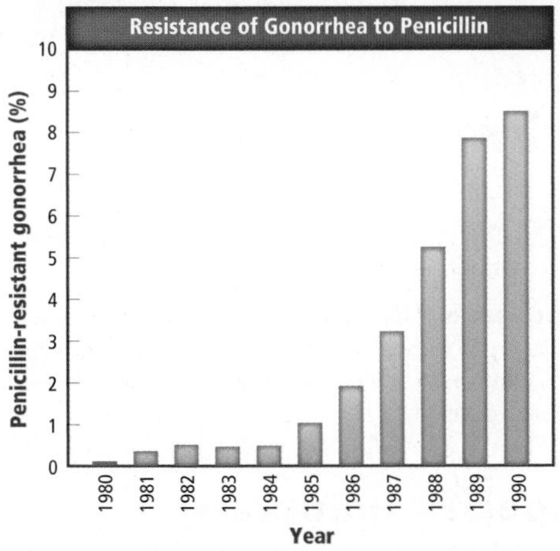

Figure 7 The graph shows the reported incidence of penicillin-resistant gonorrhea in the United States from 1980–1990.
Analyze ***What is the percentage increase from 1980 to 1990?***

D Antibiotic resistance of bacteria has presented the medical community with some problems with treating certain diseases. For example, penicillin was used effectively for many years to treat gonorrhea (gah nuh REE uh), a sexually transmitted disease, but now most strains of gonorrhea bacteria are resistant to penicillin. As a result, new drug therapies are needed to treat gonorrhea. **Figure 7** shows the increase in gonorrhea resistance as the bacteria have gained resistance to treatment with antibiotics.

Another treatment problem is with staphylococcal disease—it is acquired in high-density living conditions, which can result in skin infections, pneumonia (noo MOH nyuh), or meningitis. These staphylococci are often strains of bacteria that are resistant to many current antibiotics and can be difficult to treat.

Section 1 Assessment

Section Summary

- Pathogens, such as bacteria, viruses, protozoans, and fungi, cause infectious diseases.
- Koch's postulates demonstrate how a particular pathogen causes a certain disease.
- Pathogens are found in disease reservoirs and are transmitted to humans by direct and indirect methods.
- The symptoms of disease are caused by invasion of the pathogen and the response of the host immune system.
- Treatment of infectious disease includes the use of antibiotics and antiviral drugs.

Understand Main Ideas

1. MAIN Idea **Compare** the mode of transmission of the common cold with that of malaria.
2. **Summarize** some symptoms of bacterial infectious disease.
3. **Define** *infectious disease* and give three examples of infectious diseases.
4. **Illustrate** Koch's postulates for a bacterial infectious disease in a rabbit by drawing a graphic organizer or a concept map.
5. **Infer** why a person might be exposed to tetanus bacteria after stepping on a dirty nail.

Think Critically

6. **Evaluate** the following scenario: Two days after visiting a pet shop and observing green parrots in a display cage and fish in an aquarium, a student developed a fever, became ill, and was diagnosed with parrot fever. What might be the disease reservoir and possible transmission method?
7. **Evaluate** how the practice of medicating animal feed with a low level of antiobiotics might play a role in the development of antibiotic-resistant bacteria.

? Inquiry BioLab

The lab at the end of the chapter can be used at this point in the lesson.

D Develop Concepts

BL OL AL

Clarify a Misconception

ASK STUDENTS: ***How do you think antibiotics work?*** Some students might view antibiotics as a type of quick fix. Antibiotics work by either killing bacteria or stopping the reproduction of bacteria, which takes time. Antibiotics do not prevent diseases from spreading.

Caption Question Fig. 7 almost 8.5 percent

Formative Assessment

Evaluation Have students make a diagram illustrating Koch's postulates. Evaluate their diagram for each of the four steps.

Remediation Provide a copy of Koch's postulates without the explanations. Have students summarize each step of Koch's postulates in their own words on the diagram.

Section 1 Assessment

1. The common cold is transmitted by direct contact, by droplets, or through objects, whereas malaria is transmitted by a vector.
2. Answers might include muscle spasms, coughing, and sneezing.
3. An infectious disease is one that can be passed from one individual to another. Examples might vary but might include colds and influenza.
4. The drawing should demonstrate an understanding of Koch's postulates, shown in Figure 2.
5. Tetanus bacteria live in soil and are associated with infection in deep puncture wounds.
6. The disease reservoir likely was the parrots. The student may have acquired the infection from the parrots by coming into contact with droplets or by touching the cage.
7. The continual use of antibiotics could cause the development of antibiotic-resistant pathogens.

✓ Assessment Online Quiz

Section 2

MAIN Idea

BL OL AL Protecting the Body
ASK STUDENTS: ***How does the body fight disease?*** Answers may include various types of nonspecific immunity such as the skin, white blood cells, chemical defenses, and may include various aspects of specific immunity such as B and T cell lymphocytes. In this section, students will learn more about how these particular aspects of the immune system help protect against disease.

Develop Concepts

OL Activate Prior Knowledge Review the types of white blood cells found in the bloodstream and throughout the body tissues. Review the various functions of these white blood cells and the process of phagocytosis.

FOLDABLES®

RUBRIC A rubric for evaluating Foldables is found on your eTeacherEdition Online.
Going Further On the title pages of their Foldables, have students illustrate each type of immunity at work in the body.

C Critical Thinking

OL AL Analyze Long-term smoking damages the lining of the respiratory tract. The ciliated cells die. They often are replaced with scar tissue.
ASK STUDENTS: ***Why would smokers be more susceptible to infectious diseases?*** Cilia remove mucus, which may contain pathogens, from the respiratory tract. Without cilia to sweep them away, pathogens trapped in the mucus cannot be removed, making the person more susceptible to infections.

Section 2

Reading Preview

Essential Questions

- What are the similarities and differences between nonspecific and specific immunity?
- What is the structure and function of the lymphatic system?
- What is the importance of B cells and T cells?
- What are the differences between passive and active immunity?

Review Vocabulary

white blood cells: large, nucleated blood cells that play a major role in protecting the body from foreign substances and microorganisms

New Vocabulary

complement protein
interferon
lymphocyte
antibody
B cell
helper T cell
cytotoxic T cell
memory cell
immunization

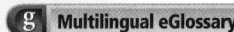

g Multilingual eGlossary

■ **Figure 8** These bacteria normally are found on human skin and provide protection from pathogens.

Color-Enhanced SEM Magnification: 14,000×

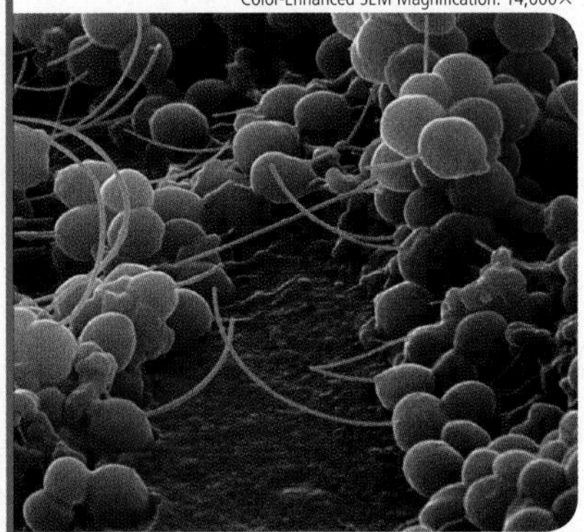

The Immune System

MAIN Idea The immune system has two main components: nonspecific immunity and specific immunity.

Real-World Reading Link We live with a number of potential pathogens such as bacteria and viruses that can cause disease. Like a fort protecting a city from attack, the immune system protects the body against these and other disease-causing organisms.

Nonspecific Immunity

At the time of birth, the body has a number of defenses in the immune system that fight off pathogens. These defenses are nonspecific because they are not aimed at a specific pathogen. They protect the body from any pathogen that the body encounters.

The nonspecific immunity provided by the body helps to prevent disease. Nonspecific immunity also helps to slow the progression of the disease while the specific immunity begins to develop its defenses. Specific immunity is the most effective immune response, but nonspecific immunity is the first line of defense.

Barriers Like the strong walls of a fort, barriers are used by the body to protect against pathogens. These barriers are found in areas of the body where pathogens might enter.

Skin barrier The first major line of defense is the unbroken skin and its secretions. Skin contains layers of living cells covered by many layers of dead skin cells. By forming a barrier, the layers of dead skin cells help protect against invasion by microorganisms. Many of the bacteria that live symbiotically on the skin digest skin oils to produce acids that inhibit many pathogens. **Figure 8** shows some normal bacteria found on the skin that protect the skin from attack.

Chemical barriers Saliva, tears, and nasal secretions contain the enzyme lysozyme. Lysozyme breaks down bacterial cell walls, which kills pathogens.

Another chemical defense is mucus, which is secreted by many inner surfaces of the body. It acts as a protective barrier, blocking bacteria from sticking to the inner epithelial cells. Cilia also line the airway. Their beating motion sends any bacteria caught in the mucus away from the lungs. When the airway becomes infected, extra mucus is secreted, which triggers coughing and sneezing to help move the infected mucus out of the body.

A third chemical defense is the hydrochloric acid secreted in your stomach. In addition to digestion, stomach acid kills many microorganisms found in food that could cause disease. C

Reading Check Compare and contrast the different types of barriers of the immune system.

Demonstration

Numbers of Microbes in the Environment Use a piece of tape or a sterile swab to remove organisms from a door knob and place the piece of tape gently on a nutrient agar plate to transfer the organisms to the agar. Seal the plate with tape. Incubate the plate at 37°C for one or two days at room temperature. Caution students not to open the plate. Use this plate to demonstrate possible disease organisms that can be found in the environment, especially where human hands touch and can transfer bacteria. Est. time: 10 min

WARNING: ***Wash hands with soap and water after handling, and thoroughly clean all surfaces used during the demonstration.***

Nonspecific responses to invasion Even if an enemy gets through the walls of a town's fort, defense doesn't end. Similarly, the body has nonspecific immune responses to pathogens that get beyond its barriers.

R **Cellular defense** If foreign microorganisms enter the body, the cells of the immune system, shown in **Table 2,** defend the body. One method of defense is phagocytosis. White blood cells, especially neutrophils and macrophages, are phagocytic. Recall that phagocytosis is the process by which phagocytic cells surround and internalize the foreign microorganisms. The phagocytes then release digestive enzymes and other harmful chemicals from their lysosomes, destroying the microorganism.

A series of about 20 proteins that are found in the blood plasma are called complement proteins. **Complement proteins** enhance phagocytosis by helping the phagocytic cells bind better to pathogens and activating the phagocytes. Some complement proteins can form a complex in the plasma membrane of a pathogen. This complex forms a pore, which aids in the destruction of the pathogen, as shown in **Figure 9.**

Interferon When a virus enters the body, another cellular defense helps prevent the virus from spreading. Virus-infected cells secrete a protein called **interferon.** Interferon binds to neighboring cells and stimulates these cells to produce antiviral proteins which can prevent viral replication in these cells.

Inflammatory response Another nonspecific response, the inflammatory response, is a complex series of events that involves many chemicals and immune cells that help enhance the overall immune response. When pathogens damage tissue, chemicals are released by both the invader and cells of the body. These chemicals attract phagocytes to the area, increase blood flow to the infected area, and make blood vessels more permeable to allow white blood cells to escape into the infected area. This response aids in the accumulation of white blood cells in the area. Some of the pain, heat, and redness experienced during an infectious disease are the result of the inflammatory response. D

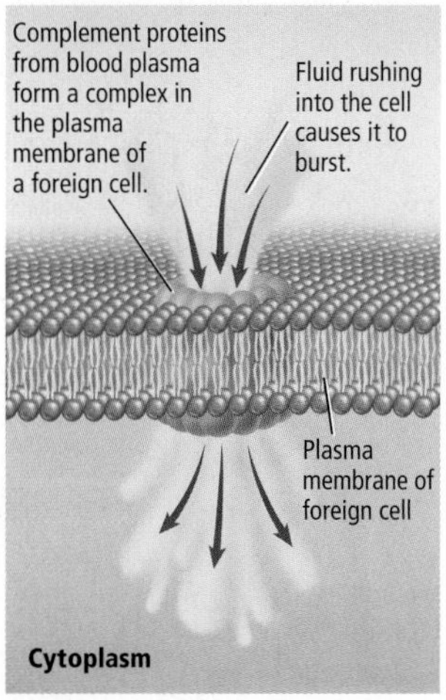

■ **Figure 9** For some pathogens, complement proteins can form a pore in the plasma membrane of the invading cell.

Concepts in Motion

Animation

Table 2 **Cells of the Immune System** Concepts in Motion Interactive Table

Type of Cell	Example	Function
Neutrophils	Stained LM Magnification: 2150× 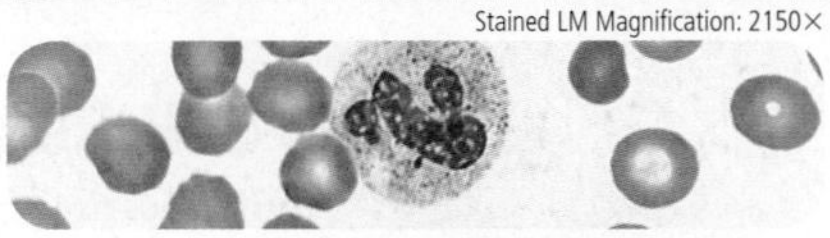	Phagocytosis: blood cells that ingest bacteria
Macrophages	Stained LM Magnification: 380× 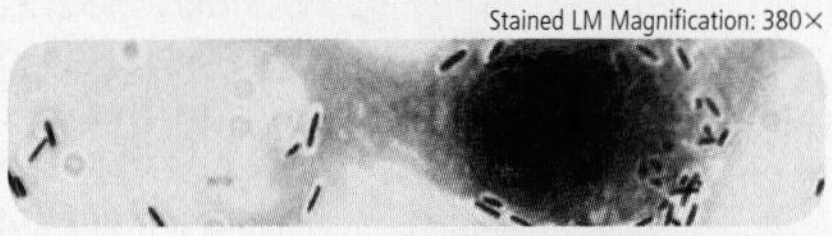	Phagocytosis: blood cells that ingest bacteria and remove dead neutrophils and other debris
Lymphocytes	Stained LM Magnification: 1800× 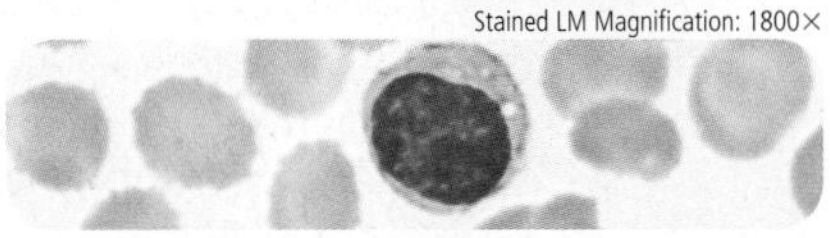	Specific immunity (antibodies and killing of pathogens): blood cells that produce antibodies and other chemicals

R Reading Strategy

BL OL AL

Content-Specific Words

Before students read the text below the heading *Cellular defense,* ask for a student volunteer.

SAY TO STUDENT: ***Use the word* phagocytes *in a sentence that helps define the term.*** A phagocyte is a cell that ingests foreign matter. Then have students review the function of phagocytes.

D Develop Concepts

BL OL AL **Activity**

SAY TO STUDENTS: ***Create a chart or make a slideshow presentation comparing red blood cells and the various types of white blood cells.*** Students can insert photos that demonstrate each type of white blood cell. Presentations should include the role of each type of white blood cell in immunity.

Concepts in Motion

Interactive Table

Differentiated Instruction

Below Level For writing activities, allow struggling students to use available technology, such as electronic spellers, word processors, and writing programs, when working on computers.

For more tips, see pages 14T–15T.

D Develop Concepts

BL OL AL

Clarify a Misconception

ASK STUDENTS: ***What purpose do your tonsils and appendix serve?*** Some students might think that the tonsils and the appendix serve no function. Both of these organs are part of the immune system. Tonsils protect the respiratory system, and the appendix channels material from the digestive tract to the lymphatic system so that the lymphatic system can monitor the contents of the intestines.

S Skill Practice

BL OL **Visual Literacy**

Obtain a diagram of the immune system and organs similar to Figure 10 and remove any labels. Have students color and label the system for practice.

C Critical Thinking

BL OL AL **Infer**

ASK STUDENTS: ***Why do doctors now rarely take out tonsils even though it used to be a common practice?*** Although tonsils were once thought to serve no function, they are now known to be important organs in the immune system. Tonsils swell when they are fighting an infection.

Video BrainPOP

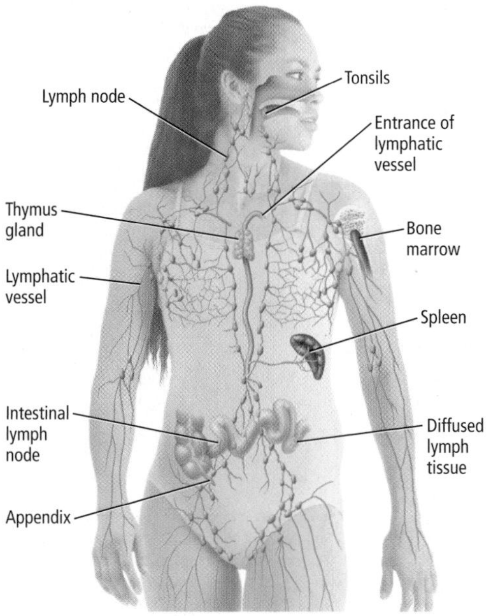

Figure 10 The lymphatic system contains the organs involved in the specific immune response.

Identify *the lymphatic organ where T cells mature.*

S

Video BrainPOP

Specific Immunity

Pathogens sometimes get past the nonspecific defense mechanisms. The body has a second line of defense that attacks these pathogens. Specific immunity is more effective, but takes time to develop. This specific response involves the tissues and organs found in the lymphatic system.

Lymphatic system The lymphatic (lim FA tihk) system, illustrated in **Figure 10,** includes organs and cells that filter lymph and blood, destroy foreign microorganisms, and absorb fat. Lymph is the fluid that leaks out of capillaries to bathe body cells. This fluid circulates among the tissue cells, is collected by lymphatic vessels, and is returned to the veins near the heart.

Lymphatic organs The organs of the lymphatic system contain lymphatic tissue, lymphocytes, a few other cell types, and connective tissue. **Lymphocytes** are a type of white blood cell that is produced in red bone marrow. These lymphatic organs include the lymph nodes, tonsils, spleen, thymus (THI mus) gland, and diffused lymphatic tissue found in mucous membranes of the intestinal, respiratory, urinary, and genital tracts.

The lymph nodes filter the lymph and remove foreign materials from the lymph. The tonsils form a protective ring of lymphatic tissue between the nasal and oral cavities. This helps protect against bacteria and other harmful materials in the nose and mouth. The spleen stores blood and destroys damaged red blood cells. It also contains lymphatic tissue that responds to foreign substances in the blood. The thymus gland, which is located above the heart, plays a role in activating a special kind of lymphocyte called T cells. T cells are produced in the bone marrow, but they mature in the thymus gland. D C

VOCABULARY

WORD ORIGIN

Thymus
comes from the Greek word *thymos,* meaning *warty excrescence*

B Cell Response

Antibodies are proteins produced by B lymphocytes that specifically react with a foreign antigen. An antigen is a substance foreign to the body that causes an immune response; it can bind to an antibody or T cell. B lymphocytes, often called **B cells,** are located in all lymphatic tissues and can be thought of as antibody factories. When a portion of a pathogen is presented by a macrophage, B cells produce antibodies. Follow along in **Figure 11,** as you learn about how B cells are activated to produce antibodies.

Caption Question Fig. 10 The thymus gland is important for T-cell development.

Research Citation

Critical Thinking Educational research indicates that asking students to use critical-thinking skills, such as the analyzing skills used in the Critical Thinking activity on this page, helps them to move beyond a simple recall of the material presented and develop a deeper understanding of the information. (Heibert, et al., 1997)

Research bibliography on pages 32T–34T

Visualizing Specific Immune Responses

Figure 11
Specific immune responses involve antigens, phagocytes, B cells, helper T cells, and cytotoxic T cells. The antibody-mediated response involves antibodies produced by B cells and memory B cells. The cytotoxic T cell response results in cytotoxic T cell activation.

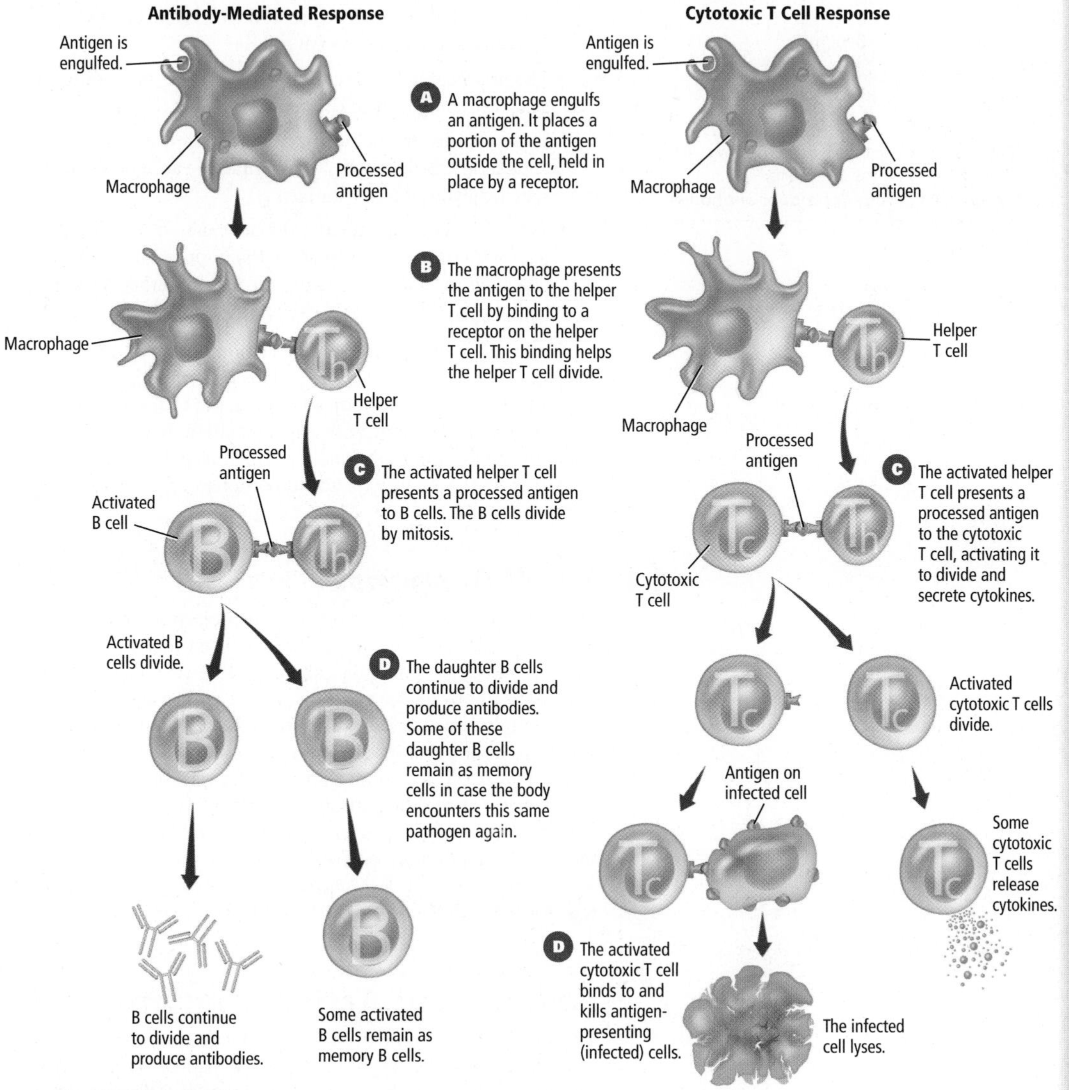
Antibody-Mediated Response
Cytotoxic T Cell Response
Antigen is engulfed.
Macrophage
Processed antigen
A A macrophage engulfs an antigen. It places a portion of the antigen outside the cell, held in place by a receptor.
Antigen is engulfed.
Macrophage
Processed antigen
Macrophage
Helper T cell
B The macrophage presents the antigen to the helper T cell by binding to a receptor on the helper T cell. This binding helps the helper T cell divide.
Helper T cell
Macrophage
Processed antigen
Activated B cell
C The activated helper T cell presents a processed antigen to B cells. The B cells divide by mitosis.
Processed antigen
C The activated helper T cell presents a processed antigen to the cytotoxic T cell, activating it to divide and secrete cytokines.
Cytotoxic T cell
Activated B cells divide.
D The daughter B cells continue to divide and produce antibodies. Some of these daughter B cells remain as memory cells in case the body encounters this same pathogen again.
Activated cytotoxic T cells divide.
Antigen on infected cell
Some cytotoxic T cells release cytokines.
B cells continue to divide and produce antibodies.
Some activated B cells remain as memory B cells.
D The activated cytotoxic T cell binds to and kills antigen-presenting (infected) cells.
The infected cell lyses.

Concepts in Motion Animation

Visualizing Specific Immune Response

Purpose

Students will summarize B-cell and T-cell response.
C.1

R Reading Strategy

BL OL COOP LEARN

Reading Circles Organize students into groups of three or four. **SAY TO STUDENTS:** ***Read and study Figure 11.*** One student should be a discussion director, one should take notes, and one should be prepared to present a summary to the class about the figure.

D Develop Concepts

BL OL AL **Activity**

SAY TO STUDENTS: ***Write a play illustrating either the B-cell response or T-cell response.*** Acting these out in class will help students visualize this multistep process. Students can use large sheets of paper to make cell diagrams to use for "costumes" to play the various types of cells. When cells bond together, students can hold hands to simulate the cellular bonding.

Concepts in Motion
Animation

Research Citation

Cooperative Learning Educational research indicates that group work, such as the Reading Strategy activity on this page, allows students to work with their peers and interact with the material presented in a variety of ways. As a result, they become more engaged in the lesson. (Wood and Turner-Vorbeck, 2001)

Research bibliography on pages 36T–38T

Reading Strategy

EL Marginal Notes

Marginal notes are questions about key concepts written on sticky note paper that help guide students in their reading. Put the notes next to the sentences in the text where the answers can be found. Questions for this section could include:

How does the skin protect a person against pathogens?
How does mucus protect the body?
What does an interferon do?
What is in the lymphatic system?
What is a lymph?
What are the lymphatic organs?
How do the lymphatic organs help protect the body?
What are antibodies?
What does a T cell do?

R Reading Strategy

BL SQ3R Have students follow SQ3R as they read the text under the heading *T-Cell Response.*
SAY TO STUDENTS: ***First Survey the section, focusing on headings. Then write Questions about the key concepts, Read the section, take notes, Recite the vocabulary, and Review for meaning.***

Develop Concepts

EL BL OL AL COOP LEARN

Analogy Group students into pairs.
SAY TO STUDENTS: ***Illustrate the immune system using the metaphor of a mythical planet under siege. Flesh out the analogy using space warriors as immune cells, invading creatures as pathogens, and any other details that seem appropriate.*** Illustrations will vary. Details in this analogy should come as close to representing actual parts of the immune system as possible.

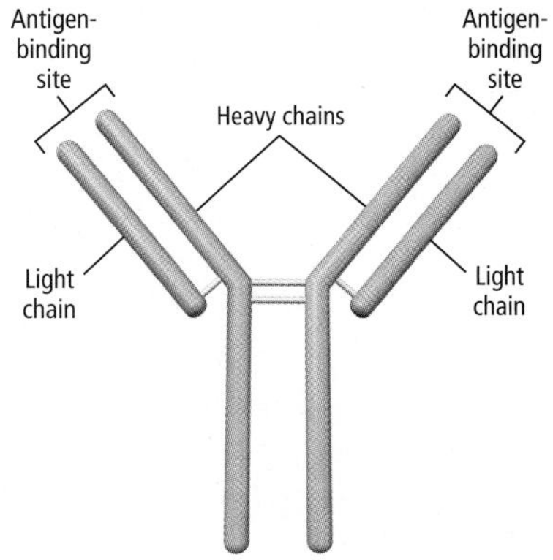

■ **Figure 12** Antibodies are made up of two types of protein chains—heavy and light chains.
Summarize *which cells produce antibodies.*

When a macrophage surrounds, internalizes, and digests a pathogen, it takes a piece of the pathogen, which is called a processed antigen, and displays it on its membrane, as illustrated in **Figure 11.** In the lymphatic tissues, such as the lymph nodes, the macrophage, with the processed antigen on its surface, binds to a type of lymphocyte called a **helper T cell.** This process activates the helper T cell. This lymphocyte is called a "helper" because it activates antibody secretion in B cells and another type of T cell, which will be discussed later, that aids in killing microorganisms:

- The activated helper T cell reproduces, binds processed antigens, and attaches to a B cell.
- The new helper T cells continue the process of binding antigens, attaching to B cells, and reproducing.
- Once an activated helper T cell binds to a B cell holding an antigen, the B cell begins to manufacture antibodies that specifically bind to the antigen.
- The antibodies can enhance the immune response by binding to microorganisms, making them more susceptible to phagocytosis and by initiating the inflammatory response, helping promote the nonspecific response.

B cells make many combinations of antibodies by using DNA that codes for the production of various heavy and light protein chains that make up antibodies as shown in **Figure 12.** Any heavy chain can combine with any light chain. If a B cell can make 16,000 different kinds of heavy chains and 1200 kinds of light chains, it can make 19,200,000 different types of antibodies ($1200 \times 16{,}000$).

R T Cell Response

Once helper T cells are activated by the presentation of an antigen by macrophages, helper T cells can also bind to and activate a group of lymphocytes called cytotoxic T cells. Activated **cytotoxic T cells** destroy pathogens and release chemicals called cytokines. Cytokines stimulate the cells of the immune system to divide and recruit immune cells to an area of infection. Cytotoxic T cells bind to pathogens, release a chemical attack, and destroy the pathogens. Multiple target cells can be destroyed by a single cytotoxic T cell. **Figure 11** summarizes the activation of cytotoxic T cells.

Reading Check **Summarize** the role that lymphocytes play in immunity.

Passive and Active Immunity

The body's first response to an invasion by a pathogen is called the primary response. For example, if the viral pathogen that causes chicken pox enters the body, nonspecific and specific immune responses eventually defeat the foreign virus and the body is cleared of the pathogen.

■ **Caption Question Fig. 12** Activated B cells produce antibodies.

Reading Check B lymphocytes are important for producing antibodies—specific chemicals that attach to antigens and increase phagocytosis. T lymphocytes include cytotoxic T cells, which can destroy foreign cells and release cytokines to stimulate the immune response. Helper T cells enhance the response of both B lymphocytes and cytotoxic T cells.

One result of the specific immune response is the production of memory B and T cells. **Memory cells** are long-living cells that are exposed to the antigen during the primary immune response. These cells are ready to respond rapidly if the body encounters the same pathogen later. Memory cells protect the body by reducing the likelihood of developing the disease if exposed again to the same pathogen.

R **Passive immunity** Sometimes temporary protection against an infectious disease is needed. This type of temporary protection occurs when antibodies are made by other people or animals and are transferred or injected into the body. For example, passive immunity occurs between a mother and her child. Antibodies produced by the mother are passed through the placenta to the developing fetus and through breast milk to the infant child. These antibodies can protect the child until the infant's immune system matures.

Antibodies developed in humans and animals that are already immune to a specific infectious disease are used to treat some infectious diseases in others. These antibodies are injected into people who have been exposed to that particular infectious disease. Passive immune therapy is available for people who have been exposed to hepatitis A and B, tetanus, and rabies. Antibodies also are available to inactivate snake and scorpion venoms.

Active immunity Active immunity occurs after the immune system is exposed to disease antigens and memory cells are produced. Active immunity can result from having an infectious disease or immunization. **Immunization,** also called vaccination, is the deliberate exposure of the body to an antigen so that a primary response and immune memory cells will develop. **Table 3** lists some of the common immunizations offered in the United States. Immunizations contain killed or weakened pathogens, which are incapable of causing the disease.

Most immunizations include more than one stimulus to the immune system, given after the first immunization. These booster shots increase the immune response, providing further protection from the disease-causing organism.

VOCABULARY

ACADEMIC VOCABULARY

Passive
not active; acted upon
The passive monkey stared lazily at the zoo visitors.

Table 3 Common Immunizations — Concepts in Motion Interactive Table

Immunization	Disease	Contents
DPT	Diphtheria (D), tetanus (T), pertussis (P) (whooping cough)	D: inactivated toxin, T: inactivated toxin, P: inactivated bacteria
Inactivated polio	Poliomyelitis	Inactivated virus
MMR	Measles, mumps, rubella	All three inactivated viruses
Varicella	Chicken pox	Inactivated virus
HIB	Haemophilus influenzae (flu) type b	Portions of bacteria cell wall covering
HBV	Hepatitis B	Subunit of virus

Activity

BL OL AL Interaction of Antibody and Antigen Bring in a young child's puzzle with large pieces. Find two pieces that fit together. Describe how an antibody and antigen fit together in a unique fashion like the puzzle pieces and they fit such that another piece will not fit. Another analogy is how a lock and key fit together. Est. time: 5 min

R Reading Strategy

BL OL AL Build a Comparison

SAY TO STUDENTS: ***Make a table comparing passive and active immunity as you read text under the headings* Passive Immunity *and* Active Immunity.**

Possible answers: Passive immunity: antibodies produced in one organism, and given to another; active immunity: antibodies produced in the person who gets the disease or immunization.

EL Provide EL students with statements and have the students write them on a table indicating whether they are related to passive or active immunity.

Skill Practice

EL BL OL AL

Compare and Contrast

As a class, create a table on the board comparing and contrasting various features of nonspecific and specific immunity.

ASK STUDENTS: ***How are specific and nonspecific immunity different? How are they similar? Record responses in the table.***

Possible answers are:

Nonspecific	Specific
Reacts to any pathogen	Reaction is tailored to individual pathogens
Rapid response	Slow-developing response
No memory	Memory
Involves skin, chemicals, and phagocytes	Involves lymphocytes

Concepts in Motion

Interactive Table

DATA ANALYSIS LAB 1

About the Lab

- Students might wish to research the side effects of some of the antiviral drugs or other therapies for AIDS. Human vaccine trials are currently being conducted.
- Also see Pilgrim, A.K., et al. 1997. Neutralizing antibody responses to human immuno-deficiency virus type 1 in primary infection and long-term-nonprogressive infection. *J Infect Dis* 176: 924–32; Kleeberger, C.D., et al. 1999. A longitudinal study of neutralizing antibodies and disease progression in HIV-1-infected subjects. *J Infect Dis* 179: 1365–74; Blick, G., et al. 1998. Passive immunotherapy in advanced HIV infection and therapeutic plasmapheresis in asymptomatic HIV-positive individuals: a four year clinical experience. *Biotherapy* 11: 7–14.

Think Critically

1. For patient 1, the virus amount sharply decreased but then increased to the original measurement. For Patient 2, the virus amount decreased and stayed down. For Patient 3, the virus amount slowly increased.
2. More research is necessary. Passive immune therapy was effective for 1 out of 3 patients.

Review Personal Tutor

Listen to a teacher explain primary and secondary responses.

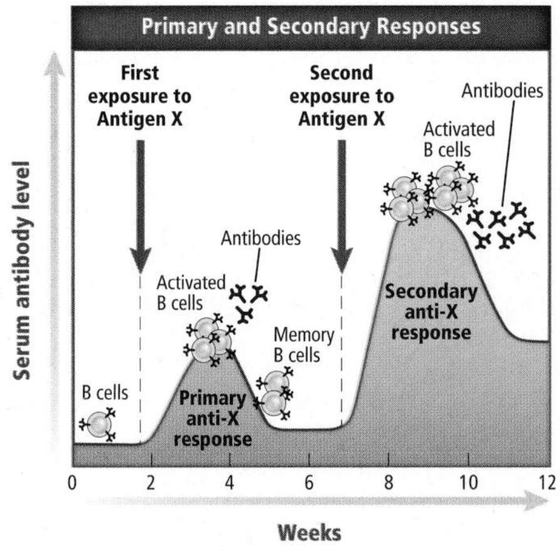

■ **Figure 13** This graph shows the difference between the primary and secondary immune responses to exposure to an antigen.
***Analyze** the differences between the primary and secondary immune responses.*

Review Personal Tutor

Inquiry Virtual Lab

Why are immunizations effective in preventing disease? The characteristics of the secondary immune response, which is the response to a second exposure to an antigen, enable immunizations to be effective in preventing disease. Study the graph in **Figure 13.** Note that the secondary response to the antigen has a number of different characteristics. First, the response is more rapid than the primary response, as shown by the greater steepness in the portion of the curves plotted in red. Second, the overall response, both B and T cell response, is greater during the second exposure. Lastly, the overall memory lasts longer after the second exposure.

Immune System Failure

Defects in the immune system can result in an increased likelihood of developing infectious diseases as well as certain types of cancers. Some diseases can affect the immune system's effectiveness. One such disease called acquired immunodeficiency syndrome (AIDS) results from an infection by human immunodeficiency virus (HIV). AIDS is a serious health problem worldwide.

In 2006, approximately 36,828 AIDS cases were diagnosed in the U.S. In 2006, 14,016 people died of AIDS in the U.S. In 2007, an estimated 33 million people globally were living with HIV infection.

DATA ANALYSIS LAB 1

Based on Real Data*

Draw a Conclusion

Is passive immune therapy effective for HIV infection? The standard treatment for a patient with an HIV infection is antiviral drug therapy. Unfortunately, the side effects and increasing prevalence of drug-resistant viruses create a need for additional therapies. One area being studied is passive immune therapy.

Data and Observations

The graph shows HIV patient responses to passive immune therapy. The number of viral copies/mL is a measure of the amount of virus in the patient's blood.

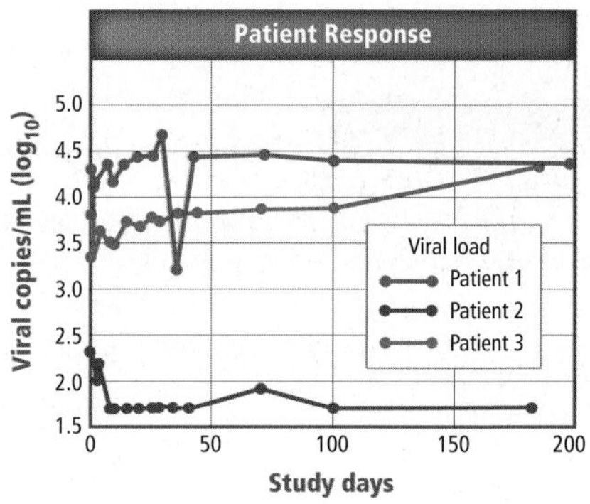

Think Critically

1. **Compare** the patient responses to passive immune therapy.
2. **Explain** whether the researchers can conclude if passive immune therapy is effective.

*Data obtained from: Stiegler G., et al. 2002. Antiviral activity of the neutralizing antibodies 2FS and 2F12 in asymptomatic HIV-1-infected humans: a phase I evaluation. *AIDS* 16: 2019-2025.

■ **Caption Question Fig. 13** The secondary response is more rapid and reaches a higher antibody level than the primary response.

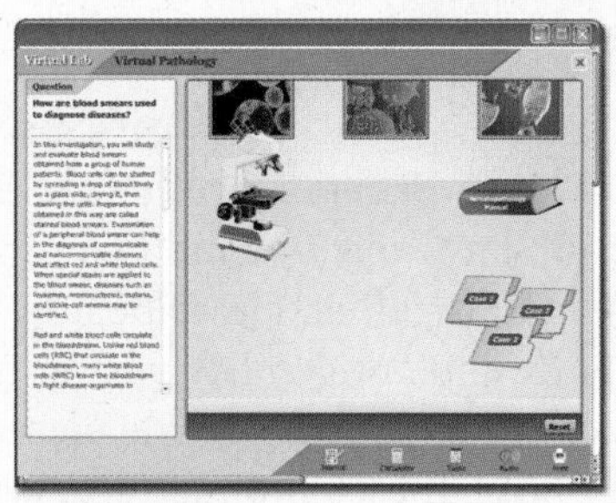

Inquiry **Virtual Lab** Students will evaluate blood samples for diseases that affect red and white blood cells.

Recall the important role that helper T cells play in specific immunity. HIV infects mainly helper T cells, also called $CD4^+$ cells because these cells have a receptor on the outside of their plasma membrane. This $CD4^+$ receptor is used by medical professionals to identify these cells, as illustrated in **Figure 14.**

HIV is an RNA virus that infects helper T cells. The helper T cells become HIV factories, producing new viruses that are released and infect other helper T cells. Over time, the number of helper T cells in an infected person decreases, making the person less able to fight disease. HIV infection usually has an early phase during the first six to twelve weeks while viruses are replicating in helper T cells.

The patient suffers symptoms such as night sweats and fever, but these symptoms are reduced after about eight to ten weeks. Then, the patient exhibits few symptoms for a period of time as long as ten years but is capable of passing the infection through sexual intercourse or blood products. HIV is a secondary immunodeficiency disease, which means that the immune system of a previously healthy person fails. Without antiviral drug therapy, the patient usually dies from a secondary infection from another pathogen after about ten years of being infected with HIV. Current antiviral drug therapy is aimed at controlling the replication of HIV in the body. Resistant strains, expensive drugs, and side effects are all issues that patients face. Researchers and health care providers are working to meet these needs and continue the search for a cure.

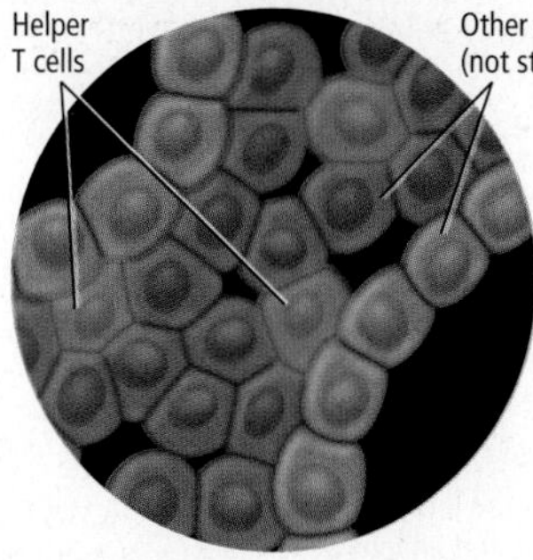

■ **Figure 14** Helper T cells have receptors on the surface that are used to identify them in the laboratory.

Writing Support

OL AL Persuasive writing

For various reasons, some parents are against vaccinating their children.

SAY TO STUDENTS: ***Research why someone might be against childhood vaccinations. Write a persuasive essay expressing your opinion about whether vaccines should be required for public school attendance.***

Formative Assessment

Evaluation Have students make a diagram, without looking at the Visualizing Page, indicating how an antigen and a helper T cell are involved in activating a B cell. Have students work in pairs to review each other's diagrams, comparing them to the Visualizing Page.

Remediation Have students build a concept map demonstrating the relationships between B cells, helper T cells, antigens, and antibody production. As they read the portion of the text about B cells, ask them to determine the cause-and-effect relationships among these words.

Section 2 Assessment

Section Summary

- The nonspecific immune response includes the skin barrier, secreted chemicals, and cellular pathways that activate phagocytosis.
- The specific immune response involves the activation of B cells, which produce antibodies, and T cells, which include helper T cells and cytotoxic T cells.
- Passive immunity involves receiving antibodies against a disease.
- Active immunity results in immune memory against a disease.
- HIV attacks helper T cells, causing an immune system failure.

Understand Main Ideas

1. MAIN Idea **Compare** specific and nonspecific immune responses.
2. **Describe** the steps involved in activating an antibody response to an antigen.
3. **Identify** ways passive and active immunity can be acquired.
4. **Describe** the structure and function of the lymphatic system.
5. **Infer** why the destruction of helper T cells in HIV infection is so devastating to specific immunity.

Think Critically

6. **Hypothesize** what happens when an HIV strain mutates such that viral-replication drugs are no longer effective.
7. **Evaluate** the effects of severe combined immune deficiency on a child born without T cell immunity.

MATH in Biology

8. Antibodies are made of two light protein chains and two heavy protein chains. If the molecular weight of a light chain is 25,000 and the molecular weight of a heavy chain is 50,000, what is the molecular weight of an antibody?

Section 2 Assessment

1. nonspecific—complement proteins and interferons; specific—B and T cells
2. The phagocyte internalizes and processes an antigen, places a piece of the antigen on its surface, and presents it to helper T cells. Helper T cells present a processed antigen to B cells to activate them so they begin producing antibodies.
3. Passive: antibodies are produced in one organism, given to another. Active: antibodies are produced in organism with the disease or immunization.
4. organs and cells that include thymus, tonsils, lymph nodes, lymphocytes; filter lymph and blood and destroy foreign microorganisms; absorb fat
5. When helper T cells decrease, both B- and T-cell immune responses are impaired.
6. More people who are infected with HIV will develop AIDS.
7. The child only will have an active nonspecific immunity and little or no specific immunity.
8. $2(25,000) + 2(50,000) = 150,000$

Section 3

MAIN Idea

BL OL AL

Noninfectious Disorders

Have students outline the section according to the boldface headings. **SAY TO STUDENTS:** ***List examples of each type of noninfectious disease under the headings.***

I. Noninfectious Disorders
   A. Genetic disorders
      1. albinism
      2. sickle-cell anemia
      3. Huntington disease
      4. hemophilia
      5. Down syndrome
      6. coronary artery disease
   B. Degenerative diseases
      1. arthritis
      2. arteriosclerosis
   C. Metabolic disease
      1. Type 1 diabetes
   D. Cancer
   E. Inflammatory diseases
      1. allergies
      2. autoimmunity

D Develop Concepts

BL OL

Clarify a Misconception

ASK STUDENTS: ***What causes diseases?*** Some students might think that all diseases are caused by pathogens. This section will help them understand that there are other kinds of diseases in addition to infectious diseases caused by pathogens.

Section 3

Reading Preview

Essential Questions

- What are the five categories of noninfectious diseases?
- What is the role of allergens in allergies?
- What is the difference between allergies and anaphylactic shock?

Review Vocabulary

cancer: uncontrolled cell division that can be caused by environmental factors or changes in enzyme production in the cell cycle

New Vocabulary

degenerative disease
metabolic disease
allergy
anaphylactic shock

g Multilingual eGlossary

Noninfectious Disorders

MAIN Idea Noninfectious disorders include genetic disorders, degenerative diseases, metabolic diseases, cancer, and inflammatory diseases.

Real-World Reading Link Maybe you have heard your parents or grandparents complain about their arthritis, which causes achy bones and joints. Perhaps some of your relatives have diabetes or have survived cancer. You or a friend might have an allergy to dust, plant pollens, or other environmental substances. These disorders are different from infectious diseases caused by pathogens.

D Genetic Disorders

Not all diseases or body disorders are caused by pathogens. Some diseases are caused by the inheritance of genes that do not function properly in the body, such as albinism, sickle cell anemia, Huntington disease, and hemophilia. There are also chromosomal disorders that result from abnormal chromosome numbers, such as Down syndrome. Many diseases are complex and have both an environmental and a genetic cause.

Coronary artery disease (CAD) is an example of a condition with environmental and genetic origins. This cardiovascular disease can result in blockage of arteries, shown in **Figure 15,** that deliver oxygenated blood to the heart muscle. There is a genetic component that increases a person's risk of developing CAD. Environmental factors such as diet contribute to the development of this complex disease. Families with a history of CAD have a two to seven times greater risk of having CAD than families without a history of CAD. The exact genetic factors, however, are not known.

Figure 15 When blood cannot flow through a coronary artery, such as the the diseased artery shown here, a heart attack or sudden death can result.

Stained LM Magnification: 5×

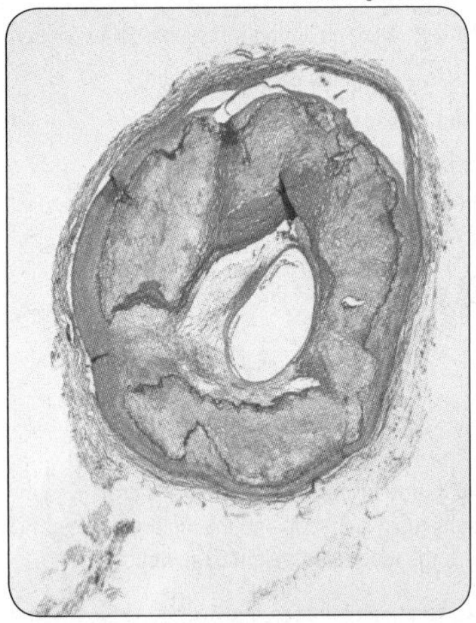

Reading Check **Summarize** the factors that cause coronary artery disease.

Degenerative Diseases

Some diseases called **degenerative** (dih JEH nuh ruh tihv) **diseases** are the result of a part of the body wearing out. This can be due to the natural aging process. However, a degenerative condition, such as degenerative arthritis, could occur sooner than would be expected if the person is genetically predisposed to the disease or if the person's joints have experienced an increased amount of wear and tear. Degenerative arthritis is common; most people have it by age 70. It is found in almost all vertebrate animals. Arteriosclerosis (ar tir ee oh skluh ROH sus), which is a hardening of the arteries, is another example of a degenerative disease. Because degenerative diseases also have a genetic component, some individuals might be more likely to develop a degenerative disease because of their genetic makeup.

Differentiated Instruction

English Learners A note-taking guide can help English learners. Modify the outline activity by providing students with a fill-in-the-blank form of the outline and a word bank. They can complete this outline as they read or listen to a lecture or discussion.

For more tips, see pages 14T–15T.

Reading Check Genetic factors and environmental components, such as diet, contribute to coronary artery disease.

Metabolic Diseases

Metabolic disease results from an error in a biochemical pathway. Some metabolic diseases result in the inability to digest specific amino acids or to regulate body processes. When the pancreas does not make the proper amount of insulin and glucose does not enter body cells normally, the condition is known as Type 2 diabetes. This results in high glucose levels in the bloodstream, which causes damage to many organs including the kidneys and the retinas of the eyes. Metabolic diseases can have a genetic component but also can involve environmental factors such as diet.

Cancer

Cancer is characterized by abnormal cell growth. Normally, certain regulatory molecules in the body control the beginning and end of the cell cycle. If this control is lost, abnormal cell growth results that could lead to various types of tumors, as shown in **Figure 16.** The abnormal cells can interfere with normal body functions and can travel throughout the body. Cancer can develop in any body tissue or organ, including the blood cells. Cancer in the blood cells is called leukemia. Both genetic and environmental factors have been shown to cause cancer.

Connection to History Cancer has been a disease that affects humans since ancient times. Egyptian mummies show evidence of bone cancer, and ancient Greek scientists described different kinds of cancer. Medieval manuscripts have reported details about cancer.

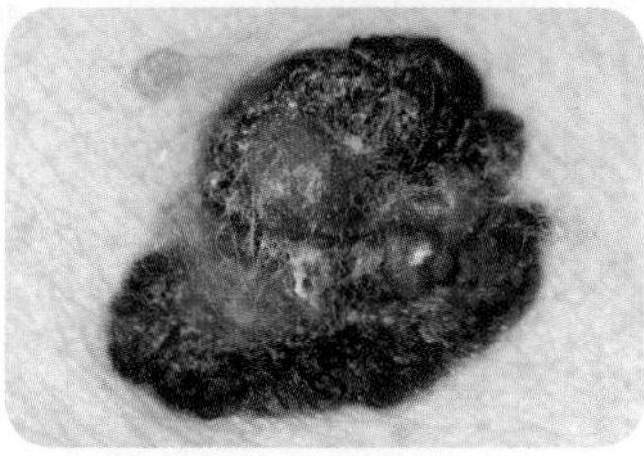

■ **Figure 16** Cancer is due to an abnormal increase in cell division in the body, resulting in a tumor such as this skin tumor.
Infer *why this large growth is so life-threatening.*

MiniLab 2

Compare Cancerous and Healthy Cells

Inquiry MiniLab

How do cancerous cells and healthy cells differ in appearance? Observe and compare liver cells afflicted with this common noninfectious disease to healthy liver cells.

Procedure

1. Read and complete the lab safety form.
2. Place a prepared **slide of healthy human liver cells** on a **microscope.**

WARNING: *Never touch broken microscope slides or other broken glass materials.*

3. Observe the healthy liver cells under several different magnifications.
4. Sketch a diagram of several healthy liver cells.
5. Repeat steps 2–4 with a prepared **slide of cancerous human liver cells.**

Analysis

1. **Compare and contrast** the features of healthy liver cells with those of cancerous liver cells.
2. **Infer** why it would not be dangerous to handle an object that was handled by a patient with liver cancer.
3. **Describe** how cancer disrupts the body's homeostasis.

LM Magnification: 50×

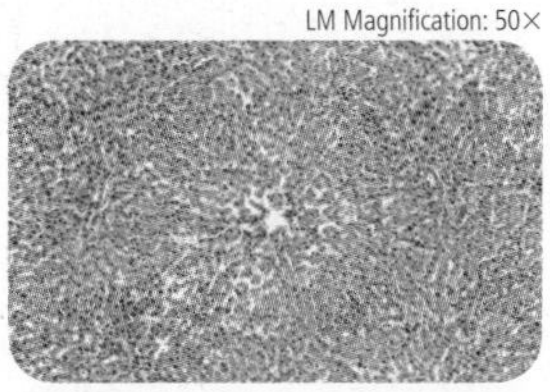

Healthy cells

LM Magnification: 50×

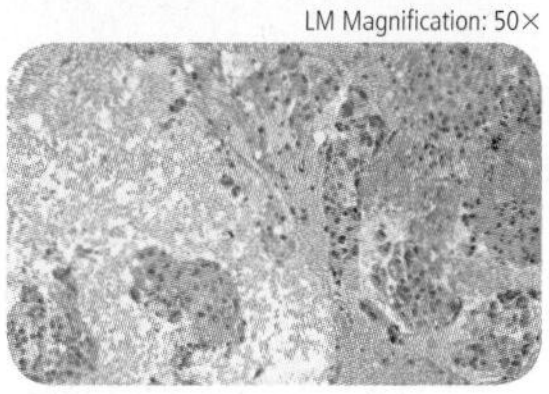

Cancerous cells

■ **Caption Question Fig. 16** Cancer cells do not function like normal cells, and they crowd out normal cells.

MiniLab 2

Inquiry MiniLab

For a lab worksheet, use your eTeacherEdition Online.

RUBRIC A rubric for evaluating MiniLabs is found on your eTeacherEdition Online.

Est. Time 10 min

Safety Precautions Approve lab safety forms before work begins. Caution students to notify you immediately if a slide breaks. Students should never touch broken glass.

Teaching Strategy Students can also compare the cancerous liver cells with healthy cheek cells they extract from their saliva. Show students how to obtain a sample by gently scraping the inside of the cheek with a toothpick.

Analysis

1. Answers might vary, but cancerous cells will vary in shape and size. They probably will be lighter in color and may form swirling patterns. Healthy cells probably will be darker in color, and they will be uniform in size and shape, and will form regular lattice shaped patterns.
2. Cancer is a noninfectious disease, not transmitted through contact.
3. Answers will vary but might include fever, fatigue, and disruption of organ functions. Cancer cells are cells that are growing out of control and no longer performing normal functions. They replicate rapidly and spread throughout the body if left unchecked.

LabManager™

Customize this lab with the LabManager™ CD-ROM.

R Reading Strategy

EL BL OL AL

Active Comprehension In groups of 3–4, have students volunteer to read the text under the heading *Inflammatory Diseases.* **SAY TO STUDENTS:** ***Write questions about topics you would like to know more about.*** Provide students learning English with several questions, and have the students keep the questions in mind when they read. Questions might include: *What is an inflammatory disease? What are some examples of allergens? What releases histamine? What happens in anaphylactic shock?*

D Develop Concepts

EL BL OL **Activity** Have students research treatments for people who have severe allergic reactions.

ASK STUDENTS: ***What should you do if you see someone suffering from a severe allergic reaction?*** Call an emergency number, such as 911, to get medical help at once. Many people at risk of severe allergic reactions carry syringes loaded with epinephrine, a hormone and neurotransmitter that helps stop the symptoms of a severe allergic reaction.

S Skill Practice

BL OL AL **Visual Literacy** Have students examine Table 4. **ASK STUDENTS:** ***What are some examples of other common allergens?*** Possible answers: medications such as penicillin, foods such as corn, insect venom

Concepts in Motion

Interactive Table

R Inflammatory Diseases

Inflammatory diseases, such as allergies and autoimmunity, are diseases in which the body produces an inflammatory response to a common substance. Recall from Section 2 that infectious diseases also result in an inflammatory response. However, the inflammatory response in an infectious disease enhances the overall immune response. This inflammatory response is a result of the immune system removing bacteria or other microorganisms from the body. In inflammatory disease, the inflammatory response is not helpful to the body.

D **Allergies** Certain individuals might have an abnormal reaction to environmental antigens. A response to environmental antigens is called an **allergy.** These antigens are called allergens and include things such as plant pollens, dust, dust mites, and various foods, as illustrated in **Table 4.** An individual becomes sensitized to the allergen and has localized inflammatory response with swollen itchy eyes, stuffy nose, sneezing, and sometimes a skin rash. These symptoms are the result of a chemical called histamine that is released by certain white blood cells. Antihistamine medications can help alleviate some of these symptoms.

Reading Check **Explain** how allergies are related to the immune system.

S

Table 4 **Common Allergens** Concepts in Motion Interactive Table

Allergen	Example	Description
Dust mite	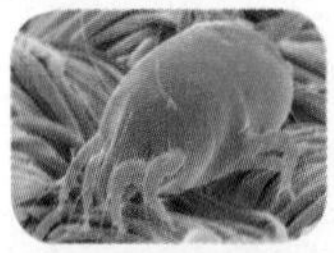 Color-Enhanced SEM Magnification: 170×	Dust mites are found in mattresses, pillows, and carpets. Mites and mite feces are allergens.
Plant pollen	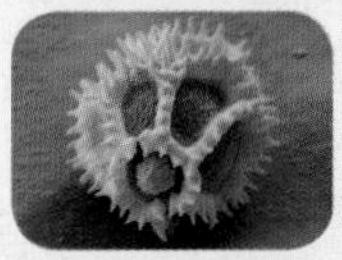 Color-Enhanced SEM Magnification: 2300×	Different parts of the country have very different pollen seasons; people can react to one or more pollens, and a person's pollen allergy season might be from early spring to late fall.
Animal dander	 Color-Enhanced SEM Magnification: 80×	Dander is skin flakes; cat and dog allergies are the most common, but people also are allergic to pets such as birds, hamsters, rabbits, mice, and gerbils.
Peanut		Allergic reaction to peanuts can result in anaphylaxis. Peanut allergy is responsible for more fatalities than any other type of allergy.
Latex	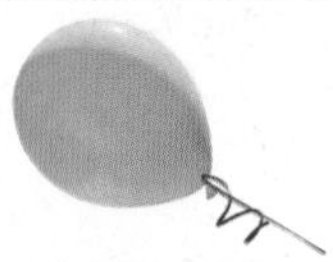	Latex comes from the milky sap of the rubber tree, found in Africa and Southeast Asia; the exact cause of latex allergy is unknown.

Demonstration

Allergens Bring in photos of common allergens. Use these photos to stimulate a discussion about allergies, allergy treatments, and how people try to stop the allergy-stimulating substance from causing an allergy attack.

Est. time: 10 min

Reading Check During an allergic response, the immune system produces an abnormal inflammatory response to a common substance such as grass or pollen.

Severe allergic reactions to particular allergens can result in **anaphylactic** (an uh fuh LAK tik) **shock,** which causes a massive release of histamine. In anaphylactic shock, the smooth muscles in the bronchioles contract, which restricts air flow into and out of the lungs.

Common allergens that cause severe allergic reactions are bee stings, penicillin, peanuts, and latex, which is used to make balloons and surgical gloves. People who are extremely sensitive to these allergens require prompt medical treatment if exposed to these agents because anaphylactic reactions are life-threatening. Allergies and anaphylactic reactions are known to have an inherited component.

Autoimmunity During the development of the immune system, the immune system learns not to attack proteins produced by the body. However, some people develop autoimmunity (aw toh ih MYOON ih tee) and do form antibodies to their own proteins, which injures their cells.

Figure 17 shows the hands of a person with rheumatoid arthritis—a form of arthritis in which antibodies attack the joints. Degenerative arthritis, the form of arthritis that you read about earlier in the section on degenerative diseases, is not caused by autoimmunity.

Rheumatic fever and lupus (LEW pus) are other examples of autoimmune disorders. Rheumatic fever is an inflammation in which antibodies attack the valves of the heart. This can lead to damage to the heart valves and cause the valves to leak or not close properly as blood moves through the heart. Lupus is a disorder in which autoantibodies are formed and attack healthy tissue. As a result, many organs are vulnerable to attack by the body's own immune system.

W

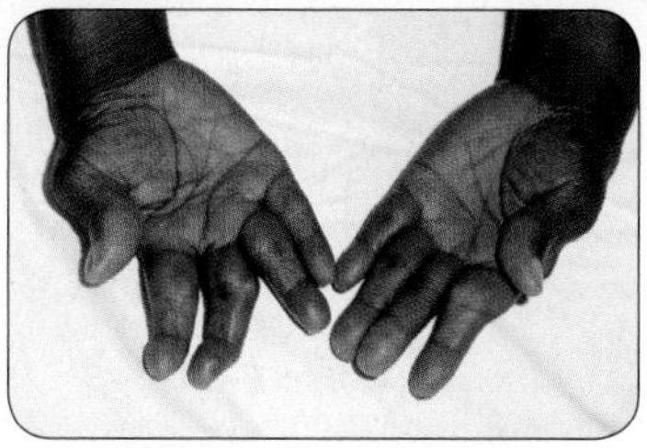

Figure 17 The large knobs and deformaties of these fingers are due to rheumatoid arthritis, an autoimmune disease.

W Writing Support

OL AL Formal Writing

Have students research and write a brief report on an autoimmune disease such as Addison's disease, Grave's disease, or myasthenia gravis.

Critical Thinking

BL OL AL Analyze

SAY TO STUDENTS: ***Cell membranes have surface proteins. These proteins are as unique as our DNA. The surfaces of tissues or organs are covered in these cellular proteins. So, before an organ is transplanted, doctors make sure that the donor and the recipient have as many matching proteins as possible. If the proteins do not match, the immune system of the recipient can reject the organ.*** **ASK STUDENTS:** ***Who is most likely to be a good match for someone who needs a transplant?*** biologically related family members because they share genes

Section 3 Assessment

Section Summary

- Noninfectious disorders often have both a genetic and an environmental component.
- The inflammatory response to an infectious disease enhances the immune response, but the inflammatory response to an inflammatory disease is not helpful to the body.
- Allergies are due to an overactive immune response to allergens found in the environment.
- Anaphylactic shock is a severe hypersensitivity to particular allergens.
- Autoimmunity results in an immune attack on body cells.

Understand Main Ideas

1. MAIN Idea **Identify** the type of noninfectious disease shown in **Figure 15.**
2. **Explain** the role of allergens in allergies.
3. **Create** a diagram demonstrating the process of anaphylactic shock.
4. **Categorize** the following diseases into the categories used in this section: sickle cell disease, diabetes, vertebral degeneration, autoimmunity, and leukemia.

Think Critically

5. **Hypothesize** several causes of chronic bronchitis (inflammation of the bronchioles) found in coal miners.
6. **Create** a plan that limits a child's exposure to cat dander when the child is found to be allergic to that allergen.

WRITING in **Biology**

7. Create a pamphlet explaining the symptoms of allergies and listing common allergens.

Formative Assessment

Evaluation Prepare a quiz that has students match a particular disorder with the noninfectious disorder category.

Remediation Students struggling with categorizing disorders can make flashcards with the disorder type (such as genetic disorders) on one side of the card and examples of disorders on the other side.

Section 3 Assessment

1. genetic
2. Allergens are the triggering antigens for allergies. They trigger the release of histamine.
3. Answers might vary, but the diagram might show a person being stung by a bee, eating peanuts, getting injected with penicillin, or being exposed to latex gloves, followed by tissue swelling in the bronchioles.
4. sickle-cell disease: genetic; diabetes: metabolic; vertebral degeneration: degenerative; autoimmunity: inflammatory disease; leukemia: cancer
5. Answers might vary but can include genetic, degenerative, or inflammatory.
6. Answers might vary but can include the following: If the child has a cat at home or at day care, the cat may need to be removed. The child might need to limit visits to homes with cats.
7. Pamphlets will vary. Allergens might include pollens, dust mites, and foods. Responses might include itchy eyes, stuffy nose, sneezing, and a rash.

Assessment Online Quiz

Purpose

Students will understand that allergic reactions are produced by a histamine reaction.
F.1, F.6

Anticipatory Guide

ASK STUDENTS: ***What do you know about allergies?*** Students may know that people can develop allergies to many things. Students may suggest that an allergic reaction includes sneezing, wheezing, or anaphylactic shock. ***Are allergies contagious?*** No. Students should know that allergies are not contagious, though because of genetic predispositions, they might occur in greater frequencies among relatives. ***What are some ways to treat allergies?*** over-the-counter medicines, prescription medicines, allergy shots, and avoidance of the allergen

Background

Buckminsterfullerines (buckyballs) are spherical cages about 1-10 nanometers in size made up of 60 carbon atoms. They were discovered in 1985 by scientists who vaporized graphite with a laser as part of an investigation into carbon compounds formed in stars. These structures are the source of much research and investigation, leading to the creation of nanotubes and other nanostructures. Recent studies have shown that buckyballs inhibit allergic responses in mice.

CUTTING-EDGE BIOLOGY

Buckyballs: A Cure for Allergies?

If you have ever had a sneezing fit after smelling flowers or become sick after eating shellfish, you might have had an allergic reaction. Many people have some type of allergy.

A Common Ailment Each year in the United States, consumers spend millions of dollars on nose sprays, pills, shots, doctor visits, and allergen avoidance in the fight against allergies. Common allergens include food, medications, animal venom and dander, and latex. Allergies, particularly food allergies, are increasingly common in the United States.

A Study A recent study gives hope to allergy sufferers in the form of a tiny, carbon ball. Buckminsterfullerenes (nicknamed buckyballs) are spherical cages about 1–10 nanometers in size made up of 60 carbon atoms. They were discovered in 1985 by scientists who vaporized graphite with a laser.

In 2007, a study revealed that buckyballs prevent allergic responses in tissue cultures and in mice. Your immune system reacts to allergens by releasing histamines and other chemicals. It is thought that buckyballs can prevent allergens from activating the histamine response.

Some buckyballs were modified by adding chemical side groups to increase their solubility. Some human immune cells called mast cells grown in tissue cultures were treated with the buckyballs while others were not.

When scientists exposed the cultures to allergenlike molecules, the buckyball-treated cultures released 50 times less histamine and inhibited 30 to 40 other chemicals involved in allergic reactions.

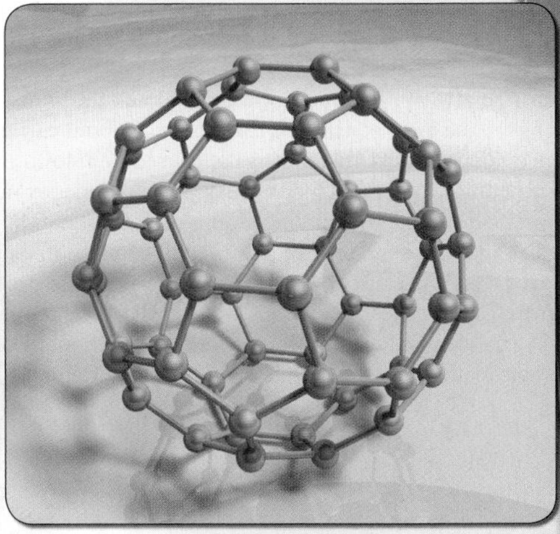

Soccer ball-shaped spheres of carbon atoms called buckyballs might provide relief for allergy sufferers in the future.

Mice injected with buckyballs also released less histamine when exposed to allergens. What scientists do not know is exactly what triggers mast cells to produce histamine and how buckyballs block that reaction.

WRITING in Biology

Research buckyballs and other new treatments for allergies. Work with a partner to develop a creative way to share your findings with the class. Ideas include a public service announcement, news article, poster, or presentation.

WRITING in Biology

RUBRIC Use the modifiable rubric found on your eTeacherEdition Online to assess writing assignments.

Activity

Have students use pipe cleaners, gumballs, and toothpicks or other creative materials to make a model of a buckyball. Encourage students to participate in a group discussion about what makes these structures special. Write down any questions that come up in the discussion on the board. Assign groups of students to research the answers to the questions and report their findings to the class.

WebQuest

BIOLAB

FORENSICS: HOW DO YOU FIND PATIENT ZERO?

Background: **Imagine that a new disease—"cellphonitis"—has invaded your school. One of the symptoms of this disease is the urge to use a cell phone during class. Cellphonitis is easily transferred from person to person by direct contact and there is no natural immunity to the disease. A student in your class has the disease, and is Patient Zero. The disease is spreading in your class and you need to track the disease to prevent the spread of an epidemic.**

Question: *Is it possible to track a disease and determine the identity of Patient Zero?*

Materials

Pasteur pipets (1 per group)
numbered test tubes of water, one infected with simulated "cellphonitis" (1 per group)
test tube racks (1 per group)
small paper cups (1 per group)
pencil and paper
testing indicator

Safety Precautions

Procedure

1. Read and complete the lab safety form.
2. Prepare a table to keep track of the contacts you make. Select a test tube and record the number of the test tube.
3. Use a Pasteur pipet and move a small amount of the fluid from the test tube to a paper cup.
4. Your teacher will divide your class into groups. When your group is called, you will simulate the sharing of saliva during drinking water by using your pipets to exchange the fluid in your test tubes with another member of your group.
5. Record who you exchanged with in your tables.
6. Roll the test tube gently between your hands to mix and repeat Step 4 every time your group is told to exchange. Be sure to pick someone different to exchange with each time.
7. When the exchanges are complete, your teacher will act as the epidemiologist and use the testing indicator to see who has the disease.
8. Share the information and work together as groups to see if you can determine the identity of Patient Zero.
9. Once each group has made their hypothesis, test the original fluid in each cup to see who really was Patient Zero.
10. Return the test tubes. Dispose of the other materials you used as instructed by your teacher.

Analyze and Conclude

1. **Analyze** Use your data and draw a diagram for each possible Patient Zero. Use arrows to show who should be infected with each possible Patient Zero.
2. **Compare and Contrast** How was the spread of "cellphonitis" in this simulation similar to the spread of disease in real life? How was it different?
3. **Think Critically** If this simulation were run in a large class, why might the disease not be passed in later exchanges?
4. **Error Analysis** What problems did you run into as you tried to determine the identity of Patient Zero?

COMMUNICATE

Newscast Research a current disease epidemic. Prepare a newscast about how epidemiologists are searching for the source of disease and present it to your class.

Analyze and Conclude

1. Every student who is infected and only had contact with other infected students is a possible patient zero. The students should draw diagrams for each of these infected individuals.
2. Sample answer: The spread of "Cellphonitis" is similar because each involved some type of contact to pass the pathogen to others. Differences include the following: no students were immune to the disease, students who were "infected" did not actually become sick, and an actual pathogen was not passed in the fluid.
3. As the fluid is passed from person to person, the NaOH becomes more dilute. The solution can eventually become too dilute to be measured by the indicator.
4. Students may have found that a person thought to be infected was not because of over-dilution or improper exchange of fluid. Students may also have forgotten to record an exchange or recorded an exchange incorrectly.

BIOLAB

Inquiry BioLab

For a lab worksheet, use your eTeacherEdition Online.

RUBRIC A rubric for evaluating BioLabs is found on your eTeacherEdition Online.

Est. Time 45 min

Content Background
In this simulation, students will use a pH test strip to trace the transmission of a "disease." One student in the class (Patient Zero) will pick a tube that has NaOH. The tube with NaOH will have a pH above 7. When other students exchange liquid with Student Zero or someone who previously exchanged with this student, the pH of their tubes will also rise. The pH test strip will then identify anyone who has been "infected."

Safety Precautions Approve lab safety forms before work begins. Make sure students are careful handling glass test tubes and do not inhale NaOH.

Teaching Strategies

- Pay attention to the student who picks the tube spiked with NaOH. Keep track of the pattern of transmission as students exchange and make sure that about 1/3 of the students are infected.
- At the end of the exchanges, have the students put all of their exchange information on a transparency that can be projected for the entire class to use. Use the projections to explain how Patient Zero was identified.

Alternative Teaching Demo
You can do this as a demonstration instead of a lab. Use several different test tube racks to help you keep track of which tubes have been contaminated.

Chapter 37

Study Guide

ConnectED

Students can use the following to review the chapter.

Review

Vocabulary eGames
Vocabulary eFlashcards
Vocabulary PuzzleMaker

Assessment

Online Quizzes
Online Test Practice
Standardized Test Practice

Use the *ExamView® Assessment Suite* CD-ROM to:

- create multiple versions of tests
- create modified tests with one mouse click
- edit existing questions and add your own questions
- build tests aligned with state standards using built-in state curriculum tags
- change English tests to Spanish with one mouse click
- track students' progress using the Teacher Management System

Chapter 37 Study Guide

THEME FOCUS Scientific Inquiry Koch's postulates were discovered through scientific inquiry and changed the way disease is diagnosed and treated.

BIG Idea The immune system attempts to protect the body from contracting an infection through pathogens.

Section 1 Infectious Diseases

infectious disease (p. 1076)
pathogen (p. 1076)
Koch's postulates (p. 1077)
reservoir (p. 1078)
endemic disease (p. 1081)
epidemic (p. 1081)
pandemic (p. 1081)
antibiotic (p. 1082)

MAIN Idea Pathogens are dispersed by people, other animals, and objects.

- Pathogens, such as bacteria, viruses, protozoans, and fungi, cause infectious diseases.
- Koch's postulates demonstrate how a particular pathogen causes a certain disease.
- Pathogens are found in disease reservoirs and are transmitted to humans by direct and indirect methods.
- The symptoms of disease are caused by invasion of the pathogen and the response of the host immune system.
- Treatment of infectious disease includes the use of antibiotics and antiviral drugs.

Section 2 The Immune System

complement protein (p. 1085)
interferon (p. 1085)
lymphocyte (p. 1086)
antibody (p. 1086)
B cell (p. 1086)
helper T cell (p. 1088)
cytotoxic T cell (p. 1088)
memory cell (p. 1089)
immunization (p. 1089)

MAIN Idea The immune system has two main components: nonspecific immunity and specific immunity.

- The nonspecific immune response includes the skin barrier, secreted chemicals, and cellular pathways that activate phagocytosis.
- The specific immune response involves the activation of B cells, which produce antibodies, and T cells, which include helper T cells and cytotoxic T cells.
- Passive immunity involves receiving antibodies against a disease.
- Active immunity results in immune memory against a disease.
- HIV attacks helper T cells, causing an immune system failure.

Section 3 Noninfectious Disorders

degenerative disease (p. 1092)
metabolic disease (p. 1093)
allergy (p. 1094)
anaphylactic shock (p. 1095)

MAIN Idea Noninfectious disorders include genetic disorders, degenerative diseases, metabolic diseases, cancer, and inflammatory diseases.

- Noninfectious disorders often have both a genetic and an environmental component.
- The inflammatory response to an infectious disease enhances the immune response, but the inflammatory response to an inflammatory disease is not helpful to the body.
- Allergies are due to an overactive immune response to allergens found in the environment.
- Anaphylactic shock is a severe hypersensitivity to particular allergens.
- Autoimmunity results in an immune attack on body cells.

Review **Vocabulary PuzzleMaker**

For additional practice with vocabulary, have students access the Vocabulary PuzzleMaker online.

Review **Vocabulary eGames**

Chapter 37 Assessment

Section 1

Vocabulary Review

Match the definitions below with a vocabulary term from the Study Guide page.

1. A(n) __________ is an agent that causes an infectious disease.

2. When a disease becomes widespread in a particular area, it is called a/an __________.

3. A source of disease organisms is called a __________.

Understand Main Ideas

4. Which national organization tracks disease patterns in the United States?
A. The Centers for Disease Control and Prevention
B. National Disease Center
C. World Health Organization
D. United Nations

5. Which scientist established a method for determining whether a microorganism caused a specific disease?
A. Koch
B. Hooke
C. Sagan
D. Mendel

6. Which is the most common way that humans acquire an infectious disease?
A. contaminated water
B. mosquito bites
C. sick animals
D. infected humans

Use the photo below to answer question 7.

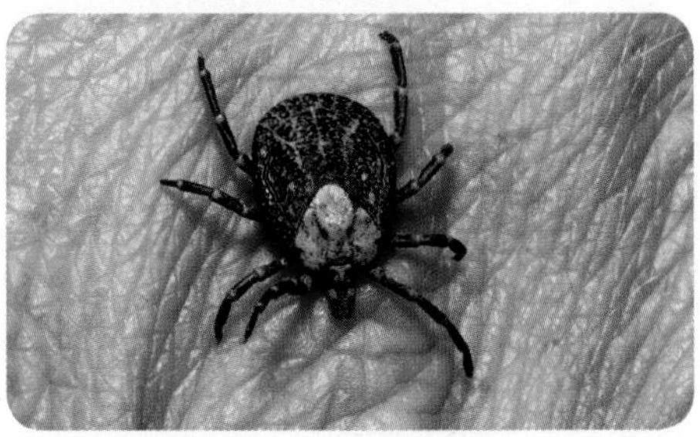

7. Which type of disease transmission is shown above?
A. direct contact
B. air transmission
C. object transmission
D. vector transmission

Use the photo below to answer question 8.

8. Which substance is secreted by the organism shown above?
A. anthrax
B. influenza
C. gentamicin
D. penicillin

Constructed Response

9. **THEME FOCUS Scientific Inquiry** Explain how you could prove that a particular bacteria was causing an infectious disease in a mouse population.

10. **Open Ended** Explain how the Centers for Disease Control and Prevention would be able to determine if an epidemic was occurring in your city.

11. **CAREERS IN BIOLOGY** Imagine you are the school nurse. Describe to students more than one way the cold virus could be transmitted from one person to another.

Think Critically

12. **MAIN Idea** Design a feasible plan that could decrease the spread of infectious disease within your school.

13. **Evaluate** why growing viruses in cell cultures would be an exception to Koch's postulates.

Section 2

Vocabulary Review

For questions 14–16, match each definition with a vocabulary term from the Study Guide page.

14. a chemical produced by B cells in response to antigen stimulation

15. a cell that activates B cells and cytotoxic T cells

16. a type of white blood cell produced in the bone marrow that includes B and T cells

Chapter 37

Assessment

Section 1

Vocabulary Review

1. pathogen
2. epidemic
3. reservoir

Understand Main Ideas

4. A
5. A
6. D
7. D
8. D

Constructed Response

9. The answer should demonstrate an understanding of Koch's postulates.

10. The Centers For Disease Control and Prevention receives information from doctors and clinics in my city and when the numbers increase dramatically, they would know that there is an epidemic occurring in my city.

11. Answers may vary, but might include direct transmission, droplet transmission, or transmission by an object such as a shared drinking glass.

Think Critically

12. Answers may vary but might include disinfecting areas that humans have direct contact with such as drinking fountains, door knobs, etc. Students who are ill could not be allowed to attend school.

13. The cell cultures would not be pure. They would contain the virus and host cells.

Section 2

Vocabulary Review

14. antibody
15. helper T cell
16. lymphocyte

Assessment Online Test Practice

Understand Main Ideas

17. C
18. C
19. C
20. D
21. A

Constructed Response

22. The T cells (after being produced in the bone marrow) mature in the thymus gland.
23. The nonspecific immune system defense is fast. It begins immediately after an organism enters the body. The specific immune response is more effective at protecting the body from particular pathogens.
24. Answers may vary, but may include that many of these diseases are not very common, so people may not be too concerned about these diseases.

Think Critically

25. A phagocyte internalizes and processes an antigen from the tetanus bacteria. The phagocyte places a piece of the antigen on its surface and presents it to helper T cells. The helper T cells present a processed antigen to the B cells, activating them to produce antibodies for tetanus.
26. The helper T cell's role is to activate both B cells and cytotoxic T cells by presenting them a processed antigen. Cytotoxic T cell's role is to release cytokines and kill pathogens after being activated by the helper T cell.

Understand Main Ideas

Use the diagram below to answer questions 17 and 18.

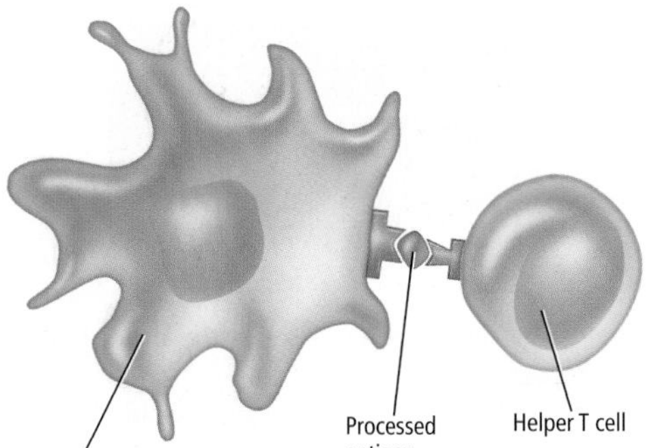

17. What kind of immune response is demonstrated in the diagram above?
A. genetic
B. nonspecific
C. specific
D. hormonal

18. To which does the activated helper T cell present its antigen?
A. a pathogen
B. bone marrow
C. a B cell
D. the thymus gland

19. Which is the first defense your body has against infectious disease?
A. the helper T cell
B. an antibody
C. your skin
D. phagocytosis

20. What is the role of complement proteins, found in the plasma, in the immune response?
A. enhance phagocytosis
B. activate phagocytes
C. enhance destruction of a pathogen
D. all of the above

21. Where are lymphocytes produced?
A. bone marrow
B. thymus gland
C. spleen
D. lymph nodes

Constructed Response

22. Short Answer Describe how the thymus gland is involved in the development of immunity.

23. MAIN Idea Evaluate why the body needs both a nonspecific and a specific immune response.

24. Open Ended Form a hypothesis as to why the proportion of unvaccinated Americans is increasing.

Think Critically

25. Organize the sequence of events that occurs to activate an antibody response to tetanus bacteria.

26. Compare the role of helper T cells and cytotoxic T cells in the specific immune response.

Section 3

Vocabulary Review

Use a vocabulary term from the Study Guide page to answer questions 27–29.

27. What type of reaction is a hypersensitivity to an allergen such as a bee sting?

28. Which type of disease occurs when people abnormally respond to environmental antigens?

29. Which type of disease is caused by a body part wearing out?

Understand Main Ideas

Use the photo below to answer question 30.

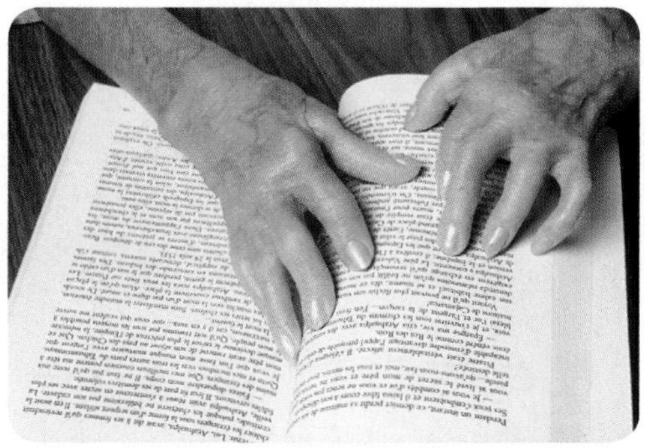

30. The above photo demonstrates which disease?
A. tetanus
B. sickle-cell disease
C. rheumatoid arthritis
D. allergy

31. Which type of noninfectious disease is defined as a problem in a biochemical pathway in the body?
A. inflammatory disease
B. metabolic disease
C. degenerative disease
D. cancer

Section 3

Vocabulary Review

27. anaphylactic shock
28. allergy
29. degenerative disease

Understand Main Ideas

30. C
31. B

Assessment Online Test Practice

32. Which of the following substances is released in the body to cause most of the symptoms of allergies?
A. insulin **C.** histamine
B. allergens **D.** acetylcholine

33. Individuals can have a dangerous response to particular allergens, such as latex, and go into anaphylactic shock. What will be the result?
A. breathing problems **C.** atherosclerosis
B. epileptic seizures **D.** arthritis

34. In autoimmunity, which attacks the body's own proteins?
A. antigens **C.** antibodies
B. allergens **D.** antihistamines

Constructed Response

35. **Short Answer** Describe how an allergy differs from a common cold, considering that the symptoms are similar.

36. **Short Answer** Discuss the effects on the organs of the body when the smooth muscles in the bronchioles constrict, causing breathing to be difficult.

37. **Short Answer** Evaluate why lupus causes systemic problems in the body.

Think Critically

38. MAIN Idea Construct a table listing each of the types of non-infectious disease and give an example of each type.

Use the graph below to answer question 39.

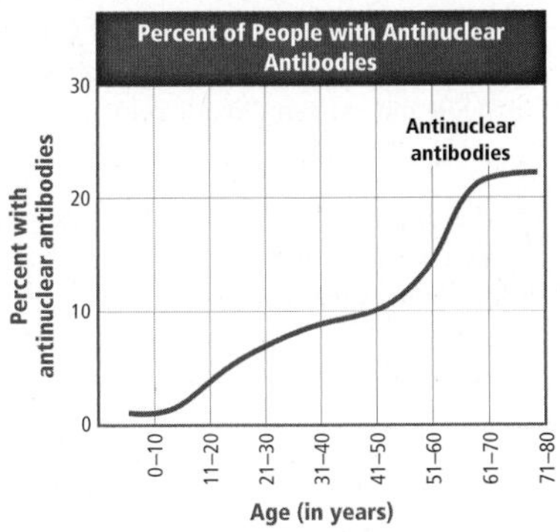

39. **Summarize** the relationship between antinuclear antibodies and age.

Summative Assessment

40. BIG Idea A friend of yours has been diagnosed with chicken pox. Describe how your body protects itself from infection and what you can do to lessen your chances of contracting the disease.

41. Choose a pathogen and make a sequence diagram showing the steps of how each type of immunity is involved in preventing or fighting infection.

42. WRITING in Biology Construct an analogy comparing the immune system to a castle being attacked by invaders from a neighboring territory.

DBQ Document-Based Questions

The table below illustrates the effectiveness of using vaccinations to prevent the contraction of disease. There was a large decrease in cases of the diseases listed after the use of vaccinations.

Data obtained from: Mandell, G. L., et al. 1995. *Principles and Practice of Infectious Diseases*, 4th ed. Churchill Livingstone, and Centers for Disease Control and Prevention. 2000. *Morbidity and Mortality Weekly Report* 48: 1162-1192.

Disease	Maximum Number of Cases in a Year	Number of Cases in 1999 in U.S.	Percent Change
Measles	894,134	60	–99.99
Mumps	152,209	352	–99.77
Polio (paralytic)	21,269	0	–100.0
Tetanus	1560	33	–97.88
Hepatitis B	26,611	6495	–75.59

43. Which disease has shown the greatest change in occurrence since the year of its maximum number of cases?

44. Tetanus has shown a large decline since the United States started vaccinating. Explain why this disease will not be completely eradicated.

45. Create a bar graph showing the percent change in number of cases as a result of vaccination for each disease.

32. C
33. A
34. C

Constructed Response

35. An allergy is an immune response to a harmless substance. A cold is caused by a virus. An allergy's symptoms come from the release of histamine, which causes the running nose and other symptoms. The symptoms of a cold come from the virus killing cells and the host's immune system trying to flush the virus out with mucus.

36. When the bronchioles constrict, less air will be available in the lungs. Less oxygen is passed into the bloodstream. Body tissues and organs may be oxygen-deficient.

37. Lupus results from antinuclear antibodies. Since all body cells have nuclei, the antibodies could attack any type of body cell.

Think Critically

38. The table should include genetic diseases, degenerative diseases, metabolic diseases, cancer, and inflammatory diseases, with an example of each.

39. There is greater incidence of antinuclear antibodies with greater age.

Summative Assessment

40. The body is protected initially by nonspecific immunity using barriers such as skin to guard against any invading pathogen. Then, if the pathogen makes it into the body, specific immunity is aimed at destroying a specific disease and involves the lymphatic system. Students should avoid contact with their friend while he or she is contagious, and clean any surfaces that their friend may have come into direct contact with.

41. Example: the virus that causes the common cold enters the body through the respiratory system. Nonspecific immunity including saliva, nasal secretions, mucus, cilia, and interferon may prevent the virus from infecting the body. Antibodies may form as part of specific immunity if nonspecific immunity is not successful.

42. Answers may vary. Answers should include references to nonspecific and specific immunity and should refer to the different parts of the lymphatic system and organs.

WRITING in Biology

RUBRIC Use the modifiable rubric found on your eTeacherEdition Online to assess writing assignments.

DBQ Document-Based Questions

Abbas, A.K., and Licktman, A.K., 2001. Basic Immunology. *MMWR* 48 (5): 1–124.

43. polio
44. Tetanus is a bacterium normally found in the soil. It will always be there.
45. Bar graph should have a title. The diseases should be labeled on the *x*-axis and percent change on the *y*-axis.

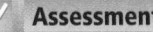

Assessment Online Test Practice

Standardized Test Practice

Multiple Choice

1. C
2. D
3. A
4. A
5. B
6. A
7. B
8. D

Short Answer

9. The number of reported cases of the disease was increasing between 1900 and 2000.
10. Answers may vary. Accept all reasonable responses.
    - **A.** Reporting systems might have improved over the course of the century, so the disease is more often recognized, or more likely to be reported.
    - **B.** The disease might be caused by an agent that is not controllable by means developed in the 20th century.
11. Answers may vary. Protists are classified together because they are not animals, plants, or fungi. Feeding habits are the main characteristics used to classify the three main groups of protists. Animal-like protists are heterotrophic. Plant-like protists are autotrophic. Fungus-like protists absorb nutrients from other organisms.
12. During dilation, the cervix opens and uterine contractions become stronger. Dilation allows the baby to pass through the birth canal. Without dilation, the only way to remove the baby from the mother would be by cutting open the mother's uterus.
13. Answers may vary. The large intestine absorbs excess water from food wastes. It contains bacteria that produce vitamin K and some B vitamins. The wastes are compacted and eliminated from the body by the large intestine.
14. Reptiles breathe by expanding and contracting their ribcage and body wall to move air into and out of their lungs. It is an efficient way of getting oxygen into the lungs and carbon dioxide out of the lungs. This means that they have lots of oxygen available for muscle activity.
15. The ganglion is a central area for the nervous system of a flatworm. Eyespots and auricles gather information about the surroundings that the flatworm responds to.

Standardized Test Practice

Cumulative

Multiple Choice

1. In the digestive system, complex carbohydrates are broken down into which substance?
A. amino acids
B. fatty acids
C. simple sugars
D. starches

Use the diagram below to answer questions 2 and 3.

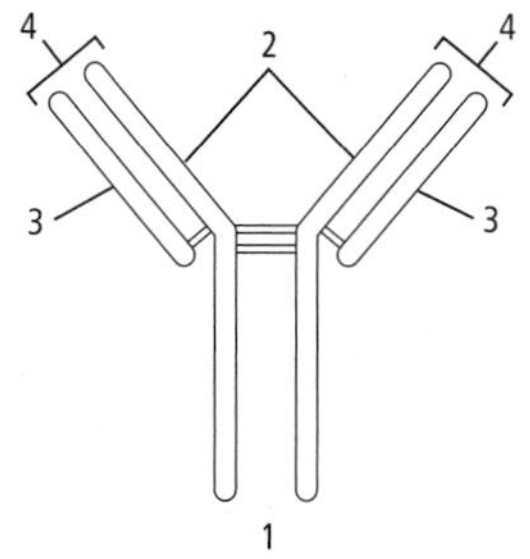

2. The diagram above shows the basic structure of an antibody. Which part of the diagram corresponds to the antigen binding site?
A. 1
B. 2
C. 3
D. 4

3. Why are parts 2 and 3 of the diagram above important for the formation of antibodies?
A. They allow for an enormous number of possible antibodies to form.
B. They are created by the T cells in the immune system.
C. They help reduce the number of antibodies that form.
D. They help stimulate the inflammatory response.

4. Which is the role of estrogen during puberty in females?
A. It causes development of the female body.
B. It causes eggs to begin to mature in the ovaries.
C. It causes meiosis to start to produce an egg.
D. It causes ovaries to release mature eggs.

5. Which is true of the appendix?
A. It absorbs sodium hydrogen carbonate to neutralize acid.
B. It has no known function in the digestive system.
C. It helps break down fats.
D. It secretes acids to help break down foods.

Use the diagram below to answer question 6.

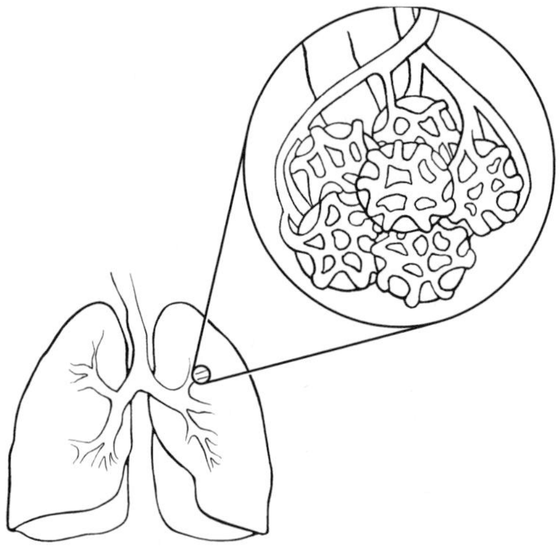

6. Which happens in the blood in these structures?
A. Carbon dioxide and oxygen are exchanged.
B. Carbon dioxide and oxygen remain constant.
C. Nitrogen and carbon dioxide are exchanged.
D. Nitrogen and carbon dioxide remain constant.

7. Puberty takes place during which transition in life?
A. adolescence to adulthood
B. childhood to adolescence
C. fetus to infant
D. zygote to fetus

8. What is the role of hormones in the body?
A. to act as reaction catalysts
B. to control breathing process
C. to help synthesize proteins
D. to regulate many body functions

Short Answer

Use the graph below to answer questions 9 and 10.

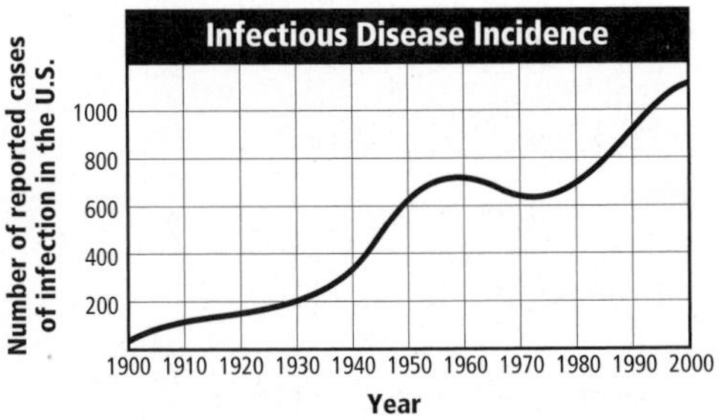

9. What is the overall trend shown in the above graph?

10. What are two possible explanations for the pattern in the above graph?

11. What characteristics are used to classify protists into three groups?

12. Describe the process of dilation during birthing. Assess why it is important.

13. Identify the function of the large intestine.

14. Assess how the respiratory system of most reptiles is adapted for life on land.

15. Free-living flatworms have some unique body structures: eyespots, a ganglion, and auricles that detect chemical stimuli. How are these body structures related to each other?

Extended Response

16. Arthropods first moved onto land about 400 million years ago and have survived several mass extinctions. Propose a hypothesis about why arthropods have been so successful.

17. Compare the production of sperm cells and egg cells during meiosis.

Essay Question

Scientist Marc Lappé wrote the following in 1981 in a book called *Germs That Won't Die.*

"Unfortunately, we played a trick on the natural world by seizing control of these [natural] chemicals, making them more perfect in a way that has changed the whole microbial constitution of the developing countries. We have organisms now proliferating that never existed before in nature. We have selected them. We have organisms that probably caused a tenth of a percent of human disease in the past that now cause twenty, thirty percent of the diseases that we're seeing. We have changed the whole face of the earth by the use of antibiotics."

Using the information in the paragraph above, answer the following question in essay format.

18. As Lappé predicted in 1981, many diseases have emerged in forms that are resistant to treatment by antibiotics and other powerful drugs. Have antibiotics "changed the whole face of the earth" for the better or for the worse? In an organized essay, discuss the advantages and disadvantages of antibiotics as they are used today.

NEED EXTRA HELP?																		
If You Missed Question . . .	1	2	3	4	5	6	7	8	9	10	11	12	13	14	15	16	17	18
Review Section . . .	35.2	37.2	37.2	36.2	35.1	34.2	36.2	35.2	37.1	37.1	19.1	36.2	35.1	29.1	25.1	26.1	36.1	37.1

Extended Response

16. Answers may vary. Students might suggest that they are successful because they are so diverse and live in many different habitats, have rapid reproduction, or have efficient food use.

17. During meiosis, the result of the divisions is the formation of sex cells. In males, four sex cells, called sperm, are produced. In females, the sex cells are one egg and one polar body that degenerates. A second polar body forms after fertilization.

Essay Question

18. The position a student takes should be supported by reasonable information about antibiotics and the immune system. Antibiotics make it possible to fight bacterial diseases that otherwise might have been untreatable. Infections can be treated easily with certain kinds of antibiotics. Many childhood diseases, and other serious diseases such as tuberculosis, can be cured. On the other hand, antibiotics have been misused. Often they have been prescribed to treat the wrong diseases. Consequently, antibiotic-resistant strains of certain diseases have developed. Some antibiotic-resistant diseases cannot be treated effectively with any antibiotics, so that now the resistant diseases are more dangerous than they were originally. Although antibiotics might be inexpensive to use, the development of new drugs to treat antibiotic-resistant diseases can be very expensive.

Student Resources

For students and parents/guardians

Investigation and experimentation are key components of your biology class. Use this reference to learn lab techniques that will enhance your lab experience. Laboratory safety is vital to a successful investigation and experiment; we've outlined basic laboratory safety principles here.

The skillbuilder handbook helps you sharpen your problem-solving skills so you can get the most out of reading and understanding scientific writing and data. Improving skills such as making comparisons, analyzing information, reading time lines, and using graphic organizers also can help you boost your test scores.

The reference handbook is another tool that will assist you. The classification tables, word origins, and the periodic table of the elements are resources that will help increase your comprehension.

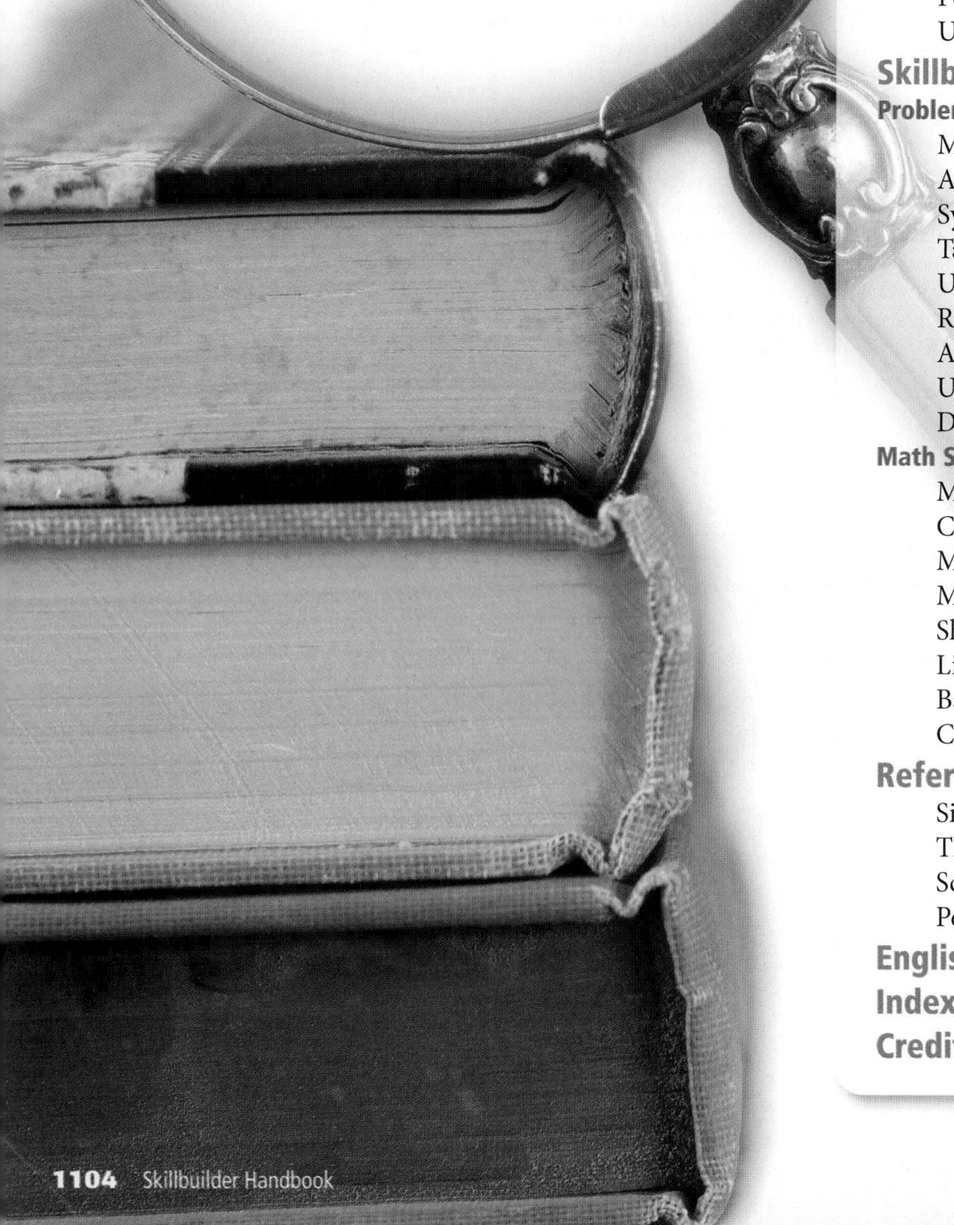

Table of Contents

Investigation and Experimentation

The foundation of scientific knowledge is Investigation and Experimentation. In this section, you will read about lab safety, the proper way to take measurements, and some laboratory techniques. While not every situation you might encounter in the laboratory is covered here, you will gain practical and useful knowledge to make your investigation and experimentation successful experiences.

Laboratory Safety

Follow these safety guidelines and rules to help protect you and others during laboratory investigations.

Complete the Lab Safety Form

- Prior to each investigation, your teacher will have you complete a lab safety form. This contract will inform your teacher that you have read the procedure and are prepared to perform the investigation.
- After your teacher reviews your comments, make any necessary corrections, and sign or initial the form.
- Use the lab safety form to help you prepare for each procedure and take responsibility for your own safety.

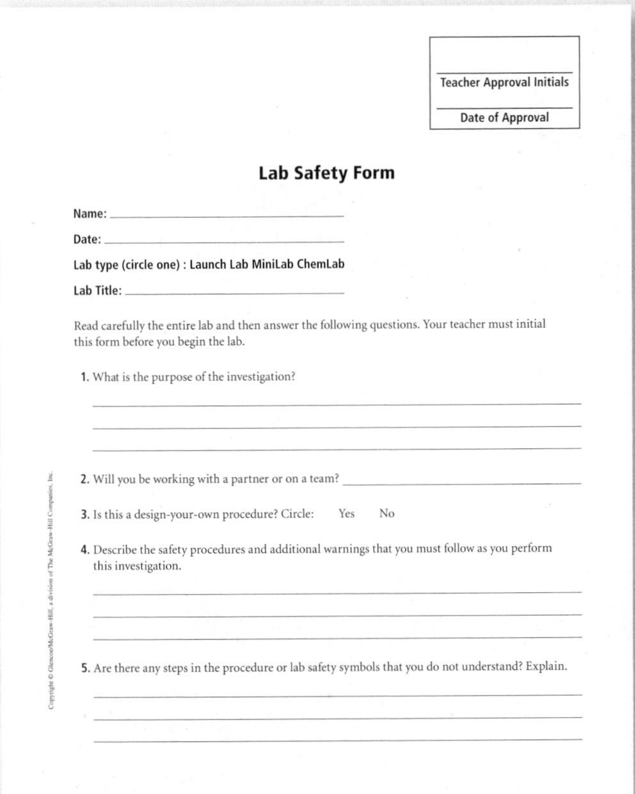

Teacher Approval Initials

Date of Approval

Lab Safety Form

Name: ____________

Date: ____________

Lab type (circle one) : Launch Lab MiniLab ChemLab

Lab Title: ____________

Read carefully the entire lab and then answer the following questions. Your teacher must initial this form before you begin the lab.

1. What is the purpose of the investigation?
2. Will you be working with a partner or on a team? ____________
3. Is this a design-your-own procedure? Circle: Yes No
4. Describe the safety procedures and additional warnings that you must follow as you perform this investigation.
5. Are there any steps in the procedure or lab safety symbols that you do not understand? Explain.

Prevent Accidents

- Always wear chemical-splash safety goggles (not glasses) in the laboratory. Goggles should fit snugly against your face to prevent any liquid from entering the eyes. Put on your goggles before beginning the lab and wear them throughout the entire activity, cleanup, and hand washing.
- Wear protective aprons and the proper type of gloves as your teacher instructs.
- Keep your hands away from your face and mouth while working in the laboratory.
- Do not wear sandals or other open-toed shoes in the lab.
- Remove jewelry on hands and wrists before doing lab work. Remove loose jewelry, such as chains and long necklaces, to prevent them from getting caught in equipment.
- Do not wear clothing loose enough to catch on anything. If clothing is loose, tape or tie it down.
- Tie back long hair to keep it away from flames and equipment.
- Do not use hair spray or other flammable hair products just before or during laboratory work when an open flame is used. These products ignite easily.
- Eating, drinking, chewing gum, applying makeup, and smoking are prohibited in the laboratory.
- You are expected to behave properly in the laboratory. Practical jokes and fooling around can lead to accidents or injury.
- Notify your teacher about allergies or other health conditions that can affect your participation in a lab.

Follow Lab Procedures

- Study all procedures before you begin a laboratory investigation. Ask questions if you do not understand any part of the procedures.
- Review and understand all safety symbols associated with the investigation. A table of the safety symbols is found on page 1108 for your reference.
- Do not begin any activity until directed to do so by your teacher.
- Use all lab equipment for its intended purpose only.
- Collect and carry all equipment and materials to your work area before beginning the lab.
- When obtaining laboratory materials, dispense only the amount you will use.
- If you have materials left over after completing the investigation, check with your teacher to determine the best choice for recycling or disposing of the materials.
- Keep your work area uncluttered.
- Learn and follow procedures for using specific laboratory equipment, such as balances, microscopes, hot plates, and burners.
- When heating or rinsing a container such as a test tube or flask, point it away from yourself and others.
- Do not taste, touch, or smell any chemical or substance in the lab.
- If your teacher instructs you to smell a substance in a container, hold the container a short distance away and fan vapors toward your nose.
- Do not substitute other chemicals or substances for those in the materials list unless instructed to do so by your teacher.
- Do not take any chemical or material outside of the laboratory.

Clean up the Lab

- Turn off all burners, gas valves, and water faucets before leaving the laboratory. Disconnect all electrical devices.

- Clean all equipment as instructed by your teacher. Return everything to the proper storage place.

- Dispose of all materials properly. Place disposable items in containers specifically marked for those types of items. Do not pour liquids down the drain unless instructed to do so by your teacher.

- **Wash your hands thoroughly with soap and warm water after each activity and before removing your goggles.**

Know How to Handle Emergencies

- **Inform your teacher immediately of any mishap, such as fire, bodily injuries, burns, electrical shock, glassware breakage, and chemical or other spills.**

- Do not attempt to clean up spills unless you are given permission and instructions on how to do so. In most instances, your teacher will clean up spills.

- Know the location of the fire extinguisher, safety shower, eyewash, fire blanket, and first-aid kit. After receiving instructions, you can use the safety shower, eyewash, and fire blanket in an emergency without your teacher's permission. However, the fire extinguisher and first-aid kit should be used only by your teacher or, in an extreme emergency, with your teacher's permission.

- If chemicals come into contact with your eyes or skin, notify your teacher immediately and flush your skin or eyes with water.

- If someone is injured or becomes ill, only a professional medical provider or someone certified in first aid should perform first-aid procedures.

Be Responsible

Because your teacher cannot anticipate every safety hazard that might occur and he or she cannot be everywhere in the room at the same time, you need to take some responsibility for your own safety. The general information below should apply to nearly every science lab.

You must:

- review any safety symbols in the labs and be certain you know what they mean;

- follow all teacher instructions for safety and make certain you understand all the hazards related to the lab you are about to perform;

- be able to explain the purpose of the lab;

- be able to explain, or demonstrate, all reasonable emergency procedures, such as:

    - how to evacuate the room during emergencies;
    - how to react to any chemical emergencies;
    - how to deal with fire emergencies;
    - how to perform a scientific investigation safely;
    - how to anticipate some safety concerns and be prepared to address them; and
    - how to use equipment properly and safely.

- be able to locate and use all safety equipment as directed by your teacher, such as:
    - fire extinguishers;
    - fire blankets;
    - eye protective equipment (goggles, safety glasses, face shield);
    - eyewash; and
    - a drench shower.

- be sure to ask questions about any safety concerns that you might have BEFORE starting any investigation.

Safety Symbols

These safety symbols are used in laboratory and field investigations in this book to indicate possible hazards. Learn the meaning of each symbol and refer to this page often. *Remember to wash your hands thoroughly after completing lab procedures.*

SAFETY SYMBOLS	HAZARD	EXAMPLES	PRECAUTION	REMEDY
DISPOSAL	Special disposal procedures need to be followed.	certain chemicals, living organisms	Do not dispose of these materials in the sink or trash can.	Dispose of wastes as directed by your teacher.
BIOLOGICAL	Organisms or other biological materials that might be harmful to humans	bacteria, fungi, blood, unpreserved tissues, plant materials	Avoid skin contact with these materials. Wear mask or gloves.	Notify your teacher if you suspect contact with material. Wash hands thoroughly.
EXTREME TEMPERATURE	Objects that can burn skin by being too cold or too hot	boiling liquids, hot plates, dry ice, liquid nitrogen	Use proper protection when handling.	Go to your teacher for first aid.
SHARP OBJECT	Use of tools or glassware that can easily puncture or slice skin	razor blades, pins, scalpels, pointed tools, dissecting probes, broken glass	Practice common-sense behavior and follow guidelines for use of the tool.	Go to your teacher for first aid.
FUME	Possible danger to respiratory tract from fumes	ammonia, acetone, nail polish remover, heated sulfur, moth balls	Make sure there is good ventilation. Never smell fumes directly. Wear a mask.	Leave foul area and notify your teacher immediately.
ELECTRICAL	Possible danger from electrical shock or burn	improper grounding, liquid spills, short circuits, exposed wires	Double-check setup with teacher. Check condition of wires and apparatus. Use GFI-protected outlets.	Do not attempt to fix electrical problems. Notify your teacher immediately.
IRRITANT	Substances that can irritate the skin or mucous membranes of the respiratory tract	pollen, moth balls, steel wool, fiberglass, potassium permanganate	Wear dust mask and gloves. Practice extra care when handling these materials.	Go to your teacher for first aid.
CHEMICAL	Chemicals that can react with and destroy tissue and other materials	bleaches such as hydrogen peroxide; acids such as sulfuric acid, hydrochloric acid; bases such as ammonia, sodium hydroxide	Wear goggles, gloves, and an apron.	Immediately flush the affected area with water and notify your teacher.
TOXIC	Substance may be poisonous if touched, inhaled, or swallowed.	mercury, many metal compounds, iodine, poinsettia plant parts	Follow your teacher's instructions.	Always wash hands thoroughly after use. Go to your teacher for first aid.
FLAMMABLE	Open flame may ignite flammable chemicals, loose clothing, or hair.	alcohol, kerosene, potassium permanganate, hair, clothing	Avoid open flames and heat when using flammable chemicals.	Notify your teacher immediately. Use fire safety equipment if applicable.
OPEN FLAME	Open flame in use, may cause fire.	hair, clothing, paper, synthetic materials	Tie back hair and loose clothing. Follow teacher's instructions on lighting and extinguishing flames.	Always wash hands thoroughly after use. Go to your teacher for first aid.

Eye Safety Proper eye protection must be worn at all times by anyone performing or observing science activities.

Clothing Protection This symbol appears when substances could stain or burn clothing.

Animal Safety This symbol appears when safety of animals and students must be ensured.

Radioactivity This symbol appears when radioactive materials are used.

Handwashing After the lab, wash hands with soap and water before removing goggles.

Field Investigation Safety

On occasion, your teacher might conduct a field investigation—an investigation on school grounds or off-campus. While many of the laboratory safety guidelines apply, the field has unique safety considerations.

Work Together

- Work with at least one other person.
- Never stray from the main group either alone or with a small group.
- Make sure that each person in your group understands his or her task and how to perform it. Ask your teacher for clarification if necessary.
- Determine how members of your group will communicate in case of a loud environment or an emergency.
- Your teacher or chaperones should be equipped with either cell phones or walkie-talkies. They should be able to communicate with one another, the school, and emergency personnel, if needed, so be sure to let your teacher know if you need help.

Dress Appropriately

- Wear your safety goggles, apron, and gloves as indicated by the procedure.
- Protect yourself from the Sun with sunblock and a hat.
- Long pants and shirts with long sleeves will protect you from the Sun, insects, and plants such as poison ivy and poison oak.

Poison ivy

Poison oak

- Insect-repellent sprays or creams may be necessary for you to use.
- Be sure to wear shoes that have closed toes and heels as well as textured soles.
- If your investigation requires that you wade into a stream, river, lake, or other body of water, wear water-resistant clothing. Do not enter the water if you have any open sores.

Consider Your Environment

- Never approach animals.
- Never drink water from a stream, river, lake, or other body of water.
- Do not remove anything from the habitat. Create a sketch of organisms you are studying.
- Stay away from power lines.
- Stay away from the edges of cliffs and ledges.
- Stay on marked trails.

Follow General Guidelines

- Treat your field investigation like a laboratory investigation. There should be no horseplay.
- A first-aid kit should be brought to the investigation site.
- Always wash your hands when you are finished. If soap and water are unavailable, use an alcohol-based hand sanitizer.

Data Collection

Biologists take measurements in many types of investigations.
- **A population biologist might count tree frogs in a rain-forest survey.**
- **A physical therapist might observe the range of motion of an injured knee.**
- **A microbiologist might measure the diameters of bacteria.**

In this section, you will learn how biologists take careful measurements. When you plan and perform your biology labs, use this section as a guide.

Accuracy, Precision, and Error

In any measurement, there always will be some error—the difference between the measured value and the real or accepted value. Error comes from several sources, including the experimenter, the equipment, and even changes in experimental conditions. Errors can affect both the accuracy and the precision of measurements.

- **Accuracy** refers to how close a measurement is to the real value or the accepted value.
- **Precision** refers to how close a series of measurements are to one another.

Examine the targets in **Figure 1** below while you consider a food scientist who measures the mass of a sample three times.

- Proper equipment setup and good technique: accurate and precise data
- Incorrect equipment setup but good technique: precise but inaccurate data
- Incorrect equipment setup and careless technique: inaccurate and imprecise data

Figure 1

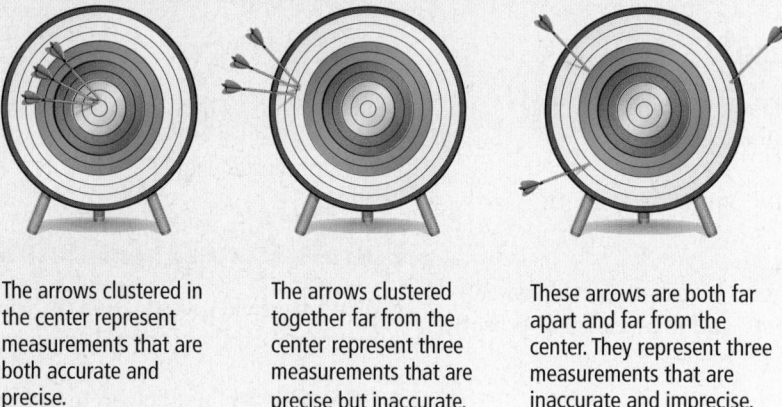

The arrows clustered in the center represent measurements that are both accurate and precise.

The arrows clustered together far from the center represent three measurements that are precise but inaccurate.

These arrows are both far apart and far from the center. They represent three measurements that are inaccurate and imprecise.

Error Analysis

Imagine that an epidemiologist (eh puh dee mee AHL uh just), a biologist who studies epidemics, tested a hypothesis about the way in which avian flu might spread from chickens to humans. All data have been gathered. The epidemiologist must now perform an error analysis, which is a process to identify and describe possible sources of error in measurements.

In your biology investigations, you will need to think of possible sources of measurement errors. Ask yourself questions such as:
- Did I take more than one reading of each measurement?
- Did I use the equipment properly?
- Was I objective, or did I make the results turn out as I expected they might?

Measure Mass

Triple-Beam Balance

A triple-beam balance has a pan and three beams with sliding masses called riders. At one end of the beams is a pointer that indicates whether the mass on the pan is equal to the masses shown on the beams.

To use:

1. Make sure the balance is zeroed before measuring the mass of an object. The balance is zeroed if the pointer is at zero when nothing is on the pan and riders are at their zero points.
2. Place the object to be measured on the pan.
3. Move the riders one notch at a time away from the pan. Begin with the largest rider. If moving the largest rider one notch brings the pointer below zero, begin measuring the mass with the next, smaller rider.
4. Change the positions of the riders until they balance the mass on the pan and the pointer is at zero. Then add the readings from the three beams to determine the mass of the object.

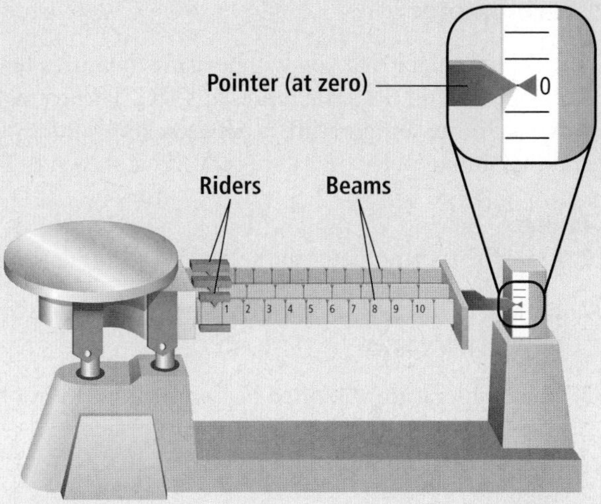

Figure 2

TIP

When using a weighing boat or weighing paper, be sure to zero the balance after you've placed the boat or paper on the pan and before you add a substance to the boat or paper.

Measure Volume

Graduated Cylinder

Use a graduated cylinder to measure the volume of a liquid.

To use:

1. Be sure to have your eyes at the level of the surface of the liquid when reading the scale on a graduated cylinder.
2. The surface of a liquid usually will be curved slightly downward when it is held in a graduated cylinder. This curve is called the meniscus. Read the volume of the liquid at the bottom of the meniscus, as shown in **Figure 3.**
3. The volume will often be between two lines on the graduated cylinder. You should estimate the final digit in your measurement. For example, if the bottom of the meniscus appears to be exactly halfway between the marks for 96 mL and 97 mL, you would read the volume as 96.5 mL.
4. To find the volume of a small solid object, record the volume of some water in a graduated cylinder. Then, measure the volume of the water after you add the object to the cylinder. The volume of the object is the difference between the first and second measurements.

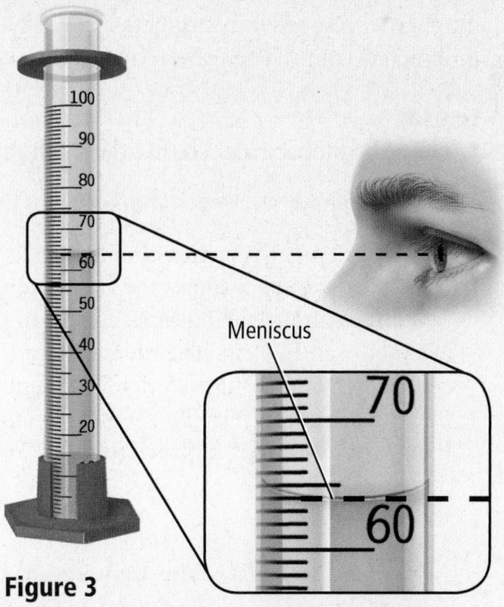

Figure 3

TIP

Do not use a beaker to measure the volume of a liquid. Beakers are used for holding and pouring liquids. To avoid overflow, be sure to use a beaker that holds roughly twice as much liquid as you need.

Measure Temperature

Thermometer

The thermometer that you will be using measures temperature in degrees Celsius (°C). Each division on the scale represents 1°C. The average human body temperature is 37°C. A typical room temperature is between 20°C and 25°C. The freezing point of water is 0°C, and the boiling point of water is 100°C, as shown in **Figure 4.**

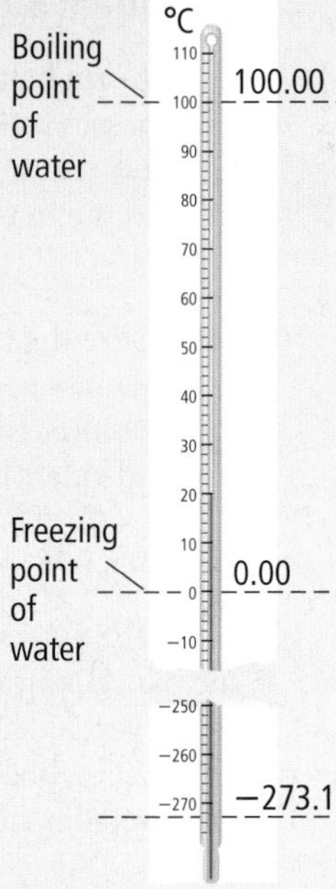

Figure 4

To use:

1. Place the thermometer in the sample and wait for 30 s before taking the reading.
2. Be sure to have your eyes at the level of the surface of the liquid when reading the scale on a thermometer.
3. The temperature will often be between two lines on the thermometer. You should estimate the final digit in your measurement. For example, if the liquid appears to be about halfway between the marks for 50°C and 51°C, you would read the temperature as 50.5°C.
4. Do not touch the sides or bottom of the container that is holding the sample with the thermometer. This can yield a false temperature.

Electronic thermometers, often called temperature probes, are used to record temperatures over a range of time or to give more accurate and precise readings.

Measure Length

Metric Ruler

Use a metric ruler or meterstick to measure the length of an object. On the ruler, each marked number represents one centimeter (cm). The smaller lines between each centimeter represent millimeters (mm). There are 10 mm in one centimeter and 100 cm in one meter (m).

To use:

1. Place the metric ruler so that the 0-cm mark lines up with the end of the object.
2. Be sure to have your eyes at the level of the object when reading the scale on the ruler.
3. The accuracy of your measurement reflects the measuring tool that you use and your technique. **Figure 5** shows the estimation of the length of the same object using two different measuring tools. Based on the bottom measuring tool, the length is between 9 and 10 cm. The measurement would be estimated to the nearest tenth of a centimeter. You would estimate the length to be 9.5 cm. Based on the top measuring tool, the length is between 9.4 and 9.5 cm. The measurement would be estimated to the nearest hundredth of a centimeter. You would estimate the length to be 9.45 cm.

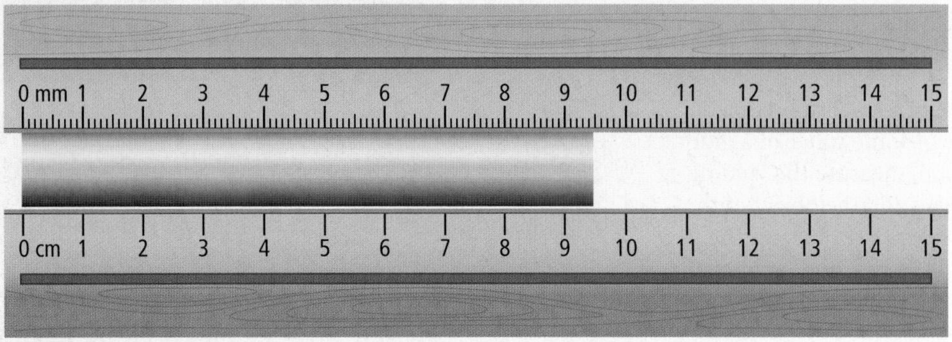

Figure 5

Laboratory Equipment and Techniques

This page and the following five pages discuss common lab equipment and techniques that you might use in a biology lab. Refer to these pages prior to performing labs that require the use of microscopes, chromatography, gel electrophoresis, or indicators.

Use a Compound Microscope

The parts of a compound microscope are listed and diagrammed in the table below.

1. Always carry the microscope by holding the arm of the microscope with one hand and supporting the base with the other hand.
2. Place the microscope on a flat surface. The arm should be positioned toward you.
3. Look through the eyepieces. Adjust the diaphragm so that the light comes through the opening in the stage.
4. Place a slide on the stage so that the specimen is in the field of view. Hold the slide firmly in place by using the stage clips.
5. Always focus first with the coarse adjustment and the low-power objective lens. Once the object is in focus on low power, the high-power objective can be used. Use only the fine adjustment to focus the high-power objective lenses.
6. Store the microscope covered.

Parts of the Compound Light Microscope

Part	Function
Base	Supports the microscope
Arm	Used to carry the microscope
Stage	Platform where the slide with specimen is placed
Stage clips	Holds the slide in place on the stage
Eyepiece	Magnifies image for the viewer
Objective lens	Low-power and high-power lenses that magnify the specimen
Coarse adjustment	Large knob used for focusing the image under low-power
Fine adjustment	Smaller knob used for focusing the image with the high-power objective
Diaphragm	Controls the amount of light that passes through the specimen
Light source	Provides light for viewing the specimen

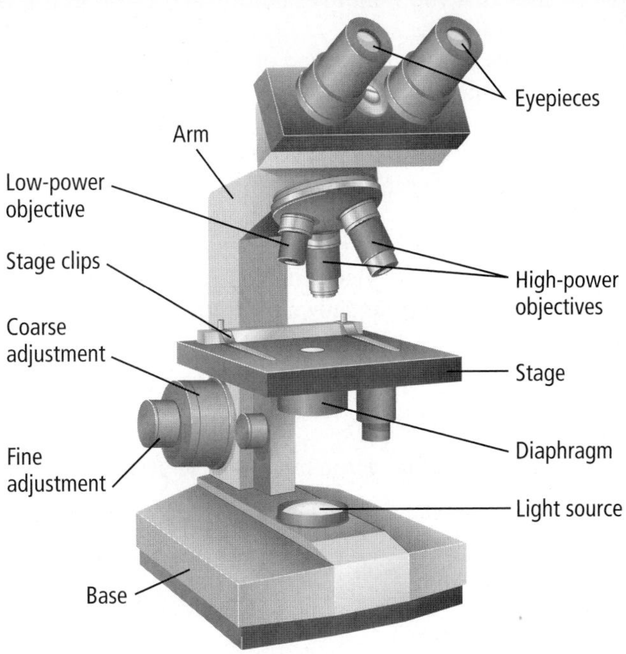

Calculate Magnification

Magnification describes how much larger an object appears when it is viewed through a microscope compared to the unaided eye. The numbers on the eyepiece and the objectives that are marked with the multiplication symbol (×) tell you how many times the lens of each microscope part magnifies an object.

- To calculate the total magnification of any object viewed under a microscope, multiply the number on the eyepiece by the number on the objective through which you are viewing the object.
- For example, if the eyepiece magnification is 4× and the low-power magnification is 10×, the total magnification under the low-power objective is 40×. With the same eyepiece and a high-power magnification of 40×, the total magnification under the high-power objective would be 160×.

Practice Problem 1 Calculate the low-power and the high-power magnifications of a microscope with an eyepiece magnification of 10×, a low-power objective of 40×, and a high-power objective of 60×.

400×; 600×

Calculate the Field of View

The area you see when you look into a microscope is called the field of view. To measure the field of view of a microscope, you must use a unit called a micrometer (μm). There are 1000 micrometers in a millimeter. Use the following steps to calculate field of view and then to determine the diameters of the microscopic specimens that you are viewing.

Diameter of Low-Power Field of View Use a low-power objective to select the section of a slide that you want to examine, such as the area where pollen grains are located.

- Place the millimeter section of a clear plastic ruler over the central opening of the microscope stage.
- Use the low-power objective to locate the lines of the ruler. Center the ruler in the field of view.
- Place one of the lines representing a millimeter at the very edge of the field of view. The distance between two lines on the ruler is 1 mm, as shown in **Figure 6.**
- Estimate the diameter, in millimeters, of the field of view on low power. Use the conversion factor $\frac{1000\ \mu\text{m}}{1\ \text{mm}}$ to calculate the diameter in micrometers. For example, if you estimate the diameter to be 1.5 mm, the field of view is 1500 μm.

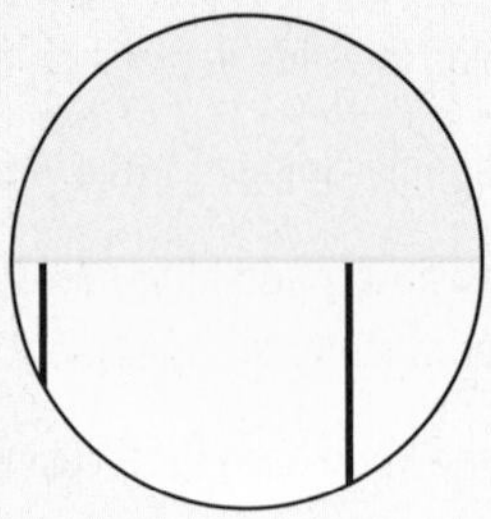

Figure 6

$$1.5\ \text{mm} \times \frac{1000\ \mu\text{m}}{1\ \text{mm}} = 1500\ \mu\text{m}$$

Diameter of High-Power Field of View After selecting a slide section on low power, use the high-power field of view to see the details on the slide, such as individual pollen grains.

- To calculate the diameter of the high-power field of view, divide the magnification of the high-power objective by the magnification of the low-power objective. For example, changing from a low power of 10× to a high power of 40×, you would write:

$$\frac{40\times}{10\times} = 4$$

- Then, divide the diameter of the low-power field of view in micrometers by this quotient. The result is the diameter of the high-power field of view in micrometers. For the low-power field of view calculated on the previous page, the diameter of the high-power field of view is

$$\frac{1500\ \mu m}{4} = 375\ \mu m$$

- To determine the diameter of a specimen in your field of view, first estimate how many of the specimens would fit end-to-end across your field of view. Then divide the diameter of the field of view by the estimated number of specimens. In the example, five specimens could fit in the field of view. The diameter of the specimen is

$$\frac{375\ \mu m}{5} = 75\ \mu m.$$

Practice Problem 2 Calculate the width of the dividing cell shown in **Figure 7** if the diameter of the low-power field of view is 720 μm, the low power is 10×, the high power is 60×, and the number of cells that fit in the field of view is 1.

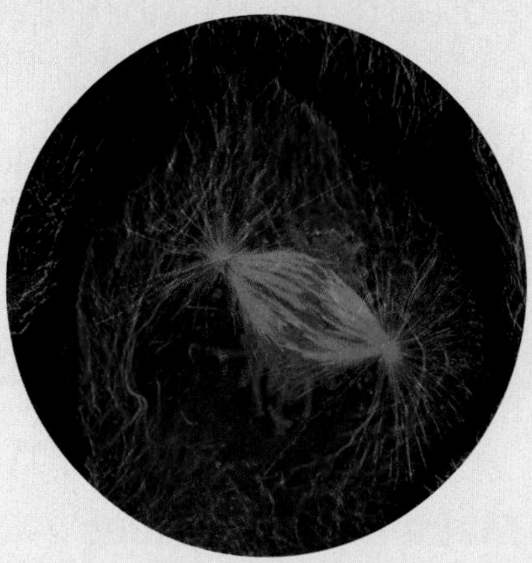

Figure 7 Dividing cell

$$\frac{60\times}{10\times} = 6;\ \frac{720\ \mu m}{6} = 120\ \mu m;\ \frac{120\ \mu m}{4} = 30\ \mu m$$

Make a Wet Mount

Many of the slides that you will prepare for observation under the microscope will be wet mounts. Wet mounts are named as such because the object to be viewed is prepared, or mounted, in water. Follow these steps to make a wet mount.

1. Obtain a clean microscope slide and a coverslip. Add a drop or two of water to the center of the microscope slide.
2. Place the specimen in the drop of water, as shown in **Figure 8.**
3. Pick up the coverslip by its edges. Do not touch the surface of the coverslip. Stand the coverslip on its edge next to the drop of water.
4. Slowly lower the coverslip over the drop of water, and the specimen, as shown in **Figure 9.**
5. Make sure that the object is totally covered with water. If it is not, remove the coverslip, add a little more water, and replace the coverslip.

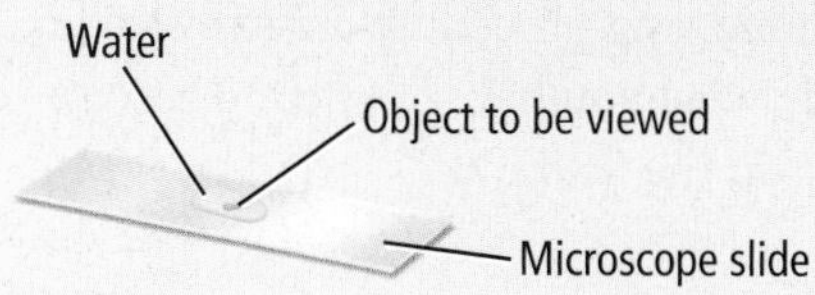

Figure 8

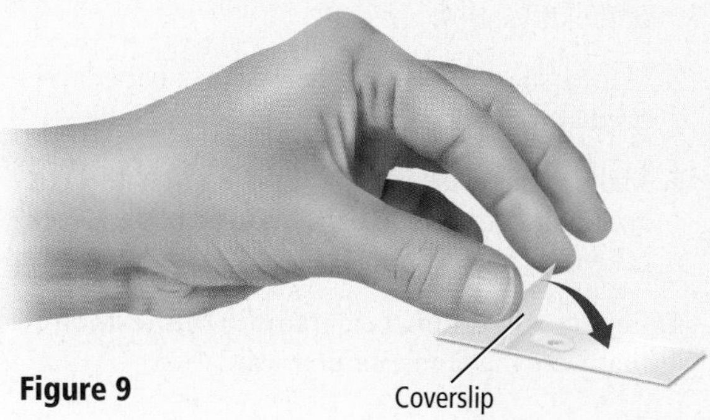

Figure 9

Stain a Slide

Staining a slide can make it easier to view a specimen. Stains enhance contrast and can emphasize certain features. For example, using iodine as a stain will cause carbohydrates in the specimen to become bluish-black in color. The following steps and **Figure 10** indicate one way to stain a microscope slide.

1. Prepare a wet mount, as indicated in the steps on the previous page.
2. Obtain the stain from your teacher. Using a dropper, place a drop of the stain at one end of the coverslip.
3. Place a paper towel at the end of the coverslip opposite the stain. The towel will draw the stain under the coverslip, staining the specimen.

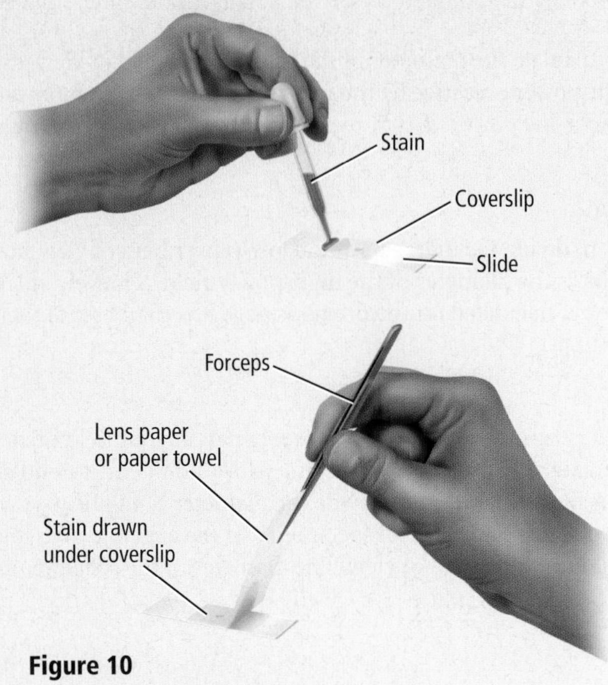

Figure 10

Make Cross Sections

When a biologist decides to study the inner structure of a biological specimen, a basic way to expose or cut a specimen to reveal its inner structure is called a cross section. A cross-sectional exposure, or cut, is made at right angles to the axis of the specimen. For example, the tree trunk in **Figure 11** has been cut at right angles to the height of the trunk. Note that microscopic cross sections reveal microscopic structures, such as the bacterium's cell wall in **Figure 11.**

Think Critically Investigate cross sections by performing the following procedure using everyday materials. Then apply what you have learned to recognize more cross sections in the textbook.

Encourage students to identify the cross section in Chapter 37. A coronary artery cross section is found on p. 1092 of this chapter.

1. Obtain log-shaped, rolled snack cakes that have contrasting color filling. The axis of this specimen runs through the center of one end to the center of the other end.
2. Place a snack cake on a sheet of wax paper and predict what a crosswise cut would look like.
3. Make a crosswise cut at a right angle to the axis and look at the cut ends. This view of the snack cake is a cross section.
4. Find cross-sectional diagrams in this textbook that were made in a similar way.

Figure 11

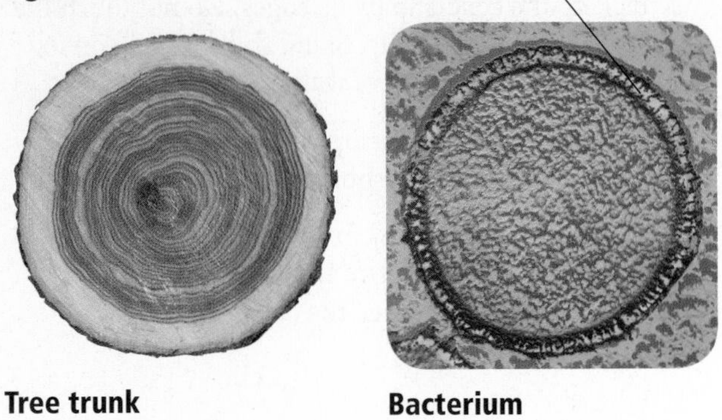

Use a Stereomicroscope

A stereomicroscope, also called a dissecting microscope, is used to observe a larger, thicker, often opaque object. A light source illuminates the object from above and a second source illuminates the object from below. The magnifying power of a stereomicroscope is much less than for a compound microscope; objects are magnified only by 10–50 diameters.

- Turn on the light source, and place the specimen on the stage so that it is in the field of view.
- Use the focus knob to adjust the focus.

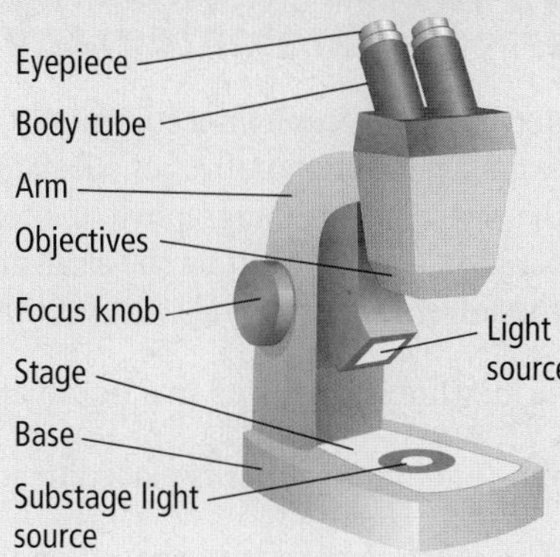

Figure 12

Perform Gel Electrophoresis

A technique called gel electrophoresis is used by scientists to separate mixtures of molecules based on their size, charge, and shape. This technique is most often used in separating DNA, RNA, and protein molecules.

Below are general guidelines for gel electrophoresis. Refer to your specific instrument's user's manual for complete instructions.

1. In the process of gel electrophoresis, scientists analyze DNA by first using special enzymes to cut a DNA sample at specific nucleotide sequences.
2. Small samples of cut DNA are prepared and placed in wells located on one end of a semisolid, gelatinlike gel, as shown in **Figure 13.**
3. The gel is placed in a buffer solution between two electrodes in a gel electrophoresis chamber. The electrodes are connected to a power supply (chamber and electrode not shown). When an electric current is applied, the buffer solution conducts the current. The current also moves through the gel. One end of the gel electrophoresis chamber becomes positively charged, and the other end becomes negatively charged.

   Negatively charged DNA fragments move toward the positive end of the gel. The shorter the fragment, the farther it moves through the gel. This allows the DNA fragments to form distinct and unique patterns for study, like those shown in **Figure 13.**

This process is also used to examine protein patterns. Proteins are extracted from cells and treated with chemicals to give them a negative charge. The prepared protein samples are placed in the wells of a gel. When an electric current is applied, the protein molecules move through the gel. The separation of protein molecules is based on the size, shape, and charge of the proteins.

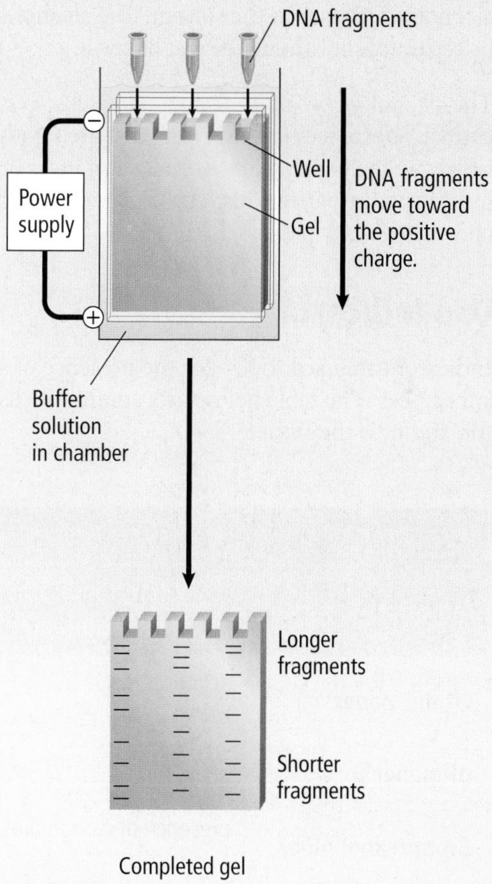

Figure 13

Perform Chromatography

Paper chromatography is a commonly used technique in the biology laboratory for separating mixtures of substances. You will perform chromatography with a special chromatography paper or with filter paper and a liquid solvent. Separation occurs based on the ability of substances in the mixture to dissolve in the solvent. The general steps for this type of chromatography follow.

1. A mixture is dissolved in a liquid and placed on the paper.
2. One end of the paper is placed in a solvent.
3. The substances separate based on their tendencies to move along the surface of the paper while in the solvent.

Figure 14

For example, chlorophyll from leaves can be separated by paper chromatography, as shown in **Figure 14.** A dot of the chlorophyll extract is placed near one end of the strip of paper. The end of the paper nearest the dot is placed in alcohol, which acts as the solvent. The alcohol should not touch the extract to be separated, but should be just below it.

The alcohol moves up the paper and picks up substances in the chlorophyll extract. Substances in the extract that are tightly held to the paper will move slowly up the paper, while extract substances that are not as tightly held move quickly up the paper. This results in bands of different substances on the chromatography paper.

Use Indicators

Indicators are used to test for the presence of specific types of chemicals or substances. The table below lists commonly used indicators, what they test for, and how they react.

Indicators

Indicator	What it indicates in a solution	Reaction
Litmus paper	acid or base	• red litmus turns blue if the solution is a base • blue litmus turns red if the solution is an acid
pH paper	pH	• a color change compared to a color chart to estimate the pH
Bromthymol blue	presence of carbon dioxide	• turns yellow if carbon dioxide is present • changes to blue from yellow when carbon dioxide is removed
Phenolphthalein solution	presence of carbon dioxide or a basic solution	• turns from clear to a bright pink in the presence of either substance
Benedict's solution	presence of simple sugars when heated	• high sugar concentration, changes from blue to red • low sugar concentration, changes from blue to yellow
Biuret solution	presence of protein	• turns from light blue to purple
Lugol's solution	presence of starch	• turns from deep brown to bluish-black

Make Comparisons

Why learn this skill?

Suppose you want to buy a portable MP3 music player, and you must choose between three models. You would probably compare the characteristics of the three models, such as price, amount of memory, sound quality, and size to determine which model is best for you. In the study of biology, you often make comparisons between the structures and functions of organisms. You will also compare scientific discoveries or events from one time period with those from another period.

Learn the Skill

When making comparisons, you examine two or more items, groups, situations, events, or theories. You must first decide what will be compared and which characteristics you will use to compare them. Then identify any similarities and differences.

For example, comparisons can be made between the two illustrations on this page. The different structures of the animal cell can be compared to the different structures of the plant cell. By reading the labels, you can see that both types of cells have a nucleus.

Practice the Skill

Create a table with the heading *Animal and Plant Cells.* Make three columns. Label the first column *Cell Structures.* Label the second column *Animal Cells.* Label the third column *Plant Cells.* List all the cell structures in the first column. Place a check mark under either *Animal Cell* or *Plant Cell* or both if that structure is shown in the illustration. When you have finished the table, answer these questions.

1. What items are being compared? How are they being compared?
2. What structures do animal and plant cells have in common?
3. What structures are unique to animal cells? What structures are unique to plant cells?

Apply the Skill

Make Comparisons In **Figure 10** of Chapter 9, you will find two images of cell division within plant and animal cells. Compare the two illustrations carefully. Then, identify the similarities and the differences between the two cells.

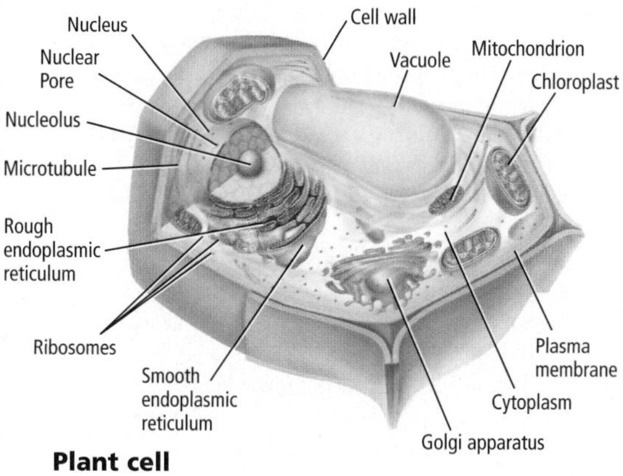

Plant cell

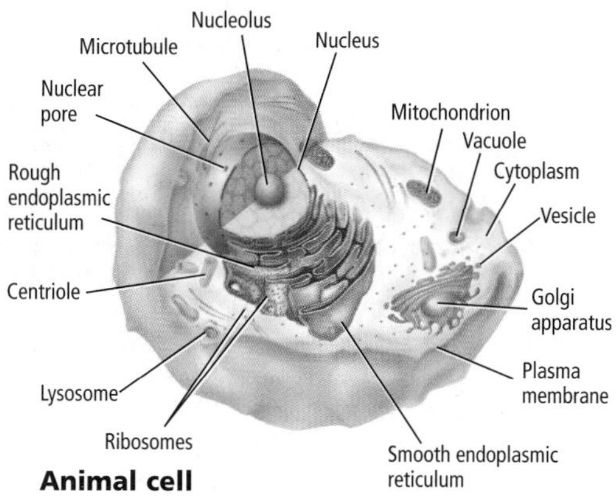

Animal cell

Practice the Skill

1. an animal cell and a plant cell; the internal structures
2. mitochondrion, vacuole, cytoplasm, Golgi apparatus, plasma membrane, smooth endoplasmic reticulum, ribosomes, rough endoplasmic reticulum, nuclear pore, microtubule, nucleolus, nucleus
3. The structures unique to animal cells are vesicles, lysosomes, and centrioles. The structures unique to plant cells are cell walls and chloroplasts.

Apply the Skill

Similarities: both create two cells; cells are genetically identical; process in both is called cytokinesis

Differences: Animal cells use microfilaments to constrict the cytoplasm in an area called a furrow. In plant cells a whole new structure, called a cell plate, forms. On either side of the cell plate cell walls form.

Practice the Skill

1. the first-ever photographic record of an *Architeuthis* (giant squid) in the wild
2. The main points are the photographic record of *Architeuthis* and the theory of the squid's daily activities.
3. Answers will vary, but should include information regarding the impediment of the squid and the subsequent photos and the theories of the squid's daily activities.

Apply the Skill

Answers will vary. Students should summarize the main points of the article and point out areas that lead to further analysis, research, and discussion. Encourage students to attach the article to their analysis.

Analyze Information

Why learn this skill?

Analyzing, or looking at separate parts of something to understand the entire piece, is a way to think critically about written work. The ability to analyze information is important when determining which ideas are the most important.

Learn the Skill

To analyze information, use the following steps:

- identify the topic being discussed
- examine how the information is organized—identify the main points
- summarize the information in your own words, and then make a statement based on your understanding of the topic and what you already know

Practice the Skill

Read the following excerpt from *National Geographic*. Use the steps listed above to analyze the information and answer the questions that follow.

Like something straight out of a Jules Verne novel, an enormous tentacled creature looms out of the inky blackness of the deep Pacific waters. But this isn't science fiction. A set of extraordinary images captured by Japanese scientists marks the first-ever record of a live giant squid (Architeuthis) in the wild.

The animal—which measures roughly 8 meters long—was photographed 900 meters beneath the North Pacific Ocean. Japanese scientists attracted the squid toward cameras attached to a baited fishing line. The scientists say they snapped more than 500 images of the massive cephalopod before it broke free after snagging itself on a hook. They also recovered one of the giant squid's two longest tentacles, which severed during its struggle.

The photo sequence, taken off Japan's Ogasawara Islands in September 2004, shows the squid homing in on the baited line and enveloping it in "a ball of tentacles." Tsunemi Kubodera of the National Science Museum in Tokyo and Kyoichi Mori of the Ogasawara Whale Watching Association report their observations in the journal Proceedings of the Royal Society B.

"Architeuthis appears to be a much more active predator than previously suspected, using its elongated feeding tentacles to strike and tangle prey," the researchers write. They add that the squid was found feeding at depths where no light penetrates even during the day.

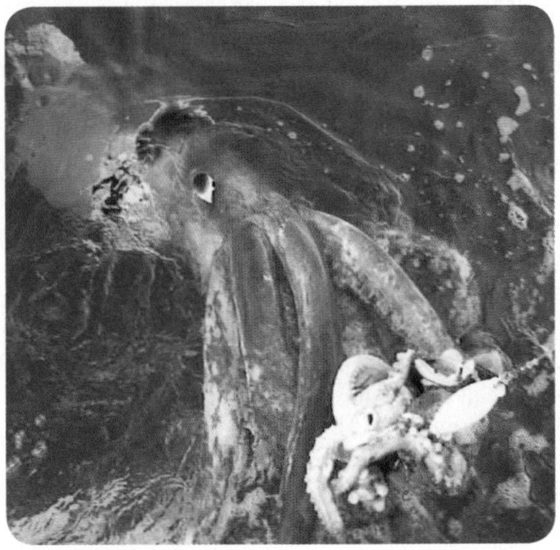

Giant squid on a fishing line

Squid expert Martin Collins of the British Antarctic Survey based in Cambridge, England is especially interested in clues the images might provide to the way giant squid swim and hunt in the deep ocean.

Collins says there were two competing schools of thought among giant squid experts. "One was the idea that [giant squid] were fairly inactive and just drifted around, dangling their tentacles below them like fishing lures to catch what came by," he said.

"The other theory was that they were actually quite active. This new evidence supports this, suggesting they are active predators which can move reasonably quickly. The efforts the squid went to untangle itself [from the baited fishing line] also shows they are capable of quite strong and rapid movement," he added.

1. What topic is being discussed?
2. What are the main points of the article?
3. Summarize the information in this article, and then provide your analysis based on this information and your own knowledge.

Apply the Skill

Analyze Information Analyze a short, informative article on a scientific discovery or technology, such as the hybrid car. Summarize the information and make a statement of your own.

Synthesize Information

Why learn this skill?

The skill of synthesizing involves combining and analyzing information gathered from separate sources or at different times to make logical connections. Being able to synthesize information can be a useful skill for you as a student when you need to gather data from several sources for a report or a presentation.

Learn the Skill

Follow these steps to synthesize information:

- select important and relevant information
- analyze the information and build connections
- reinforce or modify the connections as you acquire new information

Suppose you need to write a research paper on endangered species. You would need to synthesize what you learn to inform others. You could begin by detailing the ideas and information you already have about endangered species. A table such as the one below could help you categorize the facts.

Table 1 Endangered Species Statistics

Group	October 2000		October 2005	
	U.S.	Foreign	U.S.	Foreign
Mammals	63	251	68	251
Birds	78	175	77	175
Reptiles	14	64	14	64
Amphibians	10	8	12	8
Fishes	69	11	71	11
Clams	61	2	62	2
Snails	20	1	24	1
Insects	30	4	35	4
Arachnids	6	0	12	0
Crustaceans	18	0	19	0

Source: U.S. Fish and Wildlife Service

Then you could select a passage about endangered species like the sample below.

Stable ecosystems can be changed by the activity of other organisms, climate, or natural disasters. This natural process of extinctions is not what scientists are worried about. Many worry about a recent increase in the rate of extinction.

One of the factors that is increasing the current rate of extinction is the overexploitation, or excessive use, of species that have economic values. Historically, overexploitation was the primary cause of species extinction. However, the number one cause of species extinction today is the loss or destruction of habitat.

There are several ways that species can lose their habitats. If a habitat is destroyed or disrupted, the native species might have to relocate or die. For example, humans are clearing areas of tropical rain forests and are replacing the native plants with agricultural crops or grazing lands.

Practice the Skill

Use the table and the passage on this page to answer these questions.

1. What information is presented in the table?
2. What is the main idea of the passage? What information does the passage add to your knowledge about the topic?
3. By synthesizing the two sources and using your own knowledge, what conclusions can you draw about habitat conservation practices for endangered species?
4. Using what you learned in your studies and from this activity, contrast two types of habitat changes and their effects on the ecosystem.

Apply the Skill

Synthesize Information Find two sources of information on the same topic and write a short report. In your report, answer the following questions: What are the main ideas of each source? How does each source add to your understanding of the topic? Do the sources support or contradict each other? What conclusions can you draw from the sources?

Skillbuilder Handbook

Practice the Skill

1. endangered species statistics from October 2000 and October 2005 for the U.S. and foreign countries
2. the increase in the rate of extinction; answers will vary
3. Answers will vary based on the student's knowledge, but might include that based on the statistical data, conservation practices could be more stringent.
4. Answers will vary, but should include the characteristics of two types of habitat changes and at least one effect that change has on the ecosystem.

Apply the Skill

Answers will vary. The report should be more than a summary of the sources; the reports should be declarative. Students should include answers to the listed questions, but also go further, such as how a source could improve their point. Encourage students to attach the article to their report.

Practice the Skill

1. the mapping of DNA where differences occur
2. how researchers read DNA; diseases and disorders are caused by combinations of genetic variations; haplotypes are sets of SNPs
3. Adenine, cytosine, guanine, and thymine are the nucleotides that comprise DNA. The combination of genetic variations occurs at multiple sites on different chromosomes. Haplotypes are closely associated and are inherited as a group.
4. SNPs are often the cause of genetic diseases; no subdetail for detail 2; certain haplotypes are known to have a role in diseases

The answers to questions 2–4 are outlined below.

The mapping of DNA where differences occur.

- I. How researchers read DNA
  - A. Adenine, cytosine, guanine, and thymine are the nucleotides that comprise DNA.
    - 1. SNPs are often the cause of genetic diseases.
- II. Diseases and disorders are caused by combination of genetic variations.
  - A. The combination of genetic variations occurs at multiple sites on different chromosomes.
- III. Haplotypes are sets of SNPs.
  - A. Haplotypes are closely associated and are inherited as a group.
    - 1. Certain haplotypes are known to have a role in diseases.

Take Notes and Outline

Why learn this skill?

One of the best ways to remember something is to write it down. Taking notes—writing down information in a brief and orderly format—not only helps you remember, but also makes studying easier.

Learn the Skill

There are several styles of note taking, but all explain and put information in a logical order. As you read, identify and summarize the main ideas and details that support them and write them in your notes. Paraphrase, that is, state in your own words, the information rather than copying it directly from the text. Using note cards or developing a personal "shorthand," using symbols to represent words, can help.

You might also find it helpful to create an outline when taking notes. When outlining material, first read the material to identify the main ideas. In textbooks, section headings provide clues to main topics. Identify the subheadings. Place supporting details under the appropriate heading. The basic pattern for outlines is as follows:

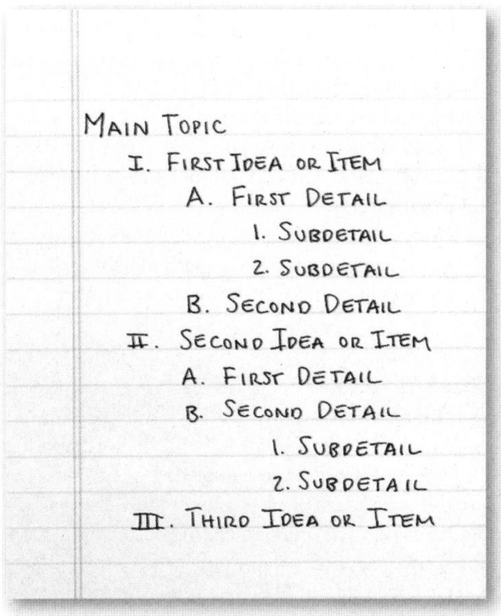

Practice the Skill

Read the following excerpt from *National Geographic*. Use the steps you just read about to take notes or create an outline. Then answer the questions that follow.

Mapping the three billion letters of the human genome has helped researchers better understand the 99.9 percent of DNA that is identical in all humans. Now a new project aims to map the 0.1 percent of DNA where differences occur. The International HapMap Project will look at variations that dictate susceptibility to genetic influences, such as environmental toxins and inherited diseases.

Researchers "read" DNA code by its structural units called nucleotides. These chemical building blocks are designated by the letters A (adenine), C (cytosine), G (guanine), and T (thymine). Single-letter variations in genes—called single nucleotide polymorphisms, or SNPs (pronounced "snips")—are often the culprits behind a wide range of genetic diseases. For example, changing an A to a T in the gene for the blood molecule hemoglobin causes sickle cell anemia.

But most diseases and disorders are not caused by a single gene. Instead they are caused by a complex combination of linked genetic variations at multiple sites on different chromosomes.

Haplotypes are sets of adjacent SNPs that are closely associated and are inherited as a group. Certain haplotypes are known to have a role in diseases, including Alzheimer's, deep vein thrombosis, type 2 diabetes, and age-related macular degeneration, a leading cause of blindness.

1. What is the main topic of the article?
2. What are the first, second, and third ideas?
3. Name one detail for each of the ideas.
4. Name one subdetail for each of the details.

Apply the Skill

Take Notes and Outline Go to Chapter 2, Section 1 and take notes by paraphrasing and using shorthand or by creating an outline. Use the section title and headings to help you create your outline. Summarize the section using only your notes.

Apply the Skill

A partial sample outline of Section 1 of Chapter 2 is shown below. Summaries will vary, but should include the information from the students' notes or outlines.

Organisms and Their Relationships

- I. Ecology is the scientific discipline in which the relationships among living organisms and the interaction the organism has with the environment are studied.
  - A. Ecologists observe, experiment, and model using a variety of tools and methods.
    - 1. Models allow ecologists to control the number of variables present.
- II. The biosphere is the portion of Earth that supports life.
  - A. Biotic factors are the living factors in an organism's environment.
    - 1. Biotic factors include all other organisms that live in the environment.
    - 2. The interactions of organisms are necessary for the health of all species in the same geographic location.
  - B. Abiotic factors are the nonliving factors in an organism's environment.
    - 1. Abiotic factors include temperature, air or water currents, sunlight, soil type, rainfall, and available nutrients.
    - 2. Organisms are adapted to surviving in the abiotic factors that are present in their natural habitat.

Understand Cause and Effect

Why learn this skill?

In order to understand an event, you should look for how that event or chain of events came about. When scientists are unsure of the cause for an event, they often design experiments. Although there might be an explanation, an experiment should be performed to be certain the cause created the event you observed. This process examines the causes and effects of events.

Learn the Skill

Every human body regulates its own temperature to maintain conditions suitable for survival. Exercise *causes* a body to heat up. The stimulated nerves in the skin are the *effect,* or result, of exercise. The figure below shows how one event—the **cause**—led to another—the **effect.**

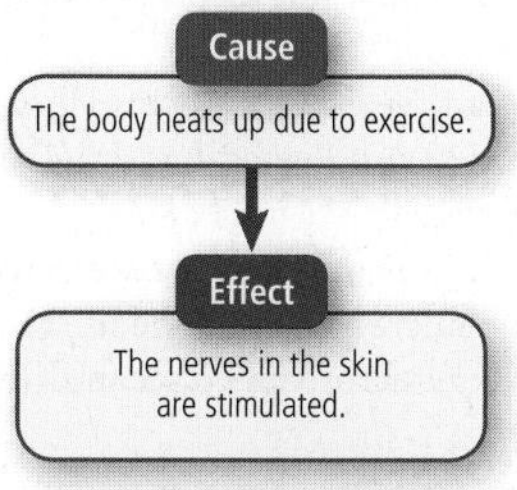

You can also identify cause-and-effect relationships in sentences from clue words such as:

because	**thus**
that is why	**due to**
led to	**for this reason**
so that	**produced**
consequently	**therefore**
as a result	**in order to**

Read the sample sentences below.

"A message is sent to sweat glands. As a result, perspiration occurs."

In the example above, the cause is a message being sent. The cause-and-effect clue words "as a result" tell you that the perspiration is the effect of the message.

In a chain of events, an effect often becomes the cause of other events. The next chart shows the complete chain of events that occur when exercise raises body temperature and the body returns to homeostasis.

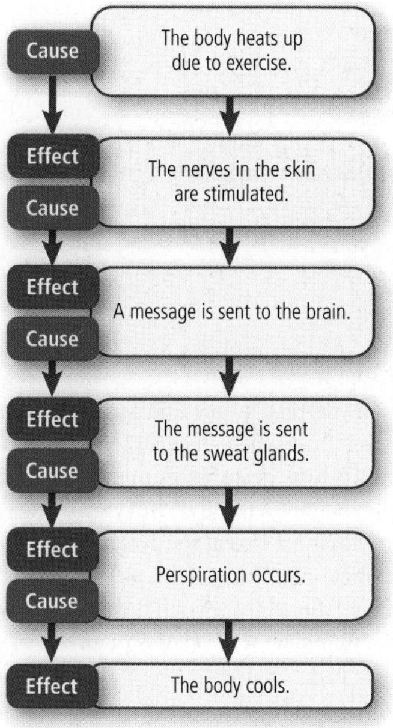

Practice the Skill

Make a chart, like the one above, showing which events are causes and which are effects using these sentences.

1. The hair cells respond by generating nerve impulses in the auditory nerve and transmitting them to the brain.
2. As the stapes vibrates, it causes the oval window to move back and forth.
3. Sound waves enter the auditory canal and cause the eardrum to vibrate.
4. Vibrations cause the fluid inside the cochlea to move like a wave against the hair cells.
5. Vibrations travel through the malleus, the incus, and the stapes.

Apply the Skill

Understand Cause and Effect Read an account of a recent scientific event or discovery in a science article. Determine the causes and effects that lead to the event or discovery. Show the chain of events in a chart.

Practice the Skill

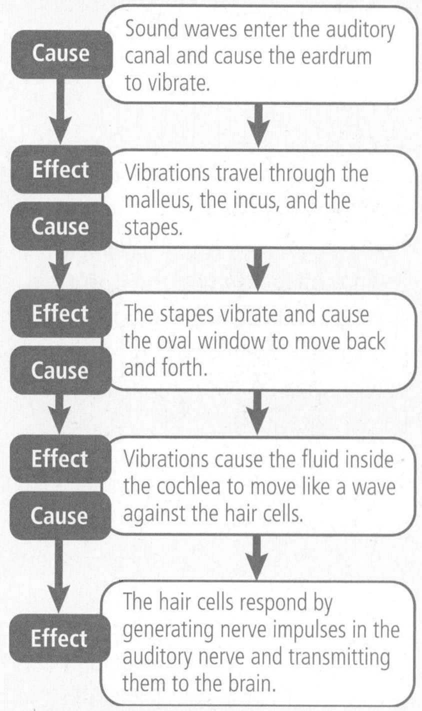

Apply the Skill

Answers will vary. As students plot out the chain of events, there should be more than just the event listed. Students should be able to explain the importance of each event and how the chain would be affected if removed. Encourage students to attach the article to their chain-of-events chart.

Practice the Skill

1. time span is 500 y, 1500–2000; intervals are 100 y
2. Robert Hooke
3. 274 y
4. 391 y

Apply the Skill

1866: Gregor Mendel published his findings on the method and the mathematics of inheritance in garden pea plants; 1928: Fredrick Griffith performed the first major experiment that led to the discovery of DNA; 1931: Oswald Avery and his colleagues identified the molecule that transformed the R strain of bacteria into the S strain; 1949: Murray Barr observed inactivated X chromosomes in female calico cats; 1951: Rosalind Franklin took a picture of wet DNA, Photo 51, which Watson and Crick use in their DNA model; 1952: Alfred Hershey and Martha Chase published experimental results that provided definitive evidence that DNA is the transforming factor of genetic material; 1953: Watson and Crick published a one-page letter in the journal *Nature* that suggested a structure for DNA; 1991: tandem repeats mutation were discovered; 2003: approximately 67.7 million hectares were planted with transgenic crops

Read a Time Line

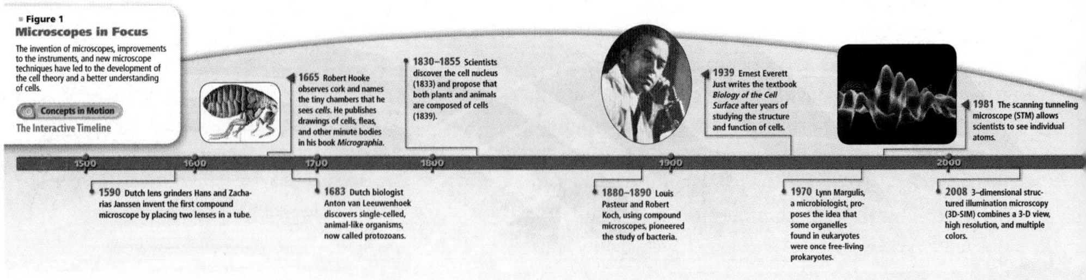

Figure 1
Microscopes in Focus
The invention of microscopes, improvements to the instruments, and new microscope techniques have led to the development of the cell theory and a better understanding of cells.

Concepts in Motion
The Interactive Timeline

Why learn this skill?

When you read a time line such as the one above, you see not only when an event took place, but also what events took place before and after it. A time line can help you develop the skill of chronological thinking. Developing a strong sense of chronology—when and in what order events took place—will help you examine relationships among the events. It will also help you understand the causes or effects of events.

Learn the Skill

A time line is a linear chart that list events that occurred on specific dates. The number of years between dates at the begining and end of the time line is the time span. A time line that begins in 1910 and ends in 1920 has a ten-year time span. Some time lines span centuries. Examine the time lines below. What time spans do they cover?

Time lines are usually divided into smaller parts called time intervals. On the two time lines below, the first time line has a 300-year time span divided into 100-year time intervals. The second time line has a six-year time span divided into two-year time intervals.

Practice the Skill

Study the time line above and then answer these questions.

1. What time span and intervals appear on this time line?
2. Which scientist was the first to observe cells with a microscope?
3. How many years after Robert Hooke observed cork did Ernest Everett Just write *Biology of the Cell Surface?*
4. What was the time span between the creation of the first microscope and the use of the scanning tunneling microscope to see individual atoms?

Apply the Skill

Read a Time Line Sometimes a time line shows events that occurred during the same period, but related to two different subjects. The time line above shows events related to cells between 1500 and 2008. Copy the time line and events onto a piece of paper. Then use a different color to add events related to genetics during this same time span. Use the chapters in Unit 3 to help you.

Analyze Media Sources

Why learn this skill?

To stay informed, people use a variety of media sources, including print media, broadcast media, and electronic media. The Internet has become an especially valuable research tool. It is convenient to use, and the information contained on the Internet is plentiful. Whichever media source you use to gather information, it is important to analyze the source to determine its accuracy and reliability.

Learn the Skill

There are a number of issues to consider when analyzing a media source. Most important is to check the accuracy of the source and content. The author and publisher or sponsors should be credible and clearly indicated. To analyze print media or broadcast media, ask yourself the following questions:

- Is the information current?
- Are the resources revealed?
- Is more than one resource used?
- Is the information biased?
- Does the information represent both sides of an issue?
- Is the information reported firsthand or secondhand?

For electronic media, ask yourself these questions in addition to the ones above.

- Is the author credible and clearly identified? Web site addresses that end in .edu, .gov, and .org tend to be credible and contain reliable information.
- Are the facts on the Web site documented?
- Are the links within the Web site appropriate and current?
- Does the Web site contain links to other useful resources?

Practice the Skill

To analyze print media, choose two articles, one from a newspaper and the other from a newsmagazine, on an issue on which public opinion is divided. Then, answer these questions.

1. What points are the articles trying to make? Were the articles successful? Can the facts be verified?
2. Did either article reflect a bias toward one viewpoint or another? List any unsupported statements.

3. Was the information reported firsthand or secondhand? Do the articles seem to represent both sides fairly?
4. How many resources can you identify in the articles? List them.

To analyze electronic media, read through the list of links provided by your teacher. Choose one link from the list, read the information on that Web site, and then answer these questions.

1. Who is the author or sponsor of the Web site?
2. What links does the Web site contain? How are they appropriate to the topic?
3. What resources were used for the information on the Web site?

Apply the Skill

Analyze Sources of Information Think of an issue in the nation on which public opinion is divided. Use a variety of media resources to read about this issue. Which news source more fairly represents the issue? Which news source has the most reliable information? Can you identify any biases? Can you verify the credibility of the news source?

Skillbuilder Handbook

Practice the Skill

Answers will vary. Encourage students to attach copies of the print media and Web pages.

Apply the Skill

Answers will vary. While it may be impossible for students to determine the fairness of the representation of information, they should be able to determine the facts. Students should identify biases and the possible reasoning used by that media source. Then, have students explain their reasoning. Encourage students to attach copies of the print media and Web pages.

Practice the Skill

1.

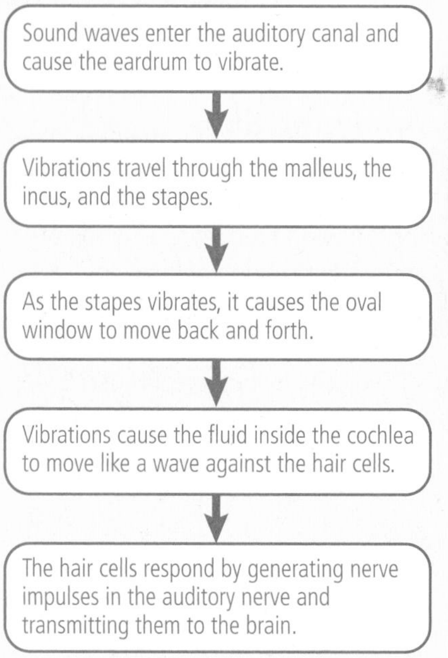

Sound waves enter the auditory canal and cause the eardrum to vibrate.
Vibrations travel through the malleus, the incus, and the stapes.
As the stapes vibrates, it causes the oval window to move back and forth.
Vibrations cause the fluid inside the cochlea to move like a wave against the hair cells.
The hair cells respond by generating nerve impulses in the auditory nerve and transmitting them to the brain.

2. **Air Travel Through the Body**

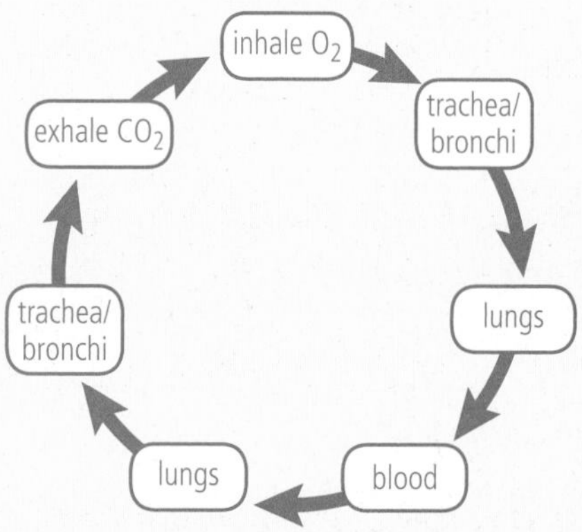

3.

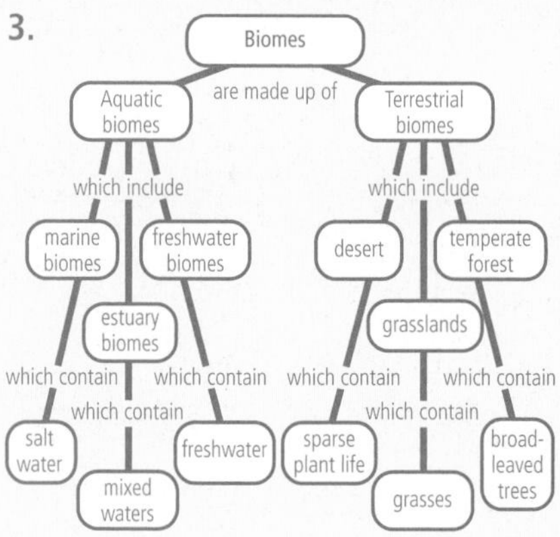

Skillbuilder Handbook

Use Graphic Organizers

Why learn this skill?

While you read this textbook, you will be looking for important ideas or concepts. One way to arrange these ideas is to create a graphic organizer. In addition to Foldables®, you will find various other graphic organizers throughout your book. Some organizers show a sequence, or flow, of events. Other organizers emphasize the relationship between concepts. Develop your own organizers to help you better understand and remember what you read.

Learn the Skill

An **events chain concept map** describes a sequence of events, such as stages of a process or procedure. When making an events-chain map, first identify the event that starts the sequence and add events in chronological order until you reach an outcome.

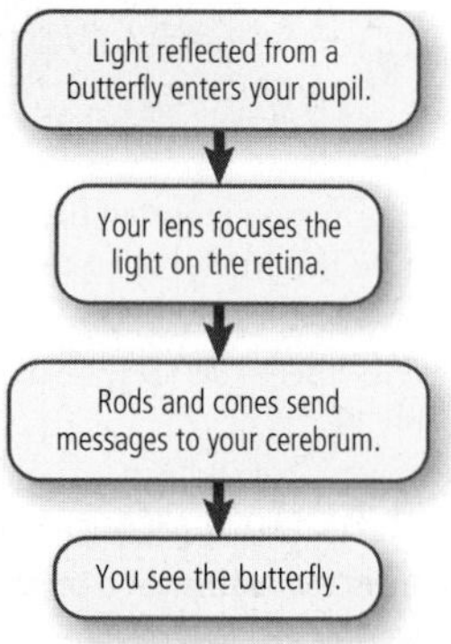

In a **cycle concept map,** the series of events do not produce a final outcome. The event that appears to be the final event relates back to the event that appears to be the initiating event. Therefore, the cycle repeats itself.

Blood Flow in the Body

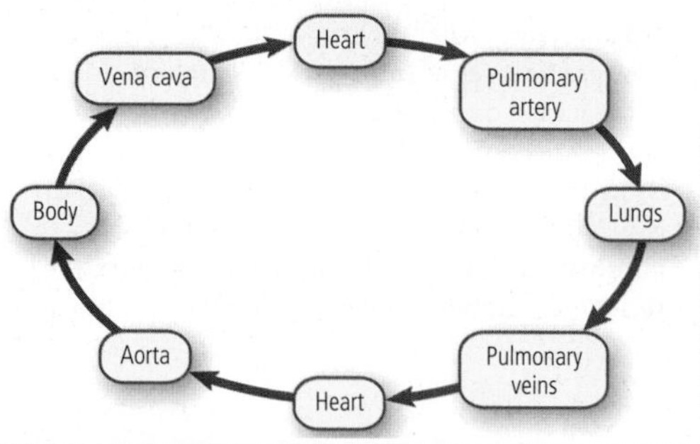

A **network tree concept map** shows the relationship among concepts, which are written in order from general to specific. The words written on the lines between the circles, called linking words, describe the relationships among the concepts; the concepts and the linking words can form a sentence.

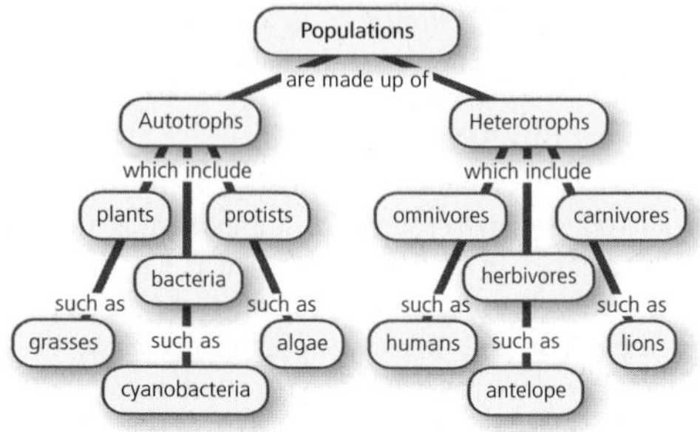

Practice the Skill

1. Create an events chain concept map that describes the process of hearing the ring of a bell. Begin with sound waves entering the outer ear. End with hearing the bell ring.
2. Create a cycle concept map of human respiration. Make sure that the cycle is complete with the event that appears to be the final event relating back to the event that appears to be the starting event.
3. Create a network tree concept map with these words: *Biomes, aquatic biomes, terrestrial biomes, marine biomes, estuary biomes, freshwater biomes, desert, grasslands, temperate forest, salt water, mixed waters, freshwater, sparse plant life, grasses,* and *broad-leaved trees.* Add linking words to describe the relationships between concepts. Refer to Chapter 3 for help.

Apply the Skill

Use Graphic Organizers Create an events chain concept map of succession using information from Chapter 3. Create a cycle concept map of the water cycle using information from Chapter 2. Create a network tree concept map of animals that includes invertebrates and vertebrates, characteristics of each type, and examples. Work with a partner.

Debate Skills

New research leads to new scientific information. There are often opposing points of view on how this research is conducted, how it is interpreted, and how it is communicated. The *Biology and Society* features in your book offer a chance to debate a current controversial topic. Here is an overview on how to conduct a debate.

Choose a Position and Research

First, choose a scientific issue that has at least two opposing viewpoints. The issue can come from current events, your textbook, or your teacher. These topics could include human cloning or environmental issues. Topics are stated as affirmative declarations, such as "Cloning human beings is beneficial to society."

One speaker will argue the viewpoint that agrees with the statement, called the positive position, and another speaker will argue the viewpoint that disagrees with the statement, called the negative position. Either individually or with a group, choose the position for which you will argue. The viewpoint that you choose does not have to reflect your personal belief. The purpose of debate is to create a strong argument supported by scientific evidence.

After choosing your position, conduct research to support your viewpoint. Use resources in your media center or library to find articles, or use your textbook to gather evidence to support your argument. A strong argument is supported by scientific evidence, expert opinions, and your own analysis of the issue. Research the opposing position also. Becoming aware of what points the other side might argue will help you to strengthen the evidence for your position.

Hold the Debate

You will have a specific amount of time, determined by your teacher, in which to present your argument. Organize your speech to fit within the time limit: explain the viewpoint that you will be arguing, present an analysis of your evidence, and conclude by summing up your most important points. Try to vary the elements of your argument. Your speech should not be a list of facts, a reading of a newspaper article, or a statement of your personal opinion, but an analysis of your evidence in an organized manner. It is also important to remember that you must never make personal attacks against your opponent. Argue the issue. You will be evaluated on your overall presentation, organization and development of ideas, and strength of support for your argument.

Additional Roles There are other roles that you or your classmates can play in a debate. You can act as the timekeeper. The timekeeper times the length of the debaters' speeches and gives quiet signals to the speaker when time is almost up (usually a hand signal).

You can also act as a judge. There are important elements to look for when judging a speech: an introduction that tells the audience what position the speaker will be arguing, strong evidence that supports the speaker's position, and organization. The speaker also must speak clearly and loudly enough for everyone to hear. It is helpful to take notes during the debate to summarize the main points of each side's argument. Then, decide which debater presented the strongest argument for his or her position. You can have a class discussion about the strengths and weaknesses of the debate and other viewpoints on this issue that could be argued.

p. 1126

Apply the Skill

example events chain concept map:

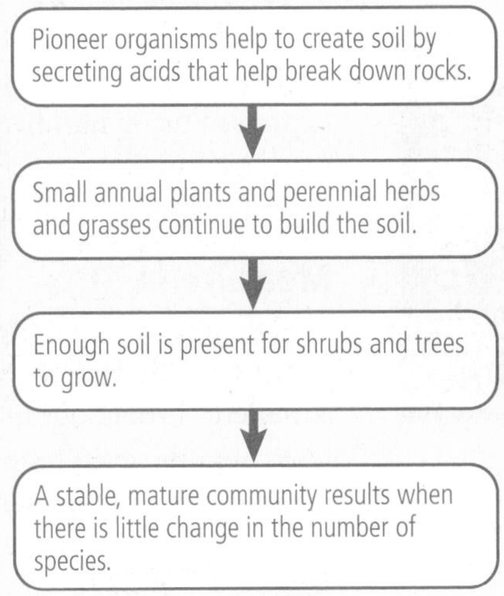
Pioneer organisms help to create soil by secreting acids that help break down rocks.
Small annual plants and perennial herbs and grasses continue to build the soil.
Enough soil is present for shrubs and trees to grow.
A stable, mature community results when there is little change in the number of species.

example cycle concept map:

Water Cycle

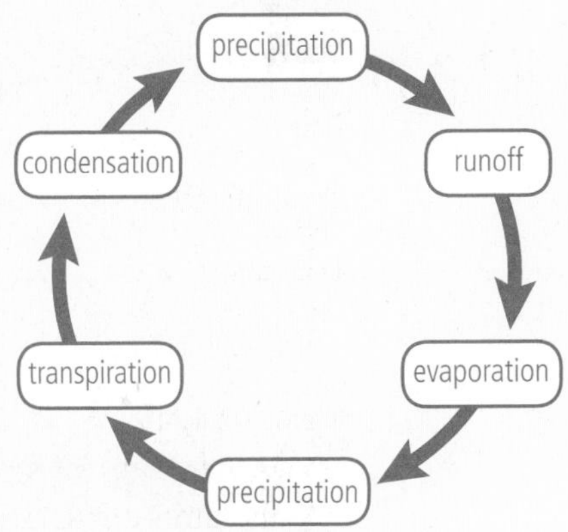
precipitation
runoff
evaporation
precipitation
transpiration
condensation

example network tree:

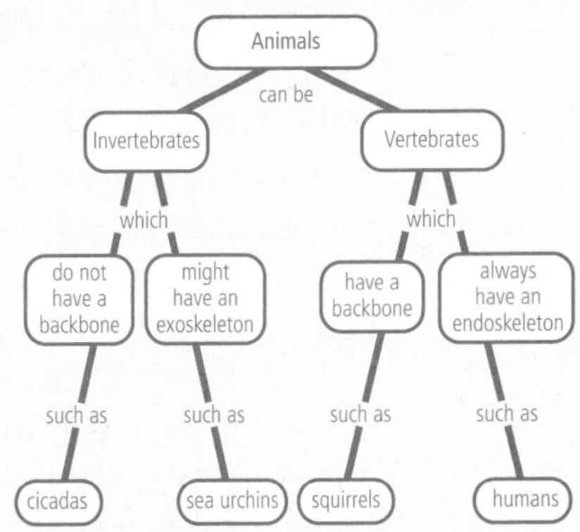
Animals
can be
Invertebrates
Vertebrates
which
which
do not have a backbone
might have an exoskeleton
have a backbone
always have an endoskeleton
such as
such as
such as
such as
cicadas
sea urchins
squirrels
humans

Math Skills

Experimental data is often quantitative and is expressed using numbers and units. The following sections provide an overview of the common system of units and some calculations involving units.

Measure in SI

The International System of Measurement, abbreviated SI, is accepted as the standard for measurement throughout most of the world. The SI system contains seven base units. All other units of measurement can be derived from these base units.

Table 2 SI Base Units

Measurement	Unit	Symbol
Length	Meter	m
Mass	Kilogram	kg
Time	Second	s
Electric current	Ampere	A
Temperature	Kelvin	K
Amount of substance	Mole	mol
Intensity of light	Candela	cd

Some units are derived by combining base units. For example, units for volume are derived from units of length. A liter (L) is a cubic decimeter ($dm^3 = dm \times dm \times dm$). Units of density (g/L) are derived from units of mass (g) and units of volume (L).

When units are multiplied by factors of ten, new units are created. For example, if a base unit is multiplied by 1000, the new unit has the prefix *kilo-*. Prefixes for some units are shown in **Table 3.**

To convert a given unit to a unit with a different factor of ten, multiply the unit by a conversion factor. A conversion factor is a ratio equal to one. The equivalents in **Table 3** can be used to make such a ratio. For example, 1 km = 1000 m. Two conversion factors can be made from this equivalent.

$$\frac{1000 \text{ m}}{1 \text{ km}} = 1 \quad \text{and} \quad \frac{1 \text{ km}}{1000 \text{ m}} = 1$$

To convert one unit to another factor of ten, choose the conversion factor that has the unit you are converting from in the denominator. For example, to convert one kilometer to meters, use the following equation.

$$1 \not{\text{km}} \times \frac{1000 \text{ m}}{1 \not{\text{km}}} = 1000 \text{ m}$$

A unit can be multiplied by several conversion factors to obtain the desired unit.

Table 3 Common SI Prefixes

Prefix	Symbol	Equivalents
mega	M	1×10^6 base units
kilo	k	1×10^3 base units
hecto	h	1×10^2 base units
deka	da	1×10^1 base units
deci	d	1×10^{-1} base units
centi	c	1×10^{-2} base units
milli	m	1×10^{-3} base units
micro	μ	1×10^{-6} base units
nano	n	1×10^{-9} base units
pico	p	1×10^{-12} base units

Practice Problem 1 How would you change 1000 micrometers to kilometers?

$$1000 \not{\mu\text{m}} \times \frac{1 \not{\text{m}}}{1{,}000{,}000 \not{\mu\text{m}}} \times \frac{1 \text{ km}}{1000 \not{\text{m}}} = 0.001 \text{ km}$$

Convert Temperature

The following formulas can be used to convert between Fahrenheit and Celsius temperatures. Notice that each equation can be obtained by algebraically rearranging the other. Therefore, you only need to remember one of the equations.

Conversion of Fahrenheit to Celsius

$$°\text{C} = \frac{(°\text{F}) - 32}{1.8}$$

Conversion of Celsius to Fahrenheit

$$°\text{F} = 1.8(°\text{C}) + 32$$

Make and Use Tables

Tables help organize data so that it can be interpreted more easily. Tables are composed of several components—a title describing the contents of the table, columns and rows that separate and organize information, and headings that describe the information in each column or row.

Table 4	Effects of Exercise on Heart Rate	
Pulse taken	Individual heart rate (Beats per min)	Class average (Beats per min)
At rest	73	72
After exercise	110	112
1 minute after exercise	94	90
5 minutes after exercise	76	75

Looking at this table, you should not only be able to pick out specific information, such as the class average heart rate after five minutes of exercise, but you should also notice trends.

Practice Problem 2 Did the exercise have an effect on the heart rate one minute after exercise? How can you tell? What can you conclude about the effects of exercise on heart rate during and after exercise?

Yes, the table shows an increase in rate from rest.

Make and Use Graphs

After scientists organize data in tables, they often display the data in graphs. A graph is a diagram that shows relationships among variables. Graphs make interpretation and analysis of data easier. The three basic types of graphs used in science are the line graph, the bar graph, and the circle graph.

Line Graphs A line graph is used to show the relationship between two variables. The independent variable is plotted on the horizontal axis, called the *x*-axis. The dependent variable is plotted on the vertical axis, called the *y*-axis. The dependent variable (y) changes as a result of a change in the independent variable (x).

Suppose a school started a bird-watching group to observe the number of birds in the school courtyard. The number of birds in the courtyard was recorded each day for four months. The average number of birds per month was calculated. A table of the birds' visitations is shown below.

Table 5	Average Number of Birds Viewed
Time (days)	Average Number of Birds per Day
30	24
60	27
90	30
120	32

To make a graph of the average number of birds over a period of time, start by determining the dependent and independent variables. The average number of birds after each period of time is the dependent variable and is plotted on the *y*-axis. The independent variable, or the number of days, is plotted on the *x*-axis.

Plain or graph paper can be used to construct graphs. Draw a grid on your paper or a box around the squares that you intend to use on your graph paper. Give your graph a title and label each axis with a title and units. In this example, label the number of days on the *x*-axis. Because the lowest average of birds viewed was 24 and the highest was 32, you know that you will have to start numbers on the *y*-axis of at least 24 and number to at least 32. You could decide to number 20–40 by intervals of two spaced at equal distances.

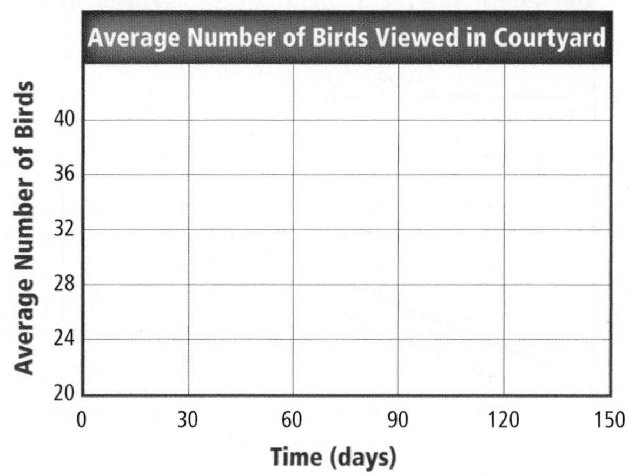

Exercise increases heart rate. After exercise, the heart rate returns to its resting rate in about 5 min.

Begin plotting points by locating 30 days on the x-axis and 24 on the y-axis. Where an imaginary vertical line from the x-axis and an imaginary horizontal line from the y-axis meet, place the first data point. Place other data points using the same process. After all the points are plotted, draw a "best fit" straight line through all the points.

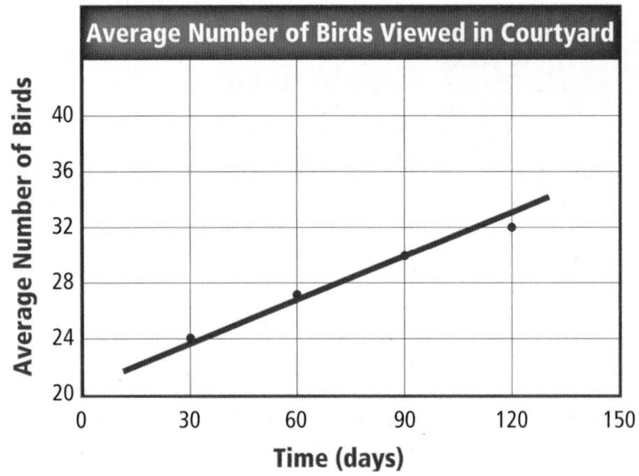

The bird-watching group also recorded the average number of brown-feathered birds they observed in the school courtyard. In the first month they averaged 21 brown-feathered birds per day. In the second month they averaged 24 brown-feathered birds. An average of 28 brown-feathered birds per day was observed in the third month. In the final month an average of 30 brown-feathered birds was observed.

What if you want to compare the average number of birds viewed with the average number of brown-feathered birds? The average brown-feathered bird data can be plotted on the same graph. Include a key with different lines indicating different sets of data.

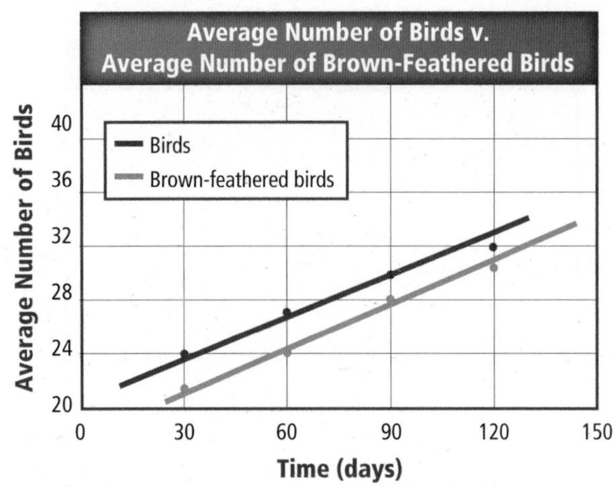

Practice Problem 3 Between 30 days and 120 days, what is the change in the average number of birds viewed? 8

Practice Problem 4 For the 120 days how did the average number of brown-feathered birds change as the average number of birds changed?
The rate of change was approximately the same.

Slope of a Linear Graph The slope of a line is a number determined by any two points on the line. This number describes how steep the line is. The greater the absolute value of the slope, the steeper the line. Slope is the ratio of the change in the y-coordinates (rise) to the change in the x-coordinates (run) as you move from one point to the other.

The graph below shows a line that passes through (5, 4) and (9, 6).

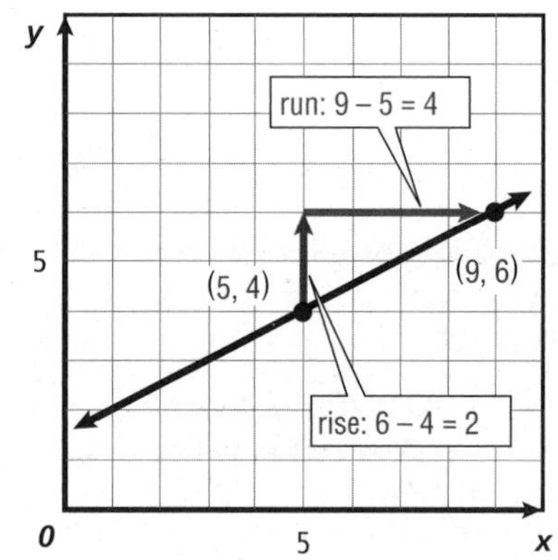

$$\text{Slope} = \frac{\text{rise}}{\text{run}}$$

$$= \frac{\text{change in } y\text{-coordinates}}{\text{change in } x\text{-coordinates}}$$

$$= \frac{6-4}{9-5}$$

$$= \frac{2}{4} \text{ or } \frac{1}{2}$$

So, the slope of the line is $\frac{1}{2}$.

A linear relationship can be translated into equation form. The equation for a straight line is

$$y = mx + b$$

where y represents the dependent variable, m is the slope of the line, x represents the independent variable, and b is the y-intercept, which is the point where the line crosses the y-axis.

Linear and Exponential Trends Two types of trends you are likely to see when you graph data in biology are linear trends and exponential trends. A linear trend has a constant increase or decrease in data values. In an exponential trend the values are increasing or decreasing more and more rapidly. The graphs below are examples of these two common trends.

In the graph below, there are two lines describing two frog species. Both lines show an increasing linear trend. As the temperature increases, so does the call pulse rates of the frogs. The rate of increase is constant.

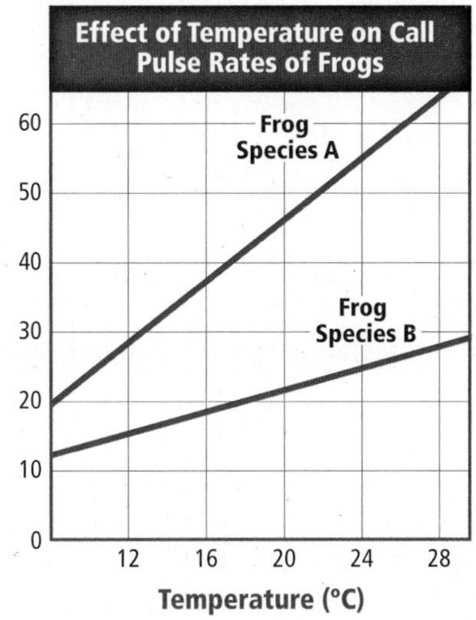

The example below shows how a mouse population would grow if the mice were allowed to reproduce unhindered. At first the population would grow slowly. The population growth rate soon accelerates because the total number of mice that are able to reproduce has increased. Notice that the portion of the graph where the population is increasing more and more rapidly is J-shaped. A J-shaped curve generally indicates exponential growth.

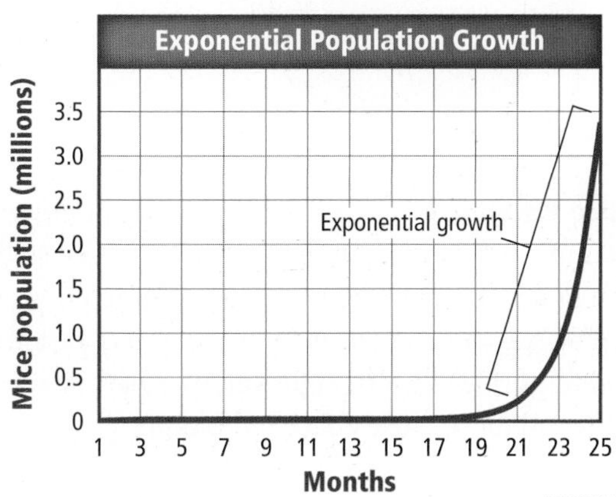

Bar Graphs A bar graph displays a comparison of different categories of data by representing each category with a bar. The length of the bar is related to the category's frequency. To make a bar graph, set up the *x*-axis and *y*-axis as you did for the line graph. Plot the data by drawing thick bars from the *x*-axis up to the *y*-axis point.

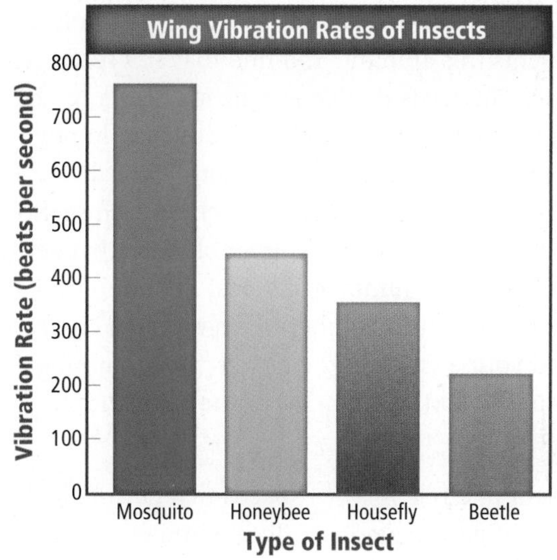

Look at the graph above. The independent variable is the type of insect. The dependent variable is the number of wing vibrations per second.

Bar graphs can also be used to display multiple sets of data in different categories at the same time. A bar graph that displays two sets of data is called a double bar graph. Double bar graphs have a legend to denote which bars represent each set of data. The graph below is an example of a double bar graph.

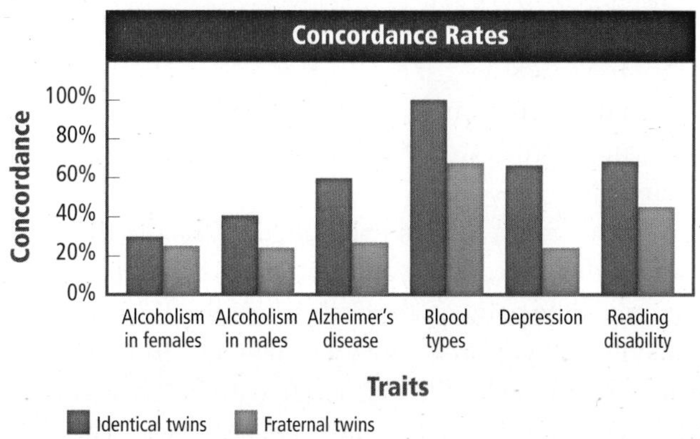

Practice Problem 5 Which type of insect has the highest number of wing vibrations per second? Is this more than twice as fast as the housefly? Explain.

mosquito; A housefly has 350 wing vibrations per s. A mosquito has 750 wing vibrations per s, which is more than twice as fast.

Circle Graphs A circle graph consists of a circle divided into sections that represent parts of a whole. When all the sections are placed together, they equal 100 percent of the whole.

Suppose you want to make a circle graph to show the number of seeds that germinate in a package. You would first determine the total number of seeds and the numbers of seeds that germinate out of the total. You plant 143 seeds. Therefore, the whole circle represents this amount. You find that 129 seeds germinate. The seeds that germinate make up one section of the circle graph and the seeds that do not germinate make up another section.

To find out how much of the circle each section should cover, divide the number of seeds that germinate by the total number of seeds. Then multiply the answer by 360, the number of degrees in a circle. Round your answer to the nearest whole number. The sum of all the segments of the circle graph should add up to 360°.

$$\text{Segment of circle for seeds that germinated} = \frac{\text{Seeds that germinated}}{\text{Total number of seeds}}$$

Divide $= \frac{129}{143}$

Multiply by number of degrees in a circle $= 0.902 \times 360°$

$= 324.72°$

Round to nearest whole number $= 325°$

Segment of circle for seeds that did not germinate $= 360° - 325°$

$= 35°$

To draw your circle graph, you will need a compass and a protractor. First, use the compass to draw a circle.

Then, draw a straight line from the center to the edge of the circle. Place your protractor on this line, and mark the point on the circle where the 35° angle will intersect the circle. Draw a straight line from the center of the circle to the intersection point. This is the section for the seeds that did not germinate. The other section represents the group of seeds that did germinate.

Circle graph should show 8% yellow blooms, 20% blue-purple blooms, 32% white blooms, and 40% red blooms.

Next, determine the percentages for each part of the whole. Calculate percentages by dividing the part by the total and multiplying by 100. Repeat this calculation for each part.

$$\text{Percent of seeds that germinate} = \frac{\text{Seeds that germinated}}{\text{Total number of seeds}}$$

$= \frac{129}{143}$

Multiply by 100 and add the % $= 0.902 \times 100$

$= 0.902$

$= 90.2\%$

Percent of seeds that did not germinate $= 100\% - 90.2\%$

$= 9.8\%$

Complete the graph by labeling the sections of the graph with percentages and giving the graph a title. Your completed graph should look similar to the one below.

If your circle graph has more than two sections, you will need to construct a segment for each entry. Place your protractor on the last line segment that you have drawn and mark off the appropriate angle. Draw a line segment from the center of the circle to the new mark on the circle. Continue this process until all of the segments have been drawn.

Percentage of Germinating and Non-Germinating Seeds

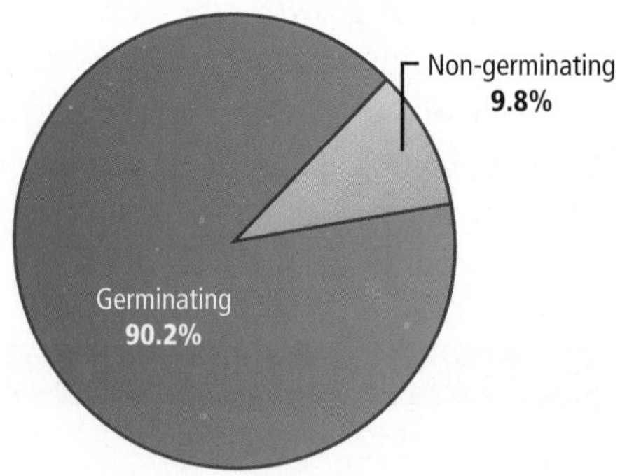

Practice Problem 6 There are 25 varieties of flowering plants growing around the high school. Construct a circle graph showing the percentage of each flower's color. Two varieties have yellow blooms, five varieties have blue-purple blooms, eight varieties have white blooms, and ten varieties have red blooms.

Six-Kingdom Classification

The classification used in this text combines information gathered from the systems of many different fields of biology. For example, phycologists—biologists who study algae—have developed their own system of classification, as have mycologists—biologists who study fungi. The naming of animals and plants is controlled by two completely different sets of rules. The six-kingdom system, although not ideal for reflecting the phylogeny of all life, is useful for showing relationships. Taxonomy is an area of biology that evolves just like the species it studies. In **Table 1,** only the major phyla are listed, and one genus is named as an example. For more information about each taxon, refer to the chapter in the text in which the group is described.

Table 1 **Six-Kingdom Classification** Concepts in Motion Interactive Table

Kingdom	Phylum/Division* (Common Name)	Typical Example (Common Name)	Characteristics
Bacteria 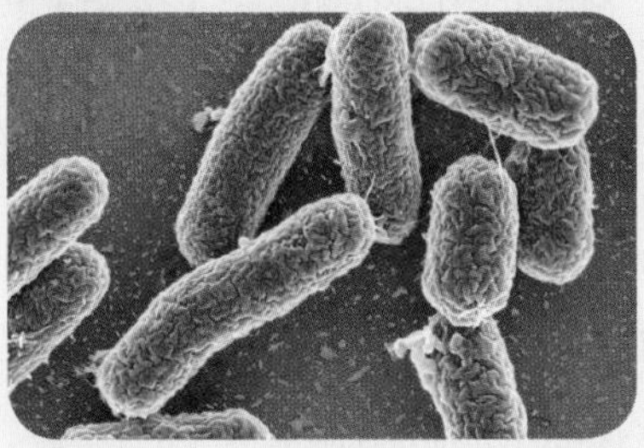 *Salmonella*	Actinobacteria	*Mycobacterium*	• unicellular • most absorb food from surroundings • some are photosynthetic • some are chemosynthetic • many are parasites • many are round, spiral, or rod-shaped • some form colonies
	Omnibacteria	*Salmonella* (salmonella)	
	Spirochaetae (spirochetes)	*Treponema*	
	Chloroxybacteria	*Prochloron*	
	Cyanobacteria (blue green algae)	*Nostoc* (nostoc)	
Archaea 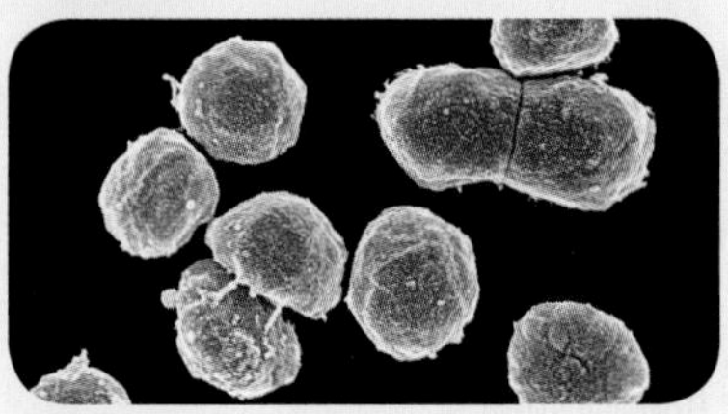 *Methanococcus jannaschii*	Aphragmabacteria	*Mycoplasma*	• unicellular • some absorb food from surroundings • some are photosynthetic • some are chemosynthetic • many are found in extremely harsh environments including salt ponds, hot springs, swamps, and deep-sea hydrothermal vents
	Halobacteria	*Halobacterium*	
	Methanocreatrices	*Methanobacillus*	
Protista 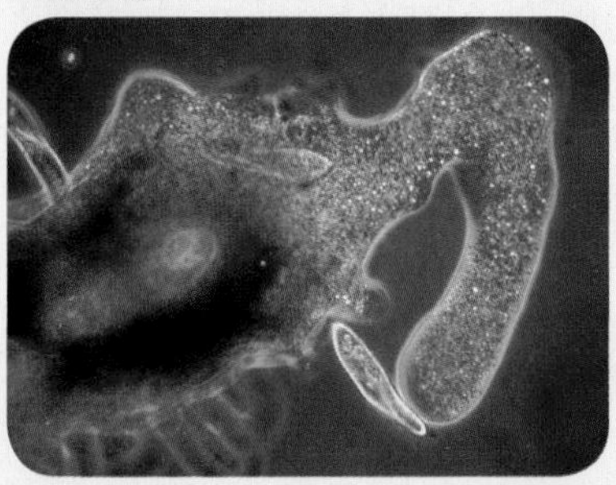 *Amoeba*	Sarcodina (amoeba)	*Amoeba* (amoeba)	• unicellular • take in food • free-living or parasitic • move by means of pseudopods
	Ciliophora (ciliates)	*Paramecium* (paramecium)	• unicellular • take in food • have large numbers of cilia
	Apicomplexa (apicomplexan)	*Plasmodium* (plasmodium)	• unicellular • take in food • no means of movement • are parasites in animals

*In the Kingdom Plantae the major phyla are referred to as "divisions."

Kingdom	Phylum/Division* (Common Name)	Typical Example (Common Name)	Characteristics
Protista *(continued)* 	Zoomastigina (zooflagellates)	*Trypanosoma*	• unicellular • take in food • free-living or parasitic • have one or more flagella
	Euglenophyta (euglenoids)	*Euglena* (euglena)	• unicellular • photosynthetic or take in food • most have one flagellum
Diatom	Bacillariophyta (diatoms)	*Navicula*	• unicellular • photosynthetic • have unique double shells made of silica
	Pyrrophyta (dinoflagellates)	*Gonyaulax*	• unicellular • photosynthetic • contain red pigments • have two flagella
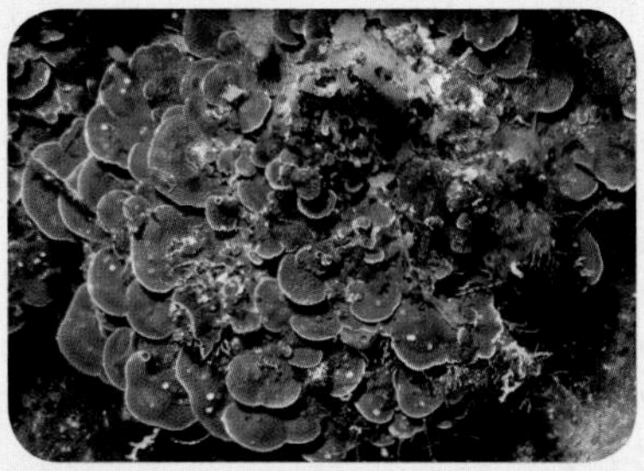	Rhodophyta (red algae)	*Chondrus*	• most are multicellular • photosynthetic • contain red pigments • most live in deep, salt water
	Phaeophyta (brown algae)	*Laminaria*	• most are multicellular • photosynthetic • contain brown pigments • most live in salt water
Red algae	Chlorophyta (green algae)	*Ulva*	• unicellular, multicellular, or colonies • photosynthetic • contain chlorophyll • live on land, in freshwater, or salt water
	Acrasiomycota (cellular slime mold)	*Dictyostelium*	• unicellular or multicellular • absorb food • change form during life cycle • cellular and plasmodial slime molds
	Myxomycota (acellular slime mold)	*Physarum*	
Slime mold	Oomycota (water mold/ downy mildew	*Phytophthora*	• multicellular • are either parasites or decomposers • live in freshwater or salt water

*In the Kingdom Plantae the major phyla are referred to as "divisions."

Kingdom	Phylum/Division* (Common Name)	Typical Example (Common Name)	Characteristics
Fungi 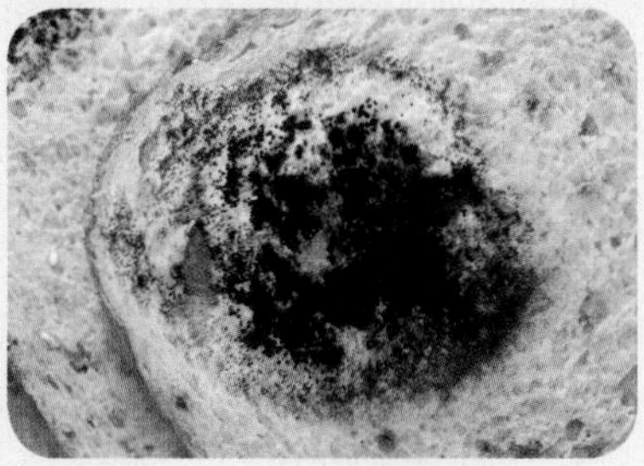 Bread mold	Zygomycota (common mold)	*Rhizopus* (bread mold)	• multicellular • absorb food • spores are produced in sporangia
	Ascomycota (sac fungi)	*Saccharomyces* (yeast)	•unicellular and multicellular • absorb food • spores produced in asci
	Basidiomycota (club fungi)	*Crucibulum* (bird's nest fungus)	• multicellular • absorb food • spores produced in basidia
	Deuteromycota (imperfect fungi)	*Penicillium* (penicillum)	• members with unknown reproductive structures • imperfect fungi
	Chytridiomycota	*Chytridium* (chrytid)	• some are saprobes • some parasitize protists, plants, and animals
Plantae  Liverwort  Wood fern	Hepaticophyta (liverworts)	*Monosolenium* (Pellia)	• multicellular nonvascular plants • reproduce by spores produced in capsules • green • grow in moist, land environments
	Anthocerophyta (hornworts)	*Anthoceros*	
	Bryophyta (moss)	*Polytrichum* (haircap moss)	
	Lycophyta (club moss)	*Lycopodium* (wolf's claw)	• multicellular vascular plants • spores are produced in cone-like structures • live on land • photosynthetic
	Arthrophyta	*Equisetum* (horsetails)	• vascular plants • ribbed and jointed stems • scale-like leaves • spores produced in cone-like structures
	Pterophyta (ferns)	*Polypodium* (ferns)	• vascular plants • leaves called fronds • spores produce in clusters or sporangia called sori • live on land or in water
	Ginkgophyta (ginko)	*Ginkgo* (ginko)	• deciduous trees • only one living species • have fan-shaped leaves with branching veins and fleshy cones with seeds

*In the Kingdom Plantae the major phyla are referred to as "divisions."

Kingdom	Phylum/Division* (Common Name)	Typical Example (Common Name)	Characteristics
Plantae *(continued)*  Welwitschia	Cycadophyta (cycad)	*Cyas* (palm tree)	• palm-like plants • have large, feather-like leaves • produce seeds in cones
	Coniferophyta (conifer)	*Pinus* (pine tree)	• deciduous or evergreen • trees or shrubs • needle-like or scale-like leaves • seeds produced in cones
	Gnetophyta (gnetophyte)	*Welwitschia* (welwitschia)	• shrubs or woody vines • seeds produced in cones • division contains only three genera
	Anthophyta (flowering plant)	*Rhododendron* (rhododendron)	• dominant group of plants • flowering plants • have fruit with seeds
Animalia  Sponge	Porifera (sponges)	*Spongilla* (sponge)	• aquatic organisms that lack true tissues and organs • asymmetrical and sessile
	Cnidaria (cnidarians)	*Hydra* (hydra)	• radially symmetrical • digestive cavity with one opening • most have tentacles armed with stinging cells • live in aquatic environments singly or in colonies
	Platyhelminthes (flatworms)	*Dugesia* (planaria)	• unsegmented, bilaterally symmetrical • no body cavity • digestive cavity, if present, has only one opening • parasitic and free-living species
 Abalone	Nematoda (roundworms)	*Trichinella* (trichinella)	• pseudocoelomate, unsegmented, bilaterally symmetrical • tubular digestive tract • without cilia • live in great numbers in soil and aquatic sediments
	Mollusca (mollusks)	*Nautilus* (nautilus)	• soft-bodied coelomates • bodies are divided into three parts: head-foot, visceral mass, and mantle • many have shells • almost all have a radula • aquatic and terrestrial species

*In the Kingdom Plantae the major phyla are referred to as "divisions."

Kingdom	Phylum/Division* (Common Name)	Typical Example (Common Name)	Characteristics
Animalia *(continued)*  Sand dollar	Annelida (segmented worms)	*Hirudo* (leech)	• coelomate, serially segmented, bilaterally symmetrical • complete digestive tract • most have setae on each segment that anchor them during crawling • terrestrial and aquatic species
	Arthropoda (arthropods)	*Colias* (butterflies)	• chitinous exoskeleton covering segmented bodies • paired, jointed appendages • many have wings • land and aquatic species
	Echinodermata (echinoderm)	*Cucumaria* (sea cucumber)	• marine organisms • have spiny or leathery skin and a water-vascular system with tube feet • radially symmetrical
	Chordata (chordates)		• segmented coelomates with a notochord • possess a dorsal nerve cord, pharyngeal slits, and a tail at some stage of life • most have paired appendages
 Sea otter	**Chordata Subphylum:** Urochordata	*Polycarpa* (sea squirt)	• young have all of the main chordate features; adults have only pharyngeal gill slits
	Chordata Subphylum: Cephalochordata	*Branchiostoma* (amphioxus)	• adults have all of the main features of chordates
	Chordata Subphylum: Vertebrata	*Panthera* (panther)	• the hallmark feature of all vertebrates is a spinal column

*In the Kingdom Plantae the major phyla are referred to as "divisions."

Three-Domain Classification

Increasingly, biologists are classifying organisms into categories larger than kingdoms called domains. The three domains are: Domain Bacteria, Domain Archaea, and Domain Eukarya. With future discoveries, this classification system might change to incorporate new information.

DOMAIN	Bacteria	Archaea	Eukarya			
KINGDOM	Bacteria	Archaea	Protista	Fungi	Plantae	Animalia

Scientific Word Origins

This list of prefixes, suffixes, and roots is provided to help you understand science terms used throughout this biology textbook. The list identifies whether the prefix, suffix, or root is of Greek *(G)* or Latin *(L)* origin. Also listed is the meaning of the prefix, suffix, or root and a science word in which it is used.

Origin	Meaning	Example
A		
ad *(L)*	to, toward	adaxial
aero *(G)*	air	aerobic
an *(G)*	without	anaerobic
ana *(G)*	up	anaphase
andro *(G)*	male	androceium
angio *(G)*	of seed	angiosperm
anth/o *(G)*	flower	anthophyte
anti *(G)*	against	antibody
aqu/a *(L)*	of water	aquatic
archae *(G)*	ancient	archaeologist
arthro, artio *(G)*	jointed	arthropod
askos *(G)*	bag	ascospore
aster *(G)*	star	Asteroidea
autos *(G)*	self	autoimmune
B		
bi *(L)*	two	bipedal
bio *(G)*	life	biosphere
C		
carn *(L)*	flesh	carnivore
ceph *(G)*	head	cephalopod
chloros *(G)*	light green	chlorophyll
chroma *(G)*	pigmented	chromosome
cide *(L)*	to kill	insecticide
circ *(L)*	circular	circadian
cocc/coccus *(G)*	small and round	streptococcus
con *(L)*	together	convergent
cyte *(G)*	cell	cytoplasm
D		
de *(L)*	remove	decompose
dendron *(G)*	tree	dendrite
dent *(L)*	tooth	edentate
derm *(G)*	skin	epidermis
di *(G)*	two	disaccharide
dia *(G)*	apart	diaphragm
dorm *(L)*	sleep	dormancy

Origin	Meaning	Example
E		
echino *(G)*	spiny	echinoderm
ec *(G)*	outer	ecosystem
ella(e) *(L)*	small	organelle
endo *(G)*	within	endosperm
epi *(G)*	upon	epidermis
eu *(G)*	true	eukaryote
exo *(G)*	outside	exoskeleton
F		
fer *(L)*	to carry	conifer
G		
gastro *(G)*	stomach	gastropod
genesis *(G)*	to originate	oogenesis
gen/(e)(o) *(G)*	kind	genotype
gon *(G)*	reproductive	archegonium
gravi *(L)*	heavy	gravitropism
gymn/o *(G)*	naked	gymnosperm
gyn/e *(G)*	female	gynecium
H		
hal(o) *(G)*	salt	halophyte
hapl(o) *(G)*	single	haploid
hemi *(G)*	half	hemisphere
hem(o) *(G)*	blood	hemoglobin
herb/a(i) *(L)*	vegetation	herbivore
heter/o *(G)*	different	heterotrophic
hom(e)/o *(G)*	same	homeostasis
hom *(L)*	human	hominid
hydr/o *(G)*	water	hydrolysis
I		
inter *(L)*	between	internode
intra *(L)*	within	intracellular
is/o *(G)*	equal	isotonic
J		
jug *(L)*	to join	jugular

Origin	Meaning	Example
K		
kary *(G)*	nucleus	eukaryote
kera *(G)*	hornlike	keratin
L		
leuc/o *(G)*	white	leukocyte
logy *(G)*	study of	biology
lymph/o *(L)*	water	lymphocyte
lysis *(G)*	break up	dialysis
M		
macr/o *(G)*	large	macromolecule
meg/a *(G)*	great	megaspore
meso *(L)*	in the middle	mesophyll
meta *(G)*	after	metaphase
micr/o *(G)*	small	microscope
mon/o *(G)*	only one	monocotyledon
morph/o *(G)*	form	morphology
N		
nema *(G)*	a thread	nematode
neuro *(G)*	nerve	neuron
nod *(L)*	knot	nodule
nomy(e) *(G)*	system of laws	taxonomy
O		
olig/o *(G)*	small, few	oligochaete
omn *(L)*	all	omnivore
orni(s) *(G)*	bird	ornithology
oste/o *(G)*	bone formation	osteocyte
ov *(L)*	an egg	oviduct
P		
pal(a)e/o *(G)*	ancient	paleontology
para *(G)*	beside	parathyroid
path/o *(G)*	suffering	pathogen
ped *(L)*	foot	centipede
per *(L)*	through	permeable
peri *(G)*	around, about	peristalsis
phag/o *(G)*	eating	phagocyte
phot/o *(G)*	light	photosynthesis
phyl *(G)*	race, class	phylogeny
phyll *(G)*	leaf	chlorophyll
phyte *(G)*	plant	epiphyte
pinna *(L)*	feather	pinnate

Origin	Meaning	Example
P (continued)		
plasm/o *(G)*	to form	plasmodium
pod *(G)*	foot	gastropod
poly *(G)*	many	polymer
post *(L)*	after	posterior
pro *(G) (L)*	before	prokaryote
prot/o *(G)*	first	protocells
pseud/o *(G)*	false	pseudopodium
R		
re *(L)*	back to original	reproduce
rhiz/o *(L)*	root	rhizoid
S		
scope *(G)*	to look	microscope
some *(G)*	body	lysome
sperm *(G)*	seed	gymnosperm
stasis *(G)*	remain constant	homeostasis
stom *(G)*	mouthlike opening	stomata
syn *(G)*	together	synapse
T		
tel/o *(G)*	end	telophase
terr *(L)*	of Earth	terrestrial
therm *(G)*	heat	endotherm
thylak *(G)*	sack	thylakoid
trans *(L)*	across	transpiration
trich *(G)*	hair	trichome
trop/o *(G)*	a change	gravitropism
trophic *(G)*	nourishment	heterotrophic
U		
uni *(L)*	one	unicellular
V		
vacc/a *(L)*	cow	vaccine
vore *(L)*	eat greedily	omnivore
X		
xer/o *(G)*	dry	xerophye
Z		
zo/o *(G)*	living being	zoology
zygous *(G)*	two joined	homozygous

PERIODIC TABLE OF THE ELEMENTS

Element — Hydrogen
Atomic number — 1
Symbol — H
Atomic mass — 1.008
State of matter

Gas
Liquid
Solid
Synthetic

Metal
Metalloid
Nonmetal
Recently observed

	1	2	3	4	5	6	7	8	9	10	11	12	13	14	15	16	17	18
1	Hydrogen 1 **H** 1.008																	Helium 2 **He** 4.003
2	Lithium 3 **Li** 6.941	Beryllium 4 **Be** 9.012											Boron 5 **B** 10.811	Carbon 6 **C** 12.011	Nitrogen 7 **N** 14.007	Oxygen 8 **O** 15.999	Fluorine 9 **F** 18.998	Neon 10 **Ne** 20.180
3	Sodium 11 **Na** 22.990	Magnesium 12 **Mg** 24.305											Aluminum 13 **Al** 26.982	Silicon 14 **Si** 28.086	Phosphorus 15 **P** 30.974	Sulfur 16 **S** 32.066	Chlorine 17 **Cl** 35.453	Argon 18 **Ar** 39.948
4	Potassium 19 **K** 39.098	Calcium 20 **Ca** 40.078	Scandium 21 **Sc** 44.956	Titanium 22 **Ti** 47.867	Vanadium 23 **V** 50.942	Chromium 24 **Cr** 51.996	Manganese 25 **Mn** 54.938	Iron 26 **Fe** 55.847	Cobalt 27 **Co** 58.933	Nickel 28 **Ni** 58.693	Copper 29 **Cu** 63.546	Zinc 30 **Zn** 65.39	Gallium 31 **Ga** 69.723	Germanium 32 **Ge** 72.61	Arsenic 33 **As** 74.922	Selenium 34 **Se** 78.96	Bromine 35 **Br** 79.904	Krypton 36 **Kr** 83.80
5	Rubidium 37 **Rb** 85.468	Strontium 38 **Sr** 87.62	Yttrium 39 **Y** 88.906	Zirconium 40 **Zr** 91.224	Niobium 41 **Nb** 92.906	Molybdenum 42 **Mo** 95.94	Technetium 43 **Tc** (98)	Ruthenium 44 **Ru** 101.07	Rhodium 45 **Rh** 102.906	Palladium 46 **Pd** 106.42	Silver 47 **Ag** 107.868	Cadmium 48 **Cd** 112.411	Indium 49 **In** 114.82	Tin 50 **Sn** 118.710	Antimony 51 **Sb** 121.757	Tellurium 52 **Te** 127.60	Iodine 53 **I** 126.904	Xenon 54 **Xe** 131.290
6	Cesium 55 **Cs** 132.905	Barium 56 **Ba** 137.327	Lanthanum 57 **La** 138.905	Hafnium 72 **Hf** 178.49	Tantalum 73 **Ta** 180.948	Tungsten 74 **W** 183.84	Rhenium 75 **Re** 186.207	Osmium 76 **Os** 190.23	Iridium 77 **Ir** 192.217	Platinum 78 **Pt** 195.08	Gold 79 **Au** 196.967	Mercury 80 **Hg** 200.59	Thallium 81 **Tl** 204.383	Lead 82 **Pb** 207.2	Bismuth 83 **Bi** 208.980	Polonium 84 **Po** 208.982	Astatine 85 **At** 209.987	Radon 86 **Rn** 222.018
7	Francium 87 **Fr** (223)	Radium 88 **Ra** (226)	Actinium 89 **Ac** (227)	Rutherfordium 104 **Rf** (261)	Dubnium 105 **Db** (262)	Seaborgium 106 **Sg** (266)	Bohrium 107 **Bh** (264)	Hassium 108 **Hs** (277)	Meitnerium 109 **Mt** (268)	Darmstadtium 110 **Ds** (281)	Roentgenium 111 **Rg** (272)	Copernicium 112 **Cn** (285)	Ununtrium * 113 **Uut** (284)	Ununquadium * 114 **Uuq** (289)	Ununpentium * 115 **Uup** (288)	Ununhexium * 116 **Uuh** (291)		Ununoctium * 118 **Uuo** (294)

The number in parentheses is the mass number of the longest lived isotope for that element.

* The names and symbols for elements 113, 114, 115, 116, and 118 are temporary. Final names will be selected when the elements' discoveries are verified.

Lanthanide series	Cerium 58 **Ce** 140.115	Praseodymium 59 **Pr** 140.908	Neodymium 60 **Nd** 144.242	Promethium 61 **Pm** (145)	Samarium 62 **Sm** 150.36	Europium 63 **Eu** 151.965	Gadolinium 64 **Gd** 157.25	Terbium 65 **Tb** 158.925	Dysprosium 66 **Dy** 162.50	Holmium 67 **Ho** 164.930	Erbium 68 **Er** 167.259	Thulium 69 **Tm** 168.934	Ytterbium 70 **Yb** 173.04	Lutetium 71 **Lu** 174.967
Actinide series	Thorium 90 **Th** 232.038	Protactinium 91 **Pa** 231.036	Uranium 92 **U** 238.029	Neptunium 93 **Np** (237)	Plutonium 94 **Pu** (244)	Americium 95 **Am** (243)	Curium 96 **Cm** (247)	Berkelium 97 **Bk** (247)	Californium 98 **Cf** (251)	Einsteinium 99 **Es** (252)	Fermium 100 **Fm** (257)	Mendelevium 101 **Md** (258)	Nobelium 102 **No** (259)	Lawrencium 103 **Lr** (262)

Glossary/Glosario

Multilingual eGlossary

The multilingual science glossary includes Arabic, Bengali, Chinese, English, Haitian Creole, Hmong, Korean, Portuguese, Russian, Spanish, Tagalog, Urdu, and Vietnamese.

Pronunciation Key

Use the following key to help you sound out words in the glossary.

a	back (BAK)	ew	food (FEWD)
ay	day (DAY)	yoo	pure (PYOOR)
ah	father (FAH thur)	yew	few (FYEW)
ow	flower (FLOW ur)	uh	comma (CAHM uh)
ar	car (CAR)	u (+ con)	rub (RUB)
e	less (LES)	sh	shelf (SHELF)
ee	leaf (LEEF)	ch	nature (NAY chur)
ih	trip (TRIHP)	g	gift (GIHFT)
i (i + con + e)	idea, life (i DEE uh, life)	j	gem (JEM)
oh	go (GOH)	ing	sing (SING)
aw	soft (SAWFT)	zh	vision (VIHZH un)
or	orbit (OR but)	k	cake (KAYK)
oy	coin (COYN)	s	seed, cent (SEED, SENT)
oo	foot (FOOT)	z	zone, raise (ZOHN, RAYZ)

Cómo usar el glorasio en español:
1. Busca el término en inglés que desees encontrar.
2. El término en español, junto con la definición, se encuentran en la columna de la derecha.

A

English	Español
abdomen: (p. 763) in invertebrates, posterior body region that contains fused segments, digestive structures, reproductive organs, and bears additional legs; in vertebrates, part of body that is between the diaphragm and pelvis.	**abdomen: (pág. 763)** región posterior del cuerpo de un invertebrado, la que contiene segmentos fusionados, estructuras digestivas, los órganos reproductores y que sostiene patas adicionales, en los vertebrados, parte del cuerpo que está entre el diafragma y la pelvis.
abiotic (ay bi AH tihk) factor: (p. 35) any nonliving factor in an organism's environment, such as soil, water temperature, and light availability.	**factor abiótico: (pág. 35)** todo factor inanimado en el ambiente de un organismo, como el suelo, el agua, la temperatura del agua y la disponibilidad de luz.
abyssal zone: (p. 81) deepest, very cold region of the open ocean.	**zona abisal: (pág. 81)** la zona más profunda y más fría del océano.
acid: (p. 164) substance that releases hydrogen ions (H^+) when dissolved in water; an acidic solution has a pH less than 7.	**ácido: (pág. 164)** sustancia que libera iones hidrógeno (H^+) cuando se halla disuelta en agua; una solución ácida contiene un pH menor que 7.
acoelomate (ay SEE lum ayt): (p. 701) animal with a solid body that lacks a fluid-filled body cavity between the gut and the body wall.	**acelomado: (pág. 701)** animal de cuerpo sólido que carece de una cavidad corporal llena de fluido entre las órganos internos y las paredes del cuerpo.
acrasin (uh KRA sun): (p. 563) chemical given off by starving amoeba-like slime mold cells that serves as a signal to the cells to form a sluglike colony.	**acrasina: (pág. 563)** sustancia química que liberan ciertas células ameboides, cuando tienen hambre, y que sirve de señal para que estas células formen una colonia viscosa.
actin: (p. 948) protein filament in muscle cells that functions with myosin in contraction.	**actina: (pág. 948)** filamento proteico de las células musculares que, junto con la miosina, participan en la contracción muscular.
action potential: (p. 964) nerve impulse.	**potencial de acción: (pág. 964)** un impulso nervioso.

activation energy: **(p. 158)** minimum amount of energy needed for reactants to form products in a chemical reaction.

active site: **(p. 160)** specific place where a substrate binds on an enzyme.

active transport: **(p. 205)** energy-requiring process by which substances move across the plasma membrane against a concentration gradient.

adaptation **(a dap TAY shun):** **(p. 10)** inherited characteristic of a species that develops over time in response to an environmental factor, enabling the species to survive.

adaptive radiation: **(p. 439)** diversification of a species into a number of different species, often over a relatively short time span.

addiction: **(p. 981)** psychological and/or physiological dependence on a drug.

adenosine triphosphate **(uh DEN uh seen • tri FAHS fayt)** **(ATP):** **(p. 221)** energy-carrying biological molecule, which, when broken down, drives cellular activities.

adolescence **(a dul ES unts):** **(p. 1063)** developmental phase that begins with puberty and ends at adulthood.

adulthood: **(p. 1064)** developmental phase that occurs at the end of adolescence, when physical growth is complete.

aerobic process: **(p. 228)** a metabolic process that requires oxygen.

aerobic respiration: **(p. 228)** metabolic process in which pyruvate is broken down and electron-carrier molecules are used to produce ATP through electron transport.

age structure: **(p. 104)** in any population, the number of individuals in their pre-reproductive, reproductive, and post-reproductive years.

agonistic **(ag oh NIHS tihk)** **behavior:** **(p. 917)** threatening or combative behavior between two members of the same species that usually does not result in injury or death.

air sac: **(p. 863)** in birds, the posterior and anterior structure used in respiration, resulting in only oxygenated air moving through the lungs.

aldosterone **(al DAWS tuh rohn):** **(p. 1035)** steroid hormone produced by the adrenal cortex that acts on the kidneys and is important for sodium reabsorption.

allele: **(p. 278)** alternative form that a single gene may have for a particular trait.

allergy: **(p. 1094)** overactive immune response to environmental antigens.

allopatric speciation: **(p. 438)** occurs when a population divided by a geographic barrier evolves into two or more populations unable to interbreed.

energía de activación: **(pág. 158)** cantidad mínima de energía que requieren los reactivos para formar productos durante una reacción química.

sitio activo: **(pág. 160)** lugar específico donde un sustrato se une a una enzima.

transporte activo: **(pág. 205)** proceso que requiere energía y que le permite a una sustancia atravesar la membrana plasmática contra un gradiente de concentración.

adaptación: **(pág. 10)** característica heredada de una especie; esta característica evoluciona a lo largo del tiempo en respuesta a un factor ambiental y le ayuda a la especie a sobrevivir.

radiación adaptativa: **(pág. 439)** diversificación de una especie en diferentes especies, a menudo en un período relativamente corto.

adicción: **(pág. 981)** dependencia psicológica o fisiológica a una droga.

trifosfato de adenosina (ATP): **(pág. 221)** molécula biológica que transporta energía, y que al desdoblarse, hace funcionar las actividades celulares.

adolescencia: **(pág. 1063)** fase del desarrollo que se inicia en la pubertad y termina al comenzar la edad adulta.

edad adulta: **(pág. 1064)** fase del desarrollo que empieza al terminar la adolescencia, cuando se completa el crecimiento físico.

proceso aeróbico: **(pág. 228)** proceso metabólico que requiere oxígeno.

respiración aeróbica: **(pág. 228)** proceso metabólico en que se desdobla el piruvato y las moléculas transportadoras de electrones ayudan a producir ATP mediante el transporte de electrones.

estructura etaria: **(pág. 104)** el número de individuos en edad prereproductora, reproductora y postreproductora en una población.

comportamiento agonístico: **(pág. 917)** comportamiento amenazador o combativo entre dos miembros de la misma especie y que normalmente no produce heridas o muerte.

sacos aéreos: **(pág. 863)** estructuras anteriores y posteriores de las aves que participan en la respiración celular y permiten sólo el paso de sangre oxigenada por los pulmones.

aldosterona: **(pág. 1035)** hormona esteroide producida por la corteza adrenal, la cual actúa sobre los riñones y es importante para la reabsorción de sodio.

alelo: **(pág. 278)** forma alternativa de un gene determinado para un rasgo dado.

alergia: **(pág. 1094)** acentuada respuesta inmune a un antígeno del ambiente.

especiación alopátrica: **(pág. 438)** sucede cuando una población separada en dos por una barrera geográfica, evoluciona y se convierte en dos poblaciones incapaces de entrecruzarse.

alternation of generations: **(p. 560)** reproductive life cycle that alternates between a diploid ($2n$) sporophyte generation and a haploid (n) gametophyte generation.

altruistic behavior: **(p. 922)** self-sacrificing behavior that benefits another individual.

alveolus: **(p. 1001)** in the lung, a thin-walled air sac surrounded by capillaries.

amino acid: **(p. 170)** carbon compound joined by peptide bonds; building block of proteins.

amnion (AM nee ahn): **(p. 852)** fluid-filled membrane that surrounds and protects a developing embryo.

amniotic egg: **(p. 853)** egg that provides a complete environment for the developing embryo with a yolk sac for nutrition, protective internal membranes and fluid, and a protective outer shell.

amniotic fluid (am nee AH tihk • FLU id): **(p. 1056)** amniotic sac fluid that cushions, insulates, and protects the embryo.

ampulla (AM pyew luh): **(p. 795)** in echinoderms, the muscular sac that contracts to force water into the tube foot, allowing it to extend.

amylase: **(p. 1020)** digestive enzyme in saliva that begins the process of chemical digestion in the mouth by breaking down starches into sugars.

anaerobic process: **(p. 228)** metabolic process that does not require oxygen.

analogous structure: **(p. 426)** structure that has the same function but different construction and was not inherited from a common ancestor.

anaphase: **(p. 251)** third stage of mitosis in which sister chromatids are pulled apart and microtubules, along with motor proteins, move the chromosomes to opposite poles of the cell.

anaphylactic (an uh fuh LAK tik) shock: **(p. 1095)** severe hypersensitivity to a specific antigen, causing a massive histamine release.

ancestral character: **(p. 495)** morphological or biochemical feature present in various groups within the line of descent.

ancestral trait: **(p. 424)** more-primitive characteristic that appeared in common ancestors.

annual: **(p. 620)** plant that completes its life span in one growing season or less.

anterior: **(p. 700)** toward the head end of an animal with bilateral symmetry.

anthropoid: **(p. 455)** part of haplorhines; humanlike primates that include New World monkeys, Old World monkeys, and hominoids.

antibiotic (an ti bi AH tihk): **(p. 1082)** substance that is able to kill or inhibit the growth of some microorganisms.

alternancia de generaciones: **(pág. 560)** ciclo de vida reproductor que se alterna entre una generación esporofita diploide ($2n$) y una generación gametofita haploide (n).

comportamiento altruista: **(pág. 922)** comportamiento de autosacrificio que beneficia a otro individuo.

alvéolo: **(pág. 1001)** saco aéreo de paredes delgadas, localizado dentro de los pulmones, y que está rodeado por capilares.

aminoácido: **(pág. 170)** compuestos de carbono con enlaces peptídicos; son la unidad básica de las proteínas.

amnios: **(pág. 852)** membrana llena de fluido que rodea y protege al embrión en desarrollo.

huevo amniótico: **(pág. 853)** huevo que provee un ambiente completo para un embrión en desarrollo. Tiene un saco vitelino para la nutrición, membranas internas y fluidos protectores, y una cubierta protectora externa.

fluido amniótico: **(pág. 1056)** fluido del saco amniótico que acojina, aísla y protege al embrión.

ampolla: **(pág. 795)** saco muscular de los equinodermos que se contrae para impulsar el agua hacia las patas ambulacrales y provocar su extensión.

amilasa: **(pág. 1020)** enzima digestiva de la saliva que inicia el proceso de digestión química en la boca, al desdoblar almidones en azúcares.

aproceso anaeróbico: **(pág. 228)** proceso metabólico que no requiere oxígeno.

estructura análoga: **(pág. 426)** estructura que tiene la misma función, pero diferente construcción y que no se originó a partir de un antepasado común.

anafase: **(pág. 251)** tercera fase de la mitosis. En ella, las cromátides hermanas se separan y los microtúbulos, junto con proteínas motoras, mueven los cromosomas hacia polos opuestos de la célula.

choque anafiláctico: **(pág. 1095)** grave hipersensibilidad a un antígeno específico que causa una liberación masiva de histamina.

carácter ancestral: **(pág. 495)** característica morfológica o bioquímica presente en varios grupos dentro de un linaje.

rasgo ancestral: **(pág. 424)** característica más primitiva que aparecían en antepasados comunes.

anual: **(pág. 620)** planta que completa su ciclo vital en una temporada de crecimiento o menos.

anterior: **(pág. 700)** extremo delantero de un animal con simetría bilateral.

antropoide: **(pág. 455)** parte de los haplorrinos; primates parecidos a humanos que incluyen los monos del Nuevo Mundo, monos del Viejo Mundo, y los homínidos.

antibiótico: **(pág. 1082)** sustancia que destruye algunos microorganismos o que inhibe su crecimiento.

antibody: **(p. 1086)** protein produced by B lymphocytes that specifically reacts with a foreign antigen.

antidiuretic (an ti di yuh REH tic) hormone: **(p. 1037)** functions in homeostasis by regulating water balance.

antigen: **(p. 1086)** a substance foreign to the body that causes an immune response; it can bind to an antibody or T cell.

aphotic zone: **(p. 80)** open-ocean zone through which sunlight cannot penetrate.

apoptosis (a pup TOH sus): **(p. 256)** programmed cell death.

appendage (uh PEN dihj): **(p. 764)** a structure such as a leg or an antenna that grows and extends from the body or body covering.

appendicular skeleton: **(p. 941)** one of the two divisions of the human skeleton; includes the bones of the arms, legs, feet, hands, hips, and shoulders.

arboreal: **(p. 455)** tree dwelling—it is a characteristic of many primates.

archaea: **(p. 500)** prokaryotes whose cell walls do not contain peptidoglycan.

artery: **(p. 993)** elastic, thick-walled blood vessel that carries oxygenated blood away from the heart.

artificial selection: **(p. 419)** Darwin's term for the selective breeding of organisms selected for certain traits in order to produce offspring having those traits.

ascocarp: **(p. 585)** in sac fungi, the reproductive structure in which haploid nuclei fuse to form a zygote.

ascospore: **(p. 585)** spore produced by an ascus.

ascus: **(p. 585)** spore-producing saclike structure of sac fungi.

atherosclerosis (a thuh roh skluh ROH sus): **(p. 999)** circulatory system disorder in which arteries are blocked, restricting blood flow.

atom: **(p. 148)** building block of matter; contains subatomic particles—neutrons, protons, and electrons.

atrium: **(p. 824)** heart chamber that receives blood from the body.

australopithecine: **(p. 465)** genus that lived in the east-central and southern part of Africa between 4.2 and 1 mya.

autonomic nervous system: **(p. 971)** part of the peripheral nervous system that transmits impulses from the central nervous system to internal organs.

anticuerpo: **(pág. 1086)** proteína producida por los linfocitos B que reacciona específicamente con un antígeno extraño.

hormona antidiurética: **(pág. 1037)** hormona que ayuda en la homeostasis al regular el equilibrio del agua.

antígeno: **(pág. 1086)** sustancia foránea al cuerpo que causa una reacción inmunológica; se puede enlazar a un anticuerpo o a una célula T.

zona afótica: **(pág. 80)** zona del mar abierto a la que no llega la luz solar.

apoptosis: **(pág. 256)** muerte celular programada.

apéndice: **(pág. 764)** estructura, como las patas o las antenas, que crece y se extiende desde el cuerpo o que la cubierta exterior del cuerpo.

esqueleto apendicular: **(pág. 941)** una de las dos divisiones del esqueleto humano; incluye los huesos de brazos, piernas, manos, pies, caderas y hombros.

arborícola: **(pág. 455)** que vive en los árboles: es una característica de muchos primates.

archaea: **(pág. 500)** procariotas cuyas paredes celulares no contienen peptidoglucanos.

arteria: **(pág. 993)** vaso sanguíneo de paredes gruesas y elásticas que transporta sangre oxigenada desde el corazón hacia el resto del cuerpo.

selección artificial: **(pág. 419)** término empleado por Darwin para referirse a la cría de selección de organismos, la cual se efectúa para seleccionar y obtener una progenie con ciertos rasgos.

ascocarpo: **(pág. 585)** estructura reproductora de los ascomicetos; la estructura reproductora en que núcleos haploides se fusionan para formar un cigoto.

ascospora: **(pág. 585)** espora producida por un asco.

asco: **(pág. 585)** estructura en forma de saco que produce esporas en los ascomicetos.

aterosclerosis: **(pág. 999)** trastorno del sistema circulatorio en que las arterias se bloquean y restringen el flujo de sangre.

átomo: **(pág. 148)** unidad básica de la materia; contiene las siguientes partículas subatómicas: neutrones, protones y electrones.

aurícula: **(pág. 824)** cavidad del corazón que recibe la sangre proveniente del cuerpo.

australopitecinos: **(pág. 465)** género que vivió en la parte centro oriental y meridional de África entre hace 4.2 y 1 millón de años.

sistema nervioso autónomo: **(pág. 971)** parte del sistema nervioso periférico que transmite impulsos desde el sistema nervioso central hacia los órganos internos.

autosome: **(p. 305)** chromosome that is not a sex chromosome.

autotroph (AW tuh trohf): **(p. 41)** organism that captures energy from sunlight or inorganic substances to produce its own food; provides the foundation of the food supply for other organisms; also called a producer.

auxin: **(p. 648)** plant hormone that moves in only one direction away from the site where it was produced and can stimulate the elongation of cells.

axial skeleton: **(p. 941)** one of the two divisions of the human skeleton; includes the bones of the vetebral column, ribs, skull, and sternum.

axon: **(p. 962)** neuron structure that transmits nerve impulses from the cell body to other neurons and muscles.

autosoma: **(pág. 305)** cromosoma que no es un cromosoma sexual.

autótrofo: **(pág. 41)** organismo que captura energía del sol o de sustancias inorgánicas para producir sus propios alimentos; es la base para la alimentación de otros organismos; también llamado productor.

auxina: **(pág. 648)** hormona vegetal que es transportada en una sola dirección, alejándose del sitio donde fue producida, y que estimula la elongación celular.

esqueleto axial: **(pág. 941)** una de las dos divisiones del esqueleto humano e incluye los huesos de la columna vertebral, las costillas, el cráneo y el esternón.

axón: **(pág. 962)** estructura de la neurona que transmite impulsos nerviosos desde el cuerpo de la célula hacia los músculos y otras neuronas.

B

B cell: **(p. 1086)** antibody-producing B lymphocyte.

background extinction: **(p. 122)** gradual process of a species becoming extinct.

bacteria: **(p. 516)** microscopic prokaryotes most are beneficial to humans and to the environment, but a small percentage can cause disease.

base: **(p. 164)** substance that releases hydroxide ions (OH^-) when dissolved in water; a basic solution has a pH greater than 7.

basidiocarp (buh SIH dee oh karp): **(p. 586)** fruiting body of basidiomycetes.

basidiospore: **(p. 586)** haploid spore released by a basidium during reproduction.

basidium: **(p. 586)** club-shaped, spore-producing hypha of basidiomycetes.

behavior: **(p. 908)** the way in which an animal responds to an external or internal stimulus.

benthic zone: **(p. 80)** ocean-floor area consisting of sand, silt, and dead organisms.

biennial: **(p. 621)** plant with a two-year life span.

bilateral (bi LA tuh rul) symmetry: **(p. 700)** body plan that can be divided into mirror images along only one plane through the central axis.

binary fission: **(p. 520)** asexual form of reproduction used by some prokaryotes in which a cell divides into two genetically identical cells.

binocular vision: **(p. 452)** overlapping fields of vision as a result of eyes located on the front of the face—a characteristic of primates.

célula B: **(pág. 1086)** linfocito B productor de antígenos.

extinción tradicional o natural: **(pág. 122)** proceso paulatino de extinción de una especie.

bacterias: **(pág. 516)** procariota microscópico; la mayoría son benéficos a los humanos y al ambiente; sólo un pequeño porcentaje puede causar enfermedades.

base: **(pág. 164)** sustancia que libera iones hidróxido (OH^-) al disolverse en agua; una solución básica tiene un pH mayor que 7.

basidiocarpo: **(pág. 586)** órgano productor de esporas en los basidiomicetos.

basidiospora: **(pág. 586)** espora haploide liberada por un basidio durante la reproducción .

basidio: **(pág. 586)** hifa productora de esporas de los basidiomicetos; tiene forma de maza.

comportamiento: **(pág. 908)** manera en que un animal responde a un estímulo externo o interno.

zona béntica: **(pág. 80)** zona del fondo marino formada por arena, limo y organismos muertos.

bienal: **(pág. 621)** planta con un ciclo de vida de dos años.

simetría bilateral: **(pág. 700)** plan corporal que se puede dividir en imágenes especulares, a lo largo de un solo plano a través del eje central.

fisión binaria: **(pág. 520)** forma de reproducción asexual de algunos procariotas, en la cual la célula se divide en dos células genéticamente idénticas.

visión binocular: **(pág. 452)** campos de visión sobrepuestos como resultado de ojos ubicados enfrente de la cara: una característica de los primates.

binomial nomenclature (bi NOH mee ul • NOH mun klay chur): (p. 485) Linnaeus's system of naming organisms, which gives a scientific two-word Latin name to each species—the first part is the genus name and the second is the specific epithet.

biodiversity: (p. 116) number of different species living in a specific area.

biogeochemical cycle: (p. 45) exchange of matter through the biosphere involving living organisms, chemical processes, and geological processes.

biogeography: (p. 428) study of the distribution of plants and animals on Earth.

bioindicator: (p. 588) living organism that is sensitive to environmental conditions and is one of the first to respond to changes.

bioinformatics: (p. 375) field of study that creates and maintains databases of biological information, especially genomic data.

biological augmentation: (p. 135) technique of adding essential materials to a degraded ecosystem.

biological community: (p. 36) all the interacting populations of different species that live in the same geographic location at the same time.

biological magnification: (p. 126) increasing concentration of toxic substances, such as DDT, in organisms as trophic levels increase in food chains or food webs.

biology: (p. 4) science of life; examines how living things interact, how systems function, and how they function at a molecular level.

bioluminescent: (p. 555) able to emit light.

biomass: (p. 44) total mass of living matter at each trophic level.

biome: (p. 36) large group of ecosystems that share the same climate and have similar types of communities.

bioremediation: (p. 134) technique using living organisms to detoxify a polluted area.

biosphere (BI uh sfihr): (p. 34) relatively thin layer of Earth and its atmosphere that supports life.

biotic (by AH tihk) factor: (p. 35) any living factor in an organism's environment.

bipedal: (p. 463) walking upright on two legs.

blastocyst: (p. 1055) a modified blastula whose inner cell mass will develop into a fetus.

blastula (BLAS chuh luh): (p. 696) fluid-filled ball of cells formed by mitotic cell division of the embryo.

nomenclatura binaria: (pág. 485) sistema desarrollado por Linneo para nombrar los organismos, en que se otorga un nombre científico de dos palabras a cada especie, la primera palabra es el género y la segunda es la especie.

biodiversidad: (pág. 116) número de especies diferentes que viven en un área determinada.

ciclo biogeoquímico: (pág. 45) intercambio de material a través de la biosfera en que participan seres vivos, procesos químicos y proceso geológicos.

biogeografía: (pág. 428) estudio de la distribución de plantas y animales en la Tierra.

bioindicador: (pág. 588) organismo vivo que es sensible a las condiciones ambientales y que es uno de los primeros en responder a los cambios.

bioinformática: (pág. 375) campo de estudio en que se crean y mantienen bases de datos con información biológica, particularmente genética.

bioaumento: (pág. 135) técnica en que se agregan materiales esenciales a un ecosistema degradado.

comunidad biológica: (pág. 36) todas las poblaciones de diferentes especies que interactúan y viven en una misma zona geográfica, al mismo tiempo.

amplificación biológica: (pág. 126) aumento en la concentración de sustancias tóxicas (como el DDT) en los organismos, a medida que aumenta el nivel trófico de cadenas y redes alimenticias.

biología: (pág. 4) ciencia que estudia la vida; examina las interacciones entre los seres vivos, el funcionamiento de sus sistemas y el funcionamiento a nivel molecular.

bioluminiscencia: (pág. 555) capacidad de emitir luz.

biomasa: (pág. 44) masa total de materia viva en cada nivel trófico.

bioma: (pág. 36) gran grupo de ecosistemas que comparte un mismo clima y que posee comunidades similares.

biorremediación: (pág. 134) técnica en que se usan organismos vivos para descontaminar un área.

biosfera: (pág. 34) capa relativamente delgada de la Tierra y su atmósfera que mantiene la vida.

factor biótico: (pág. 35) todo factor vivo en el ambiente de un organismo.

bípedo: (pág. 463) que camina erguido sobre dos piernas.

blastocisto: (pág. 1055) blástula modificada; sus células internas se convierten más tarde en el feto.

blástula: (pág. 696) esfera llena de fluido que se forma a partir de células originadas por la división mitótica de las células del embrión.

book lung (p. 767) in spiders and some other arthropods, the respiratory structure with highly folded walls whose membranes look like book pages.

filotráquea: (pág. 767) estructura respiratoria de arañas y otros artrópodos; estructura respiratoria con paredes muy plegadas, cuyas membranas semejan las páginas de un libro.

boreal forest: (p. 68) biome south of the tundra with dense evergreen forests and long, cold, dry winters.

bosque boreal: (pág. 68) bioma situado al sur de la tundra, tiene densos bosques de siempreverdes e inviernos largos, fríos y secos.

bottleneck: (p. 433) process in which a large population declines in number, then rebounds.

cuello de botella: (pág. 433) proceso en que el número de miembros de una población declina y luego aumenta.

breathing: (p. 1000) mechanical movement of air into and out of the lungs.

respiración: (pág. 1000) movimiento mecánico de entrada y salida de aire de los pulmones.

bronchus (BRAHN kuhs): (p. 1001) one of the two large tubes that carries air from the trachea to the lungs.

bronquio: (pág. 1001) uno de los dos grandes conductos por el que se introduce aire de la tráquea a los pulmones.

buffer: (p. 165) mixture that can react with an acid or a base to maintain the pH within a specific range.

amortiguador: (pág. 165) mezcla que puede reaccionar con un ácido o una base y mantener un pH dentro de cierto rango.

C

calcitonin (kal suh TOH nun): (p. 1034) thyroid hormone involved in regulation of blood calcium levels.

calcitonina: (pág. 1034) hormona tiroidea que participa en la regulación de los niveles de calcio en la sangre.

Calorie: (p. 1025) unit used to measure the energy content of food; 1 Calorie equals 1 kilocalorie, or 1000 calories.

Caloría: (pág. 1025) unidad de medida de la energía que contienen los alimentos; 1 Caloría equivale a 1 kilocaloría ó 1000 calorías.

Calvin cycle: (p. 226) light-independent reactions during phase two of photosynthesis in which energy is stored in organic molecules as glucose.

ciclo de Calvin: (pág. 226) reacciones independiente de la luz de la fase II de la fotosíntesis, en que la energía es almacenada como glucosa en moléculas orgánicas.

Cambrian explosion: (p. 398) rapid diversification of most major animal groups marking the start of the Paleozoic era.

explosión del Cámbrico: (pág. 398) rápida diversificación de la mayoría de los grupos animales que marca el inicio de la era Paleozoica.

camouflage (KA muh flahj): (p. 428) morphological adaptations that allow organisms to blend into their surroundings.

camuflaje: (pág. 428) adaptaciones morfológicas que permiten a los organismos disimularse en su ambiente.

cancer: (p. 254) uncontrolled growth and division of cells that can be caused by changes in control of the cell cycle and also may be caused by environmental factors.

cáncer: (pág. 254) crecimiento y división descontrolados de células que puede ser producido por cambios en ciclo celular o también puede ser causado por factores ambientales.

capillary: (p. 993) microscopic, one-cell-wall thick blood vessel where exchange of materials occurs between blood and body cells.

capilares: (pág. 993) vaso sanguíneo microscópico con paredes de una célula de grosor, en que sucede el intercambio de materiales entre la sangre y las células corporales.

capsid: (p. 526) outer protein layer that surrounds the genetic material of a virus.

cápsida: (pág. 526) capa externa proteica que envuelve el material genético de un virus.

capsule: (p. 518) polysaccharide layer secreted around the cell wall by some prokaryotes that prevents the cell from drying out and helps the cell attach to environmental surfaces.

cápsula: (pág. 518) capa de polisacáridos secretada alrededor de la pared celular de algunos procariotas que evita la deshidratación de la célula y que la ayuda a fijarse sobre superficies del ambiente.

carapace (KAR ah pays): (p. 857) dorsal part of a turtle's shell.

caparazón: (pág. 857) parte dorsal de la concha de una tortuga.

carbohydrate: (p. 168) organic compound containing carbon, hydrogen, and oxygen in a ratio of one oxygen and two hydrogen atoms for each carbon atom.

carbohidrato: (pág. 168) compuesto orgánico que contiene carbono, hidrógeno y oxígeno, en una razón de un átomo de oxígeno y dos átomos de hidrógeno, por cada átomo de carbono.

carcinogen **(kar SIH nuh jun): (p. 254)** cancer-causing substance.

carcinógeno: (pág. 254) sustancia que causa cáncer.

cardiac muscle: (p. 947) involuntary muscle found only in the heart.

músculo cardíaco: (pág. 947) músculo involuntario que sólo se halla en el corazón.

carnivore (KAR nuh vor): (p. 41) heterotroph that preys on other heterotrophs.

carnívoro: (pág. 41) heterótrofo que se alimenta de otros heterótrofos.

carrier: (p. 296) individual heterozygous for a recessive disorder such as cystic fibrosis or Tay-Sachs disease.

portador: (pág. 296) individuo heterocigoto para un trastorno recesivo como la fibrosis quística o la enfermedad de Tay-Sachs.

carrying capacity: (p. 98) largest number of individuals in a species that an environment can support long-term.

capacidad de carga: (pág. 98) el número mayor de individuos de una misma especie que un ambiente puede mantener a largo plazo.

cartilage (KAR tuh lihj): (p. 820) flexible, tough material that makes up vertebrate skeletons or parts of vertebrate skeletons.

cartílago: (pág. 820) material flexible y duro que forma todo o parte del esqueleto en los vertebrados.

caste: (p. 779) specialized group of individuals in an insect society that performs specific tasks.

casta: (pág. 779) grupo especializado de individuos en una sociedad de insectos que se encarga de realizar tareas específicas.

catalyst: (p. 159) substance that speeds up a chemical reaction by reducing the activation energy.

catalizador: (pág. 159) sustancia que acelera una reacción química al reducir energía de activación.

cell: (p. 182) basic unit of structure and organization of all living organisms.

célula: (pág. 182) unidad básica de estructura y organización de todos los seres vivos.

cell body: (p. 962) neuron structure that contains the nucleus and many organelles.

cuerpo celular: (pág. 962) estructura de la neurona que contiene el núcleo y muchos organelos.

cell cycle: (p. 246) process of cellular reproduction, occurring in three main stages—interphase (growth), mitosis (nuclear division), and cytokinesis (cytoplasm division).

ciclo celular: (pág. 246) proceso de reproducción celular; consta de tres fases principales: interfase (crecimiento), mitosis (división nuclear) y citoquinesis (división del citoplasma).

cell theory: (p. 183) states that (1) organisms are made of one or more cells; (2) cells are the basic unit of life; and (3) all cells come only from other cells.

teoría celular: (pág. 183) establece que (1) los organismos están formados por una o más células; (2) las células son la unidad básica de la vida y (3) todas las células provienen de otras células.

cell wall: (p. 198) in plants, the rigid barrier that surrounds the outside of the plasma membrane, is made of cellulose, and provides support and protection to the cell.

pared celular: (pág. 198) barrera rígida que rodea el exterior de la membrana plasmática de las plantas; está formada por celulosa y brinda soporte y protección a la célula.

cellular respiration: (p. 220) catabolic pathway in which organic molecules are broken down to release energy for use by the cell.

respiración celular: (pág. 220) vía catabólica en que se desdoblan moléculas orgánicas a fin de obtener energía para la célula.

central nervous system: (p. 968) consists of the brain and spinal cord and coordinates all of the body's activities.

sistema nervioso central: (pág. 968) está formado por el encéfalo y la medula espinal y coordina todas las actividades del cuerpo.

centriole: (p. 196) organelle that plays a role in cell division and is made of microtubules.

centríolo: (pág. 196) organelo formado por microtúbulos y que participa en la división celular.

centromere: (p. 248) cell structure that joins two sister chromatids.

centrómero: (pág. 248) estructura celular que une a dos cromátides hermanas.

cephalization (sef uh luh ZA shun): (p. 700) tendency to concentrate sensory organs and nervous tissue at an animal's anterior end.

cefalización: (pág. 700) tendencia a concentrar los órganos de los sentidos y el tejido nervioso en el extremo anterior del cuerpo del animal.

cephalothorax (sef uh luh THOR aks): (p. 763) in arthropods, the structure formed from the thorax region fused with the head.

cerebellum: (p. 886) part of the brain responsible for balance and coordination.

cerebral cortex: (p. 886) highly folded outer layer of the cerebrum that is responsible for coordinating conscious activities, memory, and the ability to learn.

cerebrum (suh REE brum): (p. 969) largest part of the brain; is divided into two hemispheres and carries out higher thought processes involved with language, learning, memory, and voluntary body movements.

character: (p. 492) inherited morphological or biochemical feature that varies among species and can be used to determine patterns of descent.

chelicera (kih LIH suh ruh): (p. 771) one of a pair of arachnid appendages modified to function as fangs or pincers.

cheliped: (p. 771) in most crustaceans, the first pair of legs, which has large claws to trap and crush food.

chemical digestion: (p. 1020) chemical breakdown of food by digestive enzymes such as amylase into smaller molecules that cells can absorb.

chemical reaction: (p. 156) energy-requiring process by which atoms or groups of atoms in substances are changed into different substances.

chemotaxis (KEE moh taks us): (p. 664) movement of a cell or organism in response to a particular chemical.

chitin (KI tun): (p. 577) tough, flexible polysaccharide in the exoskeletons of insects and crustaceans and in fungal cell walls.

chloroplast: (p. 197) double-membrane organelle that captures light energy and converts it to chemical energy through photosynthesis.

chordate: (p. 803) animal of the phylum Chordata having a dorsal tubular nerve cord, a notochord, pharyngeal pouches, and a postanal tail at some point in its development.

chromatin (KROH muh tun) (p. 247) relaxed form of DNA in the nucleus of a cell.

chromosome (KROH muh sohm) (p. 247) DNA-containing structure that carries genetic material from one generation to another.

cilium: (p. 198) short, hairlike projection that functions in cell movement.

circadian (sur KAY dee uhn) rhythm: (p. 919) cycle that occurs daily, such as sleeping and waking.

cefalotórax: (pág. 763) estructura de los artrópodos formada por la fusión del tórax con la cabeza.

cerebelo: (pág. 886) parte del encéfalo encargada del equilibrio y la coordinación.

corteza cerebral: (pág. 886) capa exterior del cerebro que posee muchos pliegues y que se encarga de coordinar las actividades conscientes, la memoria y la capacidad de aprender.

cerebro: (pág. 969) órgano más grande del encéfalo; se divide en dos hemisferios y realiza los procesos más complejos de pensamiento relacionados con el lenguaje, el aprendizaje, la memoria y los movimientos voluntarios del cuerpo.

carácter: (pág. 492) característica morfológica o bioquímica heredada que varía entre especies y que sirve para determinar patrones de la herencia.

quelíceros: (pág. 771) uno de los pares de apéndices de los arácnidos que están modificados para funcionar como colmillos o tenazas.

quelípedo: (pág. 771) el primer par de patas de los crustáceos y que consiste en grandes tenazas que sirven para atrapar y triturar los alimentos.

digestión química: (pág. 1020) desdoblamiento químico de los alimentos por enzimas digestivas, como la amilasa, en moléculas más pequeñas que las células puedan absorber.

reacción química: (pág. 156) proceso que requiere energía, en que los átomos o grupos de átomos se convierten en diferentes sustancias.

quimiotaxis: (pág. 664) movimiento de una célula u organismo en respuesta a una sustancia química particular.

quitina: (pág. 577) polisacárido fuerte y flexible del exoesqueleto de insectos y crustáceos y de la pared celular de los hongos.

cloroplasto: (pág. 197) organelo de doble membrana que captura la energía de la luz y la convierte en energía química mediante la fotosíntesis.

cordado: (pág. 803) animal perteneciente al filo Chordata; presenta cordón tubular nervioso dorsal, notocordio, somitas y cola postanal, en algún momento de su desarrollo.

cromatina: (pág. 247) forma no condensada de DNA en el núcleo de una célula.

cromosoma: (pág. 247) estructura que contiene DNA y que lleva el material genético de una generación a la siguiente.

cilio: (pág. 198) extensión corta y filiforme que funciona en la locomoción celular.

ritmo circadiano: (pág. 919) ciclo que sucede diariamente, como dormir y despertar.

cladistics (kla DIHS tiks): (p. 495) taxonomic method that models evolutionary relationships based on shared derived characters and phylogenetic trees.

cladogram (KLA duh gram): (p. 496) diagram with branches that represents the hypothesized phylogeny or evolution of a species or group; uses bioinformatics, morphological studies, and information from DNA studies.

class: (p. 488) taxonomic group that contains one or more related orders.

classical conditioning: (p. 913) learned behavior that occurs when an association is made between two different kinds of stimuli.

classification: (p. 484) grouping of organisms or objects based on a set of criteria that helps organize, communicate, and retain information.

climate: (p. 66) average weather conditions in a specific area, determined by latitude, elevation, ocean currents, and other factors.

climax community: (p. 63) stable, mature ecological community with little change in the composition of species.

clitellum: (p. 748) thickened band of segments that produce a cocoon from which young earthworms hatch.

cloaca (kloh AY kuh): (p. 835) the chamber that receives digestive waste, urinary waste, and eggs or sperm before they leave the body.

cloning: (p. 367) process in which large numbers of identical recombinant DNA molecules are produced.

closed circulatory system: (p. 739) blood is confined to the vessels as it moves through the body.

cnidocyte (NI duh site): (p. 710) nematocyst-containing stinging cell on a cnidarian's tentacle.

cochlea (KOH klee uh): (p. 974) snail-shaped, sound-sensitive, inner ear structure filled with fluid and lined with hair cells; generates nerve impulses sent to the brain through the auditory nerve.

codominance: (p. 302) complex inheritance pattern that occurs when neither allele is dominant and both alleles are expressed.

codon: (p. 338) three-base code in DNA or RNA.

coelom (SEE lum): (p. 701) fluid-filled body cavity completely surrounded by mesoderm.

cognitive behavior: (p. 915) learned behavior that involves thinking, reasoning, and information processing.

cladística: (pág. 495) método taxonómico que modela las relaciones evolutivas basándose en caracteres derivados compartidos y árboles filogenéticos.

cladograma: (pág. 496) diagrama con ramas que representan la filogenia hipotética, o evolución, de una especie o grupo; utiliza la bioinformática, los estudios morfológicos y la información proveniente de estudios del DNA.

clase: (pág. 488) grupo taxonómico que contiene uno o más órdenes relacionados.

condicionamiento clásico: (pág. 913) comportamiento adquirido que sucede cuando se establece una asociación entre dos diferentes tipos de estímulo.

clasificación: (pág. 484) agrupamiento de organismos u objetos en base a una serie de criterios y que permite organizar, comunicar y retener información.

clima: (pág. 66) condiciones meteorológicas promedio en un área específica; son determinadas por la latitud, la elevación, las corrientes oceánicas y otros factores.

comunidad clímax: (pág. 63) comunidad ecológica madura y estable que presenta pocos cambios en el número de especies.

clitelo: (pág. 748) banda de segmentos engrosados que produce las cápsulas de las que eclosionan las nuevas lombrices de tierra.

cloaca: (pág. 835) es la cavidad que recibe los desechos digestivos y urinarios, así como los huevos o el esperma, antes de que sean expulsados del cuerpo.

clonación: (pág. 367) proceso en que se producen grandes cantidades de moléculas idénticas de DNA recombinante.

sistema circulatorio cerrado: (pág. 739) sistema en que la sangre queda confinada en el interior de vasos cuando se desplaza a través del cuerpo.

cnidocito: (pág. 710) células urticantes, en los tentáculos de los cnidarios, que contienen nematocistos.

cóclea: (pág. 974) estructura del oído interno, con forma de caracol y sensible al sonido, que está llena de un fluido y revestida con células ciliadas; genera impulsos nerviosos que envía al encéfalo a través del nervio auditivo.

codominancia: (pág. 302) patrón hereditario complejo que sucede cuando ninguno de los alelos es dominante y ambos se expresan.

codón: (pág. 338) código de tres bases del DNA o el RNA.

celoma: (pág. 701) cavidad corporal llena de fluido y completamente rodeada por el mesodermo.

comportamiento cognitivo: (pág. 915) comportamiento adquirido que incluye razonamiento, pensamiento y procesamiento de información.

collenchyma cell: (p. 633) often elongated plant cell that provides flexibility for the plant, support for surrounding tissues, and functions in tissue repair and replacement.

colony: (p. 557) group of cells or organisms that join together, forming a close association.

commensalism (kuh MEN suh lih zum): (p. 40) symbiotic relationship in which one organism benefits and the other organism is neither helped nor harmed.

community: (p. 60) group of interacting populations that live in the same geographic area at the same time.

compact bone: (p. 942) strong, dense outer bone layer that contains Haversian systems.

companion cell: (p. 638) nucleated cell that helps the mature sieve tube member function in transporting dissolved substances in the phloem of vascular plants.

complement protein: (p. 1085) protein in blood plasma that enhances phagocytosis.

compound: (p. 151) pure substance with unique properties; formed when two or more different elements combine.

cone: (p. 618) feature that contains male or female reproductive structures of cycads and other gymnosperms. **(p. 974)** a type of cell in the retina of the eye that is responsible for sharp vision in bright light and seeing color.

conidiophore (koh NIH dee uh for): (p. 584) spore-producing hypha of sac fungi.

conjugation: (p. 520) form of reproduction used by some prokaryotes in which the prokaryotic cells attach to each other and exchange genetic material.

constant: (p. 19) a factor that remains fixed during an experiment while the independent and dependent variables change.

contour feather: (p. 862) barbed feather that covers a bird's body, wings, and tail and forms the body contour.

contractile vacuole: (p. 547) organelle that collects excess water in the cytoplasm and expels it from the cell; maintains homeostasis in hypotonic environments.

control group: (p. 19) in a controlled experiment, the group not receiving the factor being tested.

cork cambium: (p. 634) meristematic tissue that produces cells with tough cell walls that form the protective outside layer on stems and roots.

cortex: (p. 639) layer composed of ground tissues between the epidermis and vascular tissue of a root.

cortisol: (p. 1035) a glucocorticoid that raises blood glucose levels, reduces inflammation, and is produced by the adrenal cortex.

célula colenquimatosa: (pág. 633) células vegetales, a menudo alargadas, que proveen flexibilidad a la planta, sostén a los tejidos que lo rodean y que funcionan como tejido para reparar y sustituir otros tejidos.

colonia: (pág. 557) grupo de células que se unen y establecen una asociación muy estrecha.

comensalismo: (pág. 40) relación simbiótica en que un organismo se beneficia, mientras que el otro no obtiene beneficios pero tampoco es perjudicado.

comunidad: (pág. 60) grupo de poblaciones que interactúan y que viven en la misma región geográfica al mismo tiempo.

hueso compacto: (pág. 942) capa de hueso externa, más fuerte y más densa, que contiene los canales de Havers.

célula acompañante: (pág. 638) célula con núcleo que ayuda a los tubos cribosos maduros a realizar su función, en el transporte de sustancias disueltas, en el floema de las plantas vasculares.

complemento: (pág. 1085) proteínas del plasma de la sangre que estimulan la fagocitosis.

compuesto: (pág. 151) sustancia pura con propiedades particulares y que se forma cuando se combinan dos o más elementos.

cono: (pág. 618) estructura que contiene estructuras masculinas o femeninas en las cicadáceas y otras gimnospermas. **(pág. 974)** tipo de célula en la retina del ojo responsable de la visión nítida en luz brillante y de la visión a color.

conidióforo: (pág. 584) hifa de los ascomicetos que produce las esporas.

conjugación: (pág. 520) forma de reproducción de algunos procariotas en que dos células procariotas se conectan e intercambian material genético.

constante: (pág. 19) factor que permanece fijo durante un experimento mientras que las variables independiente y dependiente cambian.

pluma de contorno: (pág. 862) plumas barbadas que cubren el cuerpo, las alas y la cola de un ave y que dan contorno al cuerpo del ave.

vacuola contráctil: (pág. 547) organelo que recoge el exceso de agua en el citoplasma y lo expulsa de la célula; mantiene la homeostasis en ambientes hipotónicos.

grupo control: (pág. 19) en un experimento controlado, el grupo al que no se aplica el factor que se está probando.

cambio suberoso: (pág. 634) tejido meristemático que produce células con fuertes paredes celulares y que forma la capa protectora en el exterior de tallos y raíces.

corteza: (pág. 639) capa formada por tejido fundamental, situada entre la epidermis y el tejido vascular de la raíz.

cortisol: (pág. 1035) un glucocorticoide que eleva el nivel de glucosa en sangre, reduce la inflamación y que es producido por la corteza suprarrenal.

cotyledon (kah tuh LEE dun): (p. 617) seed structure that stores food or helps absorb food for the sporophyte of vascular seed plants.

courting behavior: (p. 921) species-specific series of movements or sounds used to attract a mate.

covalent bond: (p. 152) type of chemical bond formed when atoms share electrons.

Cro-Magnon: (p. 473) a species also referred to as *Homo sapiens;* seem to have replaced Neanderthals.

crop: (p. 746) sac in which food and soil are stored until they pass to the gizzard; found in earthworms and birds.

crossing over: (p. 272) exchange of chromosomal segments between a pair of homologous chromosomes during prophase I of meisois.

cyclin: (p. 253) one of the specific proteins that regulate the cell cycle.

cyclin-dependent kinase: (p. 253) enzyme to which cyclin binds during interphase and mitosis, triggering and controlling activities during the cell cycle.

cytokinesis (si toh kih NEE sis): (p. 246) third main stage of the cell cycle, during which the cell's cytoplasm divides, creating a new cell.

cytokinin (si tuh KI nihn): (p. 650) plant hormone that promotes cell division by stimulating production of proteins required for mitosis and cytokinesis.

cytoplasm: (p. 191) semifluid material inside the cell's plasma membrane.

cytoskeleton: (p. 191) supporting network of protein fibers that provide a framework for the cell within the cytoplasm.

cytotoxic T cell: (p. 1088) lymphocyte that destroys pathogens and releases cytokines when activated.

cotiledón: (pág. 617) estructura de la semilla que almacena alimentos o que ayuda a absorber alimentos para el esporofito de la semilla de una planta vascular.

comportamiento de cortejo: (pág. 921) serie de movimientos o sonidos específicos de cada especie, los cuales sirven para atraer a una pareja.

enlace covalente: (pág. 152) tipo de enlace químico que se forma cuando los átomos comparten electrones.

Cromañón: (pág. 473) especie también conocida como *Homo sapiens sapiens;* parece haber reemplazado a los Neandertales.

buche: (pág. 746) saco en que se almacenan los alimentos y el suelo hasta que pasan a la molleja.

entrecruzamiento: (pág. 272) intercambio de segmentos de cromosomas entre un par de cromosomas homólogos, el cual ocurre durante la profase I de la meiosis.

ciclina: (pág. 253) una de las proteínas específicas que regulan el ciclo celular.

quinasa dependiente de la ciclina: (pág. 253) enzima a la que se une la ciclina durante la interfase y la mitosis, iniciando y controlando, de este modo, las actividades del ciclo celular.

citoquinesis: (pág. 246) tercera etapa del ciclo celular; en esta etapa el citoplasma de la célula se divide y se origina una nueva célula.

citoquinina: (pág. 650) hormona vegetal que promueve la división celular al estimular la producción de las proteínas que se requieren para la mitosis y la citoquinesis.

citoplasma: (pág. 191) material semifluido que está rodeado por la membrana plasmática de la célula.

citoesqueleto: (pág. 191) red de fibras proteicas de soporte que provee una estructura para la célula, dentro del citoplasma.

linfocito T citotóxico: (pág. 1088) linfocito que al ser activado, destruye patógenos y libera citoquinas.

D

data: (p. 19) quantitative or qualitative information gained from scientific investigation.

day-neutral plant: (p. 673) plant that flowers over a wide range in the number of hours of darkness.

degenerative (di JEH nuh ruh tihv) disease: (p. 1092) noninfectious disease, such as arthritis, that results from part of the body wearing out.

demographic transition: (p. 102) population change from high birth rates and death rates to low birth rates and death rates.

datos: (pág. 19) información cualitativa o cuantitativa obtenida durante una investigación científica.

planta de días neutros: (pág. 673) planta que florece bajo un amplio rango de horas de oscuridad.

enfermedad degenerativa: (pág. 1092) trastorno no infeccioso, como la artritis, que resulta del desgaste de una parte del cuerpo.

transición demográfica: (pág. 102) cambio en una población que pasa de tener altas tasas de natalidad y de mortalidad, a tener bajas tasas de natalidad y de mortalidad.

demography: **(de MAH gra fee) (p. 100)** study of human populations based on size, density, movement, distribution, and birth and death rates.

dendrite: **(p. 962)** neuron structure that receives nerve impulses from other neurons and transmits them to the cell body.

denitrification: **(p. 48)** process in which fixed nitrogen compounds are converted back into nitrogen gas and returned to the atmosphere.

density-dependent factor: **(p. 95)** environmental factor, such as predation, disease, and competition, that depends on the number of members in a population per unit area.

density-independent factor: **(p. 94)** environmental factor, such as storms and extreme heat or cold, that affects populations regardless of their density.

dependent variable: **(p. 19)** factor being measured in a controlled experiment; its value changes because of changes to the independent variable.

depressant: **(p. 979)** substance/drug that slows down the central nervous system.

derived character: **(p. 495)** morphological or biochemical feature found in one group of a line but not in common ancestors.

derived trait: **(p. 424)** new feature that had not appeared in common ancestors.

dermis: **(p. 937)** skin layer beneath the epidermis; contains nerve cells, muscle fibers, sweat glands, oil glands, and hair follicles.

desert: **(p. 70)** area with low rainfall, whose annual rate of evaporation exceeds its annual rate of precipitation; can support cacti and some grasses and animal species such as snakes and lizards.

detritivore **(duh TRYD tuh vor): (p. 42)** heterotroph that decomposes organic material and returns the nutrients to soil, air, and water, making the nutrients available to other organisms.

deuterostome **(DEW tihr uh stohm): (p. 702)** coelomate animal whose anus develops from the opening in the gastrula.

development: **(p. 8)** changes an organism undergoes in its lifetime before reaching its adult form.

diaphragm: **(p. 885)** sheet of muscle beneath the lungs that separates the mammalian chest cavity from the abdominal cavity.

diffusion: **(p. 201)** net movement of particles from an area of higher concentration to an area of lower concentration.

dilation **(di LAY shun): (p. 1062)** the opening of the cervix during labor.

demografía: **(pág. 100)** estudio de las poblaciones humanas en base al tamaño, la densidad, el movimiento, la distribución y las tasas de natalidad y mortalidad de dichas poblaciones.

dendrita: **(pág. 962)** estructura de la neurona que recibe impulsos nerviosos de otras neuronas y que luego los transmite hacia el cuerpo de la neurona.

desnitrificación: **(pág. 48)** proceso en que los compuestos de nitrógeno fijado son convertidos a gas nitrógeno y devueltos a la atmósfera.

factor dependiente de la densidad: **(pág. 95)** factor ambiental, como la depredación, las enfermedades y la competencia, que depende del número de miembros de la población por unidad de área.

factor independiente de la densidad: **(pág. 94)** factor ambiental, como las tormentas y el calor o el frío extremos, que afectan a las poblaciones independientemente de su densidad.

variable dependiente: **(pág. 19)** factor que se mide en un experimento controlado; su valor cambia de acuerdo con los cambios en la variable independiente.

depresor: **(pág. 979)** sustancia o droga que disminuye la actividad del sistema nervioso central.

carácter derivado: **(pág. 495)** característica morfológica o bioquímica presente en un grupo de un linaje, pero no en los antepasados comunes.

rasgo derivado: **(pág. 424)** nueva característica que no aparece en antepasados comunes.

dermis: **(pág. 937)** capa de la piel situada bajo la epidermis; contiene células nerviosas, fibras musculares, glándulas sudoríparas y folículos pilosos.

desierto: **(pág. 70)** área con lluvias escasas y en que la tasa anual de evaporación excede la tasa anual de precipitación; es la morada de cactos, pastos y especies animales como serpientes y lagartijas.

detritívoro: **(pág. 42)** heterótrofo que descompone material orgánico y devuelve los nutrientes al suelo, al aire y al agua, poniendo los nutrientes a disposición de otros organismos.

deuterostomado: **(pág. 702)** animal celomado cuyo ano se desarrolla a partir de la apertura de la gástrula.

desarrollo: **(pág. 8)** cambios que sufre un organismo a lo largo de su vida, hasta alcanzar la vida adulta.

diafragma: **(pág. 885)** banda de músculos situada bajo los pulmones y que separa, en los mamíferos, el pecho de la cavidad abdominal.

difusión: **(pág. 201)** movimiento neto de partículas de una región de mayor concentración hacia una región de menor concentración.

dilatación: **(pág. 1062)** apertura del cuello uterino durante el parto.

diploid: (p. 271) having two copies of each chromosome (2*n*).

directional selection: (p. 435) shift of a population toward an extreme version of a beneficial trait.

dispersion: (p. 92) arrangement of a population in its environment.

disruptive selection: (p. 436) process in which individuals with average traits are removed, creating two populations with extreme traits.

diurnal: (p. 452) organisms that are active during the day.

division: (p. 488) taxonomic term used instead of *phylum* to group related classes of plants and bacteria.

DNA fingerprinting: (p. 373) separating an individual's unique sequence of DNA fragments to observe distinct banding patterns; can be used by forensic scientists to identify suspects and determine paternity.

DNA ligase: (p. 366) enzyme that chemically links DNA fragments together.

DNA microarray: (p. 375) silicon chips or microscope slides with DNA fragments that can allow many genes in a genome to be studied simultaneously.

DNA polymerase: (p. 334) enzyme that catalyzes synthesis of new DNA molecules.

domain: (p. 488) taxonomic group of one or more kingdoms.

dominance hierarchy (DAH muh nunts • HI rar kee): (p. 917) ranking system in which the top-ranked animal gets access to resources without conflict from others in the group.

dominant: (p. 278) Mendel's name for a specific trait that appeared in the F1 generation.

dopamine: (p. 978) neurotransmitter in the brain involved with feelings of pleasure, control of body movement, and other functions.

dormancy: (p. 679) period of little or no growth that varies from species to species; in plants, an adaptation that increases the survival rate of seeds in harsh environments.

dorsal (DOR sul): (p. 700) backside of an animal with bilateral symmetry.

dorsal tubular nerve cord: (p. 803) tube-shaped chordate nerve cord located above the digestive organs.

double helix: (p. 330) twisted-ladder shape of DNA, formed by two nucleotide strands twisted around each other.

down feather: (p. 862) soft feather beneath a bird's contour feathers that provides insulation by trapping air.

diploide: (pág. 271) células con dos copias de cada cromosoma (2*n*).

selección direccional: (pág. 435) cambio en una población hacia una versión extrema de un rasgo benéfico.

dispersión: (pág. 92) diseminación de una población en su ambiente.

selección disruptiva: (pág. 436) proceso en que los individuos con rasgos promedio son eliminados, creando dos poblaciones con rasgos extremos.

diurno: (pág. 452) organismos activos durante el día.

división: (pág. 488) término taxonómico que se usa en vez de *phylum* para agrupar clases relacionadas de plantas y bacterias.

huella genética: (pág. 373) separación de las secuencias de fragmentos de DNA propias de un individuo, para obtener su patrón único de bandas; se puede usar en estudios forenses para identificar a sospechosos o en estudios de paternidad.

DNA ligasa: (pág. 366) enzima que une químicamente entre sí, fragmentos de DNA.

micromatrices de DNA: (pág. 375) chips de silicio, o placas microscópicas con fragmentos de DNA que permiten el estudio simultáneo de todos los genes de un genoma.

DNA polimerasa: (pág. 334) enzima que cataliza la síntesis de nuevas moléculas de DNA.

dominio: (pág. 488) grupo taxonómico formado por uno o más reinos.

jerarquía de dominancia: (pág. 917) sistema de rango en que los animales de mayor jerarquía obtienen acceso a los recursos, sin conflictos con los otros miembros del grupo.

dominante: (pág. 278) nombre que dio Mendel a rasgos específicos que aparecían en la generación F1.

dopamina: (pág. 978) neurotransmisor cerebral presente en las sensaciones de placer, control de los movimientos del cuerpo y otras funciones.

latencia: (pág. 679) período en el cual ocurre muy poco o ningún crecimiento y que varía entre las especies; es una adaptación que aumenta la tasa de supervivencia de las semillas en ambientes hostiles.

dorsal: (pág. 700) parte trasera del cuerpo de un animal con simetría bilateral.

cordón nervioso tubular dorsal: (pág. 803) cordón nervioso de los cordados, de forma tubular, situado sobre los órganos digestivos.

doble hélice: (pág. 330) forma del DNA; semeja una escalera que se tuerce sobre sí misma y está constituida por dos cadenas enroscadas de nucleótidos.

plumón: (pág. 862) plumas suaves situadas bajo las plumas de contorno y que, al atrapar aire, proveen aislamiento al ave.

drug: **(p. 977)** natural or artificial substance that alters the body's function.

droga: **(pág. 977)** sustancia natural o artificial que altera las funciones corporales.

dynamic equilibrium: **(p. 202)** condition of continuous, random movement of particles but no overall change in concentration of materials.

equilibrio dinámico: **(pág. 202)** condición en que ocurre movimiento continuo y aleatorio de partículas, sin que haya un cambio general en la concentración de materiales.

E

ecological succession: **(p. 62)** process by which one community replaces another community because of changing abiotic and biotic factors.

sucesión ecológica: **(pág. 62)** proceso en que una comunidad reemplaza a otra, debido a cambios en los factores bióticos y abióticos.

ecology: **(p. 32)** scientific study of all the interrelationships between organisms and their environment.

ecología: **(pág. 32)** ciencia que estudia todas las interrelaciones entre los organismos y su ambiente.

ecosystem: **(p. 36)** biological community and all the nonliving factors that affect it.

ecosistema: **(pág. 36)** comunidad biológica y todos los factores inanimados que la afectan.

ecosystem diversity: **(p. 118)** variety of ecosystems in the biosphere.

diversidad de ecosistemas: **(pág. 118)** variedad de ecosistemas en la biosfera.

ectoderm: **(p. 697)** outer layer of cells in the gastrula that develops into nervous tissue and skin.

ectodermo: **(pág. 697)** capa exterior de células de la gástrula que origina el tejido nervioso y la piel.

ectotherm: **(p. 837)** animal that cannot regulate its body temperature through its metabolism and obtains its body heat from the external environment.

poiquilotermo: **(pág. 837)** animal que no puede regular su temperatura corporal mediante su metabolismo y que obtiene el calor corporal a partir del ambiente externo.

edge effect: **(p. 126)** any different environmental condition occurring along an ecosystem's boundaries.

efecto borde: **(pág. 126)** son todas las condiciones ambientales diferentes que suceden a lo largo de los límites de un ecosistema.

electron: **(p. 148)** negatively charged particle that occupies space around an atom's nucleus.

electrón: **(pág. 148)** partícula con carga negativa que gira alrededor del núcleo del átomo.

element: **(p. 149)** pure substance composed of only one type of atom; cannot be broken down into another substance by physical or chemical means.

elemento: **(pág. 149)** sustancia pura compuesta por un solo tipo de átomo; no se puede descomponer en otra sustancia por medios físicos ni por medios químicos.

embryo: **(p. 426)** organism's early prebirth stage of development.

embrión: **(pág. 426)** etapa inicial del desarrollo de un organismo antes del nacimiento.

emigration **(em uh GRAY shun):** **(p. 97)** movement of individuals away from a population.

emigración: **(pág. 97)** salida de individuos de una población.

endemic: **(p. 133)** found only in one specific geographic area.

endémico: **(pág. 133)** que sólo se halla en una región geográfica determinada.

endemic disease: **(p. 1081)** a disease found in only a few individuals within a population.

enfermedad endémica: **(pág. 1081)** enfermedad que sólo contraen unos cuantos individuos dentro de una población.

endocrine gland: **(p. 1031)** hormone-producing gland that releases its product into the bloodstream.

glándula endocrina: **(pág. 1031)** glándula productora de hormonas que libera su producto hacia el torrente sanguíneo.

endocytosis: **(p. 207)** energy-requiring process by which large substances from the outside environment can enter a cell.

endocitosis: **(pág. 207)** proceso que requiere energía y que permite la entrada de sustancias muy grandes a la célula.

endoderm: **(p. 697)** inner layer of cells in the gastrula that develops into digestive organs and the digestive tract lining.

endodermo: **(pág. 697)** capa interior de células de la gástrula; forma los órganos digestivos y el revestimiento del tracto digestivo.

endodermis: (p. 640) cell layer at the inner boundary of the cortex; regulates the material that enters the plant's vascular tissues.

endoplasmic reticulum (en duh PLAZ mihk • rih TIHK yuh lum): (p. 194) highly folded membrane system in eukaryotic cells that is the site for protein and lipid synthesis.

endoskeleton: (p. 693) internal skeleton that protects internal organs, provides support for the organism's body, and can provide an internal brace for muscles to pull against.

endosperm (EN duh spurm): (p. 676) tissue that provides nourishment to the developing embryo of flowering plants.

endospore: (p. 521) dormant bacterial cell able to survive for long periods of time during extreme environmental conditions.

endosymbiont theory: (p. 406) explains that eukaryotic cells may have evolved from prokaryotic cells.

endotherm: (p. 861) organism that generates its body heat internally by its own metabolism.

energy: (p. 218) ability to do work; energy cannot be created or destroyed, only transformed.

enzyme: (p. 159) protein that speeds up a biological reaction by lowering the activation energy needed to start the reaction.

eon: (p. 396) longest unit of time in the geologic time scale and can include billions of years.

epidemic: (p. 1081) large outbreak of a particular disease in a specific area.

epidermis: (p. 636) dermal tissue that makes up a plant's outer covering. **(p. 936)** in humans and some other animals, the outer superficial layer of skin made up of epithelial cells.

epididymis (eh puh DIH duh mus): (p. 1049) structure on top of each testis where sperm mature and are stored.

epiphyte: (p. 614) plant that lives anchored to an object or to another plant.

epistasis: (p. 305) interaction between alleles in which one allele hides the effects of another allele.

era: (p. 396) a large division of Earth's geologic time scale that is further divided into one or more periods.

esophagus (ih SAH fuh gus): (p. 1021) muscular tube that connects the pharynx to the stomach and moves food to the stomach by the process of peristalsis.

estuary (ES chuh wer ee): (p. 78) unique, transitional ecosystem that supports diverse species and is formed where freshwater and ocean water merge.

ethics: (p. 15) a set of values.

endodermis: (pág. 640) capa de células situada en el límite interior de la corteza y que regula los materiales que entran al tejido vascular de la planta.

retículo endoplásmico: (pág. 194) sistema de membranas de las células eucariotas; presenta numerosos pliegues y es el sitio donde ocurre la síntesis de proteínas y lípidos.

endoesqueleto: (pág. 693) esqueleto interno que protege los órganos internos, provee soporte al cuerpo del organismo y sirve como punto de apoyo para la contracción de los músculos.

endosperma: (pág. 676) tejido que provee alimentos al embrión en desarrollo de las plantas con flores.

endospora: (pág. 521) célula bacteriana en estado latente que puede sobrevivir durante largos períodos, bajo condiciones ambientales extremas.

teoría endosimbiótica: (pág. 406) propone que las células eucarióticas evolucionaron a partir de células procariotas.

homeotermo: (pág. 861) organismo que genera su calor corporal internamente, debido a su metabolismo.

energía: (pág. 218) capacidad de realizar trabajo; la energía no se puede crear o destruir, sólo se puede transformar.

enzima: (pág. 159) proteína que acelera una reacción biológica, al disminuir energía de activación que se requiere para iniciar la reacción.

eon: (pág. 396) la unidad de tiempo más larga en escala del tiempo geológico, la cual puede incluir billones de años.

epidemia: (pág. 1081) diseminación amplia de una enfermedad dada, en un área específica.

epidermis: (pág. 636) tejido dérmico que forma la cubierta más externa de una planta. **(pág. 936)** en humanos y algunos otros animales, la capa superficial externa de la piel compuesta por células epiteliales.

epidídimo: (pág. 1049) estructura situada en la parte superior del testículo en que los espermatozoides maduran y se almacenan.

epifita: (pág. 614) planta que vive sujeta a un objeto o a otra planta.

epistasis: (pág. 305) interacción entre alelos en que un alelo oculta el efecto de otro.

era: (pág. 396) gran división de la escala del tiempo geológico de la Tierra que incluye uno o más períodos.

esófago: (pág. 1021) conducto muscular que conecta la faringe con el estómago; transporta los alimentos hacia el estómago mediante movimientos peristálticos.

estuario: (pág. 78) ecosistema único de transición que mantiene gran diversidad de especies y que se forma donde el agua dulce se mezcla con el agua de los mares.

ética: (pág. 15) conjunto de valores.

ethylene: **(p. 649)** gaseous plant hormone that affects the ripening of fruits.

eukaryotic cell: **(p. 186)** unicellular organism with membrane-bound nucleus and organelles; generally larger and more complex than a prokaryotic cell.

eutrophication **(yoo troh fih KAY shun):** **(p. 127)** water pollution from nitrogen-rich and phosphorus-rich substances flowing into waterways, causing algal overgrowth.

evolution: **(p. 422)** hereditary changes in groups of living organisms over time.

exocytosis: **(p. 207)** energy-requiring process by which a cell expels wastes and secretes substances at the plasma membrane.

exon: **(p. 337)** in RNA processing, the coding sequence that remains in the final mRNA.

exoskeleton: **(p. 693)** hard or tough outer covering of many invertebrates that provides support, protects body tissues, prevents water loss, and protects the organism from predation.

experiment: **(p. 18)** procedure performed in a controlled setting to test a hypothesis and collect precise data.

experimental group: **(p. 19)** in a controlled experiment, the group receiving the factor being tested.

expulsion stage: **(p. 1062)** birthing stage during which a baby travels through the birth canal and exits the mother's body.

external fertilization: **(p. 695)** type of fertilization that occurs when sperm and egg combine outside an animal's body.

external respiration: **(p. 1000)** gas exchange between the atmosphere and the blood, occurring in the lungs.

extinction: **(p. 116)** the disappearance of a species when the last of its members dies.

etileno: **(pág. 649)** hormona gaseosa de las plantas que afecta la maduración de los frutos.

célula eucariota: **(pág. 186)** organismo unicelular con núcleo y organelos rodeados de membrana; generalmente son más grandes y complejas que las células procariotas.

eutroficación: **(pág. 127)** contaminación del agua causada por sustancias ricas en nitrógeno y fósforo que fluyen hacia masas de agua y que producen un crecimiento explosivo de algas.

evolución: **(pág. 422)** cambios hereditarios que sufren grupos de organismos a lo largo del tiempo.

exocitosis: **(pág. 207)** proceso que requiere energía y que permite a una célula expulsar desechos y secretar sustancias, a través de la membrana plasmática.

exón: **(pág. 337)** durante el procesamiento de RNA, la secuencia codificadora que queda en el mRNA final.

exoesqueleto: **(pág. 693)** cubierta exterior dura o de un material resistente que tienen muchos invertebrados; provee sostén, protege los tejidos del cuerpo, evita la pérdida de agua y los protege contra la depredación.

experimento: **(pág. 18)** procedimiento realizado bajo condiciones controladas, para recopilar datos precisos y probar una hipótesis.

grupo experimental: **(pág. 19)** grupo al que se aplica el factor que se está probando durante un experimento controlado.

etapa de expulsión: **(pág. 1062)** etapa del nacimiento durante la cual el bebé pasa a través del canal de parto y sale del cuerpo de la madre.

fecundación externa: **(pág. 695)** tipo de fecundación que ocurre cuando el esperma y el óvulo se unen fuera del cuerpo del animal.

respiración externa: **(pág. 1000)** intercambio de gases entre la atmósfera y la sangre, que ocurre en los pulmones.

extinción: **(pág. 116)** desaparición de una especie que ocurre cuando muere el último de sus miembros.

F

facilitated diffusion: **(p. 202)** passive transport of ions and small molecules across the plasma membrane by transport proteins.

family: **(p. 487)** taxonomic group of similar, related genera that is smaller than an order and larger than a genus.

feather: **(p. 861)** specialized outgrowth of the skin of birds used for flight and insulation.

fermentation: **(p. 231)** process in which NAD^+ is regenerated, allowing cells to maintain glycolysis in the absence of oxygen.

difusión facilitada: **(pág. 202)** transporte pasivo de iones y moléculas pequeñas, a través de la membrana plasmática, por medio de proteínas transportadoras.

familia: **(pág. 487)** grupo taxonómico que contiene géneros similares relacionados, está por encima del orden y por debajo del género.

pluma: **(pág. 861)** estructura especializada que crece sobre la piel de las aves y que sirve para el vuelo y como aislamiento.

fermentación: **(pág. 231)** proceso de regeneración de NAD^+ que permite a las células realizar la glucólisis en ausencia de oxígeno.

fertilization: (p. 271) process by which haploid gametes combine, forming a diploid cell with 2*n* chromosomes, with *n* chromosomes from the female parent and *n* chromosomes from the male parent.

fecundación: (pág. 271) proceso de combinación de gametos haploides que origina una célula diploide con 2*n* cromosomas; *n* cromosomas provienen de la madre y *n* cromosoma provienen del padre.

filter feeder: (p. 706) organism that filters small particles from water to get its food.

animal filtrador: (pág. 706) organismo que filtra el agua para obtener partículas que le sirven de alimento.

fin: (p. 822) paddle-shaped structure of a fish or other aquatic animal used for steering, balance, and propulsion.

aleta: (pág. 822) estructura de los peces u otros animales acuáticos, con forma de remo, que les sirve para dar dirección a sus movimientos, mantener el equilibrio y lograr propulsión.

fitness: (p. 428) measure of a trait's relative contribution to the following generation.

aptitud: (pág. 428) medida de la contribución relativa de un rasgo a la siguiente generación.

fixed action pattern: (p. 910) innate behavior that occurs in a sequence of specific actions in response to a stimulus.

pauta fija de acción: (pág. 910) comportamiento innato en respuesta a un estímulo que sucede como una secuencia de actos específicos.

flagellum: (p. 198) long, tail-like projection with whiplike or propellar motion that helps a cell move.

flagelo: (pág. 198) filamento largo y móvil que, al sacudirse como un látigo o un propellar, permite a una célula moverse.

flame cell: (p. 727) in flatworms, a cilia-lined, bulblike cell that moves water and certain substances into excretory tubules for elimination from the body.

célula flamígera: (pág. 727) células de las planarias, con forma de bulbo y revestidas con cilios, que transportan agua y ciertas sustancias hacia conductos excretorios para su posterior eliminación del cuerpo.

fluid mosaic model: (p. 190) a plasma membrane with components constantly in motion, sliding past one another within the lipid bilayer.

modelo del mosaico fluido: (pág. 190) membrana plasmática cuyos componentes se encuentran en movimiento constante, deslizándose dentro de la capa doble de lípidos.

food chain: (p. 43) simplified model that shows a single path for energy flow through an ecosystem.

cadena alimenticia: (pág. 43) modelo simplificado que muestra una sola vía para el flujo de energía en un ecosistema.

food web: (p. 43) model that shows many interconnected food chains and pathways in which energy and matter flow through an ecosystem.

red alimenticia: (pág. 43) modelo que muestra muchas cadenas alimenticias y vías interconectadas a través de las cuales fluyen la materia y la energía en un ecosistema.

foraging behavior: (p. 918) ecological behavior that involves finding and eating food.

comportamiento de forrajeo: (pág. 918) comportamiento ecológico relacionado con la búsqueda y el consumo de alimentos.

forensics: (p. 15) the field of study that applies science to matters of legal interest and other areas such as archaeology.

medicina forense: (pág. 15) campo de estudio que aplica la ciencia a asuntos de interés legal y otras áreas como la arqueología.

fossil: (p. 393) preserved evidence of an organism, often found in sedimentary rock, that provides evidence of past life.

fósil: (pág. 393) pruebas preservadas de un organismo que a menudo se hallan en rocas sedimentarias y que aportan datos y hechos sobre la vida en el pasado.

founder effect: (p. 433) random effect that can occur when a small population settles in an area separated from the rest of the population and interbreeds, producing unique allelic variations.

efecto fundador: (pág. 433) efecto aleatorio que sucede cuando una población pequeña se establece y se entrecruza en una región, separada del resto de la población, produciendo variaciones alélicas únicas.

fruiting body: (p. 577) spore-producing fungal reproductive structure.

cuerpo fructífero: (pág. 577) estructura reproductora de los hongos que produce esporas.

fungus: (p. 501) unicellular or multicellular eukaryote that is stationary, absorbs nutrients from organic materials in the environment, and has cell walls that contain chitin.

hongo: (pág. 501) eucariota sésil, unicelular o multicelular, que absorbe nutrientes de la materia orgánica del ambiente y que tiene una pared celular de quitina.

G

gametangium (ga muh TAN jee um): (p. 583) reproductive hyphal structure of zygomycetes that contains a haploid nucleus.

gametangio: (pág. 583) estructura reproductora de las hifas de los cigomicetos: contiene un núcleo haploide.

gamete: (p. 271) a haploid sex cell, formed during meiosis, that can combine with another haploid sex cell and produce a diploid fertilized egg.

gameto: (pág. 271) célula sexual haploide, formada durante la meiosis, que se puede combinar con otra célula sexual haploide y producir un huevo diploide fecundado.

ganglion: (p. 728) group of nerve-cell bodies that coordinates incoming and outgoing nerve impulses.

ganglio: (pág. 728) conjunto de cuerpos celulares de neuronas que se encargan de coordinar la entrada y salida de impulsos nerviosos.

gastrovascular (gas troh VAS kyuh lur) cavity: (p. 711) in cnidarians, the space surrounded by an inner cell layer, where digestion take place.

cavidad gastrovascular: (pág. 711) en los cnidarios, espacio rodeado por una capa interna de células y en que ocurre la digestión.

gastrula (GAS truh luh): (p. 696) two-cell-layer sac with an opening at one end that forms from the blastula during embryonic development.

gástrula: (pág. 696) saco de dos células de espesor, con una apertura en uno de sus extremos, que se forma a partir de la blástula durante el desarrollo embrionario.

gel electrophoresis: (p. 365) process that involves using electric current to separate certain biological molecules by size.

electroforesis en gel: (pág. 365) proceso en que se usa corriente eléctrica para separar ciertas moléculas biológicas, según su tamaño.

gene: (p. 270) functional unit that controls inherited trait expression that is passed on from one generation to another generation.

gene: (pág. 270) unidad funcional que controla la expresión de un rasgo heredado y que se transmite de una generación a otra.

gene regulation: (p. 342) ability of an organism to control which genes are transcribed in response to the environment.

regulación génica: (pág. 342) capacidad de un organismo para controlar los genes que se transcriben en respuesta a un ambiente.

gene therapy: (p. 378) technique to correct mutated disease-causing genes.

terapia génica: (pág. 378) técnica para corregir genes con mutaciones que causan enfermedades.

genetic diversity: (p. 116) variety of inheritable characteristics or genes in an interbreeding population.

diversidad genética: (pág. 116) variedad de características o genes heredables en una población que se entrecruza.

genetic drift: (p. 433) random change in allelic frequencies in a population.

deriva genética: (pág. 433) cambio aleatorio de frecuencias alélicas en una población.

genetic engineering: (p. 363) technology used to manipulate an organism's DNA by inserting the DNA of another organism.

ingeniería genética: (pág. 363) tecnología que se aplica para manipular el DNA de un organismo, mediante la inserción del DNA de otro organismo.

genetic recombination: (p. 283) new combination of genes produced by crossing over and independent assortment.

recombinación genética: (pág. 283) nueva combinación de genes producida por el entrecruzamiento y la distribución independiente de genes.

genetics: (p. 277) science of heredity.

genética: (pág. 277) ciencia que estudia la herencia.

genome: (p. 364) total DNA in each cell nucleus of an organism.

genoma: (pág. 364) todo el DNA en el núcleo de cada célula de un organismo.

genomics: (p. 378) study of an organism's genome.

genómica: (pág. 378) estudio del genoma de un organismo.

genotype: (p. 279) an organism's allele pairs.

genotipo: (pág. 279) pares de alelos de un organismo.

genus: (p. 487) taxonomic group of closely related species with a common ancester.

género: (pág. 487) grupo taxonómico de especies estrechamente emparentadas que comparten un antepasado común.

geologic time scale: (p. 396) model showing major geological and biological events in Earth's history.

escala del tiempo geológico: (pág. 396) modelo que muestra los principales eventos geológicos y biológicos de la historia de la Tierra.

germination: (p. 678) process in which a seed's embryo begins to grow.

germinación: (pág. 678) proceso que inicia el crecimiento del embrión de una semilla.

gestation: (p. 887) species-specific amount of time during which the young develop in the uterus before they are born.

gestación: (pág. 887) período específico para cada especie, durante el cual las crías se desarrollan en el útero, antes de nacer.

gibberellins: (p. 649) group of plant hormones that are transported in vascular tissue and that can affect seed growth, stimulate cell division, and cause cell elongation.

giberelinas: (pág. 649) grupo de hormonas vegetales que son transportadas por el tejido vascular y que pueden afectar el crecimiento de las semillas, y estimular la división y la elongacion celular.

gill (p. 738) respiratory structure of most aquatic organisms, taking many forms.

branquia: (pág. 738) estructura respiratoria de la mayoría de los organismos acuáticos, que asume muchas formas.

gizzard: (p. 746) muscular sac in earthworms and birds that contains hard particles that help grind soil and food before they pass into the intestine.

molleja: (pág. 746) saco muscular que contiene partículas duras que ayudan a moler el suelo y los alimentos, antes de que pasen al intestino.

gland: (p. 887) an organ or group of cells that secretes a substance for use elsewhere in the body.

glándula: (pág. 887) grupo de células que secretan una sustancia a usarse en alguna otra parte del cuerpo.

glucagon (GLEW kuh gahn): (p. 1034) hormone produced by the pancreas that signals liver cells to convert glycogen to glucose and release glucose into the blood.

glucagón: (pág. 1034) hormona producida por el páncreas; les indica a las células del hígado que conviertan glucógeno en glucosa y que liberen la glucosa hacia el torrente sanguíneo.

glycolysis: (p. 229) anaerobic process; first stage of cellular respiration in which glucose is broken down into two molecules of pyruvate.

glucólisis: (pág. 229) proceso anaeróbico; primera etapa de la respiración celular, en la cual la glucosa se transforma en dos moléculas de piruvato.

Golgi apparatus: (p. 195) flattened stack of tubular membranes that modifies, sorts, and packages proteins into vesicles and transports them to other organelles or out of the cell.

aparato de Golgi: (pág. 195) conjunto de membranas tubulares aplanadas que modifica, acomoda y empaca proteínas en vesículas y luego las transporta hacia otros organelos o hacia afuera de la célula.

gradualism: (p. 440) theory that evolution occurs in small, gradual steps over time.

gradualismo: (pág. 440) teoría que señala que la evolución sucede gradualmente, en pasos pequeños, a lo largo del tiempo.

granum: (p. 223) one of the stacks of pigment-containing thylakoids in a plant's chloroplasts.

grana: (pág. 223) conjunto de tilacoides con pigmentos de los cloroplastos de una planta.

grassland: (p. 70) biome characterized by fertile soils with a thick cover of grasses.

pradera: (pág. 70) bioma caracterizado por suelos fértiles con una espesa cubierta de pastos.

ground tissue: (p. 638) plant tissue consisting of parenchyma, collenchyma, and sclerenchyma.

tejido fundamental: (pág. 638) tejido vegetal que consiste en parénquima, colénquima y esclerénquima.

growth: (p. 9) process that results in mass being added to an organism; may include formation of new cells and new structures.

crecimiento: (pág. 9) proceso que provoca el aumento de masa en un organismo; puede incluir la formación de células y estructuras nuevas.

guard cell: (p. 636) one of a pair of cells that function in the opening and closing of a plant's stomata by changes in their shape.

célula guardiana: (pág. 636) una de las células del par de células cuya función es abrir y cerrar, mediante cambios en su forma, los estomas de la planta.

H

habitat: (p. 38) physical area in which an organism lives.

hábitat: (pág. 38) área física en que vive un organismo.

habitat fragmentation: (p. 127) habitat loss from separation of an ecosystem into small pieces of land.

fragmentación del hábitat: (pág. 127) pérdida de hábitat como resultado de la partición de un ecosistema en terrenos pequeños.

Glossary/ Glosario

habituation (huh bit choo AY shun): (p. 912) decrease in an animal's response after it has been repeatedly exposed to a specific stimulus that has no positive or negative effects.

habituación: (pág. 912) disminución de la respuesta de un animal, luego de haber sido expuesto repetidamente a un estímulo determinado, que no tiene efectos positivos ni negativos.

hair follicle: (p. 937) narrow cavity in the dermis from which a hair grows.

folículo piloso: (pág. 937) cavidad estrecha de la dermis de la cual crece un cabello.

half-life: (p. 395) amount of time required for half of a radioactive isotope to decay.

media vida: (pág. 395) cantidad de tiempo que se requiere para que se desintegre la mitad de un isótopo radiactivo.

haploid: (p. 271) cell with half the number of chromosomes (n) as a diploid ($2n$) cell.

haploide: (pág. 271) célula con la mitad del número de cromosomas (n) que una célula diploide ($2n$).

haplotype: (p. 378) area of linked genetic variations in the human genome.

haplotipo: (pág. 378) área del genoma humano con variaciones genéticas ligadas.

Hardy-Weinberg principle: (p. 431) states that allelic frequencies in populations stay the same unless they are affected by a factor that causes change.

principio de Hardy-Weinberg: (pág. 431) establece que las frecuencias alélicas de una población permanecen inalterables, a menos que sean afectadas por un factor que produzca un cambio.

haustorium (haws toh REE um): (p. 578) specialized hypha of parasitic fungi that grows into a host's tissues and absorbs its nutrients.

haustorio: (pág. 578) hifa especializada de los hongos parásitos cuya función es invadir los tejidos del huésped para absorber sus nutrientes.

heart: (p. 994) hollow, muscular organ that pumps oxygenated blood to the body and deoxygenated blood to the lungs.

corazón: (pág. 994) órgano muscular y hueco que bombea sangre oxigenada hacia el cuerpo y sangre desoxigenada hacia los pulmones.

helper T cell: (p. 1088) lymphocyte that activates antibody secretion in B cells and cytotoxic T cells.

célula T ayudante: (pág. 1088) linfocito que activa los linfocitos B y los linfocitos T citotóxicos para que secreten anticuerpos.

herbivore (HUR buh vor): (p. 41) heterotroph that eats only plants.

herbívoro: (pág. 41) heterótrofo que sólo se alimenta de plantas.

hermaphrodite (hur MAF ruh dite): (p. 695) animal that produces both sperm and eggs in its body, generally at different times.

hermafrodita: (pág. 695) animal que produce óvulos y espermatozoides en su cuerpo, generalmente a diferentes tiempos.

heterosporous (he tuh roh SPOR uhs): (p. 665) able to produce two types of spores—megaspores and microspores—that develop into female or male gametophytes.

heterospóreo: (pág. 665) capaz de producir dos tipos de esporas (megasporas y microsporas) que, al desarrollarse, forman el gametofito masculino o el femenino.

heterotroph (HE tuh roh trohf): (p. 41) organism that cannot make its own food and gets its nutrients and energy requirements by feeding on other organisms; also called a consumer.

heterótrofo: (pág. 41) organismo que no puede producir su propio alimento y que obtiene los nutrientes y la energía que necesita, alimentándose de otros organismos; también se llaman consumidores.

heterozygous (heh tuh roh ZI gus): (p. 279) organism with two different alleles for a specific trait.

heterocigoto: (pág. 279) organismo con dos diferentes alelos para un rasgo específico.

homeostasis (hoh mee oh STAY sus): (p. 10) regulation of an organism's internal environment to maintain conditions needed for life.

homeostasis: (pág. 10) regulación del ambiente interno de un organismo a fin de mantener las condiciones necesarias para la vida.

hominin: (p. 458) humanlike primate that appears to be more closely related to present-day humans than to present-day chimpanzees and bonobos.

hominiano: (pág. 458) primate tipo humano que parece estar más estrechamente emparentado con los humanos actuales que los chimpancés y bonobos actuales.

hominoid: (p. 461) group that includes all nonmonkey anthropoids—the living and extinct gibbons, orangutans, chimpanzees, gorillas, and humans.

hominoide: (pág. 461) grupo que incluye todos los antropoides que no son monos: los gibones, orangutanes, chimpancés, gorilas y humanos vivos y extintos.

***Homo:* (p. 467)** genus that includes living and extinct humans.

***Homo:* (pág. 467)** género que incluye a los humanos vivos y extintos.

homologous chromosome: (p. 270) one of two paired chromosomes, one from each parent, that carries genes for a specific trait at the same location.

cromosoma homólogo: (pág. 270) uno de los cromosomas, de un par de cromosomas, que contienen en un mismo sitio los genes para un rasgo específico. Cada progenitor contribuye un cromosoma de cada par.

homologous structure: (p. 424) anatomically similar structure inherited from a common ancestor.

estructura homóloga: (pág. 424) estructura anatómicamente similar heredada de un antepasado común.

homozygous (ho muh ZI gus): (p. 279) organism with two of the same alleles for a specific trait.

homocigoto: (pág. 279) organismo con dos alelos iguales para un rasgo específico.

hormone: (p. 1031) substance, such as estrogen, that is produced by an endocrine gland and acts on target cells.

hormona: (pág. 1031) sustancia, como el estrógeno, que es producida por una glándula endocrina y que actúa sobre células blanco.

hybrid: (p. 279) organism heterozygous for a specific trait.

híbrido: (pág. 279) organismo heterocigoto para un rasgo específico.

hydrogen bond: (p. 161) weak electrostatic bond formed by the attraction of opposite charges between a hydrogen atom and an oxygen, fluorine, or nitrogen atom.

enlace de hidrógeno: (pág. 161) enlace electrostático débil, formado por la atracción de cargas opuestas entre un átomo de hidrógeno y un átomo de oxígeno, flúor o nitrógeno.

hydrostatic skeleton: (p. 732) the pseudocoelom in roundworms; the fluid within a closed space that gives rigid support for muscles to work against.

esqueleto hidrostático: (pág. 732) seudoceloma de los gusanos redondos; fluido dentro de un espacio cerrado que provee un punto rígido de apoyo a los músculos.

hypertonic solution: (p. 205) a solution that has a higher concentration of solute outside than inside a cell, causing water to leave the cell by osmosis.

solución hipertónica: (pág. 205) solución que tiene una mayor concentración de soluto que el interior de la célula, la cual se encoge y arruga debido a que el agua sale de su interior por osmosis.

hypha (HI fah): (p. 577) threadlike filament that makes up the basic structural unit of a multicellular fungus.

hifa: (pág. 577) estructura con forma de filamento que constituye la unidad básica estructural de un hongo multicelular.

hypocotyl: (p. 679) region of the stem nearest the seed.

hipocótilo: (pág. 679) región del tallo más cercana a la semilla.

hypothalamus (hi poh THA luh mus): (p. 970) part of the brain that regulates body temperature, appetite, thirst, and water balance.

hipotálamo: (pág. 970) parte del encéfalo que regula la temperatura del cuerpo, el apetito, la sed y el equilibrio del agua.

hypothesis (hi PAH thuh sus): (p. 16) testable explanation of a situation.

hipótesis: (pág. 16) explicación comprobable de una situación.

hypotonic solution: (p. 204) a solution that has a lower concentration of solute outside than inside the cell, causing water to flow into the cell by osmosis.

solución hipotónica: (pág. 204) solución que tiene una menor concentración de soluto; hay más agua fuera que dentro de la célula.

I

immigration (ih muh GRAY shun): (p. 97) movement of individuals into a population.

inmigración: (pág. 97) entrada de individuos a una población.

immunization: (p. 1089) vaccination; develops active immunity.

inmunización: (pág. 1089) vacunación; desarrolla inmunidad activa.

imprinting: (p. 914) permanent learning that occurs only within a specific period of time in an animal's life.

impronta: (pág. 914) aprendizaje permanente que sucede sólo en un período específico de la vida de un animal.

inbreeding: (p. 361) selective breeding of closely related organisms to produce desired traits and eliminate undesired traits, resulting in pure lines—however, harmful recessive traits can also be passed on.

endogamia: (pág. 361) cruce selectivo de organismos emparentados para obtener rasgos deseados y eliminar rasgos indeseados; permite obtener linajes puros, aunque también puede transmitir rasgos recesivos dañinos.

incomplete dominance: (p. 302) complex inheritance pattern in which the heterozygous phenotype is intermediate between those of the two homozygous parent organisms.

incubate: (p. 866) to maintain an egg or eggs at favorable environmental conditions for hatching.

independent variable: (p. 19) the one factor that can be changed in a controlled experiment; is the factor tested and affects the experiment outcome.

infancy: (p. 1064) first two years of human life.

infectious disease: (p. 1076) pathogen-caused disease passed from one organism to another organism.

inference: (p. 16) assumption based on prior experience.

innate (ih NAYT) behavior: (p. 910) genetically based behavior.

insulin: (p. 1034) hormone produced by the pancreas that works with glucagon to maintain the level of sugar in the blood.

interferon: (p. 1085) antiviral protein secreted by virus-infected cells.

intermediate-day plant: (p. 673) plant that flowers as long as the number of hours of darkness is neither too great nor too few.

internal fertilization: (p. 695) type of fertilization that occurs when sperm and egg combine inside an animal's body.

internal respiration: (p. 1000) gas exchange between the body's cells and the blood.

interphase: (p. 246) first stage of the cell cycle, during which a cell grows, matures, and replicates its DNA.

intertidal zone: (p. 79) narrow band of shoreline where the ocean and land meet that is alternately submerged and exposed and is home to constantly changing communities.

introduced species: (p. 128) nonnative species deliberately or accidentally introduced into a new habitat.

intron: (p. 337) in RNA processing, the intervening coding sequence missing from the final mRNA.

invertebrate: (p. 693) animal without a backbone; between 95 and 99 percent of animal species are invertebrates.

invertebrate chordate: (p. 803) chordate without a backbone.

involuntary muscle: (p. 947) smooth muscle, which cannot be controlled consciously.

ion: (p. 153) atom that is negatively or positively charged because it has lost or gained one or more electrons.

dominancia incompleta: (pág. 302) patrón complejo de herencia en que el fenotipo heterocigoto es intermedio entre los dos fenotipos de los progenitores homocigotos.

incubar: (pág. 866) mantener los huevos bajo condiciones ambientales favorables para que luego eclosionen.

variable independiente: (pág. 19) el único factor que se puede cambiar en un experimento controlado; es el factor que se está probando y afecta los resultados del experimento.

lactancia: (pág. 1064) los primeros dos años de vida en los humanos.

enfermedad infecciosa: (pág. 1076) enfermedad causada por un patógeno que se transmite de un organismo a otro.

inferencia: (pág. 16) supuesto basado en la experiencia previa.

comportamiento innato: (pág. 910) comportamiento basado en la genética.

insulina: (pág. 1034) hormona producida por el páncreas que, junto con el glucagón, mantiene los niveles adecuados de azúcar en la sangre.

interferón: (pág. 1085) proteína secretada por células infectadas por virus.

planta de días intermedios: (pág. 673) planta que florece mientras el número de horas de oscuridad no sea ni muy grande ni muy pequeño.

fecundación interna: (pág. 695) tipo de fecundación que sucede cuando el espermatozoide se une al óvulo dentro del cuerpo del animal.

respiración interna: (pág. 1000) intercambio de gases entre las células del cuerpo y la sangre.

interfase: (pág. 246) primera fase del ciclo celular; en esta fase, la célula crece, madura y replica su DNA.

zona intermareal: (pág. 79) franja estrecha de la costa donde se encuentran la tierra y el mar; es inundada periódicamente por las mareas y presenta un cambio constante en su comunidad.

especie introducida: (pág. 128) especie no nativa que es introducida deliberadamente o por accidente a un nuevo hábitat.

intrón: (pág. 337) en la transcripción del RNA, la secuencia de codones que se transcribe pero que no forma parte del mRNA final.

invertebrado: (pág. 693) animal sin columna vertebral; entre el 95 y el 99 por ciento de las especies animales son invertebrados.

cordado invertebrado: (pág. 803) cordado sin columna vertebral.

músculo involuntario: (pág. 947) músculo liso, no se puede controlar a voluntad.

ion: (pág. 153) átomo con carga positiva o negativa porque ha perdido o ganado uno o más electrones.

ionic bond: (p. 153) electrical attraction between two oppositely charged atoms or groups of atoms.

enlace iónico: (pág. 153) atracción eléctrica entre dos átomos o grupos de átomos con carga opuesta.

isotonic solution: (p. 204) a solution with the same concentration of water and solutes as inside a cell, resulting in the cell retaining its normal shape because there is no net movement of water.

solución isotónica: (pág. 204) solución con la misma concentración de agua y solutos que el interior de la célula; permite a la célula mantener su forma original porque no hay movimiento neto de agua.

isotope: (p. 150) two or more atoms of the same element having different numbers of neutrons.

isótopo: (pág. 150) dos o más átomos de un mismo elemento que tienen diferente número de neutrones.

J

Jacobson's organ: (p. 855) saclike, odor-sensing structure on the roof of a snake's mouth.

órgano de Jacobson: (pág. 855) órgano con forma de saco cuya función es detectar olores; está situado en el paladar de la boca de las serpientes.

K

karyotype (KER ee uh tipe): (p. 311) micrograph in which the pairs of homologous chromosomes are arranged in decreasing size.

cariotipo: (pág. 311) micrografía en que los pares de cromosomas homólogos aparecen ordenados en tamaño decreciente.

keratin (KER uh tun): (p. 936) protein contained in the skin's outer epidermal cells that waterproofs and protects underlying cells and tissues.

queratina: (pág. 936) proteína que contienen las células más externas de la epidermis; es impermeable al agua y protege las células y tejidos subyacentes.

kidney: (p. 1006) bean-shaped, excretory system organ that filters out wastes, water, and salts from the blood and maintains blood pH.

riñón: (pág. 1006) órgano del sistema excretor con forma de frijol; mantiene el pH y elimina por filtración los desechos, el agua y las sales.

kingdom: (p. 488) taxonomic group of related phyla or divisions.

reino: (pág. 488) grupo taxonómico que incluye filos o divisiones relacionadas.

Koch's postulates: (p. 1077) rules for demonstrating that an organism causes a disease.

postulados de Koch: (pág. 1077) reglas para demostrar que un organismo causa una enfermedad.

Krebs cycle: (p. 229) series of reactions in which pyruvate is broken down into carbon dioxide inside the mitochondria of cells; also called the tricarboxylic acid cycle and the citric acid cycle.

ciclo de Krebs: (pág. 229) serie de reacciones en que el piruvato se desdobla en dióxido de carbono dentro de las mitocondrias de las células; también se llama ciclo del ácido tricarboxílico y ciclo del ácido cítrico.

K-T boundary: (p. 399) layer of iridium-rich material betweeen rocks of the Cretaceous period and rocks of the Paleogene period that provides evidence of a meteorite impact.

límite KT: (pág. 399) capa de material rico en iridio, situada entre las rocas de los períodos Cretáceo y Paleoceno; provee pruebas del impacto de un meteorito.

L

labor: (p. 1062) three-stage birthing process that begins with uterine contractions and ends with expulsion of the placenta and umbilical cord.

parto: (pág. 1062) las tres etapas del proceso de alumbramiento; se inicia con las contracciones uterinas y termina con la expulsión de la placenta y el cordón umbilical.

language: (p. 920) auditory communication in which animals use their vocal organs to produce sounds with shared meanings.

lenguaje: (pág. 920) comunicación mediante sonidos en que el animal usa sus órganos vocales para producir sonidos con significados dados.

large intestine: (p. 1024) end portion of the digestive tract; involved primarily in water absorption.

lateral line system: (p. 826) sensory receptors that enable fishes to detect vibrations, or sound waves, in water.

latitude: (p. 65) distance of a point on Earth's surface north or south of the equator.

law of independent assortment: (p. 280) Mendelian law stating that a random distribution of alleles occurs during the formation of gametes.

law of segregation: (p. 279) Mendelian law stating that two alleles for each trait separate during meiosis.

law of superposition: (p. 394) states that the oldest layers of rock are found at the bottom and the youngest layers of rock are found at the top of a formation if the rock layers have not been disturbed.

learned behavior: (p. 912) results from an interaction between innate behavior and past experience within a specific environment; includes habituation, conditioning, and imprinting.

lens: (p. 974) part of the eye behind the iris that inverts an image and focuses it on the retina.

lichen (LI ken): (p. 587) symbiotic relationship between a fungus (usually an ascomycete) and an alga or a photosynthetic partner.

ligament: (p. 944) tough connective tissue band that attaches bones to each other.

limiting factor: (p. 61) biotic or abiotic factor that restricts the number, distribution, or reproduction of a population within a community.

limnetic zone: (p. 77) well-lit, open-water area of a lake or pond.

lipid: (p. 169) hydrophobic biological molecule composed mostly of carbon and hydrogen; fats, oils, and waxes are lipids.

littoral zone: (p. 76) area of a lake or pond closest to the shore.

liver: (p. 1022) largest internal organ of the body; produces bile.

long-day plant: (p. 672) plant that flowers in the summer, when there are fewer hours of darkness than the plant's critical period.

lung: (p. 1001) largest respiratory system organ in which gas exchange takes place.

lymphocyte: (p. 1086) white blood cell involved in specific immunity; a B cell or a T cell.

intestino grueso: (pág. 1024) porción final del tracto digestivo; su función principal es la absorción de agua.

sistema de la línea lateral: (pág. 826) receptores sensoriales que permiten a los peces detectar vibraciones u ondas sonoras en el agua.

latitud: (pág. 65) distancia de un punto sobre la superficie de la Tierra, hacia el norte o hacia el sur del ecuador.

ley de la distribución independiente: (pág. 280) ley de Mendel que establece que la distribución independiente de alelos sucede durante la formación de los gametos.

ley de la segregación: (pág. 279) ley de Mendel que establece que los dos alelos para cada rasgo se separan durante la meiosis.

ley de superposición: (pág. 394) establece que, en una formación rocosa inalterada, los estratos rocosos más antiguos se hallan a mayor profundidad y los estratos más recientes se hallan más cerca de la superficie.

comportamiento adquirido: (pág. 912) es resultado de la interacción entre el comportamiento innato y las experiencias previas en un ambiente específico; incluye la habituación, el acondicionamiento y la impronta.

cristalino: (pág. 974) parte del ojo situada detrás del iris; invierte la imagen y la enfoca sobre la retina.

liquen: (pág. 587) relación simbiótica entre un hongo (a menudo un ascomiceto) y un alga u otro organismo fotosintético.

ligamento: (pág. 944) bandas fuertes de tejido conectivo que unen los huesos entre sí.

factor limitante: (pág. 61) factor biótico o abiótico que restringe el número, la distribución o la reproducción de una población en una comunidad.

zona limnética: (pág. 77) área de agua abierta y bien iluminada de un lago o laguna.

lípido: (pág. 169) molécula biológica hidrofóbica compuesta principalmente por carbono e hidrógeno; las grasas, los aceites y las ceras son lípidos.

zona litoral: (pág. 76) en lagos y lagunas, comprende la zona de agua poco profunda de la orilla y parte del fondo hasta donde penetra la luz solar.

hígado: (pág. 1022) es el órgano interno más grande del cuerpo; produce bilis.

planta de días largos: (pág. 672) planta que florece en el verano, cuando hay menos horas de oscuridad que el período crítico de la planta.

pulmón: (pág. 1001) órgano más grande del sistema respiratorio en que se lleva a cabo el intercambio de gases.

linfocito: (pág. 1086) glóbulo blanco que participa en la inmunidad específica; linfocitos B o linfocitos T.

lysogenic cycle: (p. 528) viral replication process in which viral DNA inserts into the host cell's chromosome, may remain dormant and later activate and instruct the host cell to produce more viruses.

ciclo lisogénico: (pág. 528) proceso vírico de replicación en que el DNA vírico es insertado en el cromosoma de la célula huésped; puede permanecer latente, activarse más tarde y dar instrucciones a la célula huésped para que produzca más virus.

lysosome: (p. 196) vesicle that uses enzymes to digest excess or worn-out cellular substances.

lisosoma: (pág. 196) vesícula que usa enzimas para digerir sustancias celulares gastadas o que se hallan en número excesivo.

lytic cycle: (p. 528) viral replication process in which genetic material of the virus enters the host cell's cytoplasm, the cell replicates the viral DNA or RNA, and the host cell is instructed to manufacture capsids and assemble new viral particles which then leave the cell.

ciclo lítico: (pág. 528) proceso de replicación vírica en que el material genético del virus entra al citoplasma de la célula huésped. Después, la célula replica el DNA o RNA viral y recibe instrucciones para fabricar cápsides y ensamblar nuevos virus que luego salen de la célula.

M

macromolecule: (p. 167) large molecule formed by joining smaller organic molecules together.

macromolécula: (pág. 167) molécula de gran tamaño formada por la unión de moléculas orgánicas más pequeñas.

madreporite (MA druh pohr it): (p. 795) strainerlike opening through which water enters the water-vascular system in most echinoderms.

madreporita: (pág. 795) abertura con forma de colador, a través de la cual entra y sale el agua del sistema vascular acuático.

Malpighian (mal PIH gee un) tubule: (p. 767) in most arthropods, the waste-excreting structure that also helps maintain homeostatic water balance.

túbulo de Malpighi: (pág. 767) en la mayoría de los artrópodos, la estructura excretora que también ayuda a mantener el equilibrio homeostático del agua.

mammary gland: (p. 880) mammalian gland that produces and secretes milk to nourish developing young.

glándula mamaria: (pág. 880) glándula de los mamíferos que produce y secreta leche para alimentar a las crías.

mandible (MAN duh bul): (p. 765) in most arthropods, one of a pair of mouthparts adapted for biting and chewing food; in vertebrates, one or both jaws.

mandíbulas: (pág. 765) en la mayor parte de los artrópodos, las partes bucales adaptadas para morder y masticar el alimento, en los vertebrados, uno o ambos maxilares.

mantle (MAN tuhl): (p. 737) membrane that surrounds a mollusk's internal organs.

manto: (pág. 737) membrana que rodea los órganos internos de los moluscos.

marsupial: (p. 890) pouched mammal whose offspring have a short period of development inside the uterus, then after birth have a longer period of development within the pouch.

marsupial: (pág. 890) mamífero con bolsa, cuyas crías se desarrollan en el útero durante un corto período de tiempo y completan su desarrollo dentro de la bolsa.

mass extinction: (p. 122) a large-scale dying out of a large percentage of all living organisms in an area within a short time.

extinción masiva: (pág. 122) desaparición a gran escala de un porcentaje grande de todos los organismos vivos de un área dada durante un corto tiempo.

matter: (p. 45) anything that takes up space and has mass.

materia: (pág. 45) cualquier cosa que ocupa lugar y tiene masa.

mechanical digestion: (p. 1020) physical breakdown of food that occurs when food is chewed into smaller pieces and then churned by the stomach and small intestine.

digestión mecánica: (pág. 1020) desintegración física del alimento que ocurre al masticarlo en trozos más pequeños y luego revolverlo en el estómago y el intestino delgado.

medulla oblongata: (p. 970) part of the brain stem that helps control blood pressure, heart rate, and breathing rate.

médula oblongada: (pág. 970) parte del bulbo raquídeo que ayuda a controlar la presión sanguínea y el ritmo cardíaco y el respiratorio.

medusa (mih DEW suh): (p. 712) umbrella-shaped, free-swimming body form of cnidarians.

medusa: (pág. 712) forma libre de los cnidarios que semeja un paraguas con tentáculos que cuelgan hacia abajo.

megaspore: (p. 665) spore that develops into a female gametophyte and is produced by a conifer's female cone.

megáspora: (pág. 665) espora que se desarrolla en un gametofito femenino y que produce el cono femenino de una conífera.

meiosis: (p. 271) reduction division process, occurring only in reproductive cells, in which one diploid ($2n$) cell produces four haploid (n) cells that are not genetically identical.

meiosis: (pág. 271) proceso divisorio de reducción que sólo ocurre en las células reproductoras, mediante el cual una célula diploide ($2n$) produce cuatro células haploides (n) no idénticas genéticamente.

melanin: (p. 937) pigment in the inner layer of the epidermis that protects against harmful ultraviolet radiation and influences skin color.

melanina: (pág. 937) pigmento que se encuentra en la capa interna de la epidermis; protege a las células del daño causado por la radiación solar e influye en el color de la piel.

memory cell: (p. 1089) long-lived lymphocyte produced during exposure to an antigen during the primary immune response; can function in future immune response to the same antigen.

célula de memoria: (pág. 1089) linfocito de larga vida producido debido a la exposición a un antígeno durante la respuesta inmunológica primaria; capaz de funcionar en una futura respuesta inmunológica al mismo antígeno.

menstrual (MEN strew ul) cycle: (p. 1050) monthly reproductive cycle that helps prepare the human female body for pregnancy; involves the shedding of blood, tissue fluid, mucus, and epithelial cells if an egg is not fertilized.

ciclo menstrual: (pág. 1050) ciclo reproductor mensual que ayuda a preparar el cuerpo de la hembra humana para el embarazo; comprende derrame de sangre, tejido líquido, mucosidad y células epiteliales si el óvulo no ha sido fecundado.

meristem: (p. 634) region of rapid cell division in plants; produces cells that can develop into many different types of plant cells.

meristema: (pág. 634) región de rápida división celular vegetal; produce células capaces de desarrollarse en muchos tipos de células vegetales.

mesoderm: (p. 697) layer of cells between the endoderm and the ectoderm that can become muscle tissue and tissue of the circulatory, respiratory, and excretory systems.

mesodermo: (pág. 697) capa celular entre el ectodermo y el endodermo que puede desarrollarse en tejido muscular y tejido de los sistemas circulatorio, respiratorio y excretor.

messenger RNA: (p. 336) type of RNA that carries genetic information from DNA in the nucleus to direct protein synthesis in the cytoplasm.

RNA mensajero: (pág. 336) tipo de RNA que transporta información desde el DNA en el núcleo hasta la síntesis directa de proteína en el citoplasma.

metabolic disease: (p. 1093) disease, such as type 1 diabetes, that results from an error in a biochemical pathway.

enfermedad metabólica: (pág. 1093) enfermedad, como la diabetes tipo 1, que resulta de un error en un trayecto bioquímico.

metabolism: (p. 220) all of the chemical reactions that occur within an organism.

metabolismo: (pág. 220) todas las reacciones químicas que ocurren dentro de un organismo.

metamorphosis: (p. 778) in most insects, the series of changes from a larval form to an adult form.

metamorfosis: (pág. 778) en la mayoría de los insectos, la serie de cambios desde una forma larval hasta una forma adulta.

metaphase: (p. 250) second stage of mitosis in which motor proteins pull sister chromatids to the cell's equator.

metafase: (pág. 250) segunda fase de la mitosis en la cual las proteínas motores atraen a las cromátides hermanas hacia el ecuador de la célula.

metric system: (p. 19) measurement system whose divisions are powers of ten.

sistema métrico: (pág. 19) sistema de medida cuyas divisiones son potencias de diez.

micropyle: (p. 666) opening of a conifer's ovule where a pollen grain can be trapped in a pollen drop.

micrópilo: (pág. 666) abertura en el óvulo de una conífera donde puede atraparse un grano de polen en una descarga de polen.

microspore: (p. 666) spore that develops into a male gametophyte (a pollen grain) and is produced by a conifer's male cone.

micróspora: (pág. 666) espora que se convierte en el gametofito masculino (un grano de polen) y se forma por el cono masculino de una conífera.

microsporidium (mi kroh spo RIH dee um): (p. 544) microscopic protozoan parasite that infects insects and other organisms, causing disease.

microsporídeo: (pág. 544) protozoo microscópico que vive en las tripas de termitas y produce enzimas que digieren madera.

migratory behavior: (p. 919) seasonal movement of a group of animals to a new location for feeding and breeding.

comportamiento migratorio: (pág. 919) movimiento estacional de un grupo de animales hacia una nueva localidad para alimentarse y reproducirse.

mimicry: **(p. 429)** morphological adaptation in which one species evolves to resemble another species for protection or other advantages.

mimetismo: **(pág. 429)** adaptación morfológica en la cual una especie evoluciona para parecerse a otra a modo de protección u otras ventajas.

mineral: **(p. 1028)** inorganic compound, such as calcium, that is used as building material by the body and is involved with metabolic functions.

mineral: **(pág. 1028)** compuesto inorgánico, como el calcio, utilizado por el cuerpo como material de construcción, presente en las funciones metabólicas.

mitochondrion (mi tuh KAHN dree un): **(p. 197)** membrane-bound organelle that converts fuel into energy that is available to the rest of the cell.

mitocondria: **(pág. 197)** organelo membranoso que transforman el combustible en energía disponible al resto de las célula.

mitosis (mi TOH sus): **(p. 246)** second main stage of the cell cycle during which the cell's replicated DNA divides and two genetically identical diploid daughter cells are produced.

mitosis: **(pág. 246)** segundo período principal del ciclo celular, durante el cual el DNA replicado de la célula se divide y se forman dos células hijas diploides idénticas.

mixture: **(p. 163)** combination of two or more different substances in which each substance keeps its individual characteristics; can have a uniform composition (homogeneous) or have distinct areas of substances (heterogeneous).

mezcla: **(pág. 163)** combinación de dos o más sustancias diferentes en la cual cada una mantiene sus características individuales; pueden tener una composición uniforme (homogénea) o áreas distintivas de sustancias (heterogénea).

molecular clock: **(p. 495)** model that uses comparisons of DNA sequences to estimate phylogeny and rate of evolutionary change.

reloj molecular: **(pág. 495)** modelo que usa las comparaciones secuenciales de DNA para calcular la filogenia y la tasa de cambio evolutivo.

molecule: **(p. 152)** compound whose atoms are held together by covalent bonds.

molécula: **(pág. 152)** compuesto cuyos átomos se mantienen unidos por medio de enlaces covalentes.

molting: **(p. 764)** the periodic shedding of exoskeleton, skin, feathers, or scales.

muda: **(pág. 764)** el cambio periódico del exoesqueleto, piel, plumas, o escamas.

monotreme: **(p. 889)** mammal that reproduces by laying eggs.

monotrema: **(pág. 889)** mamífero que se reproduce al poner huevos.

morula: **(p. 1055)** solid ball of embryonic cells that forms before the blastocyst.

mórula: **(pág. 1055)** bola sólida de células embrionarias que se forma antes del blastocito.

multiple alleles: **(p. 304)** having more than two alleles for a specific trait.

alelos múltiples: **(pág. 304)** presencia de más de dos alelos para un rasgo genético.

mutagen (MYEW tuh jun): **(p. 348)** substance, such as a chemical, that causes mutations.

mutágeno: **(pág. 348)** sustancia, como un químico, que causa mutaciones.

mutation: **(p. 345)** permanent change in a cell's DNA, ranging from changes in a single base pair to deletions of large sections of chromosomes.

mutación: **(pág. 345)** cambio permanente en el DNA de una célula, desde cambios en un par de base simple a eliminaciones de grandes secciones de cromosomas.

mutualism (MYEW chuh wuh lih zum): **(p. 39)** symbiotic relationship in which both organisms benefit.

mutualismo: **(pág. 39)** relación simbiótica en la cual ambos organismos se benefician.

mycelium (mi SEE lee um): **(p. 577)** complex, netlike mass made up of branching hyphae.

micelio: **(pág. 577)** masa compleja compuesta por hifas ramificadas.

mycorrhiza (my kuh RHY zuh): **(p. 589)** symbiotic relationship between a specialized fungus and plant roots; fungal hyphae help plants obtain water and minerals and plants supply carbohydrates and amino acids to the fungus.

micorriza: **(pág. 589)** asociación simbiótica de un hongo especializado con las raíces de una planta; las hifas fúngicas ayudan a las plantas a obtener agua y minerales y las plantas proveen carbohidratos y aminoácidos al hongo.

myofibril: **(p. 948)** small muscle fiber that functions in contraction and consists of myosin and actin protein filaments.

miofibrilla: **(pág. 948)** fibra muscular pequeña que funciona por contracción, compuesta por los filamentos proteicos miosina y actina.

myosin: **(p. 948)** protein filament in muscle cells that functions with actin in contraction.

miosina: **(pág. 948)** filamento proteico en las células musculares que funciona con la actina en la contracción muscular.

N

NADP+: **(p. 224)** in photosynthesis, the major electron carrier involved in electron transport.

NADP+: **(pág. 224)** en la fotosíntesis, el principal portador de electrones presente en el transporte de electrones.

nastic response: **(p. 650)** reversible, responsive movement of a plant that occurs independent of the direction of the stimulus.

respuesta nástica: **(pág. 650)** movimiento reversible y sensible de una planta que ocurre independientemente de la dirección del estímulo.

natural resource: **(p. 123)** any material or organism in the biosphere, including water, soil, fuel, and plants and animals.

recurso natural: **(pág. 123)** cualquier material u organismo en la biosfera, incluidos agua, suelo, combustible, plantas y animales.

natural selection: **(p. 420)** theory of evolution developed by Darwin, based on four ideas: excess reproduction, variations, inheritance, and the advantages of specific traits in an environment.

selección natural: **(pág. 420)** teoría de la evolución desarrollada por Darwin, basada en cuatro ideas: reproducción excesiva, variaciones, herencia y las ventajas de cualidades específicas en un medioambiente.

Neanderthal: **(p. 470)** a species also referred to as *Homo neanderthalensis* that evolved exclusively in Europe and Asia about 200,000 years ago.

Neanderthal: **(pág. 470)** especie también conocida como *Homo neanderthalensis,* la cual evolucionó exclusivamente en Europa y Asia hace unos 200,000 años.

nematocyst **(nih MA tuh sihst):** **(p. 710)** capsule whose threadlike tube contains poison and barbs and is discharged when prey touches a cnidarian.

nematocisto: **(pág. 710)** cápsula cuyo tubo filamentoso contiene veneno y bárbulas; se descarga cuando una presa toca un cnidario.

nephridium **(nih FRIH dee um):** **(p. 739)** invertebrate structure used to eliminate metabolic wastes from cellular processes.

nefridios: **(pág. 739)** estructura por los inverterados eliminan los desechos metabólicos de los procesos celulares.

nephron: **(p. 825)** filtering unit of the kidney.

nefrón: **(pág. 825)** unidad de filtración del riñón.

nerve net: **(p. 711)** nervous system that conducts impulses in cnidarians and echinoderms.

red nerviosa: **(pág. 711)** sistema nervioso cnidario y equinodermos que conduce los impulsos.

neural crest: **(p. 821)** group of cells that develops from the embryo's ectoderm and contributes to the development of many vertebrate structures.

cresta neural: **(pág. 821)** grupo de células que se desarrollan del ectodermo del embrión y contribuyen al desarrollo de muchas estructuras vertebradas.

neuron: **(p. 962)** cell that carries nerve impulses throughout the body and is composed of a cell body, an axon, and dendrites.

neurona: **(pág. 962)** célula nerviosa que conduce los impulsos a través del cuerpo y se compone de un cuerpo celular, un axón y dendritas.

neurotransmitter: **(p. 967)** chemical that diffuses across a synapse and binds to receptors on a neighboring neuron's dendrite, causing channels to open on the neighboring cell and the creation of a new action potential.

neurotransmisores: **(pág. 967)** químico que se difunde por la sinapsis y se enlaza a los receptores en la dendrita de una neurona vecina; causa la apertura de los canales en la célula vecina para crear un nuevo impulso.

neutron: **(p. 148)** particle without a charge in an atom's nucleus.

neutrón: **(pág. 148)** partícula sin carga en el núcleo de un átomo.

niche **(NIHCH):** **(p. 38)** role, or position, of an organism in its environment.

nicho: **(pág. 43)** la función o posición de un organismo en su ambiente.

nictitating membrane: **(p. 837)** in amphibians, the transparent eyelid that moves across the eye to prevent it from drying out on land and to protect it under water.

membrana nictitante: **(pág. 837)** en los anfibios, el párpado transparente que se mueve a lo largo del ojo para evitar que se seque al estar en tierra y para protegerlo bajo el agua.

nitrogen fixation: **(p. 48)** process in which nitrogen gas is captured and converted into a form plants can use.

nitrificación: **(pág. 48)** proceso mediante el cual el gas nitrógeno se captura y se convierte en una forma utilizable por las plantas.

nocturnal: **(p. 452)** organisms that are active at night.

nocturno: **(pág. 452)** organismos activos durante la noche.

node: **(p. 965)** gap in the myelin sheath along the length of an axon; nerve impulses move from node to node.

nódulo: **(pág. 965)** brecha en la vaina de mielina a lo largo de un axón; los impulsos nerviosos se desplazan de nodo a nodo.

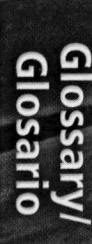

nondisjunction: **(p. 313)** cell division in which the sister chromatids do not separate correctly, resulting in gametes with an abnormal number of chromosomes.

no disyunción: **(pág. 313)** división celular en la cual las cromátides no se separan correctamente lo cual resulta en gametos con un número anormal de cromosomas.

nonrenewable resource: **(p. 130)** any natural resource available in limited amounts or replaced extremely slowly by natural processes.

recurso no renovable: **(pág. 130)** cualquier recurso natural disponible en cantidades limitadas o reemplazado en forma extremadamente lenta por los procesos naturales.

nonvascular plant: **(p. 606)** type of plant that lacks vascular tissues, moves substances slowly from cell to cell by osmosis and diffusion, and grows only in a damp environment.

plantas no vasculares: **(pág. 606)** tipo de planta que carece de tejidos vasculares, mueve sustancias lentamente de célula a célula mediante osmosis y difusión y sólo crece en un ambiente húmedo.

notochord (NOH tuh kord): **(p. 803)** flexible, rodlike structure extending the length of the chordate body, enabling the body to bend and make side-to-side movements.

notocordio: **(pág. 803)** estructura cilíndrica flexible que se extiende a lo largo del cuerpo de un cordado y le permite doblarse y realizar movimientos laterales.

nucleic acid: **(p. 171)** complex macromolecule that stores and communicates genetic information.

ácido nucleico: **(pág. 171)** macromolécula compleja que almacena y comunica información genética.

nucleoid: **(p. 518)** area in a prokaryotic cell that contains a large, circular chromosome.

nucleoide: **(pág. 518)** área de una célula procariota que contiene un cromosoma circular grande.

nucleolus: **(p. 193)** the site of ribosome production within the nucleus of eukaryotic cells.

nucléolo: **(pág. 193)** el sitio de producción de ribosomas dentro del núcleo de las células eucariotas.

nucleosome: **(p. 332)** repeating subunit of chromatin fibers, consisting of DNA coiled around histones.

nucleosoma: **(pág. 332)** subunidad repetitiva de fibras de cromatina que consiste en DNA enroscado alrededor de histonas.

nucleotide: **(p. 171)** a subunit of nucleic acid formed from a simple sugar, a phosphate group, and a nitrogenous base.

nucleótido: **(pág. 171)** subunidades de ácidos nucleicos formadas por un azúcar simple, un grupo fosfato y una base nitrogenada.

nucleus: **(p. 148)** center of an atom; contains neutrons and protons. **(p. 186)** in eukaryotic cells, the central membrane-bound organelle that manages cellular functions and contains DNA.

núcleo: **(pág. 148)** centro de un átomo; contiene neutrones y protones. **(pág. 186)** en las células eucariotas es el organelo membranoso central que se encarga de las funciones celulares y que contiene el DNA.

nurturing behavior: **(p. 921)** caretaking behavior that a parent provides to its offspring during the early stages of development.

comportamiento de crianza: **(pág. 921)** comportamiento de cuidado y formación que un progenitor provee a su cría durante las primeras etapas del desarrollo de ésta.

nutrient: **(p. 45)** chemical substance that living organisms obtain from the environment to carry out life processes and sustain life.

nutriente: **(pág. 45)** sustancia química que obtienen los organismos vivos del medioambiente para el desarrollo de los procesos vitales y el sustento de la vida.

nutrition: **(p. 1025)** process by which an individual takes in and uses food, which provides building blocks for growth and energy to maintain body mass.

nutrición: **(pág. 1025)** proceso mediante el cual un individuo consume y usa alimento, lo cual provee las bases para el crecimiento y la energía para mantener la masa corporal.

nymph (NIHMF): **(p. 778)** immature form of an insect during incomplete metamorphosis—the hatchling looks like a small adult insect and goes through several molts, eventually becoming a mature winged adult.

ninfa: **(pág. 778)** forma inmadura de un insecto durante la metamorfosis incompleta: el insecto recién salido del cascarón se parece a un insecto adulto pequeño y pasa por varias mudas hasta convertirse en un adulto alado maduro.

O

observation: **(p. 16)** orderly, direct information gathering about a natural phenomenon.

observación: **(pág. 16)** forma directa y ordenada de recopilar información sobre un fenómeno natural.

Okazaki fragment: (p. 334) short segment of DNA synthesized discontinuously in small segments in the 3' to 5' direction by DNA polymerase.

fragmento Okazaki: (pág. 334) segmento corto de DNA que la enzima polimerasa de DNA sintetiza discontinuamente en segmentos pequeños en la dirección de 3' a 5'.

omnivore (AHM nih vor): (p. 42) heterotroph that consumes both plants and animals.

omnívoro: (pág. 42) heterótrofo que consume tanto plantas como animales.

oocyte (OH uh site): (p. 1050) immature egg inside an ovary.

oocito: (pág. 1050) óvulo inmaduro dentro de un ovario.

open circulatory system: (p. 739) blood is pumped out of vessels into open spaces surrounding body organs.

sistema circulatorio abierto: (pág. 739) la sangre se bombea fuera de los vasos hacia los espacios abiertos que rodean los órganos corporales.

operant conditioning: (p. 913) learned behavior that occurs when an association is made between a response to a stimulus and a punishment or a reward.

condicionamiento operante: (pág. 913) comportamiento adquirido que ocurre al asociar una respuesta con un estímulo y un castigo o una recompensa.

operculum (oh PUR kyuh lum): (p. 824) movable, protective flap that covers a fish's gills and helps to pump water that enters the mouth and moves over the gills.

opérculo: (pág. 824) protector móvil que cubre las agallas de los peces y ayuda a bombear el agua que entra a la boca y se desplaza sobre las agallas.

operon: (p. 342) section of DNA containing genes for proteins required for a specific metabolic pathway—consists of an operator, promoter, regulatory gene, and genes coding for proteins.

operón: (pág. 342) sección de DNA que contiene los genes para las proteínas requeridas para un trayecto metabólico específico; consiste en un operador, un promotor, un gene regulador y un código de genes para las proteínas.

opposable first digit: (p. 452) a digit, either a thumb or a toe, that is set apart from the other digits and can be brought across the palm or foot so that it touches or nearly touches the other digits; this allows animals to grasp an object in a powerful grip.

primer dígito oponible: (pág. 452) dígito, ya sea un pulgar o un dígito del pie, que se diferencia del resto de los dígitos y el cual se puede cruzar a través de la palma de la mano o del pie y puede tocar o casi tocar los otros dígitos; esto les permite a los animales asir objetos fuertemente.

order: (p. 488) taxonomic group that contains related families.

orden: (pág. 488) agrupación taxonómica de familias relacionadas.

organelle: (p. 186) specialized internal cell structure that carries out specific cell functions such as protein synthesis and energy transformation.

organelo: (pág. 186) estructura celular especializada interna con funciones celulares específicas como la síntesis y la transformación de energía.

organism: (p. 6) anything that has or once had all the characteristics of life.

organismo: (pág. 6) cualquier cosa que tuvo o tiene todas las características de la vida.

organization: (p. 8) orderly structure shown by living things.

organización: (pág. 8) estructura ordenada de todos los seres vivos.

osmosis (ahs MOH sus): (p. 203) diffusion of water across a selectively permeable membrane.

osmosis: (pág. 203) difusión del agua a través de una membrana de permeabilidad selectiva.

ossification: (p. 942) formation of bone from osteoblasts.

osificación: (pág. 942) formación ósea a partir de los osteoblastos.

osteoblast: (p. 942) bone-forming cell.

osteoblasto: (pág. 942) célula formadora de hueso.

osteoclast: (p. 943) cell that breaks down bone cells.

osteoclasto: (pág. 943) célula que destruye las células óseas.

osteocyte: (p. 942) living bone cell.

osteocito: (pág. 942) célula ósea viva.

overexploitation: (p. 124) overuse of species with economic value—a factor in species extinction.

sobre-explotación: (pág. 124) uso excesivo de las especies con un valor económico; es un factor en la extinción de especies.

oviduct (OH vuh duct): (p. 1050) tube that transports an egg released from an ovary to the uterus.

oviducto: (pág. 1050) conducto que transporta un óvulo desde el ovario hasta el útero.

P

pacemaker: (p. 995) heart's sinoatrial node, which initiates contraction of the heart.

paleontologist (pay lee ahn TAH luh just): (p. 394) scientist who studies fossils.

palisade mesophyll (mehz uh fihl): (p. 644) leaf-tissue layer that contains many chloroplasts and is the site where most photosynthesis takes place.

pandemic: (p. 1081) widespread epidemic.

parasitism (PER uh suh tih zum): (p. 40) symbiotic relationship in which one organism benefits at the expense of another organism.

parasympathetic nervous system: (p. 972) branch of the autonomic nervous system that controls organs and is most active when the body is at rest.

parathyroid hormone: (p. 1034) substance produced by the parathyroid gland that increases blood calcium levels by stimulating bones to release calcium.

parenchyma (puh RENG kuh muh) cell: (p. 632) spherical, thin-walled cell found throughout most plants that can function in photosynthesis, gas exchange, protection, storage, and tissue repair and replacement.

pathogen: (p. 1076) agent, such as a bacterium, virus, protozoan, or fungus, that causes infectious disease.

pedicellaria (peh dih sih LAHR ee uh): (p. 793) small pincher that helps echinoderms catch food and remove foreign materials from the skin.

pedigree: (p. 299) diagrammed family history that is used to study inheritance patterns of a trait through several generations and that can be used to predict disorders in future offspring.

pedipalp: (p. 772) one of a pair of arachnid appendages used for sensing and holding prey and in male spiders used for reproduction.

peer review: (p. 14) a process in which the procedures used during an experiment may be repeated and the results are evaluated by scientists who are in the same field or are conducting similar research.

pellicle: (p. 547) membrane layer that encloses a paramecium and some other protists.

pepsin: (p. 1021) digestive enzyme involved in the stomach's chemical digestion of proteins.

perennial: (p. 621) plant that can live for several years.

pericycle: (p. 640) plant tissue that produces lateral roots.

marcapaso: (pág. 995) nódulo atrioventricular del corazón que inicia la contracción cardíaca.

paleontólogo: (pág. 394) científico que estudia los fósiles.

mesófilo en empalizada: (pág. 644) capa de tejido de la hoja que contiene muchos cloroplastos y donde se ubica la mayor parte de la fotosíntesis.

pandemia: (pág. 1081) epidemia que se extiende a muchos países.

parasitismo: (pág. 40) relación simbiótica en la cual un organismo se beneficia a expensas de otro.

sistema nervioso parasimpático (SNP): (pág. 972) división del sistema nervioso autónomo que controla los órganos y es más activo cuando el cuerpo está en reposo.

hormona paratiroides: (pág. 1034) sustancia producida por la glándula tiroides que aumenta los niveles de calcio en la sangre al estimular la liberación de calcio en los huesos.

célula de parénquima: (pág. 632) célula esférica con paredes delgadas que se encuentra en la mayoría de las plantas y que funciona en la fotosíntesis, el intercambio de gases, la protección, el almacenamiento y reparación o reemplazo de tejidos.

patógeno: (pág. 1076) agente, como las bacterias, los virus, los protozoarios o los hongos, causante de enfermedades infecciosas.

pedicelarios: (pág. 793) pinza minúscula de los equinodermos que los ayuda a obtener alimento y eliminar objetos extraños de la piel.

pedigrí: (pág. 299) historia familiar diagramada que se emplea para el estudio de los patrones hereditarios de un rasgo a través de varias generaciones, capaz de predecir trastornos en la progenie futura.

pedipalpo: (pág. 772) uno de un par de apéndices de los arácnidos utilizado para manipular la presa y, en las arañas macho, para la reproducción.

evaluación de compañeros: (pág. 14) proceso en que los procedimientos que se usan durante un experimento pueden repetirse y otros científicos en el mismo campo de estudio o que realizan investigaciones similares pueden evaluar los resultados.

película: (pág. 547) capa membranosa que encierra un paramecio.

pepsina: (pág. 1021) enzima digestiva presente en la digestión química de las proteínas.

perenne: (pág. 621) planta que vive por varios años.

periciclo: (pág. 640) tejido vegetal que produce raíces laterales.

period: **(p. 396)** subdivision of an era on the geologic time scale.

período: **(pág. 396)** subdivisión de una era en la escala geológica.

peripheral nervous system: **(p. 968)** consists of sensory and motor neurons that transmit information to and from the central nervous system.

sistema nervioso periférico (SNP): **(pág. 968)** compuesto por neuronas sensoriales y motoras que transportan información desde y hacia el sistema nervioso central.

peristalsis **(per uh STAHL sus): (p. 1021)** rhythmic, wavelike muscular contractions that move food throughout the digestive tract.

peristaltismo: **(pág. 1021)** serie de contracciones musculares rítmicas ondulantes que mueven el alimento por el esófago.

petal: **(p. 668)** colorful flower structure that attracts pollinators and provides them a landing place.

pétalo: **(pág. 668)** estructura floral colorida que atrae a los agentes polinizadores y les provee un lugar de aterrizaje.

petiole **(PET ee ohl): (p. 644)** stalk that connects a plant's blade to the stem.

pecíolo: **(pág. 644)** tallito de la hoja que une la lámina foliar con el tallo.

pH: **(p. 165)** measure of the concentration of hydrogen ions (H^+) in a solution.

pH: **(pág. 165)** medida de la concentración de iones de hidrógeno (H^+) en una solución.

pharmacogenomics **(far muh koh jeh NAH mihks): (p. 378)** study of how genetic inheritance affects the body's response to drugs in order to produce safer and more specific drug dosing.

farmacogenética: **(pág. 378)** estudio de la influencia de la herencia genética en la respuesta corporal a los medicamentos a fin de producir posologías más seguras y específicas.

pharyngeal pouch: **(p. 804)** in chordate embryos, one of the paired structures connecting the muscular tube lining the mouth cavity and the esophagus.

bolsa faríngea: **(pág. 804)** en los embriones de los cordados, una de las estructuras pareadas que conectan el conducto muscular que cubre la cavidad bucal con el esófago.

pharynx **(FER ingks): (p. 727)** in free-living flatworms, the tubelike muscular organ that can extend out of the mouth and suck food particles into the digestive tract.

faringe: **(pág. 727)** en las planarias, el órgano muscular tubular que se extiende desde la boca y chupa las partículas de alimento hacia el tubo digestivo.

phenotype: **(p. 279)** observable characteristic that is expressed as a result of an allele pair.

fenotipo: **(pág. 279)** apariencia externa que se expresa como resultado de un par de alelos.

pheromone **(FER uh mohn): (p. 768)** chemical secreted by an animal species to influence the behavior of other members of the same species.

feromona: **(pág. 768)** señal química que secreta una especie animal para influir en el comportamiento de otros miembros de la misma especie.

phloem **(FLOH em): (p. 638)** vascular plant tissue composed of sieve tube members and companion cells that conducts dissolved sugars and other organic compounds from the leaves and stems to the roots and from the roots to the leaves and stems.

floema: **(pág. 638)** tejido vascular vegetal formado por los miembros del tubo criboso y células acompañantes que transporta azúcares disueltos y otros compuestos orgánicos de las hojas y tallos hacia las raíces; y de allí a las hojas y tallos.

phospholipid bilayer: **(p. 188)** plasma membrane layers composed of phospholipid molecules arranged with polar heads facing the outside and nonpolar tails facing the inside.

bicapa fosfolípida: **(pág. 188)** capas membranosas del plasma compuestas por moléculas fosfolípidas cuyas cabezas polares miran hacia fuera y cuyas colas no polares miran hacia adentro.

photic zone: **(p. 80)** open-ocean zone shallow enough for sunlight to penetrate.

zona fótica: **(pág. 80)** zona a mar abierto lo suficientemente baja para que penetre la luz solar.

photoperiodism **(foh toh PIHR ee uh dih zum): (p. 672)** flowering response of a plant based on the number of hours of darkness it is exposed to.

fotoperiodicidad: **(pág. 672)** respuesta de floración de una planta al número de horas de oscuridad a la cual se expone.

photosynthesis: **(p. 220)** two-phase anabolic pathway in which the Sun's light energy is converted to chemical energy for use by the cell.

fotosíntesis: **(pág. 220)** sendero anabólico bifásico por medio del cual la energía luminosa solar se transforma en energía química para uso de la célula.

phylogeny **(fy LAH juh nee): (p. 491)** evolutionary history of a species.

filogenia: **(pág. 491)** historia evolutiva de una especie.

phylum (FI lum): (p. 488) taxonomic group of related classes.

filo: (pág. 488) agrupación taxonómica de clases que se relacionan.

pigment: (p. 223) light-absorbing colored molecule, such as chlorophyll and carotenoid, in the thylakoid membranes of chloroplasts.

pigmento: (pág. 223) molécula de color que absorbe la luz, como la clorofila y la carotenoide, en la membranas tilacoides de los cloroplastos.

pilus: (p. 518) hairlike, submicroscopic structure made of protein that can help a bacterial cell attach to environmental surfaces and act as a bridge between cells.

pilus: (pág. 518) estructura submicroscópica filiforme compuesta por proteína que ayuda a una célula bacteriana a adherirse a las superficies ambientales y actuar como puente entre las células.

pistil: (p. 669) flower's female reproductive organ; it is usually composed of a stigma, a style, and an ovary.

pistilo: (pág. 669) órgano reproductora femenina de la flor, compuesta generalmente por un estigma, un estilo y un ovario.

pituitary gland: (p. 1033) endocrine gland located at the base of the brain; called the "master gland" because it regulates many body functions.

glándula pituitaria: (pág. 1033) glándula endocrina localizada en la base del cerebro, conocida como la "glándula maestra" puesto que regula muchas funciones corporales.

placenta: (p. 887) in most mammals, the specialized organ that provides food and oxygen to the developing young and removes its wastes.

placenta: (pág. 887) en la mayoría de los mamíferos, el órgano especializado que provee alimento y oxígeno a la cría en desarrollo y elimina sus desechos.

placental mammal: (p. 891) mammal that has a placenta and gives birth to young that need no further development within a pouch.

mamífero placentario: (pág. 891) mamífero con placenta que pare a las crías que no requieren desarrollarse adicionalmente en una bolsa.

placental stage: (p. 1063) birthing stage in which the placenta and umbilical cord are expelled from the mother's body.

etapa placentaria: (pág. 1063) etapa de alumbramiento en la cual la placenta y el cordón umbilical se expulsan del cuerpo de la madre.

plankton: (p. 77) tiny marine or freshwater organisms that serve as a food source for many fish species; often autotrophic.

plancton: (pág. 77) diminutos organismos marinos o de agua dulce, que flotan libremente y constituyen la fuente alimenticia de muchas especies de peces, a menudo autótrofos.

plasma: (p. 997) clear, yellowish fluid portion of the blood.

plasma: (pág. 997) porción fluida clara y amarillenta de la sangre.

plasma membrane: (p. 185) flexible, selectively permeable boundary that helps control what enters and leaves the cell.

membrana plasmática: (pág. 185) frontera flexible, selectivamente permeable, que ayuda a controlar lo que entra y sale de la célula.

plasmid: (p. 366) any of the small, circular, double-stranded DNA molecules that can be used as a vector.

plásmido: (pág. 366) cualquiera de las pequeñas moléculas de DNA circulares de filamento doble que pueden usarse como vector.

plasmodium (plaz MOH dee um): (p. 562) feeding stage of a slime mold in which it is a mobile cytoplasmic mass with many diploid nuclei but no separate cells.

plasmodio: (pág. 562) etapa alimenticia de un hongo plasmódico en la cual es una masa de citoplasma móvil con muchos núcleos diploides pero sin membranas separadas.

plastron (PLAS trahn): (p. 857) ventral part of a turtle's shell.

plastrón: (pág. 857) parte ventral del caparazón de una tortuga.

platelet: (p. 997) flat cell fragment that functions in blood clotting.

plaqueta: (pág. 997) fragmentos celulares planos que funcionan en la coagulación de la sangre.

plate tectonics: (p. 400) geologic theory that Earth's surface is broken into several huge plates that move slowly on a partially molten rock layer.

tectónica de placas: (pág. 400) teoría geológica que afirma que la corteza terrestre se divide en varias placas enormes que se mueven lentamente sobre una capa rocosa parcialmente fundida.

polar body: (p. 1051) tiny cell that is produced and eventually disintegrates in the development of an oocyte.

cuerpo polar: (pág. 1051) célula diminuta que se produce y posteriormente se desintegra en el desarrollo de un oocito.

polar molecule: (p. 161) molecule with oppositely charged regions.

molécula polar: (pág. 161) molécula con regiones cargadas opuestamente.

polar nuclei: **(p. 674)** in anthophytes, the two nuclei in the center of a megaspore.

polygenic trait: **(p. 309)** characteristic, such as eye color or skin color, that results from the interaction of multiple gene pairs.

polymer: **(p. 167)** large molecule formed from smaller repeating units of identical, or nearly identical, compounds linked by covalent bonds.

polymerase chain reaction (PCR): **(p. 368)** genetic engineering technique that can make copies of specific regions of a DNA fragment.

polyp (PAH lup): **(p. 712)** tube-shaped, sessile body form of cnidarians.

polyploidy: **(p. 285)** having one or more extra sets of all chromosomes, which, in polyploid plants, can often result in greater size and better growth and survival.

pons: **(p. 970)** part of the brain stem that helps control breathing rate.

population: **(p. 36)** group of organisms of the same species that occupy the same geographic place at the same time.

population density: **(p. 92)** number of organisms per unit of living area.

population growth rate: **(p. 97)** how fast a specific population grows.

postanal tail: **(p. 803)** chordate structure used primarily for locomotion.

posterior: **(p. 700)** away from the head end of an animal with bilateral symmetry.

postzygotic isolating mechanism: **(p. 437)** factor that prevents a hybrid zygote from developing, or prevents hybrid offspring from reproducing; operates after fertilization.

predation (prih DAY shun): **(p. 38)** act of one organism feeding on another organism.

preen gland: **(p. 862)** oil-secreting gland located near the base of a bird's tail.

prehensile tail: **(p. 456)** functions like a fifth limb, provides the ability to grasp tree limbs or other objects and can support the body weight of some animals.

prezygotic isolating mechanism: **(p. 437)** factor that prevents individuals from different species from mating; operates before fertilization.

primary succession: **(p. 62)** establishment of a community in an area of bare rock or bare sand, where no topsoil is present.

prion (PREE ahn): **(p. 531)** protein that can cause infection or disease.

núcleos polares: **(pág. 674)** en las antofitas, los dos núcleos en el centro de una megáspora.

rasgo poligénico: **(pág. 309)** característica, como el color de los ojos o de la piel, que resulta de la interacción de múltiples pares de genes.

polímero: **(pág. 167)** molécula gigante formada por unidades pequeñas, repetitivas, idénticas, o casi idénticas, de compuestos unidos por enlaces covalentes.

reacción en cadena de polimerasa (RCP): **(pág. 368)** técnica de ingeniería genética capaz de hacer copias de regiones específicas de un fragmento de DNA.

pólipo: **(pág. 712)** cuerpo sésil cilíndrico de los cnidarios.

poliploide: **(pág. 285)** que tiene uno o más grupos de todos los cromosomas que, en plantas poliploides, puede resultar en un mayor tamaño y mejor crecimiento y supervivencia.

pons: **(pág. 970)** parte del bulbo raquídeo que ayuda a controlar el ritmo de la respiración.

población: **(pág. 36)** grupo de organismos de la misma especie que viven en la misma localidad geográfica al mismo tiempo

densidad demográfica: **(pág. 92)** número de organismos por unidad de área o superficie habitable.

tasa de crecimiento demográfico: **(pág. 97)** el grado de rapidez con que crece una población específica.

cola postnatal: **(pág. 803)** estructura de los cordados que se usa principalmente para la locomoción.

posterior: **(pág. 700)** extremo de la cola de un animal con simetría bilateral.

mecanismo de aislamiento postcigótico: **(pág. 437)** factor que impide el desarrollo de un cigoto hibrido o que impide que la progenie híbrida se reproduzca; opera después de la fecundación.

depredación: **(pág. 38)** modo de nutrición de un organismo al alimentarse de otro.

uropigio: **(pág. 862)** glándula secretora de aceite localizada cerca de la base de la cola de un ave.

cola prensil: **(pág. 456)** funciona como una quinta extremidad y permite que algunos animales se agarren de las ramas de los árboles u otros objetos y la cual puede sostener el peso de algunos animales.

mecanismo de aislamiento precigótico: **(pág. 437)** factor que imposibilita el apareamiento de individuos de diferentes especies; opera antes de la fecundación.

sucesión primaria: **(pág. 62)** colonización en un área de roca o arena desnudas, sin mantillo (capa vegetal superior).

prión: **(pág. 531)** proteína que puede causar infecciones o enfermedades.

product: (p. 157) substance formed by a chemical reaction; located on the right side of the arrow in a chemical equation.

producto: (pág. 157) sustancia formada por una reacción química; localizada en el lado derecho de la flecha en una ecuación química.

profundal zone: (p. 77) deepest, coldest area of a large lake with little light and limited biodiversity.

zona profunda: (pág. 77) el área más fría y profunda de un lago grande, con poca luz y una biodiversidad limitada.

proglottid (proh GLAH tihd): (p. 730) continuously formed, detachable section of a tapeworm that contains male and female reproductive organs, flame cells, muscles, and nerves; breaks off when its eggs are fertilized and passes out of the host's intestine.

proglótido: (pág. 730) sección de una tenia que contiene músculos, nervios, bulbos ciliados y órganos reproductores; desprende cuando sus huevos son fecundados y sale por el intestino del huésped.

prokaryotic cell: (p. 186) microscopic, unicellular organism without a nucleus or other membrane-bound organelles.

célula procariótica: (pág. 186) organismo unicelular, microscópico, sin núcleo u otros organelos limitados por membranas.

prophase: (p. 248) first stage of mitosis, during which the cell's chromatin condenses into chromosomes.

profase: (pág. 248) primera etapa de la mitosis, durante la cual la cromatina celular se condensa para formar cromosomas.

protein: (p. 170) organic compound made of amino acids joined by peptide bonds; primary building block of organisms.

proteína: (pág. 170) compuesto orgánico formado por aminoácidos unidos por enlaces pépticos; piedra angular de los organismos.

proteomics: (p. 379) study of the structure and function of proteins in the human body.

proteómica: (pág. 379) estudio de la estructura y función de proteínas en el cuerpo humano.

prothallus (pro THA lus): (p. 665) heart-shaped, tiny fern gametophyte.

prótalo: (pág. 665) gametofito diminuto de helecho, en forma de corazón.

protist: (p. 501) unicellular, multicellular, or colonial eukaryote whose cell walls may contain cellulose; can be plantlike, animal-like, or funguslike.

protista: (pág. 501) eucariota unicelular, multicelular o colonial cuyas paredes celulares pueden contener celulosa; pueden tener forma vegetal, animal o fungosa.

proton: (p. 148) positively charged particle in an atom's nucleus.

protón: (pág. 148) particular cargada positivamente en el núcleo de un átomo.

protonema: (p. 664) small, threadlike structure produced by mosses that can develop into the gametophyte plant.

protonema: (pág. 664) estructura filamentosa pequeña producida por musgos, capaz de desarrollarse en la planta gametofita.

protostome (PROH tuh stohm): (p. 702) coelomate animal whose mouth develops from the opening in the gastrula.

protostomado: (pág. 702) animal celomado cuya boca se desarrolla de la abertura de la gástrula.

protozoan (proh tuh ZOH un): (p. 542) heterotrophic, unicellular, animal-like protist.

protozoario: (pág. 542) protista unicelular heterótrofo parecido a un animal.

pseudocoelom (soo duh SEE lum): (p. 701) fluid-filled body cavity between the mesoderm and the endoderm.

seudoceloma: (pág. 701) cavidad corporal llena de fluido entre el mesodermo y el endodermo.

pseudopod (SEW duh pahd): (p. 550) temporary cytoplasmic extension that sarcodines use for feeding and movement.

seudópodos: (pág. 550) extensión citoplásmica temporal que emplean los sarcodinos en la alimentación y locomoción.

puberty: (p. 1049) growth period during which sexual maturity is reached.

pubertad: (pág. 1049) período durante el cual se llega a la madurez sexual.

punctuated equilibrium: (p. 440) theory that evolution occurs with relatively sudden periods of speciation followed by long periods of stability.

equilibrio puntuado: (pág. 440) teoría que sostiene que la evolución ocurre con períodos relativamente súbitos de especiación, seguido de largos períodos de estabilidad.

pupa (PYEW puh): (p. 778) nonfeeding stage of complete metamorphosis in which the insect changes from the larval form to the adult form.

pupa: (pág. 778) etapa no alimenticia de la metamorfosis completa de un insecto en la cual el insecto cambia de la forma larval a la adulta.

R

radial (RAY dee uhl) symmetry: (p. 700) body plan that can be divided along any plane, through a central axis, into roughly equal halves.

simetría radial: (pág. 700) plano corporal que, a través de un eje central a lo largo de cualquier plano, puede dividirse en casi dos partes iguales.

radicle: (p. 679) first part of the embryo to emerge from the seed and begin to absorb water and nutrients from the environment.

radícula: (pág. 679) primera parte del embrión que emerge de la semilla y comienza a absorber agua y nutrientes del medio ambiente.

radiometric dating: (p. 395) method used to determine the age of rocks using the rate of decay of radioactive isotopes.

datación radiométrica: (pág. 395) método utilizado para determinar la edad de las rocas mediante la tasa de desintegración de los isótopos radioactivos.

radula (RA juh luh): (p. 738) rasping tonguelike organ with rows of teeth that many mollusks use in feeding.

rádula: (pág. 738) órgano raspador parecido a una lengua con hileras de dientes que emplean muchos moluscos para alimentarse.

reactant: (p. 157) substance that exists before a chemical reaction starts; located on the left side of the arrow in a chemical equation.

reactivo: (pág. 157) sustancia que existe antes de empezar una reacción química; localizada al lado izquierdo de la flecha en una ecuación química.

recessive: (p. 278) Mendel's name for a specific trait hidden or masked in the F_1 generation.

recesivo: (pág. 256) nombre de Mendel para una rasgo específico oculto o encubierto en la generación F_1.

recombinant DNA: (p. 366) newly generated DNA fragment containing exogenous DNA.

DNA recombinante: (pág. 366) fragmento de DNA recién generado que contiene DNA exógeno.

red blood cell: (p. 997) hemoglobin-containing, disc-shaped, short-lived blood cell that lacks a nucleus and that transports oxygen to all the body's cells.

glóbulo rojo: (pág. 997) célula sanguínea de corta vida, esférica, anucleada, que contiene hemoglobina y que transporta oxígeno a todas las células del cuerpo.

red bone marrow: (p. 942) type of marrow that produces red and white blood cells and platelets.

médula roja: (pág. 942) tipo de médula que produce glóbulos rojos, glóbulos blancos y plaquetas.

reflex arc: (p. 963) nerve pathway consisting of a sensory neuron, an interneuron, and a motor neuron.

arco reflejo: (pág. 963) trayecto nervioso que consiste en una neurona sensorial, una interneurona y una neurona motora.

regeneration: (p. 728) ability to replace or regrow body parts missing due to predation or damage.

regeneración: (pág. 728) capacidad de reemplazar o regenerar partes corporales perdidas debido a la depredación o daños.

relative dating: (p. 394) method used to determine the age of rocks by comparing the rocks with younger and older rock layers.

datación relativa: (pág. 394) método empleado para determinar la edad de las rocas al compararlas con capas rocosas más recientes y más antiguas.

renewable resource: (p. 130) any resource replaced by natural processes more quickly than it is consumed.

recurso renovable: (pág. 130) cualquier recurso reemplazable por procesos naturales de manera más rápida de lo que se consume.

reproduction: (p. 9) production of offspring.

reproducción: (pág. 9) producción de la progenie.

reservoir: (p. 1078) source of a pathogen in the environment.

reservorio: (pág. 1078) fuente de un patógeno en el medio ambiente.

response: (p. 9) organism's reaction to a stimulus.

respuesta: (pág. 9) la reacción de un organismo a un estímulo.

restriction enzyme: (p. 364) bacterial protein that cuts DNA into fragments.

enzima restrictiva: (pág. 364) proteína bacterial que corta el DNA en fragmentos.

retina: (p. 974) innermost layer of the eye that contains rods and cones.

retina: (pág. 974) capa más interna del ojo que contiene bastoncillos y conos.

retrovirus: (p. 530) RNA virus, such as HIV, with reverse transcriptase in its core.

retrovirus: (pág. 530) virus RNA, como el HIV, con transcriptasa inversa en su núcleo.

rhizoid (RIH zoyd): (p. 583) type of hypha formed by a mold that penetrates a food's surface.

rhizome: (p. 615) fern's thick underground stem that functions as a food-storage organ.

ribosomal RNA (rRNA): (p. 336) type of RNA that associates with proteins to form ribosomes.

ribosome: (p. 193) simple cell organelle that helps manufacture proteins.

RNA: (p. 336) ribonucleic acid; guides protein synthesis.

RNA polymerase: (p. 337) enzyme that regulates RNA synthesis.

rod: (p. 974) one of the light-sensitive cells in the retina that sends action potentials to the brain via neurons in the optic nerve.

root cap: (p. 639) layer of parenchyma cells that covers the root tip and helps protect root tissues during growth.

rubisco: (p. 226) enzyme that converts inorganic carbon dioxide molecules into organic molecules during the final step of the Calvin cycle.

rizoide: (pág. 583) tipo de hifa formada por un musgo que penetra la superficie del alimento.

rizoma: (pág. 615) el tallo grueso subterráneo de un helecho que funciona como órgano de almacenamiento de alimento.

RNA ribosomal (rRNA): (pág. 336) tipo de RNA que se asocia con las proteínas para formar ribosomas.

ribosoma: (pág. 193) organelo celular simple que ayuda a elaborar proteínas.

RNA: (pág. 336) ácido ribonucleico; guía la síntesis de proteínas.

RNA polimerasa: (pág. 337) enzima que regula la síntesis de RNA.

bastoncillo: (pág. 974) una de las células de la retina que es sensible a la luz y que envía potenciales de acción al cerebro mediante las neuronas del nervio óptico.

piloriza: (pág. 639) capa de células del parénquima que cubre la punta de las raíces y ayuda a proteger su tejido durante el crecimiento.

rubisco: (pág. 226) enzima que convierte las moléculas inorgánicas de dióxido de carbono en moléculas orgánicas durante la etapa final del ciclo de Calvin.

S

safety symbol: (p. 21) logo representing a specific danger such as radioactivity, electrical or biological hazard, or irritants that may be present in a lab activity or field investigation.

sarcomere: (p. 948) in skeletal muscle, the functional unit that contracts and is composed of myofibrils.

scale: (p. 823) small, flat, platelike structure near the surface of the skin of most fishes; can be ctenoid, cycloid, placoid, or ganoid.

science: (p. 11) a body of knowledge based on the study of nature.

scientific methods: (p. 16) a series of problem-solving procedures that might include observations, forming a hypothesis, experimenting, gathering and analyzing data, and drawing conclusions.

sclerenchyma (skle RENG kuh muh) **cell:** (p. 633) plant cell that lacks cytoplasm and other living components when mature, leaving thick, rigid cell walls that provide support and function in transport of materials.

scolex (SKOH leks): (p. 730) parasitically adapted, knoblike anterior end of a tapeworm, having hooks and suckers that attach to the host's intestinal lining.

sebaceous gland: (p. 937) oil-producing gland in the dermis that lubricates skin and hair.

símbolo de seguridad: (pág. 21) logotipo que advierte acerca de algún peligro, como radioactividad, agentes irritantes, riesgos eléctricos o biológicos, que pudieran presentarse en una actividad de laboratorio o investigación de campo.

sarcómero: (pág. 948) en el músculo esquelético, la unidad funcional que se contrae y se compone de miofibrilla muscular.

escama: (pág. 823) estructura pequeña, plana y lameliforme, cerca de la superficie de la piel de la mayoría de los peces; puede ser serrada, cicloide, placoidea o ganoidea.

ciencia: (pág. 11) conjunto de conocimiento basado en el estudio de la naturaleza y su entorno físico.

método científico: (pág. 16) una serie de procedimientos de solución de problemas que pueden incluir observaciones, formulación de una hipótesis, experimentación, recopilación y análisis de datos y sacar conclusiones.

célula esclerénquima: (pág. 633) célula vegetal carente de citoplasma y de otros componentes vitales en su etapa madura, caracterizada por paredes celulares gruesas y rígidas que proveen soporte y funcionan en el transporte de materiales.

escólex: (pág. 730) extremidad adaptada parasitariamente con forma de perilla que poseen las tenias; posee ganchos y chupones que se adhieren a la cubierta intestinal del huésped.

glándula sebácea: (pág. 937) glándula productora de aceite en la dermis que lubrica la piel y el cabello.

secondary succession: **(p. 63)** orderly change that occurs in a place where soil remains after a community of organisms has been removed.

sucesión secundaria: **(pág. 63)** cambio ordenado que ocurre en el suelo de los lugares que experimentaron la expulsión de una comunidad de organismos.

sediment: **(p. 75)** material deposited by water, wind, or glaciers.

sedimento: **(pág. 75)** material depositado por el agua, el viento o los glaciares.

seed: **(p. 607)** adaptive reproductive structure of some vascular plants that contains an embryo, nutrients for the embryo, and is covered by a protective coat.

semilla: **(pág. 607)** estructura reproductora y adaptable de algunas plantas vasculares que contiene un embrión con su fuente de nutrientes y una capa protectora.

seed coat: **(p. 677)** protective tissue that forms from the hardening of the outside layers of the ovule.

tegumento: **(pág. 677)** tejido protector formado del endurecimiento de las capas externas del óvulo.

selective breeding: **(p. 360)** directed breeding to produce plants and animals with desired traits.

criaza selectiva: **(pág. 360)** crianza dirigida hacia la producción de plantas y animales con rasgos deseados.

selective permeability **(pur mee uh BIH luh tee): (p. 187)** property of the plasma membrane that allows it to control movement of substances into or out of the cell.

permeabilidad selectiva: **(pág. 187)** propiedad de la membrana plasmática que le permite controlar el movimiento de las sustancias dentro o fuera de la célula.

semen **(SEE mun): (p. 1049)** fluid that contains sperm, nourishment, and other fluids of the male reproductive system.

semen: **(pág. 1049)** fluido que contiene espermatozoides, nutrientes y otros fluidos del sistema reproductor masculino.

semicircular canal: **(p. 975)** inner-ear structure that transmits information about body position and balance to the brain.

canal semicircular: **(pág. 975)** estructura interna del oído que transmite al cerebro información relativa a la posición y equilibrio corporales.

semiconservative replication: **(p. 333)** method of DNA replication in which parental strands separate, act as templates, and produce molecules of DNA with one parental DNA strand and one new DNA strand.

replicación semiconservadora: **(pág. 333)** método de replicación del DNA mediante el cual los filamentos paternos se separan, actúan como plantillas y producen moléculas de DNA con un filamento paterno de DNA y otro nuevo de DNA.

seminiferous tubule **(se muh NIHF rus • TEW byul): (p. 1049)** tubule of the testis in which sperm develop.

túbulo seminífero: **(pág. 1049)** túbulo del teste donde se desarrollan los espermatozoides.

sepal: **(p. 668)** flower organ that protects the bud.

sépalo: **(pág. 668)** órgano de la flor que protege el botón.

septum: **(p. 578)** cross-wall that divides a hypha into cells.

septo: **(pág. 578)** tabique que divide una hifa en células.

serendipity: **(p. 18)** occurrence of accidental or unexpected but fortunate outcomes.

serendipia: **(pág. 18)** hecho accidental o inesperado con resultados favorables.

sessile **(SEH sul): (p. 706)** organism permanently attached to one place.

sésil: **(pág. 706)** organismo que permanece adherido a una superficie.

seta **(SEE tuh): (p. 747)** tiny bristle that digs into soil and anchors an earthworm as it moves forward.

seta: **(pág. 747)** pequeña cerda que penetra en el suelo y provee el soporte que requiere una lombriz al avanzar.

sex chromosome: **(p. 305)** X or Y chromosome; paired sex chromosomes determine an individual's gender—XX individuals are female and XY individuals are male.

cromosoma sexual: **(pág. 305)** cromosoma X o Y; los cromosomas sexuales pareados determinan el sexo del individuo: los individuos XX son femeninos y los XY, masculinos.

sex-linked trait: **(p. 307)** characteristic, such as red-green color blindness, controlled by genes on the X chromosome; also called an X-linked trait.

rasgo ligado al sexo: **(pág. 307)** característica, como el daltonismo, controlada por los genes en el cromosoma X; también denominado rasgo ligado a la X.

sexual selection: **(p. 436)** change in the frequency of a trait based on competition for a mate.

selección sexual: **(pág. 436)** cambio de la frecuencia de un rasgo basado en la rivalidad por una pareja.

short-day plant: **(p. 672)** plant that flowers in the winter, spring, or fall, when the number of hours of darkness is greater than the number of hours of light.

planta de días cortos: **(pág. 672)** planta que florece en el invierno, primavera u otoño cuando el número de horas de oscuridad es mayor que el número de horas diurnas.

SI: **(p. 19)** system of measurements used by scientists, abbreviation of the International System of Units.

SI: **(pág. 19)** sistema de medición que usan los científicos, abreviatura del Sistema Internacional de Unidades.

sieve tube member: (p. 638) nonnucleated, cytoplasmic cell of the phloem.

miembro de los tubos cribosos: (pág. 638) célula citoplasmática del floema que carece de núcleo.

single nucleotide polymorphism: (p. 376) variation in a DNA sequence occurring when a single nucleotide in a genome is altered.

polimorfismo de un nucleótido simple: (pág. 376) variación en una secuencia de DNA que ocurre al alterarse un solo nucleótido en un genoma.

siphon (p. 741) tubular organ that pumps water over the gills of most mollusks; can be use for locomotion if water is expelled focefully.

sifón: (pág. 741) órgano tubular que las bombas de agua sobre las branquias de la mayoría del los moluscos, se puede utilizar para locomotión.

sister chromatid: (p. 248) structure that contains identical DNA copies and is formed during DNA replication.

cromátides hermanas: (pág. 248) estructura formada durante la replicación del DNA, que contiene copias idénticas de DNA.

skeletal muscle: (p. 948) striated muscle that causes movement when contracted and is attached to bones by tendons.

músculo óseo: (pág. 948) músculo estriado que causa movimiento al contraerse, adherido a los huesos por los tendones.

small intestine: (p. 1022) longest part of the digestive tract; involved in mechanical and chemical digestion.

intestino delgado: (pág. 1022) parte más larga del tracto digestivo; presente en la digestión mecánica y química.

smooth muscle: (p. 947) muscle that lines many hollow internal organs, such as the stomach and uterus.

músculo liso: (pág. 947) músculo que recubre las paredes de muchos órganos internos, como el estómago y el útero.

solute: (p. 163) substance dissolved in a solvent.

soluto: (pág. 163) sustancia disuelta en un disolvente.

solution: (p. 163) homogeneous mixture formed when a substance (the solute) is dissolved in another substance (the solvent).

solución: (pág. 163) mezcla homogénea formada al disolverse una sustancia (el soluto) en otra sustancia (el disolvente).

solvent: (p. 163) substance in which another substance is dissolved.

disolvente: (pág. 163) sustancia en la cual se disuelve otra sustancia.

somatic nervous system: (p. 971) part of the peripheral nervous system that transmits impulses to and from skin and skeletal muscles.

sistema nervioso somático: (pág. 971) porción del sistema nervioso periférico que transmite impulsos hacia y desde la piel a los músculos esqueléticos.

sorus: (p. 616) fern structure formed by clusters of sporangia, usually on the undersides of a frond.

soro: (pág. 616) estructura de helecho formada por grupos de esporangios, ubicada generalmente en la super ficie inferior de una fronda.

spawning: (p. 826) process by which male and female fishes release their gametes near each other in the water.

desove: (pág. 826) proceso mediante el cual tanto los peces macho como las hembras liberan sus gametos cerca uno del otro en el agua.

species: (p. 9) group of organisms that can interbreed and produce fertile offspring.

especie: (pág. 9) grupo de organismos que pueden cruzarse y producir progenies fértiles.

species diversity: (p. 117) in a biological community, the number and abundance of different species.

diversidad de especies: (pág. 117) en una comunidad biológica, el número y la abundancia de diferentes especies.

spindle apparatus: (p. 250) structure made of spindle fibers, centrioles, and aster fibers that is involved in moving and organizing chromosomes before the cell divides.

huso: (pág. 250) estructura compuesta por fibras de microtúbulos, centriolos y áster encargada de movilizar y organizar los cromosomas antes de la división celular.

spinneret: (p. 772) in spiders, the structure that spins silk from a fluid protein secreted by their glands.

hileras: (pág. 772) en las arañas, la estructura productora de seda a partir del fluido proteico que segregan sus glándulas.

spiracle (SPIHR ih kul): (p. 767) opening in the arthropod body through which air enters and waste gases leave.

espiráculo: (pág. 767) abertura en el cuerpo de los artrópodos a través de la cual entra el aire y salen los gases de desecho.

spongy bone: (p. 942) less dense inner-bone layer with many cavities that contain bone marrow.

hueso esponjoso: (pág. 942) capa de hueso interno menos densa con muchos orificios que contienen médula.

spongy mesophyll: (p. 644) loosely packed, irregularly shaped cells with spaces around them located below the palisade mesophyll.

mesófilo esponjoso: (pág. 644) células irregulares, ligeramente empacadas, con espacios circundantes localizados bajo el mesófilo en empalizada.

spontaneous generation: (p. 401) idea that life arises from nonliving things.

generación espontánea: (pág. 401) idea de que la vida surge de la materia no viva.

sporangium: **(p. 581)** sac or case in which fungal spores are produced.

spore: **(p. 580)** reproductive haploid (*n*) cell with a hard outer shell that forms a new organism without the fusion of gametes and is produced in the asexual and sexual life cycles of most fungi and some other organisms.

stabilizing selection: **(p. 434)** most common form of natural selection in which organisms with extreme expressions of a trait are removed.

stamen: **(p. 669)** male reproductive organ of most flowers composed of a filament and an anther.

stem cell: **(p. 256)** unspecialized cell that can develop into a specialized cell under the right conditions.

sternum **(STUR num):** **(p. 862)** the breastbone in vertebrates; in birds, bone to which flight muscles are attached.

stimulant: **(p. 978)** substance/drug that increases alertness and physical activity.

stimulus: **(p. 9)** any change in an organism's internal or external environment that causes the organism to react.

stolon **(STOH lun):** **(p. 583)** type of hypha formed by a mold that spreads over a food's surface.

stomata: **(p. 606)** openings in the outer cell layer of leaf surfaces and some stems that allow the exchange of water, carbon dioxide, oxygen, and other gases between a plant and its environment.

strobilus **(STROH bih lus):** **(p. 613)** compact cluster of spore-bearing structures in some seedless vascular plant sporophytes.

stroma: **(p. 223)** fluid-filled space outside the grana in which light-dependent reactions take place.

substrate: **(p. 160)** reactant to which an enzyme binds.

sustainable use: **(p. 130)** use of resources at a rate that they can be replaced or recycled.

swim bladder: **(p. 827)** gas-filled internal space in bony fishes that allows them to regulate their buoyancy.

swimmeret: **(p. 771)** crustacean appendage that aids in swimming, balance, and egg attachment.

symbiosis **(sihm bee OH sus):** **(p. 39)** close mutualistic, parasitic, or commensal association between two or more species that live together.

symmetry **(SIH muh tree):** **(p. 700)** balance or similarity in body structures of organisms.

sympathetic nervous system: **(p. 972)** branch of the autonomic nervous system that controls organs and is most active during emergencies or stress.

esporangio: **(pág. 581)** en los hongos, un saco o envoltura donde se producen las esporas.

espora: **(pág. 580)** célula reproductora haploide (n) con una cubierta protectora dura capaz de formar un nuevo organismo sin la fusión de gametos; y se produce en los ciclos vitales sexuales y asexuales de la mayoría de los hongos.

selección estabilizadora: **(pág. 434)** la selección natural más común, mediante la cual se eliminan los organismos con expresiones extremas de un rasgo.

estambre: **(pág. 669)** órgano reproductor masculino de la mayoría de las flores, compuesto por un filamento y una antera.

célula madre: **(pág. 256)** célula no especializada capaz de desarrollarse en una célula especializada bajo las condiciones adecuadas.

esternón: **(pág. 862)** en las aves, hueso pectoral grande al cual se adhieren los músculos de vuelo.

estimulante: **(pág. 978)** sustancia / droga que aumenta la agudeza y actividad física.

estímulo: **(pág. 9)** cualquier cambio en el ambiente interno o externo de un organismo que ocasiona una reacción en el organismo.

estolón: **(pág. 583)** tipo de hifa formada por un hongo que se extiende sobre la superficie de los alimentos.

estomas: **(pág. 606)** aberturas en la capa celular externa superficial de las hojas y de algunos tallos que permiten el intercambio de agua, dióxido de carbono y otros gases entre una planta y su medioambiente.

estróbilo: **(pág. 613)** racimo compacto de estructuras que contienen esporas en algunos esporófitos de plantas vasculares sin semilla.

estroma: **(pág. 223)** espacio relleno de fluido fuera de las granas donde suceden reacciones lumino-dependientes.

sustrato: **(pág. 160)** reactivo al cual se adhiere una enzima.

uso sostenible: **(pág. 130)** uso de los recursos a una tasa tal que puedan reemplazarse o reciclarse.

vejiga natatoria: **(pág. 827)** espacio interno relleno de gas en los peces óseos que les ayuda a controlar su flotabilidad.

pleópodo: **(pág. 771)** apéndice crustáceo que ayuda en la natación, el equilibrio, y adjunción de huevos.

simbiosis: **(pág. 39)** asociación estrecha mutualista, parasítica o comensal entre dos o más especies que viven juntas.

simetría: **(pág. 700)** equilibrio o similitud en las estructuras corporales de los organismos.

sistema nervioso simpático: **(pág. 972)** rama del sistema nervioso autónomo que controla los órganos y es muy activo durante las emergencias o el estrés.

sympatric speciation: (p. 438) occurs when a species evolves into a new species in an area without a geographic barrier.

especiación simpátrica: (pág. 438) ocurre cuando una especie evoluciona en una especie nueva dentro de un área sin frontera geográfica.

synapse (SIH naps): (p. 967) gap between one neuron's axon and another nueron's dendrite.

sinapsis: (pág. 967) brecha entre el axón de una neurona y las dendritas de otra.

T

taste bud: (p. 973) one of a number of specialized chemical receptors on the tongue that can detect sweet, sour, salty, and bitter tastes.

papila gustativa: (pág. 973) una de un número de receptores químicos especializados de la lengua que detectan los sabores dulces, agrios, salados y amargos.

taxon: (p. 487) named group of organisms, such as a phylum, genus, or species.

taxón: (pág. 487) grupo nombrado de organismos, como un filo, un género o una especie.

taxonomy (tak SAH nuh mee): (p. 485) branch of biology that identifies, names, and classifies species based on their natural relationships.

taxonomía: (pág. 485) rama de la biología que identifica, nombra y clasifica las especies en base a su morfología y comportamiento.

technology (tek NAH luh jee): (p. 15) application of knowledge gained from scientific reasearch to solve society's needs and problems and improve the quality of life.

tecnología: (pág. 15) aplicación del conocimiento derivado de la investigación científica a fin de resolver los problemas y necesidades de la sociedad y mejorar la calidad de vida.

telomere: (p. 311) protective cap made of DNA that is found on the ends of a chromosome.

telómero: (pág. 311) capa protectora de DNA que se encuentra en los extremos de un cromosoma.

telophase: (p. 251) last stage of mitosis in which nucleoli reappear. Two new nuclear membranes begin to form, but the cell has not yet completely divided.

telofase: (pág. 251) fase final de la mitosis en que reaparecen los nucléolos. Comienzan a formarse dos nuevas membranas nucleares sin que la célula haya terminado de dividirse.

temperate forest: (p. 69) biome south of the boreal forest characterized by broad-leaved, deciduous trees, well-defined seasons, and average yearly precipitation of 75–150 cm.

bosque templado: (pág. 69) bioma al sur del bosque boreal compuesto por árboles caducifolios de hojas anchas, estaciones bien definidas y entre 70 y 150 cm de precipitación promedio anual.

tendon: (p. 948) tough connective-tissue band that connects muscle to bone.

tendón: (pág. 948) banda dura de tejido conectivo que adhieren los músculos a los huesos.

territorial behavior: (p. 918) competitive behavior in which an animal tries to adopt and defend a physical area against others of the same species.

comportamiento territorial: (pág. 918) comportamiento competitivo mediante el cual un animal trata de adoptar y defender un área física de otros animales de la misma especie.

test: (p. 550) hard, porous, shell-like covering of an amoeba.

testa: (pág. 550) cubierta dura, porosa, con forma de cáscara, de una ameba.

test cross: (p. 362) breeding that can be used to determine an organism's genotype.

cruzamiento de prueba: (pág. 362) cruce que puede ayudar a determinar el genotipo de un organismo.

tetrapod: (p. 830) four-footed animal with legs that have feet and toes with joints.

tetrápodo: (pág. 830) animal cuadrúpedo cuyas patas tienen pies y dedos con articulaciones.

thallose (THAL lohs): (p. 612) liverwort with a fleshy, lobed body shape.

talosa: (pág. 612) hepática con forma corporal carnosa lobulada.

theory: (p. 14) explanation of a natural phenomenon based on many observations and investigations over time.

teoría: (pág. 14) explicación de un fenómeno natural basado en muchas observaciones y experimentos con el correr del tiempo.

theory of biogenesis (bi oh JEN uh sus): (p. 402) states that only living organisms can produce other living organisms.

teoría de la biogénesis: (pág. 402) plantea que sólo los organismos vivos pueden producir otros organismos vivos.

therapsid: (p. 896) extinct mammal-like reptile from which the first mammals probably arose.

terápsido: (pág. 896) reptil extinto parecido a un mamífero del cual probablemente surgieron los primeros mamíferos.

thermodynamics: (p. 218) study of the flow and transformation of energy in the universe.

thorax: (p. 763) middle body region of an arthropod consisting of three fused main segments that may bear legs and wings.

threshold: (p. 964) minimum stimulus needed to produce a nerve impulse.

thylakoid: (p. 223) in choroplasts, one of the stacked, flattened, pigment-containing membranes in which light-dependent reactions occur.

thyroxine: (p. 1034) thyroid hormone that increases the metabolic rate of cells.

tolerance: (p. 61) organism's ability to survive biotic and abiotic factors. **(p. 981)** as the body becomes less responsive to a drug, an individual needs larger and more frequent doses to achieve the same effect.

trachea: (p. 1001) tube that carries air from the larynx to the bronchi.

tracheal (TRAY kee ul) tube: (p. 767) in most terrestrial arthropods, one of a system of tubes that branch into smaller tubules and carry oxygen throughout the body.

tracheid (TRAY key ihd): (p. 637) long, cylindrical plant cell in which water passes from cell to cell through pitted ends.

transcription (trans KRIHP shun): (p. 337) process in which mRNA is synthesized from the template DNA.

transfer RNA: (p. 336) type of RNA that transports amino acids to the ribosome.

transformation: (p. 367) process in which bacterial cells take up recombinant plasmid DNA.

transgenic organism: (p. 370) organism that is genetically engineered by inserting a gene from another organism.

translation: (p. 338) process in which mRNA attaches to the ribosome and a protein is assembled.

transpiration: (p. 645) process in which water evaporates from the inside of leaves to the outside through stomata.

transport protein: (p. 189) protein that moves substances or wastes through the plasma membrane.

trichinosis (trih kuh NOH sus): (p. 733) disease caused by eating raw or undercooked meat, usually pork, infected with *Trichinella* larvae.

trichocyst (TRIH kuh sihst): (p. 547) elongated, cylindrical structure that can discharge a spinelike structure that may function in defense, as an anchoring device, or to capture prey.

trophic (TROH fihk) level: (p. 42) each step in a food chain or food web.

termodinámica: (pág. 218) estudio del flujo y transformación de la energía del universo.

tórax: (pág. 763) región del cuerpo medio de un artrópodo compuesta por tres segmentos principales fusionados capaz de soportar patas y alas.

umbral: (pág. 964) estímulo mínimo requerido para producir un impulso nervioso.

tilacoide: (pág. 223) en los cloroplastos, una de las membranas apiladas y aplanadas que contienen pigmento donde ocurren las reacciones lumino-dependientes.

tiroxina: (pág. 1034) hormona tiroidea que aumenta la tasa metabólica de las células.

tolerancia: (pág. 61) capacidad de un organismo de sobrevivir factores bióticos y abióticos. **(pág. 981)** a medida que el cuerpo se vuelve menos sensible a una droga, un individuo necesita dosis más frecuentes y mayores para obtener el mismo efecto.

tráquea: (pág. 1001) conducto que lleva el aire desde la laringe hasta los bronquios.

tubo traqueal: (pág. 767) en la mayoría de los artrópodos terrestres, uno entre un sistema de conductos que se ramifican en otros más pequeños y transportan el oxígeno por todo el cuerpo.

traqueida: (pág. 637) célula vegetal alargada y cilíndrica en la cual pasa el agua de célula a célula a través de extremos picados.

transcripción: (pág. 337) proceso en que el mRNA se sintetiza del patrón de DNA.

RNA de transferencia: (pág. 336) tipo de RNA que transporta los aminoácidos a los ribosomas.

transformación: (pág. 367) proceso en el cual las células bacterianas recogen el DNA plásmido recombinante.

organismo transgénico: (pág. 370) organismo generado genéticamente al insertar el gene de un organismo distinto.

traducción: (pág. 338) proceso mediante el cual el mRNA se adhiere al ribosoma y se sintetiza una proteína.

transpiración: (pág. 645) proceso en el cual el agua se evapora de adentro hacia fuera de las hojas a través de los estomas.

proteína de transporte: (pág. 189) proteína que mueve sustancias o desechos a través de la membrana plasmática.

triquinosis: (pág. 733) enfermedad causada por la carne cruda o poco cocinada, generalmente de cerdo, infectada con larvas de la *Trichinella.*

tricocisto: (pág. 547) estructura alargada y cilíndrica que puede descargar una estructura husiforme capaz de reaccionar como defensa, como sistema de anclaje o captura de presa.

nivel trófico: (pág. 42) cada paso de una cadena o red alimenticia.

tropical rain forest: (p. 72) hot, wet biome with year-round humidity; contains Earth's most diverse species of plants and animals.

tropical savanna: (p. 71) biome characterized by grasses and scattered trees, and herd animals such as zebras and antelopes.

tropical seasonal forest: (p. 71) biome characterized by deciduous and evergreen trees, a dry season, and animal species that include monkeys, elephants, and Bengal tigers.

tropism (TROH pih zum): (p. 651) response to an external stimulus in a specific direction.

tube foot: (p. 795) one of the muscular, small, fluid-filled tubes with suction-cuplike ends that enable echinoderms to move and collect food.

tundra: (p. 68) treeless biome with permanently frozen soil under the surface and average yearly precipitation of 15–25 cm.

tympanic (tihm PA nihk) membrane: (p. 837) eardrum.

pluviselva tropical: (pág. 72) bioma caliente, lluvioso, con una humedad anual continua; contiene las especies más diversas de plantas y animales terrestres.

sabana tropical: (pág. 71) bioma caracterizado por hierbas, árboles dispersos y animales que se agrupan en manadas, como cebras y antílopes.

bosque estacional tropical: (pág. 71) bioma caracterizado por árboles caducifolios y siempreverdes, una estación seca y especies de animales que incluyen a los monos, los elefantes y los tigres de Bengala.

tropismo: (pág. 651) crecimiento de una planta en respuesta a estímulos externos proveniente de una dirección específica.

pie ambulacral: (pág. 795) uno de los conductos musculares pequeños rellenos de fluido y con ventosas de los equinodermos que posibilita el movimiento y la recolección de alimento.

tundra: (pág. 68) bioma carente de árboles, con suelo permanentemente congelado bajo la superficie; y una precipitación promedio anual de 15-25 cm.

membrana timpánica: (pág. 837) tímpano.

U

urea: (p. 1006) nitrogenous waste product of the excretory system.

urethra (yoo REE thruh): (p. 1049) tube that conducts semen and urine out of the body through the penis in males and transports urine out of the body in females.

uterus: (p. 887) saclike muscular female organ in which embryos develop.

urea: (pág. 1006) producto de desecho nitrogenado del sistema excretorio.

uretra: (pág. 1049) conducto que conduce el semen y la orina fuera del cuerpo a través del pene en los machos y transporta la orina fuera del cuerpo de las hembras.

útero: (pág. 887) órgano femenino muscular con forma de saco hueco donde se desarrollan los embriones.

V

vacuole: (p. 195) membrane-bound vesicle for temporary storage of materials such as food, enzymes, and wastes.

valve: (p. 994) one of the tissue flaps in veins that prevents backflow of blood.

van der Waals forces: (p. 155) attractive forces between molecules.

vascular cambium: (p. 634) thin cylinder of meristematic tissue that produces new transport cells.

vascular plant: (p. 606) type of plant with vascular tissues adapted to land environments; most widely distributed type of plant on Earth.

vascular tissue: (p. 606) specialized tissue that transports water, food, and other substances in vascular plants and can also provide structure and support.

vacuola: (pág. 195) espacio encerrado por una membrana para el almacenamiento temporal de materiales como alimento, enzimas y desechos.

válvula: (pág. 994) uno de los opérculos de los tejidos en las venas que evita que la sangre fluya hacia atrás.

fuerzas de van der Waals: (pág. 155) fuerzas de atracción entre las moléculas.

cámbium vascular: (pág. 634) cilindro delgado de tejido meristémico que produce células de transporte nuevas.

planta vascular: (pág. 606) tipo de planta con tejido vascular adaptada a ambientes terrestres; tipo de planta ampliamente distribuida en la Tierra.

tejido vascular: (pág. 606) tejido especializado que transporta agua, alimento y otras sustancias en las plantas vasculares y también proveen estructura y soporte.

vas deferens (VAS • DEF uh runz): (p. 1049) duct through which sperm move away from the testis and toward the urethra.

conducto deferente: (pág. 1049) ducto por el cual los espermatozoides se alejan de los testículos hacia la uretra.

vegetative reproduction: (p. 662) asexual reproduction in which new plants grow from parts of an existing plant.

reproducción vegetativa: (pág. 662) reproducción asexual en la cual crecen plantas nuevas de las partes de una planta existente.

vein: (p. 994) blood vessel that carries deoxygenated blood back to the heart.

vena: (pág. 994) vaso sanguíneo que devuelve la sangre desoxigenada al corazón.

ventral (VEN trul): (p. 700) underside or belly of an animal with bilateral symmetry.

ventral: (pág. 700) la superficie inferior o barriga de un animal con simetría bilateral.

ventricle: (p. 824) the heart chamber that pumps blood from the heart to the gills or lungs.

ventrículo: (pág. 894) la cavidad cardíaca que bombea la sangre del corazón a las agallas o los pulmones.

vertebrate: (p. 693) animal with an endoskeleton and a backbone.

vertebrado: (pág. 693) animal que posee endoesqueleto y columna vertebral.

vessel element: (p. 637) elongated, tubular plant cell that forms xylem strands (vessels) and conducts water and dissolved substances.

elemento vascular: (pág. 637) células vegetales alargadas, tubulares, que forman filamentos de xilema (vasos) y conducen agua y sustancias disueltas.

vestigial structure: (p. 425) reduced form of a functional structure that indicates shared ancestry.

estructura vestigial: (pág. 425) forma reducida de una estructura funcional que indica ascendencia compartida.

villus (VIH luhs): (p. 1023) fingerlike structure through which most nutrients are absorbed from within the small intestine.

vellosidad: (pág. 1023) estructura en forma de dedos por la cual el intestino delgado absorbe la mayor parte de los nutrientes.

virus: (p. 525) nonliving strand of genetic material that cannot replicate on its own, has a nucleic acid core, a protein coat, and can invade cells and alter cellular function.

virus: (pág. 525) hebra sin vida, de material genético, incapaz de duplicarse por sí misma; tiene un núcleo de ácido nucleico, un revestimiento de proteína y puede invadir las células y alterar sus funciones.

vitamin: (p. 1028) fat-soluble or water-soluble organic compound needed in very small amounts for the body's metabolic activities.

vitamina: (pág. 1028) compuesto orgánico liposoluble o hidrosoluble, que se necesita en porciones muy pequeñas para las actividades metabólicas del cuerpo.

voluntary muscle: (p. 948) consciously controlled skeletal muscle.

músculo voluntario: (pág. 948) músculo esquelético controlado en forma consciente.

W

water-vascular system: (p. 795) system of fluid-filled, closed tubes that allow echinoderms to control movement and get food.

sistema vascular acuático: (pág. 795) sistema de conductos cerrados, rellenos de fluido, que permite a los equinodermos controlar el movimiento y obtener alimento.

weather: (p. 65) atmospheric conditions such as temperature and precipitation at a specific place and time.

tiempo: (pág. 65) condiciones atmosféricas, como la temperatura y la precipitación, en un lugar y tiempo específico.

wetland: (p. 78) water-saturated land area that supports aquatic plants.

humedal: (pág. 78) terreno saturado de agua que mantiene a las plantas acuáticas.

white blood cell: (p. 998) large, nucleated, disease-fighting blood cell produced in the bone marrow.

glóbulo blanco: (pág. 998) célula sanguínea gigante y nucleada que combate las enfermedades y se produce en la médula ósea.

woodland: (p. 69) biome characterized by small trees and mixed shrub communities.

zona boscosa: (pág. 69) bioma caracterizado por árboles pequeños y comunidades de arbustos mixtas.

X

xylem (ZI lum): (p. 637) vascular plant tissue that transports water and dissolved minerals away from the roots throughout the plant and is composed of vessel elements and tracheids.

xilema: (pág. 637) tejido vegetal vascular que transporta el agua y los minerales disueltos desde las raíces hacia el resto de la planta, compuesto por elementos de los vasos y traqueidas.

Y

yellow bone marrow: (p. 942) type of marrow that consists of stored fat.

médula ósea amarilla: (pág. 942) tipo de médula que consiste en grasas almacenadas.

Z

zero population growth (ZPG): (p. 104) occurs when the birthrate equals the death rate.

zygote (ZI goht): (p. 695) fertilized egg formed when a sperm cell penetrates an egg.

crecimiento demográfico nulo (CDN): (pág. 104) sucede cuando la tasa de natalidad es igual a la tasa de mortalidad.

cigoto: (pág. 695) óvulo fecundado que se forma cuando un espermatozoide fecunda un óvulo.

Index

Index Key
Italic page numbers = illustration/photo **Bold page numbers = vocabulary term**
Italic page numbers + act = activity

A

Index

B

Index

E

Index

F

G

J

K

L

M

N

O

P

Index

Q

R

U

V

W

X

Y

Z

Art Credits

Acknowledgements: Glencoe would like to acknowledge the artists and agencies who participated in illustrating this program: Alan Male, represented by American Artists Representatives, Inc.; Annette Lasker; Argosy; Articulate Graphics, represented by Deborah Wolfe Limited; Barbara Harmon; Barbara Higgins Bond, represented by American Artists Representatives, Inc.; Michael Rothman, represented by Melissa Turk & The Artist Network; Morgan Cain & Associates; Wendy Smith, represented by Melissa Turk & The Artist Network.

Photo Credits

COV (foreground)Richard Du Toit/Getty Images, (background)Comstock/Getty Images; **Frontsheet** Peter Griffith/Masterfile; **vi** (t)Alton Biggs, (tc)Whitney Hagins, (c)William G. Holliday, (bc)Dr. Chris Kapicka, (b)Linda Lundgren; **vii** (t)Ann Haley MacKenzie, (tc)Dr. William Rogers, (bc)Dr. Marion Sewer, (b)Dinah Zike; **2-3** Myron Jay Dorf/CORBIS; **3** (t)Photo Library International/Photo Researchers, (c)CORBIS, (b)SPL/Photo Researchers; **4** Karl Ammann/CORBIS; **5** (t)Reinhard Dirscherl/Visuals Unlimited, (b)Mike Derer/AP/Wide World Photos; **6** (t)Salk Institute for Biological Studies, (b)Dr. Fred Hossler/Visuals Unlimited; **7** (t to b)M.I. Walker/Photo Researchers, (2)Tom J. Ulrich/Visuals Unlimited, (3)(4)Gary Meszaros/Visuals Unlimited, (5)Tom McHugh/Photo Researchers, (6)W. Wisniewski/zefa/CORBIS, (7)OSF/G.I. Bernard/Animals Animals, (8)Ron Fehling/Masterfile, (9)Stephen J. Krasemann/Photo Researchers; **8** (l)Alan & Sandy Carey/Peter Arnold, Inc., (c)Richard Nowitz/National Geographic Society Image Collection, (r)Joe McDonald/CORBIS; **9** (l)Hal Horwitz/CORBIS, (r)David M. Dennis/Animals Animals; **10** Gerry Ellis/Minden Pictures; **11** Jeremy Bishop/SPL/Photo Researchers; **12** The McGraw-Hill Companies; **15** David Parker/SPL/Photo Researchers; **16** (l)Frans Lanting, (r)National Geographic Society; **18** George McCarthy/CORBIS; **20** Azure Computer & Photo Services/Animals Animals; **22** (t)The McGraw-Hill Companies, (b)Dr. Jackie Buell, COSI/OSU; **23** (l)Digital Stock/CORBIS, (tr br)Ryan McVay/Getty Images, (cr)Chad Baker/Getty Images; **28-29** Ron Niebrugge; **30-31** CORBIS; **31** (t)Galen Rowell/CORBIS, (c)Paul Souders/Getty Images, (b)Dan Suzio/Photo Researchers; **32** (l)CORBIS, (r)Yann Arthus-Bertran/CORBIS; **33** (t)Flip Nicklin/Minden Pictures, (bl) ALEXANDER JOE/AFP/Newscom, (br)Radu Sigheti/Reuters/CORBIS; **34** (t)NASA, (cl)Glen Allison/Getty Images, (cr)Steve Allen/Getty Images, (b)Stockbyte/PunchStock; **35** National Geographic/Getty Images; **37** Photo Library International/ESA/Photo Researchers; **38** (t)CORBIS, (b)Martin Harvey/Foto Natura/Minden Pictures; **39** Ken Lucas/Visuals Unlimited; **40** RC Hall/Custom Medical Stock Photo; **41** Jeffrey Lepore/Photo Researchers; **42** Michael P. Gadomski/Photo Researchers; **45** K. Oster/CORBIS; **47** Kevin Schafer/CORBIS; **50** Larry Lee/CORBIS; **51** (l)David Young-Wolff/Photo Edit, (tr)D Falconer/PhotoLink, (cr)Alan Thorton/Getty Images, (br)S Meltzer/PhotoLink/Getty Images; **53** William Manning/CORBIS; **58-59** Gary Bell/Oceanwidelmages.com; **59** (t)Peter Arnold, Inc., (c)ABPL/Stephanie Lamberti/Animals Animals, (b)Taxi/Getty Images; **60** Yann Arthus-Bertrand/CORBIS; **73** Fritz Polking/Peter Arnold, Inc.; **75** Ned Therrien/Visuals Unlimited; **78** David Sieren/Visuals Unlimited; **81** CORBIS; **82** MICHAEL NICHOLS/National Geographic Stock; **83** (t)D Falconer/PhotoLink, (cl)Matt Meadows, (cr)Alan Thorton/Getty Images, (b)S Meltzer/PhotoLink/Getty Images; **85** Getty Images; **90-91** George McCarthy/CORBIS; **91** (t)Eye of Science/SPL/Photo Researchers, (b)K. Kjeldsen/Photo Researchers; **92** P. Kahl/Photo Researchers; **94** (l)Michael Ord/Photo Researchers, (r)Arco Images/Alamy Images; **95** (l)Tom Bean/CORBIS, (r)Charlie Ott/Photo Researchers; **96** Jim Cartier/Photo Researchers; **98** Pierre Holtz/Reuters/CORBIS; **99** Daryl Balfour/Photo Researchers; **102** (l)Pete Oxford/Minden Pictures, (r)Bettmann/CORBIS; **103** (l)Photo by MPI/Getty Images, (r)John Griffin/The Image Works; **106** Joanna McCarthy/Getty Images; **107** (t b)Ryan McVay/Getty Images, (c)Chad Baker/Getty Images; **108** (t)Bob Cranston/Animals Animals, (b)Bettmann/CORBIS; **109** Gary W. Carter/CORBIS; **110** CORBIS; **114-115** Roland Gerth/zefa/CORBIS; **115** (t)Terry Spivey/USDA Forest Service/www.insectimages.org, (c)Edward Kinsman/Photo Researchers, (b)Alexis Rosenfeld/Photo Researchers; **116** PSU Entomology/Photo Researchers; **117** OSF/R. Packwood/Animals Animals; **118** (l)Stefan Meyers/Animals Animals, (r)Michael and Patricia Fogden/Minden Pictures; **119** (tl)David Cavagnaro/Visuals Unlimited, (tr)David R. Frazier/Photo Researchers, (b)Nigel J. Dennis/Photo Researchers; **121** Adam Jones/Photo Researchers; **124** (tl)Michael Sewell/Peter Arnold, (tr)Adam Jones/Visuals Unlimited, (c b)Frans Lanting; **127** (t)Michael Gadomski/Earth Scenes, (b)Kirtley-Perkins/Visuals Unlimited; **130** (t)Dr. Marli Miller/Visuals Unlimited, (b)Gary Braasch/CORBIS; **133** Alan Sirulnikoff/SPL/Photo Researchers; **134** Robert Brook/Photo Researchers; **135** Anthony Bannister/Gallo Images/CORBIS; **136** Wendy Stone/CORBIS; **137** (t)D Falconer/PhotoLink, (c)Alan Thorton/Getty Images, (b)S Meltzer/PhotoLink/Getty Images; **139** DAJ/Alamy Images; **140** Alan Sirulnikoff/SPL/Photo Researchers; **144-145** Karen Kasmauski/CORBIS; **146-147** David Young-Wolff/PhotoEdit; **147** (t)David M. Phillips/Photo Researchers, Inc., (b)BSIP/Photo Researchers, Inc.; **150** (l)Custom Medical Stock Photography, (r)Neil Borden/Photo Researchers; **151** (tl)Peter Bowater/Photo Researchers, (tr)The McGraw Hill Companies, Inc. Evelyn Jo Hebert, photographer, (c)W. Cody/CORBIS, (b)Charles D. Winters/Photo Researchers; **155** (t)Zigmund Leszczynski/Animals Animals, (b)Dennis Kunkel/PhotoTake NYC; **156** (l)Julian Calder/CORBIS, (r)Charles D. Winters/Photo Researchers; **157** David Young-Wolff/PhotoEdit; **158** (t)PhotoLink/Getty Images, (b)Matt Meadows; **161** Color-Pic/Animals Animals; **162** David Whitten; **163** (t)David Young-Wolff/PhotoEdit, (bl)Matt Meadows, (br)Martin Rotker/PhotoTake NYC; **166** Elizabeth Opalenik; **167** (t)Charles D. Winters/Photo Researchers, (c)E.S. Ross/Visuals Unlimited, (b)Digital Art/CORBIS; **168** (l)John Anderson/Animals Animals, (r)Dr. Dennis Kunkel/Visuals Unlimited; **172** Tony Freeman/Photo Edit; **173** (t)Ryan McVay/Getty Images, (c)Chad Baker/Getty Images, (bl)Horizons; (br)Ryan McVay/Getty Images; **175** Steve Allen/Brand X Pictures; **176** Paul Katz/Index Stock Imagery; **180** Getty Images; **182** Bridgeman Art Library; **183** (t)Lester V. Bergman/CORBIS, (bl)SPL/Photo Researchers, (br)LBNL/SPL/Photo Researchers; **185** (t)Driscoll, Youngquist & Baldeschwieler, California Institute of Technology/Photo Researchers, (bl)Lester V. Bergman/CORBIS, (br)Biophoto Associates/Photo Researchers; **187** Jill Barton/AP/Wide World Photos; **193 194** Dr. Dennis Kunkel/Phototake NYC; **195** (t)Dr. Dennis Kunkel/Visuals Unlimited, (b)Henry Aldrich/Visuals Unlimited; **196** Gopal Murti/Phototake NYC; **197** (t)Dr. Donald Fawcett/Visuals Unlimited, (b)George Chapman/Visuals Unlimited; **198** (t)Marilyn Schaller/Photo Researchers, (bl)Dr. David M. Phillips/Visuals Unlimited, (br)Dr. Linda Stannard-Uct/Photo Researchers; **204** (l)Custom Medical Stock Photo, (r)Carolina Biological Supply/Visuals Unlimited; **205** (l)Custom Medical Stock Photo, (r)Dr. Linda Stannard-Uct/Photo Researchers; **208** SPL/Photo Researchers; **209** (t b)Ryan McVay/Getty Images, (c)Chad Baker/Getty Images; **211** Lester V. Bergman/CORBIS; **213** A.M. Siegelman/Visuals Unlimited; **216** Jose Fuste Raga/CORBIS; **218** (t)Pr. S. Cinti, University of Ancona/PhotoTake NYC, (b)CMEABG-LYON-1/PhotoTake NYC; **219** Kevin Salemme/Merrimack College; **224** CORBIS; **227** Ed Reschke/Peter Arnold, Inc.; **234** (t)Thomas Deerinck/Visuals Unlimited, Inc., (b)Collection CNRI/PhotoTake NYC; **235** (t b)Ryan McVay/Getty Images, (c)Chad Baker/Getty Images; **242-243** Radius Images/Photolibrary; **243** (t)M.I. Walker/Photo Researchers, (b)The McGraw-Hill Companies, Inc./Steven P. Lynch; **245** Dr. Gopal Murti/Visuals Unlimited; **247** Michael Abbey/Visuals Unlimited; **248** Andrew Syred/Photo Researchers; **249** Thomas Deerinck/Visuals Unlimited; **250** (t)Dr. Conley L. Rieder and Dr. Alexey Khodjakov/Visuals Unlimited, (b)Carolina Biological Supply Co./PhotoTake NYC; **251** Michael Abbey/Photo Researchers; **252** (l)RMF/Visuals Unlimited, (r)The McGraw-Hill Companies, Inc./Al Telser; **257** P. Sorrentino-Eurelios/PhotoTake NYC; **259** (t b)Ryan McVay/Getty Images, (c)Chad Baker/Getty Images; **262** Biodisc/Visuals Unlimited; **266-267** Kenneth Garrett/National Geographic Stock; **268-269** Gallo Images/Heinrich van den Berg/Getty Images; **269** (t)CNRI/Photo Researchers, Inc., (c)Manfred Kage/Peter Arnold, Inc., (b)Dr. David M. Phillips/Visuals Unlimited; **270** (l)Amie Meister/Custom Medical Stock Photography, (r)Davies & Davies/Getty Images; **277** Bettmann/CORBIS; **281** Robert Folz/Visuals Unlimited; **285** (l)Inga Spence/Getty Images, (r)Marc Moritsch/Getty Images; **287** (t b)Ryan McVay/Getty Images, (c)Chad Baker/Getty Images; **290** (l)Yann Arthus-Bertrand/CORBIS, (c)Ric Frazier/Masterfile, (r)Barbara Von Hoffmann/Animals Animals; **291** Glenn Oliver/Visuals Unlimited; **294-295** Anne Ackerman/Getty Images; **295** Addenbrookes Hospital/Photo Researchers; **303** Dr. Stanley Flegler/Visuals Unlimited; **304** (tl)Carolyn A. McKeone/Photo Researchers; (tr)Jane Burton/Photo Researchers; (bl)© ARCO/P. Wegner/age fotostock; (br)© Photolibrary/age fotostock; **305** (tl)Cheryl Ertelt/Visuals Unlimited, (tcl)Jacques Brun/Photo Researchers, (tcr)Dale C. Spartas/CORBIS, (tr)M. Claye/Photo Researchers, (b)Andrew Syred/Photo Researchers; **306** (t)Razi Searles/Bruce Coleman, Inc., (b)Dr. George Wilder/Getty Images; **307** Charles Krebs/CORBIS; **309** Carolyne A. McKeone/Photo Researchers; **311** CNRI/Photo Researchers; **313** (l)Lauren Shear/Photo Researchers, (r)CNRI/Photo Researchers; **316** Michael Newman/PhotoEdit; **317** (t b)Ryan McVay/Getty Images, (cl)Matt Meadows, (cr)Chad Baker/Getty Images; **319** Jason Edwards/National Geographic/Getty Images; **320** (l c)Michael P. Gadomski/Photo Researchers, (cr)Wally Eberhart/Visuals Unlimited, (r)CNRI/Photo Researchers; **321** CNRI/Photo Researchers; **324-325** Jennifer Waters & Adrian Salic/Photo Researchers; **325** Adrian T. Sumner/Getty Images; **326** (l)Dr. Jack M. Bostrack/Visuals Unlimited, (r)Dr. Frederick Skvara/Visuals Unlimited; **330** (t)Omikron/Photo Researchers, (b)A. Barrington Brown/Photo Researchers; **347** (t)Dr. Stanley Flegler/Visuals Unlimited, (b)Jackie Lewin, Royal Free Hospital/Photo Researchers; **350** (t)Jamey Stillings/Getty Images, (b)Bob Nichols/USDA; **351** William Fritsch/Jupiter Images; **353** Omikron/Photo Researchers; **358-359** Dr. Steve Robinow; **359** Jeffrey Plautz and Steve Kay; **360** (l c)Yann Arthus-Bertrand/CORBIS, (r)GK Hart/Vikki Hart/Getty Images; **363** Carolyn A. McKeone/SPL/Photo Researchers; **365** (l)Klaus Guldbrandsen/Photo Researchers, (r)NOAA; **371** Jim Richardson/National Geographic Society Image Collection; **374** (t)Pascal Goetgheluck/Photo Researchers, (b)Pierre Roussel/Images Distribution/Newscom; **375** USDA; **380** Frans Lanting/CORBIS; **381** William Fritsch/Jupiter Images; **388-389** Reuters/CORBIS; **390-391** Alan Morgan; **391** O. LOUIS MAZZATENTA/National Geographic Stock; **392** Roger Ressmeyer/CORBIS; **393** (l to r)John Reader/Photo Researchers, (2)Biophoto Associates/Photo Researchers, (3)Dominique Braud/Earth Scenes, (4)Bernard Edmaier/Photo Researchers, (5)Francois Gohier/Photo Researchers, (6)© Vova Pomortzeff / Alamy; **398** (t)Georgette Douwma/Photo Researchers, (b)Ken Lucas/Visuals Unlimited; **405** (t)Dr. Ken MacDonald/Photo Researchers, (b)Francois Gohier/Photo Researchers; **408** O. Louis Mazzatenta/National Geographic Society Image Collection; **409** (t b)Ryan McVay/Getty Images, (c)Chad Baker/Getty Images; **410** (t)Biophoto Associates/Photo Researchers, (b)Francois Gohier/Photo Researchers; **412** (l)Barbara Srnadova/Photo Researchers, (r)Roger Garwood & Trish Ainslie/CORBIS; **413** NPS Photo by Jim Peaco; **416-417** Michael Fogden/Animals Animals; **417** (t)Dennis Kunkel Microscopy, (c b)Michael and Patricia Fogden; **418** AKG/Photo Researchers; **423** Phyllis Greenberg/Animals Animals; **425** (t)Oliver Strewe/Lonely Planet Images, (b)Tim Fuller; **426** (tl)Alan & Sandy Carey/Getty Images, (tr)Hans Pfletschinger/Peter Arnold, Inc., (bl)David M. Dennis/Animals Animals, (br)Clouds Hill Imaging Ltd./CORBIS; **427** (t)Tom Boyden/Lonely Planet Images, (b)Gerald & Buff Corsi/Visuals Unlimited; **428** James Watt/Animals Animals; **429** (l)Erwin Bud Nielsen/Index Stock Imagery, (r)Zig Leszczynski/Animals Animals; **430** Steve Raymer/National Geographic Society Image Collection; **435** (t)Peter Parks/OSF/Animals Animals, (b)B. Frederick/OSF/Animals Animals; **436** (tl)Ohio Department of Natural Resources, (tr)Suzanne L. & Joseph T. Collins/Photo Researchers, (b)William Weber/Visuals Unlimited; **437** Gerard Lacz/Animals Animals; **438** (l)Thomas & Pat Leeson/Photo Researchers, (c)Enlightened Images/Earth Scenes, (r)Thomas & Pat Leeson/Photo Researchers; **439** Mitsuhiko Imamori/Minden Pictures; **442** (l)DEA/DANI-JESKE/De Agostini Picture Library/Getty Images, (r)Bikeadventure; **443** (t b)Ryan McVay/Getty Images, (c)Chad Baker/Getty Images; **445** (l)Zig Leszczynski/Animals Animals, (c)Alan & Sandy Carey/Getty Images, (r)Hans Pfletschinger/Peter Arnold, Inc.; **446** A.N.T./Photo Researchers; **447** Patti Murray/Animals Animals; **450-451** Frank Lukasseck/zefa/CORBIS; **451** (t)Robert Pickett/CORBIS, (c b)Theo Allofs/Visuals Unlimited; **452** Gary Retherford/Photo Researchers; **454** Jeff Cadge/Getty Images; **455** (l to r)Patti Murray/Animals Animals, (2)Studio Carlo Dani/Animals Animals, (3)OSF/David Haring/Animals Animals, (4)George Holton/Photo Researchers; **456** (t)Martin Harvey/Photodisc/Getty Images, (b)Frans Lanting/CORBIS; **457** (t)Tom McHugh/Photo Researchers, (bl)ZSSD/Minden Pictures, (br)Renee Lynn/CORBIS; **458** Jorg & Petra Wegner/Animals Animals; **459** Barry Slaven/Visuals Unlimited; **462** (t)Pascal Goetgheluck/SPL/Photo Researchers, (b)Tom McHugh/Photo Researchers; **463** João Zilhão/Portuguese Institute of Archaeology; **465** (t)Pascal Goetgheluck/Photo Researchers, (b)John Reader/Photo Researchers; **465** Pascal Goetgheluck/Photo Researchers; **468** John Gurche Illustrations; **469** (t)John Gurche Illustrations, (b)Ira Block/National Geographic Society Image Collection; **471** (1 2 4)Pascal Goetgheluck/Photo Researchers, (3 5)KAREN/Sygma/CORBIS; **473** (l)Serge de Sazo/Photo Researchers, (r)John Gurche Illustrations; **474** Handout/Reuters/CORBIS; **475** (l)Cyril Ruoso/JH Editorial/Minden Pictures, (tr br)Ryan McVay/Getty Images, (cr)Chad Baker/Getty Images; **477** Tom McHugh/Photo Researchers; **478** Pascal Goetgheluck/Photo Researchers; **482-483** Altrendo Nature/Getty Images; **483** (t)John Cancalosi/Peter Arnold, Inc., (c)Gary Braasch/CORBIS, (b)Leroy Simon/Visuals Unlimited; **485** (l)Daniel A. Bedell/Animals Animals, (c)Martin Bruce/Animals Animals, (r)Azure Computer & Photo Services/Animals

Animals; **486** Gay Bumgarner/Getty Images; **487** (l)Joe McDonald/Animals Animals, (c)Richard Sobol/Animals Animals, (r)Joseph H. Bailey/Getty Images; **489** Doug Wechsler/AG Pix; **490** Barbara Strnadova/Photo Researchers; **492** Frank Lane Picture Agency/CORBIS; **493** (l)Michael Nichols/National Geographic Society Image Collection, (c)Martin Harvey/Gallo Images/CORBIS, (r)Theo Allofs/zefa/CORBIS; **494** (l)D. Allen Photograhy/Animals Animals, (c)Peter Weimann/Animals Animals, (r)Dallas and John Heaton/Free Agents Limited/CORBIS; **497** Gerald & Buff Corsi/Visuals Unlimited; **498** Ann Ronan Picture Library/HIP/The Image Works; **499** (l)Dr. Kari Lounatmaa/Photo Researchers, (r)James Richardson/Visuals Unlimited; **500** Wolfgang Baumeister/SPL/Photo Researchers; **501** (l)G.I. Bernard/OSF/Animals Animals, (c)M.I. Walker/Photo Researchers, (r)Patti Murray/Earth Scenes; **502** (t)H. Zettl/CORBIS, (l to r) Eye of Science/Photo Researchers, (2)Dr. M. Rohde, GBF/SPL/Photo Researchers, (3)Eric V. Grave/Photo Researchers, (4)Biophoto Associates/Photo Researchers, (5)Norbert Rosing/National Geographic Society Image Collection, (6)Valerie Giles/Photo Researchers; **503** (l)Getty Images, (c)Tim Laman/National Geographic/Getty Images, (r)Eric Wanders/Foto Natura/Minden Pictures; **504** (t)H. Zettl/zefa/CORBIS, (tc)Simon Murrell/IT Stock/Alamy Images, (bc)Tim Wright/CORBIS, (b)Tom Vezo/Minden Pictures; **505** (t b)Ryan McVay/Getty Images, (c)Chad Baker/Getty Images; **508** Frank Lane Picture Agency/CORBIS; **509** Flip Nicklin/Minden Pictures; **512-513** Colin Cuthbert/Newcastle University/SPL/Photo Researchers; **514-515** CORBIS; **515** (l)ISM/Phototake NYC, (r)Dr. Richard Kessel/Visuals Unlimited; **516** (l)B. Boonyaratanakornkit & D.S. Clark, G. Vrdoljak/EM Lab, University of California at Berkley/Visuals Unlimited, (c)Dr. David M. Phillips/Visuals Unlimited, (r)Dr. Dennis Kunkel/Dennis Kunkel Microscopy; **517** (l)Jim Brandenburg/Minden Pictures, (r)Craig J. Brown/Index Stock Imagery; **518** Eye of Science/Photo Researchers; **519** (t)Eye of Science/Photo Researchers, (c)Dr. Gary Gaugler/Photo Researchers, (b)Science Source/Photo Researchers; **520** Dr. Dennis Kunkel/Phototake NYC; **522** Dr. Jeremy Burgess/SPL/Photo Researchers; **523** (l)Tim Fuller, (r)Eye of Science/Photo Researchers; **526** Archivo Iconografico, S.A./CORBIS; **527** (t)AP/Wide World Photos, (b)Bettmann/CORBIS; **531** Tim Fuller; **532** Michael Nichols/Getty Images; **533** (l)Gary Conner/Phototake NYC, (tr br)Ryan McVay/Getty Images, (cr)Chad Baker/Getty Images; **534** Dr. Gary Gaugler/Photo Researchers; **535** (t)Dr. Dennis Kunkel/Visuals Unlimited, (c)Dr. David M. Phillips/Visuals Unlimited, (b)Dr. Dennis Kunkel/Phototake NYC; **540-541** Gerald and Buff Corsi/Visuals Unlimited; **541** (t)Oliver Meckes/Nicole OttawaPhoto Researchers, (c)Gerald and Buff Corsi/Visuals Unlimited, (b)Michael Abbey/Photo Researchers; **542** Dr. Dennis Kunkel/Visuals Unlimited; **543** (l)Eric Grave/Photo Researchers, (c)Richard Herrmann/Visuals Unlimited, (r)Dwight Kuhn; **544** (l)Michel Gunter/Peter Arnold, Inc., (r)Michael & Patricia Fogden; **546** (l) Eric V. Grave/Photo Researchers, (r)Wim van Egmond/Visuals Unlimited; **547** (l)Michael Abbey/Visuals Unlimited, (r)Sinclair Stammers/SPL/Photo Researchers; **550** Andrew Syred/Photo Researchers; **552** (t)Charles Melton/Visuals Unlimited, (b)Anthony Bannister/Getty Images; **553** (l)Astrid & Hanns-Frieder Michler/Photo Researchers, (r)Michael Abbey/Visuals Unlimited; **554** (t)Astrid & Hanns-Frieder Michler/Photo Researchers, (b)Dee Breger/Photo Researchers; **556** (l)Dr. David M. Phillips/Visuals Unlimited, (r)Bill Bachman/Photo Researchers; **557** (l)Michael Abbey/Visuals Unlimited, (r)Wim Van Egmond/Visuals Unlimited; **558** (l)M.I. Walker/Photo Researchers, (c)Brad Mogen/Visuals Unlimited, (r)M.I. Walker/Photo Researchers; **559** Robert De Goursey/Visuals Unlimited; **561** (l)Biology Media/Photo Researchers, (r)Bill Beatty/Visuals Unlimited; **563** (t)Carolina Biological Supply Co./Phototake NYC, (b)Dr. Richard Kessel & Dr. Gene Shih/Getty Images; **564** James Richardson/Visuals Unlimited; **565** (l)Astrid & Hanns-Freider Michler/Photo Researchers, (r)David Munns/Photo Researchers; **566** (t)Andrew Syred/Photo Researchers, (c)Steve Gschmeissner/SPL/Photo Researchers, (b)SPL/Photo Researchers; **567** (l)M.I. Walker/Photo Researchers, (tr br)Ryan McVay/Getty Images, (cr)Chad Baker/Getty Images; **569** M.I. Walker/Photo Researchers; **570** John Burbidge/Photo Researchers; **574-575** Jeff Lepore/SPL/Photo Researchers; **575** (t)Ed Reschke/Peter Arnold Inc., (c)Biodisc/Visuals Unlimited, (b)Darlyne A. Murawski/National Geographic Society Image Collection; **576** (l)WSL Handout/Reuters/CORBIS, (r)Dr. David Phillips/Visuals Unlimited; **577** M. Kalab/Visuals Unlimited; **578** (l)Charles McRae/Visuals Unlimited, (c)Darlyne A. Murawski/Peter Arnold Inc., (r)M.F. Brown/Visuals Unlimited; **579** Loren Winters/Visuals Unlimited; **580** Dr. Dennis Kunkel/Visuals Unlimited; **581** Bill Keogh/Visuals Unlimited; **582** Joyce Longcore/University of Maine; **583** Vaughan Fleming/SPL/Photo Researchers; **584** Dr. David M. Phillips/Visuals Unlimited; **585** (1)Joyce Longcore/University of Maine, (2)Gregory G. Dimijian/Photo Researchers, Inc., (3)Ray Coleman/Visuals Unlimited, (4) Jeffrey Lepore/Photo Researchers, (5)Dr. Dennis Kunkel/Visuals Unlimited; **586** Gerald & Buff Corsi/Visuals Unlimited; **587** (l)Stephen Sharnoff/Visuals Unlimited, (r)V. Ahmadijan/Visuals Unlimited; **588** (t)Phyllis Greenberg/Earth Scenes, (b)age fotostock/SuperStock; **589** Dr. Gerald Van Dyke/Visuals Unlimited; **591** (l)Michael Busselle/CORBIS, (c)Vaughan Fleming/Photo Researchers, (r)Dr. Lucille K. Georg/Centers for Disease Control; **592** Graeme Teague Photography; **593** (t b)Ryan McVay/Getty Images, (c)Chad Baker/Getty Images; **595** M. Kalab/Visuals Unlimited; **596** Stephen Sharnoff/Visuals Unlimited; **597** Dr. Gerald Van Dyke/Visuals Unlimited; **600-601** Jim Sugar/CORBIS; **602-603** Photo Library International/ESA/Photo Researchers; **603** (t)David Muench/CORBIS, (c)George H.H. Huey/CORBIS, (b)Theo Allofs/zefa/CORBIS; **605** (l)John Lemker/Animals Animals, (r)Eye of Science/Photo Researchers; **606** (t)Dr. Gerald Van Dyke/Visuals Unlimited/Getty Images, (b)Michael Boys/CORBIS; **607** (l)Rob Simpson/Visuals Unlimited, (r)SCIMAT/Photo Researchers; **610** (l)John Heseltin/SPL/Photo Researchers, (c)Brad Mogen/Visuals Unlimited, (r)Dr. R. Calentine/Visuals Unlimited; **611** (t)Geoff Butler, (b)Henry W. Robison/Visuals Unlimited; **612** (l)Hal Horwitz/CORBIS, (r)Dr. Ken Wagner/Visuals Unlimited; **613** Winifred Wisniewski/Frank Lane Picture Agency/CORBIS; **614** (tl)Walter H. Hodge/Peter Arnold Images/Photolibrary, (bl)Clay Perry/CORBIS, (tc)Dr. Jeremy Burgess/Photo Researchers, (bc)age fotostock/SuperStock, (r)Carlyn Iverson/Photo Researchers; **615** (l)W.P. Armstrong, (r)J.B. Rapkins/Photo Researchers; **616** (l)W.P. Armstrong, (r)Steven P. Lynch; **617** (cw from top)William Harlow/Photo Researchers, (2)Peter Anderson/Dorling Kindersley/Getty Images, (3)Gail Jankus/Photo Researchers, (4)Inga Spence/Visuals Unlimited, (5)Michael Rose/CORBIS; **618** M. Philip Kahl/Photo Researchers; **619** (t)Adam Jones/Photo Researchers, (c)Dr. Daniel Nickrent and Dr. Kenneth Robertson, (bl)Dave Powell/USDA Forest Service/www.forestryimages.org, (bc)Gary Braasch/CORBIS, (br)Inga Spence/Visuals Unlimited; **621** Randall G. Prostak/University of Massachusetts; **623** (t)D Falconer/PhotoLink, (c) Alan Thorton/Getty Images, b)S Meltzer/PhotoLink/Getty Images; **625** (cw from top)Dr. Gerald Van Dyke/Visuals Unlimited/Getty Images, (2)Dr. Ken Wagner/Visuals Unlimited, (3)SCIMAT/Photo Researchers, (4)Eye of Science/Photo Researchers; **626** (tl)Steven P. Lynch, (tr)Winifred Wisniewski/Frank Lane Picture Agency/CORBIS, (bl)Walter H. Hodge/Peter Arnold Images/Photolibrary, (br)W.P. Armstrong; **627** Dr. Daniel Nickrent and Dr. Kenneth Robertson;

630-631 Lowell Georgia/CORBIS; **631** (t)Dr. David Webb/University of Hawaii at Manoa, (b) Biodisc/Visuals Unlimited; **633** (cw from top)Brad Mogen/Visuals Unlimited, (2)Dr. Arnold Karpoff/Visuals Unlimited, (3)Ed Reschke/Peter Arnold, Inc., (4)Dr. Kent Simmons, (5)Jack Bostrack/Visuals Unlimited, (b)Frank H. McClung Museum/University of Tennessee; **635** (t)Ken Wagner/Phototake NYC, (c)Sidney Moulds/SPL/Photo Researchers, (b)M.I. Walker/Photo Researchers; **636** (t)Steven P. Lynch, (bl)Dr. Richard Kessel & Dr. Gene Shih/Visuals Unlimited, (br)Brad Mogen/Visuals Unlimited; **637** Wilfred Cote, SUNY College of Environmental Forestry; **639** Dr. Jeremy Burgess/Photo Researchers; **640** (l)Science VU/Visuals Unlimited, (r)Brad Mogen/Visuals Unlimited; **641** (tl)Antonia Reeve/Photo Researchers, (tc)Science VU/Visuals Unlimited, (tr)Oregon State University Jed Colquhoun Photo Collection, (bl)Geoff Tompkinson/Photo Researchers, (br)Beatrice Neff/Photo Researchers; **642** (t)Carolina Biological Supply/Phototake NYC, (b)Robert Calentine/Visuals Unlimited; **643** (tl)Bill Beatty/Visuals Unlimited, (tc)Science Pictures Limited/Photo Researchers, (tr)De Agostini/Getty Images, (b)Matt Meadows; **646** (l)Vincent Leduc/Punchstock, (r)The Picture Store/SPL/Photo Researchers; **647** (l)Darrell Gulin/CORBIS, (r)David Sieren/Visuals Unlimited; **649** The McGraw-Hill Companies; **651** (t)Maryann Frazier/Photo Researchers, (c)David M. Dennis, (b)Adam Jones/Visuals Unlimited; **652** (l)Stocktrek/age fotostock, (r)Science Source/Photo Researchers; **653** (t)Javier Dauden/CORBIS, (c)Image Source Pink/Getty Images, (b)Daisuke Morita/Getty Images; **655** (tl)Jack Bostrack/Visuals Unlimited, (tr)Steven P. Lynch, (bl)Dr. Jeremy Burgess/Photo Researchers, (br)Dr. Richard Kessel & Dr. Gene Shih/Visuals Unlimited; **656** (tl)Brad Mogen/Visuals Unlimited, (bl)Science VU/Visuals Unlimited, (c)Carolina Biological Supply/Phototake NYC, (r)The McGraw-Hill Companies; **660-661** Roger Wilmshurst/Photo Researchers; **661** (t)Dr. Jeremy Burgess/SPL/Photo Researchers, (b)M.F. Merlet/SPL/Photo Researchers; **662** Ed Reschke/Peter Arnold; **663** Rosenfeld Images Ltd./Photo Researchers; **669** (l)Dr. Nick Kurzenko/SPL/Photo Researchers, (r)Hal Horwitz/CORBIS; **671** (l)Patti Murray/Animals Animals, (r)Jerome Wexler/Visuals Unlimited; **677** (cw from top)Tom Stack & Associates, (2)Joy Spurr/Bruce Coleman, (3)Joel W. Rogers/CORBIS, (4)Burke/Triolo Productions/Getty Images, (5)Chris Evans/www.forestryimages.org, (6)Paul Wray/Iowa State University/www.forestryimages.org, (7)Chris Hellier/CORBIS, (8)David Stuckel; **680** Getty Images/Visuals Unlimited; **681** (tr br)Ryan McVay/Getty Images, (cr)Chad Baker/Getty Images, (l)Laura Sifferlin; **683** Rosenfeld Images Ltd./Photo Researchers; **688-689** Pierre Perrin/SYGMA/CORBIS; **690-691** Taxi/Getty Images; **691** (t)Alexis Rosenfeld/Photo Researchers, (b)Dr. Brad Amos/SPL/Photo Researchers; **692** (l)E. Hanumantha Rao/Photo Researchers, (r)Darlyne A. Murawski/Peter Arnold, Inc.; **693** (t)Judy Davidson/Photo Researchers, (b)Rod Planck/Photo Researchers; **694** (t)Sheila Terry/Photo Researchers, (b)CORBIS; **695** (t)Mark Stouffer Enterprises/Animals Animals, (b) Spencer Platt/Getty Images; **696** Dr. Richard Kessel & Dr. Gene Shih/Visuals Unlimited; **698** (l)O.S.F./Animals Animals, (c)D. Robert & Lori Franz/CORBIS, (r)Shah, Manjo/Animals Animals; **704** William Dow/CORBIS; **705** Therisa Stack/Tom Stack & Associates; **707** (tl)Lawson Wood/CORBIS, (tr)CORBIS, (bl)Tom Stack/Tom Stack & Associates, (br)Patti Murray/Animals Animals; **708** Azure Computer & Photo Services/Animals Animals; **709** (t)Chris McLaughlin/Animals Animals, (b)Harbor Branch Oceanographic Institute at FAU; **710** (l)Comstock Images/PictureQuest, (r)CORBIS; **713** (t)Georgette Douwma/Photo Researchers, (b)Jeff Rotman/Photo Researchers; **716** Comstock Images/PictureQuest; **717** (t)D Falconer/PhotoLink, (cl)Matt Meadows, (cr)Alan Thorton/Getty Images, (b)S Meltzer/PhotoLink/Getty Images; **720** Lawson Wood/CORBIS; **724-725** Scott W. Smith/Animals Animals; **725** SPL/Photo Researchers; **726** (l)Arthur Seigelman/Visuals Unlimited, (r)James Robinson/Animals Animals; **728** Michael Abbey/Photo Researchers; **729** (t)Tom Adams/Visuals Unlimited, (b)E. R. Degginger/Photo Researchers; **730** (l)Scott Camazine/Newscom, (r)Dr. Richard Kessel & Dr. Gene Shih/Visuals Unlimited; **731** (l)Dr. Richard Kessel/Visuals Unlimited/Getty Images, (r)Lauritz Jensen/Visuals Unlimited; **733** (t)Sinclair Stammers/Photo Researchers, (b)Dr. Robert Calentine/Getty Images; **734** (l)Centers for Disease Control, (c)Sinclair Stammers/SPL/Photo Researchers, (r)Lester V. Bergman/CORBIS; **735** (l)Michael P. Gadomski/Photo Researchers, (c)Nigel Cattlin/Photo Researchers, (r)Nigel Cattlin/Photo Researchers; **736** John Walsh/Photo Researchers; **737** (l)age fotostock/SuperStock, (r)OSF/D. Fleetham/Animals Animals; **742** (l)age fotostock/SuperStock, (r)Andrew J. Martinez/Photo Researchers; **743** Georgette Douwma/Photo Researchers; **744** Gary Meszaros/Photo Researchers; **745** (l)John Anderson/Animals Animals, (r)Marty Snyderman/Visuals Unlimited; **748** Hans Pfletschinger/Photolibrary; **749** (tl)Robert Yin/CORBIS, (tr)Amos Nachoum/CORBIS, (b)OSF/Kathy Atkinson/Animals Animals; **752** AP Photo/Tsunemi Kubodera of the National Science Museum of Japan, HO; **753** (t b)Ryan McVay/Getty Images, (c)Chad Baker/Getty Images; **760-761** Ralph A. Clevenger/CORBIS; **761** (t)Sinclair Stammers/Photo Researchers, (c)Laguna Design/Photo Researchers, (b)Clouds Hill Imaging Ltd./CORBIS; **764** (t)Oliver Meckes/Nicole Ottawa/Photo Researchers, (b)Raymond Mendez/Animals Animals; **765** Mark Moffett/Minden Pictures; **768** (l)Harry Rogers/Photo Researchers, (c)Kjell Sandved/Visuals Unlimited, (r)Oliver Meckes/Nicole Ottawa/Photo Researchers; **770** (l)John Giustina/Getty Images, (c)CORBIS, (r)Barbara Gerlach/Visuals Unlimited; **771** Gregory G. Dimijian, M.D./Photo Researchers; **772** Niall Benvie/CORBIS; **773** (l)Brad Mogen/Visuals Unlimited, (c)Dennis Kunkel/Phototake NYC, (r)Fabio Colombini Medeiros/Animals Animals; **774** James Zipp/Photo Researchers; **777** (t)Doug Sherman/Geofile, (inset)Ralph A. Clevenger/CORBIS, (b)Getty Images; **780** (t)Raymond Coleman/Visuals Unlimited, (bl)DK Limited/CORBIS, (br)David Aubrey/CORBIS; **781** (l)DK Limited/CORBIS,(r)Diane Nelson/Visuals Unlimited; **782** Clive Druett/Papilio/CORBIS; **783** (t)Javier Dauden/CORBIS, (c)Image Source Pink/Getty Images, (b)Daisuke Morita/Getty Images; **790-791** Franklin Viola/Animals Animals; **791** Chris Newbert/Minden Pictures; **792** (l)Randy Morse/Animals Animals, (r)Fred McConaughey/Photo Researchers; **793** (l)Robert L. Dunne/Photo Researchers, (r)Douglas P. Wilson/Frank Lane Picture Agency/CORBIS; **795** Nancy Rotenberg/Animals Animals; **796** Zigmund Leszczynski/Animals Animals; **797** (l to r, t to b)Zigmund Leszczynski/Animals Animals, (2)Joyce & Frank Burek/Animals Animals, (3)C.C. Lockwood/Animals Animals, (4)Fred McConnaughey/Photo Researchers, (5)Gustav Verderber/Visuals Unlimited, (6)Science VU/Alan Baker/Visuals Unlimited, (b)Stuart Westmorland/Photo Researchers; **798** (t)Fred McConnaughey/Photo Researchers, (bl)David Wrobel/Visuals Unlimited, (br)Scott Johnson/Animals Animals; **799** (t) Ken Lucas/Visuals Unlimited, (bl)James L. Amos/Photo Researchers, (br)Borut Furlan/WaterF/age fotostock; **800** (t)David Steven Miller/Animals Animals, (b)Science VU/Alan Baker/Visuals Unlimited; **801** Minden Pictures/SuperStock; **802** (l)G.I. Bernard/OSF/Animals Animals, (r)Bruce Watkins/Animals Animals; **809** (t)Javier Dauden/CORBIS, (cl)Andrew J. Martinez/Photo Researchers, (cr)Image Source Pink/Getty Images, (b)Daisuke Morita/Getty Images; **810** (t) Robert L. Dunne/Photo Researchers, (b)G.I. Bernard/OSF/Animals Animals; **816-817** China Photos/Getty Images; **818-819** Tim Laman/National Geographic/Getty Images; **819** (t)Jeffrey L.

Rotman/CORBIS, (b)Michael Davidson/Molecular Expressions/Florida State University Research Foundation; **820** (l)Tom Brakefield/CORBIS, (r)C. Allan Morgan/Peter Arnold, Inc.; **823** CORBIS; **826** Fred Bavendam/Minden Pictures; **828** (l)Sinclair Stammers/SPL/Photo Researchers, (r)Hans Reinhard/Bruce Coleman; **829** (t)Jeffrey L. Rotman/CORBIS, (bl)Tim Davis/CORBIS, (br)Dennis Kunkel Microscopy, Inc.; **830** Jeff Rotman/Photo Researchers; **832** James L. Amos/National Geographic Society Image Collection; **833** Lee Rentz Photography; **835** Heidi & Hans-Jurgen Koch; **838** (t)FLPA/Fabio Pupin/age fotostock, (bl)Dazz DeLaMorte/Cutcaster, (br)altrendo nature/Stockbyte/Getty Images; **839** (tl)George Grall/National Geographic RF/Getty Images, (tr) Derek Middleton/FLPA/Minden Pictures, (b)Juan Manuel Renjifo/Animals Animals; **841** copyright Joseph Kiesecker; **842** (t)T. Daeschler/VIREO, (b)Zina Deretsky, National Science Foundation; **843** (tr br)Ryan McVay/Getty Images, (cr)Chad Baker/Getty Images, (l)Matt Meadows; **850-851** Joe McDonald/Visuals Unlimited; **851** (t)Jim Merli/Visuals Unlimited, (b)Joe McDonald/Visuals Unlimited; **852** Gerold and Cynthia Merker/Visuals Unlimited; **853** Heidi & Hans-Jurgen Koch/Minden Pictures; **854** Michael & Patricia Fogden/Minden Pictures; **855** (l)Francesc Muntada/CORBIS, (r)Arthur Morris/Visuals Unlimited; **856** (l)Azure Computer & Photo Services/Animals Animals, (r)David M. Dennis/Animals Animals; **857** (tl)Zigmund Leszczynski/Animals Animals., (tr)Joe McDonald/CORBIS, (b)Doug Wechsler/Animals Animals; **860** Suzanne L. and Joseph T. Collins/Photo Researchers; **864** (t)Arthur Morris/CORBIS, (bl) Michael & Patricia Fogden/CORBIS, (bc)Hal Beral/Visuals Unlimited, (br)Tom Vezo/Peter Arnold, Inc.; **865** Anthony Mercieca/Photo Researchers; **866** Steve Maslowski/Visuals Unlimited; **869** Claus Meyer/Minden Pictures; **870** Getty Images/Visuals Unlimited; **871** (l)Claus Meyer/ Minden Pictures, (tr br)Ryan McVay/Getty Images, (cr)Chad Baker/Getty Images; **872** (t)Azure Computer & Photo Services/Animals Animals, (b)Michael & Patricia Fogden/CORBIS; **873** Breck P. Kent/Animals Animals; **875** James Zipp/Photo Researchers; **878-879** Greg Stott/Masterfile; **879** (t)Michael W. Davidson/Molecular Expressions/Florida State University, (c)Susumu Nishinaga/Photo Researchers, (b)Ron Spoomer/Visuals Unlimited; **880** Kevin Schafer/zefa/ CORBIS; **881** (l)Tom & Pat Leeson/Photo Researchers, (r)Art Wolfe/Getty Images; **887** (l to r) Peter Steiner, (2)Marty Snyderman/Visuals Unlimited, (3)Kevin Schafer/CORBIS, (4)PhotoLink/ Getty Images, (5)A. & M. Shah/Animals Animals; **888** (l)Breck P. Kent/Animals Animals, (r) Stephen Dalton/Animals Animals; **889** (l)Tom McHugh/Photo Researchers, (c)J. & C. Sohns/ Animals Animals, (r)McKelvey/Rismiller; **890** (t)Stouffer Productions/Animals Animals, (bl)Keith Scholey/Getty Images, (bc)Digital Stock/CORBIS; (br)Alan Root/OSF/Animals Animals; **891** (l)Tim Davis/CORBIS, (r)Tim Shepherd/OSF/Animals Animals; **892** (tl)Michael S. Quinton/ National Geographic/Getty Images, (tr)David Lazenby/Animals Animals, (b)Tui De Roy/Minden Pictures; **893** (tl)Alan G. Nelson/Animals Animals, (tr)Alan & Sandy Carey/OSF/Animals Animals, (bl)Phyllis Greenberg/Animals Animals, (br)Panthera Productions/ABPL/Animals Animals; **894** Wally Santana/AP/Wide World Photos; **895** (l)Sirenia Project, U.S. Geological Survey, (r) Michael S. Nolan/age fotostock; **898** Joy S. Reidenberg, Ph.D.; **899** (l)Zig Leszczynski/Animals Animals, (tr)Javier Dauden/CORBIS, (cr)Image Source Pink/Getty Images, (br)Daisuke Morita/ Getty Images; **900** (t)Kevin Schafer/zefa/CORBIS, (b)Sirenia Project, U.S. Geological Survey; **906-907** Joel Simon/Getty Images; **907** (t)DLILLC/Corbis, (c)Tim Davis/CORBIS, (b)Frans Lanting/CORBIS; **908** (t)Digital Vision/Getty Images, (b)Vince Bucci/Getty; **909** (t)B&B Wells/ OSF/Animals Animals, (c)Jo McCulty/Ohio State University, (b)Dr. Tetsuro Matsuzawa; **912** (t) Ferrero/Labat/Peter Arnold, Inc., (b)Matt Meadows; **914** Scott Martin/AP/Wide World Photos; **915** Clive Bromhall/OSF/Animals Animals; **916** Ray Richardson/Animals Animals; **917** (t) Norbert Rosing/Animals Animals, (b)H. Wiesenhofer/Photolink/Getty Images; **918** Wolfgang Kaehler/CORBIS; **919** Doug Wilson/CORBIS; **920** (l)Manoj Shah/Animals Animals, (r)Juergen & Christine Sohns/Animals Animals; **921** (t)Tui De Roy/Minden Pictures, (b)Manoj Shah/Animals Animals; **922** Jennifer Jarvis/Visuals Unlimited; **924** Sharna Balfour/Gallo Images/CORBIS; **925** (t b)Ryan McVay/Getty Images, (c)Chad Baker/Getty Images; **926** (t)Digital Vision/Getty Images, (b)Norbert Rosing/Animals Animals; **932-933** Ted Horowitz/CORBIS; **934-935** Paul Conklin/PhotoEdit; **935** (t)Anatomical Travelogue/Photo Researchers, (b)Dr. Ken Wagner/ Visuals Unlimited; **937** Andrew Syred/Photo Researchers; **938** Peter Lavery/Masterfile; **940** Dr. Ken Greer/Visuals Unlimited; **941** Tim Fuller; **942** Prof. P. Motta/Department of Anatomy/University, "La Sapienza", Rome/SPL/Photo Researchers; **945** CORBIS; **950** Denis Paquin/AP/Wide World Photos; **951** (t)Corbis, (b)Matthew Stockman/Getty Images; **952** Getty Images/Photodisc; **953** (l)3B Scientific GmbH, Germany, (r)William Fritsch/Jupiter Images; **956** Tim Fuller; **960-961** Focus on Sport/Getty Images; **961** (t)Biodisc/Visuals Unlimited, (b)Dr. David M. Phillips/Visuals Unlimited; **968** (l)Hiram Bingham/National Geographic Society Image Collection, (r)Bettman/CORBIS; **969** (t)Science Pictures Limited/Photo Researchers, (b) Alfred Pasieka/SPL/Photo Researchers; **971** Tim Fuller; **977** (1)LADA/Photo Researchers, (2)Don Farrall, (3 5)Michael P. Gadomski/Photo Researchers, (4)Rosal/Photo Researchers; **979** Laura Sifferlin; **980** Dr. Susan Tapert, University of California at San Diego.; **981** Michael Newman/ PhotoEdit; **982** Duke University Photo Department; **983** (l)Horizons, (tr br)Ryan McVay/Getty Images, (cr)Chad Baker/Getty Images; **985** Science Pictures Limited/Photo Researchers; **990-991** Lee White/CORBIS; **991** (t)Susumu Nishinaga/Photo Researchers, (b)Dr. Philippa Uwins, Whistler Research Photography/SPL/Photo Researchers.; **992** (l)Art Resource, (r)SSPL/ The Image Works; **993** (t)Goldberg Diego/SYGMA/CORBIS, (b)SPL/Photo Researchers; **995** Biophoto Associates/Photo Researchers; **997** (t)Dr. Dennis Kunkel/Visuals Unlimited, (bl) Lauren Shear/Photo Researchers, (br)Dr. David Phillips/Visuals Unlimited, Inc.; **999** Scott Camazine/Photo Researchers; **1000** David Wrobel/Visuals Unlimited; **1001** (t)Tim Fuller, (b)Eye of Science/Photo Researchers; **1003** (l)Steve Gschmeissner/Photo Researchers, (r)Dr. Kessel & Dr. Kerdon/Tissues & Organs/Getty Images; **1005** Tim Fuller; **1010** Thomas Matthiesen; **1011** (l)Spencer Grant/PhotoEdit, (tr)Javier Dauden/CORBIS, (cr)Image Source Pink/Getty Images, (br)Daisuke Morita/Getty Images; **1014** Eye of Science/Photo Researchers; **1018-1019** David Young-Wolff/PhotoEdit; **1020 1021** Tim Fuller; **1022** Simon Fraser/SPL/Photo Researchers; **1026** (t)Photolibrary.com/Index Stock Imagery, (b)Tetra Images/Getty Images; **1027** Jodi Cobb/National Geographic Society Image Collection; **1029** (t to b)Getty Images, (2) CORBIS, (3)Image Source/PunchStock, (4)Foodcollection/Getty Images, (5)CORBIS, (6)Getty Images, (7)Lew Robertson/CORBIS, (8)Getty Images; **1030** C. Sherburne/PhotoLink/Getty Images; **1032** (t)Getty Images, (b)The McGraw-Hill Companies; **1033** Tim Fuller; **1038** Lester V. Bergman/CORBIS; **1039** (t b)Ryan McVay/Getty Images, (c)Chad Baker/Getty Images; **1042** Jonathan Nourok/PhotoEdit; **1043** (l)CORBIS, (r)Yang Liu/CORBIS; **1046-1047** Neil Bromhall/Genesis Films/SPL/Photo Researchers; **1047** (t)Biophoto Associates/Photo Researchers, (b)Lennart Nilsson/Bonnier-Alba; **1052** Lester V. Bergman/CORBIS; **1057** Tim Fuller; **1058** (l)Petit Format/Photo Researchers, (c)Claude Edelmann/Photo Researchers, (r)Dr. G. Moscoso/Photo Researchers; **1059** (l)Mediscan/CORBIS, (r)Steve Allen/Getty Images; **1061** Carolina Biological Supply Co./Visuals Unlimited; **1065** (l c)Hulton Archive/Stringer/Getty Images, (r)Mitchell Gerber/CORBIS; **1066** Getty Images; **1067** (l)Zephyr/Photo Researchers, (tr) Javier Dauden/CORBIS, (cr)Image Source Pink/Getty Images, (br)Daisuke Morita/Getty Images; **1074-1075** Michael Newman/PhotoEdit; **1075** (t)SIU/Visuals Unlimited, (b)Susumu Nishinaga/ SPL/Photo Researchers; **1076** Scott Camazine/Photo Researchers; **1079** (tl)SuperStock, (tr) Grapes-Michaud/Photo Researchers, (bl)Bonnie Kamin/PhotoEdit, (br)James Gathany/Centers for Disease Control; **1080** (l)A.B. Dowsett/SPL/Photo Researchers, (r)Nick Sinclair/SPL/Photo Researchers; **1081** (t)James Gathany/Centers for Disease Control, (c)Immusol Inc., (b)Steve Wood/UAB Creative and Marketing; **1082** age fotostock/SuperStock; **1084** David Scharf/Photo Researchers; **1085** (t)Michael Ross/Photo Researchers, (c)Dennis Kunkel Microscopy, (b) Hossler/Custom Medical Stock Photo; **1086** Tim Fuller; **1092** Dr. Gladden Willis/Visuals Unlimited; **1093** (t)James Stevenson/Photo Researchers, (c b)Custom Medical Stock Photography; **1094** (1)Andrew Syred/Photo Researchers, (2)Eye of Science/Photo Researchers, (3)Dr. Dennis Kunkel/Visuals Unlimited, (4)C Squared Studios/Getty Images, (5)Brian G. Green/ Getty Images; **1095** Sue Ford/Photo Researchers; **1096** Digital Art/CORBIS; **1097** William Fritsch/Jupiter Images; **1099** (t)age fotostock/SuperStock, (b)Joe McDonald/CORBIS; **1100** Publiphoto/Photo Researchers; **1104** CORBIS; **1106** Michael Newman/PhotoEdit; **1109** (l) Charles D. Winters/Photo Researchers, (r)Dr. Bayard Brattstrom/Visuals Unlimited; **1115** SCIMAT/Photo Researchers; **1116** (l)Robert Calentine/Visuals Unlimited, (r)Wolfgang Baumeister/SPL/Photo Researchers; **1118** Matt Meadows; **1120** AP Photo/Tsunemi Kubodera of the National Science Museum of Japan, HO; **1122** The McGraw-Hill Companies; **1124** (l) Bridgeman Art Library, (c)SPL/Photo Researchers, (r)LBNL/SPL/Photo Researchers; **1125 1127** Tim Fuller; **1133** (t)Gary Gaugler/The Medical File/Peter Arnold, Inc., (c)B. Boonyaratanakornkit & D.S. Clark, G. Vrdoljak/EM Lab, University of California at Berkley/Visuals Unlimited, (b)Eric Grave/Photo Researchers; **1134** (t)Dee Breger/Photo Researchers, (c)Robert De Goursey/Visuals Unlimited, (b)Biology Media/Photo Researchers; **1135** (t)Vaughan Fleming/ SPL/Photo Researchers, (c)Hal Horwitz/CORBIS, (b)age fotostock/SuperStock; **1136** (t)M. Philip Kahl/Photo Researchers, (c)Lawson Wood/CORBIS, (b)age fotostock/SuperStock; **1137** (t)Scott Johnson/Animals Animals, (b)Kevin Schafer/zefa/CORBIS.

A Biologist's Guide To The Periodic Table

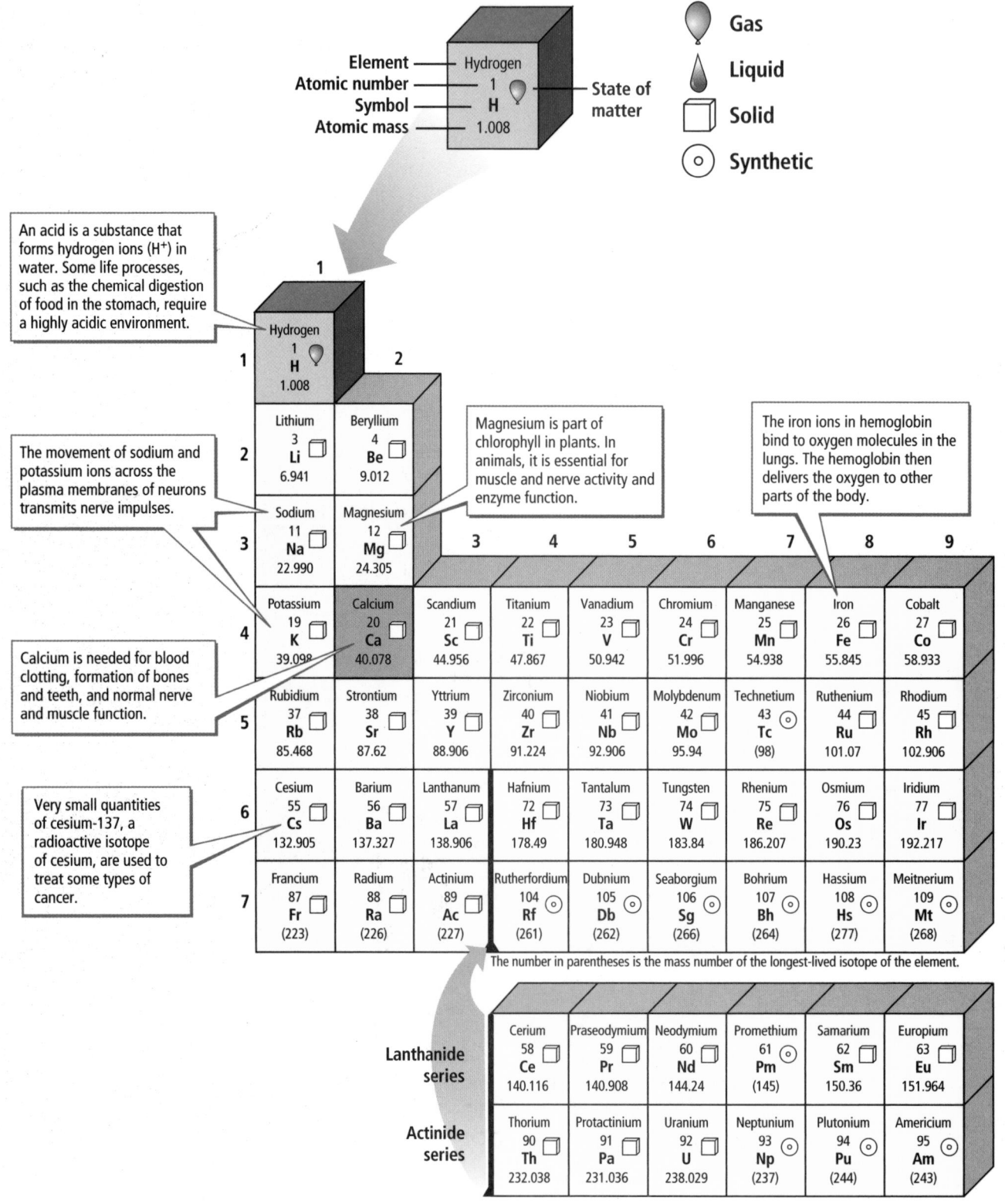

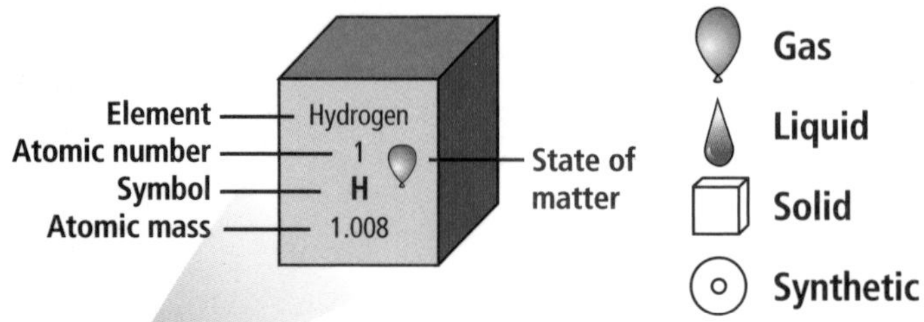

An acid is a substance that forms hydrogen ions (H^+) in water. Some life processes, such as the chemical digestion of food in the stomach, require a highly acidic environment.

The movement of sodium and potassium ions across the plasma membranes of neurons transmits nerve impulses.

Magnesium is part of chlorophyll in plants. In animals, it is essential for muscle and nerve activity and enzyme function.

The iron ions in hemoglobin bind to oxygen molecules in the lungs. The hemoglobin then delivers the oxygen to other parts of the body.

Calcium is needed for blood clotting, formation of bones and teeth, and normal nerve and muscle function.

Very small quantities of cesium-137, a radioactive isotope of cesium, are used to treat some types of cancer.

	1	2	3	4	5	6	7	8	9
1	Hydrogen 1 H 1.008								
2	Lithium 3 Li 6.941	Beryllium 4 Be 9.012							
3	Sodium 11 Na 22.990	Magnesium 12 Mg 24.305							
4	Potassium 19 K 39.098	Calcium 20 Ca 40.078	Scandium 21 Sc 44.956	Titanium 22 Ti 47.867	Vanadium 23 V 50.942	Chromium 24 Cr 51.996	Manganese 25 Mn 54.938	Iron 26 Fe 55.845	Cobalt 27 Co 58.933
5	Rubidium 37 Rb 85.468	Strontium 38 Sr 87.62	Yttrium 39 Y 88.906	Zirconium 40 Zr 91.224	Niobium 41 Nb 92.906	Molybdenum 42 Mo 95.94	Technetium 43 Tc (98)	Ruthenium 44 Ru 101.07	Rhodium 45 Rh 102.906
6	Cesium 55 Cs 132.905	Barium 56 Ba 137.327	Lanthanum 57 La 138.906	Hafnium 72 Hf 178.49	Tantalum 73 Ta 180.948	Tungsten 74 W 183.84	Rhenium 75 Re 186.207	Osmium 76 Os 190.23	Iridium 77 Ir 192.217
7	Francium 87 Fr (223)	Radium 88 Ra (226)	Actinium 89 Ac (227)	Rutherfordium 104 Rf (261)	Dubnium 105 Db (262)	Seaborgium 106 Sg (266)	Bohrium 107 Bh (264)	Hassium 108 Hs (277)	Meitnerium 109 Mt (268)

The number in parentheses is the mass number of the longest-lived isotope of the element.

Lanthanide series	Cerium 58 Ce 140.116	Praseodymium 59 Pr 140.908	Neodymium 60 Nd 144.24	Promethium 61 Pm (145)	Samarium 62 Sm 150.36	Europium 63 Eu 151.964
Actinide series	Thorium 90 Th 232.038	Protactinium 91 Pa 231.036	Uranium 92 U 238.029	Neptunium 93 Np (237)	Plutonium 94 Pu (244)	Americium 95 Am (243)